TEACHER'S EDITION

McDougal Littell
Physical SCIENCE

Chemical Interactions

Waves, Sound, and Light

Matter and Energy

Motion and Forces

Electricity and Magnetism

UNIT 1 Credits
5B Illustration by Stephen Durke; **5C** © Omni Photo Communications, Inc./Index Stock; **37C** © David Young-Wolff/PhotoEdit; **67B** © Left Lane Productions/Corbis; **67C** © Joe Sohm/Visions of America, LLC/PictureQuest.

UNIT 2 Credits
133B, 193B, 193C, 235B Illustrations by Stephen Durke; **235C** © Photodisc/Getty Images; © Greg Pease/Stock Connection/PictureQuest; © Stockbyte; © S. Feld/Robertstock.com; Jellinek & Sampson, London/Bridgeman Art Library; **271B** Illustration by Stephen Durke.

UNIT 3 Credits
341C, 377B, 73C, 415B Photographs by Sharon Hoogstraten; **445C** Illustration by Dan Stuckenschneider.

UNIT 4 Credits
549C *left* Illustrations by Dan Stuckenschneider; *right* Illustration by Eric Chadwick; **589B** Photographs by Sharon Hoogstraten; **589C** © Kim Heacox/Getty Images; **589B** Illustration by Bart Vallecoccia.

UNIT 5 Credits
626B Illustration by Stephen Durke; **629C** Illustration by Dan Stuckenschneider; **663C** © Donna Cox and Robert Patterson/National Center for Supercomputing Applications, University of Illinois, Urbana; **699B** Photograph by Sharon Hoogstraten.

Acknowledgments
Excerpts and adaptations from *National Science Education Standards* by the National Academy of Sciences. Copyright © 1996 by the National Academy of Sciences. Reprinted with permission from the National Academies Press, Washington, D.C. Excerpts and adaptations from *Benchmarks for Science Literacy: Project 2061*. Copyright © 1993 by the American Association for the Advancement of Science. Reprinted with permission.

Copyright © 2006 by McDougal Littell, a division of Houghton Mifflin Company.

All rights reserved.

Warning: No part of this work may be reproduced or transmitted in any form or by any means, electronic or mechanical, including photocopying and recording, or by any information storage or retrieval system without the prior written permission of McDougal Littell unless such copying is expressly permitted by federal copyright law. Address inquiries to Supervisor, Rights and Permissions, McDougal Littell, P.O. Box 1667, Evanston, IL 60204.

Printed in the United States of America.

ISBN-13: 978-0-618-61558-2   3 4 5 6 7 8 VJM 12 11 10 09 08 07

ISBN-10: 0-618-61558-X   Internet Web Site: http://www.mcdougallittell.com

Visit classzone.com and get connected

Online resources provide instruction, practice, and learning support correlated to your text.

- **Misconceptions database** provides solutions for common student misconceptions about science and their world.
- **Professional development links**, including SciLinks, offer additional teaching resources.
- **Animations and visualizations** help improve comprehension.
- **Math Tutorial** helps strengthen students' math skills.
- **Flashcards** help students review vocabulary.
- **State test practice** prepares students for assessments.

You have immediate access to ClassZone's teacher resources.

MCDTCOWDMSSZ

Use this code to create your own username and password.

Also visit ClassZone to learn more about these innovative and updated online resources.

- eEdition Plus Online
- eTest Plus Online
- EasyPlanner Plus Online
- Content Review Online

Now it all clicks!™

McDougal Littell

McDougal Littell Science

Effective Science Instruction Tailored for Middle School Learners

Physical Science Teacher's Edition Contents

Program Consultants and Reviewers	T4
Research-Based Solutions for Your Classroom	T6
Content Organized Around Big Ideas	T8
Many Ways to Learn	T10
Differentiated Instruction	T12
Effective Assessment	T14
Program Overview	T16
Teaching Resources	T18
Correlation to National Science Education Standards	T20
Correlation to Project 2061 Benchmarks	T22
Planning the Unit	T24
Planning the Chapter	T26
Planning the Lesson	T28
Lab Materials List	T30

Consultants and Reviewers

Science Consultants

Chief Science Consultant

James Trefil, Ph.D. is the Clarence J. Robinson Professor of Physics at George Mason University. He is the author or co-author of more than 25 books, including *Science Matters* and *The Nature of Science*. Dr. Trefil is a member of the American Association for the Advancement of Science's Committee on the Public Understanding of Science and Technology. He is also a fellow of the World Economic Forum and a frequent contributor to *Smithsonian* magazine.

Rita Ann Calvo, Ph.D. is Senior Lecturer in Molecular Biology and Genetics at Cornell University, where for 12 years she also directed the Cornell Institute for Biology Teachers. Dr. Calvo is the 1999 recipient of the College and University Teaching Award from the National Association of Biology Teachers.

Kenneth Cutler, M.S. is the Education Coordinator for the Julius L. Chambers Biomedical Biotechnology Research Institute at North Carolina Central University. A former middle school and high school science teacher, he received a 1999 Presidential Award for Excellence in Science Teaching.

Instructional Design Consultants

Douglas Carnine, Ph.D. is Professor of Education and Director of the National Center for Improving the Tools of Educators at the University of Oregon. He is the author of seven books and over 100 other scholarly publications, primarily in the areas of instructional design and effective instructional strategies and tools for diverse learners. Dr. Carnine also serves as a member of the National Institute for Literacy Advisory Board.

Linda Carnine, Ph.D. consults with school districts on curriculum development and effective instruction for students struggling academically. A former teacher and school administrator, Dr. Carnine also co-authored a popular remedial reading program.

Donald Steely, Ph.D. serves as principal investigator at the Oregon Center for Applied Science (ORCAS) on federal grants for science and language arts programs. His background also includes teaching and authoring of print and multimedia programs in science, mathematics, history, and spelling.

Sam Miller, Ph.D. is a middle school science teacher and the Teacher Development Liaison for the Eugene, Oregon, Public Schools. He is the author of curricula for teaching science, mathematics, computer skills, and language arts.

Vicky Vachon, Ph.D. consults with school districts throughout the United States and Canada on improving overall academic achievement with a focus on literacy. She is also co-author of a widely used program for remedial readers.

Content Reviewers

John Beaver, Ph.D.
Ecology
Professor, Director of Science Education Center
College of Education and Human Services
Western Illinois University
Macomb, IL

Donald J. DeCoste, Ph.D.
Matter and Energy, Chemical Interactions
Chemistry Instructor
University of Illinois
Urbana-Champaign, IL

Dorothy Ann Fallows, Ph.D., MSc
Diversity of Living Things, Microbiology
Partners in Health
Boston, MA

Michael Foote, Ph.D.
The Changing Earth, Life Over Time
Associate Professor
Department of the Geophysical Sciences
The University of Chicago
Chicago, IL

Lucy Fortson, Ph.D.
Space Science
Director of Astronomy
Adler Planetarium and Astronomy Museum
Chicago, IL

Elizabeth Godrick, Ph.D.
Human Biology
Professor, CAS Biology
Boston University
Boston, MA

Isabelle Sacramento Grilo, M.S.
The Changing Earth
Lecturer, Department of the Geological Sciences
San Diego State University
San Diego, CA

David Harbster, MSc
Diversity of Living Things
Professor of Biology
Paradise Valley Community College
Phoenix, AZ

Richard D. Norris, Ph.D.
Earth's Waters
Professor of Paleobiology
Scripps Institution of Oceanography
University of California, San Diego
La Jolla, CA

Donald B. Peck, M.S.
Motion and Forces; Waves, Sound, and Light; Electricity and Magnetism
Director of the Center for Science Education (retired)
Fairleigh Dickinson University
Madison, NJ

Javier Penalosa, Ph.D.
Diversity of Living Things, Plants
Associate Professor, Biology Department
Buffalo State College
Buffalo, NY

Raymond T. Pierrehumbert, Ph.D.
Earth's Atmosphere
Professor in Geophysical Sciences (Atmospheric Science)
The University of Chicago
Chicago, IL

Brian J. Skinner, Ph.D.
Earth's Surface
Eugene Higgins Professor of Geology and Geophysics
Yale University
New Haven, CT

Nancy E. Spaulding, M.S.
Earth's Surface, The Changing Earth, Earth's Waters
Earth Science Teacher (retired)
Elmira Free Academy
Elmira, NY

Steven S. Zumdahl, Ph.D.
Matter and Energy, Chemical Interactions
Professor Emeritus of Chemistry
University of Illinois
Urbana-Champaign, IL

Susan L. Zumdahl, M.S.
Matter and Energy, Chemical Interactions
Chemistry Education Specialist
University of Illinois
Urbana-Champaign, IL

Safety Consultant

Juliana Texley, Ph.D.
Former K–12 Science Teacher and School Superintendent
Boca Raton, FL

English Language Advisor

Judy Lewis, M.A.
Director, State and Federal Programs for reading proficiency and high risk populations
Rancho Cordova, CA

Research-Based Solutions for Your Classroom

The distinguished program consultant team and a thorough, research-based planning and development process assure that *McDougal Littell Science* supports all students in learning science concepts, acquiring inquiry skills, and thinking scientifically.

Standards-Based Instruction

Concepts and skills were selected based on careful analysis of national and state standards.

- National Science Education Standards
- Project 2061 Benchmarks for Science Literacy
- Comprehensive database of state science standards

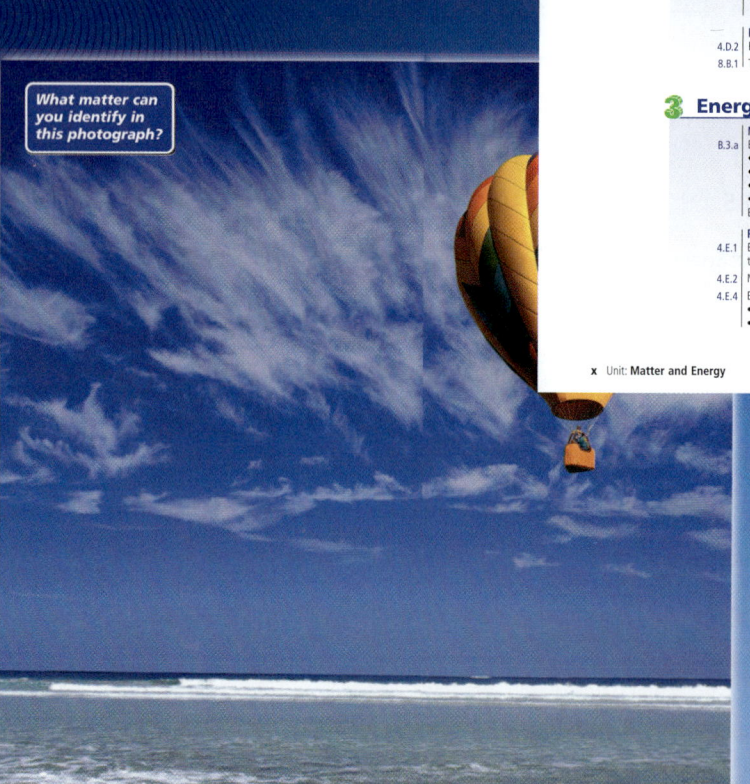

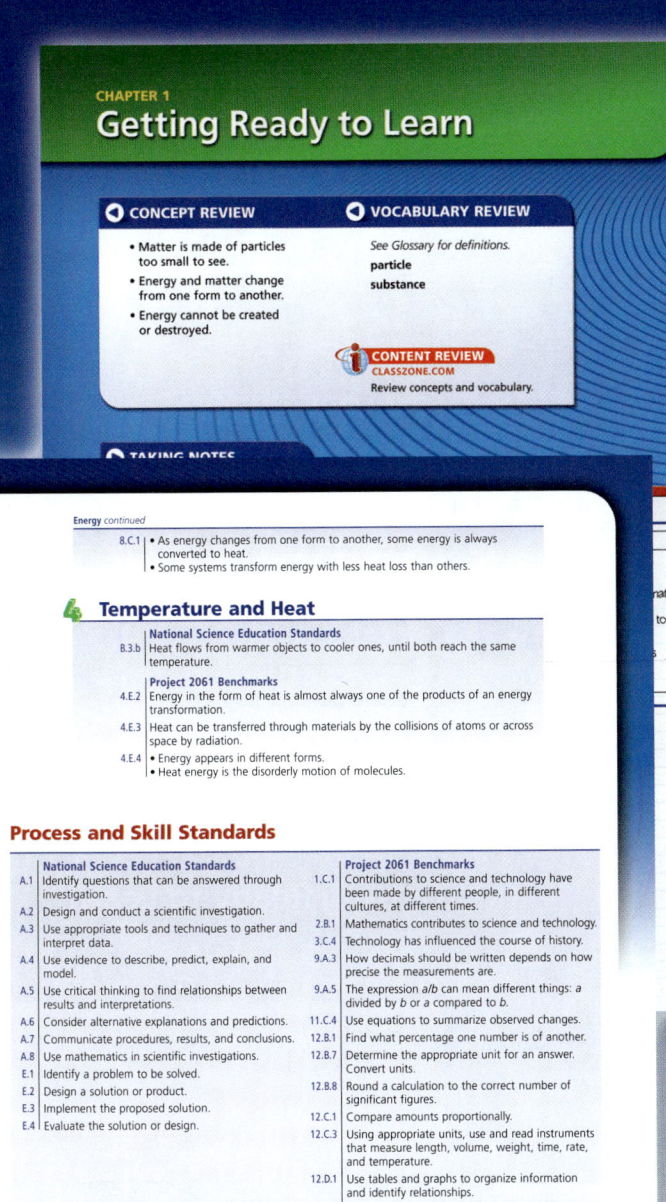

Effective Instructional Strategies

McDougal Littell Science incorporates strategies that research shows are effective in improving student achievement. These strategies include

- Note taking and nonlinguistic representations (Marzano, Pickering, and Pollock)
- A focus on big ideas (Kame'enui and Carnine)
- Background knowledge and active involvement (Project CRISS)

Robert J. Marzano, Debra J. Pickering, and Jane E. Pollock, *Classroom Instruction That Works: Research-Based Strategies for Increasing Student Achievement* (ASCD, 2001)

Edward J. Kame'enui and Douglas Carnine, *Effective Teaching Strategies That Accommodate Diverse Learners* (Pearson, 2002)

Project CRISS (Creating Independence Through Student-Owned Strategies)

Comprehensive Research, Review, and Field Testing

An ongoing program of research and review guided the development of *McDougal Littell Science*.

- Program plans based on extensive data from classroom visits, research surveys, teacher panels, and focus groups
- All pupil edition activities and labs classroom-tested by middle school teachers and students
- All chapters reviewed for clarity and scientific accuracy by the Content Reviewers listed on page T5
- Selected chapters field-tested in the classroom to assess student learning, ease of use, and student interest

Content Organized Around Big Ideas

Each chapter develops a big idea of science, helping students to place key concepts in context.

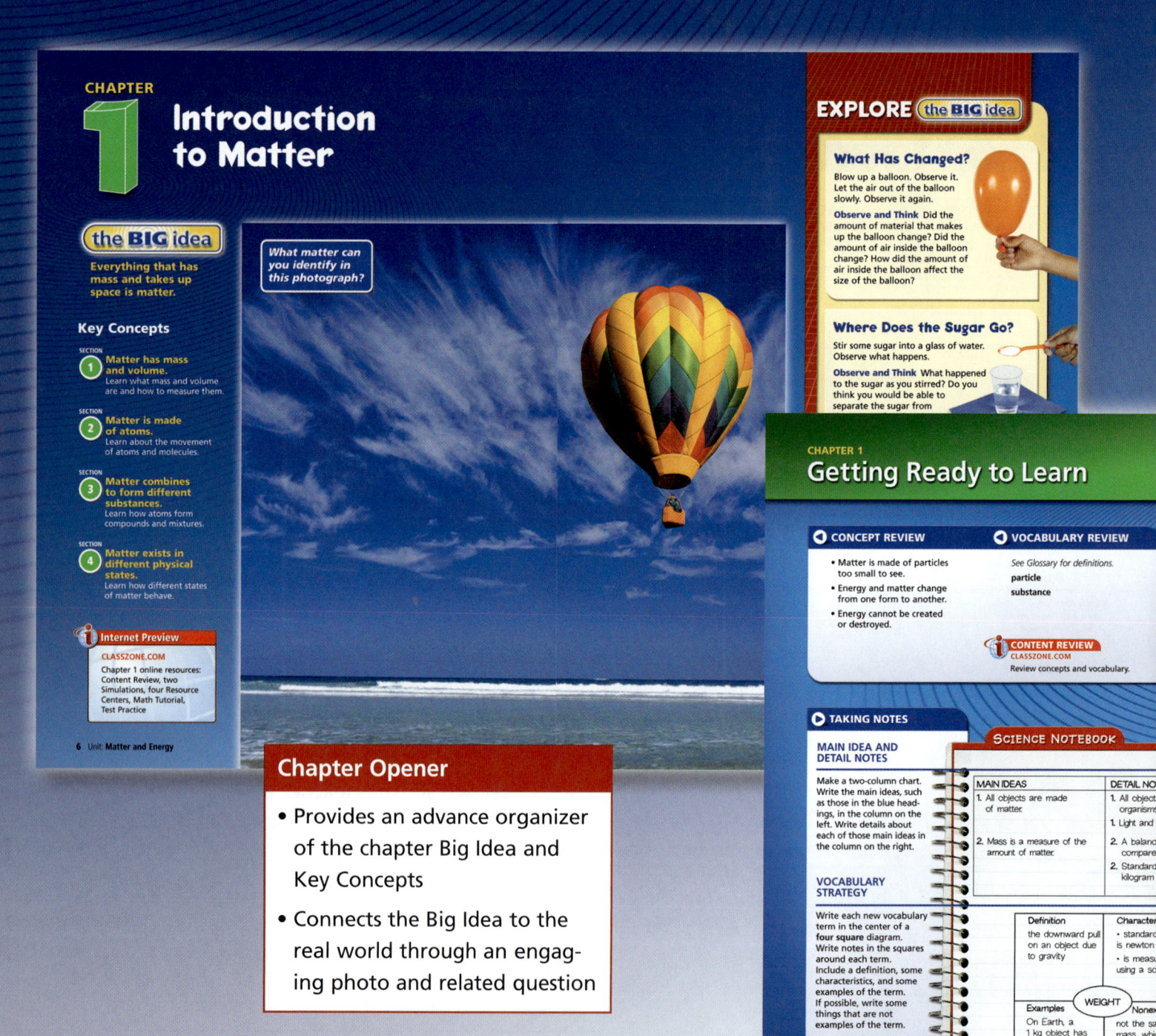

Chapter Opener

- Provides an advance organizer of the chapter Big Idea and Key Concepts
- Connects the Big Idea to the real world through an engaging photo and related question

Visual Summary

- Summarizes Key Concepts using both text and visuals
- Reinforces the connection of Key Concepts to the Big Idea

Section Opener

- Highlights the Key Concept
- Connects new learning to prior knowledge
- Previews important vocabulary

The Big Idea Questions

- Help students connect their new learning back to the Big Idea
- Prompt students to synthesize and apply the Big Idea and Key Concepts

---

1 Chapter Review

the BIG idea
Everything that has mass and takes up space is matter.

CONTENT REVIEW
CLASSZONE.COM

KEY CONCEPTS SUMMARY

1 Matter has mass and volume.

Mass is a measure of how much matter an object contains.

Volume is the measure of the amount of space matter occupies.

VOCABULARY
matter p. 9
mass p. 10
weight p. 11
volume p. 11

2 Matter is made of atoms.

An atom is the smallest basic unit of matter. Two or more atoms bonded together form a molecule. Atoms and molecules are always in motion.

VOCABULARY
atom p. 16
molecule p. 18

3 Matter combines to form different substances.

Matter can be pure, such as an element (gold), or a compound (water).

Matter can be a mixture. Mixtures contain two or

VOCABULARY
element p. 22
compound p. 23
mixture p. 23

4 Matter exists in differen

Solids have a fixed volume and a fixed shape.

Liquids ha ume but n

34 Unit: Matter and Energy

Reviewing Vocabulary

Copy and complete the chart below. If the right column is blank, give a brief description or definition. If the left column is blank, give the correct term.

Term	Description
1.	the downward pull of gravity on an object
2. liquid	
3.	the smallest basic unit of matter
4. solid	
5.	state of matter with no fixed volume and no fixed shape
6.	a combination of different substances that remain individual substances
7. matter	
8.	a measure of how much matter an object contains
9. element	
10.	a particle made of two or more atoms bonded together
11. compound	

Reviewing Key Concepts

Short Answer Answer each of the following questions in a sentence or two.

19. Describe the movement of particles in a solid, a liquid, and a gas.
20. In bright sunlight, dust particles in the air appear to dart about. What causes this effect?
21. Why is the volume of a rectangular object measured in cubic units?
22. Describe how the molecules in the air behave when you pump air into a bicycle tire.

Thinking Critically

23. **CLASSIFY** Write the headings *Matter* and *Not Matter* on your paper. Place each of these terms in the correct category: wood, water, metal, air, light, sound.
24. **INFER** If you could break up a carbon dioxide molecule, would you still have carbon dioxide? Explain your answer.
25. **MODEL** In what ways is sand in a bowl like a liquid? In what ways is it different?
26. **INFER** If you cut a hole in a basketball, what happens to the gas inside?
27. **COMPARE AND CONTRAST** Create a Venn diagram that shows how mixtures and compounds are alike and different.
28. **ANALYZE** If you place a solid rubber ball into a box, why doesn't the ball change its shape to fit the container?
29. **CALCULATE** What is the volume of an aquarium that is 120 cm long, 60 cm wide, and 100 cm high?
30. **CALCULATE** A truck whose bed is 2.5 m long, 1.5 m wide, and 1 m high is delivering sand for a sand-sculpture competition. How many trips must the truck make to deliver 7 cubic meters of sand?

Use the information in the photograph below to answer the next three questions.

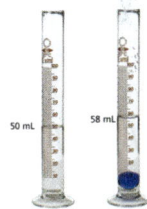

50 mL   58 mL

31. **INFER** One way to find the volume of a marble is by displacement. To determine a marble's volume, add 50 mL of water to a graduated cylinder and place the marble in the cylinder. Why does the water level change when you put the marble in the cylinder?
32. **CALCULATE** What is the volume of the marble?
33. **PREDICT** If you carefully removed the marble and let all of the water on it drain back into the cylinder, what would the volume of the water be? Explain.

the BIG idea

34. **SYNTHESIZE** Look back at the photograph on pages 6–7. Describe the picture in terms of states of matter.
35. **WRITE** Make a list of all the matter in a two-meter radius around you. Classify each as a solid, liquid, or gas.

UNIT PROJECTS

If you are doing a unit project, make a folder for your project. Include in your folder a list of the resources you will need, the date on which the project is due, and a schedule to track your progress. Begin gathering data.

36 Unit: Matter and Energy

KEY CONCEPT

1.1 Matter has mass and volume.

BEFORE, you learned
- Scientists study the world by asking questions and collecting data
- Scientists use tools such as microscopes, thermometers, and computers

NOW, you will learn
- What matter is
- How to measure the mass of matter
- How to measure the volume of matter

VOCABULARY
matter p. 9
mass p. 10
weight p. 11
volume p. 11

EXPLORE Similar Objects

How can two similar objects differ?

PROCEDURE
1. Look at the two balls but do not pick them up. Compare their sizes and shapes. Record your observations.
2. Pick up each ball. Compare the way the balls feel in your hands. Record your observations.

MATERIALS
2 balls of different sizes

WHAT DO YOU THINK?
How would your observations be different if the larger ball were made of foam?

All objects are made of matter.

Suppose your class takes a field trip to a museum. During the course of the day you see mammoth bones, sparkling crystals, hot-air balloons, and an astronaut's space suit. All of these things are matter.

Matter is what makes up all of the objects and living organisms in the universe. As you will see, **matter** is anything that has mass and takes up space. Your body is matter. The air that you breathe and the water that you drink are also matter. Matter makes up the materials around you. Matter is made of particles called atoms, which are too small to see. You will learn more about atoms in the next section.

Not everything is matter. Light and sound, for example, are not matter. Light does not take up space or have mass in the same way that a table does. Although air is made of atoms, a sound traveling through air is not.

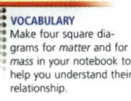

VOCABULARY
Make four square diagrams for *matter* and for *mass* in your notebook to help you understand their relationship.

CHECK YOUR READING What is matter? How can you tell if something is matter?

Chapter 1: Introduction to Matter 9

Many Ways to Learn

Because students learn in so many ways, *McDougal Littell Science* gives them a variety of experiences with important concepts and skills. Text, visuals, activities, and technology all focus on Big Ideas and Key Concepts.

Integrated Technology

- Interaction with Key Concepts through Simulations and Visualizations
- Easy access to relevant Web resources through Resource Centers and SciLinks
- Opportunities for review through Content Review and Math Tutorials

Visuals that Teach

- Information-rich visuals directly connected to the text
- Thoughtful pairing of diagrams and real-world photos
- Reading Visuals questions to support student learning

Kinetic energy and potential energy are the two general types of energy.

Learn more about kinetic energy and potential energy.

All of the forms of energy can be described in terms of two general types of energy—kinetic energy and potential energy. Anything that is moving, such as a car that is being driven or an atom in the air, has kinetic energy. All matter also has potential energy, or energy that is stored and can be released at a later time.

Kinetic Energy

READING TIP
Kinetic means "related to motion."

The energy of motion is called **kinetic energy.** It depends on both an object's mass and the speed at which the object is moving.

All objects are made of matter, and matter has mass. The more matter an object contains, the greater its mass. If you held a bowling ball in one hand and a soccer ball in the other, you could feel that the bowling ball has more mass than the soccer ball.

- **Kinetic energy increases as mass increases.** If the bowling ball and the soccer ball were moving at the same speed, the bowling ball would have more kinetic energy because of its greater mass.
- **Kinetic energy increases as speed increases.** If two identical bowling balls were rolling along at different speeds, the faster one would have more kinetic energy because of its greater speed. The speed skater in the photographs below has more kinetic energy when he is racing than he does when he is moving slowly.

High Speed

This skater has a large amount of kinetic energy when moving at a high speed.

Low Speed

When the same skater is moving more slowly, he has less kinetic energy.

READING VISUALS   **APPLY** How could a skater with less mass than another skater have more kinetic energy?

74 Unit: Matter and Energy

Potential Energy

Suppose you are holding a soccer ball in your hands. Even if the ball is not moving, it has energy because it has the potential to fall. **Potential energy** is the stored energy that an object has due to its position or chemical composition. The ball's position above the ground gives it potential energy.

The most obvious form of potential energy is potential energy that results from gravity. Gravity is the force that pulls objects toward Earth's surface. The giant boulder on the right has potential energy because of its position above the ground. The mass of the boulder and its height above the ground determine how much potential energy it has due to gravity.

It is easy to know whether an object has kinetic energy because the object is moving. It is not so easy to know how much and what form of potential energy an object has, because objects can have potential energy from several sources. For example, in addition to potential energy from gravity, substances contain potential energy due to their chemical composition—the atoms they contain.

Because the boulder could fall, it has potential energy from gravity.

 How can you tell kinetic energy and potential energy apart?

INVESTIGATE Potential Energy

How can you change the amount of potential energy?

DESIGN YOUR OWN EXPERIMENT

Use what you know about potential energy to design an experiment that shows how potential energy can be increased or decreased.

PROCEDURE

1. Using the materials in the list, design an experiment to investigate the potential energy of the model car. Use the cardboard as a ramp.
2. Write up your hypothesis and your procedure. Remember to include the variables and constants in the experiment.
3. Conduct your experiment and record your results.

WHAT DO YOU THINK?
- What variables did you change? Why?
- How do your results demonstrate a change in potential energy?

SKILL FOCUS
Designing experiments

MATERIALS
- model car
- meter stick
- weights
- balance
- tape
- cardboard
- books

TIME
30 minutes

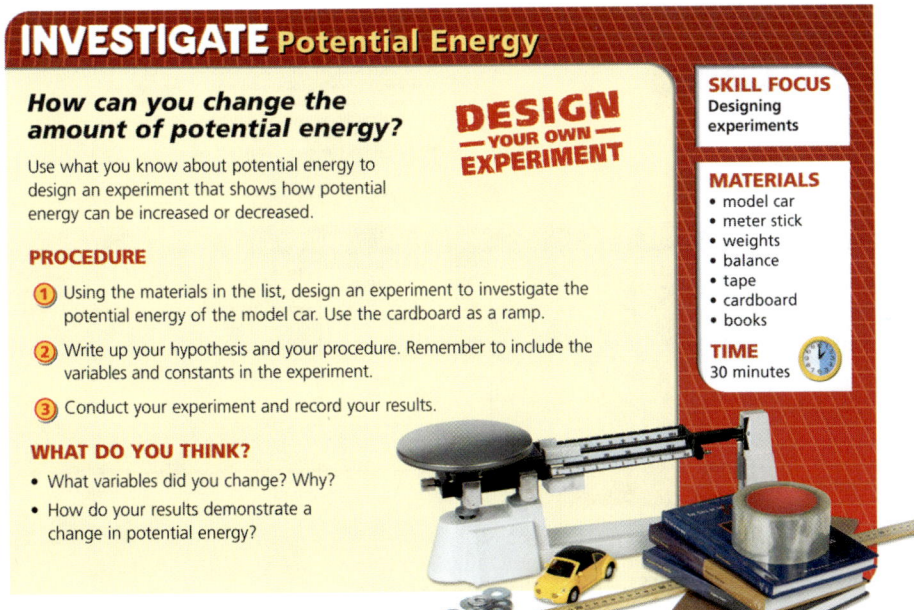

Considerate Text

- Clear structure of meaningful headings
- Information clearly connected to main ideas
- Student-friendly writing style

Hands-on Learning

- Activities that reinforce Key Concepts
- Skill Focus for important inquiry and process skills
- Multiple activities in every chapter, from quick Explores to full-period Chapter Investigations

Differentiated Instruction

A full spectrum of resources for differentiating instruction supports you in reaching the wide range of learners in your classroom.

1 INSTRUCT

Develop Critical Thinking
APPLY Tell students that enough mass cubes are not available for the entire class. Have students apply what they know about measuring mass to invent standard units of mass based on common objects. Ask them to find the mass of objects based on the invented standard units.

Teach from Visuals
To help students interpret the photographs and illustrations comparing the size and mass of a bowling ball and a basketball, ask:
- How do the sizes of the bowling ball and the basketball in the photographs compare? *They are about the same.*
- How can you tell from the illustrations which ball has more mass? *More standard cubes are needed to balance the pan with the bowling ball than the pan with the basketball.*

Ongoing Assessment
Describe how to measure the mass of matter.
Ask: How would you find the mass of an object? *Compare its mass with the mass of standard units on a balance.*

CHECK YOUR READING Answer: Mass is a measure of how much matter an object contains.

MAIN IDEA AND DETAILS As you read, write the blue headings on the left side of a two-column chart. Add details in the other column.

Mass is a measure of the amount of matter.
Different objects contain different amounts of matter. **Mass** is a measure of how much matter an object contains. A metal teaspoon, for example, contains more matter than a plastic teaspoon. Therefore, a metal teaspoon has a greater mass than a plastic teaspoon. An elephant has more mass than a mouse.

CHECK YOUR READING How are matter and mass related?

Measuring Mass
 When you measure mass, you compare the mass of the object with a standard amount, or unit, of mass. The standard unit of mass is the kilogram (kg). A large grapefruit has a mass of about one-half kilogram. Smaller masses are often measured in grams (g). There are 1000 grams in a kilogram. A penny has a mass of between two and three grams.

How can you compare the masses of two objects? One way is to use a pan balance, as shown below. If two objects balance each other on a pan balance, then they contain the same amount of matter. If a basketball balances a metal block, for example, then the basketball and the block have the same mass. Beam balances work in a similar way, but instead of comparing the masses of two objects, you compare the mass of an object with a standard mass on the beam.

A bowling ball and a basketball are about the same size, but a bowling ball has more mass.

Measuring Weight
When you hold an object such as a backpack full of books, you feel it pulling down on your hands. This is because Earth's gravity pulls the backpack toward the ground. Gravity is the force that pulls two masses toward each other. In this example, the two masses are Earth and the backpack. **Weight** is the downward pull on an object due to gravity. If the pull of the backpack is strong, you would say that the backpack weighs a lot.

Weight is measured by using a scale, such as a spring scale like the one shown on the right, that tells how hard an object is pushing or pulling on it. The standard scientific unit for weight is the newton (N). A common unit for weight is the pound (lb).

Mass and weight are closely related, but they are not the same. Mass describes the amount of matter an object has, and weight describes how strongly gravity is pulling on that matter. On Earth, a one-kilogram object has a weight of 9.8 newtons (2.2 lb). When a person says that one kilogram is equal to 2.2 pounds, he or she is really saying that one kilogram has a weight of 2.2 pounds on Earth. On the Moon, however, gravity is one-sixth as strong as it is on Earth. On the Moon, the one-kilogram object would have a weight of 1.6 newtons (0.36 lb). The amount of matter in the object, or its mass, is the same on Earth as it is on the Moon, but the pull of gravity is different.

Gravity is pulling down on both the girl and the backpack. The heavier the backpack is, the stronger the pull of gravity is on it.

SIMULATION CLASSZONE.COM
Compare weights on different planets.

CHECK YOUR READING What is the difference between mass and weight?

Volume is a measure of the space matter occupies.
Matter takes up space. A bricklayer stacks bricks on top of each other to build a wall. No two bricks can occupy the same place because the matter in each brick takes up space.

 The amount of space that matter in an object occupies is called the object's **volume**. The bowling ball and the basketball shown on page 10 take up approximately the same amount of space. Therefore, the two balls have about the same volume. Although the basketball is hollow, it is not empty. Air fills up the space inside the basketball. Air and other gases take up space and have volume.

10 Unit: Matter and Energy

Chapter 1: Introduction to Matter 11

DIFFERENTIATE INSTRUCTION

More Reading Support
A To measure mass, what do you compare the object's mass to? *standard units of mass*

English Learners Phrasal verbs such as "makes up" and "takes up" are used throughout this chapter (for example, on p. 9). Make sure students understand not to read "up" and other adverbs or prepositions in phrasal verbs as literal directions. If students are still confused, offer synonyms for phrasal verbs. For instance, "makes up" means composes, and "takes up" means occupies. English learners may also lack background knowledge of a field trip (p. 9).

DIFFERENTIATE INSTRUCTION

More Reading Support
B Which is affected by gravity, mass or weight? *weight*
C What do you call the amount of space an object takes up? *volume*

Below Level Have students make a table that compares mass and weight. Ask them to include a definition of each, the standard units used to measure them, and the tools used to measure them.

Teacher's Edition
- More Reading Support for below-level readers
- Strategies for below-level and advanced learners, English learners, and inclusion students

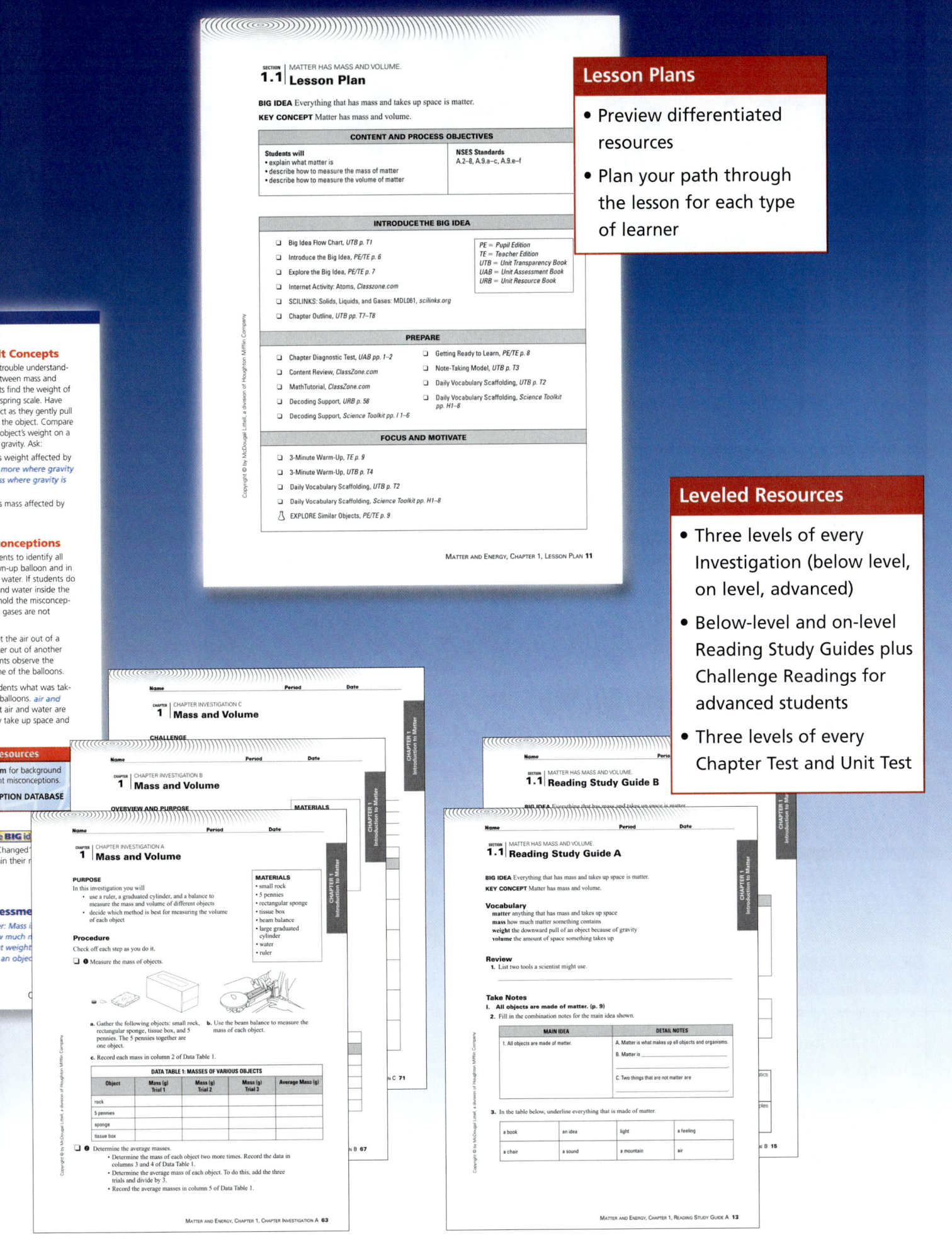

Effective Assessment

McDougal Littell Science incorporates a comprehensive set of resources for assessing student knowledge and performance before, during, and after instruction.

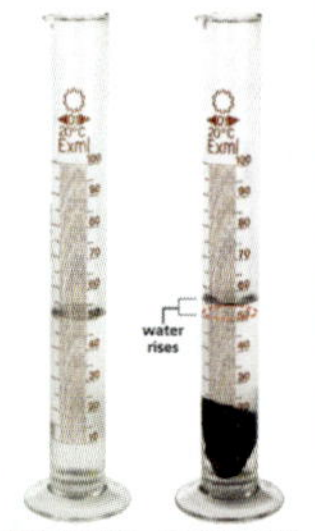

Diagnostic Tests

- Assessment of students' prior knowledge
- Readiness check for concepts and skills in the upcoming chapter

Measuring Volume by Displacement

Although a box has a regular shape, a rock does not. There is no simple formula for calculating the volume of something with an irregular shape. Instead, you can make use of the fact that two objects cannot be in the same place at the same time. This method of measuring is called displacement.

1. Add water to a graduated cylinder. Note the volume of the water by reading the water level on the cylinder.
2. Submerge the irregular object in the water. Because the object and the water cannot share the same space, the water is displaced, or moved upward. Note the new volume of the water with the object in it.
3. Subtract the volume of the water before you added the object from the volume of the water and the object together. The result is the volume of the object. The object displaces a volume of water equal to the volume of the object.

You measure the volume of a liquid by measuring how much space it takes up in a container. The volume of a liquid usually is measured in liters (L) or milliliters (mL). One liter is equal to 1000 milliliters. Milliliters and cubic centimeters are equivalent. This can be written as $1 \text{ mL} = 1 \text{ cm}^3$. If you had a box with a volume of one cubic centimeter and you filled it with water, you would have one milliliter of water.

Measure the volume of water without the rock.

Measure the volume of water with the rock in it.

In the first photograph, the graduated cylinder contains 50 mL of water. Placing a rock in the cylinder causes the water level to rise from 50 mL to 55 mL. The difference is 5 mL; therefore, the volume of the rock is 5 cm^3.

1.1 Review

KEY CONCEPTS

1. Give three examples of matter.
2. What do weight and mass measure?
3. How can you measure the volume of an object that has an irregular shape?

CRITICAL THINKING

4. **Calculate** What is the volume of a box that is 12 cm long, 6 cm wide, and 4 cm high?
5. **Synthesize** What is the relationship between the units of measurement for the volume of a liquid and of a solid object?

CHALLENGE

6. **Infer** Why might a small increase in the dimensions of an object cause a large change in its volume?

Chapter 1: **Introduction to Matter** 13

ANSWERS

1. Sample answer: air, water, a rock

2. Weight measures the downward pull on an object due to gravity. Mass measures how much matter an object contains.

3. Submerge the object in water and subtract the volume of the water before the object was added from the volume of the water and the object together.

4. 12 cm · 6 cm · 4 cm = 288 cm^3

5. One cubic centimeter of solid is equivalent to one milliliter of liquid.

6. Each of the three dimensions increases, so, for example, doubling the dimensions increases the volume by a multiple of eight.

Ongoing Assessment

Describe how to measure the volume of matter.

Ask: How would you find the volume of a box? of a small rock? *Multiply the box's length by its width and height. Put the small stone in a graduated cylinder of water and determine how much water the rock displaces.*

Teacher Demo

Place a clear glass that is full to its brim with water in a shallow tray. Ask students to predict what will happen if you slowly drop a stone into the glass. Ask them to explain their predictions.

Reinforce the BIG idea

Have students relate the section to the Big Idea.

R Reinforcing Key Concepts, p. 20

1.1 ASSESS & RETEACH

Assess

A Section 1.1 Quiz, p. 3

Reteach

Write the heading *Matter* on the board. Ask a volunteer to define *matter* and write the definition on the board. Add these two subheads under *Matter: Mass* and *Volume*. Ask a volunteer to define *mass* and *volume* and write the definitions on the board. Ask students to describe how each is measured, which tools are used for the measurements, and which units are used.

Technology Resources

Have students visit **ClassZone.com** for reteaching of Key Concepts.

CONTENT REVIEW

CONTENT REVIEW CD-ROM

Chapter 1 **13**

Ongoing Assessment

- Check Your Reading questions for student self-check of comprehension
- Consistent Teacher's Edition prompts for assessing understanding of Key Concepts

Reviewing Vocabulary

Copy and complete the chart below. If the right column is blank, give a brief description or definition. If the left column is blank, give the correct term.

Term	Description
1.	the downward pull of gravity on an object
2. liquid	
3.	the smallest basic unit of matter
4. solid	
5.	state of matter with no fixed volume and no fixed shape
6.	a combination of different substances that remain individual substances
7. matter	
8.	a measure of how much matter an object contains
9. element	
10.	a particle made of two or more atoms bonded together
11. compound	

Reviewing Key Concepts

Multiple Choice *Choose the letter of the best answer.*

12. The standard unit for measuring mass is the
- **a.** kilogram
- **b.** gram per cubic centimeter
- **c.** milliliter
- **d.** milliliter per cubic centimeter

13. A unit for measuring the volume of a liquid is the
- **a.** kilogram
- **b.** gram per cubic centimeter
- **c.** milliliter
- **d.** milliliter per cubic centimeter

14. The weight of an object is measured by using a scale that
- **a.** compares the mass of the object with a standard unit of mass
- **b.** shows the amount of space the object occupies
- **c.** indicates how much water is displaced by the object
- **d.** tells how hard the object is pushing or pulling on it

15. To find the volume of a rectangular box,
- **a.** divide the length by the height
- **b.** multiply the length, width, and height
- **c.** subtract the mass from the weight
- **d.** multiply one atom's mass by the total

16. Compounds can be separated only by
- **a.** breaking the atoms into smaller pieces
- **b.** breaking the bonds between the atoms
- **c.** using a magnet to attract certain atoms
- **d.** evaporating the liquid that contains the atoms

17. Whether a substance is a solid, a liquid, or a gas depends on how close its atoms are to one another and
- **a.** the volume of each atom
- **b.** how much matter the atoms have
- **c.** how free the atoms are to move
- **d.** the size of the container

18. A liquid has
- **a.** a fixed volume and a fixed shape
- **b.** no fixed volume and a fixed shape
- **c.** a fixed volume and no fixed shape
- **d.** no fixed volume and no fixed shape

...duction to Matter 35

Section and Chapter Reviews

- Focus on Key Concepts and critical thinking skills
- A full range of question types and levels of thinking

Short Answer *Answer each of the following questions in a sentence or two.*

19. Describe the movement of particles in a solid, a liquid, and a gas.

20. In bright sunlight, dust particles in the air appear to dart about. What causes this effect?

21. Why is the volume of a rectangular object measured in cubic units?

22. Describe how the molecules in the air behave when you pump air into a bicycle tire.

Thinking Critically

23. CLASSIFY Write the headings *Matter* and *Not Matter* on your paper. Place each of these terms in the correct category: wood, water, metal, air, light, sound.

24. INFER If you could break up a carbon dioxide molecule, would you still have carbon dioxide? Explain your answer.

25. MODEL In what ways is sand in a bowl like a liquid? In what ways is it different?

26. INFER If you cut a hole in a basketball, what happens to the gas inside?

27. COMPARE AND CONTRAST Create a Venn diagram that shows how mixtures and compounds are alike and different.

28. ANALYZE If you place a solid rubber ball into a box, why doesn't the ball change its shape to fit the container?

29. CALCULATE What is the volume of an aquarium that is 120 cm long, 60 cm wide, and 100 cm high?

30. CALCULATE A truck whose bed is 2.5 m long, 1.5 m wide, and 1 m high is delivering sand for a sand-sculpture competition. How many trips must the truck make to deliver 7 cubic meters of sand?

Use the information in the photograph below to answer the next three questions.

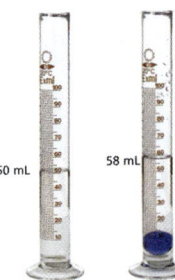

50 mL   58 mL

31. INFER One way to find the volume of a marble is by displacement. To determine a marble's volume, add 50 mL of water to a graduated cylinder and place the marble in the cylinder. Why does the water level change when you put the marble in the cylinder?

32. CALCULATE What is the volume of the marble?

33. PREDICT If you carefully removed the marble and let all of the water on it drain back into the cylinder, what would the volume of the water be? Explain.

the BIG idea

34. SYNTHESIZE Look back at the photograph on pages 6–7. Describe the picture in terms of states of matter.

35. WRITE Make a list of all the matter in a two-meter radius around you. Classify each as a solid, liquid, or gas.

UNIT PROJECTS

36 Unit: Matter and Energy

Leveled Chapter and Unit Tests

- Three levels of test for every chapter and unit
- Same Big Ideas, Key Concepts, and essential skills assessed on all levels

Rubrics

- Rubrics in Teacher's Edition for all extended-response questions
- Rubrics for all Unit Projects
- Alternative Assessment with rubric for each chapter
- A wide range of additional rubrics in the Science Toolkit

McDougal Littell Science

Science Toolkit

Transparencies, activity sheets, and teacher notes to support every aspect of science instruction
- Inquiry and experimental design
- Building science vocabulary
- Reading in the science content area
- Writing in the sciences
- Math in science
- Rubrics for investigations, projects, and presentations
- Test-taking strategies
- Daily vocabulary scaffolding
- Strategies for decoding
- Cooperative learning
- Planning for science fairs and competitions
- Lesson plans for substitute teachers

McDougal Littell Science: Life, Earth, Physical Series

Each book in this three-book series provides comprehensive coverage of life, earth, or physical science.

- Carefully sequenced units and chapters that consistently connect new learning to prior knowledge
- Focused integration of selected concepts from other sciences and technology
- Complete Student Resource Handbooks in every book

Life Science Units

1 ▶ Cells and Heredity
1. The Cell
2. How Cells Function
3. Cell Division
4. Patterns of Heredity
5. DNA and Modern Genetics

2 ▶ Life Over Time
6. The History of Life on Earth
7. Classification of Living Things
8. Population Dynamics

3 ▶ Diversity of Living Things
9. Single-Celled Organisms and Viruses
10. Introduction to Multicellular Organisms
11. Plants
12. Invertebrate Animals
13. Vertebrate Animals

4 ▶ Ecology
14. Ecosystems and Biomes
15. Interactions Within Ecosystems
16. Human Impact on Ecosystems

5 ▶ Human Biology
17. Systems, Support, and Movement
18. Absorption, Digestion, and Exchange
19. Transport and Protection
20. Control and Reproduction
21. Growth, Development, and Health

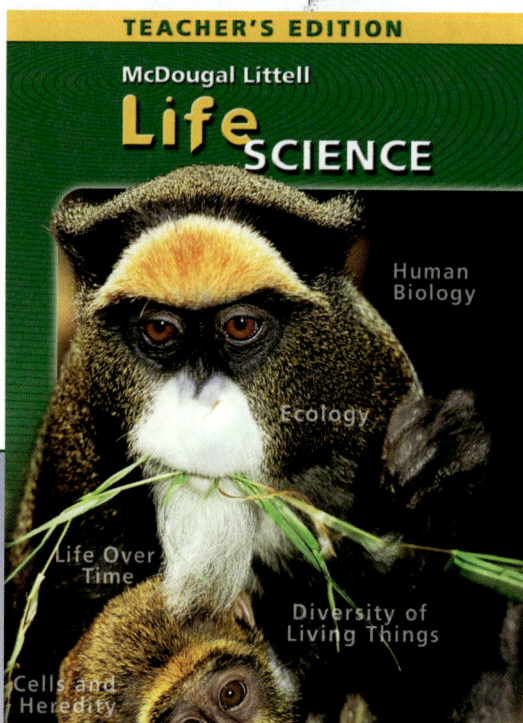

Earth Science Units

1 ▶ Earth's Surface
1. Views of Earth Today
2. Minerals
3. Rocks
4. Weathering and Soil Formation
5. Erosion and Deposition

2 ▶ The Changing Earth
6. Plate Tectonics
7. Earthquakes
8. Mountains and Volcanoes
9. Views of Earth's Past
10. Natural Resources

3 ▶ Earth's Waters
11. The Water Planet
12. Freshwater Resources
13. Ocean Systems
14. Ocean Environments

4 ▶ Earth's Atmosphere
15. Earth's Changing Atmosphere
16. Weather Patterns
17. Weather Fronts and Storms
18. Climate and Climate Change

5 ▶ Space Science
19. Exploring Space
20. Earth, Moon, and Sun
21. Our Solar System
22. Stars, Galaxies, and the Universe

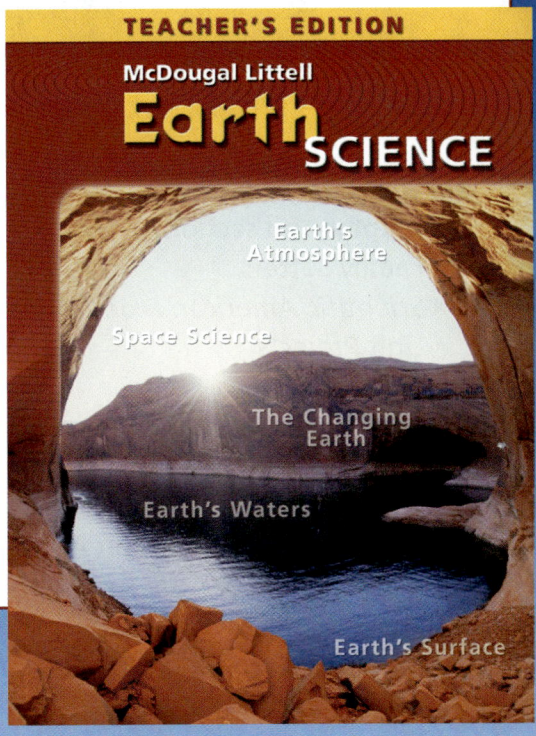

Physical Science Units

1 ▶ Matter and Energy
1. Introduction to Matter
2. Properties of Matter
3. Energy
4. Temperature and Heat

2 ▶ Chemical Interactions
5. Atomic Structure and the Periodic Table
6. Chemical Bonds and Compounds
7. Chemical Reactions
8. Solutions
9. Carbon in Life and Materials

3 ▶ Motion and Forces
10. Motion
11. Forces
12. Gravity, Friction, and Pressure
13. Work and Energy
14. Machines

4 ▶ Waves, Sound, and Light
15. Waves
16. Sound
17. Electromagnetic Waves
18. Light and Optics

5 ▶ Electricity and Magnetism
19. Electricity
20. Circuits and Electronics
21. Magnetism

Teaching Resources

A wealth of print and technology resources help you adapt the program to your teaching style and to the specific needs of your students.

Book-Specific Print Resources

Unit Resource Book provides all of the teaching resources for the unit organized by chapter and section.
- Family Letters
- *Scientific American Frontiers* Video Guide
- Unit Projects
- Lesson Plans
- Reading Study Guides (Levels A and B)
- Spanish Reading Study Guides
- Challenge Readings
- Challenge and Extension Activities
- Reinforcing Key Concepts
- Vocabulary Practice
- Math Support and Practice
- Investigation Datasheets
- Chapter Investigations (Levels A, B, and C)
- Additional Investigations (Levels A, B, and C)
- Summarizing the Chapter

Unit Assessment Book contains complete resources for assessing student knowledge and performance.
- Chapter Diagnostic Tests
- Section Quizzes
- Chapter Tests (Levels A, B, and C)
- Alternative Assessments
- Unit Tests (Levels A, B, and C)

Unit Transparency Book includes instructional visuals for each chapter.
- Three-Minute Warm-Ups
- Note-Taking Models
- Daily Vocabulary Scaffolding
- Chapter Outlines
- Big Idea Flow Charts
- Chapter Teaching Visuals

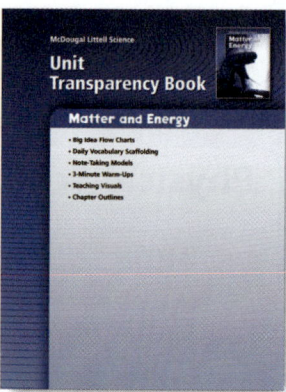

Lab Manual

Note-Taking/ Reading Study Guide

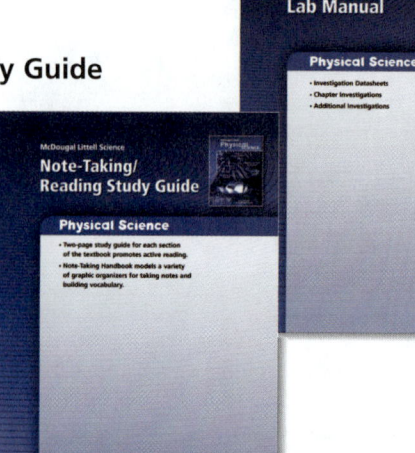

Program-Wide Print Resources

Process and Lab Skills

Problem Solving and Critical Thinking

Standardized Test Practice

Science Toolkit

City Science

Visual Glossary

Multi-Language Glossary

English Learners Package

Scientific American Frontiers Video Guide

How Stuff Works Express This quarterly magazine offers opportunities to explore current science topics.

Technology Resources

Scientific American Frontiers Video Program
Each specially tailored segment from this award-winning PBS series correlates to a unit; available on VHS and DVD

Audio CDs Complete chapter texts read in both English and Spanish

Lab Generator CD-ROM A searchable database of all activities from the program plus additional labs for each unit; edit and print your own version of labs

Test Generator CD-ROM

eEdition CD-ROM

EasyPlanner CD-ROM

Content Review CD-ROM

Power Presentations CD-ROM

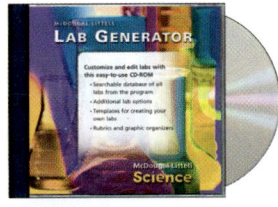

Online Resources

ClassZone.com

Content Review Online

eEdition Plus Online

EasyPlanner Plus Online

eTest Plus Online

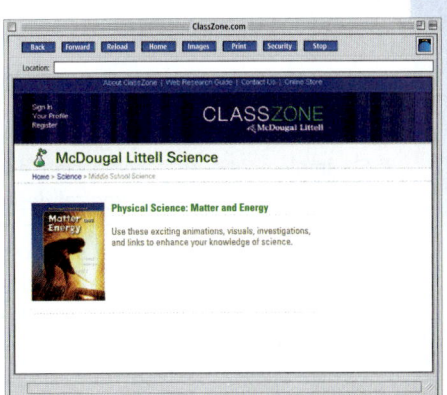

Correlation to National Science Education Standards

This chart provides an overview of how the five units of *McDougal Littell Physical Science* address the National Science Education Standards. The complete wording of the standards can be found at the end of this Teacher's Edition.

A. Science as Inquiry	Chapter and Section
A.1–A.8 **Abilities necessary to do scientific inquiry** Identify questions for investigation; design and conduct investigations; use evidence; think critically and logically; analyze alternative explanations; communicate; use mathematics.	pp. R2–R44, all Chapter Investigations, all Think Science features
A.9 **Understandings about scientific inquiry** Different kinds of investigations for different questions; investigations guided by current scientific knowledge; importance of mathematics and technology for data gathering and analysis; importance of evidence, logical argument, principles, models, and theories; role of legitimate skepticism; scientific investigations lead to new investigations.	pp. xxxviii–xli, 3.1, 6.2, 13.2, 17.2, 21.1

B. Physical Science	Chapter and Section
B.1 **Properties and changes of properties in matter** Physical properties; substances, elements, and compounds; chemical reactions.	1.1, 1.2, 1.3, 1.4, 2.1, 2.2, 5, 7.2, 8.1, 8.2, 8.3, 9.1, 9.3, 12.4
B.2 **Motions and forces** Position, speed, direction of motion; balanced and unbalanced forces.	10.1, 10.2, 10.3, 11.1, 11.3, 12.1, 12.2, 12.3, 12.4, 13.1
B.3 **Transfer of energy** Energy transfer; forms of energy; heat and light; electrical circuits; sun as source of Earth's energy.	3.1, 3.2, 3.3, 4.1, 4.2, 4.3, 7.3, 13.2, 15.1, 17.3, 17.4, 18.1, 18.2, 18.3, 19.1, 19.2, 19.3, 20.1, 20.2

C. Life Science	Chapter and Section
C.1 **Structure and function in living systems** Systems; structure and function; levels of organization; cells and cell activities; specialization; human body systems; disease.	5.1 (Connecting Sciences), 9.2, 14.2 (Connecting Sciences)

D. Earth and Space Science	Chapter and Section
D.1 **Earth's changing atmosphere**	8.2 (Connecting Sciences)
D.3 **Earth in the solar system** Sun, planets, asteroids, comets; regular and predictable motion and day, year, phases of the moon, and eclipses; gravity and orbits; sun as source of energy for earth; cause of seasons.	3.2, 3.3, 12.1, 17.3

E. Science and Technology	Chapter and Section
E.1–E.5 **Abilities of technological design** Identify problems; design a solution or product; implement a proposed design; evaluate completed designs or products; communicate the process of technological design.	2.3, 3.1, 4.3, Unit 2 (p. 5), 8.2, 10.2, 11.1, 12.2, 14.3, 16.4, 17.1, 17.3, 18.4, 20.3
E.6 **Understandings about science and technology** Similarities and differences between scientific inquiry and technological design; contributions of people in different cultures; reciprocal nature of science and technology; nonexistence of perfectly designed solutions; constraints, benefits, and unintended consequences of technological designs.	pp. xlii–xliii, All Frontiers in Science and Timelines in Science features, 1.2, 3.3, 7.1, 7.3, 7.4, 14.3, 18.4, 19.2, 19.3

F.	Science in Personal and Social Perspectives	Chapter and Section
F.1	**Personal health** Exercise; fitness; hazards and safety; tobacco, alcohol, and other drugs; nutrition; STDs; environmental health.	8.2, 9.2
F.2	**Populations, resources, and environments** Overpopulation and resource depletion; environmental degradation.	3.1
F.3	**Natural hazards** Earthquakes, landslides, wildfires, volcanic eruptions, floods, storms; hazards from human activity; personal and societal challenges.	7.2, 17.2, 19.2
F.4	**Risks and benefits** Risk analysis; natural, chemical, biological, social, and personal hazards; decisions based on risks and benefits.	8.3
F.5	**Science and technology in society** Science's influence on knowledge and world view; societal challenges and scientific research; technological influences on society; contributions from people of different cultures and times; work of scientists and engineers; ethical codes; limitations of science and technology.	All Timelines in Science features, 1.2, 3.2, 3.3, 7.4, 8.4, 14.3, 16, 17.2, 17.3, 18.4, 19.2, 19.3

G.	History and Nature of Science	Chapter and Section
G.1	**Science as a human endeavor** Diversity of people working in science, technology, and related fields; abilities required by science.	pp. xxxviii–xli, all Frontiers in Science features
G.2	**Nature of science** Observations, experiments, and models; tentative nature of scientific ideas; differences in interpretation of evidence; evaluation of results of investigations, experiments, observations, theoretical models, and explanations; importance of questioning, response to criticism, and communication.	5.2, 6.1, 6.3, 21.2
G.3	**History of science** Historical examples of inquiry and relationships between science and society; scientists and engineers as valued contributors to culture; challenges of breaking through accepted ideas.	All Frontiers in Science and Timelines in Science features, 5.2, 7.2, 11.1, 16.4

Correlations to Benchmarks

This chart provides an overview of how the five units of *McDougal Littell Physical Science* address the Project 2061 Benchmarks for Science Literacy. The complete wording of the benchmarks can be found at the end of this Teacher's Edition.

1. The Nature of Science	Chapter and Section
	The Nature of Science (pp. xxxviii–xli); 20.3; Think Science Features: 3.1, 6.2, 11.1, 13.2, 17.2, 21.1; Scientific Thinking Handbook (pp. R2–R9); Lab Handbook (pp. R10–R35)

3. The Nature of Technology	Chapter and Section
	The Nature of Technology (pp. xlii–xliii); 3.3, 8.4, 18.4, 19, 20.3, 21.2, 21.3, 21.4; Timelines in Science Features

4. The Physical Setting		Chapter and Section
4.B	THE EARTH	3.1, 4.3, 12.1
4.D	STRUCTURE OF MATTER	
4.D.1	All matter is made of atoms; atoms of any element are alike but different from atoms of other elements; different arrangements of atoms into groups compose all substances.	1.2, 1.3, 5.1, 6.1, 6.2
4.D.2	Equal volumes of different substances usually have different weights.	2.1, 2.3
4.D.3	Atoms and molecules are perpetually in motion; increased temperature means greater average energy of motion; states of matter: solids, liquids, gases.	1.2, 4.1
4.D.4	Temperature and acidity of a solution influence reaction rates. Many substances dissolve in water, which may facilitate reactions between them.	7.1, 8.2, 8.3
4.D.5	Greek philosophers' scientific ideas about elements; most elements tend to combine with others, so few elements are found in their pure form.	5.1
4.D.6	Groups of elements have similar properties; oxidation; some elements, like carbon and hydrogen, don't fit into any category and are essential elements of living matter.	5.2, 5.3, 7.1, 9.1, 9.2
4.D.7	Conservation of matter: the total weight of a closed system remains the same because the total number of atoms stays the same regardless of how they interact with one another.	7.2
4.E	ENERGY TRANSFORMATIONS	
4.E.1	Energy cannot be created or destroyed, but only changed from one form into another.	3.2, 13.2
4.E.2	Most of what goes on in the universe involves energy transformations.	3, 4.2, 4.3
4.E.3	Heat can be transferred through materials by the collisions of atoms or across space by radiation; convection currents transfer heat in fluid materials.	4.2, 4.3
4.E.4	Energy appears in many different forms, including heat energy, chemical energy, mechanical energy, and gravitational energy.	3.1, 4.2, 4.3, 13.2
4.F	MOTION	
4.F.1	Light from the Sun is made up of many different colors of light; objects that give off or reflect light have a different mix of colors.	17.3, 17.4

4.F.2 Something can be "seen" when light waves emitted or reflected by it enter the eye.	18.1, 18.3
4.F.3 An unbalanced force acting on an object changes its speed or direction of motion, or both. If the force acts toward a single center, the object's path may curve into an orbit around the center.	11.1, 11.2, 12.1
4.F.4 Vibrations in materials set up wavelike disturbances (such as sound) that spread away from the source; waves move at different speeds in different materials.	15, 16.1, 16.2, 17.1, 17.4
4.F.5 Human eyes respond to only a narrow range of wavelengths of electromagnetic radiation—visible light. Differences of wavelengths within that range are perceived as differences in color.	17.2, 17.4, 18.3
4.G FORCES OF NATURE	
4.G.1 Objects exerts gravitational forces on one another, but these forces depend on the mass and distance of objects, and may be too small to detect.	12.1
4.G.2 The Sun's gravitational pull holds Earth and other planets in their orbits; planets' gravitational pull keeps their moons in orbit around them.	12.1
4.G.3 Electric currents and magnets can exert a force on each other.	21.1, 21.2, 21.3

5. The Living Environment	**Chapter and Section**
5.E Flow of Matter and Energy	9.2
8. The Designed World	2.1, 2.3, 3.3, 7.4, 8.4, 9.3, 14.3, 20.3, 21.2
9. The Mathematical World	All Math in Science Features, 20.3
10. Historical Perspectives	5, 6, 7.2, 10.1, 11, 18.4
12. Habits of Mind	**Chapter and Section**
12.A VALUES AND ATTITUDES	Think Science Features: 3.1, 6.2, 11.1, 13.2, 17.2, 21.1
12.B COMPUTATION AND ESTIMATION	All Math in Science Features, Lab Handbook (pp. R10–R35)
12.C MANIPULATION AND OBSERVATION	All Investigates and Chapter Investigations
12.D COMMUNICATION SKILLS	All Chapter Investigations, Lab Handbook (pp. R10–R35)
12.E CRITICAL-RESPONSE SKILLS	Think Science Features: 3.1, 6.2, 11.1, 13.2, 17.2, 21.1; Scientific Thinking Handbook (pp. R2–R9)

Planning the Unit

The Pacing Guide provides suggested pacing for all chapters in the unit as well as the two unit features shown below.

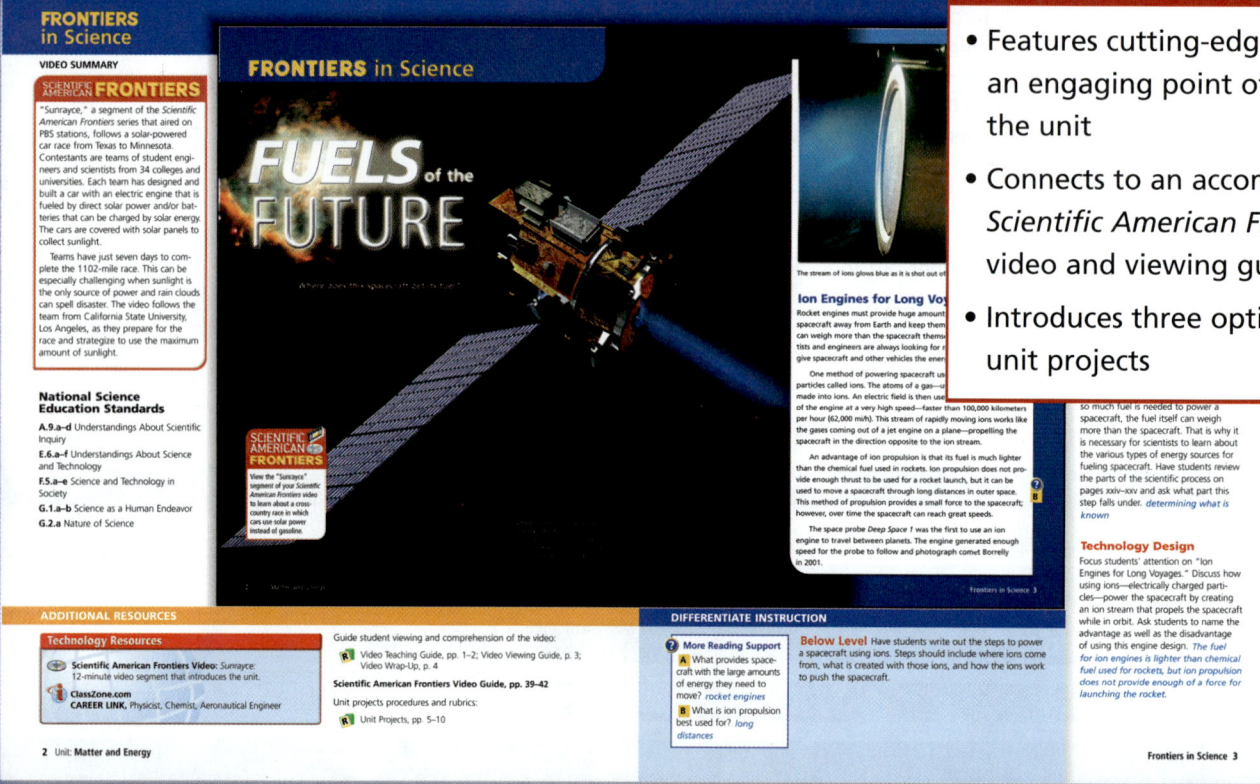

Frontiers in Science

- Features cutting-edge research as an engaging point of entry into the unit
- Connects to an accompanying *Scientific American Frontiers* video and viewing guide
- Introduces three options for unit projects

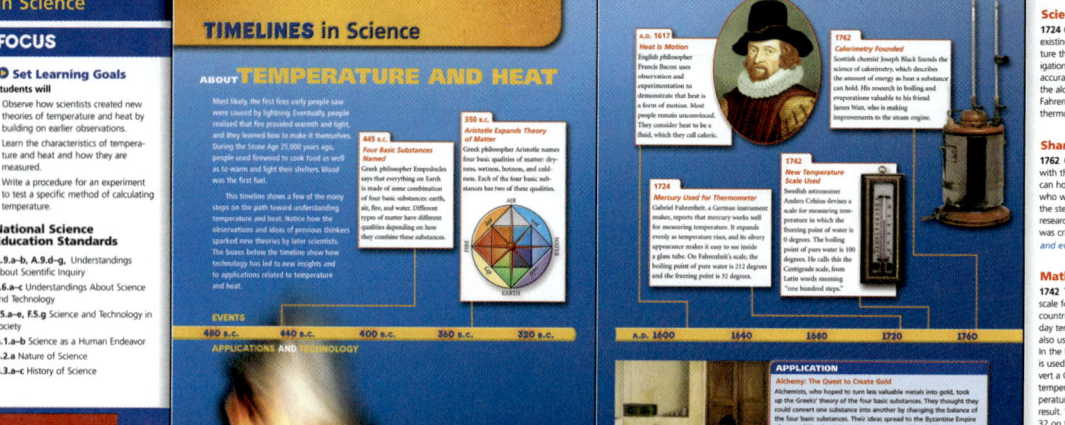

Timelines in Science

- Traces the history of key scientific discoveries
- Highlights interactions between science and technology

Matter and Energy Pacing Guide

The following pacing guide shows how the chapters in *Matter and Energy* can be adapted to fit your specific course needs. If you need to cover 5 units in a year, reduce the number of periods spent on the last section of each chapter by making the Chapter Review the homework.

	TRADITIONAL SCHEDULE (DAYS)	BLOCK SCHEDULE (DAYS)
Frontiers in Science: Fuels of the Future	1	0.5
Chapter 1 Introduction to Matter		
1.1 Matter has mass and volume.	2	1
1.2 Matter is made of atoms.	2	1
1.3 Matter combines to form different substances.	2	1
1.4 Matter exists in different physical states.	3	1.5
Chapter Investigation	1	0.5
Chapter 2 Properties of Matter		
2.1 Matter has observable properties.	2	1
2.2 Changes of state are physical changes.	2	1
2.3 Properties are used to identify substances.	3	1.5
Chapter Investigation	1	0.5
Chapter 3 Energy		
3.1 Energy exists in different forms.	2	1
3.2 Energy can change forms but is never lost.	2	1
3.3 Technology improves the way people use energy.	3	1.5
Chapter Investigation	1	0.5
Timelines in Science: About Temperature and Heat	1	0.5
Chapter 4 Temperature and Heat		
4.1 Temperature depends on particle movement.	2	1
4.2 Energy flows from warmer to cooler objects.	2	1
4.3 The transfer of energy as heat can be controlled.	3	1.5
Chapter Investigation	1	0.5
Total Days for Unit	**36**	**18**

Chemical Interactions Pacing Guide

The following pacing guide shows how the chapters in *Chemical Interactions* can be adapted to fit your specific course needs. If you need to cover 5 units in a year, reduce the number of periods spent on the last section of each chapter by making the Chapter Review the homework.

	TRADITIONAL SCHEDULE (DAYS)	BLOCK SCHEDULE (DAYS)
Frontiers in Science: Medicines from Nature	1	0.5
Chapter 5 Atomic Structure and the Periodic Table		
5.1 Atoms are the smallest form of elements.	2	1
5.2 Elements make up the periodic table.	2	1
5.3 The periodic table is a map of the elements.	3	1.5
Chapter Investigation	1	0.5
Chapter 6 Chemical Bonds and Compounds		
6.1 Elements combine to form compounds.	2	1
6.2 Chemical bonds hold compounds together.	2	1
6.3 Substances' properties depend on their bonds.	3	1.5
Chapter Investigation	1	0.5
Chapter 7 Chemical Reactions		
7.1 Chemical reactions alter arrangements of atoms.	2	1
7.2 The masses of reactants and products are equal.	2	1
7.3 Chemical reactions involve energy changes.	2	1
7.4 Life and industry depend on chemical reactions.	3	1.5
Chapter Investigation	1	0.5
Timelines in Science: The Story of Atomic Structure	1	0.5
Chapter 8 Solutions		
8.1 A solution is a type of mixture.	2	1
8.2 The amount of solute that dissolves can vary.	2	1
8.3 Solutions can be acidic, basic, or neutral.	2	1
8.4 Metal alloys are solid mixtures.	3	1.5
Chapter Investigation	1	0.5
Chapter 9 Carbon in Life and Materials		
9.1 Carbon-based molecules have many structures.	2	1
9.2 Carbon-based molecules are life's building blocks.	2	1
9.3 Carbon-based molecules are in many materials.	3	1.5
Chapter Investigation	1	0.5
Total Days for Unit	**46**	**23**

Motion and Forces Pacing Guide

The following pacing guide shows how the chapters in *Motion and Forces* can be adapted to fit your specific course needs. If you need to cover 5 units in a year, reduce the number of periods spent on the last section of each chapter by making the Chapter Review the homework.

	TRADITIONAL SCHEDULE (DAYS)	BLOCK SCHEDULE (DAYS)
Frontiers in Science: Robots on Mars	1	0.5
Chapter 10 Motion		
10.1 An object in motion changes position.	2	1
10.2 Speed measures how fast positions change.	2	1
10.3 Acceleration measures how fast velocity changes.	3	1.5
Chapter Investigation	1	0.5
Chapter 11 Forces		
11.1 Forces change motion.	2	1
11.2 Force and mass determine acceleration.	2	1
11.3 Forces act in pairs.	2	1
11.4 Forces transfer momentum.	3	1.5
Chapter Investigation	1	0.5
Chapter 12 Gravity, Friction, and Pressure		
12.1 Gravity is a force exerted by masses.	2	1
12.2 Friction is a force that opposes motion.	2	1
12.3 Pressure depends on force and area.	2	1
12.4 Fluids can exert a force on objects.	3	1.5
Chapter Investigation	1	0.5
Timelines in Science: Understanding Forces	1	0.5
Chapter 13 Work and Energy		
13.1 Work is the use of force to move an object.	2	1
13.2 Energy is transferred when work is done.	2	1
13.3 Power is the rate at which work is done.	3	1.5
Chapter Investigation	1	0.5
Chapter 14 Machines		
14.1 Machines help people do work.	2	1
14.2 Six simple machines have many uses.	2	1
14.3 Modern technology uses compound machines.	3	1.5
Chapter Investigation	1	0.5
Total Days for Unit	**46**	**23**

Waves, Sound, and Light Pacing Guide

The following pacing guide shows how the chapters in *Waves, Sound, and Light* can be adapted to fit your specific course needs. If you need to cover 5 units in a year, reduce the number of periods spent on the last section of each chapter by making the Chapter Review the homework.

	TRADITIONAL SCHEDULE (DAYS)	BLOCK SCHEDULE (DAYS)
Frontiers in Science: Sound Medicine	1	0.5
Chapter 15 Waves		
15.1 Waves transfer energy.	2	1
15.2 Waves have measurable properties.	2	1
15.3 Waves behave in predictable ways.	3	1.5
Chapter Investigation	1	0.5
Chapter 16 Sound		
16.1 Sound is a wave.	2	1
16.2 Frequency determines pitch.	2	1
16.3 Intensity determines loudness.	2	1
16.4 Sound has many uses.	3	1.5
Chapter Investigation	1	0.5
Chapter 17 Electromagnetic Waves		
17.1 Electromagnetic waves have unique traits.	2	1
17.2 Electromagnetic waves have many uses.	2	1
17.3 The Sun is the source of most visible light.	2	1
17.4 Light waves interact with materials.	3	1.5
Chapter Investigation	1	0.5
Timelines in Science: The Story of Light	1	0.5
Chapter 18 Light and Optics		
18.1 Mirrors form images by reflecting light.	2	1
18.2 Lenses form images by refracting light.	2	1
18.3 The eye is a natural optical tool.	2	1
18.4 Optical technology makes use of light waves.	3	1.5
Chapter Investigation	1	0.5
Total Days for Unit	**40**	**20**

Electricity and Magnetism Pacing Guide

The following pacing guide shows how the chapters in *Electricity and Magnetism* can be adapted to fit your specific course needs. If you need to cover 5 units in a year, reduce the number of periods spent on the last section of each chapter by making the Chapter Review the homework.

	TRADITIONAL SCHEDULE (DAYS)	BLOCK SCHEDULE (DAYS)
Frontiers in Science: Electronics in Music	1	0.5
Chapter 19 Electricity		
19.1 Materials can become electrically charged.	2	1
19.2 Charges can move from one place to another.	2	1
19.3 Electrical current is a flow of charge.	3	1.5
Chapter Investigation	1	0.5
Chapter 20 Circuits and Electronics		
20.1 Charge needs a continuous path to flow.	2	1
20.2 Circuits make electric current useful.	2	1
20.3 Electronic technology is based on circuits.	3	1.5
Chapter Investigation	1	0.5
Timelines in Science: The Story of Electronics	1	0.5
Chapter 21 Magnetism		
21.1 Magnetism is a force that acts at a distance.	2	1
21.2 Current can produce magnetism.	2	1
21.3 Magnetism can produce current.	2	1
21.4 Generators supply electrical energy.	3	1.5
Chapter Investigation	1	0.5
Total Days for Unit	**28**	**14**

Planning the Chapter

Complete planning support precedes each chapter.

Previewing Content
- Section-by-section science background notes
- Common Misconceptions notes

CHAPTER 1

Introduction to Matter

Physical Science
UNIFYING PRINCIPLES

PRINCIPLE 1	PRINCIPLE 2	PRINCIPLE 3	PRINCIPLE 4
Matter is made of particles too small to see.	Matter changes form and moves from place to place.	Energy changes form to another cannot be created or destroyed.	

Unit: Matter and Energy
BIG IDEAS

CHAPTER 1 Introduction to Matter	CHAPTER 2 Properties of Matter	CHAPTER 3 Energy
Everything that has mass and takes up space is matter.	Matter has properties that can be changed by physical and chemical processes.	Energy has different but it is always cons

CHAPTER 1 KEY CONCEPTS

SECTION 1	SECTION 2	SECTION
Matter has mass and volume. 1. All objects are made of matter. 2. Mass is a measure of the amount of matter. 3. Volume is a measure of the space matter occupies.	**Matter is made of atoms.** 1. Atoms are extremely small. 2. Atoms and molecules are always in motion.	**Matter comb different sub** 1. Matter can mixed. 2. Parts of mix the same or throughout.

 The Big Idea Flow Chart is available on p. T1 in the UNIT TRANSPARENCY BOOK.

5A Unit: Matter and Energy

Previewing Content

SECTION 1 **Matter has mass and volume.** pp. 9–15

1. **All objects are made of matter.**
   Anything that has **mass** and takes up space is **matter**. All the objects, liquids, gases, and living things in the universe are made of matter. Energy is not matter. However, under special circumstances, such as a nuclear reaction, energy can become matter and matter can become energy.

SECTION 2
1. **Ato**
   All m spoo atom have
   Ato

Previewing Content

SECTION 3 **Matter combines to form different substances.** pp. 21–26

1. **Matter can be pure or mixed.**
   Matter that contains only one kind of atom or molecule is pure. Matter often contains two or more substances mixed together. Substances can be composed of elements, compounds, or mixtures.
   - An **element** is a substance that contains only one kind of atom. Gold is the element represented in the diagram on the left below.

   Element: Gold 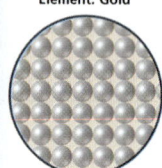   **Compound: Dry Ice**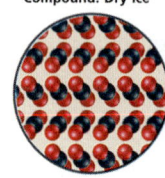

   - A **compound** is a substance that consists of two or more different types of atoms bonded together as shown in the diagram on the right above. Water molecules are compounds because they contain two kinds of atom bonded covalently. A molecule of oxygen is not a compound. Some compounds, such as table salt, are bonded ionically.
   - A **mixture** is a combination of different substances that retain their individual properties and can be separated by physical means.

2. **Parts of mixtures can be the same or different throughout.**
   Mixtures can be either heterogeneous or homogeneous.
   - A heterogeneous mixture has different properties in different parts of the mixture because the substances in different parts of the mixture vary.
   - A homogeneous mixture has substances evenly spread out throughout the mixture.

SECTION 4 **Matter exists in different physical states.** pp. 27–33

1. **Particle arrangement and motion determine the state of matter.**
   Solid, liquid, and gas are three common states of matter. When a substance changes from one state to another, the arrangement of its molecules changes. The distance between molecules and the attraction they have for one another change.

2. **Solid, liquid, and gas are common states of matter.**
   The state of a substance depends on the space between its particles and the way in which the particles move.
   - A **solid** has particles that are close together. The particles are attached to one another and can vibrate in place, but they cannot move from place to place.
   - A **liquid** has particles that are attracted to one another and are close together. The particles can slide over one another and move from one place to another.
   - A **gas** has particles that are not close to one another and can move about freely.

   The diagrams below show the arrangement and motion of particles in different states of matter.

   ① Solid 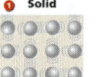   **② Liquid** 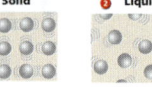   **③ Gas**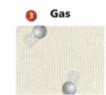

3. **Solids have a definite volume and shape.**
   A solid has a fixed volume and shape. The particles in some solids are in regular patterns and form crystals.

4. **Liquids have a definite volume but no definite shape.**
   A liquid has a definite volume because its particles are close enough together that they cannot move about freely, although they slide past each other. A liquid takes the shape of the container that it is in.

5. **Gases have no definite volume or shape.**
   A gas has no definite volume or shape. The volume, pressure, and temperature of a gas are related to one another, and changing one can change the others.

Common Misconceptions
ATOMS AND COLOR Students often think that individual atoms and molecules have the same properties as the substance they make up. For example, students might think a gold atom is hard and solid or a gas molecule is transparent.

 This misconception is addressed in the Teacher Demo on p. 22.

 MISCONCEPTION DATABASE CLASSZONE.COM Background on student misconceptions

5C Unit: Matter and Energy

T30

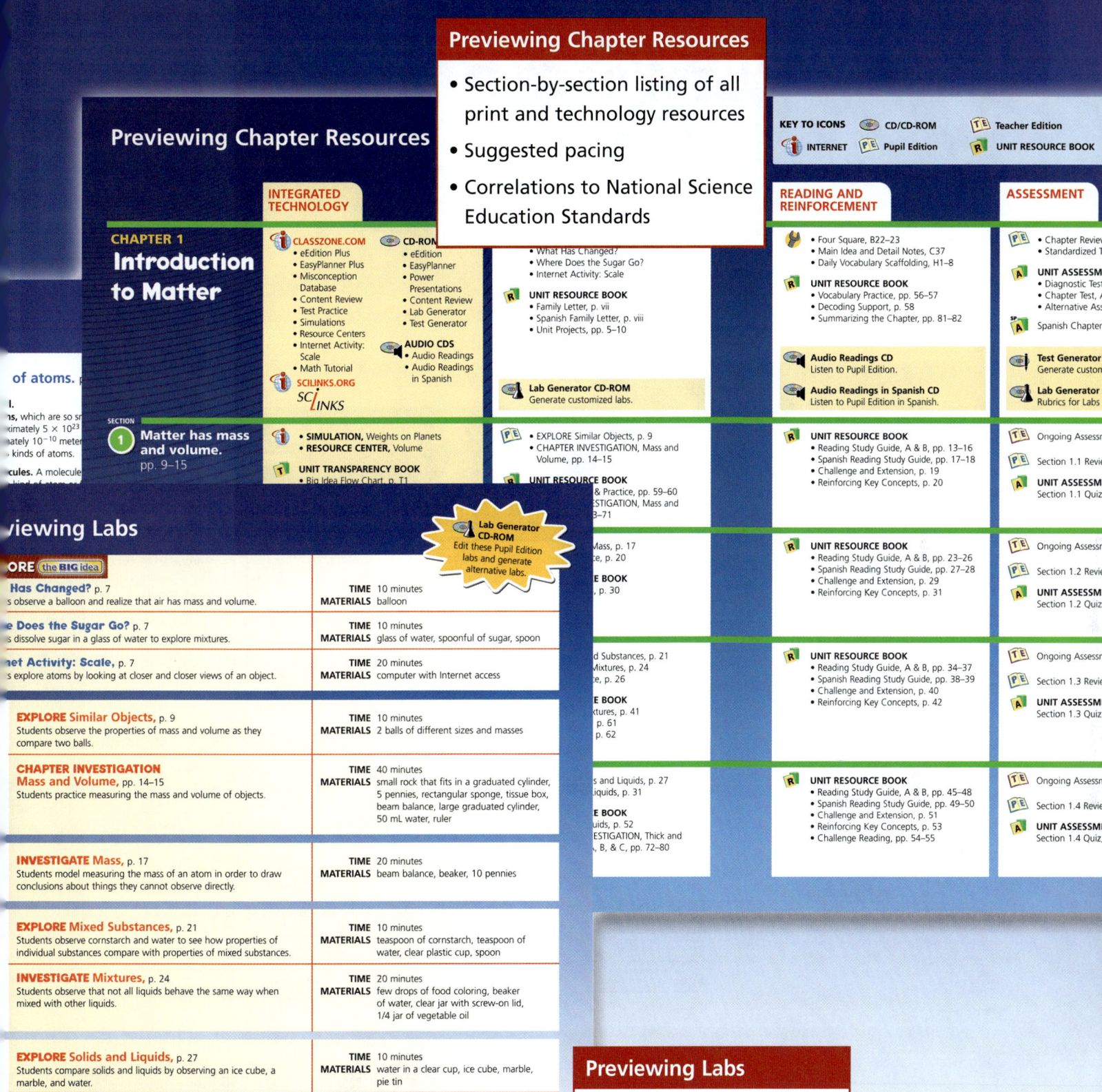

Planning the Lesson

Point-of-use support for each lesson provides a wealth of teaching options.

1. Prepare
- Concept and vocabulary review
- Note-taking and vocabulary strategies

2. Focus
- Set Learning Goals
- 3-Minute Warm-up

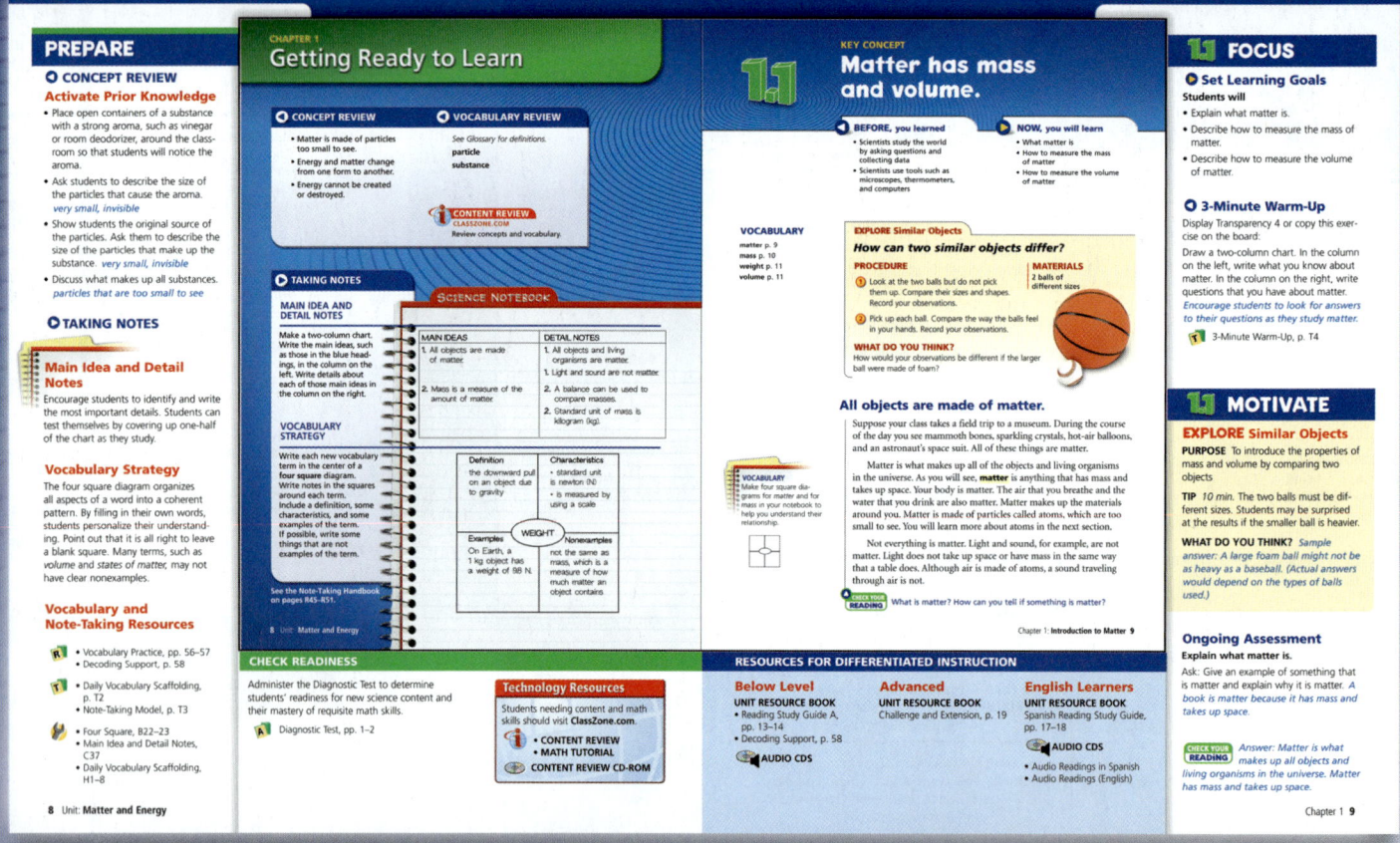

3. Motivate
- Engaging entry into the section
- Explore activity or Think About question

Lab Materials List

The following charts list the consumables, nonconsumables, and equipment needed for all activities. Quantities are per group of four students. Lab aprons, goggles, water, books, paper, pens, pencils, and calculators are assumed to be available for all activities.

Materials kits are available. For more information, please call McDougal Littell at 1-800-323-5435.

Consumables

Description	Quantity per Group	Explore page	Investigate page	Chapter Investigation page
acetate, blue, 4" x 4"	1			580
acetate, green, 4" x 4"	1			580
acetate, red, 4" x 4"	1			580
aluminum foil	11 ft	593, 667	89, 112, 638, 709	84, 122, 690
antacid tablet with calcium carbonate	2	253		
ashes	1/2 tsp		223	
bag, paper	1	159		
bag, plastic grocery	1	633		
bag, zip-top sandwich	2	506		298
baking powder	1 tsp	58		
baking soda	6 tsp	58	207	220, 260
ball, Styrofoam, 1"	6		277	
ball, Styrofoam, 3"	2		277	
balloon	4	642	207, 521, 638	
borax	2 tsp			298
bottle, plastic, 1/2 liter	2			366, 400
bottle, plastic, 1 liter	4		107, 241	366, 400
bottle, plastic, 2 liter with cap	1			298
bottle, plastic, pint	3		207	122
box, empty tissue	1			14
bread, cube 1/4"	1		286	
can, aluminum soda	1			84
candle, tea light	4	169, 282	223	188
cardboard tube, 12"	4	538	614	
cardboard, 10 cm x 25 cm	1		533	
cardboard, 12" x 24"	1		75	
cardboard, 20 cm x 20 cm	1			690
cardboard, 8.5" x 11"	1		331	
carrot, 1/4" slice	1	282		
carton, milk, 1/2 gallon	1		595	
clay, modeling	7 sticks	41, 611	107, 323, 608, 638	84, 122, 366, 604, 650

T34

Description	Quantity per Group	Explore page	Investigate page	Chapter Investigation page
coffee filter, basket	4		61, 578	
coffee filter, cone	1		241	
corn syrup, dark	10 mL		31	
cornstarch	2 tsp	21	47	
cornstarch solution	1–2 mL		286	
craft stick	3		181	690
crouton	1			84
cup, clear plastic	42	21, 27, 58, 214, 239, 245, 253, 345, 402, 434, 599	47, 61, 89, 112, 202, 248, 404, 578, 638	188, 220, 260
cup, paper, 6oz	1		386	
cup, Styrofoam	1			724
detergent powder	1 tsp			260
Epsom salts	10 tsp	214		188
feather	1	345		
flour	1 tsp	239		
foam packing pellet	1 cup			122
food coloring	1 bottle	504	24, 31, 107, 404, 506	298
fruit juice	30 mL			260
fruit or vegetable, various	1–3		655	
gelatin, liquid	1–2 mL		286	
glue stick	1		331	
glue, white	40 mL			298
hydrogen peroxide	30 mL			220
ice cube	1	27		
index card	8	86, 611	61, 608	604
iodine solution	2 mL		286	
iron filings	20 grams			188
isopropyl alcohol	250 mL		107	
lemon	1		655	
Lugol's iodine solution	6 mL		47	
marker, colored	1			604, 724
marker, permanent black	1		277, 404, 564	260
marker, water soluble black, various brands	3		241, 578	
marshmallow, small	1	282		
match, wood	16	169, 282	223	84
mechanical pencil lead	10 cm	652		
milk	2 tsp	573		
mineral oil	3–4 oz	599		
nail, iron, 3"	5	197	265, 714	
nail, small	1			400

Description	Quantity per Group	Explore page	Investigate page	Chapter Investigation page
nail, steel, 3"	3		265	
newspaper, 3 cm x 30 cm	2	633		
newspaper, sheet	1		358	
paper, construction, 8.5" x 11"	3			366, 502
paper, graph 8.5" x 11"	4	159	683, 729	152
paper, white 8.5" x 11"	3		564, 683	502
paper clip	33	353, 402	141, 181, 638, 655, 714	84, 650, 690, 724
paper towel	2–5			260
pencil, colored	4–6		729	
pepper, ground	1 tsp		61	
pH test strip, universal	7			260
pie plate, aluminum	6	27, 282	61	84, 650
plastic garbage bag, black, 4" x 4" piece	1		89	
plastic, garbage bag, white 4" x 4" piece	1		89	
plastic wrap	3–4 ft			122
plate, stiff paper, white	2		358, 608	
plate, Styrofoam	1			650
poster paint	1 oz		358	
posterboard, white, 20 cm x 20 cm	2	652		604
rice cake, caramel	1/4			84
rubber band, large	40	103	89, 521, 528, 533	122, 544, 690
salt, table	2 cups	197, 239	61, 248, 521	260
sand	3 lbs	71, 506	61	122, 502
sandpaper	2		455, 722	
seltzer tablet	2		202	
shampoo	30 mL			260
shoe box, cardboard	2		528	580
shoebox, cardboard with lid	1			544
soda water	1 1/2 cup	245		260
soil, potting	1/4 lb			122
sponge	1			14
spoon, plastic	8	21, 197, 214, 239	47, 61, 248	188, 220, 298
stearic acid	30 mL			56
steel wool	1 strand		672	
straw, clear drinking	10		107, 323, 404	298, 366
straw, jumbo drinking	1			366
string	14 meters	353, 402, 517	181, 323, 331, 350, 437, 500	440, 502

Description	Quantity per Group	Explore page	Investigate page	Chapter Investigation page
sugar	3 1/2 cups	169	181	188
sugar cube	2		223	
tape, duct	1 roll		614, 646	
tape, electrical	1 roll	559, 652, 667, 712	714, 722	690
tape, masking	2 rolls	184, 320, 538	429, 437, 500, 528, 595, 672	260, 336, 502, 580, 604, 724,
tape, packing	8"		75	
tape, transparent	1 roll			366
tofu, cube 1/4"	1		286	
toothpick	15		277, 323	690
vegetable oil	1 cup		24, 31	
vinegar	4 cups	197, 253	207	220, 260
vitamin C tablet, 100 mg	1		47	
water, distilled	200 mL			188, 260
wire, copper, insulated	1 meter		714	
wire, copper, uninsulated	250 cm	184, 559, 712		56, 690
wire, low voltage	150 cm	652	646	
wire, magnet	4 meters		722	724
yeast	1 gram			220

Nonconsumables

Description	Quantity per Group	Explore page	Investigate page	Chapter Investigation page
balance, triple beam	1		17, 75, 112, 141, 207, 248, 265, 323, 429	14, 84, 152, 220
ball, golf	1	381		
ball, baseball	1	9, 368		
ball, basketball	1	9, 368		
ball, racquetball	1		350, 429	
ball, table tennis	1	381		
ball, tennis	1	320, 345	316, 350	
battery holder, D cell	2		678	
battery, 6 volt	1		672	188
battery, AA	1	712, 719		
battery, D cell	2	184, 559, 652, 667	646, 678, 714, 722	690
beaker, 50 mL	1		17	
beaker, 100 mL	2	169	112, 181	188, 220
beaker, 200 mL	2	116		122
beaker, 500 mL	2	116	24, 248	
bolt with matching nut	10		171	

Description	Quantity per Group	Explore page	Investigate page	Chapter Investigation page
bowl, clear plastic, large	1	71, 197	107	
bowl, plastic, small	2		709	298
button, assortment	20	145		
calculator	1		429	336
can opener	1			84
carbon sample	1	169		
chair	1	489		440
cloth, wool, 8" x 8"	1	642	61	650
clothespin, wood, lever type	1	703		690
coffee can with lid, 1 lb	1	122		400
coin, penny	50	159, 197	17, 112, 655	14
coin, quarter	1	345		
comb, plastic	1		61	
compass	1	712	722	
dishpan, plastic	1		386	400
dowel rod, 1/4" diameter	6"	703		84
dowel rod, 1/4" diameter	24"			474
electrode, copper	1			188
electrode, zinc	1			188
eyedropper	3		47, 241, 286	
film canister with lid	5			152
flashlight with batteries	1	573		604
fork, steel	1	559		
funnel	1		61, 207	
graduated cylinder, 100 mL	1	214	31, 47, 61, 112, 265	14, 84, 122, 220, 260, 502
hand lens	1		181	188
jar, clear plastic, 2 liter with lid	1	573		
jar, baby food with lid	1		24, 521, 672	298
lamp, gooseneck desk	1		570, 608	580
lens, convex	2	611	608, 614	604
lid, baby food jar	4		286	
lid, film canister	4		323	
light bulb holder	1	184, 652, 719	646, 678	188, 690
light bulb, compact fluorescent, 15 watt	1		570	
light bulb, flashlight	1	184, 652, 667, 719	646, 678	188, 690
light bulb, incandescent, 60 watt	1		570	
light bulb, incandescent, 75 watt	1		608	580
light bulb, incandescent, 100 watt	1		570	
light bulb, small fluorescent tube	1	642		
machine, small (stapler, screw driver, can opener, etc.)	1	449		

Description	Quantity per Group	Explore page	Investigate page	Chapter Investigation page
magnet, bar	1		709	
magnet, high strength	1			724
magnet, low strength	1			724
magnet, medium strength	1			724
magnet, disc	3	703		
marble, metal	10	27, 434	358, 370	336
measuring spoon, teaspoon	1	573	207	220, 260, 298
meter stick	2	320	75, 350, 422, 437, 455	336, 366, 400, 440, 474, 502, 604
mirror on a stand	1	553		
mirror, 3 1/2" x 3 1/2"	2		595	
motor, small ultra-sensitive	1	719		
multimeter	1		655	
paint brush	1		358	
pan, glass, 10" x 14"	1	504	506	
pebble	1	71		
prism	1		564	
protractor	1		595	
pulley cord	4 ft		461	474
pulley, large	2			474
pulley, medium	2		461	474
pulley, small	2			474
radio, portable with batteries	1	559		
radiometer	1		556	
ribbon	20 cm	489		
ring stand with ring	1		461	84, 298
rock, medium	1	71		
rock, small	1			14
rope	2–3 m	489		
ruler, metric	2	86, 506, 525, 703	370, 404, 429, 533, 722	14, 336, 400, 544, 580, 724
scissors	1	137	89, 323, 331, 358, 521, 533, 578, 595	298, 366, 502, 544, 580, 690
sewing needle	1		709	
small object, black	1			580
small object, red	1			580
small object, white	1			580
small object, yellow	1			580
solar calculator with no battery backup	1	86		
spiral notebook	1		422	

Description	Quantity per Group	Explore page	Investigate page	Chapter Investigation page
spoon, large metal	1	517		
spring scale	2		362, 422, 437, 455, 461	440, 474
spring toy	1		493	
stereo system or boom box	1			724
stopper, cork	1			84
stopwatch	1	116, 214, 320, 434	89, 112, 202, 286, 323, 429, 437, 500	122, 220, 298, 336, 440
Styrofoam board, 2 cm x 20 cm x 20 cm	1	395		
test tube	3	169	31	56, 188
test tube rack	1		31	56
thermometer	3	116, 214	89, 112, 248, 564	122, 220
thermometer, 12"	1			56, 84
tongs	1	282	223	
tongs, test tube	1	169		56, 188
toy car, large	1		75	440
TV with infrared remote control	1	553		
washer, metal 1"	20		75, 331, 500	
washer, metal 7/16"	21			152
weight, hooked, 100 gram	1		437, 461	474
weight, hooked, 500 gram	1			474
wire cutters	1			690
wire lead with alligator clips	4		672, 678	188, 690, 724
wood block, 2" cube	1		350	
wood block, 2" with eye hook	1		455	
wood block, 3" x 3" x 1"	1	506		
wood board, 1 m x 15 cm	1		323, 455	440, 474
wood board, 30 cm x 30 cm	1		429	

Unit Resource Book Datasheets

Description	Explore page	Investigate page	Chapter Investigation page
Morse Code Chart			690
Tool Template		331	

Safety Equipment

Description	Explore page	Investigate page	Chapter Investigation page
gloves		286	122

McDougal Littell
Physical SCIENCE

- Chemical Interactions
- Waves, Sound, and Light
- Matter and Energy
- Motion and Forces
- Electricity and Magnetism

PHYSICAL SCIENCE

Standards and Benchmarks	xxiv
Introducing Physical Science	xxviii
Unifying Principles of Physical Science	xxx
The Nature of Science	xxxviii
The Nature of Technology	xlii
Using *McDougal Littell Science*	xliv

1 Matter and Energy
Introduction to Matter
Properties of Matter
Energy
Temperature and Heat

2 Chemical Interactions
Atomic Structure and the Periodic Table
Chemical Bonds and Compounds
Chemical Reactions
Solutions
Carbon in Life and Materials

3 Motion and Forces
Motion
Forces
Gravity, Friction, and Pressure
Work and Energy
Machines

4 Waves, Sound, and Light
Waves
Sound
Electromagnetic Waves
Light and Optics

5 Electricity and Magnetism
Electricity
Circuits and Electronics
Magnetism

Scientific Thinking Handbook	R2
Lab Handbook	R10
Math Handbook	R36
Note-Taking Handbook	R45
Glossary	R52
Index	R71
Acknowledgments	R92

Acknowledgments: Excerpts and adaptations from *National Science Education Standards* by the National Academy of Sciences. Copyright © 1996 by the National Academy of Sciences. Reprinted with permission from the National Academies Press, Washington, D.C.

Excerpts and adaptations from *Benchmarks for Science Literacy: Project 2061*. Copyright © 1993 by the American Association for the Advancement of Science. Reprinted with permission.

Copyright © 2006 by McDougal Littell, a division of Houghton Mifflin Company.

No part of this work may be reproduced or transmitted in any form or by any means, electronic or mechanical, including photocopy and recording, or by any information storage or retrieval system without the prior written permission of McDougal Littell unless such copying is expressly permitted by federal copyright law. Address inquiries to Supervisor, Rights and Permissions, McDougal Littell, P.O. Box 1667, Evanston, IL 60204.

Printed in the United States of America

ISBN: 0-618-61557-1   X 2 3 4 5 6 7 8 VJM 09 08 07 06 05

Internet Web Site: http://www.mcdougallittell.com

Science Consultants

Chief Science Consultant

James Trefil, Ph.D. is the Clarence J. Robinson Professor of Physics at George Mason University. He is the author or co-author of more than 25 books, including *Science Matters* and *The Nature of Science*. Dr. Trefil is a member of the American Association for the Advancement of Science's Committee on the Public Understanding of Science and Technology. He is also a fellow of the World Economic Forum and a frequent contributor to *Smithsonian* magazine.

Rita Ann Calvo, Ph.D. is Senior Lecturer in Molecular Biology and Genetics at Cornell University, where for 12 years she also directed the Cornell Institute for Biology Teachers. Dr. Calvo is the 1999 recipient of the College and University Teaching Award from the National Association of Biology Teachers.

Kenneth Cutler, M.S. is the Education Coordinator for the Julius L. Chambers Biomedical Biotechnology Research Institute at North Carolina Central University. A former middle school and high school science teacher, he received a 1999 Presidential Award for Excellence in Science Teaching.

Instructional Design Consultants

Douglas Carnine, Ph.D. is Professor of Education and Director of the National Center for Improving the Tools of Educators at the University of Oregon. He is the author of seven books and over 100 other scholarly publications, primarily in the areas of instructional design and effective instructional strategies and tools for diverse learners. Dr. Carnine also serves as a member of the National Institute for Literacy Advisory Board.

Linda Carnine, Ph.D. consults with school districts on curriculum development and effective instruction for students struggling academically. A former teacher and school administrator, Dr. Carnine also co-authored a popular remedial reading program.

Donald Steely, Ph.D. serves as principal investigator at the Oregon Center for Applied Science (ORCAS) on federal grants for science and language arts programs. His background also includes teaching and authoring of print and multimedia programs in science, mathematics, history, and spelling.

Sam Miller, Ph.D. is a middle school science teacher and the Teacher Development Liaison for the Eugene, Oregon, Public Schools. He is the author of curricula for teaching science, mathematics, computer skills, and language arts.

Vicky Vachon, Ph.D. consults with school districts throughout the United States and Canada on improving overall academic achievement with a focus on literacy. She is also co-author of a widely used program for remedial readers.

Content Reviewers

John Beaver, Ph.D.
Ecology
Professor, Director of Science Education Center
College of Education and Human Services
Western Illinois University
Macomb, IL

Donald J. DeCoste, Ph.D.
Matter and Energy, Chemical Interactions
Chemistry Instructor
University of Illinois
Urbana-Champaign, IL

Dorothy Ann Fallows, Ph.D., MSc
Diversity of Living Things, Microbiology
Partners in Health
Boston, MA

Michael Foote, Ph.D.
The Changing Earth, Life Over Time
Associate Professor
Department of the Geophysical Sciences
The University of Chicago
Chicago, IL

Lucy Fortson, Ph.D.
Space Science
Director of Astronomy
Adler Planetarium and Astronomy Museum
Chicago, IL

Elizabeth Godrick, Ph.D.
Human Biology
Professor, CAS Biology
Boston University
Boston, MA

Isabelle Sacramento Grilo, M.S.
The Changing Earth
Lecturer, Department of the Geological Sciences
San Diego State University
San Diego, CA

David Harbster, MSc
Diversity of Living Things
Professor of Biology
Paradise Valley Community College
Phoenix, AZ

Richard D. Norris, Ph.D.
Earth's Waters
Professor of Paleobiology
Scripps Institution of Oceanography
University of California, San Diego
La Jolla, CA

Donald B. Peck, M.S.
Motion and Forces; Waves, Sound, and Light; Electricity and Magnetism
Director of the Center for Science Education (retired)
Fairleigh Dickinson University
Madison, NJ

Javier Penalosa, Ph.D.
Diversity of Living Things, Plants
Associate Professor, Biology Department
Buffalo State College
Buffalo, NY

Raymond T. Pierrehumbert, Ph.D.
Earth's Atmosphere
Professor in Geophysical Sciences (Atmospheric Science)
The University of Chicago
Chicago, IL

Brian J. Skinner, Ph.D.
Earth's Surface
Eugene Higgins Professor of Geology and Geophysics
Yale University
New Haven, CT

Nancy E. Spaulding, M.S.
Earth's Surface, The Changing Earth, Earth's Waters
Earth Science Teacher (retired)
Elmira Free Academy
Elmira, NY

Steven S. Zumdahl, Ph.D.
Matter and Energy, Chemical Interactions
Professor Emeritus of Chemistry
University of Illinois
Urbana-Champaign, IL

Susan L. Zumdahl, M.S.
Matter and Energy, Chemical Interactions
Chemistry Education Specialist
University of Illinois
Urbana-Champaign, IL

Safety Consultant

Juliana Texley, Ph.D.
Former K–12 Science Teacher and School Superintendent
Boca Raton, FL

English Language Advisor

Judy Lewis, M.A.
Director, State and Federal Programs for reading proficiency and high risk populations
Rancho Cordova, CA

Teacher Panel Members

Carol Arbour
Tallmadge Middle School,
Tallmadge, OH

Patty Belcher
Goodrich Middle School,
Akron, OH

Gwen Broestl
Luis Munoz Marin Middle School,
Cleveland, OH

Al Brofman
Tehipite Middle School,
Fresno, CA

John Cockrell
Clinton Middle School,
Columbus, OH

Jenifer Cox
Sylvan Middle School,
Citrus Heights, CA

Linda Culpepper
Martin Middle School,
Charlotte, NC

Melvin Figueroa
New River Middle School,
Ft. Lauderdale, FL

Doretha Grier
Kannapolis Middle School,
Kannapolis, NC

Robert Hood
Alexander Hamilton Middle School,
Cleveland, OH

Scott Hudson
Covedale Elementary School,
Cincinnati, OH

Loretta Langdon
Princeton Middle School,
Princeton, NC

Carlyn Little
Glades Middle School,
Miami, FL

Ann Marie Lynn
Amelia Earhart Middle School,
Riverside, CA

James Minogue
Lowe's Grove Middle School,
Durham, NC

Kathleen Montagnino-DeMatteo
Jefferson Davis Middle School,
West Palm Beach, FL

Joann Myers
Buchanan Middle School,
Tampa, FL

Barbara Newell
Charles Evans Hughes Middle School,
Long Beach, CA

Anita Parker
Kannapolis Middle School,
Kannapolis, NC

Greg Pirolo
Golden Valley Middle School,
San Bernardino, CA

Laura Pottmyer
Apex Middle School,
Apex, NC

Lynn Prichard
Williams Middle Magnet School,
Tampa, FL

Jacque Quick
Walter Williams High School,
Burlington, NC

Robert Glenn Reynolds
Hillman Middle School,
Youngstown, OH

Stacy Rinehart
Lufkin Road Middle School,
Apex, NC

Theresa Short
Abbott Middle School,
Fayetteville, NC

Rita Slivka
Alexander Hamilton Middle School,
Cleveland, OH

Marie Sofsak
B F Stanton Middle School,
Alliance, OH

Nancy Stubbs
Sweetwater Union Unified School District,
Chula Vista, CA

Sharon Stull
Quail Hollow Middle School,
Charlotte, NC

Donna Taylor
Bak Middle School of the Arts,
West Palm Beach, FL

Sandi Thompson
Harding Middle School,
Lakewood, OH

Lori Walker
Audubon Middle School & Magnet Center,
Los Angeles, CA

Teacher Lab Evaluators

Andrew Boy
W.E.B. DuBois Academy,
Cincinnati, OH

Jill Brimm-Byrne
Albany Park Academy,
Chicago, IL

Gwen Broestl
Luis Munoz Marin Middle School,
Cleveland, OH

Al Brofman
Tehipite Middle School,
Fresno, CA

Michael A. Burstein
The Rashi School,
Newton, MA

Trudi Coutts
Madison Middle School,
Naperville, IL

Jenifer Cox
Sylvan Middle School,
Citrus Heights, CA

Larry Cwik
Madison Middle School,
Naperville, IL

Jennifer Donatelli
Kennedy Junior High School,
Lisle, IL

Melissa Dupree
Lakeside Middle School,
Evans, GA

Carl Fechko
Luis Munoz Marin Middle School,
Cleveland, OH

Paige Fullhart
Highland Middle School,
Libertyville, IL

Sue Hood
Glen Crest Middle School,
Glen Ellyn, IL

William Luzader
Plymouth Community Intermediate School,
Plymouth, MA

Ann Min
Beardsley Middle School,
Crystal Lake, IL

Aileen Mueller
Kennedy Junior High School,
Lisle, IL

Nancy Nega
Churchville Middle School,
Elmhurst, IL

Oscar Newman
Sumner Math and Science Academy,
Chicago, IL

Lynn Prichard
Williams Middle Magnet School,
Tampa, FL

Jacque Quick
Walter Williams High School,
Burlington, NC

Stacy Rinehart
Lufkin Road Middle School,
Apex, NC

Seth Robey
Gwendolyn Brooks Middle School,
Oak Park, IL

Kevin Steele
Grissom Middle School,
Tinley Park, IL

UNIT 1
Matter and Energy

Unit Features

SCIENTIFIC AMERICAN **FRONTIERS IN SCIENCE** *Fuels of the Future* — 2

TIMELINES IN SCIENCE *About Temperature and Heat* — 96

1 Introduction to Matter — 6

the BIG idea
Everything that has mass and takes up space is matter.

1. **Matter has mass and volume.** — 9
   CHAPTER INVESTIGATION *Mass and Volume* — 14
2. **Matter is made of atoms.** — 16
   EXTREME SCIENCE *Particles Too Small to See* — 20
3. **Matter combines to form different substances.** — 21
   MATH IN SCIENCE *Making a Circle Graph* — 26
4. **Matter exists in different physical states.** — 27

2 Properties of Matter — 38

the BIG idea
Matter has properties that can be changed by physical and chemical processes.

1. **Matter has observable properties.** — 41
   MATH IN SCIENCE *Solving Proportions* — 49
2. **Changes of state are physical changes.** — 50
   CHAPTER INVESTIGATION *Freezing Point* — 56
3. **Properties are used to identify substances.** — 58
   CONNECTING SCIENCES *Separating Minerals* — 63

What properties could help you identify this sculpture as sugar? page 38

vi Physical Science

What different forms of energy are shown in this photograph? page 68

3 Energy — 68

the BIG idea
Energy has different forms, but it is always conserved.

1. **Energy exists in different forms.** — 71
   THINK SCIENCE *Gasoline or Electric?* — 77
2. **Energy can change forms but is never lost.** — 78
   CHAPTER INVESTIGATION *Energy Conversions* — 84
3. **Technology improves the ways people use energy.** — 86
   MATH IN SCIENCE *Using Formulas* — 91

4 Temperature and Heat — 100

the BIG idea
Heat is a flow of energy due to temperature differences.

1. **Temperature depends on particle movement.** — 103
   MATH IN SCIENCE *Metric Conversions* — 109
2. **Energy flows from warmer to cooler objects.** — 110
   SCIENCE ON THE JOB *Cooking with Heat* — 115
3. **The transfer of energy as heat can be controlled.** — 116
   CHAPTER INVESTIGATION *Insulators* — 122

Visual Highlights

States of Matter	29
Physical Changes	45
Converting Energy	81
Insulation	120

Table of Contents vii

UNIT 2
Chemical Interactions

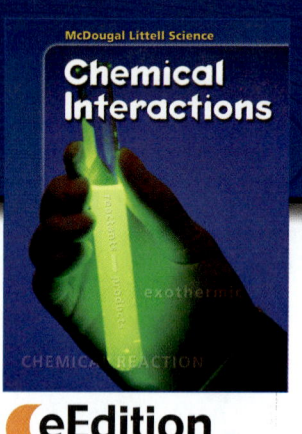
eEdition

Unit Features

FRONTIERS IN SCIENCE *Medicines from Nature* — 130

TIMELINES IN SCIENCE *The Story of Atomic Structure* — 232

5 Atomic Structure and the Periodic Table — 134

the BIG idea
A substance's atomic structure determines its physical and chemical properties.

1. **Atoms are the smallest form of elements.** — 137
   CONNECTING SCIENCES *Elements of Life* — 144
2. **Elements make up the periodic table.** — 145
   CHAPTER INVESTIGATION *Modeling Atomic Masses* — 152
3. **The periodic table is a map of the elements.** — 154
   MATH IN SCIENCE *Using Scientific Notation* — 161

6 Chemical Bonds and Compounds — 166

the BIG idea
The properties of compounds depend on their atoms and chemical bonds.

1. **Elements combine to form compounds.** — 169
   MATH IN SCIENCE *Calculating Ratios* — 174
2. **Chemical bonds hold compounds together.** — 175
   THINK SCIENCE *Stick to It* — 183
3. **Substances' properties depend on their bonds.** — 184
   CHAPTER INVESTIGATION *Chemical Bonds* — 188

How do these skydivers stay together? How is this similar to the way atoms stay together? page 166

viii Physical Science

7 Chemical Reactions — 194

the BIG idea
Chemical reactions form new substances by breaking and making chemical bonds.

1. **Chemical reactions alter arrangements of atoms.** — 197
   MATH IN SCIENCE *Analyzing Line Graphs* — 205
2. **The masses of reactants and products are equal.** — 206
   SCIENCE ON THE JOB *Chemistry in Firefighting* — 213
3. **Chemical reactions involve energy changes.** — 214
   CHAPTER INVESTIGATION *Exothermic or Endothermic?* — 220
4. **Life and industry depend on chemical reactions.** — 222

8 Solutions — 236

the BIG idea
When substances dissolve to form a solution, the properties of the mixture change.

1. **A solution is a type of mixture.** — 239
2. **The amount of solute that dissolves can vary.** — 245
   CONNECTING SCIENCES *Cool, Clear Water* — 252
3. **Solutions can be acidic, basic, or neutral.** — 253
   CHAPTER INVESTIGATION *Acids and Bases* — 260
4. **Metal alloys are solid mixtures.** — 262
   MATH IN SCIENCE *Calculating Percentages* — 267

9 Carbon in Life and Materials — 272

the BIG idea
Carbon is essential to living things and to modern materials.

1. **Carbon-based molecules have many structures.** — 275
   EXTREME SCIENCE *Stronger Than Steel* — 281
2. **Carbon-based molecules are life's building blocks.** — 282
   MATH IN SCIENCE *Making Bar Graphs* — 290
3. **Carbon-based molecules are in many materials.** — 291
   CHAPTER INVESTIGATION *Polymers* — 298

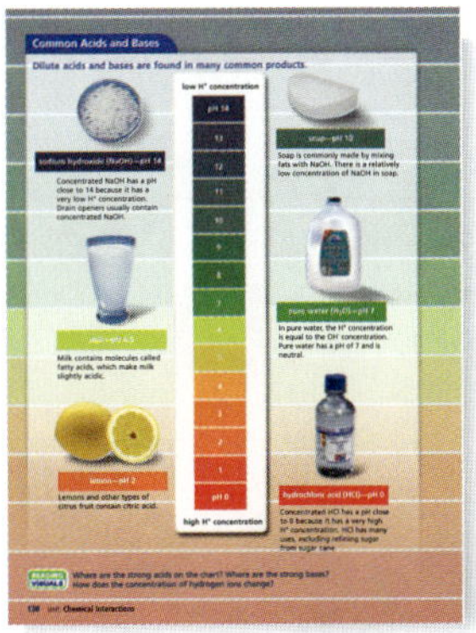

Visual Highlights

The Periodic Table of the Elements	148
Comparing Bonds	180
Balancing Equations with Coefficients	211
Chemical Reactions in Catalytic Converters	225
Common Acids and Bases	258
Carbon Chains and Carbon Rings	279
Nucleic Acid Structure and Function	288
Using Petroleum	293

Table of Contents ix

UNIT 3
Motion and Forces

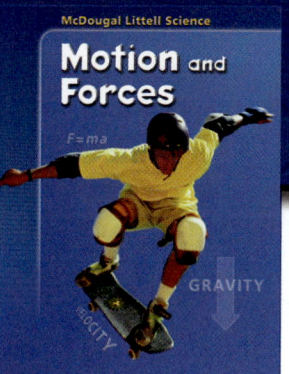

Unit Features

 **FRONTIERS IN SCIENCE** *Robots on Mars* — 306

TIMELINES IN SCIENCE *Understanding Forces* — 412

10 Motion — 310

the BIG idea
The motion of an object can be described and predicted.

1. **An object in motion changes position.** — 313
   SCIENCE ON THE JOB *Physics for Rescuers* — 319
2. **Speed measures how fast position changes.** — 420
   MATH IN SCIENCE *Working with Units* — 328
3. **Acceleration measures how fast velocity changes.** — 329
   CHAPTER INVESTIGATION *Acceleration and Slope* — 336

11 Forces — 342

the BIG idea
Forces change the motion of objects in predictable ways.

1. **Forces change motion.** — 345
   THINK SCIENCE *Why Do These Rocks Slide?* — 352
2. **Force and mass determine acceleration.** — 353
   MATH IN SCIENCE *Using Significant Figures* — 360
3. **Forces act in pairs.** — 361
   CHAPTER INVESTIGATION *Newton's Laws of Motion* — 366
4. **Forces transfer momentum.** — 368

What must happen for a team to win this tug of war? page 342

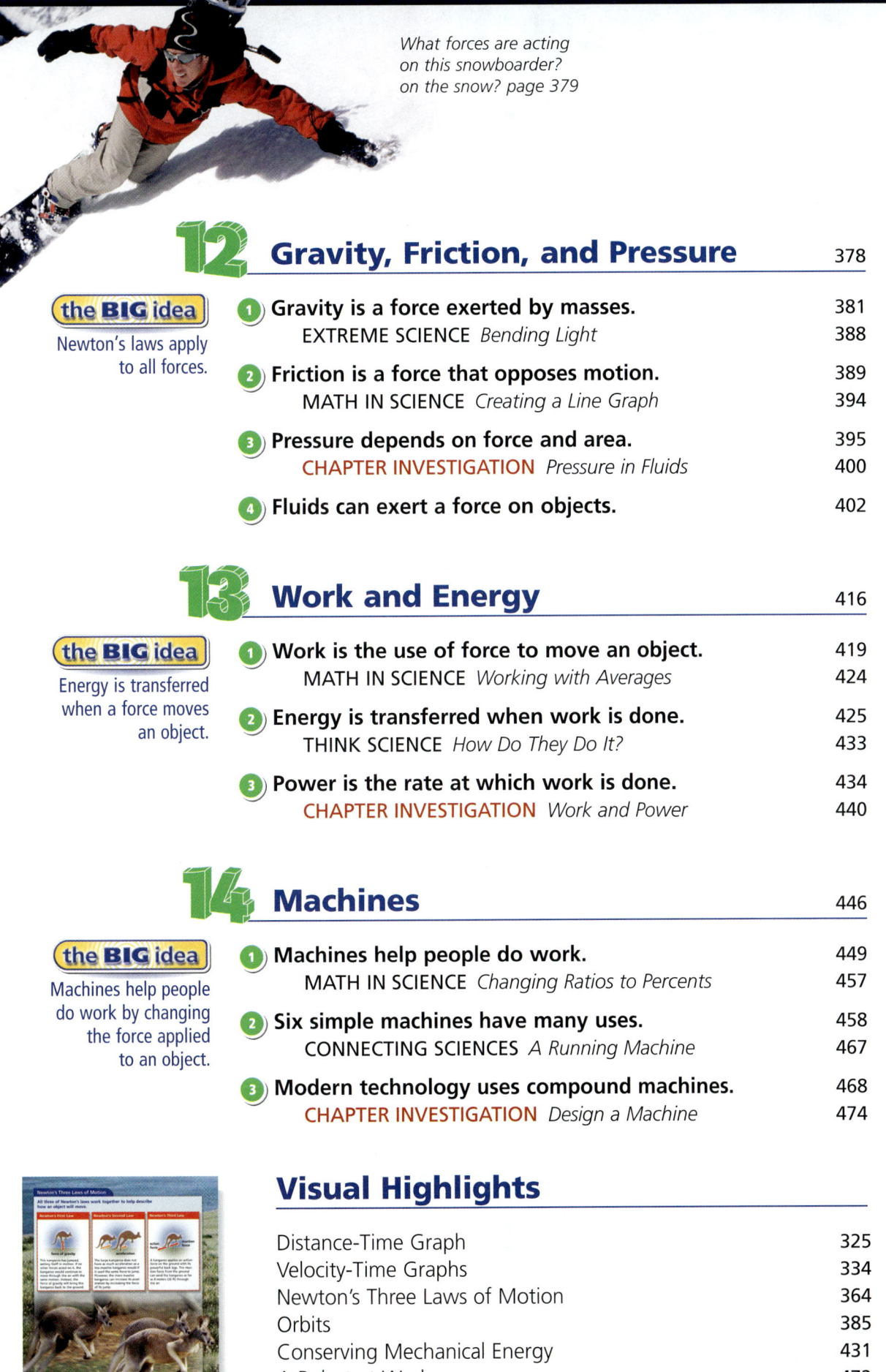

What forces are acting on this snowboarder? on the snow? page 379

12 Gravity, Friction, and Pressure — 378

the BIG idea
Newton's laws apply to all forces.

1. **Gravity is a force exerted by masses.** — 381
   EXTREME SCIENCE *Bending Light* — 388
2. **Friction is a force that opposes motion.** — 389
   MATH IN SCIENCE *Creating a Line Graph* — 394
3. **Pressure depends on force and area.** — 395
   CHAPTER INVESTIGATION *Pressure in Fluids* — 400
4. **Fluids can exert a force on objects.** — 402

13 Work and Energy — 416

the BIG idea
Energy is transferred when a force moves an object.

1. **Work is the use of force to move an object.** — 419
   MATH IN SCIENCE *Working with Averages* — 424
2. **Energy is transferred when work is done.** — 425
   THINK SCIENCE *How Do They Do It?* — 433
3. **Power is the rate at which work is done.** — 434
   CHAPTER INVESTIGATION *Work and Power* — 440

14 Machines — 446

the BIG idea
Machines help people do work by changing the force applied to an object.

1. **Machines help people do work.** — 449
   MATH IN SCIENCE *Changing Ratios to Percents* — 457
2. **Six simple machines have many uses.** — 458
   CONNECTING SCIENCES *A Running Machine* — 467
3. **Modern technology uses compound machines.** — 468
   CHAPTER INVESTIGATION *Design a Machine* — 474

Visual Highlights

Distance-Time Graph	325
Velocity-Time Graphs	334
Newton's Three Laws of Motion	364
Orbits	385
Conserving Mechanical Energy	431
A Robot at Work	472

Table of Contents xi

UNIT 4
Waves, Sound, and Light

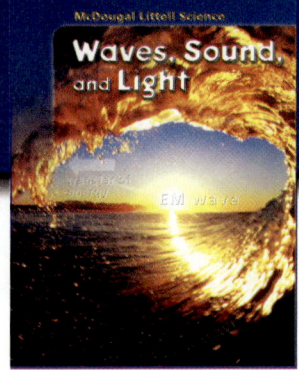
eEdition

Unit Features

FRONTIERS IN SCIENCE *Sound Medicine* — 482

TIMELINES IN SCIENCE *The Story of Light* — 586

15 Waves — 486

the BIG idea
Waves transfer energy and interact in predictable ways.

1. **Waves transfer energy.** — 489
   MATH IN SCIENCE *Mean, Median, and Mode* — 495
2. **Waves have measurable properties.** — 496
   CHAPTER INVESTIGATION *Wavelength* — 502
3. **Waves behave in predictable ways.** — 504
   CONNECTING SCIENCES *Tsunamis!* — 509

16 Sound — 514

the BIG idea
Sound waves transfer energy through vibrations.

1. **Sound is a wave.** — 517
   EXTREME SCIENCE *Sonic Booms* — 524
2. **Frequency determines pitch.** — 545
3. **Intensity determines loudness.** — 532
   MATH IN SCIENCE *Interpreting Graphs* — 537
4. **Sound has many uses.** — 538
   CHAPTER INVESTIGATION *Build a Stringed Instrument* — 544

How is this guitar player producing sound? page 514

xii Physical Science

How does this phone stay connected? page 550

17 Electromagnetic Waves — 550

the BIG idea
Electromagnetic waves transfer energy through radiation.

1. **Electromagnetic waves have unique traits.** — 553
   MATH IN SCIENCE *Using Exponents* — 558
2. **Electromagnetic waves have many uses.** — 559
   THINK SCIENCE *Are Cell Phones Harmful?* — 567
3. **The Sun is the source of most visible light.** — 568
4. **Light waves interact with materials.** — 573
   CHAPTER INVESTIGATION *Wavelength and Color* — 580

18 Light and Optics — 590

the BIG idea
Optical tools depend on the wave behavior of light.

1. **Mirrors form images by reflecting light.** — 593
   MATH IN SCIENCE *Measuring Angles* — 598
2. **Lenses form images by refracting light.** — 599
   CHAPTER INVESTIGATION *Looking at Lenses* — 604
3. **The eye is a natural optical tool.** — 606
4. **Optical technology makes use of light waves.** — 611
   SCIENCE ON THE JOB *Optics in Photography* — 619

Visual Highlights

Graphing a Wave	499
Sound Frequencies Heard by Animals	527
How Musical Instruments Work	541
The Electromagnetic Spectrum	560
How a Convex Lens Forms an Image	602
Microscopes and Telescopes	613

Table of Contents xiii

UNIT 5
Electricity and Magnetism

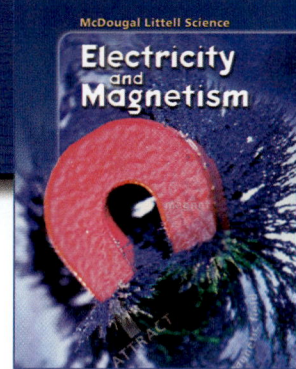
eEdition

Unit Features

SCIENTIFIC AMERICAN FRONTIERS IN SCIENCE Electronics in Music — 626

TIMELINES IN SCIENCE The Story of Electronics — 696

19 Electricity — 630

the BIG idea
Moving electric charges transfer energy.

1. **Materials can become electrically charged.** — 633
   CONNECTING SCIENCES Electric Eels — 641
2. **Charges can move from one place to another.** — 642
   CHAPTER INVESTIGATION Lightning — 650
3. **Electric current is a flow of charge.** — 652
   MATH IN SCIENCE Using Variables — 659

20 Circuits and Electronics — 664

the BIG idea
Circuits control the flow of electric charge.

1. **Charge needs a continuous path to flow.** — 667
   SCIENCE ON THE JOB The Science of Electrical Work — 674
2. **Circuits make electric current useful.** — 675
   MATH IN SCIENCE Solving Percent Problems — 680
3. **Electronic technology is based on circuits.** — 681
   CHAPTER INVESTIGATION Design an Electronic Communication Device — 690

How can circuits control the flow of charge? page 664

xiv Physical Science

What force is acting on this compass needle? page 700

21 Magnetism — 700

the BIG idea
Current can produce magnetism, and magnetism can produce current.

1. **Magnetism is a force that acts at a distance.** — 703
   THINK SCIENCE *Can Magnets Heal People?* — 711
2. **Current can produce magnetism.** — 712
3. **Magnetism can produce current.** — 719
   CHAPTER INVESTIGATION *Build a Speaker* — 724
4. **Generators supply electrical energy.** — 726
   MATH IN SCIENCE *Using Significant Figures* — 731

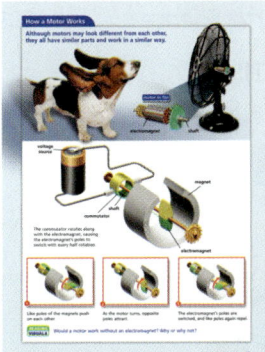

Visual Highlights

How a Photocopier Works	639
How Lightning Forms	645
Batteries	657
How a PC Works	686
How Magnets Differ from Other Materials	707
How a Motor Works	717

Features

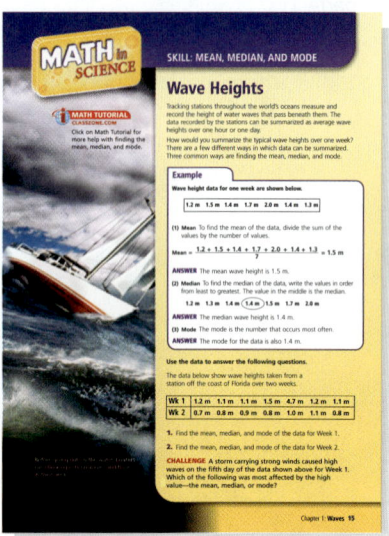

Math in Science

MATTER AND ENERGY
Making a Circle Graph	26
Solving Proportions	49
Using Formulas	91
Metric Conversions	109

CHEMICAL INTERACTIONS
Using Scientific Notation	161
Calculating Ratios	174
Analyzing Line Graphs	205
Calculating Percentages	267
Making Bar Graphs	290

MOTION AND FORCES
Working with Units	328
Using Significant Figures	360
Creating a Line Graph	364
Working with Averages	424
Changing Ratios to Percents	457

WAVES, SOUND, AND LIGHT
Mean, Median, and Mode	495
Interpreting Graphs	537
Using Exponents	558
Measuring Angles	598

ELECTRICITY AND MAGNETISM
Using Variables	659
Solving Percent Problems	680
Using Significant Figures	731

Think Science

MATTER AND ENERGY
Finding Solutions	77

CHEMICAL INTERACTIONS
Isolating Variables	183

MOTION AND FORCES
Evaluating Hypotheses	352
Isolating Variables	433

WAVES, SOUND, AND LIGHT
Determining Relevance	567

ELECTRICITY AND MAGNETISM
Evaluating Conclusions	711

Connecting Sciences

MATTER AND ENERGY
Physical Science and Earth Science	63

CHEMICAL INTERACTIONS
Physical Science and Life Science	144
Physical Science and Earth Science	252

MOTION AND FORCES
Physical Science and Life Science	467

WAVES, SOUND, AND LIGHT
Physical Science and Earth Science	509

ELECTRICITY AND MAGNETISM
Physical Science and Life Science	641

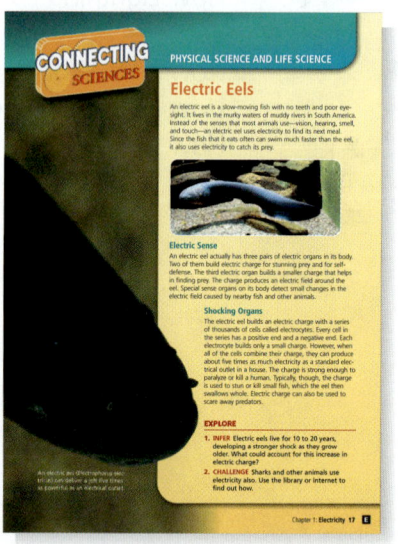

xvi Physical Science

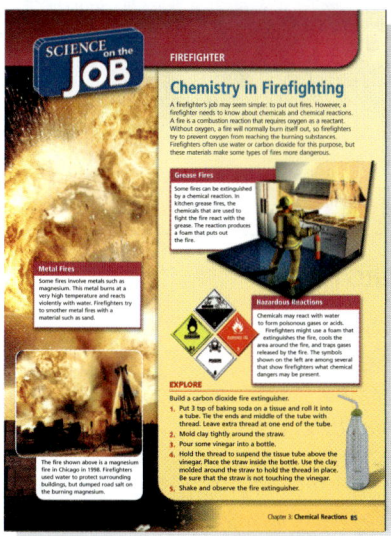

Science on the Job

MATTER AND ENERGY
Cooking with Heat — 115

CHEMICAL INTERACTIONS
Chemistry in Firefighting — 213

MOTION AND FORCES
Physics for Rescuers — 319

WAVES, SOUND, AND LIGHT
Optics in Photography — 619

ELECTRICITY AND MAGNETISM
The Science of Electrical Work — 674

Extreme Science

MATTER AND ENERGY
Particles Too Small to See — 20

CHEMICAL INTERACTIONS
Stronger Than Steel — 281

MOTION AND FORCES
Bending Light — 388

WAVES, SOUND, AND LIGHT
Sonic Booms — 524

Frontiers in Science

MATTER AND ENERGY
Fuels of the Future — 2

CHEMICAL INTERACTIONS
Medicines from Nature — 130

MOTION AND FORCES
Robots on Mars — 306

WAVES, SOUND, AND LIGHT
Sound Medicine — 482

ELECTRICITY AND MAGNETISM
Electronics in Music — 626

Timelines in Science

MATTER AND ENERGY
About Temperature and Heat — 96

CHEMICAL INTERACTIONS
The Story of Atomic Structure — 232

MOTION AND FORCES
Understanding Forces — 412

WAVES, SOUND, AND LIGHT
The Story of Light — 586

ELECTRICITY AND MAGNETISM
The Story of Electronics — 696

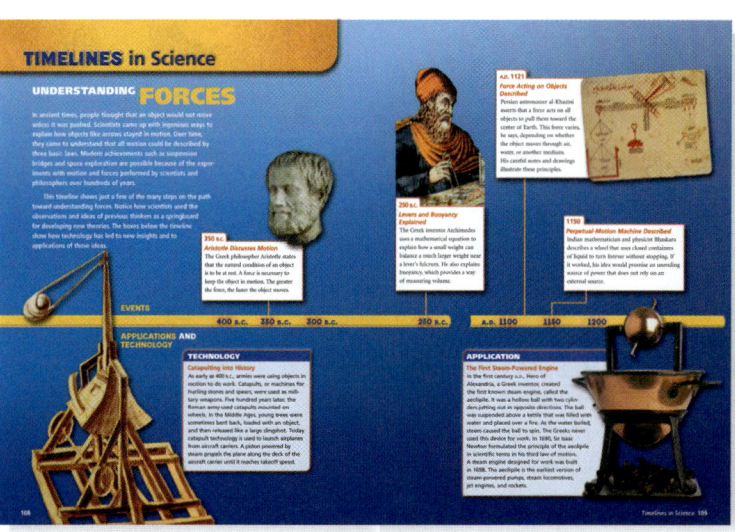

Table of Contents xvii

Internet Resources @ ClassZone.com

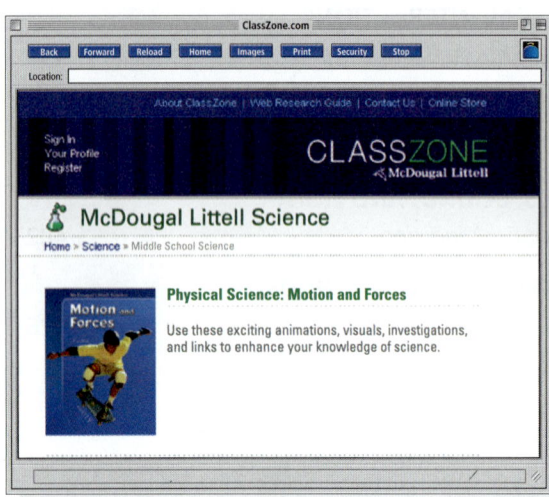

Simulations

MATTER AND ENERGY
Weight on Different Planets	11
Gas Behavior	33
Physical and Chemical Changes	39
Potential Energy and Kinetic Energy	69
Kinetic Energy and Temperature	101
Conduction, Convection, or Radiation	119

CHEMICAL INTERACTIONS
Build an Atom	140
Mixing Alloys	237
3-D Carbon Molecules	278

MOTION AND FORCES
Changing Acceleration	335
Applying Force	343
Newton's Second Law	354
Fluids and Pressure	397
Work	417
Mechanical Advantage	465

WAVES, SOUND, AND LIGHT
Forces and Waves	487
The Sun at Different Wavelengths	551
Using Lenses to Form Images	603

ELECTRICITY AND MAGNETISM
Static Electricity	631
Ohm's Law	653
Circuits	665
Electromagnets	701

Visualizations

MATTER AND ENERGY
Solar Cells	88

CHEMICAL INTERACTIONS
Radioactive Decay	160
Ionic and Covalent Bonds	167
Polar Electron Cloud	179
Concentration and Reaction Rate	202
Endothermic and Exothermic Reactions	218
Supersaturated Solutions and Precipitation	246
Petroleum Distillation	292

MOTION AND FORCES
Relative Motion	311
Effect of Gravity in a Vacuum	383
Transfer of Potential and Kinetic Energy	430

WAVES, SOUND, AND LIGHT
Wave Graphing	498
How Sound Travels	515
Doppler Effect	531
Electromagnetic Waves	554
Reflection	595

ELECTRICITY AND MAGNETISM
Hard Drive	687
Motor	716

Career Centers

Electrical Engineering	5
Chemistry	133
Physics and Engineering	309
Audiology	485
Music and Computer Science	629

Resource Centers

MATTER AND ENERGY
Resources for the following topics may be found at ClassZone.com: *Scale Views of Matter; Volume; Scanning Tunneling Microscope Images; Mixtures; Chemical Properties of Matter; Melting Points and Boiling Points; Separating Materials from Mixtures; Kinetic Energy and Potential Energy; Electric Cars; Alternative Energy Sources; Temperature and Heat Research; Temperature and Temperature Scales; Thermal Energy.*

CHEMICAL INTERACTIONS
Resources for the following topics may be found at ClassZone.com: *Periodic Table; Atom; Elements Important to Life; Chemical Formulas; Properties of Ionic and Covalent Compounds; Balancing Chemical Equations; Catalysts in Living Things; Atomic Research; Aquifers and Purification; Acids and Bases; Alloys; Polymers; Nanotubes; Carbohydrates, Lipids, Proteins, and Nucleic Acids; Petroleum and Hydrocarbons.*

MOTION AND FORCES
Resources for the following topics may be found at ClassZone.com: *Finding Position; Acceleration; Inertia; Moving Rocks; Newton's Laws of Motion; Momentum; Gravity; Gravitational Lenses; Friction, Forces, and Surfaces; Force and Motion Research; Work; Power; Machines in Everyday Objects; Artificial Limbs; Nanomachines; Robots.*

WAVES, SOUND, AND LIGHT
Resources for the following topics may be found at ClassZone.com: *Waves; Wave Speed; Supersonic Aircraft; Sound Safety; Musical Instruments; The Electromagnetic Spectrum; Visible Light; Light Research; Optics; Microscopes and Telescopes; Lasers.*

ELECTRICITY AND MAGNETISM
Resources for the following topics may be found at ClassZone.com: *Lightning and Lightning Safety; Electrochemical Cells; Electrical Safety; Electronics; Electronic and Computer Research; Magnetism; Dams and Electricity; Energy Use and Conservation.*

Math Tutorials

MATTER AND ENERGY
Circle Graphs	26
Solving Proportions	49
Rates	91
Temperature Conversions	109

CHEMICAL INTERACTIONS
Scientific Notation	161
Ratios	174
Interpreting Line Graphs	205
Understanding Percents	267
Bar Graphs	290

MOTION AND FORCES
Units and Rates	328
Rounding Decimals	360
Creating a Line Graph	394
Finding the Mean	424
Percents and Fractions	457

WAVES, SOUND, AND LIGHT
Finding the Mean, Median, and Mode	495
Interpreting Line Graphs	537
Positive and Negative Exponents	558
Measuring Angles	598

ELECTRICITY AND MAGNETISM
Equations	659
Percents and Proportions	680
Rounding Decimals	731

NSTA SciLinks

Codes for use with the NSTA SciLinks site may be found on every chapter opener.

Content Reviews

There is a content review for every chapter at ClassZone.com.

Test Practice

There is a standardized test practice for every chapter at ClassZone.com.

Explore the Big idea

Chapter Opening Inquiry

Each chapter opens with hands-on explorations that introduce the chapter's Big Idea.

Matter and Energy

What Has Changed? Where Does the Sugar Go?	7
Float or Sink; Hot Chocolate	39
A Penny for Your Energy; Hot Dog!	69
Moving Colors, Does It Chill?	101

Chemical Interactions

That's Far! Element Safari	135
Mixing It Up; The Shape of Things	167
Changing Steel Wool; A Different Rate	195
Does It Dissolve? Acid Test	237
Structure and Function; Sweet Crackers	273

Motion and Forces

Off the Wall; Rolling Along	311
Popping Ping-Pong Balls; Take Off!	343
Let It Slide; Under Pressure	379
Bouncing Ball; Power Climbing	417
Changing Direction; Shut the Door!	447

Waves, Sound, and Light

How Can Energy Be Passed Along? How Can You Change a Wave?	487
What Gives a Sound Its Qualities? How Does Size Affect Sound?	515
What Melts the Ice Cubes? What Is White Light Made Of?	551
How Does a Spoon Reflect Your Face? Why Do Things Look Different Through Water?	591

Electricity and Magnetism

How Do the Pieces of Tape Interact? Why Does the Water React Differently?	631
Will the Flashlight Still Work? What's Inside a Calculator?	665
Is It Magnetic? How Can You Make a Chain?	701

Chapter Investigations

Full-Period Labs

The Chapter Investigations are in-depth labs that let you form and test a hypothesis, build a model, or sometimes design your own investigation.

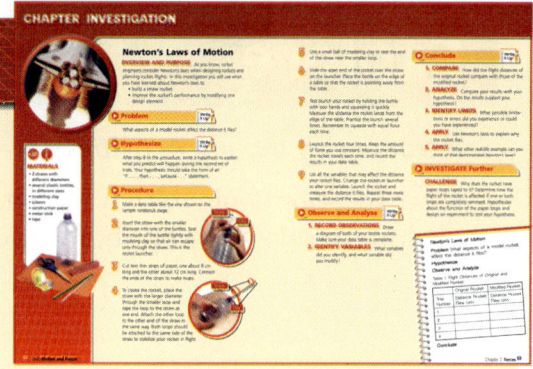

Matter and Energy

Mass and Volume	14
Freezing Point	56
Energy Conversions	84
Insulators *Design Your Own*	122

Chemical Interactions

Modeling Atomic Masses	152
Chemical Bonds	188
Exothermic or Endothermic?	220
Acids and Bases	260
Polymers	298

Motion and Forces

Acceleration and Slope	336
Newton's Laws of Motion	366
Pressure in Fluids	400
Work and Power	440
Design a Machine *Design Your Own*	474

Waves, Sound, and Light

Wavelength	502
Build a Stringed Instrument *Design Your Own*	544
Wavelength and Color	580
Looking at Lenses	604

Electricity and Magnetism

Lightning	650
Design an Electronic Communication Device *Design Your Own*	690
Build a Speaker	724

Table of Contents xxi

Explore

Introductory Inquiry Activities

Most sections begin with a simple activity that lets you explore the Key Concept before you read the section.

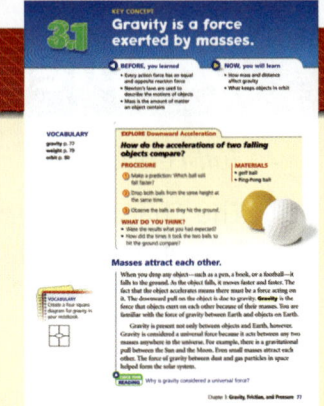

Matter and Energy

Similar Objects	9
Mixed Substances	21
Solids and Liquids	27
Physical Properties	41
Identifying Substances	58
Energy	71
Solar Cells	86
Temperature	103
Conduction	116

Chemical Interactions

The Size of Atoms	137
Similarities and Differences of Objects	145
Compounds	169
Bonds in Metals	184
Chemical Changes	197
Energy Changes	214
Mixtures	239
Solutions and Temperature	245
Acids and Bases	253
Carbon in Food	282

Motion and Forces

Location	313
Speed	320
Changing Motion	345
Acceleration	353
Collisions	368
Downward Acceleration	381
Pressure	395
Forces in Liquid	402
Work	419
Power	434
Machines	449
Changing Forces	458

Waves, Sound, and Light

Waves	489
Reflection	504
Sound	517
Pitch	525
Echoes	538
Electromagnetic Waves	553
Radio Waves	559
Light and Matter	573
Reflection	593
Refraction	599
Focusing Vision	606
Combining Lenses	611

Electricity and Magnetism

Static Electricity	633
Static Discharge	642
Current	652
Circuits	667
Codes	681
Magnetism	703
Magnetism from Electric Current	712
Energy Conversion	719

Investigate

Skill Labs

Each Investigate activity gives you a chance to practice a specific science skill related to the content that you're studying.

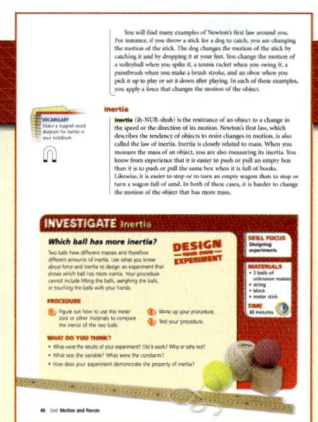

Matter and Energy

Mass	Modeling	17
Mixtures	Inferring	24
Liquids	Measuring	31
Chemical Changes	Measuring	47
Separating Mixtures	Design Your Own	61
Potential Energy	Design Your Own	75
Solar Energy	Observing	89
Temperature Measurements	Modeling	107
Heat Transfer	Measuring	112

Chemical Interactions

Masses of Atomic Particles	Modeling	141
Radioactivity	Modeling	159
Element Ratios	Modeling	171
Crystals	Observing	181
Chemical Reactions	Inferring	202
Conservation of Mass	Measuring	207
Sugar Combustion	Inferring	223
Solutions	Observing	241
Solubility	Design Your Own	248
Alloys	Observing	265
Carbon Bonding	Modeling	277
Organic Molecules	Inferring	286

Motion and Forces

Changing Positions	Observing	316
Speed and Distance	Design Your Own	323
Acceleration	Measuring	331
Inertia	Design Your Own	350
Motion and Force	Hypothesizing	358
Newton's Third Law	Observing	362
Momentum	Observing	370
Gravity	Predicting	386
Friction in Air	Design Your Own	392

Bernoulli's Principle	Observing	404
Work	Measuring	422
Mechanical Energy	Analyzing Data	429
Power	Measuring	437
Efficiency	Analyzing Data	455
Pulleys	Inferring	461

Waves, Sound, and Light

Wave Types	Comparing	493
Frequency	Collecting Data	500
Diffraction	Predicting	506
Sound Energy	Observing	521
Sound Frequency	Inferring	528
Loudness	Observing	533
Wave Behavior	Design Your Own	556
The Electromagnetic Spectrum	Drawing Conclusions	564
Artificial Lighting	Design Your Own	570
Mixing Colors	Observing	578
The Law of Reflection	Analyzing	595
Vision	Observing	608
Optical Tools	Design Your Own	614

Electricity and Magnetism

Making a Static Detector	Inferring	638
Conductors and Insulators	Interpreting Data	646
Electric Cells	Inferring	655
Fuses	Making Models	672
Circuits	Inferring	678
Digital Information	Making Models	683
Earth's Magnetic Field	Inferring	709
Electromagnets	Observing	714
Electric Current	Inferring	722
Power	Making Models	729

Standards and Benchmarks

Each unit in **Physical Science** addresses some of the learning goals described in the *National Science Education Standards* (NSES) and the Project 2061 *Benchmarks for Science Literacy.* The following National Science Education Standards are also addressed in the book introduction, unit and chapter features, and lab investigations in all the units: A.9 Understandings About Scientific Inquiry, E.6 Understandings About Science and Technology, F.5 Science and Technology in Society, G.1 Science as a Human Endeavor, G.2 Nature of Science, G.3 History of Science.

National Science Education Standards

Content Standards

UNIT 1 Matter and Energy

B.1.a	A substance has characteristic properties, such as density, a boiling point, and solubility. A mixture of substances often can be separated into the original substances using these properties.	B.3.a	Energy is a property of substances and is often associated with heat, light, electricity, mechanical motion, and sound. Energy is transferred in many ways.
B.1.c	There are more than 100 known elements that combine to produce compounds.	B.3.b	Heat flows from warmer objects to cooler ones, until both reach the same temperature.

UNIT 2 Chemical Interactions

B.1.a	A substance has characteristic properties, such as density, a boiling point, and solubility, all of which do not depend on the amount of the sample.	B.1.c	Chemical elements do not break down during normal reactions involving heating, electric current, or acids. There are more than 100 known elements that combine in many ways to produce compounds. Compounds account for the living and non-living substances that we encounter.
B.1.b	Substances react chemically in characteristic ways with other substances to form new substances, or compounds. These compounds have different properties from the original substances. In chemical reactions, the total mass is conserved. Substances are placed in groups, such as metals, if they react in similar ways.	C.1.a	Living systems demonstrate the complementary nature of structure and function.
		D.1.h	The atmosphere is a mixture of nitrogen, oxygen, and small amounts of other gases such as water vapor.

UNIT 3 Motion and Forces

B.1.a	A substances has characteristic properties, such as density.	D.3.c	Gravity is the force that keeps planets in orbit around the Sun, governs motion within the solar system, holds us to Earth's surface, and produces tides.
B.2.a	An object's motion is described by its position, direction of motion, and speed. That motion can be measured and shown on a graph.	E.6.c	Science and technology often work together. Science helps drive technology. Technology is used to improve scientific investigations.
B.2.b	An object will move in a straight line at a constant speed unless a force acts on it.	E.6.d	Perfectly designed solutions do not exist. All technological solutions have trade-offs, such as cost, safety, and efficiency.
B.2.c	If more than one force acts on an object along a straight line, then the forces will reinforce or cancel each other.	E.6.e	All designs have limits, including those having to do with material properties, safety, and environmental protection.
B.3.a	Energy is often associated with heat, sound, and mechanical motion. Energy is transferred in many ways.		

UNIT 4 Waves, Sound, and Light

B.3.a	Energy is often associated with sound, light, and mechanical motion. Energy is transferred in many ways.	B.3.f	Energy from the Sun is transferred to Earth in the form of visible light, infrared light, and ultraviolet light.
B.3.c	Light interacts with matter by transmission, absorption, or scattering. To see an object, light from that object must enter the eye.		

UNIT 5 Electricity and Magnetism

B.3.a	Energy is the property of substances that is often associated with electricity. Energy is transferred in many ways.	B.3.e	In most chemical reactions, energy is transferred into or out of a system. Heat, light, motion, or electricity all might be involved in such transfers.
B.3.d	Circuits transfer electrical energy. Heat, light, sound, and chemical changes are produced.		

Process and Skill Standards

A.1	Identify questions that can be answered through investigation.	A.7	Communicate procedures, results, and conclusions.
A.2	Design and conduct a scientific investigation.	A.8	Use mathematics in scientific inquiry.
A.3	Use appropriate tools and techniques to gather, analyze, and interpret data.	E.1	Identify a problem to be solved.
		E.2	Design a solution or product.
A.4	Use evidence to describe, predict, explain, and model.	E.3	Implement the proposed solution.
		E.4	Evaluate the solution or design.
A.5	Use critical thinking to find relationships between results and interpretations.	E.5	Communicate the process of technological design.
A.6	Consider alternative explanations and predictions.	F.4.c	Use systematic thinking to estimate risks.

Project 2061 Benchmarks

Content Benchmarks

UNIT 1 Matter and Energy

4.D.1	All matter is made up of atoms.	4.E.4	Energy appears in different forms, including heat, mechanical, chemical, and gravitational.
4.D.2	Equal volumes of different substances usually have different weights.	8.B.1	The choice of materials for a job depends on their properties.
4.D.3	Atoms and molecules are always in motion.	8.C.1	Energy can change from one form to another. In the process, some energy is always converted to heat.
4.E.1	Energy cannot be created or destroyed, but it can be changed from one form to another.		Some systems transform energy with less loss of heat than others.
4.E.2	Most of what goes on in the universe involves energy transformations.		
4.E.3	Heat can be transferred through materials by the collisions of atoms or across space by radiation.		

UNIT 2 Chemical Interactions

4.D.1	All matter is made of atoms, which are far too small to see. The atoms of any element are alike but are different from atoms of other elements. Atoms may stick together in molecules or may be packed together in large arrays.	4.D.7	No matter how substances in a closed system interact with one another, the total weight of the system remains the same.
		10.F.3	The work of scientist Antoine Lavoisier led to the modern science of chemistry.
4.D.4	The temperature and acidity of a solution influence reaction rates.	10.F.4	Lavoisier tested the concept of conservation of matter by measuring the substances involved in burning.
4.D.6	There are groups of elements that have similar properties, including highly reactive metals, less-reactive metals, highly reactive nonmetals, and some almost completely nonreactive gases. Carbon and hydrogen are essential elements of living matter.	10.G.1	The discovery that minerals containing uranium darken photographic film led to the idea of radioactivity.
		10.G.2	Scientists Marie Curie and Pierre Curie isolated the elements radium and polonium.

UNIT 3 Motion and Forces

4.B.3	Everything on or near Earth is pulled toward Earth's center by the force of gravity.	4.G.2	The sun's gravitational pull holds the earth and other planets in their orbits. The planets' gravity keeps their moons in orbit around them.
4.E.1	Energy cannot be created or destroyed, but it can be changed from one form to another.	8.B.4	The use of robots has changed the nature of work in many fields, including manufacturing.
4.E.4	Energy appears in many different forms, including heat, chemical, mechanical, and gravitational.	10.A.1	An object's motion is relative to some other object or point in space.
4.F.3	An unbalanced force acting on an object changes its speed and/or direction of motion.	10.B.1	Newton's Laws describe motion everywhere in the universe.
4.G.1	Every object exerts the force of gravity on every other object.	11.C.2	A system may stay the same because no forces are acting on the system, or forces are acting on the system but they all cancel each other out.

UNIT 4 Waves, Sound, and Light

4.F.1	Light from the sun is made up of a mixture of many different colors of light, even though the light looks almost white.	4.F.4	Vibrations in materials set up wavelike disturbances that spread away from the source. Sound and earthquake waves are examples. These and other waves move at different speeds through different materials.
4.F.2	Something can be "seen" when light waves emitted or reflected by it enter the eye—just as something can be "heard" when sound waves from it enter the ear.	4.F.5	Human eyes respond to only a narrow range of wavelengths of electromagnetic radiation—visible light. Differences of wavelength within that range are perceived as differences in color.

UNIT 5 Electricity and Magnetism

1.C.6	Computers are important in science.	8.D.2	The ability to code information as electric currents in wires has made communication many times faster than is possible by mail or sound.
3.A.2	Technology is essential to science.		
3.A.3	Engineers and others who work in design and technology use scientific knowledge to solve practical problems.		
4.G.3	Electric currents and magnets can exert a force on each other.	8.E.1	Computers use digital codes containing only two symbols to perform all operations.
8.C.4	Electrical energy can be produced from a variety of energy sources and can be transformed into almost any other form of energy.	9.A.6	Numbers can be represented by using only 1 and 0.

Process and Skill Benchmarks

1.A.3	Some knowledge in science is very old and yet is still used today.	9.C.4	Graphs show patterns and can be used to make predictions.
1.C.1	Contributions to science and technology have been made by different kinds of people, in different cultures, at different times.	9.D.3	The mean, median, and mode tell different things about the middle of a data set.
2.B.1	Mathematics contributes to science and technology.	12.B.1	Find what percentage one number is of another.
3.B.1	Design requires taking constraints into account.	12.B.7	Determine the appropriate unit for an answer. Convert units.
3.B.2	Technologies have effects other than those intended.	12.B.8	Round a calculation to the correct number of significant figures.
3.C.4	Technology has influenced the course of history.	12.C.3	Use and read instruments that measure length, volume, weight, time, rate, and temperature.
8.B.1	The choice of materials for a job depends on their properties.		
9.A.3	How decimals should be written depends on how precise the measurements are.	12.D.1	Use tables and graphs to organize information and identify relationships.
9.B.3	Graphs can show the relationship between two variables.	12.E.3	Be skeptical of arguments based on very small samples for which there was no control group.

Standards and Benchmarks xxvii

Introducing Physical Science

Scientists are curious. Since ancient times, they have been asking and answering questions about the world around them. Scientists are also very suspicious of the answers they get. They carefully collect evidence and test their answers many times before accepting an idea as correct.

In this book you will see how scientific knowledge keeps growing and changing as scientists ask new questions and rethink what was known before. The following sections will help get you started.

Unifying Principles of Physical Science — xxix

What do scientists know about matter and energy? These pages introduce four unifying principles that will give you a big picture of physical science.

The Nature of Science — xxxviii

How do scientists learn? This section provides an overview of scientific thinking and the processes that scientists use to ask questions and to find answers.

The Nature of Technology — xlii

How do we use what scientists learn? These pages introduce you to how people develop and use technologies to design solutions to real-world problems.

Using McDougal Littell Science — xliv

How can you learn more about science? This section provides helpful tips on how to learn and use science from the key parts of this program—the text, the visuals, the activities, and the Internet resources.

UNIFYING PRINCIPLES of Physical Science

What Is Physical Science?

In the simplest terms, physical science is the study of what things are made of and how they change. It combines the studies of both physics and chemistry. Physics is the science of matter, energy, and forces. It includes the study of topics such as motion, light, and electricity and magnetism. Chemistry is the study of the structure and properties of matter, and it especially focuses on how substances change into different substances.

The text and pictures in this book will help you learn key concepts and important facts about physical science. A variety of activities will help you investigate these concepts. As you learn, it helps to have a big picture of physical science as a framework for this new information. The four unifying principles listed below will give you this big picture. Read the next few pages to get an overview of each of these principles and a sense of why they are so important.

- **Matter is made of particles too small to see.**
- **Matter changes form and moves from place to place.**
- **Energy changes from one form to another, but it cannot be created or destroyed.**
- **Physical forces affect the movement of all matter on Earth and throughout the universe.**

the BIG idea

Each chapter begins with a big idea. Keep in mind that each big idea relates to one or more of the unifying principles.

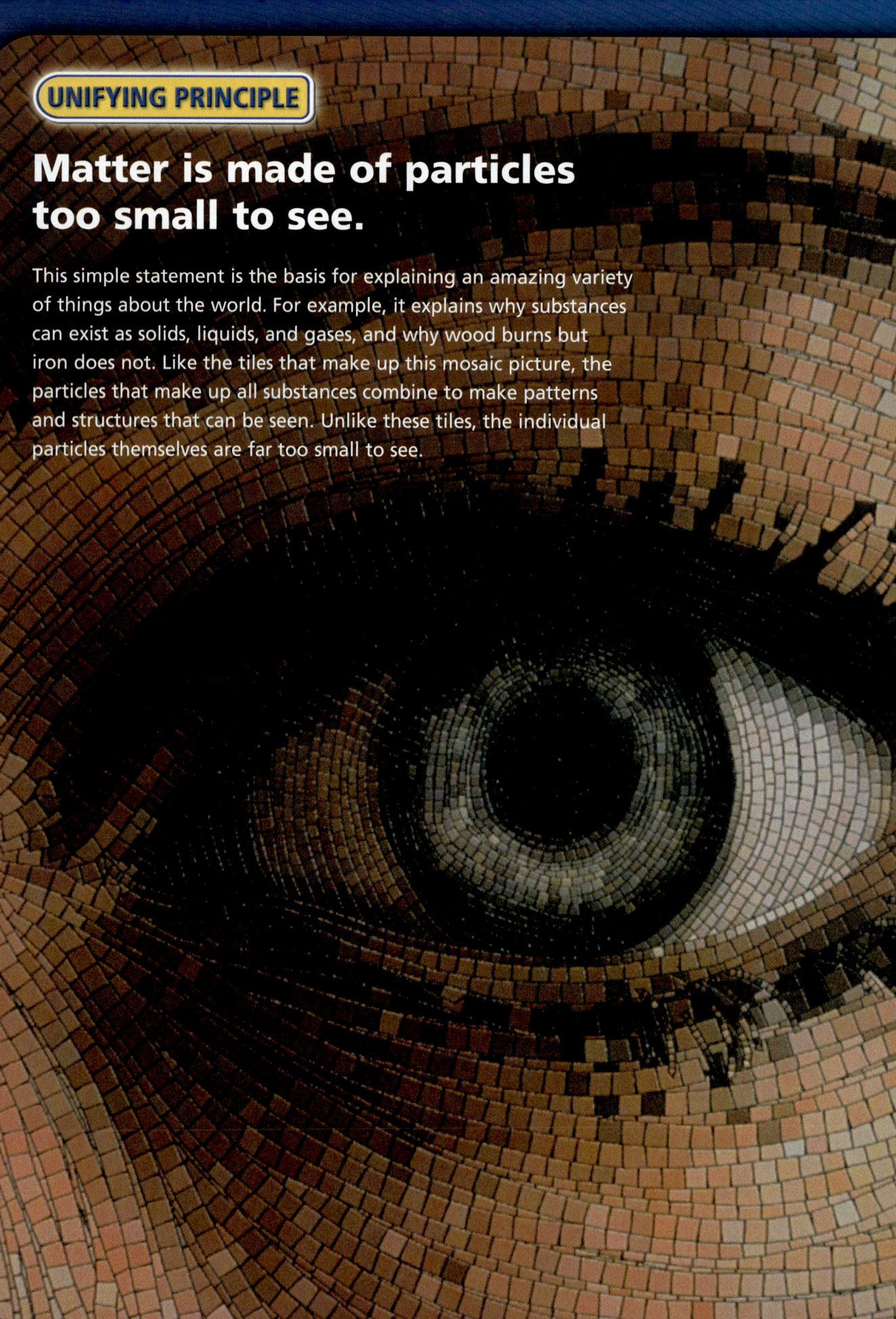

UNIFYING PRINCIPLE

Matter is made of particles too small to see.

This simple statement is the basis for explaining an amazing variety of things about the world. For example, it explains why substances can exist as solids, liquids, and gases, and why wood burns but iron does not. Like the tiles that make up this mosaic picture, the particles that make up all substances combine to make patterns and structures that can be seen. Unlike these tiles, the individual particles themselves are far too small to see.

What It Means

To understand this principle better, let's take a closer look at the two key words: *matter* and *particles*.

Matter

Objects you can see and touch are all around you. The materials that these objects are made of are called **matter.** All living things—even you—are also matter. Even though you can't see it, the air around you is matter too. Scientists often say that matter is anything that has mass and takes up space. **Mass** is a measure of the amount of matter in an object. We use the word **volume** to refer to the amount of space an object or a substance takes up.

Particles

The tiny particles that make up all matter are called **atoms.** Just how tiny are atoms? They are far too small to see, even through a powerful microscope. In fact, an atom is more than a million times smaller than the period at the end of this sentence.

There are more than 100 basic kinds of matter called **elements.** For example, iron, gold, and oxygen are three common elements. Each element has its own unique kind of atom. The atoms of any element are all alike but different from the atoms of any other element.

Many familiar materials are made of particles called molecules. In a **molecule,** two or more atoms stick together to form a larger particle. For example, a water molecule is made of two atoms of hydrogen and one atom of oxygen.

Why It's Important

Understanding atoms and molecules makes it possible to explain and predict the behavior of matter. Among other things, this knowledge allows scientists to

- explain why different materials have different characteristics
- predict how a material will change when heated or cooled
- figure out how to combine atoms and molecules to make new and useful materials

UNIFYING PRINCIPLE

Matter changes form and moves from place to place.

You see matter change form every day. You see the ice in your glass of juice disappear without a trace. You see a black metal gate slowly develop a flaky, orange coating. Matter is constantly changing and moving.

What It Means

Remember that matter is made of tiny particles called atoms. Atoms are constantly moving and combining with one another. All changes in matter are the result of atoms moving and combining in different ways.

Matter Changes and Moves

You can look at water to see how matter changes and moves. A block of ice is hard like a rock. Leave the ice out in sunlight, however, and it changes into a puddle of water. That puddle of water can eventually change into water vapor and disappear into the air. The water vapor in the air can become raindrops, which may fall on rocks, causing them to weather and wear away. The water that flows in rivers and streams picks up tiny bits of rock and carries them from one shore to another. Understanding how the world works requires an understanding of how matter changes and moves.

Matter Is Conserved

No matter was lost in any of the changes described above. The ice turned to water because its molecules began to move more quickly as they got warmer. The bits of rock carried away by the flowing river were not gone forever. They simply ended up farther down the river. The puddles of rainwater didn't really disappear; their molecules slowly mixed with molecules in the air.

Under ordinary conditions, when matter changes form, no matter is created or destroyed. The water created by melting ice has the same mass as the ice did. If you could measure the water vapor that mixes with the air, you would find it had the same mass as the water in the puddle did.

Why It's Important

Understanding how mass is conserved when matter changes form has helped scientists to

- describe changes they see in the world
- predict what will happen when two substances are mixed
- explain where matter goes when it seems to disappear

UNIFYING PRINCIPLE

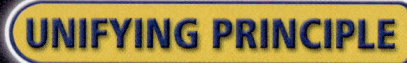

Energy changes from one form to another, but it cannot be created or destroyed.

When you use energy to warm your food or to turn on a flashlight, you may think that you "use up" the energy. Even though the camp-stove fuel is gone and the flashlight battery no longer functions, the energy they provided has not disappeared. It has been changed into a form you can no longer use. Understanding how energy changes forms is the basis for understanding how heat, light, and motion are produced.

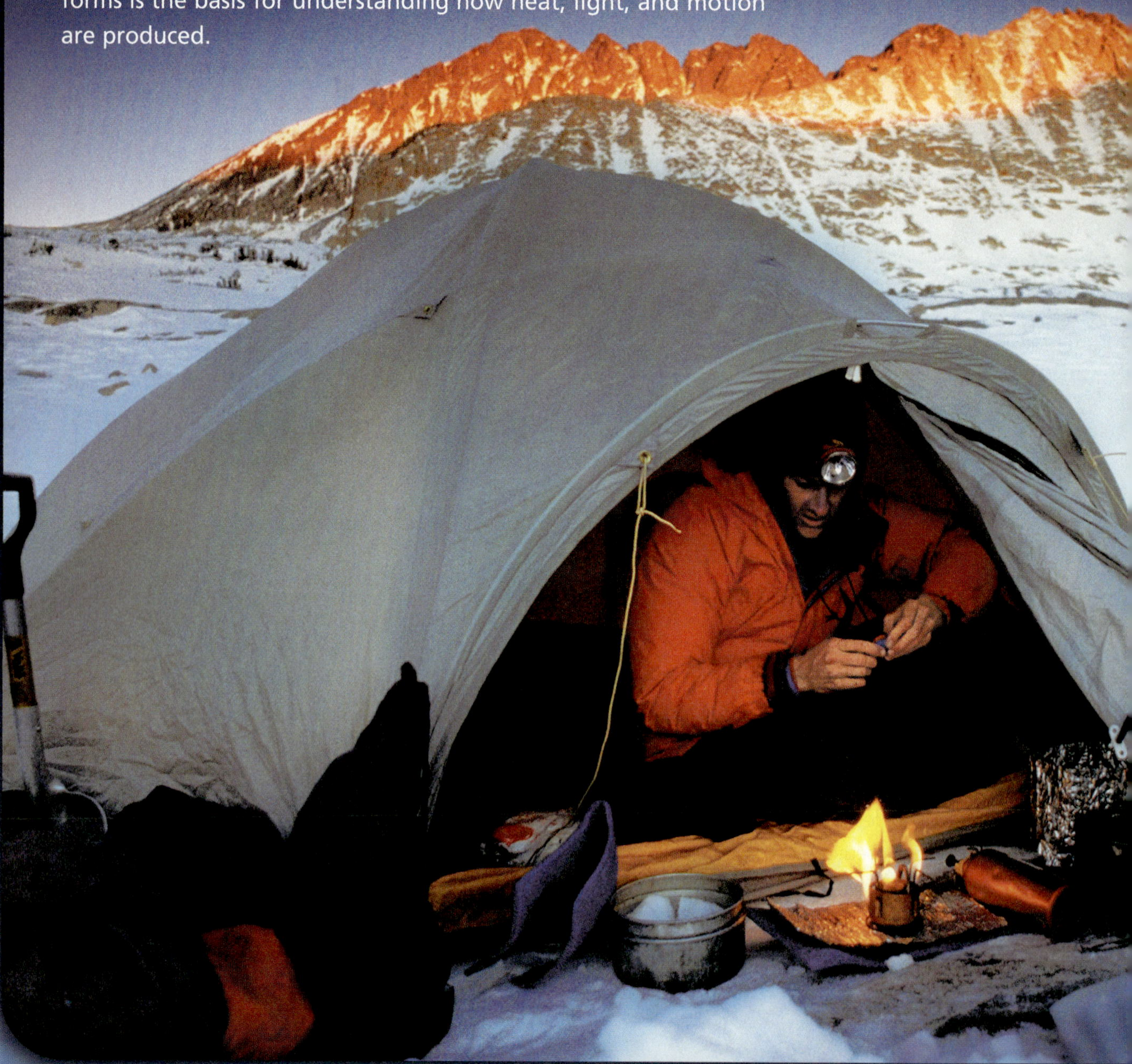

What It Means

Changes that you see around you depend on energy. **Energy,** in fact, means the ability to cause change. The electrical energy from an outlet changes into light and heat in a light bulb. Plants change the light energy from the Sun into chemical energy, which animals use to power their muscles.

Energy Changes Forms

Using energy means changing energy. You probably have seen electric energy changing into light, heat, sound, and mechanical energy in household appliances. Fuels like wood, coal, and oil contain chemical energy that produces heat when burned. Electric power plants make electrical energy from a variety of energy sources, including falling water, nuclear energy, and fossil fuels.

Energy Is Conserved

Energy can be converted into forms that can be used for specific purposes. During the conversion, some of the original energy is converted into unwanted forms. For instance, when a power plant converts the energy of falling water into electrical energy, some of the energy is lost to friction and sound.

Similarly, when electrical energy is used to run an appliance, some of the energy is converted into forms that are not useful. Only a small percentage of the energy used in a light bulb, for instance, produces light; most of the energy becomes heat. Nonetheless, the total amount of energy remains the same through all these conversions.

The fact that energy does not disappear is a law of physical science. The **law of conservation of energy** states that energy cannot be created or destroyed. It can only change form.

Why It's Important

Understanding that energy changes form but does not disappear has helped scientists to

- predict how energy will change form
- manage energy conversions in useful ways
- build and improve machines

UNIFYING PRINCIPLE

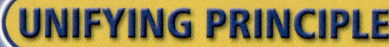

Physical forces affect the movement of all matter on Earth and throughout the universe.

What makes the world go around? The answer is simple: forces. Forces allow you to walk across the room, and forces keep the stars together in galaxies. Consider the forces acting on the rafts below. The rushing water is pushing the rafts forward. The force from the people paddling helps to steer the rafts.

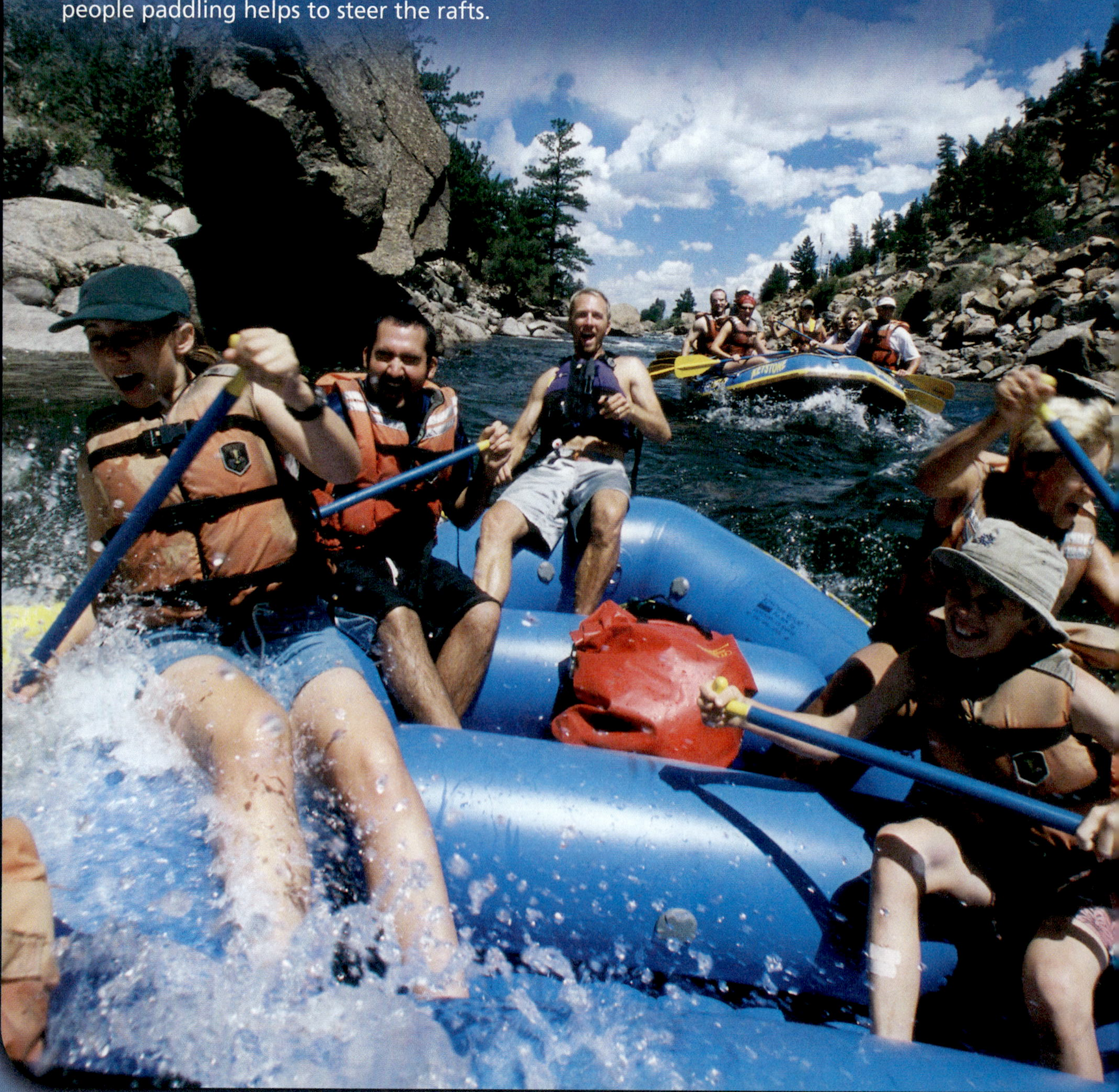

What It Means

A **force** is a push or a pull. Every time you push or pull an object, you're applying a force to that object, whether or not the object moves. There are several forces—several pushes and pulls—acting on you right now. All these forces are necessary for you to do the things you do, even sitting and reading.

- You are already familiar with the force of gravity. **Gravity** is the force of attraction between two objects. Right now gravity is at work pulling you to Earth and Earth to you. The Moon stays in orbit around Earth because gravity holds it close.

- A contact force occurs when one object pushes or pulls another object by touching it. If you kick a soccer ball, for instance, you apply a contact force to the ball. You apply a contact force to a shopping cart that you push down a grocery aisle or a sled that you pull up a hill.

- **Friction** is the force that resists motion between two surfaces pressed together. If you've ever tried to walk on an icy sidewalk, you know how important friction can be. If you lightly rub your finger across a smooth page in a book and then across a piece of sandpaper, you can feel how the different surfaces produce different frictional forces. Which is easier to do?

- There are other forces at work in the world too. For example, a compass needle responds to the magnetic force exerted by Earth's magnetic field, and objects made of certain metals are attracted by magnets. In addition to magnetic forces, there are electrical forces operating between particles and between objects. For example, you can demonstrate electrical forces by rubbing an inflated balloon on your hair. The balloon will then stick to your head or to a wall without additional means of support.

Why It's Important

Although some of these forces are more obvious than others, physical forces at work in the world are necessary for you to do the things you do. Understanding forces allows scientists to

- predict how objects will move
- design machines that perform complex tasks
- predict where planets and stars will be in the sky from one night to the next

The Nature of Science

You may think of science as a body of knowledge or a collection of facts. More important, however, science is an active process that involves certain ways of looking at the world.

Scientific Habits of Mind

Scientists are curious. They are always asking questions. Scientists have asked questions such as, "What is the smallest form of matter?" and "How do the smallest particles behave?" These and other important questions are being investigated by scientists around the world.

Scientists are observant. They are always looking closely at the world around them. Scientists once thought the smallest parts of atoms were protons, neutrons, and electrons. Later, protons and neutrons were found to be made of even smaller particles called quarks.

Scientists are creative. They draw on what they know to form possible explanations for a pattern, an event, or an interesting phenomenon that they have observed. Then scientists create a plan for testing their ideas.

Scientists are skeptical. Scientists don't accept an explanation or answer unless it is based on evidence and logical reasoning. They continually question their own conclusions and the conclusions suggested by other scientists. Scientists trust only evidence that is confirmed by other people or methods.

Scientists cannot always make observations with their own eyes. They have developed technology, such as this particle detector, to help them gather information about the smallest particles of matter.

Scientists ask questions about the physical world and seek answers through carefully controlled procedures. Here a researcher works with supercooled magnets.

Science Processes at Work

You can think of science as a continuous cycle of asking and seeking answers to questions about the world. Although there are many processes that scientists use, scientists typically do each of the following:

- Observe and ask a question
- Determine what is known
- Investigate
- Interpret results
- Share results

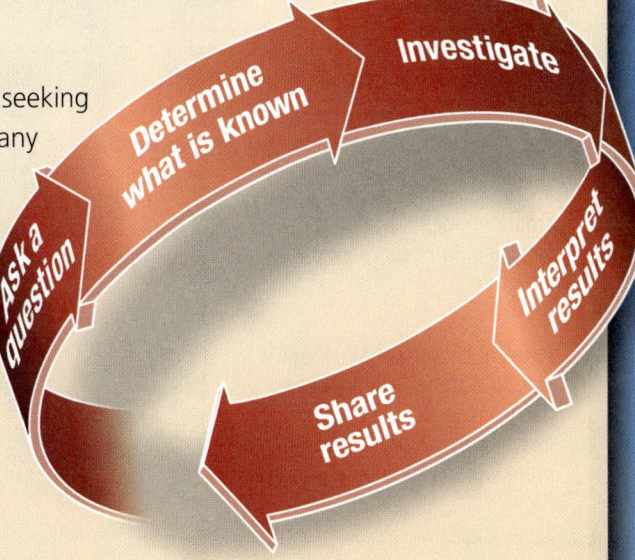

Observe and Ask a Question

It may surprise you that asking questions is an important skill. A scientific process may start when a scientist asks a question. Perhaps scientists observe an event or a process that they don't understand, or perhaps answering one question leads to another.

Determine What Is Known

When beginning an inquiry, scientists find out what is already known about a question. They study results from other scientific investigations, read journals, and talk with other scientists. A scientist working on subatomic particles is most likely a member of a large team using sophisticated equipment. Before beginning original research, the team analyzes results from previous studies.

The Nature of Science

Investigate

Investigating is the process of collecting evidence. Two important ways of investigating are observing and experimenting.

Observing is the act of noting and recording an event, a characteristic, or anything else detected with an instrument or with the senses. A researcher may study the properties of a substance by handling it, finding its mass, warming or cooling it, stretching it, and so on. For information about the behavior of subatomic particles, however, a researcher may rely on technology such as scanning tunneling microscopes, which produce images of structures that cannot be seen with the eye.

An **experiment** is an organized procedure to study something under controlled conditions. In order to study the effect of wing shape on the motion of a glider, for instance, a researcher would need to conduct controlled studies in which gliders made of the same materials and with the same masses differed only in the shape of their wings.

Scanning tunneling microscopes create images that allow scientists to observe molecular structure.

Physical chemists have found a way to observe chemical reactions at the atomic level. Using lasers, they can watch bonds breaking and new bonds forming.

Forming hypotheses and making predictions are two of the skills involved in scientific investigations. A **hypothesis** is a tentative explanation for an observation, a phenomenon, or a scientific problem that can be tested by further investigation. For example, in the mid-1800s astronomers noticed that the planet Uranus departed slightly from its expected orbit. One astronomer hypothesized that the irregularities in the planet's orbit were due to the gravitational effect of another planet—one that had not yet been detected.
A **prediction** is an expectation of what will be observed or what will happen. A prediction can be used to test a hypothesis. The astronomers predicted that they would discover a new planet in the position calculated, and their prediction was confirmed with the discovery of the planet Neptune.

Interpret Results

As scientists investigate, they analyze their evidence, or data, and begin to draw conclusions. **Analyzing data** involves looking at the evidence gathered through observations or experiments and trying to identify any patterns that might exist in the data. Scientists often need to make additional observations or perform more experiments before they are sure of their conclusions. Many times scientists make new predictions or revise their hypotheses.

Often scientists use computers to help them analyze data. Computers reveal patterns that might otherwise be missed.

Scientists use computers to create models of objects or processes they are studying. This model shows carbon atoms forming a sphere.

Share Results

An important part of scientific investigation is sharing results of experiments. Scientists read and publish in journals and attend conferences to communicate with other scientists around the world. Sharing data and procedures gives them a way to test one another's results. They also share results with the public through newspapers, television, and other media.

The Nature of Science xli

The Nature of Technology

When you think of technology, you may think of cars, computers, and cell phones, as well as refrigerators, radios, and bicycles. Technology is not only the machines and devices that make modern lives easier, however. It is also a process in which new methods and devices are created. Technology makes use of scientific knowledge to design solutions to real-world problems.

Science and Technology

Science and technology go hand in hand. Each depends upon the other. Even designing a device as simple as a toaster requires knowledge of how heat flows and which materials are the best conductors of heat. Just as technology based on scientific knowledge makes our lives easier, some technology is used to advance scientific inquiry itself. For example, researchers use a number of specialized instruments to help them collect data. Microscopes, telescopes, spectrographs, and computers are just a few of the tools that help scientists learn more about the world. The more information these tools provide, the more devices can be developed to aid scientific research and to improve modern lives.

The Process of Technological Design

The process of technology involves many choices. For example, how does an automobile engineer design a better car? Is a better car faster? safer? cheaper? Before designing any new machine, the engineer must decide exactly what he or she wants the machine to do as well as what may be given up for the machine to do it. A faster car may get people to their destinations more quickly, but it may cost more and be less safe. As you study the technological process, think about all the choices that were made to build the technologies you use.

Identify a Need
Successful technology fills a need; it helps us perform a task we need or want to do. For example, as more cars appear on the road, noise and air pollution become serious threats to the environment and to people's health. Gas consumption also depletes precious petroleum resources. There is a need to find a fuel source for a car that will not pollute the air and that will never run out.

Design and Develop
Hydrogen fuel cells are a potential solution to this need. These cells combine hydrogen and oxygen into water, producing electricity in the process. Engineers have found a way to make fuel cells small enough to fit into a car, yet able to produce enough electricity to power an electric motor. Before arriving at this final design, engineers tried many others.

Test and Improve
Just because a technology works doesn't mean it cannot be improved. A fuel-cell-powered car has been driven from San Francisco to Washington, D.C., but it probably will be a while before it's in dealer showrooms. Engineers won't know how these cars will perform until they're driven in real-world conditions. Engineers also won't know if the average driver will be able to handle the necessary maintenance on the car until the car is made available to ordinary drivers. Improvements in the future may well bring cars powered by fuel cells into garages everywhere.

Using McDougal Littell Science

Reading Text and Visuals

This book is organized to help you learn. Use these boxed pointers as a path to help you learn and remember the **Big Ideas** and **Key Concepts**.

Read the Big Idea.

As you read **Key Concepts** for the chapter, relate them to **the Big Idea**.

Take notes.

Use the strategies on the **Getting Ready to Learn** page.

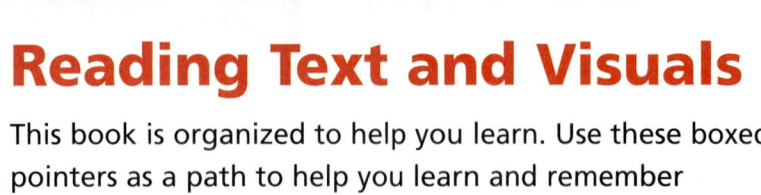

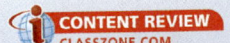
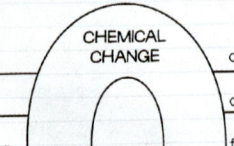

Read each heading.

See how it fits into the outline of the chapter.

KEY CONCEPT
2.1 Matter has observable properties.

BEFORE, you learned
- Matter has mass and volume
- Matter is made of atoms
- Matter exists in different states

NOW, you will learn
- About physical and chemical properties
- About physical changes
- About chemical changes

VOCABULARY
physical property p. 41
density p. 43
physical change p. 44
chemical property p. 46
chemical change p. 46

EXPLORE Physical Properties

How can a substance be changed?

PROCEDURE
1. Observe the clay. Note its physical characteristics, such as color, shape, texture, and size.
2. Change the shape of the clay. Note which characteristics changed and which ones stayed the same.

MATERIAL
rectangular piece of clay

WHAT DO YOU THINK?
- How did reshaping the clay change its physical characteristics?
- How were the mass and the volume of the clay affected?

Remember what you know.

Think about concepts you learned earlier and preview what you'll learn now.

Try the activities.

They will introduce you to science concepts.

Physical properties describe a substance.

What words would you use to describe a table? a chair? the sandwich you ate for lunch? You would probably say something about the shape, color, and size of each item. Next you might consider whether it is hard or soft, smooth or rough to the touch. Normally, when describing an object, you identify the characteristics of the object that you can observe without changing the identity of the object.

The characteristics of a substance that can be observed without changing the identity of the substance are called **physical properties**. In science, observation can include measuring and handling a substance. All of your senses can be used to detect physical properties. Color, shape, size, texture, volume, and mass are a few of the physical properties you probably have encountered.

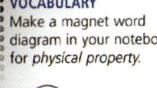
VOCABULARY
Make a magnet word diagram in your notebook for *physical property*.

 Describe some of the physical properties of your desk.

Learn the vocabulary.

Take notes on each term.

Answer the questions.

Check Your Reading questions will help you remember what you read.

Chapter 2: **Properties of Matter** 41

Using McDougal Littell Science **xlv**

Reading Text and Visuals

Read one paragraph at a time.

Look for a topic sentence that explains the main idea of the paragraph. Figure out how the details relate to that idea. One paragraph might have several important ideas; you may have to reread to understand.

Answer the questions.

Check Your Reading questions will help you remember what you read.

Study the visuals.

- Read the title.
- Read all labels and captions.
- Figure out what the picture is showing. Notice colors, arrows, and lines.
- Answer the question. **Reading Visuals** questions will help you understand the picture.

Physical Properties

How do you know which characteristics are physical properties? Just ask yourself whether observing the property involves changing the substance to a different substance. For example, you can stretch a rubber band. Does stretching the rubber band change what it is made of? No. The rubber band is still a rubber band before and after it is stretched. It may look a little different, but it is still a rubber band.

Mass and volume are two physical properties. Measuring these properties does not change the identity of a substance. For example, a lump of clay might have a mass of 200 grams (g) and a volume of 100 cubic centimeters (cm^3). If you were to break the clay in half, you would have two 100 g pieces of clay, each with a volume of 50 cm^3. You can bend and shape the clay too. Even if you were to mold a realistic model of a car out of the clay, it still would be a piece of clay. Although you have changed some of the properties of the object, such as its shape and volume, you have not changed the fact that the substance you are observing is clay.

▼ **REMINDER**
Because all formulas for volume involve the multiplication of three measurements, volume has a unit that is cubed (such as cm^3).

CHECK YOUR READING Which physical properties listed above are found by taking measurements? Which are not?

Physical Properties

Physical properties of clay—such as volume, mass, color, texture, and shape—can be observed without changing the fact that the substance is clay.

Block of Clay

Shaped Clay

READING VISUALS COMPARE AND CONTRAST Which physical properties do the two pieces of clay have in common? Which are different?

Doing Labs

To understand science, you have to see it in action. Doing labs helps you understand how things really work.

1. **Read the entire lab first.**
2. **Form a hypothesis.**
3. **Follow the procedure.**
4. **Record the data.**
5. **Analyze your results.**
6. **Write your lab report.**

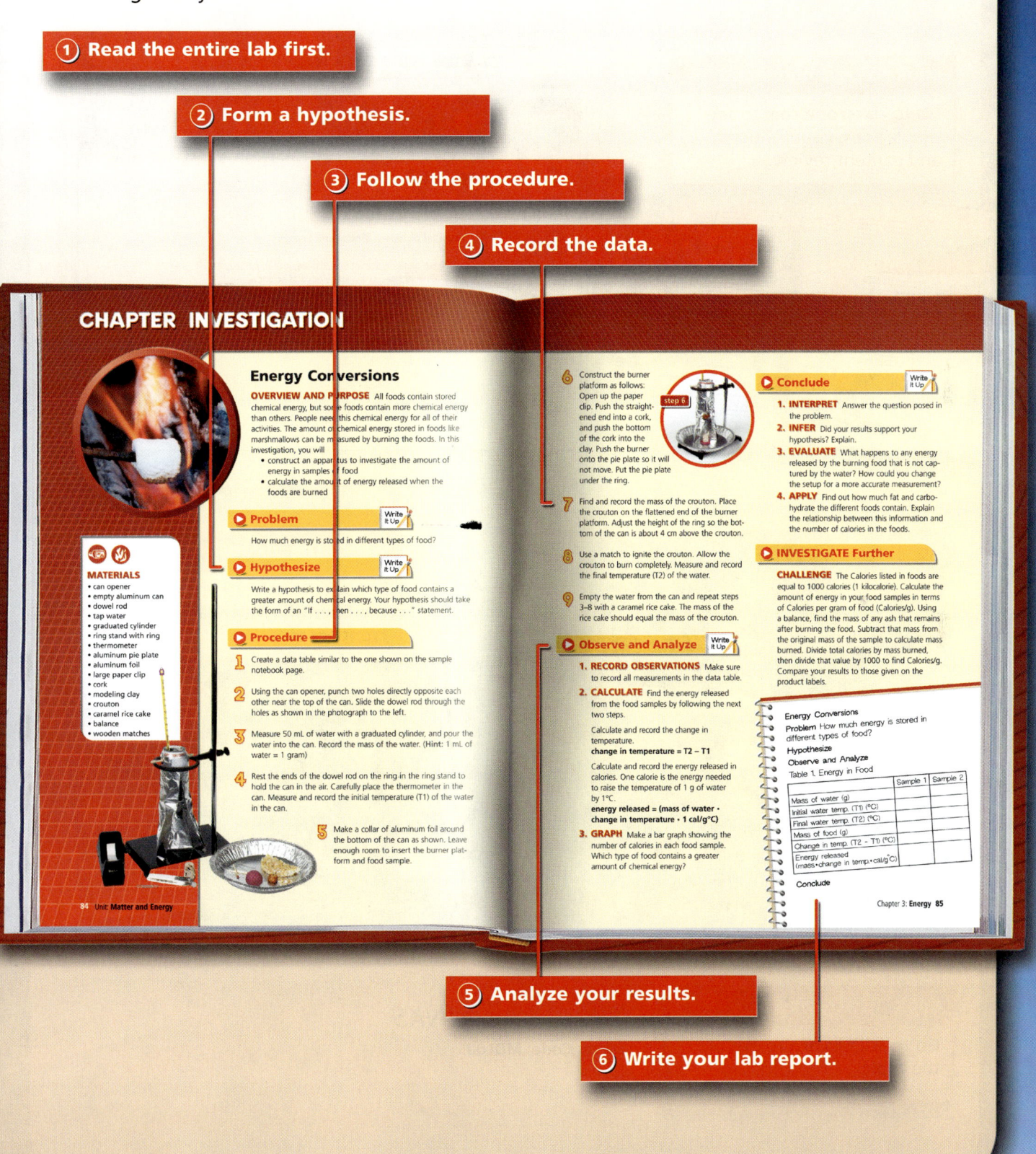

Using Technology

The Internet is a great source of information about up-to-date science. The ClassZone Web site and SciLinks have exciting sites for you to explore. Video clips and simulations can make science come alive.

Look for red banners.

Go to **classzone.com** to see simulations, visualizations, and content review.

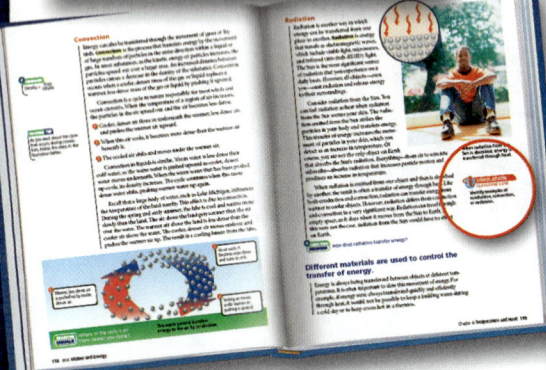

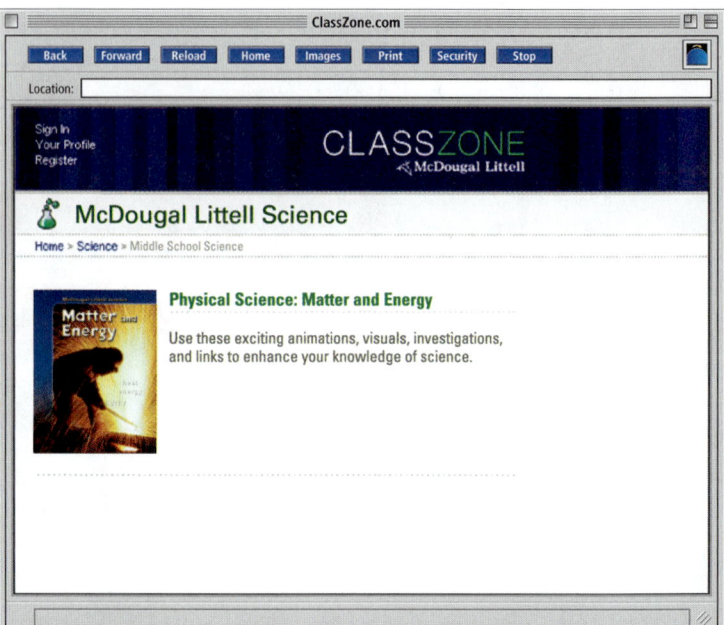

Watch the videos.

See science at work in the **Scientific American Frontiers** video.

Look up SciLinks.

Go to **scilinks.org** to explore the topic.

Forces **Code: MDL005**

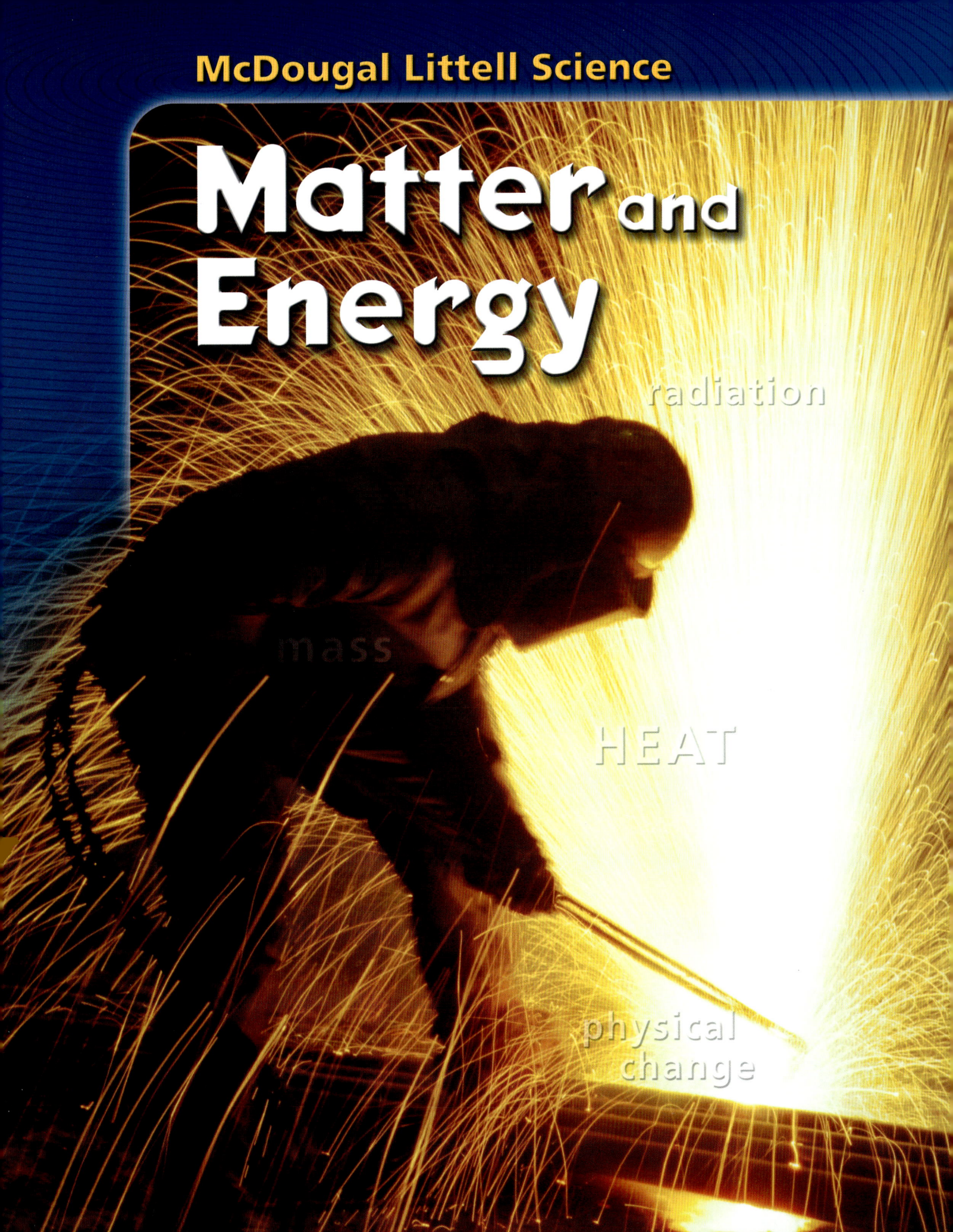

Matter and Energy
Contents Overview

Unit Features

FRONTIERS IN SCIENCE Fuels of the Future — 2
TIMELINES IN SCIENCE About Temperature and Heat — 96

1 Introduction to Matter — 6
the BIG idea
Everything that has mass and takes up space is matter.

2 Properties of Matter — 38
the BIG idea
Matter has properties that can be changed by physical and chemical processes.

3 Energy — 68
the BIG idea
Energy has different forms, but it is always conserved.

4 Temperature and Heat — 100
the BIG idea
Heat is a flow of energy due to temperature differences.

FRONTIERS in Science

VIDEO SUMMARY

SCIENTIFIC AMERICAN FRONTIERS

"Sunrayce," a segment of the *Scientific American Frontiers* series that aired on PBS stations, follows a solar-powered car race from Texas to Minnesota. Contestants are teams of student engineers and scientists from 34 colleges and universities. Each team has designed and built a car with an electric engine that is fueled by direct solar power and/or batteries that can be charged by solar energy. The cars are covered with solar panels to collect sunlight.

Teams have just seven days to complete the 1102-mile race. This can be especially challenging when sunlight is the only source of power and rain clouds can spell disaster. The video follows the team from California State University, Los Angeles, as they prepare for the race and strategize to use the maximum amount of sunlight.

National Science Education Standards

A.9.a–d Understandings About Scientific Inquiry

E.6.a–f Understandings About Science and Technology

F.5.a–e Science and Technology in Society

G.1.a–b Science as a Human Endeavor

G.2.a Nature of Science

FRONTIERS in Science

FUELS of the FUTURE

Where does this spacecraft get its fuel?

SCIENTIFIC AMERICAN FRONTIERS

View the "Sunrayce" segment of your *Scientific American Frontiers* video to learn about a cross-country race in which cars use solar power instead of gasoline.

Deep Space 1 was an experimental design. Its successful mission prepared the way to the development of more ion-propelled spacecraft.

ADDITIONAL RESOURCES

Technology Resources

Scientific American Frontiers Video: *Sunrayce:* 12-minute video segment that introduces the unit.

ClassZone.com
CAREER LINK, Physicist, Chemist, Aeronautical Engineer

Guide student viewing and comprehension of the video:

 Video Teaching Guide, pp. 1–2; Video Viewing Guide, p. 3; Video Wrap-Up, p. 4

Scientific American Frontiers Video Guide, pp. 39–42

Unit projects procedures and rubrics:

 Unit Projects, pp. 5–10

The stream of ions glows blue as it is shot out of an ion-propulsion engine.

Ion Engines for Long Voyages

Rocket engines must provide huge amounts of energy to move spacecraft away from Earth and keep them in orbit. The fuel required can weigh more than the spacecraft themselves. That is why scientists and engineers are always looking for more efficient ways to give spacecraft and other vehicles the energy to move.

One method of powering spacecraft uses electrically charged particles called ions. The atoms of a gas—usually xenon—are first made into ions. An electric field is then used to pull these ions out of the engine at a very high speed—faster than 100,000 kilometers per hour (62,000 mi/h). This stream of rapidly moving ions works like the gases coming out of a jet engine on a plane—propelling the spacecraft in the direction opposite to the ion stream.

An advantage of ion propulsion is that its fuel is much lighter than the chemical fuel used in rockets. Ion propulsion does not provide enough thrust to be used for a rocket launch, but it can be used to move a spacecraft through long distances in outer space. This method of propulsion provides a small force to the spacecraft; however, over time the spacecraft can reach great speeds.

The space probe *Deep Space 1* was the first to use an ion engine to travel between planets. The engine generated enough speed for the probe to follow and photograph comet Borrelly in 2001.

FOCUS

▶ Set Learning Goals

Students will
- Examine how spacecraft are powered.
- Explore alternative types of fuels.
- Determine how solar energy works.

Remind students that frontiers are undeveloped fields for discovery or research, and that the "Sunrayce" video shows engineers and scientists testing designs to find answers or solve problems. Have students look at the photographs of the spacecraft and engine and predict what problem the engineers and scientists are trying to solve.

INSTRUCT

Scientific Process

Emphasize to students that in order to move spacecraft out into orbit, large amounts of energy are required. Because so much fuel is needed to power a spacecraft, the fuel itself can weigh more than the spacecraft. That is why it is necessary for scientists to learn about the various types of energy sources for fueling spacecraft. Have students review the parts of the scientific process on pages xxiv–xxv and ask what part this step falls under. *determining what is known*

Technology Design

Focus students' attention on "Ion Engines for Long Voyages." Discuss how using ions—electrically charged particles—power the spacecraft by creating an ion stream that propels the spacecraft while in orbit. Ask students to name the advantage as well as the disadvantage of using this engine design. *The fuel for ion engines is lighter than chemical fuel used for rockets, but ion propulsion does not provide enough of a force for launching the rocket.*

DIFFERENTIATE INSTRUCTION

? More Reading Support

A What provides spacecraft with the large amounts of energy they need to move? *rocket engines*

B What is ion propulsion best used for? *long distances*

Below Level Have students write out the steps to power a spacecraft using ions. Steps should include where ions come from, what is created with those ions, and how the ions work to push the spacecraft.

Teach from Visuals

Have students look at the photograph of the solar sails. Ask:

- What is one problem with using solar energy for powering spacecraft? *Once the spacecraft moves far from the Sun, it does not collect as much sunlight and loses energy.*

- For what purpose might scientists use solar sails? *Sample answer: Solar sails are used to reflect sunlight to provide the solar energy to move spacecraft farther through space to the outer planets.*

Technology Design

Remind students about the problem to be solved: providing enough power for spacecraft to move far from Earth and the Sun. Ask: How did the scientists improve the recovery of solar energy? *using sails as mirrors to reflect sunlight* How did they further supplement the energy source? *by beaming energy from Earth to the solar sails through microwaves and laser lights*

Solar sails will reflect sunlight to move a spacecraft through space.

Running on Sunlight

Solar energy is used for travel in outer space, where there is plenty of sunlight and very little friction to slow down a spacecraft. However, once a spacecraft travels far away from the Sun—as far as the outer planets Jupiter and Saturn—the amount of energy reaching it is far less than the energy it was getting near Earth. The sunlight can be helpful only if solar cells on the vehicle can collect enough of it. One solution is to reflect sunlight. Scientists are developing solar sails, which will act like enormous mirrors. The pressure of reflected sunlight on the sails can be used to move a large ship through space—even far from the Sun.

Beaming Energy from Earth

Another way to power a spacecraft is to send energy to it all the way from Earth. This idea is called beamed energy propulsion. A beam delivers energy to solar sails on the spacecraft. The energy can be in the form of microwaves—the same energy that heats food in a microwave oven or delivers calls on a cell phone. Or it can be in the form of laser light, a very concentrated beam of visible light. This method has already been used successfully to power very small vehicles, 10 centimeters (4 in.) long. Experiments are under way with larger spacecraft.

Combined Technologies

Some recent space flights have combined common and experimental technologies. For example, the *Cassini* space probe has two regular rocket engines for propulsion. Other energy comes from three generators powered by radioactive decay. This combination of engines allowed *Cassini* to be the largest and most complicated spacecraft ever launched. Its goal is to explore Saturn.

SCIENTIFIC AMERICAN FRONTIERS

View the "Sunrayce" segment of your *Scientific American Frontiers* video to see what is involved in solar-car racing.

IN THIS SCENE FROM THE VIDEO ▶ Students from California State University, Los Angeles, work on their solar car.

CATCHING THE SUN'S RAYS Since 1990 teams of college students have built and raced solar-powered cars. The races are held every two years to promote awareness of solar energy and to inspire young people to work in science and engineering.

Solar cells on the cars' bodies convert sunlight into electricity. The goal is to make lightweight cars that convert sunlight efficiently. Today's solar cars can reach speeds of up to 75 miles per hour, but the average racing speed is 25 miles per hour. On cloudy or rainy days, the teams conserve power by traveling more slowly—or risk running down their batteries.

In 2003 the American Solar Challenge took place on historic Route 66 from Chicago to Claremont, California. At 3700 kilometers (2300 mi), the ten-day event was the longest solar-car race in the world.

4 Unit 1: Matter and Energy

DIFFERENTIATE INSTRUCTION

More Reading Support

C What type of energy uses sunlight for fuel? *solar energy*

D What are two sources of energy beams? *microwaves and laser light*

English Learners English learners may be unfamiliar with some of the vocabulary used to describe how spacecraft and other vehicles are fueled. The examples below use different words to indicate the same idea.

"... collect enough sunlight to drive a large ship ..."

"Another way to power a spacecraft ..."

If read literally, "to drive" and "to power" might be confusing. Help students learn the multiple meanings of words such as these.

Alternative Fuels on Earth

Scientists and inventors have long been looking for practical alternative fuels to power vehicles on Earth as well as in outer space. Most vehicle engines on Earth use gasoline or other fossil fuels. These fuels are based on resources, such as petroleum, that are found in underground deposits. Those deposits will not be replaced for millions of years. Solar energy, by contrast, is endlessly renewable, so it seems to be a good alternative to nonrenewable fossil fuels.

Solar-powered cars rely on solar cells, which convert the energy of sunlight directly into electrical energy that can be stored in batteries. One outstanding solar car was built by Dutch students and entered in the 2001 World Solar Challenge.

The students' car, called the *Nuna*, used several technologies that had been developed for space travel. Its body was reinforced with Kevlar, a space-age material that is also used in satellites, space suits, and bulletproof vests. During the race, the *Nuna* covered 3010 kilometers of desert in Australia, breaking solar-car speed records, and won the race.

Does the development of solar cars like the *Nuna* mean that most people will be driving solar cars soon? Unfortunately, such cars run only when the Sun is shining unless they rely on batteries—and it takes hundreds of pounds of batteries to store the amount of energy in a gallon of gasoline. As with spacecraft, the goal is to design a vehicle in which the fuel doesn't outweigh the vehicle itself.

UNANSWERED Questions

Even as scientists and inventors solve problems in solar technology, new questions arise.
- Can solar technology be made affordable?
- Is solar technology practical for large-scale public transportation?
- Are there any hidden costs to the use of alternative fuels?

UNIT PROJECTS

As you study this unit, work alone or with a group on one of these projects.

Build a Solar Oven

Design and build a solar oven that can boil a quarter cup of water.
- Plan and sketch a design for a solar oven that can reach 100°C.
- Collect materials and assemble your oven. Then conduct trials and improve your design.

Multimedia Presentation

Create an informative program on solar race cars and the way they work.
- Collect information about solar race cars. Research how they are powered.
- Examine why solar cars have specific shapes. Learn how the solar panels and batteries work together.
- Give a multimedia presentation describing what you learned.

Design an Experiment

Design an experiment that compares how well two of the following alternative energy sources move an object: solar energy, wind power, biomass (fuel from plant material), waste-material fuel, hydrogen fuel cells, heat exchangers.
- Research the energy sources, and pick two types to compare.
- List materials for your experiment. Create a data table and write up your procedure.
- Describe your experiment for the class.

 CAREER CENTER CLASSZONE.COM

Learn more about careers in electrical engineering.

Frontiers in Science 5

DIFFERENTIATE INSTRUCTION

 **More Reading Support**

E What is the difference between fossil fuels and solar energy? *Solar energy is renewable while fossil fuels take millions of years to be replaced.*

Differentiate Unit Projects Projects are appropriate for varying abilities. Allow students to choose the ones that interest them the most. Encourage them to vary the products they produce throughout the year.

Below Level Encourage students to try "Build a Solar Oven."

Advanced Challenge students to complete "Design an Experiment."

UNANSWERED Questions

Have students read the questions and think of some of their own. Remind them that scientists usually end up with more questions—that inquiry is the driving force of science.
- With the class, generate on the board a list of new questions.
- Students can add to the list after they watch the *Scientific American Frontiers* Video.
- Students can use the list as a springboard for choosing their Unit Projects.

UNIT PROJECTS

Encourage students to pick the project that most appeals to them. Point out that each is long-term and will take several weeks to complete. You might group or pair students to work on projects and in some cases guide student choice. Some of the projects have student choice built into them.

Each project has two worksheet pages, including a rubric. Use the pages to guide students through criteria, process, and schedule.

 Unit Projects, pp. 5–10

REVISIT concepts introduced in this article:

Chapter 1
- Matter has mass and volume, pp. 9–13
- Matter is made up of atoms, pp. 16–19
- Matter combines, pp. 21–25

Chapter 2
- Observable properties, pp. 41–48
- Changes of state, pp. 50–55
- Identifying substances, pp. 58–62

Chapter 3
- Energy exists in different forms, pp. 71–76
- Energy is never lost, pp. 78–83
- Technology improves energy use, pp. 86–90

Chapter 4
- Temperature depends on particle movement, pp. 103–108
- Energy flows from warmer to cooler objects, pp. 110–114
- The transfer of energy as heat, pp. 116–121

Frontiers in Science 5

CHAPTER 1
Introduction to Matter

Physical Science
UNIFYING PRINCIPLES

PRINCIPLE 1
Matter is made of particles too small to see.

PRINCIPLE 2
Matter changes form and moves from place to place.

PRINCIPLE 3
Energy changes from one form to another, but it cannot be created or destroyed.

PRINCIPLE 4
Physical forces affect the movement of all matter on Earth and throughout the universe.

Unit 1: Matter and Energy
BIG IDEAS

CHAPTER 1
Introduction to Matter
Everything that has mass and takes up space is matter.

CHAPTER 2
Properties of Matter
Matter has properties that can be changed by physical and chemical processes.

CHAPTER 3
Energy
Energy has different forms, but it is always conserved.

CHAPTER 4
Temperature and Heat
Heat is a flow of energy due to temperature differences.

CHAPTER 1
KEY CONCEPTS

SECTION 1
Matter has mass and volume.
1. All objects are made of matter.
2. Mass is a measure of the amount of matter.
3. Volume is a measure of the space matter occupies.

SECTION 2
Matter is made of atoms.
1. Atoms are extremely small.
2. Atoms and molecules are always in motion.

SECTION 3
Matter combines to form different substances.
1. Matter can be pure or mixed.
2. Parts of mixtures can be the same or different throughout.

SECTION 4
Matter exists in different physical states.
1. Particle arrangement and motion determine the state of matter.
2. Solid, liquid, and gas are common states of matter.

 The Big Idea Flow Chart is available on p. T1 in the **UNIT TRANSPARENCY BOOK**.

5A   Unit 1: **Matter and Energy**

Previewing Content

SECTION

 1 Matter has mass and volume. pp. 9–15

1. **All objects are made of matter.**
   Anything that has **mass** and takes up space is **matter**. All the objects, liquids, gases, and living things in the universe are made of matter. Energy is not matter. However, under special circumstances, such as a nuclear reaction, energy can become matter and matter can become energy.

2. **Mass is a measure of the amount of matter.**
   Mass is measured by comparing the mass of an object with the mass of known units or standard units of mass. Units of mass are the kilogram and gram. **Weight** is the downward pull of gravity on an object. An object's mass is invariable, but an object's weight varies, depending on the amount of gravity. Weight is measured in newtons.

3. **Volume is a measure of the space matter occupies.**
   Units of **volume** are the cubic centimeter or milliliter. One milliliter is equal to one cubic centimeter. The amount of space that matter takes up can be measured in two ways.
   - Use a formula to determine the volume of regular objects. For example, the volume of an object shaped like a square or a rectangular box is length times width times height.
     $V = lwh$
   - Use displacement to measure the volume of solids with an irregular shape. Submerge the object in a known amount of water. The increase in the volume of the water is the volume of the object. This technique will not work if the solid can dissolve.

SECTION

 2 Matter is made of atoms. pp. 16–20

1. **Atoms are extremely small.**
   All matter is made up of **atoms**, which are so small that a teaspoon full of water has approximately 5×10^{23} atoms. An atom has a radius of approximately 10^{-10} meters. Scientists have identified more than 100 kinds of atoms.

   Atoms combine to form **molecules.** A molecule can be made from two or more of the same kind of atom or from two or more different kinds of atoms. For example, water molecules are made up of hydrogen and oxygen, but ozone molecules are made up of only oxygen. The diagram below shows the makeup of a water molecule and an ozone molecule.

   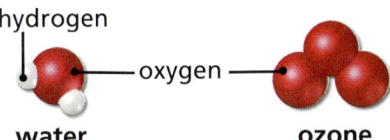

2. **Atoms and molecules are always in motion.**
   Atoms and molecules are always moving. You can see evidence of moving air molecules as they collide with dust or other particles in the air. You can see liquids move when you add a drop of food coloring to water. Even the atoms and molecules in a solid constantly vibrate.

Common Misconceptions

LIQUIDS AND GASES ARE MATTER Students may think that liquids and gases are not matter. Liquids and gases are both matter because they have mass and take up space.

 This misconception is addressed on p. 11.

MISCONCEPTION DATABASE
CLASSZONE.COM Background on student misconceptions

SUBSTANCES ARE MADE OF ATOMS AND MOLECULES Students may think that atoms or molecules are merely parts of substances and that there is something other than empty space between the molecules. Rather, substances are composed entirely of atoms and molecules. Molecules of a gas (air) can fill spaces between other molecules. Other space is just empty space.

 This misconception is addressed on p. 18.

Previewing Content

SECTION

3 Matter combines to form different substances. pp. 21–26

1. **Matter can be pure or mixed.**
   Matter that contains only one kind of atom or molecule is pure. Matter often contains two or more substances mixed together. Substances can be composed of elements, compounds, or mixtures.
   - An **element** is a substance that contains only one kind of atom. Gold is the element represented in the diagram on the left below.

   Element: Gold **Compound: Dry Ice**

   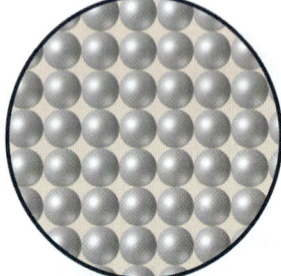 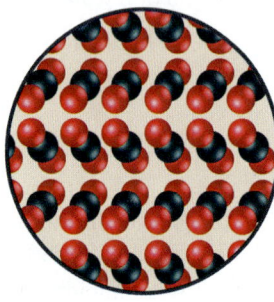

   - A **compound** is a substance that consists of two or more different types of atoms bonded together as shown in the diagram on the right above. Water molecules are compounds because they contain two kinds of atom bonded covalently. A molecule of oxygen is not a compound. Some compounds, such as table salt, are bonded ionically.
   - A **mixture** is a combination of different substances that retain their individual properties and can be separated by physical means.

2. **Parts of mixtures can be the same or different throughout.**
   Mixtures can be either heterogeneous or homogeneous.
   - A heterogeneous mixture has different properties in different parts of the mixture because the substances in different parts of the mixture vary.
   - A homogeneous mixture has substances evenly spread out throughout the mixture.

Common Misconceptions

ATOMS AND COLOR Students often think that individual atoms and molecules have the same properties as the substance they make up. For example, students might think a gold atom is hard and solid or a gas molecule is transparent.

 This misconception is addressed in the Teacher Demo on p. 22.

SECTION

4 Matter exists in different physical states. pp. 27–33

1. **Particle arrangement and motion determine the state of matter.**
   Solid, liquid, and gas are three common **states of matter**. When a substance changes from one state to another, the arrangement of its molecules changes. The distance between molecules and the attraction they have for one another change.

2. **Solid, liquid, and gas are common states of matter.**
   The state of a substance depends on the space between its particles and the way in which the particles move.
   - A **solid** has particles that are close together. The particles are attached to one another and can vibrate in place, but they cannot move from place to place.
   - A **liquid** has particles that are attracted to one another and are close together. The particles can slide over one another and move from one place to another.
   - A **gas** has particles that are not close to one another and can move about freely.

   The diagrams below show the arrangement and motion of particles in different states of matter.

   ① Solid   ② Liquid   ③ Gas

   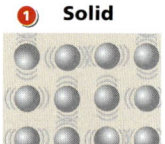 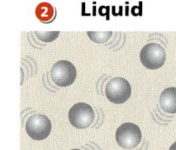 

3. **Solids have a definite volume and shape.**
   A solid has a fixed volume and shape. The particles in some solids are in regular patterns and form crystals.

4. **Liquids have a definite volume but no definite shape.**
   A liquid has a definite volume because its particles are close enough together that they cannot move about freely, although they slide past each other. A liquid takes the shape of the container that it is in.

5. **Gases have no definite volume or shape.**
   A gas has no definite volume or shape. The volume, pressure, and temperature of a gas are related to one another, and changing one can change the others.

 MISCONCEPTION DATABASE
CLASSZONE.COM Background on student misconceptions

Previewing Labs

EXPLORE the BIG idea

What Has Changed? p. 7
Students observe a balloon and realize that air has mass and volume.
- TIME: 10 minutes
- MATERIALS: balloon

Where Does the Sugar Go? p. 7
Students dissolve sugar in a glass of water to explore mixtures.
- TIME: 10 minutes
- MATERIALS: glass of water, spoonful of sugar, spoon

Internet Activity: Scale, p. 7
Students explore atoms by looking at closer and closer views of an object.
- TIME: 20 minutes
- MATERIALS: computer with Internet access

SECTION 1

EXPLORE Similar Objects, p. 9
Students observe the properties of mass and volume as they compare two balls.
- TIME: 10 minutes
- MATERIALS: 2 balls of different sizes and masses

CHAPTER INVESTIGATION
Mass and Volume, pp. 14–15
Students practice measuring the mass and volume of objects.
- TIME: 40 minutes
- MATERIALS: small rock that fits in a graduated cylinder, 5 pennies, rectangular sponge, tissue box, beam balance, large graduated cylinder, 50 mL water, ruler

SECTION 2

INVESTIGATE Mass, p. 17
Students model measuring the mass of an atom in order to draw conclusions about things they cannot observe directly.
- TIME: 20 minutes
- MATERIALS: beam balance, beaker, 10 pennies

SECTION 3

EXPLORE Mixed Substances, p. 21
Students observe cornstarch and water to see how properties of individual substances compare with properties of mixed substances.
- TIME: 10 minutes
- MATERIALS: teaspoon of cornstarch, teaspoon of water, clear plastic cup, spoon

INVESTIGATE Mixtures, p. 24
Students observe that not all liquids behave the same way when mixed with other liquids.
- TIME: 20 minutes
- MATERIALS: few drops of food coloring, beaker of water, clear jar with screw-on lid, 1/4 jar of vegetable oil

SECTION 4

EXPLORE Solids and Liquids, p. 27
Students compare solids and liquids by observing an ice cube, a marble, and water.
- TIME: 10 minutes
- MATERIALS: water in a clear cup, ice cube, marble, pie tin

INVESTIGATE Liquids, p. 31
Students measure and make inferences about the behavior of different liquids.
- TIME: 20 minutes
- MATERIALS: graduated cylinder, 15 mL colored water, test tube, test-tube rack, 10 mL vegetable oil, 10 mL corn syrup

R Additional INVESTIGATION, Thick and Thin Liquids, A, B, & C, pp. 72–80; Teacher Instructions, pp. 262–263

Previewing Chapter Resources

	INTEGRATED TECHNOLOGY	LABS AND ACTIVITIES
CHAPTER 1 **Introduction to Matter**	**CLASSZONE.COM** • eEdition Plus • EasyPlanner Plus • Misconception Database • Content Review • Test Practice • Simulations • Resource Centers • Internet Activity: Scale • Math Tutorial **SCILINKS.ORG** **CD-ROMS** • eEdition • EasyPlanner • Power Presentations • Content Review • Lab Generator • Test Generator **AUDIO CDS** • Audio Readings • Audio Readings in Spanish	**EXPLORE the Big Idea, p. 7** • What Has Changed? • Where Does the Sugar Go? • Internet Activity: Scale **UNIT RESOURCE BOOK** • Family Letter, p. vii • Spanish Family Letter, p. viii • Unit Projects, pp. 5–10 **Lab Generator CD-ROM** Generate customized labs.
SECTION 1 **Matter has mass and volume.** pp. 9–15 Time: 3 periods (1.5 blocks) Lesson Plan, pp. 11–12	• **SIMULATION,** Weights on Planets • **RESOURCE CENTER,** Volume **UNIT TRANSPARENCY BOOK** • Big Idea Flow Chart, p. T1 • Daily Vocabulary Scaffolding, p. T2 • Note-Taking Model, p. T3 • 3-Minute Warm-Up, p. T4	• EXPLORE Similar Objects, p. 9 • CHAPTER INVESTIGATION, Mass and Volume, pp. 14–15 **UNIT RESOURCE BOOK** • Math Support & Practice, pp. 59–60 • CHAPTER INVESTIGATION, Mass and Volume, pp. 63–71
SECTION 2 **Matter is made of atoms.** pp. 16–20 Time: 2 periods (1 block) Lesson Plan, pp. 21–22	• **RESOURCE CENTER,** Scanning Tunneling Microscope Images **UNIT TRANSPARENCY BOOK** • Daily Vocabulary Scaffolding, p. T2 • 3-Minute Warm-Up, p. T4	• INVESTIGATE Mass, p. 17 • Extreme Science, p. 20 **UNIT RESOURCE BOOK** Datasheet, Mass, p. 30
SECTION 3 **Matter combines to form different substances.** pp. 21–26 Time: 2 periods (1 block) Lesson Plan, pp. 32–33	• **RESOURCE CENTER,** Mixtures • **MATH TUTORIAL** **UNIT TRANSPARENCY BOOK** • Daily Vocabulary Scaffolding, p. T2 • 3-Minute Warm-Up, p. T5	• EXPLORE Mixed Substances, p. 21 • INVESTIGATE Mixtures, p. 24 • Math in Science, p. 26 **UNIT RESOURCE BOOK** • Datasheet, Mixtures, p. 41 • Math Support, p. 61 • Math Practice, p. 62
SECTION 4 **Matter exists in different physical states.** pp. 27–33 Time: 3 periods (1.5 blocks) Lesson Plan, pp. 43–44	**SIMULATION,** Gas Behavior **UNIT TRANSPARENCY BOOK** • Big Idea Flow Chart, p. T1 • Daily Vocabulary Scaffolding, p. T2 • 3-Minute Warm-Up, p. T5 • "States of Matter" Visual, p. T6 • Chapter Outline, pp. T7–T8	• EXPLORE Solids and Liquids, p. 27 • INVESTIGATE Liquids, p. 31 **UNIT RESOURCE BOOK** • Datasheet, Liquids, p. 52 • Additional INVESTIGATION, Thick and Thin Liquids, A, B, & C, pp. 72–80

KEY TO ICONS   CD/CD-ROM    Teacher Edition   UNIT TRANSPARENCY BOOK   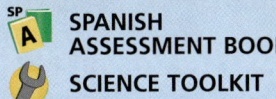 SPANISH ASSESSMENT BOOK
 INTERNET   Pupil Edition   UNIT RESOURCE BOOK   UNIT ASSESSMENT BOOK   SCIENCE TOOLKIT

READING AND REINFORCEMENT

- Four Square, B22–23
- Main Idea and Detail Notes, C37
- Daily Vocabulary Scaffolding, H1–8

 UNIT RESOURCE BOOK
- Vocabulary Practice, pp. 56–57
- Decoding Support, p. 58
- Summarizing the Chapter, pp. 81–82

 Audio Readings CD
Listen to Pupil Edition.

 Audio Readings in Spanish CD
Listen to Pupil Edition in Spanish.

 UNIT RESOURCE BOOK
- Reading Study Guide, A & B, pp. 13–16
- Spanish Reading Study Guide, pp. 17–18
- Challenge and Extension, p. 19
- Reinforcing Key Concepts, p. 20

UNIT RESOURCE BOOK
- Reading Study Guide, A & B, pp. 23–26
- Spanish Reading Study Guide, pp. 27–28
- Challenge and Extension, p. 29
- Reinforcing Key Concepts, p. 31

UNIT RESOURCE BOOK
- Reading Study Guide, A & B, pp. 34–37
- Spanish Reading Study Guide, pp. 38–39
- Challenge and Extension, p. 40
- Reinforcing Key Concepts, p. 42

 UNIT RESOURCE BOOK
- Reading Study Guide, A & B, pp. 45–48
- Spanish Reading Study Guide, pp. 49–50
- Challenge and Extension, p. 51
- Reinforcing Key Concepts, p. 53
- Challenge Reading, pp. 54–55

ASSESSMENT

- Chapter Review, pp. 35–36
- Standardized Test Practice, p. 37

 UNIT ASSESSMENT BOOK
- Diagnostic Test, pp. 1–2
- Chapter Test, A, B, & C, pp. 7–18
- Alternative Assessment, pp. 19–20

 Spanish Chapter Test, pp. 213–216

 Test Generator CD-ROM
Generate customized tests.

 Lab Generator CD-ROM
Rubrics for Labs

 Ongoing Assessment, pp. 9–13

Section 1.1 Review, p. 13

UNIT ASSESSMENT BOOK
Section 1.1 Quiz, p. 3

 Ongoing Assessment, pp. 16–19

 Section 1.2 Review, p. 19

 UNIT ASSESSMENT BOOK
Section 1.2 Quiz, p. 4

 Ongoing Assessment, pp. 22–24

 Section 1.3 Review, p. 25

 UNIT ASSESSMENT BOOK
Section 1.3 Quiz, p. 5

 Ongoing Assessment, pp. 28, 30–32

 Section 1.4 Review, p. 33

 UNIT ASSESSMENT BOOK
Section 1.4 Quiz, p. 6

STANDARDS

National Standards
A.2–8, A.9.a–c, A.9.e–f, B.1.c, E.6.c, F.5.c

See p. 6 for the standards.

National Standards
A.2–8, A.9.a–c, A.9.e–f

National Standards
A.2–7, A.9.a–b, A.9.e–f, E.6.c, F.5.c

National Standards
A.2–8, A.9.a–c, A.9.e–f

National Standards
A.2–7, A.9.a–b, A.9.e–f

Chapter 1: **Introduction to Matter** 5F

Previewing Resources for Differentiated Instruction

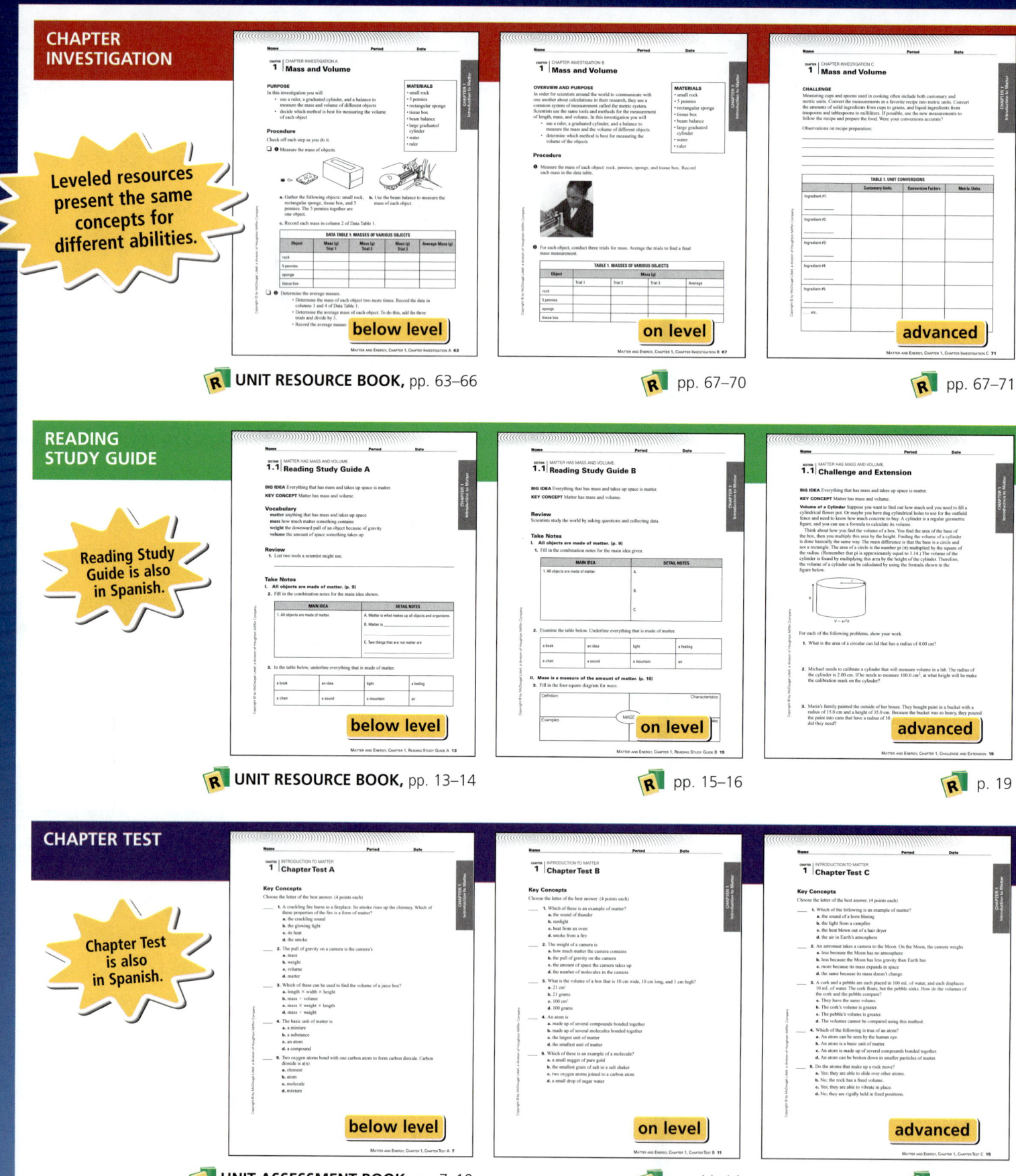

5G Unit 1: Matter and Energy

TECHNOLOGY

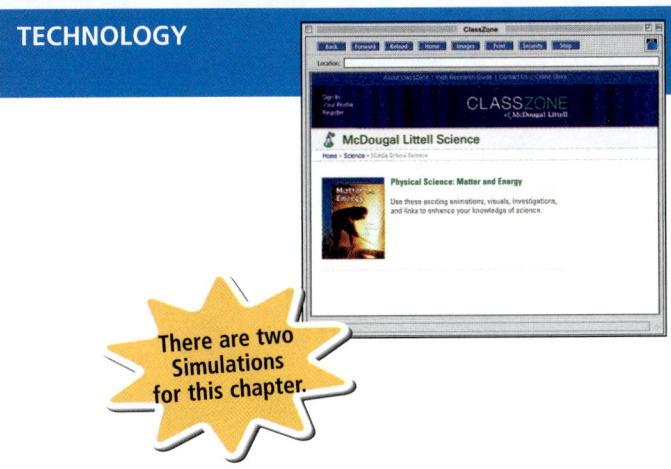
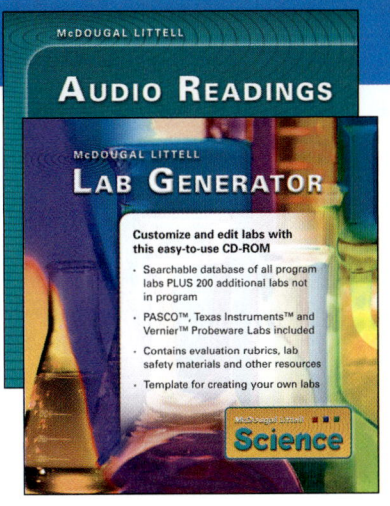
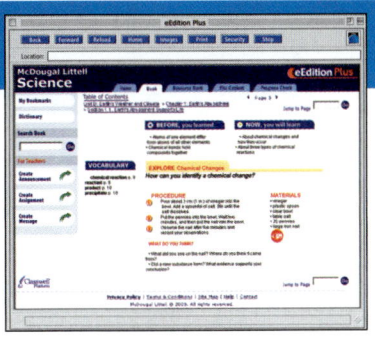

There are two Simulations for this chapter.

i CLASSZONE.COM   **CD/CD-ROMS**   **i CLASSZONE.COM**

VISUAL CONTENT

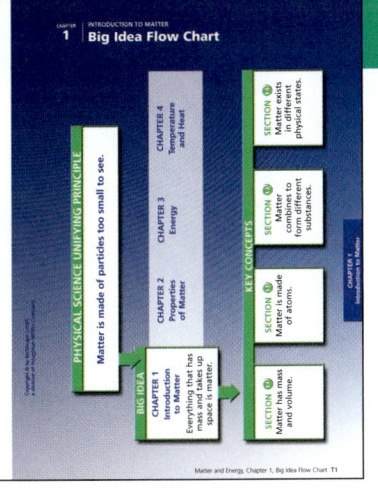
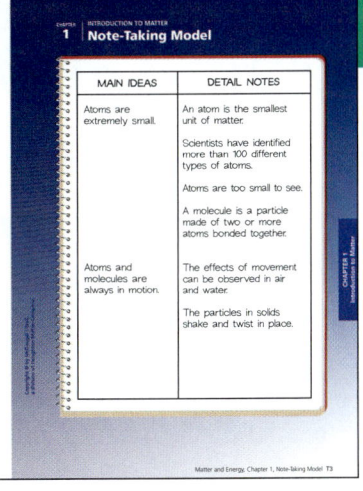

T UNIT TRANSPARENCY BOOK, p. T1   **T** p. T3   **T** p. T6

MORE SUPPORT

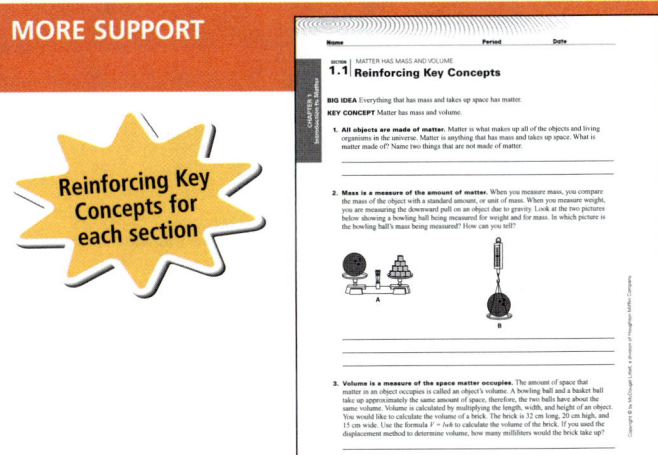
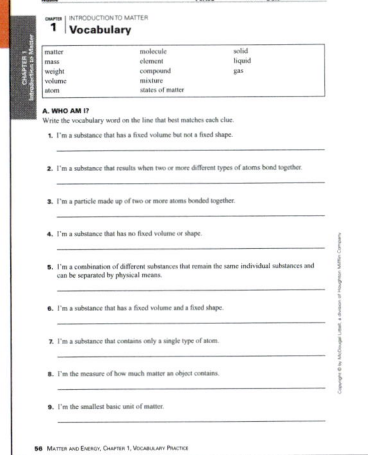
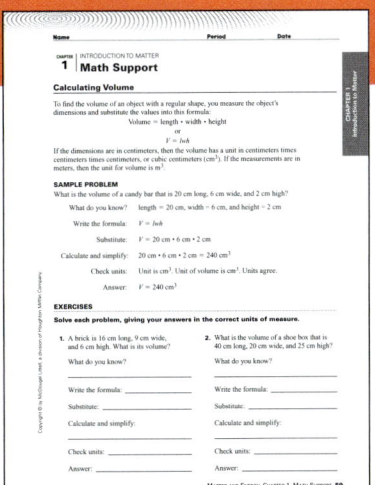

Reinforcing Key Concepts for each section

R UNIT RESOURCE BOOK, p. 20   **R** pp. 56–57   **R** p. 59

Chapter 1: **Introduction to Matter 5H**

CHAPTER 1 Introduction to Matter

INTRODUCE

Have students look at the photograph of the beach and discuss how the question in the box links to the Big Idea:

- Which substances in the photograph have mass and take up space?
- How do the substances differ?
- What isn't matter?

National Science Education Standards

Content

B.1.c Chemical elements do not break down during normal laboratory reactions involving such treatments as heating, exposure to electric current, or reaction with acids. There are more than 100 known elements that combine in a multitude of ways to produce compounds, which account for the living and nonliving substances that we encounter.

Process

A.2–8 Design and conduct an investigation; use tools to gather and interpret data; use evidence to describe, predict, explain, model; think critically to make relationships between evidence and explanation; recognize different explanations and predictions; communicate scientific procedures and explanations; use mathematics.

A.9.a–c, A.9.e–f Understand scientific inquiry by using different investigations, methods, mathematics, and explanations based on logic, evidence, and skepticism.

E.6.c Science drives technology and technology drives science

F.5.c Technology influences society through its products and processes.

6 Unit 1: **Matter and Energy**

CHAPTER 1 Introduction to Matter

the BIG idea

Everything that has mass and takes up space is matter.

What matter can you identify in this photograph?

Key Concepts

SECTION 1 Matter has mass and volume.
Learn what mass and volume are and how to measure them.

SECTION 2 Matter is made of atoms.
Learn about the movement of atoms and molecules.

SECTION 3 Matter combines to form different substances.
Learn how atoms form compounds and mixtures.

SECTION 4 Matter exists in different physical states.
Learn how different states of matter behave.

Internet Preview

CLASSZONE.COM
Chapter 1 online resources: Content Review, two Simulations, four Resource Centers, Math Tutorial, Test Practice

6 Unit 1: **Matter and Energy**

 **INTERNET PREVIEW**

CLASSZONE.COM For student use with the following pages:

Review and Practice
- Content Review, pp. 8, 34
- Math Tutorial: Circle Graphs, p. 26
- Test Practice, p. 37

Activities and Resources
- Internet Activity: p. 7
- Simulations: Weights on Different Planets, p. 11; Gas Behavior, p. 33
- Resource Centers: Volume, p. 12; STM Images, p. 20; Mixtures, p. 24

Solids, Liquids, and Gases
Code: MDL061

EXPLORE the BIG idea

What Has Changed?
Blow up a balloon. Observe it. Let the air out of the balloon slowly. Observe it again.

Observe and Think Did the amount of material that makes up the balloon change? Did the amount of air inside the balloon change? How did the amount of air inside the balloon affect the size of the balloon?

Where Does the Sugar Go?
Stir some sugar into a glass of water. Observe what happens.

Observe and Think What happened to the sugar as you stirred? Do you think you would be able to separate the sugar from the water? If so, how?

Internet Activity: Scale
Go to **ClassZone.com** to explore the smallest units of matter. Start with a faraway view of an object. Then try closer and closer views until you see that object at the atomic level.

Observe and Think Are all objects seen at faraway views made up of the same parts at an atomic level? Explain your answer.

NSTA scilinks.org SCLINKS
Solids, Liquids, and Gases **Code:** MDL061

Chapter 1: **Introduction to Matter** 7

TEACHING WITH TECHNOLOGY

Video Camera Students can use a video camera to record real-world examples that model the movement of particles in the different states of matter on p. 28.

Scanning Tunneling Microscope In addition to the ClassZone site, you can search the Internet for other images from SEM (scanning electron microscopes) or STM technology while discussing p. 20.

EXPLORE the BIG idea

These inquiry-based activities are appropriate for use at home or as a supplement to classroom instruction.

What Has Changed?
PURPOSE To introduce the idea that air takes up space and is matter. Students observe a balloon as they blow it up and then slowly let the air out.

TIP *10 min.* For health reasons, do not allow students to share the task of blowing up a balloon. Caution students not to overfill the balloons. Have extra balloons available.

Answer: The amount of matter that made up the balloon did not change. The amount of air inside the balloon changed. The less air in the balloon, the smaller the balloon gets.

REVISIT after p. 11.

Where Does the Sugar Go?
PURPOSE To introduce the concept of two substances forming a mixture. Students dissolve sugar in a glass of water.

TIP *10 min.* If the sugar does not dissolve, have students add more water and stir the mixture for a longer time.

Answer: The sugar dissolved in the water. You could boil the water or let it evaporate. The sugar will be left behind.

REVISIT after p. 25.

Internet Activity: Scale
PURPOSE To introduce students to atoms, the smallest units of matter.

TIP *20 min.* Have students observe more than one object.

Answer: Yes; matter is made up of atoms.

REVISIT after p. 18.

Chapter 1 **7**

PREPARE

◉ CONCEPT REVIEW

Activate Prior Knowledge

- Place open containers of a substance with a strong aroma, such as vinegar or room deodorizer, around the classroom so that students will notice the aroma.
- Ask students to describe the size of the particles that cause the aroma. *very small, invisible*
- Show students the original source of the particles. Ask them to describe the size of the particles that make up the substance. *very small, invisible*
- Discuss what makes up all substances. *particles that are too small to see*

◉ TAKING NOTES

Main Idea and Detail Notes

Encourage students to identify and write the most important details. Students can test themselves by covering up one-half of the chart as they study.

Vocabulary Strategy

The four square diagram organizes all aspects of a word into a coherent pattern. By filling in their own words, students personalize their understanding. Point out that it is all right to leave a blank square. Many terms, such as *volume* and *states of matter*, may not have clear nonexamples.

Vocabulary and Note-Taking Resources

- Vocabulary Practice, pp. 56–57
- Decoding Support, p. 58

- Daily Vocabulary Scaffolding, p. T2
- Note-Taking Model, p. T3

- Four Square, B22–23
- Main Idea and Detail Notes, C37
- Daily Vocabulary Scaffolding, H1–8

8 Unit 1: **Matter and Energy**

CHAPTER 1
Getting Ready to Learn

◉ CONCEPT REVIEW

- Matter is made of particles too small to see.
- Energy and matter change from one form to another.
- Energy cannot be created or destroyed.

◉ VOCABULARY REVIEW

See Glossary for definitions.

particle
substance

CONTENT REVIEW
CLASSZONE.COM
Review concepts and vocabulary.

▶ TAKING NOTES

MAIN IDEA AND DETAIL NOTES

Make a two-column chart. Write the main ideas, such as those in the blue headings, in the column on the left. Write details about each of those main ideas in the column on the right.

VOCABULARY STRATEGY

Write each new vocabulary term in the center of a **four square** diagram. Write notes in the squares around each term. Include a definition, some characteristics, and some examples of the term. If possible, write some things that are not examples of the term.

See the Note-Taking Handbook on pages R45–R51.

SCIENCE NOTEBOOK

MAIN IDEAS	DETAIL NOTES
1. All objects are made of matter.	1. All objects and living organisms are matter.
	1. Light and sound are not matter.
2. Mass is a measure of the amount of matter.	2. A balance can be used to compare masses.
	2. Standard unit of mass is kilogram (kg).

Definition	Characteristics
the downward pull on an object due to gravity	• standard unit is newton (N) • is measured by using a scale

WEIGHT

Examples	Nonexamples
On Earth, a 1 kg object has a weight of 9.8 N.	not the same as mass, which is a measure of how much matter an object contains

CHECK READINESS

Administer the Diagnostic Test to determine students' readiness for new science content and their mastery of requisite math skills.

 Diagnostic Test, pp. 1–2

Technology Resources

Students needing content and math skills should visit **ClassZone.com**.

- **CONTENT REVIEW**
- **MATH TUTORIAL**

 CONTENT REVIEW CD-ROM

1.1 KEY CONCEPT
Matter has mass and volume.

◀ **BEFORE, you learned**
- Scientists study the world by asking questions and collecting data
- Scientists use tools such as microscopes, thermometers, and computers

▶ **NOW, you will learn**
- What matter is
- How to measure the mass of matter
- How to measure the volume of matter

VOCABULARY
matter p. 9
mass p. 10
weight p. 11
volume p. 11

EXPLORE Similar Objects
How can two similar objects differ?

PROCEDURE
1. Look at the two balls but do not pick them up. Compare their sizes and shapes. Record your observations.
2. Pick up each ball. Compare the way the balls feel in your hands. Record your observations.

MATERIALS
2 balls of different sizes

WHAT DO YOU THINK?
How would your observation be different if the larger ball were made of foam?

VOCABULARY
Make four square diagrams for *matter* and for *mass* in your notebook to help you understand their relationship.

All objects are made of matter.

Suppose your class takes a field trip to a museum. During the course of the day you see mammoth bones, sparkling crystals, hot-air balloons, and an astronaut's space suit. All of these things are matter.

Matter is what makes up all of the objects and living organisms in the universe. As you will see, **matter** is anything that has mass and takes up space. Your body is matter. The air that you breathe and the water that you drink are also matter. Matter makes up the materials around you. Matter is made of particles called atoms, which are too small to see. You will learn more about atoms in the next section.

Not everything is matter. Light and sound, for example, are not matter. Light does not take up space or have mass in the same way that a table does. Although air is made of atoms, a sound traveling through air is not.

 What is matter? How can you tell if something is matter?

Chapter 1: Introduction to Matter 9

RESOURCES FOR DIFFERENTIATED INSTRUCTION

Below Level
UNIT RESOURCE BOOK
- Reading Study Guide A, pp. 13–14
- Decoding Support, p. 58

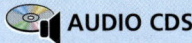 AUDIO CDS

Advanced
UNIT RESOURCE BOOK
Challenge and Extension, p. 19

English Learners
UNIT RESOURCE BOOK
Spanish Reading Study Guide, pp. 17–18

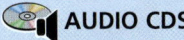 AUDIO CDS
- Audio Readings in Spanish
- Audio Readings (English)

1.1 FOCUS

▶ **Set Learning Goals**
Students will
- Explain what matter is.
- Describe how to measure the mass of matter.
- Describe how to measure the volume of matter.

◯ **3-Minute Warm-Up**
Display Transparency 4 or copy this exercise on the board:

Draw a two-column chart. In the column on the left, write what you know about matter. In the column on the right, write questions that you have about matter. *Encourage students to look for answers to their questions as they study matter.*

[T] 3-Minute Warm-Up, p. T4

1.1 MOTIVATE

EXPLORE Similar Objects

PURPOSE To introduce the properties of mass and volume by comparing two objects

TIP 10 min. The two balls must be different sizes. Students may be surprised at the results if the smaller ball is heavier.

WHAT DO YOU THINK? *Sample answer: A large foam ball might not be as heavy as a baseball. (Actual answers would depend on the types of balls used.)*

Ongoing Assessment
Explain what matter is.

Ask: Give an example of something that is matter and explain why it is matter. *A book is matter because it has mass and takes up space.*

 *Answer: Matter is what makes up all objects and living organisms in the universe. Matter has mass and takes up space.*

Chapter 1 **9**

1.1 INSTRUCT

Develop Critical Thinking

APPLY Tell students that enough mass cubes are not available for the entire class. Have students apply what they know about measuring mass to invent standard units of mass based on common objects. Ask them to find the mass of objects based on the invented standard units.

Teach from Visuals

To help students interpret the photographs and illustrations comparing the size and mass of a bowling ball and a basketball, ask:

- How do the sizes of the bowling ball and the basketball in the photographs compare? *They are about the same.*
- How can you tell from the illustrations which ball has more mass? *More standard cubes are needed to balance the pan with the bowling ball than the pan with the basketball.*

Ongoing Assessment

Describe how to measure the mass of matter.

Ask: How would you find the mass of an object? *Compare its mass with the mass of standard units on a balance.*

 Answer: Mass is a measure of how much matter an object contains.

 **MAIN IDEA AND DETAILS**
As you read, write the blue headings on the left side of a two-column chart. Add details in the other column.

Mass is a measure of the amount of matter.

Different objects contain different amounts of matter. **Mass** is a measure of how much matter an object contains. A metal teaspoon, for example, contains more matter than a plastic teaspoon. Therefore, a metal teaspoon has a greater mass than a plastic teaspoon. An elephant has more mass than a mouse.

CHECK YOUR READING How are matter and mass related?

Measuring Mass

When you measure mass, you compare the mass of the object with a standard amount, or unit, of mass. The standard unit of mass is the kilogram (kg). A large grapefruit has a mass of about one-half kilogram. Smaller masses are often measured in grams (g). There are 1000 grams in a kilogram. A penny has a mass of between two and three grams.

How can you compare the masses of two objects? One way is to use a pan balance, as shown below. If two objects balance each other on a pan balance, then they contain the same amount of matter. If a basketball balances a metal block, for example, then the basketball and the block have the same mass. Beam balances work in a similar way, but instead of comparing the masses of two objects, you compare the mass of an object with a standard mass on the beam.

A bowling ball and a basketball are about the same size, but a bowling ball has more mass.

DIFFERENTIATE INSTRUCTION

More Reading Support

A To measure mass, what do you compare the object's mass to? *standard units of mass*

English Learners Phrasal verbs such as "makes up" and "takes up" are used throughout this chapter (for example, on p. 9). Make sure students understand not to read "up" and other adverbs or prepositions in phrasal verbs as literal directions. If students are still confused, offer synonyms for phrasal verbs. For instance, "makes up" means composes, and "takes up" means occupies. English learners may also lack background knowledge of a field trip (p. 9).

Measuring Weight

When you hold an object such as a backpack full of books, you feel it pulling down on your hands. This is because Earth's gravity pulls the backpack toward the ground. Gravity is the force that pulls two masses toward each other. In this example, the two masses are Earth and the backpack. **Weight** is the downward pull on an object due to gravity. If the pull of the backpack is strong, you would say that the backpack weighs a lot.

Gravity is pulling down on both the girl and the backpack. The heavier the backpack is, the stronger the pull of gravity is on it.

Weight is measured by using a scale, such as a spring scale like the one shown on the right, that tells how hard an object is pushing or pulling on it. The standard scientific unit for weight is the newton (N). A common unit for weight is the pound (lb).

Mass and weight are closely related, but they are not the same. Mass describes the amount of matter an object has, and weight describes how strongly gravity is pulling on that matter. On Earth, a one-kilogram object has a weight of 9.8 newtons (2.2 lb). When a person says that one kilogram is equal to 2.2 pounds, he or she is really saying that one kilogram has a weight of 2.2 pounds on Earth. On the Moon, however, gravity is one-sixth as strong as it is on Earth. On the Moon, the one-kilogram object would have a weight of 1.6 newtons (0.36 lb). The amount of matter in the object, or its mass, is the same on Earth as it is on the Moon, but the pull of gravity is different.

Compare weights on different planets.

CHECK YOUR READING What is the difference between mass and weight?

Volume is a measure of the space matter occupies.

Matter takes up space. A bricklayer stacks bricks on top of each other to build a wall. No two bricks can occupy the same place because the matter in each brick takes up space.

The amount of space that matter in an object occupies is called the object's **volume**. The bowling ball and the basketball shown on page 10 take up approximately the same amount of space. Therefore, the two balls have about the same volume. Although the basketball is hollow, it is not empty. Air fills up the space inside the basketball. Air and other gases take up space and have volume.

Chapter 1: Introduction to Matter 11

Real World Example

The amount of some products is determined by volume. For example, bags of mulch used for gardens and yards are sold by cubic feet. A bag often tells consumers how large of an area the bag will cover, although amounts can vary depending on the depth of the mulch. Soil and cement are also sold by volume.

Ongoing Assessment

 **Practice the Math** Answers:

1. 10 cm · 5 cm · 7 cm = 350 cm^3
2. 1 m · 0.5 m · 0.5 m = 0.25 m^3

- Math Support, p. 59
- Math Practice, p. 60

 Find out more about volume.

Determining Volume by Formula

There are different ways to find the volume of an object. For objects that have well-defined shapes, such as a brick or a ball, you can take a few measurements of the object and calculate the volume by substituting these values into a formula.

A rectangular box, for example, has a length, a width, and a height that can be measured. To find the volume of the box, multiply the three values.

$$\text{Volume} = \text{length} \cdot \text{width} \cdot \text{height}$$
$$V = lwh$$

If you measure the length, the width, and the height of the box in centimeters (cm), the volume has a unit of centimeters times centimeters times centimeters, or centimeters cubed (cm^3). If the measurements are meters, the unit of volume is meters cubed (m^3). All measurements must be in the same unit to calculate volume.

Other regular solids, such as spheres and cylinders, also have formulas for calculating volumes. All formulas for volume require multiplying three dimensions. Units for volume are often expressed in terms of a length unit cubed, that is, a length to the third power.

Calculating Volume

Sample Problem

What is the volume of a pizza box that is 8 cm high, 38 cm wide, and 38 cm long?

What do you know?	length = 38 cm, width = 38 cm, height = 8 cm
What do you want to find out?	Volume
Write the formula:	$V = lwh$
Substitute into the formula:	$V = 38$ cm · 38 cm · 8 cm
Calculate and simplify:	11,552 cm · cm · cm = 11,552 cm^3
Check that your units agree:	Unit is cm^3. Unit of volume is cm^3. Units agree.
Answer:	11,552 cm^3

 **Practice the Math**

1. A bar of gold is 10 cm long, 5 cm wide, and 7 cm high. What is its volume?
2. What is the volume of a large block of wood that is 1 m long, 0.5 m high, and 50 cm wide?

DIFFERENTIATE INSTRUCTION

 More Reading Support

D A formula can be used to find the volume of which type of objects? *regular objects with well-defined shapes*

Advanced Have students find the formulas for calculating the volume of a sphere and a cylinder. Encourage them to use the formulas to find the volume of objects in the classroom.

 Challenge and Extension, p. 19

Measuring Volume by Displacement

Although a box has a regular shape, a rock does not. There is no simple formula for calculating the volume of something with an irregular shape. Instead, you can make use of the fact that two objects cannot be in the same place at the same time. This method of measuring is called displacement.

 Add water to a graduated cylinder. Note the volume of the water by reading the water level on the cylinder.

 Submerge the irregular object in the water. Because the object and the water cannot share the same space, the water is displaced, or moved upward. Note the new volume of the water with the object in it.

❸ Subtract the volume of the water before you added the object from the volume of the water and the object together. The result is the volume of the object. The object displaces a volume of water equal to the volume of the object.

You measure the volume of a liquid by measuring how much space it takes up in a container. The volume of a liquid usually is measured in liters (L) or milliliters (mL). One liter is equal to 1000 milliliters. Milliliters and cubic centimeters are equivalent. This can be written as $1 \text{ mL} = 1 \text{ cm}^3$. If you had a box with a volume of one cubic centimeter and you filled it with water, you would have one milliliter of water.

In the first photograph, the graduated cylinder contains 50 mL of water. Placing a rock in the cylinder causes the water level to rise from 50 mL to 55 mL. The difference is 5 mL; therefore, the volume of the rock is 5 cm^3.

Measure the volume of water without the rock.

Measure the volume of water with the rock in it.

1.1 Review

KEY CONCEPTS
1. Give three examples of matter.
2. What do weight and mass measure?
3. How can you measure the volume of an object that has an irregular shape?

CRITICAL THINKING
4. **Calculate** What is the volume of a box that is 12 cm long, 6 cm wide, and 4 cm high?
5. **Synthesize** What is the relationship between the units of measurement for the volume of a liquid and of a solid object?

⚠ CHALLENGE
6. **Infer** Why might a small increase in the dimensions of an object cause a large change in its volume?

Chapter 1: **Introduction to Matter** 13

ANSWERS

1. Sample answer: air, water, a rock

2. Weight measures the downward pull on an object due to gravity. Mass measures how much matter an object contains.

3. Submerge the object in water and subtract the volume of the water before the object was added from the volume of the water and the object together.

4. 12 cm · 6 cm · 4 cm = 288 cm^3

5. One cubic centimeter of solid is equivalent to one milliliter of liquid.

6. Each of the three dimensions increases, so, for example, doubling the dimensions increases the volume by a multiple of eight.

CHAPTER INVESTIGATION

Focus

PURPOSE To practice measuring mass and volume

OVERVIEW Students will measure the mass and volume of four objects and find the average of three trials for each object. Students will find:

- the volume of a rectangular object by multiplying the object's length by its width and height.
- the volume of an irregular object by subtracting the volume of water in a graduated cylinder without the object from the volume of the water with the object.

Lab Preparation

- Collect small rocks that will fit into graduated cylinders, pennies, sponges, and tissue boxes. You also could substitute a variety of other objects from the classroom. You could ask students to bring pennies from home.
- Prior to the investigation, have students read through the investigation and prepare their data tables. Or you may wish to copy and distribute datasheets and rubrics.

 UNIT RESOURCE BOOK, pp. 63–71

 SCIENCE TOOLKIT, F15

Lab Management

- Review with students how to use a beam balance and a graduated cylinder. Remind them to read the volume of the water at the bottom of the meniscus in the cylinder.
- If time is a factor, you could reduce the number of objects to be tested.
- Point out that three trials and an average are used because sometimes there are human errors in measuring.

INCLUSION Students with disabilities might need help making accurate measurements of mass and volume.

14 Unit 1: **Matter and Energy**

CHAPTER INVESTIGATION

Mass and Volume

OVERVIEW AND PURPOSE In order for scientists around the world to communicate with one another about calculations in their research, they use a common system of measurement called the metric system. Scientists use the same tools and methods for the measurement of length, mass, and volume. In this investigation you will

- use a ruler, a graduated cylinder, and a balance to measure the mass and the volume of different objects
- determine which method is best for measuring the volume of the objects

Procedure

MATERIALS
- small rock
- 5 pennies
- rectangular sponge
- tissue box
- beam balance
- large graduated cylinder
- water
- ruler

1. Make a data table like the one shown on the sample notebook page.

2. Measure the mass of each object: rock, pennies, sponge, and tissue box. Record each mass.

step 2

3. For each object, conduct three trials for mass. Average the trials to find a final mass measurement.

4. Decide how you will find the volume of each object.

   For rectangular objects, you will use the following formula:

   $$\text{Volume} = \text{length} \cdot \text{width} \cdot \text{height}$$

   For irregular objects, you will use the displacement method and the following formula:

   $$\text{Volume of object} = \text{volume of water with object} - \text{volume of water without object}$$

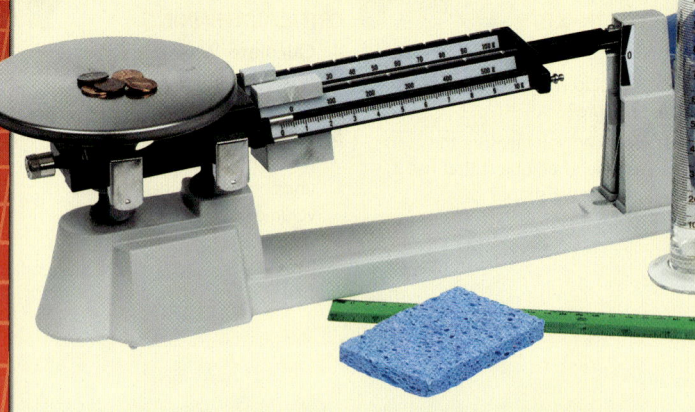

14 Unit 1: **Matter and Energy**

INVESTIGATION RESOURCES

 CHAPTER INVESTIGATION, Mass and Volume
- Level A, pp. 63–66
- Level B, pp. 67–70
- Level C, p. 71

Advanced students should complete Levels B & C.

 Writing a Lab Report, D12–13

Technology Resources

Customize this student lab as needed or look for an alternative. Print rubrics to assess student lab reports.

 Lab Generator CD-ROM

5. For each object, you will conduct three trials for measuring volume. Average the trials to find a final volume measurement.

6. For rectangular objects, use metric units for measuring the length, width, and height. Record the measurements in your data table.

step 6

7. For irregular objects, fill the graduated cylinder about half full with water. Record the exact volume of water in the cylinder. **Note:** The surface of the liquid will be curved in the graduated cylinder. Read the volume of the liquid at the bottom of the curve called the meniscus.

step 7

8. Carefully place the object you are measuring into the cylinder. The object must be completely under the water. Record the exact volume of water in the cylinder containing the object by reading the meniscus.

Observe and Analyze

1. **RECORD OBSERVATIONS** Make sure you have filled out your data table completely.
2. **INTERPRET** For each object, explain why you chose a particular method for measuring the volume.

Conclude

1. **IDENTIFY LIMITS** Which sources of error might have affected your measurements?
2. **APPLY** Doctors need to know the mass of a patient before deciding how much of a medication to prescribe. Why is it important to measure each patient's mass before prescribing medicine?
3. **APPLY** Scientists in the United States work closely with scientists in other countries to develop new technology. What are the advantages of having a single system of measurement?

INVESTIGATE Further

CHALLENGE Measuring cups and spoons used in cooking often include both customary and metric units. Convert the measurements in a favorite recipe into metric units. Convert the amounts of solid ingredients to grams, and liquid ingredients to milliliters or liters. If possible, use the new measurements to follow the recipe and prepare the food. Were your conversions accurate?

Mass and Volume
Observe and Analyze
Table 1. Masses of Various Objects

Object	Mass (g)			
	Trial 1	Trial 2	Trial 3	Average
rock				
5 pennies				
sponge				
tissue box				

Table 2. Volumes of Various Objects

Object	Method Used	Volume (cm^3 or mL)			
		Trial 1	Trial 2	Trial 3	Average
rock					
5 pennies					
sponge					
tissue box					

Chapter 1: **Introduction to Matter** 15

Observe and Analyze

1. SAMPLE DATA Table 1 Masses of Various Objects, Average: rock, 3 g; 5 pennies, 12.33 g; sponge, 8.9 g; tissue box, 293.66 g. Table 2 Volumes of Various Objects, Average: rock, 4 mL; 5 pennies, 2 mL; sponge, 129.4 cm^3; tissue box, 2448 cm^3. See students' tables.

2. Students should have chosen the correct formula for measuring the volume of objects with a regular shape (i.e., sponge, tissue box) and the displacement method for measuring the volume of objects with an irregular shape (i.e., rock, pennies).

Conclude

1. incorrect readings of volume or length
2. Doctors prescribe a dosage based on a patient's body mass. Smaller patients should receive less medicine.
3. Scientists should use the same system of measurements so that they can share information without having to convert their results to another measurement system.

INVESTIGATE Further

CHALLENGE Answers will vary.

Post-Lab Discussion

Have groups compare their measurements and averages. Discuss the importance of doing a number of trials and finding the average. Ask:
- Based on your measurements, why is finding an average measurement important? *Measurements might vary due to small errors in individual measurements. An average measurement is more accurate.*
- Which methods or tools did you use to measure mass and volume? *a beam balance for mass, a formula for the volume of objects with a regular shape, and displacement for the volume of objects with an irregular shape*

1.2 FOCUS

▶ Set Learning Goals

Students will
- Identify the smallest particles of matter.
- Describe how atoms combine into molecules.
- Describe how atoms and molecules move.
- Use modeling to draw conclusions about atoms and their masses.

◀ 3-Minute Warm-Up

Display Transparency 4 or copy this exercise on the board:

Decide if these statements are true. If not, correct them.

1. Substances you can see are matter, but substances you cannot see are not matter. *All substances are matter.*
2. Mass and weight are the same thing. *They are not the same.*
3. Formulas can be used to calculate the volume of many solids with a regular shape. *true*

[T] 3-Minute Warm-Up, p. T4

1.2 MOTIVATE

THINK ABOUT

PURPOSE To understand the size of atoms

DISCUSS Brainstorm examples of scales in which a length or a size represents a much larger length or size. Ask: If an atom were the size of the round head of the pin in the photograph, how large would the pin be? *It would cover about 90 square miles and be about 80 miles high.*

Ongoing Assessment

 **Answer:** Atoms are the smallest basic units of matter. Like building blocks, atoms are the small parts that make up a larger structure.

16 Unit 1: **Matter and Energy**

KEY CONCEPT
1.2 Matter is made of atoms.

◀ **BEFORE, you learned**
- Matter has mass
- Matter has volume

▶ **NOW, you will learn**
- About the smallest particles of matter
- How atoms combine into molecules
- How atoms and molecules move

VOCABULARY
atom p. 16
molecule p. 18

THINK ABOUT

How small is an atom?

All matter is made up of very tiny particles called atoms. It is hard to imagine exactly how small these particles are. Suppose that each of the particles making up the pin shown in the photograph on the right were actually the size of the round head on the pin. How large would the pin be in that case? If you could stick such a pin in the ground, it would cover about 90 square miles—about one-seventh the area of London, England. It would also be about 80 miles high—almost 15 times the height of Mount Everest.

VOCABULARY
Make a four square diagram for *atom* that includes details that will help you remember the term.

Atoms are extremely small.

How small can things get? If you break a stone wall into smaller and smaller pieces, you would have a pile of smaller stones. If you could break the smaller stones into the smallest pieces possible, you would have a pile of atoms. An **atom** is the smallest basic unit of matter.

The idea that all matter is made of extremely tiny particles dates back to the fifth century B.C., when Greek philosophers proposed the first atomic theory of matter. All matter, they said, was made of only a few different types of tiny particles called atoms. The different arrangements of atoms explained the differences among the substances that make up the world. Although the modern view of the atom is different from the ancient view, the idea of atoms as basic building blocks has been confirmed. Today scientists have identified more than 100 different types of atoms.

 What are atoms? How are they like building blocks?

16 Unit 1: Matter and Energy

RESOURCES FOR DIFFERENTIATED INSTRUCTION

Below Level
UNIT RESOURCE BOOK
- Reading Study Guide A, pp. 23–24
- Decoding Support, p. 58

 AUDIO CDS

Advanced
UNIT RESOURCE BOOK
Challenge and Extension, p. 29

English Learners
UNIT RESOURCE BOOK
Spanish Reading Study Guide, pp. 27–28

🎧 AUDIO CDS
- Audio Readings in Spanish
- Audio Readings (English)

Atoms

It is hard to imagine that visible matter is composed of particles too tiny to see. Although you cannot see an individual atom, you are constantly seeing large collections of them. You are a collection of atoms. So are your textbook, a desk, and all the other matter around you. Matter is not something that contains atoms; matter is atoms. A desk, for example, is a collection of atoms and the empty space between those atoms. Without the atoms, there would be no desk—just empty space.

Atoms are so small that they cannot be seen even with very strong optical microscopes. Try to imagine the size of an atom by considering that a single teaspoonful of water contains approximately 500,000,000,000,000,000,000,000 atoms. Although atoms are extremely small, they do have a mass. The mass of a single teaspoonful of water is about 5 grams. This mass is equal to the mass of all the atoms that the water is made of added together.

READING TIP
The word *atom* comes from the Greek word *atomos*, meaning "indivisible," or "cannot be divided."

INVESTIGATE Mass

How do you measure the mass of an atom?

PROCEDURE
1. Find the mass of the empty beaker. Record your result.
2. Place 10 pennies into the beaker. Find the mass of the beaker with the pennies in it. Record your result.
3. Subtract the mass of the empty beaker from the mass of the beaker with the pennies. Record your result.
4. Divide the difference in mass by 10. Record your result.

WHAT DO YOU THINK?
- What is the mass of one penny? What assumptions do you make when you answer this question?
- How might scientists use a similar process to find the mass of a single atom?

CHALLENGE All pennies may not be the same. After years of use, some pennies may have had some of their metal rubbed away. Also, the materials that make up pennies have changed. Find the individual mass of several pennies and compare the masses. Do all pennies have exactly the same mass?

SKILL FOCUS Modeling

MATERIALS
- beam balance
- beaker
- 10 pennies

TIME 20 minutes

Chapter 1: **Introduction to Matter** 17

DIFFERENTIATE INSTRUCTION

More Reading Support

A What makes up all matter? *atoms*

English Learners The phrase "hard to imagine" is used several times in this section. Make sure English learners do not interpret the word "hard" as physically hard—like metal is hard. Rather, stress that hard in this context means difficult. Help students understand that some words have more than one meaning.

Advanced Large numbers can be written in scientific notation. Have students learn how to use scientific notation to write large numbers.

 Challenge and Extension, p. 29

1.2 INSTRUCT

History of Science

The Greek philosophers Leucippus and Democritus developed the first atomic theory in the fifth century B.C. Their view of the atom was different from the modern view of the atom. For example, they thought that objects had different physical properties because their atoms had different shapes. Something that tasted sweet was thought to be made of large, round atoms and sour things made of rough, sharp atoms.

INVESTIGATE Mass

PURPOSE To use modeling to draw conclusions about things that cannot be directly observed

TIPS 20 min.
- You may want to have students bring pennies from home.
- If necessary, explain that the pennies represent a substance and that each individual penny represents an atom of the substance.

WHAT DO YOU THINK? *About 2.3–2.7 grams; like atoms in a single substance, the pennies are all alike. Scientists could find the mass of a large amount of a substance and divide by the number of atoms to estimate the mass of one atom.*

CHALLENGE *Pennies vary in mass by tiny amounts.*

 Datasheet, Mass, p. 30

Technology Resources

Customize this student lab as needed or look for an alternative. Print rubrics to assess students' lab reports.

 Lab Generator CD-ROM

Ongoing Assessment

Identify the smallest particles of matter.

Ask: What is the smallest particle that makes up all matter? *atom*

Chapter 1 **17**

Address Misconceptions

IDENTIFY Ask students to identify what makes up substances besides atoms and molecules. If students do not answer "nothing" or "empty space," they may hold the misconception that atoms and molecules are just some of the parts in a substance, not the substance itself.

CORRECT Explain that atoms or combinations of atoms, such as molecules, are the only matter in a substance. Empty space between atoms is too small to see and has no mass.

REASSESS Ask students what makes up substances. *atoms and combinations of atoms, such as molecules*

Technology Resources

Visit **ClassZone.com** for background on common student misconceptions.

MISCONCEPTION DATABASE

History of Science

Antoine Laurent Lavoisier was a French scientist during the 1700s. Many of his experiments involved breaking compounds into smaller substances and recombining them. He wrote a book that synthesized the chemical knowledge of his time and laid the groundwork for modern atomic theory.

EXPLORE the BIG idea

Revisit "Internet Activity: Scale" on p. 7. Have students compare a substance and its smallest parts.

Ongoing Assessment

Describe how atoms combine into molecules.

Ask: Compare and contrast carbon monoxide molecules with vitamin E molecules. *Both molecules combine atoms, but have different types and numbers of atoms.*

 Answer: A molecule consists of two or more atoms bonded together.

18 Unit 1: **Matter and Energy**

Molecules

When two or more atoms bond together, or combine, they make a particle called a **molecule**. A molecule can be made of atoms that are different or atoms that are alike. A molecule of water, for example, is a combination of different atoms—two hydrogen atoms and one oxygen atom (also written as H_2O). Hydrogen gas molecules are made of the same atom—two hydrogen atoms bonded together.

A molecule is the smallest amount of a substance made of combined atoms that is considered to be that substance. Think about what would happen if you tried to divide water to find its smallest part. Ultimately you would reach a single molecule of water. What would you have if you divided this molecule into its individual atoms of hydrogen and oxygen? If you break up a water molecule, it is no longer water. Instead, you would have hydrogen and oxygen, two different substances.

READING TIP
Not all atoms and molecules have color. In this book atoms and molecules are given colors to make them easier to identify.

CHECK YOUR READING How is a molecule related to an atom?

The droplets of water in this spider web are made of water molecules. Each molecule contains two hydrogen atoms (shown in white) and one oxygen atom (shown in red).

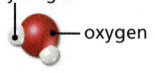
water

Molecules can be made up of different numbers of atoms. For example, carbon monoxide is a molecule that is composed of one carbon atom and one oxygen atom. Molecules also can be composed of a large number of atoms. The most common type of vitamin E molecule, for example, contains 29 carbon atoms, 50 hydrogen atoms, and 2 oxygen atoms.

oxygen   ozone

Molecules made of different numbers of the same atom are different substances. For example, an oxygen gas molecule is made of two oxygen atoms bonded together. Ozone is also composed of oxygen atoms, but an ozone molecule is three oxygen atoms bonded together. The extra oxygen atom gives ozone properties that are different from those of oxygen gas.

18 Unit 1: **Matter and Energy**

DIFFERENTIATE INSTRUCTION

More Reading Support

B What makes up a molecule? *atoms*

C How do an oxygen atom and an oxygen molecule differ? *O atom = one atom; O_2 molecule = O_2 atoms bond together.*

Below Level Have students draw and label a water molecule and the atoms that are in it.

Inclusion Have tactile learners and students with visual impairments make a model of a water molecule by using two identical gumdrops, a marshmallow, and toothpicks.

This photograph shows the interior of Grand Central Terminal in New York City. Light from the window reflects off dust particles that are being moved by the motion of the molecules in air.

Atoms and molecules are always in motion.

If you have ever looked at a bright beam of sunlight, you may have seen dust particles floating in the air. If you were to watch carefully, you might notice that the dust does not fall toward the floor but instead seems to dart about in all different directions. Molecules in air are constantly moving and hitting the dust particles. Because the molecules are moving in many directions, they collide with the dust particles from different directions. This action causes the darting motion of the dust that you observe.

Atoms and molecules are always in motion. Sometimes this motion is easy to observe, such as when you see evidence of molecules in air bouncing dust particles around. Water molecules move too. When you place a drop of food coloring into water, the motion of the water molecules eventually causes the food coloring to spread throughout the water.

The motion of individual atoms and molecules is hard to observe in solid objects, such as a table. The atoms and molecules in a table cannot move about freely like the ones in water and air. However, the atoms and molecules in a table are constantly moving—by shaking back and forth, or by twisting—even if they stay in the same place.

1.2 Review

KEY CONCEPTS
1. What are atoms?
2. What is the smallest particle of a substance that is still considered to be that substance?
3. Why do dust particles in the air appear to be moving in different directions?

CRITICAL THINKING
4. **Apply** How does tea flavor spread from a tea bag throughout a cup of hot water?
5. **Infer** If a water molecule (H_2O) has two hydrogen atoms and one oxygen atom, how would you describe the make-up of a carbon dioxide molecule (CO_2)?

CHALLENGE
6. **Synthesize** Assume that a water balloon has the same number of water molecules as a helium balloon has helium atoms. If the mass of the water is 4.5 times greater than the mass of the helium, how does the mass of a water molecule compare with the mass of a helium atom?

Chapter 1: Introduction to Matter 19

EXTREME SCIENCE
Fun and Motivating Science

Set Learning Goal
To understand how scanning tunneling microscopes make images of atoms

Present the Science
Gerd Binnig and Heinrich Rohrer invented the scanning tunneling microscope in 1981. It is the first microscope that can make three-dimensional images of the atoms on surfaces. Organic molecules, such as DNA, can be attached to a surface and scanned to image their structure.

Discussion Questions
Ask: What does a scanning tunneling microscope measure to make an image of atoms on the surface of a material? *the interaction between the electrically charged needle tip and the nearest atom on the surface of the material*

Ask: What does the series of bumps on the image show? *where the atoms are located*

Ask: Besides making images, what can the tip of a STM needle do? *move atoms around on a surface*

Close
Ask: How do the structures in a scanning tunneling microscope compare with what you can see with your eyes or a regular light microscope? *You cannot see atoms with your eyes or an optical microscope. Scanning tunneling microscopes give you images similar to those of a contour map.*

Technology Resources
Have students visit **ClassZone.com** to find more images from scanning tunneling microscopes

 RESOURCE CENTER

20 Unit 1: **Matter and Energy**

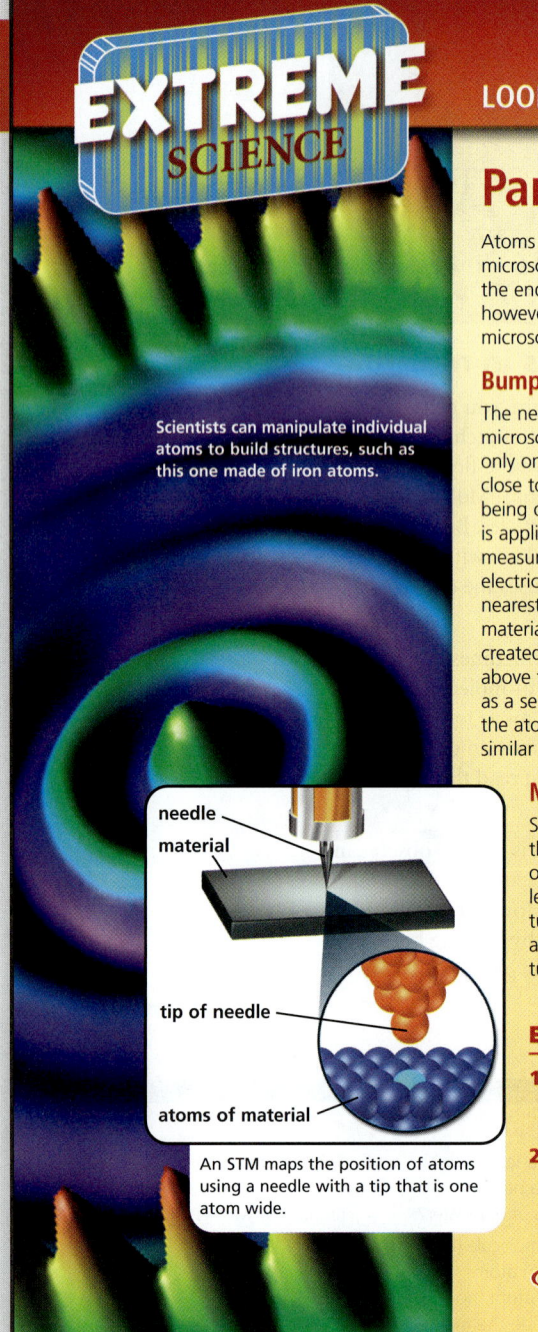

LOOKING AT ATOMS

Particles Too Small to See

Atoms are so small that you cannot see them through an ordinary microscope. In fact, millions of them could fit in the period at the end of this sentence. Scientists can make images of atoms, however, using an instrument called a scanning tunneling microscope (STM).

Bumps on a Surface
The needle of the scanning tunneling microscope has a very sharp tip that is only one atom wide. The tip is brought close to the surface of the material being observed, and an electric current is applied to the tip. The microscope measures the interaction between the electrically charged needle tip and the nearest atom on the surface of the material. An image of the surface is created by moving the needle just above the surface. The image appears as a series of bumps that shows where the atoms are located. The result is similar to a contour map.

Moving Atoms
Scientists also can use the tip of the STM needle to move atoms on a surface. The large image at left is an STM image of a structure made by pushing individual atoms into place on a very smooth metal surface. This structure was designed as a corral to trap individual atoms inside.

Tiny Pieces of Matter
- Images of atoms did not exist until 1970.
- Atoms are so small that a single raindrop contains more than 500 billion trillion atoms.
- If each atom were the size of a pea, your fingerprint would be larger than Alaska.
- In the space between stars, matter is so spread out that a volume of one liter contains only about 1000 atoms.

Scientists can manipulate individual atoms to build structures, such as this one made of iron atoms.

An STM maps the position of atoms using a needle with a tip that is one atom wide.

EXPLORE
1. **INFER** Why must the tip of a scanning tunneling microscope be only one atom wide to make an image of atoms on a surface?
2. **CHALLENGE** Find out more about images of atoms on the Internet. How are STM images used in research to design better materials?

 **RESOURCE CENTER**
CLASSZONE.COM
Find more images from scanning tunneling microscopes.

EXPLORE
1. **INFER** The tip needs to get close to one atom to be able to measure the interaction between the atom and the tip.
2. **CHALLENGE** STM images can be used to help scientists understand structural details and alter the structures for a specific task.

KEY CONCEPT 1.3
Matter combines to form different substances.

◀ **BEFORE, you learned**
- Matter is made of tiny particles called atoms
- Atoms combine to form molecules

▶ **NOW, you will learn**
- How pure matter and mixed matter are different
- How atoms and elements are related
- How atoms form compounds

VOCABULARY
element p. 22
compound p. 23
mixture p. 23

EXPLORE Mixed Substances
What happens when substances are mixed?

PROCEDURE
1. Observe and describe a teaspoon of cornstarch and a teaspoon of water.
2. Mix the two substances together in the cup. Observe and describe the result.

MATERIALS
- cornstarch
- water
- small cup
- spoon

WHAT DO YOU THINK?
- After you mixed the substances, could you still see each substance?
- How was the new substance different from the original substances?

Matter can be pure or mixed.

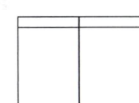
MAIN IDEA AND DETAILS
Continue to organize your notes in a two-column chart as you read.

Matter can be pure, or it can be two or more substances mixed together. Most of the substances you see around you are mixed, although you can't always tell that by looking at them. For example, the air you breathe is a combination of several substances. Wood, paper, steel, and lemonade are all mixed substances.

You might think that the water that you drink from a bottle or from the tap is a pure substance. However, drinking water has minerals dissolved in it and chemicals added to it that you cannot see. Often the difference between pure and mixed substances is apparent only on the atomic or molecular level.

A pure substance has only one type of component. For example, pure water contains only water molecules. Pure silver contains only silver atoms. Coins and jewelry that look like silver are often made of silver in combination with other metals.

Chapter 1: Introduction to Matter 21

1.3 FOCUS

▶ Set Learning Goals
Students will
- Describe how pure and mixed matter are different.
- Explain how atoms and elements are related.
- Describe how atoms form compounds.
- Observe and compare in an experiment the properties of individual substances with the properties of mixtures.

◉ 3-Minute Warm-Up
Display Transparency 5 or copy this exercise on the board:

Match each definition with the correct term.

Definitions
1. the smallest basic unit of matter c
2. a particle made when two or more atoms combine e
3. anything that has mass and takes up space a

Terms
a. matter
b. volume
c. atom
d. weight
e. molecule

 3-Minute Warm-Up, p. T5

1.3 MOTIVATE

EXPLORE Mixed Substances
PURPOSE To introduce students to mixtures

TIP *10 min.* Ask students to clean up any spills immediately.

WHAT DO YOU THINK? *No; after the two substances were mixed, the new substance had a consistency different from the one that either substance had alone.*

RESOURCES FOR DIFFERENTIATED INSTRUCTION

Below Level
UNIT RESOURCE BOOK
- Reading Study Guide A, pp. 34–35
- Decoding Support, p. 58

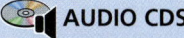 **AUDIO CDS**

Advanced
UNIT RESOURCE BOOK
Challenge and Extension, p. 40

English Learners
UNIT RESOURCE BOOK
Spanish Reading Study Guide, pp. 38–39

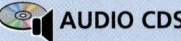 **AUDIO CDS**
- Audio Readings in Spanish
- Audio Readings (English)

1.3 INSTRUCT

Teacher Demo

Many students have the misconception that atoms and molecules have the same properties as the substances they make up. To help students understand that properties they are familiar with, such as color and texture, are not the same as the properties of atoms, try the following:

- Show students pictures or samples of graphite and diamond. Explain that both are pure substances.
- Have students discuss whether or not graphite and diamond are made up of the same atoms or molecules.
- Explain to students that graphite and diamond are both made of carbon atoms. Although the individual atoms all have the same properties, different arrangements of carbon atoms give graphite and diamond very different properties.

Teach from Visuals

To help students interpret the photographs of gold and dry ice along with the diagrams of atoms and molecules, ask:

- Based on the diagram, what does the gold in the photograph consist of? *atoms of gold*
- Based on the diagram, what does the dry ice consist of? *molecules of carbon dioxide, which consist of one carbon atom and two oxygen atoms*
- Is dry ice a pure substance? Why? *Yes; it contains only one kind of molecule.*

Ongoing Assessment

Explain how atoms and elements are related.

Ask: What is the smallest possible amount of an element? *an atom*

 Answer: An element contains only one type of atom.

22 Unit 1: **Matter and Energy**

> **REMINDER**
> A molecule consists of two or more atoms that are bonded together.

If you could look at the atoms in a bar of pure gold, you would find only gold atoms. If you looked at the atoms in a container of pure water, you would find water molecules, which are a combination of hydrogen and oxygen atoms. Does the presence of two types of atoms mean that water is not really a pure substance after all?

A substance is considered pure if it contains only a single type of atom, such as gold, or a single combination of atoms that are bonded together, such as a water molecule. Because the hydrogen and oxygen atoms are bonded together as molecules, water that has nothing else in it is considered a pure substance.

Elements

One type of pure substance is an element. An **element** is a substance that contains only a single type of atom. The number of atoms is not important as long as all the atoms are of the same type. You cannot separate an element into other substances.

You are probably familiar with many elements, such as silver, oxygen, hydrogen, helium, and aluminum. There are as many elements as there are types of atoms—more than 100. You can see the orderly arrangement of atoms in the element gold, on the left below.

 Why is an element considered to be a pure substance?

Element: Gold

The atoms in gold are all the same type of atom. Therefore, gold is an element.

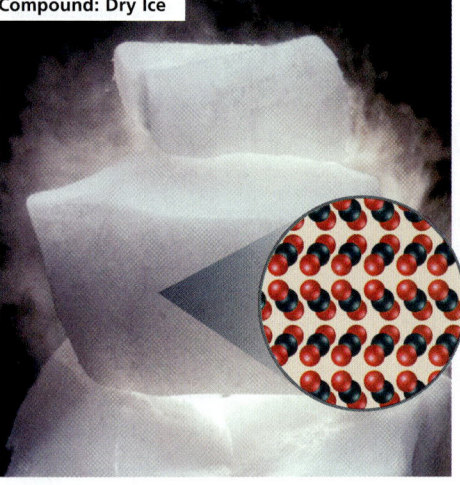

Compound: Dry Ice

Dry ice is frozen carbon dioxide, a compound. Each molecule is made of one carbon atom and two oxygen atoms.

22 Unit 1: Matter and Energy

DIFFERENTIATE INSTRUCTION

More Reading Support

A Why is water a pure substance even though it contains two types of atoms? *The atoms are bonded in one type of molecule.*

English Learners Help English learners recognize cause-and-effect relationships in sentences that do not follow the *If/then* convention. For example, on p. 22, *then* is implied and not stated; "If you could look at the atoms in a bar of pure gold, you would find only gold atoms." Likewise, the sentence beginning with *because* in the second paragraph conveys a cause-and-effect relationship; the fact that hydrogen and oxygen atoms are bonded together in water molecules makes water a pure substance.

Compounds

A **compound** is a substance that consists of two or more different types of atoms bonded together. A large variety of substances can be made by combining different types of atoms to make different compounds. Some types of compounds are made of molecules, such as water and carbon dioxide, shown on page 22. Other compounds are made of atoms that are bonded together in a different way. Table salt is an example.

A compound can have very different properties from the individual elements that make up that compound. Pure table salt is a common compound that is a combination of sodium and chlorine. Although table salt is safe to eat, the individual elements that go into making it—sodium and chlorine—are poisonous.

 What is the relationship between atoms and a compound?

Mixtures

Most of the matter around you is a mixture of different substances. Seawater, for instance, contains water, salt, and other minerals mixed together. Your blood is a mixture of blood cells and plasma. Plasma is also a mixture, made up of water, sugar, fat, protein, salts, and minerals.

 A **mixture** is a combination of different substances that remain the same individual substances and can be separated by physical means. For example, if you mix apples, oranges, and bananas to make a fruit salad, you do not change the different fruits into a new kind of fruit. Mixtures do not always contain the same amount of the various substances. For example, depending on how the salad is made, the amount of each type of fruit it contains will vary.

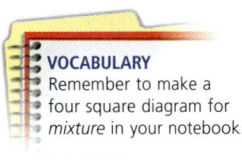

VOCABULARY
Remember to make a four square diagram for *mixture* in your notebook.

APPLY In what ways can a city population be considered a mixture?

DIFFERENTIATE INSTRUCTION

 **More Reading Support**

B What is a combination of substances that remain the same individual substances? *a mixture*

Below Level Have students draw and label a graphic organizer or table that compares atoms, elements, molecules, compounds, and mixtures. Ask students to include a definition and an example of each.

Teach Difficult Concepts

Explain that if you break a pure compound into the smallest parts that are still that substance, you do not have individual atoms or elements. If you break a pure element into the smallest parts that are still that substance, you have atoms of that element. Ask: What do you have if you break a compound into the parts that compose it? *atoms of the elements that compose it*

Integrate the Sciences

The human body and other organisms contain organic compounds and inorganic compounds. Organic compounds always contain the element carbon. Carbon can bond with other elements and with thousands of other carbon atoms to make huge molecules. Proteins and carbohydrates are organic compounds. Most inorganic compounds do not contain carbon and are small. Oxygen, carbon dioxide, and water are some inorganic compounds in the human body.

Ongoing Assessment

Describe how pure and mixed matter are different.

Ask: Are most of the substances around you pure or mixed matter? *mixed*

Ask: What is the difference between a pure substance and a mixed substance? *A pure substance has only one type of atom or molecule, while a mixed substance contains two or more different substances.*

Describe how atoms form compounds.

Ask: What is the lowest number of types of atoms that can bond to form a compound? *two*

CHECK YOUR READING Answer: *A compound is made up of two or more different types of atoms bonded together.*

PHOTO CAPTION Answer: *A city population is a mixture of men and women, people of different ages, and people of different ethnic backgrounds.*

INVESTIGATE Mixtures

PURPOSE To show that not all liquids behave the same way when mixed with other liquids

TIPS 20 min.

- You may want to have students bring clear, plastic jars with screw-on lids from home.
- Test tubes with stoppers could be substituted for the jars.

WHAT DO YOU THINK? Yes; the water changes color. No; the oil floats on the water. The oil floats to the new "top." Some liquids mix easily; others do not.

CHALLENGE The soap breaks up the oil into smaller droplets. This helps water mix with the oil.

 Datasheet, Mixtures, p. 41

Technology Resources

Customize this student lab as needed or look for an alternative. Print rubrics to assess student lab reports.

 Lab Generator CD-ROM

Ongoing Assessment

CHECK YOUR READING *Answer: A mixture combines different substances that remain those substances. A compound has different properties than the individual elements that make it up.*

INVESTIGATE Mixtures

How well do oil and water mix?

PROCEDURE

1. Add a few drops of food coloring to the water in the beaker. Swirl the water around in the beaker until the water is evenly colored throughout.
2. Pour the colored water from the beaker into the jar until the jar is about one-fourth full.
3. Add the same amount of vegetable oil to the jar. Screw the lid tightly on the jar.
4. Carefully shake the jar several times with your hand over the cover, and then set it on the table. Observe and record what happens to the liquids in the jar.
5. Turn the jar upside down and hold it that way. Observe what happens to the liquids and record your observations.

WHAT DO YOU THINK?
- Does water mix with food coloring? What evidence supports your answer?
- Do water and oil mix? What evidence supports your answer?
- What happened when you turned the jar upside down?
- Based on your observations, what can you infer about the ability of different liquids to mix?

CHALLENGE To clean greasy dishes, you add soap to the dishwater. Try adding soap to your mixture. What does the soap do?

SKILL FOCUS Inferring

MATERIALS
- food coloring
- beaker of water
- jar with lid
- vegetable oil
  for Challenge:
- dish soap

TIME 20 minutes

Comparing Mixtures and Compounds

 Find out more about mixtures.

Although mixtures and compounds may seem similar, they are very different. Consider how mixtures and compounds compare with each other.

- The substances in mixtures remain the same substances. Compounds are new substances formed by atoms that bond together.
- Mixtures can be separated by physical means. Compounds can be separated only by breaking the bonds between atoms.
- The proportions of different substances in a mixture can vary throughout the mixture or from mixture to mixture. The proportions of different substances in a compound are fixed because the type and number of atoms that make up a basic unit of the compound are always the same.

 How is a mixture different from a compound?

24 Unit 1: **Matter and Energy**

DIFFERENTIATE INSTRUCTION

 More Reading Support

C If two substances bond together, is the new substance a compound or a mixture? *compound*

Advanced

 Challenge and Extension, p. 40

Parts of mixtures can be the same or different throughout.

It is obvious that something is a mixture when you can see the different substances in it. For example, if you scoop up a handful of soil, you might see that it contains dirt, small rocks, leaves, and even insects. You can separate the soil into its different parts.

Exactly what you see depends on what part of the soil you scoop up. One handful of soil might have more pebbles or insects in it than another handful would. There are many mixtures, such as soil, that have different properties in different areas of the mixture. Such a mixture is called a heterogeneous (HEHT-uhr-uh-JEE-nee-uhs) mixture.

In some types of mixtures, however, you cannot see the individual substances. For example, if you mix sugar into a cup of water and stir it well, the sugar seems to disappear. You can tell that the sugar is still there because the water tastes sweet, but you cannot see the sugar or easily separate it out again.

When substances are evenly spread throughout a mixture, you cannot tell one part of the mixture from another part. For instance, one drop of sugar water will be almost exactly like any other drop. Such a mixture is called a homogeneous (HOH-muh-JEE-nee-uhs) mixture. Homogenized milk is processed so that it becomes a homogeneous mixture of water and milk fat. Milk that has not been homogenized will separate—most of the milk fat will float to the top as cream while leaving the rest of the milk low in fat.

READING TIP
The prefix *hetero* means "different," and the prefix *homo* means "same." The Greek root *genos* means "kind."

1.3 Review

KEY CONCEPTS
1. What is the difference between pure and mixed matter?
2. How are atoms and elements related?
3. How are compounds different from mixtures?

CRITICAL THINKING
4. **Infer** What can you infer about the size of sugar particles that are dissolved in a mixture of sugar and water?
5. **Infer** Why is it easier to remove the ice cubes from cold lemonade than it is to remove the sugar?

CHALLENGE
6. **Apply** A unit of sulfuric acid is a molecule of 2 atoms of hydrogen, 1 atom of sulfur, and 4 atoms of oxygen. How many of each type of atom are there in 2 molecules of sulfuric acid?

Chapter 1: **Introduction to Matter** 25

ANSWERS

1. Pure matter is made of only one type of atom or molecule; mixed matter has two or more substances.

2. An element is composed of only one type of atom.

3. Mixtures combine two or more substances that remain the same substances. Compounds contain two or more types of atoms bonded together. Mixtures can be separated by physical means, but compounds can be separated only by breaking the bond between atoms.

4. The sugar particles are very small.

5. The ice cubes are bigger.

6. 4 hydrogen atoms, 2 sulfur atoms, 8 oxygen atoms

Integrate the Sciences

Crops grow best in soil that is a mixture of sand, silt, clay, and a large amount of humus. This mixture retains water long enough for plants to use it but allows water to drain well enough that the soil doesn't stay too wet. Soil dries out more quickly when it contains more sand. Soil with a larger amount of clay particles doesn't drain as well and is more difficult for plant roots to grow in. Soil with a large amount of humus retains moisture, drains well, and contains nutrients that plants need to grow.

EXPLORE the BIG idea

Revisit "Where Does the Sugar Go?" on p. 7. Have students explain their observations and answer the questions again.

Reinforce the BIG idea

Have students relate the section to the Big Idea.

 Reinforcing Key Concepts, p. 42

1.3 ASSESS & RETEACH

Assess
 Section 1.3 Quiz, p. 5

Reteach

Ask students to compare each pair of terms below and give a definition and examples.

- pure matter and mixed matter
- elements and atoms
- elements and compounds
- mixtures and compounds
- heterogeneous mixtures and homogeneous mixtures

Technology Resources

Have students visit **ClassZone.com** for reteaching of Key Concepts.

 CONTENT REVIEW

 CONTENT REVIEW CD-ROM

Chapter 1 25

MATH IN SCIENCE
Math Skills Practice for Science

Set Learning Goal
To make circle graphs to show the amount of different substances in mixtures

Present the Science
Cumin is from the dried seedlike fruit of a cumin plant. Ginger is from the underground stems, or rhizomes, of a ginger plant. Nutmeg is from the seed of a tree. Spice and herb mixtures that vary in terms of amounts of each ingredient include chili powder, curry powder, and poultry seasoning.

Develop Graphing Skills
- Remind students that when they multiply a number by a fraction, they first multiply the number by the numerator of the fraction and then divide by the denominator.
- Remind students that the number of degrees of the individual substances in a circle graph must add up to 360.
- Review how to use a protractor.

DIFFERENTIATION TIP Allow students who have trouble with fine motor skills or who are visually impaired to round the numbers to whole numbers, which are easier to see on the protractor and easier to draw.

Close
Ask students what they can learn about mixtures from a circle graph and its labels. *how much of different substances make up the mixture*

- Math Support, p. 61
- Math Practice, p. 62

Technology Resources
Students can visit ClassZone.com for practice in making circle graphs.

 MATH TUTORIAL

Click on Math Tutorial for more help with circle graphs.

SKILL: MAKING A CIRCLE GRAPH

A Mixture of Spices

Two different mixtures of spices may contain the exact same ingredients but have very different flavors. For example, a mixture of cumin, nutmeg, and ginger powder can be made using more cumin than ginger, or it can be made using more ginger than cumin.

One way to show how much of each substance a mixture contains is to use a circle graph. A circle graph is a visual way to show how a quantity is divided into different parts. A circle graph represents quantities as parts of a whole.

Example
Make a circle graph to represent a spice mixture that is 1/2 cumin, 1/3 nutmeg, and 1/6 ginger.

(1) To find the angle measure for each sector of the circle graph, multiply each fraction in your mixture by 360°.

Cumin: $\frac{1}{2} \cdot 360° = 180°$

Nutmeg: $\frac{1}{3} \cdot 360° = 120°$

Ginger: $\frac{1}{6} \cdot 360° = 60°$

(2) Use a compass to draw a circle. Use a protractor to draw the angle for each sector.

(3) Label each sector and give your graph a title.

ANSWER

Spice Mixture

Answer the following questions.

1. Draw a circle graph representing a spice mixture that is 1/2 ginger, 1/4 cumin, and 1/4 crushed red pepper.

2. A jeweler creates a ring that is 3/4 gold, 3/16 silver, and 1/16 copper. Draw a circle graph representing the mixture of metals in the ring.

3. Draw a circle graph representing a mixture that is 1/5 sand, 2/5 water, and 2/5 salt.

CHALLENGE Dry air is a mixture of about 78 percent nitrogen, 21 percent oxygen, and 1 percent other elements. Create a circle graph representing the elements found in air.

ANSWERS

1. Graphs should show 180° ginger, 90° cumin, and 90° crushed red pepper.

2. Graphs should show 270° gold, 67.5° silver, and 22.5° copper.

3. Graphs should show 72° sand, 144° water, and 144° salt.

CHALLENGE Graphs should show 280.8° nitrogen, 75.6° oxygen, and 3.6° other elements.

1.4 Matter exists in different physical states.

KEY CONCEPT

BEFORE, you learned
- Matter has mass
- Matter is made of atoms
- Atoms and molecules in matter are always moving

NOW, you will learn
- About the different states of matter
- How the different states of matter behave

VOCABULARY
states of matter p. 27
solid p. 28
liquid p. 28
gas p. 28

EXPLORE Solids and Liquids

How do solids and liquids compare?

PROCEDURE
1. Observe the water, ice, and marble. Pick them up and feel them. Can you change their shape? their volume?
2. Record your observations. Compare and contrast each object with the other two.

MATERIALS
- water in a cup
- ice cube
- marble
- pie tin

WHAT DO YOU THINK?
- How are the ice and the water in the cup similar? How are they different?
- How are the ice and the marble similar? How are they different?

Particle arrangement and motion determine the state of matter.

When you put water in a freezer, the water freezes into a solid (ice). When you place an ice cube on a warm plate, the ice melts into liquid water again. If you leave the plate in the sun, the water becomes water vapor. Ice, water, and water vapor are made of exactly the same type of molecule—a molecule of two hydrogen atoms and one oxygen atom. What, then, makes them different?

Ice, water, and water vapor are different states of water. **States of matter** are the different forms in which matter can exist. The three familiar states are solid, liquid, and gas. When a substance changes from one state to another, the molecules in the substance do not change. However, the arrangement of the molecules does change, giving each state of matter its own characteristics.

Chapter 1: Introduction to Matter 27

1.4 FOCUS

▶ Set Learning Goals
Students will
- Describe the different states of matter.
- Describe how the different states of matter behave.
- Experiment with the behavior of different liquids.

◀ 3-Minute Warm-Up
Display Transparency 5 or copy this exercise on the board:

Draw and label a diagram that shows the relationship between atoms and molecules. Write a caption for your diagram that explains the relationship.
Diagrams should show at least two atoms bonded together. The atoms may be different or alike. Sample caption: Atoms combine to form a molecule.

T 3-Minute Warm-Up, p. T5

1.4 MOTIVATE

EXPLORE Solids and Liquids

PURPOSE To compare solids and liquids

TIP *10 min.* Ask students to clean up any spills immediately.

WHAT DO YOU THINK? *The ice and water are both made of water molecules; however, one is solid and the other is liquid. The ice and the marble are both solid; however, the ice can melt and change shape.*

RESOURCES FOR DIFFERENTIATED INSTRUCTION

Below Level
UNIT RESOURCE BOOK
- Reading Study Guide A, pp. 45–46
- Decoding Support, p. 58

🎧 **AUDIO CDS**

R Additional INVESTIGATION,
Thick and Thin Liquids, A, B, & C, pp. 72–80;
Teacher Instructions, pp. 262–263

Advanced
UNIT RESOURCE BOOK
- Challenge and Extension, p. 51
- Challenge Reading, pp. 54–55

English Learners
UNIT RESOURCE BOOK
Spanish Reading Study Guide, pp. 49–50

🎧 **AUDIO CDS**
- Audio Readings in Spanish
- Audio Readings (English)

Chapter 1 27

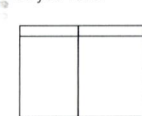

1.4 INSTRUCT

Develop Critical Thinking

COMPARE Have students compare the three states of matter in a table while listing the characteristics of each. The tables should include at least one example of each state of matter.

Teaching with Technology

If a video camera is available, have students record real-world models of the movements of particles in solids, liquids, and gases. Encourage students to narrate a comparison of the movements they record.

Real World Example

The expansion of water as it freezes often causes damage. Put a can of soda in a freezer, and it will expand enough to break the seal. Pipes carrying water may freeze and burst if temperatures drop too low. Frost in the ground can push posts and pavement out of alignment. Ice expanding in small cracks and in the road base leads to potholes.

Ongoing Assessment

CHECK YOUR READING Answer: *A solid has a fixed volume and shape, but a gas has neither. Particles in a solid are fixed in one place, but particles in a gas can move easily in any direction.*

Solid, liquid, and gas are common states of matter.

MAIN IDEA AND DETAILS Remember to organize your notes in a two-column chart as you read.

A substance can exist as a solid, a liquid, or a gas. The state of a substance depends on the space between its particles and on the way in which the particles move. The illustration on page 29 shows how particles are arranged in the three different states.

① A **solid** is a substance that has a fixed volume and a fixed shape. In a solid, the particles are close together and usually form a regular pattern. Particles in a solid can vibrate but are fixed in one place. Because each particle is attached to several others, individual particles cannot move from one location to another, and the solid is rigid.

② A **liquid** has a fixed volume but does not have a fixed shape. Liquids take on the shape of the container they are in. The particles in a liquid are attracted to one another and are close together. However, particles in a liquid are not fixed in place and can move from one place to another.

③ A **gas** has no fixed volume or shape. A gas can take on both the shape and the volume of a container. Gas particles are not close to one another and can move easily in any direction. There is much more space between gas particles than there is between particles in a liquid or a solid. The space between gas particles can increase or decrease with changes in temperature and pressure.

 Describe two differences between a solid and a gas.

The particles in a solid are usually closer together than the particles in a liquid. For example, the particles in solid steel are closer together than the particles in molten—or melted—steel. However, water is an important exception. The molecules that make up ice actually have more space between them than the molecules in liquid water do.

The fact that the molecules in ice are farther apart than the molecules in liquid water has important consequences for life on Earth. Because there is more space between its molecules, ice floats on liquid water. By contrast, a piece of solid steel would not float in molten steel but would sink to the bottom.

Because ice floats, it remains on the surface of rivers and lakes when they freeze. The ice layer helps insulate the water and slow down the freezing process. Animals living in rivers and lakes can survive in the liquid water layer below the ice layer.

28 Unit 1: Matter and Energy

DIFFERENTIATE INSTRUCTION

 More Reading Support

A What are three common states of matter? *solid, liquid, gas*

B What substance's molecules are farther apart when it is a solid than when it is a liquid? *water*

English Learners English learners may have trouble comprehending certain words and phrases used repeatedly in this section. Tell students that the terms *fixed, regular, definite,* and *rigid* describe things that do not change.

Use the Chapter Summary page to help students focus on key concepts and vocabulary.

States of Matter

Matter can exist in different states. The state of matter depends on the arrangement and motion of the particles.

① Solid

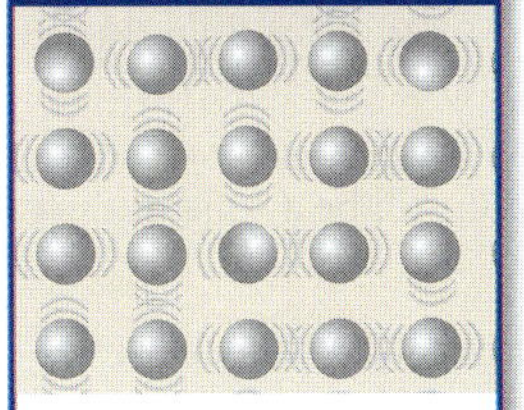

The particles in a solid are close together. They are fixed in place but can vibrate.

② Liquid

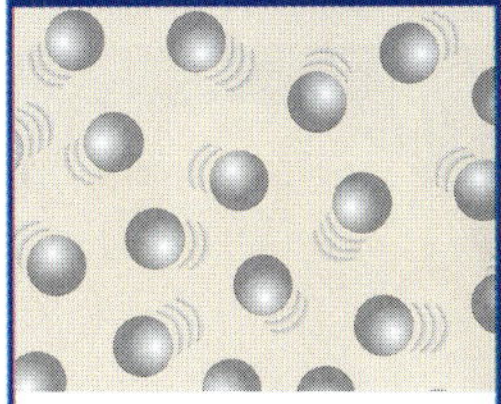

The particles that make up a liquid are close together but usually farther apart than the particles in a solid are. They can slide freely past one another.

③ Gas

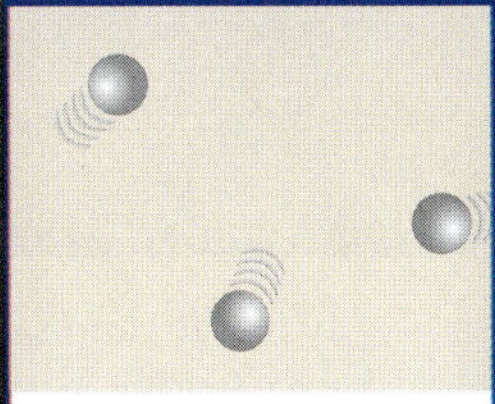

The particles in a gas are farther apart than particles in liquids and solids. Gas particles move freely in any direction.

① The particles that make up a solid are similar to a crowd of people sitting in a theater. People can move back and forth in their seats but must stay in the same general place.

② The particles in a liquid are similar to people moving in a crowd. Although one person can move past another, the surrounding people limit how far he or she can move.

③ Gas particles are similar to a few people moving about in a large space. Each person moves freely and independently of the others, and there is plenty of space between them.

Chapter 1: **Introduction to Matter** 29

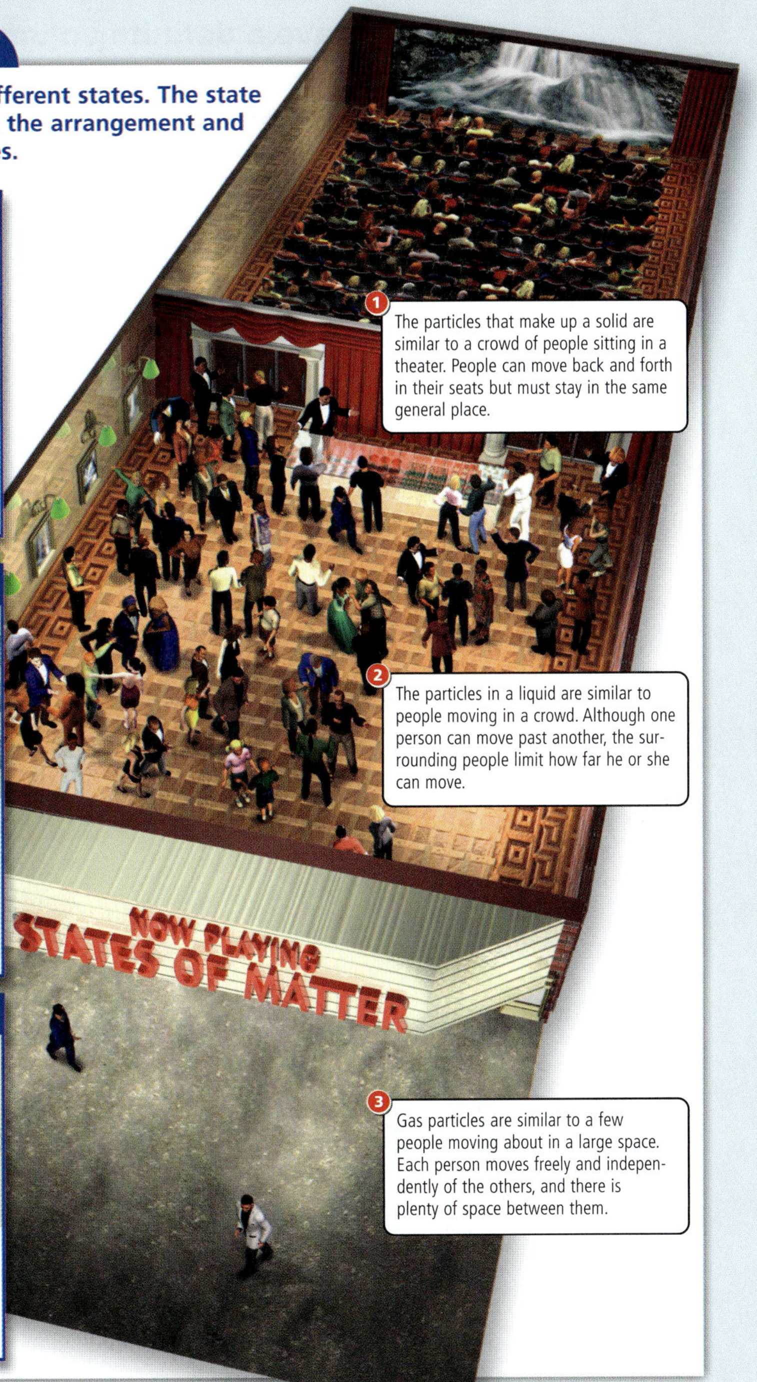

Teach from Visuals

To help students interpret the diagrams of the arrangement and motion of particles in three states of matter, ask:

- Which two characteristics determine the state of matter? *arrangement and motion of particles*
- Which state of matter has particles that are farthest apart? *gas*
- Which state of matter has particles that are generally closest together? *solid*
- Which state of matter has particles that can slide past each other but cannot move freely in any direction? *liquid*

 This visual is also available as T6 in the Unit Transparency Book.

Teach Difficult Concepts

Students may have difficulty appreciating how much farther apart gas molecules are compared with the molecules in liquids and solids. On average, gas molecules are spaced about ten times farther apart than molecules in a liquid or solid. Have students model the relative spacing of the three states of matter with their own bodies in a large room.

DIFFERENTIATE INSTRUCTION

Advanced Plasma is a fourth state of matter and makes up at least 99 percent of the universe. The Sun and lightning are made up of plasma. Have students make a list of other examples of where plasma exists. Ask them to identify examples of artificial plasma and natural plasma.

 Challenge and Extension, p. 51

Have students who are interested in quarks, the fundamental building blocks of matter, read the following article.

 Challenge Reading, pp. 54–55

Chapter 1 **29**

Teach Difficult Concepts

In most cases when a solid is broken, the volume of the pieces will add up to the volume of the original solid. For example, if you saw a block of wood into two pieces, the volume of each piece will add up to the original volume of the block. However, if a solid is divided into small enough pieces, such as when wood is ground into sawdust, the total volume might change.

Teach from Visuals

Have students identify the hexagonal pattern of the water molecules in the visual. Compare the hexagonal pattern with the solid shown in the illustration on p. 29. Point out that it is the relatively large amount of space between the molecules in ice that causes ice to float in water.

Ongoing Assessment

 *Answer: a definite shape and a definite volume*

▼ **REMINDER**
Volume is the amount of space that an object occupies.

Solids have a definite volume and shape.

A piece of ice, a block of wood, and a ceramic cup are solids. They have shapes that do not change and volumes that can be measured. Any matter that is a solid has a definite shape and a definite volume.

The molecules in a solid are in fixed positions and are close together. Although the molecules can still vibrate, they cannot move from one part of the solid to another part. As a result, a solid does not easily change its shape or its volume. If you force the molecules apart, you can change the shape and the volume of a solid by breaking it into pieces. However, each of those pieces will still be a solid and have its own particular shape and volume.

The particles in some solids, such as ice or table salt, occur in a very regular pattern. The pattern of the water molecules in ice, for example, can be seen when you look at a snowflake like the one shown below. The water molecules in a snowflake are arranged in hexagonal shapes that are layered on top of one another. Because the molecular pattern has six sides, snowflakes form with six sides or six points. Salt also has a regular structure, although it takes a different shape.

The particles in many solids, such as the water molecules in this snowflake, have a regular pattern.

Not all solids have regular shapes in the same way that ice and salt do, however. Some solids, such as plastic or glass, have particles that are not arranged in a regular pattern.

 What two characteristics are needed for a substance to be a solid?

30 Unit 1: **Matter and Energy**

DIFFERENTIATE INSTRUCTION

? More Reading Support

C Which state of matter has a definite volume and a definite shape? *solid*

Below Level Point out that different words sometimes refer to the same concept. For example, *arrangement of particles* refers to the space between particles. The words *fixed* and *definite* mean the same thing when referring to the volume and the shape of matter.

30 Unit 1: **Matter and Energy**

Liquids have a definite volume but no definite shape.

Water, milk, and oil are liquids. A liquid has a definite volume but does not have a definite shape. The volume of a certain amount of oil can be measured, but the shape that the oil takes depends on what container it is in. If the oil is in a tall, thin container, it has a tall, thin shape. If it is in a short, wide container, it has a short, wide shape. Liquids take the shape of their containers.

The molecules in a liquid are close together, but they are not tightly attached to one another as the molecules in a solid are. Instead, molecules in liquids can move independently. As a result, liquids can flow. Instead of having a rigid form, the molecules in a liquid move and fill the bottom of the container they are in.

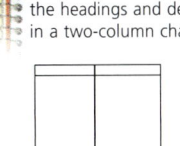

MAIN IDEA AND DETAILS As you read, organize the headings and details in a two-column chart.

 How is a liquid different from a solid?

INVESTIGATE Liquids

How do different liquids behave?

PROCEDURE

1. Using the graduated cylinder, measure 5 mL of colored water. Add it to the test tube.
2. Measure 5 mL of vegetable oil. Pour the oil into the test tube. Record your observations.
3. Pour a small amount of corn syrup directly into the test tube. Record what happens to all three liquids.
4. Add 10 mL more of colored water to the test tube and record what happens.
5. Add 5 mL more of vegetable oil and record what happens.

WHAT DO YOU THINK?
- How did the layers change as more liquid was added?
- What are some behaviors of each of the liquids in this experiment that can be used to tell them apart?
- What would happen if you changed the order in which you added the liquids?

CHALLENGE Think of a liquid you are familiar with that was not used in this experiment. What do you think would happen if you added that liquid to your test tube? Explain.

SKILL FOCUS Measuring

MATERIALS
- graduated cylinder
- colored water
- test tube
- test-tube rack
- vegetable oil
- corn syrup

TIME 20 minutes

Chapter 1: **Introduction to Matter** 31

DIFFERENTIATE INSTRUCTION

D What determines the shape of a liquid? *the container it is in*

Additional Investigation To reinforce Section 1.4 learning goals, use the following full-period investigation:

 Additional **INVESTIGATION**, Thick and Thin Liquids, A, B, & C, pp. 72–80, 262–263
(Advanced students should complete levels B and C.)

Advanced Have students investigate the role of density in determining if liquids mix or not. For example, students can create a colored salt solution with the same density as the corn syrup and see if they get the same results.

INVESTIGATE Liquids

PURPOSE To practice measuring liquids and to learn about the behavior of different liquids

TIPS 20 min.
- Use dark corn syrup so that it cannot be confused with the oil.
- Have students wipe up spills immediately.
- If students have trouble measuring accurately, the results will not be affected.

INCLUSION Students can draw pictures of the layers of liquids each time a liquid is added instead of answering the questions.

WHAT DO YOU THINK? *The layers change positions and get thicker. The oil layer floats on top of the other layers, the corn syrup layer sinks to the bottom, and the water layer is in the middle. Changing the order of adding the liquids would not affect where they settle.*

CHALLENGE *The density of a new liquid will determine whether it combines with one of the existing layers or forms a new layer.*

Datasheet, Liquids, p. 52

Technology Resources

Customize this student lab as needed or look for an alternative. Print rubrics to assess students' lab reports.

Lab Generator CD-ROM

Ongoing Assessment

CHECK YOUR READING *Answer: A liquid has a definite volume but not a definite shape. It takes the shape of its container. A solid has a rigid form, and the molecules are more tightly attached to one another than they are in a liquid.*

Teacher Demo

Demonstrate gas pressure by placing a small piece of dry ice in a small container with a lid that can easily pop off. Wear safety goggles and use tongs or gloves; keep students at a safe distance. Dry ice changes from solid carbon dioxide directly to a gas.

Teach from Visuals

To help students understand the diagrams of the helium tanks, ask:
- What happened to the molecules of gas in the container after half of them were removed? *They moved farther apart.*
- What happened to the volume of the gas in the container when half the gas molecules were removed? *It stayed the same.*

Ongoing Assessment

Describe the different states of matter.

Ask: How would you describe the volume and shape of the different states of matter? *A solid has a definite volume and a definite shape. A liquid has a definite volume but no definite shape. A gas has no definite volume or shape.*

Describe how the different states of matter behave.

Ask: How do particles in a solid, liquid, and gas move? *Particles in a solid vibrate in place, particles in a liquid slide over one another, and particles in a gas move about easily in any direction.*

 *Answer: Gas molecules are far apart compared with molecules in a solid or a liquid. The amount of space between gas molecules varies with the size of the container.*

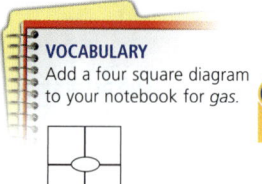

VOCABULARY
Add a four square diagram to your notebook for *gas*.

Gases have no definite volume or shape.

The air that you breathe, the helium in a balloon, and the neon inside the tube in a neon light are gases. A gas is a substance with no definite volume and no definite shape. Solids and liquids have volumes that do not change easily. If you have a container filled with one liter of a liquid that you pour into a two-liter container, the liquid will occupy only half of the new container. A gas, on the other hand, has a volume that changes to match the volume of its container.

Gas Composition

The molecules in a gas are very far apart compared with the molecules in a solid or a liquid. The amount of space between the molecules in a gas can change easily. If a rigid container—one that cannot change its shape—has a certain amount of air and more air is pumped in, the volume of the gas does not change. However, there is less space between the molecules than there was before. If the container is opened, the molecules spread out and mix with the air in the atmosphere.

As you saw, gas molecules in a container can be compared to a group of people in a room. If the room is small, there is less space between people. If the room is large, people can spread out so that there is more space between them. When people leave the room, they go in all different directions and mix with all of the other people in the surrounding area.

CHECK YOUR READING Contrast the molecules in a gas with those of a liquid and a solid.

Gas and Volume

The amount of space between gas particles depends on how many particles are in the container.

Before Use
The atoms of helium gas are constantly in motion. The atoms are spread throughout the entire tank.

After Use
Although there are fewer helium atoms in the tank after many balloons have been inflated, the remaining atoms are still spread throughout the tank. However, the atoms are farther apart than before.

DIFFERENTIATE INSTRUCTION

More Reading Support

E What state of matter has no definite volume or shape? *gas*

F How easily can the space between gas molecules change? *very easily*

Gas Behavior

Because gas molecules are always in motion, they are continually hitting one another and the sides of any container they may be in. As the molecules bounce off one another and the surfaces of the container, they apply a pressure against the container. You can feel the effects of gas pressure if you pump air into a bicycle tire. The more air you put into the tire, the harder it feels because more gas molecules are pressing the tire outward.

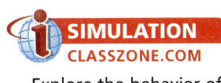
Explore the behavior of a gas.

The speed at which gas molecules move depends on the temperature of the gas. Gas molecules move faster at higher temperatures than at lower temperatures. The volume, pressure, and temperature of a gas are related to one another, and changing one can change the others.

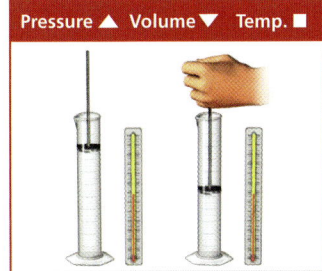

If the temperature of a gas stays the same, increasing the pressure of the gas decreases its volume.

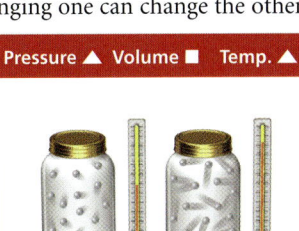

If the volume of a gas stays the same, increasing the temperature of the gas also increases the pressure.

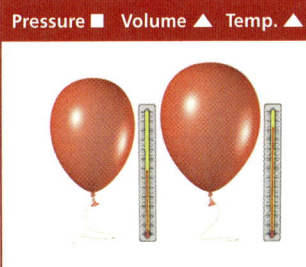

If the pressure of a gas stays the same, increasing the temperature of the gas also increases the volume.

In nature, volume, pressure, and temperature may all be changing at the same time. By studying how gas behaves when one property is kept constant, scientists can predict how gas will behave when all three properties change.

1.4 Review

KEY CONCEPTS

1. What are the characteristics of the three familiar states of matter?
2. How can you change the shape and volume of a liquid?
3. How does gas behave inside a closed container?

CRITICAL THINKING

4. **Infer** What happens to a liquid that is not in a container?
5. **Synthesize** What is the relationship between the temperature and the volume of a gas?

CHALLENGE

6. **Synthesize** Can an oxygen canister ever be half empty? Explain.

Chapter 1: **Introduction to Matter** 33

ANSWERS

1. Solids have a definite volume and shape, liquids have a definite volume but not a definite shape, and gases have no definite volume or shape.
2. You can change the shape of a liquid by pouring it into a different container with a different shape. You can't change the volume of a liquid unless you remove some of the liquid or add liquid to it.
3. Gas molecules are always in motion; they bounce off one another and the insides of the container.
4. It spreads out.
5. Increasing the temperature of a gas increases its volume.
6. No; it can have half as much oxygen, but the molecules will spread out evenly to fill the canister.

Teach from Visuals

Point out the symbols at the top of each box. Ask students what they mean. To help students understand the diagrams of gas behavior, ask:

- What happens to the volume of a gas if the temperature stays the same and the pressure on the gas increases? *It decreases.*
- What happens to the pressure of a gas if the volume stays the same and the temperature increases? *It increases.*
- What happens to the volume of a gas if the pressure stays the same and the temperature increases? *It increases.*

Reinforce the BIG idea

Have students relate the section to the Big Idea.

 Reinforcing Key Concepts, p. 53

1.4 ASSESS & RETEACH

Assess

 Section 1.4 Quiz, p. 6

Reteach

Have students make a set of flashcards. One side of each card should show a diagram of a characteristic of a solid, liquid, or gas. The other side should name the state of matter that the diagram describes. Students should make enough flashcards to include all the characteristics in the text. Pairs of students can use the cards to test each other's knowledge.

Technology Resources

Have students visit ClassZone.com for reteaching of Key Concepts.

 CONTENT REVIEW

 CONTENT REVIEW CD-ROM

Chapter 1 **33**

CHAPTER 1 • REVIEW

BACK TO

Have students look at the photograph on pp. 6–7. Ask them to list ten objects or substances that represent different states of matter in the photograph. Have them explain what makes each object matter. *Each object has mass and takes up space.*

◯ KEY CONCEPTS SUMMARY

SECTION 1.1
Ask: Which tools are being used to measure mass and volume? *a pan balance to measure mass and a graduated cylinder to measure volume* Ask: Which tool would you use to measure the volume of a box? *a ruler or meter stick*

SECTION 1.2
Ask: How many different kinds of atoms formed the molecule? *two*

SECTION 1.3
Ask: Which picture shows a pure substance? Explain. *The picture on the left of the gold coins shows a pure substance. The coins contain only one substance, the element gold.*

SECTION 1.4
Ask: Which state of matter has a fixed volume but takes the shape of the container it is in? *liquid*

Review Concepts

- Big Idea Flow Chart, p. T1
- Chapter Outline, pp. T7–T8

Chapter Review

 the BIG idea
Everything that has mass and takes up space is matter.

◯ KEY CONCEPTS SUMMARY

1 Matter has mass and volume.

Mass is a measure of how much matter an object contains.

Volume is the measure of the amount of space matter occupies.

VOCABULARY
matter p. 9
mass p. 10
weight p. 11
volume p. 11

2 Matter is made of atoms.

An atom is the smallest basic unit of matter. Two or more atoms bonded together form a molecule. Atoms and molecules are always in motion.

VOCABULARY
atom p. 16
molecule p. 18

3 Matter combines to form different substances.

Matter can be pure, such as an element (gold), or a compound (water).

Matter can be a mixture. Mixtures contain two or more pure substances.

VOCABULARY
element p. 22
compound p. 23
mixture p. 23

4 Matter exists in different physical states.

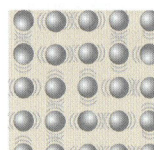 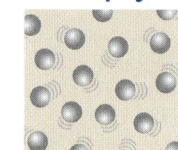 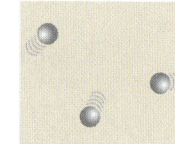

Solids have a fixed volume and a fixed shape.

Liquids have a fixed volume but no fixed shape.

Gases have no fixed volume and no fixed shape.

VOCABULARY
states of matter p. 27
solid p. 28
liquid p. 28
gas p. 28

Technology Resources

Have students visit **ClassZone.com** or use the CD-ROM for a cumulative review of concepts.

 CONTENT REVIEW

 CONTENT REVIEW CD-ROM

Engage students in a whole-class interactive review of Key Concepts. Edit content as you wish.

 POWER PRESENTATIONS

Reviewing Vocabulary

Copy and complete the chart below. If the right column is blank, give a brief description or definition. If the left column is blank, give the correct term.

Term	Description
1.	the downward pull of gravity on an object
2. liquid	
3.	the smallest basic unit of matter
4. solid	
5.	state of matter with no fixed volume and no fixed shape
6.	a combination of different substances that remain individual substances
7. matter	
8.	a measure of how much matter an object contains
9. element	
10.	a particle made of two or more atoms bonded together
11. compound	

Reviewing Key Concepts

Multiple Choice Choose the letter of the best answer.

12. The standard unit for measuring mass is the
    a. kilogram
    b. gram per cubic centimeter
    c. milliliter
    d. milliliter per cubic centimeter

13. A unit for measuring the volume of a liquid is the
    a. kilogram
    b. gram per cubic centimeter
    c. milliliter
    d. milliliter per cubic centimeter

14. The weight of an object is measured by using a scale that
    a. compares the mass of the object with a standard unit of mass
    b. shows the amount of space the object occupies
    c. indicates how much water is displaced by the object
    d. tells how hard the object is pushing or pulling on it

15. To find the volume of a rectangular box,
    a. divide the length by the height
    b. multiply the length, width, and height
    c. subtract the mass from the weight
    d. multiply one atom's mass by the total

16. Compounds can be separated only by
    a. breaking the atoms into smaller pieces
    b. breaking the bonds between the atoms
    c. using a magnet to attract certain atoms
    d. evaporating the liquid that contains the atoms

17. Whether a substance is a solid, a liquid, or a gas depends on how close its atoms are to one another and
    a. the volume of each atom
    b. how much matter the atoms have
    c. how free the atoms are to move
    d. the size of the container

18. A liquid has
    a. a fixed volume and a fixed shape
    b. no fixed volume and a fixed shape
    c. a fixed volume and no fixed shape
    d. no fixed volume and no fixed shape

Chapter 1: **Introduction to Matter** 35

Reviewing Vocabulary

1. weight
2. matter with a definite volume but no definite shape
3. atom
4. matter with a definite volume and shape
5. gas
6. mixture
7. anything that has mass and takes up space
8. mass
9. a substance that contains only a single type of atom
10. molecule
11. a substance that results when two or more different types of atoms bond together

Reviewing Key Concepts

12. a
13. c
14. d
15. b
16. b
17. c
18. c

(Answers to items that appear on p. 36)

19. Particles in a solid vibrate in position. Particles in a liquid slide past one another. Particles in a gas move freely in any direction.
20. Molecules in the air are moving, hitting the dust particles, and pushing them from different directions.
21. because three one-dimensional units are multiplied
22. The molecules apply pressure inside the tire, expanding the tire.

ASSESSMENT RESOURCES

ASSESSMENT BOOK
- Chapter Test A, pp. 7–10
- Chapter Test B, pp. 11–14
- Chapter Test C, pp. 15–18
- Alternative Assessment, pp. 19–20

SPANISH ASSESSMENT BOOK
Spanish Chapter Test, pp. 213–216

Technology Resources

Edit test items and answer choices.

 Test Generator CD-ROM

Visit **ClassZone.com** to extend test practice.

 Test Practice

Chapter 1 **35**

(Answers for items 19–22 appear on p. 35.)

Thinking Critically

23. Matter: wood, metal, water, air; Not Matter: light, sound

24. No; you would have carbon and oxygen atoms. A molecule is the smallest part of a compound that is still that compound.

25. Like a liquid, sand has a definite volume but takes the shape of its container as sand grains slide around. Unlike a liquid, sand is made up of individual grains that each have a definite volume and a definite shape.

26. Many of the gas molecules escape into the air outside the ball.

27. Mixtures: substances remain the same, separated by physical means, percentages of substances can vary; Compounds: new substances formed, separated by breaking bonds, percentages of substances fixed; Alike: combinations of substances

28. The ball is a solid; the molecules are fixed in place and cannot move easily.

29. 720,000 cm³

30. 2 trips

31. The marble displaces the liquid.

32. 8 mL or 8 cm³

33. 50 mL; the volume of the water does not change and the marble is no longer displacing any of it.

the BIG idea

34. Answers should categorize items as solids, liquids, and gases.

35. Answers might include water (liquid), air (gas), and table (solid).

UNIT PROJECTS

Give students the appropriate Unit Project worksheets from the URB for their projects. Both directions and rubrics can be used as a guide.

 Unit Projects, pp. 5–10

Short Answer *Answer each of the following questions in a sentence or two.*

19. Describe the movement of particles in a solid, a liquid, and a gas.

20. In bright sunlight, dust particles in the air appear to dart about. What causes this effect?

21. Why is the volume of a rectangular object measured in cubic units?

22. Describe how the molecules in the air behave when you pump air into a bicycle tire.

Thinking Critically

23. **CLASSIFY** Write the headings *Matter* and *Not Matter* on your paper. Place each of these terms in the correct category: wood, water, metal, air, light, sound.

24. **INFER** If you could break up a carbon dioxide molecule, would you still have carbon dioxide? Explain your answer.

25. **MODEL** In what ways is sand in a bowl like a liquid? In what ways is it different?

26. **INFER** If you cut a hole in a basketball, what happens to the gas inside?

27. **COMPARE AND CONTRAST** Create a Venn diagram that shows how mixtures and compounds are alike and different.

28. **ANALYZE** If you place a solid rubber ball into a box, why doesn't the ball change its shape to fit the container?

29. **CALCULATE** What is the volume of an aquarium that is 120 cm long, 60 cm wide, and 100 cm high?

30. **CALCULATE** A truck whose bed is 2.5 m long, 1.5 m wide, and 1 m high is delivering sand for a sand-sculpture competition. How many trips must the truck make to deliver 7 cubic meters of sand?

Use the information in the photograph below to answer the next three questions.

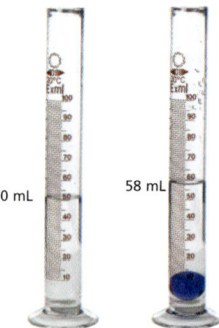

50 mL   58 mL

31. **INFER** One way to find the volume of a marble is by displacement. To determine a marble's volume, add 50 mL of water to a graduated cylinder and place the marble in the cylinder. Why does the water level change when you put the marble in the cylinder?

32. **CALCULATE** What is the volume of the marble?

33. **PREDICT** If you carefully removed the marble and let all of the water on it drain back into the cylinder, what would the volume of the water be? Explain.

the BIG idea

34. **SYNTHESIZE** Look back at the photograph on pages 6–7. Describe the picture in terms of states of matter.

35. **WRITE** Make a list of all the matter in a two-meter radius around you. Classify each as a solid, liquid, or gas.

UNIT PROJECTS

If you are doing a unit project, make a folder for your project. Include in your folder a list of the resources you will need, the date on which the project is due, and a schedule to track your progress. Begin gathering data.

MONITOR AND RETEACH

If students have trouble applying the concepts in items 29–33, suggest that they review pp. 12–13. Have students make a table that lists standard units of volume in one column and describes the units in the other column.

Students may benefit from summarizing one or more sections of the chapter.

 Summarizing the Chapter, pp. 81–82

Standardized Test Practice

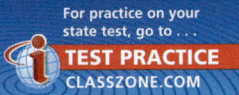

For practice on your state test, go to...
TEST PRACTICE
CLASSZONE.COM

Interpreting Graphs

The graph below shows the changing volume of a gas as it was slowly heated, with the pressure held constant.

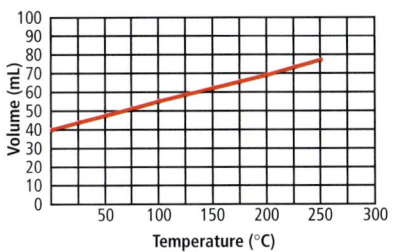

Use the graph to answer the questions.

1. As the temperature of the gas rises, what happens to its volume?
   a. It increases.
   b. It stays the same.
   c. It decreases.
   d. It changes without pattern.

2. What is the volume of the gas at 250°C as compared with the volume at 0°C?
   a. about three times greater
   b. about double
   c. about one-half
   d. about the same

3. What happens to a gas as it is cooled below 0°C?
   a. The volume would increase.
   b. The volume would continue to decrease.
   c. The volume would remain at 40 mL.
   d. A gas cannot be cooled below 0°C.

4. If you raised the temperature of this gas to 300°C, what would be its approximate volume?
   a. 70 mL
   b. 75 mL
   c. 80 mL
   d. 85 mL

5. If the volume of the gas at 0°C was 80 mL instead of 40 mL, what would you expect the volume to be at 200°C?
   a. 35 mL
   b. 70 mL
   c. 80 mL
   d. 140 mL

Extended Response

Answer the two questions below in detail. Include some of the terms from the word box. Underline each term you use in your answer.

| gravity | mass | molecule |
| states of matter | weight | |

6. An astronaut's helmet, measured on a balance, has the same number of kilograms on both Earth and the Moon. On a spring scale, though, it registers more newtons on Earth than on the Moon. Why?

7. Explain how water changes as it moves from a solid to a liquid and then to a gas.

Chapter 1: Introduction to Matter 37

METACOGNITIVE ACTIVITY

Have students answer the following questions in their **Science Notebook**:

1. What concept about matter did you find the most challenging to understand?
2. Describe a substance that you think is hard to categorize as a gas, liquid, or solid.
3. What goals have you set for your Unit Project? What is the next step you will complete?

Interpreting Graphs

1. a   3. b   5. d
2. b   4. d

Extended Response

6. RUBRIC

4 points for a response that correctly explains both results and uses the following terms accurately:

- mass
- gravity
- weight

Sample: The balance measures mass, or the amount of matter. Mass is the same on Earth and the moon. The spring scale measures weight, or the force of gravity pulling on an object. Gravity on the moon pulls on the helmet less than gravity on Earth, so the helmet weighs less on the moon.

3 points correctly explains both results and uses two terms correctly
2 points correctly explains both results and uses one term correctly
1 point correctly explains one of the results

7. RUBRIC

4 points for a response that correctly identifies solid, liquid, and gas as states of matter, explains how the arrangement and movement of the molecules change for each state, and uses the following terms accurately:

- states of matter
- molecule

Sample: As water changes from a solid to a liquid and then to a gas, it is changing states of matter. The arrangement of its molecules changes and the movement of the molecules changes. As it changes from a solid to a liquid, its molecules can slide past each other. When water changes to a gas, its molecules can move freely in any direction and are much farther apart.

3 points for a response that correctly identifies solid, liquid, and gas as states of matter, explains how the arrangement and movement of the molecules change for two states of matter, and uses both terms accurately
2 points correctly identifies solid, liquid, and gas as states of matter, explains how the arrangement and movement of the molecules change for one state of matter, and uses both terms accurately
1 point correctly identifies solid, liquid, and gas as states of matter and uses both terms accurately

Chapter 1 37

CHAPTER 2  Properties of Matter

Physical Science
UNIFYING PRINCIPLES

PRINCIPLE 1
Matter is made of particles too small to see.

PRINCIPLE 2
Matter changes form and moves from place to place.

PRINCIPLE 3
Energy changes from one form to another, but it cannot be created or destroyed.

PRINCIPLE 4
Physical forces affect the movement of all matter on Earth and throughout the universe.

Unit 1: Matter and Energy
BIG IDEAS

CHAPTER 1
Introduction to Matter
Everything that has mass and takes up space is matter.

CHAPTER 2
Properties of Matter
Matter has properties that can be changed by physical and chemical processes.

CHAPTER 3
Energy
Energy has different forms, but it is always conserved.

CHAPTER 4
Temperature and Heat
Heat is a flow of energy due to temperature differences.

CHAPTER 2
KEY CONCEPTS

SECTION 1

Matter has observable properties.
1. Physical properties describe a substance.
2. Chemical properties describe how substances form new substances.

SECTION 2

Changes of state are physical changes.
1. Matter can change from one state to another.
2. Solids can become liquids, and liquids can become solids.
3. Liquids can become gases, and gases can become liquids.

SECTION 3

Properties are used to identify substances.
1. Substances have characteristic properties.
2. Mixtures can be separated by using the properties of the substances in them.

 The Big Idea Flow Chart is available on p. T9 in the **UNIT TRANSPARENCY BOOK**.

37A Unit 1: **Matter and Energy**

Previewing Content

SECTION Matter has observable properties. pp. 41–49

1. **Physical properties describe a substance.**
   Physical properties of a substance can be observed without changing the identity of the substance. Density, mass, color, size, volume, and texture are examples of physical properties.
   - **Density** is the relationship between the mass and the volume of a substance.
   - Calculate density by dividing mass by volume, as shown in the sample problem below.

   A glass marble has a volume of 5 cm³ and a mass of 13 g. What is the density of glass?

   What do you know? Volume = 5 cm³, mass = 13 g

   What do you want to find out? Density

   Write the formula: $D = \dfrac{m}{V}$

   Substitute into the formula: $D = \dfrac{13\ g}{5\ cm^3}$

   Calculate and simplify: $D = 2.6\ g/cm^3$.

   Any change in a physical property of a substance is a **physical change.** The identity of the material remains the same during the change. Examples of physical changes include cutting a material, breaking it, and changing its state.

2. **Chemical properties describe how substances form new substances.**
   To observe **chemical properties** in a substance, you must see a **chemical change.**
   - To observe the combustibility of a piece of paper, for example, the paper must burn. The products that result from burning the paper differ in identity from the paper itself.
   - Signs of a chemical change include the production of an odor, a gas, or a solid and a change in temperature or color.
   - Other examples of chemical properties include reactivity, tendency to corrode, and toxicity.

SECTION Changes of state are physical changes. pp. 50–57

1. **Matter can change from one state to another.**
   Matter has three common states—solid, liquid, and gas. Matter can physically change from one state to another.
   - A solid has a fixed volume and a fixed shape.
   - A liquid has a fixed volume but assumes the shape of its container.
   - Both the volume and shape of a gas depend on the volume and shape of its container.

2. **Solids can become liquids, and liquids can become solids.**
   When a substance **melts,** added energy as heat breaks the tight bonds between particles. This process occurs at a temperature called the **melting point** of the substance. For some substances, the melting point is not a well-defined temperature. **Freezing** is the process by which particles of a liquid lose energy and bond tightly to form a solid. The **freezing point** of a substance is the same as its melting point. While a substance with a well-defined melting point is freezing or melting, the temperature will not change.

3. **Liquids can become gases, and gases can become liquids.**
   During **condensation,** a gas is changed to a liquid. Energy is removed from the gas, and the particles form loose bonds.
   - High-energy particles can escape from the surface of a liquid by **evaporation.**
   - If energy as heat is added to a liquid, bubbles of gas can form throughout the liquid in a process called **boiling.**
   - **Sublimation** is the process by which solids become gases, and deposition is the process by which gases become solids. Sublimation and deposition happen only under certain pressure and temperature conditions.

Common Misconceptions

DENSITY Students may think that *heavy* and *dense* mean the same thing. How heavy something feels depends on its mass. Density, however, depends on both mass and volume. For example, an object can have a low density but still be heavy if the volume is large.

 This misconception is addressed on p. 43.

MISCONCEPTION DATABASE
CLASSZONE.COM Background on student misconceptions

EVAPORATION Students may not understand that a liquid does not simply disappear when it evaporates. Instead, evaporation involves a change of state: some of the liquid becomes a gas.

 This misconception is addressed on p. 53.

Previewing Content

SECTION

Properties are used to identify substances. pp. 58–63

1. **Substances have characteristic properties.**
   The physical and chemical properties of a substance can be used to identify it. Although a substance may share properties with another substance, no two substances have identical sets of properties. The following properties can be used to identify substances because they are the same for every sample of a particular substance:
   - density
   - heating properties
   - solubility
   - conductivity
   - magnetic properties

2. **Mixtures can be separated by using the properties of the substances in them.**
   Substances can be separated by using differences in physical properties.
   - A magnet will separate materials that have magnetic properties from those that don't.
   - Filtration can separate solids from liquids and can separate solids that differ in particle size.
   - Evaporation can separate a liquid and the substances dissolved in it.

Previewing Labs

EXPLORE the BIG idea

Float or Sink, p. 39 Students mold clay and float it to observe the effect of shape on overall density.	**TIME** 10 minutes **MATERIALS** ball of clay, bowl, water
Hot Chocolate, p. 39 Students melt chocolate, observing the effect of heat on the state of a material.	**TIME** 10 minutes **MATERIALS** four candy-coated chocolates, paper towel
Internet Activity: Physical and Chemical Changes, p. 39 Students are introduced to examples of physical and chemical changes.	**TIME** 20 minutes **MATERIALS** computer with Internet access

SECTION 1

EXPLORE Physical Properties, p. 41 Students observe physical properties of a material and how they can change.	**TIME** 10 minutes **MATERIALS** rectangular piece of clay
INVESTIGATE Chemical Changes, p. 47 Students observe signs of a chemical change in two solutions.	**TIME** 15 minutes **MATERIALS** 100-mL graduated cylinder, water, 2 clear plastic cups, 2 eyedroppers, iodine solution, cornstarch, spoon, vitamin C tablet

SECTION 2

CHAPTER INVESTIGATION **Freezing Point,** pp. 56–57 Students freeze melted stearic acid and measure its freezing point.	**TIME** 40 minutes **MATERIALS** large test tube, pure stearic acid, test-tube holder, test-tube rack, wire-loop stirrer, thermometer

SECTION 3

EXPLORE Identifying Substances, p. 58 Students examine how properties can be used to identify two unknown substances.	**TIME** 10 minutes **MATERIALS** baking soda, baking powder, 2 cups, beaker, water
INVESTIGATE Separating Mixtures, p. 61 Students design a way to separate a mixture of sand, salt, and pepper.	**TIME** 30 minutes **MATERIALS** spoon; mixture of sand, table salt, and pepper; 2 index cards; comb; felt; 100-mL graduated cylinder; water; coffee filter; funnel; small cup; pie tin

R **Additional INVESTIGATION,** Measuring Density, A, B, & C, pp. 133–141; Teacher Instructions, pp. 262–263

Chapter 2: **Properties of Matter** 37D

Previewing Chapter Resources

	INTEGRATED TECHNOLOGY	LABS AND ACTIVITIES
CHAPTER 2 **Properties of Matter**	**CLASSZONE.COM** • eEdition Plus • EasyPlanner • Misconception Database • Content Review • Test Practice • Simulation • Resource Centers • Internet Activity: Physical and Chemical Changes • Math Tutorial 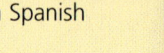 **SCILINKS.ORG** **CD-ROMS** • eEdition • EasyPlanner • Power Presentations • Content Review • Lab Generator • Test Generator **AUDIO CDS** • Audio Readings • Audio Readings in Spanish	EXPLORE the Big Idea, p. 39 • Float or Sink • Hot Chocolate • Internet Activity: Physical and Chemical Changes **UNIT RESOURCE BOOK** Unit Projects, pp. 5–10 **Lab Generator CD-ROM** Generate customized labs.
SECTION 1 **Matter has observable properties.** pp. 41–49 Time: 2 periods (1 block) Lesson Plan, pp. 83–84	• **RESOURCE CENTER**, Chemical Properties of Matter • **MATH TUTORIAL** **UNIT TRANSPARENCY BOOK** • Big Idea Flow Chart, p. T9 • Daily Vocabulary Scaffolding, p. T10 • Note-Taking Model, p. T11 • 3-Minute Warm-Up, p. T12 • "Physical Changes" Visual, p. T14	• EXPLORE Physical Properties, p. 41 • INVESTIGATE Chemical Changes, p. 47 • Math in Science, p. 49 **UNIT RESOURCE BOOK** • Datasheet, Chemical Changes, p. 92 • Math Support, pp. 120, 122 • Math Practice, pp. 121, 123 • Additional INVESTIGATION, Measuring Density, A, B, & C, pp. 133–141
SECTION 2 **Changes of state are physical changes.** pp. 50–57 Time: 3 periods (1.5 blocks) Lesson Plan, pp. 94–95	**RESOURCE CENTER**, Melting Points and Boiling Points **UNIT TRANSPARENCY BOOK** • Daily Vocabulary Scaffolding, p. T10 • 3-Minute Warm-Up, p. T12	CHAPTER INVESTIGATION, Freezing Point, pp. 56-57 **UNIT RESOURCE BOOK** CHAPTER INVESTIGATION, Freezing Point, pp. 124–132
SECTION 3 **Properties are used to identify substances.** pp. 58–63 Time: 3 periods (1.5 blocks) Lesson Plan, pp. 104–105	**RESOURCE CENTER**, Separating Materials from Mixtures **UNIT TRANSPARENCY BOOK** • Big Idea Flow Chart, p. T9 • Daily Vocabulary Scaffolding, p. T10 • 3-Minute Warm-Up, p. T13 • Chapter Outline, p. T15–T16	• EXPLORE Identifying Substances, p. 58 • INVESTIGATE Separating Mixtures, p. 61 • Connecting Sciences, p. 63 **UNIT RESOURCE BOOK** Datasheet, Separating Mixtures, p. 113

KEY TO ICONS CD/CD-ROM  Teacher Edition UNIT TRANSPARENCY BOOK 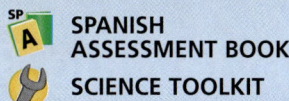 SPANISH ASSESSMENT BOOK
 INTERNET  Pupil Edition 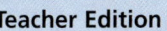 UNIT RESOURCE BOOK UNIT ASSESSMENT BOOK SCIENCE TOOLKIT

READING AND REINFORCEMENT

ASSESSMENT

STANDARDS

- Magnet Word, B24–25
- Main Idea Web, C38–39
- Daily Vocabulary Scaffolding, H1–8

 UNIT RESOURCE BOOK
- Vocabulary Practice, pp. 117–118
- Decoding Support, p. 119
- Summarizing the Chapter, pp. 142–143

- Chapter Review, pp. 65–66
- Standardized Test Practice, p. 67

 UNIT ASSESSMENT BOOK
- Diagnostic Test, pp. 21–22
- Chapter Test, A, B, & C, pp. 26–37
- Alternative Assessment, pp. 38–39

 Spanish Chapter Test, pp. 217–220

National Standards
A.2–8, A.9.a–f, B.1.a, E.2–5

See p. 38 for the standards.

 Audio Readings CD
Listen to Pupil Edition.

 **Audio Readings in Spanish CD**
Listen to Pupil Edition in Spanish.

 **Test Generator CD-ROM**
Generate customized tests.

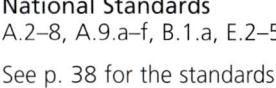 **Lab Generator CD-ROM**
Rubrics for Labs

 UNIT RESOURCE BOOK
- Reading Study Guide, A & B, pp. 85–88
- Spanish Reading Study Guide, pp. 89–90
- Challenge and Extension, p. 91
- Reinforcing Key Concepts, p. 93
- Challenge Reading, pp. 115–116

 Ongoing Assessment, pp. 41–48

 Section 2.1 Review, p. 48

 UNIT ASSESSMENT BOOK
Section 2.1 Quiz, p. 23

National Standards
A.2–8, A.9.a–c, A.9.e–f, B.1.a

 UNIT RESOURCE BOOK
- Reading Study Guide, A & B, pp. 96–99
- Spanish Reading Study Guide, pp. 100–101
- Challenge and Extension, p. 102
- Reinforcing Key Concepts, p. 103

 Ongoing Assessment, pp. 50–55

 Section 2.2 Review, p. 55

 UNIT ASSESSMENT BOOK
Section 2.2 Quiz, p. 24

National Standards
A.2–7, A.9.a–b, A.9.d–f, B.1.a

 UNIT RESOURCE BOOK
- Reading Study Guide, A & B, pp. 106–109
- Spanish Reading Study Guide, pp. 110–111
- Challenge and Extension, p. 112
- Reinforcing Key Concepts, p. 114

 Ongoing Assessment, pp. 58–59, 61–62

 Section 2.3 Review, p. 62

 UNIT ASSESSMENT BOOK
Section 2.3 Quiz, p. 25

National Standards
A.2–7, A.9.a–b, A.9.e–f, E.2–5

Previewing Resources for Differentiated Instruction

CHAPTER INVESTIGATION

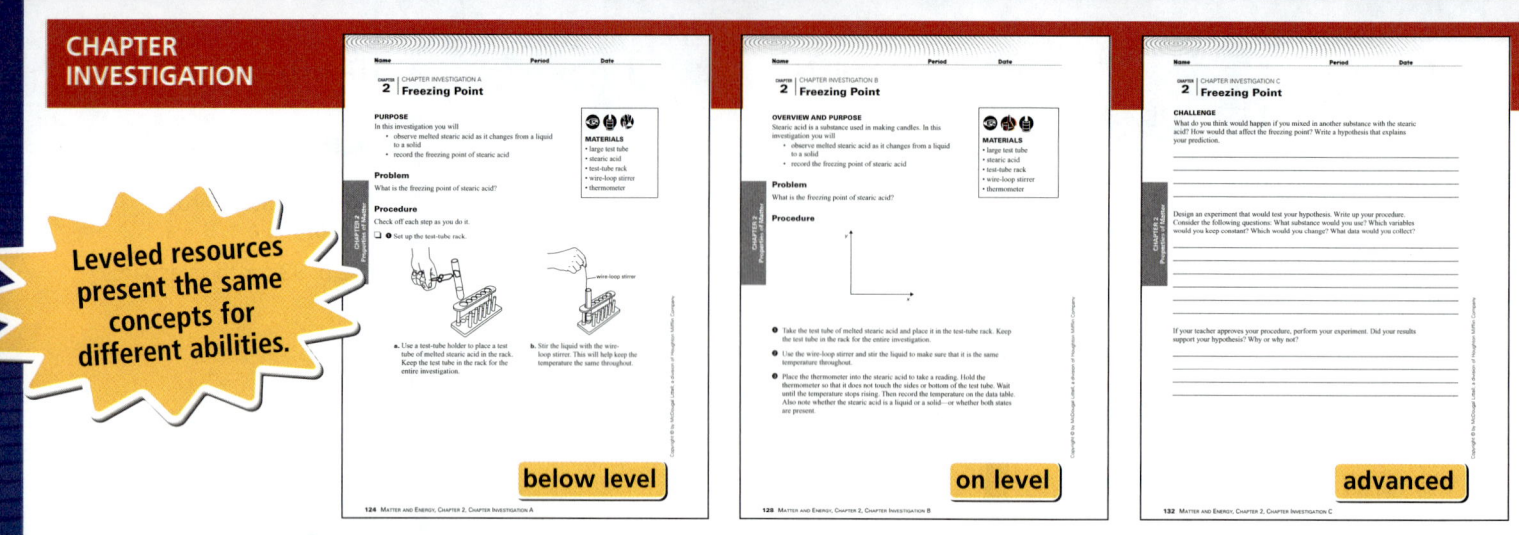

Leveled resources present the same concepts for different abilities.

R UNIT RESOURCE BOOK, pp. 124–127   **R** pp. 128–131   **R** pp. 128–132

READING STUDY GUIDE

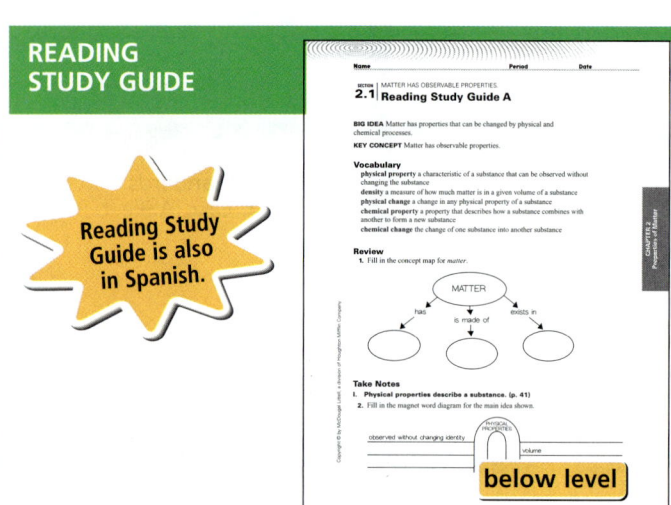 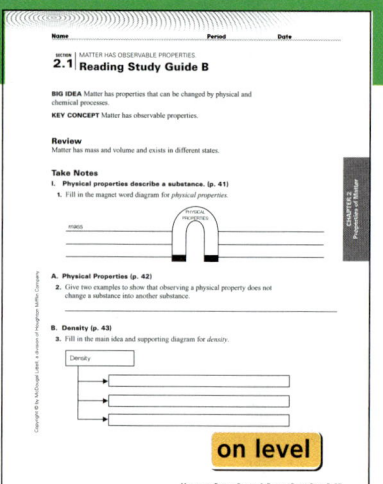 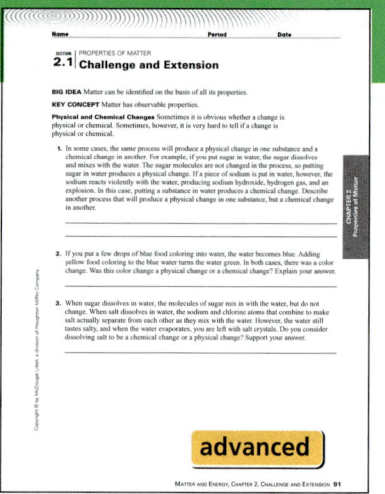

Reading Study Guide is also in Spanish.

R UNIT RESOURCE BOOK, pp. 85–86   **R** pp. 87–88   **R** p. 91

CHAPTER TEST

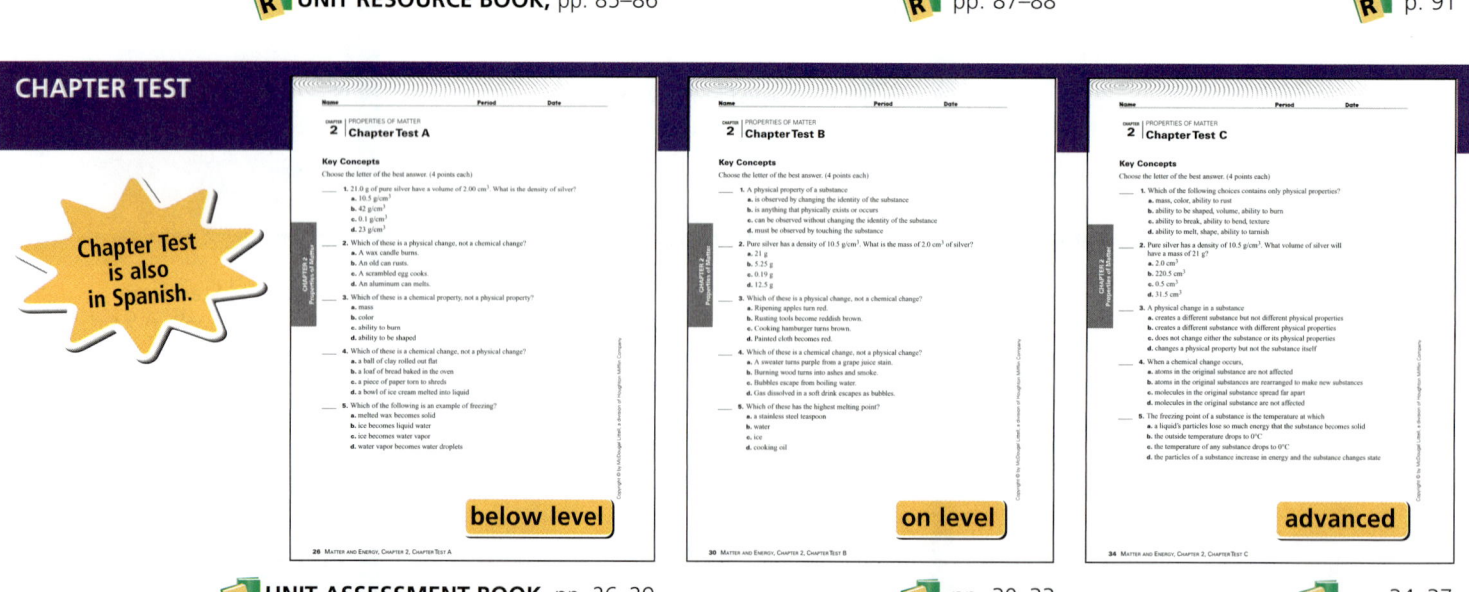

Chapter Test is also in Spanish.

A UNIT ASSESSMENT BOOK, pp. 26–29   **A** pp. 30–33   **A** pp. 34–37

37G   Unit 1: **Matter and Energy**

TECHNOLOGY

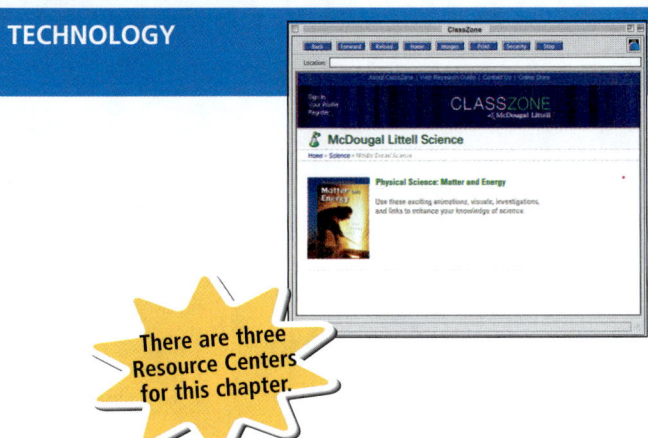
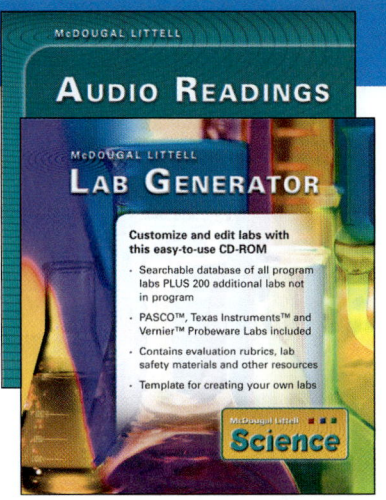
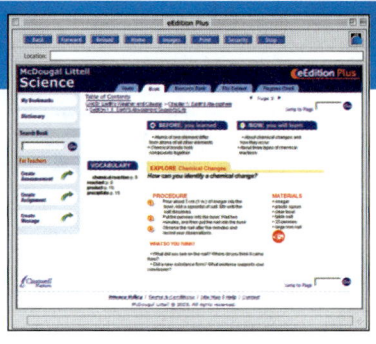

There are three Resource Centers for this chapter.

CLASSZONE.COM   **CD/CD-ROMS**   **CLASSZONE.COM**

VISUAL CONTENT

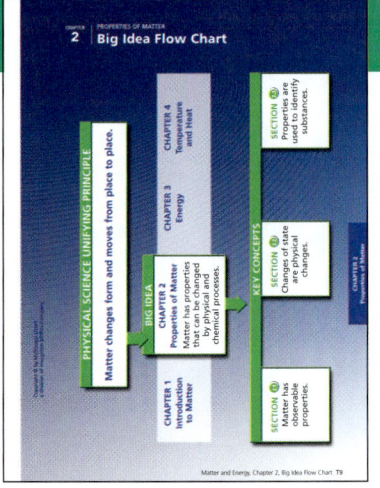
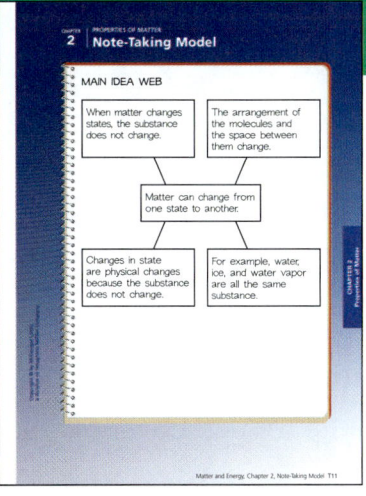

UNIT TRANSPARENCY BOOK, p. 9   p. 11   p. 14

MORE SUPPORT

Reinforcing Key Concepts for each section

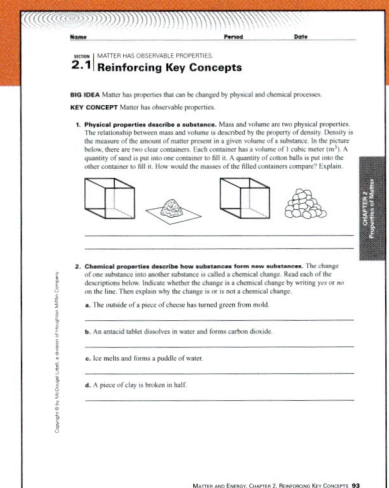
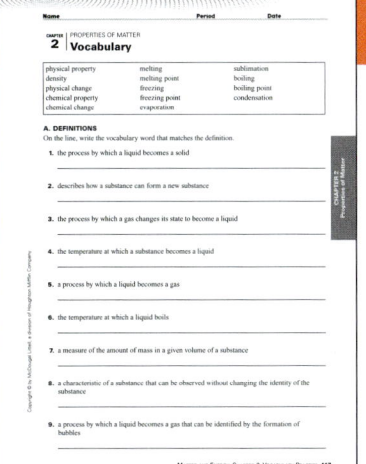
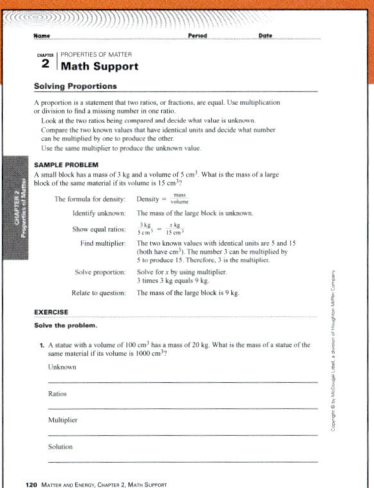

UNIT RESOURCE BOOK, p. 93   pp. 117–118   p. 120

Chapter 2: **Properties of Matter** 37H

CHAPTER 2 Properties of Matter

INTRODUCE

Have students look at the photograph of the chef making a sugar sculpture. Discuss how the question in the box relates to the Big Idea:
- How does the sugar in the sculpture compare to granular sugar?
- What is added to the sugar to make it harden?
- In what ways can food change when it is cooked?

National Science Education Standards

Content

B.1.a A substance has characteristic properties, such as density, a boiling point, and solubility, all of which are independent of the amount of the sample. A mixture of substances often can be separated into the original substances using one or more of the characteristic properties.

Process

A.2–8 Design and conduct an investigation; use tools to gather and interpret data; use evidence to describe, predict, explain, model; think critically to make relationships between evidence and explanation; recognize different explanations and predictions; communicate scientific procedures and explanations; use mathematics.

A.9.a–f Understand scientific inquiry by using different investigations, methods, mathematics, technology, explanations based on logic, evidence, and skepticism.

E.2–5 Design, implement, and evaluate a solution or product; communicate technological design.

CHAPTER 2 Properties of Matter

the BIG idea
Matter has properties that can be changed by physical and chemical processes.

What properties could help you identify this sculpture as sugar?

Key Concepts

SECTION 1 — Matter has observable properties.
Learn how to recognize physical and chemical properties.

SECTION 2 — Changes of state are physical changes.
Learn how energy is related to changes of state.

SECTION 3 — Properties are used to identify substances.
Learn how the properties of substances can be used to identify them and to separate mixtures.

Internet Preview
CLASSZONE.COM
Chapter 2 online resources: Content Review, Simulation, three Resource Centers, Math Tutorial, Test Practice

38 Unit 1: Matter and Energy

INTERNET PREVIEW

CLASSZONE.COM For student use with the following pages:

Review and Practice
- Content Review, pp. 40, 64
- Math Tutorial: Solving Proportions, p. 49
- Test Practice, p. 67

Activities and Resources
- Internet Activity: Physical/Chemical Changes, p. 39
- Resource Centers: Chemical Properties of Matter, p. 46; Melting Points and Boiling Points, p. 54; Separating Materials from Mixtures, p. 63

Physical Properties of Matter
Code: MDL062

EXPLORE the BIG idea

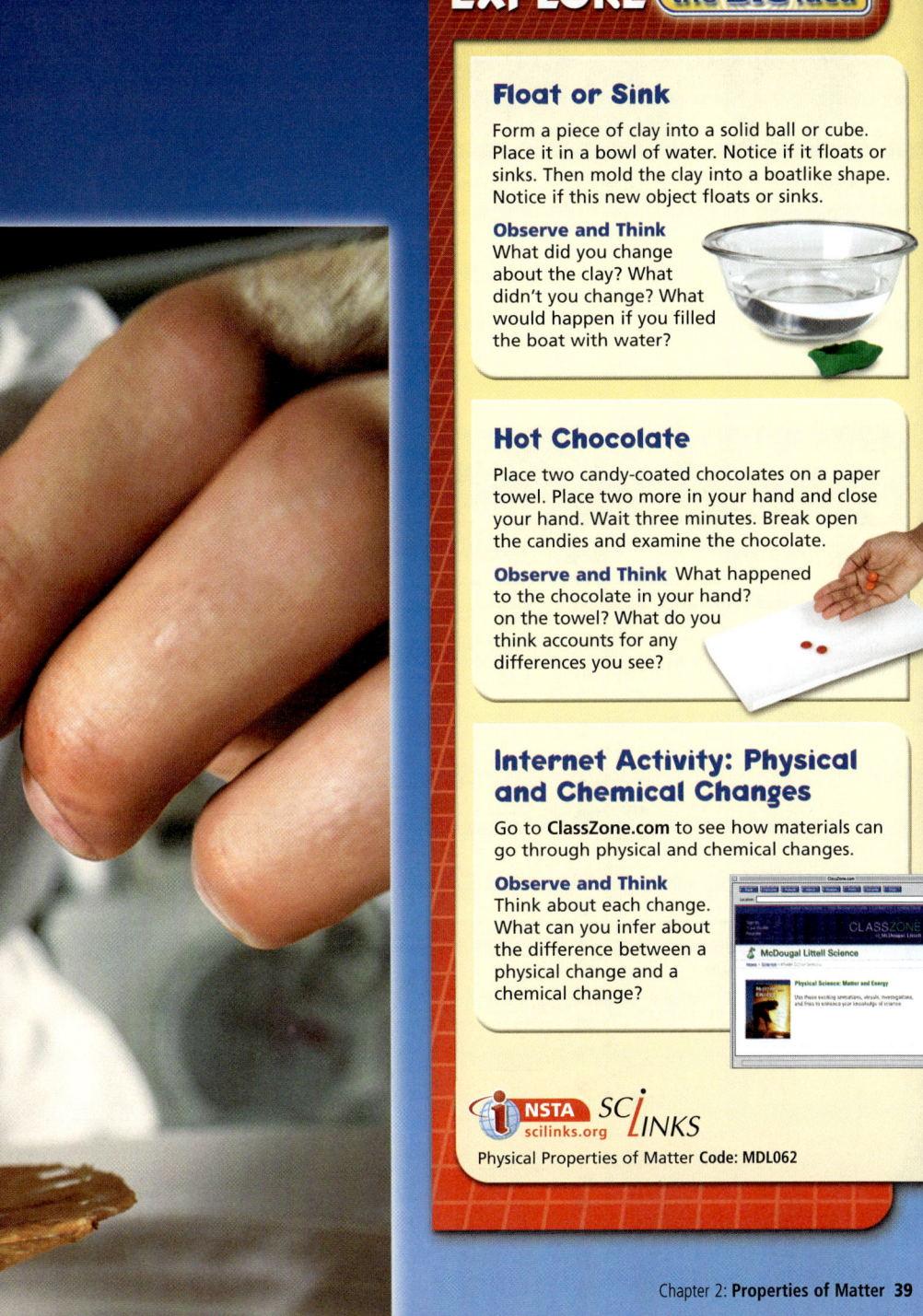

Float or Sink
Form a piece of clay into a solid ball or cube. Place it in a bowl of water. Notice if it floats or sinks. Then mold the clay into a boatlike shape. Notice if this new object floats or sinks.

Observe and Think What did you change about the clay? What didn't you change? What would happen if you filled the boat with water?

Hot Chocolate
Place two candy-coated chocolates on a paper towel. Place two more in your hand and close your hand. Wait three minutes. Break open the candies and examine the chocolate.

Observe and Think What happened to the chocolate in your hand? on the towel? What do you think accounts for any differences you see?

Internet Activity: Physical and Chemical Changes
Go to ClassZone.com to see how materials can go through physical and chemical changes.

Observe and Think Think about each change. What can you infer about the difference between a physical change and a chemical change?

NSTA scilinks.org SCLINKS
Physical Properties of Matter **Code:** MDL062

Chapter 2: **Properties of Matter** 39

TEACHING WITH TECHNOLOGY

Digital Camera While students perform the Chapter Investigation on pp. 56–57, have them photograph the various steps of the procedure. Have them prepare a slide show of the photographs on a computer.

CBL and Probeware Use a temperature probe instead of a thermometer in the Chapter Investigation, pp. 56–57.

EXPLORE the BIG idea

These inquiry-based activities are appropriate for use at home or as a supplement to classroom instruction.

Float or Sink
PURPOSE To introduce students to the effect of shape on overall density. Students shape clay to explore its density and volume.

TIP *10 min.* Be sure the boatlike shape contains no holes through which water can enter.

Answer: The shape of the clay changed. By creating a shape that held air, the clay boat was able to float. Other properties, such as total amount of clay, mass, weight, and color, didn't change. If the boat were filled with water, it would sink.

REVISIT after p. 43.

Hot Chocolate
PURPOSE To introduce students to the effect of heat on the state of a material. Students apply heat to chocolate and observe that it changes state.

TIP *10 min.* Remind students never to eat anything in a laboratory setting.

Answer: It melted; it stayed the same; an increase in temperature melts chocolate.

REVISIT after p. 51.

Internet Activity: Physical and Chemical Changes
PURPOSE To introduce students to examples of physical and chemical changes.

TIP *20 min.* Encourage students to generalize about what physical changes have in common and what chemical changes have in common.

Answer: The identity of a substance changes during a chemical change but does not during a physical change.

REVISIT after p. 46.

Chapter 2 **39**

PREPARE

◉ CONCEPT REVIEW

Activate Prior Knowledge

- At the beginning of class, place an ice cube in a transparent cup in the front of the room. Ask students if the ice is matter. *It is.*
- After 15 minutes, ask students if what is in the cup is still matter. *yes*
- Ask them to describe any changes the matter has undergone. *Some of the solid matter is now a liquid.*

◉ TAKING NOTES

Main Idea Web

Point out that different webs can have different numbers of boxes around them. Some might have only two connected to the heading box. Suggest that students limit the number of boxes surrounding the center box to reflect an appropriate level of detail.

Vocabulary Strategy

Discuss why a magnet is a good representation of the central concept.

Vocabulary and Note-Taking Resources

- Vocabulary Practice, pp. 117–118
- Decoding Support, p. 119

- Daily Vocabulary Scaffolding, p. T10
- Note-Taking Model, p. T11

- Magnet Word, B24–25
- Main Idea Web, C38–39
- Daily Vocabulary Scaffolding, H1–8

CHAPTER 2
Getting Ready to Learn

◉ CONCEPT REVIEW
- Everything is made of matter.
- Matter has mass and volume.
- Atoms combine to form molecules.

◉ VOCABULARY REVIEW
mass p. 10
volume p. 11
molecule p. 18
states of matter p. 27

CONTENT REVIEW
CLASSZONE.COM
Review concepts and vocabulary.

◉ TAKING NOTES

MAIN IDEA WEB

Write each new blue heading in a box. Then write notes in boxes around the center box that give important terms and details about that heading.

VOCABULARY STRATEGY

Think about a vocabulary term as a **magnet word** diagram. Write related terms and ideas in boxes around it.

SCIENCE NOTEBOOK

- color, shape, size, texture, volume, mass
- melting point, boiling point
- Physical properties describe a substance.
- density: a measure of the amount of matter in a given volume

CHEMICAL CHANGE
- burning
- rusting
- tarnishing
- change in temperature
- change in color
- formation of bubbles

See the Note-Taking Handbook on pages R45–R51.

40 Unit 1: Matter and Energy

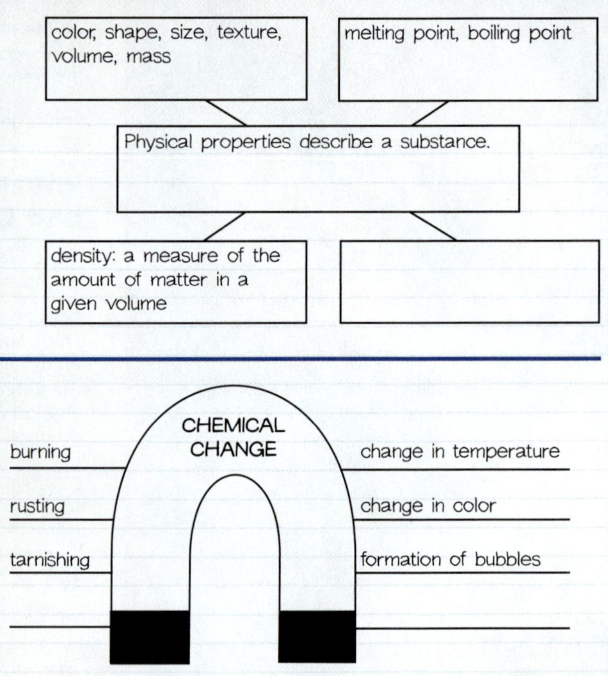

CHECK READINESS

Administer the Diagnostic Test to determine students' readiness for new science content and requisite math skills.

 Diagnostic Test, pp. 21–22

Technology Resources

Students needing content and math skills should visit ClassZone.com.

- CONTENT REVIEW
- MATH TUTORIAL

 CONTENT REVIEW CD-ROM

40 Unit 1: **Matter and Energy**

KEY CONCEPT
Matter has observable properties.

BEFORE, you learned
- Matter has mass and volume
- Matter is made of atoms
- Matter exists in different states

NOW, you will learn
- About physical and chemical properties
- About physical changes
- About chemical changes

VOCABULARY
physical property p. 41
density p. 43
physical change p. 44
chemical property p. 46
chemical change p. 46

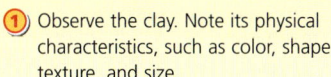

How can a substance be changed?

PROCEDURE
1. Observe the clay. Note its physical characteristics, such as color, shape, texture, and size.
2. Change the shape of the clay. Note which characteristics changed and which ones stayed the same.

MATERIAL
rectangular piece of clay

WHAT DO YOU THINK?
- How did reshaping the clay change its physical characteristics?
- How were the mass and the volume of the clay affected?

Physical properties describe a substance.

What words would you use to describe a table? a chair? the sandwich you ate for lunch? You would probably say something about the shape, color, and size of each item. Next you might consider whether it is hard or soft, smooth or rough to the touch. Normally, when describing an object, you identify the characteristics of the object that you can observe without changing the identity of the object.

VOCABULARY
Make a magnet word diagram in your notebook for *physical property*.

The characteristics of a substance that can be observed without changing the identity of the substance are called **physical properties.** In science, observation can include measuring and handling a substance. All of your senses can be used to detect physical properties. Color, shape, size, texture, volume, and mass are a few of the physical properties you probably have encountered.

 Describe some of the physical properties of your desk.

Chapter 2: **Properties of Matter** 41

2.1 FOCUS

▶ Set Learning Goals
Students will
- Describe physical and chemical properties.
- Give examples of physical changes.
- Explain that chemical changes form new substances.
- Observe signs of chemical change in an experiment.

◆ 3-Minute Warm-Up
Display Transparency 12 or copy this exercise on the board:

Describe a common object by naming its distinctive properties. Trade your mystery-object description with a partner's and try to guess what object he or she has described.

 3-Minute Warm-Up, p. T12

2.1 MOTIVATE

EXPLORE Physical Properties

PURPOSE To observe the physical properties of a material before and after a physical change

TIP *10 min.* Students can use the same clay they used for the exploration on p. 39.

WHAT DO YOU THINK? *The shape changed, but the color and texture stayed the same. Mass and volume stayed the same.*

Ongoing Assessment
 *Answer: Answers should include color, texture, and shape.*

RESOURCES FOR DIFFERENTIATED INSTRUCTION

Below Level
UNIT RESOURCE BOOK
- Reading Study Guide A, pp. 85–86
- Decoding Support, p. 119

 **AUDIO CDS**

 **Additional INVESTIGATION,**
Measuring Density, A, B, & C, pp. 133–141; Teacher Instructions, pp. 262–263

Advanced
UNIT RESOURCE BOOK
- Challenge and Extension, p. 91
- Challenge Reading, pp. 115–116

English Learners
UNIT RESOURCE BOOK
Spanish Reading Study Guide, pp. 89–90

 **AUDIO CDS**
- Audio Readings in Spanish
- Audio Readings (English)

Chapter 2 **41**

2.1 INSTRUCT

Real World Example

A centrifuge is a machine that separates the components of a liquid on the basis of the physical property of density. It spins a liquid at great speed so that denser materials sink to the bottom of the container that holds the liquid. One liquid whose components are separated in a centrifuge is blood. Blood cells are denser than plasma, the liquid part of blood. As a result, the cells end up at the bottom, with the plasma on top. Why would anyone want to separate blood? Sometimes blood tests are done on only one part of blood, so that part must be isolated. Also, some blood transfusions involve only plasma or cells.

Develop Critical Thinking

APPLY This activity illustrates the concept of density.

- Collect two groups of items. One group should have items of the same mass but different volumes. The second group should have items of the same volume, but different masses.
- Have students order the items in each group according to which they think have the greatest mass. Students should write down and explain their choices without touching or picking up the objects.
- Next, have students pick up the items and adjust their lists based on the new information.
- Ask: How does the relationship between mass and volume depend on the material? *Some materials have a greater mass per unit volume than other materials.*

Ongoing Assessment

Answer: mass, volume; shape, ability to stretch

Answer: texture, color; volume, shape, mass

Physical Properties

How do you know which characteristics are physical properties? Just ask yourself whether observing the property involves changing the substance to a different substance. For example, you can stretch a rubber band. Does stretching the rubber band change what it is made of? No. The rubber band is still a rubber band before and after it is stretched. It may look a little different, but it is still a rubber band.

Mass and volume are two physical properties. Measuring these properties does not change the identity of a substance. For example, a lump of clay might have a mass of 200 grams (g) and a volume of 100 cubic centimeters (cm^3). If you were to break the clay in half, you would have two 100 g pieces of clay, each with a volume of 50 cm^3. You can bend and shape the clay too. Even if you were to mold a realistic model of a car out of the clay, it still would be a piece of clay. Although you have changed some of the properties of the object, such as its shape and volume, you have not changed the fact that the substance you are observing is clay.

REMINDER Because all formulas for volume involve the multiplication of three measurements, volume has a unit that is cubed (such as cm^3).

CHECK YOUR READING Which physical properties listed above are found by taking measurements? Which are not?

Physical Properties

Physical properties of clay—such as volume, mass, color, texture, and shape—can be observed without changing the fact that the substance is clay.

Block of Clay

Shaped Clay

READING VISUALS **COMPARE AND CONTRAST** Which physical properties do the two pieces of clay have in common? Which are different?

42 Unit 1: Matter and Energy

DIFFERENTIATE INSTRUCTION

More Reading Support

A If observing a property doesn't change a substance, what kind of property is it? *physical*

B What type of property is texture? *physical*

English Learners The words *would*, *should*, and *could* are not universal in all languages. Help students understand sentences that contain these words. For example, guide them to see that the condition expressed in the following sentence is hypothetical: "If you were to break the clay in half, you would have two 100 g pieces of clay."

Density

The relationship between the mass and the volume of a substance is another important physical property. For any substance, the amount of mass in a unit of volume is constant. For different substances, the amount of mass in a unit of volume may differ. This relationship explains why you can easily lift a shoebox full of feathers but not one filled with pennies, even though both are the same size. A volume of pennies contains more mass than an equal volume of feathers. The relationship between mass and volume is called density.

? C **Density** is a measure of the amount of matter present in a given volume of a substance. Density is normally expressed in units of grams per cubic centimeter (g/cm^3). In other words, density is the
? D mass in grams divided by the volume in cubic centimeters.

$$\text{Density} = \frac{\text{mass}}{\text{Volume}} \qquad D = \frac{m}{V}$$

How would you find the density of 200 g of clay with a volume of 100 cm^3? You calculate that the clay has a density of 200 g divided by 100 cm^3, or 2 g/cm^3. If you divide the clay in half and find the density of one piece of clay, it will be 100 g/50 cm^3, or 2 g/cm^3—the same as the original piece. Notice that density is a property of a substance that remains the same no matter how much of the substance you have.

READING TIP

The density of solids is usually measured in grams per cubic centimeter (g/cm^3). The density of liquids is usually measured in grams per milliliter (g/mL). Recall that 1 mL = 1 cm^3.

Calculating Density

Sample Problem

A glass marble has a volume of 5 cm^3 and a mass of 13 g. What is the density of glass?

What do you know? Volume = 5 cm^3, mass = 13 g

What do you want to find out? Density

Write the formula: $D = \frac{m}{V}$

Substitute into the formula: $D = \frac{13\text{ g}}{5\text{ cm}^3}$

Calculate and simplify: $D = 2.6\text{ g/cm}^3$

Check that your units agree: Unit is g/cm^3. Unit of density is g/cm^3. Units agree.

Answer: $D = 2.6\text{ g/cm}^3$

Practice the Math

1. A lead sinker has a mass of 227 g and a volume of 20 cm^3. What is the density of lead?
2. A glass of milk has a volume of 100 mL. If the milk has a mass of 103 g, what is the density of milk?

Address Misconceptions

IDENTIFY Place a ball of modeling clay and a Styrofoam ball in water. Ask why one floats and the other doesn't. If students suggest the clay sinks because it is heavier, they may hold the misconception that *dense* and *heavy* mean the same thing.

CORRECT Remove a small portion of clay that has less mass than the Styrofoam ball. Have students compare the weights of the small portion of clay and the ball. Ask them to predict what will happen if both are put in water again. Demonstrate. Explain that the clay sinks not because it is heavier, but because it is more dense than water.

REASSESS Ask students to discuss how large a Styrofoam ball would have to be before it would sink in water. Students should reach the conclusion that any amount of Styrofoam should float because Styrofoam is less dense than water.

Technology Resources

Visit **ClassZone.com** for background on common student misconceptions.

MISCONCEPTION DATABASE

Develop Algebra Skills

Remind students of the importance of using correct units to determine whether a problem is set up correctly. If correct units are used at each step, the answer should have the correct units.

EXPLORE the BIG idea

Revisit "Float or Sink" on p. 39. Ask students how the density of air affects the average density of the boat. *The average density is decreased because the volume of the boat is filled with air.*

DIFFERENTIATE INSTRUCTION

More Reading Support

C What physical property compares mass and volume? *density*

D How do you calculate density? *Divide mass by volume.*

Additional Investigation To reinforce Section 2.1 learning goals, use the following full-period investigation:

R **Additional INVESTIGATION,** Measuring Density, A, B, & C, pp. 133–141, 262–263 (Advanced students should complete Levels B and C.)

Below Level Have students pan for copper using a mixture of pennies and objects that are less dense, such as buttons. Have students move the pan around so the pennies "sink" to the bottom and the less dense items rise to the top.

Ongoing Assessment

Practice the Math *Answers:*

1. *11.35 g/cm^3*
2. *1.03 g/cm^3*

R
- Math Support, p. 120
- Math Practice, p. 121

Integrate the Sciences

There are two types of weathering: physical and chemical. In physical weathering, rock is broken down into smaller pieces. It also undergoes mechanical weathering, a type of physical weathering. Plant-root growth helps break up rocks, as does ice wedging. The latter works as follows: Water seeps into cracks in rocks. When the temperature drops below freezing, the water freezes and expands, applying pressure to the sides of the crack. A series of freezing and thawing cycles will break the rock into small pieces.

In chemical weathering, chemical reactions occur that create new substances. Soil, for example, is formed from decaying organic matter and weathered rock. Rock can weather chemically by the action of acids and other chemicals in the environment.

Teacher Demo

Use a raw egg to show the difference between physical changes and other changes. Have students list each change below and decide whether it is a physical change or not.

- Break a raw egg open and place it in a beaker. *physical*
- Use a fork to beat the egg. *physical*
- Cook the egg over a hot plate. *other*

Ongoing Assessment

CHECK YOUR READING *Answer: It changes a physical property, not the substance itself. For example, cutting paper will change its shape and volume, but will not change the substance of the paper.*

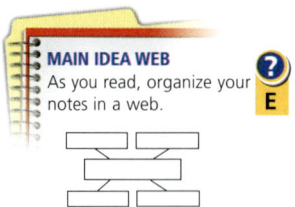

MAIN IDEA WEB
As you read, organize your notes in a web.

Physical Changes

You have read that a physical property is any property that can be observed without changing the identity of the substance. What then would be a physical change? A **physical change** is a change in any physical property of a substance, not in the substance itself. Breaking a piece of clay in half is a physical change because it changes only the size and shape of the clay. Stretching a rubber band is a physical change because the size of the rubber band changes. The color of the rubber band sometimes can change as well when it is stretched. However, the material that the rubber band is made of does not change. The rubber band is still rubber.

What happens when water changes from a liquid into water vapor or ice? Is this a physical change? Remember to ask yourself what has changed about the material. Ice is a solid and water is a liquid, but both are the same substance—both are composed of H_2O molecules. As you will read in more detail in the next section, a change in a substance's state of matter is a physical change.

CHECK YOUR READING How is a physical change related to a substance's physical properties?

A substance can go through many different physical changes and still remain the same substance. Consider, for example, the changes that happen to the wool that ultimately becomes a sweater.

1. Wool is sheared from the sheep. The wool is then cleaned and placed into a machine that separates the wool fibers from one another. Shearing and separating the fibers are physical changes that change the shape, volume, and texture of the wool.

2. The wool fibers are spun into yarn. Again, the shape and volume of the wool change. The fibers are twisted so that they are packed more closely together and are intertwined with one another.

3. The yarn is dyed. The dye changes the color of the wool, but it does not change the wool into another substance. This type of color change is a physical change.

4. Knitting the yarn into a sweater also does not change the wool into another substance. A wool sweater is still wool, even though it no longer resembles the wool on a sheep.

It can be difficult to determine if a specific change is a physical change or not. Some changes, such as a change in color, also can occur when new substances are formed during the change. When deciding whether a change is a physical change or not, ask yourself whether you have the same substance you started with. If the substance is the same, then the changes it underwent were all physical changes.

44 Unit 1: Matter and Energy

DIFFERENTIATE INSTRUCTION

 **More Reading Support**

E Is cutting paper a physical change? *yes*

Advanced Have students select two or three samples of several different substances. Then have them identify properties of each substance—such as mass, volume, and density—and categorize them as "Depends on amount of substance (extensive)" or "Does not depend on amount of substance (intensive)."

Have students who are interested in physical properties of unusual substances read the following article:

 Challenge Reading, pp. 115–116

Physical Changes

The process of turning wool into a sweater requires that the wool undergo physical changes. Changes in shape, volume, texture, and color occur as raw wool is turned into a colorful sweater.

① Shearing

Preparing the wool produces physical changes. The wool is removed from the sheep and then cleaned before the wool fibers are separated.

② Spinning

Further physical changes occur as a machine twists the wool fibers into a long, thin rope of yarn.

③ Dyeing
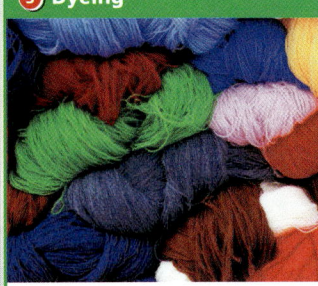
Dyeing produces color changes but does not change the basic substance of the wool.

④ The final product, a wool sweater, is still wool.

READING VISUALS How does the yarn in the sweater differ from the wool on the sheep?

Chapter 2: Properties of Matter **45**

DIFFERENTIATE INSTRUCTION

Inclusion Bring a wool sweater and some raw wool to class so that students who are visually impaired can feel and compare the two forms of wool.

Teach Difficult Concepts

Color change produced by covering a material with a pigment, such as paint or dye, is usually considered a physical change. Although many dyes and paints attach to the surface of a material by chemical bonds, these bonds do not change the nature of the original substance. Instead, the bonds cause the pigment to adhere to the material. Ask: How do you think dye colors wool without changing the wool's identity? *It coats the fibers.*

Teach from Visuals

The visual "Physical Changes" is available as T14 in the Unit Transparency Book.

Art Connection

In many cultures, people use dyes to produce textile artwork. Examples include the colorful kente cloth woven in Ghana and the detailed batik images produced in Indonesia and India. The oldest known dyes are indigo, which comes from the indigo plant, and Tyrian purple, which is extracted from snails. Many natural dyes color fabric with no other additive, but some require the use of metal salts, often called mordants, that fix the dye to the fabric. Most dyes used today are synthetic, although some artists still prefer to make their own dyes from natural sources.

Ongoing Assessment

Give examples of physical changes.
Ask: How can you physically change a substance without changing what it is? *by cutting it up, by changing its shape, by changing its color*

READING VISUALS *Answer: The yarn was twisted into strands, dyed, and knit to form the sweater. However, it is still wool.*

Chapter 2 **45**

Teach Difficult Concepts

Students might have difficulty understanding color as it relates to properties and changes. Color itself is a physical property, because it can be observed without changing the identity of the object. But when color changes, it is usually a sign of a chemical change. Ask students for examples of color changes that indicate a chemical change. To help students understand this concept, try the following demonstration.

Teacher Demo

Fill a small, transparent container halfway with water. Dissolve a crystal of potassium permanganate in the water. Point out that dissolving is a physical change. Add about one gram of sodium hydrogen sulfite to the solution. As it dissolves, the solution loses its color because of a chemical change.

EXPLORE the BIG idea

Revisit "Internet Activity: Physical and Chemical Changes" on p. 39. Have students state the difference between a chemical change and a physical change.

Ongoing Assessment

Describe physical and chemical properties.

Ask: List some physical properties of wood. *hardness, density, color* What chemical properties does wood have? *ability to burn, turns into other substances*

PHOTO CAPTION Answer: *When people rub the nose, the oils on their skin remove tarnish, revealing the untarnished bronze. Oils from people's hands also protect the bronze from reacting with the air and forming more tarnish.*

Learn about the chemical properties of matter.

Chemical properties describe how substances form new substances.

If you wanted to keep a campfire burning, would you add a piece of wood or a piece of iron? You would add wood, of course, because you know that wood burns but iron does not. Is the ability to burn a physical property of the wood? The ability to burn seems to be quite different from physical properties such as color, density, and shape. More important, after the wood burns, all that is left is a pile of ashes and some new substances in the air. The wood has obviously changed into something else. The ability to burn, therefore, must describe another kind of property that substances have—not a physical property but a chemical property.

Chemical Properties and Changes

Chemical properties describe how substances can form new substances. Combustibility, for example, describes how well an object can burn. Wood burns well and turns into ashes and other substances. Can you think of a chemical property for the metal iron? Especially when left outdoors in wet weather, iron rusts. The ability to rust is a chemical property of iron. The metal silver does not rust, but eventually a darker substance called tarnish forms on its surface. You may have noticed a layer of tarnish on some silver spoons or jewelry.

INFER The bust of Abraham Lincoln is made of bronze. Why is the nose a different color from the rest of the head?

The chemical properties of copper cause it to become a blue-green color when it is exposed to air. A famous example of tarnished copper is the Statue of Liberty. The chemical properties of bronze are different. Some bronze objects tarnish to a dark brown color, like the bust of Abraham Lincoln in the photograph on the left.

Chemical properties can be identified by the changes they produce. The change of one substance into another substance is called a **chemical change.** A piece of wood burning, an iron fence rusting, and a silver spoon tarnishing are all examples of chemical changes. A chemical change affects the substances involved in the change. During a chemical change, combinations of atoms in the original substances are rearranged to make new substances. For example, when rust forms on iron, the iron atoms combine with oxygen atoms in the air to form a new substance that is made of both iron and oxygen.

A chemical change is also involved when an antacid tablet is dropped into a glass of water. As the tablet dissolves, bubbles of gas appear. The water and the substances in the tablet react to form new substances. One of these substances is carbon dioxide gas, which forms the bubbles that you see.

46 Unit 1: Matter and Energy

DIFFERENTIATE INSTRUCTION

 More Reading Support

F What happens to atoms during a chemical change? *They are rearranged.*

Advanced Have students place an old discolored penny in a jar containing a few milliliters of household ammonia. Have them close the jar quickly to avoid breathing the vapors. After 30 minutes, check the penny and ask them to explain what happened in terms of a chemical change. *The ammonia chemically changed the tarnish on the penny. Evidence of this change is the color change of the penny—it became brighter—and the color change of the solution—it turned blue.*

 Challenge and Extension, p. 91

Not all chemical changes are as destructive as burning, rusting, or tarnishing. Chemical changes are also involved in cooking. When you boil an egg, for example, the substances in the raw egg change into new substances as energy is added to the egg. When you eat the egg, further chemical changes take place as your body digests the egg. The process forms new molecules that your body then can use to function.

CHECK YOUR READING Give three examples of chemical changes.

The only true indication of a chemical change is that a new substance has been formed. Sometimes, however, it is difficult to tell whether new substances have been formed or not. In many cases you have to judge which type of change has occurred only on the basis of your observations of the change and your previous experience. However, some common signs can suggest that a chemical change has occurred. You can use these signs to guide you as you try to classify a change that you are observing.

INVESTIGATE Chemical Changes

What are some signs of a chemical change?

PROCEDURE

1. Measure 80 mL of water and pour it into one of the cups.
2. Add 3 full droppers of iodine solution. Record your observations.
3. Add 1 spoonful of cornstarch to the iodine solution and stir. Record your observations.
4. Measure 50 mL of water and pour it into the second cup.
5. Using a clean eyedropper, add 4 full droppers of the iodine/cornstarch solution to the second cup.
6. Drop a vitamin C tablet into the second cup and stir the liquid with a clean spoon until the tablet is dissolved. Record your observations.

WHAT DO YOU THINK?
- What changes did you observe in the first cup? in the second cup?
- Do you think that chemical changes occurred? Why or why not?
- What are some characteristics of chemical changes?

CHALLENGE Describe some chemical changes that you have seen take place in your home or school.

SKILL FOCUS Measuring

MATERIALS
- graduated cylinder
- water
- 2 clear plastic cups
- 2 eyedroppers
- iodine solution
- cornstarch
- spoon
- vitamin C tablet

TIME 15 minutes

DIFFERENTIATE INSTRUCTION

More Reading Support

G What type of change occurs when an egg cooks? *chemical*

H What is an indication of chemical change? *A new substance forms.*

English Learners Offer synonyms and simplifications for word combinations that may confuse an English learner. For example, "a few" (p. 41) means *some*, "go through" (p. 44) means *experience* or *undergo*, and "most likely" (p. 48) means *probably*.

INVESTIGATE Chemical Changes

PURPOSE To observe signs of a chemical change

TIPS *15 min.*
- Use Lugol's solution as a source of iodine. Add enough iodine to make the solution yellow.
- If vitamin C tablets are not available, use orange juice.

WHAT DO YOU THINK? *The color changed from orange to blue-black in the first cup. In the second cup, the color changed and bubbles formed. Yes; new substances formed, as evidenced by the color changes and bubbles. Some signs of a chemical change are a change in color and the formation of bubbles.*

CHALLENGE *Sample answer: food cooking, tarnish forming on doorknobs, and fuel burning for heat*

Datasheet, Chemical Changes, p. 92

Technology Resources

Customize this student lab as needed or look for an alternative. Print rubrics to assess student lab reports.

Lab Generator CD-ROM

Metacognitive Strategy

Ask students to write a paragraph focusing on questions that occurred to them during the investigation. Have them underline the questions they could answer after completing the activity.

Integrate the Sciences

After a thunderstorm, the air often smells different. As lightning passes through oxygen gas, the oxygen chemically changes to ozone. The results of this chemical reaction can be detected as a change in odor. Ozone, however, is unstable and soon forms oxygen gas again.

Ongoing Assessment

CHECK YOUR READING *Sample answer: burning, rusting, tarnishing*

Chapter 2 **47**

Ongoing Assessment

Explain that chemical changes form new substances.

Ask: If you mix water and antacid and they react chemically, what substances are you likely to have after the reaction? *new chemicals and maybe a little leftover water or antacid*

 **Sample answer: change in odor, temperature, and color**

Reinforce the BIG idea

Have students relate the section to the Big Idea.

 Reinforcing Key Concepts, p. 93

Assess

 Section 2.1 Quiz, p. 23

Reteach

Light a previously unburned candle and have students observe it. Ask students to list signs of a chemical change in the burning candle. *Students should notice a change in odor, a rise in temperature, formation of a gas, and a change in wick color.*

Technology Resources

Have students visit ClassZone.com for reteaching of Key Concepts.

 CONTENT REVIEW

 CONTENT REVIEW CD-ROM

Carbon dioxide bubbles form as substances in the tablet react with water.

Signs of a Chemical Change

You may not be able to see that any new substances have formed during a change. Below are some signs that a chemical change may have occurred. If you observe two or more of these signs during a change, you most likely are observing a chemical change.

Production of an Odor Some chemical changes produce new smells. The chemical change that occurs when an egg is rotting produces the smell of sulfur. If you go outdoors after a thunderstorm, you may detect an unusual odor in the air. The odor is an indication that lightning has caused a chemical change in the air.

Change in Temperature Chemical changes often are accompanied by a change in temperature. You may have noticed that the temperature is higher near logs burning in a campfire.

Change in Color A change in color is often an indication of a chemical change. For example, fruit may change color when it ripens.

Formation of Bubbles When an antacid tablet makes contact with water, it begins to bubble. The formation of gas bubbles is another indicator that a chemical change may have occurred.

Formation of a Solid When two liquids are combined, a solid called a precipitate can form. The shells of animals such as clams and mussels are precipitates. They are the result of a chemical change involving substances in seawater combining with substances from the creatures.

 Give three signs of chemical changes. Describe one that you have seen recently.

2.1 Review

KEY CONCEPTS
1. What effect does observing a substance's physical properties have on the substance?
2. Describe how a physical property such as mass or texture can change without causing a change in the substance.
3. Explain why burning is a chemical change in wood.

CRITICAL THINKING
4. **Synthesize** Why does the density of a substance remain the same for different amounts of the substance?
5. **Calculate** What is the density of a block of wood with a mass of 120 g and a volume of 200 cm^3?

CHALLENGE
6. **Infer** Iron can rust when it is exposed to oxygen. What method could be used to prevent iron from rusting?

48 Unit 1: Matter and Energy

ANSWERS

1. The identity of the substance does not change.

2. Sample answer: Some mass can be removed from the object, but the object still has the same identity.

3. The products of the change are no longer wood.

4. As mass increases or decreases, so does volume. The relationship between mass and volume remains the same.

5. D = m/V = 120 g/200 cm^3 = 0.6 g/cm^3

6. Paint the iron so that it does not come into contact with the oxygen.

MATH in SCIENCE

SKILL: SOLVING PROPORTIONS

Density of Materials

Two statues are made of the same type of marble. One is larger than the other. However, they both have the same density because they are made of the same material. Recall the formula for density.

$$\text{Density} = \frac{\text{mass}}{\text{Volume}}$$

Because the density is the same, you know that the mass of one statue divided by its volume is the same as the mass of the other statue divided by its volume. You can set this up and solve it as a proportion.

Example

A small marble statue has a mass of 2.5 kg and a volume of 1000 cm^3. A large marble statue with the same density has a mass of 10 kg. What is the volume of the large statue?

(1) Write the information as an equation showing the proportion.

$$\frac{\text{mass of small statue}}{\text{volume of small statue}} = \frac{\text{mass of large statue}}{\text{volume of large statue}}$$

(2) Insert the known values into your equation.

$$\frac{2.5 \text{ kg}}{1000 \text{ cm}^3} = \frac{10 \text{ kg}}{\text{volume of large statue}}$$

(3) Compare the numerators: 10 kg is 4 times greater than 2.5 kg.

(4) The denominators of the fractions are related in the same way. Therefore, the volume of the large statue is 4 times the volume of the small one.

volume of large statue = 4 • 1000 cm^3 = 4000 cm^3

ANSWER The volume of the large statue is 4000 cm^3.

Answer the following questions.

1. A lump of gold has a volume of 10 cm^3 and a mass of 193 g. Another lump of gold has a mass of 96.5 g. What is the volume of the second lump of gold?

2. A carpenter saws a wooden beam into two pieces. One piece has a mass of 600 g and a volume of 1000 cm^3. What is the mass of the second piece if its volume is 250 cm^3?

3. A 200 mL bottle is completely filled with cooking oil. The oil has a mass of 180 g. If 150 mL of the oil is poured into a pot, what is the mass of the poured oil?

CHALLENGE You have two spheres made of the same material. One has a diameter that is twice as large as the other. How do their masses compare?

If the marble statue and the marble bust both have the same density, their masses are proportional to their volumes.

MATH IN SCIENCE
Math Skills Practice for Science

Set Learning Goal
To solve proportions in the context of density

Present the Science
Density can be reliably used for identifying many solids because it remains the same for any-sized sample of the solid. The density of a mineral is a key characteristic in identifying it.

Develop Algebra Skills
- Remind students that a proportion is two ratios in fraction form with an equal sign between them.
- If three of the four parts of a proportion are known, multiplication and division can be used to find the unknown quantity.

Close
Ask: A 450-gram sample of nickel has a volume of 50 cm^3. A sample of iron has a mass of 300 grams. Can you use this information to set up a proportion to find the volume of iron? Explain. *No; the densities of the elements differ, so the ratios are not equal to each other.*

- Math Support, p. 122
- Math Practice, p. 123

Technology Resources
Students can visit **ClassZone.com** for practice in solving proportions.

MATH TUTORIAL

ANSWERS

1. 193 g • 0.5 = 96.5 g; 10 cm^3 • 0.5 = 5 cm^3

2. $\frac{1000 \text{ cm}^3}{4} = 250 \text{ cm}^3$; $\frac{600 \text{ g}}{4} = 150 \text{ g}$

3. 200 mL • 0.75 = 150 mL; 180 g • 0.75 = 135 g

CHALLENGE The formula for the volume of a sphere is 4/3 πr^3. If the diameter doubles, the radius also doubles. Thus, the volume is 2^3, or 8, times greater. The density is the same for both, so if the volume is 8 times greater, the mass will also be 8 times greater.

2.2 FOCUS

▶ Set Learning Goals

Students will
- Describe how liquids can become solids, and solids can become liquids.
- Explain how liquids can become gases, and gases can become liquids.
- Determine how energy is related to changes in state.

◀ 3-Minute Warm-Up

Display Transparency 12 or copy this exercise on the board:

Decide if the statements are true. If not, correct them.

1. Density is a chemical property. *physical property*
2. Cutting a carrot in half is a physical change. *true*
3. Silver tarnishing is an example of a physical change. *chemical change*

 3-Minute Warm-Up, p. T12

2.2 MOTIVATE

THINK ABOUT

PURPOSE To understand how liquid water forms from water vapor

DISCUSS How does the formation of dew compare with the formation of water on the outside of a glass of ice water? *In both cases, liquid water forms from water vapor in the air.*

Ongoing Assessment

 Answer: The identity of the substance does not change.

KEY CONCEPT

Changes of state are physical changes.

◀ **BEFORE, you learned**
- Substances have physical and chemical properties
- Physical changes do not change a substance into a new substance
- Chemical changes result in new substances

▶ **NOW, you will learn**
- How liquids can become solids, and solids can become liquids
- How liquids can become gases, and gases can become liquids
- How energy is related to changes of state

VOCABULARY
melting p. 51
melting point p. 51
freezing p. 52
freezing point p. 52
evaporation p. 53
sublimation p. 53
boiling p. 54
boiling point p. 54
condensation p. 55

THINK ABOUT

Where does dew come from?

On a cool morning, droplets of dew cover the grass. Where does this water come from? You might think it had rained recently. However, dew forms even if it has not rained. Air is made of a mixture of different gases, including water vapor. Some of the water vapor condenses—or becomes a liquid—on the cool grass and forms drops of liquid water.

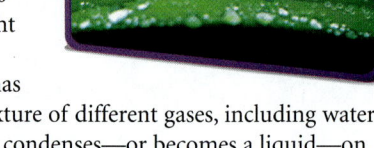

MAIN IDEA WEB
Remember to place each blue heading in a box. Add details around it to form a web.

Matter can change from one state to another.

Matter is commonly found in three states: solid, liquid, and gas. A solid has a fixed volume and a fixed shape. A liquid also has a fixed volume but takes the shape of its container. A gas has neither a fixed volume nor a fixed shape. Matter always exists in one of these states, but it can change from one state to another.

When matter changes from one state to another, the substance itself does not change. Water, ice, and water vapor are all the same basic substance. As water turns into ice or water vapor, the water molecules themselves do not change. What changes are the arrangement of the molecules and the amount of space between them. Changes in state are physical changes because changes in state do not change the basic substance.

 Why is a change in state a physical change rather than a chemical change?

50 Unit 1: **Matter and Energy**

RESOURCES FOR DIFFERENTIATED INSTRUCTION

Below Level
UNIT RESOURCE BOOK
- Reading Study Guide A, pp. 96–97
- Decoding Support, p. 119

 AUDIO CDS

Advanced
UNIT RESOURCE BOOK
Challenge and Extension, p. 102

English Learners
UNIT RESOURCE BOOK
Spanish Reading Study Guide, pp. 100–101

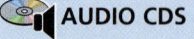 AUDIO CDS
- Audio Readings in Spanish
- Audio Readings (English)

Solids can become liquids, and liquids can become solids.

If you leave an ice cube on a kitchen counter, it changes to the liquid form of water. Water changes to the solid form of water, ice, when it is placed in a freezer. In a similar way, if a bar of iron is heated to a high enough temperature, it will become liquid iron. As the liquid iron cools, it becomes solid iron again.

Melting

Melting is the process by which a solid becomes a liquid. Different solids melt at different temperatures. The lowest temperature at which a substance begins to melt is called its **melting point.** Although the melting point of ice is 0°C (32°F), iron must be heated to a much higher temperature before it will melt.

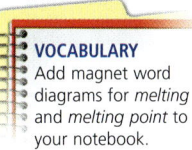

VOCABULARY
Add magnet word diagrams for *melting* and *melting point* to your notebook.

Remember that particles are always in motion, even in a solid. Because the particles in a solid are bound together, they do not move from place to place—but they do vibrate. As a solid heats up, its particles gain energy and vibrate faster. If the vibrations are fast enough, the particles break loose and slide past one another. In other words, the solid melts and becomes a liquid.

Some substances have a well-defined melting point. If you are melting ice, for example, you can predict that when the temperature reaches 0°C, the ice will start to melt. Substances with an orderly structure start melting when they reach a specific temperature.

Melting a Solid

Steel melts at very high temperatures. Liquid steel can be poured into molds to form the beams that are used in bridges like the one shown on the left.

 What would happen to the steel in this bridge if it became as hot as the steel in the bucket?

Chapter 2: **Properties of Matter** 51

DIFFERENTIATE INSTRUCTION

A What happens to ice at 0°C? *It melts.*

 B How do the particles in a liquid differ from those in a solid? *The particles in a liquid can move past each other.*

English Learners English learners may think the sentence "What changes are the arrangement of the molecules and the amount of space between them," (p. 50) is a question because the phrase *what changes* begins the sentence.

Advanced Have students use a high school chemistry book to investigate phase diagrams. Have them write a paragraph that explains the meaning of each area of a phase diagram.

R Challenge and Extension, p. 102

2.2 INSTRUCT

Real World Example
Fuses and circuit breakers control the amount of electric current in a wire so that it does not overheat. A fuse contains a small piece of metal with a low melting point. When the metal in the fuse becomes hot enough to melt, the circuit breaks, and current no longer flows through the wire. Circuit breakers contain a piece of metal that bends when it becomes hot. The bending opens the circuit.

EXPLORE the BIG idea
Revisit "Hot Chocolate" on p. 39. Have students explain the source of the energy that caused the change of state.

Teach from Visuals
To help students interpret the photographs of solid and liquid steel, ask: What generalization can you make about the melting points of structural materials? *They must be high enough that they will not melt under normal conditions.*

Ongoing Assessment
Describe how liquids can become solids, and solids can become liquids.

Ask: What process does iron ore undergo when it is liquefied to remove the impurities? *melting*

Answer: It would melt, and the bridge would collapse.

Chapter 2 **51**

Teach Difficult Concepts

Students might think that melting and dissolving are the same process because in both processes a solid ends up as a liquid. Point out that melting involves changing state and dissolving doesn't. To help students understand the difference, you might try the following demonstration.

Teacher Demo

Take two sugar cubes. Wrap one tightly in plastic wrap. Drop both into a cup of warm water and stir. Discuss the results. If students suggest that the unwrapped cube melted, ask: Were both cubes at the same temperature? *yes* If the wrapped sugar stays in the warm water, will it become a liquid? *no* Explain that the melting point of sugar is about 185°C (365°F). The unwrapped sugar did not melt but broke up into pieces too small to see and then mixed with the water.

Ongoing Assessment

 *Answer: Particles move fast enough to slide past one another.*

 *Answer: They are the same temperature.*

Other substances, such as plastic and chocolate, do not have a well-defined melting point. Chocolate becomes soft when the temperature is high enough, but it still maintains its shape. Eventually, the chocolate becomes a liquid, but there is no specific temperature at which you can say the change happened. Instead, the melting happens gradually over a range of temperatures.

 Describe the movement of molecules in a substance that is at its melting point.

Icicles grow as water drips down them, freezes, and sticks to the ice that is already there. On a warm day, the frozen icicles melt again.

Freezing

READING TIP
On the Celsius temperature scale, under normal conditions, water freezes at 0°C and boils at 100°C. On the Fahrenheit scale, water freezes at 32°F and boils at 212°F.

Freezing is the process by which a liquid becomes a solid. Although you may think of cold temperatures when you hear the word *freezing*, many substances are solid, or frozen, at room temperature and above. Think about a soda can and a candle. The can and the candle are frozen at temperatures you would find in a classroom.

As the temperature of a liquid is lowered, its particles lose energy. As a result, the particles move more slowly. Eventually, the particles move slowly enough that the attractions among them cause the liquid to become a solid. The temperature at which a specific liquid becomes a solid is called the **freezing point** of the substance.

The freezing point of a substance is the same as that substance's melting point. At this particular temperature, the substance can exist as either a solid or a liquid. At temperatures below the freezing/melting point, the substance is a solid. At temperatures above the freezing/melting point, the substance is a liquid.

 What is the relationship between a substance's melting point and freezing point?

52 Unit 1: **Matter and Energy**

DIFFERENTIATE INSTRUCTION

More Reading Support

C How does a liquid become a solid? *It freezes.*

D What state is a substance in if its temperature is slightly above its freezing point? *liquid*

Alternative Assessment Have students put together a bulletin board about the three states of matter and the processes that change matter from one state to another. They can use drawings, pictures from magazines, concept maps, or other means of displaying information.

Liquids can become gases, and gases can become liquids.

Suppose you spill water on a picnic table on a warm day. You might notice that the water eventually disappears from the table. What has happened to the water molecules? The liquid water has become water vapor, a gas. The water vapor mixes with the surrounding air. At the same picnic, you might also notice that a cold can of soda has beads of water forming on it. The water vapor in the air has become the liquid water found on the soda can.

Evaporation

Evaporation is a process by which a liquid becomes a gas. It usually occurs at the surface of a liquid. Although all particles in a liquid move, they do not all move at the same speed. Some particles move faster than others. The fastest moving particles at the surface of the liquid can break away from the liquid and escape to become gas particles.

As the temperature increases, the energy in the liquid increases. More particles can escape from the surface of the liquid. As a result, the liquid evaporates more quickly. This is why spilled water will evaporate faster in hot weather than in cold weather.

READING TIP
The root of the word *evaporation* is *vapor*, a Latin word meaning "steam."

CHECK YOUR READING Describe the movement of particles in a liquid as it evaporates.

It is interesting to note that under certain conditions, solids can lose particles through a process similar to evaporation. When a solid changes directly to a gas, the process is called **sublimation**. You may have seen dry ice being used in a cooler to keep foods cold. Dry ice is frozen carbon dioxide that sublimates in normal atmospheric conditions.

Evaporation

During evaporation, fast-moving particles escape from the surface of a liquid and become gas particles.

Chapter 2: **Properties of Matter** 53

DIFFERENTIATE INSTRUCTION

More Reading Support

E Where does evaporation usually occur? *at the surface of a liquid*

F By what process does a solid change directly to a gas? *sublimation*

Inclusion Have students place a few drops of rubbing alcohol on their arm. Ask them to describe how it feels. Tell them that as the particles of alcohol escape from the liquid, the overall energy decreases, so their skin temperature also decreases.

Real World Example

Two problems in a car's fuel line involve changes in state. Fuel-line freeze-up occurs when water in the fuel tank freezes during cold weather. The resulting ice can block the fuel line, and gasoline cannot reach the engine. To avoid this problem, car owners add materials to the gas tank that absorb the water in gasoline. The second problem, vapor lock, occurs during warmer weather. At a hot spot in the gasoline line, gasoline can vaporize, forming a pocket of gas. The engine stalls because the fuel pump in the car is designed to pump a liquid, not a gas.

History of Science

In 1846, Norbert Rillieux patented a vacuum evaporator to crystallize sugar from sugar-cane juice. The first pan in the evaporator held heated cane juice. The vapors from this pan heated the juice in the next pan, and so forth, with the last pan being connected to a condenser that removed water from the system. The whole system worked in a partial vacuum. Decreasing the pressure from pan to pan lowered the boiling point, so less energy was needed for water molecules to escape. Rillieux's vacuum evaporator has been adapted for use in processing sugar beets, soap, and glue.

Ongoing Assessment

Explain how liquids can become gases, and gases can become liquids.

Name two processes by which a liquid becomes a gas. *evaporation, boiling*

Explore melting points and boiling points.

Boiling

Boiling is another process by which a liquid becomes a gas. Unlike evaporation, boiling produces bubbles. If you heat a pot of water on the stove, you will notice that after a while tiny bubbles begin to form. These bubbles contain dissolved air that is escaping from the liquid. As you continue to heat the water, large bubbles suddenly form and rise to the surface. These bubbles contain energetic water molecules that have escaped from the liquid water to form a gas. This process is boiling.

Boiling can occur only when the liquid reaches a certain temperature, called the **boiling point** of the liquid. Liquids evaporate over a wide range of temperatures. Boiling, however, occurs at a specific temperature for each liquid. Water, for example, has a boiling point of 100°C (212°F) at normal atmospheric pressure.

In the mountains, water boils at a temperature lower than 100°C. For example, in Leadville, Colorado, which has an elevation of 3094 m (10,152 ft) above sea level, water boils at 89°C (192°F). This happens because at high elevations the air pressure is much lower than at sea level. Because less pressure is pushing down on the surface of the water, bubbles can form inside the liquid at a lower temperature. Less energetic water molecules are needed to expand the bubbles under these conditions. The lower boiling point of water means that foods cooked in water, such as pasta, require a longer time to prepare.

Different substances boil at different temperatures. Helium, which is a gas at room temperature, boils at −270°C (−454°F). Aluminum, on the other hand, boils at 2519°C (4566°F). This fact explains why some substances usually are found as gases but others are not.

Bubbles of vapor form inside the boiling water.

54 Unit 1: **Matter and Energy**

DIFFERENTIATE INSTRUCTION

More Reading Support

G How does the boiling point of a liquid at a high elevation differ from the boiling point of that liquid at sea level? *It is lower.*

Below Level Have students plan a demonstration of the difference in particle motion in evaporation and boiling. They can use the figures on pp. 53 and 54 to help them. Allow them to use other students or appropriate objects to represent particles.

54 Unit 1: **Matter and Energy**

Tiny droplets of water form on a window as water vapor from the air condenses into liquid water.

Condensation

The process by which a gas changes its state to become a liquid is called **condensation.** You probably have seen an example of condensation when you enjoyed a cold drink on a warm day. The beads of water that formed on the glass or can were water vapor that condensed from the surrounding air.

The cold can or glass cooled the air surrounding it. When you cool a gas, it loses energy. As the particles move more slowly, the attractions among them cause droplets of liquid to form. Condensed water often forms when warm air containing water vapor comes into contact with a cold surface, such as a glass of ice or ground that has cooled during the night.

As with evaporation, condensation can occur over a wide range of temperatures. Like the particles in liquids, the individual particles in a gas are moving at many different speeds. Slowly moving particles near the cool surface condense as they lose energy. The faster moving particles also slow down but continue to move too fast to stick to the other particles in the liquid that is forming. However, if you cool a gas to a temperature below its boiling point, almost all of the gas will condense.

READING TIP
The root of the word *condensation* is *condense*, which comes from a Latin word meaning "to thicken."

2.2 Review

KEY CONCEPTS
1. Describe three ways in which matter can change from one state to another.
2. Compare and contrast the processes of evaporation and condensation.
3. How does adding energy to matter by heating it affect the energy of its particles?

CRITICAL THINKING
4. **Synthesize** Explain how water can exist as both a solid and a liquid at 0°C.
5. **Apply** Explain how a pat of butter at room temperature can be considered to be frozen.

CHALLENGE
6. **Infer** You know that water vapor condenses from air when the air temperature is lowered. Should it be possible to condense oxygen from air? What would have to happen?

Chapter 2: **Properties of Matter** 55

ANSWERS

1. any three: melting, freezing, evaporation, sublimation, boiling, condensation

2. During evaporation, particles in a liquid have enough energy to escape the liquid and become a gas. During condensation, gas particles cool enough to slow down and form attractions to other particles, becoming a liquid.

3. It increases the energy of the particles.

4. That temperature is both the freezing point and the melting point of water. Both processes are occurring, so both states can exist.

5. The butter is solid.

6. Yes; oxygen could condense from air if the temperature were lowered to oxygen's boiling point.

Ongoing Assessment
Determine how energy is related to changes in state.

Ask: If you remove energy from a liquid, will it become a solid or a gas? *a solid*

Reinforce the BIG idea
Have students relate the section to the Big Idea.

  Reinforcing Key Concepts, p. 103

2.2 ASSESS & RETEACH

Assess
  Section 2.2 Quiz, p. 24

Reteach
Have pairs of students label index cards *condensation, melting, freezing, evaporation, sublimation, solid, liquid,* and *gas.* If you wish to include the gas to solid process, include an index card labeled *deposition*. Otherwise, tell students to ignore the gas to solid transition. Have one student lay down side-by-side two of the cards that list states of matter. Have the other student lay down any cards that name the processes that change matter from the state on the left to the state on the right.

Technology Resources
Have students visit **ClassZone.com** for reteaching of Key Concepts.

  CONTENT REVIEW
  CONTENT REVIEW CD-ROM

CHAPTER INVESTIGATION

Focus

PURPOSE To observe the change in state from a liquid to a solid and to measure the freezing point of a substance

OVERVIEW Students will use a thermometer to measure the temperature at which liquid stearic acid solidifies. Students will find the following:

- Pure stearic acid starts to harden at about 69°C. Some brands may be mixtures with a melting point of 55°C.
- The temperature remains the same until the stearic acid becomes completely solid.

Lab Preparation

- Prepare the wire-loop stirrers. The loop must fit around the thermometer and into the test tube.
- Obtain stearic acid, or stearin, which is available in most craft stores.
- Melt the stearic acid before class. Keep it liquid by immersing the container in hot water.
- Have students read pp. 56–57 and make data tables in advance or copy and distribute datasheets and rubrics.

   UNIT RESOURCE BOOK, pp. 124–132

   SCIENCE TOOLKIT, F15

Lab Management

- Have students stir with an up-and-down motion so as not to disturb the thermometer.
- To clean the test tubes, place them upright in hot water to melt the acid. Carefully remove the thermometers and stirrers and wipe them clean. Pour the acid into a metal can and wipe the test tubes clean. Cool the can completely before discarding it.

SAFETY Students should wear safety goggles throughout the activity and use care in handling the warm stearic acid.

Teaching with Technology

If probeware is available, use temperature probes instead of thermometers.

CHAPTER INVESTIGATION

Freezing Point

OVERVIEW AND PURPOSE Stearic acid is a substance used in making candles. In this experiment you will
- observe melted stearic acid as it changes from a liquid to a solid
- record the freezing point of stearic acid

Problem

What is the freezing point of stearic acid?

MATERIALS
- large test tube
- stearic acid
- test-tube tongs
- test-tube rack
- wire-loop stirrer
- thermometer

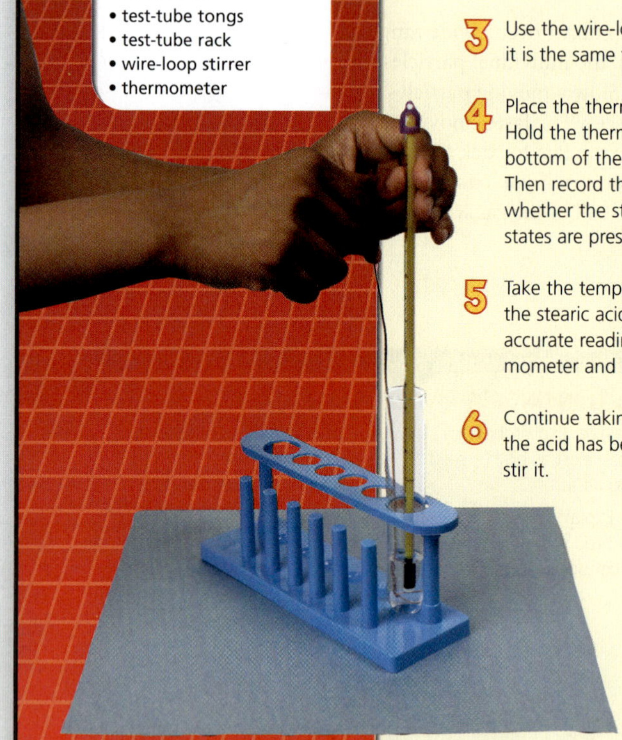

Procedure

1. Make a data table like the one shown on the sample notebook page.

2. Use the test-tube tongs to take the test tube of melted stearic acid and place it in the test-tube rack. Keep the test tube in the rack for the entire experiment.

3. Use the wire-loop stirrer and stir the liquid to make sure that it is the same temperature throughout.

4. Place the thermometer into the stearic acid to take a reading. Hold the thermometer so that it does not touch the sides or bottom of the test tube. Wait until the temperature stops rising. Then record the temperature on your data table. Also note whether the stearic acid is a liquid or a solid—or whether both states are present.

5. Take the temperature of the stearic acid every minute, stirring the stearic acid with the stirrer before each reading. To get an accurate reading, place the loop of the stirrer around the thermometer and use an up-and-down motion.

6. Continue taking temperature readings until two minutes after the acid has become totally solid or you are no longer able to stir it.

INVESTIGATION RESOURCES

CHAPTER INVESTIGATION, Freezing Point
- Level A, pp. 124–127
- Level B, pp. 128–131
- Level C, p. 132

Advanced students should complete Levels B & C.

Writing a Lab Report, D12–13

Technology Resources

Customize this student lab as needed or look for an alternative. Print rubrics to assess student lab reports.

Lab Generator CD-ROM

7. Make a note of the temperature on your data table when the first signs of a solid formation appear.

8. Make a note of the temperature on your data table when the stearic acid is completely solid.

9. Leave the thermometer and stirrer in the test tube and carry it carefully in the test-tube rack to your teacher.

Observe and Analyze *Write It Up*

1. **RECORD OBSERVATIONS** Make a line graph showing the freezing curve of stearic acid. Label the vertical axis **Temperature** and the horizontal axis **Time**.

2. **RECORD OBSERVATIONS** Label your graph to show when the stearic acid was a liquid, when it was a solid, and when it was present in both states.

3. **ANALYZE** Explain how your graph tells you the freezing point of stearic acid.

Conclude *Write It Up*

1. **INTERPRET** Answer the question in the problem.

2. **IDENTIFY** How does the freezing point of stearic acid compare with the freezing point of water?

3. **INFER** What happened to the energy of the molecules as the stearic acid changed from a liquid to a solid?

4. **INFER** From your observations, infer the melting point of stearic acid. How is the melting point of stearic acid related to its freezing point?

5. **APPLY** Why do you think stearic acid is used as an ingredient in bar soaps but not in liquid soaps?

INVESTIGATE Further

CHALLENGE What do you think would happen if you mixed in another substance with the stearic acid? How would that affect the freezing point? What experiment would you perform to find the answer?

Freezing Point

Problem What is the freezing point of stearic acid?

Observe and Analyze

Table 1. Freezing Point of Stearic Acid

Time (min)	Temperature (°C)	Liquid	Solid	Both
0.0				
1.0				
2.0				
3.0				
4.0				
5.0				
6.0				
7.0				

Chapter 2: **Properties of Matter** 57

Observe and Analyze *Write It Up*

1. See students' graphs. Sample data: 0 min, 73°C; 1 min, 66°C; 2 min, 60°C; 3 min, 57°C; 4 min, 55°C; 5 min, 55°C; 6 min, 55°C; 7 min, 55°C; 8 min, 53°C; 9 min, 52°C

2. The slope to the left of the flat part of the line on the graph indicates when the acid was liquid. The slope to the right indicates when the acid was solid. The flat line indicates when the acid was both a solid and a liquid.

3. The flat part of the line indicates that both states exist, so the temperature indicated by the flat part of the line is the freezing point.

Conclude *Write It Up*

1. The freezing point of stearic acid is about 69°C (or 55°C for some brands).

2. The freezing point of stearic acid is higher.

3. It decreased.

4. Answer should match students' freezing point in question 1. Melting and freezing point are the same.

5. It keeps bar soaps from liquefying in hot water. Liquid soap is supposed to be liquid, even at room temperature.

INVESTIGATE Further

CHALLENGE Adding impurities tends to lower the freezing point of a mixture.

Post-Lab Discussion

Commercial stearic acid, such as the acid used in this lab, is usually a mixture of stearic acid and palmitic acid. The freezing point of palmitic acid is about 63°C. Ask: How do you think using a mixture might affect your results? *Freezing point will change. Freezing point may not be a well-defined temperature.*

Chapter 2 **57**

2.3 FOCUS

◆ Set Learning Goals
Students will
- Describe how properties can help you identify substances.
- Explain how properties of substances can be used to separate substances.
- Design an experiment to separate a mixture.

◆ 3-Minute Warm-Up
Display Transparency 13 or copy this exercise on the board:

Create an events-chain concept map that shows the formation of a liquid from a solid, then a gas from a liquid. Use arrows to show energy being added or released. *Map should show a material going from a solid to a liquid to a gas. Arrows between states should show that energy is added or released.*

 3-Minute Warm-Up, p. 13

2.3 MOTIVATE

EXPLORE Identifying Substances

PURPOSE To use properties to identify a substance

TIP 10 min. Remind students that both chemical and physical properties can be used for identification.

WHAT DO YOU THINK? *When water was added to substance A, the substance dissolved but did not change identity. When water was added to substance B, a new substance formed during the chemical change that occurred. Substance B is baking powder.*

Ongoing Assessment

Answer: Compare the properties of the unknown substance with the properties of known substances.

58 Unit 1: **Matter and Energy**

KEY CONCEPT

 Properties are used to identify substances.

◀ BEFORE, you learned
- Matter can change from one state to another
- Changes in state require energy changes

▶ NOW, you will learn
- How properties can help you identify substances
- How properties of substances can be used to separate substances

---

EXPLORE Identifying Substances

How can properties help you identify a substance?

PROCEDURE

① Place some of substance A into one cup and some of substance B into the other cup. Label the cups.

② Carefully add some water to each cup. Observe and record what happens.

MATERIALS
- substance A
- substance B
- 2 cups
- water

WHAT DO YOU THINK?
- Which result was a physical change? a chemical change? Explain.
- The substances are baking soda and baking powder. Baking powder and water produce carbon dioxide gas. Which substance is baking powder?

MAIN IDEA WEB
As you read, place each blue heading in a box. Add details around it to form a web.

Substances have characteristic properties.

You often use the properties of a substance to identify it. For example, when you reach into your pocket, you can tell the difference between a ticket stub and a folded piece of tissue because one is stiff and smooth and the other is soft. You can identify nickels, dimes, and quarters without looking at them by feeling their shapes and comparing their sizes. To tell the difference between a nickel and a subway token, however, you might have to use another property, such as color. Texture, shape, and color are physical properties that you use all the time to identify and sort objects.

 CHECK YOUR READING How can physical properties be used to identify a substance?

58 Unit 1: Matter and Energy

RESOURCES FOR DIFFERENTIATED INSTRUCTION

Below Level
UNIT RESOURCE BOOK
- Reading Study Guide A, pp. 106–107
- Decoding Support, p. 119

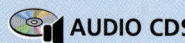 **AUDIO CDS**

Advanced
UNIT RESOURCE BOOK
Challenge and Extension, p. 112

English Learners
UNIT RESOURCE BOOK
Spanish Reading Study Guide, pp. 110–111

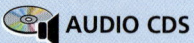 **AUDIO CDS**

- Audio Readings in Spanish
- Audio Readings (English)

Identifying Unknown Substances

Suppose you have a glass of an unknown liquid that you want to identify. It looks like milk, but you cannot be sure. How could you determine what it is? Of course, you would not taste an unknown substance, but there are many properties other than taste that you could use to identify the substance safely.

To proceed scientifically, you could measure several properties of the unknown liquid and compare them with the properties of known substances. You might observe and measure such properties as color, odor, texture, density, boiling point, and freezing point. A few of these properties might be enough to tell you that your white liquid is glue rather than milk.

To determine the difference among several colorless liquids, scientists would use additional tests. Their tests, however, would rely on the same idea of measuring and comparing the properties of an unknown with something that is already known.

Properties Used for Identifying Substances

You are already familiar with the most common physical properties of matter. Some of these properties, such as mass and volume, depend upon the specific object in question. You cannot use mass to tell one substance from another because two very different objects can have the same mass—a kilogram of feathers has the same mass as a kilogram of peanut butter, for example.

Other properties, such as density, can be used to identify substances. They do not vary from one sample of the same substance to another. For example, you could see a difference between a kilogram of liquid soap and a kilogram of honey by measuring their densities.

The physical properties described below can be used to identify a substance.

Density The densities of wood, plastic, and steel are all different. Scientists already have determined the densities of many substances. As a result, you can conveniently compare the density of an unknown substance with the densities of known substances. Finding any matching densities will give you information about the possible identity of the unknown substance. However, it is possible for two different substances to have the same density. In that case, in order to identify the substance positively, you would need additional data.

Aerogel, an extremely lightweight material used in the space program, has such a low density that it can float on soap bubbles.

Why can't you identify a substance on the basis of density alone?

Chapter 2: **Properties of Matter** 59

Teach from Visuals

The fibers in the photograph contain spaces filled with air.

- Ask: Why do you think the fibers contain spaces filled with air? *Air is not a good conductor of heat, so the air helps insulate the clothing.*

- The fibers themselves act as insulators, as does the air. Ask: If the fibers insulate anyway, why are the spaces for the air desirable? *Air is less dense than the material that makes up the fiber, so using the spaces reduces the weight of the clothing.*

Develop Critical Thinking

ANALYZE Water that is suitable for drinking and other purposes is limited worldwide. One possible source of potable water is salt water. Ask:

- What properties of water and salt might be used to separate them? *Their boiling and melting points are quite different.*

- Could you use a filter to separate water and salt? Explain. *No; a solution is a homogeneous mixture, and all the particles are about the same size.*

- If you boiled or evaporated the water from salt water, how could you reclaim the fresh water that forms? *The water vapor could be collected, cooled, and condensed into liquid water.*

These fibers act as heat insulators to keep the inside of the sleeping bag warm.

READING TiP
The root of the word *solubility* is the Latin word *solvere*, which means "to loosen."

Iron filings are attracted by the magnet. The wood chips, however, are not.

Heating Properties Substances respond to heating in different ways. Some warm up very quickly, and others take a long while to increase in temperature. This property is important in selecting materials for different uses. Aluminum and iron are good materials for making pots and pans because they conduct heat well. Various materials used in household insulation are poor heat conductors. Therefore, these insulators are used to keep warm air inside a home on a cold day. You can measure the rate at which a substance conducts heat and compare that rate with the heat conduction rates of other substances.

Solubility Solubility is a measure of how much of a substance dissolves in a given volume of a liquid. Sugar and dirt, for instance, have very different solubilities in water. If you put a spoonful of sugar into a cup of water and stir, the sugar dissolves in the water very rapidly. If you put a spoonful of dirt into water and stir, most of the dirt settles to the bottom as soon as you stop stirring.

Electric Properties Some substances conduct electricity better than others. This means that they allow electric charge to move through them easily. Copper wire is used to carry electricity because it is a good conductor. Materials that do not conduct easily, such as rubber and plastics, are used to block the flow of charge. With the proper equipment, scientists can test the electric conductivity of an unknown substance.

Magnetic Properties Some substances are attracted to magnets, but others are not. You can use a magnet to pick up a paper clip but not a plastic button or a wooden match. The elements iron, cobalt, and nickel are magnetic—meaning they respond to magnets—but copper, aluminum, and zinc are not. Steel, which contains iron, is also magnetic.

DIFFERENTIATE INSTRUCTION

More Reading Support

B Does insulation heat up slowly or quickly?
slowly

C What do you call the ability of a substance to dissolve in a liquid?
solubility

English Learners Clarify for English learners that the phrase *used to* (p. 60) explains the function of materials, and does not mean formerly, as students familiar with the phrase *use to* might think. Also caution them against reading "up" as a literal direction in the phrasal verb *break up* on p. 62.

Mixtures can be separated by using the properties of the substances in them.

Suppose you have a bag of cans that you want to recycle. The recycling center accepts only aluminum cans. You know that some of your cans contain steel. You would probably find it difficult to tell aluminum cans from steel ones just by looking at them. How could you separate the cans? Aluminum and steel may look similar, but they have different magnetic properties. You could use a magnet to test each can. If the magnet sticks to the can, the can contains steel. Recycling centers often use magnets to separate aluminum cans from steel cans.

Some mixtures contain solids mixed with liquids. A filter can be used to separate the solid from the liquid. One example of this is a tea bag. The paper filter allows the liquid water to mix with the tea, because water molecules are small enough to pass through the filter. The large pieces of tea, however, cannot pass through the filter and remain inside the tea bag.

INVESTIGATE Separating Mixtures

How can a mixture of sand, salt, and pepper be separated?

DESIGN YOUR OWN EXPERIMENT

Scientists often have to isolate a single substance from a mixture. Use your knowledge of the properties of sand, salt, and pepper to design a method for separating each of these substances from the mixture.

PROCEDURE

1. Examine the mixture and the materials provided. Design a procedure for separating the different substances in your mixture. Carefully consider the order in which you will try each step.
2. Write up your procedure. Explain why you chose the steps you did for each substance.
3. Carry out your procedure.

WHAT DO YOU THINK?
- Was your procedure successful? How would you modify your procedure if you were to perform the separation again?
- How does knowing the properties of matter help you separate the substances in mixtures?

SKILL FOCUS
Designing experiments

MATERIALS
- mixture of sand, salt, and pepper
- 2 index cards
- comb
- felt
- graduated cylinder
- spoon
- water
- coffee filter
- funnel
- small cup
- pie tin

TIME
30 minutes

INVESTIGATE Separating Mixtures

PURPOSE To design an experiment to separate different substances

TIPS 30 min.
- Iron filings can be part of the mixture, with a magnet available to use for separation.
- Use coarse salt so it is easily seen.
- Use plenty of pepper in the mixture.
- Students might need to be told that they can use static electricity and the comb to separate materials.

WHAT DO YOU THINK? *You can use your knowledge to create situations where one property will separate one substance from the others.*

Datasheet, Separating Mixtures, p. 113

Technology Resources

Customize this student lab as needed or look for an alternative. Print rubrics to assess student lab reports.

Lab Generator CD-ROM

Ongoing Assessment

Explain how properties of substances can be used to separate substances.

Ask: How could small pebbles be separated from larger gravel? *You could use a sieve with holes large enough for the pebbles to pass through.*

DIFFERENTIATE INSTRUCTION

More Reading Support

D What metal will a magnet attract? *steel*

E What method can be used to separate a solid from a liquid? *using a filter*

Advanced Have students create a poster or bulletin board that shows how relative boiling points are used to separate different petroleum products by the process of fractional distillation. Diagrams and explanations of this process can be found in most chemistry books or on the Internet.

Challenge and Extension, p. 112

Ongoing Assessment

 CHECK YOUR READING Sample answer: making water safe to drink, separating aluminum cans from those containing steel

Reinforce

Have students relate the section to the Big Idea.

 Reinforcing Key Concepts, p. 114

2.3 ASSESS & RETEACH

Assess

 Section 2.3 Quiz, p. 25

Reteach

List on the board as the head of a column each of the properties described on pp. 59–60. Then have students brainstorm sets of two objects. Ask them to explain how the properties could be used to compare the objects. For example, if paper and copper are compared, copper is denser, a conductor of heat and electricity, insoluble in water, and nonmagnetic; paper is less dense, an insulator, insoluble in water, and nonmagnetic. Point out that not all properties can be used to identify each item. For example, both paper and copper are insoluble in water and nonmagnetic.

Technology Resources

Have students visit **ClassZone.com** for reteaching of Key Concepts.

- CONTENT REVIEW
- CONTENT REVIEW CD-ROM

This water-treatment plant separates harmful substances from the water.

Some mixtures are more difficult to separate than others. For example, if you stir sugar into water, the sugar dissolves and breaks up into individual molecules that are too tiny to filter out. In this case, you can take advantage of the fact that water is a liquid and will evaporate from an open dish. Sugar, however, does not evaporate. The mixture can be heated to speed the evaporation of the water, leaving the sugar behind.

There are many important reasons for separating substances. One reason is to make a substance safe to consume, such as drinking water. In order to produce drinking water, workers at a water-treatment plant must separate many of the substances that are mixed in with the water.

The process in water-treatment plants generally includes these steps:

- First, a chemical is added to the water that causes the larger particles to stick together. They settle to the bottom of the water, where they can be removed.
- Next, the water is run through a series of special molecular filters. Each filter removes smaller particles than the one before.
- Finally, another chemical, chlorine, is added to disinfect the water and make it safe to drink.

Water-treatment plants use the properties of the substances found in water to produce the clean water that flows from your tap.

 **CHECK YOUR READING** What are two situations in which separating substances is useful?

2.3 Review

KEY CONCEPTS

1. How can properties help you distinguish one substance from another?
2. What are two physical properties that can help you identify a substance?
3. How can understanding properties help you separate substances from a mixture?

CRITICAL THINKING

4. **Apply** Why might an archaeologist digging in ancient ruins sift dirt through a screen?
5. **Synthesize** Suppose you had a mixture of iron pellets, pebbles, and small wood spheres, all of which were about the same size. How would you separate this mixture?

CHALLENGE

6. **Synthesize** You have two solid substances that look the same. What measurements would you take and which tests would you perform to determine whether they actually are the same?

62 Unit 1: **Matter and Energy**

ANSWERS

1. You can notice the physical properties of the two substances that are different.

2. Sample answer: density and color

3. Properties that differ from substance to substance can be used to separate them.

4. Artifacts are likely to be bigger than soil particles, and the screen would catch the artifacts.

5. Pull out the iron with a magnet. Add water to float the wood, and skim it from the top. The pebbles would be left.

6. Sample answer: Compare their conductivity and density.

Connecting Sciences

PHYSICAL SCIENCE AND EARTH SCIENCE

Separating Minerals

A few minerals, such as rock salt, occur in large deposits that can be mined in a form that is ready to use. Most minerals, however, are combined with other materials, so they need to be separated from the mixtures of which they are a part. Scientists and miners use the differences in physical properties to analyze samples and to separate the materials removed from a mine.

Appearance
Gemstones are prized because of their obvious physical properties, such as color, shininess, and hardness. Particularly valuable minerals, such as diamonds and emeralds, are often located by digging underground and noting the differences between the gemstone and the surrounding dirt and rock.

Density
When gold deposits wash into a streambed, tiny particles of gold mix with the sand. It is hard to separate them by appearance because the pieces are so small. In the 1800s, as prospectors swirled this sand around in a pan, the lighter particles of sand washed away with the water. The denser gold particles collected in the bottom of the pan. Some modern gold mines use the same principle in machines that handle tons of material, washing away the lighter dirt and rock to leave bits of gold.

Magnetism
Machines called magnetic separators divide a mixture into magnetic and nonmagnetic materials. In order to separate iron from other materials, rocks are crushed and carried past a strong magnet. Particles that contain iron are drawn toward the magnet and fall into one bin, while the nonmagnetic materials fall into another bin.

Melting Point
Thousands of years ago, people discovered that when some minerals are placed in a very hot fire, metals—such as copper, tin, and zinc—can be separated from the rock around them. When the ores reach a certain temperature, the metal melts and can be collected as a liquid.

EXPLORE

1. **INFER** At a copper ore mine in Chile, one of the world's largest magnets is used to remove pieces of iron from the ore. What can you infer about the copper ore?
2. **CHALLENGE** Electrostatic precipitators are important tools for protecting the environment from pollution. Use the Internet to learn how they are used in power plants and other factories that burn fuels.

RESOURCE CENTER *CLASSZONE.COM* — Find out more about separating materials from mixtures.

Chapter 2: Properties of Matter 63

Workers can identify garnets in a mine because their physical properties are different from the physical properties of their surroundings.

EXPLORE

1. **INFER** Copper ore has no magnetic properties.
2. **CHALLENGE** Electrostatic precipitators use electricity to charge particles that are products of burning fuels. These charged particles are attracted to a charged plate, so they aren't released into the environment.

CONNECTING SCIENCES
Integration of Sciences

Set Learning Goal
To learn how the physical properties of minerals are used to sort them from other materials

Present the Science
Chemical properties are useful in separating a mineral from compounds. For example, iron ore can be concentrated by physical means, but iron almost always exists in compounds in nature. Chemical changes are necessary to produce metallic iron from its compounds. When you heat iron ore and charcoal, oxygen in the ore combines with carbon in the charcoal to form carbon dioxide. Carbon dioxide and carbon monoxide are released, leaving metallic iron behind.

Discussion Question
Tell students that a deposit of silver is mixed in with sulfur. Silver has a density of 10.5 g/cm^3 and a melting point of 962°C. Sulfur has a density of 2.07 g/cm^3 and a melting point of 115°C. Ask: How can these physical properties be used to separate silver and sulfur? *Heat the mixture until the sulfur melts. Because it is denser, the solid silver will fall to the bottom and can be removed.*

Close
Tell the class that the melting point of iron is 1538°C and of nickel is 1455°C. Ask: Why wouldn't melting point be a good physical property to use to separate nickel and iron? *The melting points are too close together.*

Technology Resources
Have students visit **ClassZone.com** to find more about separating materials from mixtures.

 RESOURCE CENTER

Chapter 2 63

CHAPTER 2 • REVIEW

BACK TO

Have students look at the photograph on pp. 38–39. Ask them to use the photograph to summarize what they have learned about cooking in relation to properties and changes. Have them include examples. *Sample answer: Cooking changes the identity of the substances being cooked, so cooking involves chemical changes. A cake baking, an egg frying, and bread toasting are examples. All have different physical and chemical properties after they have been cooked.*

◀ KEY CONCEPTS SUMMARY

SECTION 2.1
Ask: Which of the photos shows a substance that can be identified as a metal because it has luster? *the one on the right*

SECTION 2.2
Ask: What do the arrows in the diagrams indicate? *the direction of the process*

Ask: What two processes represent what happens to a Popsicle left outside on a warm day? *melting and evaporation*

SECTION 2.3
Ask: Which of the physical properties is being used in the photograph to separate substances? *magnetic properties*

Review Concepts

- Big Idea Flow Chart, p. T9
- Chapter Outline, pp. T15–T16

---

2 Chapter Review

the BIG idea
Matter has properties that can be changed by physical and chemical processes.

CONTENT REVIEW
CLASSZONE.COM

◀ KEY CONCEPTS SUMMARY

 Matter has observable properties.

- Physical properties can be observed without changing the substance.
- Physical changes can change some physical properties but do not change the substance.
- Chemical properties describe how substances form new substances.
- Chemical changes create new substances.

VOCABULARY
physical property p. 41
density p. 43
physical change p. 44
chemical property p. 46
chemical change p. 46

 Changes of states are physical changes.
Matter is commonly found in three states: solid, liquid, and gas.

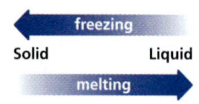 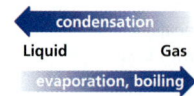

VOCABULARY
melting p. 51
melting point p. 51
freezing p. 52
freezing point p. 52
evaporation p. 53
sublimation p. 53
boiling p. 54
boiling point p. 54
condensation p. 55

 Properties are used to identify substances.
Physical properties that can be used to identify substances include:
- density
- heating properties
- solubility
- electric properties
- magnetic properties

Mixtures can be separated by using the properties of the substances they contain.

64 Unit 1: Matter and Energy

Technology Resources

Have students visit ClassZone.com or use the CD-ROM for a cumulative review of concepts.

 CONTENT REVIEW

 CONTENT REVIEW CD-ROM

Engage students in a whole-class interactive review of Key Concepts. Edit content as you wish.

 POWER PRESENTATIONS

Reviewing Vocabulary

Describe how the terms in the following sets of terms are related.

1. physical property, physical change
2. chemical property, chemical change
3. density, matter
4. melting, melting point, freezing point
5. boiling, boiling point, liquid
6. evaporation, condensation
7. sublimation, solid

Reviewing Key Concepts

Multiple Choice *Choose the letter of the best answer.*

8. Color, shape, size, and texture are
   a. physical properties
   b. chemical properties
   c. physical changes
   d. chemical changes

9. Density describes the relationship between a substance's
   a. matter and mass
   b. mass and volume
   c. volume and area
   d. temperature and mass

10. Dissolving sugar in water is an example of a
    a. physical change
    b. chemical change
    c. change in state
    d. pressure change

11. An electric current can be used to decompose, or break down, water into oxygen gas and hydrogen gas. This is an example of a
    a. physical change
    b. chemical change
    c. change in state
    d. pressure change

12. The formation of rust on iron is a chemical change because
    a. the color and shape have changed
    b. the mass and volume have changed
    c. the substance remains the same
    d. a new substance has been formed

13. The process by which a solid becomes a liquid is called
    a. boiling
    b. freezing
    c. melting
    d. evaporating

14. The process by which a liquid becomes a solid is called
    a. boiling
    b. freezing
    c. melting
    d. evaporating

15. Two processes by which a liquid can become a gas are
    a. evaporation and boiling
    b. melting and freezing
    c. sublimation and condensation
    d. evaporation and condensation

Short Answer *Answer each of the following questions in a sentence or two.*

16. When a sculptor shapes marble to make a statue, is this a physical or a chemical change? Explain your answer.
17. Describe and identify various physical changes that water can undergo.
18. Why does dew often form on grass on a cool morning, even if there has been no rain?
19. Describe the difference between evaporation and boiling in terms of the movement of the liquid's particles in each case.
20. What effect does altitude have on the boiling point of water?

Chapter 2: **Properties of Matter** 65

ASSESSMENT RESOURCES

UNIT ASSESSMENT BOOK
- Chapter Test A, pp. 26–29
- Chapter Test B, pp. 30–33
- Chapter Test C, pp. 34–37
- Alternative Assessment, pp. 38–39

SPANISH ASSESSMENT BOOK
Spanish Chapter Test, pp. 217–220

Technology Resources

Edit test items and answer choices.

 Test Generator CD-ROM

Visit **ClassZone.com** to extend test practice.

 Test Practice

Reviewing Vocabulary

1. A physical change is a change in any physical property of a substance.
2. A chemical property describes how a substance can form a new substance during a chemical change.
3. Density is a measure of the amount of matter in a given volume of a substance.
4. A substance melts at its melting point, which is the same temperature as its freezing point.
5. A liquid boils, or changes to a gas, at its boiling point.
6. Evaporation is a process by which a liquid changes to a gas, and condensation is the reverse process.
7. Sublimation is the process by which a solid changes directly to a gas.

Reviewing Key Concepts

8. a
9. b
10. a
11. b
12. d
13. c
14. b
15. a

16. The change is physical. The shape changes, but the material does not change identity.
17. Liquid water can freeze into ice or evaporate or boil into water vapor. Solid water can melt into liquid water or sublimate into water vapor. Water vapor can condense into liquid water.
18. Water vapor from the air cools and condenses.
19. During evaporation, only a few liquid particles have enough energy to escape the surface of a liquid and become a gas. During boiling, many particles with enough energy form bubbles of gas throughout the liquid.
20. It lowers the boiling point because atmospheric pressure is lower.

Chapter 2 **65**

Thinking Critically

21. From materials originally in the milk, a new substance (lactic acid) forms.
22. The shavings and the sharpened pencil still have the identity of the original materials.
23. Water is a liquid and thus has ability to flow; spaghetti, which is a solid, is too large to go through the holes.
24. It is spoiled.
25. Its size and volume change, and the substances dissolved and suspended in it become more concentrated. The water is still liquid, but the solution gets denser.
26. Yes. Water can evaporate over a range of temperatures. It will evaporate more slowly, however.
27. They would remain behind as solids.
28. If the object is only one substance, it is silver. However, if it is a mixture, it could be a combination of elements that have densities greater than and less than 10.5 g/cm^3.
29. With a density of 8.91 g/cm^3, nickel would fall between iron and copper.

the BIG idea

30. The sugar undergoes physical changes as it is melted and shaped. The sugar undergoes chemical changes when it is heated, changing in color and flavor.
31. Students should mention which properties of the matter they might research. Sources of information may include science books and the Internet.

UNIT PROJECTS

Collect schedules, materials lists, and questions. Be sure dates and materials are obtainable, and questions are focused.

   Unit Projects, pp. 5–10

Thinking Critically

21. **ANALYZE** Whole milk is a mixture. When bacteria in the milk digest part of the mixture, changes occur. Lactic acid is produced, and the milk tastes sour. Explain why this process is a chemical change.

22. **INFER** Sharpening a pencil leaves behind pencil shavings. Why is sharpening a pencil a physical change instead of a chemical change?

23. **ANALYZE** Dumping cooked spaghetti and water into a colander separates the two substances because the liquid water can run through the holes in the colander but the solid spaghetti cannot. Explain how this is an example of separating a mixture based on the physical properties of its components.

24. **INFER** The density of water is 1.0 g/mL. Anything with a density less than 1.0 g/mL will float in water. The density of a fresh egg is about 1.2 g/mL. The density of a spoiled egg is about 0.9 g/mL. If you place an egg in water and it floats, what does that tell you about the egg?

Use the photograph below to answer the next three questions.

25. **COMPARE** Which physical properties of the puddle change as the water evaporates? Which physical properties remain the same?

26. **ANALYZE** Can water evaporate from this puddle on a cold day? Explain your answer.

27. **PREDICT** What would happen to any minerals and salts in the water if the water completely evaporated?

Use the chart below to answer the next two questions.

Densities Measured at 20°C

Material	Density (g/cm^3)
gold	19.3
lead	11.3
silver	10.5
copper	9.0
iron	7.9

28. **PREDICT** Suppose you measure the mass and the volume of a shiny metal object and find that its density is 10.5 g/mL. Could you make a reasonable guess as to what material the object is made of? What factor or factors might affect your guess?

29. **CALCULATE** A solid nickel bar has a mass of 2.75 kg and a volume of 308.71 cm^3. Between which two materials would nickel fall on the chart?

the BIG idea

30. **PREDICT** Look again at the photograph on pages 38–39. The chef has melted sugar to make a sculpture. Describe how the sugar has changed in terms of its physical and chemical properties. Predict what will happen to the sculpture over time.

31. **RESEARCH** Think of a question you have about the properties of matter that is still unanswered. For example, there may be a specific type of matter about which you are curious. What information do you need in order to answer your question? How might you find the information?

UNIT PROJECTS

Check your schedule for your unit project. How are you doing? Be sure that you have placed data or notes from your research in your project folder.

MONITOR AND RETEACH

If students have trouble applying the concepts in items 28 and 29, have them determine the densities of several common objects in the classroom and compare them. They can create a similar table, using the densities of these materials. Students can benefit from holding equal volumes of these materials in their hands and comparing how "heavy" they are.

Students may benefit from summarizing one or more sections of the chapter.

   Summarizing the Chapter, pp. 142–143

Standardized Test Practice

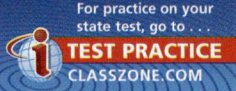

For practice on your state test, go to...
TEST PRACTICE
CLASSZONE.COM

Analyzing Experiments

Read the following description of an experiment together with the chart. Then answer the questions that follow.

Archimedes was a Greek mathematician and scientist who lived in the third century B.C. He figured out that any object placed in a liquid displaced a volume of that liquid equal to its own volume. He used this knowledge to solve a problem.

The king of Syracuse had been given a crown of gold. But he was not sure whether the crown was pure gold. Archimedes solved the king's problem by testing the crown's density.

He immersed the crown in water and measured the volume of water it displaced. Archimedes compared the amount of water displaced by the crown with the amount of water displaced by a bar of pure gold with the same mass. The comparison told him whether the crown was all gold or a mixture of gold and another element.

Element	Density (g/cm³)
copper	8.96
gold	19.30
iron	7.86
lead	11.34
silver	10.50
tin	7.31

1. Which problem was Archimedes trying to solve?
   a. what the density of gold was
   b. what the crown was made of
   c. what the mass of the crown was
   d. how much water the crown displaced

2. Archimedes used the method that he did because a crown has an irregular shape and the volume of such an object cannot be measured in any other way. Which one of the following objects would also require this method?
   a. a square wooden box
   b. a cylindrical tin can
   c. a small bronze statue
   d. a rectangular piece of glass

3. Suppose Archimedes found that the crown had a mass of 772 grams and displaced 40 milliliters of water. Using the formula $D = m/V$, what would you determine the crown to be made of?
   a. pure gold
   b. half gold and half another element
   c. some other element with gold plating
   d. cannot be determined from the data

4. Using the formula, compare how much water a gold crown would displace if it had a mass of 579 grams.
   a. 10 mL
   b. 20 mL
   c. 30 mL
   d. 193 mL

5. If you had crowns made of each element in the chart that were the same mass, which would displace more water than a gold crown of that mass?
   a. all
   b. lead only
   c. tin only
   d. none

Extended Response

Answer the two questions below in detail.

6. What is the difference between a physical change and a chemical change? Include examples of each type in your explanation.

7. Why does someone cooking spaghetti at a high elevation need to boil it longer than someone cooking spaghetti at a lower elevation?

Analyzing Experiments

1. b   3. a   5. a
2. c   4. c

Extended Response

6. RUBRIC
4 points for a response that correctly answers the question, gives at least two examples of each change, and uses the following terms accurately:
- physical change
- chemical change

Sample: Physical changes, such as a change in shape or state, do not change the identity of the material. Chemical changes, such as burning or tarnishing, change the identity of the original material.

3 points correctly answers the question, gives one example of each change, and uses both terms accurately
2 points correctly answers the question, but without examples, and uses both terms accurately
1 point correctly answers the question but without providing examples or using terms accurately

7. RUBRIC
4 points for a response that correctly answers the question and uses the following terms accurately:
- air pressure
- boiling point
- temperature

Sample: The air pressure is less at higher elevations. The energy of the particles doesn't have to be as high to escape, so the boiling point of the water will be at a lower temperature. A lower temperature means a longer cooking time.

3 points correctly answers the question and uses two terms accurately
2 points correctly answers the question and uses one term accurately
1 point correctly answers the question but fails to use any of the terms accurately

METACOGNITIVE ACTIVITY

Have students answer the following questions in their **Science Notebook**:

1. Describe a chemical change that is important in your life.
2. What questions do you still have about physical and chemical properties?
3. How have you solved a problem while working on your Unit Project?

CHAPTER 3 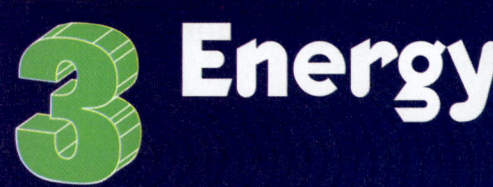 Energy

Physical Science
UNIFYING PRINCIPLES

PRINCIPLE 1
Matter is made of particles too small to see.

PRINCIPLE 2
Matter changes form and moves from place to place.

PRINCIPLE 3
Energy changes from one form to another, but it cannot be created or destroyed.

PRINCIPLE 4
Physical forces affect the movement of all matter on Earth and throughout the universe.

Unit 1: Matter and Energy
BIG IDEAS

CHAPTER 1
Introduction to Matter
Everything that has mass and takes up space is matter.

CHAPTER 2
Properties of Matter
Matter has properties that can be changed by physical and chemical processes.

CHAPTER 3
Energy
Energy has different forms, but it is always conserved.

CHAPTER 4
Temperature and Heat
Heat is a flow of energy due to temperature differences.

CHAPTER 3
KEY CONCEPTS

SECTION 1

Energy exists in different forms.
1. Different forms of energy have different uses.
2. Kinetic energy and potential energy are the two general types of energy.

SECTION 2

Energy can change forms but is never lost.
1. Energy changes forms.
2. Energy is always conserved.
3. Energy conversions may produce unwanted forms of energy.

SECTION 3

Technology improves the ways people use energy.
1. Technology improves energy conversions.
2. Technology improves the use of energy resources.

 The Big Idea Flow Chart is available on p. T17 in the **UNIT TRANSPARENCY BOOK**.

Previewing Content

SECTION

 Energy exists in different forms. pp. 71–77

1. **Different forms of energy have different uses.**
   Energy is the ability to cause a change. Different forms of energy cause different changes to occur.
   • Mechanical energy involves the position and motion of objects. Mechanical energy is a combination of potential energy and kinetic energy; it may be either or both.
   • Sound energy is energy associated with a transfer of vibrations through a solid, liquid, or gas.
   • Chemical energy is energy that is stored in the chemical composition of matter due to the atoms, bonds, and arrangement of atoms in substances.
   • Thermal energy is the total amount of energy within an object due to the motion of all of the object's particles.
   • Electromagnetic energy is energy in electromagnetic waves, including visible light, ultraviolet light, x rays, and microwaves. Electromagnetic energy can travel through a vacuum.
   • Nuclear energy holds atomic nuclei together.

2. **Kinetic energy and potential energy are the two general types of energy.**
   Kinetic energy (KE) is the energy of motion. The amount of kinetic energy that any object has depends on its mass and speed. An increase in speed causes a much larger increase in kinetic energy than does an increase in mass.
   Potential energy (PE) is energy that is stored in an object as a result of its position, shape, or chemical composition.
   • Gravitational potential energy is due to an object's position above Earth's surface. Gravitational potential energy is related to an object's mass and its height above the ground.
   • Elastic potential energy is due to position and shape in an object being compressed or flexed. Examples include a compressed spring or a stretched rubber band. Not every object that is compressed will contain elastic potential energy, for example, aluminum foil crumpled into a ball.
   • Chemical potential energy is due to a substance's chemical composition—the atoms and bonds contained within the substance. Different substances contain different amounts of chemical potential energy. Examples include energy stored in fossil fuels and in molecules of foods.

SECTION

 Energy can change forms but is never lost. pp. 78–85

1. **Energy changes forms.**
   Energy can be converted from one form to another. Often, energy must change forms in order for it to be useful. Many energy transformations occur between potential and kinetic energy. A ski jumper at the top of a slope has gravitational potential energy, which is converted into kinetic energy as the ski jumper moves down the slope. The ski jumper can regain potential energy through the kinetic energy of a chairlift that carries the jumper back up the hill. When gasoline is burned in a car's engine, the chemical potential energy of the fuel is converted into the car's motion, and energy released as heat from the car's engine is the kinetic energy of particle motion.

2. **Energy is always conserved.**
   The **law of conservation of energy** states that energy is neither created nor destroyed. When it appears that energy has been lost, it has simply changed form or been transferred to another object. In the soccer ball photograph below, the soccer ball's kinetic energy decreases, but the energy is converted into sound and heat. As a result, the total amount of energy never changes.

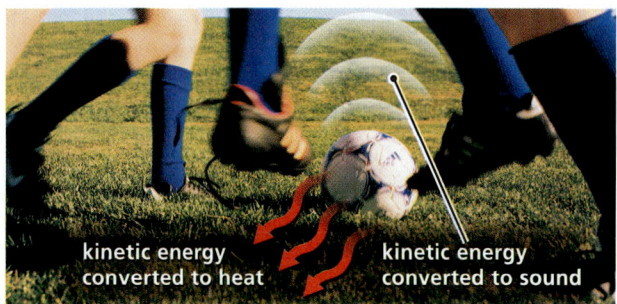
kinetic energy converted to heat   kinetic energy converted to sound

3. **Energy conversions may produce unwanted forms of energy.**
   When energy changes forms, the total amount of energy does not change, but some of the energy may convert to unusable or unwanted forms. **Energy efficiency** is a measure of usable energy after an energy conversion. The more energy-efficient the energy conversion, the more energy is changed into the desired form.

Common Misconceptions

ENERGY AND MATTER Students may think that everything that exists is matter, including heat, light, and electricity. Matter has mass and takes up space, whereas energy does not.

 This misconception is addressed on p. 72.

 MISCONCEPTION DATABASE
CLASSZONE.COM Background on student misconceptions

ENERGY AT REST Many students might think that objects at rest do not have any energy. Objects that are not moving do possess different forms of energy, such as gravitational potential energy and chemical potential energy.

 This misconception is addressed on p. 75.

Chapter 3: **Energy** 67B

Previewing Content

SECTION

 Technology improves the ways people use energy. pp. 86–91

1. **Technology improves energy conversions.**
   Because most energy conversions are very inefficient, an important goal of technology is to improve energy efficiency.
   • LEDs convert almost all the electricity they use into light.
   • Hybrid cars, which use both a gasoline engine and electrical energy from batteries, are more efficient than conventional gasoline-powered cars.

2. **Technology improves the use of energy resources.**
   Fossil fuels, the most commonly used energy source, are a non-renewable resource. A major goal of technology research is a more efficient usage of other energy sources.
   • Solar cells convert sunlight to electrical energy. Solar energy is available in unlimited amounts, is quiet and clean, and is nonpolluting. It is inefficient, however, and the materials used to make solar cells are expensive.
   • Windmills are used to convert the kinetic energy of wind into electrical energy. Like solar energy, wind energy is an inexhaustible source of energy that is nonpolluting, but there are limitations to the usefulness of wind power. It takes a large number of windmills to produce enough electrical energy to make a windfarm economically viable. Also, wind power is limited to regions of the country where wind is relatively constant.

Common Misconceptions

CONSERVATION OF ENERGY Students may think that "conservation of energy" means that energy should be conserved; this misconception arises due to different uses of the word *conservation*. In terms of the law of conservation of energy, conservation means that the total amount of energy in the universe does not change.

 This misconception is addressed on p. 82.

 MISCONCEPTION DATABASE
CLASSZONE.COM Background on student misconceptions

67C Unit 1: **Matter and Energy**

Previewing Labs

EXPLORE the BIG idea

A Penny for Your Energy, p. 69
Students explore the transfer of energy from a warm object to a cold object.

TIME 10 minutes
MATERIALS cold glass bottle, cooking oil, coin

Hot Dog! p. 69
Students use a solar-energy collector to cook a hot dog.

TIME 40 minutes
MATERIALS cardboard, aluminum foil, wooden skewer, hot dog, 2 corks

Internet Activity: Energy, p. 69
Students investigate the relationship between potential and kinetic energy.

TIME 20 minutes
MATERIALS computer with Internet access

EXPLORE Energy, p. 71
Students observe that all objects, even when stationary, have energy.

TIME 10 minutes
MATERIALS large plastic bowl, sand, pebble, rock

INVESTIGATE Potential Energy, p. 75
Students design an experiment to change the amount of potential energy an object has.

TIME 30 minutes
MATERIALS model car, meter stick, weights, balance, tape, cardboard, books

CHAPTER INVESTIGATION
Energy Conversions, pp. 84–85
Students investigate the amount of energy stored in different kinds of food by constructing a simple calorimeter and burning food samples.

TIME 40 minutes
MATERIALS can opener, empty aluminum can, dowel rod, tap water, graduated cylinder, ring stand with ring, thermometer, aluminum pie plate, aluminum foil, large paper clip, cork, modeling clay, croutons, caramel rice cakes, balance, wooden matches

EXPLORE Solar Cells, p. 86
Students investigate the size of a solar cell needed to provide electrical energy for a solar calculator.

TIME 10 minutes
MATERIALS solar calculator without backup battery, ruler, index card

INVESTIGATE Solar Energy, p. 89
Students observe how the color of a solar-energy collector affects the amount of energy collected.

TIME 20 minutes
MATERIALS 2 plastic cups, white and black plastic to cover cups, 2 rubber bands, scissors, 2 thermometers, stopwatch, aluminum foil

R Additional INVESTIGATION, Build a Roller Coaster, A, B, & C, pp. 192–200; Teacher Instructions, pp. 262–263

Previewing Chapter Resources

	INTEGRATED TECHNOLOGY	LABS AND ACTIVITIES
CHAPTER 3 **Energy**	**CLASSZONE.COM** • eEdition Plus • EasyPlanner Plus • Misconception Database • Content Review • Test Practice • Simulation • Visualization • Resource Centers • Internet Activity: Energy • Math Tutorial **SCILINKS.ORG** **CD-ROMS** • eEdition • EasyPlanner • Power Presentations • Content Review • Lab Generator • Test Generator **AUDIO CDS** • Audio Readings • Audio Readings in Spanish	EXPLORE the Big Idea, p. 69 • A Penny for Your Energy • Hot Dog! • Internet Activity: Energy **UNIT RESOURCE BOOK** Unit Projects, pp. 5–10 **Lab Generator CD-ROM** Generate customized labs.
SECTION 1 **Energy exists in different forms.** pp. 71–77 Time: 2 periods (1 block) Lesson Plan, pp. 144–145	**RESOURCE CENTERS,** Kinetic Energy and Potential Energy; Electric Cars **UNIT TRANSPARENCY BOOK** • Big Idea Flow Chart, p. T17 • Daily Vocabulary Scaffolding, p. T18 • Note-Taking Model, p. T19 • 3-Minute Warm-Up, p. T20	• EXPLORE Energy, p. 71 • INVESTIGATE Potential Energy, p. 75 • Think Science, p. 77 **UNIT RESOURCE BOOK** Datasheet, Potential Energy, p. 153
SECTION 2 **Energy can change forms but is never lost.** pp. 78–85 Time: 3 periods (1.5 blocks) Lesson Plan, pp. 155–156	**UNIT TRANSPARENCY BOOK** • Daily Vocabulary Scaffolding, p. T18 • 3-Minute Warm-Up, p. T20 • "Converting Energy" Visual, p. T22	CHAPTER INVESTIGATION, Energy Conversions, pp. 84–85 **UNIT RESOURCE BOOK** • Additional INVESTIGATION, Build a Roller Coaster, A, B, & C, pp. 192–200 • CHAPTER INVESTIGATION, Energy Conversions, A, B, & C, pp. 183–191
SECTION 3 **Technology improves the ways people use energy.** pp. 86–91 Time: 3 periods (1.5 blocks) Lesson Plan, pp. 165–166	• **VISUALIZATION,** Solar Cells • **RESOURCE CENTER,** Alternative Energy Sources • **MATH TUTORIAL** **UNIT TRANSPARENCY BOOK** • Big Idea Flow Chart, p. T17 • Daily Vocabulary Scaffolding, p. T18 • 3-Minute Warm-Up, p. T21 • Chapter Outline, pp. T23–T24	• EXPLORE Solar Cells, p. 86 • INVESTIGATE Solar Energy, p. 89 • Math in Science, p. 91 **UNIT RESOURCE BOOK** • Datasheet, Solar Energy, p. 174 • Math Support, p. 181 • Math Practice, p. 182

KEY TO ICONS	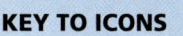 CD/CD-ROM	Teacher Edition	UNIT TRANSPARENCY BOOK	 SPANISH ASSESSMENT BOOK
INTERNET	Pupil Edition	UNIT RESOURCE BOOK	UNIT ASSESSMENT BOOK	SCIENCE TOOLKIT

READING AND REINFORCEMENT | ASSESSMENT | STANDARDS

- Frame Game, B26–27
- Mind Map, C40–41
- Daily Vocabulary Scaffolding, H1–8

UNIT RESOURCE BOOK
- Vocabulary Practice, pp. 178–179
- Decoding Support, p. 180
- Summarizing the Chapter, pp. 201–202

 Audio Readings CD
Listen to Pupil Edition.

 Audio Readings in Spanish CD
Listen to Pupil Edition in Spanish.

 UNIT RESOURCE BOOK
- Reading Study Guide, A & B, pp. 146–149
- Spanish Reading Study Guide, pp. 150–151
- Challenge and Extension, p. 152
- Reinforcing Key Concepts, p. 154

 **UNIT RESOURCE BOOK**
- Reading Study Guide, A & B, pp. 157–160
- Spanish Reading Study Guide, pp. 161–162
- Challenge and Extension, p. 163
- Reinforcing Key Concepts, p. 164

 UNIT RESOURCE BOOK
- Reading Study Guide, A & B, pp. 167–170
- Spanish Reading Study Guide, pp. 171–172
- Challenge and Extension, p. 173
- Reinforcing Key Concepts, p. 175
- Challenge Reading, pp. 176–177

- Chapter Review, pp. 93–94
- Standardized Test Practice, p. 95

 UNIT ASSESSMENT BOOK
- Diagnostic Test, pp. 40–41
- Chapter Test, A, B, & C, pp. 45–56
- Alternative Assessment, pp. 57–58

 Spanish Chapter Test, pp. 221–224

 Test Generator CD-ROM
Generate customized tests.

Lab Generator CD-ROM
Rubrics for Labs

 Ongoing Assessment, pp. 72–76

 Section 3.1 Review, p. 76

 UNIT ASSESSMENT BOOK
Section 3.1 Quiz, p. 42

Ongoing Assessment, pp. 78–83

Section 3.2 Review, p. 83

 UNIT ASSESSMENT BOOK
Section 3.2 Quiz, p. 43

 Ongoing Assessment, pp. 87–90

 Section 3.3 Review, p. 90

 UNIT ASSESSMENT BOOK
Section 3.3 Quiz, p. 44

National Standards
A.2–8, A.9.a–f, B.3.a, E.2–5, E.6.c–e, F.5.a–c

See p. 68 for the standards.

National Standards
A.2–7, A.9.a–b, A.9.e–f, B.3.a, E.2–5, E.6.d–e

National Standards
A.2–8, A.9.a–f, B.3.a, E.6.c–e, F.5.a–c

National Standards
A.2–8, A.9.a–f, B.3.a, E.6.c–e, F.5.a–c

Chapter 3: **Energy** 67F

Previewing Resources for Differentiated Instruction

CHAPTER INVESTIGATION

Leveled resources present the same concepts for different abilities.

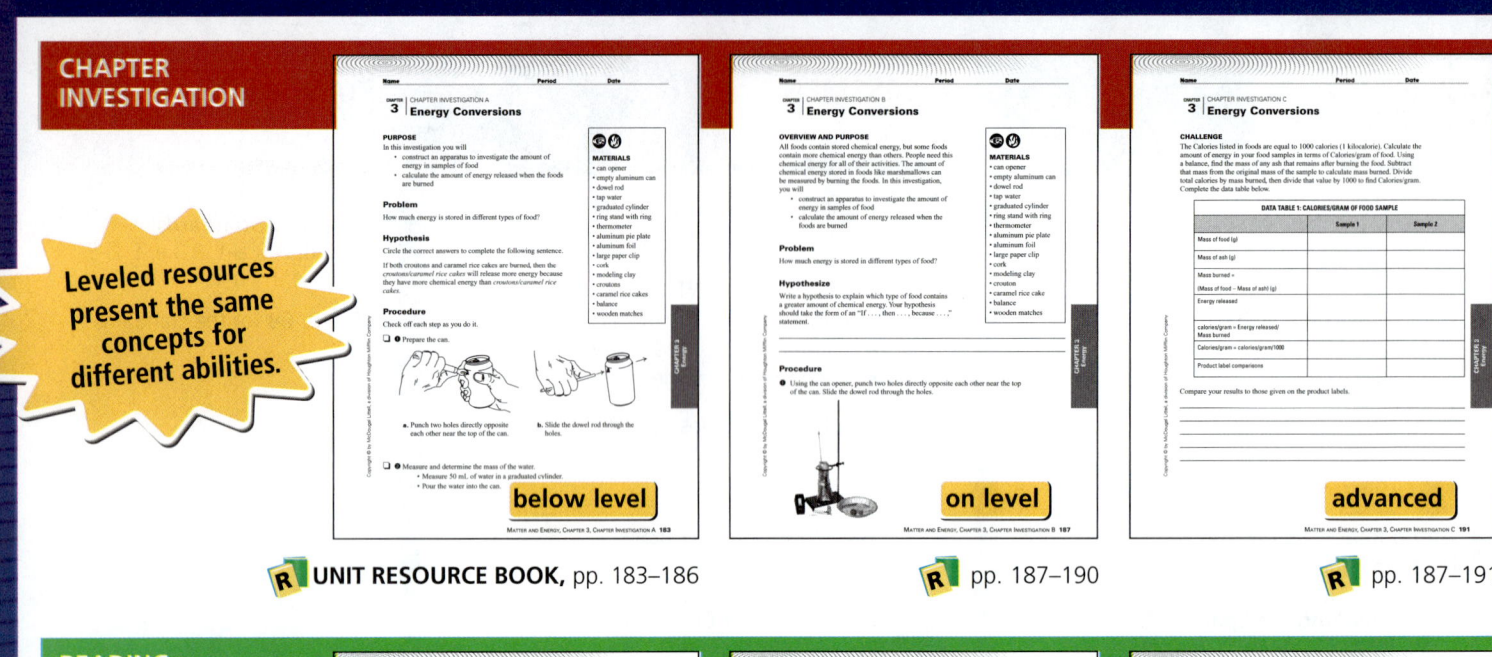

R UNIT RESOURCE BOOK, pp. 183–186   **R** pp. 187–190   **R** pp. 187–191

READING STUDY GUIDE

Reading Study Guide is also in Spanish.

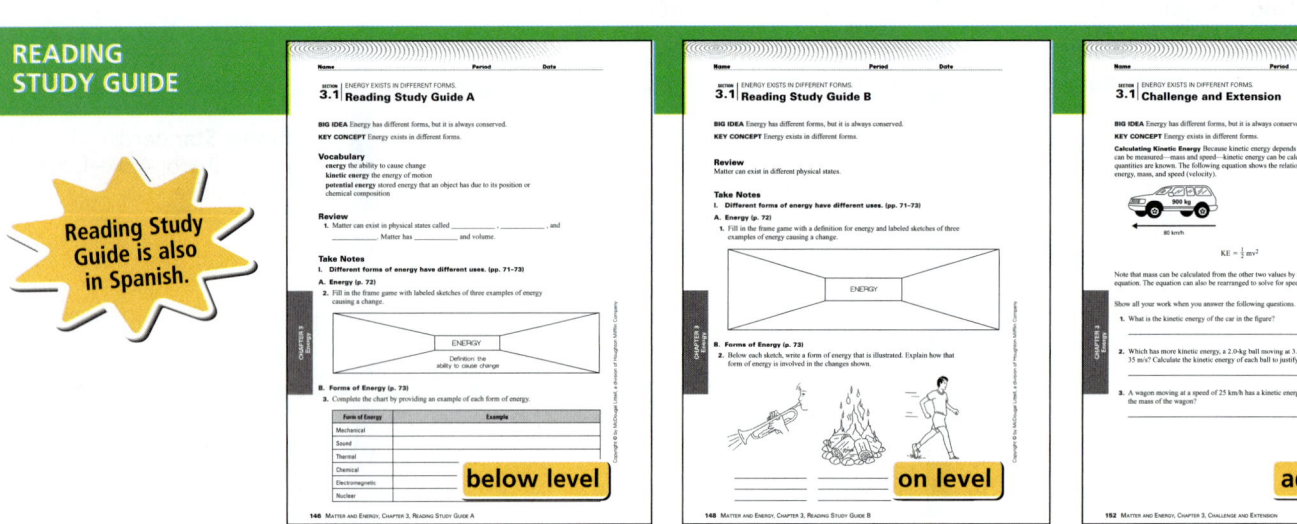
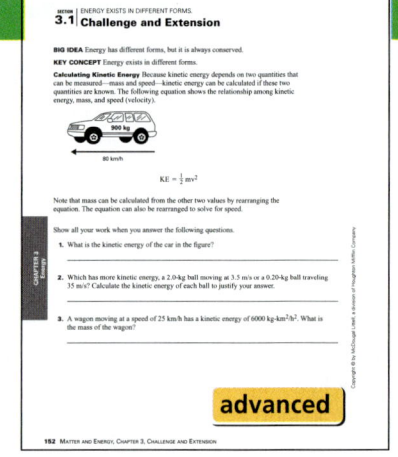

R UNIT RESOURCE BOOK, pp. 146–147   **R** pp. 148–149   **R** p. 152

CHAPTER TEST

Chapter Test is also in Spanish.

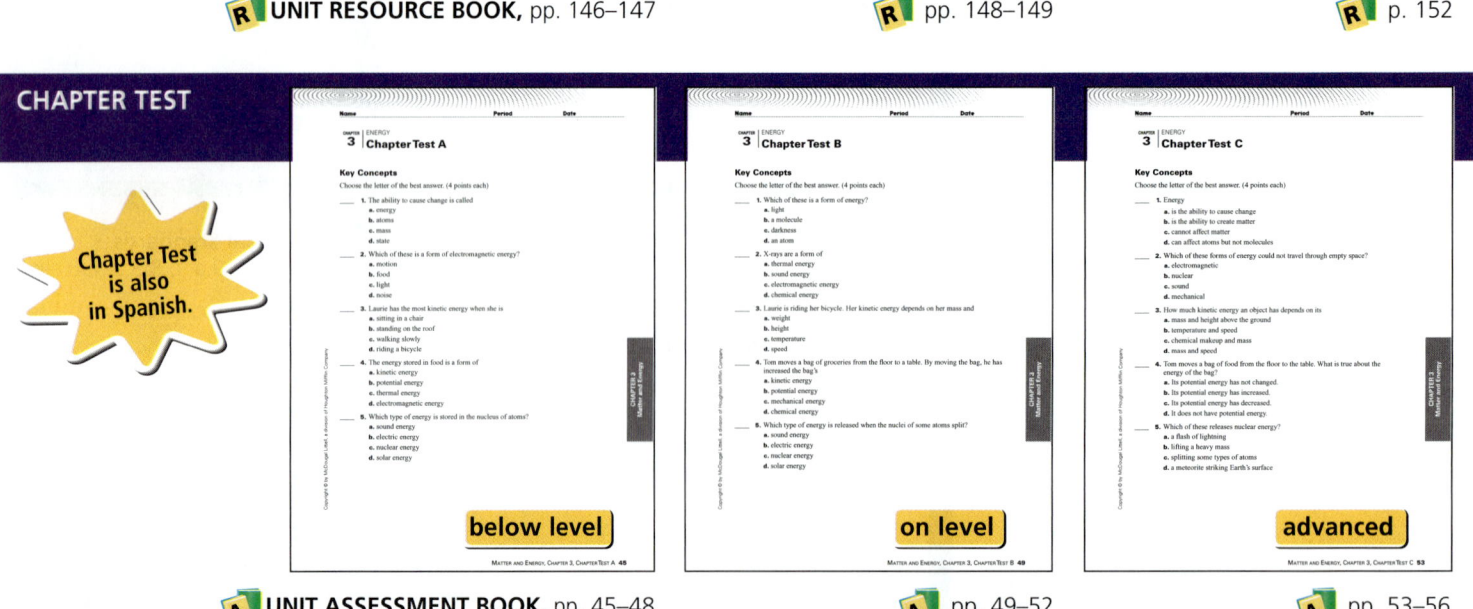

A UNIT ASSESSMENT BOOK, pp. 45–48   **A** pp. 49–52   **A** pp. 53–56

67G   Unit 1: **Matter and Energy**

TECHNOLOGY

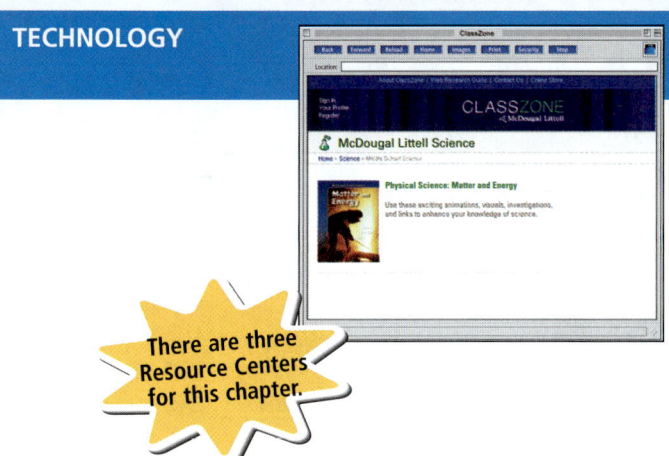
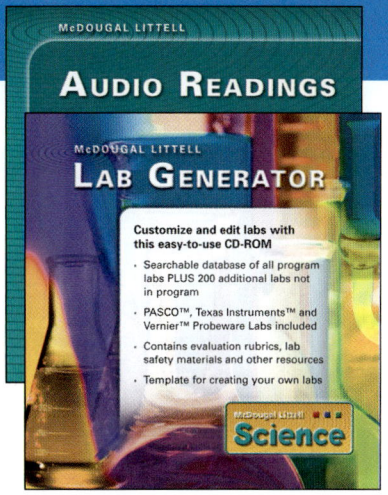
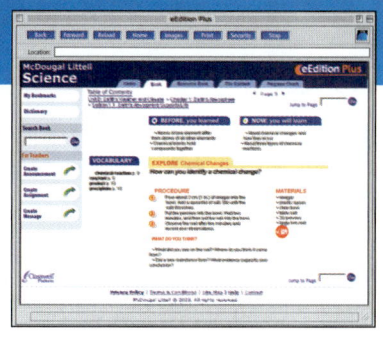

There are three Resource Centers for this chapter.

 CLASSZONE.COM    CD/CD-ROMS    CLASSZONE.COM

VISUAL CONTENT

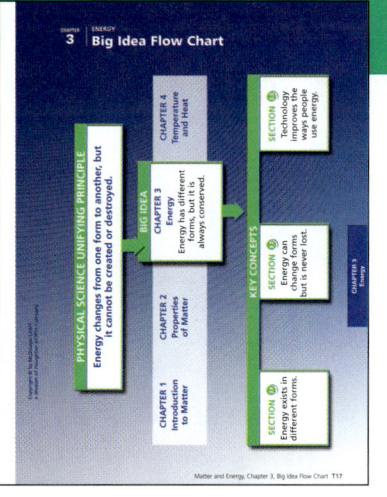
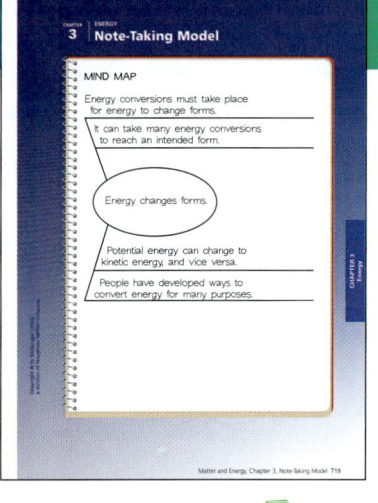
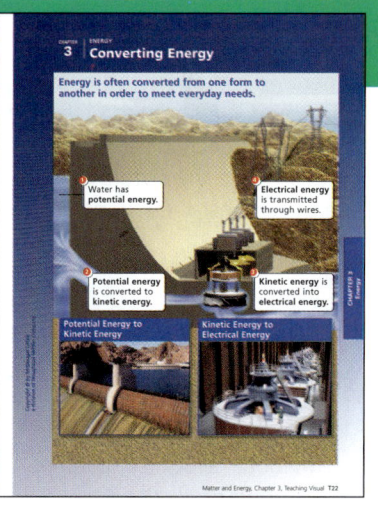

UNIT TRANSPARENCY BOOK, p. T17    p. T19   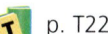 p. T22

MORE SUPPORT

Reinforcing Key Concepts for each section

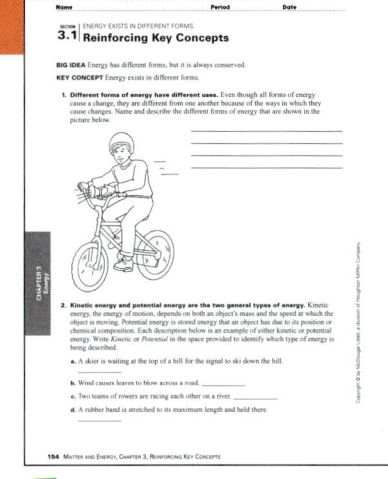
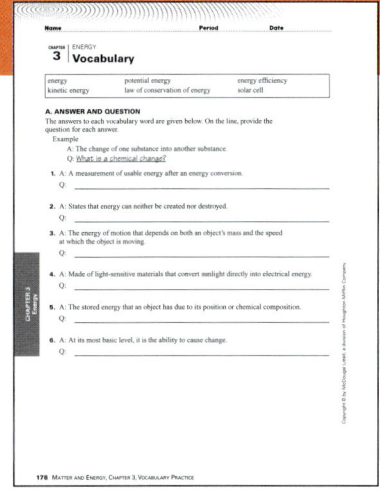
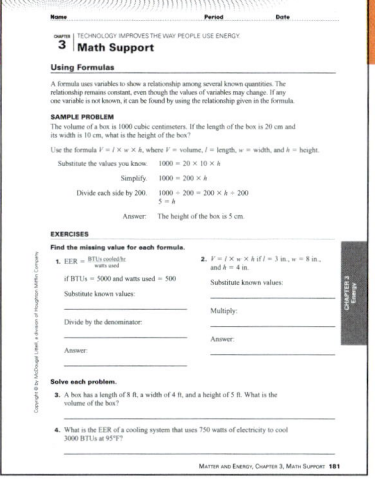

UNIT RESOURCE BOOK, p. 154   pp. 178–179   p. 181

Chapter 3: **Energy** 67H

CHAPTER 3 Energy

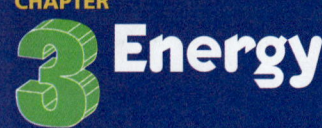

INTRODUCE

Have students look at the photograph of cyclists and discuss how the question in the box links to the Big Idea:

- Where in the photograph can energy be observed?
- Where in the photograph can energy be inferred?

National Science Education Standards

Content

B.3.a Energy is a property of many substances and is associated with heat, light, electricity, mechanical motion, sound, nuclei, and the nature of a chemical. Energy is transferred in many ways.

Process

A.2–8 Design and conduct an investigation; use tools to gather and interpret data; use evidence to describe, predict, explain, model; think critically to make relationships between evidence and explanation; recognize different explanations and predictions; communicate scientific procedures and explanations; use mathematics.

A.9.a–f Understand scientific inquiry by using different investigations, methods, mathematics, technology, explanations based on logic, evidence, and skeptisicm.

E.2–5 Design, implement, and evaluate a solution or product; communicate technological design.

E.6.c–e Science and technology are reciprocal; technological designs have constraints.

F.5.a–c Science and technology in society.

G.1.b Science requires different abilities.

CHAPTER 3 Energy

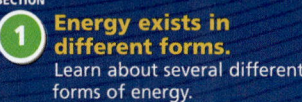

Energy has different forms, but it is always conserved.

What different forms of energy are shown in this photograph?

Key Concepts

SECTION 1 Energy exists in different forms.
Learn about several different forms of energy.

SECTION 2 Energy can change forms but is never lost.
Learn about the law of conservation of energy.

SECTION 3 Technology improves the ways people use energy.
Learn how technology can be used to make energy conversions more efficient.

 Internet Preview

CLASSZONE.COM
Chapter 3 online resources: Content Review, Simulation, Visualization, three Resource Centers, Math Tutorial, Test Practice

68 Unit 1: Matter and Energy

 INTERNET PREVIEW

CLASSZONE.COM For student use with the following pages:

Review and Practice
- Content Review, pp. 70, 92
- Math Tutorial: Rates, p. 91
- Test Practice, p. 95

Activities and Resources
- Internet Activity: p. 69
- Resource Centers: Kinetic and Potential Energy, p. 74; Electric Cars, p. 77; Alternative Energy Sources, p. 90. Visualization: Solar Cells, p. 88

Forms of Energy
Code: MDL063

EXPLORE the BIG idea

A Penny for Your Energy
Chill an empty glass bottle. Immediately complete the following steps: Rub a drop of cooking oil around the rim of the bottle. Place a coin on the rim so the oil forms a seal between the coin and the bottle. Wrap your hands around the bottle.

Observe and Think What happened to the coin? What do you think caused this to happen?

Hot Dog!
Cover a piece of cardboard with aluminum foil, and bend it into the shape of a U. Poke a wooden skewer through a hot dog, and through each side of the cardboard. Push corks over both ends of the skewer so the cardboard does not flatten out. Place your setup in direct sunlight for 30 minutes.

Observe and Think What happened to the hot dog? Were there any changes you had to make while the hot dog was in sunlight?

Internet Activity: Energy
Go to ClassZone.com to investigate the relationship between potential energy and kinetic energy.

Observe and Think How did you change potential energy? How do these changes affect kinetic energy?

NSTA SciLinks
scilinks.org
Forms of Energy Code: MDL063

Chapter 3: Energy 69

EXPLORE the BIG idea

These inquiry-based activities are appropriate for use at home or as a supplement to classroom instruction.

A Penny for Your Energy
PURPOSE To explore the transfer of energy from a warm object to a cold object. Students make a coin vibrate by causing air to warm and expand.

TIP *10 min.* Make sure the coin will completely cover the opening of the bottle but not extend too far over the rim.

Answer: The coin vibrated and jumped on the top of the bottle. The air sealed inside the bottle warmed and expanded as a result of energy transferred from the student's hands to the trapped air.

REVISIT after p. 80.

Hot Dog!
PURPOSE To observe and use a solar-energy collector. Students cook a hot dog with solar energy.

TIPS *40 min.* Students should not eat the hot dog. Students should try this at home with an adult. The experiment should be done in direct sunlight during the middle of the day.

Answer: The hot dog cooked. The solar collector needed adjustment to keep sunlight reflected on the hot dog.

REVISIT after p. 89.

Internet Activity: Energy
PURPOSE To investigate the relationship between potential and kinetic energy.

TIP *20 min.* Students should understand that potential energy is related to position.

Answer: As the mass and height of an object was increased, the potential energy increased. The object will thus have more kinetic energy.

REVISIT after p. 76.

TEACHING WITH TECHNOLOGY

Video Camera You may wish to film students as they design their experiments for "Investigate Potential Energy" on p. 75. As they watch the video, encourage them to write down ideas for how to improve the design of their experiments.

CBL and Probeware If CBL equipment and probeware are available, have students substitute a temperature probe for the thermometer in the Chapter Investigation on pp. 84–85 and "Investigate Solar Energy" on p. 89.

Chapter 3 **69**

PREPARE

CONCEPT REVIEW

Activate Prior Knowledge

- To demonstrate that matter has mass and volume, have students measure a small object such as a domino and calculate its volume. Have them find the mass of the object on a balance.

- Ask: Does all matter, even a gas that cannot be seen, have mass and volume? *Yes; the atoms or molecules that make up a gas have mass and take up space.*

TAKING NOTES

Mind Map

A mind map allows students to include as much information and detail about a concept as they choose. Encourage students to use the mind map to take notes in a way that will help them to remember relationships between concepts, definitions, and examples.

Vocabulary Strategy

A frame game diagram organizes characteristics of a vocabulary term into a coherent pattern. By filling in their own words, examples, and descriptions around the frame, students personalize their understanding of the term and can connect personal experience to the term's meaning.

Vocabulary and Note-Taking Resources

- Vocabulary Practice, pp. 178–179
- Decoding Support, p. 180

- Daily Vocabulary Scaffolding, p. T18
- Note-Taking Model, p. T19

- Frame Game, B26–27
- Mind Map, C40–41
- Daily Vocabulary Scaffolding, H1–8

CHAPTER 3
Getting Ready to Learn

CONCEPT REVIEW

- Matter has mass and is made of tiny particles.
- Matter can be changed physically or chemically.
- A change in the state of matter is a physical change.

VOCABULARY REVIEW

matter p. 9
mass p. 10
atom p. 16
physical change p. 44
chemical change p. 46

CONTENT REVIEW
CLASSZONE.COM
Review concepts and vocabulary.

TAKING NOTES

MIND MAP

Write each main idea, or blue heading, in an oval; then write details that relate to each other and to the main idea. Organize the details so that each spoke of the web has notes about one part of the main idea.

VOCABULARY STRATEGY

Write each new vocabulary term in the center of a **frame game** diagram. Decide what information to frame it with. Use examples, descriptions, parts, sentences that use the term in context, or pictures. You can change the frame to fit each term.

See the Note-Taking Handbook on pages R45–R51.

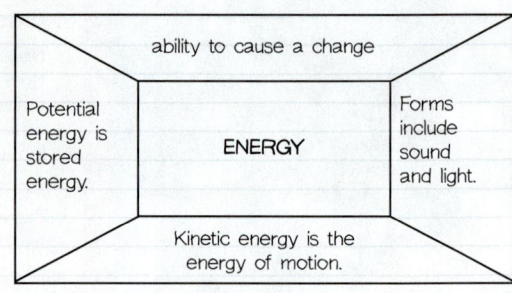

CHECK READINESS

Administer the Diagnostic Test to determine students' readiness for new science content and their mastery of requisite math skills.

 Diagnostic Test, pp. 40–41

Technology Resources

Students needing content and math skills should visit **ClassZone.com**.

- CONTENT REVIEW
- MATH TUTORIAL

 CONTENT REVIEW CD-ROM

3.1 Energy exists in different forms.

KEY CONCEPT

BEFORE, you learned
- All substances are made of matter
- Matter has both physical and chemical properties
- Matter can exist in different physical states

NOW, you will learn
- How energy causes change
- About common forms of energy
- About kinetic energy and potential energy

VOCABULARY
energy p. 72
kinetic energy p. 74
potential energy p. 75

EXPLORE Energy

How can you demonstrate energy?

PROCEDURE

1. Fill the bowl halfway with sand. Place the bowl on the floor as shown. Make sure the sand is level.
2. Place a pebble and a rock near the edge of a table above the bowl of sand.
3. Gently push the pebble off the table into the sand. Record your observations.
4. Remove the pebble, and make sure the sand is level. Gently push the rock off the table into the sand. Record your observations.

MATERIALS
- large plastic bowl
- sand
- pebble
- rock

WHAT DO YOU THINK?
- What happened to the sand when you dropped the pebble? when you dropped the rock?
- How can you explain any differences you observed?

Different forms of energy have different uses.

Energy takes many different forms and has many different effects. Just about everything you see happening around you involves energy. Lamps and other appliances in your home operate on electrical energy. Plants use energy from the Sun to grow. You use energy provided by the food you eat to carry out all of your everyday activities—eating, exercising, reading, and even sitting and thinking. In this chapter, you will learn what these and other forms of energy have in common.

Chapter 3: Energy 71

3.1 FOCUS

◉ Set Learning Goals
Students will
- Recognize how energy causes change.
- Describe common forms of energy.
- Illustrate that the two general types of energy are kinetic energy and potential energy.
- Design an experiment to investigate and change potential energy.

◉ 3-Minute Warm-Up
Display Transparency 20 or copy this exercise on the board:

Draw diagrams that show the motion of particles in a solid, such as ice, and the motion of particles in a liquid, such as water. What is the process that changes the solid into the liquid? *melting* What must be added to cause the solid to change into the liquid? *energy*

[T] 3-Minute Warm-Up, p. T20

3.1 MOTIVATE

EXPLORE Energy

PURPOSE To observe that all objects have energy, even when they are stationary

TIPS 10 min.
- Bowls with wide openings work best.
- Packing peanuts may be used instead of sand.

WHAT DO YOU THINK? *The pebble made a small dent in the sand; the rock made a much larger dent in the sand. The rock contains more (potential) energy due to the force of gravity.*

RESOURCES FOR DIFFERENTIATED INSTRUCTION

Below Level
UNIT RESOURCE BOOK
- Reading Study Guide A, pp. 146–147
- Decoding Support, p. 180

🔊 **AUDIO CDS**

Advanced
UNIT RESOURCE BOOK
Challenge and Extension, p. 152

English Learners
UNIT RESOURCE BOOK
Spanish Reading Study Guide, pp. 150–151

🔊 **AUDIO CDS**
- Audio Readings in Spanish
- Audio Readings (English)

Chapter 3 **71**

3.1 INSTRUCT

Address Misconceptions

IDENTIFY Ask: Is light a substance? If students say yes, they may hold the misconception that energy is a form of matter, that is, an object.

CORRECT Have students list the properties that matter must have. Discuss whether light and other forms of energy have mass and volume.

REASSESS Ask students to write a short paragraph differentiating between an object and a property of an object. Ask: Which is energy? *a property of an object*

Technology Resources
Visit **ClassZone.com** for background on common student misconceptions.

 MISCONCEPTION DATABASE

Teach Difficult Concepts

Students may think that energy is associated only with living things. In fact, all things, both living and nonliving, have energy.

Place a domino at the base of a ramp. Have students roll a marble down the ramp so that it knocks over the domino. Ask: What knocked the domino over? *the marble's energy* Ask students to design another way to demonstrate that inanimate objects have energy that can cause a change.

Teach from Visuals

To help students identify energy and its effects, ask: What other changes might be occurring in the picture? *people moving in cars; trees moving; sounds*

Ongoing Assessment

Recognize how energy causes change.
Ask: What is the most fundamental quality of energy? *Its ability to cause change.*

 Sample answer: Hitting a baseball changes its direction and speed.

Energy

All forms of energy have one important point in common—they cause changes to occur. The flow of electrical energy through a wire causes a cool, dark bulb to get hot and glow. The energy of the wind causes a flag to flutter.

You are a source of energy that makes changes in your environment. For example, when you pick up a tennis racquet or a paintbrush, you change the position of that object. When you hit a tennis ball or smooth paint on a canvas, you cause further changes. Energy is involved in every one of these actions. At its most basic level, **energy** is the ability to cause change.

 **VOCABULARY** Remember to use a frame game diagram for *energy* and other vocabulary terms.

CHECK YOUR READING Provide your own example of energy and how it causes a change.

The photograph below shows a city street. All of the activities that take place on every street in any city require energy, so there are many changes taking place in the picture. Consider one of the cars. A person's energy is used to turn the key that starts the car. The key's movement starts the car's engine and gasoline begins burning. Gasoline provides the energy for the car to move. The person's hand, the turning key, and the burning gasoline all contain energy that causes change.

The motion of the cars and the glow of the streetlights are changes produced by energy.

72 Unit 1: Matter and Energy

DIFFERENTIATE INSTRUCTION

More Reading Support

A What do all forms of energy have in common? *They cause changes.*

English Learners Help English learners understand complex sentences. Give students several difficult sentences and ask them to circle the subject and verb. Be sure students circle the entire subject—often it is more than one word. For example, in the sentence "Just about everything you see happening around you involves energy" (p. 71), students should circle "Just about everything you see happening around you" as the subject and "involves" as the verb.

Forms of Energy

Scientists classify energy into many forms, each of which causes change in a different way. Some of these forms are described below.

Mechanical Energy The energy that moves objects is mechanical energy. The energy that you use to put a book on a shelf is mechanical energy, as is energy that a person uses to turn a car key.

Sound Energy Sound results from the vibration of particles in a solid, liquid, or gas. People and other animals are able to detect these tiny vibrations with structures in their ears that vibrate due to the sound. So, when you hear a car drive past, you are detecting vibrations in the air produced by sound energy. Sound cannot travel through empty space. If there were no air or other substance between you and the car, you would not hear sounds from the car.

Chemical Energy Energy that is stored in the chemical composition of matter is chemical energy. The amount of chemical energy in a substance depends on the types and arrangement of atoms in the substance. When wood or gasoline burns, chemical energy produces heat. The energy used by the cells in your body comes from chemical energy stored in the foods you eat.

Thermal Energy The total amount of energy from the movement of particles in matter is thermal energy. Recall that matter is made of atoms, and atoms combined in molecules. The atoms and molecules in matter are always moving. The energy of this motion in an object is the object's thermal energy. You will learn more about thermal energy in the next chapter.

Electromagnetic Energy Electromagnetic (ih-LEHK-troh-mag-NEHT-ihk) energy is transmitted through space in the form of electromagnetic waves. Unlike sound, electromagnetic waves can travel through empty space. These waves include visible light, x-rays, and microwaves. X-rays are high energy waves used by doctors and dentists to look at your bones and teeth. Microwaves can be used to cook food or to transmit cellular telephone calls but contain far less energy than x-rays. The Sun releases a large amount of electromagnetic energy, some of which is absorbed by Earth.

Nuclear Energy The center of an atom—its nucleus—is the source of nuclear energy. A large amount of energy in the nucleus holds the nuclear particles together. When a heavy atom's nucleus breaks apart, or when the nuclei (NOO-klee-EYE) of two small atoms join together, energy is released. Nuclear energy released from the fusing of small nuclei to form larger nuclei keeps the Sun burning.

CHECK YOUR READING How does chemical energy cause a change? What about electromagnetic energy?

APPLY Where in this photograph can you find chemical, sound, and mechanical energy?

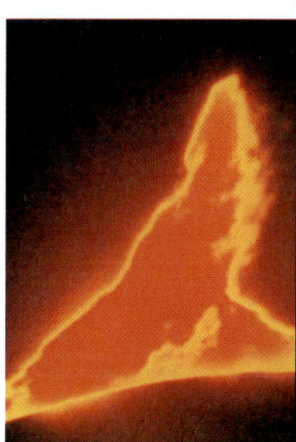

This solar flare releases electromagnetic energy and thermal energy produced by nuclear energy in the Sun.

Teacher Demo

To help students understand that decreasing an object's speed decreases its kinetic energy, do the following demonstration. Set up a ramp. Position a small object at the end of the ramp. Roll a small ball down the ramp so that it knocks over the object. Decrease the angle of the ramp to decrease the speed of the ball, then roll the ball down again. Continue to decrease the speed in this way until the ball has insufficient kinetic energy to knock over the object. To demonstrate the relationship between mass and kinetic energy, repeat the above procedure, keeping the ramp at the same angle but using balls with different mass. Find a ball with so little mass that the ball cannot knock over the object. Use a balance (or kitchen scale to measure objects in increments of 10 grams) to measure the mass of the balls to confirm that they have different masses.

Teach Difficult Concepts

Mechanical energy is a combination of potential energy and kinetic energy. Mechanical energy results from the position of objects (potential energy), the movement of objects (kinetic energy), or both.

Teach from Visuals

To help students interpret the photos of the speed skater, ask: Where did the skater's kinetic energy come from? *from chemical energy stored in the skater's muscles*

Ongoing Assessment

 Answer: If the skater with less mass is moving faster, he or she could have more kinetic energy.

Kinetic energy and potential energy are the two general types of energy.

RESOURCE CENTER
CLASSZONE.COM
Learn more about kinetic energy and potential energy.

All of the forms of energy can be described in terms of two general types of energy—kinetic energy and potential energy. Anything that is moving, such as a car that is being driven or an atom in the air, has kinetic energy. All matter also has potential energy, or energy that is stored and can be released at a later time.

Kinetic Energy

READING TIP
Kinetic means "related to motion."

D

The energy of motion is called **kinetic energy**. It depends on both an object's mass and the speed at which the object is moving.

All objects are made of matter, and matter has mass. The more matter an object contains, the greater its mass. If you held a bowling ball in one hand and a soccer ball in the other, you could feel that the bowling ball has more mass than the soccer ball.

- **Kinetic energy increases as mass increases.** If the bowling ball and the soccer ball were moving at the same speed, the bowling ball would have more kinetic energy because of its greater mass.

E

- **Kinetic energy increases as speed increases.** If two identical bowling balls were rolling along at different speeds, the faster one would have more kinetic energy because of its greater speed. The speed skater in the photographs below has more kinetic energy when he is racing than he does when he is moving slowly.

High Speed
This skater has a large amount of kinetic energy when moving at a high speed.

Low Speed
When the same skater is moving more slowly, he has less kinetic energy.

READING VISUALS **APPLY** How could a skater with less mass than another skater have more kinetic energy?

74 Unit 1: Matter and Energy

DIFFERENTIATE INSTRUCTION

 More Reading Support

D What is kinetic energy? *the energy of motion*

E What is the relationship between speed and kinetic energy? *As speed increases, kinetic energy increases.*

Advanced Introduce students to the formula for kinetic energy, $KE = 1/2\ mv^2$. Use examples to show that the kinetic energy of an object varies directly with its mass and with the square of the velocity (speed). Ask students to explain why changing the velocity of an object has a much greater impact on its kinetic energy than changing its mass.

R Challenge and Extension, p. 152

Potential Energy

Suppose you are holding a soccer ball in your hands. Even if the ball is not moving, it has energy because it has the potential to fall. **Potential energy** is the stored energy that an object has due to its position or chemical composition. The ball's position above the ground gives it potential energy.

The most obvious form of potential energy is potential energy that results from gravity. Gravity is the force that pulls objects toward Earth's surface. The giant boulder on the right has potential energy because of its position above the ground. The mass of the boulder and its height above the ground determine how much potential energy it has due to gravity.

It is easy to know whether an object has kinetic energy because the object is moving. It is not so easy to know how much and what form of potential energy an object has, because objects can have potential energy from several sources. For example, in addition to potential energy from gravity, substances contain potential energy due to their chemical composition—the atoms they contain.

Because the boulder could fall, it has potential energy from gravity.

CHECK YOUR READING How can you tell kinetic energy and potential energy apart?

INVESTIGATE Potential Energy

How can you change the amount of potential energy?
DESIGN YOUR OWN EXPERIMENT

Use what you know about potential energy to design an experiment that shows how potential energy can be increased or decreased.

PROCEDURE

1. Using the materials in the list, design an experiment to investigate the potential energy of the model car. Use the cardboard as a ramp.
2. Write up your hypothesis and your procedure. Remember to include the variables and constants in the experiment.
3. Conduct your experiment and record your results.

WHAT DO YOU THINK?
- What variables did you change? Why?
- How do your results demonstrate a change in potential energy?

SKILL FOCUS
Designing experiments

MATERIALS
- model car
- meter stick
- weights
- balance
- tape
- cardboard
- books

TIME
30 minutes

Address Misconceptions

IDENTIFY Ask: What happens to energy when an object is at rest? If students reply the object has no energy, they may hold the misconception that objects at rest do not have any energy.

CORRECT Explain how potential energy relates to various forms of energy. Even though an object may be at rest, it has stored energy. Different substances have potential energy because of the types of atoms in them. Have students make a list of objects with potential energy.

REASSESS Ask: What type of energy is found in food? *chemical energy*

Technology Resources
Visit ClassZone.com for background on common student misconceptions.

MISCONCEPTION DATABASE

INVESTIGATE Potential Energy

PURPOSE To design an experiment that shows how potential energy can change

TIPS 30 min. Pennies or washers can be used as the weights. Ask students to bring a toy car from home.

WHAT DO YOU THINK? *mass of car, height of ramp. Both alter the potential energy the car has. The farther the car travels, the greater its kinetic energy; thus the greater was its potential energy.*

Datasheet, Potential Energy, p. 153

Technology Resources
Customize this student lab as needed or look for an alternative. Print rubrics to assess student lab reports.

Lab Generator CD-ROM

DIFFERENTIATE INSTRUCTION

More Reading Support
F What is potential energy? *stored energy*

G What causes an object to have potential energy due to its position above the ground? *gravity*

Ongoing Assessment

CHECK YOUR READING *Answer: Kinetic energy— an object is in motion; potential energy—stored energy due to position or chemical composition.*

Chapter 3   75

Ongoing Assessment

Illustrate that the two general types of energy are kinetic energy and potential energy.

Ask: How might riding down a waterslide involve both potential and kinetic energy? *At the top of the slide, you have potential energy and no kinetic energy. As you move down the slide, potential energy changes to kinetic energy.*

 Answer: It is energy that is stored in molecules.

EXPLORE the BIG idea

Revisit "Internet Activity: Energy" on p. 69. Have students explain the relationship between potential and kinetic energy.

Reinforce the BIG idea

Have students relate the section to the Big Idea.

 Reinforcing Key Concepts, p. 154

3.1 ASSESS & RETEACH

Assess

 Section 3.1 Quiz, p. 42

Reteach

Ask students how water flowing over a waterfall involves kinetic and potential energy. *Flowing water has kinetic energy; the water has potential energy due to gravity.* Ask: What forms of energy can be observed? *mechanical in the motion of the water; sound from the water*

Technology Resources

Have students visit ClassZone.com for reteaching of Key Concepts.

 CONTENT REVIEW

 CONTENT REVIEW CD-ROM

Pulling the string, which bends the bow, gives the bow potential energy.

Chemical energy in the fuel of a model rocket engine is potential energy.

Another form of potential energy related to an object's position comes from stretching or compressing an object. Think about the spring that is pushed down in a jack-in-the-box. The spring's potential energy increases when the spring is compressed and decreases when it is released. Look at the bow that is being bent in the photograph on the left. When the bowstring is pulled, the bow bends and stores energy. When the string is released, both the string and the bow return to their normal shape. Stored energy is released as the bow and the string straighten out and the arrow is pushed forward.

When a rock falls or a bow straightens, potential energy is released. In fact, in these examples, the potential energy produced either by gravity or by bending is changed into kinetic energy.

Chemical energy, such as the energy stored in food, is less visible, but it is also a form of potential energy. This form of potential energy depends on chemical composition rather than position. It is the result of the atoms, and the bonds between atoms, that make up the molecules in food. When these molecules are broken apart, and their atoms rearranged through a series of chemical changes, energy is released.

The fuel in a model rocket engine also contains chemical energy. Like the molecules that provide energy in your body, the molecules in the fuel store potential energy. When the fuel ignites in the rocket engine, the arrangement of atoms in the chemical fuel changes and its potential energy is released.

 Why is chemical energy a form of potential energy?

3.1 Review

KEY CONCEPTS

1. List three ways you use energy. How does each example involve a change?
2. What are some changes that can be caused by sound energy? by electromagnetic energy?
3. What two factors determine an object's kinetic energy?

CRITICAL THINKING

4. **Synthesize** How do the different forms of potential energy depend on an object's position or chemical composition?
5. **Infer** What forms of potential energy would be found in an apple on the branch of a tree? Explain.

CHALLENGE

6. **Synthesize** Describe a stone falling off a tabletop in terms of both kinetic energy and potential energy.

76 Unit 1: Matter and Energy

ANSWERS

1. Answers could include any activity, but should indicate what change results.
2. sound—vibrations in a solid, liquid, or gas; electromagnetic—lighting a dark room
3. mass and speed
4. an object's position above the ground; an object's compressed or stretched position; chemical potential depends on the atoms and bonds in an object.
5. gravitational, because of the apple's position; chemical, because the apple can be eaten for chemical energy
6. The stone has potential energy due to gravity. The amount of energy depends on its mass and height. The greater its potential energy, the greater its kinetic energy when it falls.

Think SCIENCE

SKILL: FINDING SOLUTIONS

Gasoline or Electric?

Cars use a significant amount of the world's energy. Most cars get their energy from the chemical energy of gasoline, a fossil fuel. Cars can also get their energy from sources other than gasoline. For many years, engineers have been working to design cars that run only on electricity. The goals of developing these new cars include reducing air pollution and decreasing the use of fossil fuels. So why have electric cars not replaced gasoline-powered cars?

● Advantages of Electric Cars

- Electric motors are more simple than gasoline engines.
- Electric cars use energy more efficiently than gasoline-powered cars, so they are cheaper to operate.
- Controlling pollution at power plants that produce electricity is easier than controlling pollution from cars.
- Electric motors are quieter than gasoline engines.
- Electric cars do not produce smog, which is a major health concern in large cities.

● Disadvantages of Electric Cars

- At this time, electric cars can travel only about 100 miles on a single battery charge.
- It takes several hours to recharge the batteries of an electric car using today's charging systems.
- The batteries of an electric car need to be replaced after being recharged about 600 times.
- An electric car's range is decreased by heating or cooling the inside of the car because, unlike batteries in gasoline-powered cars, its batteries are not recharged during driving.

● Finding Solutions

As a Group
What technology would need to be improved for electric cars to replace gasoline-powered cars? What facilities that do not exist today would be needed to serve electric cars?

As a Class
Compare your group's solutions to those of other groups. Use the Internet to research hybrid vehicles. How would these vehicles solve some of the problems that you identified?

 Find out more about electric cars.

Chapter 3: **Energy** 77

THINK SCIENCE
Scientific Methods of Thinking

Set Learning Goal
To learn about electric cars and weigh their advantages and disadvantages

Present the Science
Batteries are the weak link in the development of economical and practical electric cars. The batteries are heavy, bulky, and expensive. They must be recharged (a slow process) and have to be replaced regularly. For this reason, research has centered on hybrid electric vehicles (HEVs) and on fuel cells. HEVs are an intermediate step between purely electric cars and gasoline-powered cars, and were meant to be a temporary solution until better batteries were developed.

Guide the Activity
DIFFERENTIATION TIP Have slower learners discuss the general characteristics of the advantages and disadvantages of electric cars and organize them into a chart. Be sure students identify health and the environment as advantages, and convenience as a disadvantage.

Point out that most energy sources have advantages and disadvantages. Discuss a major energy source for your area and how it benefits people and what problems it causes.

COOPERATIVE LEARNING STRATEGY Divide the class into groups of four. Have each group discuss what would have to be done to make electric cars convenient and practical.

Close
Ask: What might be the advantages if all future cars were electric powered? *Smog and pollution would be decreased.*

Technology Resources
Have students visit **ClassZone.com** to find out more about electric cars

 RESOURCE CENTER

ANSWERS

AS A GROUP Battery technology needs to improve and facilities for recharging car batteries have to be built.

AS A CLASS Hybrid electric vehicles solve some of the problems of electric cars because they combine electric power with the power of the internal combustion engine. They are more efficient and less polluting.

3.2 FOCUS

Set Learning Goals

Students will

- Explain how energy can be converted from one form to another.
- Restate the law of conservation of energy.
- Understand that energy conversions may be inefficient.

3-Minute Warm-Up

Display Transparency 20 or copy this exercise on the board:

Decide if these statements are true. If not true, correct them.

1. Chemical energy is based on the movement of particles within matter. *thermal energy*
2. Nuclear energy holds an atom's nucleus together. *true*
3. Electromagnetic energy is the energy used to move objects. *mechanical energy*
4. Kinetic energy is energy of motion, and potential energy is stored energy. *true*

3-Minute Warm-Up, p. T20

3.2 MOTIVATE

THINK ABOUT

PURPOSE To identify how energy changes forms several times when a match is lit

DISCUSS Have students suggest energy changes in other everyday events. *Using a stove, turning on a light, and using an electric appliance all involve energy changing forms.*

Answer: The energy to strike the match initially comes from the person who uses the match.

Ongoing Assessment

Answer: Chemical energy becomes mechanical energy in the match. The match's mechanical energy changes into heat and light released by the burning match.

78 Unit 1: Matter and Energy

KEY CONCEPT

3.2 Energy can change forms but is never lost.

BEFORE, you learned
- Energy causes change
- Energy has different forms
- Kinetic energy and potential energy are the two general types of energy

NOW, you will learn
- How energy can be converted from one form to another
- About the law of conservation of energy
- How energy conversions may be inefficient

VOCABULARY

law of conservation of energy p. 82
energy efficiency p. 83

THINK ABOUT

How does energy change form?

Potential energy is stored in the chemicals on the head of a match. The flame of a burning match releases that energy as light and heat. Where does the energy to strike the match come from in the first place?

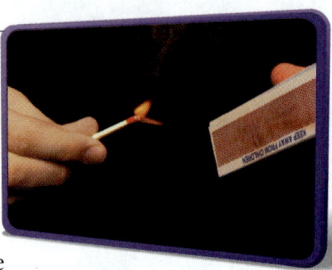

MIND MAP Use a mind map to take notes about how energy changes forms.

Energy changes forms.

A match may not appear to have any energy by itself, but it does contain potential energy that can be released. The chemical energy stored in a match can be changed into light and heat. Before the chemical energy in the match changes forms, however, other energy conversions must take place.

Plants convert energy from the Sun into chemical energy, which is stored in the form of sugars in their cells. When a person eats food that comes from plants—or from animals that have eaten plants—the person's cells can release this chemical energy. Some of this chemical energy is converted into the kinetic energy that a person uses to rub the match over a rough surface to strike it. The friction between the match and the striking surface produces heat. The heat provides the energy needed to start the chemical changes that produce the flame. From the Sun to the flame, at least five energy conversions have taken place.

CHECK YOUR READING How is a person's chemical energy changed into another form of energy in the lighting of a match?

78 Unit 1: Matter and Energy

RESOURCES FOR DIFFERENTIATED INSTRUCTION

Below Level
UNIT RESOURCE BOOK
- Reading Study Guide A, pp. 157–158
- Decoding Support, p. 180

AUDIO CDS

Additional INVESTIGATION, Build a Roller Coaster, A, B, & C, pp. 192–200; Teacher Instructions, pp. 262–263

Advanced
UNIT RESOURCE BOOK
Challenge and Extension, p. 163

English Learners
UNIT RESOURCE BOOK
Spanish Reading Study Guide, pp. 161–162

AUDIO CDS

- Audio Readings in Spanish
- Audio Readings (English)

Conversions Between Potential Energy and Kinetic Energy

The results of some energy conversions are obvious, such as when electrical energy in a light bulb is changed into light and heat. Other energy conversions are not so obvious. The examples below and on page 80 explore, step by step, some ways in which energy conversions occur in the world around you.

Potential energy can be changed into kinetic energy and back into potential energy. Look at the illustrations and photograph of the ski jumper shown below.

① At first, the ski jumper is at the top of the hill. This position gives him potential energy (PE) due to gravity.

② As the ski jumper starts moving downhill, some of his potential energy changes into kinetic energy (KE). Kinetic energy moves him down the slope to the ramp.

③ When the ski jumper takes off from the ramp, some of his kinetic energy is changed back into potential energy as he rises in the air.

When the ski jumper descends to the ground, his potential energy once again changes into kinetic energy. After the ski jumper lands and stops moving, how might he regain the potential energy that he had at the top of the hill? The kinetic energy of a ski lift can move the ski jumper back up the mountain and give him potential energy again.

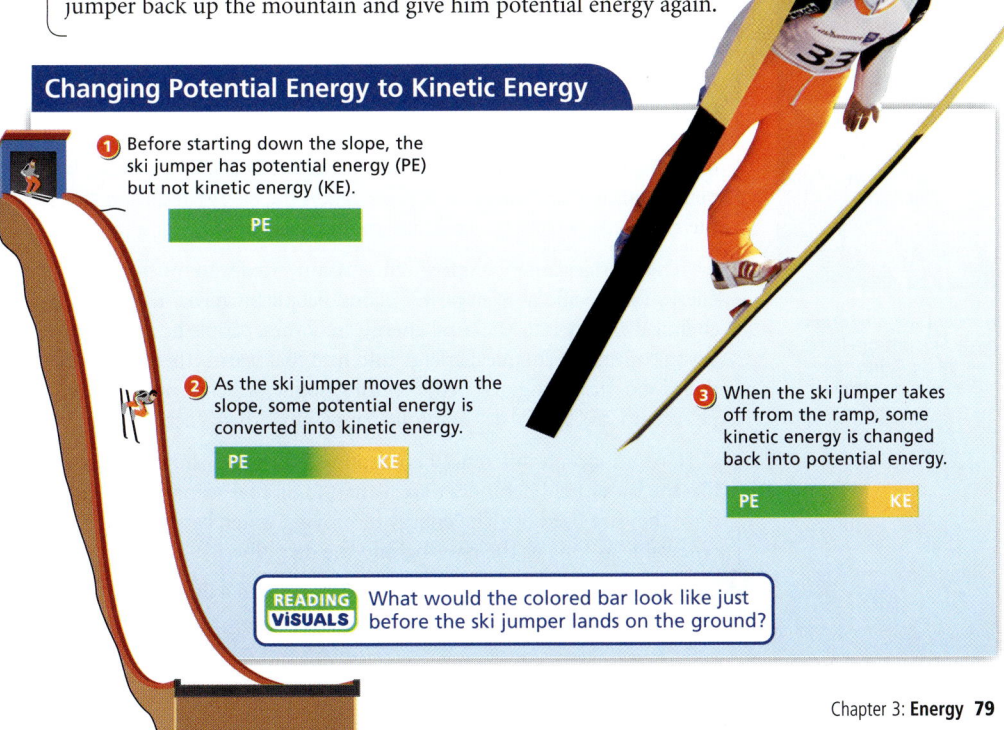

Changing Potential Energy to Kinetic Energy

① Before starting down the slope, the ski jumper has potential energy (PE) but not kinetic energy (KE).

② As the ski jumper moves down the slope, some potential energy is converted into kinetic energy.

③ When the ski jumper takes off from the ramp, some kinetic energy is changed back into potential energy.

READING VISUALS What would the colored bar look like just before the ski jumper lands on the ground?

Chapter 3: **Energy** 79

3.2 INSTRUCT

Teach from Visuals
To help students interpret the graphic of energy changes in ski jumping, ask:

- Why does the ski jumper have potential energy? *At the top, he has potential energy due to gravity.*
- Why is some potential energy converted to kinetic energy in step 2? *The skier has descended and moves faster as a result. Kinetic energy is the energy of motion.*
- When does the ski jumper have the most potential energy after he takes off from the jump? *at the skier's point of greatest height*
- Why does the ski jumper's potential energy increase for a short time after taking off from the jump? *because his height above the ground increases*

Develop Critical Thinking
INFER Have students infer what energy changes are involved if a different ski jumper slides down the slope. Ask:

- How could another ski jumper have a greater amount of potential energy than the one shown in the illustration? *start from a greater height, have a greater mass*
- How would the energies involved change if the ski jumper was much heavier? *His mass would be larger, and therefore his potential and kinetic energy would also be larger; he would exert a greater force on the ground when he landed.*
- When the ski jumper has landed and stopped moving, does he still possess a form of potential energy? Explain. *yes; chemical potential energy from molecules obtained from food.*

Ongoing Assessment
READING VISUALS *Answer: It would be all yellow.*

DIFFERENTIATE INSTRUCTION

More Reading Support
A What type of energy moves a skier down a hill? *kinetic energy*

Additional Investigation To reinforce Section 3.2 learning goals, use the following full-period investigation:

R **Additional INVESTIGATION,** Build a Roller Coaster, A, B, & C, pp. 192–200, 262–263 (Advanced students should complete Levels B and C.)

English Learners Students may need background knowledge of a ski jumper and ski lifts (p. 79). For the section review (p. 83), tell students what a trampoline is and make sure English learners understand the direction *Suppose*.

Chapter 3 **79**

EXPLORE the BIG idea

Revisit "A Penny for Your Energy" on p. 69. Have students describe the energy transfer that took place.

Teach Difficult Concepts

Students may confuse the transfer of energy with transformation of energy. In a transfer of energy, energy moves from one object to another. This occurs in the activity "A Penny for Your Energy," where thermal energy is transferred from warm hands to the cold bottle. Transformation of energy is the conversion of one energy form to another, such as when generators convert the mechanical energy of moving water to electrical energy. Ask students to describe examples of energy transfer and transformation. Make a table listing student responses on the board.

Teacher Demo

To demonstrate the conversion of sound energy to mechanical energy, position a fully inflated balloon in front of a stereo speaker. Students will be able to feel the vibrations from a loud sound by placing their hands lightly on the balloon.

Ongoing Assessment

Explain how energy can be converted from one form to another.
Ask: What energy conversions take place when fireworks explode? *Chemical energy in the firework chemicals is converted into light, heat, and sound energy.*

CHECK YOUR READING *Sample answer: The potential energy of water behind a dam can be changed into electrical energy.*

READING TIP
As you read about the process for producing electrical energy, follow the steps on page 81.

Using Energy Conversions

People have developed ways to convert energy from one form to another for many purposes. Read about the energy conversion process below, and follow that process in the illustrations on page 81 to see how energy in water that is stored behind a dam is changed into electrical energy.

① The water held behind the dam has potential energy because of its position.

② Some of the water is allowed to flow through a tunnel within the dam. The potential energy in the stored water changes into kinetic energy when the water moves through the tunnel.

③ The kinetic energy of the moving water turns turbines within the dam. The water's kinetic energy becomes kinetic energy in the turbines. The kinetic energy of the turning turbines is converted into electrical energy by electrical generators.

④ Electrical energy is transported away from the dam through wires. The electrical energy is converted into many different forms of energy and is used in many different ways. For example, at a concert or a play, electrical energy is converted into light and heat by lighting systems and into sound energy by sound systems.

As you can see, several energy conversions occur in order to produce a usable form of energy—potential energy becomes kinetic energy, and kinetic energy becomes electrical energy.

Other sources of useful energy begin with electromagnetic energy from the Sun. In fact, almost all of the energy on Earth began as electromagnetic energy from the Sun. This energy can be converted into many other forms of energy. Plants convert the electromagnetic energy of sunlight into chemical energy as they grow. This energy, stored by plants hundreds of millions of years ago, is the energy found in fossil fuels, such as petroleum, coal, and natural gas.

The chemical energy in fossil fuels is converted into other forms of energy for specific uses. In power plants, people burn coal to convert its chemical energy into electrical energy. In homes, people burn natural gas to convert its chemical energy into heat that warms them and cooks their food. In car engines, people burn gasoline, which is made from petroleum, to convert its chemical energy into kinetic energy.

One important difference between fossil fuels and sources of energy like the water held behind a dam, is that fossil fuels cannot be replaced once they are used up. The energy of moving water, by contrast, is renewable as long as the river behind the dam flows.

CHECK YOUR READING How can potential energy be changed into a usable form of energy?

Hoover Dam produces a large amount of electrical energy for California, Nevada, and Arizona.

80 Unit 1: **Matter and Energy**

DIFFERENTIATE INSTRUCTION

? More Reading Support

B How did almost all of Earth's energy begin? *as electromagnetic energy from the Sun*

C What kind of energy do fossil fuels contain? *chemical energy*

Below Level Have students make a flow chart that follows the path of energy from the Sun to plants to fossil fuels to a coal-burning power plant to students' homes. Students should label each stage of energy conversion with the forms of energy.

Converting Energy

Energy is often converted from one form to another in order to meet everyday needs.

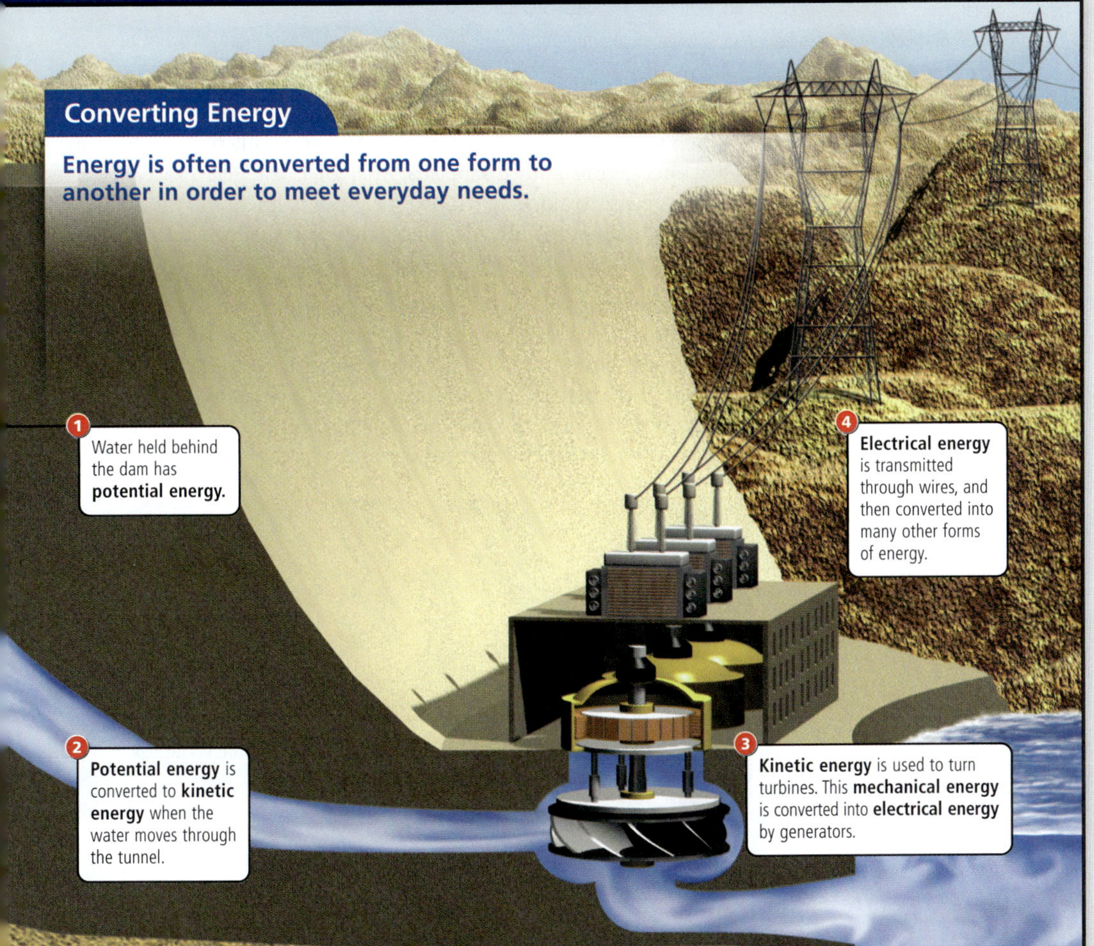

① Water held behind the dam has **potential energy**.

② **Potential energy** is converted to **kinetic energy** when the water moves through the tunnel.

③ **Kinetic energy** is used to turn turbines. This **mechanical energy** is converted into **electrical energy** by generators.

④ **Electrical energy** is transmitted through wires, and then converted into many other forms of energy.

Potential Energy to Kinetic Energy
The potential energy of water behind the dam becomes the kinetic energy of moving water. 

Kinetic Energy to Electrical Energy
The kinetic energy of turning turbines becomes electrical energy in these generators.

READING VISUALS How many different energy conversions are described in this diagram?

Chapter 3: Energy 81

DIFFERENTIATE INSTRUCTION

Advanced Students could extend their knowledge of a hydroelectric dam by thinking about why a dam is needed. Ask: Why can't water simply be removed from a river and made to turn turbines? Ask them to design experiments using water and a pin wheel to observe that there must be a difference in elevation because the energy to turn the turbines comes from falling water.

 Challenge and Extension, p. 163

Teach from Visuals

To help students interpret the diagrams of energy conversions in a hydroelectric power plant, ask:

- Why does the water behind the dam have potential energy? *Because of its position, it has potential energy due to gravity.*
- What is the function of the moving water? *It turns the blades of turbines, which power the generators.*

 The visual "Converting Energy" is available as T22 in the Unit Transparency Book.

Metacognitive Strategy

Ask students to discuss whether or not they find it easier to understand the conversion of energy from one form to another if they study a large diagram. What changes would they make in the diagram on this page to make it more useful?

Real World Example

The Hoover Dam does more than provide electric power to a large portion of the southwestern United States. It also prevents annual spring flooding by the lower Colorado River, provides water for irrigation, and helps form an artificial lake (Lake Mead). During dam construction, the Colorado River was diverted through four concrete tunnels. At one time, Hoover Dam, which was completed in 1935, was the largest hydroelectric plant in the world.

Ongoing Assessment

READING VISUALS *Answer: three; potential to kinetic, kinetic (mechanical) to electrical, electrical to many other forms*

Chapter 3 **81**

Address Misconceptions

IDENTIFY Ask: Is Earth running out of energy? If students answer yes, they may be confusing the idea of the "conservation of energy" with the meaning of conservation as preservation or protection.

CORRECT Explain that an energy source is a fuel that can provide energy. Energy sources are not conserved according to the law of conservation of energy and can be used up, but the energy itself is converted rather than lost. Have students make a list of energy sources and discuss those that are in danger of being used up.

REASSESS Ask: What happens to the energy produced by fuels? *It is converted into other forms of energy such as heat and light, and the total amount of energy remains the same.*

Technology Resources
Visit **ClassZone.com** for background on common student misconceptions.
MISCONCEPTION DATABASE

History of Science

Arguably the most famous equation of the 20th century is Albert Einstein's $E = mc^2$, which demonstrates that matter and energy are actually the same. Mass can be considered to be "solidified energy." Because the equation states that energy is equal to mass multiplied by the speed of light squared, a very small mass is equal to a very large amount of energy.

Ongoing Assessment

Restate the law of conservation of energy.

Ask students to restate the law of conservation of energy in their own words. *Sample answer: Energy is converted to other forms, not used up or created.*

 Answer: Energy can neither be created nor destroyed.

Energy is always conserved.

When you observe energy conversions in your daily life, it may seem that energy constantly disappears. After all, if you give a soccer ball kinetic energy by kicking it along the ground, it will roll for a while but eventually stop. Consider what might have happened to the ball's kinetic energy.

As the ball rolls, it rubs against the ground. Some kinetic energy changes into heat as a result of friction. Some of the ball's energy also changes into sound energy that you can hear as the ball moves. Although the ball loses kinetic energy, the overall amount of energy in the universe does not decrease. The photograph below shows how the soccer ball's kinetic energy decreases.

The soccer ball's kinetic energy decreases as that energy is changed into sound energy and heat.

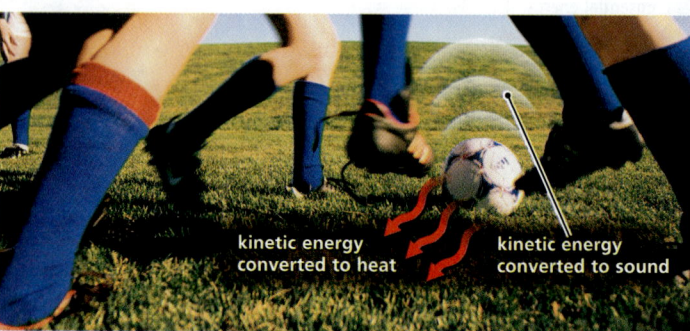
kinetic energy converted to heat
kinetic energy converted to sound

READING TIP
Conservation refers to a total that does not change.

In the soccer ball example, the ball loses energy, but this energy is transferred to other parts of the universe. Energy is conserved. The **law of conservation of energy** states that energy can neither be created nor destroyed. Conservation of energy is called a law because this rule is true in all known cases. Although in many instances it may appear that energy is gained or lost, it is really only changed in form.

CHECK YOUR READING Explain what is meant by the law of conservation of energy.

Conservation of energy is a balance of energy in the universe. When a soccer ball is kicked, a certain amount of energy is transferred by the kick. The ball gains an equal amount of energy, mostly in the form of kinetic energy. However, the ball's kinetic energy decreases as some of that energy is converted into sound energy and heat from the friction between the ball and the ground.

According to the law of conservation of energy, the amount of energy that a soccer player gives to the ball by kicking it is equal to the energy the ball gains. The energy the ball loses, in turn, is equal to the amount of energy that is transferred to the universe as sound energy and heat as the ball slows down.

DIFFERENTIATE INSTRUCTION

More Reading Support

D Why is conservation of energy a law? *It is true in all known cases.*

E How does a ball's kinetic energy decrease? *It changes to heat and sound.*

Alternative Assessment Have students think of examples to explain the law of conservation of energy. For example, when food is warmed in a microwave oven, the thermal energy of the food increases through energy conversions. Electrical energy enters the microwave oven, in which it is converted into other forms of energy including electromagnetic energy (microwaves). The microwaves transfer energy to the food, but the total amount of energy is not changed.

Energy conversions may produce unwanted forms of energy.

When energy changes forms, the total amount of energy is conserved. However, the amount of useful energy is almost always less than the total amount of energy. For example, consider the energy used by an electric fan. The amount of electrical energy used is greater than the kinetic energy of the moving fan blades. Because energy is always conserved, some of the electrical energy flowing into the fan's motor is obviously changed into unusable or unwanted forms.

The fan converts a significant portion of the electrical energy into the kinetic energy of the fan blades. At the same time, some electrical energy changes into heat in the fan's motor. If the fan shakes, some of the electrical energy is being turned into unwanted kinetic energy. The more efficiently the fan uses electrical energy, though, the more energy will be transformed into kinetic energy that moves the air.

Energy efficiency is a measurement of usable energy after an energy conversion. You may be familiar with energy-efficient household appliances. These appliances convert a greater percentage of energy into the desired form than inefficient ones. The more energy-efficient a fan is, the more electrical energy it turns into kinetic energy in the moving blades. Less electrical energy is needed to operate appliances that are energy efficient.

 What does it mean when an energy conversion is efficient?

Some electrical energy is converted into unwanted sound energy.

Some electrical energy is converted into kinetic energy of the fan blades.

Some electrical energy is converted into unwanted heat.

Ongoing Assessment
Understand that energy conversions may be inefficient.

Ask: Which energy conversion is more efficient—a soccer ball kicked along a smooth sidewalk or a soccer ball kicked in a field of tall weeds? Why? *the sidewalk, because less energy will be changed into heat by friction*

 Answer: Most of the energy that enters an energy conversion changes into the desired form of energy.

Reinforce
Have students relate the section to the Big Idea.

R Reinforcing Key Concepts, p. 164

3.2 ASSESS & RETEACH

Assess
 Section 3.2 Quiz, p. 43

Reteach
Remind students about the law of conservation of energy and the concept of conversions between potential and kinetic energy. A roller coaster is a good example of these concepts. Draw a simple roller coaster on the board. Make sure each hill is lower than the previous hill. Ask students to identify points of substantial potential energy (at the top of hills) and kinetic energy (at the bottom of hills). Ask: Why must each hill be lower than the previous hill? *Kinetic energy decreases due to friction. If two adjacent hills were the same height, the coaster would not be able to make it to the top of the second hill because it would not have enough kinetic energy.*

3.2 Review

KEY CONCEPTS
1. Describe an energy conversion you have observed in your own life.
2. Explain the law of conservation of energy in your own words.
3. Give an example of an energy conversion that produces unwanted forms of energy.

CRITICAL THINKING
4. **Synthesize** Suppose you are jumping on a trampoline. Describe the conversions that occur between kinetic energy and potential energy.
5. **Infer** Look at the ski jumper on page 79. Has all of his potential energy likely been changed into kinetic energy at the moment he lands? Explain.

CHALLENGE
6. **Communicate** Draw and label a diagram that shows at least three different energy conversions that might occur when a light bulb is turned on.

Chapter 3: **Energy** 83

Technology Resources
Have students visit ClassZone.com for reteaching of Key Concepts.

 CONTENT REVIEW

 CONTENT REVIEW CD-ROM

ANSWERS
1. Sample answer: a flashlight, chemical energy becomes electrical energy, which becomes visible light.
2. Energy can change forms, but the overall amount of energy is constant.
3. Sample answer: Incandescent bulbs release heat in addition to light.
4. Potential energy is greatest at the highest point. Potential energy converts into kinetic energy until hitting the trampoline. Kinetic energy converts to potential energy in the trampoline to the lowest point, and is converted to kinetic energy back into the air.
5. No; some energy changed into heat and sound.
6. chemical energy to mechanical energy when turning a switch; mechanical energy to electrical energy; electrical energy to light and heat in the bulb

CHAPTER INVESTIGATION

Focus

PURPOSE To investigate the amount of energy stored in different types of food

OVERVIEW Students will construct an apparatus to trap the energy released from different food samples when they burn. Students will collect data and calculate the amount of energy each food contained. They will find the following:

- The water in the can traps the energy that is released by the burning food.
- The temperature increase in the water is greater when burning foods high in fats than when burning foods high in carbohydrates.
- Fats contain more energy than carbohydrates.

Lab Preparation

- Students can bring many of the materials, such as aluminum cans, from home.
- Punch holes in the cans before class to save time.
- Prior to the investigation, have students read through the investigation and prepare their data tables. You may wish to copy and distribute datasheets and rubrics.

 UNIT RESOURCE BOOK, pp. 183–191

 SCIENCE TOOLKIT, F14

Lab Management

- Warn students not to eat the food samples.

SAFETY Advise students with long hair to tie it back. Students wearing long, loose sleeves should roll them up. Desks should be cleared of all non-essential and flammable materials.

Teaching with Technology

Have students use a temperature probe to record temperature changes.

84 Unit 1: **Matter and Energy**

CHAPTER INVESTIGATION

Energy Conversions

OVERVIEW AND PURPOSE All foods contain stored chemical energy, but some foods contain more chemical energy than others. People need this chemical energy for all of their activities. The amount of chemical energy stored in foods like marshmallows can be measured by burning the foods. In this investigation, you will

- construct an apparatus to investigate the amount of energy in samples of food
- calculate the amount of energy released when the foods are burned

▶ Problem

Write It Up

How much energy is stored in different types of food?

▶ Hypothesize

Write It Up

Write a hypothesis to explain which type of food contains a greater amount of chemical energy. Your hypothesis should take the form of an "If . . . , then . . . , because . . ." statement.

▶ Procedure

MATERIALS
- can opener
- empty aluminum can
- dowel rod
- water
- graduated cylinder
- ring stand with ring
- thermometer
- aluminum pie plate
- aluminum foil
- tape
- large paper clip
- cork
- modeling clay
- crouton
- caramel rice cake
- balance
- wooden matches

1. Create a data table similar to the one shown on the sample notebook page.

2. Using the can opener, punch two holes directly opposite each other near the top of the can. Slide the dowel rod through the holes as shown in the photograph to the left.

3. Measure 50 mL of water with a graduated cylinder, and pour the water into the can. Record the mass of the water. (Hint: 1 mL of water = 1 gram)

4. Rest the ends of the dowel rod on the ring in the ring stand to hold the can in the air. Carefully place the thermometer in the can. Measure and record the initial temperature (T1) of the water in the can.

5. Make a collar of aluminum foil and tape it around the can as shown. Leave enough room to insert the burner platform and food sample.

84 Unit 1: **Matter and Energy**

INVESTIGATION RESOURCES

 CHAPTER INVESTIGATION, Energy Conversions
- Level A, pp. 183–186
- Level B, pp. 187–190
- Level C, p. 191

Advanced students should complete Levels B & C.

 Writing a Lab Report, D12–13

Technology Resources

Customize this student lab as needed or look for an alternative. Print rubrics to assess student lab reports.

 Lab Generator CD-ROM

6. Construct the burner platform as follows: Open up the paper clip. Push the straightened end into a cork, and push the bottom of the cork into the clay. Push the burner onto the pie plate so it will not move. Put the pie plate under the ring.

step 6

7. Find and record the mass of the crouton. Place the crouton on the flattened end of the burner platform. Adjust the height of the ring so the bottom of the can is about 4 cm above the crouton.

8. Use a match to ignite the crouton. Allow the crouton to burn completely. Measure and record the final temperature (T2) of the water.

9. Empty the water from the can and repeat steps 3–8 with a caramel rice cake. The mass of the rice cake should equal the mass of the crouton.

Observe and Analyze Write It Up

1. **RECORD OBSERVATIONS** Make sure to record all measurements in the data table.

2. **CALCULATE** Find the energy released from the food samples by following the next two steps.

   Calculate and record the change in temperature.
   change in temperature = T2 – T1

   Calculate and record the energy released in calories. One calorie is the energy needed to raise the temperature of 1 g of water by 1°C.
   energy released = (mass of water · change in temperature · 1 cal/g°C)

3. **GRAPH** Make a bar graph showing the number of calories in each food sample. Which type of food contains a greater amount of chemical energy?

Conclude — Write It Up

1. **INTERPRET** Answer the question posed in the problem.
2. **INFER** Did your results support your hypothesis? Explain.
3. **EVALUATE** What happens to any energy released by the burning food that is not captured by the water? How could you change the setup for a more accurate measurement?
4. **APPLY** Find out how much fat and carbohydrate the different foods contain. Explain the relationship between this information and the number of calories in the foods.

INVESTIGATE Further

CHALLENGE The Calories listed in foods are equal to 1000 calories (1 kilocalorie). Calculate the amount of energy in your food samples in terms of Calories per gram of food (Calories/g). Using a balance, find the mass of any ash that remains after burning the food. Subtract that mass from the original mass of the sample to calculate mass burned. Divide total calories by mass burned, then divide that value by 1000 to find Calories/g. Compare your results to those given on the product labels.

Energy Conversions

Problem How much energy is stored in different types of food?

Hypothesize

Observe and Analyze

Table 1. Energy in Food

	Sample 1	Sample 2
Mass of water (g)		
Initial water temp. (T1) (°C)		
Final water temp. (T2) (°C)		
Mass of food (g)		
Change in temp. (T2 – T1) (°C)		
Energy released (mass · change in temp. · cal/g°C)		

Conclude

Chapter 3: Energy 85

Observe and Analyze Write It Up

1. Sample data: Rice snack (Sample 1): mass of water 50 g; T1 20°C; T2 24°C; Crouton (Sample 2): mass of water 50 g; T1 20°C; T2 32°C. Mass of food will depend on the size of the sample.

2. For the sample data, the rice snack produced 200 calories and the crouton 600 calories.

3. See students' graphs; croutons

Conclude Write It Up

1. The amount of energy stored in food depends on the nutrients in it. Fats store more energy than carbohydrates.

2. Answers will vary depending on the initial hypothesis.

3. It went into the air. A container that is completely closed and insulated to prevent the loss of heat would improve accuracy.

4. Fats contain more calories than carbohydrates, so the food that contains more fat should release more energy when it is burned.

INVESTIGATE Further

CHALLENGE Students will need to keep the ashes from their food samples to find how much the mass changed. Students' results will probably vary from the values given on product labels because the equipment used is crude, contributing to a high percent of error.

Post-Lab Discussion

• Ask: Why was it important that the same amount of water be used in each trial? *A greater mass of water would heat up more slowly with a given amount of energy.*

• Ask: What energy conversions occurred in this lab? Where was energy transferred to? *Chemical energy from the food molecules changed to thermal energy (heat), electromagnetic energy (light), and sound energy when the food was burned. Some of the thermal energy was captured by the water. Additional thermal energy was lost to the air and to the equipment.*

Chapter 3 **85**

3.3 FOCUS

▶ Set Learning Goals

Students will

- Summarize how technology can improve energy conversions.
- Evaluate advantages and disadvantages of different types of energy conversions.
- Recognize how technology can improve the use of natural resources.
- Experiment to observe how the collection of solar energy is affected by the color of a solar collector.

▶ 3-Minute Warm-Up

Display Transparency 21 or copy this exercise on the board:

Match each definition with the correct term.

Definitions

1. energy you have when you are running *b*
2. energy you have while standing still on a diving board *d*
3. measure of useable energy after an energy conversion *e*

Terms

a. conservation of energy
b. kinetic energy
c. sound energy
d. potential energy
e. energy efficiency

 3-Minute Warm-Up, p. T21

3.3 MOTIVATE

EXPLORE Solar Cells

PURPOSE To explore the size of a solar cell needed to provide electrical energy for a solar calculator

TIP *10 min.* The calculator must not have a battery backup.

WHAT DO YOU THINK? *Answers will depend on the calculator and light conditions. A large solar cell would keep the calculator working under relatively poor lighting conditions.*

86 Unit 1: Matter and Energy

KEY CONCEPT
3.3 Technology improves the ways people use energy.

◀ BEFORE, you learned	▶ NOW, you will learn
• Energy can change forms	• How technology can improve energy conversions
• When energy changes forms, the overall amount of energy remains the same	• About advantages and disadvantages of different types of energy conversions
• Energy conversions usually produce unwanted forms of energy	• How technology can improve the use of natural resources

VOCABULARY

solar cell p. 88

EXPLORE Solar Cells

Why does a solar calculator need a large solar cell?

PROCEDURE

1. Measure the area of the calculator's solar cell. (**Hint:** area = length • width)
2. Turn the calculator on. Make sure that there is enough light for the calculator to work.
3. Gradually cover the solar cell with the index card. Observe the calculator's display as you cover more of the cell.
4. Measure the uncovered area of the solar cell when the calculator no longer works.

WHAT DO YOU THINK?

- How much of the solar cell is needed to keep the calculator working?
- Why might a solar calculator have a solar cell that is larger than necessary?

MATERIALS
- solar calculator without backup battery
- ruler
- index card

 **MIND MAP**
Use a mind map to take notes about technology that improves energy conversions.

Technology improves energy conversions.

In many common energy conversions, most of the wasted energy is released as heat. One example is the common incandescent light bulb. Amazingly, only about 5 percent of the electrical energy that enters an incandescent light bulb is converted into light. That means that 95 percent of the electrical energy turns into unwanted forms of energy. Most is released as heat and ends up in the form of thermal energy in the surrounding air. To decrease this amount of wasted energy, scientists have investigated several more efficient types of lights.

86 Unit 1: Matter and Energy

RESOURCES FOR DIFFERENTIATED INSTRUCTION

Below Level
UNIT RESOURCE BOOK
- Reading Study Guide A, pp. 167–168
- Decoding Support, p. 180

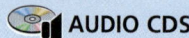 AUDIO CDS

Advanced
UNIT RESOURCE BOOK
- Challenge and Extension, p. 173
- Challenge Reading, pp. 176–177

English Learners
UNIT RESOURCE BOOK
Spanish Reading Study Guide, pp. 171–172

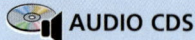 AUDIO CDS

- Audio Readings in Spanish
- Audio Readings (English)

Efficient Lights

A Research to replace light bulbs with a more energy-efficient source of light has resulted in the light-emitting diode, or LED. LEDs have the advantage of converting almost all of the electrical energy they use into light.

The first LEDs were not nearly as bright as typical light bulbs, but over time scientists and engineers have been able to produce brighter LEDs. LEDs have many uses, including television remote controls, computer displays, outdoor signs, giant video boards in stadiums, and traffic signals. LEDs are also used to transmit information through fiber optic cables that connect home audio and visual systems.

CHECK YOUR READING How are LEDs more efficient than incandescent lights?

LEDs that produce infrared light are used in remote controls.

Efficient Cars

B Another common but inefficient energy conversion is the burning of gasoline in cars. A large percentage of gasoline's chemical energy is not converted into the car's kinetic energy. Some of the kinetic energy is then wasted as heat from the car's engine, tires, and brakes. Here, too, efficiency can be improved through advances in technology.

Fuel injectors, common in cars since the 1980s, have improved the efficiency of engines. These devices carefully monitor and control the amount of gasoline that is fed into a car's engine. This precise control of fuel provides a significant increase in the distance a car can travel on a tank of gasoline. More recently, hybrid cars have been developed. These cars use both gasoline and electrical energy from batteries. These cars are very fuel efficient. Even better, some of the kinetic energy lost during braking in hybrid cars is used to generate electrical energy to recharge the car's batteries.

Hybrid cars may look very similar to typical gasoline-powered cars, but their engines are different.

Chapter 3: **Energy** 87

3.3 INSTRUCT

Teach Difficult Concepts

Students may think that some energy conversions are 100% efficient. Have students hammer a nail into a board. They should immediately feel the nail head, which should be warm. Ask students to write a short description of the energy conversions that took place and an explanation of why the nail head became warm. *Chemical energy in muscles converted to mechanical energy. Some mechanical energy was converted into heat due to friction.*

History of Science

The first visible LED, a red light, was developed in the late 1960s. LEDs that produce yellow, orange, green, blue, and white light were later developed. LED technology is known as electroluminescence and uses semiconductors such as gallium arsenide. Different semiconductors have different properties, so they can be used to produce LEDs with different characteristics.

Ongoing Assessment

Summarize how technology can improve energy conversions.

Ask: What is one aspect of an energy conversion that technology tries to improve? *efficiency*

CHECK YOUR READING *Answer: They convert almost all of the electrical energy that enters them into light.*

DIFFERENTIATE INSTRUCTION

More Reading Support

A Why replace light bulbs with LEDs? *LEDs are more efficient*

B How is a large amount of gasoline's energy wasted? *as heat*

English Learners The English language uses many words and phrases in ways that make little sense when taken literally. Examples from this section include "ends up" (p. 86) and "over time" (p. 90 in the Check Your Reading question). Help students by pointing out such phrases and tell them not to read such prepositions literally. Encourage them to use the context of the sentence to decipher the phrases' meanings.

Real World Example

In July 2003, teams of university students from the United States and Canada raced the solar-powered cars they had spent months designing and building. The race, called the American Solar Challenge, is sponsored by the U.S. Department of Energy. The route follows Route 66 across the Great Plains, the Rocky Mountains, and the southwestern desert, from Chicago to southern California. In the 2003 race, speeds of 75 miles per hour were recorded.

Teacher Demo

Connect a set of solar cells to a small electric motor that drives a propeller. Have students predict what will happen when the apparatus is placed under a light source. This will work outdoors on a bright, sunny day or in the classroom with a bright lamp. Ask: where does the energy come from and where does it go? *Electromagnetic energy is converted into mechanical energy in the propeller.*

Teach from Visuals

To help students interpret the visual of the solar car, ask:

- Where would the solar cells have to be on the car? *on the top exterior*
- Why might such a large area of the car be covered with solar cells? *to capture as much light as possible because solar cells are inefficient*
- What would happen to the car on a rainy day? *The car would not run unless it had a backup energy supply.*

Develop Critical Thinking

COMPARE Have students compare the conversion of solar energy in a solar car and in the leaves of a plant. *In a solar car, solar energy is converted to electrical energy. In a plant, solar energy is converted to chemical energy during photosynthesis.*

Ongoing Assessment

unlimited supplies, no harmful waste products

Technology improves the use of energy resources.

Much of the energy used on Earth comes from fossil fuels such as coal, petroleum, and natural gas. However, the supply of fossil fuels is limited. So, scientists and engineers are exploring the use of several alternative energy sources. Today, for example, both solar energy and wind energy are used on a small scale to generate electrical energy.

Solar energy and wind energy have several advantages compared to fossil fuels. Their supply is not limited, and they do not produce the same harmful waste products that fossil fuels do. However, there are also many obstacles that must be overcome before solar energy and wind energy, among other alternative energy sources, are as widely used as fossil fuels.

 What are the advantages of solar energy and wind energy as compared to fossil fuels?

Solar Energy

Observe how solar cells produce electricity.

Solar cells are important in today's solar energy technology. Modern **solar cells** are made of several layers of light-sensitive materials, which convert sunlight directly into electrical energy. Solar cells provide the electrical energy for such things as satellites in orbit around Earth, hand-held calculators, and, as shown below, experimental cars.

Solar Energy for Electricity

Solar cells can produce electricity to run a car.

A solar car requires 8 square meters of solar cells to provide sufficient electrical energy to power the car.

88 Unit 1: Matter and Energy

DIFFERENTIATE INSTRUCTION

 **More Reading Support**

C What energy conversion occurs in solar cells? *Sunlight is converted to electrical energy.*

Below Level Have students compare solar and wind energy to fossil fuel energy. Students should make a table that lists each type of energy source and some of the characteristics of each type. Have students mark an "X" in the box on the table to indicate that the energy has that characteristic. Discuss with students how the energy sources are alike and how they are different.

88 Unit 1: **Matter and Energy**

Solar cells produce electrical energy quietly and cleanly. However, they are not yet commonly used because the materials used to make them are very expensive. What's more, solar cells are not very efficient in producing electrical energy. Large numbers of solar cells produce only a relatively small amount of electrical energy. Typical solar cells convert only about 12 to 15 percent of the sunlight that reaches them into electrical energy. However, solar cells currently being developed could have efficiencies close to 40 percent.

In addition to converting the Sun's light directly into electrical energy, people have used the Sun's radiation for heating. In ancient Rome, glass was used to trap solar energy indoors so that plants could be grown in the winter. Today radiation from the Sun is still used to grow plants in greenhouses and to warm buildings. The photograph above shows a house that uses solar energy in both ways. The solar cells on the roof provide electrical energy, and the large windows help to trap the warmth. In fact, some solar power systems also use that warmth to produce additional electrical energy.

Solar energy can be used in homes to provide heat and electrical energy.

How can energy from the Sun be used by people?

INVESTIGATE Solar Energy

What improves the collection of solar energy?

PROCEDURE

1. Cover the top of one cup with white plastic, and cover the top of the other cup with black plastic. Secure the plastic with a rubber band.
2. Use the scissors to make a small hole in the center of each cup's plastic lid. Insert a thermometer through each opening.
3. Place the cups in direct sunlight, and record their temperatures every minute for 10 minutes.

WHAT DO YOU THINK?
- Which cup showed a greater temperature change? Why do you think this happened?
- Make a line graph of your results to show the change in temperature in each cup.

CHALLENGE Try the experiment again, using aluminum foil instead of white plastic. How do the results differ with the aluminum foil? Why might this be the case?

SKILL FOCUS
Observing

MATERIALS
- 2 plastic cups
- white plastic
- black plastic
- 2 rubber bands
- scissors
- 2 thermometers
- stopwatch
for Challenge:
- aluminum foil

TIME
20 minutes

Chapter 3: Energy 89

INVESTIGATE Solar Energy

PURPOSE To observe how the collection of solar energy is affected by the color of the collector

TIPS 20 min.
- The plastics should be the same thickness; garbage bags can be used.
- Be careful not to rip the plastic and aluminum; a faulty seal may lead to inaccurate data.

WHAT DO YOU THINK? *The cup with black plastic; the black plastic absorbs more sunlight. Check students' graphs.*

CHALLENGE *Aluminum foil will reflect sunlight but absorb more energy than the white plastic; a cup covered with aluminum foil should show a temperature increase between black plastic and white plastic.*

Datasheet, Solar Energy, p. 174

Technology Resources

Customize this student lab as needed or look for an alternative. Print rubrics to assess student lab reports.

Lab Generator CD-ROM

Teaching with Technology

If probeware is available, students can use a temperature probe in place of a thermometer. Graphing calculators can be used to graph students' data.

EXPLORE the BIG idea

Revisit "Hot Dog!" on p. 69. Have students explain why the hot dog cooked.

Ongoing Assessment

Evaluate advantages and disadvantages in energy conversions.

Ask: What is an advantage to heating a home with solar power? What is a disadvantage? *advantage: nonpolluting; disadvantage: materials are expensive*

Sample answer: *to produce electrical energy; to warm buildings*

DIFFERENTIATE INSTRUCTION

More Reading Support

D Why is solar power not commonly used? *It is inefficient and expensive.*

E How can the Sun's heat be used? *It can be trapped to provide heat.*

Alternative Assessment Have small groups orally present their data and graphs for peer review. Then lead a discussion to reach a consensus for each question.

Advanced Have interested students conduct research and make a poster presenting limitations and real sites or locations of one of the alternative energy sources discussed on pp. 88–90.

- Challenge and Extension, p. 173
- Challenge Reading, pp. 176–177

Chapter 3 **89**

Ongoing Assessment

Recognize how technology can improve the use of natural resources.

Ask: How can technology help conserve natural resources? *by making energy conversion more efficient*

CHECK YOUR READING Answer: *Wind has been used to propel ships, pump water, and grind grains. Now it is also used to produce electricity at windfarms.*

PHOTO CAPTION Answer: *to capture as much energy from the wind as possible*

Integrate the Sciences

A new branch of meteorology involves offshore wind power. Wind and wave characteristics are studied at sea for the purpose of developing offshore wind farms for electric power. Denmark is a global leader in this field because of strong political support and the mandatory purchase of wind power output by utilities.

Reinforce the BIG idea

Have students relate the section to the Big Idea.

 Reinforcing Key Concepts, p. 175

3.3 ASSESS & RETEACH

Assess

 Section 3.3 Quiz, p. 44

Reteach

Have students brainstorm the best locations (in terms of weather conditions) for using solar and wind energy. Use a weather map for reference. Then ask students to list the limitations of these alternative energy sources and brainstorm how technology might help.

Technology Resources

Have students visit ClassZone.com for reteaching of Key Concepts.

 CONTENT REVIEW

 CONTENT REVIEW CD-ROM

90 Unit 1: **Matter and Energy**

INFER Why might so many windmills be needed at a windfarm?

 Find out more about alternative energy sources.

Wind Energy

For many centuries, people have used the kinetic energy of wind to sail ships, and, by using windmills, to grind grain and pump water. More recently, windmills have been used to generate electrical energy. In the early 1900s, for example, windmills were already being used to produce electrical energy in rural areas of the United States.

Like the technological advances in the use of solar energy, advances in capturing and using wind energy have helped to improve its efficiency and usefulness. One way to better capture the wind's energy has been to build huge windmill farms in areas that receive a consistent amount of wind. Windmill farms are found in several states, including Kansas, California, and New York. Other methods of more efficiently capturing wind energy include the use of specially shaped windmill blades that are made of new, more flexible materials.

 How has the use of wind energy changed over time?

3.3 Review

KEY CONCEPTS

1. Provide an example of a common technology that does not efficiently convert energy. Explain.
2. Describe two ways in which hybrid cars are more energy-efficient than gasoline-powered cars.
3. List two advantages and two disadvantages of solar power.

CRITICAL THINKING

4. **Compare and Contrast** How are LEDs similar to incandescent light bulbs? How are they different?
5. **Synthesize** What are two ways in which the Sun's energy can be captured and used? How can both be used in a home?

CHALLENGE

6. **Draw Conclusions** Satellites orbiting Earth use solar cells as their source of electrical energy. Why are solar cells ideal energy sources for satellites?

90 Unit 1: **Matter and Energy**

ANSWERS

1. Sample answer: incandescent lights—heat instead of light

2. They use less fuel and convert heat from brakes into electrical energy.

3. advantages: clean, unlimited supplies; disadvantages: inefficient, expensive materials

4. Both produce light. LEDs are more efficient and have several applications. Incandescent lights are brighter than most LEDs.

5. solar cells for electricity; trapping heat to warm the building

6. They receive more constant sunlight.

MATH in SCIENCE

MATH TUTORIAL
CLASSZONE.COM
Click on Math Tutorial for more help with rates.

Indoor ice rinks require cooling systems that can keep ice frozen even when the outdoor temperature is 95°F.

SKILL: USING FORMULAS

Cool Efficiency

Energy efficiency is important because energy supplies are limited. The energy used by appliances such as air conditioners is measured in British thermal units, or BTUs. One BTU warms one pound of water by 1°F. The cooling ability of an air conditioner is measured by the number of BTUs it can move. Consider the number of BTUs that an air conditioning system must move in an ice rink.

An air conditioner typically has an energy efficiency ratio (EER) rating. The EER measures how efficiently a cooling system operates when the outdoor temperature is 95°F. The EER is the ratio of cooling per hour to the amount of electricity used, which is measured in watts. The higher the EER, the more energy efficient the air conditioner is.

$$EER = \frac{BTUs/hr}{watts\ used}$$

Example

Suppose an air conditioner uses 750 watts of electricity to cool 6000 BTUs per hour at 95°F. Calculate the air conditioner's EER.

(1) Use the formula above to calculate the EER.

$$EER = \frac{BTUs/hr}{watts\ used}$$

(2) Enter the known values into the formula.

$$EER = \frac{6000\ BTUs/hr}{750\ watts\ used}$$

(3) Solve the formula for the unknown value.

$$EER = \frac{6000\ BTUs/hr}{750\ watts\ used} = 8$$

ANSWER EER = 8 BTUs/hr per watt used

Answer the following questions.

1. What is the EER of a cooling system that uses 500 watts of electricity to move 6000 BTUs per hour at 95°F?

2. What is the EER of a cooling system that uses 1500 watts of electricity to move 12,000 BTUs per hour at 95°F?

3. Which air conditioner in the two questions above is more efficient?

CHALLENGE How many BTUs per hour would an air conditioner move at 95°F if it had an EER of 10 and used 1200 watts of electricity?

Chapter 3: Energy 91

MATH IN SCIENCE
Math Skills Practice for Science

Set Learning Goal
To use a mathematical formula to calculate the energy efficiency of cooling systems

Present the Science
A cooling system with a high EER rating is more efficient in that it uses less electricity to deliver a given amount of cooling power. Similarly, heating systems with high EER ratings more efficiently use energy to produce a given amount of warming power. An EER of 14 is close to the upper limit of current technology. Efficient window air conditioners have EER ratings of about 10. Central air conditioning systems have EER ratings of around 12.

Develop Algebra Skills
- Remind students that the numerator of a fraction is above the line and the denominator is below.
- To help students use the formula for calculating EER, remind them that the line in the formula means "divided by." Thus, the numerator, BTUs, per hour, should be divided by the denominator, watts.
- The units of an EER rating are BTUs per hour per watt. The rating measures output of the air conditioner divided by input.

Close
Ask: What other types of appliances could have an EER rating? *refrigerators, freezers, furnaces, hot water heaters*

 • Math Support, p. 181
• Math Practice, p. 182

Technology Resources
Students can visit **ClassZone.com** for practice with rates.

 MATH TUTORIAL

ANSWERS

1. 6000 BTUs/500 watts = 12 BTUs cooled/hr per watt used
2. 12,000 BTUs/1500 watts = 8 BTUs cooled/hr per watt used
3. the one in item 1

CHALLENGE EER = 10 = x BTUs/1200 watts
x = 10 (1200) = 12,000

Chapter 3 **91**

CHAPTER 3 • REVIEW

BACK TO

Make two sets of index cards with each card naming a form of energy. One set should be labeled "Original energy form" and the other "Converted to." Call on students to choose one card from each set and give an example of that energy conversion.

◑ KEY CONCEPTS SUMMARY

SECTION 3.1

Ask: What do all forms of energy have in common? *They all have the ability to produce a change.*

Ask: How does changing a skater's mass and speed affect his or her kinetic energy? *Increasing mass or speed increases kinetic energy. Decreasing either decreases kinetic energy.*

SECTION 3.2

Ask: When will kinetic energy decrease and potential energy increase? *after taking off from the jump as the skier is rising in the air*

Ask: Is kinetic energy destroyed when that occurs? *No, energy is never created nor destroyed*

SECTION 3.3

Ask: Why is it important to use technology to better use natural resources? *Many sources of energy are limited in supply, and those that aren't limited are used inefficiently.*

Review Concepts

- Big Idea Flow Chart, p. T17
- Chapter Outline, pp. T23–T24

Chapter Review

the BIG idea
Energy has different forms, but it is always conserved.

CONTENT REVIEW
CLASSZONE.COM

◑ KEY CONCEPTS SUMMARY

 Energy exists in different forms.
- Energy is the ability to cause a change.
- Different forms of energy produce changes in different ways.
- Kinetic energy depends on mass and speed.

Potential energy depends on position and chemical composition.

VOCABULARY
energy p. 72
kinetic energy p. 74
potential energy p. 75

 Energy can change forms but is never lost.
- Energy often needs to be transformed in order to produce a useful form of energy.
- The law of conservation of energy states that energy is never created or destroyed.

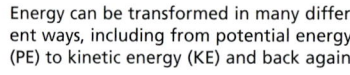
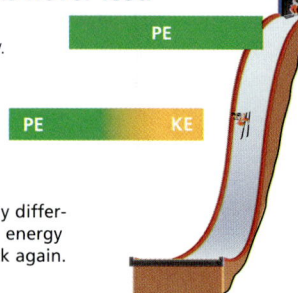

Energy can be transformed in many different ways, including from potential energy (PE) to kinetic energy (KE) and back again.

VOCABULARY
law of conservation of energy p. 82
energy efficiency p. 83

Technology improves the ways people use energy.
- Different forms of technology are being developed and used to improve the efficiency of energy conversions.
- Solar cells convert sunlight into electrical energy.

New solar cells convert light into electrical energy more efficiently than those in the past.

VOCABULARY
solar cell p. 88

92 Unit 1: Matter and Energy

Technology Resources

Have students visit **ClassZone.com** or use the CD-ROM for a cumulative review of concepts.

 CONTENT REVIEW

 CONTENT REVIEW CD-ROM

Engage students in a whole-class interactive review of Key Concepts. Edit content as you wish.

 POWER PRESENTATIONS

Reviewing Vocabulary

Review vocabulary terms by making a four square diagram for each term as shown in the example below. Include a definition, characteristics, examples from real life, and, if possible, nonexamples of the term.

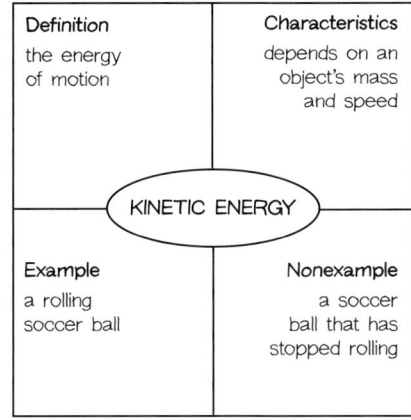

1. energy
2. potential energy
3. conservation of energy
4. energy efficiency

Reviewing Key Concepts

Multiple Choice *Choose the letter of the best answer.*

5. All forms of energy are a combination of
   a. mechanical energy and chemical energy
   b. chemical energy and kinetic energy
   c. potential energy and thermal energy
   d. potential energy and kinetic energy

6. Which type of energy is transmitted by vibrations of air?
   a. electromagnetic   c. nuclear
   b. sound   d. chemical

7. When energy is converted from one form to another, what is usually produced?
   a. chemical energy   c. heat
   b. gravity   d. nuclear energy

8. An object's kinetic energy is determined by its
   a. position and composition
   b. speed and position
   c. mass and speed
   d. height and width

9. Which of the following is a conversion from chemical energy to mechanical energy?
   a. a dark light bulb starting to glow
   b. food being heated in an oven
   c. a ball rolling down a hill
   d. a person lifting a weight

10. An energy-efficient electric fan converts a large portion of the electrical energy that enters it into
    a. an unwanted form of energy
    b. kinetic energy of the fan blades
    c. thermal energy in the fan's motor
    d. sound energy in the fan's motor

11. The energy in wind used to generate electricity is
    a. chemical energy
    b. sound energy
    c. potential energy
    d. kinetic energy

12. A skier on a hill has potential energy due to
    a. speed   c. compression
    b. energy efficiency   d. position

Short Answer *Write a short answer to each question.*

13. Explain how the law of conservation of energy might apply to an energy conversion that you observe in your daily life.

14. Describe a situation in which chemical energy is converted into mechanical energy. Explain each step of the energy conversion process.

Chapter 3: **Energy** 93

Reviewing Vocabulary

1. Sample answer—Definition: the ability to cause a change; Characteristics: is conserved; Examples: sound, chemical, mechanical; Nonexample: matter

2. Sample answer—Definition: stored energy; Characteristics: depends on position or chemical composition; Example: skier at top of ramp; Nonexample: skier at bottom of hill due to position

3. Sample answer—Definition: energy cannot be created or destroyed; Characteristics: energy may seem to disappear when it changes form, but it is transferred or changed; Example: air gains thermal energy (heat) transferred during a conversion

4. Sample answer—Definition: useful energy after an energy conversion; Characteristics: high efficiency—less energy is needed to run the appliance; Example: Inefficient light bulbs convert electrical energy to light and a large amount of heat.

Reviewing Key Concepts

5. d
6. b
7. c
8. c
9. d
10. b
11. d
12. d
13. Answers should suggest that the amount of energy entering a process may appear to decrease during an energy conversion but actually changes into a different energy form.
14. Answers could involve a process that uses chemical energy in a person's muscles to move or lift an object.

ASSESSMENT RESOURCES

UNIT ASSESSMENT BOOK
- Chapter Test A, pp. 45–48
- Chapter Test B, pp. 49–52
- Chapter Test C, pp. 53–56
- Alternative Assessment, pp. 57–58

SPANISH ASSESSMENT BOOK
Spanish Chapter Test, pp. 221–224

Technology Resources

Edit test items and answer choices.

 Test Generator CD-ROM

Visit ClassZone.com to extend test practice.

 Test Practice

Chapter 3 **93**

Thinking Critically

15. potential energy: 5 (or 1) because height is greatest; kinetic energy: 4 (or 2), because speed is greatest

16. 2; the skater's height above the ground begins to increase.

17. No, because the conversions between potential and kinetic energy are not 100% efficient, so some energy is being converted into unwanted forms.

18. Energy will be converted into heat and sound due to the friction of the skates against the ramp.

19. 5—all potential; 4—mostly kinetic, some potential; 3—all kinetic; 2—mostly kinetic, some potential; 1—all potential

20. Both convert sunlight into another energy form. Plants turn light into chemical energy; solar cells convert light into electrical energy.

21. Both are relatively inefficient and require a steady input of light or wind. New materials are being developed, and large groups of solar cells or windmills are used to capture as much energy as possible.

22. the machine that does not get hot, because less energy is being transformed through unwanted heat and more is being turned into the desired form of energy

23. 40; Energy must be conserved.

24. Answers might include striking a match; check students' diagrams.

the BIG idea

25. Answers will vary; check students' answers.

26. Answers will vary; check students' answers.

UNIT PROJECTS

Students should have begun designing their models or presentations by this time. Remind them to continue researching as needed. Encourage them to try different solutions to the problems they encounter.

 Unit Projects, pp. 5–10

94 Unit 1: **Matter and Energy**

Thinking Critically

The illustrations below show an in-line skater on a ramp. Use the illustrations to answer the next five questions.

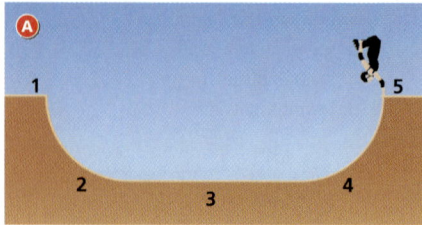

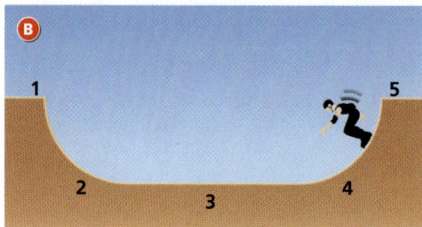

15. **OBSERVE** At what point in the illustrations would the skater have the most potential energy? the most kinetic energy? Explain.

16. **SYNTHESIZE** At what point in illustration B will the skater's kinetic energy begin to be changed back into potential energy? Explain.

17. **INFER** When the skater's kinetic energy is changed back into potential energy, will this amount of potential energy likely be equal to the skater's potential energy in illustration A? Why or why not?

18. **PREDICT** Describe how energy may appear to decrease in the example shown above. What energy conversions that produce unwanted forms of energy are occurring? Explain.

19. **SYNTHESIZE** Draw colored bars that might represent the potential energy and kinetic energy of the skater at each of the five labeled points on illustration A. Explain why you drew the bars the way you did. (*Hint:* See the illustration on p. 79.)

20. **SYNTHESIZE** How are plants and solar cells similar? How are the ways in which they capture sunlight and convert it into other forms of energy different? Explain.

21. **COMPARE** Explain how energy sources such as solar energy and wind energy have similar problems that must be overcome. How have scientists tried to address these problems?

22. **INFER** Suppose that one air conditioner becomes very hot when it is working but another air conditioner does not. Which air conditioner is more energy efficient? How can you tell?

23. **DRAW CONCLUSIONS** Suppose a vacuum cleaner uses 100 units of electrical energy. All of this energy is converted into thermal and sound energy (from the motor), and into the kinetic energy of air being pulled into the vacuum cleaner. If 60 units of electrical energy are converted into thermal energy and sound energy, how much electrical energy is converted into the desired form of energy? How do you know?

24. **COMMUNICATE** Describe a process in which energy changes forms at least twice. Draw and label a diagram that shows these energy conversions.

the BIG idea

25. **APPLY** Look again at the photograph on pages 68 and 69 and consider the opening question. How might your answer have changed after reading the chapter?

26. **COMMUNICATE** How have your ideas about energy and its different forms changed after reading the chapter? Provide an example from your life to describe how you would have thought of energy compared to how you might think about it now.

UNIT PROJECTS

If you need to do an experiment for your unit project, gather the materials. Be sure to allow enough time to observe results before the project is due.

94 Unit 1: **Matter and Energy**

MONITOR AND RETEACH

If students have trouble applying the concept of conservation of energy in items 13, 17, 18, and 23, explain that when one object gains energy, another object must have lost the same amount of energy. Divide a group of 25 paper clips into several smaller groups that represent different forms of energy. Explain that the paper clips can be moved from group to group, but that the total number will still equal 25.

Students may benefit from summarizing one or more sections of the chapter.

 Summarizing the Chapter, pp. 201–202

Standardized Test Practice

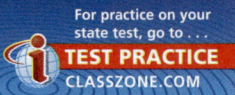

For practice on your state test, go to...
TEST PRACTICE
CLASSZONE.COM

Interpreting Graphs

Study the graph below. Then answer the first five questions.

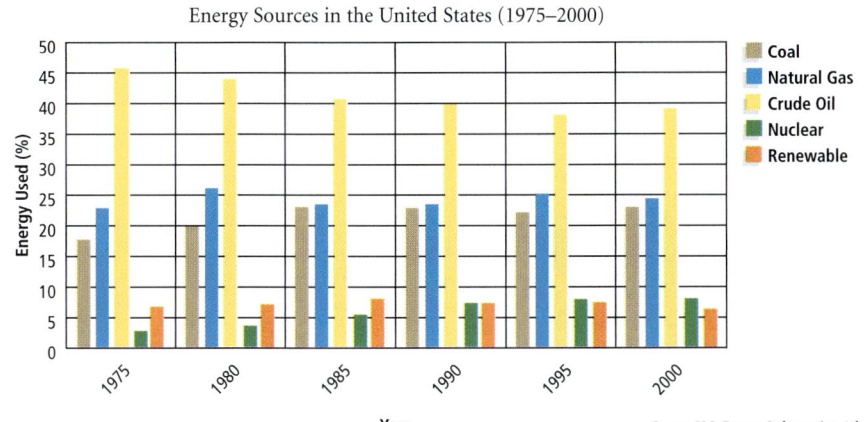

Energy Sources in the United States (1975–2000)

Source: U.S. Energy Information Administration, Monthly Energy Review (June 2003)

1. In which year did the greatest percentage of energy used in the United States come from crude oil?
   a. 1975
   b. 1980
   c. 1995
   d. 2000

2. What three sources of energy account for about 80 percent of all energy used in each year shown?
   a. coal, crude oil, nuclear
   b. natural gas, crude oil, renewable
   c. coal, natural gas, crude oil
   d. crude oil, nuclear, renewable

3. Which sources of energy show a greater percentage in 2000 as compared to 1980?
   a. crude oil, renewable
   b. natural gas, crude oil
   c. coal, nuclear
   d. coal, crude oil

4. The use of which energy source tended to decrease between 1975 and 2000?
   a. coal
   b. natural gas
   c. crude oil
   d. nuclear

5. The use of which source of energy steadily increased between 1975 and 1995?
   a. coal
   b. crude oil
   c. nuclear
   d. renewable

Extended Response

Answer the questions in detail. Include some of the terms from the word box on the right. Underline each term you use in your answers.

chemical energy	potential energy
electrical energy	sound energy
mechanical energy	thermal energy

6. When gasoline is burned in a moving car's engine, which forms of energy are being used? Which forms of energy are produced? Explain.

7. Name two appliances in your home that you believe are inefficient. What about them indicates that they may be inefficient?

Chapter 3: **Energy** 95

METACOGNITIVE ACTIVITY

Have students answer the following questions in their **Science Notebook:**

1. What misconceptions about energy did you have? Have these misconceptions been corrected?

2. Which topics in this chapter would you like to learn more about?

3. What have you learned from your research on your Unit Project?

Interpreting Graphs

1. a   2. c   3. c   4. c   5. c

Extended Response

6. RUBRIC
4 points for a response that correctly answers both questions, gives an accurate explanation, and uses the following terms correctly:
- chemical energy
- mechanical energy
- sound energy
- thermal energy
- potential energy

Sample: The <u>chemical energy</u> of gasoline is <u>potential energy</u> that is converted into several other forms of energy listed when a car is driven. For example, <u>sound energy</u> and <u>thermal energy</u> are produced in the car's engine and <u>mechanical energy</u> moves the car.

3 points correctly answers one of the questions, gives an accurate explanation, and uses the terms correctly
2 points correctly answers at least one question but fails to give an accurate explanation, and uses at least three terms correctly
1 point does not correctly answer either question and fails to give an accurate explanation, but uses at least three terms correctly

7. RUBRIC
4 points for a response that correctly answers both questions and gives two correct examples.

Sample: The refrigerator and air conditioner are inefficient. They produce unwanted heat and <u>sound energy</u> from <u>electrical energy</u>.

3 points correctly answers both questions and gives one correct example
2 points correctly answers both questions but does not give any correct examples
1 point correctly answers one question and gives one correct example

Chapter 3

TIMELINES in Science

FOCUS

▶ Set Learning Goals
Students will
- Observe how scientists created new theories of temperature and heat by building on earlier observations.
- Learn the characteristics of temperature and heat and how they are measured.
- Write a procedure for an experiment to test a specific method of calculating temperature.

National Science Education Standards
A.9.a–b, A.9.d–g, Understandings About Scientific Inquiry

E.6.a–c Understandings About Science and Technology

F.5.a–e, F.5.g Science and Technology in Society

G.1.a–b Science as a Human Endeavor

G.2.a Nature of Science

G.3.a–c History of Science

INSTRUCT

Point out to students that the top half of the timeline shows major events in the scientific study of temperature and heat and the years in which they occurred. The bottom half addresses the developments in technology based on the scientific discoveries in the top half. The gap between 320 B.C. and A.D. 1600 represents a block of time that has been omitted.

Teach from Visuals
350 B.C. To help students better understand the ancient Greek theory of matter, have them review the diagram of the basic qualities of matter. Ask students to create a table of the four basic substances and their characteristics to illustrate which substances were thought to have which two qualities.

96 Unit 1: **Matter and Energy**

TIMELINES in Science

ABOUT TEMPERATURE AND HEAT

Most likely, the first fires early people saw were caused by lightning. Eventually, people realized that fire provided warmth and light, and they learned how to make it themselves. During the Stone Age 25,000 years ago, people used firewood to cook food as well as to warm and light their shelters. Wood was the first fuel.

This timeline shows a few of the many steps on the path toward understanding temperature and heat. Notice how the observations and ideas of previous thinkers sparked new theories by later scientists. The boxes below the timeline show how technology has led to new insights and to applications related to temperature and heat.

445 B.C.
Four Basic Substances Named
Greek philosopher Empedocles says that everything on Earth is made of some combination of four basic substances: earth, air, fire, and water. Different types of matter have different qualities depending on how they combine these substances.

350 B.C.
Aristotle Expands Theory of Matter
Greek philosopher Aristotle names four basic qualities of matter: dryness, wetness, hotness, and coldness. Each of the four basic substances has two of these qualities.

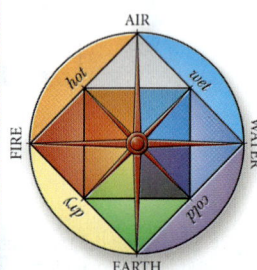

EVENTS
480 B.C.   440 B.C.   400 B.C.   360 B.C.   320 B.C.

APPLICATIONS AND TECHNOLOGY

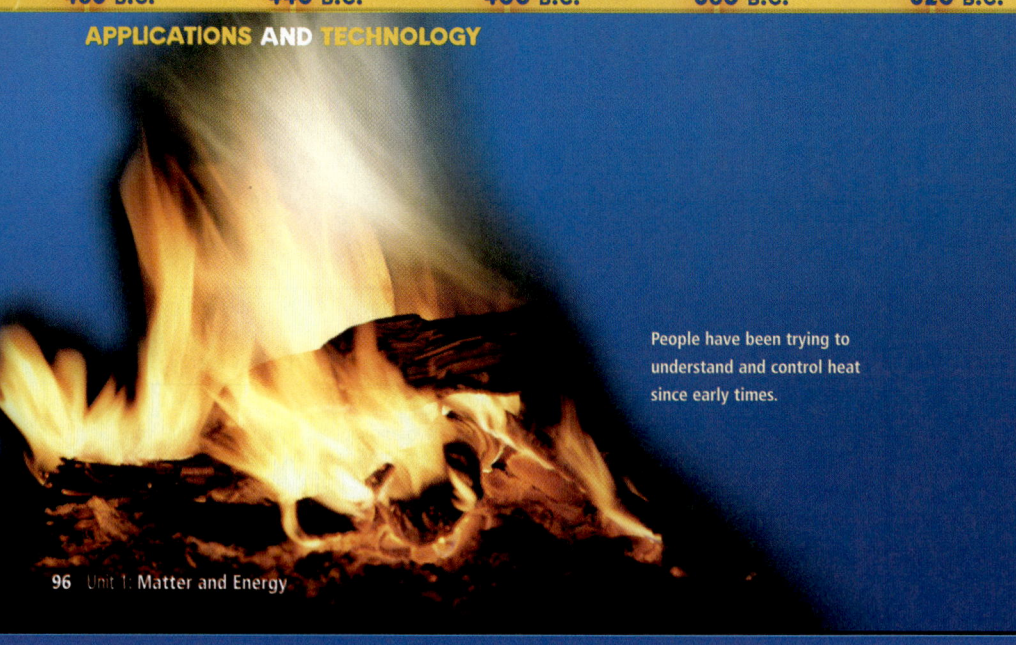

People have been trying to understand and control heat since early times.

96 Unit 1: Matter and Energy

DIFFERENTIATE INSTRUCTION

Below Level For students who may have difficulty understanding how information is organized on a timeline, point out the dates on the center line. Explain how the dates become more recent when read from left to right. Show them the lines connecting the event boxes to the specific dates on the timeline. Discuss how timelines are a good way to show the order in which events happened.

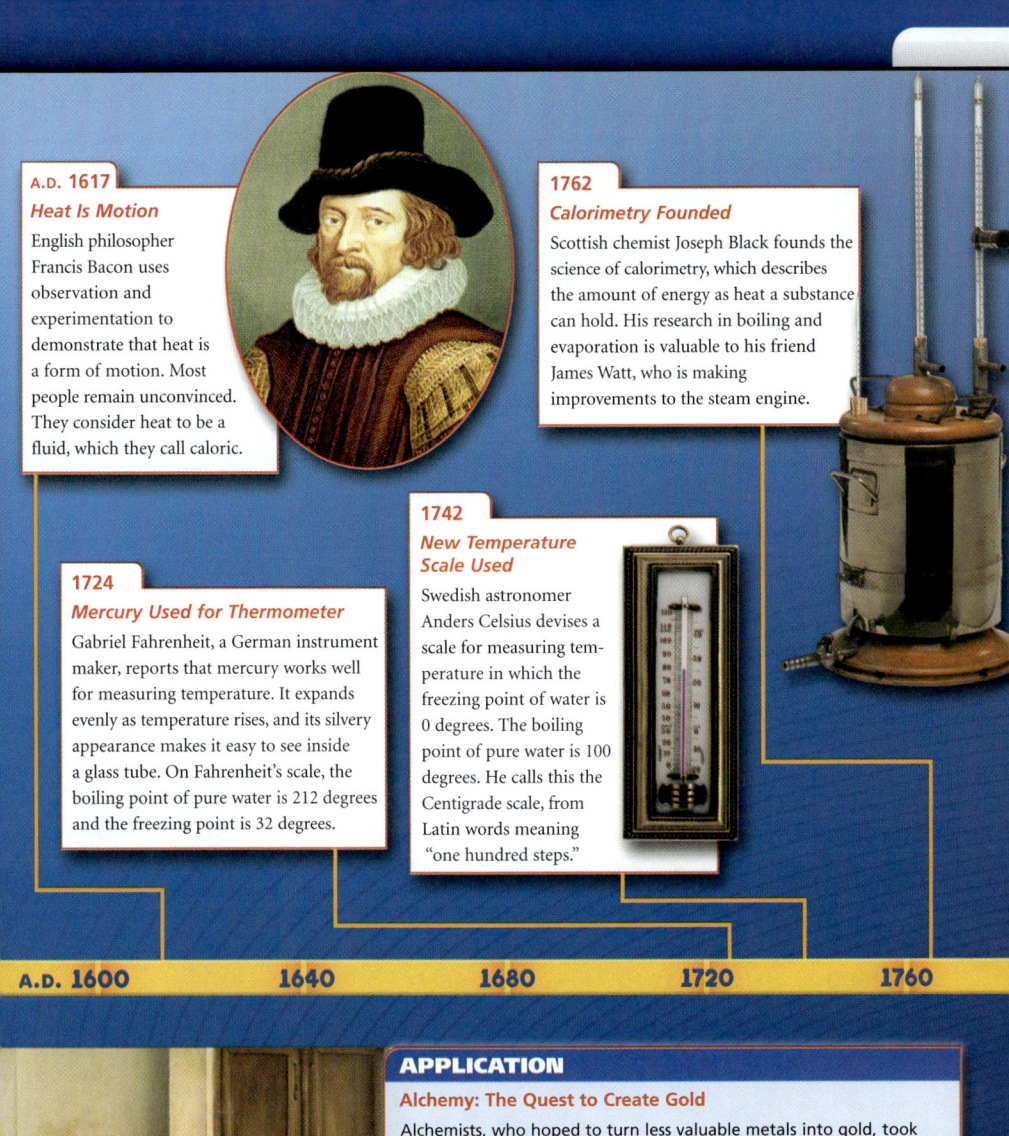

A.D. 1617
Heat Is Motion
English philosopher Francis Bacon uses observation and experimentation to demonstrate that heat is a form of motion. Most people remain unconvinced. They consider heat to be a fluid, which they call caloric.

1762
Calorimetry Founded
Scottish chemist Joseph Black founds the science of calorimetry, which describes the amount of energy as heat a substance can hold. His research in boiling and evaporation is valuable to his friend James Watt, who is making improvements to the steam engine.

1724
Mercury Used for Thermometer
Gabriel Fahrenheit, a German instrument maker, reports that mercury works well for measuring temperature. It expands evenly as temperature rises, and its silvery appearance makes it easy to see inside a glass tube. On Fahrenheit's scale, the boiling point of pure water is 212 degrees and the freezing point is 32 degrees.

1742
New Temperature Scale Used
Swedish astronomer Anders Celsius devises a scale for measuring temperature in which the freezing point of water is 0 degrees. The boiling point of pure water is 100 degrees. He calls this the Centigrade scale, from Latin words meaning "one hundred steps."

A.D. 1600 — 1640 — 1680 — 1720 — 1760

APPLICATION
Alchemy: The Quest to Create Gold
Alchemists, who hoped to turn less valuable metals into gold, took up the Greeks' theory of the four basic substances. They thought they could convert one substance into another by changing the balance of the four basic substances. Their ideas spread to the Byzantine Empire after A.D. 641, where these concepts were combined with advances in techniques for manipulating heat. Alchemy spread to Western Europe during the 1100s and 1200s.

Alchemists used chemical processes such as heating in furnaces, boiling in pots or cauldrons, distillation, pounding, and grinding. Because it was difficult to control the temperature, and thermometers had not yet been invented, alchemists usually had many different kinds of furnaces. Although alchemy is not considered a true science today, it did contribute methods and processes still used by chemists. It remained popular until around 1700.

Scientific Process
1724 Gabriel Fahrenheit improved on existing technology to measure temperature through his observations and investigations. He found that mercury was more accurate in measuring temperature than the alcohol thermometers of the time. Fahrenheit then developed the mercury thermometer, which we still use today.

Sharing Results
1762 Chemist Joseph Black experimented with the amount of heat a substance can hold. His results helped James Watt, who was working on improvements to the steam engine. Ask students what research Black was conducting that was critical to Watt's work. *boiling and evaporation*

Mathematics Connection
1742 The Celsius scale is the metric scale for measuring temperature. Most countries use the Celsius scale for everyday temperature measurement. Scientists also use this scale for their experiments. In the United States, the Fahrenheit scale is used to measure temperature. To convert a Celsius temperature to a Fahrenheit temperature, multiply the Celsius temperature by 9/5 and then add 32 to the result. Write the formula °F = 9/5(°C) + 32 on the board. Ask students to convert 35°C to Fahrenheit. *95°F*

Application
ALCHEMY While alchemy is no longer considered a true science, for some time it was a major source of chemical knowledge. Because alchemists experimented with turning metals such as lead into gold, they gained wide knowledge about chemical substances. The alchemist's workshop became the forerunner of the modern chemistry laboratory. Alchemists used tools such as funnels, beakers, and balances. Although alchemists failed to produce gold from other materials, their experimentation was successful in other ways. Ask students what impact alchemy had on science and technology. *Alchemy created many chemical processes and tools that are still used by chemists today.*

DIFFERENTIATE INSTRUCTION
Advanced Have students use the temperature conversion formula shown in the Mathematics Connection on this page to convert Fahrenheit to Celsius. Ask students what the formula for the conversion is. *°C = 5/9 (°F − 32)* Then ask students to convert 98.6°F to Celsius. *37°C*

Scientific Process

Refer students to Francis Bacon's observations on page 97. Despite his experiments, people still believed that heat is fluid rather than a form of motion. Thompson's observations about friction and heat provided evidence that contradicted the leading hypothesis of the time. With evidence against the fluid theory of heat mounting, scientists began to consider seriously other ideas about the nature of heat.

Technology

VACUUM FLASK The reflective silver coating that a vacuum flask, or thermos, uses to keep fluids hot is the same type of technology that NASA used on the Mars rover. To keep heat from escaping out of the rover body and cold air from entering during landing, the outside of the rover's body was painted gold. This coating helps reduce energy that is spread outward from the rover's body. It also prevents the body from emitting heat energy into its cold surroundings.

Integrate the Sciences

One way in which clouds are formed is by convection, that is, when warm air rises. The Sun's heat causes Earth's water (from lakes, oceans, and rivers) to evaporate into the air. When that air is heated, it becomes less dense than the surrounding air. As a result, it rises. As the moist air continues to rise, it expands and becomes cooler. The water vapor in the air condenses and forms clouds.

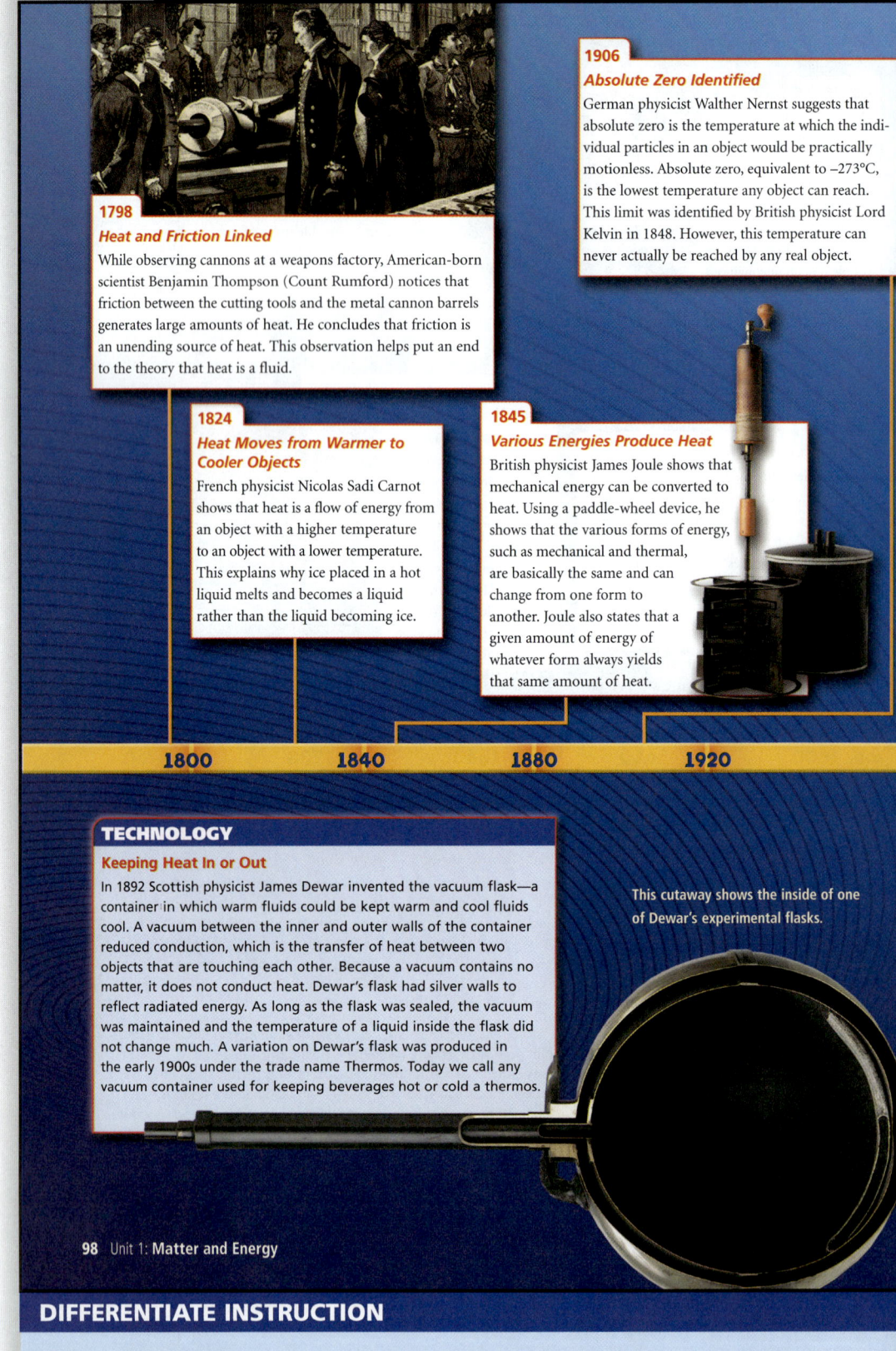

1798
Heat and Friction Linked
While observing cannons at a weapons factory, American-born scientist Benjamin Thompson (Count Rumford) notices that friction between the cutting tools and the metal cannon barrels generates large amounts of heat. He concludes that friction is an unending source of heat. This observation helps put an end to the theory that heat is a fluid.

1824
Heat Moves from Warmer to Cooler Objects
French physicist Nicolas Sadi Carnot shows that heat is a flow of energy from an object with a higher temperature to an object with a lower temperature. This explains why ice placed in a hot liquid melts and becomes a liquid rather than the liquid becoming ice.

1845
Various Energies Produce Heat
British physicist James Joule shows that mechanical energy can be converted to heat. Using a paddle-wheel device, he shows that the various forms of energy, such as mechanical and thermal, are basically the same and can change from one form to another. Joule also states that a given amount of energy of whatever form always yields that same amount of heat.

1906
Absolute Zero Identified
German physicist Walther Nernst suggests that absolute zero is the temperature at which the individual particles in an object would be practically motionless. Absolute zero, equivalent to −273°C, is the lowest temperature any object can reach. This limit was identified by British physicist Lord Kelvin in 1848. However, this temperature can never actually be reached by any real object.

TECHNOLOGY
Keeping Heat In or Out
In 1892 Scottish physicist James Dewar invented the vacuum flask—a container in which warm fluids could be kept warm and cool fluids cool. A vacuum between the inner and outer walls of the container reduced conduction, which is the transfer of heat between two objects that are touching each other. Because a vacuum contains no matter, it does not conduct heat. Dewar's flask had silver walls to reflect radiated energy. As long as the flask was sealed, the vacuum was maintained and the temperature of a liquid inside the flask did not change much. A variation on Dewar's flask was produced in the early 1900s under the trade name Thermos. Today we call any vacuum container used for keeping beverages hot or cold a thermos.

This cutaway shows the inside of one of Dewar's experimental flasks.

DIFFERENTIATE INSTRUCTION

Below Level **1798** Have students rub their hands together to demonstrate how friction produces heat.

2003
Wasps Stay Cool
Scientists in Israel have found evidence that some wasps have an internal air-conditioning system. Like a refrigerator, the wasp uses energy to stay cooler than the air around it. The energy may come from several sources, such as the energy generated by an electric current produced when the wasp's shell is exposed to sunlight. This ability to stay cool allows wasps to hunt for food even on very hot days.

RESOURCE CENTER
CLASSZONE.COM
Learn about current temperature and heat research.

1960   2000

INTO THE FUTURE

As scientists are able to create colder and colder temperatures in the laboratory, they gain new insight into the scientific theories that explain temperature and heat. Advances in our knowledge of temperature and heat will lead to future applications.

- Scientists have developed a car that can run on hydrogen cooled into its liquid state. Before cars that run on this supercooled fuel become common, a system of refueling stations must be established.
- Understanding how some materials, such as silicon, conduct energy as heat may result in medical advances through better scanning and imaging technology.
- At temperatures approaching absolute zero (−273°C), a unique state of matter can be formed that is different from a solid, liquid, or gas. This rare state of matter could possibly be used to help produce extremely small circuits for use in miniature computers or other electronics.

ACTIVITIES

Design a Procedure
Many people claim that it is possible to determine the temperature by listening to the chirping of crickets. Crickets are sensitive to changes in air temperature and chirp more quickly when the temperature rises. To calculate the temperature in degrees Celsius, count the number of chirps in 7 seconds and add 5.

Write a procedure for an experiment that would test this claim. What factors would you consider testing? What range of temperatures would you test?

Writing About Science
Alchemy has fascinated people for centuries. Research its influence on both the technology and procedures of modern chemistry. Write a short report.

APPLICATION
Using Thermal Energy from Ponds
Ponds can be used to store solar energy. The goal is to turn the solar energy into energy people can use. Salt must be added to the ponds, however, so that the water at the bottom is denser than the water at the top. This prevents thermal energy stored on the bottom from moving up to the surface, where it would be lost to the air through evaporation. A net on the surface helps prevent wind from mixing the water layers.

DIFFERENTIATE INSTRUCTION

Advanced Encourage students to trace the development of ideas from the ancient Greeks to the present. Students might create a visual or model that represents each new idea as building on the previous idea.

Application
USING THERMAL ENERGY FROM PONDS The idea of using ponds with a salt gradient to collect and store thermal energy was developed after natural examples of such ponds were discovered. The energy from these ponds can be used for applications such as purifying water and producing electricity. Ask students what some of the benefits of using solar-energy ponds might be. *provides clean, cost-effective electricity*

INTO THE FUTURE

Have students divide into small groups. Have each group come up with a list of possible inventions or ideas based on what they read about temperature and heat. An example might be a portable solar-powered DVD player. Then have each group prepare a presentation about their invention, describing what it is and how it works. Presentations might consist of bulletin-board displays, videos done as news segments, or oral reports with visual aids.

ACTIVITIES

Design a Procedure
Refer students to the steps of the scientific process as they write their procedure for the experiment. Remind them to include in their procedure ways to record findings clearly.

Writing About Science
Suggest that students look up the history of alchemy on the Internet or in the library. Some might focus on contributions of a specific culture, such as Egyptian, Chinese, Indian, or Islamic alchemists.

Technology Resources
Students can visit **ClassZone.com** for information about temperature and heat.

CHAPTER 4: Temperature and Heat

Physical Science
UNIFYING PRINCIPLES

PRINCIPLE 1
Matter is made of particles too small to see.

PRINCIPLE 2
Matter changes form and moves from place to place.

PRINCIPLE 3
Energy changes from one form to another, but it cannot be created or destroyed.

PRINCIPLE 4
Physical forces affect the movement of all matter on Earth and throughout the universe.

Unit 1: Matter and Energy
BIG IDEAS

**CHAPTER 1
Introduction to Matter**
Everything that has mass and takes up space is matter.

**CHAPTER 2
Properties of Matter**
Matter has properties that can be changed by physical and chemical processes.

**CHAPTER 3
Energy**
Energy has different forms, but it is always conserved.

**CHAPTER 4
Temperature and Heat**
Heat is a flow of energy due to temperature differences.

CHAPTER 4
KEY CONCEPTS

SECTION 1
Temperature depends on particle movement.
1. All matter is made of moving particles.
2. Temperature can be measured.

SECTION 2
Energy flows from warmer to cooler objects.
1. Heat is different from temperature.
2. Some substances change temperature more easily than others.

SECTION 3
The transfer of energy as heat can be controlled.
1. Energy moves as heat in three ways.
2. Different materials are used to control the transfer of energy.

 The Big Idea Flow Chart is available on p. T25 in the **UNIT TRANSPARENCY BOOK**.

99A Unit 1: Matter Tend Energy

Previewing Content

SECTION

 Temperature depends on particle movement. pp. 103–109

1. **All matter is made of moving particles.**
   The **kinetic theory of matter** states that all the particles in matter are constantly in motion. As a result, all particles have kinetic energy. Particles in solids, liquids, and gases move differently.
   - Particles in a solid vibrate in fixed positions but do not move past each other. Particles in a liquid are not tightly bound to each other, as in a solid, and slide past each other. Particles in a gas are separated by greater distances than those in a solid or liquid.
   - All the particles in a substance are not moving at the same speed and can change speeds.
   - **Temperature** is a measurement of the average kinetic energy of all particles in an object or location.

2. **Temperature can be measured.**
   The two common temperature scales (Fahrenheit and Celsius) are based on the physical properties of pure water and are expressed in terms of degrees. A third temperature scale is the Kelvin scale, which is an absolute temperature scale. The zero point of the Kelvin scale is absolute zero, which is the complete absence of particle movement. Absolute zero is 0 K, which is equal to −273.15°C.

   Thermometers measure temperature. Often, the physical property used to measure temperature is expansion or contraction. All gases, many liquids, and most solids expand when temperature increases.
   - Thermometers filled with a liquid (alcohol or mercury) measure temperature through the uniform expansion or contraction of the liquid over a wide range of temperatures.
   - Thermometers can also measure temperature through electrical resistance, infrared radiation, and the differential expansion of materials.

SECTION

 Energy flows from warmer to cooler objects. pp. 110–115

1. **Heat is different from temperature.**
   Heat, temperature, and thermal energy are closely related but not the same.
   - **Temperature** is the average kinetic energy of particles in a substance or location.
   - **Heat** is a flow of energy from an object or location at a higher temperature to an object or location at a lower temperature. The transfer of energy through heat continues as long as the temperature difference exists. When energy is transferred in this way, the thermal energy of both objects or locations changes.
   - **Thermal energy** is the total kinetic energy of particles in a substance or location.

   The most common units of heat measurement are the calorie and the joule.
   - A **calorie** is the amount of energy needed to raise the temperature of 1 gram of water by 1° C.
   - A Calorie with a capital *C*—the measure used with food and nutrition—is a kilocalorie, or 1000 calories.
   - A **joule** is the standard scientific unit for measuring energy. One calorie is equal to 4.18 joules, so 4.18 joules of energy raises the temperature of 1 gram of water by 1°C.

2. **Some substances change temperature more easily than others.**
   Each substance needs to absorb a different amount of energy in order for its temperature to increase. A substance's **specific heat** is the amount of energy that is required for 1 gram of that substance to increase in temperature by 1°C.

   Any amount of a particular substance has the same specific heat. However, the more mass an object has, the more energy is required to produce an increase in its temperature and, conversely, the more energy must be released to produce a decrease in temperature.

 MISCONCEPTION DATABASE
CLASSZONE.COM Background on student misconceptions

Common Misconceptions

CONSTANT MOTION OF PARTICLES Students may have difficulty understanding that all particles in matter are in constant motion. Particles in solids vibrate in place, particles in liquids slide past one another, and particles in gases move freely in all directions.

 This misconception is addressed on p. 104.

DEFINITION OF TEMPERATURE Students may think that temperature is a measure of an object's heat. Temperature measures the average kinetic energy of the particles in an object.

 This misconception is addressed in Teach Difficult Concepts on p. 105.

Previewing Content

SECTION

 The transfer of energy as heat can be controlled. pp. 116–123

1. **Energy moves as heat in three ways.**
   Energy is transferred between objects or locations when there are temperature differences between them. Depending on both the medium and the objects themselves, energy can be transferred by conduction, convection, or radiation.
   - **Conduction** is the process through which energy is transferred through physical contact. Particles of a warmer object collide with particles of a cooler object and transfer some of their energy to the cooler object. Materials that easily transfer energy are **conductors**; those that are poor conductors are called **insulators**.
   - **Convection** is the process that transfers energy in gases and liquids. Differences in density between substances are produced by differences in temperature. A warmer region of gas or liquid is less dense than a cooler region, due to thermal expansion. The warmer, less dense gas or liquid is pushed up by cooler, denser gas or liquid that sinks in underneath. The cycle of convection accounts for currents in bodies of water and winds in the atmosphere.
   - **Radiation** is energy that travels as electromagnetic waves, such as visible light, infrared light, and x-rays. All objects radiate at least a small amount of energy. Often, when radiation is absorbed by an object, the transfer of energy as heat occurs. Radiation differs from conduction and convection in that it can transfer energy through a vacuum.

2. **Different materials are used to control the transfer of energy.**
   Materials are used for different purposes depending on whether they are good or poor conductors of energy. Many insulators contain or trap a layer of air, which is a poor conductor. Human-made insulators are similar to, and often based upon, insulators found in nature.

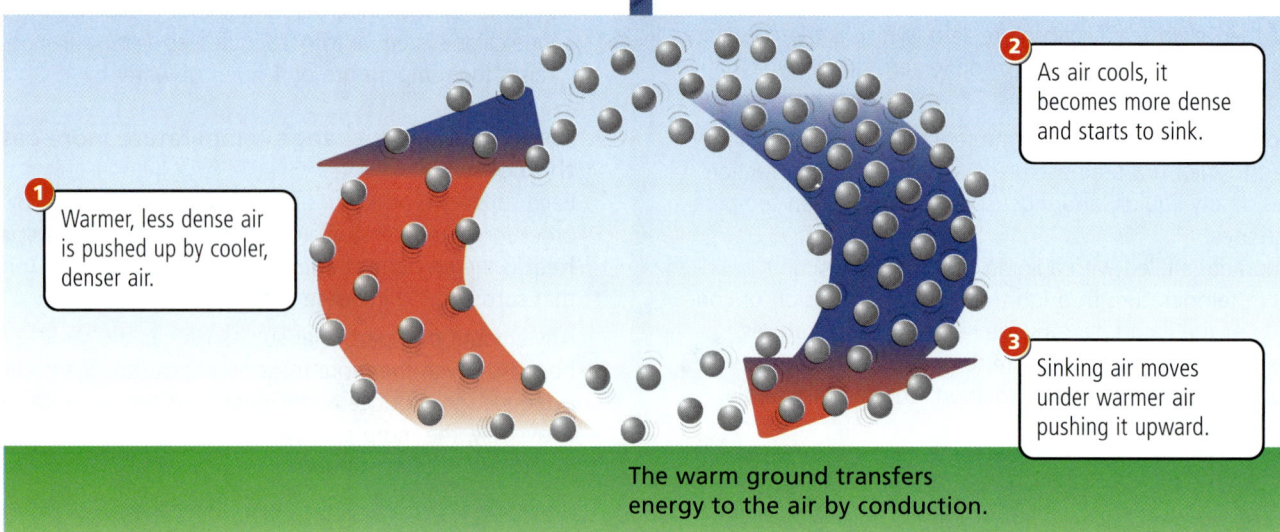

1. Warmer, less dense air is pushed up by cooler, denser air.
2. As air cools, it becomes more dense and starts to sink.
3. Sinking air moves under warmer air pushing it upward.

The warm ground transfers energy to the air by conduction.

Common Misconceptions

HEAT Some students may think that heat is a fluid that literally flows from one object to another and that heat and cold are different, rather than being at opposite ends of an energy flow. Heat is the flow of energy from a warm substance to a cooler substance.

 This misconception is addressed on p. 111.

 MISCONCEPTION DATABASE
CLASSZONE.COM Background on student misconceptions

DIRECTION OF HEAT FLOW Because students have often heard that heat rises, they may think that heat only travels upward. Heat can transfer energy in all directions, depending upon the process that is involved.

 This misconception is addressed on p. 118.

99C   Unit 1: Matter and Energy

Previewing Labs

EXPLORE the BIG idea

Moving Colors, p. 101
Students observe food coloring in hot and cold water to investigate motion and temperature.

TIME 10 minutes
MATERIALS 2 plastic cups, hot and cold water, eyedropper, food coloring

Does It Chill? p. 101
Students investigate how soil acts as an insulator.

TIME 30 minutes
MATERIALS outdoor thermometer, paper cup, freezer, soil, stopwatch

Internet Activity: Kinetic Theory, p. 101
Students observe the relationship between the kinetic energy of particles and temperature.

TIME 20 minutes
MATERIALS computer with Internet access

SECTION 1

EXPLORE Temperature, p. 103
Students discover how a transfer of energy and increased motion produce an increase in temperature.

TIME 10 minutes
MATERIALS large rubber band

INVESTIGATE Temperature Measurements, p. 107
Students make thermometers and observe how thermal expansion can be used to measure temperature.

TIME 30 minutes
MATERIALS small plastic bottle, alcohol solution, food coloring, clear plastic straw, clay, bowl, ice water, hot tap water

SECTION 2

INVESTIGATE Heat Transfer, p. 112
Students investigate the specific heat of different materials by measuring a change in temperature.

TIME 30 minutes
MATERIALS graduated cylinder, balance, room-temperature water, pennies, aluminum foil, 100 mL beaker, 3 plastic cups, hot tap water, thermometer, stopwatch

SECTION 3

EXPLORE Conduction, p. 116
Students observe the direction in which energy is transferred through direct contact between objects at different temperatures.

TIME 10 minutes
MATERIALS 500 mL beaker, hot tap water, cold water, 2 thermometers, stopwatch, 200 mL beaker

CHAPTER INVESTIGATION
Insulators, pp. 122–123
Students design and test an insulated bottle to slow a change in the temperature of water as compared to a noninsulated control bottle.

TIME 40 minutes
MATERIALS 2 small plastic bottles, 2 thermometers, modeling clay, graduated cylinder, hot or cold tap water, foam packing peanuts, plastic wrap, aluminum foil, soil, sand, rubber bands, coffee can, beaker, stopwatch, graph paper

R Additional INVESTIGATION, Observing Convection, A, B, & C, pp. 251–259; Teacher Instructions, pp. 262–263

Chapter 4: **Temperature and Heat** 99D

Previewing Chapter Resources

	INTEGRATED TECHNOLOGY	LABS AND ACTIVITIES
CHAPTER 4 **Temperature and Heat**	**CLASSZONE.COM** • eEdition Plus • EasyPlanner Plus • Misconception Database • Content Review • Test Practice • Simulations • Resource Centers • Internet Activity: Kinetic Theory • Math Tutorial **SCILINKS.ORG** **CD-ROMS** • eEdition • EasyPlanner • Power Presentations • Content Review • Lab Generator • Test Generator **AUDIO CDS** • Audio Readings • Audio Readings in Spanish	EXPLORE the Big Idea, p. 101 • Moving Colors • Does It Chill? • Internet Activity: Kinetic Theory **UNIT RESOURCE BOOK** Unit Projects, pp. 5–10 **Lab Generator CD-ROM** Generate customized labs.
SECTION 1 **Temperature depends on particle movement.** pp. 103–109 Time: 2 periods (1 block) Lesson Plan, pp. 203–204	• **RESOURCE CENTER,** Temperature and Temperature Scales • **MATH TUTORIAL** **UNIT TRANSPARENCY BOOK** • Big Idea Flow Chart, p. T25 • Daily Vocabulary Scaffolding, p. T26 • Note-Taking Model, p. T27 • 3-Minute Warm-Up, p. T28	• EXPLORE Temperature, p. 103 • INVESTIGATE Temperature Measurements, p. 107 • Math in Science, p. 109 **UNIT RESOURCE BOOK** • Datasheet, Temperature Measurements, p. 212 • Math Support, p. 240 • Math Practice, p. 241
SECTION 2 **Energy flows from warmer to cooler objects.** pp. 110–115 Time: 2 periods (1 block) Lesson Plan, pp. 214–215	**RESOURCE CENTER,** Thermal Energy **UNIT TRANSPARENCY BOOK** • Daily Vocabulary Scaffolding, p. T26 • 3-Minute Warm-Up, p. T28	• INVESTIGATE Heat Transfer, p. 112 • Science on the Job, p. 115 **UNIT RESOURCE BOOK** Datasheet, Heat Transfer, p. 223
SECTION 3 **The transfer of energy as heat can be controlled.** pp. 116–123 Time: 4 periods (2 blocks) Lesson Plan, pp. 225–226	**SIMULATION,** Conduction, Convection, or Radiation **UNIT TRANSPARENCY BOOK** • Big Idea Flow Chart, p. T25 • Daily Vocabulary Scaffolding, p. T26 • 3-Minute Warm-Up, p. T29 • "Insulation" Visual, p. T30 • Chapter Outline, pp. T31–T32	• EXPLORE Conduction, p. 116 • CHAPTER INVESTIGATION, Insulators, pp. 122–123 **UNIT RESOURCE BOOK** • CHAPTER INVESTIGATION, Insulators, A, B, & C, pp. 242–250 • Additional INVESTIGATION, Observing Convection, A, B, & C, pp. 251–259

99E Unit 1: **Matter and Energy**

KEY TO ICONS CD/CD-ROM  Teacher Edition UNIT TRANSPARENCY BOOK  SPANISH ASSESSMENT BOOK
 INTERNET Pupil Edition  UNIT RESOURCE BOOK UNIT ASSESSMENT BOOK  SCIENCE TOOLKIT

READING AND REINFORCEMENT

ASSESSMENT

STANDARDS

- Description Wheel, B20–21
- Choose Your Own Strategy, C35–44
- Daily Vocabulary Scaffolding, H1–8

 UNIT RESOURCE BOOK
- Vocabulary Practice, pp. 237–238
- Decoding Support, p. 239
- Summarizing the Chapter, pp. 260–261

- Chapter Review, pp. 125–126
- Standardized Test Practice, p. 127

 UNIT ASSESSMENT BOOK
- Diagnostic Test, pp. 59–60
- Chapter Test, A, B, & C, pp. 64–75
- Alternative Assessment, pp. 76–77
- Unit Test, A, B, C, pp. 78–89

- Spanish Chapter Test, pp. 225–228
- Spanish Unit Test, pp. 229–232

National Standards
A.1–8, A.9.a–g, B.3.a–b, E.2–5

See p. 100 for the standards.

 Audio Readings CD
Listen to Pupil Edition.

 Audio Readings in Spanish CD
Listen to Pupil Edition in Spanish.

 Test Generator CD-ROM
Generate customized tests.

 Lab Generator CD-ROM
Rubrics for Labs

 UNIT RESOURCE BOOK
- Reading Study Guide, A & B, pp. 205–208
- Spanish Reading Study Guide, pp. 209–210
- Challenge and Extension, p. 211
- Reinforcing Key Concepts, p. 213

 Ongoing Assessment, pp. 104–108

 Section 4.1 Review, p. 108

 UNIT ASSESSMENT BOOK
Section 4.1 Quiz, p. 61

National Standards
A.2–8, A.9.a–c, A.9.e–f, B.3.a

 UNIT RESOURCE BOOK
- Reading Study Guide, A & B, pp. 216–219
- Spanish Reading Study Guide, pp. 220–221
- Challenge and Extension, p. 222
- Reinforcing Key Concepts, p. 224

 Ongoing Assessment, pp. 110–114

 Section 4.2 Review, p. 114

 UNIT ASSESSMENT BOOK
Section 4.2 Quiz, p. 62

National Standards
A.2–7, A.9.a–b, A.9.d–f, B.3.a–b

 UNIT RESOURCE BOOK
- Reading Study Guide, A & B, pp. 227–230
- Spanish Reading Study Guide, pp. 231–232
- Challenge and Extension, p. 233
- Reinforcing Key Concepts, p. 234
- Challenge Reading, pp. 235–236

 Ongoing Assessment, pp. 117–121

 Section 4.3 Review, p. 121

 UNIT ASSESSMENT BOOK
Section 4.3 Quiz, p. 63

National Standards
A.1–8, A.9.a–g, B.3.a, E.2–5

Chapter 4: **Temperature and Heat** 99F

Previewing Resources for Differentiated Instruction

CHAPTER INVESTIGATION

Leveled resources present the same concepts for different abilities.

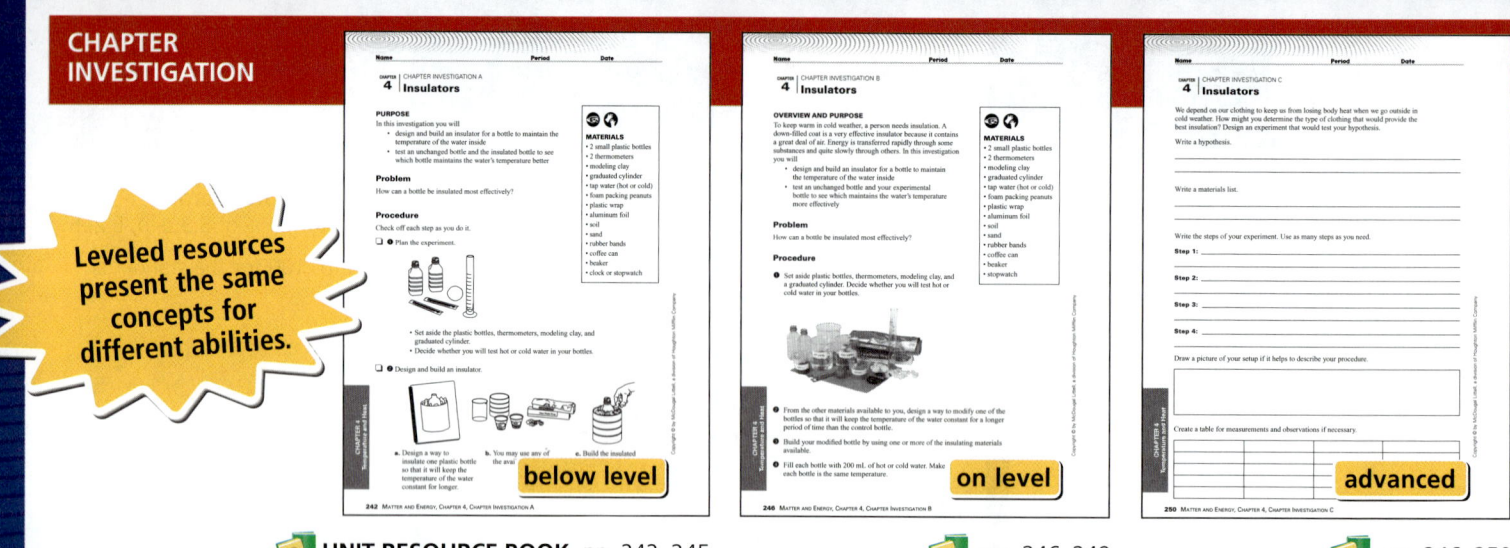

R UNIT RESOURCE BOOK, pp. 242–245   **R** pp. 246–249   **R** pp. 246–250

READING STUDY GUIDE

Reading Study Guide is also in Spanish.

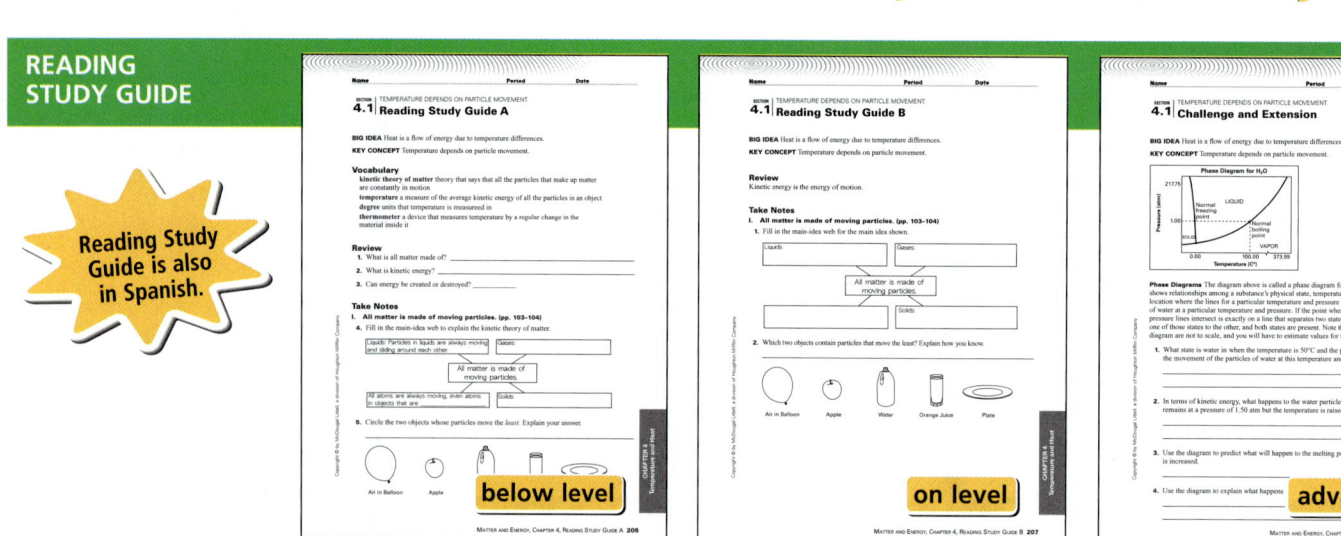
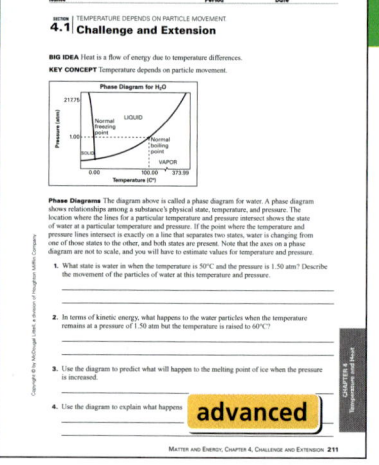

R UNIT RESOURCE BOOK, pp. 205–206   **R** pp. 207–208   **R** p. 211

CHAPTER TEST

Chapter Test is also in Spanish.

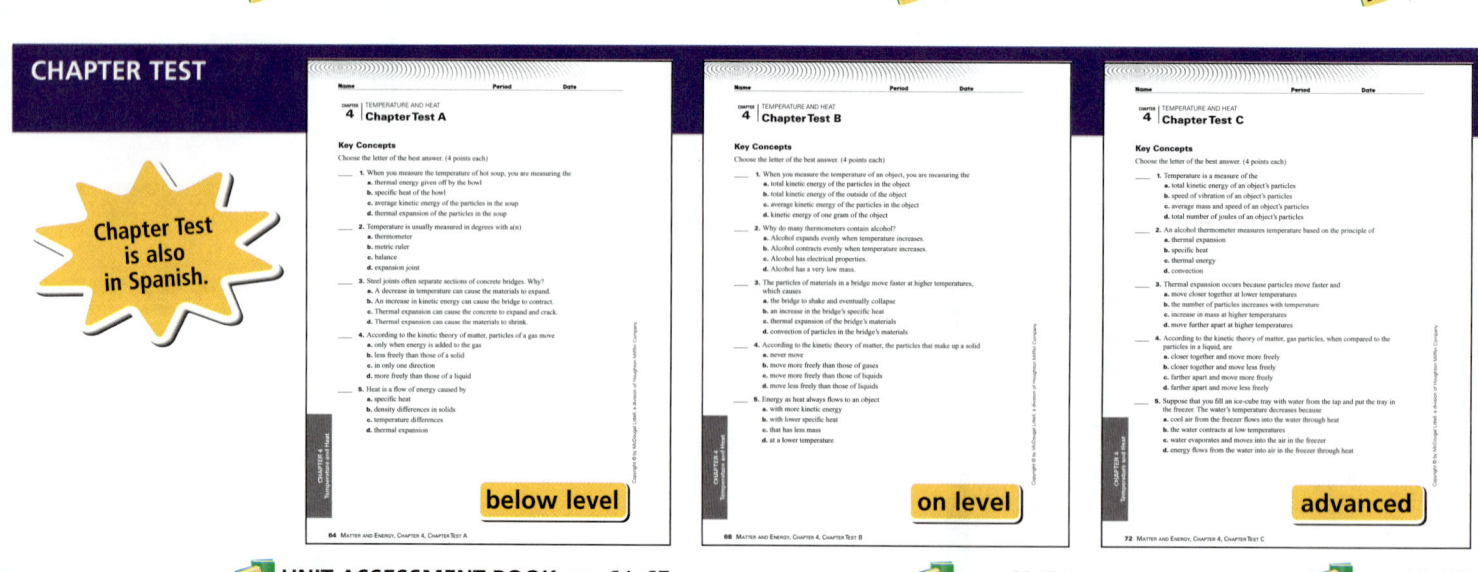

A UNIT ASSESSMENT BOOK, pp. 64–67   **A** pp. 68–71   **A** pp. 72–75

TECHNOLOGY

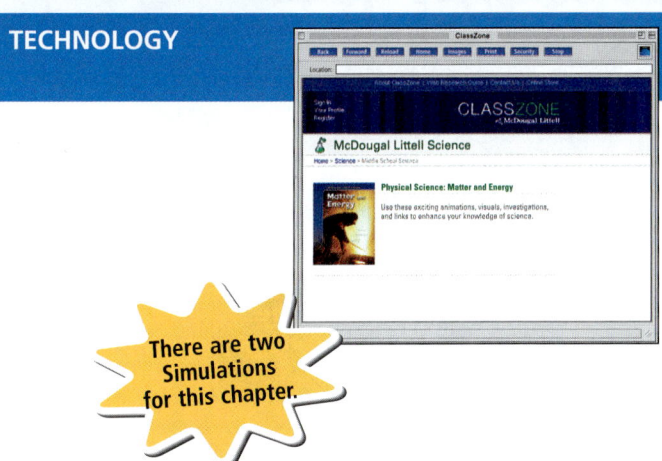
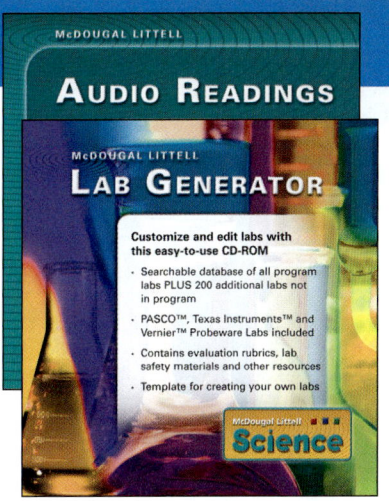
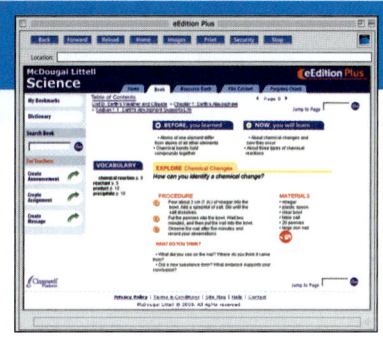

There are two Simulations for this chapter.

 **CLASSZONE.COM**  **CD/CD-ROMS**  **CLASSZONE.COM**

VISUAL CONTENT

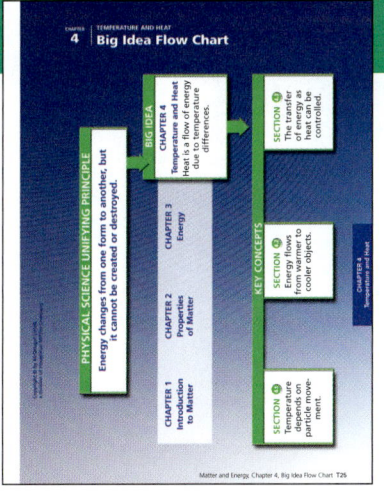
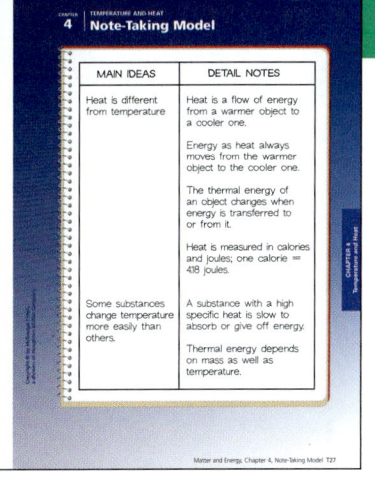

 UNIT TRANSPARENCY BOOK, p. T25   p. T27   p. T30

MORE SUPPORT

Reinforcing Key Concepts for each section

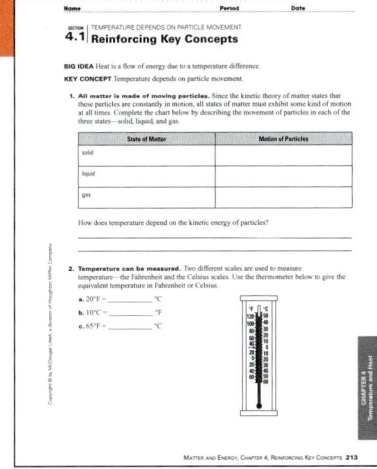
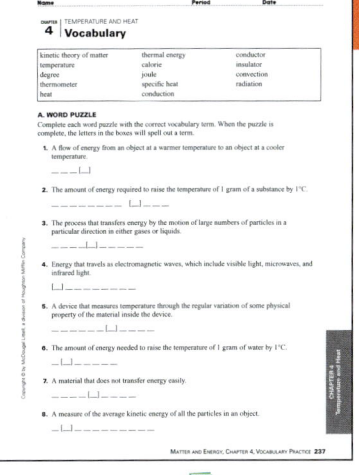
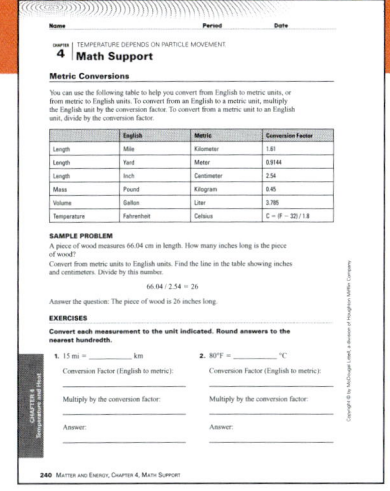

 UNIT RESOURCE BOOK, p. 213   pp. 237–238   p. 240

Chapter 4: **Temperature and Heat 99H**

CHAPTER 4
Temperature and Heat

INTRODUCE
the BIG idea

Have students look at the photograph of a giraffe in a sunny environment and discuss how the question in the box links to the Big Idea. Ask:

- How can you tell that energy travels from the Sun to Earth?
- What sources of energy are there after the Sun has set?

National Science Education Standards

Content

B.3.a Energy is a property of many substances, is associated with heat, and is transferred in many ways.

B.3.b Heat moves in predictable ways, flowing from warmer objects to cooler ones, until both reach the same temperature.

Process

A.1–8 Identify questions that can be answered through scientific investigations; design and conduct an investigation; use tools to gather and interpret data; use evidence to describe, predict, explain, model; think critically to make relationships between evidence and explanation; recognize different explanations and predictions; communicate scientific procedures and explanations; use mathematics.

A.9.a–g Understand scientific inquiry by using different investigations, methods, mathematics, technology, and explanations based on logic, evidence, and skepticism. Data often results in new investigations.

E.2–5 Design, implement, and evaluate a solution or product; communicate technological design.

100 Unit 1: **Matter and Energy**

CHAPTER 4
Temperature and Heat

the BIG idea
Heat is a flow of energy due to temperature differences.

How does heat from the Sun increase this giraffe's temperature?

Key Concepts

SECTION 1
Temperature depends on particle movement.
Learn how kinetic energy is the basis of temperature.

SECTION 2
Energy flows from warmer to cooler objects.
Learn about differences between temperature and heat, and how temperature changes in different substances.

SECTION 3
The transfer of energy as heat can be controlled.
Learn how energy is transferred through heat, and how that transfer can be controlled.

Internet Preview
CLASSZONE.COM
Chapter 4 online resources: Content Review, two Simulations, two Resource Centers, Math Tutorial, Test Practice

100 Unit 1: **Matter and Energy**

INTERNET PREVIEW

CLASSZONE.COM For student use with the following pages:

Review and Practice
- Content Review, pp. 102, 124
- Math Tutorial: Temperature Conversions, p. 109
- Test Practice, p. 127

Activities and Resources
- Internet Activity, p. 101
- Resource Centers: Temperature & Temperature Scales, p. 106; Thermal Energy, p. 111
- Simulations: Conduction, Convection, or Radiation, p. 119

NSTA scilinks.org SciLINKS
Kinetic Theory
Code: MDL064

EXPLORE the BIG idea

Moving Colors
Fill a clear plastic cup halfway with cold water. Fill another cup halfway with hot water. Using an eyedropper, place a drop of food coloring at the very bottom of each cup. Observe.

Observe and Think What happened to the drop of food coloring in cold water? in hot water? Why might this have happened?

Does It Chill?
Place an outdoor thermometer in an empty paper cup, and place the cup in the freezer. Check the thermometer every minute and record the time it takes for the temperature to reach 0°C (32°F). Remove the cup from the freezer. After it returns to room temperature, fill the cup with soil and repeat the experiment.

Observe and Think How long did it take for the temperature to reach 0°C each time? Why might there have been a difference?

Internet Activity: Kinetic Theory
Go to ClassZone.com to explore how temperature affects the speed of particles. Examine the effects of particle size as well.

Observe and Think What is the relationship between temperature and kinetic energy? How does particle mass affect temperature?

NSTA scilinks.org SCLINKS
Kinetic Theory **Code: MDL064**

Chapter 4: Temperature and Heat 101

EXPLORE the BIG idea

These inquiry-based activities are appropriate for use at home or as a supplement to classroom instruction.

Moving Colors
PURPOSE To observe that particles in matter move faster at higher temperatures than at lower temperatures. Students observe a drop of food coloring in cold water and in hot water.

TIP *10 min.* Have students use clear cups. Caution students not to get food coloring on their hands or clothing.

Answer: The food coloring spreads out faster in hot water than in cold water because the molecules in the hot water are moving faster.

REVISIT after p. 105.

Does It Chill?
PURPOSE To investigate how soil, as an insulator, slows changes in temperature. Students observe and record the temperature in a freezer.

TIP *30 min.* Have students read the thermometer and return it to the freezer as quickly as possible each time. Remind students to keep track of the time.

Answer: The thermometer in the soil should take longer to reach 0°C because soil acts as an insulator.

REVISIT after p. 117.

Internet Activity: Kinetic Theory
PURPOSE To observe that particle size and speed are related to temperature.

TIP *20 min.* Students should observe the kinetic energy of particles.

Answer: Temperature is the average kinetic energy of particles in an object; the greater the kinetic energy, the higher the temperature. The size of a particle affects its average kinetic energy.

REVISIT after p. 104.

TEACHING WITH TECHNOLOGY

CBL and Probeware If a probeware system is available, students can use a temperature probe to measure temperature changes for "Investigate Heat Transfer" on p. 112, "Explore Conduction" on p. 116, and to record and graph temperature changes in the Chapter Investigation, pp. 122–123.

PREPARE

◐ CONCEPT REVIEW

Activate Prior Knowledge

Place an ice cube in a beaker, and place the beaker on a hot plate. Ask:

- How will the ice cube change? *It will melt into water, then evaporate and boil into water vapor.*
- What stays the same when the ice cube undergoes these changes? *The molecules remain as water.*
- How is energy related to these changes? *The addition of energy raises the temperature and produces the changes in physical state.*

◐ TAKING NOTES

Choose Your Own Strategy

Choosing different strategies for taking notes can help students learn which strategies work best for them. Students can choose their own strategy or use the strategy suggested on the first page of each section. Encourage students to use their notes to test themselves.

Vocabulary Strategy

Description wheels can include as much information as students want to add. They are handy study devices when students look back through their notes.

Vocabulary and Note-Taking Resources

- Vocabulary Practice, pp. 237–238
- Decoding Support, p. 239

- Daily Vocabulary Scaffolding, p T26
- Note-Taking Model, p. T27

- Description Wheel, B20–21
- Choose Your Own Strategy, C35–44
- Daily Vocabulary Scaffolding, H1–8

CHAPTER 4
Getting Ready to Learn

◐ CONCEPT REVIEW
- Matter is made of particles too small to see.
- Matter can be solid, liquid, or gas.
- Energy is the ability to cause a change.
- There are different forms of energy.

◐ VOCABULARY REVIEW
matter p. 9
energy p. 72
kinetic energy p. 74

Review concepts and vocabulary.

▶ TAKING NOTES

CHOOSE YOUR OWN STRATEGY

Take notes using one or more of the strategies from earlier chapters—**main idea and detail notes, main idea web,** or **mind map.** Feel free to mix and match the strategies, or use an entirely different note-taking strategy.

VOCABULARY STRATEGY

Place each vocabulary term at the center of a **description wheel** diagram. Write some words describing it on the spokes.

See the Note-Taking Handbook on pages R45–R51.

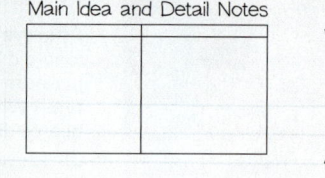

CHECK READINESS

Administer the Diagnostic Test to determine students' readiness for new science content and their mastery of requisite math skills.

 Diagnostic Test, pp. 59–60

Technology Resources

Students needing content and math skills should visit **ClassZone.com**.

- CONTENT REVIEW
- MATH TUTORIAL

 CONTENT REVIEW CD-ROM

KEY CONCEPT

Temperature depends on particle movement.

> **BEFORE, you learned**
> - All matter is made of particles
> - Kinetic energy is the energy of motion
> - Energy can be transferred or changed but is never created or destroyed

> **NOW, you will learn**
> - How temperature depends on kinetic energy
> - How temperature is measured
> - How changes in temperature can affect matter

VOCABULARY

kinetic theory of matter p. 104
temperature p. 105
degree p. 106
thermometer p. 107

EXPLORE Temperature

What can cause a change in temperature?

PROCEDURE

1. Work with a partner. Hold the rubber band with both hands. Without stretching it, hold it to the underside of your partner's wrist.
2. Move the rubber band away, then quickly stretch it once and keep it stretched. Hold it to the underside of your partner's wrist.
3. Move the rubber band away and quickly let it return to its normal size. Hold it to the underside of your partner's wrist.

WHAT DO YOU THINK?
- What effect did stretching the rubber band have on the temperature of the rubber band?
- What may have caused this change to occur?

MATERIALS
large rubber band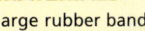

All matter is made of moving particles.

NOTE-TAKING STRATEGY
You could take notes on the movement of particles in matter by using a main idea web.

You have read that any object in motion has kinetic energy. All the moving objects you see around you—from cars to planes to butterflies—have kinetic energy. Even objects so small that you cannot see them, such as atoms, are in motion and have kinetic energy.

You might think that a large unmoving object, such as a house or a wooden chair, does not have any kinetic energy. However, all matter is made of atoms, and atoms are always in motion, even if the objects themselves do not change their position. The motion of these tiny particles gives the object energy. The chair you are sitting on has some amount of energy. You also have energy, even when you are not moving.

Chapter 4: **Temperature and Heat** 103

4.1 FOCUS

▶ Set Learning Goals
Students will
- Explain how temperature depends on kinetic energy.
- Describe how temperature is measured.
- Describe how changes in temperature can affect matter.
- Observe experimentally how thermal expansion can be used to measure temperature.

● 3-Minute Warm-Up
Display Transparency 28 or copy this exercise on the board:

Decide if these statements are true. If not, correct them.

1. Solids and liquids are made of particles, but gases are made of air, which is not made of particles. *Gases are also made of particles.*
2. Kinetic energy is the energy of motion. *true*
3. Kinetic energy depends on position and chemical composition. *Kinetic energy depends on mass and speed. (Potential energy depends on position and chemical composition.)*

 3-Minute Warm-Up, p. T28

4.1 MOTIVATE

EXPLORE Temperature

PURPOSE To discover how a transfer of energy and increased motion produce an increase in temperature

TIP *10 min.* Use thick rubber bands that will not break easily. Students should wear safety goggles. Caution students to avoid stretching the rubber bands to their breaking point.

WHAT DO YOU THINK? *The temperature increased because stretching the rubber band added energy to it.*

RESOURCES FOR DIFFERENTIATED INSTRUCTION

Below Level
UNIT RESOURCE BOOK
- Reading Study Guide A, pp. 205–206
- Decoding Support, p. 239

 **AUDIO CDS**

Advanced
UNIT RESOURCE BOOK
Challenge and Extension, p. 211

English Learners
UNIT RESOURCE BOOK
Spanish Reading Study Guide, pp. 209–210

AUDIO CDS
- Audio Readings in Spanish
- Audio Readings (English)

Chapter 4 **103**

INSTRUCT

Address Misconceptions

IDENTIFY Ask: What states of matter have particles always in motion? If students do not mention all states of matter, they may think that some particles in matter are not in constant motion.

CORRECT Demonstrate the kinetic theory of matter in relation to solids, liquids, and gases using a clear plastic container holding beads or other small objects. Fill the container. Shake it to demonstrate a solid. If the container is completely full, the "particles" will move around slightly and will be in constant contact. Remove a portion of the objects, then shake the container to demonstrate a liquid. The "particles" will still collide but will move past each other and move more freely. Finally, remove all but a few objects, then shake the container to demonstrate a gas. The "particles" will move most freely and barely interact.

REASSESS Ask students to describe the motion of particles in their desks and chairs. *Particles are vibrating in place.* Reiterate that particles in all matter are always in motion.

Technology Resources

Visit **ClassZone.com** for background on common student misconceptions.

MISCONCEPTION DATABASE

Teach from Visuals

To help students interpret the diagrams of particles in solid, liquid, and gas, ask:

- What do the particles in the solid, liquid, and gas have in common? *They are all in constant motion.*
- How are the solid, liquid, and gas different? *The freedom with which the particles can move varies.*

EXPLORE the BIG idea

Revisit "Internet Activity: Kinetic Theory" on p. 101. Have students explain their observations.

Ongoing Assessment

CHECK YOUR READING that particles in matter are in constant motion and have kinetic energy

104 Unit 1: **Matter and Energy**

REMINDER
Kinetic energy is the energy of motion.

READING TIP
In illustrations of particle movement, more motion lines mean a greater speed.

The Kinetic Theory of Matter

Physical properties and physical changes are the result of how particles of matter behave. The **kinetic theory of matter** states that all of the particles that make up matter are constantly in motion. As a result, all particles in matter have kinetic energy. The kinetic theory of matter helps explain the different states of matter—solid, liquid, and gas.

① The particles in a solid, such as concrete, are not free to move around very much. They vibrate back and forth in the same position and are held tightly together by forces of attraction.

② The particles in a liquid, such as water in a pool, move much more freely than particles in a solid. They are constantly sliding around and tumbling over each other as they move.

③ In a gas, such as the air around you or in a bubble in water, particles are far apart and move around at high speeds. Particles might collide with one another, but otherwise they do not interact much.

Particles do not always move at the same speed. Within any group of particles, some are moving faster than others. A fast-moving particle might collide with another particle and lose some of its speed. A slow-moving particle might be struck by a faster one and start moving faster. Particles have a wide range of speeds and often change speeds.

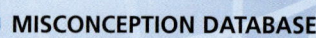 What is the kinetic theory of matter?

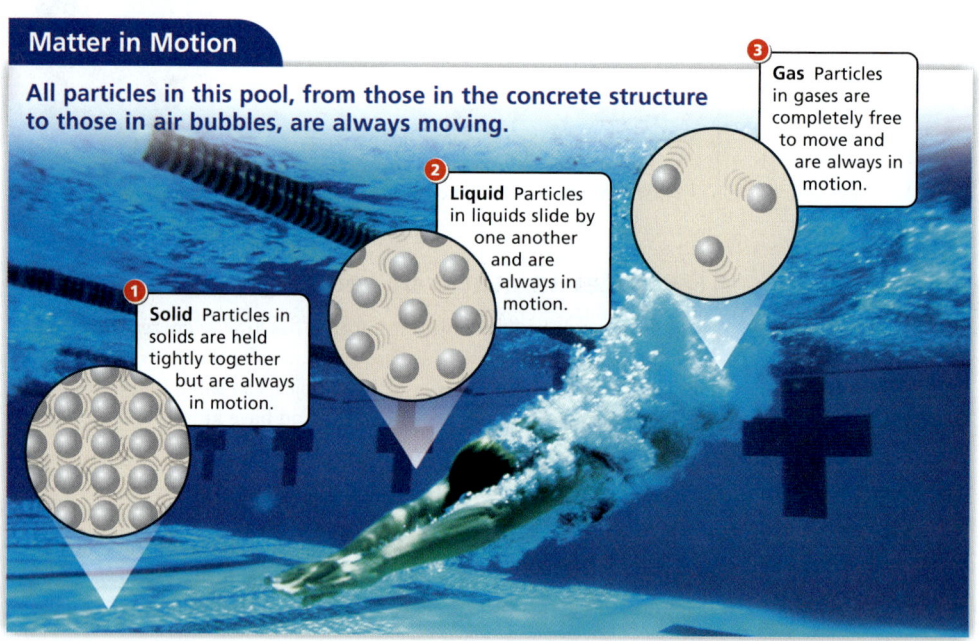

Matter in Motion

All particles in this pool, from those in the concrete structure to those in air bubbles, are always moving.

① **Solid** Particles in solids are held tightly together but are always in motion.

② **Liquid** Particles in liquids slide by one another and are always in motion.

③ **Gas** Particles in gases are completely free to move and are always in motion.

104 Unit 1: **Matter and Energy**

DIFFERENTIATE INSTRUCTION

More Reading Support

 What does the kinetic theory of matter say? *All the particles in matter are constantly in motion.*

English Learners Have students write the definitions of *temperature*, *degree*, and *thermometer* in their Science Word Dictionaries. English learners may require background knowledge of "smoothie" (p. 105), and the phrase "into account" (p. 108). Tell students to take something into account means to consider it.

Temperature and Kinetic Energy

Particles of matter moving at different speeds have different kinetic energies because kinetic energy depends on speed. It is not possible to know the kinetic energy of each particle in an object. However, the average kinetic energy of all the particles in an object can be determined.

Temperature is a measure of the average kinetic energy of all the particles in an object. If a liquid, such as hot cocoa, has a high temperature, the particles in the liquid are moving very fast and have a high average kinetic energy. The cocoa feels hot. If a drink, such as a fruit smoothie, has a low temperature, the particles in the liquid are moving more slowly and have a lower average kinetic energy. The smoothie feels cold.

VOCABULARY
Remember to make a description wheel diagram for *temperature* and other vocabulary terms.

You experience the connection between temperature and the kinetic energy of particles every day. For example, to raise the temperature of your hands on a cold day—to warm your hands—you have to add energy, perhaps by putting your hands near a fire or a hot stove. The added energy makes the particles in your hands move faster. If you let a hot bowl sit on a table for a while, the particles in the bowl slow down due to collisions with particles in the air and in the table. The temperature of the bowl decreases, and it becomes cooler.

Temperature is the measurement of the average kinetic energy of particles, not just their speed. Recall that kinetic energy depends on mass as well as speed. Particles in a metal doorknob do not move as fast as particles in air. However, the particles in a doorknob have more mass and they can have the same amount of kinetic energy as particles in air. As a result, the doorknob and the air can have equal temperatures.

How does temperature change when kinetic energy increases?

Chapter 4: **Temperature and Heat** 105

History of Science

In the 1800s, scientist William Thomson, Lord Kelvin, developed an absolute temperature scale with 0 representing absolute zero. At this theoretical temperature the particles in matter stop moving and have no kinetic energy. The Celsius scale uses the same magnitude of units as the Kelvin scale, and 0 K is equal to −273.15° Celsius. Therefore, to convert Celsius to Kelvin, add 273.15° to the Celsius temperature. This conversion is only necessary in the case of particular temperature values, but not for a change in temperature. That is, an increase of 10 K is equal to an increase of 10°C.

Note that the Kelvin scale employs no degree symbol, unlike the Fahrenheit and Celsius scales.

Teach from Visuals

To help students interpret the photograph of the temperature scales, ask:

- What is the temperature of Death Valley in the photograph? *49°C or 120°F*
- Why is it important to include the scale when giving a temperature? *The number is meaningless if the scale is unknown.*

Ongoing Assessment

 *Answer: They both measure temperature in terms of degrees. They have different numbers of degrees between the freezing point and boiling point of water, and the zero point of the Celsius scale is fixed at the freezing point of water, whereas the zero point of the Fahrenheit scale is not.*

Find out more about temperature and temperature scales.

During a summer day in Death Valley, California, the temperature can reach 49°C (120°F).

Temperature can be measured.

You have read that a warmer temperature means a greater average kinetic energy. How is temperature measured and what does that measurement mean? Suppose you hear on the radio that the temperature outside is 30 degrees. Do you need to wear a warm coat to spend the day outside? The answer depends on the temperature scale being used. There are two common temperature scales, both of which measure the average kinetic energy of particles. However, 30 degrees on one scale is quite different from 30 degrees on the other scale.

Temperature Scales

To establish a temperature scale, two known values and the number of units between the values are needed. The freezing and boiling points of pure water are often used as the standard values. These points are always the same under the same conditions and they are easy to reproduce. In the two common scales, temperature is measured in units called **degrees** (°), which are equally spaced units between two points.

The scale used most commonly in the United States for measuring temperature—in uses ranging from cooking directions to weather reports—is the Fahrenheit (FAR-uhn-HYT) scale (°F). It was developed in the early 1700s by Gabriel Fahrenheit. On the Fahrenheit scale, pure water freezes at 32°F and boils at 212°F. Thus, there are 180 degrees—180 equal units—between the freezing point and the boiling point of water.

The temperature scale most commonly used in the rest of the world, and also used more often in science, is the Celsius (SEHL-see-uhs) scale (°C). This scale was developed in the 1740s by Anders Celsius. On the Celsius scale, pure water freezes at 0°C and boils at 100°C, so there are 100 degrees—100 equal units—between these two temperatures.

Recall the question asked in the first paragraph of this page. If the outside temperature is 30 degrees, do you need to wear a warm coat? If the temperature is 30°F, the answer is yes, because that temperature is colder than the freezing point of water. If the temperature is 30°C, the answer is no—it is a nice warm day (86°F).

 How are the Fahrenheit and Celsius temperature scales different? How are they similar?

106 Unit 1: Matter and Energy

DIFFERENTIATE INSTRUCTION

More Reading Support

D What are the equally spaced units between two points? *degrees*

E What temperature scale is often used by scientists? *Celsius*

Advanced Have students calibrate the thermometers they make in the investigation on p. 107. Students should make a mark on the straw to indicate the alcohol level at a low temperature, and another mark for the level at a high temperature. The actual temperature should be measured with a real thermometer at the same time. Have students test a temperature midway between their calibration points.

Challenge and Extension, p. 211

Thermometers

Temperature is measured by using a device called a thermometer. A **thermometer** measures temperature through the regular variation of some physical property of the material inside the thermometer. A mercury or alcohol thermometer, for example, can measure temperature because the liquid inside the thermometer always expands or contracts by a certain amount in response to a change in temperature.

Liquid-filled thermometers measure how much the liquid expands in a narrow tube as the temperature increases. The distances along the tube are marked so that the temperature can be read. At one time, thermometers were filled with liquid mercury because it expands or contracts evenly at both high and low temperatures. This means that mercury expands or contracts by the same amount in response to a given change in temperature. However, mercury is dangerous to handle, so many thermometers today are filled with alcohol instead.

Some thermometers work in a different way—they use a material whose electrical properties change when the temperature changes. These thermometers can be read by computers. Some show the temperature on a display panel and are often used in cars and in homes.

 How do liquid-filled thermometers work?

INVESTIGATE Temperature Measurements

How does a thermometer work?

PROCEDURE

1. To make your own thermometer, fill the bottle halfway with the alcohol solution. Add a small amount of food coloring and mix thoroughly.
2. Place the straw into the bottle. Use clay to suspend the straw above the bottom of the bottle and to seal the bottle's mouth completely.
3. Pour ice water into the bowl and place the bottle into the ice water. Record your observations, and then empty the bowl.
4. Pour hot water into the bowl and place the bottle into the hot water. Record your observations.

WHAT DO YOU THINK?

- What happened to the level of the alcohol solution in the straw when the bottle was put into the ice water? into the hot water?
- Why do you think these changes happened?

CHALLENGE How could you modify your thermometer so that you could use it to measure a temperature?

SKILL FOCUS
Modeling

MATERIALS
- plastic bottle
- alcohol solution
- food coloring
- clear plastic straw
- clay
- bowl
- ice water
- hot tap water

TIME
30 minutes

INVESTIGATE Temperature Measurements

PURPOSE To observe how thermal expansion can be used to measure temperature

TIPS 30 min.
- The mouth of the bottle must be completely sealed.
- You might want students to bring small plastic bottles from home.

WHAT DO YOU THINK? *The level dropped in ice water and rose in hot water. The liquid contracted and expanded in response to a change in temperature.*

CHALLENGE *Two known temperatures and levels on the straw are needed. The expansion and contraction would need to be observed several times.*

 Datasheet, Temperature Measurements, p. 212

Technology Resources

Customize this student lab as needed or look for an alternative. Print rubrics to assess student lab reports.

 Lab Generator CD-ROM

History of Science

Scientists developed tools to measure temperature changes in the 1500s and 1600s. These thermoscopes used air instead of liquid. At first they did not have temperature scales. Eventually, scientists developed many different scales and could not compare their measurements with those using other scales.

Ongoing Assessment

Describe how temperature is measured.

Ask: What are two things a thermometer needs to measure temperature? *a substance that varies regularly with changing temperatures and a scale with two known values.*

 Answer: *The liquid expands or contracts by a consistent amount due to a change in temperature.*

DIFFERENTIATE INSTRUCTION

More Reading Support

F What device measures temperature?
thermometer

Alternative Assessment Students can answer and extend the questions in "Investigate Temperature Measurements" by drawing and labeling their results and ideas.

Chapter 4 **107**

Ongoing Assessment

Describe how changes in temperature can affect matter.

Ask: What happens to all gases, many liquids, and most solids when their temperature increases? *They expand.*

 *Answer: The particles move faster and move apart from each other very slightly.*

Real World Example

Thermal expansion can be used to solve problems. For example, a metal lid stuck on a jar will expand if held under hot tap water, and the jar will open more easily. Also, home thermostats contain a coil made of two metals with different rates of expansion. When the temperature drops, the coil bends one way, and when the temperature rises, it bends the other way.

Reinforce the BIG idea

Have students relate the section to the Big Idea.

 Reinforcing Key Concepts, p. 213

4.1 ASSESS & RETEACH

Assess
 Section 4.1 Quiz, p. 61

Reteach
Ask volunteers to explain each concept and give examples.
- how temperature depends on kinetic energy
- what is needed for a temperature scale
- how a thermometer works
- what thermal expansion is

Technology Resources
Have students visit ClassZone.com for reteaching of Key Concepts.

 CONTENT REVIEW

 CONTENT REVIEW CD-ROM

108 Unit 1: **Matter and Energy**

During construction of the Gateway Arch in St. Louis, engineers had to account for thermal expansion.

Thermal Expansion

The property that makes liquid-filled thermometers work is called thermal expansion. Thermal expansion affects many substances, not just alcohol and liquid mercury. All gases, many liquids, and most solids expand when their temperature increases.

Construction engineers often have to take thermal expansion into account because steel and concrete both expand with increasing temperature. An interesting example involves the construction of the Gateway Arch in St. Louis, which is built mostly of steel.

The final piece of the Arch to be put into place was the top segment joining the two legs. The Arch was scheduled to be completed in the middle of the day for its opening ceremony. However, engineers knew that the side of the Arch facing the Sun would get hot and expand due to thermal expansion.

This expansion would narrow the gap between the legs and prevent the last piece from fitting into place. In order to complete the Arch, workers sprayed water on the side facing the Sun. The water helped cool the Arch and decreased the amount of thermal expansion. Once the final segment was in place, engineers made the connection strong enough to withstand the force of the expanding material.

Thermal expansion occurs in solids because the particles of solids vibrate more at higher temperatures. Solids expand as the particles move ever so slightly farther apart. This is why bridges and highways are built in short segments with slight breaks in them, called expansion joints. These joints allow the material to expand safely.

 Why do objects expand when their temperatures increase?

4.1 Review

KEY CONCEPTS
1. Describe the relationship between temperature and kinetic energy.
2. Describe the way in which thermometers measure temperature.
3. How can you explain thermal expansion in terms of kinetic energy?

CRITICAL THINKING
4. **Synthesize** Suppose a mercury thermometer shows that the air temperature is 22°C (72°F). Do particles in the air have more average kinetic energy than particles in the mercury? Explain.
5. **Infer** If a puddle of water is frozen, do particles in the ice have kinetic energy? Explain.

CHALLENGE
6. **Apply** Why might a sidewalk be built with periodic breaks in it?

108 Unit 1: **Matter and Energy**

ANSWERS

1. Temperature is a measurement of average kinetic energy of particles in a substance. As the average kinetic energy increases, so does temperature.

2. through the regular variation of a physical property in response to a change in temperature

3. When the kinetic energy of particles in an object increases, they move faster and move farther apart from one another.

4. No; the temperatures are the same, so the particles of both have the same average kinetic energy.

5. Yes; particles in solids are always in motion.

6. As concrete expands and contracts with changes in temperature, it needs room to move.

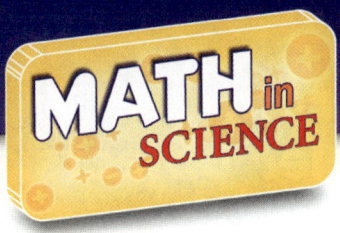

MATH in SCIENCE

Click on Math Tutorial for more help with temperature conversions.

SKILL: METRIC CONVERSIONS

How Hot Is Hot?

Temperatures on Earth can vary greatly, from extremely hot in some deserts to frigid in polar regions. The meaning of a temperature measurement depends on which temperature scale is being used. A very high temperature on the Fahrenheit scale is equal to a much lower temperature on the Celsius scale. The table shows the formulas used to convert temperatures between the two scales.

Conversion	Formula
Fahrenheit to Celsius	$°C = \frac{5}{9}(°F - 32)$
Celsius to Fahrenheit	$°F = \frac{9}{5}°C + 32$

Example

The boiling point of pure water is 212°F. Convert that temperature to a measurement on the Celsius scale.

(1) Use the correct conversion formula.

$$°C = \frac{5}{9}(°F - 32)$$

(2) Substitute the temperature given for the correct variable in the formula.

$$°C = \frac{5}{9}(212 - 32) = \frac{5}{9} \cdot 180 = 100$$

ANSWER °C = 100

Use the information in the table below to answer the questions that follow.

Highest and Lowest Temperatures Recorded on Earth

Location	Highest Temp. (°F)	Location	Lowest Temp. (°F)
El Azizia, Libya	136	Vostok, Antarctica	−129
Death Valley, California	134	Oimekon, Russia	−90
Tirat Tsvi, Israel	129	Verkhoyansk, Russia	−90
Cloncurry, Australia	128	Northice, Greenland	−87
Seville, Spain	122	Snag, Yukon, Canada	−81

1. What is the highest temperature in °C?
2. What is the temperature difference in °C between the highest and second highest temperatures?
3. What is the difference between the highest and lowest temperatures in °F? in °C?

CHALLENGE The surface of the Sun is approximately 5500°C. What is this temperature in °F?

Temperatures on Earth, ranging from the extremes of frigid polar regions to the hottest deserts, can differ by more than 250°F.

Chapter 4: **Temperature and Heat** 109

ANSWERS

1. $°C = 5/9 (136−32) = 5/9 (104) = 57.8$
2. $°C = 5/9 (134−32) = 5/9 (104) = 56.7; 57.8 − 56.7 = 1.1$
3. $136 − (−129) = 265°F; 57.8 − (−89.4) = 147.2°C$

CHALLENGE $°F = 9/5 (5500) + 32 = 9900 + 32 = 9932$

MATH IN SCIENCE
Math Skills Practice for Science

Set Learning Goal
To convert temperatures from Fahrenheit to Celsius and Celsius to Fahrenheit

Present the Science
Both common temperature scales have advantages. The Fahrenheit scale uses smaller degrees, so it is more accurate for weather reports. The Celsius scale is more closely tied to a physical constant (water's freezing point) and is more commonly used in science.

Develop Algebra Skills
- Remind students that the numerator of the fraction is above the line, and the denominator is below. To help them remember which part of the fraction to multiply, emphasize that they divide by the denominator.
- Point out that when converting from Fahrenheit to Celsius, the parentheses mean that the 32 is subtracted before multiplying by 5/9. When converting Celsius to Fahrenheit, the 32 is added after multiplying by 9/5.

DIFFERENTIATION TIP Use graph paper to model multiplying the fractions 1/5 and 1/9 by a number such as 45. Shade squares that show the fraction as a portion of a larger number.

Close
Ask: Why is knowing how to convert from one temperature scale to another useful? *Sample answer: Most people are more familiar with one scale than the other. Without conversion, temperatures given in an unfamiliar scale are meaningless.*

- Math Support, p. 240
- Math Practice, p. 241

Technology Resources
Students can visit ClassZone.com for practice with temperature conversions.

 MATH TUTORIAL

Chapter 4 **109**

4.2 FOCUS

▶ Set Learning Goals
Students will
- Compare heat and temperature.
- Describe how heat is measured.
- Understand why some substances change temperature more easily than others.
- Measure heat transfer in an experiment.

⏺ 3-Minute Warm-Up
Display Transparency 28 or copy this exercise on the board:

Match the correct temperature scale to the descriptions.

Temperature Scale
1. Fahrenheit *b*
2. Celsius *a, c, d*

Description
a. freezing point of water is 0°
b. freezing point of water is 32°
c. used by scientists and most countries
d. 100 units between freezing and boiling points of water

 3-Minute Warm-Up, p. T28

4.2 MOTIVATE

THINK ABOUT
PURPOSE To introduce that different substances warm up at different rates

DISCUSS Have students brainstorm answers to the question in the text.
More energy is needed to warm water.

Ongoing Assessment
Explain how heat is different from temperature.
Ask: How does heat differ from temperature? *Heat is the flow of energy; temperature is a measure of it.*

 *Answer: the flow of energy from warmer to cooler objects*

KEY CONCEPT

4.2 Energy flows from warmer to cooler objects.

◀ **BEFORE, you learned**
- All matter is made of moving particles
- Temperature is the measurement of average kinetic energy of particles in an object
- Temperature can be measured

▶ **NOW, you will learn**
- How heat is different from temperature
- How heat is measured
- Why some substances change temperature more easily than others

VOCABULARY
heat p. 110
thermal energy p. 111
calorie p. 112
joule p. 112
specific heat p. 113

THINK ABOUT

Why does water warm up so slowly?

If you have ever seen food being fried in oil or butter, you know that the metal frying pan heats up very quickly, as does the oil or butter used to coat the pan's surface.

However, if you put the same amount of water as you put oil in the same pan, the water warms up more slowly. Why does water behave so differently from the metal, oil, or butter?

NOTE-TAKING STRATEGY
The mind map organizer would be a good choice for taking notes on heat.

Heat is different from temperature.

Heat and temperature are very closely related. As a result, people often confuse the concepts of heat and temperature. However, they are not the same. Temperature is a measurement of the average kinetic energy of particles in an object. **Heat** is a flow of energy from an object at a higher temperature to an object at a lower temperature.

If you add energy as heat to a pot of water, the water's temperature starts to increase. The added energy increases the average kinetic energy of the water molecules. Once the water starts to boil, however, adding energy no longer changes the temperature of the water. Instead, the heat goes into changing the physical state of the water from liquid to gas rather than increasing the kinetic energy of the water molecules. This fact is one demonstration that heat and temperature are not the same thing.

 What is heat?

110 Unit 1: Matter and Energy

RESOURCES FOR DIFFERENTIATED INSTRUCTION

Below Level
UNIT RESOURCE BOOK
- Reading Study Guide A, pp. 216–217
- Decoding Support, p. 239

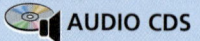 AUDIO CDS

Advanced
UNIT RESOURCE BOOK
Challenge and Extension, p. 222

English Learners
UNIT RESOURCE BOOK
Spanish Reading Study Guide, pp. 220–221

AUDIO CDS
- Audio Readings in Spanish
- Audio Readings (English)

Heat and Thermal Energy

Suppose you place an ice cube in a bowl on a table. At first, the bowl and the ice cube have different temperatures. However, the ice cube melts, and the water that comes from the ice will eventually have the same temperature as the bowl. This temperature will be lower than the original temperature of the bowl but higher than the original temperature of the ice cube. The water and the bowl end up at the same temperature because the particles in the ice cube and the particles in the bowl continually bump into each other and energy is transferred from the bowl to the ice.

Learn more about thermal energy.

Heat is always the transfer of energy from an object at a higher temperature to an object at a lower temperature. So energy flows from the particles in the warmer bowl to the particles in the cold ice and, later, the cooler water. If energy flowed in the opposite direction—from cooler to warmer—the ice would get colder and the bowl would get hotter, and you know that never happens.

 In which direction does heat always transfer energy?

When energy flows from a warmer object to a cooler object, the thermal energy of both of the objects changes. **Thermal energy** is the total random kinetic energy of particles in an object. Note that temperature and thermal energy are different from each other. Temperature is an average and thermal energy is a total. A glass of water can have the same temperature as Lake Superior, but the lake has far more thermal energy because the lake contains many more water molecules.

Another example of how energy is transferred through heat is shown on the right. Soon after you put ice cubes into a pitcher of lemonade, energy is transferred from the warmer lemonade to the colder ice. The lemonade's thermal energy decreases and the ice's thermal energy increases. Because the particles in the lemonade have transferred some of their energy to the particles in the ice, the average kinetic energy of the particles in the lemonade decreases. As a result, the temperature of the lemonade decreases.

Energy is transferred from the warmer lemonade to the cold ice through heat until their temperatures are equal.

 How are heat and thermal energy related to each other?

Chapter 4: **Temperature and Heat** 111

DIFFERENTIATE INSTRUCTION

More Reading Support

A What does heat do? *transfers energy*

B What is the total random kinetic energy of all particles in an object? *thermal energy*

English Learners English learners rely on patterns and conventions in the English language, and may not recognize cause-and-effect relationships in sentences that do not follow *if/then* format. Point out the cause-and-effect relationship in the following sentence from this page: "Because the particles in the lemonade have transferred . . ., the average kinetic energy of the particles in the lemonade decreases." Encourage students to look for introductory clauses and phrases rather than a particular word, such as *if*.

4.2 INSTRUCT

Address Misconceptions

IDENTIFY Ask students how a flow of energy through heat differs from the flow of a fluid such as water. If students fail to recognize that heat is not a physical form of matter like water, they may hold the misconception that heat is a form of matter that literally flows from one object to another.

CORRECT Hold an ice cube in the palm of your hand. Ask students to describe the flow of heat. Point out that energy, not particles of matter, flows from your hand to the ice cube.

REASSESS Ask: What flows from one place to another when an object is heated? *energy*

Technology Resources
Visit **ClassZone.com** for background on common student misconceptions.

MISCONCEPTION DATABASE

Teach from Visuals

To help students interpret the diagram of heat transfer from lemonade to ice, ask:

- In what direction does heat transfer energy in the diagram? *from the warm lemonade to the cold ice*
- What happens to the ice's thermal energy? *It increases.*
- What happens to the lemonade's thermal energy? *It decreases.*

Teach Difficult Concepts

Heat is often thought of as both a form of energy and a way in which energy can be transferred. Point out that in this chapter, heat is not a form of energy but rather the flow of energy.

Ongoing Assessment

 *Answer: from warmer to cooler*

 *Answer: As heat transfers energy, the thermal energy of the warmer object decreases, and the thermal energy of the cooler object increases.*

Chapter 4 **111**

INVESTIGATE Heat Transfer

PURPOSE To investigate the specific heat of different materials by measuring a change in temperature

TIPS 30 min.

- You might want to have students bring pennies from home.
- The hot water should be at least 60°C for the best results.

WHAT DO YOU THINK? *The cup to which water is added will show the greatest change in temperature; the cup to which the pennies are added will show the smallest change in temperature. Different substances absorb different amounts of energy to show changes in temperature.*

CHALLENGE *Little energy is required to increase their temperatures.*

 Datasheet, Heat Transfer, p. 223

Technology Resources

Customize this student lab as needed or look for an alternative. Print rubrics to assess student lab reports.

 Lab Generator CD-ROM

Teaching with Technology

A probeware system with a temperature probe can be used to measure temperatures.

Metacognitive Strategy

Ask students what they could do to improve the accuracy of their results.

Ongoing Assessment

Describe how heat is measured.

Ask: What is a calorie? *energy to raise the temperature of 1 g of water 1°C*

 Answer: *in calories or joules; the amount of energy transferred between substances*

112 Unit 1: Matter and Energy

VOCABULARY Remember to make description wheel diagrams for *calorie, joule,* and other vocabulary terms.

Measuring Heat

The most common units of heat measurement are the calorie and the joule (jool). One **calorie** is the amount of energy needed to raise the temperature of 1 gram of water by 1°C. The **joule** (J) is the standard scientific unit in which energy is measured. One calorie is equal to 4.18 joules.

You probably think of calories in terms of food. However, in nutrition, one Calorie—written with a capital C—is actually one kilocalorie, or 1000 calories. This means that one Calorie in food contains enough energy to raise the temperature of 1 kilogram of water by 1°C. So, each Calorie in food contains 1000 calories of energy.

How do we know how many Calories are in a food, such as a piece of chocolate cake? The cake is burned inside an instrument called a calorimeter. The amount of energy released from the cake through heat is the number of Calories transferred from the cake to the calorimeter. The energy transferred to the calorimeter is equal to the amount of energy originally in the cake. A thermometer inside the calorimeter measures the increase in temperature from the burning cake, which is used to calculate how much energy is released.

 How is heat measured?

INVESTIGATE Heat Transfer

Which substances change temperature faster?

PROCEDURE

1. Using the graduated cylinder and the balance, separately measure 20 g of room-temperature water, 20 g of pennies, and 20 g of aluminum foil. Pour the water into a beaker until it is needed.

2. Using the graduated cylinder, pour 50 mL of hot water into each of the cups. Record the water temperature in each cup.

3. Pour the room-temperature water into one cup. Place the pennies in the second cup and the foil in the third. After 5 minutes, record the temperature of the water in each of the cups.

WHAT DO YOU THINK?
- How did the temperature changes in the three cups compare?
- What might account for the differences you observed?

CHALLENGE Why might items such as pots and pans be made of materials like copper, stainless steel, or iron?

SKILL FOCUS Measuring

MATERIALS
- graduated cylinder
- balance
- room-temperature water
- pennies
- aluminum foil
- hot tap water
- 100 mL beaker
- 3 plastic cups
- thermometer
- stopwatch

TIME 30 minutes

112 Unit 1: Matter and Energy

DIFFERENTIATE INSTRUCTION

More Reading Support

C What are two common units for measuring heat? *calorie and joule*

D How many calories are in a Calorie, with a capital C? *1000*

Advanced Have students investigate and compare the number of Calories in fats, carbohydrates, and proteins; the number of Calories in foods they like; or the number of Calories that different people need. Have students make a table of their results to share with the class. What happens when too many Calories are consumed?

 Challenge and Extension, p. 222

Some substances change temperature more easily than others.

Have you ever seen an apple pie taken right out of the oven? If you put a piece of pie on a plate to cool, you can touch the pie crust in a few minutes and it will feel only slightly warm. But if you try to take a bite, the hot pie filling will burn your mouth. The pie crust cools much more quickly than the filling, which is mostly water.

Specific Heat

The amount of energy required to raise the temperature of 1 gram of a substance by 1°C is the **specific heat** of that substance. Every substance has its own specific heat value. So, each substance absorbs a different amount of energy in order to show the same increase in temperature.

If you look back at the definition of a calorie, you will see that it is defined in terms of water—one calorie raises the temperature of 1 gram of water by 1°C. So, water has a specific heat of exactly 1.00 calorie per gram per °C. Because one calorie is equal to 4.18 J, it takes 4.18 J to raise the temperature of one gram of water by 1°C. In joules, water's specific heat is 4.18 J per gram per °C. If you look at the specific heat graph shown below, you will see that 4.18 is an unusually large value. For example, one gram of iron has to absorb only 0.45 joules for its temperature to increase by 1°C.

A substance with a high specific heat value, like water, not only has to absorb a large quantity of energy for its temperature to increase, but it also must release a large quantity of energy for its temperature to decrease. This is why the apple pie filling can still be hot while the pie crust is cool. The liquid filling takes longer to cool. The high specific heat of water is also one reason it is used as a coolant in car radiators. The water can absorb a great deal of energy and protect the engine from getting too hot.

READING TIP
Joules per gram per °C is shown as $\frac{J}{g°C}$.

Specific Heat of Substances

Substance	Specific Heat ($\frac{J}{g°C}$)
water	4.18
wood	1.76
aluminum	0.90
sand	0.67
glass	0.66
iron	0.45

CHECK YOUR READING How is specific heat related to a change in temperature?

APPLY More energy is needed to warm water than many other substances. What materials in this photograph might be warmer than the water?

Chapter 4: Temperature and Heat 113

DIFFERENTIATE INSTRUCTION

 More Reading Support

E What is the amount of energy needed to raise the temperature of 1 gram of a specific substance by 1°C? *the substance's specific heat*

Below Level If students have trouble understanding the concept of specific heat, ask them for examples of substances that get hot faster and stay hot longer than other substances. Possible examples include fruit or other fillings with a high water content inside muffins or pies. Explain that substances that stay hot longer have a higher specific heat value.

Teach from Visuals

To help students interpret the graph of specific heat, ask: What is the specific heat of wood? *1.76 J/g°C* What does this mean? *One gram of wood absorbs 1.76 J for its temperature to rise 1°C.*

Teach Difficult Concepts

As the atoms of elements become larger, less energy is required to produce an increase in temperature. Hydrogen has the greatest specific heat value (14.3 J/g°C) and is the smallest atom. The general relationship between atomic mass and specific heat was expressed by the Dulong-Petit law in 1819, about 50 years before Mendeleyev's modern periodic table.

Teacher Demo

To help students understand how substances absorb varying amounts of energy, do the following demonstration. Light a candle and ask students what will happen if you hold an index card over the flame. Hold the card over the flame; it will catch fire. (Keep a bucket of water nearby to put out the fire.) Gather some crayon shavings and place them on top of a second index card. Ask students what they think will happen this time. Hold the card and shavings over the flame. The shavings will melt, but the card will not burn. Remove the card after the wax is melted. Ask students why this second index card did not burn.

Ongoing Assessment

Understand why some substances change temperature more easily than others.

Ask: What determines the amount of energy a substance needs to absorb to increase its temperature? *specific heat*

PHOTO CAPTION Answer: *metals, sand, wood, glass*

CHECK YOUR READING Answer: *The greater a substance's specific heat, the more energy is required to raise that substance's temperature.*

Chapter 4 113

Ongoing Assessment

 Answer: The more mass an object has, the more thermal energy it has.

Teach Difficult Concepts

To help students understand that a substance with a low temperature can have more thermal energy than a substance with a higher temperature, place a gallon jug of hot water and a cup of hotter water on a table. Record the temperature of the water in both containers and have students carefully feel the outside of the containers. Wait 20 minutes and repeat the observations. The gallon of hot water should be warmer. Point out that the mass of a substance, in addition to its temperature, determines how much thermal energy it has.

Reinforce

Have students relate the section to the Big Idea.

R *Reinforcing Key Concepts, p. 224*

4.2 ASSESS & RETEACH

Assess

 Section 4.2 Quiz, p. 62

Reteach

Divide the class into groups. Make a three-column chart on the board to compare and contrast heat, thermal energy, and specific heat. Ask volunteers to fill in the chart with examples, characteristics, and misconceptions for each term.

Technology Resources

Have students visit ClassZone.com for reteaching of Key Concepts.

- CONTENT REVIEW
- CONTENT REVIEW CD-ROM

114 Unit 1: **Matter and Energy**

Specific Heat and Mass

Recall that thermal energy is the total kinetic energy of all particles in an object. So, thermal energy depends on the object's mass. Suppose you have a cup of water at a temperature of 90°C (194°F) and a bathtub full of water at a temperature of 40°C (104°F). Which mass of water has more thermal energy? There are many more water molecules in the bathtub, so the water in the tub has more thermal energy.

Specific Heat, Mass, and Weather

The temperature of a large body of water influences the temperature of nearby land. The green shading shows how far this effect extends.

The water in the cup has the same specific heat as the water in the tub. However, the cup of water will cool more quickly than the water in the bathtub. The tub of water has to release more thermal energy to its surroundings, through heat, to show a decrease in temperature because it has so much more mass.

This idea is particularly relevant to very large masses. For example, Lake Michigan holds 4.92 quadrillion liters (1.30 quadrillion gallons) of water. Because of the high specific heat of water and the mass of water in the lake, the temperature of Lake Michigan changes very slowly.

The temperature of the lake affects the temperatures on its shores. During spring and early summer, the lake warms slowly, which helps keep the nearby land cooler. During the winter, the lake cools slowly, which helps keep the nearby land warmer. Temperatures within about 15 miles of the lake can differ by as much as 6°C (about 10°F) from areas farther away from the lake.

As you will read in the next section, the way in which a large body of water can influence temperatures on land depends on how energy is transferred through heat.

 How does an object's thermal energy depend on its mass?

4.2 Review

KEY CONCEPTS

1. How is temperature related to heat?
2. How do the units that are used to measure heat differ from the units that are used to measure temperature?
3. Describe specific heat in your own words.

CRITICAL THINKING

4. **Compare and Contrast** How are a calorie and a joule similar? How are they different?
5. **Synthesize** Describe the relationships among kinetic energy, temperature, heat, and thermal energy.

⬤ CHALLENGE

6. **Infer** Suppose you are spending a hot summer day by a pool. Why might the water in the pool cool the air near the pool?

114 Unit 1: **Matter and Energy**

ANSWERS

1. Heat transfers energy because a temperature difference exists.

2. Heat is measured in terms of temperature change.

3. the amount of energy that 1 gram of a substance needs to absorb to increase in temperature by 1°C

4. Both are used to measure heat. The joule is the standard unit for energy. One calorie equals 4.18 joules.

5. Temperature is the average kinetic energy of particles in an object; thermal energy is the total kinetic energy of particles in an object. Heat transfers thermal energy between objects due to temperature differences.

6. Water has a high specific heat, and heat transfers energy from the air to the cooler water.

SCIENCE on the JOB

CHEF

Bread vs. Meat

Chefs have to understand how energy as heat is transferred to different foods. For example, the fluffy texture of bread comes from pockets of gas that separate its fibers. The gas is a poor conductor of energy. Therefore, more energy and a longer cooking time are needed to cook bread than to cook an equal amount of meat.

What Temperature?

Eggs cook very differently under different temperatures. For example, temperature is important when baking meringue, which is made of egg whites and sugar. A Key lime pie topped with meringue is baked at 400°F to make a meringue that is soft. However, meringue baked at 275°F makes light and crisp dessert shells.

Cooking with Heat

A chef makes many decisions about cooking a meal based on heat and temperature. The appropriate temperature and cooking method must be used. A chef must calculate the cooking time of each part of the meal so that everything is finished at the same time. A chef also needs to understand how heat moves through food. For example, if an oven temperature is too hot, meat can be overcooked on the outside and undercooked on the inside.

Roasting and Heat

The shape of the food being roasted is just as important as what is being roasted. Heat moves more quickly through food with a thin shape than it will through food with a thicker shape.

EXPLORE

1. **COMPARE** Using a cookbook, find the oven temperatures for baking biscuits, potatoes, and beef. Could you successfully cook a roast and biscuits in the oven at the same time?
2. **CHALLENGE** Crack open three eggs. Lightly beat one egg in each of three separate bowls. Follow the steps below.
   1. Heat about two cups of water to 75°C in a small pan.
   2. Pour one of the eggs into the water in the pan.
   3. Observe the egg and record your observations.
   4. Repeat steps 1–3 twice, once with boiling water and then with room-temperature water.

   Describe the differences that you observed among the three eggs. What may account for these differences?

Chapter 4: **Temperature and Heat** 115

SCIENCE ON THE JOB
Relevance of Science to Non-science Jobs

Set Learning Goal
To understand why chefs need knowledge of heat and temperature

Present the Science
Many foods, such as beef, chicken, pork, and eggs, can contain microorganisms such as bacteria that cause food poisoning. Cooking foods until they reach a certain temperature kills these bacteria. Meat thermometers and other thermometers help ensure that foods reach the correct temperature. In addition, refrigerating leftovers and keeping foods cold help slow the growth of bacteria. Heat and temperature are also important to a chef because part of the job involves the presentation and appeal of food. The structure of protein changes when exposed to high temperatures, so a chef has to know how the texture of foods containing a large amount of protein will change during and after cooking.

Discussion Questions
- Ask: What can cause meat to be overcooked on the outside and undercooked on the inside? *an oven temperature that is too hot*
- Ask: How does the shape of a roast affect how fast it cooks? *Heat moves more quickly through a thin roast than a thick roast.*

Close
Ask: How do chefs use their knowledge of heat and temperature? *to choose the right temperature and cooking method; to finish cooking every part of the meal at the right time; to understand how heat moves through food*

EXPLORE

1. **COMPARE** By changing the length of time they are in the oven, or by putting them in the oven at different times.
2. **CHALLENGE** The egg in room-temperature water doesn't visibly change. In boiling water it stays in one piece and turns white right away. In 75°C water it spreads out and slowly turns slightly white. The water temperature determines what happens to the eggs.

Chapter 4 **115**

4.3 FOCUS

Set Learning Goals

Students will

- Explain how energy is transferred through heat.
- Describe how materials are used to control the transfer of energy through heat.

3-Minute Warm-Up

Display Transparency 29 or copy this exercise on the board:

Match each definition with the correct term.

Definitions

1. the flow of energy from warmer objects to cooler objects *c*
2. the average kinetic energy of particles in an object *a*
3. the total kinetic energy of particles in an object *d*

Terms

a. temperature
b. specific heat
c. heat
d. thermal energy
e. kinetic energy

 3-Minute Warm-Up, p. T29

4.3 MOTIVATE

EXPLORE Conduction

PURPOSE To observe the transfer of energy between objects in direct contact

TIP 10 min. Make sure the hot water in the large beaker does not overflow into the smaller beaker.

WHAT DO YOU THINK? *The temperature of the cold water increased, and the temperature of the hot water decreased. Energy flowed from warm to cooler; the changes in temperature are indicated by the two thermometers.*

KEY CONCEPT
4.3 The transfer of energy as heat can be controlled.

▸ **BEFORE, you learned**
- Temperature is the average amount of kinetic energy of particles in an object
- Heat is the flow of energy from warmer objects to cooler objects

▸ **NOW, you will learn**
- How energy is transferred through heat
- How materials are used to control the transfer of energy through heat

VOCABULARY

conduction p. 117
conductor p. 117
insulator p. 117
convection p. 118
radiation p. 119

EXPLORE Conduction

How can you observe a flow of energy?

PROCEDURE

1. Fill the large beaker halfway with hot tap water. Fill the small beaker halfway with cold water. Place a thermometer in each beaker. Record the temperature of the water in each beaker.

2. Without removing the water in either beaker, place the small beaker inside the large beaker. Record the temperature in each beaker every 30 seconds for 2 minutes.

WHAT DO YOU THINK?
- How did the water temperature in each beaker change?
- In which direction did energy flow? How do you know?

MATERIALS
- 500 mL beaker
- hot tap water
- 200 mL beaker
- cold water
- 2 thermometers
- stopwatch

NOTE-TAKING STRATEGY
Main idea and detail notes would be a useful strategy for taking notes on how heat transfers energy.

Energy moves as heat in three ways.

Think about what you do to keep warm on a cold day. You may wear several layers of clothing, sit next to a heater, or avoid drafty windows. On a hot day, you may wear light clothing and sit in the shade of a tree. In all of these situations, you are trying to control the transfer of energy between yourself and your surroundings.

Recall that heat is always a transfer of energy from objects at a higher temperature to objects at a lower temperature. How does energy get transferred from a warmer object to a cooler one? There are three different ways in which this transfer of energy can occur—by conduction, convection, and radiation. So, in trying to control heat, it is necessary to control conduction, convection, and radiation.

116 Unit 1: Matter and Energy

RESOURCES FOR DIFFERENTIATED INSTRUCTION

Below Level
UNIT RESOURCE BOOK
- Reading Study Guide A, pp. 227–228
- Decoding Support, p. 239

🅒 **AUDIO CDS**

🅡 **Additional INVESTIGATION,**
Observing Convection, A, B, & C, pp. 251–259;
Teacher Instructions, pp. 262–263

Advanced
UNIT RESOURCE BOOK
- Challenge and Extension, p. 233
- Challenge Reading, pp. 235–236

English Learners
UNIT RESOURCE BOOK
Spanish Reading Study Guide, pp. 231–232

🅒 **AUDIO CDS**
- Audio Readings in Spanish
- Audio Readings (English)

Conduction

One way in which energy is transferred as heat is through direct contact between objects. **Conduction** is the process that moves energy from one object to another when they are touching physically. If you have ever picked up a bowl of hot soup, you have experienced conduction.

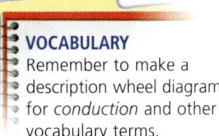

VOCABULARY
Remember to make a description wheel diagram for *conduction* and other vocabulary terms.

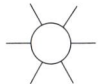

Conduction occurs any time that objects at different temperatures come into contact with each other. The average kinetic energy of particles in the warmer object is greater than that of the particles in the cooler object. When particles of the objects collide, some of the kinetic energy of the particles in the warmer object is transferred to the cooler object. As long as the objects are in contact, conduction continues until the temperatures of the objects are equal.

Conduction can also occur within a single object. In this case, energy is transferred from the warmer part of the object to the cooler part of the object by heat. Suppose you put a metal spoon into a cup of hot cocoa. Energy will be conducted from the warm end of the spoon to the cool end until the temperature of the entire spoon is the same.

Some materials transfer the kinetic energy of particles better than others. **Conductors** are materials that transfer energy easily. Often, conductors also have a low specific heat. For example, metals are typically good conductors. You know that when one end of a metal object gets hot, the other end quickly becomes hot as well. Consider pots or pans that have metal handles. A metal handle becomes too hot to touch soon after the pan is placed on a stove that has been turned on.

Other materials, called **insulators,** are poor conductors. Insulators often have high specific heats. Some examples of insulators are wood, paper, and plastic foam. In fact, plastic foam is a good insulator because it contains many small spaces that are filled with air. A plastic foam cup will not easily transfer energy by conduction. As a result, plastic foam is often used to keep cold drinks cold or hot drinks hot. Think about the pan handle mentioned above. Often, the handle is made of a material that is an insulator, such as wood or plastic. Although a wood or plastic handle will get hot when the pan is on a stove, it takes a much longer time for wood or plastic to get hot as compared to a metal handle.

Conduction transfers energy from the cocoa to the mug to the person's hands.

 How are conductors and insulators different?

Chapter 4: **Temperature and Heat** 117

DIFFERENTIATE INSTRUCTION

More Reading Support

A What do two objects need for conduction to occur? *touch and a temperature difference*

B What are poor conductors of energy? *insulators*

English Learners Point out different word forms to English learners as they appear in the text.

| conductor | insulator | radiate |
| conduction | insulation | radiation |

Have students look up one of the pairs of words and compare their definitions. Ask students what they might conclude about the word ending *-tion*.

4.3 INSTRUCT

Teacher Demo
To help students understand heat conduction, place a small amount of wax at various spots on a copper rod and ask students to predict what will happen to the wax if the rod is heated on one end. Have students share their predictions about what will happen and their reasons for those predictions. Then use a candle to heat one end of the copper rod so students can test their predictions. The wax closest to the heat source will melt first, and the wax farthest away will melt last. Based on their observations, have them discuss the behavior of heat when a copper rod is heated.

Teach from Visuals
To help students interpret the photograph of conduction from the mug of cocoa, ask: What is happening in the photograph? *The hot cocoa transfers energy through the wall of the mug to the hand holding the mug and to the air.*

Develop Critical Thinking
PREDICT Have students predict what will happen in terms of particle movement when energy is conducted from the hot cocoa through the mug to a person's hands. *Particles that are moving faster will bump into slower particles and transfer energy.*

EXPLORE the BIG idea
Revisit "Does It Chill?" on p. 101. Have students explain their results.

Ongoing Assessment
CHECK YOUR READING *Answer: Conductors easily transfer energy, but insulators do not. Conductors often have low specific heats, and insulators often have high specific heats.*

Chapter 4 **117**

Address Misconceptions

IDENTIFY Ask: In what direction, such as upward, downward, or sideways, is energy transferred through heat? If students say only upward, they may hold the misconception that heat only rises.

CORRECT Point out that the common phrase "Heat rises" is misleading. Have students look at the diagram again. Point out that warm air is pushed up by cooler, denser air. To show that heat can travel in any direction, use a radiant heat source. Have students put their hand close to the heat source, but not above it, to observe that heat travels in all directions. The demonstration on p. 117 also shows how heat travels in different directions.

REASSESS Ask students to describe what causes warm air to rise. *It is pushed up by cooler, denser air.*

Technology Resources
Visit **ClassZone.com** for background on common student misconceptions.

 MISCONCEPTION DATABASE

Teach from Visuals

To help students interpret the diagram of convection in air, ask:

- What happens to air as it cools? *It becomes more dense and sinks.*
- What happens to cooler, denser air when it moves under warm air? *It is warmed by conduction from the ground.*

Integrate the Sciences

Convection is the process thought to be responsible for the movement of Earth's internal energy. As hot mantle near Earth's core rises toward the crust, it cools and is pushed aside by hot mantle rising beneath it. It continues to cool, becomes more dense, and sinks back toward Earth's core, creating convection currents.

Ongoing Assessment

 more dense at 2 where air is cool; less dense at 1 where air is warmer

---

Convection

Energy can also be transferred through the movement of gases or liquids. **Convection** is the process that transfers energy by the movement of large numbers of particles in the same direction within a liquid or gas. In most substances, as the kinetic energy of particles increases, the particles spread out over a larger area. An increased distance between particles causes a decrease in the density of the substance. Convection occurs when a cooler, denser mass of the gas or liquid replaces a warmer, less dense mass of the gas or liquid by pushing it upward.

REMINDER
Density = mass / Volume

READING TIP
As you read about the cycle that occurs during convection, follow the steps in the illustration below.

Convection is a cycle in nature responsible for most winds and ocean currents. When the temperature of a region of air increases, the particles in the air spread out and the air becomes less dense.

① Cooler, denser air flows in underneath the warmer, less dense air, and pushes the warmer air upward.

② When this air cools, it becomes more dense than the warmer air beneath it.

③ The cooled air sinks and moves under the warmer air.

Convection in liquids is similar. Warm water is less dense than cold water, so the warm water is pushed upward as cooler, denser water moves underneath. When the warm water that has been pushed up cools, its density increases. The cycle continues when this more dense water sinks, pushing warmer water up again.

Recall that a large body of water, such as Lake Michigan, influences the temperature of the land nearby. This effect is due to convection. During the spring and early summer, the lake is cool and warms more slowly than the land. The air above the land gets warmer than the air over the water. The warmer air above the land is less dense than the cooler air above the water. The cooler, denser air moves onshore and pushes the warmer air up. The result is a cooling breeze from the lake.

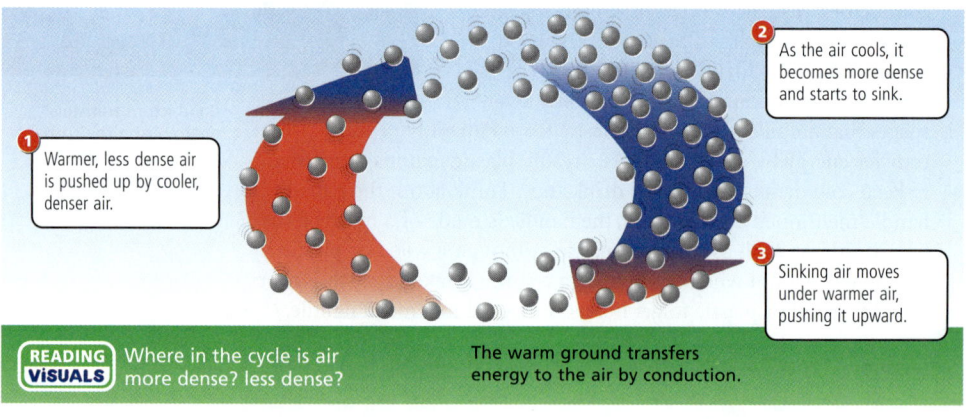

① Warmer, less dense air is pushed up by cooler, denser air.

② As the air cools, it becomes more dense and starts to sink.

③ Sinking air moves under warmer air, pushing it upward.

The warm ground transfers energy to the air by conduction.

 READING VISUALS Where in the cycle is air more dense? less dense?

DIFFERENTIATE INSTRUCTION

 More Reading Support

C What is the process that transfers energy by the motion of many particles in liquids or gases? *convection*

Additional Investigation To reinforce Section 4.3 learning goals, use the following full-period investigation:

R **Additional INVESTIGATION,** Observing Convection, A, B, & C, pp. 251–259, 262–263

Below Level Remind students that density is the amount of mass of a substance in a certain volume. Because the particles in warm air are farther apart than the particles in cold air, a certain volume of warm air has fewer particles than the same volume of cold air. Warm air therefore is less dense than cold air.

Radiation

Radiation is another way in which energy can be transferred from one place to another. **Radiation** is energy that travels as electromagnetic waves, which include visible light, microwaves, and infrared (IHN-fruh-REHD) light. The Sun is the most significant source of radiation that you experience on a daily basis. However, all objects—even you—emit radiation and release energy to their surroundings.

Consider radiation from the Sun. You can feel radiation as heat when radiation from the Sun warms your skin. The radiation emitted from the Sun strikes the particles in your body and transfers energy. This transfer of energy increases the movement of particles in your skin, which you detect as an increase in temperature. Of course, you are not the only object on Earth that absorbs the Sun's radiation. Everything—from air to concrete sidewalks—absorbs radiation that increases particle motion and produces an increase in temperature.

When radiation is emitted from one object and then is absorbed by another, the result is often a transfer of energy through heat. Like both conduction and convection, radiation can transfer energy from warmer to cooler objects. However, radiation differs from conduction and convection in a very significant way. Radiation can travel through empty space, as it does when it moves from the Sun to Earth. If this were not the case, radiation from the Sun would have no effect on Earth.

When radiation from the Sun is absorbed, energy is transferred through heat.

Identify examples of conduction, convection, or radiation.

 How does radiation transfer energy?

Different materials are used to control the transfer of energy.

Energy is always being transferred between objects at different temperatures. It is often important to slow this movement of energy. For example, if energy were always transferred quickly and efficiently through heat, it would not be possible to keep a building warm during a cold day or to keep cocoa hot in a thermos.

Chapter 4: **Temperature and Heat** 119

DIFFERENTIATE INSTRUCTION

D What is both a form of energy and a way that heat transfers energy? *radiation*

Advanced Have students research solar air heaters and try to construct one in a window. Solar air heaters typically have the following characteristics: clear covers, dark interior surfaces, and insulating materials.

 Challenge and Extension, p. 233

Have students who are interested in how heat is transferred on the sun read the following article:

 Challenge Reading, pp. 235–236

Teach from Visuals

To help students interpret the diagram and photograph of the person being warmed by radiation from the sun, ask:

- What is striking particles of this person's skin and transferring energy? *radiation*
- What happens to the particles of skin? *Their movement increases, and the person detects an increase in temperature.*

Real World Example

Radiation from the Sun is used in buildings designed for passive solar heating. In the Northern Hemisphere, these buildings have many windows facing south, so that more sunlight will shine into the building. The walls and floors are designed to absorb radiation, and their temperature increases when sunlight hits them. Conduction transfers the energy from the walls and floor to the air in the building.

Integrate the Sciences

Cold-blooded animals cannot maintain their own internal body temperature, so it remains about the same as the temperature of their environment. Some animals, such as turtles, frogs, lizards, and butterflies, lie in sunlight to absorb radiation from the Sun; others use muscle movement to increase their body temperature.

Ongoing Assessment

Explain how energy is transferred through heat.

Ask: What are three ways that energy can be transferred? *conduction, convection, radiation*

 Answer: When electromagnetic waves strike an object, they transfer energy to the object.

Chapter 4 **119**

Teach from Visuals

To help students interpret the diagrams and photographs of the polar bear and the vacuum flask, ask:

- Why is the polar bear's hollow hair an effective insulator? *Air inside the hair does not easily conduct energy from the warm bear to the cold air.*
- What is the insulator in the vacuum flask? *empty space*

 This visual is also available as T30 in the Unit Transparency Book.

Integrate the Sciences

In some homes, much of the energy used for heating is wasted because energy flows through leaks around windows and doors and in floors, walls, and ceilings. Using more fuel and electricity adds to the pollution of the environment and to the depletion of nonrenewable resources. Properly insulating a home makes it more energy efficient and saves money.

Develop Critical Thinking

EVALUATE In addition to hollow guard hairs and a thick layer of fat, polar bears have other characteristics that help keep them warm in their environment. Their fur is oily, and their skin is black. How might these characteristics help? *Radiation that penetrates a polar bear's fur is absorbed more readily by the black pigment of the skin; the oily fur repels water so a polar bear can easily shake off water before the water freezes into ice.*

Ongoing Assessment

READING VISUALS Sample answer: It provides insulation and slows the transfer of energy through conduction. In the hair, air is the insulator; in the vacuum flask, empty space is the insulator.

Insulation

Insulators used by people are similar to insulators in nature. Polar bears are so well insulated that they tend to overheat.

Vacuum Flask

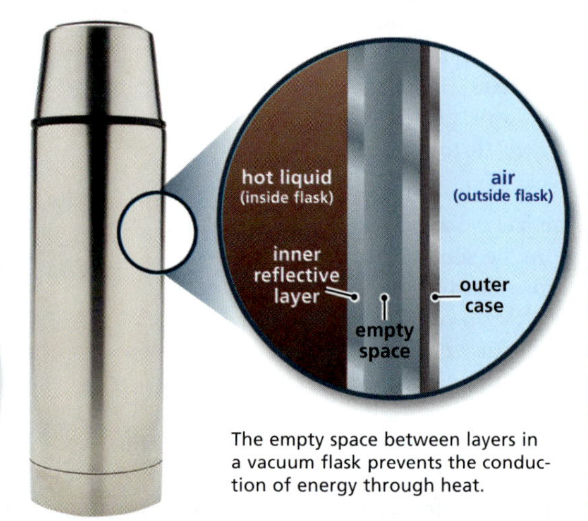

The polar bear's hollow guard hair is an effective insulator because air inside the hair does not easily conduct energy.

hollow hair

hot liquid (inside flask) — air (outside flask)
inner reflective layer — outer case
empty space

The empty space between layers in a vacuum flask prevents the conduction of energy through heat.

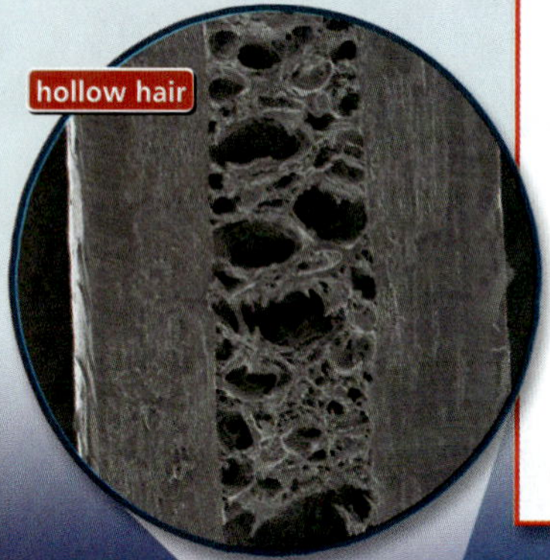

Polar bears have several layers of insulation. They have a layer of fat up to 11 cm thick, a 2.5–5.0 cm thick layer of fur, and an outer layer of hollow guard hairs.

READING VISUALS How is the polar bear's hollow hair similar to the empty space in a vacuum flask? How is it different?

120 Unit 1: Matter and Energy

DIFFERENTIATE INSTRUCTION

Alternative Assessment Have students write a paragraph describing the insulators in the photograph and how they work.

Insulators are used to control and slow the transfer of energy from warmer objects to cooler objects because they are poor conductors of energy. You can think of an insulator as a material that keeps cold things cold or hot things hot.

Sometimes people say that insulation "keeps out the cold." An insulator actually works by trapping energy. During the winter, you use insulators such as wool to slow the loss of your body heat to cold air. The wool traps air against your body, and because both air and wool are poor conductors, you lose body heat at a slower rate. Fiberglass insulation in the outer walls of a building works in the same way. The fiberglass slows the movement of energy from a building to the outside during cold weather, and it slows the movement of energy into the building during hot weather.

A vacuum flask, or thermos, works in a slightly different way to keep liquids either hot or cold. Between two layers of the flask is an empty space. This space prevents conduction between the inside and outside walls of the flask. Also, the inside of the flask is covered with a shiny material that reflects much of the radiation that strikes it. This prevents radiation from either entering or leaving the flask.

Insulators that people use are often very similar to insulators in nature. Look at the photograph of the polar bear on page 120. Because of the arctic environment in which the polar bear lives, it needs several different types of insulation. The polar bear's fur helps to trap a layer of air against its body to keep warmth inside. Polar bears also have guard hairs that extend beyond the fur. These guard hairs are hollow and contain air. Because air is a poor conductor, the bear's body heat is not easily released into the air.

 How does insulation keep a building warm?

4.3 Review

KEY CONCEPTS
1. What are three ways in which energy can be transferred through heat? Provide an example of each.
2. Explain how convection is a cycle in nature.
3. Describe how an insulator can slow a transfer of energy.

CRITICAL THINKING
4. **Compare and Contrast** Describe the similarities and differences among conduction, convection, and radiation.
5. **Synthesize** Do you think solids can undergo convection? Why or why not? Explain.

CHALLENGE
6. **Infer** During the day, wind often blows from a body of water to the land. What do you think would happen at night? Explain.

Chapter 4: **Temperature and Heat** 121

ANSWERS

1. Sample answer: conduction, metal spoon in hot cocoa; convection, air moving in a cycle; radiation, sunlight transferring energy to skin

2. Warm air is pushed up by cooler, denser air. As air cools, it becomes more dense, sinks, and moves under warmer air.

3. It is a poor conductor, so energy is only slowly transferred.

4. All are ways that heat transfers energy. Conduction occurs only with direct contact. Convection occurs in a cycle in gases or liquids. Radiation travels as EM waves through empty space.

5. No; particles in a solid cannot move freely.

6. The land cools more quickly than the water, and wind blows from the land to the water.

CHAPTER INVESTIGATION

Focus

PURPOSE To design and test an insulated bottle that slows a change in the temperature of water as compared to a noninsulated control bottle

OVERVIEW Students will design and build an insulated bottle. They will measure the temperature change of water in the insulated bottle and a control bottle. Students will find the following:

- The temperature of the water in the control bottle should change more than that of the water in the insulated bottle.
- Insulation slows the transfer of energy through heat.

Lab Preparation

- Have students bring in small plastic bottles that hold over 200 mL. Each group should use two identical bottles.
- Prior to the investigation, have students read through the investigation and prepare their data tables. Or you may wish to copy and distribute datasheets and rubrics.

 UNIT RESOURCE BOOK, pp. 242–250

 SCIENCE TOOLKIT, F13

Lab Management

- Review with students how to put the thermometers in the bottles and hold them in place with clay so that they do not touch the bottom or sides of the bottle.
- Students should be ready to insert the thermometers and clay before getting the hot or cold water.

Teaching with Technology

A probeware system with a temperature probe can be used to measure and record temperatures. A CBL system can graph the data.

122 Unit 1: **Matter and Energy**

CHAPTER INVESTIGATION

Insulators

OVERVIEW AND PURPOSE

 DESIGN YOUR OWN

To keep warm in cold weather, a person needs insulation. A down-filled coat, such as the one worn by the girl in the photograph, is a very effective insulator because it contains a great deal of air. Energy is transferred rapidly through some substances and quite slowly through others. In this investigation, you will

- design and build an insulator for a bottle to maintain the temperature of the water inside
- test an unchanged bottle and your experimental bottle to see which maintains the water's temperature more effectively

▶ Problem

How can a bottle be insulated most effectively?

MATERIALS
- 2 small plastic bottles
- 2 thermometers
- modeling clay
- graduated cylinder
- tap water (hot or cold)
- foam packing peanuts
- plastic wrap
- aluminum foil
- soil
- sand
- rubber bands
- coffee can
- beaker
- stopwatch

▶ Procedure

1. Create a data table similar to the one shown on the sample notebook page to record your measurements.

2. Set aside plastic bottles, thermometers, modeling clay, and a graduated cylinder. Decide whether you will test hot or cold water in your bottles.

3. From the other materials available to you, design a way to modify one of the bottles so that it will keep the temperature of the water constant for a longer period of time than the control bottle.

4. Build your modified bottle by using one or more of the insulating materials available.

122 Unit 1: **Matter and Energy**

INVESTIGATION RESOURCES

 CHAPTER INVESTIGATION, Insulators
- Level A, pp. 242–245
- Level B, pp. 246–249
- Level C, p. 250

Advanced students should complete Levels B & C.

 Writing a Lab Report, D12–13

Technology Resources

Customize this student lab as needed or look for an alternative. Print rubrics to assess student lab reports.

 Lab Generator CD-ROM

5. Fill each bottle with 200 mL of hot or cold water. Make sure that the water in each bottle is the same temperature.

6. Place a thermometer into each bottle. The thermometers should touch only the water, not the bottom or sides of the bottles. Use modeling clay to hold the thermometers in place in the bottles.

7. Record the starting temperature of the water in both bottles. Continue to observe and record the temperature of the water in both bottles every 2 minutes for 30 minutes. Record these temperatures in your data table.

step 6

Observe and Analyze

1. **COMMUNICATE** Draw the setup of your experimental bottle in your notebook. Be sure to label the materials that you used to insulate your experimental bottle.

2. **RECORD OBSERVATIONS** Make sure you record all of your measurements and observations in the data table.

3. **GRAPH** Make a double line graph of the temperature data. Graph temperature versus time. Plot the temperature on the vertical axis, or *y*-axis, and the time on the horizontal axis, or *x*-axis. Use different colors to show the data from the different bottles.

4. **IDENTIFY VARIABLES, CONTROLS, AND CONSTANTS** Which bottle was the control? What was the variable? What were the constants in both setups?

5. **ANALYZE** Obtain the experimental results from two other groups that used a different insulator. Compare your results with the results from the other groups. Which bottle changed temperature most quickly?

Conclude

1. **EVALUATE** Explain why the materials used by different groups might have been more or less effective as insulators. How might you change your design to improve its insulating properties?

2. **IDENTIFY LIMITS** Describe possible sources of error in the procedure or any points at which errors might have occurred. Why is it important to use the same amount of water in both bottles?

3. **APPLY** Energy can be transferred as heat by radiation, conduction, and convection. Which of these processes might be slowed by the insulation around your bottle? Explain.

INVESTIGATE Further

CHALLENGE We depend on our clothing to keep us from losing body heat when we go outside in cold weather. How might you determine the type of clothing that would provide the best insulation? Design an experiment that would test your hypothesis.

Insulators
Problem How can a bottle be insulated most effectively?
Observe and Analyze
Table 1. Water Temperature Measurements

Time (min)	Control Bottle Temperature (°C)	Experimental Bottle Temperature (°C)
0		
2		
4		
6		
8		
10		

Conclude

Chapter 4: **Temperature and Heat** 123

Observe and Analyze

1. See students' drawings.
2. See students' tables.
3. The graph should indicate that the water in the insulated bottle has a more stable temperature than the water in the control bottle.
4. The control was the unmodified bottle. The variable was the insulating material used. The amount and the starting temperature of the water were the same for both setups.
5. Answers will vary depending on the different insulators being compared.

Conclude

1. Sample answer: The most effective designs used materials that have the highest specific heats and contain a large amount of air. Materials that are tightly packed are less effective. A design may be improved by using a material with more effective insulating properties.
2. Possible sources of error include different starting temperatures, inaccurate volume measurements, thermometers touching the bottom or sides of the bottles, inaccurate temperature measurements, different-sized bottles, and one bottle being disturbed more than the other. The same amount of water is important because both bottles need to start with the same thermal energy.
3. Conduction is the form of energy transfer that will be most affected by the materials available, although transfer by radiation will also be affected.

INVESTIGATE Further

CHALLENGE Answer: Students' experiments should have a control and test different types of clothing materials.

Post-Lab Discussion

Ask: Why didn't it matter if you used hot or cold water? *Heat is the transfer of energy from a warmer substance to a colder substance. The insulating material slows down the transfer of energy either from the hot water to the cooler bottle and air or from the warm air and bottle to the colder water.*

CHAPTER 4 • REVIEW

BACK TO

Have students look at the photograph on pp. 100–101. Ask them to summarize how heat affects temperatures in the photograph. *Radiation from the Sun is transferring energy to particles in the ground and the giraffe's skin. This increases the kinetic energy of the particles in the ground and skin, which increases their temperatures.*

KEY CONCEPTS SUMMARY

SECTION 4.1
Ask: Which liquid has particles with a higher average kinetic energy, and how do you know? *The particles in the hot liquid have a higher average kinetic energy and are moving faster, as shown by the motion lines.*

SECTION 4.2
Ask: What is happening to energy in the lemonade and ice? *Energy is transferred through heat from the lemonade to the cooler ice.*

Ask: When will the transfer of energy stop? *when there is no temperature difference*

SECTION 4.3
Ask: How does energy transfer differently by conduction, convection, and radiation? *Conduction requires direct contact, convection requires movement of gases or liquids, and radiation travels via electromagnetic waves.*

Review Concepts

- Big Idea Flow Chart, p. T25
- Chapter Outline, pp. T31–T32

---

4 Chapter Review

the BIG idea
Heat is a flow of energy due to temperature differences.

CONTENT REVIEW
CLASSZONE.COM

 KEY CONCEPTS SUMMARY

1 Temperature depends on particle movement.
- All particles in matter have kinetic energy.
- Temperature is the measurement of the average kinetic energy of particles in an object.
- Temperature is commonly measured on the Fahrenheit or Celsius scales.

hot liquid

cold liquid

Particles in a warmer substance have a greater average kinetic energy than particles in a cooler substance.

VOCABULARY
kinetic theory of matter p. 104
temperature p. 105
degree p. 106
thermometer p. 107

2 Energy flows from warmer to cooler objects.
- Heat is a transfer of energy from an object at a higher temperature to an object at a lower temperature.
- Different materials require different amounts of energy to change temperature.

Energy is transferred from the warmer lemonade to the cold ice through heat.

VOCABULARY
heat p. 110
thermal energy p. 111
calorie p. 112
joule p. 112
specific heat p. 113

3 The transfer of energy as heat can be controlled.
- Energy can be transferred by conduction, convection, and radiation.
- Different materials are used to control the transfer of energy.

Types of Energy Transfer		
Conduction	**Convection**	**Radiation**
• Energy transferred by direct contact • Energy flows directly from warmer object to cooler object • Can occur within one object • Continues until object temperatures are equal	• Occurs in gases and liquids • Movement of large number of particles in same direction • Occurs due to difference in density • Cycle occurs while temperature differences exist	• Energy transferred by electromagnetic waves such as light, microwaves, and infrared radiation • All objects radiate energy • Can transfer energy through empty space

VOCABULARY
conduction p. 117
conductor p. 117
insulator p. 117
convection p. 118
radiation p. 119

124 Unit 1: Matter and Energy

Technology Resources

Have students visit ClassZone.com or use the CD-ROM for a cumulative review of concepts.

 CONTENT REVIEW

 CONTENT REVIEW CD-ROM

Engage students in a whole-class interactive review of Key Concepts. Edit content as you wish.

 POWER PRESENTATIONS

Reviewing Vocabulary

Make a frame for each of the vocabulary terms listed below. Write the term in the center. Decide what information to frame it with. Use definitions, examples, descriptions, parts, or pictures.

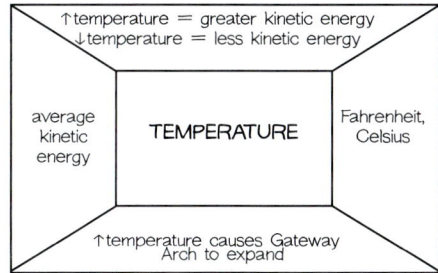

1. kinetic theory of matter
2. heat
3. thermal energy
4. conduction
5. convection
6. radiation

In two or three sentences, describe how the terms in the following pairs are related to each other. Underline each term in your answers.

7. calorie, joule
8. conductor, insulator

Reviewing Key Concepts

Multiple Choice *Choose the letter of the best answer.*

9. What is the zero point in the Celsius scale?
   a. the freezing point of pure water
   b. the boiling point of pure water
   c. the freezing point of mercury
   d. the boiling point of alcohol

10. Energy is always transferred through heat from?
    a. an object with a lower specific heat to one with a higher specific heat
    b. a cooler object to a warmer object
    c. an object with a higher specific heat to one with a lower specific heat
    d. a warmer object to a cooler object

11. The average kinetic energy of particles in an object can be measured by its
    a. heat
    b. thermal energy
    c. calories
    d. temperature

12. How is energy transferred by convection?
    a. by direct contact between objects
    b. by electromagnetic waves
    c. by movement of groups of particles in gases or liquids
    d. by movement of groups of particles in solid objects

13. The total kinetic energy of particles in an object is
    a. heat
    b. thermal energy
    c. calories
    d. temperature

14. Water requires more energy than an equal mass of iron for its temperature to increase by a given amount because water has a greater
    a. thermal energy
    b. specific heat
    c. temperature
    d. kinetic energy

15. Energy from the Sun travels to Earth through which process?
    a. temperature
    b. conduction
    c. radiation
    d. convection

16. An insulator keeps a home warm by
    a. slowing the transfer of cold particles from outside to inside
    b. increasing the specific heat of the air inside
    c. slowing the transfer of energy from inside to outside
    d. increasing the thermal energy of the walls

17. Conduction is the transfer of energy from a warmer object to a cooler object through
    a. a vacuum
    b. a gas
    c. direct contact
    d. empty space

Short Answer *Write a short answer to each question.*

18. How are kinetic energy and temperature related to each other?

19. What is the difference between heat and temperature?

Chapter 4: **Temperature and Heat** 125

ASSESSMENT RESOURCES

UNIT ASSESSMENT BOOK
- Chapter Test A, pp. 64–67
- Chapter Test B, pp. 68–71
- Chapter Test C, pp. 72–75
- Alternative Assessment, pp. 76–77
- Unit Test, A, B, & C, pp. 78–89

SPANISH ASSESSMENT BOOK
- Spanish Chapter Test, pp. 225–228
- Spanish Unit Test, pp. 229–232

Technology Resources

Edit test items and answer choices.

 Test Generator CD-ROM

Visit ClassZone.com to extend test practice.

 Test Practice

Reviewing Vocabulary

1. Frames should include that the kinetic theory of matter states that all particles in matter are in constant motion.
2. Frames should include that heat is the transfer of energy from an object at a higher temperature to one at a lower temperature.
3. Frames should include that thermal energy is the total amount of kinetic energy of the particles in an object.
4. Frames should include that conduction transfers energy through direct contact between objects.
5. Frames should include that convection transfers energy through the movement of many particles of a gas or liquid.
6. Frames should include that radiation transfers energy through electromagnetic waves.
7. Sample answer: The calorie and the joule are measures of heat. One calorie is the amount of energy needed to raise the temperature of 1 g of water by 1°C. One calorie is equal to 4.18 joules.
8. Sample answer: Conductors easily transfer energy, and insulators slow the transfer of energy. Conductors typically have a low specific heat, and insulators typically have a high specific heat.

Reviewing Key Concepts

9. a
10. d
11. d
12. c
13. b
14. b
15. c
16. c
17. c

18. Temperature measures the average kinetic energy of particles in a substance.
19. Heat is the transfer of energy between objects that differ in temperature. Temperature is a measurement of the average kinetic energy of particles in an object.

Chapter 4 **125**

Thinking Critically

20. B has the higher temperature because its particles are moving faster.

21. If A were chilled, its particles would slow down and become more tightly packed. If B were warmed, its particles would speed up and have more space between them.

22. Energy would flow from B to A because B is warmer and heat always transfers energy from warm substances to cooler substances.

23. The illustrations would be identical because heat will transfer energy until the substances are the same temperature.

24. Both processes transfer energy. Convection occurs in large regions of gases and liquids, but not in solids. Conduction occurs by direct contact between substances.

25. Radiation directly from the Sun is being avoided. Conduction to any part of the body in contact with the ground is still felt. Convection might be felt if air is moving.

26. Check students' diagrams; answers should be similar in concept to the convection diagram on p. 118

Using Math Skills in Science

27. about 20°F
28. 100 calories
29. 418 joules
30. 45 joules

the BIG idea

31. Answers will vary.
32. Answers should indicate that the kinetic theory of matter states that all particles of matter are in constant motion.

UNIT PROJECTS

Have students present their projects. Use the appropriate rubrics from the URB to evaluate their work.

 Unit Projects, pp. 5–10

Thinking Critically

The illustrations below show particle movement in a substance at two different temperatures. Use the illustrations to answer the next four questions.

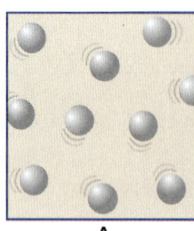 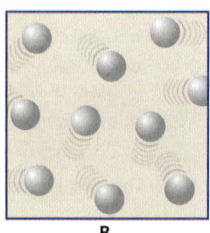

A   B

20. **OBSERVE** Which illustration represents the substance when it is at a higher temperature? Explain.

21. **PREDICT** What would happen to the particles in illustration A if the substance were chilled? What would happen if the particles in illustration B were warmed?

22. **PREDICT** If energy is transferred from one of the substances to the other through heat, in which direction would the energy flow (from A to B, or from B to A)? Why?

23. **COMMUNICATE** Suppose energy is transferred from one of the substances to the other through heat. Draw a sketch that shows what the particles of both substances would look like when the transfer of energy is complete. Explain.

24. **COMPARE AND CONTRAST** How are conduction and convection similar? How are they different?

25. **DRAW CONCLUSIONS** Suppose you are outdoors on a hot day and you move into the shade of a tree. Which form of energy transfer are you avoiding? Which type of energy transfer are you still feeling? Explain.

26. **COMMUNICATE** Draw a sketch that shows how convection occurs in a liquid. Label the sketch to indicate how the process occurs in a cycle.

126 Unit 1: Matter and Energy

Using Math Skills in Science

Use the illustrations of the two thermometers below to answer the next four questions.

A   B

27. How much of a change in temperature occurred between A and B in the Fahrenheit scale?

28. Suppose the temperatures were measured in 10 g of water. How much energy, in calories, would have been added to cause that increase in temperature? (**Hint:** 1 calorie raises the temperature of 1 g of water by 1°C.)

29. Again, suppose the temperatures shown above were measured in 10 g of water. How much energy, in joules, would have been added? (**Hint:** 1 calorie = 4.18 joules.)

30. Suppose that the temperatures were measured for 10 g of iron. How much energy, in joules, would have been added to cause the increase in temperature? (**Hint:** see graph on p. 113.)

the BIG idea

31. **ANALYZE** Look back at the photograph and the question on pages 100 and 101. How has your understanding of temperature and heat changed after reading the chapter?

32. **COMMUNICATE** Explain the kinetic theory of matter in your own words. What, if anything, about the kinetic theory of matter surprised you?

UNIT PROJECTS

Evaluate all the data, results, and information from your project folder. Prepare to present your project.

MONITOR AND RETEACH

If students have trouble applying the concepts of heat transfer in items 24–26, suggest that they review the diagrams on pp. 117–119. Have them draw and label a diagram that includes all three processes (conduction, convection, and radiation) in a natural setting.

Students may benefit from summarizing one or more sections of the chapter.

 Summarizing the Chapter, pp. 260–261

Standardized Test Practice

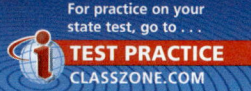

For practice on your state test, go to...
TEST PRACTICE
CLASSZONE.COM

Interpreting Diagrams

The diagrams below illustrate the process that occurs in sea and land breezes.

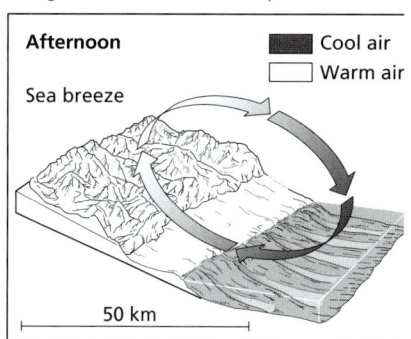

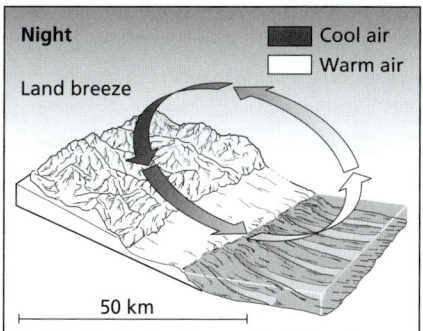

Use the diagrams above to answer the next five questions.

1. What happens during the day?
   a. Cool air from the land flows out to sea.
   b. Warm air from the land flows out to sea close to sea level.
   c. Cool air from the sea flows to the land.
   d. Warm air from the sea flows to the land.

2. What characteristic of large bodies of water explains why the seawater is cooler than the land in the hot afternoon sun?
   a. Water is liquid while the land is solid.
   b. Water has a higher specific heat than land.
   c. Land is a better insulator than water.
   d. Land has a higher specific heat than water.

3. What process causes the warm air to move upward over the land during the day?
   a. convection   c. evaporation
   b. condensation   d. radiation

4. Warm air is pushed upwards by cooler air during convection because the warm air
   a. is more dense   c. is less dense
   b. has more mass   d. has less mass

5. About how far over water does this land breeze extend?
   a. 1 kilometer   c. 25 kilometers
   b. 10 kilometers   d. 50 kilometers

Extended Response

Answer the two questions below in detail. Include some of the terms from the word box on the right. Underline each term that you use in your answer.

| boiling point | heat | specific heat |
| conduction | freezing point | zero point |

6. What are the differences between the Fahrenheit and Celsius temperature scales? Which one is used in science? Why might this be the case?

7. Suppose you place three spoons—one metal, one plastic, and one wood—into a cup filled with hot water. The bowl end of the spoon is inside the cup and the handle is sticking up into the air. On each handle, you place a bead, held to the spoon by a dab of margarine. From which spoon will the bead fall first, and why?

Chapter 4: **Temperature and Heat** 127

Interpreting Diagrams
1. c   2. b   3. a   4. c   5. c

Extended Response

6. RUBRIC
4 points for a response that correctly answers the three questions and uses the following terms accurately:
- freezing point
- boiling point
- zero point

Sample: The Fahrenheit and Celsius scales have a different number of degrees between the <u>freezing point</u> and <u>boiling point</u> of water. On the Fahrenheit scale, the freezing point of water is 32° and the boiling point is 212°. On the Celsius scale, the freezing point of water is 0° and the boiling point is 100°. Scientists use the Celsius scale because it has a well-defined <u>zero point</u>.

3 points correctly answers two questions and uses two terms correctly
2 points correctly answers two questions and uses one term correctly
1 point correctly answers one of the questions

7. RUBRIC
4 points for a response that answers the question correctly and uses the following terms accurately:
- conduction
- specific heat
- heat

Sample: The bead will fall first from the metal spoon because metal has a higher conductivity and a lower <u>specific heat</u> than wood and plastic, so it warms up faster. <u>Heat</u> transfers energy from the hot water to the metal spoon by <u>conduction</u>. Heat transfers energy through the spoon and melts the margarine.

3 points correctly answers the question and uses one term accurately
2 points correctly answers the question
1 point does not correctly answer the question but uses the terms accurately

METACOGNITIVE ACTIVITY

Have students answer the following questions in their **Science Notebook:**
1. What did you find the most challenging to understand about temperature and heat?
2. Which topics in this chapter would you like to learn more about?
3. What are the strongest pieces right now in your Unit Project?

Chapter 4 **127**

McDougal Littell Science

Chemical Interactions

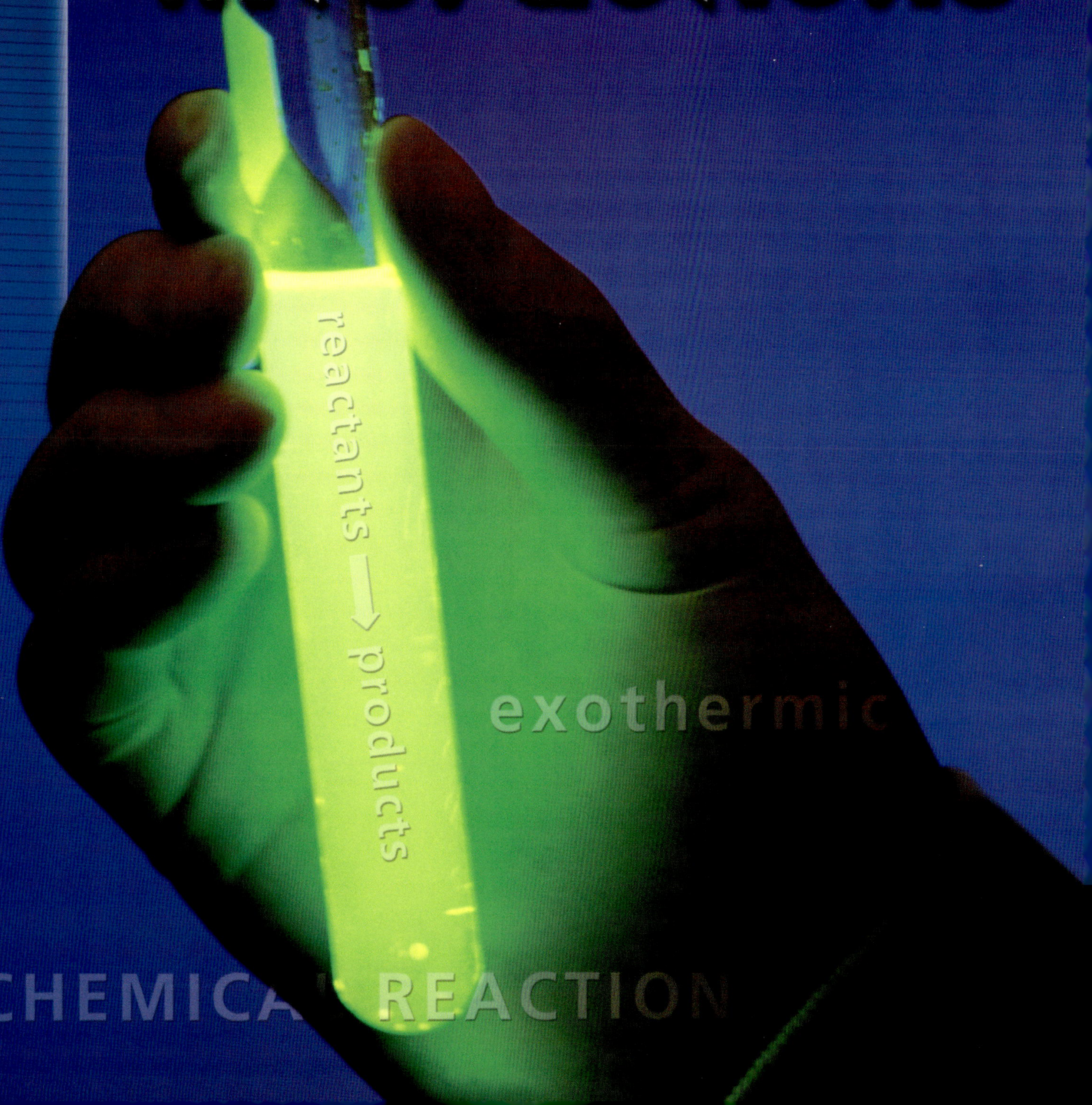

reactants → products

exothermic

CHEMICAL REACTION

Chemical Interactions
Contents Overview

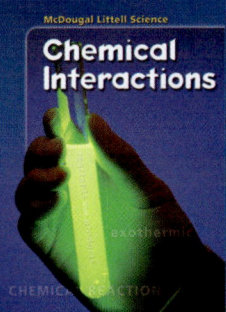

Unit Features

FRONTIERS IN SCIENCE Medicines from Nature — 130
TIMELINES IN SCIENCE The Story of Atomic Structure — 232

5 Atomic Structure and the Periodic Table — 134

the BIG idea
A substance's atomic structure determines its physical and chemical properties.

6 Chemical Bonds and Compounds — 166

the BIG idea
The properties of compounds depend on their atoms and chemical bonds.

7 Chemical Reactions — 194

the BIG idea
Chemical reactions form new substances by breaking and making chemical bonds.

8 Solutions — 236

the BIG idea
When substances dissolve to form a solution, the properties of the mixture change.

9 Carbon in Life and Materials — 272

the BIG idea
Carbon is essential to living things and to modern materials.

FRONTIERS in Science

VIDEO SUMMARY

SCIENTIFIC AMERICAN FRONTIERS

"Endangered Wonder Drug," a segment of the *Scientific American Frontiers* series that aired on PBS stations, traces the development of the cancer-fighting drug Taxol. The drug comes from the bark of the increasingly rare Pacific yew tree. Scientists are trying to find alternative sources in nature and in the laboratory. Taxol has been clinically tested as a treatment for women with ovarian cancer. If the drug succeeds as a cancer treatment and the demand increases, the natural supply of Taxol will soon be used up. One alternative is to grow yew trees in nurseries; another is to extract Taxol from the needles rather than the bark. Chemists are also working to make synthetic Taxol in large quantities. The ultimate solution may be a hybrid of natural and synthetic chemical compounds.

National Science Education Standards

A.9.a–d Understandings About Scientific Inquiry

E.6.a–f Understandings About Science and Technology

F.5.a–e Science and Technology in Society

G.1.a–b Science as a Human Endeavor

G.2.a Nature of Science

FRONTIERS in Science

Medicines from Nature

Where have people found medicines?

SCIENTIFIC AMERICAN FRONTIERS

View the "Endangered Wonder Drug" segment of your Scientific American Frontiers video to see how chemicals found in nature can improve the health of people.

ADDITIONAL RESOURCES

Technology Resources

Scientific American Frontiers Video: *Endangered Wonder Drug:* 11-minute video segment that introduces the unit.

ClassZone.com
CAREER LINK, Chemist

Guide student viewing and comprehension of the video:

 Video Teaching Guide, pp. 1–2; Video Viewing Guide, p. 3; Video Wrap-Up, p. 4

Scientific American Frontiers Video Guide, pp. 43–46

Unit projects procedures and rubrics:

 Unit Projects, pp. 5–10

In Brazil, extracts from plants are used to treat everything from Parkinson's Disease to arthritis.

Finding Natural Remedies

In the 1960s, people were searching desperately for new cancer-fighting agents. Scientists tested over 35,000 compounds, some of which came from the bark of the Pacific yew tree, long known to have strong effects on the body. The tests indicated that something in the bark stopped the growth of cancerous tumors. Scientists eventually derived the drug Taxol from the compounds found in the yew tree.

Natural medicines are much more than simple folk cures, like the sapi karta leaves that the Kuna people of Panama believe increase creativity. Many powerful medicines are based on compounds found in nature. But even though these natural compounds may be very effective at treating diseases, they can be limited in supply and can have harmful side effects. Organic chemists must find ways to make these compounds safer and produce them in greater amounts.

Modeling the Molecule

To make a compound, a chemist must know what its molecule looks like, atom by atom. Many useful drugs have structures that contain many atoms arranged in complicated ways. The chemist must know exactly how many atoms of each kind are in the molecule and how they are arranged. One atom in the wrong place might mean that the drug won't work the way it should.

Scientific Process

Natural sources of drugs can be unreliable because climate variation and differences in growing conditions, harvesting, and storage affect the amount of the compound produced. This variability makes it hard to test a drug or assign a dosage. Ask students to brainstorm some of the issues involved in producing reliable results under these circumstances.

Technology Design

Discuss the problem presented in "Assembling the Puzzle." Ask:

- Suppose you know the types and numbers of atoms in a molecule. What else do you need to find out to synthesize the molecule? *its structure and how to assemble it*
- How can you learn about molecular structure? *using spectroscopy and modeling*

History of Science

The drug-development process is rarely straightforward. Sometimes, a drug developed for one purpose is found to treat a completely unrelated medical condition. For example, many years ago a drug developed to treat tuberculosis was administered to patients suffering from tuberculosis in a psychiatric hospital. The drug was found to be effective, but it was also observed to have an unexpected effect. The patients given the drug were observed to become cheerful and more optimistic. By chance, a new antidepressant drug had been developed.

Updates in Science

Remind students that science changes very quickly. For example, despite the complexity of the molecule (as shown in the video segment), Taxol has now been synthesized in the laboratory. Taxol has been a boon to many cancer patients, although it is not a cure. However, some patients develop a resistance to it over time, and some types of tumors do not respond to Taxol at all.

132 Unit 2: **Chemical Interactions**

 To study the structures of molecules, chemists use a method called spectroscopy. Spectroscopy is a process that shows how the molecules of a compound respond to certain forms of radiation. Three important types of spectroscopy are

- NMR (nuclear magnetic resonance) spectroscopy, which allows chemists to identify small groups of atoms within larger molecules
- IR (infrared) spectroscopy, which shows the presence of certain types of bonds in molecules
- X-ray studies, which show details such as how much space there is between atoms and what the overall physical shapes of molecules are

Chemists put all this information together to determine the structure of a molecule. They might even build a model of the molecule.

Assembling the Puzzle

Once chemists know the structure of the molecule, they must figure out the starting reactants and the specific sequence of chemical reactions that will produce that molecule as a final product. It is a lot like doing a jigsaw puzzle when you know what the final picture looks like but still have to fit together all the pieces. Only in this case, the chemists may not even be sure what the little pieces look like.

Organic chemists often prefer to complete the process backward. They look at a model of the complete molecule and then figure out how they might build one just like it. How do chemists know what kinds of reactions might produce a certain molecule? Chemists have classified chemical reactions into different types. They determine how combinations of reactions will put the various kinds of atoms into their correct places in the molecule. Chemists may need to combine dozens of reactions to get the desired molecule.

Testing the Medicine

Once chemists have produced the desired drug molecule, the synthetic compound must be carefully tested to make sure it works like the natural substance does. The sequence of reactions must also be tested to make sure they produce the same compound when larger amounts of chemicals are used.

View the "Endangered Wonder Drug" segment of your *Scientific American Frontiers* video to see how modern medicines can be developed from chemical compounds found in nature.

IN THIS SCENE FROM THE VIDEO
A researcher works with a substance found in bark.

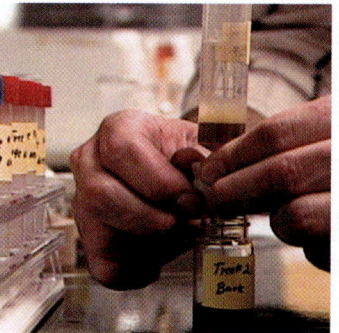

SAVING LIVES THROUGH NATURE AND CHEMISTRY
Medicines from plants and other natural sources have been used by different cultures around the world for thousands of years. The ephedra plant contains the raw material for many decongestants, which help shrink swollen nasal passages. It was used by the Chinese more than 5000 years ago. Today, the bark of the Pacific yew tree is being used as the source of the anticancer drug Taxol. A large amount of bark from the tree, however, is needed to make just one dose of the drug, and very few Pacific yew trees are available. Chemists, therefore, are trying to make this medicine in the laboratory.

132 Unit 2: Chemical Interactions

DIFFERENTIATE INSTRUCTION

 More Reading Support

C What process uses radiation to show the shape of molecules in a compound? *spectroscopy*

Below Level Ask students to make a chart showing the steps in synthesizing a molecule. Have a group of students write down each task described in the text, then organize them into a flow chart of the sequence of events.

Once a potential new drug is found in nature, it may take several years, or even decades, to figure out how to produce the drug synthetically and test it for safety. Only a small percentage of drugs tested ever goes to market, because the drugs must undergo several stages of testing on both animals and humans. Today, chemists routinely search the seas and the forests for marine organisms and rare plants that might have the power to fight cancer, heart disease, or viruses.

Chemists often use computers to make models of drug molecules. Computers allow the chemists to see how the drug molecules will interact with other molecules.

UNANSWERED Questions

The search for new chemical compounds that can be used to treat human illnesses raises many questions. Scientists need to find ways to investigate, produce, and test new, more powerful drugs.

- How might scientists more quickly test the safety and effectiveness of new medicines?
- Can easily synthesized compounds be just as effective as natural medicines?
- Might the processes that produce these drugs in nature be duplicated in a lab?
- Can we discover other new sources of medicines in the natural world?

UNIT PROJECTS

As you study this unit, work alone or with a group on one of these projects.

Medicines Around You

Present a report about a plant in your region that has medicinal properties.

- Collect samples of a plant that has medicinal properties.
- Bring your plant samples into your classroom. Prepare and present a report about the plant and the way it is used in medicine.

Model Medicine

Build a scale model of a molecule that is used to treat a certain illness.

- Using the Internet or an encyclopedia, determine the structure of a compound that interests you.
- Using foam balls, toothpicks, water colors, string, and other materials, construct a model of the molecule. Describe your model to the class.

Remedies

Write a news report about a popular herbal remedy, such as Saint John's Wort.

- To learn more about the herbal remedy, try interviewing a personal fitness trainer or an employee of a health-food store.
- Deliver a news report to the class telling of the advantages of the remedy and warning of its potential dangers.

Learn more about careers in chemistry.

Frontiers in Science 133

DIFFERENTIATE INSTRUCTION

 More Reading Support

D Where are chemists looking for natural drug sources? *the sea and forest*

UNANSWERED Questions

Have students read the questions and think of some of their own. Remind them that scientists usually end up with more questions—that inquiry is the driving force of science.

- With the class, generate on the board a list of new questions.
- Students can add to the list after they watch the *Scientific American Frontiers* Video.
- Students can use the list as a springboard for choosing their Unit Projects.

UNIT PROJECTS

Encourage students to pick the project that most appeals to them. Point out that each is long-term and will take several weeks to complete. You might group or pair students to work on projects and in some cases guide student choice. Some of the projects have student choice built into them. Each project has two worksheet pages, including a rubric. Use the pages to guide students through criteria, process, and schedule.

 Unit Projects, pp. 5–10

REVISIT concepts introduced in this article:

Chapter 5
- Atoms and elements, pp. 137–143
- The periodic table, pp. 145–151
- Map of the elements, pp. 154–160

Chapter 6
- Elements form compounds, pp. 169–173
- Chemical bonds, pp. 175–182
- Substances' properties depend on bonds, pp. 184–187

Chapter 7
- Chemical reactions alter arrangements, pp. 197–204
- Masses of reactants and products, pp. 206–212
- Life and industry, pp. 222–227

Chapter 8
- Solutes, pp. 245–251

Chapter 9
- Carbon-based molecules, pp. 275–280
- Carbon-based molecules are life's building blocks, pp. 282–289

Frontiers in Science 133

CHAPTER 5: Atomic Structure and the Periodic Table

Physical Science
UNIFYING PRINCIPLES

PRINCIPLE 1
Matter is made of particles too small to see.

PRINCIPLE 2
Matter changes form and moves from place to place.

PRINCIPLE 3
Energy changes from one form to another, but it cannot be created or destroyed.

PRINCIPLE 4
Physical forces affect the movement of all matter on Earth and throughout the universe.

Unit 2: Chemical Interactions
BIG IDEAS

CHAPTER 5
Atomic Structure and the Periodic Table
A substance's atomic structure determines its physical and chemical properties.

CHAPTER 6
Chemical Bonds and Compounds
The properties of compounds depend on their atoms and chemical bonds.

CHAPTER 7
Chemical Reactions
Chemical reactions form new substances by breaking and making chemical bonds.

CHAPTER 8
Solutions
When substances dissolve to form a solution, the properties of a mixture change.

CHAPTER 9
Carbon in Life and Materials
Carbon is essential to living things and to modern materials.

CHAPTER 5 KEY CONCEPTS

SECTION 1
Atoms are the smallest form of elements.
1. All matter is made of atoms.
2. Each element is made of a different atom.
3. Atoms form ions.

SECTION 2
Elements make up the periodic table.
1. Elements can be organized by similarities.
2. The periodic table organizes the atoms of the elements by properties and atomic number.

SECTION 3
The periodic table is a map of the elements.
1. The periodic table has distinct regions.
2. Most elements are metals.
3. Nonmetals and metalloids have a wide range of properties.
4. Some atoms can change their identity.

 The Big Idea Flow Chart is available on p. T1 in the **UNIT TRANSPARENCY BOOK.**

Previewing Content

SECTION

 Atoms are the smallest form of elements. pp. 137–144

1. **All matter is made of atoms.**
   All matter is made up of atoms of about 100 elements, or basic substances. Hydrogen is the most abundant element in the universe; oxygen is the most abundant element in Earth's crust. Every element has a unique name and symbol. Names and symbols of the elements come from many sources.

2. **Each element is made of a different atom.**
   Atoms are made of three smaller particles: protons, neutrons, electrons.
   - At the center of an atom is the **nucleus,** which contains almost all of the atom's mass.
   - The nucleus contains protons and neutrons. Protons have a positive charge and neutrons have no charge. Protons and neutrons have approximately the same mass.
   - In a cloud around the nucleus are **electrons.** Electrons are 2000 times smaller than protons or neutrons. The figure below shows the position of the electron cloud and the nucleus in an atom.

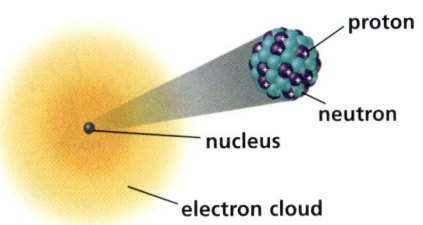

   The **atomic number** is the number of protons in an atom. **Atomic mass number** is the number of protons plus the number of neutrons in the nucleus. Electrons have negligible mass. **Isotopes** are atoms of the same element with different numbers of neutrons. Since isotopes occur in various amounts in nature, the atomic mass number of an atom is the average mass of all its isotopes.

3. **Atoms form ions.**
   Atoms form **ions** when they gain or lose electrons. Gaining electrons results in negative ions. Losing electrons results in positive ions. Atoms normally lose and gain electrons in pairs.

Common Misconceptions

NATURE OF ATOMS Students may hold the misconception that atoms are solid bits that vary in size and shape and have no space between them. Atoms of the same substance are identical in size and shape and are mostly empty space, not solid.

 This misconception is addressed on p. 138.

SECTION

 Elements make up the periodic table. pp. 145–153

1. **Elements can be organized by similarities.**
   Many scientists thought the elements could be organized by their properties. Dmitri Mendeleev made the first periodic table. Mendeleev used atomic mass to order the elements and placed elements with similar properties in the same rows.

2. **The periodic table organizes the atoms of the elements by properties and atomic number.**
   The modern periodic table is organized by atomic number. The periodic table gives the following information about each element: atomic number, chemical symbol, name, average atomic mass. It also indicates state at room temperature.

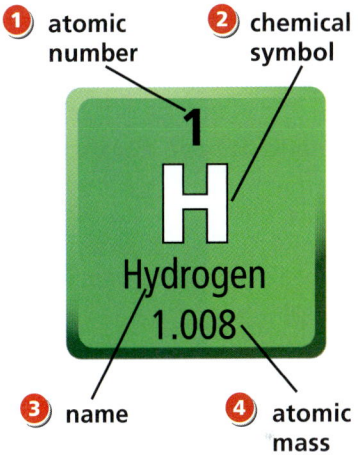

   - A **group** is a column of elements. The elements in a group have similar properties.
   - A **period** is a row of elements. These elements have chemical properties that tend to change the same way across the table. Properties like atomic size, density, and likelihood to form ions vary in regular ways up, down, and across the periodic table.

MISCONCEPTION DATABASE
CLASSZONE.COM Background on student misconceptions

SIZE OF ATOMS Students may hold the misconception that atoms can be viewed under a regular optical microscope. Atoms are unimaginably small, many magnitudes smaller than microscopic objects such as cells of organisms.

 This misconception is addressed on p. 140.

Chapter 5: **Atomic Structure and the Periodic Table** 133B

Previewing Content

SECTION

 3 The periodic table is a map of the elements. pp. 154–161

1. **The periodic table has distinct regions.**
   Position in the periodic table reveals something about how **reactive** an element is. Elements in Groups 1 and 17 are especially reactive. Elements in Group 18 are the least reactive.

2. **Most elements are metals.**
   Metals are usually shiny, often conduct electricity and heat well, and can be easily shaped and drawn into a wire.
   - Alkali metals and alkaline earth metals are at the left of the periodic table and are very reactive.
   - Transition metals are near the center of the periodic table and include copper, gold, silver, and iron.
   - Rare earth metals are in the top row of the two rows of metals shown outside the main body of the periodic table.
   - The two bottom rows are separated from the table to save space.

3. **Nonmetals and metalloids have a wide range of properties.**
   Nonmetals appear on the right side of the periodic table. They include elements with a wide range of properties. Carbon, nitrogen, oxygen, and sulfur are nonmetals, as are the extremely reactive halogens, such as chlorine, and noble, or inert, gases, such as neon.
   Metalloids lie between metals and nonmetals in the periodic table. They have characteristics of both. An important use of metalloids is in the making of semiconductors for electronic devices.

4. **Some atoms can change their identity.**
   The atomic nucleus is held together by forces. Sometimes there can be too many or too few neutrons in a nucleus, and so the forces holding it together cannot hold it together properly. To regain its stability, the nucleus will produce particles and eject them. This process is called radioactivity. The identity of radioactive atoms changes when the number of protons change. This is called radioactive decay. Radioactive decay occurs at a steady rate that is characteristic of the particular isotope. The amount of time that it takes for one-half of the atoms in a particular sample to decay is called the half-life of the isotope. The chart shown below illustrates the progress of radioactive decay.

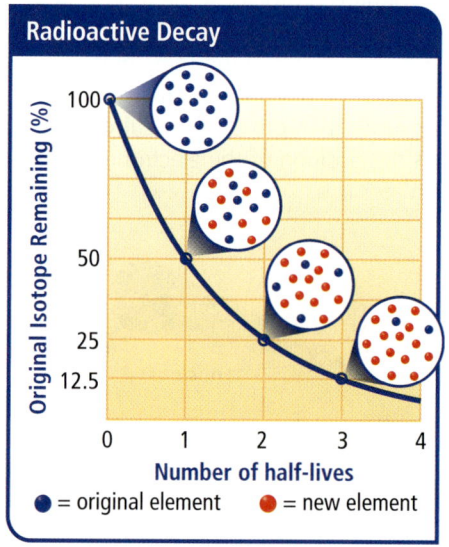

Common Misconceptions

PROPERTIES OF ELEMENTS Students may hold the misconception that a single atom of an element will exhibit the same properties as the element in bulk. Samples of elements exhibit particular, identifiable chemical properties. At the atomic level, properties such as color and texture are meaningless.

 This misconception is addressed on p. 155.

 MISCONCEPTION DATABASE
CLASSZONE.COM Background on student misconceptions

133C   Unit 2: Chemical Interactions

Previewing Labs

EXPLORE the BIG idea

That's Far! p. 135
Students pace out the relative distance between an electron and a nucleus, demonstrating that most of the volume of an atom is empty space.

TIME 10 minutes
MATERIALS baseball, dime

Element Safari, p. 135
Students look at labels on food packages to learn that elements make up common materials.

TIME 10 minutes
MATERIALS periodic table; packages of (or labels from) baking soda, vinegar, cereal flakes, antacid tablets

Internet Activity: Periodic Table, p. 135
Students explore the organization of the periodic table.

TIME 20 minutes
MATERIALS computer with Internet access

SECTION 1

EXPLORE The Size of Atoms, p. 137
Students model the particulate nature of matter by cutting paper into smaller and smaller pieces.

TIME 10 minutes
MATERIALS 30 cm strip of paper, pair of scissors

INVESTIGATE Masses of Atomic Particles, p. 141
Students use common objects to model the relative masses of atomic particles.

TIME 20 minutes
MATERIALS balance; large paper clip; items available in bulk, such as sand, clay, or water

SECTION 2

EXPLORE Similarities and Differences of Objects, p. 145
Students classify an assortment of buttons to see how objects can be organized using different criteria.

TIME 15 minutes
MATERIALS assorted buttons like those found on shirts, etc.

CHAPTER INVESTIGATION Modeling Atomic Masses, pp. 152–153
Students make model atoms from film cans and washers to determine the atom's relative masses.

TIME 40 minutes
MATERIALS 5 film cans, 21 washers, balance

SECTION 3

INVESTIGATE Radioactivity, p. 159
Students use pennies to model the half-life of radioactive elements.

TIME 30 minutes
MATERIALS 50 pennies, bag, graph paper

 Additional INVESTIGATION, Investigating the Unseen, A, B, & C, pp. 59–67; Teacher Instructions, pp. 329–330

Previewing Chapter Resources

	INTEGRATED TECHNOLOGY	**LABS AND ACTIVITIES**
CHAPTER 5 **Atomic Structure and the Periodic Table**	 **CLASSZONE.COM** • eEdition Plus • EasyPlanner • Misconception Database • Content Review • Test Practice • Simulation • Visualization • Resource Centers • Internet Activity: Periodic Table • Math Tutorial **SCILINKS.ORG** **CD-ROMS** • eEdition • EasyPlanner • Power Presentations • Content Review • Lab Generator • Test Generator **AUDIO CDS** • Audio Readings • Audio Readings in Spanish	EXPLORE the Big Idea, p. 135 • That's Far! • Element Safari • Internet Activity: Periodic Table **UNIT RESOURCE BOOK** • Family Letter, p. ix • Spanish Family Letter, p. x • Unit Projects, pp. 5–10 **Lab Generator CD-ROM** Generate customized labs.
SECTION **Atoms are the smallest form of elements.** pp. 137–144 Time: 2 periods (1 block) Lesson Plan, pp. 11–12	• **RESOURCE CENTER,** The Atom, Elements Important to Life • **SIMULATION,** Build an Atom **T** **UNIT TRANSPARENCY BOOK** • Big Idea Flow Chart, p. T1 • Daily Vocabulary Scaffolding, p. T2 • Note-Taking Model, p. T3 • 3-Minute Warm-Up, p. T4 • "The Atomic Model" Visual, "Isotopes" Visual, p. T6	• EXPLORE The Size of Atoms, p. 137 • INVESTIGATE Masses of Atomic Particles, p. 141 • Connecting Sciences, p. 144 **UNIT RESOURCE BOOK** • Datasheet, Masses of Atomic Particles, p. 20 • Additional INVESTIGATION, Investigating the Unseen, A, B, & C, pp. 59–67
SECTION 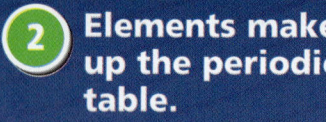 **Elements make up the periodic table.** pp. 145–153 Time: 3 periods (1.5 blocks) Lesson Plan, pp. 22–23	**T** **UNIT TRANSPARENCY BOOK** • Daily Vocabulary Scaffolding, p. T2 • 3-Minute Warm-Up, p. T4	• EXPLORE Similarities and Differences of Objects, p. 145 • CHAPTER INVESTIGATION, Modeling Atomic Masses, pp. 152–153 **UNIT RESOURCE BOOK** CHAPTER INVESTIGATION, Modeling Atomic Masses, A, B, & C, pp. 50–58
SECTION 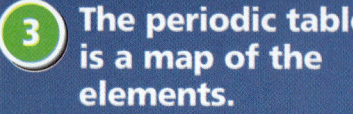 **The periodic table is a map of the elements.** pp. 154–161 Time: 3 periods (1.5 block) Lesson Plan, pp. 32–33	• **VISUALIZATION,** Radioactive Decay • **MATH TUTORIAL** **T** **UNIT TRANSPARENCY BOOK** • Big Idea Flow Chart, p. T1 • Daily Vocabulary Scaffolding, p. T2 • 3-Minute Warm-Up, p. T5 • Chapter Outline, pp. T7–T8	• INVESTIGATE Radioactivity, p. 159 • Math in Science, p. 161 **UNIT RESOURCE BOOK** • Datasheet, Radioactivity, p. 41 • Math Support, p. 48 • Math Practice, p. 49

KEY TO ICONS	CD/CD-ROM	Teacher Edition	UNIT TRANSPARENCY BOOK	SPANISH ASSESSMENT BOOK
INTERNET	Pupil Edition	UNIT RESOURCE BOOK	UNIT ASSESSMENT BOOK	SCIENCE TOOLKIT

READING AND REINFORCEMENT

- Frame Game, B26–27
- Main Idea Web, C38–39
- Daily Vocabulary Scaffolding, H1–8

UNIT RESOURCE BOOK
- Vocabulary Practice, pp. 45–46
- Decoding Support, p. 47
- Summarizing the Chapter, pp. 68–69

Audio Readings CD
Listen to Pupil Edition.

Audio Readings in Spanish CD
Listen to Pupil Edition in Spanish.

ASSESSMENT

- Chapter Review, pp. 163–164
- Standardized Test Practice, p. 165

UNIT ASSESSMENT BOOK
- Diagnostic Test, pp. 1–2
- Chapter Test, A, B, & C, pp. 6–17
- Alternative Assessment, pp. 18–19

Spanish Chapter Test, pp. 233–236

Test Generator CD-ROM
Generate customized tests.

Lab Generator CD-ROM
Rubrics for Labs

STANDARDS

National Standards
A.2–8, A.9.a–c, A.9.e–f, B.1.b, B.1.c, G.1.b, G.2.a–b

See p. 134 for the standards.

UNIT RESOURCE BOOK
- Reading Study Guide, A & B, pp. 13–16
- Spanish Reading Study Guide, pp. 17–18
- Challenge and Extension, p. 19
- Reinforcing Key Concepts, p. 21

Ongoing Assessment, pp. 138–140, 142

Section 5.1 Review, p. 143

UNIT ASSESSMENT BOOK
Section 5.1 Quiz, p. 3

National Standards
A.2–8, A.9.a–b, A.9.e–f, B.1.c

UNIT RESOURCE BOOK
- Reading Study Guide, A & B, pp. 24–27
- Spanish Reading Study Guide, pp. 28–29
- Challenge and Extension, p. 30
- Reinforcing Key Concepts, p. 31

Ongoing Assessment, pp. 146, 150–151

Section 5.2 Review, p. 151

UNIT ASSESSMENT BOOK
Section 5.2 Quiz, p. 4

National Standards
A.2–8, A.9.a–c, A.9.e–f, B.1.b, G.2.a–b

UNIT RESOURCE BOOK
- Reading Study Guide, A & B, pp. 34–37
- Spanish Reading Study Guide, pp. 38–39
- Challenge and Extension, p. 40
- Reinforcing Key Concepts, p. 42
- Challenge Reading, pp. 43–44

Ongoing Assessment, pp. 154–155, 157–158

Section 5.3 Review, p. 160

UNIT ASSESSMENT BOOK
Section 5.3 Quiz, p. 5

National Standards
A.2–8, A-9.a–c, A.9.e–f, B.1.b

Chapter 5: **Atomic Structure and the Periodic Table** 133F

Previewing Resources for Differentiated Instruction

CHAPTER INVESTIGATION

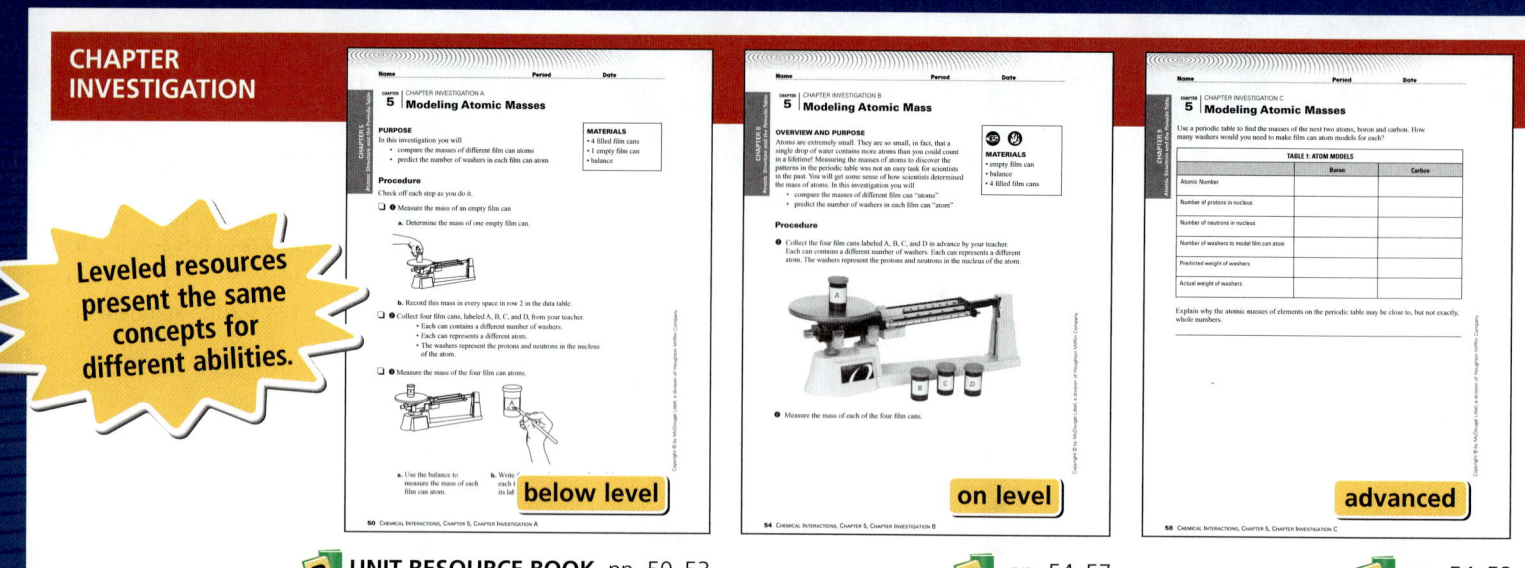

UNIT RESOURCE BOOK, pp. 50–53 | pp. 54–57 | pp. 54–58

READING STUDY GUIDE

Leveled resources present the same concepts for different abilities.

Reading Study Guide is also in Spanish.

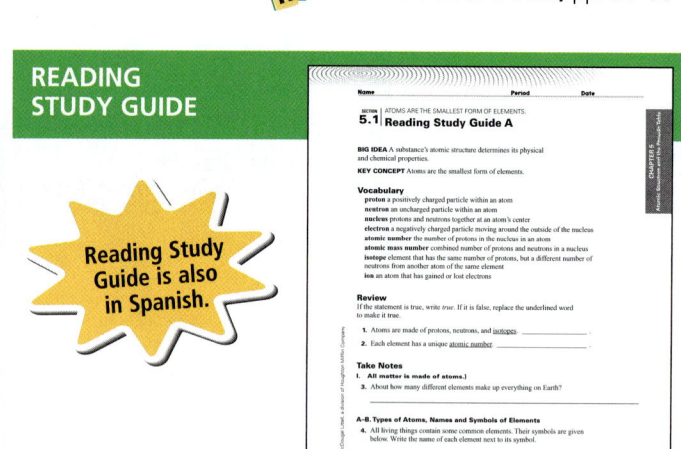
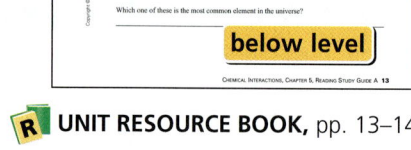
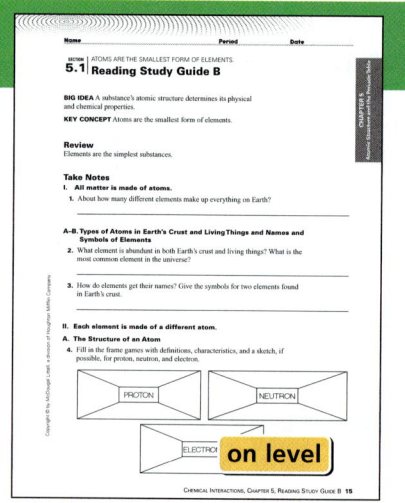
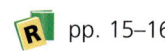
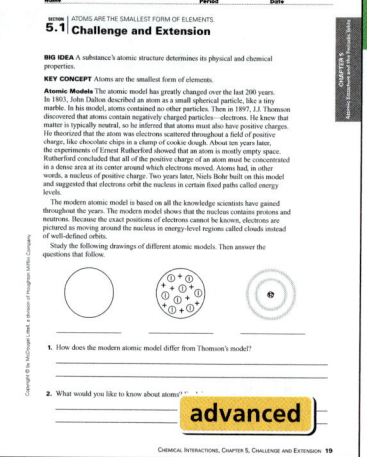

UNIT RESOURCE BOOK, pp. 13–14 | pp. 15–16 | p. 19

CHAPTER TEST

Chapter Test is also in Spanish.

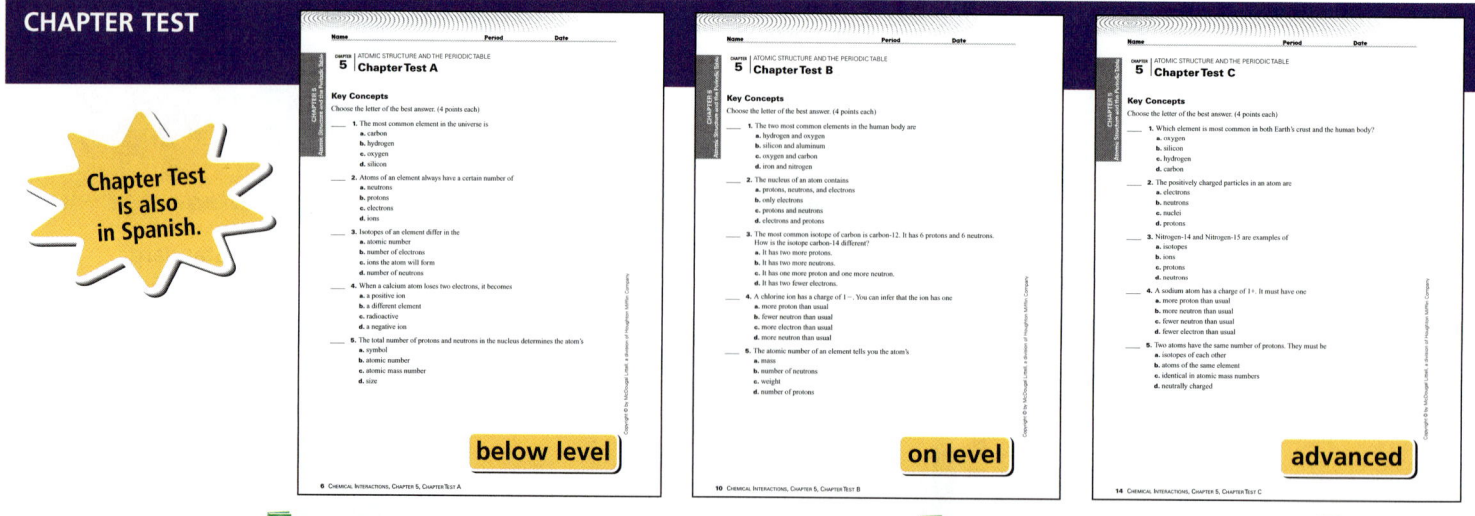

UNIT ASSESSMENT BOOK, pp. 6–9 | pp. 10–13 | pp. 14–17

133G Unit 2: **Chemical Interactions**

TECHNOLOGY

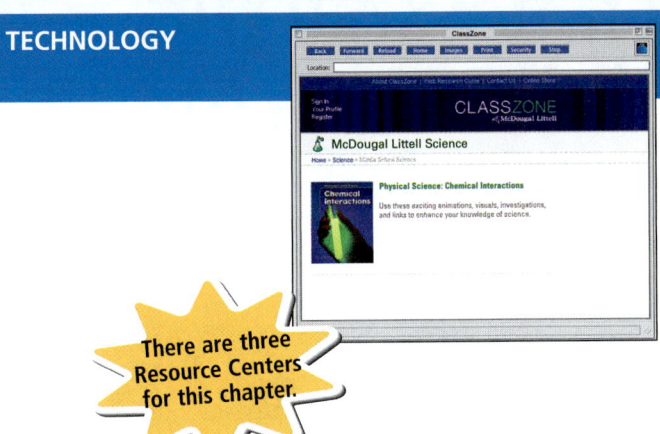
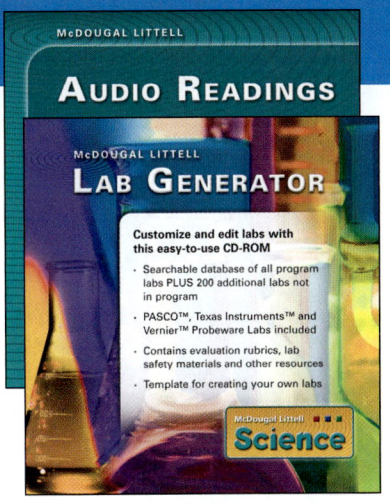
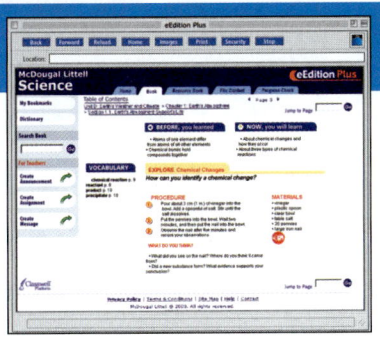

There are three Resource Centers for this chapter.

CLASSZONE.COM   CD/CD-ROMS   CLASSZONE.COM

VISUAL CONTENT

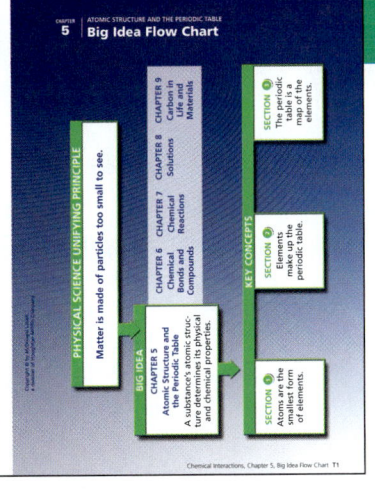
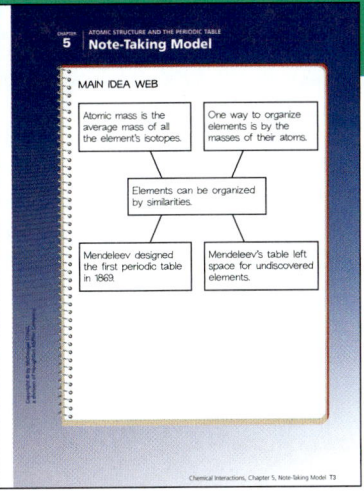
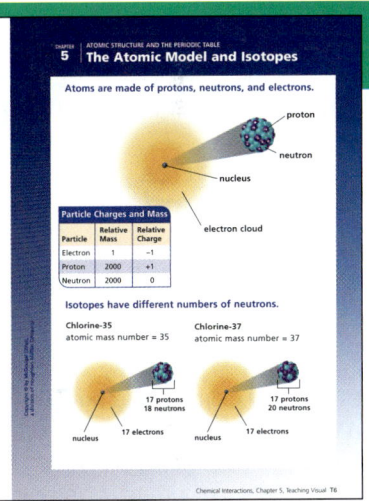

UNIT TRANSPARENCY BOOK, p. T1   p. T3   p. T6

MORE SUPPORT

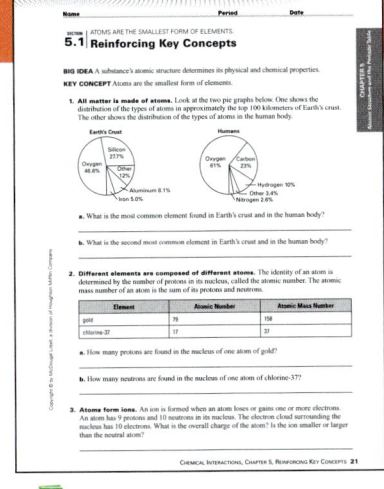
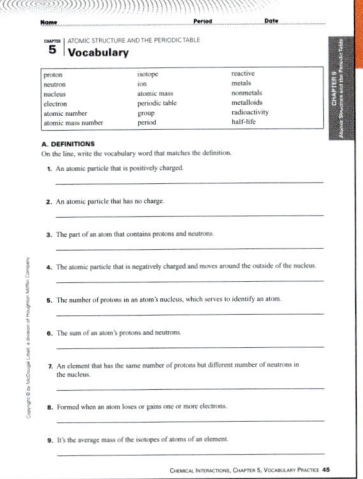
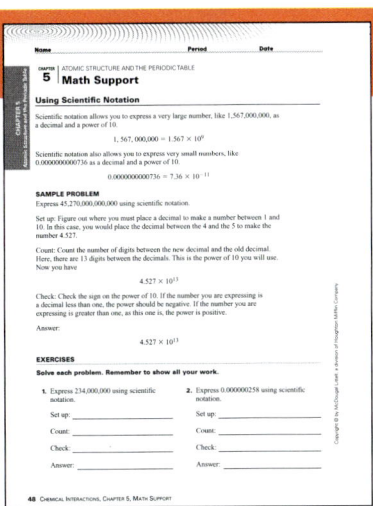

Reinforcing Key Concepts for each section

UNIT RESOURCE BOOK, p. 21   pp. 45–46   p. 48

Chapter 5: **Atomic Structure and the Periodic Table**   **133H**

CHAPTER 5
Atomic Structure and the Periodic Table

INTRODUCE

Have students look at the image of nickel atoms and discuss how the question in the box links to the Big Idea:

- How do you know the picture of this object is not the way you would normally view the object?
- Could you reproduce this view by holding an ordinary magnifying glass over a nickel-plated cup? Explain why or why not.
- What might account for the differences in the way nickel looks in the photo and on a nickel-plated cup?

National Science Education Standards

Content

B.1.b Substances often are placed in categories or groups if they react in similar ways; metals is such a group.

B.1.c Chemical elements do not break down during normal laboratory reactions involving such treatments as heating, exposure to electric current, or reaction with acids. There are more than 100 known elements that combine in a multitude of ways to produce compounds, which account for the living and non-living substances that we encounter.

Process

A.2–8 Design and conduct an investigation; use tools to gather and interpret data; use evidence; think critically between evidence and explanation; recognize different explanations and predictions; communicate scientific procedures and explanations; use mathematics.

A.9.a–c, A.9.e–f Understand scientific inquiry by using different investigations, methods, mathematics, and explanations based on logic, evidence, and skepticism.

G.1.b Science requires different abilities.

G.2.a–b Nature of Science

134   Unit 2: Chemical Interactions

CHAPTER 5
Atomic Structure and the Periodic Table

the BIG idea
A substance's atomic structure determines its physical and chemical properties.

You can't zoom in any closer than this! The picture is an extremely close-up view of nickel. How do things look different the closer you get to them?

Key Concepts

SECTION 1 — Atoms are the smallest form of elements.
Learn about the structure of atoms and how each element's atoms are different.

SECTION 2 — Elements make up the periodic table.
Learn how the periodic table of the elements is organized.

SECTION 3 — The periodic table is a map of the elements.
Learn more about the groups of elements in the periodic table.

Internet Preview
CLASSZONE.COM
Chapter 5 online resources: Content Review, Simulation, Visualization, three Resource Centers, Math Tutorial, Test Practice

134 Unit 2: Chemical Interactions

INTERNET PREVIEW

CLASSZONE.COM   For student use with the following pages:

Review and Practice
- Content Review, pp. 136, 162
- Math Tutorial: Scientific Notation, p. 161
- Test Practice, p. 165

Activities and Resources
- Internet Activity, p. 135
- Resource Center: The Atom, p. 139, Elements Important to Life, p. 144
- Simulation: Build an Atom, p. 140
- Visualization: Radioactive Decay, p. 160

NSTA scilinks.org
Atomic Theory
Code: MDL022

EXPLORE the BIG idea

That's Far!
Place a baseball in the middle of a large field. Hold a dime and count off the number of steps from the baseball to the edge of the field. If the baseball were an atom's nucleus and the dime an electron, you would need to go about 6000 steps to walk the distance between the nucleus and the electrons.

Observe and Think How far were you able to go? How much farther would you need to go to model the proportion of an atom? What does this tell you about atomic structure?

Element Safari
Locate the following products in your home or in a grocery store: baking soda, vinegar, cereal flakes, and antacid tablets. You may examine other products if you wish. Look at the labels on the products. Can you recognize the names of any elements? Use your periodic table as a reference.

Observe and Think Which element names did you find?

Internet Activity: Periodic Table
Go to ClassZone.com to explore the periodic table. See different ways to set up the table and learn more about the listed elements.

Observe and Think How do atomic number and mass change as you move across the periodic table?

NSTA scilinks.org
SCLINKS
Atomic Theory Code: MDL022

Chapter 5: **Atomic Structure and the Periodic Table** 135

EXPLORE the BIG idea

These inquiry-based activities are appropriate for use at home or as a supplement to classroom instruction.

That's Far!
PURPOSE To introduce the concept that most of the volume of an atom is empty space between the nucleus and electrons. Students demonstrate this by pacing out the distance between an electron and a nucleus.

TIP *10 min.* Emphasize that although the scale isn't exactly correct, the idea is the great amount of space.

Answer: probably 50 to 100 steps; if students took 50 steps, they'd need to go more than 100 times that distance to model the proportion of an atom. An atom has a lot of empty space.

REVISIT after p. 140.

Element Safari
PURPOSE To introduce the concept that common materials are made up of elements. Students look for names on product packages.

TIP *10 min.* Encourage students to work with their parents on this activity. Inform students that the names of elements in compound names may be spelled differently than they are in the periodic table.

Answer: Students will probably find sodium (Na), hydrogen (H), and oxygen (O), and perhaps chlorine (Cl).

REVISIT after p. 149.

Internet Activity: Periodic Table
PURPOSE To introduce the logical arrangement of the periodic table.

TIP *20 min.* Encourage students to have a parent assist them with this activity.

Answer: They increase.

REVISIT after p. 158.

TEACHING WITH TECHNOLOGY

Graphing Software If you have graphing software, have students make a pie chart using figures from the "Mass of Elements in 50 kg Human" table on p. 144. Students can also use software or a graphing calculator to create graphs for "Modeling Atomic Masses," pp. 152–153, or "Investigate Radioactivity" on p. 159.

Scanning Electron Microscope Tell students that the photograph on pp. 134–135 is an image from a scanning electron microscope (SEM). Search the Internet for other images from SEM or STM (scanning tunneling microscope) technology.

Chapter 5 **135**

PREPARE

◀ CONCEPT REVIEW

Activate Prior Knowledge

- Place a penny, an iron nail, and a piece of graphite from a broken pencil point on a white sheet of paper.
- Ask students if they think that each of these samples is a basic substance that contains only one kind of atom.
- Remind students that even the tiniest sample of a simple substance contains millions and billions of the same kind of atom, because atoms are so tiny.
- Point out that if any of the three substances contains more than one kind of atom, it can be broken down chemically into two or more different substances. Substances are not simple because they look simple; substances are simple because they contain only one kind of atom.

▶ TAKING NOTES

Main Idea Web

Students should make clear which box contains the main idea by centering the box and highlighting it in some way.

Vocabulary Strategy

The frame game is a good way for students to make associations by grouping information around a vocabulary word. The framing data might include examples, a definition, details, and characteristics.

Vocabulary and Note-Taking Resources

- Vocabulary Practice, pp. 45–46
- Decoding Support, p. 47

- Daily Vocabulary Scaffolding, p. T2
- Note-Taking Model, p. T3

- Frame Game, B26–27
- Main Idea Web, C38–39
- Daily Vocabulary Scaffolding, H1–8

136 Unit 2: **Chemical Interactions**

CHAPTER 5
Getting Ready to Learn

◀ CONCEPT REVIEW
- Matter is made of particles called atoms that are too small to see with the eyes.
- Matter can be an element, a compound, or a mixture.
- Matter can undergo physical and chemical changes.

◀ VOCABULARY REVIEW
See Glossary for definitions.
atom
compound
element

CONTENT REVIEW
CLASSZONE.COM
Review concepts and vocabulary.

▶ TAKING NOTES

MAIN IDEA WEB

Write each new blue heading in a box. Then write notes in boxes around the center box that give important terms and details about that blue heading.

VOCABULARY STRATEGY

Write each new vocabulary term in the center of a **frame game** diagram. Decide what information to frame it with. Use examples, descriptions, parts, sentences that use the term in context, or pictures. You can change the frame to fit each term.

See the Note-Taking Handbook on pages R45–R51.

SCIENCE NOTEBOOK

- Atoms are made of protons, neutrons, and electrons.
- The atomic number is the number of protons in the nucleus.
- Each element is made of a different atom.
- Every element has a certain number of protons in its nucleus.

Central part of atom
Contains most of an atom's mass — **NUCLEUS** — Electrons move about it
Is made of protons and neutrons

136 Unit 2: Chemical Interactions

CHECK READINESS

Administer the Diagnostic Test to determine students' readiness for new science content and their mastery of requisite math skills.

 Diagnostic Test, pp. 1–2

Technology Resources

Students needing content and math skills should visit ClassZone.com.

- **CONTENT REVIEW**
- **MATH TUTORIAL**

 CONTENT REVIEW CD-ROM

KEY CONCEPT
5.1 Atoms are the smallest form of elements.

 BEFORE, you learned
- All matter is made of atoms
- Elements are the simplest substances

▶ **NOW, you will learn**
- Where atoms are found and how they are named
- About the structure of atoms
- How ions are formed from atoms

VOCABULARY
proton p. 139
neutron p. 139
nucleus p. 139
electron p. 139
atomic number p. 140
atomic mass number p. 140
isotope p. 140
ion p. 142

EXPLORE The Size of Atoms

How small can you cut paper?

PROCEDURE
1. Cut the strip of paper in half. Cut one of these halves in half.
2. Continue cutting one piece of paper in half as many times as you can.

WHAT DO YOU THINK?
- How many cuts were you able to make?
- Do you think you could keep cutting the paper forever? Why or why not?

MATERIALS
- strip of paper about 30 centimeters long
- scissors

All matter is made of atoms.

Think of all the substances you see and touch every day. Are all of these substances the same? Obviously, the substances that make up this book you're reading are quite different from the substances in the air around you. So how many different substances can there be? This is a question people have been asking for thousands of years.

About 2400 years ago, Greek philosophers proposed that everything on Earth was made of only four basic substances—air, water, fire, and earth. Everything else contained a mixture of these four substances. As time went on, chemists came to realize that there had to be more than four basic substances. Today chemists know that about 100 basic substances, or elements, account for everything we see and touch. Sometimes these elements appear by themselves. Most often, however, these elements appear in combination with other elements to make new substances. In this section, you'll learn about the atoms of the elements that make up the world and how these atoms differ from one another.

READING TIP
The word *element* is related to *elementary*, which means "basic."

Chapter 5: **Atomic Structure and the Periodic Table** 137

5.1 INSTRUCT

Mathematics Connection
Explain to students that not all pie charts (or other charts that display gathered information) are completely secure in their data. Deviations might occur.

Address Misconceptions
IDENTIFY Ask: If you had a microscope powerful enough to see atoms in pure gold, what would the atoms look like? Ask students to sketch them. If students draw atoms of various shapes and sizes with no space between them, they hold the misconception that atoms of the same element are solid bits that vary in size and shape and are jammed together.

CORRECT Have students imagine a wall covered with evenly spaced black dots. Then have them imagine backing away from the wall: the dots would appear smaller and closer together as students get farther away. Eventually, the wall would look solid black. Say that the black dots are like the atoms in matter, which merge into the form of the matter—solid, liquid, or gas.

REASSESS Ask: If you could see the atoms in a grain of sand, what would they look like? *dots with space around them*

Technology Resources
Visit **ClassZone.com** for background on common student misconceptions.

MISCONCEPTION DATABASE

Ongoing Assessment
Recognize where atoms of common elements are found and how they are named.

Ask: In terms of percentages, which has more oxygen, Earth's crust or a human body? *a human body*

 Answer: hydrogen

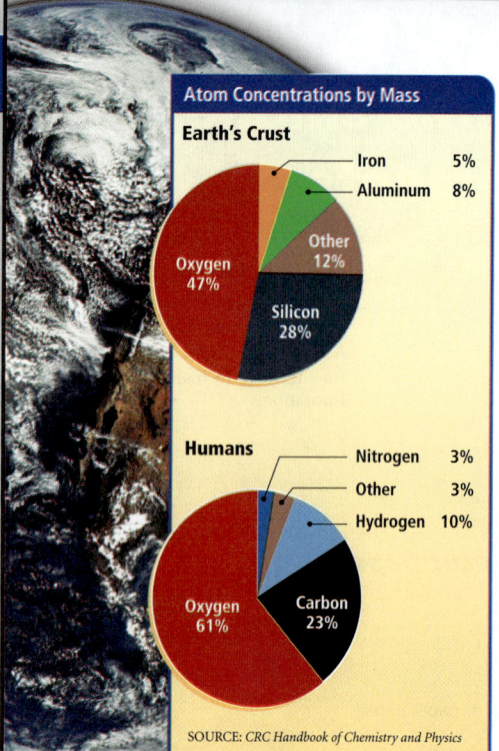

SOURCE: CRC Handbook of Chemistry and Physics

Types of Atoms in Earth's Crust and Living Things
Atoms of the element hydrogen account for about 90 percent of the total mass of the universe. Hydrogen atoms make up only about 1 percent of Earth's crust, however, and most of those hydrogen atoms are combined with oxygen atoms in the form of water. The graph on the left shows the types of atoms in approximately the top 100 kilometers of Earth's crust.

The distribution of the atoms of the elements in living things is very different from what it is in Earth's crust. Living things contain at least 25 types of atoms. Although the amounts of these atoms vary somewhat, all living things—animals, plants, and bacteria—are composed primarily of atoms of oxygen, carbon, hydrogen, and nitrogen. As you can see in the lower graph on the left, oxygen atoms account for more than half your body's mass.

 What is the most common element in the universe?

Names and Symbols of Elements
 Elements get their names in many different ways. Magnesium, for example, was named for the region in Greece known as Magnesia. Lithium comes from the Greek word *lithos*, which means "stone." Neptunium was named after the planet Neptune. The elements einsteinium and fermium were named after scientists Albert Einstein and Enrico Fermi.

Each element has its own unique symbol. For some elements, the symbol is simply the first letter of its name.

hydrogen (H)   sulfur (S)   carbon (C)

The symbols for other elements use the first letter plus one other letter of the element's name. Notice that the first letter is capitalized but the second letter is not.

aluminum (Al)   platinum (Pt)   cadmium (Cd)   zinc (Zn)

The origins of some symbols, however, are less obvious. The symbol for gold (Au), for example, doesn't seem to have anything to do with the element's name. The symbol refers instead to gold's name in Latin, *aurum*. Lead (Pb), iron (Fe), and copper (Cu) are a few other elements whose symbols come from Latin names.

138 Unit 2: Chemical Interactions

DIFFERENTIATE INSTRUCTION

A What element makes up more than half of your body's mass? *oxygen*

B From where do elements get their names? *from people, places, Greek words*

English Learners Some English learners may not be familiar with how pie charts display information. Use a simpler example than the "Atoms Concentrations by Mass" charts. For example, create a pie chart displaying the numbers of different hair colors among students in the class.

Inclusion Help students with hearing impairments identify the names of elements presented on this page. Write each element's name on the board; then pronounce it distinctly for the students.

Each element is made of a different atom.

In the early 1800s British scientist John Dalton proposed that each element is made of tiny particles called atoms. Dalton stated that all of the atoms of a particular element are identical but are different from atoms of all other elements. Every atom of silver, for example, is similar to every other atom of silver but different from an atom of iron.

Dalton's theory also assumed that atoms could not be divided into anything simpler. Scientists later discovered that this was not exactly true. They found that atoms are made of even smaller particles.

Learn more about the atom.

The Structure of an Atom

A key discovery leading to the current model of the atom was that atoms contain charged particles. The charge on a particle can be either positive or negative. Particles with the same type of charge repel each other—they are pushed apart. Particles with different charges attract each other—they are drawn toward each other.

Atoms are composed of three types of particles—electrons, protons, and neutrons. A **proton** is a positively charged particle, and a **neutron** is an uncharged particle. The neutron has approximately the same mass as a proton. The protons and neutrons of an atom are grouped together in the atom's center. This combination of protons and neutrons is called the **nucleus** of the atom. Because it contains protons, the nucleus has a positive charge. **Electrons** are negatively charged particles that move around outside the nucleus.

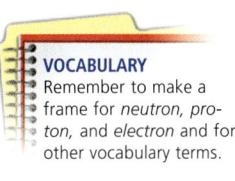

VOCABULARY
Remember to make a frame for *neutron*, *proton*, and *electron* and for other vocabulary terms.

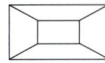

The Atomic Model

Atoms are made of protons, neutrons, and electrons.

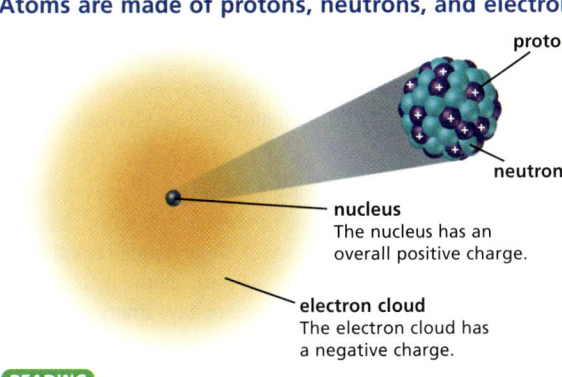

- proton
- neutron
- **nucleus** The nucleus has an overall positive charge.
- **electron cloud** The electron cloud has a negative charge.

Particle Charges and Mass

Particle	Relative Mass	Relative Charge
Electron	1	−1
Proton	2000	+1
Neutron	2000	0

 Which part of the atom has a negative charge?

Chapter 5: **Atomic Structure and the Periodic Table** 139

DIFFERENTIATE INSTRUCTION

 More Reading Support

C What particles are grouped in the atom's nucleus? *protons and neutrons*

D What particles move around outside the nucleus? *electrons*

Advanced Challenge students to find out about quarks—smaller, more fundamental particles of atoms. Since quarks' existence is still hypothetical, have students report on the evidence used to support their existence.

Challenge and Extension, p. 19

English Learners Have English learners write each vocabulary term and its definition on separate index cards, or put the terms on the Science Word Wall so students have quick and easy reminders to refer to during the lesson.

History of Science

Around 450 B.C., the Greek philosopher Democritus described matter as being made of small, indestructible atoms. Although some other Greeks contributed to this theory, most others rejected it, and it was discredited until the 18th century. In 1704, Isaac Newton described matter as being made of indivisible particles. In 1803, John Dalton proposed the modern atomic theory, which stated that each element had its own atom.

Real World Example

Beams of electrons have many practical uses. In a television or computer, rapidly moving electron beams create the images on the screen. In a scanning electron microscope, an electron beam produces images of very small objects.

Teach from Visuals

To help students interpret the diagram "The Atomic Model," ask:

- What part of the atom is pulled out and enlarged to show more detail? *the nucleus, in order to show protons and neutrons*
- Why would it be impossible to show the exact dimensions of an atom on paper? *because the nucleus is so small compared with total atom space, and because the distance between the nucleus and electrons is so great*

 This visual is also available as T6 in the Unit Transparency Book.

Ongoing Assessment

Describe atomic structure.

Ask: What are the major parts of an atom? *protons and neutrons in the nucleus, electrons in a cloud around the nucleus*

 Answer: the electron

Chapter 5 **139**

Teach Difficult Concepts

Students may conceive of the electron cloud as a mostly filled-in space, such as cotton candy or plastic foam. Point out that electrons take up almost no space—they have a tiny mass. The electron cloud is drawn to show where electrons are likely to be around the atom. The electron cloud is not a physical thing.

EXPLORE the BIG idea

Revisit "That's Far!" on p. 135. Have students reinterpret their observations.

Address Misconceptions

IDENTIFY Ask: If you put a grain of sand under a microscope, would you be able to see the atoms in the sand, or would the atoms be too small? If students answer that they would be able to see the atoms, they hold a misconception of the size of atoms.

CORRECT Point out that even a grain of sand has room for millions of atoms. Nothing in the classroom could possibly magnify an atom enough to make it visible.

REASSESS Ask: How many times would you have to enlarge the period at the end of a sentence in order to view any atoms? *at least a million times*

Technology Resources
Visit **ClassZone.com** for background on common student misconceptions.
MISCONCEPTION DATABASE

Ongoing Assessment

 Answer: Atomic mass number includes the protons and neutrons in the nucleus. Atomic number is the number of protons in the nucleus.

Build a model of an atom.

Atoms are extremely small, about 10^{-10} meters in diameter. This means that you could fit millions of atoms in the period at the end of this sentence. The diagram on page 139, picturing the basic structure of the atom, is not drawn to scale. In an atom the electron cloud is about 10,000 times the diameter of the nucleus.

Electrons are much smaller than protons or neutrons—about 2000 times smaller. Electrons also move about the nucleus very quickly. Scientists have found that it is not possible to determine their exact positions with any certainty. This is why we picture the electrons as being in a cloud around the nucleus.

The negative electrons remain associated with the nucleus because they are attracted to the positively charged protons. Also, because electrical charges that are alike (such as two negative charges) repel each other, electrons remain spread out in the electron cloud. Neutral atoms have no overall electrical charge because they have an equal number of protons and electrons.

Atom Size
Millions of atoms could fit in a space the size of this dot. It would take you 500 years to count the number of atoms in a grain of salt.

Gold has 79 protons and 79 electrons.

Atomic Numbers

If all atoms are composed of the same particles, how can there be more than 100 different elements? The identity of an atom is determined by the number of protons in its nucleus, called the **atomic number.** Every hydrogen atom—atomic number 1—has exactly one proton in its nucleus. Every gold atom has 79 protons, which means the atomic number of gold is 79.

Atomic Mass Numbers

The total number of protons and neutrons in an atom's nucleus is called its **atomic mass number.** While the atoms of a certain element always have the same number of protons, they may not always have the same number of neutrons, so not all atoms of an element have the same atomic mass number.

All chlorine atoms, for instance, have 17 protons. However, some chlorine atoms have 18 neutrons, while other chlorine atoms have 20 neutrons. Atoms of chlorine with 18 and 20 neutrons are called chlorine isotopes. **Isotopes** are atoms of the same element that have a different number of neutrons. Some elements have many isotopes, while other elements have just a few.

READING TIP
The *iso-* in *isotope* is from the Greek language, and it means "equal."

CHECK YOUR READING How is atomic mass number different from atomic number?

DIFFERENTIATE INSTRUCTION

More Reading Support

E What particles are counted to determine atomic number? *protons*

F What particles are counted for atomic mass number? *protons and neutrons*

Below Level Use this analogy to illustrate the distinction between atomic number and atomic mass number: Suppose you have a bag of hard candies. There are 10 "hot red" candies and 10 "cool white" candies in the bag. Imagine that this bag stands for an atom, and that the hot red candies are protons and the cool white candies are neutrons. How would you figure out the atomic number? *You'd count the hot red candies—10.* How would you figure out the atomic mass number? *You'd add up all the candies—20.*

Isotopes

Isotopes have different numbers of neutrons.

Chlorine-35
atomic mass number = 35

Chlorine-37
atomic mass number = 37

- 17 protons
- 18 neutrons
- nucleus
- 17 electrons

- 17 protons
- 20 neutrons
- nucleus
- 17 electrons

A particular isotope is designated by the name of the element and the total number of its protons and neutrons. You can find the number of neutrons in a particular isotope by subtracting the atomic number from the atomic mass number. For example, chlorine-35 indicates the isotope of chlorine that has 18 neutrons. Chlorine-37 has 20 neutrons. Every atom of a given element always has the same atomic number because it has the same number of protons. However, the atomic mass number varies depending on the number of neutrons.

INVESTIGATE Masses of Atomic Particles

How can you model the relative masses of atomic particles?

PROCEDURE

1. Use a paper clip to represent an electron. Determine its mass.
2. Find a substance in the classroom (sand, clay, water) from which you could make a model representing the mass of a proton or neutron. The mass of a proton or neutron is about 2000 times the mass of an electron.
3. Measure out the substance until you have enough of it to make your model.

WHAT DO YOU THINK?
- What substance did you use to make your model?
- What was the model's mass?
- What do you conclude about the masses of atomic particles?

CHALLENGE The diameter of an electron is approximately 1/2000 that of a proton. What two objects could represent each of these to scale?

SKILL FOCUS
Modeling

MATERIALS
- balance
- large paper clip
- other items

TIME
20 minutes

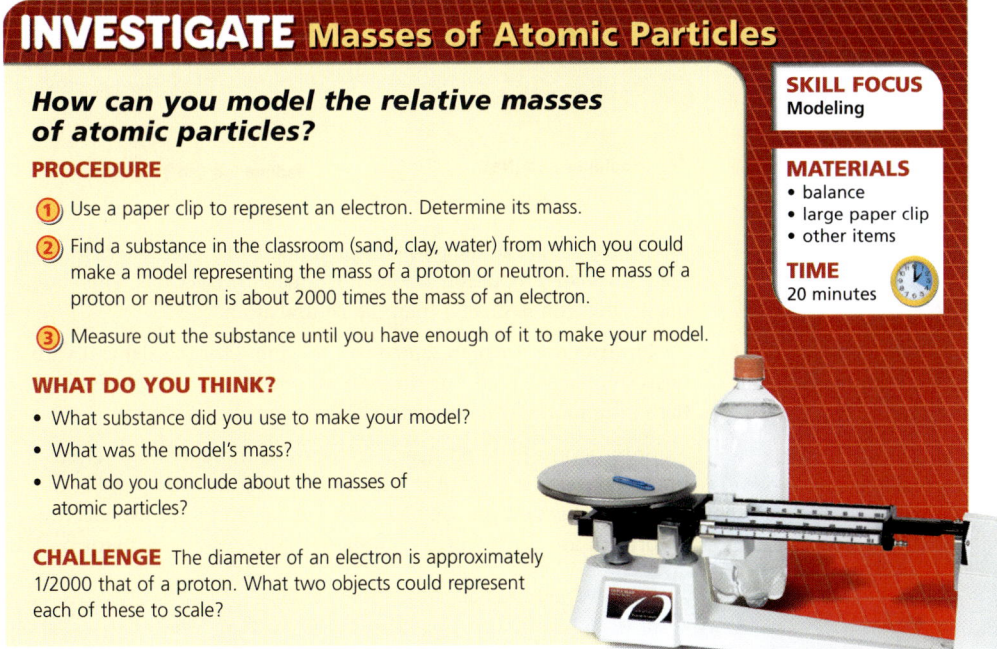

Chapter 5: **Atomic Structure and the Periodic Table** 141

Teach from Visuals

To help students interpret the "Isotopes" visual, ask:

- How are the two chlorine atoms similar? *Both have 17 electrons, and a nucleus with 17 protons.*
- How are they different? *The first has 18 neutrons, and the second has 20 neutrons.*

This visual is also available as T6 in the Unit Transparency Book.

INVESTIGATE Masses of Atomic Particles

PURPOSE To model the relative masses of atomic particles

TIPS 20 min.

- At the beginning of the activity, ask students to state what the paper clip stands for (electron) and what the other object stands for (proton or neutron).
- During the activity, have students restate what the objects with which they are working represent.

WHAT DO YOU THINK? *Answers will vary. Students should conclude that protons (or neutrons) are much more massive than electrons.*

CHALLENGE *The diameter of a proton is 1×10^{-15} meter and of the electron, about 1×10^{-18} meter. Emphasize to students that as yet it is impossible for scientists to determine exactly the relative sizes of protons and electrons.*

Datasheet, Masses of Atomic Particles, p. 20

Technology Resources

Customize this student lab as needed or look for an alternative. Print rubrics to assess student lab reports.

 Lab Generator CD-ROM

DIFFERENTIATE INSTRUCTION

More Reading Support

G Do isotopes have different numbers of protons or of neutrons? *neutrons*

Additional Investigation To reinforce Section 5.1 learning goals, use the following full-period investigation:

Additional INVESTIGATION, Investigating the Unseen, A, B, & C, pp. 59–67, 329–330
(Advanced students should complete Levels B and C.)

Chapter 5 **141**

Teach from Visuals

To help students interpret the diagrams of the sodium atom and ion, ask:

- In each of the two pictures, what does the dark clump in the center stand for? *the nucleus*
- What does the surrounding cloud stand for? *the electrons*
- What charge does each part have? *The nucleus has a positive charge. The electron cloud has a negative charge.*
- What creates the difference in size between the atom and the ion? *the number of electrons; the positive ion has fewer electrons*

Teach Difficult Concepts

Students may have difficulty understanding why atoms sometimes lose or gain electrons to form ions. Explain that atoms often form ions because having a certain number of electrons in the electron cloud is more electrically stable. Also emphasize that ions form in pairs: when one atom loses an electron, another atom gains an electron.

Ongoing Assessment

Explain how ions form from atoms.
Ask: If an atom gains an electron, what does it become? *a negative ion*

 *Answer: An atom must lose an electron.*

MAIN IDEA WEB Make a main idea web to organize what you know about ions.

Atoms form ions.

An atom has an equal number of electrons and protons. Since each electron has one negative charge and each proton has one positive charge, atoms have no overall electrical charge. An **ion** is formed when an atom loses or gains one or more electrons. Because the number of electrons in an ion is different from the number of protons, an ion does have an overall electric charge.

Formation of Positive Ions

Consider how a positive ion can be formed from an atom. The left side of the illustration below represents a sodium (Na) atom. Its nucleus contains 11 protons and some neutrons. Because the electron cloud surrounding the nucleus consists of 11 electrons, there is no overall charge on the atom. If the atom loses one electron, however, the charges are no longer balanced. There is now one more proton than there are electrons. The ion formed, therefore, has a positive charge.

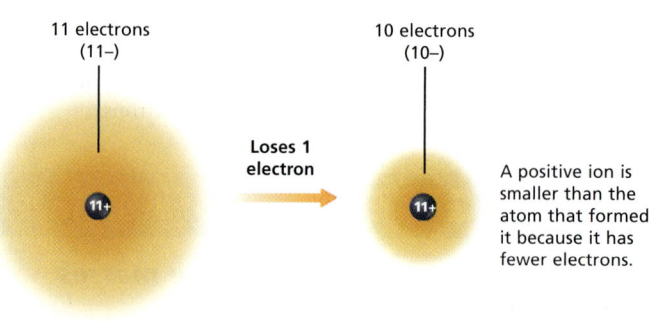

Sodium Atom (Na) — 11 electrons (11–), 11+

Loses 1 electron →

Sodium Ion (Na⁺) — 10 electrons (10–), 11+

A positive ion is smaller than the atom that formed it because it has fewer electrons.

Notice the size of the positive ion. Because there are fewer electrons, there is less of a repulsion among the remaining electrons. Therefore, the positive ion is smaller than the neutral atom.

Positive ions are represented by the symbol for the element with a raised plus sign to indicate the positive charge. In the above example, the sodium ion is represented as Na^+.

Some atoms form positive ions by losing more than one electron. In those cases, the symbol for the ion also indicates the number of positive charges on the ion. For example, calcium loses two electrons to form an ion Ca^{2+}, and aluminum loses three electrons to form Al^{3+}.

 What must happen to form a positive ion?

DIFFERENTIATE INSTRUCTION

 More Reading Support

H What kind of charge does an electron have? *negative*

I After an atom has lost an electron, what kind of charge does it have? *positive*

Below Level To help students understand ions, draw a diagram of an atom on the board. Draw the nucleus and the surrounding electron cloud. In the nucleus, draw three plus marks; in the cloud, draw three minus marks. Have students identify the marks as protons and electrons. Emphasize that the protons' positive charges balance the electrons' negative charges. Erase one minus sign in the electron cloud. Have students discuss how this change will affect the atom.

Formation of Negative Ions

The illustration below shows how a negative ion is formed. In this case the atom is chlorine (Cl). The nucleus of a chlorine atom contains 17 protons and some neutrons. The electron cloud has 17 electrons, so the atom has no overall charge. When an electron is added to the chlorine atom, a negatively charged ion is formed. Notice that a negative ion is larger than the neutral atom that formed it. The extra electron increases the repulsion within the cloud, causing it to expand.

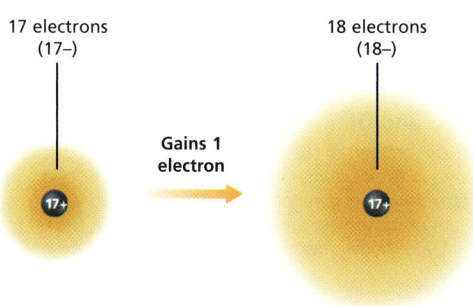

A negative ion is larger than the atom that formed it because it has more electrons.

Negative ions are represented by placing a minus sign to the right and slightly above the element's symbol. The negative chloride ion in the example, therefore, would be written as Cl$^-$. If an ion has gained more than one electron, the number of added electrons is indicated by a number in front of the minus sign. Oxygen (O), for example, gains two electrons when it forms an ion. Its symbol is O^{2-}.

5.1 Review

KEY CONCEPTS
1. Which two atoms are most common in Earth's crust? in the human body?
2. What are the particles that make up an atom?
3. What happens when an atom forms an ion?

CRITICAL THINKING
4. **Infer** Magnesium and sodium atoms are about the same size. How does the size of a magnesium ion with a 2+ charge compare with that of a sodium ion with a single + charge?
5. **Compare** The atomic number of potassium is 19. How does potassium-39 differ from potassium-41?

CHALLENGE
6. **Analyze** When determining the mass of an atom, the electrons are not considered. Why can scientists disregard the electrons?

Chapter 5: **Atomic Structure and the Periodic Table** 143

ANSWERS

1. oxygen and silicon; oxygen and carbon
2. protons, neutrons, and electrons
3. It gains or loses an electron.
4. The magnesium ion is smaller.
5. Potassium-41 has two more neutrons.
6. Scientists can disregard electrons because they have such a small mass.

CONNECTING SCIENCES
Integration of Sciences

Set Learning Goal
To identify chemical elements in the human body and the roles they play

Present the Science
Fluoride ions protect teeth by replacing other ions in the tooth's enamel, or hard covering. The new compound is much more resistant to the acids that can form in the mouth and so helps prevent the spread of tooth decay.

Discussion Questions
- Ask: Where do you find iron in the human body? *in the hemoglobin in red blood cells*
- Ask: What are two important functions of sodium and potassium in the body? *to regulate the amount and location of water and to make up sweat to control temperature*
- Ask: In what parts of the body is most of the calcium found? *bones and teeth*
- Ask: What element makes up part of the hard coating on teeth? *fluorine*

Teaching with Technology
Have students use graphics software to construct a pie graph of the chart data. They can convert each amount into a percentage by dividing by 50 kilograms.

Close
Tell students that any element, no matter how important for life, can be harmful if taken in too large a dose. Ask: Why do you think this is so? *A human's body chemistry will be upset if elements are not balanced as they need to be.*

Technology Resources
Have students visit ClassZone.com to find more about the elements important to life.

RESOURCE CENTER

144 Unit 2: **Chemical Interactions**

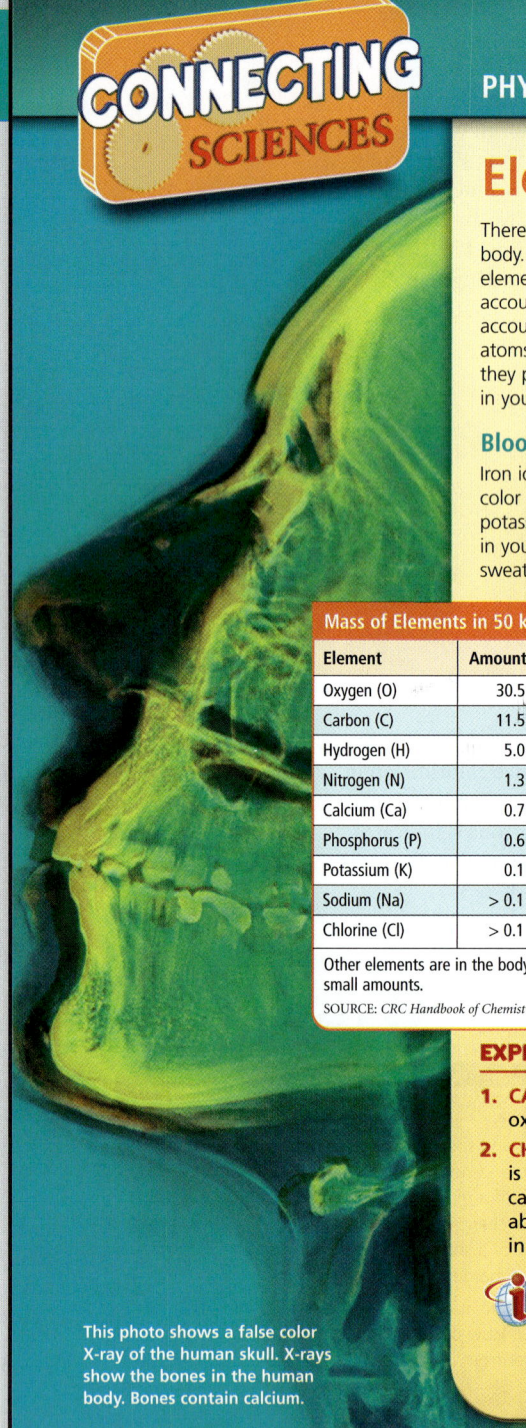

Connecting Sciences
PHYSICAL SCIENCE AND LIFE SCIENCE

Elements of Life

There are more than 25 different types of atoms in the cells of your body. The table below shows the amount of atoms of some of the elements in a 50-kilogram human. Atoms of the element oxygen account for about 61 percent of a person's mass. Atoms of carbon account for about 23 percent of a person's mass. Although the atoms of some elements are present only in very small amounts, they play an important role in the chemical processes that occur in your cells.

Blood and Other Fluids
Iron ions are part of the hemoglobin that gives your blood its red color and carries oxygen to cells throughout your body. Sodium and potassium ions help regulate the amount and location of the water in your body. Sodium and potassium ions also make up part of the sweat your body produces to regulate temperature.

Bones and Teeth
The sturdier structures of your body get their strength from calcium, magnesium, and phosphorus. You have less than a kilogram of calcium in your body, almost all of which is in your bones and teeth. Fluoride ions make up part of the hard coating on your teeth. This is why you'll often find fluoride ions added to toothpaste.

Elements to Avoid
In some way, the atoms of every element in the periodic table play a role in human lives. Many of them, however, can be hazardous if handled improperly. For example, arsenic and mercury are poisonous.

| Mass of Elements in 50 kg Human ||
Element	Amount (kg)
Oxygen (O)	30.5
Carbon (C)	11.5
Hydrogen (H)	5.0
Nitrogen (N)	1.3
Calcium (Ca)	0.7
Phosphorus (P)	0.6
Potassium (K)	0.1
Sodium (Na)	> 0.1
Chlorine (Cl)	> 0.1

Other elements are in the body in very small amounts.
SOURCE: *CRC Handbook of Chemistry and Physics*

EXPLORE
1. **CALCULATE** What percentage of your body is made up of oxygen, carbon, hydrogen, and nitrogen?
2. **CHALLENGE** Salt, made of sodium ions and chloride ions, is an essential part of your diet. However, too much salt can cause health problems. Use the Internet to find out about the problems caused by too much or too little salt in your diet.

 **RESOURCE CENTER** Find out more about the elements important to life.
CLASSZONE.COM

This photo shows a false color X-ray of the human skull. X-rays show the bones in the human body. Bones contain calcium.

144 Unit 2: **Chemical Interactions**

EXPLORE
1. **CALCULATE** oxygen: 30.5 kg/50 kg = 61.0%;
   carbon: 11.5 kg/50 kg = 23.0%;
   hydrogen: 5 kg/50 kg = 10.0%;
   nitrogen: 1.3 kg/50 kg = 2.6%
2. **CHALLENGE** Too much salt can lead to too much sodium, which can cause high blood pressure. Sodium is an essential nutrient, however, in maintaining the electrolyte balance in the body.

KEY CONCEPT

5.2 Elements make up the periodic table.

BEFORE, you learned
- Atoms have a structure
- Every element is made from a different type of atom

NOW, you will learn
- How the periodic table is organized
- How properties of elements are shown by the periodic table

VOCABULARY

atomic mass p. 145
periodic table p. 146
group p. 150
period p. 150

EXPLORE Similarities and Differences of Objects

How can different objects be organized?

PROCEDURE

1. With several classmates, organize the buttons into three or more groups.
2. Compare your team's organization of the buttons with another team's organization.

MATERIALS
buttons

WHAT DO YOU THINK?
- What characteristics did you use to organize the buttons?
- In what other ways could you have organized the buttons?

Elements can be organized by similarities.

One way of organizing elements is by the masses of their atoms. Finding the masses of atoms was a difficult task for the chemists of the past. They could not place an atom on a pan balance. All they could do was find the mass of a very large number of atoms of a certain element and then infer the mass of a single one of them.

Remember that not all the atoms of an element have the same atomic mass number. Elements have isotopes. When chemists attempt to measure the mass of an atom, therefore, they are actually finding the average mass of all its isotopes. The **atomic mass** of the atoms of an element is the average mass of all the element's isotopes. Even before chemists knew how the atoms of different elements could be different, they knew atoms had different atomic masses.

Chapter 5: **Atomic Structure and the Periodic Table** 145

5.2 FOCUS

▶ Set Learning Goals

Students will
- Describe how the periodic table is organized.
- Identify how properties of elements are shown by the periodic table.

◀ 3-Minute Warm-Up

Display Transparency 4 or copy the following exercise on the board:

Correct any statements that are not true.

1. The atomic number of an atom is the number of protons and neutrons in the nucleus. *atomic mass number*
2. Isotopes are atoms of the same element, but with a different number of neutrons. *true*
3. When an atom gives up an electron, it becomes an ion with a negative charge. *positive*

3-Minute Warm-Up, p. T4

5.2 MOTIVATE

EXPLORE Similarities and Differences of Objects

PURPOSE To classify logically a variety of objects

TIP *15 min.* Even if students do not physically sort the buttons, have them suggest ways they can organize them.

WHAT DO YOU THINK? *Size, shape, color, number of holes, and texture are likely criteria for organizing the buttons.*

RESOURCES FOR DIFFERENTIATED INSTRUCTION

Below Level
UNIT RESOURCE BOOK
- Reading Study Guide A, pp. 24–25
- Decoding Support, p. 47

AUDIO CDS

Advanced
UNIT RESOURCE BOOK
Challenge and Extension, p. 30

English Learners
UNIT RESOURCE BOOK
Spanish Reading Study Guide, pp. 28–29

AUDIO CDS
- Audio Readings in Spanish
- Audio Readings (English)

Chapter 5 **145**

5.2 INSTRUCT

Teach from Visuals

To help students interpret the visual of Mendeleev's periodic table, ask: **What do the question marks in the table represent?** *missing elements that Mendeleev thought should be there, based on the properties of other elements in the column and the changes in atomic mass.*

Integrate the Sciences

The concept of periodic patterns—patterns that repeat consistently at regular intervals—appears in many areas of science. In astronomy, the planets move in periodic patterns: they travel in elliptical paths around the Sun, passing the same points in space repeatedly. This particular periodic movement is the basis of a year as a measure of time.

Social Studies Connection

In his periodic table, Mendeleev used the Latin alphabet for element symbols and the Cyrillic alphabet for the text. Cyrillic letters are based on the Greek alphabet. Slavic languages that use Cyrillic include Russian, Serbian, Bulgarian, and Ukrainian.

Ongoing Assessment

 *increasing atomic mass and similar chemical properties*

Mendeleev's Periodic Table

In the early 1800s several scientists proposed systems to organize the elements based on their properties. None of these suggested methods worked very well until a Russian chemist named Dmitri Mendeleev (MENH-duh-LAY-uhf) decided to work on the problem.

In the 1860s, Mendeleev began thinking about how he could organize the elements based on their physical and chemical properties. He made a set of element cards. Each card contained the atomic mass of an atom of an element as well as any information about the element's properties. Mendeleev spent hours arranging the cards in various ways, looking for a relationship between properties and atomic mass.

The exercise led Mendeleev to think of listing the elements in a chart. In the rows of the chart, he placed those elements showing similar chemical properties. He arranged the rows so the atomic masses increased as one moved down each vertical column. It took Mendeleev quite a bit of thinking and rethinking to get all the relationships correct, but in 1869 he produced the first **periodic table** of the elements. We call it the periodic table because it shows a periodic, or repeating, pattern of properties of the elements. In the reproduction of Mendeleev's first table shown below, notice how he placed carbon (C) and silicon (Si), two elements known for their similarities, in the same row.

CHECK YOUR READING What organizing method did Mendeleev use?

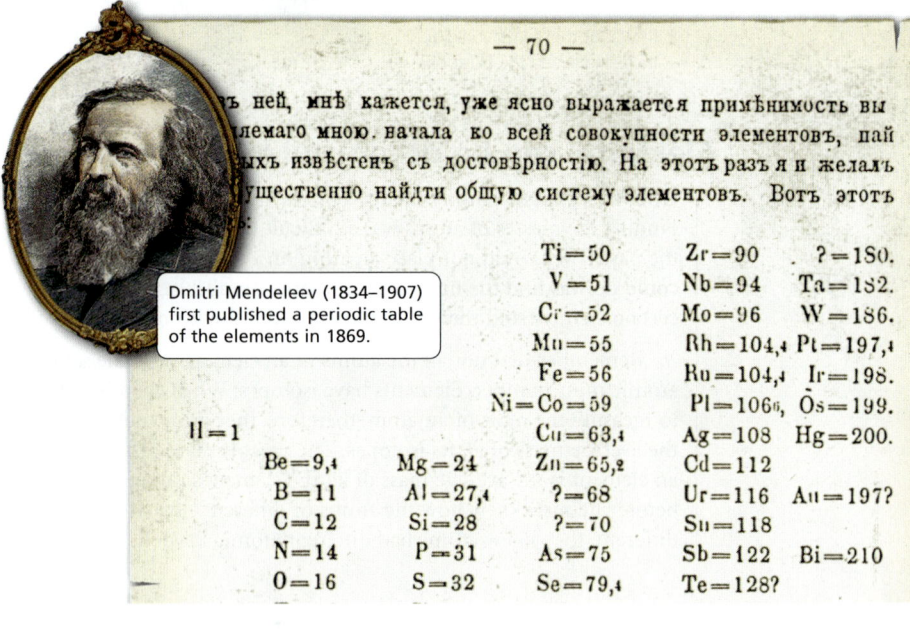

Dmitri Mendeleev (1834–1907) first published a periodic table of the elements in 1869.

146 Unit 2: Chemical Interactions

DIFFERENTIATE INSTRUCTION

 More Reading Support

A Who produced the first periodic table of elements? *Dmitri Mendeleev*

B What pattern repeats in the periodic table? *the properties of the elements*

English Learners Within this section are sentences with a variety of introductory clauses and phrases. Give students the following examples and have them identify the subject of the sentence: "In the rows of the chart, *he* placed those elements showing similar chemical properties." (p. 146)

"At the start, many *chemists* found it hard to accept Mendeleev's predictions of unknown elements." (p. 147)

Encourage students to use introductory clauses and phrases in their own writing.

Predicting New Elements

When Mendeleev constructed his table, he left some empty spaces where no known elements fit the pattern. He predicted that new elements that would complete the chart would eventually be discovered. He even described some of the properties of these unknown elements.

At the start, many chemists found it hard to accept Mendeleev's predictions of unknown elements. Only six years after he published the table, however, the first of these elements—represented by the question mark after aluminum (Al) on his table—was discovered. This element was given the name gallium, after the country France (Gaul) where it was discovered. In the next 20 years, two other elements Mendeleev predicted would be discovered.

The periodic table organizes the atoms of the elements by properties and atomic number.

The modern periodic table on pages 148 and 149 differs from Mendeleev's table in several ways. For one thing, elements with similar properties are found in columns, not rows. More important, the elements are not arranged by atomic mass but by atomic number.

MAIN IDEA WEB Make a main idea web to summarize the information you can learn from the periodic table.

Reading the Periodic Table

Each square of the periodic table gives particular information about the atoms of an element.

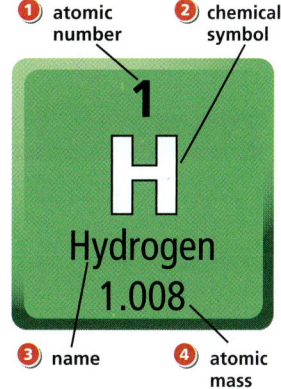
① atomic number ② chemical symbol
③ name ④ atomic mass

① The number at the top of the square is the atomic number, which is the number of protons in the nucleus of an atom of that element.

② The chemical symbol is an abbreviation for the element's name. It contains one or two letters. Some elements that have not yet been named are designated by temporary three-letter symbols.

③ The name of the element is written below the symbol.

④ The number below the name indicates the average atomic mass of all the isotopes of the element.

The color of the element's symbol indicates the physical state of the element at room temperature. White letters—such as the *H* for hydrogen in the box to the right—indicate a gas. Blue letters indicate a liquid, and black letters indicate a solid. The background colors of the squares indicate whether the element is a metal, nonmetal, or metalloid. These terms will be explained in the next section.

Chapter 5: **Atomic Structure and the Periodic Table** 147

Mathematics Connection

Atomic masses that are not whole numbers may baffle students. Remind students that different isotopes of an element have different atomic mass numbers. The atomic mass number represents the average atomic mass of all the isotopes of the elements. If there is only 30 percent of isotope A and 70 percent of isotope B, the average mass will be closer to the mass of isotope B, but not that exact mass.

History of Science

In 1913, the British chemist Henry Moseley began examining the x-ray radiation produced by some of the elements in the periodic table. Moseley noticed that the wavelengths produced by the elements changed in a predictable way that coincided with the element's position in the periodic table. Moseley concluded that there must be some other fundamental quantity that determined an element's position in the periodic table. This was how scientists came to reorder the periodic table by atomic number instead of atomic mass.

Social Studies Connection

Many of today's chemical symbols are based on old names for elements that were in use hundreds or thousands of years ago. Tell students that old alchemical symbols exist for elements such as iron, mercury, gold, and silver. Students may want to find pictures of alchemical symbols on the Internet.

DIFFERENTIATE INSTRUCTION

More Reading Support

C In the periodic table, where does the atomic number appear? *at the top of each square*

Below Level Help students interpret the details of the element square. Ask: Can different elements have the same atomic number? Why? *No; the atomic number is the number of protons, which is used to identify elements. Every element has a different atomic number.* What parts of the square besides atomic number are unique? *symbol, name*

Discuss whether the atomic mass is unique for each element, and why it could be the same.

Chapter 5 **147**

Teach from Visuals

To help students interpret the periodic table, ask:

- What color are most of the elements in the table? *yellow*
- According to the key at the bottom, what are those elements? *metals*
- How many nonmetals are in the table? *17*
- Why do you think the lanthanide and actinide series are listed below the others? *to save space*

Teacher Demo

You can demonstrate a flame test of elements if you have the following equipment: Bunsen burner; flame-test wires; test solutions of 0.5M barium chloride, calcium chloride, copper sulfate, potassium nitrate, and sodium chloride; 5M hydrochloric acid. Clean the metal loop by dipping it in the hydrochloric acid and putting it in the flame: the flame should not change color. Then dip the loop in a test solution (use the NaCl last, since it can be hard to clean from the wire). Put the loop in the flame and ask students to identify the color change. Tell students what element the solution contains. (Repeat this process for each solution.) Barium produces a light green flame; calcium, reddish yellow; copper, blue green; potassium, lilac; and sodium, yellow.

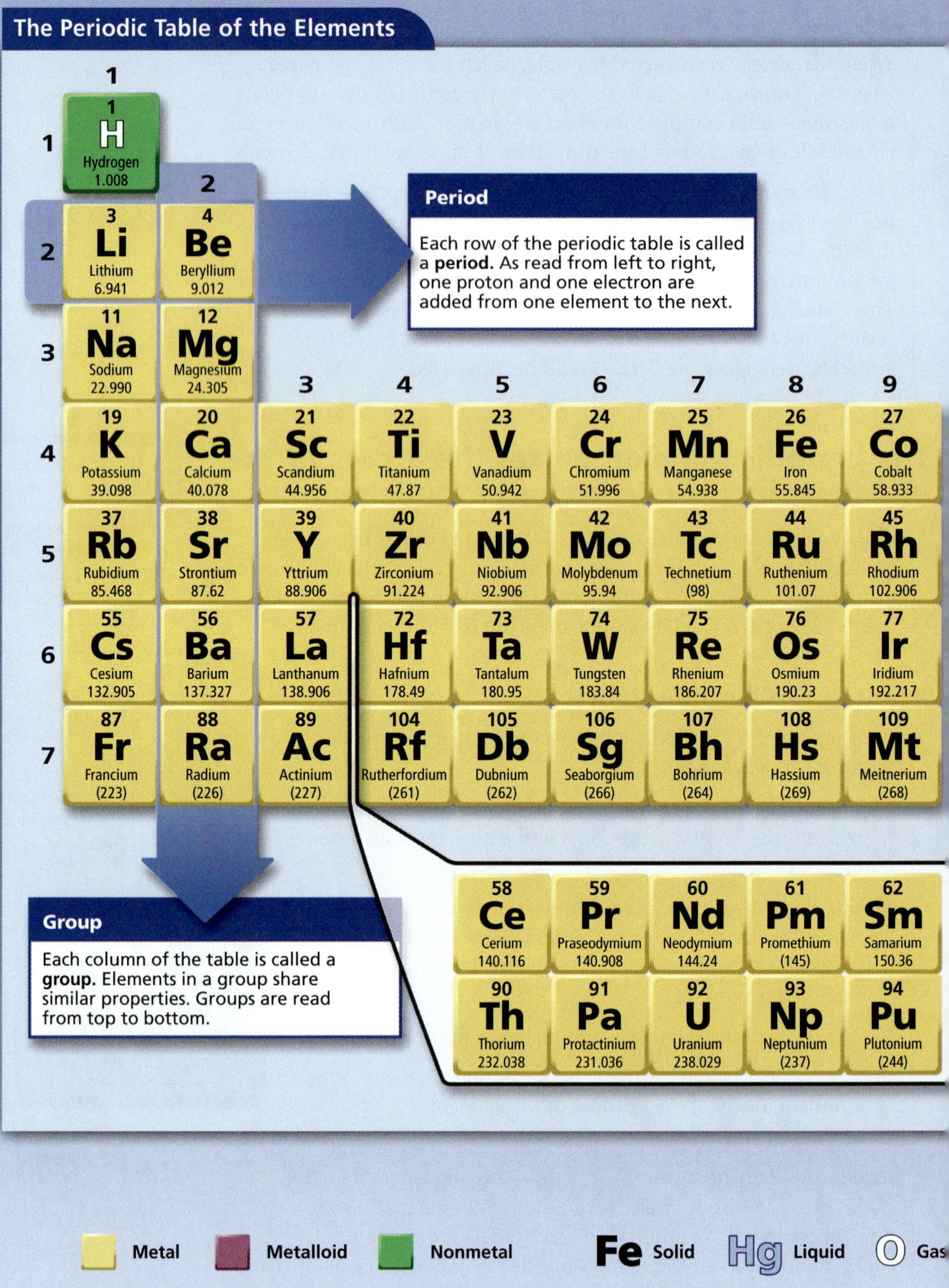

148 Unit 2: **Chemical Interactions**

The Periodic Table of the Elements

Period Each row of the periodic table is called a **period**. As read from left to right, one proton and one electron are added from one element to the next.

Group Each column of the table is called a **group**. Elements in a group share similar properties. Groups are read from top to bottom.

Key: Metal, Metalloid, Nonmetal, Fe Solid, Hg Liquid, O Gas

148 Unit 2: **Chemical Interactions**

DIFFERENTIATE INSTRUCTION

Inclusion Distribute enlarged copies of the periodic table so students with visual impairment can understand the table's layout. Tactile periodic tables are available from the American Printing House for the Blind.

Advanced Have students identify elements that are named after scientists, and then have them research one of the scientists. Point out that the higher-numbered elements are the most likely to have such names.

 Challenge and Extension, p. 30

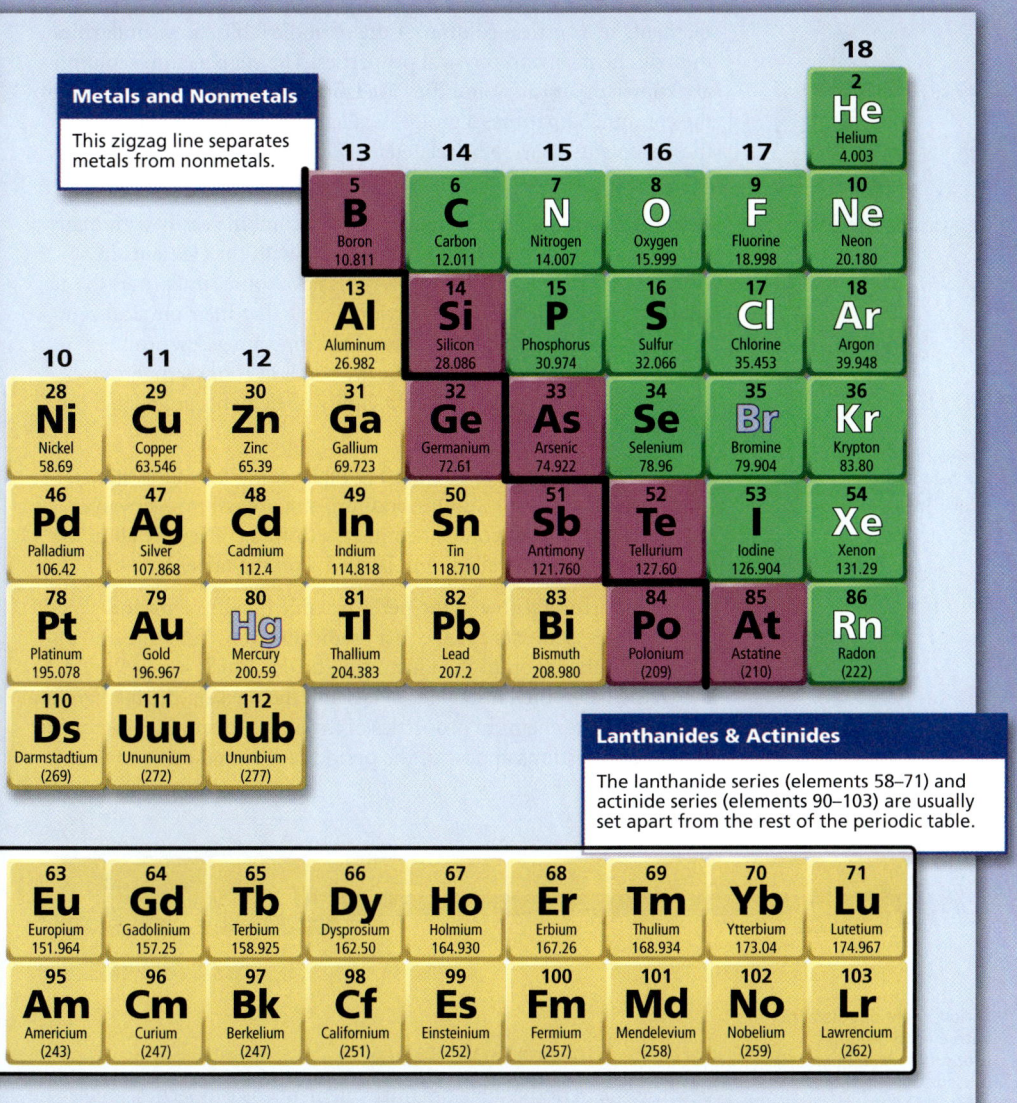

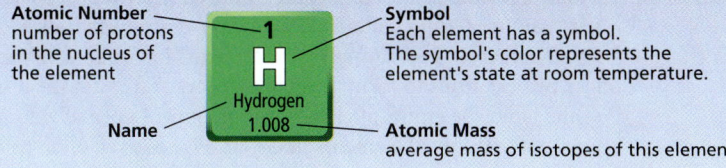

Chapter 5: **Atomic Structure and the Periodic Table** 149

Develop Critical Thinking

SEQUENCE Have students relate sequence to periodicity in the periodic table. Ask:

- What role does sequence of numbers play in the periodic table? *The atomic number increases by one as you go from left to right and then jump to the start of the next row (period).*
- Why are the rows broken where they are? *to align groups that have similar properties*

EXPLORE the BIG idea

Revisit "Element Safari" on p. 135. Have students locate on the periodic table each element they found in the safari, and then have them find the symbol, atomic number, and atomic mass for each element.

Language Arts Connection

Students have learned that some symbols for elements are based on Latin words. One interesting example is Hg, for mercury. The symbol comes from the Latin *hydrargyrum,* meaning "liquid silver." Students may have seen a drop of mercury, which does indeed look like liquid silver.

DIFFERENTIATE INSTRUCTION

Advanced Have students investigate an element and determine when it was discovered and how it was named. Helium, for example, was found first in the Sun (Greek *hēlios*) and later on Earth.

Chapter 5 **149**

Teach from Visuals

To help students connect the visuals of a row and a column to the larger periodic table, ask:

- From what part of the periodic table is the column labeled "Group 17" taken? *the far right*
- From what part is the row labeled "Period 3" taken? *the upper part*

Metacognitive Strategy

Discuss mnemonic devices and other strategies that students can use to remember the difference between group and period. For example, periods run horizontally, like a sentence, and a sentence ends with a period.

Health Connection

People who for health reasons cannot have table salt (NaCl) can instead use potassium chloride (KCl). The taste is somewhat bitter. Potassium and sodium are in the same group and so have similar properties.

Ongoing Assessment

Describe how the periodic table is organized.

Ask: Why is a group sometimes called a family of elements? *A group is sometimes called a family of elements because the elements are related in terms of properties and traits they share.*

Groups and Periods

Elements in a vertical column of the periodic table show similarities in their chemical and physical properties. The elements in a column are known as a **group**, and they are labeled by a number at the top of the column. Sometimes a group is called a family of elements, because these elements seem to be related.

The elements in Group 17, the halogens, show many similarities.

The illustration at the left shows Group 17, commonly referred to as the halogen group. Halogens tend to combine easily with many other elements and compounds, especially with the elements in Groups 1 and 2. Although the halogens have some similarities to one another, you can see from the periodic table that their physical properties are not the same. Fluorine and chlorine are gases, bromine is a liquid, and iodine and astatine are solids at room temperature. Remember that the members of a family of elements are related but not identical.

Metals like copper can be used to make containers for water. Some metals—such as lithium, sodium, and potassium—however, react violently if they come in contact with water. They are all in the same group, the vertical column labeled 1 on the table.

Each horizontal row in the periodic table is called a **period**. Properties of elements change in a predictable way from one end of a period to the other. In the illustration below, which shows Period 3, the elements on the far left are metals and the ones on the far right are nonmetals. The chemical properties of the elements show a progression; similar progressions appear in the periods above and below this one.

Period 3 contains elements with a wide range of properties. Aluminum (Al) is used to make drink cans, while argon (Ar) is a gas used in light bulbs.

Trends in the Periodic Table

Because the periodic table organizes elements by properties, an element's position in the table can give information about the element. Remember that atoms form ions by gaining or losing electrons. Atoms of elements on the left side of the table form positive ions easily. For example, Group 1 atoms lose an electron to form ions with one positive charge (1+). Atoms of the elements in Group 2, likewise, can lose two electrons to form ions with a charge of 2+. At the other side of the table, the atoms of elements in Group 18 normally do not form ions at all. Atoms of elements in Group 17, however, often gain one

150 Unit 2: Chemical Interactions

DIFFERENTIATE INSTRUCTION

 More Reading Support

D What do you call a column of the periodic table? *a group*

E What do you call a row of the periodic table? *a period*

English Learners The use of dashes in writing may be confusing to English learners. The dash can function like a comma or parentheses, and introduce an appositive phrase. For example, "Some metals—such as lithium, sodium, and potassium—however, react violently if they come in contact with water."

electron to form a negative ion (1–). Similarly, the atoms of elements in Group 16 can gain two electrons to form a 2– ion. The atoms of the elements in Groups 3 to 12 all form positive ions, but the charge can vary.

Other information about atoms can be determined by their position in the table. The illustration to the right shows how the sizes of atoms vary across periods and within groups. An atom's size is important because it affects how the atom will react with another atom.

The densities of elements also follow a pattern. Density generally increases from the top of a group to the bottom. Within a period, however, the elements at the left and right sides of the table are the least dense, and the elements in the middle are the most dense. The element osmium (Os) has the highest known density, and it is located at the center of the table.

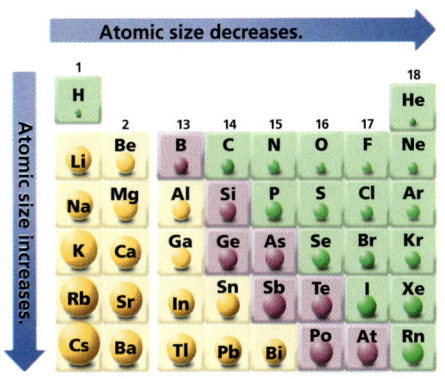

Atomic size is one property that changes in a predictable way across, up, and down the periodic table.

Chemists cannot predict the exact size or density of an atom of one element based on that of another. These trends, nonetheless, are a valuable tool in predicting the properties of different substances. The fact that the trends appeared after the periodic table was organized by atomic number was a victory for all of the scientists like Mendeleev who went looking for them all those years before.

CHECK YOUR READING What are some properties that can be related to position on the periodic table?

5.2 Review

KEY CONCEPTS
1. How is the modern periodic table organized?
2. What information about an atom's properties can you read from the periodic table?
3. How are the relationships of elements in a group different from the relationships of elements in a period?

CRITICAL THINKING
4. **Infer** Would you expect strontium (Sr) to be more like potassium (K) or bromine (Br)? Why?
5. **Predict** Barium (Ba) is in Group 2. Recall that atoms in Group 1 lose one electron to form ions with a 1+ charge. What type of ion does barium form?

CHALLENGE
6. **Analyze** Explain how chemists can state with certainty that no one will discover an element between sulfur (S) and chlorine (Cl).

Chapter 5: **Atomic Structure and the Periodic Table** 151

ANSWERS

1. by atomic number

2. the number of protons in an atom's nucleus, the average mass of one atom of that element, the element's symbol, and the element's name

3. The elements in a group have similar properties. The elements in a period have varying properties.

4. potassium, because it is closer on the periodic table

5. positive ion with 2+ charge

6. Chlorine has an atomic number one greater than sulfur. This means it has one more proton in its nucleus. Each element is defined by its atomic number, which is an integer.

CHAPTER INVESTIGATION

Focus

PURPOSE Students model atoms and determine the atoms' relative masses.

OVERVIEW Students will use washers in film cans to represent protons and neutrons in atomic nuclei. They will designate one can to be the baseline with an atomic mass of 1 and will compare the masses of the remaining cans with the baseline. Students will find that you can use relative weights to determine atomic mass number.

Lab Preparation

- Ahead of time fill four film cans for each group of students as follows: 1 washer in A, 4 washers in B, 7 washers in C, and 9 washers in D. One empty can is also used in the investigation.
- You could use pennies or quarters instead of washers.
- Prior to the investigation, have students read through the investigation and prepare their data tables. Or you may wish to copy and distribute datasheets and rubrics.

 UNIT RESOURCE BOOK, pp. 50–58

 SCIENCE TOOLKIT, F12

Lab Management

- Encourage multiple measurements of the masses to ensure accuracy.
- Students should use the same mass of the empty can for all the samples.
- Make sure students understand that the data in rows 1–4 of the table represent actual measurements that may not be all whole numbers. The data in row 5, however, are their estimations of the numbers of washers in each film can and so must be a whole number.

INCLUSION Have students with visual impairments work the balance so they can feel when the mass is equal, and have a partner relate the measured mass.

152 Unit 2: **Chemical Interactions**

CHAPTER INVESTIGATION

Modeling Atomic Masses

OVERVIEW AND PURPOSE Atoms are extremely small. They are so small, in fact, that a single drop of water contains more atoms than you could count in a lifetime! Measuring the masses of atoms to discover the patterns in the periodic table was not an easy task for scientists in the past. This investigation will give you some sense of how scientists determined the mass of atoms. You will
- compare the masses of different film can "atoms"
- predict the number of washers in each film can "atom"

Procedure

MATERIALS
- empty film can
- balance
- 4 filled film cans

1. Create a data table similar to the one shown on the sample notebook page.

2. Find the mass of one empty film can. Record this mass in the second row of the table.

3. Collect the four film cans labeled A, B, C, and D in advance by your teacher. Each can contains a different number of washers and represents a different atom. The washers represent the protons and neutrons in an atom's nucleus.

4. Measure the mass of each of the four film cans. Record the masses of the film can atoms in the first row of your data table.

5. Subtract the mass of an empty film can from the mass of each film can atom. Record the differences in the correct spaces in your data table. These masses represent the masses of the washers in your film can atoms. Think of these masses as the masses of the nuclei.

6. Divide the mass of the washers in can B by the mass of the washers in can A. Record the value under the mass of the washers in can B.

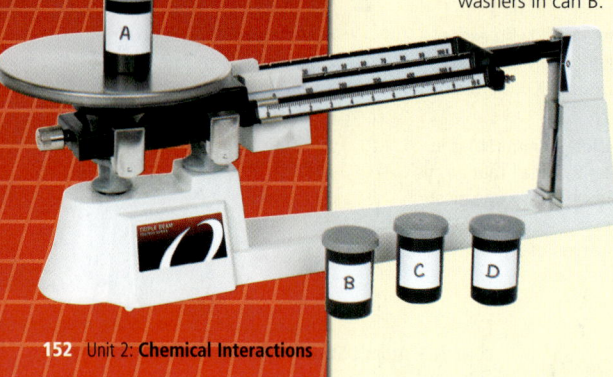

152 Unit 2: **Chemical Interactions**

INVESTIGATION RESOURCES

 CHAPTER INVESTIGATION, Modeling Atomic Masses
- Level A, pp. 50–53
- Level B, pp. 54–57
- Level C, p. 58

Advanced students should complete Levels B & C.

 Writing a Lab Report, D12–13

Technology Resources

Customize this student lab as needed or look for an alternative. Print rubrics to assess student lab reports.

 Lab Generator CD-ROM

7. Repeat step 6 for film can atoms A, C, and D. Record the value under the masses of the washers in each can.

8. Round the values you obtained in steps 6 and 7 to the nearest whole number. Record the rounded figures in the next row of the table.

Observe and Analyze

1. **RECORD OBSERVATIONS** Be sure your data table and calculations are complete. Double-check your arithmetic.

2. **ANALYZE DATA** Examine your data table. Do you notice any patterns in how the masses increase? Given that all the washers in the film can atoms have identical masses, what might the ratio of the mass of the washers to the smallest mass tell you?

3. **PREDICT** Assume there is only one washer in can A. Estimate the number of washers in the other cans and record your estimates in the last row of the table.

4. **GRAPH DATA** On a sheet of graph paper, plot the masses (in grams) of the washers in the film can atoms on the y-axis and the number of washers in each can on the x-axis. Connect the points on the graph.

5. **INTERPRET DATA** Compare the masses of your film can atoms with the masses of the first four atoms on the periodic table. Which represents which?

Conclude

1. **IDENTIFY LIMITS** What can't this activity tell you about the identity of your film can atoms? (Hint: Protons and neutrons in real atoms have about the same mass.)

2. **INFER** Hydrogen has only a single proton in its nucleus. If your film can atoms represent the first four elements in the periodic table, what are the numbers of protons and neutrons in each atom?

3. **APPLY** Single atoms are far too small to place on a balance. How do you think scientists determine the masses of real atoms?

INVESTIGATE Further

CHALLENGE Use a periodic table to find the masses of the next two atoms (boron and carbon). How many washers would you need to make film can atom models for each?

Modeling Atomic Masses
Observe and Analyze
Table 1. Masses of Film Can Atoms

	A	B	C	D
Mass of film can atom (g)				
Mass of empty film can (g)				
Mass of washers (g)				
Mass of washers divided by can A				
Value rounded to nearest whole number				
Estimated number of washers in each can				

Atomic Structure and the Periodic Table 153

Observe and Analyze

1. SAMPLE DATA Empty film can, 7.3 g. Can A, 11.8 g; washers, 4.5 g. Can B, 24.4 g; washers, 17.1 g. Can C, 39.4 g; washers, 32.1 g. Can D, 47.9 g; washers, 42.6 g.

2. Students may notice that the mass of B is about four times the mass of A. The ratio of the mass of the washers to the smallest mass might tell you that the smallest mass might be the mass of one washer.

3. 1, 4, 7, 9

4. See students' graphs.

5. A represents hydrogen; B represents helium; C represents lithium; D represents beryllium

Conclude

1. The activity cannot tell you how the mass divides between protons and neutrons.

2. A = 1 proton, 0 neutrons; B = 2 protons and 2 neutrons; C = 3 protons and 4 neutrons; D = 4 protons and 5 neutrons

3. They measure the masses of many atoms, then divide by the number of atoms to find the mass of a single atom.

INVESTIGATE Further

CHALLENGE 11 washers for boron and 12 washers for carbon

Post-Lab Discussion

Ask: Why did you subtract the mass of the empty film can from the mass of each of the filled cans? *You want to know the mass of the "atoms" in the can; adding the mass of the container would skew the results.* Also ask if students have an appreciation for what Mendeleev and others went through to determine atomic masses.

5.3 FOCUS

▶ Set Learning Goals

Students will
- Classify elements as metals, non-metals, and metalloids.
- Identify different groups of elements.
- Describe radioactive elements.
- Model half-life in an experiment.

◯ 3-Minute Warm-Up

Display Transparency 5 or copy the following exercise on the board:

Look for the elements below in the periodic table on pp. 148–149. Write how each pair of elements are related.

1. calcium and barium *in the same group*
2. lithium and carbon *in the same period*
3. uranium and curium *in the same period and in the actinide series*

 3-Minute Warm-Up, p. T5

5.3 MOTIVATE

THINK ABOUT

PURPOSE To reinforce the concept that elements with similar properties are in the same part of the periodic table

DISCUSS Help students locate these elements in the periodic table. Discuss the other elements that are near them. *Fluorine, krypton, neon, chlorine, and bromine are near argon. Boron, carbon, silicon, gallium, and germanium are near aluminum. Nickel, palladium, silver, zinc, and cadmium are near copper.*

Ongoing Assessment

 Answer: Elements with similar properties are near each other in the periodic table.

154 Unit 2: **Chemical Interactions**

KEY CONCEPT
5.3 The periodic table is a map of the elements.

◀ BEFORE, you learned	▶ NOW, you will learn
• The periodic table is organized into groups of elements with similar characteristics	• How elements are classified as metals, nonmetals, and metalloids
• The periodic table organizes elements according to their properties	• About different groups of elements
	• About radioactive elements

VOCABULARY

reactive p. 154
metal p. 155
nonmetal p. 157
metalloid p. 158
radioactivity p. 158
half-life p. 160

THINK ABOUT

How are elements different?

The photograph shows common uses of the elements copper, aluminum, and argon: copper in a penny, aluminum in a pie plate, and argon in a light bulb. Each element is located in a different part of the periodic table, and each has a very different use. Find these elements on the periodic table. What other elements are near these?

The periodic table has distinct regions.

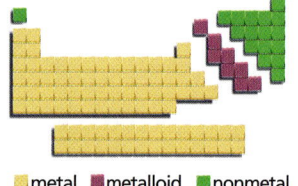

■ metal ■ metalloid ■ nonmetal

The periodic table is a kind of map of the elements. Just as a country's location on the globe gives you information about its climate, an atom's position on the periodic table indicates the properties of its element. The periodic table has three main regions—metals on the left, nonmetals (except hydrogen) on the right, and metalloids in between. The periodic table on pages 148 and 149 indicates these regions with different colors. A yellow box indicates a metal; green, a nonmetal; and purple, a metalloid.

An element's position in the table also indicates how reactive it is. The term **reactive** indicates how likely an element is to undergo a chemical change. Most elements are somewhat reactive and combine with other materials. The atoms of the elements in Groups 1 and 17 are the most reactive. The elements of Group 18 are the least reactive of all the elements.

 How does the periodic table resemble a map?

154 Unit 2: **Chemical Interactions**

RESOURCES FOR DIFFERENTIATED INSTRUCTION

Below Level
UNIT RESOURCE BOOK
- Reading Study Guide A, pp. 34–35
- Decoding Support, p. 47

 AUDIO CDS

Advanced
UNIT RESOURCE BOOK
- Challenge and Extension, p. 40
- Challenge Reading, pp. 43–44

English Learners
UNIT RESOURCE BOOK
Spanish Reading Study Guide, pp. 38–39

 AUDIO CDS

- Audio Readings in Spanish
- Audio Readings (English)

Most elements are metals.

When you look at the periodic table, it is obvious from the color that most of the elements are metals. In general, **metals** are elements that conduct electricity and heat well and have a shiny appearance. Metals can be shaped easily by pounding, bending, or being drawn into a long wire. Except for mercury, which is a liquid, metals are solids at room temperature.

Sodium is a metal that is so soft it can be cut with a knife at room temperature.

You probably can name many uses for the metal **copper**.

Aluminum is often used for devices that must be strong and light.

Reactive Metals

The metals in Group 1 of the periodic table, the alkali metals, are very reactive. Sodium and potassium are often stored in oil to keep them away from air. When exposed to air, these elements react rapidly with oxygen and water vapor. The ions of these metals, Na^+ and K^+, are important for life, and play an essential role in the functioning of living cells.

The metals in Group 2, the alkaline earth metals, are less reactive than the alkali metals. They are still more reactive than most other metals, however. Calcium ions are an essential part of your diet. Your bones and teeth contain calcium ions. Magnesium is a light, inexpensive metal that is often combined with other metals when a lightweight material is needed, such as for airplane frames.

Transition Metals

The elements in Groups 3–12 are called the transition metals. Among these metals are some of the earliest known elements, such as copper, gold, silver, and iron. Transition metals are generally less reactive than most other metals. Because gold and silver are easily shaped and do not react easily, they have been used for thousands of years to make jewelry and coins. Ancient artifacts made from transition metals can be found in many museums and remain relatively unchanged since the time they were made. Today, dimes and quarters are made of copper and nickel, and pennies are made of zinc with a coating of copper. Transition metal ions even are found in the foods you eat.

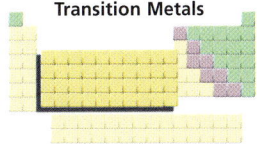
Reactive Metals

Transition Metals

Chapter 5: Atomic Structure and the Periodic Table 155

Integrate the Sciences

The human body needs a number of transition metals, in small amounts, to function properly. One of the most important transition metals for humans is iron, which is a key component of hemoglobin in red blood cells. Other important transition metals include zinc, molybdenum, copper, chromium, iron, and manganese.

Teacher Demo

Bring a box of iron-rich breakfast cereal and a vial of iron filings to class. Crush a small sample of cereal. Put it in a beaker of hot distilled water and stir with a magnetic stirrer. After about 15 minutes of stirring, remove the stirrer and show the dark slivers of iron on the magnet. Have students inspect the iron from the cereal and compare it with the iron filings. Point out that humans need iron in their diet for several important functions, including the carrying of oxygen in the red blood cells.

Real World Example

Although many transition metals are widespread in Earth's crust, their distribution in economically useful concentrations (ores) is uneven. The United States and Canada have many of these metals in abundance, but often choose to acquire them from countries that have higher-quality ores or lower costs for the labor to recover them.

The properties of the transition metals make them particularly important to industry. Iron is the main part of steel, a material used for bridges and buildings. Most electric wires and many other electrical devices are made of copper. Copper is also used to make water pipes. Indeed, it would be hard to think of an industry that doesn't make use of transition metals.

Although other transition metals may be less familiar, many of them are important for modern technology. The tiny coil of wire inside incandescent light bulbs is made of tungsten. Platinum is in the catalytic converters that reduce pollution from automobile engines.

For many applications, two or more metals are combined to form an alloy. Alloys can be stronger, less likely to corrode, or easier to shape than pure metals. Steel, which is stronger than the pure iron it contains, often includes other transition metals, such as nickel, chromium, or manganese. Brass, an alloy of copper and zinc, is stronger than either metal alone. Jewelry is often made of an alloy of silver and copper, which is stronger than pure silver.

Rare Earth Elements

The rare earth elements are the elements in the top row of the two rows of metals that are usually shown outside the main body of the periodic table. Taking these elements out of the main body of the table makes the table more compact. The rare earth elements are often referred to as lanthanides because they follow the element lanthanum (La) on the table. They are called rare earth elements because scientists once thought that these elements were available only in tiny amounts in Earth's crust. As mining methods improved, scientists learned that the rare earths were actually not so rare at all—only hard to isolate in pure form.

More and more uses are being found for the rare earth elements. Europium (Eu), for example, is used as a coating for some television tubes. Praseodymium (Pr) provides a protective coating against harmful radiation in the welder's helmet in the photograph on the right.

Rare Earth Elements

DIFFERENTIATE INSTRUCTION

 More Reading Support

C What is the combination of two or more metals called? *alloy*

D Where are the rare earth metals in the table? *in the top row of the rows below the table*

Advanced Have students use the Internet to research and report on the discovery of an element. You might suggest Marie Curie's discovery of polonium and radium or the contributions of Karl Scheele, Sir Humphry Davy, and Bernard Courtois in the discovery of chlorine and iodine.

- Challenge and Extension, p. 40
- Challenge Reading, pp. 43–44

Nonmetals and metalloids have a wide range of properties.

The elements to the right side of the periodic table are called **nonmetals.** As the name implies, the properties of nonmetals tend to be the opposite of those of metals. The properties of nonmetals also tend to vary more from element to element than the properties of the metals do. Many of them are gases at room temperature, and one—bromine—is a liquid. The solid nonmetals often have dull surfaces and cannot be shaped by hammering or drawing into wires. Nonmetals are generally poor conductors of heat and electric current.

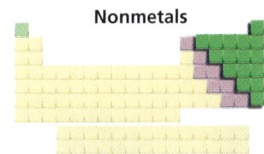
Nonmetals

The main components of the air that you breathe are the nonmetal elements nitrogen and oxygen. Nitrogen is a fairly unreactive element, but oxygen reacts easily to form compounds with many other elements. Burning and rusting are two familiar types of reactions involving oxygen. Compounds containing carbon are essential to living things. Two forms of the element carbon are graphite, which is a soft, slippery black material, and diamond, a hard crystal. Sulfur is a bright yellow powder that can be mined from deposits of the pure element.

Halogens

The elements in Group 17 are commonly known as halogens, from Greek words meaning "forming salts." Halogens are very reactive nonmetals that easily form compounds called salts with many metals. Because they are so reactive, halogens are often used to kill harmful microorganisms. For example, the halogen chlorine is used to clean drinking water and to prevent the growth of algae in swimming pools. Solutions containing iodine are often used in hospitals and doctors' offices to kill germs on skin.

Halogens and Noble Gases

Noble Gases

Group 18 elements are called the noble, or inert, gases because they almost never react with other elements. Argon gas makes up about one percent of the atmosphere. The other noble gases are found in the atmosphere in smaller amounts. Colorful lights, such as those in the photograph on the right, are made by passing an electric current through tubes filled with neon, krypton, xenon, or argon gas. Argon gas also is placed in tungsten filament light bulbs, because it will not react with the hot filament.

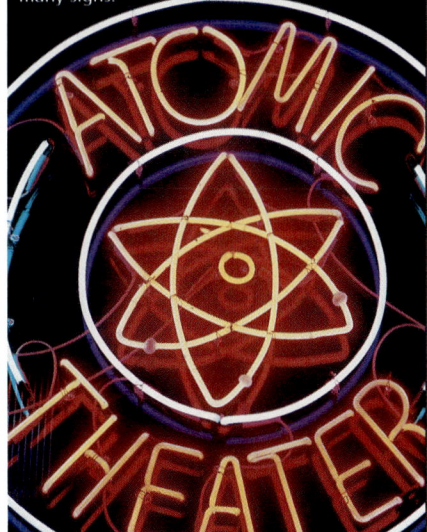
Noble gases produce the light for many signs.

 Where on Earth can you find noble gases?

DIFFERENTIATE INSTRUCTION

 More Reading Support

E What type of elements are on the right of the table? *nonmetals*

F What is true of group 18 elements? *They almost never react with other elements.*

Alternative Assessment Have students create a two-column chart to list the differences between noble gases and halogens. *Halogens: Group 17 in periodic table, very reactive nonmetals that form salt compounds with metals, used to kill harmful microorganisms because they are so reactive. Noble gases: Group 18 in periodic table, almost never react with other elements, used in lighting materials because they are not reactive.*

Develop Critical Thinking

CLASSIFY Have students classify each of the following elements as a metal or a nonmetal. They should be able to explain their classification.

calcium	metal
sulfur	nonmetal
tin	metal
neon	nonmetal
nitrogen	nonmetal
carbon	nonmetal
mercury	metal

Art Connection

Have students look for interesting photographs of "neon" signs. Point out that each noble gas produces a particular color; for example, neon glows reddish orange. A greater variety of colors can be produced by having a glowing gas interact with a coating on the inside of a tube.

Ongoing Assessment

Identify different groups of elements.

Ask: Where in the periodic table are the gases that almost never react with other elements? *Group 18 (noble gases) on the right side* Where in the periodic table are the very reactive nonmetals that easily form salt compounds with metals? *Group 17 (halogens) on the right side*

 Answer: in the colorful lights in many signs

EXPLORE the BIG idea

Revisit "Internet Activity: Periodic Table" on p. 135. Have students review the definition of atomic number, the definition of atomic mass, and the relationship between these measures.

History of Science

Marie Curie (1867–1934) blazed a path for women scientists by making huge contributions to physics and chemistry. Curie was the first woman to win a Nobel Prize in physics (1903, shared) and in chemistry (1911, alone). In 1906, she became the first woman professor at the Paris Sorbonne, one of France's great universities.

Ongoing Assessment

Describe radioactive elements.

Ask: What makes a radioactive isotope unstable? *If the nucleus has too many or too few neutrons, it may become unstable and emit particles and energy.*

 *Answer: radioactivity*

Metalloids

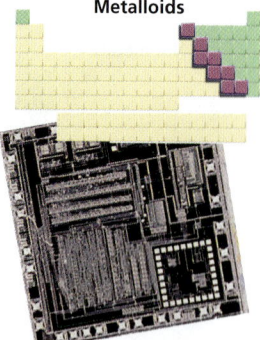

The metalloid silicon is found in sand and in computer microchips.

Radioactive Elements

Metalloids are elements that have properties of both metals and nonmetals. In the periodic table, they lie on either side of a zigzag line separating metals from nonmetals. The most common metalloid is silicon. Silicon atoms are the second most common atoms in Earth's crust.

Metalloids often make up the semiconductors found in electronic devices. Semiconductors are special materials that conduct electricity under some conditions and not under others. Silicon, gallium, and germanium are three semiconductors used in computer chips.

Some atoms can change their identity.

The identity of an element is determined by the number of protons in its nucleus. Chemical changes do not affect the nucleus, so chemical changes don't change one type of atom into another. There are, however, conditions under which the number of protons in a nucleus can change and so change the identity of an atom.

Recall that the nucleus of an atom contains protons and neutrons. Attractive forces between protons and neutrons hold the nucleus together even though protons repel one another. We say an atomic nucleus is stable when these attractive forces keep it together.

Each element has isotopes with different numbers of neutrons. The stability of a nucleus depends on the right balance of protons and neutrons. If there are too few or too many neutrons, the nucleus may become unstable. When this happens, particles are produced from the nucleus of the atom to restore the balance. This change is accompanied by a release of energy.

If the production of particles changes the number of protons, the atom is transformed into an atom of a different element. In the early 1900s, physicist Marie Curie named the process by which atoms produce energy and particles **radioactivity**. Curie was the first person to isolate polonium and radium, two radioactive elements.

An isotope is radioactive if the nucleus has too many or too few neutrons. Most elements have radioactive isotopes, although these isotopes are rare for small atoms. For the heaviest of elements—those beyond bismuth (Bi)—all of the isotopes are radioactive.

Scientists study radioactivity with a device called a Geiger counter. The Geiger counter detects the particles from the breakup of the atomic nucleus with audible clicks. More clicks indicate that more particles are being produced.

 How can an atom of one element change into an atom of a different element?

158 Unit 2: Chemical Interactions

DIFFERENTIATE INSTRUCTION

More Reading Support

G What are metalloids? *elements that have properties of both metals and nonmetals*

H What do radioactive atoms produce? *particles and energy*

Below Level Use wheel-and-spoke diagrams to clarify relationships among element groupings. At the center of one wheel will be metals; spokes will be reactive metals, transition metals, and rare earth elements. At the center of a second wheel will be nonmetals; spokes will be halogens, nonhalogens, and noble gases. The two wheels can be connected by a dotted line labeled *metalloids,* signifying that metalloids bridge the metals and nonmetals. Ask students to list the symbol of each metalloid on the line.

158 Unit 2: **Chemical Interactions**

Uses of Radioactivity in Medicine

The radiation produced from unstable nuclei is used in hospitals to diagnose and treat patients. Some forms of radiation from nuclei are used to destroy harmful tumors inside a person's body without performing an operation. Another medical use of radiation is to monitor the activity of certain organs in the body. A patient is injected with a solution containing a radioactive isotope. Isotopes of a given atom move through the body in the same way whether or not they are radioactive. Doctors detect the particles produced by the radioactive isotopes to determine where and how the body is using the substance.

Although radiation has its benefits, in large doses it is harmful to living things and should be avoided. Radiation can damage or kill cells, and the energy from its particles can burn the skin. Prolonged exposure to radiation has been linked to cancer and other health problems.

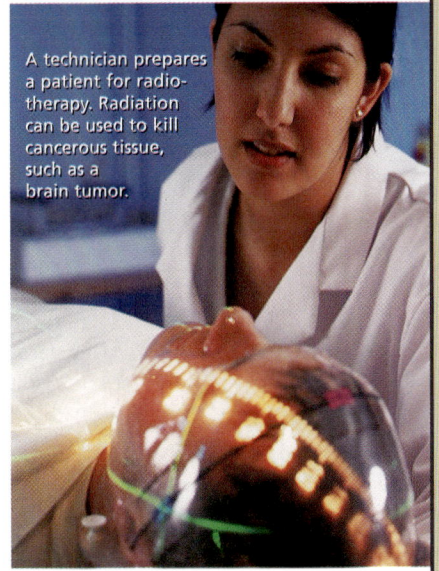

A technician prepares a patient for radiotherapy. Radiation can be used to kill cancerous tissue, such as a brain tumor.

INVESTIGATE Radioactivity

PURPOSE To model how quickly atoms of radioactive elements can change

TIP 30 min. Any common coin will work; all coins should be the same denomination.

WHAT DO YOU THINK? About one-half of the atoms did not change. Two tries will change three-fourths of the atoms. It should take up to seven times for all the atoms to turn. Each time, about half the atoms change.

CHALLENGE Yes; it would take longer to get down to no atoms of the original. The curve of the graph would be the same.

Datasheet, Radioactivity, p. 41

Technology Resources

Customize this student lab as needed or look for an alternative. Print rubrics to assess student lab reports.

Lab Generator CD-ROM

Teaching with Technology

Students can use graphing software or calculators to construct their graphs. Ask them to compare their graphs to the half-life graph pictured on p. 160.

Real World Example

One radioactive element that people often encounter in the natural environment is radon, a gas with a short half-life. Uranium-rich rock and soil emit radon, which can enter homes through the foundations. High levels of radon appear to contribute to lung cancer. What level of radon is safe for humans is a topic of debate and study.

INVESTIGATE Radioactivity

How quickly can atoms change?

PROCEDURE

1. Put 50 pennies in a bag. The pennies represent 50 atoms.
2. Pour out the pennies.
3. Count the number of pennies that landed head side up. These represent atoms whose nuclei changed.
4. Refill the bag with only the pennies that landed tail side up.
5. Repeat steps 2–4 until all of the pennies have landed head side up. Each time you pour out the pennies counts as one turn.
6. Construct a graph with the number of atoms that changed on the y-axis and the number of turns on the x-axis.

SKILL FOCUS Modeling

MATERIALS
- 50 pennies
- bag
- graph paper

TIME 30 minutes

WHAT DO YOU THINK?
- After one turn, how many atoms had changed? had not changed?
- In how many turns did all the atoms change?
- From looking at your graph, what can you conclude about the rate of radioactive change?

CHALLENGE If you used a different number of pennies, would your results be different? In what way?

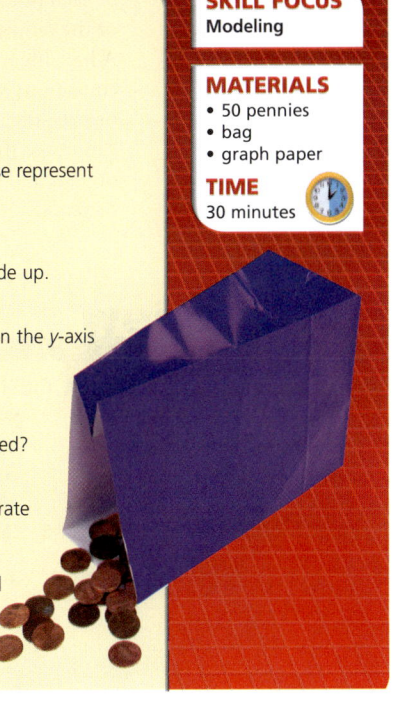

Chapter 5: **Atomic Structure and the Periodic Table** 159

DIFFERENTIATE INSTRUCTION

More Reading Support

I Why should we avoid large doses of radiation?
It harms living things.

Below Level Point out that because atoms are so small, they cannot be counted like heads and tails on a coin. Tell students that scientists have instruments, such as the Geiger counter, that can intercept and count the radiation particles from an unstable element. These instruments are analogous to a baseball backstop that counts the number of balls that hit it; many balls hit it during a highly active "inning," and few during a stable "inning."

Chapter 5 **159**

Teach from Visuals

To help students interpret the graph of radioactive decay, ask: How are the graph and the circles connected? *The circles show pictorially the amount of radioisotope (y-axis) that is left at each time (x-axis).*

Integrate the Sciences

Living things have the same concentration of carbon-14 when they are alive. When they die, organisms stop taking in carbon-14. Knowing how fast carbon-14 decays, scientists can calculate how long ago an organism lived.

Reinforce *the BIG idea*

Have students relate the section to the Big Idea.

 Reinforcing Key Concepts, p. 42

5.3 ASSESS & RETEACH

Assess

 Section 5.3 Quiz, p. 5

Reteach

Distribute copies of the periodic table to groups of students. Suggest they flip through the text in this section to help them identify the following: reactive metals *(Groups 1 and 2)*, transition metals *(Groups 3–12)*, rare earth elements *(top row of the two rows of metals outside main body of periodic table)*, nonmetals *(upper right corner of table)*, halogens *(Group 17)*, noble gases *(Group 18)*, and metalloids *(upper right corner between metals and nonmetals; B, Si, Ge, As, Sb, Te, At)*.

Technology Resources

Have students visit ClassZone.com for reteaching of Key Concepts.

 CONTENT REVIEW

 CONTENT REVIEW CD-ROM

160   Unit 2: **Chemical Interactions**

VISUALIZATION
CLASSZONE.COM
Watch how a radioactive element decays over time.

Radioactive Decay

Radioactive atoms produce energy and particles from their nuclei. The identity of these atoms changes because the number of protons changes. This process is known as radioactive decay. Over time, all of the atoms of a radioactive isotope will change into atoms of another element.

Radioactive decay occurs at a steady rate that is characteristic of the particular isotope. The amount of time that it takes for one-half of the atoms in a particular sample to decay is called the **half-life** of the isotope. For example, if you had 1000 atoms of a radioactive isotope with a half-life of 1 year, 500 of the atoms would change into another element over the course of a year. In the next year, 250 more atoms would decay. The illustration to the right shows how the amount of the original isotope would decrease over time.

The half-life is a characteristic of each isotope and is independent of the amount of material. A half-life is also not affected by conditions such as temperature or pressure. Half-lives of isotopes can range from a small fraction of a second to many billions of years.

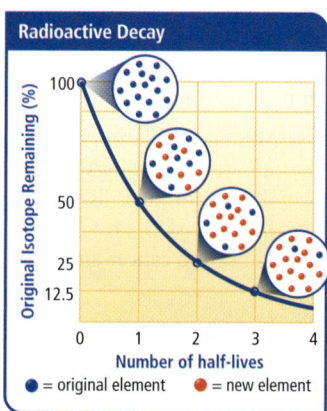

Half-Lives of Selected Elements

Isotope	Half-Life
Uranium-238	4,510,000,000 years
Carbon-14	5,730 years
Radon-222	3.82 days
Lead-214	27 minutes
Polonium-214	.00016 seconds

5.3 Review

KEY CONCEPTS

1. What are the three main classes of elements in the periodic table?
2. What are the major characteristics of metals?
3. How can an atom of one element change to an atom of another element?

CRITICAL THINKING

4. **Compare** Use the periodic table to determine whether a carbon or a fluorine atom would be more reactive.
5. **Calculate** What fraction of a radioactive sample remains after three half-lives?

CHALLENGE

6. **Analyze** Why do you think the noble gases were among the last of the naturally occurring elements to be discovered?

160   Unit 2: **Chemical Interactions**

ANSWERS

1. metals, metalloids, and nonmetals

2. Metals usually are shiny, easily bent or drawn into a wire, and good conductors of electricity and heat.

3. Radioactive decay causes the number of protons in the nucleus to change.

4. fluorine

5. one-eighth

6. The noble gases were hard to notice, because they don't often combine or react with other elements.

MATH in SCIENCE

SKILL: USING SCIENTIFIC NOTATION

Numbers with Many Zeros

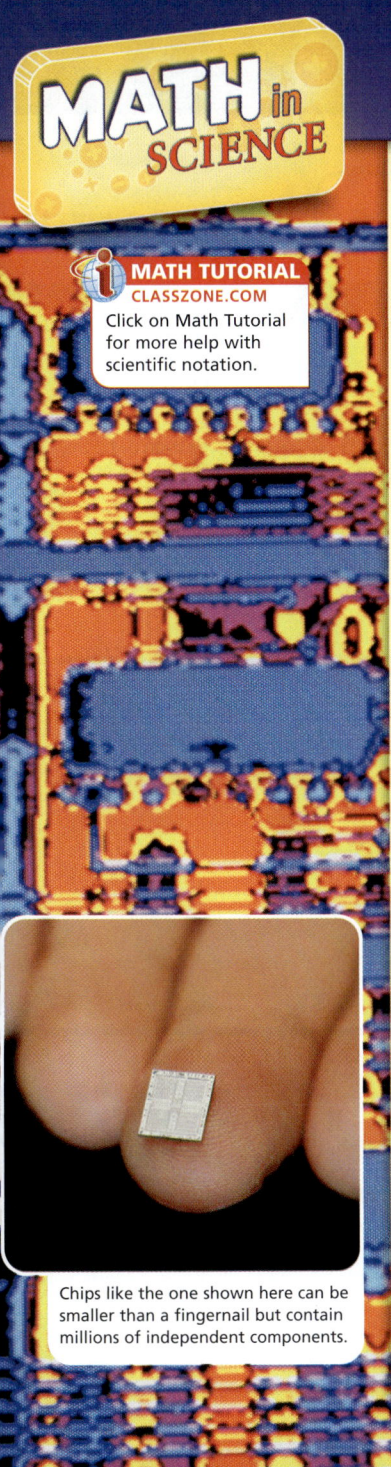

Click on Math Tutorial for more help with scientific notation.

Chips like the one shown here can be smaller than a fingernail but contain millions of independent components.

Semiconductor devices are at the heart of the modern personal computer. Today tiny chips can contain more than 42,000,000 connections and perform about 3,000,000,000 calculations per second. Computers have little problem working with such large numbers. Scientists, however, use a scientific notation as a shorthand way to write large numbers. Scientific notation expresses a very large or very small number as the product of a number between 1 and 10 and a power of 10.

Example

Large Number How would you express the number 6,400,000,000—the approximate population of the world—in scientific notation?

(1) Look at the number and count how many spaces you would need to move the decimal point to get a number between 1 and 10.

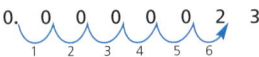

6,400,000,000 (positions 9 8 7 6 5 4 3 2 1)

(2) Place the decimal point in the space and multiply the number by the appropriate power of 10. The power of 10 will be equivalent to the number of spaces you moved the decimal point.

ANSWER 6.4×10^9

Small Number How would you express 0.0000023 in scientific notation?

(1) Count the number of places you need to move the decimal point to get a number between 1 and 10. This time you move the decimal point to the right, not the left.

0.0000023 (positions 1 2 3 4 5 6)

(2) The power of 10 you need to multiply this number by is still equal to the number of places you moved the decimal point. Place a negative sign in front of it to indicate that you moved the decimal point to the right.

ANSWER 2.3×10^{-6}

Answer the following questions.

1. Express the following numbers in scientific notation:
   (a) 75,000   (b) 54,000,000,000   (c) 0.0000064

2. Express these numbers in decimal form:
   (a) 6.0×10^{24} (b) 7.4×10^{22} (c) 5.7×10^{-10}

CHALLENGE What is 2.2×10^{22} subtracted from 4.6×10^{22}?

Chapter 5: **Atomic Structure and the Periodic Table** 161

ANSWERS

1. 7.5×10^4; 5.4×10^{10}; 6.4×10^{-6}
2. 6,000,000,000,000,000,000,000,000; 74,000,000,000,000,000,000,000; 0.00000000057

CHALLENGE 2.4×10^{22}

MATH IN SCIENCE
Math Skills Practice for Science

Set Learning Goal
To express very large or very small numbers using scientific notation

Present the Science
Scientists often work with extreme numbers. A good example is the number indicating the size of an atom—or conversely, the number of atoms in a sample of matter. Writing out all the zeros would be time-consuming and very prone to error. Scientific notation avoids confusion.

Develop Number Sense
- Make sure students distinguish between the procedures for handling large numbers and small numbers. In large numbers, the zeros are strung out to the right, so the decimal is moved to the left. In small numbers, the procedure is just the reverse.
- For the Challenge question, prompt students to compare the exponents of 10 in the two scientific notations.

DIFFERENTIATION TIP Some students might benefit from counting the decimal places themselves. Write the number 6,400,000,000 or 0.0000023 on the board, leaving space between the numbers. Students can use colored chalk (or a colored dry erase marker) to count off the decimal places.

Close
Have students contrast the procedures for expressing a large number and a small decimal number in scientific notation. *For the large number, you move the decimal to the left and use a positive exponent; for the small number, you move the decimal to the right and use a negative exponent.*

- Math Support, p. 48
- Math Practice, p. 49

Technology Resources
Students can visit ClassZone.com for practice in scientific notation.

MATH TUTORIAL

CHAPTER 5 • REVIEW

BACK TO

Have students look back at the atoms photograph of nickel on pp. 134–135. Ask what an even more highly magnified photograph might show. *individual protons and neutrons, but probably not electrons*

◐ KEY CONCEPTS SUMMARY

SECTION 5.1
Ask: How is the mass of an atom distributed? *most is concentrated in nucleus*
Ask: Why is an electron cloud pictured, rather than individual electrons? *Electrons are about 2000 times smaller than protons, and move very quickly around the nucleus. Since it is not possible to determine their exact positions, the electron cloud represents them.*

SECTION 5.2
Ask: Suppose an element is brittle and a poor conductor of electricity. To find another element with similar properties, would you look up and down or side to side in the periodic chart? *up and down*

SECTION 5.3
Ask: Would an element near the upper-right corner of the periodic table be shiny and easily formed into wire? Why? *No; those are properties of metals, and the elements near the upper-right corner of the periodic table are nonmetals.*

Review Concepts

- Big Idea Flow Chart, p. T1
- Chapter Outline, pp. T7–T8

---

5 Chapter Review

the BIG idea

A substance's atomic structure determines its physical and chemical properties.

CONTENT REVIEW
CLASSZONE.COM

◐ KEY CONCEPTS SUMMARY

① Atoms are the smallest form of elements.
- All matter is made of the atoms of approximately 100 elements.
- Atoms are made of protons, neutrons, and electrons.
- Different elements are made of different atoms.
- Atoms form ions by gaining or losing electrons.

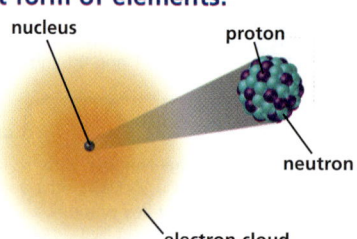

VOCABULARY
proton p. 139
neutron p. 139
nucleus p. 139
electron p. 139
atomic number p. 140
atomic mass number p. 140
isotope p. 140
ion p. 142

② Elements make up the periodic table.
- Elements can be organized by similarities.
- The periodic table organizes the atoms of the elements by properties and atomic number.

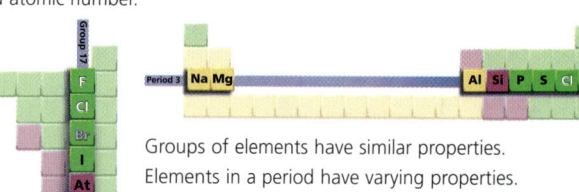

Groups of elements have similar properties.
Elements in a period have varying properties.

VOCABULARY
atomic mass p. 145
periodic table p. 146
group p. 150
period p. 150

③ The periodic table is a map of the elements.
- The periodic table has distinct regions.
- Most elements are metals.
- Nonmetals and metalloids have a wide range of properties.
- Some atoms can change their identity through radioactive decay.

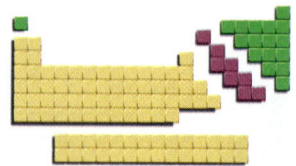

metal   metalloid   nonmetal

VOCABULARY
reactive p. 154
metal p. 155
nonmetal p. 157
metalloid p. 158
radioactivity p. 158
half-life p. 160

162 Unit 2: Chemical Interactions

Technology Resources

Have students visit **ClassZone.com** or use the CD-ROM for a cumulative review of concepts.

 CONTENT REVIEW

 CONTENT REVIEW CD-ROM

Engage students in a whole-class interactive review of Key Concepts. Edit content as you wish.

 POWER PRESENTATIONS

Reviewing Vocabulary

Describe how the vocabulary terms in the following pairs are related to each other. Explain the relationship in a one- or two-sentence answer. Underline each vocabulary term in your answer.

1. isotope, nucleus
2. atomic mass, atomic number
3. electron, proton
4. atomic number, atomic mass number
5. group, period
6. metals, nonmetals
7. radioactivity, half-life

Reviewing Key Concepts

Multiple Choice *Choose the letter of the best answer.*

8. The central part of an atom is called the
   a. electron   c. proton
   b. nucleus   d. neutron

9. The electric charge on a proton is
   a. positive   c. neutral
   b. negative   d. changing

10. The number of protons in the nucleus is the
    a. atomic mass   c. atomic number
    b. isotope   d. half-life

11. Nitrogen has atomic number 7. An isotope of nitrogen containing seven neutrons would be
    a. nitrogen-13   c. nitrogen-15
    b. nitrogen-14   d. nitrogen-16

12. How does the size of a negative ion compare to the size of the atom that formed it?
    a. It's smaller.
    b. It's larger.
    c. It's the same size.
    d. It varies.

13. The modern periodic table is organized by
    a. size of atom
    b. atomic mass
    c. number of neutrons
    d. atomic number

14. Elements in a group have
    a. a wide range of chemical properties
    b. the same atomic radius
    c. similar chemical properties
    d. the same number of protons

15. Elements in a period have
    a. a wide range of chemical properties
    b. the same atomic radius
    c. similar chemical properties
    d. the same number of protons

16. From left to right in a period, the size of atoms
    a. increases   c. remains the same
    b. decreases   d. shows no pattern

17. The elements in Group 1 of the periodic table are commonly called the
    a. alkali metals   c. alkaline earth metals
    b. transition metals   d. rare earth metals

18. The isotope nitrogen-13 has a half-life of 10 minutes. If you start with 40 grams of this isotope, how many grams will you have left after 20 minutes?
    a. 10   c. 20
    b. 15   d. 30

Short Answer *Write a short answer to each question. You may need to consult a periodic table.*

19. Rubidium forms the positive ion Rb^+. Is this ion larger or smaller than the neutral atom? Explain.

20. How can you find the number of neutrons in the isotope nitrogen-16?

21. Explain how density varies across and up and down the periodic table.

22. Place these elements in order from least reactive to most reactive: nickel (Ni), xenon (Xe), lithium (Li). How did you determine the order?

Chapter 5: **Atomic Structure and the Periodic Table** 163

ASSESSMENT RESOURCES

UNIT ASSESSMENT BOOK
- Chapter Test A, pp. 6–9
- Chapter Test B, pp. 10–13
- Chapter Test C, pp. 14–17
- Alternative Assessment, pp. 18–19

SPANISH ASSESSMENT BOOK
Spanish Chapter Test, pp. 233–236

Technology Resources

Edit test items and answer choices.

 Test Generator CD-ROM

Visit **ClassZone.com** to extend test practice.

 Test Practice

Reviewing Vocabulary

1. An <u>isotope</u> of an element has a different number of neutrons in its <u>nucleus</u> than another atom of that element.

2. The <u>atomic mass</u> of an element is basically the mass of the protons and neutrons in the nucleus, whereas the <u>atomic number</u> is the number of protons in the nucleus.

3. An <u>electron</u> is a particle with a negative charge, and a <u>proton</u> is a particle with a positive charge.

4. <u>Atomic number</u> is the number of protons in a nucleus, whereas <u>atomic mass number</u> is the number of protons and neutrons in the nucleus.

5. A <u>group</u> is a vertical columns in the periodic table that contains elements with similar properties, whereas a <u>period</u> is a horizontal row of elements with varying properties.

6. <u>Metals</u> are usually solids at room temperature, while <u>nonmetals</u> are usually gas or liquid at room temperature.

7. <u>Radioactivity</u> is measured in <u>half-life</u>, the amount of time it takes for one-half of a substance's atoms to decay.

Reviewing Key Concepts

8. b   14. c
9. a   15. a
10. c   16. b
11. b   17. a
12. b   18. a
13. d

19. smaller because the atom lost an electron

20. Subtract its atomic number from 16.

21. Density generally increases as one moves down a group. Elements at the ends of a period are least dense, and elements in the middle are most dense.

22. Xenon, nickel, lithium. Xenon is a noble gas and thus very nonreactive. Nickel is a transition metal and so not very reactive. Lithium is an alkali metal and thus very reactive.

Chapter 5 **163**

Thinking Critically

23. B, C, and F are metals; they look shiny and conduct electricity. E is a metalloid; it is a semiconductor. A and D are nonmetals; they do not have any of the properties of metals.

24. a cube of A

25. Element E; it is a semiconductor.

26. The decreased occurrence of thyroid disease is linked to increased ingestion of iodine.

27. It is larger.

28. because halogens are the most reactive nonmetals

29. 120 neutrons and 80 protons

30. larger

31. 12.5 g

32. thorium

the BIG idea

33. Nickel is a smooth, shiny metal. When magnified enough to see individual atoms, however, we see that it can appear bumpy and rough.

34. Remove three protons from the nucleus of a lead atom to make it into a gold atom (82 − 3 = 79). You might need to remove some neutrons to stabilize the new atom.

35. Atoms are arranged in the periodic table by their atomic number, which is the number of protons in an atom's nucleus. The structure of an atom's nucleus determines its place in the periodic table.

UNIT PROJECTS

Give students the appropriate Unit Project worksheets from the URB for their projects. Both directions and rubrics can be used as a guide.

 Unit Projects, pp. 5–10

Thinking Critically

The table below lists some properties of six elements. Use the information and your knowledge of the properties of elements to answer the next three questions.

Element	Appearance	Density (g/cm³)	Conducts Electricity
A	dark purple crystals	4.93	no
B	shiny silvery solid	0.97	yes
C	shiny silvery solid	22.65	yes
D	yellow powder	2.07	no
E	shiny gray solid	5.32	semiconductor
F	shiny bluish solid	8.91	yes

23. **ANALYZE** Based on the listed properties, identify each of the elements as a metal, nonmetal, or metalloid.

24. **APPLY** Which would weigh more: a cube of element A or a same-sized cube of element D?

25. **HYPOTHESIZE** Which element(s) do you think you might find in electronic devices? Why?

26. **HYPOTHESIZE** The thyroid gland, located in your throat, secretes hormones. In 1924 iodine was added to table salt. As more and more Americans used iodized salt, the number of cases of thyroid diseases decreased. Write a hypothesis that explains the observed decrease in thyroid-related diseases.

27. **INFER** How does the size of a beryllium (Be) atom compare with the size of an oxygen (O) atom?

28. **PREDICT** Although noble gases do not naturally react with other elements, xenon and krypton have been made to react with halogens such as chlorine in laboratories. Why are the halogens most likely to react with the noble gases?

Below is an element square from the periodic table. Use it to answer the next two questions.

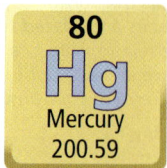

29. **CALCULATE** One of the more common isotopes of mercury is mercury-200. How many protons and neutrons are in the nucleus of mercury-200?

30. **INFER** Cadmium occupies the square directly above mercury on the periodic table. Is a cadmium atom larger or smaller than a mercury atom?

31. **CALCULATE** An isotope has a half-life of 40 minutes. How much of a 100-gram sample would remain unchanged after two hours?

32. **APPLY** When a uranium atom with 92 protons and 146 neutrons undergoes radioactive decay, it produces a particle that consists of two protons and two neutrons from its nucleus. Into which element is the uranium atom transformed?

the BIG idea

33. **ANALYZE** Look again at the photograph on pages 134–135. Answer the question again, using what you have learned in the chapter.

34. **DRAW CONCLUSIONS** Suppose you've been given the ability to take apart and assemble atoms. How could you turn lead into gold?

35. **ANALYZE** Explain how the structure of an atom determines its place in the periodic table.

UNIT PROJECTS

If you are doing a unit project, make a folder for your project. Include in your folder a list of the resources you will need, the date on which the project is due, and a schedule to track your progress. Begin gathering data.

MONITOR AND RETEACH

If students still have difficulty with atomic mass number and atomic mass, create a simple atomic diagram clearly showing all the protons and neutrons in the nucleus. Have students find atomic number by counting protons, and find atomic mass by counting neutrons and protons.

To review isotopes, draw two more atomic diagrams, in which only the number of neutrons varies from the original diagram. Then have students average the atomic masses of the isotopes.

Students may benefit from summarizing sections of the chapter.

 Summarizing the Chapter, pp. 68–69

Standardized Test Practice

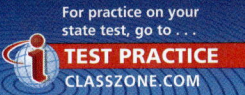

For practice on your state test, go to...
TEST PRACTICE
CLASSZONE.COM

Interpreting Tables

The table below shows part of the periodic table of elements.

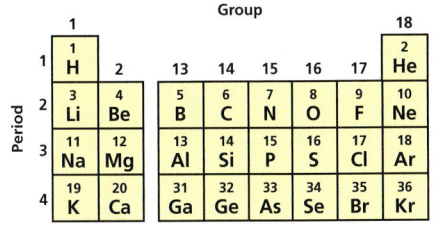

Answer the questions based on the information given in the table.

1. What does the number above the symbol for each element represent?
   a. Its number of isotopes
   b. Its atomic number
   c. Its number of neutrons
   d. Its atomic mass

2. The atom of what element is in Period 4, Group 13?
   a. Na   c. Al
   b. Ga   d. K

3. What do the elements on the far right of the table (He, Ne, Ar, and Kr) have in common?
   a. They do not generally react with other elements.
   b. They are in liquids under normal conditions.
   c. They are metals that rust easily.
   d. They are very reactive gases.

4. How many electrons does a neutral chlorine (Cl) atom contain?
   a. 16   c. 18
   b. 17   d. 19

5. If a sodium (Na) atom loses one electron to form a positive ion, how many electrons would lithium (Li) lose to form a positive ion?
   a. 0   c. 2
   b. 1   d. 3

6. If a fluorine (F) atom gains one electron to form a negative ion, how many electrons would bromine (Br) gain to form a negative ion?
   a. 0   c. 2
   b. 1   d. 3

Extended Response

Answer the following two questions in detail. Include some of the terms shown in the word box at right. Underline each term you use in your answer.

| electron | nucleus | proton |
| isotope | neutron | radioactivity |

7. Democritus was an ancient Greek philosopher who claimed that all matter was made of tiny particles he called atoms. Democritus said that all atoms were made of the same material. The objects of the world differed because each was made of atoms of different sizes and shapes. How does the modern view of atoms differ from this ancient view? How is it similar?

8. Half-life is a measure of the time it takes half of the radioactive atoms in a substance to decay into other atoms. If you know how much radioactive material an object had to begin with, how could you use half-life to determine its age now?

Interpreting Tables

1. b   3. a   5. b
2. b   4. b   6. b

Extended Response

7. RUBRIC
4 points for a response that correctly answers the question and uses the following terms accurately:
- protons
- neutrons
- electrons

Sample: Democritus' atomic theory is like the atomic theory of today because we now know that all atoms are made of the same stuff—<u>protons, neutrons, and electrons</u>—and that atoms are different sizes. However, we no longer think, as Democritus did, that atoms are shaped differently.

3 points correctly answers the question and uses two terms accurately
2 points correctly answers the question and uses one term accurately
1 point correctly answers the question or uses one term accurately

8. RUBRIC
4 points for a response that correctly answers the question and uses the following terms accurately:
- radioactive
- isotope

Sample: One way to figure it out is by seeing how much of the new element is there and how much of the <u>radioactive isotope</u> is left, and then using the ratio to find how many years since the organism died.

3 points correctly answers the question and uses one term accurately
2 points partly answers the question and uses one term accurately
1 point partly answers the question or uses one term accurately

METACOGNITIVE ACTIVITY

Have students answer the following questions in their **Science Notebook:**

1. What questions do you still have about atomic structure?
2. Which topics in this chapter would you like to learn more about?
3. What have you learned in this chapter that can be applied to your Unit Project?

CHAPTER 6: Chemical Bonds and Compounds

Physical Science
UNIFYING PRINCIPLES

PRINCIPLE 1
Matter is made of particles too small to see.

PRINCIPLE 2
Matter changes form and moves from place to place.

PRINCIPLE 3
Energy changes from one form to another, but it cannot be created or destroyed.

PRINCIPLE 4
Physical forces affect the movement of all matter on Earth and throughout the universe.

Unit 2: Chemical Interactions
BIG IDEAS

CHAPTER 5
Atomic Structure and the Periodic Table
A substance's atomic structure determines its physical and chemical properties.

CHAPTER 6
Chemical Bonds and Compounds
The properties of compounds depend on their atoms and chemical bonds.

CHAPTER 7
Chemical Reactions
Chemical reactions form new substances by breaking and making chemical bonds.

CHAPTER 8
Solutions
When substances dissolve to form a solution, the properties of the mixture change.

CHAPTER 9
Carbon in Life and Materials
Carbon is essential to living things and to modern materials.

CHAPTER 6 KEY CONCEPTS

SECTION 1
Elements combine to form compounds.
1. Compounds have different properties from the elements that make them.
2. Atoms combine in predictable numbers.

SECTION 2
Chemical bonds hold compounds together.
1. Chemical bonds between atoms involve electrons.
2. Atoms can transfer electrons.
3. Atoms can share electrons.
4. Chemical bonds give all materials their structures.

SECTION 3
Substances' properties depend on their bonds.
1. Metals have unique bonds.
2. Ionic and covalent bonds give compounds certain properties.
3. Bonds can make the same element look different.

 The Big Idea Flow Chart is available on p. T9 in the **UNIT TRANSPARENCY BOOK**.

Previewing Content

SECTION

 Elements combine to form compounds. pp. 169–174

1. **Compounds have different properties from the elements that make them.**
   A compound is a combination of two or more elements. What makes a compound different from a mixture is that atoms of the elements in a compound are held together by chemical bonds. The properties of a compound are often quite different from the properties of the elements that make it.

2. **Atoms combine in predictable numbers.**
   Compounds have a definite composition. Each compound contains a specific ratio of atoms held together by chemical bonds. The compound formed when one nitrogen atom combines with one oxygen atom is different from the compound formed when two nitrogen atoms combine with one oxygen atom. Compounds are not like simple mixtures, which have no definite combination.

   A chemical compound is represented by a **chemical formula**. Chemical formulas use the symbols for the elements to show the different elements that make up a compound. To show the ratios of the atoms of those elements in the compound, subscripts are used. A **subscript** is a number written to the right of the chemical symbol and slightly below the line. Carbon dioxide, for example, has two oxygen atoms for each carbon atom. The chemical formula for carbon dioxide is therefore CO_2. In the table below, notice the ratios of the atoms in each compound.

Compound Name	Atomic Ratio	Chemical Formula
Hydrogen chloride	1:1	HCl
Water	2:1	H_2O
Ammonia	1:3	NH_3
Methane	1:4	CH_4
Propane	3:8	C_3H_8

Different compounds, such as H_2O and H_2O_2, can be composed of the same elements. Because they are different compounds, they have different properties.

SECTION

 Chemical bonds hold compounds together. pp. 175–183

1. **Chemical bonds between atoms involve electrons.**
   Chemical bonds are the glue holding the atoms in compounds together. Chemical bonds are the result of interactions between the electron clouds of two or more atoms.

2. **Atoms can transfer electrons.**
   Ions are formed when atoms gain or lose electrons. When one atom loses an electron, another atom picks up that electron, forming a negative and positive ion pair. A positive ion is attracted to a negative ion. This attraction is called an **ionic bond**.

   Ionic bonds produce large crystal networks of atoms, because the attraction between the positive and negative ions acts in all directions. In an ionic compound, positive ions are attracted to all negative ions, and negative ions are attracted to all positive ions.

   Ionic compounds bear the name of the positive ion followed by the name of the negative ion, with the suffix –*ide*. The ionic compound made of lithium and chlorine is lithium chloride.

3. **Atoms can share electrons.**
   Atoms that share a pair of electrons have what is called a **covalent bond**. Atoms form covalent bonds because they are more energetically stable when they have a certain number of electrons around their nuclei. Covalent bonds can form between two atoms of the same element or two atoms of different elements. A **molecule** is a group of atoms held together by covalent bonds. It has no electrical charge.

   In some cases, two atoms can form as many as four covalent bonds. Most often, the electrons shared in a covalent bond spend more time closer to one of the nuclei than the other. When electrons stay much closer to one nucleus than the other, this is a **polar covalent bond**.

4. **Chemical bonds give all materials their structures.**
   The shape of the crystal formed by an ionic compound depends on the ratio, shapes, and sizes of the ions. Covalent compounds do not form crystals; they form individual molecules.

   Molecules have characteristic shapes, or molecular structures. Molecular structure affects many properties of the compounds.

 MISCONCEPTION DATABASE
CLASSZONE.COM Background on student misconceptions

Common Misconceptions

PHYSICAL VERSUS CHEMICAL COMBINATIONS Students might think that chemical combinations are the same as physical combinations. For chemical compounds to be created, chemical bonds must be formed.

 This misconception is addressed on p. 176.

Chapter 6: **Chemical Bonds and Compounds** 165B

Previewing Content

SECTION 3 **Substances' properties depend on their bonds.** pp. 184–189

1. **Metals have unique bonds.**
   Metal atoms share electrons in all directions with other metal atoms in a type of bond called a **metallic bond.** The figure shows how the electrons in a metal are shared by many metal atoms.

   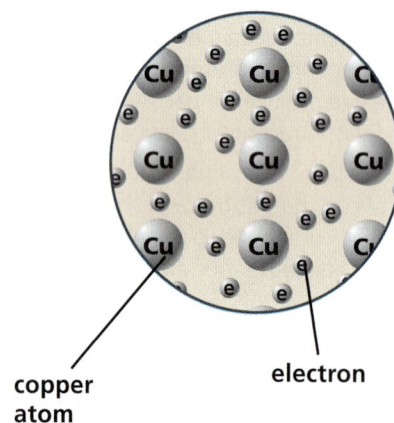

   copper atom   electron

   Properties of metals are determined by the mobility of the electrons in a metallic bond. These properties include conductivity, ductility, and malleability.

2. **Ionic and covalent bonds give compounds certain properties.**
   Ions are tightly locked into place in the structure of a crystal, so ionic bonds are difficult to break. Ionic compounds generally
   - have high melting and boiling points
   - are hard and brittle and do not conduct electricity when a solid
   - break up into negative and positive ions when dissolved and will conduct an electric current in solution

   The molecules of covalent compounds are not held together as tightly.
   - Boiling and melting points of covalent compounds are relatively low.
   - Molecules stay intact when dissolved in water.
   - Molecule size and shape affect properties also.

3. **Bonds can make the same element look different.**
   Different forms of the same element, called allotropes, can result from different covalent bonds. Carbon forms three different allotropes, all with different properties: diamond, graphite, and fullerene.

165C Unit 2: **Chemical Interactions**

Previewing Labs

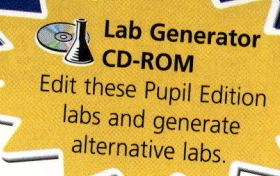

EXPLORE the BIG idea

Mixing It Up, p. 167 Students observe that the properties of a combination differ from the properties of the components.	**TIME** 10 minutes **MATERIALS** red and yellow modeling compound
The Shape of Things, p. 167 Students observe the crystal structure of an ionic compound, salt.	**TIME** 10 minutes **MATERIALS** table salt, dark paper, hand lens
Internet Activity: Bonding, p. 167 Students are introduced to differences in ionic and covalent bonding.	**TIME** 20 minutes **MATERIALS** computer with Internet access

SECTION 1

EXPLORE Compounds, p. 169 Students compare the properties of a compound with those of the elements that compose it.	**TIME** 10 minutes **MATERIALS** carbon, beaker of water, sugar, test tube, test-tube holder, candle, matches
INVESTIGATE Element Ratios, p. 171 Students model a compound and determine the ratio of its "elements." Modeling Compounds Datasheet	**TIME** 20 minutes **MATERIALS** nuts and bolts, Modeling Compounds Datasheet

SECTION 2

INVESTIGATE Crystals, p. 181 Students observe how a crystal grows over a period of time.	**TIME** 30 minutes **MATERIALS** crystal-growing substance (sugar, table salt, alum, or copper sulfate), 2 glass beakers, hot tap water, stirring stick, cotton string, paper clip, pencil, hand lens

SECTION 3

EXPLORE Bonds in Metals, p. 184 Students examine conductivity of metals.	**TIME** 10 minutes **MATERIALS** masking tape, 3 6-inch pieces of copper wire, D-cell battery, light bulb and holder, objects to test
CHAPTER INVESTIGATION **Chemical Bonds,** pp. 188–189 Students investigate properties of substances with different types of bonds.	**TIME** 40 minutes **MATERIALS** 3 wire leads with alligator clips; battery; zinc strip; copper strip; light bulb and socket; 20 grams each of Epsom salts, sugar, and iron filings; 3 plastic cups; distilled water; beaker; constuction paper; hand lens; plastic spoon; 3 test tubes; test-tube rack; candle; matches; wire test-tube holder

 Additional INVESTIGATION, Weird Water, A, B, & C, pp. 119–127; Teacher Instructions, pp. 329–330

Chapter 6: **Chemical Bonds and Compounds** 165D

Previewing Chapter Resources

	INTEGRATED TECHNOLOGY	LABS AND ACTIVITIES
CHAPTER 6 **Chemical Bonds and Compounds**	**CLASSZONE.COM** • eEdition Plus • EasyPlanner • Misconception Database • Content Review • Test Practice • Visualization • Resource Centers • Internet Activity: Bonding • Math Tutorial **SCILINKS.ORG**	 **CD-ROMS** • eEdition • EasyPlanner • Power Presentations • Content Review • Lab Generator • Test Generator **AUDIO CDS** • Audio Readings • Audio Readings in Spanish	EXPLORE the Big Idea, p. 167 • Mixing It Up • The Shape of Things • Internet Activity: Bonding **UNIT RESOURCE BOOK** Unit Projects, pp. 5–10 **Lab Generator CD-ROM** Generate customized labs.
SECTION 1 **Elements combine to form compounds.** pp. 169–174 Time: 2 periods (1 block) Lesson Plan, pp. 70–71	• **RESOURCE CENTER,** Chemical Formulas • **MATH TUTORIAL** **UNIT TRANSPARENCY BOOK** • Big Idea Flow Chart, p. T9 • Daily Vocabulary Scaffolding, p. T10 • Note-Taking Model, p. T11 • 3-Minute Warm-Up, p. T12	• EXPLORE Compounds, p. 169 • INVESTIGATE Element Ratios, p. 171 • Math in Science, p. 174 **UNIT RESOURCE BOOK** • Modeling Compounds Datasheet, p. 79 • Datasheet, Element Ratios, p. 80 • Math Support, p. 108 • Math Practice, p. 109
SECTION 2 **Chemical bonds hold compounds together.** pp. 175–183 Time: 2 periods (1 block) Lesson Plan, pp. 82–83	• **VISUALIZATION,** Polar Electron Clouds **UNIT TRANSPARENCY BOOK** • Daily Vocabulary Scaffolding, p. T10 • 3-Minute Warm-Up, p. T12 • "Comparing Bonds" Visual, p. T14	• INVESTIGATE Crystals, p. 181 • Think Science, p. 183 **UNIT RESOURCE BOOK** Datasheet, Crystals, p. 91
SECTION 3 **Substances' properties depend on their bonds.** pp. 184–189 Time: 4 periods (2 blocks) Lesson Plan, pp. 93–94	• **RESOURCE CENTER,** Properties of Ionic and Covalent Compounds **UNIT TRANSPARENCY BOOK** • Big Idea Flow Chart, p. T9 • Daily Vocabulary Scaffolding, p. T10 • 3-Minute Warm-Up, p. T13 • Chapter Outline, pp. T15–T16	• EXPLORE Bonds in Metals, p. 184 • CHAPTER INVESTIGATION, Chemical Bonds, pp. 188–189 **UNIT RESOURCE BOOK** • CHAPTER INVESTIGATION, Chemical Bonds, A, B, & C, pp. 110–118 • Additional INVESTIGATION, Weird Water, A, B, & C, pp. 119–127

165E   Unit 2: **Chemical Interactions**

KEY TO ICONS 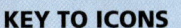 CD/CD-ROM  Teacher Edition  UNIT TRANSPARENCY BOOK 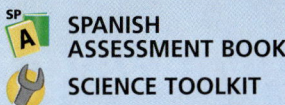 SPANISH ASSESSMENT BOOK

 INTERNET Pupil Edition UNIT RESOURCE BOOK UNIT ASSESSMENT BOOK SCIENCE TOOLKIT

READING AND REINFORCEMENT

ASSESSMENT

STANDARDS

- Description Wheel, B20–21
- Main Idea and Detail Notes, C37
- Daily Vocabulary Scaffolding, H1–8

 UNIT RESOURCE BOOK
- Vocabulary Practice, pp. 105–106
- Decoding Support, p. 107
- Summarizing the Chapter, pp. 128–129

- Chapter Review, pp. 191–192
- Standardized Test Practice, p. 193

 UNIT ASSESSMENT BOOK
- Diagnostic Test, pp. 20–21
- Chapter Test, A, B, & C, pp. 25–36
- Alternative Assessment, pp. 37–38

 Spanish Chapter Test, pp. 237–240

National Standards
A.2–8, A.9.a–c, A.9.e–f, B.1.b

See p. 166 for the standards.

 Audio Readings CD
Listen to Pupil Edition.

 Audio Readings in Spanish CD
Listen to Pupil Edition in Spanish.

 Test Generator CD-ROM
Generate customized tests.

 Lab Generator CD-ROM
Rubrics for Labs

 UNIT RESOURCE BOOK
- Reading Study Guide, A & B, pp. 72–75
- Spanish Reading Study Guide, pp. 76–77
- Challenge and Extension, p. 78
- Reinforcing Key Concepts, p. 81

 Ongoing Assessment, pp. 170, 172–173

 Section 6.1 Review, p. 173

 UNIT ASSESSMENT BOOK
Section 6.1 Quiz, p. 22

National Standards
A.2–8, A.9.a–c, A.9.e–f, B.1.b

 UNIT RESOURCE BOOK
- Reading Study Guide, A & B, pp. 84–87
- Spanish Reading Study Guide, pp. 88–89
- Challenge and Extension, p. 90
- Reinforcing Key Concepts, p. 92
- Challenge Reading, pp. 103–104

 Ongoing Assessment, pp. 175–176, 179–180, 182

 Section 6.2 Review, p. 182

 UNIT ASSESSMENT BOOK
Section 6.2 Quiz, p. 23

National Standards
A.2–7, A.9.a–b, A.9.e–f

 UNIT RESOURCE BOOK
- Reading Study Guide, A & B, pp. 95–98
- Spanish Reading Study Guide, pp. 99–100
- Challenge and Extension, p. 101
- Reinforcing Key Concepts, p. 102

 Ongoing Assessment, pp. 184–186

 Section 6.3 Review, p. 187

 UNIT ASSESSMENT BOOK
Section 6.3 Quiz, p. 24

National Standards
A.2–7, A.9.a–b, A.9.e–f, B.1.b

Chapter 6: **Chemical Bonds and Compounds** 165F

Previewing Resources for Differentiated Instruction

CHAPTER INVESTIGATION

Leveled resources present the same concepts for different abilities.

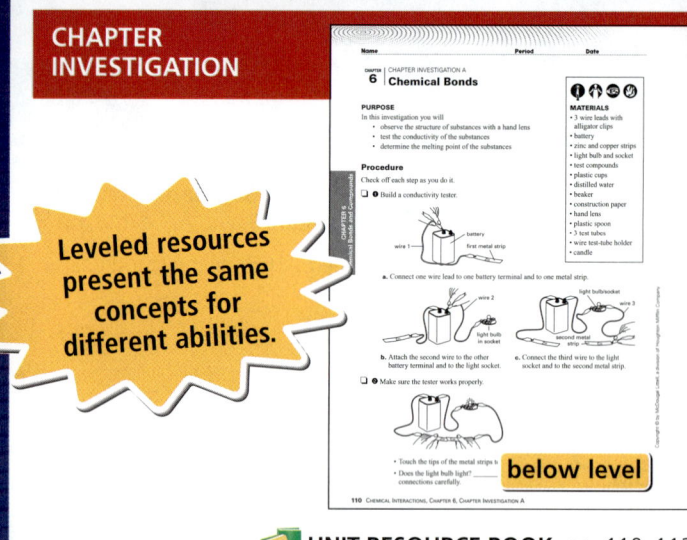
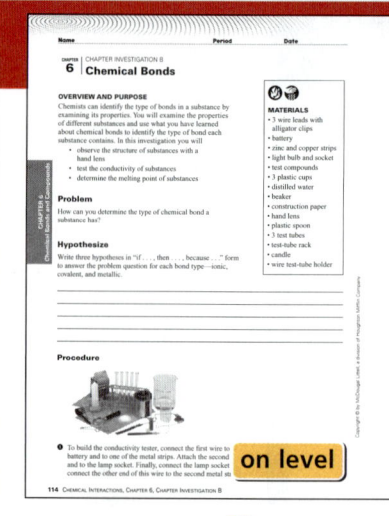
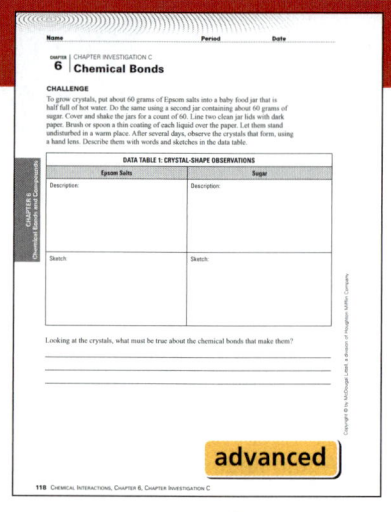

R UNIT RESOURCE BOOK, pp. 110–113   **R** pp. 114–117   **R** pp. 114–118

READING STUDY GUIDE

Reading Study Guide is also in Spanish.

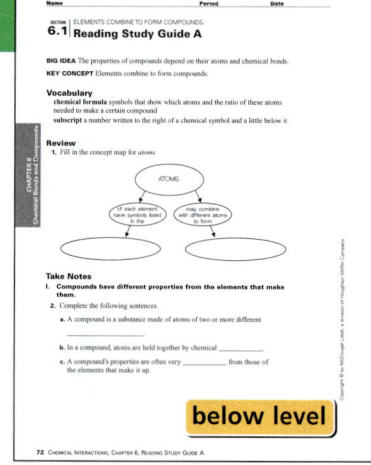
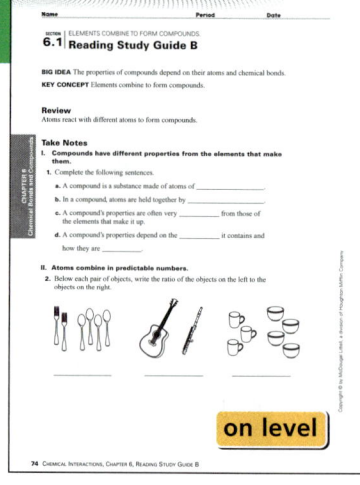
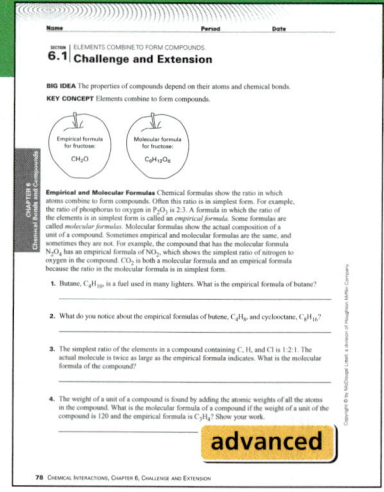

R UNIT RESOURCE BOOK, pp. 72–73   **R** pp. 74–75   **R** p. 78

CHAPTER TEST

Chapter Test is also in Spanish.

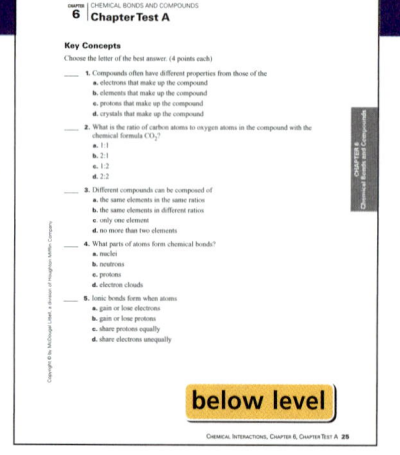
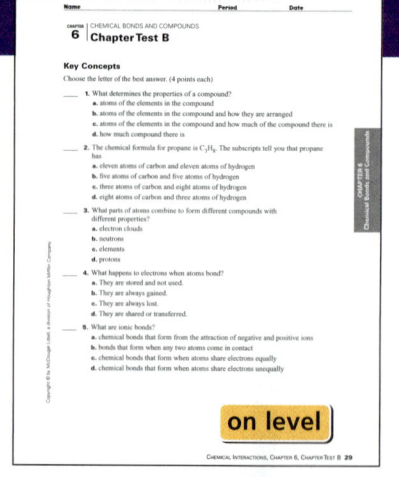
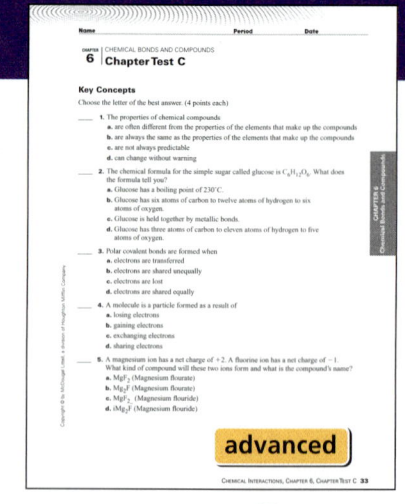

A UNIT ASSESSMENT BOOK, pp. 25–28   **A** pp. 29–32   **A** pp. 33–36

165G Unit 2: **Chemical Interactions**

TECHNOLOGY

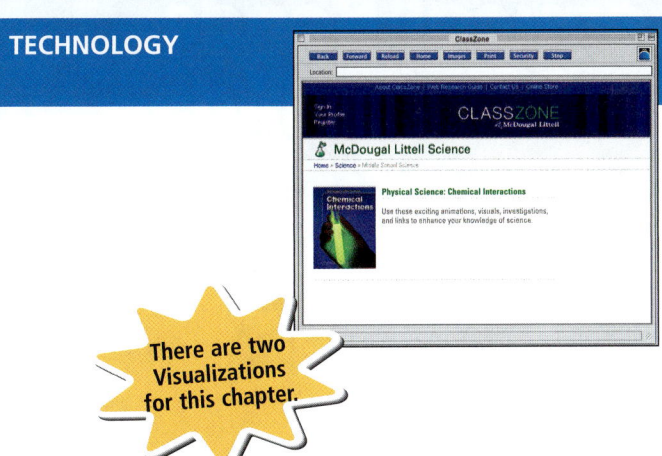
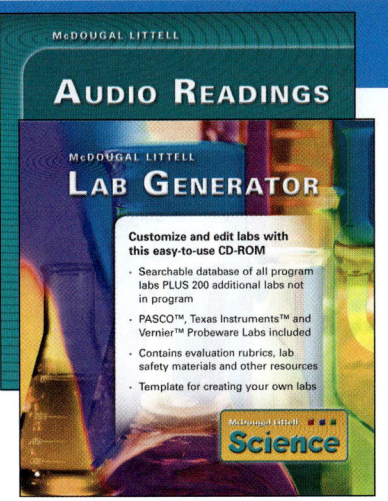
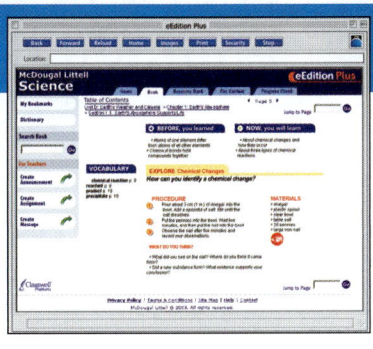

There are two Visualizations for this chapter.

 CLASSZONE.COM  CD/CD-ROMS  CLASSZONE.COM

VISUAL CONTENT

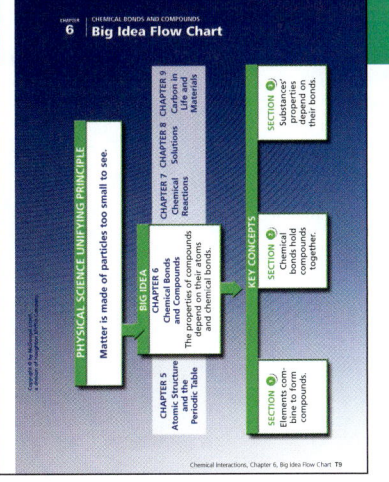
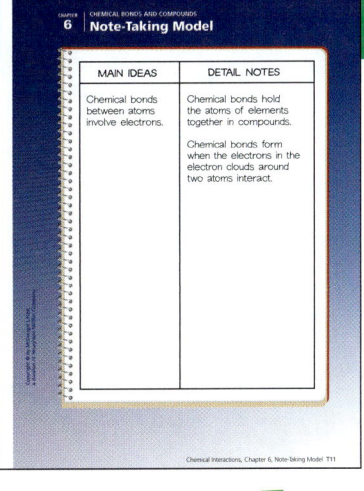
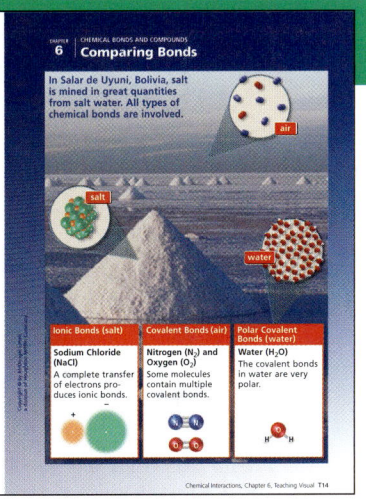

T UNIT TRANSPARENCY BOOK, p. T9   **T** p. T11   **T** p. T14

MORE SUPPORT

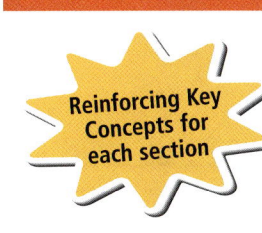

Reinforcing Key Concepts for each section

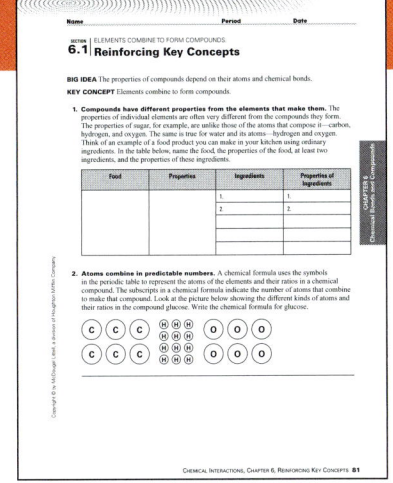
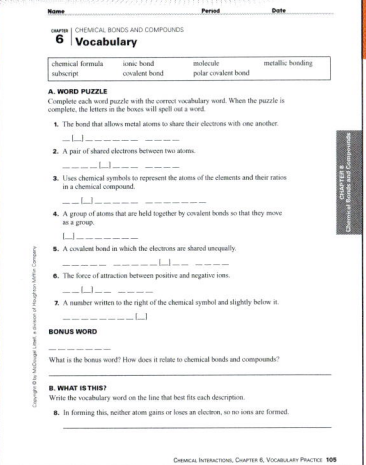
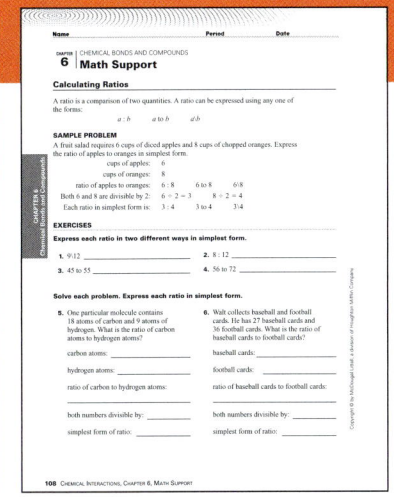

R UNIT RESOURCE BOOK, p. 81   **R** pp. 105–106   **R** p. 108

Chapter 6: **Chemical Bonds and Compounds** 165H

CHAPTER 6
Chemical Bonds and Compounds

INTRODUCE

Have students look at the photograph of skydivers diving as a group. Discuss how the question in the box links to the Big Idea:

- If you described the characteristics of the group of skydivers, how would the group characteristics compare to those of the individual skydivers?
- Based on the formation, to how many other skydivers can one skydiver connect?

National Science Education Standards

Content

B.1.b Substances react chemically in characteristic ways with other substances to form new substances (compounds) with different characteristic properties. In chemical reactions, the total mass is conserved. Substances often are placed in categories or groups if they react in similar ways; metals is an example of such a group.

Process

A.2–8 Design and conduct an investigation; use tools to gather and interpret data; use evidence to describe, predict, explain, model; think critically to make relationships between evidence and explanation; recognize different explanations and predictions; communicate scientific procedures and explanations; use mathematics.

A.9.a–c, A.9.e–f Understand scientific inquiry by using different investigations, methods, mathematics, and explanations based on logic, evidence, and skepticism.

CHAPTER 6
Chemical Bonds and Compounds

the BIG idea
The properties of compounds depend on their atoms and chemical bonds.

How do these skydivers stay together? How is this similar to the way atoms stay together?

Key Concepts

SECTION 1: Elements combine to form compounds.
Learn the difference between elements and compounds. Learn how to write and name chemical compounds.

SECTION 2: Chemical bonds hold compounds together.
Learn about the different types of chemical bonds.

SECTION 3: Substances' properties depend on their bonds.
Learn how bonds give compounds certain properties.

Internet Preview
CLASSZONE.COM
Chapter 6 online resources: Content Review, two Visualizations, two Resource Centers, Math Tutorial, Test Practice

166 Unit 2: Chemical Interactions

INTERNET PREVIEW

CLASSZONE.COM For student use with the following pages:

Review and Practice
- Content Review, pp. 168, 190
- Math Tutorial: Ratios, p. 174
- Test Practice, p. 193

Activities and Resources
- Internet Activity: Bonding, p. 167
- Resource Centers: Chemical Formulas, p. 172; Properties of Compounds, p. 186
- Visualization: Polar Electron Clouds, p. 179

Compounds Code: MDL023

EXPLORE the BIG idea

Mixing It Up

Get some red and yellow modeling compound. Make three red and two yellow balls, each about the diameter of a nickel. Blend one red and one yellow ball together. Blend one yellow and two red balls together.

Observe and Think How different do your combinations look from the original? from each other?

The Shape of Things

Pour some salt onto dark paper. Look at the grains through a hand lens. Try to observe a single grain.

Observe and Think What do you notice about the salt grains? What do you think might affect the way the grains look?

Internet Activity: Bonding

Go to **ClassZone.com** and watch the animation showing ionic and covalent bonding. Observe the differences in the two types of bonding.

Observe and Think What's the difference between an ionic and a covalent bond? Explain how covalent bonding can have different characteristics.

NSTA SCILINKS
scilinks.org
Compounds Code: MDL023

Chapter 6: **Chemical Bonds and Compounds** 167

EXPLORE the BIG idea

These inquiry-based activities are appropriate for use at home or as a supplement to classroom instruction.

Mixing It Up

PURPOSE To introduce how properties of a compound differ from the properties of its components. Students observe changes in properties when modeling the modeling compound alone and when combined.

TIP *10 min.* Different colors of food coloring in water can be used instead of modeling compound.

Answer: The resulting colors are different from the original colors. The second combination is darker.

REVISIT after p. 170.

The Shape of Things

PURPOSE To introduce the crystal structure of an ionic compound. Students observe the structure of salt.

TIP *10 min.* Have students draw what they see.

Answer: They are cubes with sharp edges. Size might affect how the crystals look, but the shape would be the same.

REVISIT after p. 177.

Internet Activity: Bonding

PURPOSE To introduce students to differences in ionic and covalent bonding.

TIP *20 min.* Have students list characteristics of each type of bond as they go through the examples.

Answer: In ionic compounds, electrons are transferred. In covalent compounds, electrons are shared.

REVISIT after p. 179.

TEACHING WITH TECHNOLOGY

Molecule Modeling Software As students discuss molecular shape, have them use molecule modeling software to examine the shapes of several different molecules. Two opportunities are when they read about carbon dioxide and the molecules shown on p. 182 and when you discuss the polyatomic ions described in Teach Difficult Concepts, p. 186.

Chapter 6 **167**

PREPARE

CONCEPT REVIEW

Activate Prior Knowledge

- Tell students they will draw a helium atom, which has two protons and two neutrons.
- Have students identify where to put the protons. Ask where they would put the neutrons.
- Ask students how many electrons are needed to balance the charges. Have students note the charge on the electron cloud.

TAKING NOTES

Main Idea and Detail Notes

Have small groups of students compare their charts. Have them discuss similarities and differences.

Vocabulary Strategy

Encourage students to make at least three spokes describing each term. Examine their descriptions to see whether they are too general and should be more specific. If a description is too detailed, advise the student to split the information between two spokes.

Vocabulary and Note-Taking Resources

- Vocabulary Practice, pp. 105–106
- Decoding Support, p. 107

- Daily Vocabulary Scaffolding, p. T10
- Note-Taking Model, p. T11

- Description Wheel, B20–21
- Main Idea and Detail Notes, C37
- Daily Vocabulary Scaffolding, H1–8

CHAPTER 6
Getting Ready to Learn

CONCEPT REVIEW
- Electrons occupy a cloud around an atom's nucleus.
- Atoms form ions by losing or gaining electrons.

VOCABULARY REVIEW
electron p. 139
element *See Glossary.*

Review concepts and vocabulary.

TAKING NOTES

MAIN IDEA AND DETAIL NOTES

Make a two-column chart. Write the main ideas, such as those in the blue headings, in the column on the left. Write details about each of those main ideas in the column on the right.

VOCABULARY STRATEGY

Place each vocabulary term at the center of a **description wheel** diagram. Write some words describing it on the spokes.

MAIN IDEAS	DETAIL NOTES
Atoms combine in predictable numbers.	• Each compound has a specific ratio of atoms. • A ratio is a comparison between two quantities.
Writing chemical formulas	• Find symbols on the periodic table. • Note ratio of atoms with subscripts.

Description wheel for SUBSCRIPT:
- written to the right of a symbol
- indicates number of atoms per molecule
- slightly below the symbol

See the Note-Taking Handbook on pages R45–R51.

168 Unit 2: Chemical Interactions

CHECK READINESS

Administer the Diagnostic Test to determine students' readiness for new science content and their mastery of requisite math skills.

 Diagnostic Test, pp. 20–21

Technology Resources

Students needing content and math skills should visit **ClassZone.com**.

- CONTENT REVIEW
- MATH TUTORIAL

 CONTENT REVIEW CD-ROM

KEY CONCEPT

Elements combine to form compounds.

◀ **BEFORE, you learned**
- Atoms make up everything on Earth
- Atoms react with different atoms to form compounds

▶ **NOW, you will learn**
- How compounds differ from the elements that make them
- How a chemical formula represents the ratio of atoms in a compound
- How the same atoms can form different compounds

VOCABULARY
chemical formula p. 171
subscript p. 171

EXPLORE Compounds

How are compounds different from elements?

PROCEDURE

1. Examine the lump of carbon, the beaker of water, and the sugar. Record your observations of each.

2. Light the candle. Pour some sugar into a test tube and heat it over the candle for several minutes. Record your observations.

WHAT DO YOU THINK?
- The sugar is made up of atoms of the same elements that are in the carbon and water. How are sugar, carbon, and water different from one another?
- Does heating the sugar give you any clue that sugar contains more than one element?

MATERIALS
- carbon
- water
- sugar
- test tube
- test-tube holder
- candle
- matches

Compounds have different properties from the elements that make them.

MAIN IDEA AND DETAILS
Make a two-column chart to start organizing information on compounds.

If you think about all of the different substances around you, it is clear that they cannot all be elements. In fact, while there are just over 100 elements, there are millions of different substances. Most substances are compounds. A compound is a substance made of atoms of two or more different elements. Just as the 26 letters in the alphabet can form thousands of words, the elements in the periodic table can form millions of compounds.

The atoms of different elements are held together in compounds by chemical bonds. Chemical bonds can hold atoms together in large networks or in small groups. Bonds help determine the properties of a compound.

Chapter 6: Chemical Bonds and Compounds 169

RESOURCES FOR DIFFERENTIATED INSTRUCTION

Below Level
UNIT RESOURCE BOOK
- Reading Study Guide A, pp. 72–73
- Decoding Support, p. 107

 **AUDIO CDS**

Advanced
UNIT RESOURCE BOOK
Challenge and Extension, p. 78

English Learners
UNIT RESOURCE BOOK
Spanish Reading Study Guide, pp. 76–77

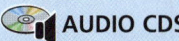 **AUDIO CDS**

- Audio Readings in Spanish
- Audio Readings (English)

6.1 FOCUS

▶ Set Learning Goals
Students will
- Describe how compounds are made from combinations of atoms.
- Explain how chemical formulas represent compounds.
- Model a compound in an experiment.

◯ 3-Minute Warm-Up
Display Transparency 12 or copy this exercise on the board:

Draw a diagram of a neutral carbon atom. A neutral carbon atom has six protons in its nucleus. On your diagram, label the nucleus and electron cloud, and indicate the total positive or negative charge on each. *Diagrams should show the nucleus as a dot within the electron cloud. The electron cloud should be labeled 6− and a line to the nucleus should be labeled 6+.*

T 3-Minute Warm-Up, p. T12

6.1 MOTIVATE

EXPLORE Compounds
PURPOSE To compare the properties of a compound and those of its elements

TIP *10 min.* Extend the activity, using a piece of uncorroded iron and a piece of rusty iron.

WHAT DO YOU THINK? *They differ in color, texture, and state. If the sugar is heated enough, it turns black, like carbon, and droplets of water form at the top of the test tube.*

Chapter 6 169

INSTRUCT

History of Science
In the early 1800s, John Dalton and other scientists noticed that atoms combine in whole number volumes. Two liters of hydrogen, for example, always combined with one liter of oxygen to make two liters of water. This happens because these volumes contain the correct ratio of atoms to form the compound.

EXPLORE the BIG idea
Revisit "Mixing It Up" on p. 167. Have students make an analogy between their results and chemical compounds.

Integrate the Sciences
Although the air is approximately 78 percent nitrogen, this nitrogen is not in a form that plants can use. Nitrogen is quite unreactive in its elemental form. Things such as bacteria in the soil can change elemental nitrogen into compounds. These compounds have properties such that plants are able to absorb and use nitrogen.

Ongoing Assessment
Describe how compounds are made from combinations of atoms.
Ask: What can you predict about the properties of the compound potassium fluoride compared to the properties of the elements potassium and fluorine? *They are different.*

 Answer: They are often quite different.

The properties of a compound depend not only on which atoms the compound contains, but also on how the atoms are arranged. Atoms of carbon and hydrogen, for example, can combine to form many thousands of different compounds. These compounds include natural gas, components of automobile gasoline, the hard waxes in candles, and many plastics. Each of these compounds has a certain number of carbon and hydrogen atoms arranged in a specific way.

The properties of compounds are often very different from the properties of the elements that make them. For example, water is made from two atoms of hydrogen bonded to one atom of oxygen. At room temperature, hydrogen and oxygen are both colorless, odorless gases, and they remain gases down to extremely low temperatures. Water, however, is a liquid at temperatures up to 100°C (212°F) and a solid below 0°C (32°F). Sugar is a compound composed of atoms of carbon, hydrogen, and oxygen. Its properties, however, are unlike those of carbon, hydrogen, or oxygen.

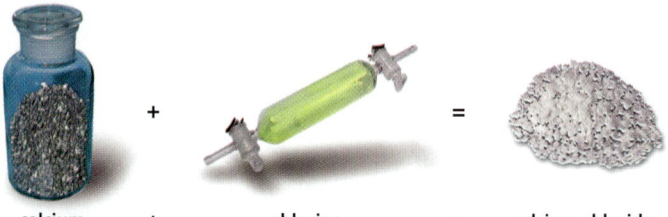

calcium + chlorine = calcium chloride

The picture above shows what happens when the elements calcium and chlorine combine to form the compound calcium chloride. Calcium is a soft, silvery metallic solid. Chlorine is a greenish-yellow gas that is extremely reactive and poisonous to humans. Calcium chloride, however, is a nonpoisonous white solid. People who live in cold climates often use calcium chloride to melt the ice that forms on streets in the wintertime.

 How do the properties of a compound compare with the properties of the elements that make it?

Atoms combine in predictable numbers.

A given compound always contains atoms of elements in a specific ratio. For example, the compound ammonia always has three hydrogen atoms for every nitrogen atom—a 3 to 1 ratio of hydrogen to nitrogen. This same 3:1 ratio holds for every sample of ammonia, under all physical conditions. A substance with a different ratio of hydrogen to nitrogen atoms is not ammonia. For example, hydrazoic acid also contains atoms of hydrogen and nitrogen but in a ratio of one hydrogen atom to three nitrogen atoms, or 1:3.

READING TIP
A ratio is a numerical relationship between two values. If you had 3 apples for every 1 orange, you'd have a ratio of 3 to 1.

170 Unit 2: Chemical Interactions

DIFFERENTIATE INSTRUCTION

 More Reading Support
A What two factors determine the properties of a compound? *the types of atoms it contains and how the atoms are arranged*

English Learners Put the definitions for the terms *compound*, *chemical formula*, and *subscript* on your classroom Science Word Wall or have English learners make flash cards for quick reference.

"Investigate Element Ratios" on p. 171 has directions that use the imperative mood, in which "you" is implied. Make sure English learners understand how to read and follow these directions.

INVESTIGATE Element Ratios

How can you model a compound?

PROCEDURE

1. Collect a number of nuts and bolts. The nuts represent hydrogen atoms. The bolts represent carbon atoms.
2. Connect the nuts to the bolts to model the compound methane. Methane contains four hydrogen atoms attached to one carbon atom. Make as many of these models as you can.
3. Count the nuts and bolts left over.

WHAT DO YOU THINK?
- What ratio of nuts to bolts did you use to make a model of a methane atom?
- How many methane models did you make? Why couldn't you make more?

CHALLENGE The compound ammonia has one nitrogen atom and three hydrogen atoms. How would you use the nuts and bolts to model this compound?

SKILL FOCUS Modeling

MATERIAL
- nuts and bolts
- Modeling Compounds Datasheet

TIME 20 minutes

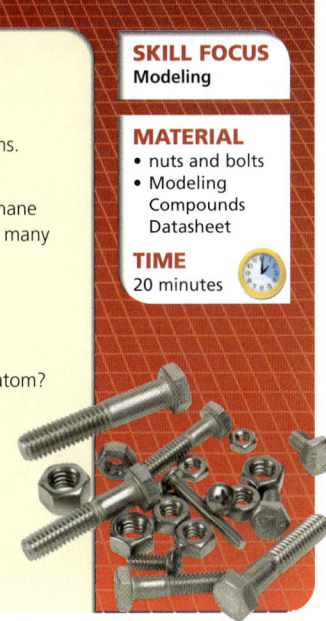

Chemical Formulas

Remember that atoms of elements can be represented by their chemical symbols, as given in the periodic table. A **chemical formula** uses these chemical symbols to represent the atoms of the elements and their ratios in a chemical compound.

Carbon dioxide is a compound consisting of one atom of carbon attached by chemical bonds to two atoms of oxygen. Here is how you would write the chemical formula for carbon dioxide:

- Find the symbols for carbon (C) and oxygen (O) on the periodic table. Write these symbols side by side.
- To indicate that there are two oxygen atoms for every carbon atom, place the subscript 2 to the right of the oxygen atom's symbol. A **subscript** is a number written to the right of a chemical symbol and slightly below it.
- Because there is only one atom of carbon in carbon dioxide, you need no subscript for carbon. The subscript 1 is never used. The chemical formula for carbon dioxide is, therefore,

$$CO_2$$

The chemical formula shows one carbon atom bonded to two oxygen atoms.

VOCABULARY Remember to create a description wheel for *chemical formula* and other vocabulary words.

READING TIP The word *subscript* comes from the prefix *sub-*, which means "under," and the Latin word *scriptum,* which means "written." A subscript is something written under something else.

Chapter 6: **Chemical Bonds and Compounds** 171

DIFFERENTIATE INSTRUCTION

More Reading Support

B How do we represent compounds? *by a chemical formula*

C $NaNO_3$ has how many oxygen atoms? *three*

Alternative Assessment Have students design a similar experiment, in which other materials are used to model carbon dioxide, CO_2, and phosphorus pentachloride, PCl_5.

INVESTIGATE Element Ratios

PURPOSE To model a compound using representations of atoms in definite proportions

TIP 20 min. Provide students with a random number of nuts and bolts allowing for some of one to be left over. An excess "reactant" encourages students to think in terms of proportions.

WHAT DO YOU THINK? *Four nuts were attached to one bolt. The number of models is limited by the number of either nuts or bolts. If you do not have exactly the right ratio, you cannot make the compound.*

CHALLENGE *You would use one bolt to represent nitrogen and three nuts to represent hydrogen.*

For additional practice, have students use the Modeling Compounds Datasheet.

- Modeling Compounds Datasheet, p. 79
- Datasheet, Element Ratios, p. 80

Technology Resources

Customize this student lab as needed or look for an alternative. Print rubrics to assess student lab reports.

Lab Generator CD-ROM

Metacognitive Strategy

Ask students to discuss how performing this investigation helped them make generalizations about compounds and their element ratios. Students should remark that there need to be a certain number of atoms for compounds to form.

Teach from Visuals

Have students review the table of chemical formulas. Ask:

- Phosphorus trichloride has the formula PCl_3. What would be the entries for the second and third columns if this compound were included in the table? *the diagram of one phosphorus atom and three chlorine atoms and the ratio 1:3*

- A unit of barium chloride contains one barium ion and two chloride ions. What are the atomic ratio and the chemical formula for this compound? *1:2, $BaCl_2$*

Mathematics Connection

In some compounds, the ratio of the atoms is not expressed in simplest terms. Ask:

- A butane molecule contains four carbon atoms, and the simplest ratio of carbon to hydrogen atoms is 2:5. What is the chemical formula for butane? *C_4H_{10}*

- A molecule of glucose has the formula $C_6H_{12}O_6$. What is the ratio of atoms in this molecule? *6:12:6* What is this ratio in simplest form? *1:2:1*

Ongoing Assessment

Explain how chemical formulas represent compounds.

Ask: How many carbon atoms are in a molecule of $C_{12}H_{22}O_{11}$? *twelve*

READING VISUALS Answer: *four*

CHECK YOUR READING Answer: *Different ratios of elements indicate different compounds.*

Chemical Formulas

Chemical formulas show the ratios of atoms in a chemical compound.

Compound Name	Atoms	Atomic Ratio	Chemical Formula
Hydrogen chloride		1:1	HCl
Water		2:1	H_2O
Ammonia		1:3	NH_3
Methane		1:4	CH_4
Propane		3:8	C_3H_8

READING VISUALS How many more hydrogen atoms does propane have than methane?

RESOURCE CENTER CLASSZONE.COM
Find out more about chemical formulas.

The chart above shows the names, atoms, ratios, and chemical formulas for several chemical compounds. The subscripts for each compound indicate the number of atoms that combine to make that compound. Notice how hydrogen combines with different atoms in different ratios. Notice in particular that methane and propane are made of atoms of the same elements, carbon and hydrogen, only in different ratios. This example shows why it's important to pay attention to ratios when writing chemical formulas.

CHECK YOUR READING Why is the ratio of atoms in a chemical formula so important?

Same Elements, Different Compounds

Even before chemists devised a way to write chemical formulas, they realized that different compounds could be composed of atoms of the same elements. Nitrogen and oxygen, for example, form several compounds. One compound consists of one atom of nitrogen attached to one atom of oxygen. This compound's formula is NO. A second compound has one atom of nitrogen attached to two atoms of oxygen, so its formula is NO_2. A third compound has two nitrogen atoms attached to one oxygen atom; its formula is N_2O. The properties of these compounds are different, even though they are made of atoms of the same elements.

DIFFERENTIATE INSTRUCTION

D What compounds contain the same two elements? *methane and propane*

E Write the formula for one atom of nitrogen and one atom of oxygen. *NO*

Advanced Have students research the work of John Dalton to find his symbols for the elements. Have students make a table comparing his symbols to the modern chemical symbols of the periodic table.

 Challenge and Extension, p. 78

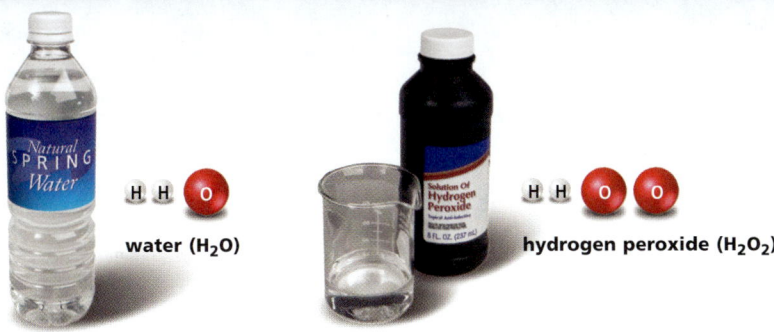

water (H₂O)   hydrogen peroxide (H₂O₂)

There are many other examples of atoms of the same elements forming different compounds. The photographs above show two bottles filled with clear, colorless liquids. You might use the liquid in the first bottle to cool off after a soccer game. The bottle contains water, which is a compound made from two atoms of hydrogen and one atom of oxygen (H_2O). You could not survive for long without water.

You definitely would not want to drink the liquid in the second bottle, although this liquid resembles water. This bottle also contains a compound of hydrogen and oxygen, hydrogen peroxide, but hydrogen peroxide has two hydrogen and two oxygen atoms (H_2O_2). Hydrogen peroxide is commonly used to kill bacteria on skin. One way to tell these two compounds apart is to test them using a potato. A drop of hydrogen peroxide on a raw potato will bubble; a drop of water on the potato will not.

The difference between the two compounds is greater than the labels or their appearance would indicate. The hydrogen peroxide that you buy at a drugstore is a mixture of hydrogen peroxide and water. In its concentrated form, hydrogen peroxide is a thick, syrupy liquid that boils at 150°C (302°F). Hydrogen peroxide can even be used as a fuel.

 What are the chemical formulas for water and hydrogen peroxide?

6.1 Review

KEY CONCEPTS

1. How do the properties of compounds often compare with the properties of the elements that make them?
2. How many atoms are in the compound represented by the formula $C_{12}H_{22}O_{11}$?
3. How can millions of compounds be made from the atoms of about 100 elements?

CRITICAL THINKING

4. **Apply** If a chemical formula has no subscripts, what can you conclude about the ratio of the atoms in it?
5. **Infer** How might you distinguish between hydrogen peroxide and water?

CHALLENGE

6. **Analyze** A chemist analyzes two compounds and finds that they both contain only carbon and oxygen. The two compounds, however, have different properties. How can two compounds made from the same elements be different?

Chapter 6: **Chemical Bonds and Compounds** 173

ANSWERS

1. In many cases they are quite different.

2. 12 carbon atoms + 22 hydrogen atoms + 11 oxygen atoms = 45 total atoms

3. Atoms can combine in many different ratios.

4. All atoms are in a 1:1 ratio.

5. Compare how they react with another substance.

6. The carbon and oxygen atoms are in different ratios in the compounds.

Ongoing Assessment

 Answer: H_2O, H_2O_2

Reinforce

Have students relate the section to the Big Idea.

 Reinforcing Key Concepts, p. 81

6.1 ASSESS & RETEACH

Assess

 Section 6.1 Quiz, p. 22

Reteach

Draw models for the following compounds on the board: water (two hydrogen atoms with an oxygen atom between them), methane (one carbon atom in the center of hydrogen atoms in a three-dimensional pyramid structure), and carbon dioxide (one carbon atom between two oxygen atoms). From the models, have students write the chemical formulas for the compounds. *H_2O, CH_4, CO_2* Next, write the formulas $C_6H_{12}O_6$ (glucose), NaCl (table salt), and NH_3 (ammonia) on the board. Ask students to identify the numbers of atoms in each compound. Ask students also to note different ratios in the compounds. *Glucose has six carbon atoms, 12 hydrogen atoms, and 6 oxygen atoms, a ratio of 1:2:1. Table salt has one sodium atom and one chlorine atom, a ratio of 1:1. Ammonia has one nitrogen atom and three hydrogen atoms, a ratio of 1:3.*

Technology Resources

Have students visit **ClassZone.com** for reteaching of Key Concepts.

 CONTENT REVIEW

 CONTENT REVIEW CD-ROM

Chapter 6 **173**

MATH IN SCIENCE
Math Skills Practice for Science

Set Learning Goal
To determine and use ratios to represent relative numbers of atoms in a chemical formula

Present the Science
A given compound contains the same elements in the same proportion by mass. For example, ammonia is always NH_3, with nitrogen and hydrogen in a 1:3 ratio. According to the law of multiple proportions, different compounds can form from the same elements, but the elements will be in different ratios in the different compounds. For example, copper and oxygen form CuO and Cu_2O. The ratios of elements in these compounds are 1:1 and 2:1, respectively.

Develop Number Sense
Students are used to writing ratios in simplest form where the numbers in the ratios have no common factor. Ask why representing ratios in simplest form may not always give accurate information. *Because atoms often combine in ratios that are not the lowest possible numerically.*

Close
Ask: How does the ratio of hydrogen to oxygen compare for water and glucose? *It is the same for both.* If this ratio is the same, why are they different compounds? *Glucose also contains carbon.*

- Math Support, p. 108
- Math Practice, p. 109

Technology Resources
Students can visit **ClassZone.com** for practice in calculating ratios.

 MATH TUTORIAL

174 Unit 2: **Chemical Interactions**

Math in Science

MATH TUTORIAL
CLASSZONE.COM
Click on Math Tutorial for more help with ratios.

A good strikeout-to-walk ratio for a baseball pitcher is 2:1. This means that for every two strikeouts achieved, the pitcher only allows one walk.

174 Unit 2: **Chemical Interactions**

SKILL: CALCULATING RATIOS

Regarding Ratios

No pitcher gets a batter out every time. Sometimes even the worst pitchers have spectacular games. If you're a fan of professional baseball, you've probably seen the quality of certain players rated by using a ratio. A ratio is a comparison of two quantities. For a major league baseball pitcher, for example, one ratio you might hear reported is the number of strikeouts to the number of walks during a season. Chemical formulas are also ratios—ratios that compare the numbers of atoms in a compound.

Example
Consider the chemical formula for the compound glucose:

$$C_6H_{12}O_6$$

From this formula you can write several ratios. To find the ratio of carbon atoms to hydrogen atoms, for instance, do the following:

(1) Find the number of each kind of atom by noting the subscripts.

6 carbon, 12 hydrogen

(2) Write the first number on the left and the second on the right, and place a colon between them.

6:12

(3) Reduce the ratio by dividing each side by the largest number that goes into each evenly, in this case 6.

1:2

ANSWER The ratio of carbon to hydrogen in glucose is 1:2.

Use the table below to answer the following questions.

Compounds and Formulas	
Compound Name	**Chemical Formula**
Carbon dioxide	CO_2
Methane	CH_4
Sulfuric acid	H_2SO_4
Glucose	$C_6H_{12}O_6$
Formic acid	CH_2O_2

1. In carbon dioxide, what is the ratio of carbon to oxygen?
2. What is the ratio of carbon to hydrogen in methane?
3. In sulfuric acid, what is the ratio of hydrogen to sulfur? the ratio of sulfur to oxygen?

CHALLENGE What two chemical compounds in the table have the same ratio of carbon atoms to oxygen atoms?

ANSWERS
1. 1:2
2. 1:4
3. 2:1, 1:4

CHALLENGE carbon dioxide and formic acid

KEY CONCEPT
Chemical bonds hold compounds together.

BEFORE, you learned
- Elements combine to form compounds
- Electrons are located in a cloud around the nucleus
- Atoms can lose or gain electrons to form ions

NOW, you will learn
- How electrons are involved in chemical bonding
- About the different types of chemical bonds
- How chemical bonds affect structure

VOCABULARY
ionic bond p. 176
covalent bond p. 178
molecule p. 179
polar covalent bond p. 179

THINK ABOUT

How do you keep things together?

Think about the different ways the workers at this construction site connect materials. They may use nails, screws, or even glue, depending on the materials they wish to keep together. Why would they choose the method they do? What factors do you consider when you join two objects?

MAIN IDEA AND DETAILS
Make a two-column chart to organize information on chemical bonds.

Chemical bonds between atoms involve electrons.

Water is a compound of hydrogen and oxygen. The air you breathe, however, contains oxygen gas, a small amount of hydrogen gas, as well as some water vapor. How can hydrogen and oxygen be water sometimes and at other times not? The answer is by forming chemical bonds.

Chemical bonds are the "glue" that holds the atoms of elements together in compounds. Chemical bonds are what make compounds more than just mixtures of atoms.

Remember that an atom has a positively charged nucleus surrounded by a cloud of electrons. Chemical bonds form when the electrons in the electron clouds around two atoms interact. How the electron clouds interact determines the kind of chemical bond that is formed. Chemical bonds have a great effect on the chemical and physical properties of compounds. Chemical bonds also influence how different substances interact. You'll learn more about how substances interact in a later chapter.

Chapter 6: **Chemical Bonds and Compounds** 175

RESOURCES FOR DIFFERENTIATED INSTRUCTION

Below Level
UNIT RESOURCE BOOK
- Reading Study Guide A, pp. 84–85
- Decoding Support, p. 107

 **AUDIO CDS**

Advanced
UNIT RESOURCE BOOK
- Challenge and Extension, p. 90
- Challenge Reading, pp. 103–104

English Learners
UNIT RESOURCE BOOK
Spanish Reading Study Guide, pp. 88–89

 **AUDIO CDS**

- Audio Readings in Spanish
- Audio Readings (English)

6.2 FOCUS

Set Learning Goals
Students will
- Explain how electrons are involved in chemical bonding.
- Describe what the different types of chemical bonds are.
- Determine how chemical bonds affect structure.
- Observe how a crystal grows in an experiment.

3-Minute Warm-Up
Display Transparency 12 or copy this exercise on the board:

Match each definition to a term.

Definitions
1. a negatively charged particle that moves around an atom's nucleus *a*
2. an atom that has lost an electron *c*
3. an atom that has gained an electron *b*

Terms
a. electron
b. negative ion
c. positive ion

 3-Minute Warm-Up, p. T12

6.2 MOTIVATE

THINK ABOUT
PURPOSE To understand how things can be connected in different ways

DEMONSTRATE Show students several connections on clothing, such as buttons, zippers, and Velcro. Ask them to explain why they would use one method and not another, based on the situation. (Snaps may be too bulky for some materials; buttons may not stay attached well on certain other materials.)

Ongoing Assessment
Explain how electrons are involved in chemical bonding.

Ask: What determines the kind of chemical bond formed? *how the electron clouds interact*

Chapter 6 **175**

6.2 INSTRUCT

Teach from Visuals
Have students examine the table of groups 1, 2, and 17. Ask what shows the charges on individual elements. *+/– signs to the right of each element's symbol.* Remind them that compounds have no overall charge. Point out that an element from group 1 can combine with an element from group 17 in single molecules: Li + Br = LiBr. An element from group 2 combines with an element from group 17 by doubling the molecules of the element from group 17: Ca + F = CaF_2.

Address Misconceptions
IDENTIFY Ask students what would happen if they were to mix a bottle of hydrogen gas with a bottle of oxygen gas. If they answer, "Water would form," they hold the misconception that chemical combination is no different from physical combination.

CORRECT Take either the graphite from a pencil or a piece of charcoal (carbon) and place it in a glass of water. Tell students that here they have all the chemical ingredients for sugar but they have no sugar, only a mess. To make a chemical compound, like sugar, chemical bonds must be formed.

REASSESS Ask students why simply mixing the eggs, flour, water, and other ingredients for a cake does not make a cake. *Because bonds need to form. Baking is what forms the bonds.*

Technology Resources
Visit ClassZone.com for background on common student misconceptions.

 MISCONCEPTION DATABASE

Ongoing Assessment
 Answer: positive

---

Atoms can transfer electrons.

REMINDER Remember that elements in columns show similar chemical properties.

Ions are formed when atoms gain or lose electrons. Gaining electrons changes an atom into a negative ion. Losing electrons changes an atom into a positive ion. Individual atoms do not form ions by themselves. Instead, ions typically form in pairs when one atom transfers one or more electrons to another atom.

An element's location on the periodic table can give a clue as to the type of ions the atoms of that element will form. The illustration to the left shows the characteristic ions formed by several groups. Notice that all metals lose electrons to form positive ions. Group 1 metals commonly lose only one electron to form ions with a single positive charge. Group 2 metals commonly lose two electrons to form ions with two positive charges. Other metals, like the transition metals, also always form positive ions, but the number of electrons they may lose varies.

Nonmetals form ions by gaining electrons. Group 17 nonmetals, for example, gain one electron to form ions with a 1– charge. The nonmetals in Group 16 gain two electrons to form ions with a 2– charge. The noble gases do not normally gain or lose electrons and so do not normally form ions.

 **CHECK YOUR READING** What type of ions do metals form?

Ionic Bonds
What happens when an atom of an element from Group 1, like sodium, meets an atom of an element from Group 17, like chlorine? Sodium is likely to lose an electron to form a positive ion. Chlorine is likely to gain an electron to form a negative ion. An electron, therefore, moves from the sodium atom to the chlorine atom.

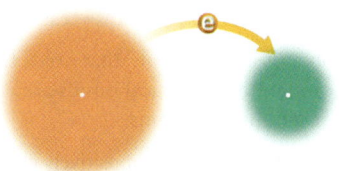
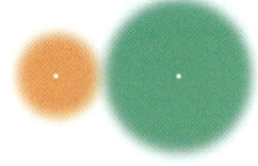

sodium atom (Na)   chlorine atom (Cl)   sodium ion (Na^+)   chloride ion (Cl^-)

Remember that particles with opposite electrical charges attract one another. When the ions are created, therefore, they are drawn toward one another by electrical attraction. This force of attraction between positive and negative ions is called an **ionic bond**.

176 Unit 2: **Chemical Interactions**

DIFFERENTIATE INSTRUCTION

More Reading Support

A What do you get when an atom loses or gains an electron? *an ion*

B What do you call the force of attraction between positive and negative ions? *an ionic bond*

English Learners English learners may need help understanding different word forms. Look at the words *ionic* and *ionize*. Adding *-ic* to the end of *ion*, produces an adjective. Adding *-ize* to the end of the same word produces a verb. Help English learners recognize indicators such as these when learning new terms.

Electrical forces act in all directions. Each ion, therefore, attracts all other nearby ions with the opposite charge. The next illustration shows how this all-around attraction produces a network of sodium and chloride ions known as a sodium chloride crystal.

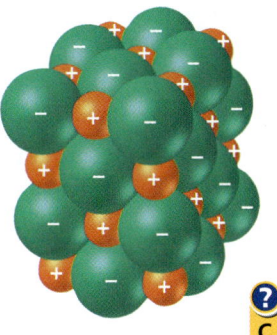

Notice how each positive ion is surrounded by six negative ions, and each negative ion is surrounded by six positive ions. This regular arrangement gives the sodium chloride crystal its characteristic cubic shape. You can see this distinctive crystal shape when you look at table salt crystals through a magnifying glass.

Ionic bonds form between all nearby ions of opposite charge. These interactions make ionic compounds very stable and their crystals very strong. Although sodium chloride crystals have a cubic shape, other ionic compounds form crystals with different regular patterns. The shape of the crystals of an ionic compound depends, in part, on the ratio of positive and negative ions and the sizes of the ions.

The cubic shape of sodium chloride crystals is a result of how the ions form crystals.

Names of Ionic Compounds

The name of an ionic compound is based on the names of the ions it is made of. The name for a positive ion is the same as the name of the atom from which it is formed. The name of a negative ion is formed by dropping the last part of the name of the atom and adding the suffix *-ide*. To name an ionic compound, the name of the positive ion is placed first, followed by the name of the negative ion. For example, the chemical name for table salt is sodium chloride. *Sodium* is the positive sodium ion and *chloride* is the negative ion formed from chlorine.

Therefore, to name the compound with the chemical formula BaI_2

- First, take the name of the positive metal element: barium.
- Second, take the name of the negative, nonmetal element, iodine, and give it the ending *-ide*: iodide.
- Third, combine the two names: barium iodide.

Similarly, the name for KBr is potassium bromide, and the name for MgF_2 is magnesium fluoride.

Chapter 6: **Chemical Bonds and Compounds** 177

History of Science

Before the work of chemist Gilbert Newton Lewis in the early 1900s, bonding theory was limited to electron transfer. Lewis was the first to suggest that atoms share electrons when forming a bond. His theory was that atoms could only have a certain number of electrons around them. Atoms would share electrons so they would have this maximum number.

Teach Difficult Concepts

Have students investigate the role of electronegativity in determining the nature of bonds. Electronegativity is a measure of the attraction of an atom for electrons in a chemical bond. Some periodic tables list electronegativity. Tell students that the highest electronegativities are associated with the atoms that have the greatest attraction for electrons.

Atoms can share electrons.

In general, an ionic bond forms between atoms that lose electrons easily to form positive ions, such as metals, and atoms that gain electrons easily to form negative ions, such as nonmetals. Another way in which atoms can bond together is by sharing electrons. Nonmetal atoms usually form bonds with each other by sharing electrons.

Covalent Bonds

VOCABULARY Make a description wheel for *covalent bond* and other vocabulary words.

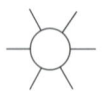

A pair of shared electrons between two atoms is called a **covalent bond**. In forming a covalent bond, neither atom gains or loses an electron, so no ions are formed. The shared electrons are attracted to both positively charged nuclei. The illustrations below show a covalent bond between two iodine atoms. In the first illustration, notice how the electron clouds overlap. A covalent bond is also often represented as a line between the two atoms, as in the second illustration.

Iodine (I₂)

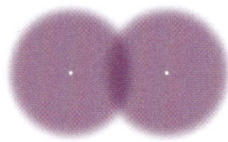
electron cloud model

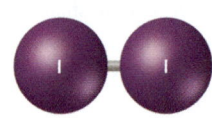
ball-and-stick model

READING TIP To help yourself remember that a covalent bond involves a sharing of electrons, remember that the prefix *co-* means "partner."

The number of covalent bonds that an atom can form depends on the number of electrons that it has available for sharing. For example, atoms of the halogen group and hydrogen can contribute only one electron to a covalent bond. These atoms, therefore, can form only one covalent bond. Atoms of Group 16 elements can form two covalent bonds. Atoms of the elements of Group 15 can form three bonds. Carbon and silicon in Group 14 can form four bonds. For example, in methane (CH₄), carbon forms four covalent bonds with four hydrogen atoms, as shown below.

Methane (CH₄)

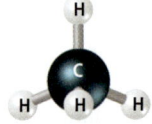
ball-and-stick model

space-filling model

We don't always show the lines representing the covalent bonds between the atoms. The space-filling model still shows the general shape of the bonded atoms, but occupies far less space on the page.

178 Unit 2: **Chemical Interactions**

DIFFERENTIATE INSTRUCTION

 More Reading Support

E What type of bond is formed when electrons are shared? *covalent*

Below Level Have students model a single bond by using a toothpick and two gumdrops. Have students test how easily they can turn the gumdrops. Have them model a double bond by using two toothpicks. Again test how easily the "atoms" can spin. Then have them model a triple bond by using three toothpicks. Test again how easily the gumdrops can spin. Ask students how the three bonds compare and which bond would be the strongest? *Each additional bond is more rigid. A triple bond would be the strongest.*

Each carbon-hydrogen bond in methane is a single bond because one pair of electrons is shared between the atoms. Sometimes atoms may share more than one pair of electrons with another atom. For example, the carbon atom in carbon dioxide (CO_2) forms double bonds with each of the oxygen atoms. A double bond consists of four (two pairs of) shared electrons. Two nitrogen atoms form a triple bond, meaning that they share six (three pairs of) electrons.

Carbon Dioxide (CO_2)   **Nitrogen (N_2)**

READING TIP
Remember that each line in the model stands for a covalent bond—one shared pair of electrons.

A group of atoms held together by covalent bonds is called a **molecule**. A molecule can contain from two to many thousand atoms. Most molecules contain the atoms of two or more elements. For example, water (H_2O), ammonia (NH_3), and methane (CH_4) are all compounds made up of molecules. However, some molecules contain atoms of only one element. The following elements exist as two-atom molecules: H_2, N_2, O_2, F_2, Cl_2, Br_2, and I_2.

 What is a molecule?

Polar Covalent Bonds

In an iodine molecule, both atoms are exactly the same. The shared electrons therefore are attracted equally to both nuclei. If the two atoms involved in a covalent bond are very different, however, the electrons have a stronger attraction to one nucleus than to the other and spend more time near that nucleus. A covalent bond in which the electrons are shared unequally is called a **polar covalent bond**. The word *polar* refers to anything that has two extremes, like a magnet with its two opposite poles.

Water (H_2O)

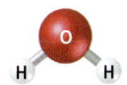

ball-and-stick model   space-filling model

READING TIP
To remind yourself that polar covalent bonds have opposite partial charges, remember that Earth has both a North Pole and a South Pole.

In a water molecule (H_2O), the oxygen atom attracts electrons far more strongly than the hydrogen atoms do. The oxygen nucleus has eight protons, and the hydrogen nucleus has only one proton. The oxygen atom pulls the shared electrons more strongly toward it. In a water molecule, therefore, the oxygen side has a slightly negative charge, and the hydrogen side has a slightly positive charge.

VISUALIZATION
CLASSZONE.COM
Examine how electrons move in a polar covalent molecule.

DIFFERENTIATE INSTRUCTION

More Reading Support

F What type of bond forms from unequal sharing of electrons? *polar covalent*

Inclusion Prepare physical models of the molecules on pp. 178–179 by using small Styrofoam balls and toothpicks or molecular model kits. Have these molecules available for students who need a tactile model.

Teach Difficult Concepts

What makes a molecule is difficult to explain completely. A molecule is often described as the "smallest part of a substance that retains all the properties of that substance." In this sense, one NaCl pair would be considered a molecule. We do not use the term *molecule* to refer to ionic compounds simply because it is rare to find a single pair of sodium and chloride ions.

Real World Example

In the water molecule, oxygen attracts electrons more strongly than hydrogen. The molecule is so polar that the negative end of one water molecule is attracted to the positive end of another molecule to form a bond called a hydrogen bond. Hydrogen bonding is what is responsible for water's high surface tension and higher than expected boiling point.

EXPLORE the BIG idea

Revisit "Internet Activity: Bonding" on p. 167. Have students revise their answers if necessary.

Ongoing Assessment

CHECK YOUR READING Answer: a group of atoms held together by covalent bonds

Teach Difficult Concepts

Students may think that scientists can always classify chemical bonds with certainty. Explain that the bond between two atoms is not always completely ionic or completely covalent. To illustrate this, hang a piece of white paper and a piece of black paper on the board. Ask students to pick out black and white objects in the room. Then hold up several objects or pieces of paper that are various shades of gray. Point out that although some things are entirely black or white, many objects are in the range that goes from black to white. Point out that only identical atoms bond by 100 percent covalent bonds.

Teach from Visuals

Ask: Why is there no line between the sodium and chloride ions? *There is no line because electrons are not shared.*

 This visual is also available as T14 in the Unit Transparency Book.

Ongoing Assessment

Describe the different types of chemical bonds.

Ask: What type of bond has molecules with negative and positive ends? *polar covalent*

 Answer: nitrogen, oxygen, and water

Comparing Bonds

In Salar de Uyuni, Bolivia, salt is mined in great quantities from salt water. The salt is harvested as the water evaporates into the air, leaving the salt behind. All types of chemical bonds are involved.

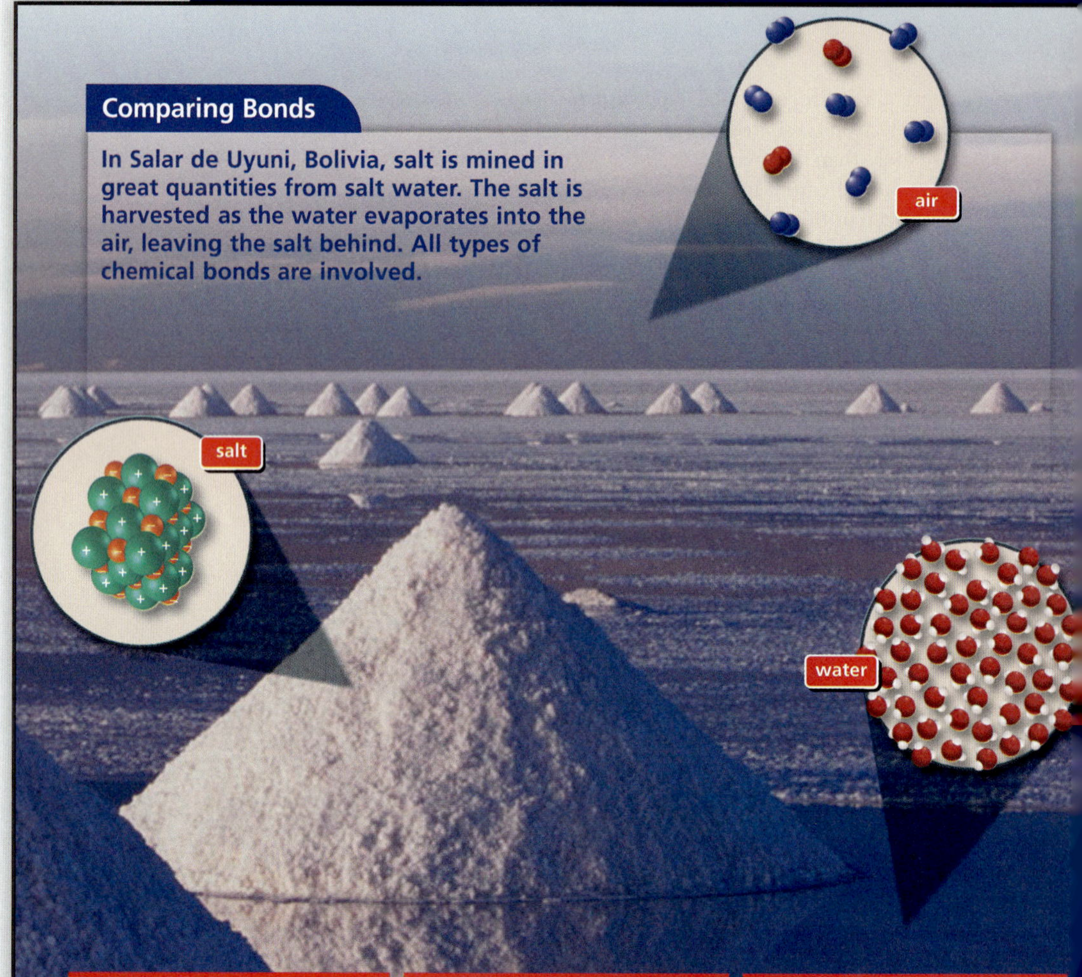

Ionic Bonds (salt)
Sodium Chloride (NaCl)
A complete transfer of electrons produces the ionic bonds that hold sodium chloride (table salt) crystals together.

Covalent Bonds (air)
Nitrogen (N_2) and Oxygen (O_2)
Some molecules in air contain multiple covalent bonds. Nitrogen has triple bonds. Oxygen has double bonds.

Polar Covalent Bonds (water)
Water (H_2O)
The covalent bonds in water are very polar because oxygen attracts electrons far more strongly than hydrogen does.

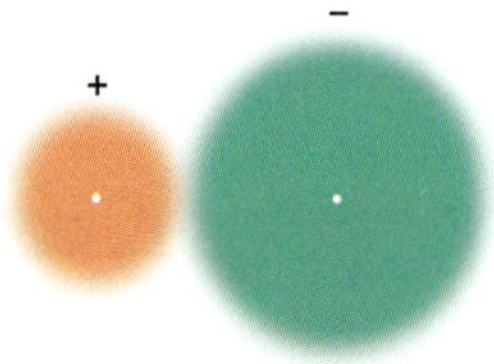

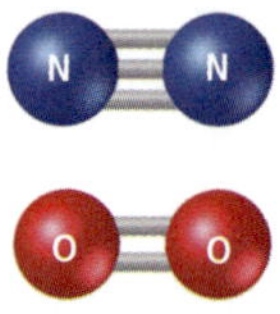

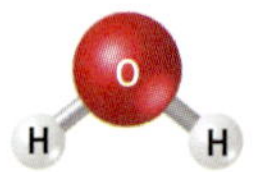

READING ViSUALS Atoms of which element are shown both in the air and in the water?

DIFFERENTIATE INSTRUCTION

Alternative Assessment Have students prepare bar graphs showing the mixture of compounds in air in terms of the types of bonds that make up the compounds. Each graph should contain four bars, one each for the three types of bonds and one for no bonding. Have them include the covalent bonds of nitrogen at 78% and oxygen at 21%, and polar water vapor at 4%. (The amount of water vapor in air can vary from 0% to 4%.) The bar for ionic compounds will be at 0. Argon has no bonds, just single atoms.

Chemical bonds give all materials their structures.

The substances around you have many different properties. The structure of the crystals and molecules that make up these substances are responsible for many of these properties. For example, crystals bend rays of light, metals shine, and medications attack certain diseases in the body because their atoms are arranged in specific ways.

Ionic Compounds

Most ionic compounds have a regular crystal structure. Remember how the size, shape, and ratio of the sodium ions and chloride ions give the sodium chloride crystal its shape. Other ionic compounds, such as calcium chloride, have different but equally regular structures that depend upon the ratio and sizes of the ions. One consequence of such rigid structures is that, when enough force is applied to the crystal, it shatters rather than bends.

INVESTIGATE Crystals

How does a crystal grow?
PROCEDURE

1. Add a small amount of the crystal-growing substance to a beaker of hot tap water. Stir until it mixes completely with the water. Keep adding the substance and stirring until no more will dissolve.
2. Pour the mixture into another beaker.
3. Tie one end of the string to the paper clip and the other end to a pencil. Lower the paper clip into the solution and lay the pencil across the top of the beaker. The paper clip should hang at about the middle of the beaker.
4. Use a hand lens to observe the paper clip several times a week for three weeks.

WHAT DO YOU THINK?
- Describe the crystals you see forming on the paper clip. Do the crystals look different as they get larger?
- Compare your crystals to those of other groups. What similarities do you see among them? What differences?

CHALLENGE Try growing larger crystals by selecting one of the crystals from your paper clip, tying it to a piece of string, and sinking it into a solution of the same crystal-growing substance.

SKILL FOCUS
Observing

MATERIALS
- crystal-growing substance
- 2 glass beakers
- hot tap water
- stirring stick
- cotton string
- paper clip
- pencil
- hand lens

TIME
30 minutes

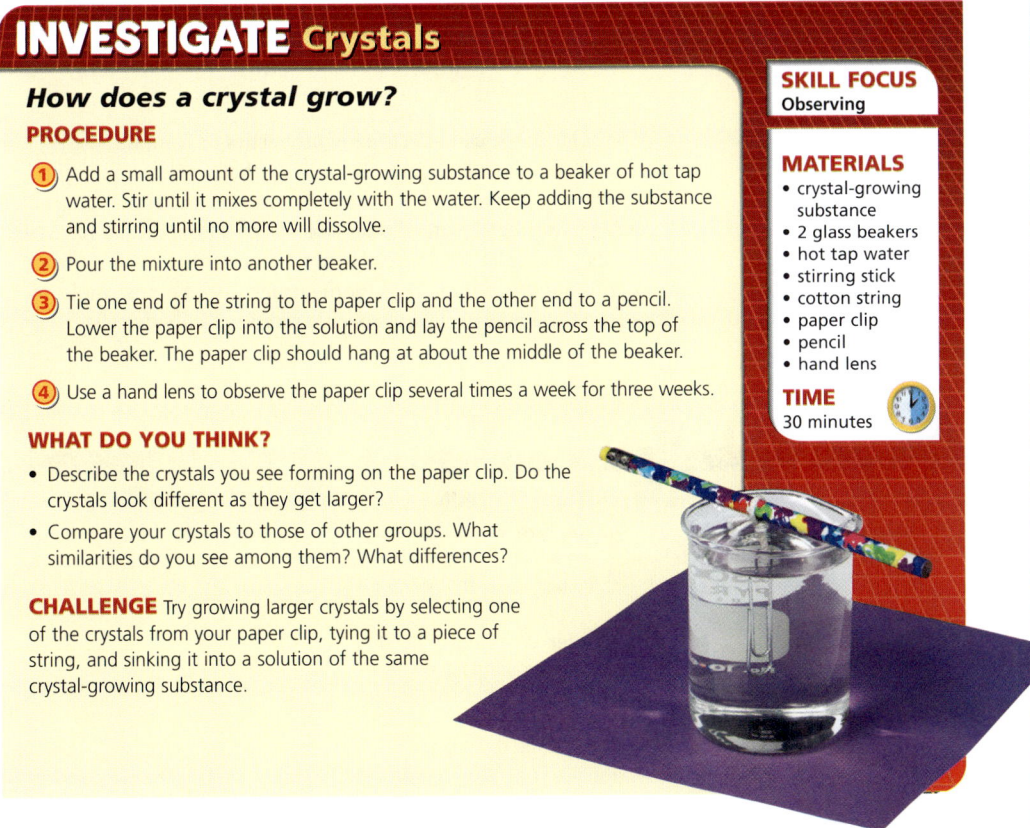

Chapter 6: **Chemical Bonds and Compounds** 181

DIFFERENTIATE INSTRUCTION

 More Reading Support

G What is responsible for many of the properties of substances? *their structure*

Advanced Have students research the uses for crystals in the electronics industry.

Have students who are interested in nuclear magnetic resonance (NMR), which can detect how atoms are bonded together, read the following article:

 Challenge Reading, pp. 103–104

INVESTIGATE Crystals

PURPOSE To observe how a crystal grows

TIPS 30 min.
- Check toxicity and other safety factors before using a laboratory chemical.
- If possible, have different groups use different crystal-growing substances. Use either sugar, salt, alum, or copper sulfate.
- Alum, which can be purchased at a pharmacy or some grocery stores, grows good crystals and is inexpensive.
- Hot distilled water will produce more regular crystals because of the lack of impurities.
- While crystals are growing, it is important to keep the beaker free of dust and undisturbed. You might try putting a coffee filter over the cup.

WHAT DO YOU THINK? *The shape of the crystal will depend on the solute chosen. The shape remains the same as the crystal grows.*

CHALLENGE *As the water evaporates, the crystal should remain the same shape but grow larger.*

 Datasheet, Crystals, p. 91

Technology Resources

Customize this student lab as needed or look for an alternative. Print rubrics to assess student lab reports.

 Lab Generator CD-ROM

Metacognitive Strategy

Ask students to think about how often they should take a picture of the crystal growth if they wanted to make a presentation of the investigation.

Covalent Compounds

Unlike ionic compounds, covalent compounds exist as individual molecules. Chemical bonds give each molecule a specific, three-dimensional shape called its molecular structure. Molecular structure can influence everything from how a specific substance feels to the touch to how well it interacts with other substances.

A few basic molecular structures are shown below. Molecules can have a simple linear shape, like iodine (I_2), or they can be bent, like a water molecule (H_2O). The atoms in an ammonia molecule (NH_3) form a pyramid, and methane (CH_4) molecules even have a slightly more complex shape. The shape of a molecule depends on the atoms it contains and the bonds holding it together.

READING TIP To help yourself appreciate the differences among these structures, try making three-dimensional models of them.

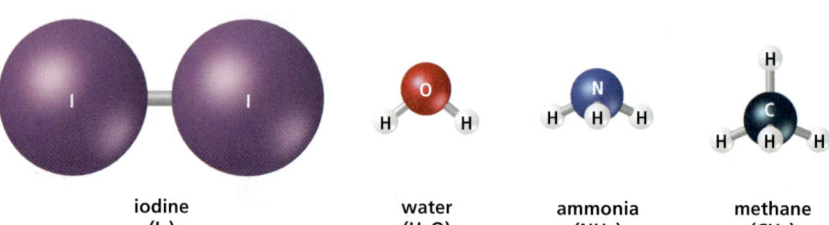

iodine (I_2)   water (H_2O)   ammonia (NH_3)   methane (CH_4)

Molecular shape can affect many properties of compounds. For example, there is some evidence to indicate that we detect scents because molecules with certain shapes fit into certain smell receptors in the nose. Molecules with similar shapes, therefore, should have similar smells. Molecular structure also plays an essential role in how our bodies respond to certain drugs. Some drugs work because molecules with certain shapes can fit into specific receptors in body cells.

6.2 Review

KEY CONCEPTS
1. What part of an atom is involved in chemical bonding?
2. How are ionic bonds and covalent bonds different?
3. Describe two ways that crystal and molecular structures affect the properties of ionic and covalent compounds.

CRITICAL THINKING
4. **Analyze** Would you expect the bonds in ammonia to be polar covalent? Why or why not?
5. **Infer** What kind of bond would you expect atoms of strontium and iodine to form? Why? Write the formula and name the compound.

CHALLENGE
6. **Conclude** Is the element silicon likely to form ionic or covalent bonds? Explain.

ANSWERS
1. the electron cloud
2. An ionic bond results from the attraction of oppositely charged ions. Covalent bonds result from atoms sharing electrons.
3. Their crystal structures make ionic compounds shatter when enough force is applied. Molecular structures can influence how a compound smells and how it reacts with other compounds.
4. Yes; nitrogen has more protons in its nucleus and thus has more attraction for the shared electrons.
5. Strontium is in Group 2 and forms Sr^{2+} ions. Iodine is in Group 17 and forms I^- ions. Strontium iodide is ionic, SrI_2.
6. Silicon is in the same group as carbon. Carbon forms covalent bonds, so silicon probably does, too.

Think SCIENCE

SKILL: ISOLATING VARIABLES

Stick to It

Glues join objects by forming something like chemical bonds between their surfaces. While glue manufacturers try to make glues as strong as possible, simply being strong does not mean that a glue will join all surfaces equally well. For example, a glue that will hold two pieces of wood together very well may not be able to form a lasting bond between two pieces of plastic piping or two metal sheets.

Variables

When testing a new glue, a scientist wants to know exactly how that glue will perform under all conditions. In any test, however, there are a number of variables that could affect the quality of the bonds formed by the glue. The scientist needs to discover exactly which of these variables most affects the glue's ability to form lasting bonds. Identifying these variables and the effects each has on the glue's strength and lifetime enables glue makers to recommend the best uses for the glue. Following are a few of the variables a glue maker may consider when testing a glue.

- What surfaces the glue is being used to join
- How much glue is used in a test
- How evenly the glue is applied to the surface
- How much force the glue can withstand
- Over how long a time the force is applied
- The environment the glue is used in (wet, dry, or dusty)

The glue on the back of a postage stamp must be activated somehow. This scanning electron microscope photo shows postage stamp glue before (green) and after (blue) it has been activated by moisture.

Variables to Test

On Your Own You are a scientist at a glue company. You have developed a new type of glue and need to know how specific conditions will affect its ability to hold surfaces together. First, select one variable you wish to test. Next, outline how you would ensure that only that variable will differ in each test. You might start out by listing all the variables you can think of and then put a check by each one and describe how you are controlling it.

As a Group Discuss the outlines of your tests with others. Are there any variables you haven't accounted for?

CHALLENGE Adhesive tapes come in many different types. Outline how you would test how well a certain tape holds in a wet environment and in a dry environment.

This highly magnified photograph shows the attachment formed by a colorless, waterproof wood glue.

Chapter 6: **Chemical Bonds and Compounds** 183

THINK SCIENCE
Scientific Methods of Thinking

Set Learning Goal
To isolate and identify the variables involved in testing a glue

Present the Science
- One very strong glue is made from an acrylic resin. The glue bonds with whatever it touches when it comes in contact with water. Almost any surface contains at least trace amounts of water, so this type of glue bonds readily. Acrylic glues can do more than repair broken vases. They are sometimes used to close wounds and detect fingerprints.
- White glues bond when the solvent they contain evaporates. The solvent in most white glues is water, so when the glue dries, it bonds to the object it contacts.
- The glue that is used on repositionable papers forms tiny spheres. Therefore, the overall hold of the glue is weak.

Guide the Activity
- As students are making their lists of variables, ask them to think of what they do when they apply a glue.
- Next to each variable, have students state exactly how it is accounted for in their experiments.

Close
Ask students why doing tests at the same time is better than doing them days or weeks apart. *You can be more familiar with the variables and so control them better.*

ANSWERS

Check student lists for numbers of variables. More important than the number of variables identified, however, is the number students have successfully accounted for in their tests.
CHALLENGE *Check to ensure students have addressed the special effects of moisture on tape.*

6.3 FOCUS

▶ Set Learning Goals

Students will
- Describe how metal atoms form chemical bonds with one another.
- Analyze how ionic and covalent bonds influence substances' properties.
- Identify different forms of the same element.

◀ 3-Minute Warm-Up

Display Transparency 13 or copy this exercise on the board:

Decide if these statements are true. If they are not true, correct them.

1. An atom can form more than one covalent bond with another atom. *true*
2. Covalent bonds always have equal sharing of electrons. *usually unequal sharing of electrons*
3. A molecule's structure can influence how it reacts with other molecules. *true*

 3-Minute Warm-Up, p. T13

6.3 MOTIVATE

EXPLORE Bonds in Metals

PURPOSE To determine what objects will conduct an electric current

TIP 10 min. Ask students to bring a D-cell battery from home.

WHAT DO YOU THINK? *Most metal objects will conduct a current.*

Ongoing Assessment

Describe how metal atoms form chemical bonds with one another.

Ask: Why are metals able to carry an electrical current? *The electrons in a metal are free to move.*

6.3 KEY CONCEPT
Substances' properties depend on their bonds.

◀ BEFORE, you learned	▶ NOW, you will learn
• Chemical bonds hold the atoms of compounds together	• How metal atoms form chemical bonds with one another
• Chemical bonds involve the transfer or sharing of electrons	• How ionic and covalent bonds influence substances' properties
• Molecules have a structure	

VOCABULARY
metallic bond p. 184

EXPLORE Bonds in Metals
What objects conduct electricity?

PROCEDURE

1. Tape one end of a copper wire to one terminal of the battery. Attach the other end of the copper wire to the light bulb holder. Attach a second wire to the holder. Tape a third wire to the other terminal of the battery.

2. Touch the ends of both wires to objects around the classroom. Notice if the bulb lights or not.

WHAT DO YOU THINK?
- Which objects make the bulb light?
- How are these objects similar?

MATERIALS
- masking tape
- 3 pieces of copper wire (15 cm)
- D cell (battery)
- light bulb and holder
- objects to test

▼ **REMINDER**
Chemical bonds involve the sharing of or transfer of electrons.

Metals have unique bonds.

Metal atoms bond together by sharing their electrons with one another. The atoms share the electrons equally in all directions. The equal sharing allows the electrons to move easily among the atoms of the metal. This special type of bond is called a **metallic bond**.

The properties of metals are determined by metallic bonds. One common property of metals is that they are good conductors of electric current. The electrons in a metal flow through the material, carrying the electric current. The free movement of electrons among metal atoms also means that metals are good conductors of heat. Metals also typically have high melting points. Except for mercury, all metals are solids at room temperature.

184 Unit 2: Chemical Interactions

RESOURCES FOR DIFFERENTIATED INSTRUCTION

Below Level
UNIT RESOURCE BOOK
- Reading Study Guide A, pp. 95–96
- Decoding Support, p. 107

 **AUDIO CDS**

 Additional INVESTIGATION,
Weird Water, A, B, & C, pp. 119–127;
Teacher Instructions, pp. 329–330

Advanced
UNIT RESOURCE BOOK
Challenge and Extension, p. 101

English Learners
UNIT RESOURCE BOOK
Spanish Reading Study Guide, pp. 99–100

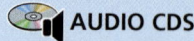 **AUDIO CDS**
- Audio Readings in Spanish
- Audio Readings (English)

Metallic Properties

Copper and other metals get their properties from metallic bonds.

The ability of electrons to move freely makes metals
- good conductors of electricity
- good conductors of heat
- easy to shape

copper wire
copper atom
electron

Two other properties of metals are that they are easily shaped by pounding and can be drawn into a wire. These properties are also explained by the nature of the metallic bond. In metallic compounds, atoms can slide past one another. It is as if the atoms are swimming in a pool of surrounding electrons. Pounding the metal simply moves these atoms into other positions. This property makes metals ideal for making coins.

 **What three properties do metals have because of metallic bonds?**

Ionic and covalent bonds give compounds certain properties.

The properties of a compound depend on the chemical bonds that hold its atoms together. For example, you can be pretty certain an ionic compound will be a solid at room temperature. Ionic compounds, in fact, usually have extremely high melting and boiling points because it takes a lot of energy to break all the bonds among all the ions in the crystal. The rigid crystal network also makes ionic compounds hard, brittle, and poor conductors of electricity. No moving electrical charges means no current will flow.

Ionic compounds, however, often dissolve easily in water, separating into positive ions and negative ions. The separated ions can move freely, making solutions of ionic compounds good conductors of electricity. Your body, in fact, uses ionic solutions to help transmit impulses between nerve and muscle cells. Exercise can rapidly deplete these ionic solutions in the body, so sports drinks contain ionic compounds.

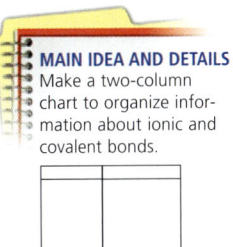

MAIN IDEA AND DETAILS
Make a two-column chart to organize information about ionic and covalent bonds.

Chapter 6: **Chemical Bonds and Compounds** 185

6.3 INSTRUCT

Real World Example
Most metals you use are not pure elements but mixtures of metals called alloys. Brass, bronze, and steel are all alloys. Alloys are most commonly formed from two metals that have similar atom sizes.

Teach Difficult Concepts
Students may have trouble with the distinction between chemical and physical properties. Consider copper and iron, two common metals used extensively in many everyday objects. Both elements have melting points over 1000°C, are easily shaped, and are good conductors of heat and electricity. All these properties are physical properties. The chemical properties of these elements are quite different.

- Iron is relatively reactive. It rusts and reacts with acids.
- Copper is relatively unreactive. It slowly reacts with materials in the air, as demonstrated by discolored pennies and the green patina that appears on copper items.

Ongoing Assessment
 *Answer: Metals are good conductors of heat and electricity and are easy to shape.*

DIFFERENTIATE INSTRUCTION

More Reading Support

A What property of the electrons in a metal gives the metal its properties?
They move easily.

English Learners Students may not understand how bulleted text can be read as three endings to the same sentence, as in the graphic at the top of this page.

The ability of electrons to move freely makes metals
- good conductors of electricity
- good conductors of heat
- easy to shape

Point out that each bulleted line completes the sentence.

Real World Example

Petroleum is a mixture of hydrocarbons, all of which are covalent compounds. The component parts of this mixture can be separated because some of the molecules are larger than others. The smaller molecules, such as those in gasoline, have lower boiling points. The larger molecules, such as those in lubricating oil, have higher boiling points. In fractional distillation, the different parts of petroleum are heated until they reach their boiling points. The vapors rise through a fractionating tower, where they cool. As each component liquifies, it is removed from the mixture.

Teach Difficult Concepts

Sometimes both covalent and ionic bonds occur in the same compound. Some ionic compounds contain ions called polyatomic ions. Polyatomic ions are covalently bonded groups of atoms that act as a single ion. Nitrate (NO_3^-), sulfate (SO_4^{2-}), and ammonium (NH_4^+) are examples of polyatomic ions. Explain that chemists often treat these groups as single ions because they commonly appear together.

Teaching with Technology

Have students use software to model polyatomic ions. Using one of the many periodic tables available on the Web, have students note common compounds formed by various elements. Challenge students to identify other elements that have different forms.

Ongoing Assessment

Analyze how ionic and covalent bonds influence substances' properties.

Ask: You can see that a specific compound comes in crystal form, but it melts at a fairly low temperature. What can you infer? *The compound probably has covalent bonds.*

A hot pool in Yellowstone Park's Upper Geyser Basin. These pools are often characterized by their striking colors.

Find out more about the properties of ionic and covalent compounds.

These compounds, such as potassium chloride, replace the ions lost during physical activity.

Mineral hot springs, like those found in Yellowstone National Park, are another example of ionic solutions. Many of the ionic compounds dissolved in these hot springs contain the element sulfur, which can have an unpleasant odor. Evidence of these ionic compounds can be seen in the white deposits around the pool's rim.

Covalent compounds have almost the exact opposite properties of ionic compounds. Since the atoms are organized as individual molecules, melting or boiling a covalent compound does not require breaking chemical bonds. Therefore, covalent compounds often melt and boil at lower temperatures than ionic compounds. Unlike ionic compounds, molecules stay together when dissolved in water, which means covalent compounds are poor conductors of electricity. Table sugar, for example, does not conduct an electric current when in solution.

Bonds can make the same element look different.

Covalent bonds do not always form small individual molecules. This explains how the element carbon can exist in three very different forms—diamond, graphite, and fullerene. The properties of each form depend on how the carbon atoms are bonded to each other.

Diamond is the hardest natural substance. This property makes diamond useful for cutting other substances. Diamonds are made entirely of carbon. Each carbon atom forms covalent bonds with four other carbon atoms. The pattern of linked atoms extends throughout the entire volume of a diamond crystal. This three-dimensional structure of carbon atoms gives diamonds their strength—diamond bonds do not break easily.

186 Unit 2: Chemical Interactions

DIFFERENTIATE INSTRUCTION

 **More Reading Support**

B Are covalent compounds good conductors of electricity when dissolved? Why or why not? *No, molecules stay together and do not conduct an electric current.*

Advanced Have students investigate buckminsterfullerene. Why do scientists want to make it? What uses could it have?

 Challenge and Extension, p. 101

Additional Investigation To reinforce Section 2.3 learning goals, use the following full-period investigation:

Additional INVESTIGATION, Weird Water, A, B, & C, pp. 119–127, 329–330
(Advanced students should complete Levels B and C.)

Another form of carbon is graphite. Graphite is the dark, slippery component of pencil "lead." Graphite has a different structure from diamond, although both are networks of interconnected atoms. Each carbon atom in graphite forms covalent bonds with three other atoms to form two-dimensional layers. These layers stack on top of one another like sheets of paper. The layers can slide past one another easily. Graphite feels slippery and is used as a lubricant to reduce friction between metal parts of machines.

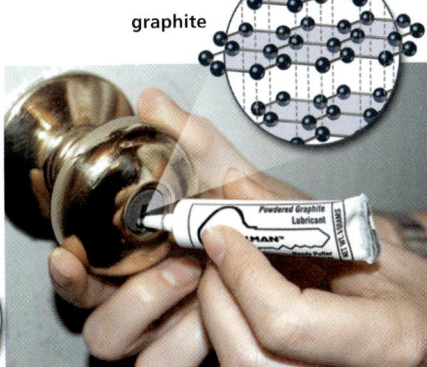
graphite

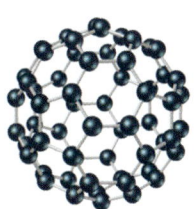
diamond

A third form of carbon, fullerene, contains large molecules. One type of fullerene, called buckminsterfullerene, has molecules shaped like a soccer ball. In 1985 chemists made a fullerene molecule consisting of 60 carbon atoms. Since then, many similar molecules have been made, ranging from 20 to more than 100 atoms per molecule.

buckminsterfullerene

6.3 Review

KEY CONCEPTS
1. How do metal atoms bond together?
2. Why do ionic compounds have high melting points?
3. What are three forms of the element carbon?

CRITICAL THINKING
4. **Apply** A compound known as cubic boron nitride has a structure similar to that of a diamond. What properties would you expect it to have?
5. **Infer** Sterling silver is a combination of silver and copper. How are the silver and copper atoms held together?

CHALLENGE
6. **Infer** Why might the water in mineral springs be a better conductor of electricity than drinking water?

Chapter 6: **Chemical Bonds and Compounds** 187

CHAPTER INVESTIGATION

Focus

PURPOSE To investigate properties of substances that have different types of bonds

OVERVIEW Students will examine ionic and covalent compounds and metals to determine their properties. They will use the properties to characterize three compounds. Students will find the following:

- Sugar is a covalent compound.
- Epsom salts is an ionic compound.
- Iron is a metal.

Lab Preparation

- Epsom salts and sugar can be purchased from local sources.
- If time is limited, assemble the conductivity testers ahead of time and place the samples in labeled cups.
- Prior to the investigation, have students read through the investigation and prepare their data tables. Or you may wish to copy and distribute datasheets and rubrics.

 UNIT RESOURCE BOOK, pp. 110–118

 SCIENCE TOOLKIT, F14

Lab Management

- Have students use laboratory scoops or small pieces of paper to add the materials to the test tubes.
- Any solutions can be poured down the drain with plenty of water. Save uncontaminated iron for reuse.

SAFETY Students should wear safety goggles and aprons throughout the investigation. Be sure proper fire safety is observed when candles are being used.

INCLUSION For students who are visually impaired, wire the conductivity tester to a low-voltage buzzer instead of a light bulb.

CHAPTER INVESTIGATION

Chemical Bonds

OVERVIEW AND PURPOSE Chemists can identify the type of bonds in a substance by examining its properties. In this investigation you will examine the properties of different substances and use what you have learned about chemical bonds to identify the type of bond each substance contains. You will

- observe the structure of substances with a hand lens
- test the conductivity of substances
- determine the melting point of substances

 Problem

How can you determine the type of chemical bond a substance has?

 Hypothesize

Write three hypotheses in "if . . . , then . . . , because . . ." form to answer the problem question for each bond type—ionic, covalent, and metallic.

 Procedure

MATERIALS
- 3 wire leads with alligator clips
- battery
- zinc and copper strips
- light bulb and socket
- test compounds
- 3 plastic cups
- distilled water
- beaker
- construction paper
- hand lens
- plastic spoon
- 3 test tubes
- test-tube rack
- candle
- wire test-tube holder

1. Create a data table similar to the one shown on the sample notebook page.

2. To build the conductivity tester, connect the first wire to one terminal of the battery and to one of the metal strips. Attach the second wire to the other terminal and to the lamp socket. Finally, connect the lamp socket to the third wire, and connect the other end of this wire to the second metal strip.

3. To make sure your tester works properly, touch the tips of the metal strips together. If the bulb lights, the tester is working properly. If not, check the connections carefully.

4. Get the following test compounds from your teacher: Epsom salts ($MgSO_4$), sugar ($C_{12}H_{22}O_{11}$), and iron filings (Fe). For each substance, put about 20 grams in a cup and label it.

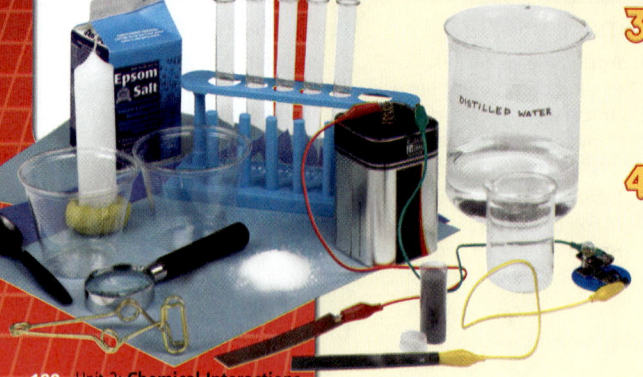

188 Unit 2: **Chemical Interactions**

INVESTIGATION RESOURCES

 CHAPTER INVESTIGATION, Chemical Bonds
- Level A, pp. 110–113
- Level B, pp. 114–117
- Level C, p. 118

Advanced students should complete Levels B & C.

 Writing a Lab Report, D12–13

Technology Resources

Customize this student lab as needed or look for an alternative. Print rubrics to assess student lab reports.

 Lab Generator CD-ROM

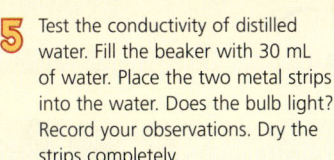

5. Test the conductivity of distilled water. Fill the beaker with 30 mL of water. Place the two metal strips into the water. Does the bulb light? Record your observations. Dry the strips completely.

6. Place dry Epsom salts on dark paper. Observe them with a hand lens. Do you see any kind of patterns in the different grains? Put the salts between the metal strips. Can you get the bulb to light by bringing the strips closer together? Record your observations.

7. Add all but a small amount of the Epsom salts to the beaker of water. Stir well. Repeat the conductivity test. What happens when you put the metal strips into the solution? Record your results.

8. Rinse and dry the beaker. Repeat steps 6–7 with other test substances. Record your results.

9. Put the remainder of each test substance into its own clean, dry test tube. Label the tubes. Light the candle. Use a test tube holder to hold each compound over the candle flame for 2 minutes. Do you notice any signs of melting? Record your observations.

Observe and Analyze

1. **RECORD OBSERVATIONS** Be sure you have entered all your observations in your data table.

2. **CLASSIFY** Using the periodic table, find the elements these compounds contain. How might consulting the periodic table help you determine what type of bond exists in the compound?

Conclude

1. **INTERPRET** Review your recorded observations. Classify the compounds as having ionic, covalent, or metallic bonds. Fill in the last row of the data table with your conclusions.

2. **INFER** Compare your results with your hypotheses. Did your results support your hypotheses?

3. **EVALUATE** Describe possible limitations, errors, or places where errors might have occurred.

4. **APPLY** Electrocardiograms are graphs that show the electrical activity of the heart. When an electrocardiogram is made, a paste of sodium chloride is used to hold small metal discs on the patient's skin. What property of ionic compounds does this medical test make use of?

INVESTIGATE Further

CHALLENGE To grow crystals, put about 60 grams of Epsom salts into a baby-food jar that is half full of hot water. Do the same using a second jar containing about 60 grams of sugar. Cover and shake the jars for a count of 60. Line two clean jar lids with dark paper. Brush or spoon a thin coating of each liquid over the paper. Let them stand in a warm place. After several days, observe the crystals that form, using a hand lens.

Chemical Bonds
Problem How can you determine the type of chemical bond a substance has?

Hypothesize

Observe and Analyze

Table 1: Properties of Bonds

Property	Epsom Salts (MgSO4)	Sugar (C12H22O11)	Iron Filings (Fe)
Crystal structure			
Conductivity of solid			
Conductivity in water			
Melting			
Bond type			

Conclude

Chapter 6: **Chemical Bonds and Compounds** 189

Observe and Analyze

1. The solid iron and the Epsom-salts solution conduct a current. Only the sugar melts. Sugar and Epsom salts have a crystal structure. The sugar crystal and Epsom salts have a regular shape.

2. Epsom salts contains magnesium, which is a group 2 metal, so it is probably ionic. Sugar ($C_{12}H_{22}O_{11}$) contains no metals, so it is probably covalent. Iron is a transition metal, so it has metallic bonds.

Conclude

1. Epsom salts is ionic, sugar is covalent, and iron contains metallic bonds.

2. Answers will vary.

3. Sample answer: The water used might have contained ions, the solutions might not have contained enough solute, or the hand lens may not have been powerful enough to reveal crystal structure.

4. They conduct electric current.

INVESTIGATE Further

CHALLENGE The crystals will look irregular.

Post-Lab Discussion

Ask: Why did you need to do more than one test to determine sugar was a covalent compound? *Sugar was soluble in water and had a crystal shape just like ionic compounds.*

CHAPTER 6 • REVIEW

BACK TO

Have students look back at the photograph on pp. 166–167. Ask them to use the photograph to summarize what they have learned about chemical bonding and to use the skydiving analogy to describe bonding. *Just as the skydivers joined hands, atoms connect by chemical bonds. Skydivers hold hands just as atoms share electrons.*

◯ KEY CONCEPTS SUMMARY

SECTION 6.1
Ask: At room temperature, the element nitrogen is a gas. Can you assume that all compounds containing nitrogen are gases? *No. Compounds often have very different physical properties.*

SECTION 6.2
Ask: How is a polar covalent bond similar to both an ionic bond and a covalent bond? *Although electrons are still being shared by the atoms, they spend more time nearer to one atom.*

SECTION 6.3
Ask: What kind of compound would you expect to find in a battery, ionic or covalent? Why? *ionic; ionic compounds conduct electricity in solution.*

Review Concepts

- Big Idea Flow Chart, p. T9
- Chapter Outline, pp. T15–T16

---

6 Chapter Review

the BIG idea
The properties of compounds depend on their atoms and chemical bonds.

CONTENT REVIEW
CLASSZONE.COM

◯ KEY CONCEPTS SUMMARY

 Elements combine to form compounds.
- Compounds have different properties from the elements that made them.
- Atoms combine in predictable numbers.

calcium (Ca) + chlorine (Cl$_2$) = calcium chloride (CaCl$_2$)

VOCABULARY
chemical formula p. 171
subscript p. 171

2 Chemical bonds hold compounds together.
- Chemical bonds between atoms involve electrons.
- Atoms can transfer electrons.
- Atoms can share electrons.
- Chemical bonds give all materials their structure.

ionic bond   covalent bond

VOCABULARY
ionic bond p. 176
covalent bond p. 178
molecule p. 179
polar covalent bond p. 179

3 Substances' properties depend on their bonds.
- Metals have unique bonds.
- Ionic and covalent bonds give compounds certain properties.
- Bonds can make the same element look different.

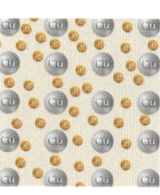  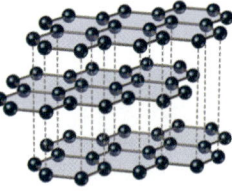

copper   diamond fragment   graphite fragment

VOCABULARY
metallic bond p. 184

Technology Resources

Have students visit **ClassZone.com** or use the CD-ROM for a cumulative review of concepts.

 CONTENT REVIEW

 CONTENT REVIEW CD-ROM

Engage students in a whole-class interactive review of Key Concepts. Edit content as you wish.

 POWER PRESENTATIONS

Reviewing Vocabulary

Copy and complete the table below. Under each bond type, describe
- how electrons are distributed
- how the compound is structured
- one of the properties of the compound containing this type of bond

Some of the table has been filled out for you.

Ionic Bonds	Covalent Bonds	Metallic Bonds
1.	shared electron pair	2.
3.	4.	close-packed atoms in sea of electrons
have high melting points	5.	6.

Reviewing Key Concepts

Multiple Choice *Choose the letter of the best answer.*

7. Most substances are
   a. elements
   b. compounds
   c. metals
   d. nonmetals

8. All compounds are made of
   a. atoms of two or more elements
   b. two or more atoms of the same element
   c. atoms arranged in a crystal
   d. atoms joined by covalent bonds

9. The chemical formula for a compound having one barium (Ba) ion and two chloride (Cl) ions is
   a. BCl
   b. BaCl
   c. BaCl$_2$
   d. Ba$_2$Cl$_2$

10. The 4 in the chemical formula CH$_4$ means there are
    a. four carbon atoms to one hydrogen atom
    b. four carbon and four hydrogen atoms
    c. four hydrogen atoms to one carbon atom
    d. four total carbon CH combinations

11. The compound KBr has the name
    a. potassium bromide
    b. potassium bromine
    c. bromide potassium
    d. bromine potassium

12. An atom becomes a positive ion when it
    a. is attracted to all nearby atoms
    b. gains an electron from another atom
    c. loses an electron to another atom
    d. shares an electron with another atom

13. A polar covalent bond forms when two atoms
    a. share one electron equally
    b. share two electrons equally
    c. share one electron unequally
    d. share two electrons unequally

14. Metallic bonds make many metals
    a. poor conductors of heat
    b. liquid at room temperature
    c. difficult to shape
    d. good conductors of electricity

15. Three forms of carbon are
    a. diamond, graphite, and salt
    b. diamond, graphite, and fullerene
    c. graphite, salt, and carbonate
    d. diamond, salt, and fullerene

Short Answer *Write a short answer to each question.*

16. Why does a mixture of sodium chloride and water conduct electricity but a sodium chloride crystal does not?

17. Describe what makes diamond and graphite, two forms of the element carbon, so different.

Chapter 6: **Chemical Bonds and Compounds** 191

Reviewing Vocabulary

1. transferred electrons
2. sea of electrons
3. crystal
4. individual molecules
5. have low melting points
6. conduct an electric current

Reviewing Key Concepts

7. b
8. a
9. c
10. c
11. a
12. c
13. d
14. d
15. b
16. Charged particles are free to move in a solution of sodium and chloride ions in water.
17. The carbon atoms are bonded differently, giving them different structures.

ASSESSMENT RESOURCES

UNIT ASSESSMENT BOOK
- Chapter Test A, pp. 25–28
- Chapter Test B, pp. 29–32
- Chapter Test C, pp. 33–36
- Alternative Assessment, pp. 37–38

SPANISH ASSESSMENT BOOK
Spanish Chapter Test, pp. 237–240

Technology Resources

Edit test items and answer choices.

 Test Generator CD-ROM

Visit **ClassZone.com** to extend test practice.

 Test Practice

Thinking Critically

18. NH_3

19. There should be a negative charge by nitrogen and positive charge by hydrogen.

20. $MgCl_2$

21. Temperature and heat cause bonds to be rearranged.

22. Seawater has a greater concentration of ions.

23. The attraction among the metal atoms is the same in all directions so they can slide past each other when pressure is applied.

24. All elements detected on Mars are present on Earth. Thus, it is unlikely that different bonds exist there.

25. Ions attract other ions from all sides, and so do not form individual molecules.

26. potassium chloride; ionic

27. I. potassium, sulfur, and oxygen; 7
    II. carbon and fluorine; 5
    III. carbon and hydrogen; 14
    IV. potassium and chlorine; 2

28. II. 1:4; III. 4:10; IV. 1:1; I. potassium to sulfur 2:1, sulfur to oxygen 1:4, potassium to oxygen 2:4

29. The metals gain and lose electrons relatively easily. Both metals and saltwater conduct an electric current well.

30. Hydrogen can form only one bond. It has only one electron.

the BIG idea

31. Skydivers hold hands much as atoms share electrons to form bonds. Skydivers might also hold onto a rope; they can share a rope.

32. Phosphorus can have different patterns of bonding.

UNIT PROJECTS

Collect schedules, materials lists, and questions. Be sure dates and materials are obtainable and questions are focused.

 Unit Projects, pp. 5–10

192 Unit 2: **Chemical Interactions**

Thinking Critically

Use the illustration above to answer the next two questions.

18. **IDENTIFY** Write the chemical formula for the molecule pictured above.

19. **ANALYZE** The nitrogen atom has a far greater attraction for electrons than hydrogen atoms. Copy the molecule pictured above and indicate which parts of the molecule have a slightly positive charge and which parts have a slightly negative charge.

20. **PREDICT** The chemical formula for calcium chloride is $CaCl_2$. What would you predict the formula for magnesium chloride to be? [**Hint:** Find magnesium on the periodic table.]

21. **INFER** When scientists make artificial diamonds, they sometimes subject graphite to very high temperatures and pressures. What do you think happens to change the graphite into diamond?

22. **SYNTHESIZE** Why would seawater be a better conductor of electricity than river water?

23. **ANALYZE** How does the nature of the metallic bond explain the observation that most metals can be drawn into a wire?

24. **EVALUATE** Do you think the types of bonds you've studied occur on the planet Mars? Explain.

25. **INFER** Why don't we use the term *ionic molecule*?

Use the chemical formulas below and a periodic table to answer the next three questions.

Compound
I. K_2SO_4
II. CF_4
III. C_4H_{10}
IV. KCl

26. **APPLY** Name compound IV. Does this compound have ionic or covalent bonds?

27. **ANALYZE** Name the elements in each compound. Tell how many atoms are in each compound.

28. **CALCULATE** Express the ratio of atoms in compounds II, III, and IV. For compound I, express all three ratios.

29. **APPLY** By 1800 Alessandro Volta had made the first electric battery. He placed pieces of cardboard soaked in saltwater in between alternating zinc and silver discs. What properties of the metals and the saltwater made them good materials for a battery?

30. **PREDICT** What is the maximum number of covalent bonds that a hydrogen atom can form? Explain your answer.

the BIG idea

31. **DRAW CONCLUSIONS** Look at the photograph on pages 166–167 again. Can you now recognize any similarities between how the skydivers stay together and how atoms stay together?

32. **APPLY** Phosphorus can be a strange element. Pure phosphorus is sometimes white, black, or red. What can account for the differences in appearance?

UNIT PROJECTS

If you need to create graphs or other visuals for your project, be sure you have graph paper, poster board, markers, or other supplies.

192 Unit 2: Chemical Interactions

MONITOR AND RETEACH

If students have trouble applying the concepts in items 26–28, have them make a labeled diagram of groups 1, 2, and 17 from the periodic table. Their diagrams need to include only the symbols of the elements. Students can use these diagrams to familiarize themselves with what elements are in the same group and thus form similar bonds.

Students may benefit from summarizing one or more sections of the chapter.

 Summarizing the Chapter, pp. 128–129

Standardized Test Practice

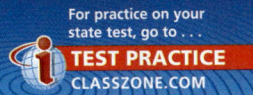

For practice on your state test, go to...
TEST PRACTICE
CLASSZONE.COM

Interpreting Tables

The table below lists some of the characteristics of substances that contain different types of bonds. Use the table to answer the questions.

Bond Type	Usually Forms Between	Electrons	Properties	Examples
Ionic	an atom of a metal and an atom of a nonmetal	transferred between atoms	• high melting points • conducts electricity when in water	BaS, BaBr$_2$, Ca$_3$N$_2$, LiCl, ZnO
Covalent	atoms of nonmetallic elements	shared between atoms but often not equally	• low melting points • does not conduct electricity	C$_2$H$_6$, C, Cl$_2$, H$_2$, AsCl$_3$
Metallic	atoms of metallic elements	freely moving about the atoms	• high melting points • conducts electricity at all times • easily shaped	Ca, Fe, Na, Cu, Zn

1. Which of these compounds would you expect to have the highest melting point?
   a. C$_2$H$_6$ c. AsCl$_3$
   b. Cl$_2$ d. BaBr$_2$

2. Which substance is likely to be easily shaped?
   a. BaBr$_2$ c. Na
   b. LiCl   d. C

3. In the compound LiCl, electrons are
   a. shared equally
   b. shared but not equally
   c. transferred between atoms to form ions
   d. freely moving among the atoms

4. Which of the following is an ionic compound?
   a. C$_2$H$_6$ c. AsCl$_3$
   b. Cl$_2$ d. ZnO

5. Which of the following compounds has a low melting point?
   a. Cl$_2$ c. Cu
   b. ZnO   d. BaBr$_2$

6. A solid mass of which substance would conduct electricity?
   a. Ca$_3$N$_2$ c. Cu
   b. LiCl   d. AsCl$_3$

Extended Response

Answer the next two questions in detail. Include some of the terms from the list in the box. Underline each term you use in your answer.

share electron	transfer electron
freely moving electrons	charge
compound	chemical formula

7. Compare how electrons are involved in making the three main types of bonds: ionic, covalent, and metallic.

8. Just about 100 elements occur naturally. There are, however, millions of different materials. How can so few basic substances make so many different materials?

Chapter 6: **Chemical Bonds and Compounds** 193

Interpreting Tables
1. d   3. c   5. a
2. c   4. d   6. c

Extended Response

7. RUBRIC

4 points for a response that correctly describes all three types of bonds and uses the following terms accurately:
- share electron
- freely moving electrons
- compound
- transfer electron
- charge

An atom might <u>transfer</u> one or more <u>electrons</u> to another atom to form <u>charged</u> particles. An ionic bond forms when these oppositely charged particles attract each other. Atoms <u>share electrons</u> when covalent bonds form. Both ionic and covalent bonds form compounds. Metallic bonds form when <u>freely moving electrons</u> surround metal ions and are easily attracted to all of them.

3 points correctly describes two types and uses four terms accurately
2 points correctly describes two types and uses two terms accurately
1 point correctly describes one type and uses one term accurately

8. RUBRIC

4 points for a response that answers the question completely and uses the following term accurately:
- compound

Sample: Atoms of one element can combine with the atoms of different elements. The same two atoms can sometimes combine in different ratios. Just as the same letters may form several different words, the same atoms may form several different <u>compounds</u>.

3 points incomplete answer to the question and uses the term accurately
2 points incomplete answer to the question and uses the term inaccurately
1 point incomplete answer to the question and does not use the term

METACOGNITIVE ACTIVITY

Have students answer the following questions in their **Science Notebook:**
1. What did you find the most challenging to understand about chemical bonds?
2. What questions do you still have about chemical bonds?
3. How have you solved a problem while working on your Unit Project?

CHAPTER 7 Chemical Reactions

Physical Science
UNIFYING PRINCIPLES

PRINCIPLE 1
Matter is made of particles too small to see.

PRINCIPLE 2
Matter changes form and moves from place to place.

PRINCIPLE 3
Energy changes from one form to another, but it cannot be created or destroyed.

PRINCIPLE 4
Physical forces affect the movement of all matter on Earth and throughout the universe.

Unit 2: Chemical Interactions
BIG IDEAS

CHAPTER 5
Atomic Structure and the Periodic Table
A substance's atomic structure determines its physical and chemical properties.

CHAPTER 6
Chemical Bonds and Compounds
The properties of compounds depend on their atoms and chemical bonds.

CHAPTER 7
Chemical Reactions
Chemical reactions form new substances by breaking and making chemical bonds.

CHAPTER 8
Solutions
When substances dissolve to form a solution, the properties of the mixture change.

CHAPTER 9
Carbon in Life and Materials
Carbon is essential to living things and to modern materials.

CHAPTER 7
KEY CONCEPTS

SECTION 1	SECTION 2	SECTION 3	SECTION 4
Chemical reactions alter arrangements of atoms.	**The masses of reactants and products are equal.**	**Chemical reactions involve energy changes.**	**Life and industry depend on chemical reactions.**
1. Atoms interact in chemical reactions. 2. Chemical reactions can be classified. 3. The rates of chemical reactions can vary.	1. Careful observations led to the discovery of the conservation of mass. 2. Chemical reactions can be described by chemical equations. 3. Chemical equations must be balanced.	1. Chemical reactions release or absorb energy. 2–3. Exothermic reactions release energy; endothermic reactions absorb energy. 4. Exothermic and endothermic reactions work together to supply energy.	1. Living things require chemical reactions. 2. Chemical reactions are used in technology. 3. Industry uses chemical reactions to make useful products.

The Big Idea Flow Chart is available on p. T17 in the **UNIT TRANSPARENCY BOOK**.

Previewing Content

SECTION

Chemical reactions alter arrangements of atoms. pp. 197–205

1. Atoms interact in chemical reactions.
Substances change in two ways.
- In physical changes, the substance itself does not change, although its appearance or some of its properties may change.
- In chemical changes, a substance changes into different substances. A **chemical reaction** rearranges atoms. Bonds are broken in **reactants,** and new bonds are formed in the **products.**

Evidence of a chemical reaction includes a change in color or temperature or the formation of a **precipitate** or a gas.

2. Chemical reactions can be classified.
A synthesis reaction combines two or more simpler reactants to form a new, more complex product. A decomposition reaction breaks a reactant into two or more simpler products. A combustion reaction always involves oxygen. The other reactant often contains carbon and hydrogen.

3. The rates of chemical reactions can vary.
Four factors can change the rate of a chemical reaction:
- the concentration of reactants
- the surface area of reactants
- the temperature of the reaction mixture
- the presence of a catalyst

A **catalyst** takes part in a reaction but is not consumed during the reaction. It decreases the energy needed to start a reaction, and it increases the reaction rate. The diagram below represents the effect of a catalyst called an enzyme on a reaction.

Reactants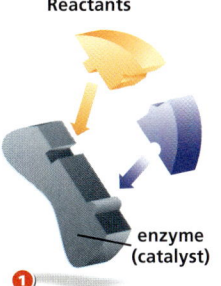
① An enzyme is a catalyst for chemical reactions in living things.

Reactants combined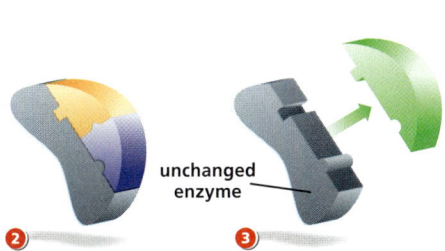
② Enzymes allow reactions that would not normally take place to occur.

New product
③ A new product is made, but the enzyme is not changed by the reaction.

SECTION

The masses of reactants and products are equal. pp. 206–213

1. Careful observations led to the discovery of the conservation of mass.
Antoine Lavoisier's careful quantitative experiments showed that in a chemical reaction, the total mass of reactants is always equal to the total mass of products. In other words, mass is neither created nor destroyed during chemical reactions.

2. Chemical reactions can be described by chemical equations.
A chemical equation represents the way in which a reaction rearranges the atoms in chemicals. To write an equation, you must know the reactants and products, their chemical formulas, and the direction of the reaction. The arrow in an equation indicates the direction of the reaction.

$$C + O_2 \rightarrow CO_2$$

3. Chemical equations must be balanced.
A chemical equation must reflect the law of conservation of mass, so each side of an equation must have the same number of atoms of each element.

- An equation is balanced by changing the number of molecules of reactants or products represented. This is done by adding coefficients in front of some of the chemical formulas, as shown in the equations below.

$$N_2 + H_2 \rightarrow NH_3 \qquad N_2 + 3H_2 \rightarrow 2NH_3$$
Unbalanced Equation Balanced Equation

- When balancing an equation, subscripts in the chemical formulas of the reactants and products cannot be changed. Changing a subscript in a chemical formula changes the substance represented by the formula. Therefore, equations must be balanced by changing coefficients, which changes only the amounts of the reactants and products represented by the equation.

Common Misconceptions

BURNING IS A CHEMICAL CHANGE Students often think that burning is a physical change. Burning, a combustion reaction, is a chemical change that requires oxygen and usually produces water, carbon, and carbon dioxide.

 This misconception is addressed on p. 199.

MISCONCEPTION DATABASE
CLASSZONE.COM Background on student misconceptions

THE INTRINSIC MOTION OF PARTICLES IN MATTER Students may not understand that all particles in matter, including those in solid objects, have kinetic energy and are in constant, random motion.

 This misconception is addressed on p. 203.

Previewing Content

SECTION 3 Chemical reactions involve energy changes. pp. 214–221

1. Chemical reactions release or absorb energy.
Chemical reactions break the chemical bonds in reactants and make new bonds in the products. Breaking bonds requires energy; forming bonds releases energy. The energy in chemical bonds is called **bond energy.**
- If more energy is released when the bonds in products form than is used to break the bonds in reactants, energy is released by the **exothermic reaction.**
- If more energy is needed to break the bonds in reactants than is released when the bonds in products form, energy is absorbed by the **endothermic reaction.**

2. Exothermic reactions release energy.
In exothermic reactions, the reactants have lower bond energies than the products, so energy is released, often as heat and light. All common combustion reactions are exothermic. Below is an energy diagram showing an exothermic reaction.

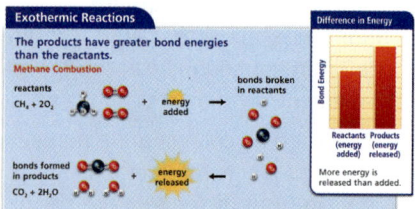

3. Endothermic reactions absorb energy.
In endothermic reactions, the reactants have higher bond energies than the products, so energy is absorbed. Below is an energy diagram showing an endothermic reaction.

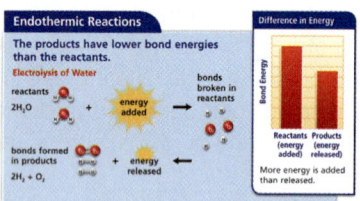

4. Exothermic and endothermic reactions work together to supply energy.
Endothermic and exothermic reactions can form a cycle. For example, the energy stored by the series of endothermic reactions in photosynthesis can be released by exothermic reactions such as combustion.

Common Misconceptions

BALANCING EQUATIONS Some students may try to balance chemical equations by changing the chemical formulas rather than adding coefficients. Changing the formulas changes the substances involved, not the amounts.

 This misconception is addressed on p. 210.

SECTION 4 Life and industry depend on chemical reactions. pp. 222–227

1. Living things require chemical reactions.
Photosynthesis is an endothermic process. During photosynthesis, plants absorb energy from sunlight and store this energy in the chemical bonds of sugars. These sugars are broken down during the exothermic reactions of **respiration,** the process that produces energy for living organisms. The processes of photosynthesis and respiration are essentially the reverse of one another.

Photosynthesis:
$6CO_2 + 6H_2O + \text{energy} \rightarrow C_6H_{12}O_6 + 6O_2$

Respiration:
$C_6H_{12}O_6 + 6O_2 \rightarrow 6CO_2 + 6H_2O + \text{energy}$

Most reactions that take place in living organisms use enzymes, catalysts that cause reactions to take place at the relatively low temperatures of living tissue.

2. Chemical reactions are used in technology.
Combustion engines use gasoline in a chemical reaction that releases energy. Catalytic converters are technological devices that remove unwanted pollutants from the burning of gasoline in automobile engines. These devices use metals as catalysts. The metal catalysts in a catalytic converter, which include platinum, palladium, and rhodium, allow reactions between exhaust gases to occur. These reactions change the exhaust gases into gases that are typical parts of Earth's atmosphere, such as oxygen, nitrogen, water vapor, and carbon dioxide.

3. Industry uses chemical reactions to make useful products.
The electronics industry produces silicon for microchips by refining SiO_2 (quartz) into pure silicon. Silicon treated with photoresist and light produces miniature electronic circuits.

MISCONCEPTION DATABASE
CLASSZONE.COM Background on student misconceptions

BREAKING BONDS A very common misconception is that energy is released when bonds are broken. The overall reaction may release energy, but energy is always required to break bonds.

 This misconception is addressed on p. 215.

Previewing Labs

EXPLORE the BIG idea

Changing Steel Wool, p. 195
Students observe a chemical reaction that involves the rusting of steel wool.

TIME 10 minutes
MATERIALS small lump of steel wool, cup, vinegar, tongs, small plastic bottle, balloon

A Different Rate, p. 195
Students vary the temperature of a reaction mixture to explore how reaction rate is affected by temperature.

TIME 10 minutes
MATERIALS 2 plastic cups, hot and cold tap water, 2 seltzer tablets, stopwatch

Internet Activity: Reactions, p. 195
Students explore chemical reactions and how to balance chemical equations.

TIME 20 minutes
MATERIALS computer with Internet access

SECTION 1

EXPLORE Chemical Changes, p. 197
Students examine the evidence for a chemical change caused by a chemical reaction.

TIME 10 minutes
MATERIALS 25 mL vinegar, clear bowl, plastic spoon, spoonful of table salt, 20 pennies, large ungalvanized iron nail

INVESTIGATE Chemical Reactions, p. 202
Students vary the surface area of a reactant in a chemical reaction to infer how surface area affects reaction rate.

TIME 15 minutes
MATERIALS 2 seltzer tablets, 2 plastic cups, warm tap water, stopwatch

SECTION 2

INVESTIGATE Conservation of Mass, p. 207
Students measure the mass of the reactants, products, and experimental setup in a chemical reaction in order to observe the law of conservation of mass.

TIME 35 minutes
MATERIALS teaspoon, 2 tsp baking soda, funnel, balloon, 2 tsp vinegar, plastic bottle, balance

SECTION 3

EXPLORE Energy Changes, p. 214
Students measure changes in temperature during a chemical process in order to identify a transfer of energy.

TIME 10 minutes
MATERIALS graduated cylinder, hot tap water, plastic cup, thermometer, stopwatch, plastic spoon, 5 tsp Epsom salts

**CHAPTER INVESTIGATION
Exothermic or Endothermic?,** pp. 220–221
Students classify each of two processes as exothermic or endothermic by measuring the change in temperature of reaction mixtures.

TIME 40 minutes
MATERIALS graduated cylinder, 30 mL hydrogen peroxide, 2 100 mL beakers, 2 thermometers, stopwatch, measuring spoons, 1 g yeast, balance, plastic spoon, large plastic cup, hot tap water, 30 mL vinegar, 1 g baking soda

SECTION 4

INVESTIGATE Sugar Combustion, p. 223
Students infer that different experimental conditions can determine whether a reaction happens.

TIME 20 minutes
MATERIALS candle, matches, tongs, 2 sugar cubes, stopwatch, ashes

Additional INVESTIGATION, Modeling Chemical Reactions, A, B, & C, pp. 189–197; Teacher Instructions, pp. 329–330

Previewing Chapter Resources

	INTEGRATED TECHNOLOGY	LABS AND ACTIVITIES
CHAPTER 7 **Chemical Reactions**	**CLASSZONE.COM** • eEdition Plus • EasyPlanner Plus • Misconception Database • Content Review • Test Practice • Visualizations • Resource Centers • Internet Activity: Reactions • Math Tutorial **SCILINKS.ORG** **CD-ROMS** • eEdition • EasyPlanner • Power Presentations • Content Review • Lab Generator • Test Generator **AUDIO CDS** • Audio Readings • Audio Readings in Spanish	EXPLORE the Big Idea, p. 195 • Changing Steel Wool • A Different Rate • Internet Activity: Reactions **UNIT RESOURCE BOOK** Unit Projects, pp. 5–10 **Lab Generator CD-ROM** Generate customized labs.
SECTION 1 **Chemical reactions alter arrangements of atoms.** pp. 197–205 Time: 2 periods (1 block) Lesson Plan, pp. 130–131	• **VISUALIZATION,** Concentration and Reaction Rate • **RESOURCE CENTER,** Catalysts • **MATH TUTORIAL** **UNIT TRANSPARENCY BOOK** • Big Idea Flow Chart, p. T17 • Daily Vocabulary Scaffolding, p. T18 • Note-Taking Model, p. T19 • 3-Minute Warm-Up, p. T20	• EXPLORE Chemical Changes, p. 197 • INVESTIGATE Chemical Reactions, p. 202 • Math in Science, p. 205 **UNIT RESOURCE BOOK** • Datasheet, Chemical Reactions, p. 139 • Additional INVESTIGATION, Modeling Chemical Reactions, A, B, & C, pp. 189–197 • Math Support & Practice, pp. 178–179
SECTION 2 **The masses of reactants and products are equal.** pp. 206–213 Time: 2 periods (1 block) Lesson Plan, pp. 141–142	**UNIT TRANSPARENCY BOOK** • Daily Vocabulary Scaffolding, p. T18 • 3-Minute Warm-Up, p. T20	• INVESTIGATE Conservation of Mass, p. 207 • Science on the Job, p. 213 **UNIT RESOURCE BOOK** Datasheet, Conservation of Mass, p. 150
SECTION 3 **Chemical reactions involve energy changes.** pp. 214–221 Time: 3 periods (1.5 blocks) Lesson Plan, pp. 152–153	**VISUALIZATION,** Endothermic and Exothermic Reactions **UNIT TRANSPARENCY BOOK** • Daily Vocabulary Scaffolding, p. T18 • 3-Minute Warm-Up, p. T21	• EXPLORE Energy Changes, p. 214 • CHAPTER INVESTIGATION, Exothermic or Endothermic?, pp. 220–221 **UNIT RESOURCE BOOK** CHAPTER INVESTIGATION, Exothermic or Endothermic?, A, B, & C, pp. 180–188
SECTION 4 **Life and industry depend on chemical reactions.** pp. 222–227 Time: 3 periods (1.5 blocks) Lesson Plan, pp. 162–163	**UNIT TRANSPARENCY BOOK** • Big Idea Flow Chart, p. T17 • Daily Vocabulary Scaffolding, p. T18 • 3-Minute Warm-Up, p. T21 • "Chemical Reactions in Catalytic Converters" Visual, p. T22 • Chapter Outline, pp. T23–T24	INVESTIGATE Sugar Combustion, p. 223 **UNIT RESOURCE BOOK** Datasheet, Sugar Combustion, p. 171

KEY TO ICONS 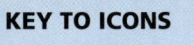 CD/CD-ROM Teacher Edition UNIT TRANSPARENCY BOOK 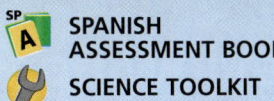 SPANISH ASSESSMENT BOOK
INTERNET 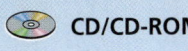 Pupil Edition UNIT RESOURCE BOOK UNIT ASSESSMENT BOOK SCIENCE TOOLKIT

READING AND REINFORCEMENT

- Four Square, B22–23
- Combination Notes, C36
- Daily Vocabulary Scaffolding, H1–8

 UNIT RESOURCE BOOK
- Vocabulary Practice, pp. 175–176
- Decoding Support, p. 177
- Summarizing the Chapter, pp. 198–199

Audio Readings CD
Listen to Pupil Edition.

Audio Readings in Spanish CD
Listen to Pupil Edition in Spanish.

 UNIT RESOURCE BOOK
- Reading Study Guide, A & B, pp. 132–135
- Spanish Reading Study Guide, pp. 136–137
- Challenge and Extension, p. 138
- Reinforcing Key Concepts, p. 140

 UNIT RESOURCE BOOK
- Reading Study Guide, A & B, pp. 143–146
- Spanish Reading Study Guide, pp. 147–148
- Challenge and Extension, p. 149
- Reinforcing Key Concepts, p. 151

 UNIT RESOURCE BOOK
- Reading Study Guide, A & B, pp. 154–157
- Spanish Reading Study Guide, pp. 158–159
- Challenge and Extension, p. 160
- Reinforcing Key Concepts, p. 161
- Challenge Reading, pp. 173–174

 UNIT RESOURCE BOOK
- Reading Study Guide, A & B, pp. 164–167
- Spanish Reading Study Guide, pp. 168–169
- Challenge and Extension, p. 170
- Reinforcing Key Concepts, p. 172

ASSESSMENT

- Chapter Review, pp. 229–230
- Standardized Test Practice, p. 231

 UNIT ASSESSMENT BOOK
- Diagnostic Test, pp. 39–40
- Chapter Test, A, B, & C, pp. 45–56
- Alternative Assessment, pp. 57–58

 Spanish Chapter Test, pp. 241–244

Test Generator CD-ROM
Generate customized tests.

Lab Generator CD-ROM
Rubrics for Labs

 Ongoing Assessment, pp. 198–199, 201, 203–204

 Section 7.1 Review, p. 204

 UNIT ASSESSMENT BOOK
Section 7.1 Quiz, p. 41

 Ongoing Assessment, pp. 207–208, 210–212

 Section 7.2 Review, p. 212

 UNIT ASSESSMENT BOOK
Section 7.2 Quiz, p. 42

 Ongoing Assessment, pp. 214–219

 Section 7.3 Review, p. 219

 UNIT ASSESSMENT BOOK
Section 7.3 Quiz, p. 43

 Ongoing Assessment, pp. 223–227

 Section 7.4 Review, p. 227

 UNIT ASSESSMENT BOOK
Section 7.4 Quiz, p. 44

STANDARDS

National Standards
A.2–8, A.9.a–f, B.1.b, B.3.e, E.6.c, F.5.c, G.1.b

See p. 194 for the standards.

National Standards
A.2–8, A.9.a, A.9.c–e, G.1.b

National Standards
A.2–8, A.9.a, A.9.c–e, B.1.b, G.1.b

National Standards
A.2–8, A.9.a, A.9.c–e, B.3.e, G.1.b

National Standards
A.2–8, A.9.a, A.9.c–e, E.6.c, F.5.c, G.1.b

Chapter 7: **Chemical Reactions** 193F

Previewing Resources for Differentiated Instruction

CHAPTER INVESTIGATION

Leveled resources present the same concepts for different abilities.

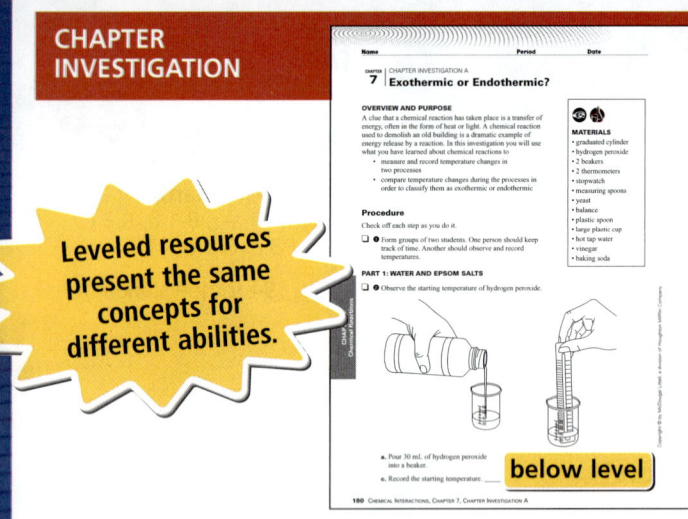
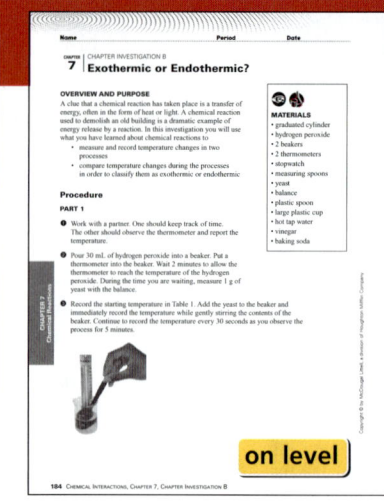
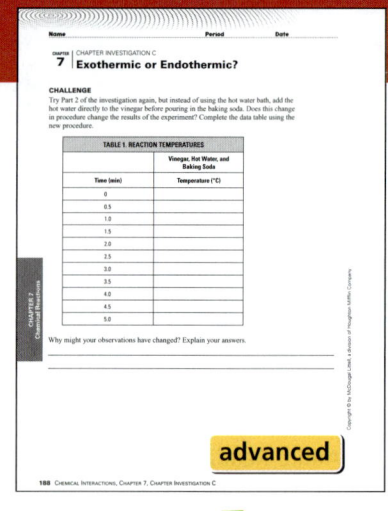

UNIT RESOURCE BOOK, pp. 180–183 | pp. 184–187 | pp. 184–188

READING STUDY GUIDE

Reading Study Guide is also in Spanish.

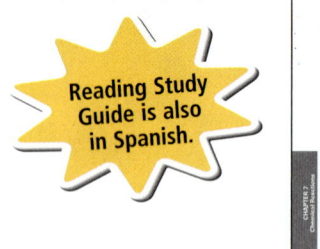
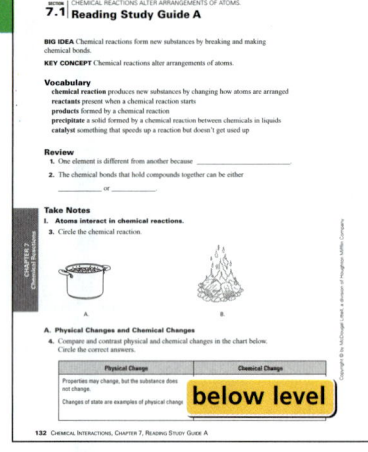
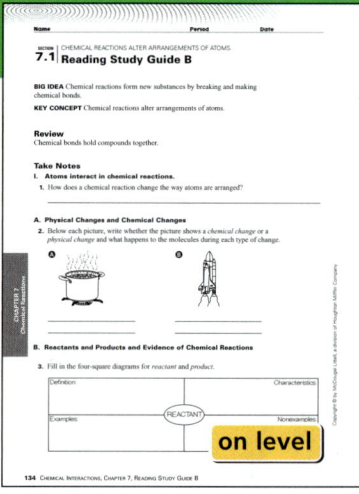
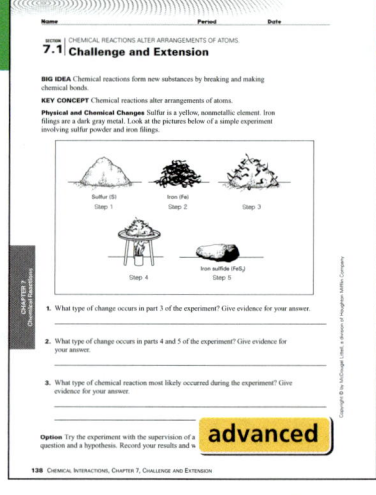

UNIT RESOURCE BOOK, pp. 132–133 | pp. 134–135 | p. 138

CHAPTER TEST

Chapter Test is also in Spanish.

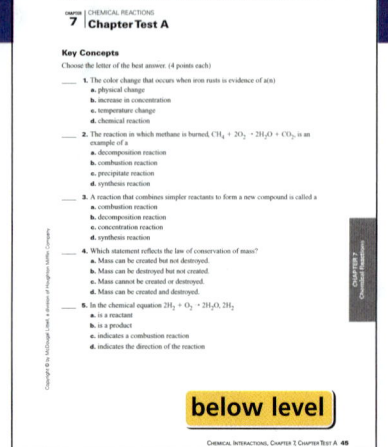
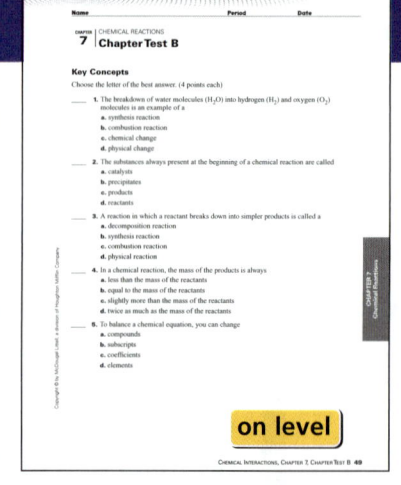
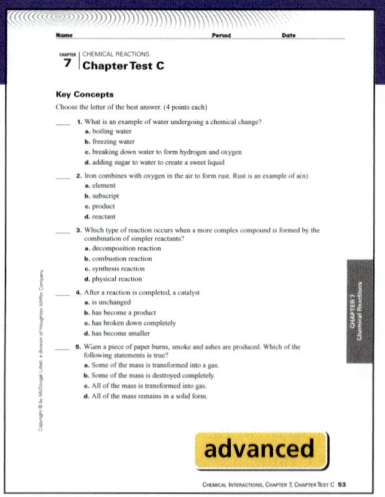

UNIT ASSESSMENT BOOK, pp. 45–48 | pp. 49–52 | pp. 53–56

Unit 2: Chemical Interactions

TECHNOLOGY

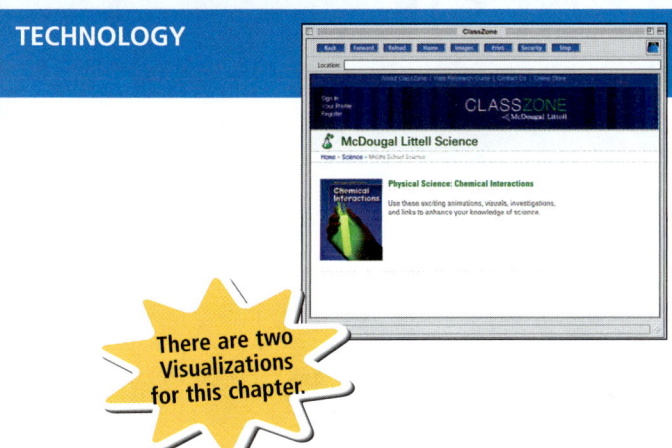
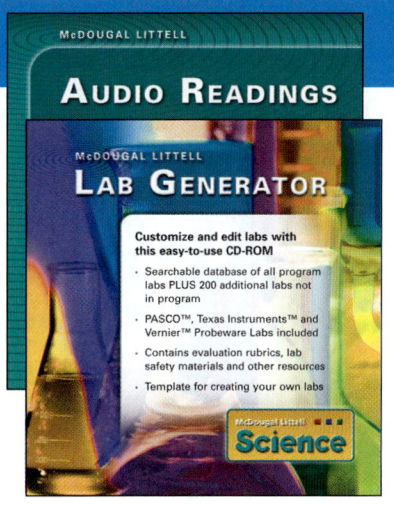
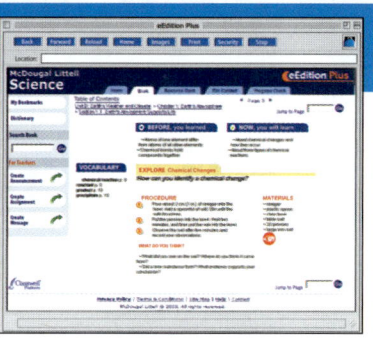

There are two Visualizations for this chapter.

VISUAL CONTENT

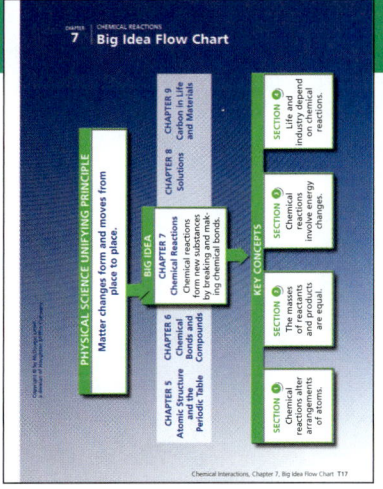
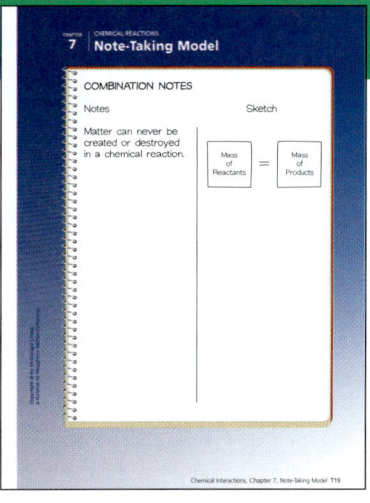
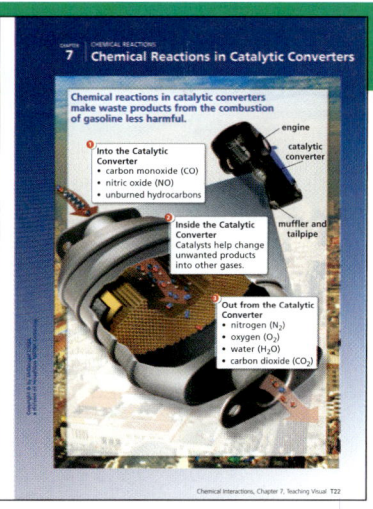

UNIT TRANSPARENCY BOOK, p. T17    p. T19   p. T22

MORE SUPPORT

Reinforcing Key Concepts for each section

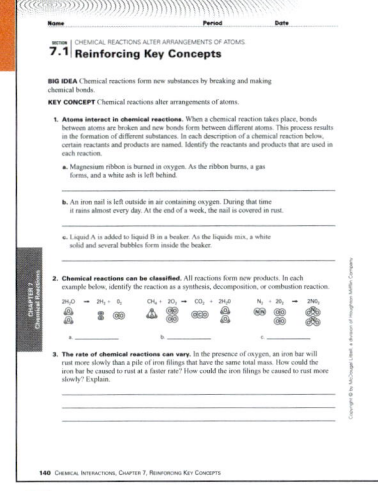
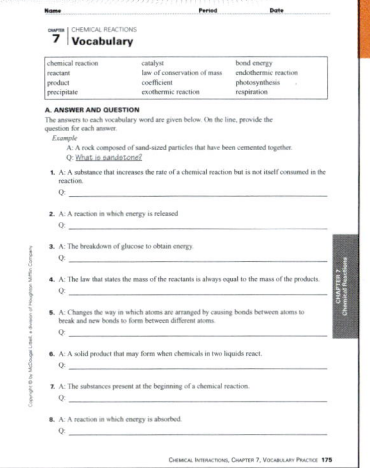
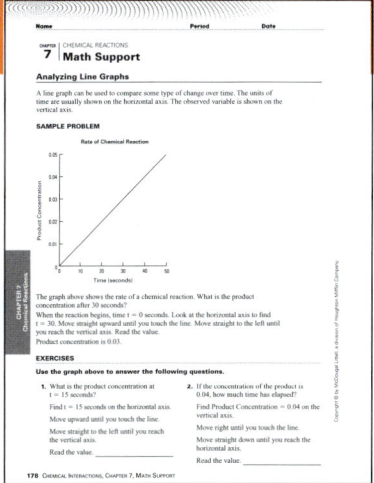

UNIT RESOURCE BOOK, p. 140   pp. 175–176   p. 178

Chapter 7: Chemical Reactions 193H

CHAPTER 7 Chemical Reactions

INTRODUCE

Have students look at the photograph of the chemical reaction and discuss how the question in the box links to the Big Idea. For further discussion:
- How might new substances be formed by a chemical reaction?
- What types of changes might indicate that a chemical reaction has occurred?

National Science Education Standards

Content

B.1.b Substances react chemically in characteristic ways with other substances to form new substances (compounds) with different characteristic properties. In chemical reactions, the total mass is conserved.

B.3.e In most chemical and nuclear reactions, energy is transferred into or out of a system.

Process

A.2–8 Design and conduct an investigation; use tools to gather and interpret data; use evidence to describe, predict, explain, model; think critically to make relationships between evidence and explanation; recognize different explanations and predictions; communicate scientific procedures and explanations; use mathematics.

A.9.a–f Understand scientific inquiry by using different investigations, methods, mathematics, technology, explanations based on logic, evidence, and skepticism.

E.6.c Science drives technology; technology drives science.

F.5.c Technology influences society through its products and processes.

G.1.b Science requires different abilities.

CHAPTER 7 Chemical Reactions

the BIG idea

Chemical reactions form new substances by breaking and making chemical bonds.

What changes are happening in this chemical reaction?

Key Concepts

SECTION 1 Chemical reactions alter arrangements of atoms.
Learn how chemical reactions are identified and controlled.

SECTION 2 The masses of reactants and products are equal.
Learn how chemical equations show the conservation of mass.

SECTION 3 Chemical reactions involve energy changes.
Learn how energy is absorbed or released by chemical reactions.

SECTION 4 Life and industry depend on chemical reactions.
Learn about some chemical reactions in everyday life.

Internet Preview

CLASSZONE.COM
Chapter 7 online resources: Content Review, two Visualizations, two Resource Centers, Math Tutorial, Test Practice

---

INTERNET PREVIEW

CLASSZONE.COM For student use with the following pages:

Review and Practice
- Content Review, pp. 196, 228
- Math Tutorial: Interpreting Line Graphs, p. 205
- Test Practice, p. 231

Activities and Resources
- Internet Activity: p. 195
- Visualizations: Concentration and Reaction Rate, p. 202; Endothermic and Exothermic Reactions, p. 218
- Resource Center: Catalysts in Living Things, p. 204

Chemical Reactions
Code: MDL024

EXPLORE the BIG idea

Changing Steel Wool

Place a small lump of steel wool in a cup. Pour in enough vinegar to cover the steel wool. After five minutes, take the steel wool out of the vinegar. Shake the steel wool to remove any excess vinegar. Place the steel wool in a small plastic bottle, and cover the mouth of the bottle with a balloon. Observe the steel wool and balloon after one hour.

Observe and Think What happened to the steel wool and balloon? What might have caused this to occur?

A Different Rate

Half fill one cup with hot tap water and a second cup with cold tap water. Drop a seltzer tablet into each cup at the same time. Time how long it takes for each tablet to stop fizzing.

Observe and Think Which tablet fizzed for a longer period of time? How might you explain any differences?

Internet Activity: Reactions

Go to **ClassZone.com** to explore chemical reactions and chemical equations. Learn how a chemical equation can be balanced.

Observe and Think How do chemical equations show what happens during a chemical reaction?

NSTA scilinks.org SCLINKS
Chemical Reactions Code: MDL024

Chapter 7: **Chemical Reactions** 195

EXPLORE the BIG idea

These inquiry-based activities are appropriate for use at home or as a supplement to classroom instruction.

Changing Steel Wool

PURPOSE To observe a chemical change. Students observe a chemical reaction that involves the rusting of steel wool.

TIP *10 min.* Do not use scouring pads that contain soap.

Answer: The steel wool rusted, and the balloon was pulled into the bottle because oxygen from the air in the bottle reacted with the metal.

REVISIT after p. 200.

A Different Rate

PURPOSE To explore how reaction rate is affected by temperature. Students vary the temperature of a reaction mixture and measure changes in reaction rate.

TIP *10 min.* Use effervescent tablets.

Answer: The tablet in cold water fizzed longer because the reaction proceeded more slowly.

REVISIT after p. 203.

Internet Activity: Reactions

PURPOSE To examine chemical equations and learn how to balance them.

TIP *20 min.* Students should check their work by tallying the number of atoms of each element on each side of the equation.

Answer: The same number of atoms of each element in the reaction is on each side of the equation, which indicates that atoms are neither created nor destroyed during a chemical reaction.

REVISIT after p. 211.

TEACHING WITH TECHNOLOGY

Video Camera Use a video camera to record sugar combustion (p. 223). The reaction takes place quickly; videotaping it will allow students to observe it again.

CBL and Probeware If you have probeware, you may use a temperature probe to record temperature changes in the Chapter Investigation on pp. 220–221. Students can then use a graphing calculator (or graphing software) to make graphs of the temperatures they record.

Chapter 7 **195**

PREPARE

◉ CONCEPT REVIEW

Activate Prior Knowledge

Make a model of a water molecule by attaching two identical gumdrops to a marshmallow with toothpicks. The angle between the toothpicks should be slightly greater than a right angle (about 105°).

- Ask: What do the toothpicks represent? **covalent bonds** What does the marshmallow represent? **an oxygen atom** The gumdrops? **hydrogen atoms**
- Ask: Are electrons shared or are they gained and lost by the atoms within the molecule? **shared**

◉ TAKING NOTES

Combination Notes

Combining a sketch with notes will help students to visualize a new concept and connect it with an example. Students should use a two-column format, writing their notes in one column and drawing their sketch in the other.

Vocabulary Strategy

The four square diagram organizes all aspects of a term into a coherent pattern. By filling in their own words, students personalize their understanding. Point out that it's okay to leave a blank square if there is no clear nonexample for the term.

Vocabulary and Note-Taking Resources

- Vocabulary Practice, pp. 175–176
- Decoding Support, p. 177

- Daily Vocabulary Scaffolding, p. T18
- Note-Taking Model, p. T19

- Four Square, B22–23
- Combination Notes, C36
- Daily Vocabulary Scaffolding, H1–8

196 Unit 2: **Chemical Interactions**

CHAPTER 7
Getting Ready to Learn

◉ CONCEPT REVIEW

- Atoms combine to form compounds.
- Atoms gain or lose electrons when they form ionic bonds.
- Atoms share electrons in covalent bonds.

◉ VOCABULARY REVIEW

electron p. 139
ionic bond p. 176
covalent bond p. 178

See Glossary for definitions.

atom, chemical change

CONTENT REVIEW
CLASSZONE.COM
Review concepts and vocabulary.

▶ TAKING NOTES

COMBINATION NOTES

To take notes about a new concept, first make an informal outline of the information. Then make a sketch of the concept and label it so you can study it later.

VOCABULARY STRATEGY

Write each new vocabulary term in the center of a **four square** diagram. Write notes in the squares around each term. Include a definition, some characteristics, and some examples of the term. If possible, write some things that are not examples of the term.

SCIENCE NOTEBOOK

NOTES

Chemical reactions
- cause chemical changes
- make new substances
- change reactants into products

Evidence of Chemical Reactions

before · after

increase in temperature

Definition	Characteristics
substance present before a chemical reaction occurs	its bonds are broken during a reaction

REACTANT

Examples	Nonexample
oxygen in a combustion reaction	carbon dioxide in a combustion reaction

See the Note-Taking Handbook on pages R45–R51.

196 Unit 2: **Chemical Interactions**

CHECK READINESS

Administer the Diagnostic Test to determine students' readiness for new science content and their mastery of requisite math skills.

 Diagnostic Test, pp. 39–40

Technology Resources

Students needing content and math skills should visit **ClassZone.com**.

- **CONTENT REVIEW**
- **MATH TUTORIAL**

 CONTENT REVIEW CD-ROM

KEY CONCEPT

Chemical reactions alter arrangements of atoms.

> **BEFORE, you learned**
> - Atoms of one element differ from atoms of all other elements
> - Chemical bonds hold compounds together
> - Chemical bonds may be ionic or covalent

> **NOW, you will learn**
> - About chemical changes and how they occur
> - About three types of chemical reactions
> - How the rate of a chemical reaction can be changed

VOCABULARY
chemical reaction p. 197
reactant p. 199
product p. 199
precipitate p. 200
catalyst p. 204

EXPLORE Chemical Changes

How can you identify a chemical change?

PROCEDURE

1. Pour about 3 cm (1 in.) of vinegar into the bowl. Add a spoonful of salt. Stir until the salt dissolves.
2. Put the pennies into the bowl. Wait two minutes, and then put the nail into the bowl.
3. Observe the nail after five minutes and record your observations.

MATERIALS
- vinegar
- clear bowl
- plastic spoon
- table salt
- 20 pennies
- large iron nail

WHAT DO YOU THINK?
- What did you see on the nail? Where do you think it came from?
- Did a new substance form? What evidence supports your conclusion?

Atoms interact in chemical reactions.

You see substances change every day. Some changes are physical, such as when liquid water changes to water vapor during boiling. Other changes are chemical, such as when wood burns to form smoke and ash, or when rust forms on iron. During a chemical change, substances change into one or more different substances.

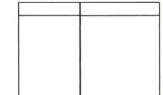

COMBINATION NOTES
Use combination notes to organize information about how atoms interact during chemical reactions.

A **chemical reaction** produces new substances by changing the way in which atoms are arranged. In a chemical reaction, bonds between atoms are broken and new bonds form between different atoms. This breaking and forming of bonds takes place when particles of the original materials collide with one another. After a chemical reaction, the new arrangements of atoms form different substances.

Chapter 7: **Chemical Reactions** 197

RESOURCES FOR DIFFERENTIATED INSTRUCTION

Below Level
UNIT RESOURCE BOOK
- Reading Study Guide A, pp. 132–133
- Decoding Support, p. 177

AUDIO CDS

Additional INVESTIGATION,
Modeling Chemical Reactions, A, B, & C, pp. 189–197; Teacher Instructions, pp. 329–330

Advanced
UNIT RESOURCE BOOK
Challenge and Extension, p. 138

English Learners
UNIT RESOURCE BOOK
Spanish Reading Study Guide, pp. 136–137

 **AUDIO CDS**
- Audio Readings in Spanish
- Audio Readings (English)

7.1 FOCUS

▶ Set Learning Goals
Students will
- Recognize evidence of chemical changes and describe how these changes occur.
- Identify three types of chemical reactions.
- Describe how the rate of a chemical reaction can be changed.
- Infer through an experiment how the rate of a reaction can be changed by physically changing the reactants.

⚫ 3-Minute Warm-Up
Display Transparency 20 or copy this exercise on the board:

Draw a diagram showing a sodium atom, a chlorine atom, and the two of them bonded together as sodium chloride. How do sodium and chlorine bond to each other in this compound? *The diagram should show that sodium loses an electron to chlorine and that sodium ions and chloride ions bond to form sodium chloride. The ions are held together by the attraction between the oppositely charged particles.*

 3-Minute Warm-Up, p. T20

7.1 MOTIVATE

EXPLORE Chemical Changes

PURPOSE To identify a chemical change

TIP *10 min.* Do not use iron nails that are galvanized or coated.

WHAT DO YOU THINK? *Copper appeared on the nail; the copper came from the pennies. A new substance did form, as shown by a change in color.*

Chapter 7 **197**

7.1 INSTRUCT

Teach from Visuals

To help students interpret the blow-up diagrams, ask what happens to the water molecules when water changes from the solid state to the liquid state. *The water molecules from the ice are no longer locked in place, allowing the molecules to move freely past each other.*

Real World Example

Making popcorn involves a physical change of water. Unpopped popcorn kernels contain about 14 percent water. When you heat the kernels, the water expands and turns to steam. Pressure builds up inside the kernel. Eventually, the kernel explodes. As it explodes, the soft starch inside the kernel inflates and bursts, turning the kernel inside out. The kernel releases the steam, and the popcorn is popped.

Ongoing Assessment

CHECK YOUR READING *Answer: Its physical form changes, but the substance itself remains unchanged.*

Physical Changes

A change in the state of a substance is an example of a physical change. The substance may have some different properties after a physical change, but it is still the same substance. For example, you know that water can exist in three different physical states: the solid state (ice), the liquid state (water), and the gas state (water vapor). However, regardless of what state water is in, it still remains water, that is, H_2O molecules. As ice melts, the molecules of water move around more quickly, but the molecules do not change. As water vapor condenses, the molecules of water move more slowly, but they are still the same molecules.

Substances can undergo different kinds of physical changes. For example, sugar dissolves in water but still tastes sweet because the molecules that make up sugar do not change when it dissolves. The pressure of helium changes when it is pumped from a high-pressure tank into a balloon, but the gas still remains helium.

CHECK YOUR READING What happens to a substance when it undergoes a physical change?

When water changes from a liquid to a solid, it undergoes a physical change.

Ice is composed of water molecules that are locked together.

Liquid water is composed of molecules that move freely past each other.

198 Unit 2: Chemical Interactions

DIFFERENTIATE INSTRUCTION

More Reading Support

A What kind of change occurs when a substance changes state? *a physical change*

English Learners Have students write the definitions for *chemical reaction*, *precipitate*, and *catalyst* in their Science Word Dictionaries. Help English learners understand reactants and products by using an analogy. For example, reactants are like the ingredients in a cake recipe, and the product is like the cake. Encourage students to think of other analogies for reactants and products.

Chemical Changes

Water can also undergo a chemical change. Water molecules can be broken down into hydrogen and oxygen molecules by a chemical reaction called electrolysis. When an electric current is passed through liquid water (H_2O), it changes the water into two gases—hydrogen and oxygen. The molecules of water break apart into individual atoms, which then recombine into hydrogen molecules (H_2) and oxygen molecules (O_2). The original material (water) changes into different substances through a chemical reaction.

Hydrogen and oxygen are used as rocket fuel for the space shuttle. During liftoff, liquid hydrogen and liquid oxygen are combined in a reaction that is the opposite of electrolysis. This reaction produces water and a large amount of energy that helps push the shuttle into orbit.

 How does a chemical change differ from a physical change?

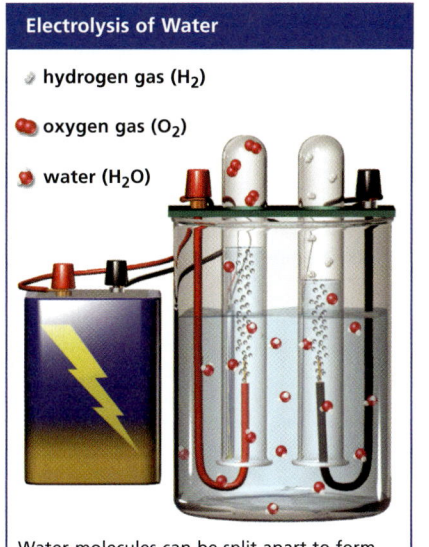

Electrolysis of Water
- hydrogen gas (H_2)
- oxygen gas (O_2)
- water (H_2O)

Water molecules can be split apart to form separate hydrogen and oxygen molecules.

Reactants and Products

Reactants are the substances present at the beginning of a chemical reaction. In the burning of natural gas, for example, methane (CH_4) and oxygen (O_2) are the reactants in the chemical reaction. **Products** are the substances formed by a chemical reaction. In the burning of natural gas, carbon dioxide (CO_2) and water (H_2O) are the products formed by the reaction. Reactants and products can be elements or compounds, depending on the reaction taking place.

During a chemical reaction, bonds between atoms in the reactants are broken and new bonds are formed in the products. When natural gas is burned, bonds between the carbon and hydrogen atoms in methane are broken, as are the bonds between the oxygen atoms in oxygen molecules. New bonds are formed between carbon and oxygen in carbon dioxide gas and between hydrogen and oxygen in water vapor.

Reactants—bonds broken	Products—new bonds formed
methane + oxygen (CH_4) (O_2)	carbon dioxide + water (CO_2) (H_2O)

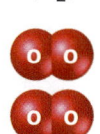 

 What must happen for reactants to be changed into products?

Chapter 7: **Chemical Reactions** 199

Teacher Demo

Set up chemical reactions to show evidence of each type of chemical change.

- To demonstrate a color change, place some dry cornstarch in a small dish. Put a few drops of iodine solution on the starch. A dark blue iodine-starch complex will form. Caution: Iodine solution can stain hands and clothing.

- To produce a precipitate, pour about 5 mL of 0.1M silver nitrate solution (2 g $AgNO_3$ dissolved in 100 mL water) into a flask. Slowly add about 5 mL of 0.1M potassium iodide solution (2 g KI dissolved in 100 mL water). A bright yellow precipitate of silver iodide (AgI) will form. Caution: Silver nitrate solution can stain hands and clothing.

- To produce a gas, place a spoonful of baking soda ($NaHCO_3$) in a small beaker. Add about 10 mL of vinegar (acetic acid). Bubbles of carbon dioxide will appear.

- To demonstrate a temperature change, burn a small amount of rubbing alcohol in an evaporating dish. Tell students that heat is produced during the combustion reaction. Caution: Make sure students maintain a safe distance.

EXPLORE the BIG idea

Revisit "Changing Steel Wool" on p. 195. Have students explain their results.

Real World Example

The rusting of iron and corrosion of other metals are very costly chemical reactions. Millions of dollars are spent worldwide each year to paint building parts, bridges, ships, machinery, storage tanks, and other metal structures. In addition, rust takes an enormous toll on automobiles. The salt used to melt snow and ice on roads enhances the reaction that produces rust.

VOCABULARY Remember to use a four square diagram for *precipitate* and other vocabulary terms.

Evidence of Chemical Reactions

Some chemical changes are easy to observe—the products formed by the rearrangement of atoms look different than the reactants. Other changes are not easy to see but can be detected in other ways.

Color Change Substances often change color during a chemical reaction. For example, when gray iron rusts, the product that forms is brown, as shown in the photograph below.

Formation of a Precipitate Many chemical reactions form products that exist in a different physical state from the reactants. A solid product called a **precipitate** may form when chemicals in two liquids react, as shown in the photograph below. Seashells are often formed this way when a sea creature releases a liquid that reacts with seawater.

Color Change

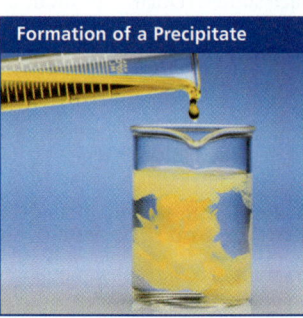
Formation of a Precipitate

Formation of a Gas Chemical reactions may produce a gas, like that often formed when antacid pills are mixed with excess stomach acid. The photograph below shows an example in which carbon dioxide gas is produced by a chemical reaction.

Temperature Change Most chemical reactions involve a temperature change. Sometimes this change can be inferred from the observation of a flame, as in the burning of the metal magnesium in the photograph below. Other temperature changes are not immediately obvious. If you have touched concrete before it hardens, you may have noticed that it felt warm. This warmth is due to a chemical reaction.

Formation of a Gas

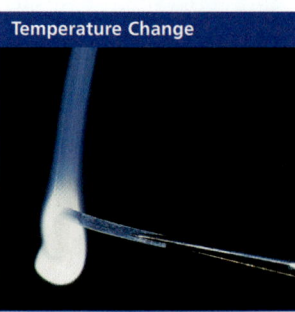
Temperature Change

200 Unit 2: Chemical Interactions

DIFFERENTIATE INSTRUCTION

More Reading Support

C What is a precipitate? *a solid product*

D How can a temperature change in a reaction be observed? *seeing a flame or feeling warmth*

Advanced Have students investigate the reaction of various antacids with excess stomach acid. What gas is sometimes produced? *carbon dioxide* What happens to the excess stomach acid? *It changes to a harmless salt and water.*

R Challenge and Extension, p. 138

Chemical reactions can be classified.

Scientists classify chemical reactions in several ways to help make the different types of reactions easier to understand. All reactions form new products, but the ways in which products are made can differ.

Synthesis In a synthesis reaction, a new compound is formed by the combination of simpler reactants. For example, nitrogen dioxide (NO_2), a component of smog, forms when nitrogen and oxygen combine in the air.

> **READING TIP**
> *Synthesis* means "making a substance from simpler substances."

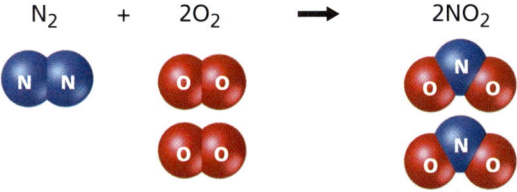

$$N_2 + 2O_2 \rightarrow 2NO_2$$

Decomposition In a decomposition reaction, a reactant breaks down into simpler products, which could be elements or other compounds. Decomposition reactions can be thought of as being the reverse of synthesis reactions. For example, water can be decomposed into its elements—hydrogen and oxygen.

> **READING TIP**
> *Decomposition* means "separation into parts."

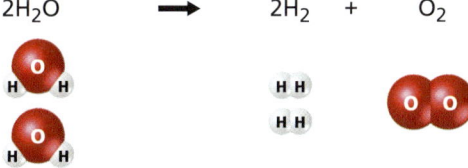

$$2H_2O \rightarrow 2H_2 + O_2$$

Combustion In a combustion reaction, one reactant is always oxygen and another reactant often contains carbon and hydrogen. The carbon and hydrogen atoms combine with oxygen, producing carbon dioxide and water. The burning of methane is a combustion reaction.

> **READING TIP**
> *Combustion* is the process of burning with oxygen.

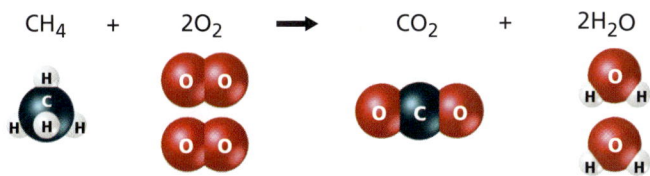

$$CH_4 + 2O_2 \rightarrow CO_2 + 2H_2O$$

CHECK YOUR READING How are synthesis reactions different from decomposition reactions?

Chapter 7: **Chemical Reactions** 201

INVESTIGATE Chemical Reactions

PURPOSE To infer how the surface area of reactants affects reaction rate

TIP 15 min. Only antacids containing carbonate or a bicarbonate will fizz. Use effervescent seltzer tablets.

WHAT DO YOU THINK *The whole tablet should fizz longer than the crushed tablet. The crushed tablet has a greater total surface area, so the reaction proceeds more rapidly.*

CHALLENGE *A greater surface area means that more particles are available to react, so they collide more frequently.*

 Datasheet, Chemical Reactions, p. 139

Technology Resources
Customize this student lab as needed or look for an alternative. Print rubrics to assess student lab reports.

 Lab Generator CD-ROM

Teach Difficult Concepts

Students often have trouble visualizing that a large particle has less surface area than many small particles with an equal mass or volume. Have students calculate the volume and surface area of a cube 4 cm on each side. *V = 64 cm³, area = 96 cm²* Then have them calculate the volume and surface area of 64 cubes, each is 1 cm on each side. Point out that these 64 cubes would fit inside the larger cube. *V = 64 cm³, area = 384 cm²*

202 Unit 2: **Chemical Interactions**

The rates of chemical reactions can vary.

Most chemical reactions take place when particles of reactants collide with enough force to react. Chemical reactions can occur at different rates. Striking a match causes a very quick chemical reaction, while the rusting of an iron nail may take months. However, the rate of a reaction can be changed. For instance, a nail can be made to rust more quickly. Three physical factors—concentration, surface area, and temperature—and a chemical factor—a catalyst—can greatly affect the rate of a chemical reaction.

Concentration

Observe how changing the concentration of a reactant can change the rate of a reaction.

Concentration measures the number of particles present in a certain volume. A high concentration of reactants means that there is a large number of particles that can collide and react. Turning the valve on a gas stove to increase the flow of gas increases the concentration of methane molecules that can combine with oxygen in the air. The result is a bigger flame and a faster combustion reaction.

Surface Area

Suppose one of the reactants in a chemical reaction is present as a single large piece of material. Particles of the second reactant cannot get inside the large piece, so they can react only with particles on the surface. To make the reaction go faster, the large piece of material could be broken into smaller pieces before the reaction starts.

INVESTIGATE Chemical Reactions

How can the rate of a reaction be changed?
PROCEDURE

1. Place a whole seltzer tablet in one cup. Crush the second tablet and place it in the second cup.
2. At the same time, fill both cups halfway with water.
3. Time how long the tablet in each cup fizzes.

WHAT DO YOU THINK?
- How long did the whole tablet fizz? What about the crushed tablet?
- How are these results related to the rate of a chemical reaction? Explain.

CHALLENGE How might your results be related to collisions between particles during a chemical reaction?

SKILL FOCUS
Inferring

MATERIALS
- 2 seltzer tablets
- 2 plastic cups
- tap water
- stopwatch

TIME
15 minutes

202 Unit 2: **Chemical Interactions**

DIFFERENTIATE INSTRUCTION

 More Reading Support

F What three physical factors affect reaction rate? *concentration, surface area, and temperature*

Alternative Assessment Students can answer and extend the Challenge question visually by making a drawing or model. Students should understand that more collisions between reactant particles take place when more surface area is exposed.

Breaking a large piece of material into smaller parts increases the surface area of the material. All of the inner material has no surface when it is inside a larger piece. Each time the large piece is broken, however, more surfaces are exposed. The amount of material does not change, but breaking it into smaller parts increases its surface area. Increasing the surface area increases the rate of the reaction.

 Why does a reaction proceed faster when the reactants have greater surface areas?

Temperature

The rate of a reaction can be increased by making the particles move faster. The result is that more collisions take place per second and occur with greater force. The most common way to make the particles move faster is to add energy to the reactants, which will raise their temperature.

Many chemical reactions during cooking go very slowly, or do not take place at all, unless energy is added to the reactants. Too much heat can make a reaction go too fast, and food ends up burned. Chemical reactions can also be slowed or stopped by decreasing the temperature of the reactants. Again, think about cooking. The reactions that take place during cooking can be stopped by removing the food from the heat source.

▼ REMINDER
Temperature is the average amount of kinetic energy of the particles in a substance.

Particles and Reaction Rates

Changes in Reactants	Normal Reaction Rate	Increased Reaction Rate
Concentration An increase in concentration of the reactants increases the number of particles that can interact.		
Surface area An increase in the surface area of the reactants increases the number of particles that can interact.		
Temperature Adding energy makes particles move faster and increases temperature. The increase in motion allows reactants to collide and react more frequently.		

Chapter 7: **Chemical Reactions** 203

DIFFERENTIATE INSTRUCTION

 More Reading Support

G Why are collisions between particles important in chemical reactions? *Particles of reactants must collide to react.*

English Learners Point out that the word *rate* has several meanings. Have students look up the meanings in a dictionary. Then have them use each meaning in a sentence and indicate which meaning is used in this section. *Rate here is the speed of reaction in relation to time.*

Ongoing Assessment

Describe how the rate of a chemical reaction can be changed.

Ask: Why does increased temperature increase the rate of a reaction? *The particles of reactants move faster, and they collide harder and more often.*

 Answer: *They increase the rate of chemical reactions. Some reactions would proceed slowly or not at all without a catalyst.*

Teach from Visuals

To help students interpret the sequence of enzyme action, have them examine the diagram. Ask: How do you think an enzyme might increase the rate of a reaction? *An enzyme precisely lines up two molecules so they can react quickly.*

Reinforce

Have students relate the section to the Big Idea.

 Reinforcing Key Concepts, p. 140

7.1 ASSESS & RETEACH

Assess

 Section 7.1 Quiz, p. 41

Reteach

Have students make a set of flash cards. On one side of each card, they should write one type of chemical reaction. On the other side, they should write the definition, important criteria, and an example of that type of reaction. Have pairs of students trade cards to learn from each other's ideas.

Technology Resources

Have students visit ClassZone.com for reteaching of Key Concepts.

 CONTENT REVIEW

 CONTENT REVIEW CD-ROM

Catalysts

Learn more about catalysts and how they work in living things.

The rate of a reaction can be changed chemically by adding a catalyst. A **catalyst** is a substance that increases the rate of a chemical reaction but is not itself consumed in the reaction. This means that after the reaction is complete, the catalyst remains unchanged. Catalysts are very important for many industrial and biological reactions. In fact, many chemical reactions would proceed slowly or not take place at all without catalysts.

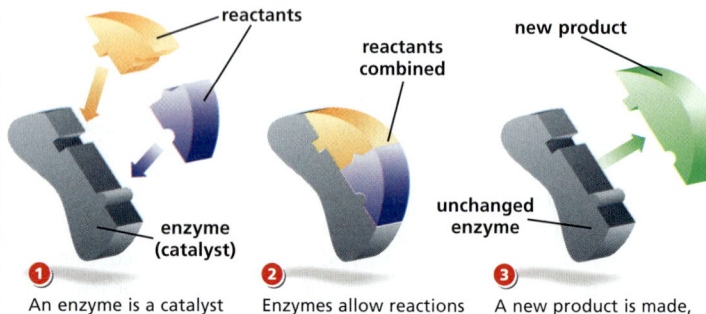

1. An enzyme is a catalyst for chemical reactions in living things.
2. Enzymes allow reactions that would not normally take place to occur.
3. A new product is made, but the enzyme is not changed by the reaction.

In living things, catalysts called enzymes are absolutely necessary for life. Without them, many important reactions could not take place under the conditions within your body. In fact, in 2003, scientists reported that they had discovered the slowest known chemical reaction in living things. This reaction would normally take one trillion years. Enzymes, though, allow the reaction to occur in 0.01 seconds.

 Why are catalysts important in chemical reactions?

7.1 Review

KEY CONCEPTS

1. How do physical changes differ from chemical changes? Explain.
2. Describe four types of evidence of a chemical reaction.
3. Describe the ways in which the rate of a chemical reaction can be changed.

CRITICAL THINKING

4. **Synthesize** What evidence shows that the burning of methane is a chemical reaction?
5. **Compare** What about combustion reactions makes them different from either synthesis or decomposition reactions?

⬥ CHALLENGE

6. **Apply** How might the chewing of food be related to the rate of a chemical reaction— digestion—that occurs in your body? Explain.

204 Unit 2: Chemical Interactions

ANSWERS

1. A physical change alters the characteristics of a substance, but not the substance itself. A chemical change produces different substances.

2. a color change, formation of a precipitate or a gas, a temperature change

3. Change the concentration, surface area, or temperature of reactants, or add a catalyst.

4. a change in temperature and the production of gases

5. Oxygen is always a reactant, and another reactant often contains carbon and hydrogen.

6. Chewing increases the surface area of food, which speeds up chemical reactions involved in digestion.

MATH in SCIENCE

SKILL: ANALYZING LINE GRAPHS

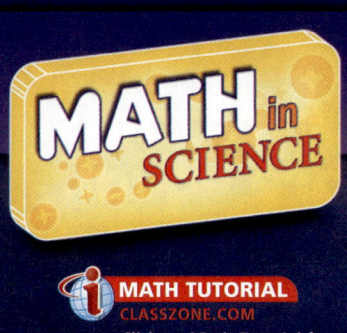

MATH TUTORIAL
CLASSZONE.COM
Click on Math Tutorial for more help with interpreting line graphs.

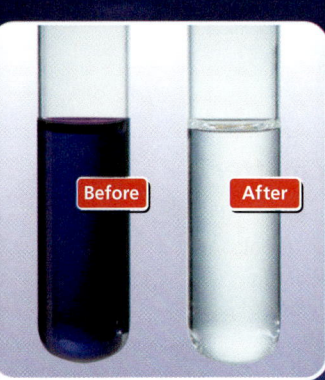

The reactants in the iodine clock reaction produce a sudden color change several seconds after the reactants are mixed.

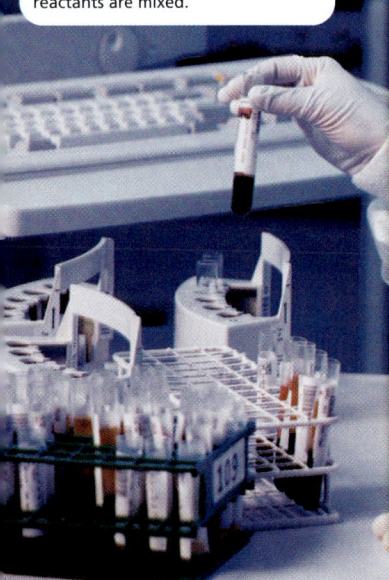

The Iodine Clock

Can a chemical reaction be timed? In the iodine clock reaction, a sudden color change indicates that the reaction has occurred. The length of time that passes before the color changes depends on the concentration ratios of the reactants. As shown in the graph below, the greater the concentration of the reactants, the faster the reaction.

Example

Suppose you are given an unknown iodine concentration to test in the iodine clock reaction. What is the concentration ratio of the iodine if it takes 40 seconds for the color change to occur?

(1) Find 40 seconds on the *x*-axis of the graph below and follow the vertical line up to the plotted data.

(2) Draw a horizontal line from that point on the curve to the *y*-axis to find the iodine concentration ratio in your sample.

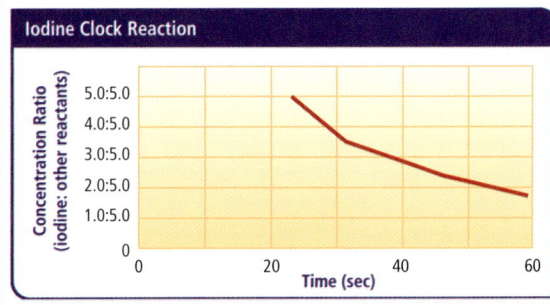

ANSWER The unknown concentration ratio is approximately 3.0:5.0.

Answer the following questions using the information in the graph above.

1. Approximately how long will it take for the reaction to occur if the concentration ratio is 4.0:5.0? 2.0:5.0?

2. Suppose you could extend the curve on the graph. If the reaction took 70 seconds to occur, what would be the approximate iodine concentration ratio?

CHALLENGE Using the following concentration ratios and times for another reactant, draw a reaction rate graph similar to the one shown above.
Concentration Ratios = 5.0:5.0, 4.0:5.0, 3.0:5.0, 2.0:5.0
Times = 24 sec, 25 sec, 43 sec, 68 sec

Chapter 7: **Chemical Reactions** 205

MATH IN SCIENCE
Math Skills Practice for Science

Set Learning Goal
To use a line graph to find reactant concentration

Present the Science
Two reactions are happening simultaneously in the iodine clock. A slow reaction produces triiodide, and a fast one makes the triiodide disappear. When the reactant for the fast reaction is used up, the triiodide no longer disappears but suddenly colors the solution dark blue as it reacts with starch.

Develop Graph Skills
- Point out the use and labeling of the two axes. The *y*-axis usually represents the dependent variable (the variable being studied), and the *x*-axis the independent variable (variable that is known or manipulated).
- Ask: Why might it be difficult to estimate untested values outside the data endpoints? *The curve outside the endpoints might suddenly drop or rise.*

DIFFERENTIATION TIP For students with visual impairments who have trouble reading the *x* and *y* values, provide a transparency of a grid that will help them determine alignment of a point with the axes.

Close
Ask students how they could make sure that the line of the graph continues in the same arc below 20 seconds and above 60. *Measure the reaction rate when the concentration ratio is less than 1.0:5.0 and greater than 5.0:5.0.*

 • Math Support, p. 178
• Math Practice, p. 179

Technology Resources

Students can visit **ClassZone.com** for practice in interpreting line graphs.

 MATH TUTORIAL

ANSWERS
1. approximately 28 sec; approximately 55 sec
2. 1.5 : 5.0

CHALLENGE Check students' graphs.

Chapter 7 **205**

7.2 FOCUS

◗ Set Learning Goals
Students will
- Explain why total mass does not change in a chemical reaction.
- Recognize how a chemical equation represents a chemical reaction.
- Outline how to balance a simple chemical equation.
- Measure in an experiment the mass of reactants and products in a chemical reaction.

◗ 3-Minute Warm-Up
Display Transparency 20 or copy this exercise on the board:

Decide if these statements are true. If not, correct them.

1. Reactants are changed into products by a physical change. *chemical change*
2. Changing the concentration of reactants can change the reaction rate. *true*
3. A color change in a reaction mixture is evidence that a chemical reaction has taken place. *true*

 3-Minute Warm-Up, p. T20

7.2 MOTIVATE

THINK ABOUT
PURPOSE To examine how substances change during a chemical reaction

DISCUSS Brainstorm with students what happens to the matter that undergoes a chemical reaction. Ask: What happens to matter that seems to disappear? *A gas may form and escape into the air.*

Integrate the Sciences
Matter can, in fact, be destroyed, but not through chemical reactions. Matter is destroyed and converted into energy through nuclear reactions. This is the principle behind nuclear power.

206 Unit 2: **Chemical Interactions**

KEY CONCEPT
7.2 The masses of reactants and products are equal.

◀ BEFORE, you learned
- Chemical reactions turn reactants into products by rearranging atoms
- Chemical reactions can be observed and identified
- The rate of chemical reactions can be changed

▶ NOW, you will learn
- About the law of conservation of mass
- How a chemical equation represents a chemical reaction
- How to balance a simple chemical equation

VOCABULARY
law of conservation of mass p. 207
coefficient p. 210

THINK ABOUT
What happens to burning matter?
You have probably watched a fire burn in a fireplace, a campfire, or a candle flame. It looks as if the wood or candle disappears over time, leaving a small pile of ashes or wax when the fire has finished burning. But does matter really disappear? Combustion is a chemical reaction, and chemical reactions involve rearrangements of atoms. The atoms do not disappear, so where do they go?

COMBINATION NOTES
Take notes on the conservation of mass using combination notes.

Careful observations led to the discovery of the conservation of mass.

The ashes left over from a wood fire contain less mass than the wood. In many other chemical reactions, mass also appears to decrease. That is, the mass of the products appears to be less than the mass of the reactants. In other reactions, the products appear to gain mass. For example, plants grow through a complex series of reactions, but where does their extra mass come from? At one time, scientists thought that chemical reactions could create or destroy matter.

During the 1780s the French chemist Antoine Lavoisier (luh-VWAH-zee-ay) showed that matter can never be created or destroyed in a chemical reaction. Lavoisier emphasized the importance of making very careful measurements in his experiments. Because of his methods, he was able to show that reactions that seem to gain mass or lose mass actually involve reactions with gases in the air. These gases could not be seen, but their masses could be measured.

206 Unit 2: **Chemical Interactions**

RESOURCES FOR DIFFERENTIATED INSTRUCTION

Below Level
UNIT RESOURCE BOOK
- Reading Study Guide A, pp. 143–144
- Decoding Support, p. 177

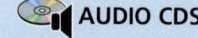 **AUDIO CDS**

Advanced
UNIT RESOURCE BOOK
Challenge and Extension, p. 149

English Learners
UNIT RESOURCE BOOK
Spanish Reading Study Guide, pp. 147–148

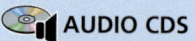 **AUDIO CDS**

- Audio Readings in Spanish
- Audio Readings (English)

An example of Lavoisier's work is his study of the reaction of the metal mercury when heated in air. In this reaction, the reddish-orange product formed has more mass than the original metal. Lavoisier placed some mercury in a jar, sealed the jar, and recorded the total mass of the setup. After the mercury had been heated in the jar, the total mass of the jar and its contents had not changed.

Lavoisier showed that the air left in the jar would no longer support burning—a candle flame was snuffed out by this air. He concluded that a gas in the air, which he called oxygen, had combined with the mercury to form the new product.

Lavoisier conducted many experiments of this type and found in all cases that the mass of the reactants is equal to the mass of the products. This conclusion, called the **law of conservation of mass,** states that in a chemical reaction atoms are neither created nor destroyed. All atoms present in the reactants are also present in the products.

Lavoisier carefully measured both the reactants and the products of chemical reactions.

CHECK YOUR READING How did Lavoisier investigate the conservation of mass?

INVESTIGATE Conservation of Mass

Why is it important to measure the masses of reactants and products?

PROCEDURE

1. Measure 2 tsp of baking soda. Use a funnel to put the baking soda in a balloon.
2. Pour 2 tsp of vinegar into the plastic bottle.
3. Secure the balloon over the mouth of the bottle with the balloon hanging to the side of the bottle. Find and record the mass of the experimental setup.
4. Lift the balloon so that the baking soda drops into the bottle. Observe for five minutes, and then find and record the mass of the setup again.

WHAT DO YOU THINK?
- Did the mass of the experimental setup change?
- How do your observations demonstrate the conservation of mass?

CHALLENGE What do you think you would have observed if you had not used the balloon? Explain.

SKILL FOCUS Measuring

MATERIALS
- teaspoon
- baking soda
- funnel
- balloon
- vinegar
- plastic bottle
- balance

TIME 35 minutes

Chapter 7: **Chemical Reactions** 207

DIFFERENTIATE INSTRUCTION

More Reading Support

A What scientific law states that the mass of the reactants is always equal to the mass of the products? *the law of conservation of mass*

English Learners Help English learners clearly understand the law of conservation of mass. If two or more students speak the same first language, encourage them to discuss the law of conservation of mass together in their native language. Then, encourage them to try the conversation in English, or pair them with more advanced students for help.

7.2 INSTRUCT

INVESTIGATE Conservation of Mass

PURPOSE To show that mass is conserved in a chemical reaction

TIPS *35 min.*
- Different amounts of vinegar and baking soda can be used, but they should be kept in the same proportions.
- Students with small motor-skill disabilities may need help from a partner in manipulating the balloon.

WHAT DO YOU THINK? *No; all of the products were collected. The equal masses of the setup before and after the reaction show the conservation of mass.*

CHALLENGE *The mass would have been different after the reaction because any gas produced would have escaped.*

Datasheet, Conservation of Mass, p. 150

Technology Resources

Customize this student lab as needed or look for an alternative. Print rubrics to assess student lab reports.

Lab Generator CD-ROM

Ongoing Assessment

Explain why total mass does not change in a chemical reaction.

Ask: Why is mass conserved in a chemical reaction? *Atoms are not created or destroyed in a chemical reaction.*

CHECK YOUR READING *Answer: By carefully observing and measuring all of the reactants and products in chemical reactions, he found that the total masses were always equal.*

Chapter 7 **207**

Mathematics Connection

Ask: How many atoms are present in each of the following compounds? CH_4, C_2H_5OH, $MgSO_4$, $NaCl$ *5, 9, 6, 2*

Ask: How many atoms of hydrogen are in a molecule of C_2H_5OH? *6*

Develop Critical Thinking

PREDICT Although equations are shown in this chapter with the arrow pointing to the right, many chemical reactions are reversible. Have students predict what will happen if a reaction is reversible. *Many reactions will continue in both directions until they reach a point of equilibrium, where the formation of products from the reactants equals the formation of reactants from products.*

Teach Difficult Concepts

Chemical reactions rarely occur in the one step shown by a chemical equation. Rather, the chemical equation shows the overall process that occurs during the reaction.

Ongoing Assessment

Recognize that a chemical equation represents a chemical reaction.

Ask: What information is presented in a chemical equation? *reactants, products, direction of the reaction, the atomic symbols and chemical formulas of the reactants and products*

 Answer: by showing on each side of the equation the same number of atoms of each element involved in the reaction

Chemical reactions can be described by chemical equations.

The law of conservation of mass states that in a chemical reaction, the total mass of reactants is equal to the total mass of products. For example, the mass of sodium plus the mass of chlorine that reacts with the sodium equals the mass of the product sodium chloride. Because atoms are rearranged in a chemical reaction, there must be the same number of sodium atoms and chlorine atoms in both the reactants and products.

Chemical equations represent how atoms are rearranged in a chemical reaction. The atoms in the reactants are shown on the left side of the equation. The atoms in the products are shown on the right side of the equation. Because atoms are rearranged and not created or destroyed, the number of atoms of each different element must be the same on each side of the equation.

CHECK YOUR READING How does a chemical equation show the conservation of mass?

In order to write a chemical equation, the information that you need to know is

- the reactants and products in the reaction
- the atomic symbols and chemical formulas of the reactants and products in the reaction
- the direction of the reaction

Carbon dioxide is a gas that animals exhale.

The following equation describes the formation of carbon dioxide from carbon and oxygen. In words, this equation says "Carbon reacts with oxygen to yield carbon dioxide." Notice that instead of an equal sign, an arrow appears between the reactants and the products. The arrow shows which way the reaction proceeds—from reactants on the left to the product or the products on the right.

reactants	direction of reaction	product
$C + O_2$	$\longrightarrow$	CO_2

Remember, the numbers below the chemical formulas for oxygen and carbon dioxide are called subscripts. A subscript indicates the number of atoms of an element in a molecule. You can see in the equation above that the oxygen molecule has two oxygen atoms, and the carbon dioxide molecule also has two oxygen atoms. If the chemical formula of a reactant or product does not have a subscript, it means that only one atom of each element is present in the molecule.

208 Unit 2: Chemical Interactions

DIFFERENTIATE INSTRUCTION

 More Reading Support

B What does an arrow show in a chemical equation? *which way the reaction proceeds*

Advanced Chemical equations show the overall process that occurs during a reaction. Reactions, however, rarely occur in the single step shown by an equation. Have interested students do research to find a step reaction. Have them write the step reaction on the board and then discuss each step in order to learn more about how each one affects the overall reaction.

R Challenge and Extension, p. 149

Chemical equations must be balanced.

Remember, chemical reactions follow the law of conservation of mass. Chemical equations show this conservation, or equality, in terms of atoms. The same number of atoms of each element must appear on both sides of a chemical equation. However, simply writing down the chemical formulas of reactants and products does not always result in equal numbers of atoms. You have to balance the equation to make the number of atoms equal on each side of an equation.

Balancing Chemical Equations

To learn how to balance an equation, look at the example of the combustion of natural gas, which is mostly methane (CH_4). The reactants are methane and oxygen. The products are carbon dioxide and water. You can write this reaction as the following equation.

REMINDER Oxygen is always a reactant in a combustion reaction.

Unbalanced Equation

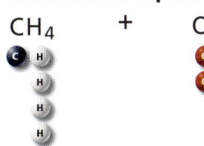 + →  +

$$CH_4 + O_2 \rightarrow CO_2 + H_2O$$

This equation is not balanced. There is one C on each side of the equation, so C is balanced. However, on the left side, H has a subscript of 4, which means there are four hydrogen atoms. On the right side, H has a subscript of 2, which means there are two hydrogen atoms. Also, there are two oxygen atoms on the left and three oxygen atoms on the right. Because of the conservation of mass, you know that hydrogen atoms do not disappear and oxygen atoms do not suddenly appear.

READING TIP As you read how to balance the equation, look at the illustrations and count the atoms. The number of each type of atom is shown below the formula.

You can balance a chemical equation by changing the amounts of reactants or products represented.

- To balance H first, add another H_2O molecule on the right. Now, both C and H are balanced.
- There are now two oxygen atoms on the left side and four oxygen atoms on the right side. To balance O, add another O_2 molecule on the left.

Balanced Equation

$$CH_4 + O_2 + O_2 \rightarrow CO_2 + H_2O + H_2O$$

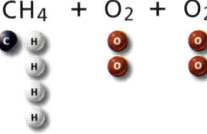    →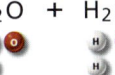

Chapter 7: **Chemical Reactions** 209

DIFFERENTIATE INSTRUCTION

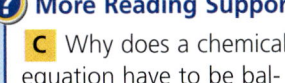

C Why does a chemical equation have to be balanced? *to make the number of atoms equal on both sides of the equation*

English Learners Point out to English learners that the word *subscript* comes from two Latin root words meaning "to write under." Subscripts are always written next to and slightly below the symbol for an atom. Tell English learners that word parts can often serve as clues to a word's meaning.

Teach from Visuals

To help students interpret a chemical equation, ask: Why can you add coefficients to an equation but not change subscripts of a formula? *Different subscripts change the formula for the substance. It would no longer be the same substance. Adding coefficients to an equation indicates the number of molecules that are involved in the reaction so that mass is conserved.*

Address Misconceptions

IDENTIFY If students balance equations by changing the formulas of compounds, they do not realize that changing the formula is not the same as changing the amount of a chemical.

CORRECT Ask: What does 2CO mean? *two molecules of carbon monoxide* What does CO_2 mean? *a molecule of carbon dioxide*

Point out that even though both formulas (2CO and CO_2) have the number 2 in them, the number means different things. When a number is in front of a chemical formula, it represents the amount of the compound that is present. When a number appears as a subscript in a formula, it represents the number of atoms of that element in the compound.

REASSESS Write the equation $NaN_3 \rightarrow Na + N_2$ on the board. Ask students to describe, without using numbers, how they would balance this equation. Then ask them to write the balanced equation. *Change the coefficients until the same numbers of atoms are on each side of the arrow. Balanced equation: $2NaN_3 \rightarrow 2Na + 3N_2$*

Technology Resources

Visit **ClassZone.com** for background on common student misconceptions.

MISCONCEPTION DATABASE

Ongoing Assessment

 Answer: They give equal numbers of atoms on each side of an equation by indicating the amounts of reactants and products.

210 Unit 2: **Chemical Interactions**

Using Coefficients to Balance Equations

The balanced equation for the combustion of methane shows that one molecule of methane reacts with two molecules of oxygen to produce one molecule of carbon dioxide and two molecules of water. The equation can be simplified by writing $2O_2$ instead of $O_2 + O_2$, and $2H_2O$ instead of $H_2O + H_2O$.

The numbers in front of the chemical formulas are called coefficients. **Coefficients** indicate how many molecules take part in the reaction. If there is no coefficient, then only one molecule of that type takes part in the reaction. The balanced equation, with coefficients, for the combustion of methane is shown below.

REMINDER
A subscript shows the number of atoms in a molecule. If a subscript is changed, the molecule represented by the formula is changed.

Balanced Equation with Coefficients

$$CH_4 + 2O_2 \rightarrow CO_2 + 2H_2O$$

coefficient — subscript

Chemical formulas can have both coefficients and subscripts. In these cases, multiply the two numbers together to find the number of atoms involved in the reaction. For example, two water molecules ($2H_2O$) contain $2 \cdot 2 = 4$ hydrogen atoms and $2 \cdot 1 = 2$ oxygen atoms. Remember, coefficients in a chemical equation indicate how many molecules of each type take part in the reaction.

Only coefficients can be changed in order to balance a chemical equation. Subscripts are part of the chemical formula for reactants or products and cannot be changed to balance an equation. Changing a subscript changes the substance represented by the formula.

For example, the equation for the combustion of methane cannot be balanced by changing the formula CO_2 to CO. The formula CO_2 represents carbon dioxide gas, which animals exhale when they breathe. The formula CO represents carbon monoxide gas, which is a very different compound from CO_2. Carbon monoxide gas is poisonous, and breathing too much of it can be fatal.

 **CHECK YOUR READING** Why are coefficients used to balance equations?

The combustion of methane (CH_4) is used to melt glass.

210 Unit 2: Chemical Interactions

DIFFERENTIATE INSTRUCTION

 **More Reading Support**

D What are the numbers in front of chemical formulas called? *coefficients*

E What numbers can you change to balance a chemical equation? *coefficients*

Below Level If students have trouble understanding the concept of a balanced equation, write an equation using everyday objects instead of chemical formulas. For example, wheels + frame + handlebar $\rightarrow$ bike. This equation can be balanced by adding a coefficient of 2 in front of the wheels. One bike contains 2 wheels, 1 frame, and 1 handlebar.

Students may also need to be reminded that there is only one atom of an element present in a molecule when there is no subscript following the element's symbol.

Balancing Equations with Coefficients

The steps below show how to balance the equation for the synthesis reaction between nitrogen (N_2) and hydrogen (H_2), which produces ammonia (NH_3).

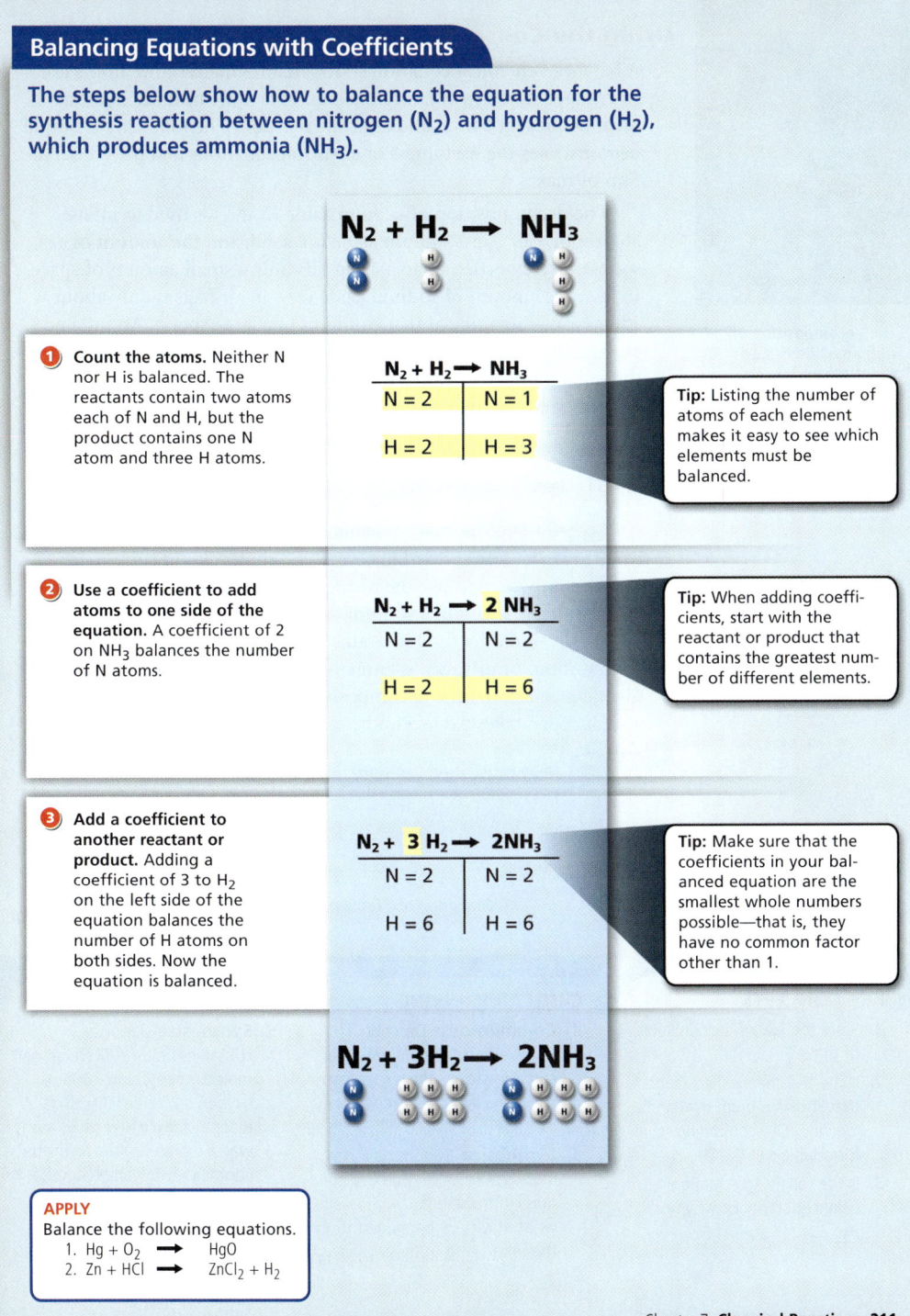

1. **Count the atoms.** Neither N nor H is balanced. The reactants contain two atoms each of N and H, but the product contains one N atom and three H atoms.

   Tip: Listing the number of atoms of each element makes it easy to see which elements must be balanced.

2. **Use a coefficient to add atoms to one side of the equation.** A coefficient of 2 on NH_3 balances the number of N atoms.

   Tip: When adding coefficients, start with the reactant or product that contains the greatest number of different elements.

3. **Add a coefficient to another reactant or product.** Adding a coefficient of 3 to H_2 on the left side of the equation balances the number of H atoms on both sides. Now the equation is balanced.

   Tip: Make sure that the coefficients in your balanced equation are the smallest whole numbers possible—that is, they have no common factor other than 1.

APPLY
Balance the following equations.
1. $Hg + O_2 \rightarrow HgO$
2. $Zn + HCl \rightarrow ZnCl_2 + H_2$

Chapter 7: Chemical Reactions 211

DIFFERENTIATE INSTRUCTION

Inclusion Kinesthetic learners and students with visual impairments can use three-dimensional objects, such as small foam balls, cardboard cutouts, or marshmallows, to create chemical equations. Distinguish for students what kind of atom each object represents.

Teach Difficult Concepts

To help students balance chemical equations, write the following equation on the board: $NO + H_2 \rightarrow NH_3 + H_2O$. Use red, blue, and white construction paper to represent oxygen, nitrogen, and hydrogen atoms respectively. Have students cut out circles. (four blue, four red, and twenty white).

Have students tape the circles together to model molecules of the reactants and products. Have them continue until they have used all the circles and have the same number of each color on both sides of the equation. The equation is balanced once they have two blue (nitrogen) circles, two red (oxygen) circles, and ten white (hydrogen) circles on each side. $2NO + 5H_2 \rightarrow 2NH_3 + 2H_2O$

Metacognitive Strategy

Have students write a short paragraph explaining whether a visual model helps them learn how to balance equations.

Develop Algebra Skills

When coefficients are used to balance an equation, the least common multiple of the coefficients should be used. Ask: Is $2N_2 + 6H_2 \rightarrow 4NH_3$ balanced? *yes* Ask: How can the equation be expressed in a simpler form? $N_2 + 3H_2 \rightarrow 2NH_3$ Point out that the smallest whole numbers possible should be used.

EXPLORE the BIG idea

Revisit "Internet Activity: Reactions" on p. 195. Have students explain the steps they use to balance equations.

Ongoing Assessment

Outline how to balance a simple chemical equation.

Ask: What steps do you follow to balance a chemical equation? *Count the atoms of each element. Use coefficients to add atoms to one side at a time. Repeat until balanced.*

CAPTION Answers:
1. $2Hg + O_2 \rightarrow 2HgO$
2. $Zn + 2HCl \rightarrow ZnCl_2 + H_2$

Ongoing Assessment

 Answer: The law of conservation of mass says that matter is neither created nor destroyed during a chemical reaction, so the number of atoms of each element must be the same on both sides of the equation.

Reinforce

Have students relate the section to the Big Idea.

 Reinforcing Key Concepts, p. 151

7.2 ASSESS & RETEACH

Assess
 Section 7.2 Quiz, p. 42

Reteach
Remind students about the law of conservation of mass and the concept of using chemical equations to represent chemical reactions. List the information needed in order to write a chemical equation, and then write the equation $2Li + H_2O \rightarrow LiOH + H_2$ on the board. Ask students to identify the key points of the equation (reactants on the left and products on right) and how many atoms are on each side of the equation. Then have students balance the equation by using coefficients to show that the number of atoms of each element is the same on both sides of the equation.
$2Li + 2H_2O \rightarrow 2LiOH + H_2$

Technology Resources
Have students visit **ClassZone.com** for reteaching of Key Concepts.

 CONTENT REVIEW

CONTENT REVIEW CD-ROM

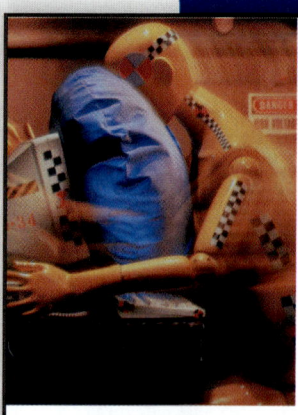

The decomposition of sodium azide is used to inflate air bags in automobiles.

Using the Conservation of Mass

A balanced chemical equation shows that no matter how atoms are rearranged during a chemical reaction, the same number of atoms must be present before and after the reaction. The following example demonstrates the usefulness of chemical equations and the conservation of mass.

The decomposition of sodium azide (NaN_3) is used to inflate automobile air bags. Sodium azide is a solid, and the amount of sodium azide needed in an air bag fills only a small amount of space. In fact, the amount of sodium azide used in air bags is only about 130 grams—an amount that would fit in a large spoon. An inflated air bag, though, takes up much more space even though it contains the same number of atoms that entered the reaction. The reason is illustrated by the chemical equation for this reaction.

Balanced Equation

$2NaN_3 \rightarrow 2Na + 3N_2$

According to the balanced equation shown above, three molecules of nitrogen gas are formed for every two molecules of sodium azide that decompose. Because the nitrogen is a gas, it fills a much greater volume than the original sodium azide. In fact, 67 liters of nitrogen gas are produced by the 130 grams of sodium azide in the reaction. This amount of nitrogen is enough to quickly inflate the air bag during a collision—the decomposition of sodium azide to sodium and nitrogen takes 0.03 seconds.

 Why must chemical equations be balanced?

7.2 Review

KEY CONCEPTS

1. State the law of conservation of mass.
2. Write the chemical equation that shows sodium (Na) and chlorine (Cl_2) combining to form table salt (NaCl).
3. Is the following equation balanced? Why or why not?
   $CO \rightarrow C + O_2$

CRITICAL THINKING

4. **Communicate** Describe Lavoisier's experiment with mercury. How does this experiment show the law of conservation of mass?
5. **Synthesize** Suppose a log's mass is 5 kg. After burning, the mass of the ash is 1 kg. Explain what may have happened to the other 4 kg of mass.

CHALLENGE

6. **Synthesize** Suppose a container holds 1000 hydrogen molecules (H_2) and 1000 oxygen molecules (O_2) that react to form water. How many water molecules will be in the container? Will anything else be in the container? If so, what?

ANSWERS

1. During a chemical reaction, matter is neither created nor destroyed; the mass of reactants always equals the mass of the products.

2. $2Na + Cl_2 \rightarrow 2NaCl$

3. No; one oxygen atom is on the left side of the arrow, and two are on the right side.

4. Mass in the system as a whole did not increase. This indicates that the mass of the product had to come from within the system, presumably from the air within the jar.

5. It was released into the air as a gas because it was not collected during the reaction.

6. 1000 water molecules; yes; 500 O_2 molecules

SCIENCE on the JOB

FIREFIGHTER

Chemistry in Firefighting

A firefighter's job may seem simple: to put out fires. However, a firefighter needs to know about chemicals and chemical reactions. A fire is a combustion reaction that requires oxygen as a reactant. Without oxygen, a fire will normally burn itself out, so firefighters try to prevent oxygen from reaching the burning substances. Firefighters often use water or carbon dioxide for this purpose, but these materials make some types of fires more dangerous.

Grease Fires

Some fires can be extinguished by a chemical reaction. In kitchen grease fires, the chemicals that are used to fight the fire react with the grease. The reaction produces a foam that puts out the fire.

Metal Fires

Some fires involve metals such as magnesium. This metal burns at a very high temperature and reacts violently with water. Firefighters try to smother metal fires with a material such as sand.

Hazardous Reactions

Chemicals may react with water to form poisonous gases or acids. Firefighters might use a foam that extinguishes the fire, cools the area around the fire, and traps gases released by the fire. The symbols shown on the left are among several that show firefighters what chemical dangers may be present.

The fire shown above is a magnesium fire in Chicago in 1998. Firefighters used water to protect surrounding buildings, but dumped road salt on the burning magnesium.

EXPLORE

Build a carbon dioxide fire extinguisher.

1. Put 3 tsp of baking soda on a tissue and roll it into a tube. Tie the ends and middle of the tube with thread. Leave extra thread at one end of the tube.
2. Mold clay tightly around a straw.
3. Pour some vinegar into a bottle.
4. Hold the thread to suspend the tissue tube above the vinegar. Place the straw inside the bottle. Use the clay molded around the straw to hold the thread in place. Be sure that the straw is not touching the vinegar.
5. Shake and observe the fire extinguisher.

Chapter 7: **Chemical Reactions** 213

EXPLORE

To avoid submerging the bottom of the straw in the vinegar, students should measure the distance between the top of the bottle and the vinegar before figuring out where to put the clay on the straw. After they create the fire extinguisher, make sure they understand that when they shake it up, the baking soda and vinegar combine to make carbon dioxide, which will smother a fire (i.e., keep it from getting oxygen).

SCIENCE ON THE JOB
Relevance of Science to Non-science Jobs

Set Learning Goal
To understand why firefighters need a knowledge of chemistry

Present the Science
Remind students that there are three elements to almost every fire: heat, a fuel source, and oxygen. Extinguishing a fire requires the removal of at least one of these elements. Water is useful for extinguishing fires in materials such as paper and wood, but can make other fires more dangerous.

GREASE FIRES Dry chemical extinguishers contain bases such as sodium bicarbonate (baking soda) and ammonium phosphate that react with fatty acids in grease. The resulting foam cuts off the fire's oxygen supply. Water may cause a grease fire to spread rather than extinguish it.

METAL FIRES The fire's oxygen supply must be cut off. Usually it will be smothered with a nonflammable material. When water is added directly on burning magnesium, massive fireballs can be produced.

HAZARDOUS MATERIALS Discuss the word *corrosive*. Water reacts with many chemicals, including cyanide salts. These chemicals contain a metal and a cyanide (CN^-) group. When most cyanide salts combine with water, deadly hydrogen cyanide (HCN) is produced.

Discussion Question
Ask: Why do most home fire extinguishers use dry chemicals instead of water? *Water can cause grease or chemical fires to spread, and water should never be used on an electrical fire. Dry chemicals are a safer choice.*

Close
Ask: Why do firefighters need a knowledge of chemistry? *to understand which materials will put out different types of fires; to avoid making a fire worse*

Chapter 7 213

7.3 FOCUS

▶ Set Learning Goals
Students will
- Describe how energy changes in a chemical reaction.
- Explain how some chemical reactions release energy.
- Explain how some chemical reactions absorb energy.

◀ 3-Minute Warm-Up
Display Transparency 21 or copy this exercise on the board:

Balance the equation.

Al + Br$_2$ → AlBr$_3$ *2Al + 3Br$_2$ → 2AlBr$_3$*

How can you tell if an equation is balanced? *An equation is balanced if the number of atoms of each element is the same on both sides of the equation.*

How does the law of conservation of mass relate to balanced equations? *The total mass of reactants and products must be the same, so the number of atoms of each element must be the same for both reactants and products.*

3-Minute Warm-Up, p. T21

7.3 MOTIVATE

EXPLORE Energy Changes
PURPOSE To observe the energy changes in an endothermic chemical process

TIPS 10 min. Make sure that students are measuring the temperature of the water as they are adding the Epsom salts.

WHAT DO YOU THINK? *The temperature decreased. Energy was absorbed by the process.*

Ongoing Assessment
Describe how energy changes in a chemical reaction.

Ask: Does breaking a chemical bond require energy or release energy? *requires energy*

KEY CONCEPT

7.3 Chemical reactions involve energy changes.

◀ BEFORE, you learned
- Bonds are broken and made during chemical reactions
- Mass is conserved in all chemical reactions
- Chemical reactions are represented by balanced chemical equations

▶ NOW, you will learn
- About the energy in chemical bonds between atoms
- Why some chemical reactions release energy
- Why some chemical reactions absorb energy

VOCABULARY
bond energy p. 214
exothermic reaction p. 215
endothermic reaction p. 215
photosynthesis p. 218

EXPLORE Energy Changes
How can you identify a transfer of energy?

PROCEDURE
1. Pour 50 mL of hot tap water into the cup and place the thermometer in the cup.
2. Wait 30 seconds, then record the temperature of the water.
3. Measure 5 tsp of Epsom salts. Add the Epsom salts to the cup and immediately record the temperature while stirring the contents of the cup.
4. Continue to record the temperature every 30 seconds for 2 minutes.

WHAT DO YOU THINK?
- What happened to the temperature after you added the Epsom salts?
- What do you think caused this change to occur?

MATERIALS
- graduated cylinder
- hot tap water
- plastic cup
- thermometer
- stopwatch
- plastic spoon
- Epsom salts

COMBINATION NOTES
Use combination notes to organize information on how chemical reactions absorb or release energy.

Chemical reactions release or absorb energy.

Chemical reactions involve breaking bonds in reactants and forming new bonds in products. Breaking bonds requires energy, and forming bonds releases energy. The energy associated with bonds is called **bond energy.** What happens to this energy during a chemical reaction?

Chemists have determined the bond energy for bonds between atoms. Breaking a bond between carbon and hydrogen requires a certain amount of energy. This amount of energy is different from the amount of energy needed to break a bond between carbon and oxygen, or between hydrogen and oxygen.

214 Unit 2: Chemical Interactions

RESOURCES FOR DIFFERENTIATED INSTRUCTION

Below Level
UNIT RESOURCE BOOK
- Reading Study Guide A, pp. 154–155
- Decoding Support, p. 177

🎧 **AUDIO CDS**

Advanced
UNIT RESOURCE BOOK
- Challenge and Extension, p. 160
- Challenge Reading, pp. 173–174

English Learners
UNIT RESOURCE BOOK
Spanish Reading Study Guide, pp. 158–159

🎧 **AUDIO CDS**
- Audio Readings in Spanish
- Audio Readings (English)

Energy is needed to break bonds in reactant molecules. Energy is released when bonds are formed in product molecules. By adding up the bond energies in the reactants and products, you can determine whether energy will be released or absorbed.

If more energy is released when the products form than is needed to break the bonds in the reactants, then energy is released during the reaction. A reaction in which energy is released is called an **exothermic reaction.**

If more energy is required to break the bonds in the reactants than is released when the products form, then energy must be added to the reaction. That is, the reaction absorbs energy. A reaction in which energy is absorbed is called an **endothermic reaction.**

These types of energy changes can also be observed in different physical changes such as dissolving or changing state. The state change from a liquid to a solid, or freezing, releases energy—this is an exothermic process. The state change from a solid to a liquid, or melting, absorbs energy—this is an endothermic process.

CHECK YOUR READING How are exothermic and endothermic reactions different?

The white clouds of water vapor are formed by the exothermic reaction between hydrogen and oxygen.

$2H_2 + O_2 \longrightarrow 2H_2O$

Exothermic reactions release energy.

Exothermic chemical reactions often produce an increase in temperature. In exothermic reactions, the bond energies of the reactants are less than the bond energies of the products. As a result, less energy is needed to break the bonds in the reactants than is released during the formation of the products. This energy difference between reactants and products is often released as heat. The release of heat causes a change in the temperature of the reaction mixture.

Even though energy is released by exothermic reactions, some energy must first be added to break bonds in the reactants. In exothermic reactions, the formation of bonds in the products releases more energy. Overall, more energy is released than is added.

Some reactions are highly exothermic. These reactions produce a great deal of heat and significantly raise the temperature of their surroundings. One example is the reaction of powdered aluminum metal with a type of iron oxide, a reaction known as the thermite reaction. The equation for this reaction is

$2Al + Fe_2O_3 \longrightarrow Al_2O_3 + 2Fe$

This reaction releases enough heat to melt the iron that is produced. In fact, this reaction is used to weld iron rails together.

The thermite reaction releases enough heat to weld pieces of iron together.

CHECK YOUR READING What is evidence for an exothermic chemical reaction?

Chapter 7: Chemical Reactions 215

DIFFERENTIATE INSTRUCTION

More Reading Support

A What is a chemical reaction that releases energy? *exothermic reaction*

B What happens during an endothermic reaction? *Energy is absorbed.*

English Learners To help English learners remember the definitions of *exothermic reaction* and *endothermic reaction*, explain the prefixes *endo-* and *exo-*. The prefix *endo-* means "inside" or "within." An endothermic reaction takes in, or absorbs, energy. The prefix *exo-* means "outside" or "external." An exothermic reaction gives off, or releases, energy.

7.3 INSTRUCT

Address Misconceptions

IDENTIFY Ask: Where does the energy that is released by an exothermic reaction come from? If students say it comes from breaking bonds, they may hold the misconception that breaking bonds releases energy.

CORRECT Show students the energy diagram on p. 216. Point out the yellow energy bursts that indicate energy must be added to the reactants before the reaction can take place, and that a larger amount of energy is released when new bonds form.

REASSESS Ask students to describe where energy is absorbed and released in an exothermic reaction. *Energy is always absorbed to break bonds and start a reaction. An exothermic reaction releases energy because, when new bonds form, more energy is released than is required to break the bonds in the reactants.*

Technology Resources

Visit **ClassZone.com** for background on common student misconceptions.

MISCONCEPTION DATABASE

Teach Difficult Concepts

Explain the difference between temperature and heat. Temperature is a measure of the average amount of kinetic energy of the particles within a substance. Heat is the transfer of energy from an object of higher temperature to an object of lower temperature. Ask: What decreases an object's temperature? *a transfer of energy through heat*

Ongoing Assessment

CHECK YOUR READING *Answer: Exothermic reactions release energy, and endothermic reactions absorb energy.*

CHECK YOUR READING *Answer: change in temperature caused by a release of energy*

Chapter 7 215

Teach from Visuals

To help students interpret the diagrams and graph of energy changes in an exothermic reaction, ask:

- Is more energy added or released during this reaction? *released*
- What does the graph show about reactants and products in an exothermic reaction? *Reactants have a lower bond energy than products, so more energy is released by bond formation than is absorbed to break bonds.*

Real World Example

The production of light by living organisms occurs mainly among marine animals and is the main source of light in the deep ocean. Almost all light produced by marine animals is blue light, because it is visible at the greatest distance under water, and most animals are sensitive only to blue light. The black dragonfish, also called loosejaws, is an exception because it produces red light.

Ongoing Assessment

Identify some chemical reactions that release energy.

Ask: What two forms of energy can be released in exothermic reactions? Identify reactions that release these energy forms. *Energy can be released as heat (all common combustion reactions) or light (the reaction between oxygen and luciferin).*

READING VISUALS *Answer: The size of the yellow energy bursts and the height of the bars in the bar graph indicate that more energy is released than is absorbed.*

CHECK YOUR READING *Answer: as heat or light*

Exothermic Reactions

The products have greater bond energies than the reactants.

Methane Combustion

reactants
$CH_4 + 2O_2$ + energy added → bonds broken in reactants

bonds formed in products
$CO_2 + 2H_2O$ + energy released ←

Difference in Energy

Bond Energy

Reactants (energy added) Products (energy released)

More energy is released than added.

READING VISUALS What information in the diagram shows that methane combustion is exothermic?

All common combustion reactions, such as the combustion of methane, are exothermic. To determine how energy changes in this reaction, the bond energies in the reactants—oxygen and methane—and in the products—carbon dioxide and water—can be added and compared. This process is illustrated by the diagram shown above. The difference in energy is released to the surrounding air as heat.

Some chemical reactions release excess energy as light instead of heat. For example, glow sticks work by a chemical reaction that releases energy as light. One of the reactants, a solution of hydrogen peroxide, is contained in a thin glass tube within the plastic stick. The rest of the stick is filled with a second chemical and a brightly colored dye. When you bend the stick, the glass tube inside it breaks and the two solutions mix. The result is a bright glow of light.

These cup coral polyps glow because of exothermic chemical reactions.

Exothermic chemical reactions also occur in living things. Some of these reactions release energy as heat, and others release energy as light. Fireflies light up due to a reaction that takes place between oxygen and a chemical called luciferin. This type of exothermic reaction is not unique to fireflies. In fact, similar reactions are found in several different species of fish, squid, jellyfish, and shrimp.

CHECK YOUR READING In which ways might an exothermic reaction release energy?

DIFFERENTIATE INSTRUCTION

More Reading Support

C Are combustion reactions exothermic or endothermic? *exothermic*

Below Level Review the use of bar graphs. Have students identify the *x*- and *y*-axes on the bar graph on this page. Ask them to explain what the bar graph is telling them.

Advanced Have students who are interested in learning more about how glow sticks work read the following article:

- Challenge Reading, pp. 173–174
- Challenge and Extension, p. 160

The bombardier beetle, shown in the photograph on the right, uses natural exothermic reactions to defend itself. Although several chemical reactions are involved, the end result is the production of a hot, toxic spray. The most important reaction in the process is the decomposition of hydrogen peroxide into water and oxygen.

$$2H_2O_2 \longrightarrow 2H_2O + O_2$$

When the hydrogen peroxide rapidly breaks down, the hot, toxic mixture made by the series of reactions is pressurized by the oxygen gas from the reaction in the equation above. After enough pressure builds up, the beetle can spray the mixture.

Endothermic reactions absorb energy.

Endothermic reactions often produce a decrease in temperature. In endothermic reactions, the bond energies of the reactants are greater than the bond energies of the products. As a result, more energy is needed to break the bonds in the reactants than is released during the formation of the products. The difference in energy is usually absorbed from the surroundings as heat. This often causes a decrease in the temperature of the reaction mixture.

All endothermic reactions absorb energy. However, they do not all absorb energy as heat. One example of an endothermic reaction of this type is the decomposition of water by electrolysis. In this case, the energy that is absorbed is in the form of electrical energy. When the electric current is turned off, the reaction stops. The change in energy that occurs in this reaction is shown below.

READING TIP
The prefix *endo-* means "inside."

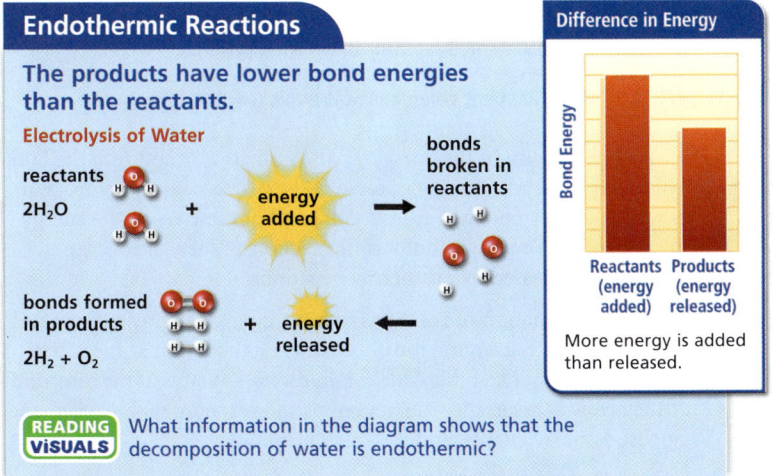

Endothermic Reactions
The products have lower bond energies than the reactants.
Electrolysis of Water
reactants $2H_2O$ + energy added → bonds broken in reactants
bonds formed in products $2H_2 + O_2$ + energy released ←

Difference in Energy
Reactants (energy added) Products (energy released)
More energy is added than released.

READING VISUALS What information in the diagram shows that the decomposition of water is endothermic?

Chapter 7: Chemical Reactions 217

DIFFERENTIATE INSTRUCTION

 More Reading Support

D In endothermic reactions, which has greater bond energies, the reactants or the products? *the reactants*

Alternative Assessment Have students write a paragraph summarizing the diagram on this page. They should describe the reaction that takes place, the energy changes, and the bond energies of the reactants and products.

History of Science

Many scientists were involved in working out how photosynthesis uses light. In 1905, the English plant physiologist F. F. Blackman showed that photosynthesis is a two-step process and that only one of the steps involves light. The role of light was clarified by Cornelis van Niel when he was a graduate student at Stanford University in the 1930s. Ultimately, photosynthesis takes place in the chloroplasts of leaves and chlorophyll absorbs light during the first step, called the light reaction.

Teacher Demo

Purchase or grow two small plants of the same species. Water both plants well. Place one plant in a window or under a bright light. Place the other plant under a foil-wrapped box or in a dark incubator. Have students examine the plants after a week. Ask: Do the results suggest that photosynthesis is an endothermic or exothermic reaction? Why? *Endothermic; the plant exposed to sunlight grew because it absorbed energy.*

Language Arts Connection

Tell students that the word *exothermic* comes from the Greek root words *exo* and *therm,* meaning "heat out." The word *endothermic* comes from the Greek words meaning "heat in." Have students find other *exo* and *endo* words and use them in sentences.

Ongoing Assessment

Identify some chemical reactions that absorb energy.

Ask: What endothermic reaction absorbs light energy rather than heat? *photosynthesis*

 Answer: The temperature of the reaction mixture decreases.

 Answer: It becomes an endothermic reaction that absorbs energy.

218 Unit 2: **Chemical Interactions**

 Probably the most important series of endothermic reactions on Earth is photosynthesis. Many steps occur in the process, but the overall chemical reaction is

$$6CO_2 + 6H_2O \longrightarrow C_6H_{12}O_6 + 6O_2$$

Unlike many other endothermic reactions, photosynthesis does not absorb energy as heat. Instead, during **photosynthesis,** plants absorb energy from sunlight to turn carbon dioxide and water into oxygen and glucose, which is a type of sugar molecule. The energy is stored in the glucose molecules, ready to be used when needed.

 How can you determine if a reaction is endothermic?

Exothermic and endothermic reactions work together to supply energy.

When thinking about exothermic and endothermic reactions, it is often useful to consider energy as part of the reaction. An exothermic reaction releases energy, so energy is on the product side of the chemical equation. An endothermic reaction absorbs energy, so energy is on the reactant side of the chemical equation.

Exothermic Reaction
Reactants ⟶ Products + Energy

Endothermic Reaction
Reactants + Energy ⟶ Products

As you can see in the general reactions above, exothermic and endothermic reactions have opposite energy changes. This means that if an exothermic chemical reaction proceeds in the opposite direction, it becomes an endothermic reaction that absorbs energy. Similarly, if an endothermic reaction proceeds in the opposite direction, it becomes an exothermic reaction that releases energy.

 What happens when an exothermic reaction is reversed?

 A large amount of the energy we use on Earth comes from the Sun. This energy includes energy in fossil fuels such as coal and petroleum, as well as energy obtained from food. In all of these cases, the energy in sunlight is stored by endothermic reactions. When the energy is needed, it is released by exothermic reactions.

This combination of reactions forms a cycle of energy storage and use. For example, examine the photosynthesis equation at the top of the page. If you look at this equation in reverse—that is, if the direction of the arrow is reversed—it is a combustion reaction, with oxygen and glucose as the reactants, and it is exothermic.

218 Unit 2: Chemical Interactions

View examples of endothermic and exothermic reactions.

DIFFERENTIATE INSTRUCTION

 More Reading Support

E What is the most important endothermic reaction in nature? *photosynthesis*

F Where does much of the energy on Earth come from? *the Sun*

Advanced Have students list additional examples of exothermic and endothermic reactions and describe what happens when these reactions are reversed, as in the photosynthesis equation on this page. Ask students for examples of other cycles of energy storage and use.

Plants such as trees store energy through photosynthesis. Cars and trucks release this energy through combustion.

Plants store energy through the endothermic reactions of photosynthesis. Living things can release this energy through a series of exothermic reactions that will be described in the next section.

The energy stored in plants through photosynthesis can also be released in other ways. Consider energy from fossil fuels. Fossil fuels include petroleum, natural gas, and coal. These substances formed from fossilized materials, mainly plants, that had been under high pressures and temperatures for millions of years. When these plants were alive, they used photosynthesis to produce glucose and other molecules from carbon dioxide and water.

The energy stored in the bonds of these molecules remains, even though the molecules have changed over time. The burning of gasoline in a car releases this energy, enabling the car's engine to work. Similarly, the burning of coal in a power plant, or the burning of natural gas in a stove, releases the energy originally stored by the endothermic series of photosynthesis reactions.

 How can endothermic and exothermic reactions work together?

7.3 Review

KEY CONCEPTS
1. What are the differences between exothermic and endothermic reactions?
2. Is the combustion of methane an exothermic or endothermic reaction? Explain.
3. Is photosynthesis an exothermic or endothermic reaction? Explain.

CRITICAL THINKING
4. **Synthesize** Describe the connections between the processes of photosynthesis and combustion.
5. **Communicate** Explain how most energy used on Earth can be traced back to the Sun.

CHALLENGE
6. **Synthesize** Electrolysis of water is endothermic. What does this indicate about the bond energy in the reactants and products? What happens when this reaction is reversed?

Chapter 7: **Chemical Reactions** 219

Ongoing Assessment

 Answer: Energy can be stored in molecules as a result of an endothermic reaction and then released through exothermic reactions.

Reinforce

Have students relate the section to the Big Idea.

R Reinforcing Key Concepts, p. 161

7.3 ASSESS & RETEACH

Assess
 Section 7.3 Quiz, p. 43

Reteach
Write the definitions for *endothermic reaction*, *exothermic reaction*, and *photosynthesis* on the board. Ask students whether energy is released or absorbed in each process. Then have students think about the process of baking a cake. Ask:

- Is the process of baking a cake endothermic or exothermic? *endothermic*
- How do you know? *The cake batter will not bake unless it absorbs energy.*
- Where does the energy needed to bake the cake come from? *heat from the oven*

Technology Resources

Have students visit ClassZone.com for reteaching of Key Concepts.

 CONTENT REVIEW

CONTENT REVIEW CD-ROM

ANSWERS

1. Exothermic reactions: products have higher bond energy than reactants and energy is released; endothermic reactions: reactants have higher bond energy than products and energy is absorbed.

2. Exothermic; energy is released as heat and light.

3. Endothermic; energy from light is absorbed in order for the reactions to occur.

4. They are approximately opposite reactions in terms of energy as well as reactants and products.

5. Sample answer: Fossil fuels contain the carbon stored in plants by photosynthesis hundreds of millions of years ago. So, energy in fossil fuels started as energy from the Sun.

6. Bond energy is greater in the reactants; when the reaction is reversed, the bond energy is greater in the products and energy is released.

Chapter 7 **219**

CHAPTER INVESTIGATION

Focus

PURPOSE To observe energy changes that result from chemical reactions

OVERVIEW Students will measure temperature changes during one exothermic reaction and one endothermic reaction. Students will find the following:

- Adding yeast to hydrogen peroxide produces an increase in temperature due to an exothermic process.
- The reaction between vinegar and baking soda is endothermic, with a decrease in temperature.

Lab Preparation

- Have students bring in stopwatches if you do not have enough for the entire class. A wristwatch with a second hand can substitute for a stopwatch.
- Have students read through the investigation and prepare their data tables. Or you may wish to copy and distribute datasheets and rubrics.

 UNIT RESOURCE BOOK, pp. 180–188

 SCIENCE TOOLKIT, F15

Lab Management

- Make sure students include necessary time intervals when making data tables.
- Review with students how to use a balance and a graduated cylinder. Remind them to read the bottom of the meniscus in the cylinder.
- Students should measure the yeast on the balance during the 2-minute waiting period. Students should measure the baking soda on the balance while the vinegar is warming.

INCLUSION Ask students if they can observe temperature changes by feeling the beakers.

Teaching with Technology

Temperature probes can be used to measure and record temperatures. Graphing calculators can be used to graph students' data.

220 Unit 2: **Chemical Interactions**

CHAPTER INVESTIGATION

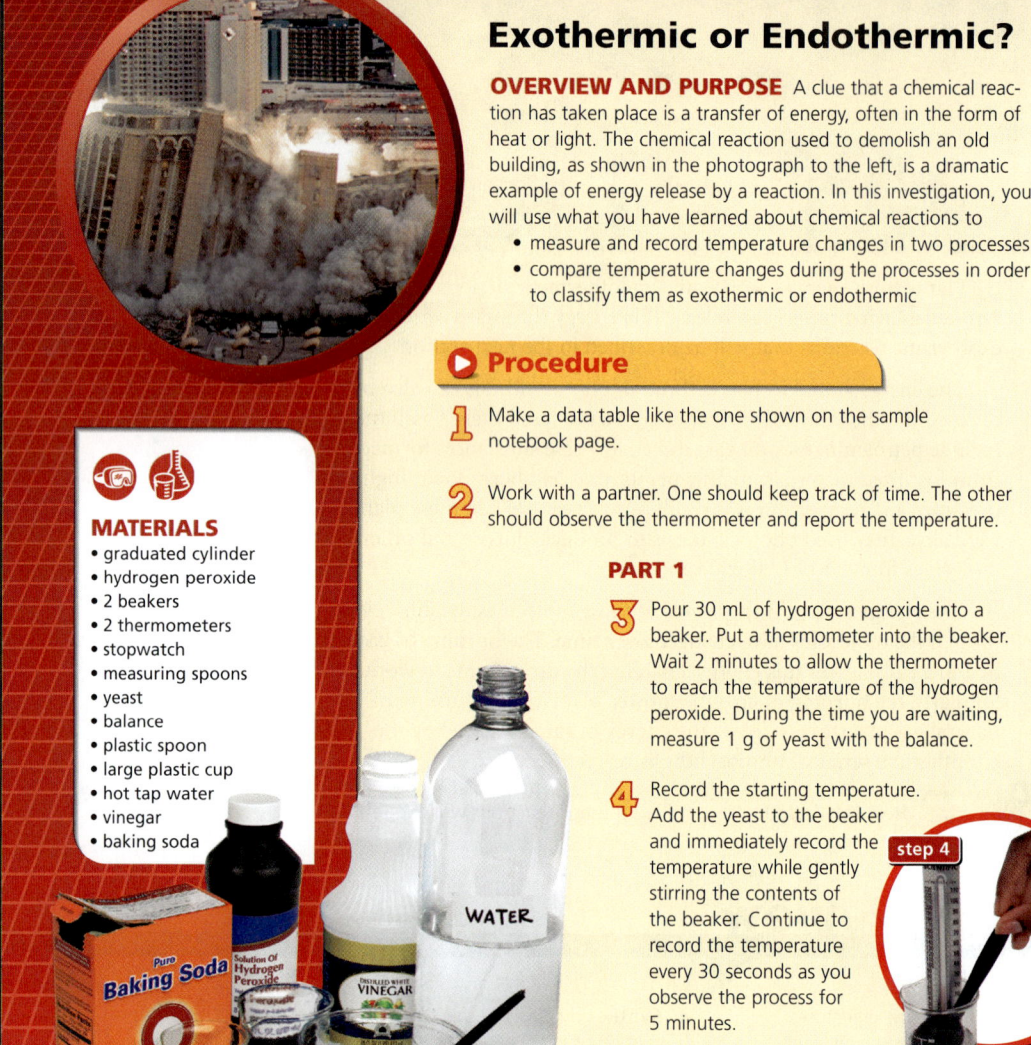

Exothermic or Endothermic?

OVERVIEW AND PURPOSE A clue that a chemical reaction has taken place is a transfer of energy, often in the form of heat or light. The chemical reaction used to demolish an old building, as shown in the photograph to the left, is a dramatic example of energy release by a reaction. In this investigation, you will use what you have learned about chemical reactions to
- measure and record temperature changes in two processes
- compare temperature changes during the processes in order to classify them as exothermic or endothermic

▶ Procedure

1. Make a data table like the one shown on the sample notebook page.

2. Work with a partner. One should keep track of time. The other should observe the thermometer and report the temperature.

PART 1

3. Pour 30 mL of hydrogen peroxide into a beaker. Put a thermometer into the beaker. Wait 2 minutes to allow the thermometer to reach the temperature of the hydrogen peroxide. During the time you are waiting, measure 1 g of yeast with the balance.

4. Record the starting temperature. Add the yeast to the beaker and immediately record the temperature while gently stirring the contents of the beaker. Continue to record the temperature every 30 seconds as you observe the process for 5 minutes.

MATERIALS
- graduated cylinder
- hydrogen peroxide
- 2 beakers
- 2 thermometers
- stopwatch
- measuring spoons
- yeast
- balance
- plastic spoon
- large plastic cup
- hot tap water
- vinegar
- baking soda

step 4

220 Unit 2: **Chemical Interactions**

INVESTIGATION RESOURCES

 CHAPTER INVESTIGATION, Exothermic or Endothermic?
- Level A, pp. 180–183
- Level B, pp. 184–187
- Level C, p. 188

Advanced students should complete Levels B & C.

 Writing a Lab Report, pp. D12–13

Technology Resources

Customize this student lab as needed or look for an alternative. Print rubrics to assess student lab reports.

 Lab Generator CD-ROM

PART 2

5. Make a hot water bath by filling a large plastic cup halfway with hot tap water.

6. Measure and pour 30 mL of vinegar into a small beaker. Set this beaker in the hot water bath and place a thermometer in the vinegar. Wait until the temperature of the vinegar rises to between 32 and 38°C (90 to 100°F). While waiting for the vinegar's temperature to increase, measure 1 g of baking soda.

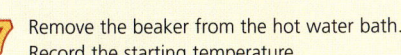

7. Remove the beaker from the hot water bath. Record the starting temperature.

8. Add the baking soda to the vinegar and immediately record the temperature as you swirl the contents of the beaker. Continue to record the temperature every 30 seconds as you observe the reaction for 5 minutes.

Observe and Analyze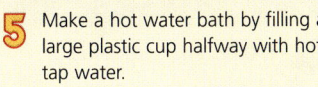

1. **RECORD OBSERVATIONS** Remember to complete your data table.

2. **GRAPH** Use the information from your data table to graph your results. Make a double-line graph, plotting your data in a different color for each part of the investigation. Plot temperature in degrees Celsius on the vertical, or y-axis. Plot the time in minutes on the horizontal, or x-axis.

3. **ANALYZE DATA** Examine the graph. When did the temperature change the most in each part of the investigation? When did it change the least? Compare the temperature at the start of each process with the temperature after 5 minutes. How do the temperature changes compare?

Conclude

1. **CLASSIFY** Is the mixture of hydrogen peroxide and yeast endothermic or exothermic? Is the reaction between vinegar and baking soda endothermic or exothermic? Provide evidence for your answers.

2. **EVALUATE** Did you have any difficulties obtaining accurate measurements? Describe possible limitations or sources of error.

3. **APPLY** What does the reaction between baking soda and vinegar tell you about their bond energies?

INVESTIGATE Further

CHALLENGE Repeat Part 2, but instead of using the hot water bath, add the hot water directly to the vinegar before pouring in the baking soda. Does this change in procedure change the results of the experiment? Why might your observations have changed? Explain your answers.

Exothermic or Endothermic?
Observe and Analyze
Table 1. Temperature Measurements

Time (min)	Hydrogen Peroxide and Yeast Temperature (°C)	Vinegar and Baking Soda Temperature (°C)
0		
0.5		
1.0		
....		
5.0		

Conclude

Chapter 7: **Chemical Reactions** 221

Observe and Analyze

1. **SAMPLE DATA** Hydrogen peroxide and yeast: 0 minutes, 21°C; 0.5–2 minutes, 24°C; 2.5–5 minutes, 23°C. Vinegar and baking soda: 0 minutes, 33°C; 0.5–2 minutes, 28°C; 2.5–5 minutes, 27°C.

2. See students' graphs.

3. The reaction involving yeast and hydrogen peroxide showed an immediate increase in temperature. The reaction between vinegar and baking soda showed an immediate decrease in temperature.

Conclude

1. The first reaction is exothermic, as indicated by an increase in temperature; the second reaction is endothermic, as indicated by a decrease in temperature.

2. Answers will vary but could include difficulties with temperature measurements, inconsistent times between measurements, or measurement error during the experimental setup.

3. The bond energies of the reactants are greater than the bond energies of the products.

INVESTIGATE Further

CHALLENGE Answer: Yes; adding water to the reaction mix decreases the concentrations of the reactants, thus slowing the reaction rate. Temperature change should be less after 5 minutes.

Post-Lab Discussion

- Discuss variables in the lab. Ask: What was the independent variable? *time* What was the dependent variable? *temperature*
- Ask: Why was it helpful to heat the vinegar to 32–38°C? *to increase the reaction rate and provide a greater contrast in the change in temperature*
- Ask: Why is it important to record the temperature immediately as the reaction starts? *because the temperature change is relatively large at the beginning of the reaction, but then levels off*

7.4 FOCUS

◉ Set Learning Goals
Students will
- Identify the relationship between the reactions of respiration and the reactions of photosynthesis.
- Recognize how chemistry has been used to develop new technology.
- Infer through an experiment how catalysts affect a chemical reaction.

◉ 3-Minute Warm-Up
Display Transparency 21 or copy this exercise on the board:

Match the definition to the correct term.

Definitions
1. substances formed by a reaction *e*
2. reaction in which energy is released *a*
3. reaction in which energy is absorbed by plants to make glucose and oxygen *c*

Terms
a. exothermic reaction
b. reactants
c. photosynthesis
d. catalysts
e. products

 3-Minute Warm-Up, p. T21

7.4 MOTIVATE

THINK ABOUT

PURPOSE To explore examples of chemical reactions in modern life and technology that are adapted from reactions found in nature

DISCUSS Brainstorm possible examples of reactions with students. *Sample answer: reactions involved in the manufacturing of pesticides, fertilizers, medicines, clothing fibers, artificial rubber, dyes*

KEY CONCEPT

7.4 Life and industry depend on chemical reactions.

◁ BEFORE, you learned
- Chemical reactions turn reactants into products by rearranging atoms
- Mass is conserved during chemical reactions
- Chemical reactions involve energy changes

▷ NOW, you will learn
- About the importance of chemical reactions in living things
- How chemistry has helped the development of new technology

VOCABULARY
respiration p. 222

THINK ABOUT

How is a glow stick like a firefly?

When a firefly glows in the dark, a chemical reaction that emits light is taking place. Similarly, when you activate a glow stick, a chemical reaction that causes the glow stick to emit light occurs. Many reactions in modern life and technology adapt chemical reactions found in nature. Can you think of other examples?

Living things require chemical reactions.

In section 3, you saw that photosynthesis stores energy from the Sun in forms that can be used later. These forms of stored energy include fossil fuels and the sugar glucose. The glucose molecules produced by photosynthesis make up the basic food used for energy by almost all living things. For example, animals obtain glucose molecules by eating plants or eating other animals that have eaten plants.

Living cells obtain energy from glucose molecules through the process of **respiration,** which is the "combustion" of glucose to obtain energy. This series of chemical reactions is, in general, the reverse of photosynthesis. It produces carbon dioxide and water from oxygen and glucose. The overall reactions for both photosynthesis and respiration are shown on the top of page 223. From a chemical point of view, respiration is the same as any other combustion reaction.

VOCABULARY
Remember to make a four square diagram for *respiration*.

222 Unit 2: Chemical Interactions

RESOURCES FOR DIFFERENTIATED INSTRUCTION

Below Level
UNIT RESOURCE BOOK
- Reading Study Guide A, pp. 164–165
- Decoding Support, p. 177

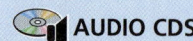 **AUDIO CDS**

Advanced
UNIT RESOURCE BOOK
Challenge and Extension, p. 170

English Learners
UNIT RESOURCE BOOK
Spanish Reading Study Guide, pp. 168–169

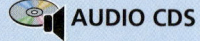 **AUDIO CDS**

- Audio Readings in Spanish
- Audio Readings (English)

Photosynthesis
$6CO_2 + 6H_2O + energy \rightarrow C_6H_{12}O_6 + 6O_2$

Respiration
$C_6H_{12}O_6 + 6O_2 \rightarrow 6CO_2 + 6H_2O + energy$

The energy released by respiration can be used for growth of new cells, movement, or any other life function. Suppose that you are late for school and have to run to get to class on time. Your body needs to activate nerves and muscles right away, without waiting for you to first eat some food as a source of energy. The glucose molecules in food are stored in your body until you need energy. Then, respiration consumes them in a process that includes several steps.

To make these steps go quickly, the body uses catalysts—enzymes—for each step. Some enzymes break the glucose molecules into smaller pieces, while other enzymes break bonds within each piece. Still other enzymes help form the reaction products—carbon dioxide and water. With the help of enzymes, these reactions take place quickly and automatically. You do not have to think about breaking down glucose when you run—you just start to run and the energy is there.

 How are photosynthesis and respiration opposites?

INVESTIGATE Sugar Combustion

How are catalysts important in the combustion of sugar?

PROCEDURE
1. Using the tongs, hold a sugar cube in a candle flame for 30 seconds. Observe what happens.
2. Rub ashes on the second sugar cube.
3. Using the tongs, hold the second sugar cube in the candle flame for 30 seconds. Observe what happens.

WHAT DO YOU THINK?
- What happened to the first sugar cube? What happened to the second sugar cube?
- What may have caused any differences that you observed?

CHALLENGE How might the ashes used in this experiment have a similar function to enzymes in your cells? Explain.

SKILL Inferring

MATERIALS
- candle
- matches
- tongs
- 2 sugar cubes
- stopwatch
- ashes

TIME 20 minutes

Chapter 7: **Chemical Reactions** 223

DIFFERENTIATE INSTRUCTION

More Reading Support

A What series of chemical reactions in the body releases energy that is used for growth and movement? *respiration*

English Learners English learners may not fully understand that respiration is the reverse of photosynthesis. Place the terms and their definitions on the Science Word Wall. Also, point out the chemical equations at the top of this page. The reactants in photosynthesis are the products in respiration. The reactants in respiration are the products in photosynthesis.

7.4 INSTRUCT

INVESTIGATE Sugar Combustion

PURPOSE To infer how catalysts affect a chemical reaction

TIP *20 min.* Remind students not to touch melted sugar. It is very hot.

WHAT DO YOU THINK? *The first cube melted. The second cube burned. The ash-covered sugar cube burned because it was covered with ash.*

CHALLENGE *The ashes act as a catalyst, as enzymes do in living cells.*

Datasheet, Sugar Combustion, p. 171

Technology Resources

Customize this student lab as needed or look for an alternative. Print rubrics to assess student lab reports.

Lab Generator CD-ROM

Integrating the Sciences

Cells in most organisms, including humans, use a molecule called ATP, not glucose, as the source of energy. However, cells break down glucose to make ATP. The enzymes involved in respiration, and other reactions in cells, are vital because most reactions will not normally occur at the temperatures of living cells.

Ongoing Assessment

Identify the chemical reactions that take place in living cells.

Ask: How is respiration similar to a combustion reaction? *One reactant is oxygen and the other contains carbon and hydrogen, the products are carbon dioxide and water, and it is exothermic.*

CHECK YOUR READING Answer: *Photosynthesis makes glucose and oxygen from carbon dioxide and water. The process is endothermic. Respiration is an exothermic process. Glucose and oxygen are the reactants, and carbon dioxide and water are the products.*

Real World Example

Another reaction between chemicals made by humans and natural reactants is the atmospheric reaction between chlorofluorocarbons (CFCs) and ozone (O_3). CFCs, as well as other chemicals, are involved in the decomposition of ozone. A decrease in ozone in the ozone layer high in the atmosphere allows more ultraviolet radiation to reach Earth's surface.

Develop Critical Thinking

COMPARE Ask students to write and compare the chemical equations for the complete and incomplete combustion of methane (CH_4). Tell students that incomplete combustion takes place when insufficient oxygen is present and that it produces carbon monoxide gas (CO) rather than carbon dioxide (CO_2). *complete: $CH_4 + 2O_2 \rightarrow CO_2 + 2H_2O$; incomplete: $2CH_4 + 3O_2 \rightarrow 2CO + 4H_2O$*

Teach Difficult Concepts

The process that occurs inside a catalytic converter takes place in two steps. First, platinum and rhodium are used to change NO and NO_2 into oxygen (O_2) and nitrogen (N_2) by separating the nitrogen and oxygen. Then, platinum and palladium are used in the second step to change CO and unburned hydrocarbons into CO_2 and H_2O.

Ongoing Assessment

 *Answer: to reduce pollution released into the air from vehicles*

Chemical reactions are used in technology.

Every time your cells need energy, they essentially complete respiration—the "combustion" of glucose. The series of chemical reactions in respiration involves enzymes, which are catalysts. Every time someone drives a car, another combustion reaction occurs—the combustion of gasoline. While the combustion of gasoline does not require a catalyst, the chemical reactions that change a car's exhaust gases do use a catalyst.

No chemical reaction is ever completely efficient. It does not matter what the reaction is or how the reaction conditions are set up. There are always some reactants that do not change completely into products. Sometimes a chemical reaction makes unwanted waste products.

In the case of gasoline combustion, some of the original carbon compounds, called hydrocarbons, do not burn completely, and carbon monoxide gas (CO) is produced. Also, nitrogen in the air reacts with oxygen in a car's engine to produce compounds of nitrogen and oxygen, including nitric oxide (NO). The production of these gases lowers the overall efficiency of combustion. More importantly, these gases can react with water vapor in the air to form smog and acid rain.

Sometimes, as you can see with gasoline combustion, chemical technology causes a problem. Then, new chemical technology is designed to treat the problem. For example, it was necessary to reduce carbon monoxide and nitric oxide emissions from car exhaust. As a result, engineers in the 1970s developed a device called a catalytic converter. This device causes chemical reactions that remove the unwanted waste products from the combustion of gasoline.

Catalytic converters contain metal catalysts such as platinum, palladium, and rhodium. The products of the reactions in the catalytic converter are nitrogen (N_2), oxygen (O_2), water (H_2O), and carbon dioxide (CO_2), which are all ordinary parts of Earth's atmosphere.

Even though catalytic converters have been used for many years, scientists and engineers are still trying to improve them. One goal of this research is to use less expensive metals, such as magnesium and zinc, inside catalytic converters, while forming the same exhaust products.

 Why were catalytic converters developed?

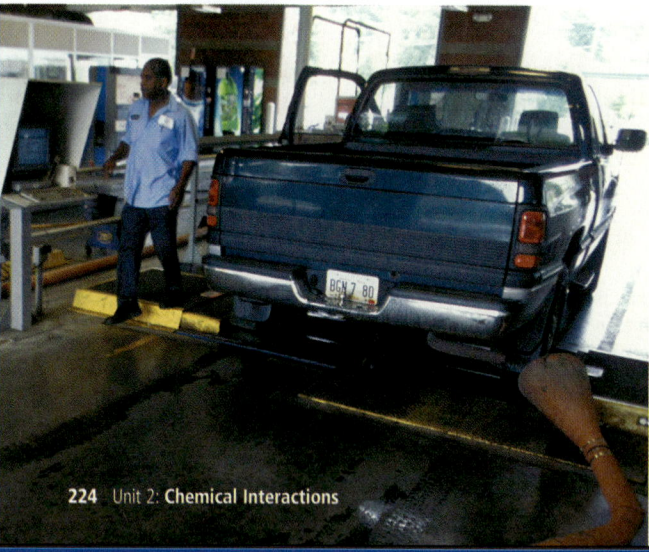

Many states inspect vehicles to test the pollutants in their exhaust gases.

224 Unit 2: Chemical Interactions

DIFFERENTIATE INSTRUCTION

More Reading Support

B What are waste products of gasoline combustion? *carbon monoxide and nitric oxide*

C What device reduces gasoline's waste products? *catalytic converter*

Alternative Assessment Have students in groups quiz each other on section material. One student can ask a question of the others. The student who correctly answers the question then asks the group another question.

Chemical Reactions in Catalytic Converters

The combustion of gasoline makes harmful waste products. Chemical reactions in catalytic converters make these waste products less harmful.

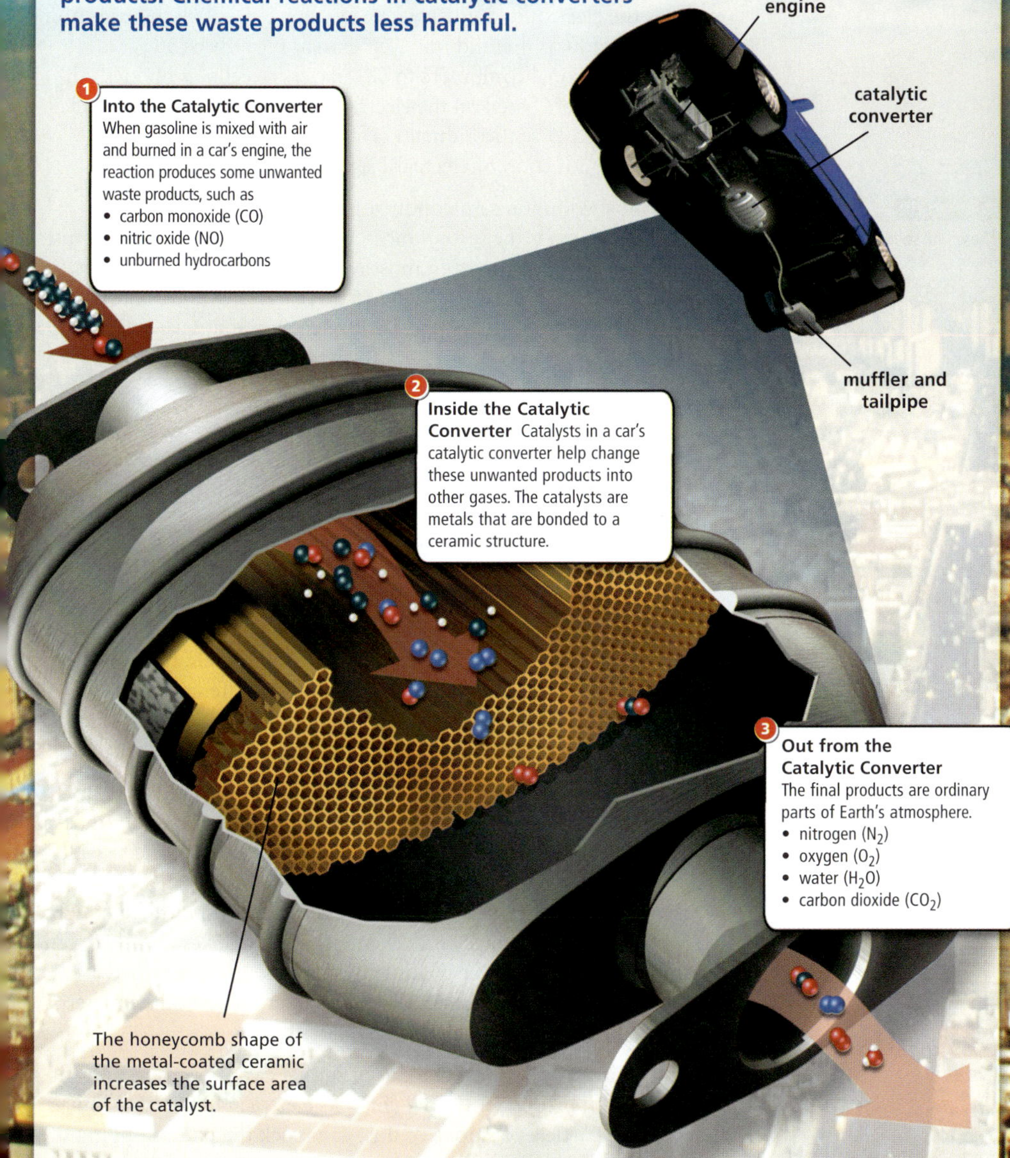

1 Into the Catalytic Converter When gasoline is mixed with air and burned in a car's engine, the reaction produces some unwanted waste products, such as
- carbon monoxide (CO)
- nitric oxide (NO)
- unburned hydrocarbons

engine

catalytic converter

muffler and tailpipe

2 Inside the Catalytic Converter Catalysts in a car's catalytic converter help change these unwanted products into other gases. The catalysts are metals that are bonded to a ceramic structure.

3 Out from the Catalytic Converter The final products are ordinary parts of Earth's atmosphere.
- nitrogen (N_2)
- oxygen (O_2)
- water (H_2O)
- carbon dioxide (CO_2)

The honeycomb shape of the metal-coated ceramic increases the surface area of the catalyst.

READING VISUALS What are CO and NO changed into by a catalytic converter?

Chapter 7: Chemical Reactions 225

DIFFERENTIATE INSTRUCTION

Below Level If students have a difficult time reading, have them give an oral summary of the diagram depicting how a catalytic converter works. They should describe the reactants and products involved and the function of catalysts in the reaction.

Teach from Visuals

To help students interpret the diagram of a catalytic converter, ask:
- What are the reactants that enter the catalytic converter? *carbon monoxide, nitric oxide, and unburned hydrocarbons*
- What are these reactants the original products of? What are the original reactants? *gasoline combustion; hydrocarbons (gasoline) and air (nitrogen, oxygen, carbon dioxide, water vapor, and trace gases)*
- Why does a catalytic converter have a honeycomb structure? *It increases the surface area of the catalyst, which increases the reaction rate.*
- What does a catalytic converter change unburned hydrocarbons into? *carbon dioxide and water*

This visual is also available as T22 in the Unit Transparency Book.

Integrating the Sciences

Even though catalytic converters change the original emissions of cars into less harmful products, evidence indicates that the carbon dioxide released may contribute to global warming through the greenhouse effect. Carbon dioxide is a gas that traps heat in the atmosphere.

Metacognitive Strategy

Have students write a short paragraph examining whether it is easier for them to learn how a catalytic converter works from a diagram, as on this page, or from text, as on p. 224.

Ongoing Assessment

READING VISUALS *Answer: nitrogen, oxygen, and carbon dioxide*

Chapter 7 225

History of Science

The development of modern personal computers relied on the invention of the integrated circuit, or microchip. The first silicon chip was invented by Jack St. Claire Kilby at Texas Instruments, and it was produced in September 1958. Computers using chips began to appear in 1962.

Teacher Demo

Discarded silicon chips are usually available from stores that repair computers or other electronic devices. Obtain one, and pass it around the room with a magnifying glass, so that students can examine it.

Develop Number Sense

In order to be used in microchips, silicon must have less than 1 part per billion of impurities. In scientific notation, this value can be expressed as 1×10^{-9}. The larger the absolute value of a negative exponent, the smaller the number. Ask: Is a purity of 1×10^{-11} good enough for microchips? What about a purity of 1×10^{-7}? Why? *Yes; no; 1×10^{-11} is 1 part per hundred billion, which is pure enough, but 1×10^{-7} is 1 part per 10 million, which is not pure enough.*

Ongoing Assessment

Recognize how chemistry has helped develop new technology.

Ask: Why is the element silicon so important to modern technology? *Silicon is a semiconductor. All common electronic devices are based on the electrical properties of semiconductors.*

 *Answer: It is a semiconductor.*

Industry uses chemical reactions to make useful products.

No area of science and technology has changed today's society as much as the electronics industry has. Just think about all the common electronic products that did not even exist as recently as 30 years ago—from personal computers to CD players to cellular phones. All of these devices are based on the electrical properties of materials called semiconductors. A semiconductor is a material that can precisely control the conduction of electrical signals.

READING TIP
The prefix *semi-* means "partial," so a semiconductor partially conducts electricity.

The most common semiconductor material is the element silicon (Si). Silicon is the second most common element in Earth's crust after oxygen, and it is found in most rocks and sand. Pure silicon is obtained from quartz (SiO_2). The quartz is heated with carbon in an electric furnace at 3000°C. The chemical reaction that takes place is

$$SiO_2 + 2C \rightarrow Si + 2CO$$

This reaction produces silicon that is about 98 percent pure. However, this silicon is still not pure enough to be used in electronics. Several other refining steps must be used to make silicon that is more than 99.999999999 percent pure.

CHECK YOUR READING What property makes silicon useful in electronic devices?

Early electronic devices had to be large enough to fit various types of glass tubes and connecting wires inside. In the 1950s, however, engineers figured out how to replace all of these different tubes and wires with thin layers of material placed on a piece of silicon. The resulting circuits are often called microchips, or simply chips.

In order to make these chips, another reaction is used. This reaction involves a material called photoresist (FOH-toh-rih-ZIST), whose properties change when it is exposed to ultraviolet light. Silicon wafers are first coated with photoresist. A stencil is placed over the surface, which allows some areas of the wafer to be exposed to ultraviolet light while other areas are protected. A chemical reaction takes place between the ultraviolet light and the coating of photoresist. The exposed areas of photoresist remain on the silicon surface after the rest of the material is washed away.

The entire process is carried out in special clean rooms to prevent contamination by dust. A typical chip has electrical pathways so small that a single particle of smoke or dust can block the path, stopping the chip from working properly. The process is automated, and no human hand ever touches a chip.

Quartz (SiO_2) is the source of silicon for chips.

226 Unit 2: Chemical Interactions

DIFFERENTIATE INSTRUCTION

 More Reading Support

D What property of semiconductors is used in electronic devices? *their electrical properties*

E What is the most common semiconductor material? *silicon*

Advanced Silicon's electrical conductivity can be improved by adding tiny amounts of certain elements, a process called doping. Have students research the process of doping, find out what elements are used, and learn how it improves conductivity of silicon.

 Challenge and Extension, p. 170

From Quartz to Microchips

A chemical reaction makes the tiny circuits that are used to run electronic devices such as cellular phones.

① After silicon is sliced into very thin wafers, it is coated with photoresist. The silicon is covered with a stencil and exposed to ultraviolet light, which reacts with the photoresist.

② The entire process takes place in clean rooms, where workers wear special clothing to prevent dust from reaching the chips.

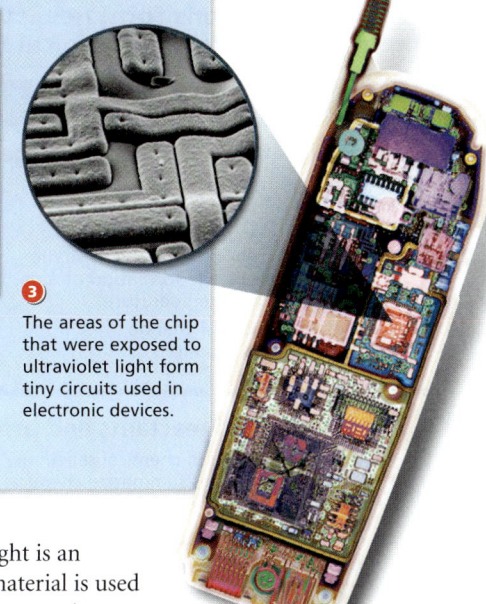

③ The areas of the chip that were exposed to ultraviolet light form tiny circuits used in electronic devices.

One of the many uses of silicon chips is in cellular phones.

The reaction of photoresist with ultraviolet light is an important chemical reaction. The same type of material is used in the printing of books and newspapers. A similar reaction occurs in photocopiers and laser printers. This is an example of how one type of chemical reaction has helped change industry and society in important ways.

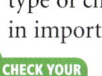 **CHECK YOUR READING** Describe how chemical reactions are important in industry.

7.4 Review

KEY CONCEPTS
1. Explain how respiration and photosynthesis are chemically opposite from each other.
2. Provide an example of how catalysts are used in technology.
3. Describe two chemical reactions used in making silicon chips.

CRITICAL THINKING
4. **Compare and Contrast** How are respiration and the combustion of gasoline similar? How are they different?
5. **Analyze** In microchip manufacture, what would happen if the clean rooms had outside windows? Explain.

⚠ CHALLENGE
6. **Infer** The gases released from a catalytic converter include N_2, O_2, H_2O, and CO_2. The original reactants must contain atoms of which elements?

Chapter 7: **Chemical Reactions** 227

ANSWERS

1. The reactants of one process are the products of the other process. Respiration is exothermic; photosynthesis is endothermic.

2. Sample answer: Metal catalysts such as platinum and palladium are used in catalytic converters.

3. Silicon dioxide reacts with carbon to purify silicon. Under ultraviolet light, photoresist creates pathways for electronic circuits.

4. Both release energy and require oxygen; both have reactants that depend on photosynthesis. Respiration occurs naturally in living cells and requires catalysts, while gasoline combustion does not.

5. The microchips would likely become contaminated, which would make them unusable.

6. carbon, nitrogen, oxygen, and hydrogen

CHAPTER 7 • REVIEW

BACK TO

Have students look at the photograph on pp. 194–195. Ask them to summarize the evidence that a chemical reaction is taking place in the beaker. Ask how this evidence is related to the breaking and forming of bonds. *Color change, gas formation, apparent temperature increase. Bonds are broken in the reactants to form products with a different color and in a different physical state (a gas). Energy is released, and the temperature increases, because more energy is released by the formation of new bonds than was required to break the original bonds.*

KEY CONCEPTS SUMMARY

SECTION 7.1
Ask: What happens when the reactant enters the substance in the beaker? *Bonds of the reactants break. Bonds form to make at least one product, which is visible as a precipitate.*

SECTION 7.2
Ask: How do you know that this equation is balanced? *An equal number of atoms of each element appears on both sides of the equation.*

Ask: How does the equation uphold the law of conservation of mass? *Atoms are neither created nor destroyed.*

SECTION 7.3
Ask: What happens to the chemical energy that is released during an exothermic reaction? *It is converted to other forms of energy, including heat and light.*

SECTION 7.4
Ask: What process in living things releases energy from molecules of glucose? *respiration*

Review Concepts

- Big Idea Flow Chart, p. T17
- Chapter Outline, pp. T23–T24

228 Unit 2: **Chemical Interactions**

---

7 Chapter Review

the BIG idea
Chemical reactions form new substances by breaking and making chemical bonds.

CONTENT REVIEW
CLASSZONE.COM

KEY CONCEPTS SUMMARY

Chemical reactions alter arrangements of atoms.
- Chemical changes occur through chemical reactions.
- Evidence of a chemical reaction includes a color change, the formation of a precipitate, the formation of a gas, and a change in temperature.
- Chemical reactions change reactants into products.

VOCABULARY
chemical reaction p. 197
reactant p. 199
product p. 199
precipitate p. 200
catalyst p. 204

2 The masses of reactants and products are equal.
- Mass is conserved in chemical reactions.
- Chemical equations summarize chemical reactions.
- Balanced chemical equations show the conservation of mass.

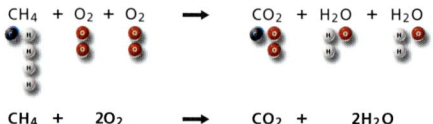

$$CH_4 + 2O_2 \rightarrow CO_2 + 2H_2O$$

VOCABULARY
law of conservation of mass p. 207
coefficient p. 210

Chemical reactions involve energy changes.
- Different bonds contain different amounts of energy.
- In an exothermic reaction, more energy is released than added.
- In an endothermic reaction, more energy is added than released.

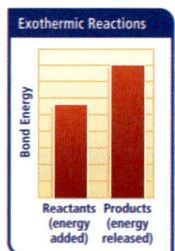 

VOCABULARY
bond energy p. 214
exothermic reaction p. 215
endothermic reaction p. 215
photosynthesis p. 218

4 Life and industry depend on chemical reactions.
- Living things rely on chemical reactions that release energy from molecules.
- Different parts of modern society rely on chemical reactions.

VOCABULARY
respiration p. 222

228 Unit 2: **Chemical Interactions**

Technology Resources

Have students visit **ClassZone.com** or use the CD-ROM for a cumulative review of concepts.

 CONTENT REVIEW

 CONTENT REVIEW CD-ROM

Engage students in a whole-class interactive review of Key Concepts. Edit content as you wish.

 POWER PRESENTATIONS

Reviewing Vocabulary

Describe how the vocabulary terms in the following pairs are related to each other. Explain the relationship in a one- or two-sentence answer.

1. reactant, product
2. law of conservation of mass, chemical reaction
3. endothermic, exothermic
4. respiration, photosynthesis

Reviewing Key Concepts

Multiple Choice Choose the letter of the best answer.

5. During a chemical reaction, reactants always
   a. become more complex
   b. require catalysts
   c. lose mass
   d. form products

6. The splitting of water molecules into hydrogen and oxygen molecules is an example of a
   a. combination reaction
   b. chemical change
   c. synthesis reaction
   d. physical change

7. Combustion reactions
   a. destroy atoms   c. form precipitates
   b. require glucose   d. require oxygen

8. Which of the following will increase the rate of a reaction?
   a. breaking solid reactants into smaller pieces
   b. removing a catalyst
   c. decreasing the temperature
   d. decreasing the concentration

9. What does a catalyst do in a chemical reaction?
   a. It slows the reaction down.
   b. It speeds the reaction up.
   c. It becomes a product.
   d. It is a reactant.

10. During a chemical reaction, the total amount of mass present
    a. increases
    b. decreases
    c. may increase or decrease
    d. does not change

11. Chemical equations show summaries of
    a. physical changes
    b. changes of state
    c. chemical reactions
    d. changes in temperature

12. A chemical equation must
    a. show energy   c. use subscripts
    b. be balanced   d. use coefficients

13. What type of reaction occurs if the reactants have a greater total bond energy than the products?
    a. an endothermic reaction
    b. a synthesis reaction
    c. an exothermic reaction
    d. a decomposition reaction

14. Endothermic reactions always
    a. absorb energy
    b. make more complex products
    c. release energy
    d. make less complex products

Short Answer Write a short answer to each question.

15. Describe the differences between physical and chemical changes. How can each be identified?

16. Compare and contrast the overall chemical reactions of photosynthesis and respiration. How can these reactions be described in terms of bond energy in the reactants and products?

17. Describe an example of an advance in technology that makes use of a chemical reaction.

18. When you balance a chemical equation, why can you change coefficients of reactants or products, but not subscripts?

Chapter 7: **Chemical Reactions** 229

ASSESSMENT RESOURCES

UNIT ASSESSMENT BOOK
- Chapter Test A, pp. 45–48
- Chapter Test B, pp. 49–52
- Chapter Test C, pp. 53–56
- Alternative Assessment, pp. 57–58

SPANISH ASSESSMENT BOOK
Spanish Chapter Test, pp. 241–244

Technology Resources

Edit test items and answer choices.

 Test Generator CD-ROM

Visit **ClassZone.com** to extend test practice.

 Test Practice

Reviewing Vocabulary

1. The bonds in <u>reactants</u> are broken, and new bonds form to make <u>products</u>.

2. Matter is not created or destroyed during a <u>chemical reaction</u>, so the <u>law of conservation of mass</u> is upheld.

3. <u>Endothermic</u> reactions absorb energy, whereas <u>exothermic</u> reactions release energy.

4. <u>Photosynthesis</u> is an endothermic process. The overall process that occurs during photosynthesis can be considered to be the reverse of the overall process that occurs during <u>respiration,</u> which is exothermic.

Reviewing Key Concepts

5. d	10. d
6. b	11. c
7. d	12. b
8. a	13. a
9. b	14. a

15. A physical change alters the physical characteristics of a substance, but not the substance itself. A chemical change, through a chemical reaction, produces different substances. Chemical changes can be identified by color or temperature change or by formation of a precipitate or a gas.

16. Overall, they are opposite processes. In photosynthesis, the bond energies of the reactants are greater than the bond energies of the products. The process is endothermic. In respiration, the bond energies of the reactants in the overall chemical reaction are less than those of the products of the overall reaction. As a result, the overall process of respiration is exothermic.

17. Answers might cover the reaction that purifies silicon, the reactions in catalytic converters, or the reaction involving photoresist.

18. Changing coefficients changes the amount of the substances. Changing subscripts changes the formula of a substance which makes it a different substance.

Chapter 7 **229**

Thinking Critically

19. It increased.
20. Yes; a gas is still being produced, and the temperature is continuing to change.
21. Exothermic; energy is being released, as shown by an increase in temperature.
22. The rate of the reaction increased because catalysts increase reaction rate.
23. All of it, because catalysts are not consumed during a chemical reaction.
24. Bonds are broken in the reactants, and the products that form will be simpler than the reactants.

Using Math Skills in Science

25. $2HgO \rightarrow 2Hg + O_2$
26. 2 to HgO and 2 to Hg
27. 2
28. $4Al + 3O_2 \rightarrow 2Al_2O_3$
29. 4 to Al, 3 to O_2, and 2 to Al_2O_3
30. 6
31. $S_8 + 12O_2 \rightarrow 8SO_3$
32. 12 to O_2 and 8 to SO_3
33. 8
34. 24

the BIG idea

35. Answers will vary but could include life processes and technological applications.
36. Answers will vary but should describe how bonds break in reactants and form in products, and how the energy associated with these bonds determines whether energy will be absorbed or released by a chemical reaction.

UNIT PROJECTS

 Collect schedules, materials lists, and questions. Be sure dates and materials are obtainable, and questions are focused.

 Unit Projects, pp. 5–10

Thinking Critically

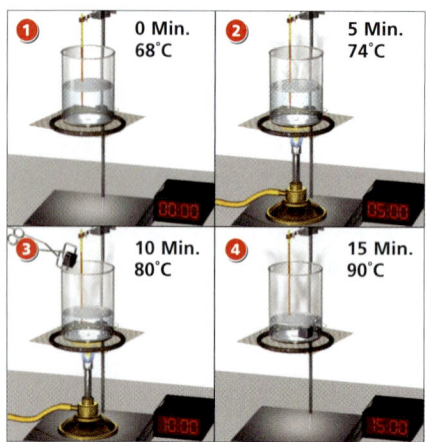

The series of illustrations above shows a chemical reaction at five-minute intervals. Use the information in the illustrations to answer the following six questions.

19. **OBSERVE** What happened to the temperature of the substance in the beaker from the beginning to the end of each five-minute interval?
20. **ANALYZE** Does the reaction appear to continue in step 4? What evidence tells you?
21. **CLASSIFY** Is this an endothermic or exothermic reaction? Explain.
22. **INFER** Suppose the metal cube placed in the beaker in step 3 is a catalyst. What effect did the metal have on the reaction? Why?
23. **PREDICT** If the metal cube is a catalyst, how much of the metal cube will be left in the beaker when the reaction is completed? Explain.
24. **SYNTHESIZE** Assume that the reaction shown is a decomposition reaction. Describe what happens to the reactants.

Using Math Skills in Science

Answer the following ten questions based on the equations below.

Equation 1—$HgO \rightarrow Hg + O_2$

Equation 2—$Al + O_2 \rightarrow Al_2O_3$

Equation 3—$S_8 + O_2 \rightarrow SO_3$

25. Copy and balance equation 1.
26. What coefficients, if any, did you add to equation 1 to balance it?
27. How many Hg atoms take part in the reaction represented by equation 1 when it is balanced?
28. Copy and balance equation 2.
29. What coefficients, if any, did you add to equation 2 to balance it?
30. How many O atoms take part in the reaction represented by equation 2 when it is balanced?
31. Copy and balance equation 3.
32. What coefficients, if any, did you add to equation 3 to balance it?
33. How many S atoms take part in the reaction represented by equation 3 when it is balanced?
34. How many O atoms take part in the reaction represented by equation 3 when it is balanced?

the BIG idea

35. **DRAW CONCLUSIONS** Describe three ways in which chemical reactions are important in your life.
36. **ANALYZE** Look back at the photograph and question on pages 194 and 195. Answer the question in terms of the chapter's Big Idea.

UNIT PROJECTS

Check your schedule for your unit project. How are you doing? Be sure that you have placed data or notes from your research in your project folder.

MONITOR AND RETEACH

If students have trouble applying the concept of relative bond energies in reactants and products in items 3, 13, 14, and 16, suggest that they review the diagrams and graphs on pp. 216 and 217.

Students may benefit from summarizing one or more sections of the chapter.

Summarizing the Chapter, pp. 198–199

Standardized Test Practice

For practice on your state test, go to...
TEST PRACTICE CLASSZONE.COM

Analyzing Theories

Answer the questions based on the information in the following passage.

During the 1700s, scientists thought that matter contained a substance called phlogiston. According to this theory, wood was made of phlogiston and ash. When wood burned, the phlogiston was released and the ash was left behind.

The ash that remained had less mass than the original wood. This decrease in mass was explained by the release of phlogiston. However, when substances such as phosphorus and mercury burned, the material that remained had more mass than the original substances. This increase in mass did not make sense to some scientists.

The scientists who supported the phlogiston theory said that the phlogiston in some substances had negative mass. So, when the substances burned, they released phlogiston and gained mass. Other scientists disagreed, and their research led to the discovery of a scientific law. Antoine Lavoisier carried out several experiments by burning metals in sealed containers. He showed that mass is never lost or gained in a chemical reaction.

1. What did the phlogiston theory successfully explain?
   a. the presence of ash in unburned wood
   b. the apparent gain of mass in some reactions
   c. the chemical makeup of the air
   d. the apparent decrease in mass in some situations

2. Why did some scientists disagree with the phlogiston theory?
   a. Burning a substance always produced an increase in mass.
   b. Burning a substance always produced a decrease in mass.
   c. Burning could produce either an increase or decrease in mass.
   d. Burning wood produced ash and phlogiston.

3. What law did Lavoisier's work establish?
   a. conservation of energy
   b. conservation of mass
   c. conservation of momentum
   d. conservation of resources

4. To carry out his experiments, what kind of equipment did Lavoisier need?
   a. devices to separate the different elements in the air
   b. machines that could separate wood from ash
   c. microscopes that could be used to study rust and ash
   d. balances that could measure mass very accurately

Extended Response

Answer the following questions in detail. Include some of the terms from the list on the right. Underline each term you use in your answers.

catalyst	coefficient	concentration
temperature	reaction	subscript
surface area		

5. Suppose you wanted to change the rate of a chemical reaction. What might you change in the reaction? Explain each factor.

6. Is the chemical equation shown below balanced? Why or why not? How are balanced chemical equations related to conservation of mass?

$$6CO_2 + 6H_2O \longrightarrow C_6H_{12}O_6 + O_2$$

Chapter 7: **Chemical Reactions** 231

Analyzing Theories

1. d   2. c   3. b   4. d

Extended Response

5. RUBRIC

4 points for a response that answers the question and uses the following terms accurately:
- temperature
- concentration
- surface area
- catalyst

Sample: <u>Temperature</u>, <u>concentration</u>, or <u>surface area</u> of reactants might be changed. Increases in any of these factors would increase the reaction rate. Decreases in any of these factors would decrease the reaction rate. The addition of a <u>catalyst</u> would also increase reaction rate.

3 points for a response that correctly answers the question and uses three terms correctly

2 points for a response that correctly answers the question and uses two terms correctly

1 point for a response that correctly answers the question and uses one term correctly

6. RUBRIC

4 points for a response that answers the three questions correctly and uses the three following terms accurately:
- subscript
- coefficient
- reaction

The chemical equation is not balanced because oxygen's <u>subscripts</u> on the right side of the equation only give 8 atoms, but the <u>coefficients</u> and subscripts on the left side represent 18 atoms of oxygen. Chemical equations must be balanced because they summarize chemical <u>reactions</u>, which obey the law of conservation of mass.

3 points for a response that answers two of the questions correctly and uses two of the terms correctly

2 points for a response that correctly answers two of the questions

1 point for a response that correctly answers one of the questions

Chapter 7 **231**

METACOGNITIVE ACTIVITY

Have students answer the following questions in their **Science Notebook:**

1. Why do you think it is important for you to learn about chemical reactions?
2. Which topics in this chapter would you like to learn more about?
3. What are the strongest pieces right now in your Unit Project?

TIMELINES in Science

FOCUS

▶ Set Learning Goals
Students will
- Examine how the concept of atomic structure has changed over the years.
- Learn about the tools used to study atoms and subatomic particles.
- Model the discovery of the atomic nucleus.

National Science Education Standards
A.9.a–g Understandings About Scientific Inquiry

E.6.a–c Understandings About Science and Technology

F.5.a–e, F.5.g Science and Technology in Society

G.1.a–b Science as a Human Endeavor

G.2.a Nature of Science

G.3.a–c History of Science

INSTRUCT

Point out that the top half of the timeline depicts scientific progress in describing the atom. The bottom half of the timeline shows technology that has been used to study atoms and their structure and how greater knowledge of atomic structure led to advances in technology.

Teach from Visuals
COLLECTING GASES Discuss the diagram. Tell students that pneumatic troughs are still used today to collect gases from a reaction, so they don't just mix into the air. Ask:
- Where is the gas collected? *over water in a bulb*
- Where does the gas come from? *the fire*

232 Unit 2: Chemical Interactions

TIMELINES in Science

THE STORY OF ATOMIC STRUCTURE

About 2500 years ago, certain Greek thinkers proposed that all matter consisted of extremely tiny particles called atoms. The sizes and shapes of different atoms, they reasoned, was what determined the properties of a substance. This early atomic theory, however, was not widely accepted. Many at the time found these tiny, invisible particles difficult to accept.

What everyone could observe was that all substances were liquid, solid, or gas, light or heavy, hot or cold. Everything, they thought, must then be made of only a few basic substances or elements. They reasoned these elements must be water, air, fire, and earth. Different substances contained different amounts of each of these four substances.

The timeline shows a few of the major events that led scientists to accept the idea that matter is made of atoms and agree on the basic structure of atoms. With the revised atomic theory, scientists were able to explain how elements could be basic but different.

1661
Boyle Challenges Concept of the Four Elements
British chemist Robert Boyle proposes that more than four basic substances exist. Boyle also concludes that all matter is made of very tiny particles he calls corpuscles.

EVENTS
1600 — 1620 — 1640 — 1660

APPLICATIONS AND TECHNOLOGY

TECHNOLOGY
Collecting and Studying Gases
Throughout the 1600s, scientists tried to study gases but had difficulty collecting them. English biologist Stephen Hales designed an apparatus to collect gases. The "pneumatic trough" was a breakthrough in chemistry because it allowed scientists to collect and study gases for the first time. The pneumatic trough was later used by such chemists as Joseph Black, Henry Cavendish, and Joseph Priestley to study the gases that make up the air we breathe. The work of these scientists showed that air was made of more than a single gas.

232 Unit 2: Chemical Interactions

DIFFERENTIATE INSTRUCTION

Below Level Point out the structure of the timeline. Tell students that events get closer to the present as you read the line from left to right. Discuss how one discovery often leads to another, farther to the right. Ask: How did electricity, produced by Volta in 1800, lead to Davy's isolation of elements? *Electricity gave investigators a new tool to use to try to break down substances.*

1808
John Dalton Says: "Bring Back the Atom"
English chemist John Dalton revives the ancient Greek idea that all matter is made of atoms. Dalton claims that each element has its own type of atom and that the atoms combine in fixed and predictable ratios with one another in different substances.

1897
It's Smaller Than the Atom!
English physicist Joseph John Thomson discovers the electron—the first subatomic particle to be identified. Thomson concludes that these tiny particles have a negative charge. Thomson will later propose that atoms are made of a great many of these negative particles floating in a sea of positive charge. Thomson suggests that each atom resembles a dish of pudding with raisins in it. The electrons are the raisins and the pudding the positive charge in which they float.

1808
Humphrey Davy Shocks Chemistry
English chemist Humphrey Davy applies an electric current to different materials. He discovers that many materials once thought to be elements break apart into even simpler materials. Davy succeeds in isolating the elements sodium, calcium, strontium, and barium.

1800 1820 1840 1860 1880

TECHNOLOGY
Chemistry and Electric Charge
In 1800 Italian physicist Alessandro Volta announced that he had produced an electric current from a pile, or battery, of alternating zinc and silver discs. Volta's invention was important for the study of atoms and elements in two ways. First, the fact that the contact of two different metals could produce an electric current suggested that electric charge must be part of matter. Second, the powerful electric current produced by the batteries enabled chemists to break apart many other substances, showing that there were more elements than previously thought.

Timelines in Science 233

DIFFERENTIATE INSTRUCTION
Advanced Have students research batteries today. They should chart what types are available, what they are used for, and the chemical reaction that produces electricity.

Scientific Process
Ask: What old theory did Thomson's atomic model prove false? *Atoms are the smallest form of matter.*

Technology
1815 Davy and other scientists were using batteries to produce electricity for experiments, but otherwise batteries weren't used by most people. Ask: Why do you think ordinary people weren't using electricity at that time? *Batteries were large, expensive, and difficult to maintain in working order. Also, uses had to be developed for batteries before they could be used.*

Language Arts Connection
Mary Shelley wrote one of the first science fiction novels, *Frankenstein*, about a scientist who created a monster. He used electricity to give it life. Electricity was a new and exciting subject when Shelley wrote her novel.

Timelines in Science 233

Scientific Process

Discuss how atomic researchers gathered data in the early 1900s. Point out that they couldn't observe small particles directly; they had to infer what the particles are like by observing what effects they had on other events. Ask: **What areas of science can you think of where this process is still essential?** *Sample answer: astronomy*

Technology

CHEMISTRY OF COMMUNICATIONS
The audion was the first radio tube to use a control grid as well as a cathode and anode. It became known as a triode. It received radio waves and amplified them.

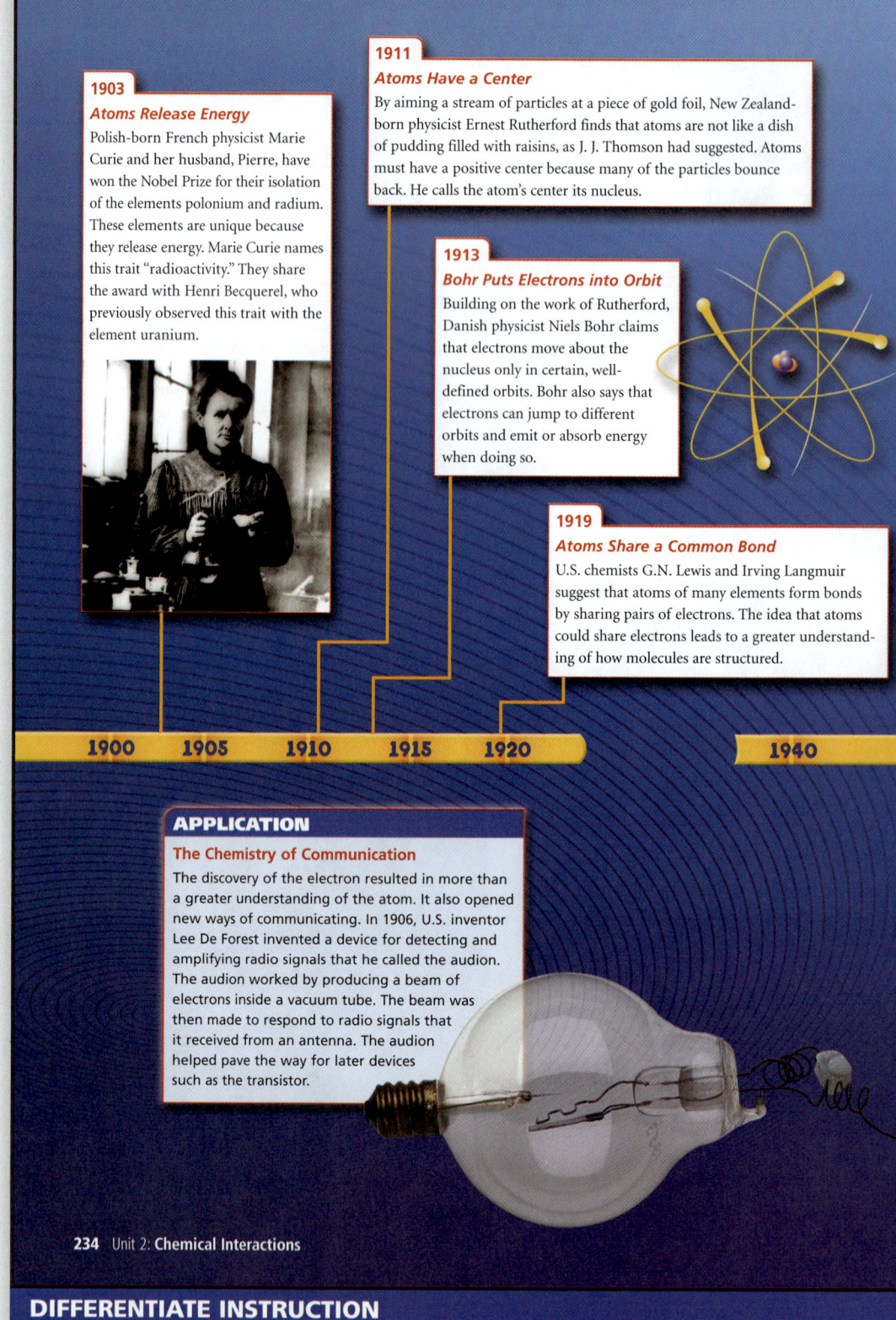

1903
Atoms Release Energy
Polish-born French physicist Marie Curie and her husband, Pierre, have won the Nobel Prize for their isolation of the elements polonium and radium. These elements are unique because they release energy. Marie Curie names this trait "radioactivity." They share the award with Henri Becquerel, who previously observed this trait with the element uranium.

1911
Atoms Have a Center
By aiming a stream of particles at a piece of gold foil, New Zealand-born physicist Ernest Rutherford finds that atoms are not like a dish of pudding filled with raisins, as J. J. Thomson had suggested. Atoms must have a positive center because many of the particles bounce back. He calls the atom's center its nucleus.

1913
Bohr Puts Electrons into Orbit
Building on the work of Rutherford, Danish physicist Niels Bohr claims that electrons move about the nucleus only in certain, well-defined orbits. Bohr also says that electrons can jump to different orbits and emit or absorb energy when doing so.

1919
Atoms Share a Common Bond
U.S. chemists G.N. Lewis and Irving Langmuir suggest that atoms of many elements form bonds by sharing pairs of electrons. The idea that atoms could share electrons leads to a greater understanding of how molecules are structured.

1900 1905 1910 1915 1920 1940

APPLICATION
The Chemistry of Communication
The discovery of the electron resulted in more than a greater understanding of the atom. It also opened new ways of communicating. In 1906, U.S. inventor Lee De Forest invented a device for detecting and amplifying radio signals that he called the audion. The audion worked by producing a beam of electrons inside a vacuum tube. The beam was then made to respond to radio signals that it received from an antenna. The audion helped pave the way for later devices such as the transistor.

DIFFERENTIATE INSTRUCTION

English Learners Tell students that the word *audion* was assembled from old words to describe a new technology. *Audio* means "to hear," and *ion* means "to go." List other neologisms on the board, such as *radioactivity* and *electron*. Show how they are made of other words.

1960s
Smaller Particles Discovered
By smashing atoms into one another, scientists discover that protons and neutrons are themselves composed of even smaller particles. In a bit of scientific humor, these smaller particles are named "quarks," a nonsense word taken from a novel. Scientists detect these particles by observing the tracks they make in special detectors.

1980s
Tunneling to the Atomic Level
Scanning tunneling microscopes (STMs) allow scientists to interact with matter at the atomic level. Electrons on the tiny tip of an STM "tunnel" through the gap between the tip and target surface. By recording changes in the tunneling current, researchers get an accurate picture.

 RESOURCE CENTER
CLASSZONE.COM
Explore advances in atomic research.

1960   1980   2000

TECHNOLOGY
Particle Accelerators
Particle accelerators speed up charged particles by passing them through an electric field. By smashing subatomic particles into one another, scientists are able to learn what these particles are made of as well as the forces holding them together. The H1 particle detector in Hamburg, Germany, can accelerate protons to 800 billion volts and is used to study the quarks that make up protons.

INTO THE FUTURE
Humans have gone from hypothesizing atoms exist to being able to see and move them. People once considered only four substances to be true elements; today we understand how there are more than a hundred simple substances. Not only have scientists learned atoms contain electric charges, they have also learned how to use these charges.

As scientists learn more and more about the atom, it is difficult to say what they will find next. Is there something smaller than a quark? Is there one type of particle from which all other particles are made? Will we one day be able to move and connect atoms in any way we want? Are there other kinds of atoms to discover? Maybe one day we will find answers to these questions.

ACTIVITIES
Explore a Model Atom
The discovery of the nucleus was one of the most important discoveries in human history. Rutherford's experiment, however, was a simple one that you can model. Take an aluminum pie plate and place a table tennis ball-sized piece of clay at its center. The clay represents a nucleus. Place the end of a grooved ruler at the edge of the plate. Hold the other end up to form a ramp. Roll a marble down the groove toward the clay. Move the ruler to different angles with each roll. Roll the marble 20 times. How many rolls out of 20 hit the clay ball? How do you think the results would be different if the atoms looked like pudding with raisins in it, as Thomson suggested?

Writing About Science
Suppose you are an atom. Choose one of the events on the timeline and describe it from the atom's point of view.

Application
1960s People keep inventing new prefixes for the basic SI units, to indicate smaller and smaller units. Particle physics has been one reason these terms became necessary. Besides the familiar *nano* (10^{-9}), prefixes from *pico* to *yocto* span factors of 10^{-12} to 10^{-24}.

INTO THE FUTURE
Ask students what they think would be the consequences of being able to take apart and assemble atoms and molecules. Would all consequences be good or would there be some bad results? *Materials such as gold and silver would no longer be valuable because we could make as much as we want. But some people could use this technology to destroy instead of make things.*

ACTIVITIES
Explore a Model Atom
Discuss how the model is like Rutherford's experiment and how it differs. *The plum pudding model would have bounced all the electrons back.*

Writing About Science
Students can have fun with this assignment by imagining themselves as small as an atom. Tell them to think of themselves as the recipient or victim of an attack from whichever historic event they choose. They should write using the first-person noun *I*.

Technology Resources
Students can visit **ClassZone.com** for current news on atomic research.

DIFFERENTIATE INSTRUCTION
Alternative Writing Project Have groups of students research how diagrams of the atom have changed to reflect new ideas. Have them produce labeled diagrams for different atomic theories and write brief descriptions of what made the theory change.

CHAPTER 8
Solutions

Physical Science
UNIFYING PRINCIPLES

PRINCIPLE 1
Matter is made of particles too small to see.

PRINCIPLE 2
Matter changes form and moves from place to place.

PRINCIPLE 3
Energy changes from one form to another, but it cannot be created or destroyed.

PRINCIPLE 4
Physical forces affect the movement of all matter on Earth and throughout the universe.

Unit 2: Chemical Interactions
BIG IDEAS

CHAPTER 5
Atomic Structure and the Periodic Table
A substance's atomic structure determines its physical and chemical properties.

CHAPTER 6
Chemical Bonds and Compounds
The properties of compounds depend on their atoms and chemical bonds.

CHAPTER 7
Chemical Reactions
Chemical reactions form new substances by breaking and making chemical bonds.

CHAPTER 8
Solutions
When substances dissolve to form a solution, the properties of the mixture change.

CHAPTER 9
Carbon in Life and Materials
Carbon is essential to living things and to modern materials.

CHAPTER 8
KEY CONCEPTS

SECTION 1
A solution is a type of mixture.
1. The parts of a solution are mixed evenly.
2. Solvent and solute particles interact.
3. Properties of solvents change in solutions.

SECTION 2
The amount of solute that dissolves can vary.
1. A solution with a high concentration contains a large amount of solute.
2. The solubility of a solute can be changed.
3. Solubility depends on molecular structure.

SECTION 3
Solutions can be acidic, basic, or neutral.
1. Acids and bases have distinct properties.
2. The strengths of acids and bases can be measured.
3. Acids and bases neutralize each other.

SECTION 4
Metal alloys are solid mixtures.
1. Humans have made alloys for thousands of years.
2. Alloys have many uses in modern life.

 The Big Idea Flow Chart is available on p. T25 in the **UNIT TRANSPARENCY BOOK**.

Previewing Content

SECTION A solution is a type of mixture. pp. 239–244

1. The parts of a solution are mixed evenly.
A **solution** is a homogeneous mixture; all portions of a solution have identical properties. The **solute** is the substance that is dissolved. The **solvent** dissolves the solute.
- Solutes, solvents, and solutions can be liquids, solids, or gases.
- The solute and solvent can be in the same or in different physical states.
- A **suspension** is a mixture with large particles. The particles do not dissolve, and the mixture is not a solution.

2. Solvent and solute particles interact.
When a solid dissolves in a liquid, the solute breaks apart. Solute particles are surrounded by solvent particles and are evenly distributed in the solution.
- Ionic compounds break up into individual ions when they dissolve, as the diagram below shows.

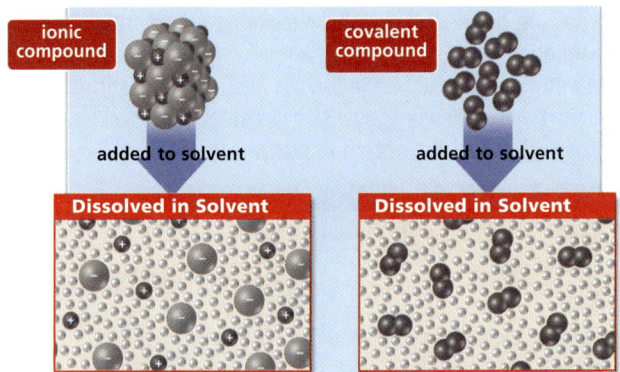

- When a covalent compound dissolves, the molecules separate from each other, but the covalent bonds remain intact and the individual molecules remain whole.

3. Properties of solvents change in solutions.
A solute changes the physical properties of a solvent.
- The freezing point of a solution is lower than the freezing point of the pure solvent.
- The boiling point of a solution is higher than the boiling point of the pure solvent.

SECTION The amount of solute that dissolves can vary. pp. 245–252

1. A solution with a high concentration contains a large amount of solute.
The **concentration** of a solution is the amount of solute dissolved in it at a particular temperature. Solutions can be made more concentrated by adding solute, or more **dilute** by adding solvent.

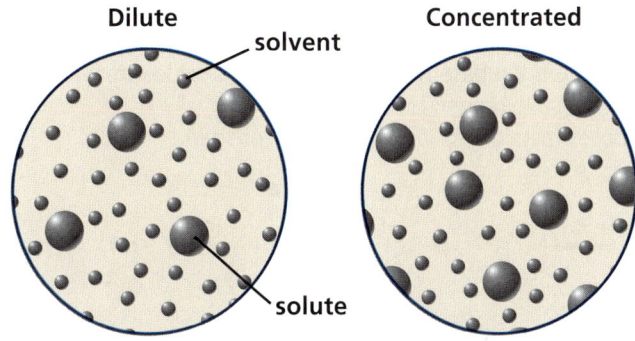

- A **saturated** solution holds as much of a given solute as it can at a given temperature. If a solution contains more solute than can normally dissolve at a given temperature, it is supersaturated. Supersaturated solutions are very unstable, and disturbing the solution will cause the excess solute to come out of the solution as a precipitate.
- Every substance has a characteristic **solubility,** the amount that will dissolve in a certain amount of a certain solvent at a given temperature.

2. The solubility of a solute can be changed.
An increase in temperature increases the solubility of most solid solutes and decreases the solubility of gaseous solutes. An increase in pressure increases the solubility of gaseous solutes. The solubility of solid and liquid solutes are not usually affected by changes in pressure.

3. Solubility depends on molecular structure.
Solubility depends on charges of solute and solvent particles. Molecules with regions of electrical charge (polar molecules) and ions dissolve in polar solvents such as water. Nonpolar molecules (oils) do not have charged regions and do not dissolve in polar solvents, but they will dissolve in nonpolar solvents.

Common Misconceptions

WHY DO MATERIALS DISSOLVE? Students often think that sand does not dissolve in water because it is too dense, too thick, or too hard. Solubility depends instead on the molecular makeup of the solute and solvent and on the polarity of their bonding.

 This misconception is addressed on p. 242.

MISCONCEPTION DATABASE
CLASSZONE.COM Background on student misconceptions

PROPERTIES OF SOLUTIONS Students may think that the mass of the solute is lost when it dissolves in a solvent. Although the solute seems to disappear, it is still present, and therefore the mass of the solution is equal to the mass of the solute and solvent together.

 This misconception is addressed on p. 243.

Previewing Content

SECTION 3

Solutions can be acidic, basic, or neutral. pp. 253–261

1. Acids and bases have distinct properties.
An **acid** can donate a hydrogen ion to another substance when the acid is dissolved in water.
- HCl is an acid and donates a hydrogen ion in a water solution.
- Acids taste sour, react with carbonates to form carbon dioxide, and react with many metals.

A **base** can accept a hydrogen ion from another substance.
- In water, the base NaOH releases a hydroxide ion, which can accept a hydrogen ion.
- Bases taste bitter and feel slippery or soapy.

Acid

$HCl \xrightarrow{H_2O} H^+ + Cl^-$

Base

$NaOH \xrightarrow{H_2O} Na^+ + OH^-$

2. The strengths of acids and bases can be measured.
Strong acids and bases break apart completely into individual ions. No complete molecules of the acid or base remain in the solution. A weak acid or base does not break apart completely into ions, and contains both molecules of the acid or base and its ions.
The acidity of a solution is measured on the **pH** scale.
- Acids produce a high hydrogen ion concentration and have a low pH—from 0 to 7.
- Bases produce a low hydrogen ion concentration and have a high pH—from 7 to 14.
- Solutions of pH 7 are **neutral,** neither acidic nor basic.

3. Acids and bases neutralize each other.
When an acid and a base come in contact with each other, they undergo a neutralization reaction. The hydrogen ion from the acid and the hydroxide ion from the base combine to form water. The negative ion from the acid and the positive ion from the base combine to form a salt. The products of a neutralization reaction—water and a salt—are neutral substances.

Common Misconceptions

ACIDS AND BASES Students often think of a base as a substance that counteracts the dangerous corrosive properties of an acid, and that bases are "good" and acids are "bad." Strong bases have corrosive properties just as do strong acids.

 This misconception is addressed on p. 255.

SECTION 4

Metal alloys are solid mixtures. pp. 262–267

1. Humans have made alloys for thousands of years.
An **alloy** is a solid mixture that has many of the characteristics of a solution. In an alloy, a solid (usually metal) solute is mixed with a solid metallic solvent. Alloys are made by melting the metal components and mixing them in the liquid state. The physical properties of an alloy are different from those of the solvent metal.
There are two general types of alloys. Brass is an example of one type, called a substitutional alloy, in which some of the copper atoms are replaced by zinc atoms. Steel is an example of the other type, called an interstitial alloy, in which carbon atoms occupy gaps between iron atoms.

2. Alloys have many uses in modern life.
New alloys are constantly being developed in response to the development of new technologies. In the transportation industry, medicine, and the aerospace industry, new alloys with unique properties are developed to fulfill specific requirements. For example, aluminum alloys, which have a relatively low density and are lightweight, but very strong, are used in such applications as cars and aircraft. More dense alloys, such as steel, are used in applications in which weight is not an important feature.

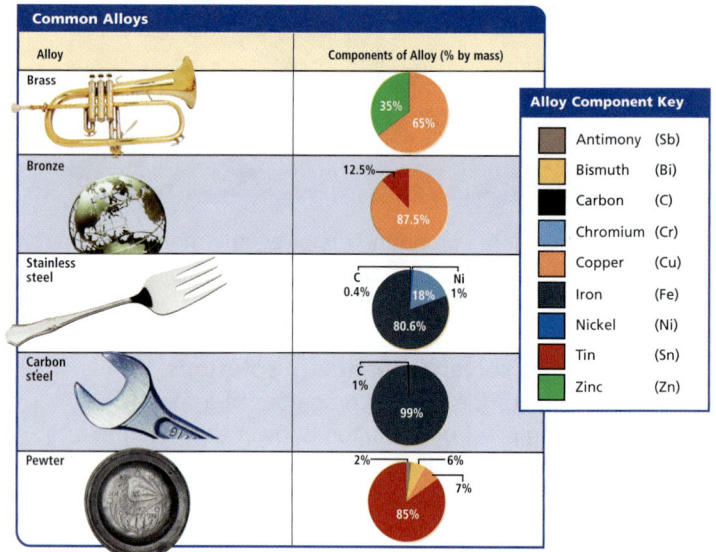

 MISCONCEPTION DATABASE
CLASSZONE.COM Background on student misconceptions

Previewing Labs

EXPLORE the BIG idea

Does it Dissolve? p. 237
Students distinguish between solutions and mixtures by observing different substances in water.

TIME 10 minutes
MATERIALS tap water; 4 small clear plastic cups; plastic spoon; 1 teaspoon each of powdered drink mix, vinegar, milk, and sand

Acid Test, p. 237
Students use a radish as a pH indicator.

TIME 10 minutes
MATERIALS radish; 3 blank index cards; 3 cotton swabs; a few drops of lemon juice, tap water, and soda water

Internet Activity: Alloys, p. 237
Students investigate virtual alloys and change their composition.

TIME 20 minutes
MATERIALS computer with Internet access

SECTION 1

EXPLORE Mixtures, p. 239
Students try to dissolve table salt and flour in water to compare the physical properties of a solution and a suspension.

TIME 10 minutes
MATERIALS water, 2 clear plastic cups, plastic spoon, 1 teaspoon each of table salt and flour

INVESTIGATE Solutions, p. 241
Students make a paper chromatogram to observe that the parts of a solution can be separated.

TIME 15 minutes
MATERIALS washable black marking pen, coffee filter, plastic bottle, eyedropper, water, watch

SECTION 2

EXPLORE Solutions and Temperature, p. 245
Students observe the fizzing of warm and cold soda water to determine how temperature affects a solution of a gas in a liquid.

TIME 10 minutes
MATERIALS 50 mL each of warm and cold soda water, 2 clear plastic cups

INVESTIGATE Solubility, p. 248
Students design an experiment to determine how a change in temperature affects the solubility of table salt in water.

TIME 20 minutes
MATERIALS clear plastic cups, thermometer, water, salt, balance, spoon, hot and cold water baths

SECTION 3

EXPLORE Acids and Bases, p. 253
Students dissolve an antacid in vinegar to observe the chemical reaction between a base and an acid.

TIME 10 minutes
MATERIALS clear plastic cup, 30 mL of vinegar, 2 antacid tablets containing a carbonate

**CHAPTER INVESTIGATION
Acids and Bases,** pp. 260–261
Students use pH indicator paper to test and classify common substances as acids or bases.

TIME 40 minutes
MATERIALS 7 plastic cups; 1 tsp. baking soda; salt; 30 mL fruit juice; shampoo; soda water; detergent powder; vinegar; masking tape; marking pen; measuring spoons; graduated cylinder; 90 mL distilled water; paper towels; 7 strips universal pH indicator paper

SECTION 4

INVESTIGATE Alloys, p. 265
Students find the density of alloys and a pure metal to observe that they have different physical properties.

TIME 30 minutes
MATERIALS 3 iron nails, 3 steel nails or 3 stainless steel nails, balance, graduated cylinder, water

Additional INVESTIGATION, Rates of Solution, A, B, & C, pp. 259–267; Teacher Instructions, pp. 329–330

Previewing Chapter Resources

	INTEGRATED TECHNOLOGY	LABS AND ACTIVITIES

CHAPTER 8
Solutions

 CLASSZONE.COM
- eEdition Plus
- EasyPlanner Plus
- Misconception Database
- Content Review
- Test Practice
- Simulation
- Visualization
- Resource Centers
- Internet Activity: Alloys
- Math Tutorial

 CD-ROMS
- eEdition
- EasyPlanner
- Power Presentations
- Content Review
- Lab Generator
- Test Generator

 AUDIO CDS
- Audio Readings
- Audio Readings in Spanish

 SCILINKS.ORG

EXPLORE the Big Idea, p. 237
- Does It Dissolve?
- Acid Test
- Internet Activity: Alloys

UNIT RESOURCE BOOK
Unit Projects, pp. 5–10

 Lab Generator CD-ROM
Generate customized labs.

SECTION 1
A solution is a type of mixture.
pp. 239–244

Time: 2 periods (1 block)

 Lesson Plan, pp. 200–201

 UNIT TRANSPARENCY BOOK
- Big Idea Flow Chart, p. T25
- Daily Vocabulary Scaffolding, p. T26
- Note-Taking Model, p. T27
- 3-Minute Warm-Up, p. T28

 • EXPLORE Mixtures, p. 239
• INVESTIGATE Solutions, p. 241

 UNIT RESOURCE BOOK
Datasheet, Solutions, p. 209

SECTION 2
The amount of solute that dissolves can vary.
pp. 245–252

Time: 2 periods (1 block)

 Lesson Plan, pp. 211–212

 • **VISUALIZATION,** Supersaturated Solutions and Precipitation
• **RESOURCE CENTER,** Aquifers and Purification

 UNIT TRANSPARENCY BOOK
- Daily Vocabulary Scaffolding, p. T26
- 3-Minute Warm-Up, p. T28

 • EXPLORE Solutions and Temperature, p. 245
• INVESTIGATE Solubility, p. 248
• Connecting Sciences, p. 252

 UNIT RESOURCE BOOK
- Datasheet, Solubility, p. 220
- Additional INVESTIGATION, Rates of Solution, A, B, & C, pp. 259–267

SECTION 3
Solutions can be acidic, basic, or neutral.
pp. 253–261

Time: 3 periods (1.5 blocks)

 Lesson Plan, pp. 222–223

 RESOURCE CENTER, Acids and Bases

 UNIT TRANSPARENCY BOOK
- Daily Vocabulary Scaffolding, p. T26
- 3-Minute Warm-Up, p. T29
- "Common Acids and Bases" Visual, p. T30

 • EXPLORE Acids and Bases, p. 253
• CHAPTER INVESTIGATION, Acids and Bases, pp. 260–261

 UNIT RESOURCE BOOK
CHAPTER INVESTIGATION, Acids and Bases, A, B, & C, pp. 250–258

SECTION 4
Metal alloys are solid mixtures.
pp. 262–267

Time: 3 periods (1.5 blocks)

 Lesson Plan, pp. 232–233

 • **RESOURCE CENTER,** Alloys
• **MATH TUTORIAL**

 UNIT TRANSPARENCY BOOK
- Big Idea Flow Chart, p. T25
- Daily Vocabulary Scaffolding, p. T26
- 3-Minute Warm-Up, p. T29
- Chapter Outline, pp. T31–T32

 • INVESTIGATE Alloys, p. 265
• Math in Science, p. 267

 UNIT RESOURCE BOOK
- Datasheet, Alloys, p. 241
- Math Support, p. 248
- Math Practice, p. 249

235E Unit 2: **Chemical Interactions**

KEY TO ICONS	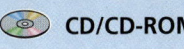 CD/CD-ROM	Teacher Edition	T UNIT TRANSPARENCY BOOK	SP A SPANISH ASSESSMENT BOOK
i INTERNET	PE Pupil Edition	R UNIT RESOURCE BOOK	A UNIT ASSESSMENT BOOK	SCIENCE TOOLKIT

READING AND REINFORCEMENT

ASSESSMENT

STANDARDS

- Choose Your Own Strategy, B18–27
- Mind Map, C40–41
- Daily Vocabulary Scaffolding, H1–8

 UNIT RESOURCE BOOK
- Vocabulary Practice, pp. 245–246
- Decoding Support, p. 247
- Summarizing the Chapter, pp. 268–269

- Chapter Review, pp. 269–270
- Standardized Test Practice, p. 271

 UNIT ASSESSMENT BOOK
- Diagnostic Test, pp. 59–60
- Chapter Test, A, B, & C, pp. 65–76
- Alternative Assessment, pp. 77–78

SP A Spanish Chapter Test, pp. 245–248

National Standards
A.1–8, A.9.a–g, B.1.a, B.1.c, E.2–5

See p. 236 for the standards.

 Audio Readings CD
Listen to Pupil Edition.

 Audio Readings in Spanish CD
Listen to Pupil Edition in Spanish.

 Test Generator CD-ROM
Generate customized tests.

 Lab Generator CD-ROM
Rubrics for Labs

 UNIT RESOURCE BOOK
- Reading Study Guide, A & B, pp. 202–205
- Spanish Reading Study Guide, pp. 206–207
- Challenge and Extension, p. 208
- Reinforcing Key Concepts, p. 210

TE Ongoing Assessment, pp. 239–240, 242–244

 Section 8.1 Review, p. 244

 UNIT ASSESSMENT BOOK
Section 8.1 Quiz, p. 61

National Standards
A.2–7, A.9.a–b, A.9.e–f, B.1.c

 UNIT RESOURCE BOOK
- Reading Study Guide, A & B, pp. 213–216
- Spanish Reading Study Guide, pp. 217–218
- Challenge and Extension, p. 219
- Reinforcing Key Concepts, p. 221

TE Ongoing Assessment, pp. 246–251

 Section 8.2 Review, p. 251

 UNIT ASSESSMENT BOOK
Section 8.2 Quiz, p. 62

National Standards
A.2–7, A.9.a–b, A.9.e–f, B.1.a, E.2–5

 UNIT RESOURCE BOOK
- Reading Study Guide, A & B, pp. 224–227
- Spanish Reading Study Guide, pp. 228–229
- Challenge and Extension, p. 230
- Reinforcing Key Concepts, p. 231
- Challenge Reading, pp. 243–244

TE Ongoing Assessment, pp. 254–255, 257–259

 Section 8.3 Review, p. 259

 UNIT ASSESSMENT BOOK
Section 8.3 Quiz, p. 63

National Standards
A.1–7, A.9.a–c, A.9.d–g, B.1.c

UNIT RESOURCE BOOK
- Reading Study Guide, A & B, pp. 234–237
- Spanish Reading Study Guide, pp. 238–239
- Challenge and Extension, p. 240
- Reinforcing Key Concepts, p. 242

TE Ongoing Assessment, pp. 263–266

Section 8.4 Review, p. 266

 UNIT ASSESSMENT BOOK
Section 8.4 Quiz, p. 64

National Standards
A.2–8, A.9.a–c, A.9.e–f

Chapter 8: **Solutions** 235F

Previewing Resources for Differentiated Instruction

CHAPTER INVESTIGATION

Leveled resources present the same concepts for different abilities.

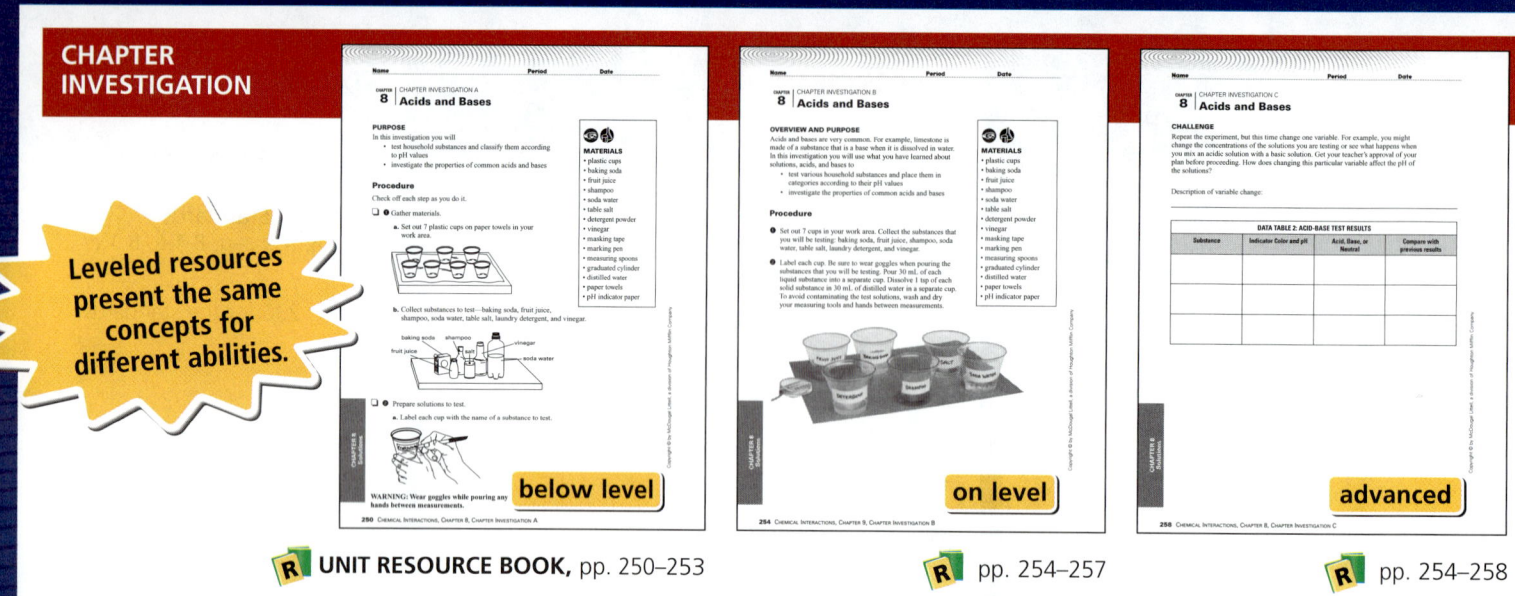

UNIT RESOURCE BOOK, pp. 250–253 | pp. 254–257 | pp. 254–258

READING STUDY GUIDE

Reading Study Guide is also in Spanish.

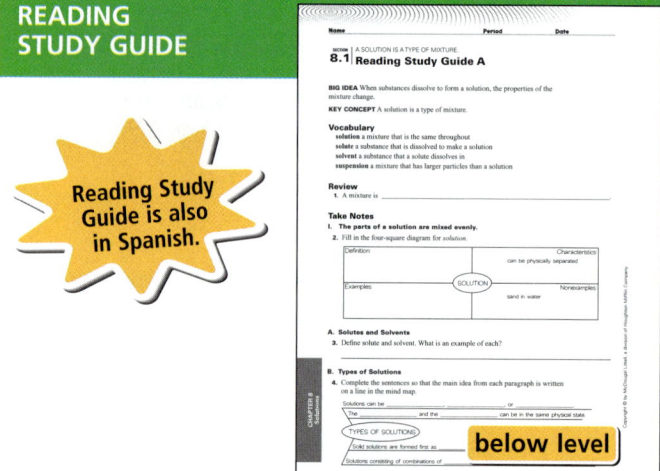 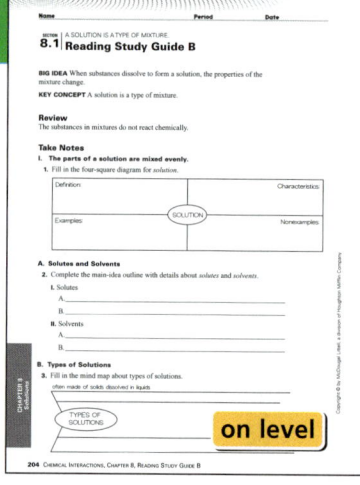 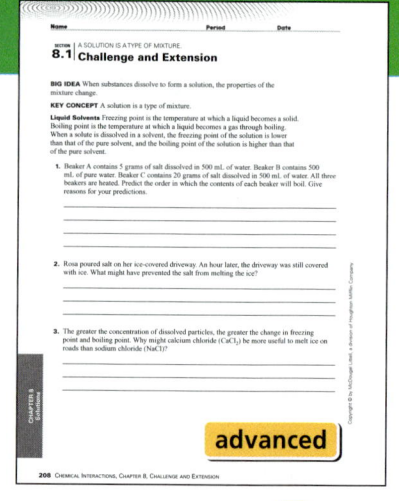

UNIT RESOURCE BOOK, pp. 202–203 | pp. 204–205 | p. 208

CHAPTER TEST

Chapter Test is also in Spanish.

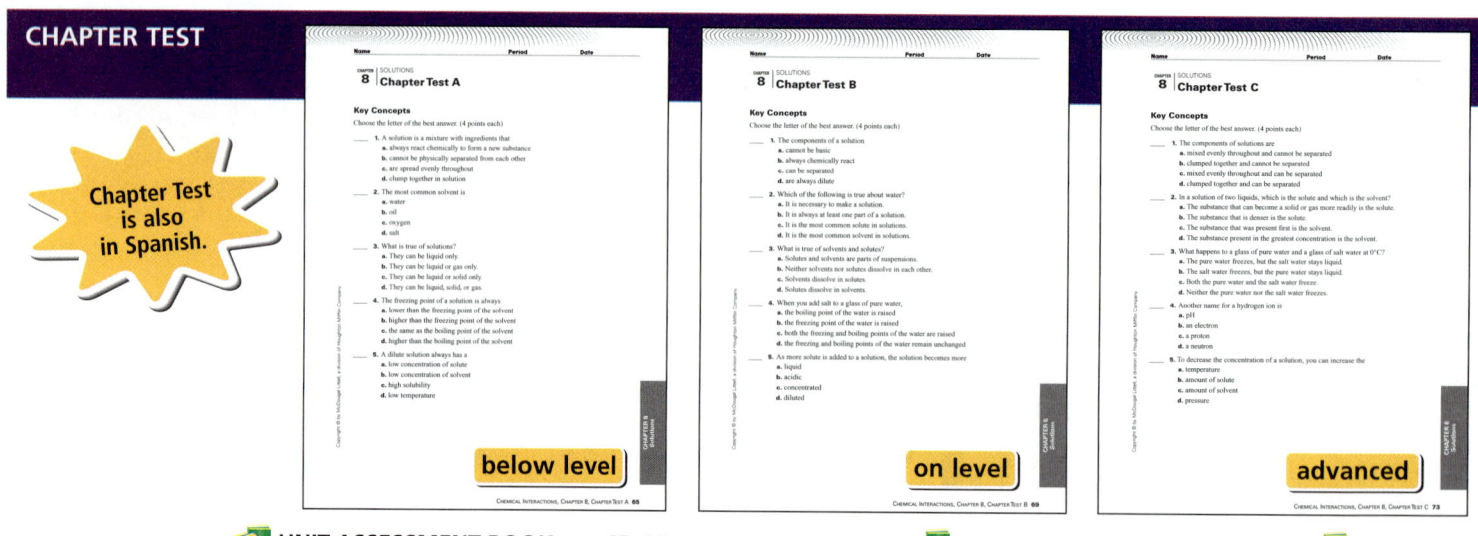

UNIT ASSESSMENT BOOK, pp. 65–68 | pp. 69–72 | pp. 73–76

235G Unit 2: **Chemical Interactions**

TECHNOLOGY

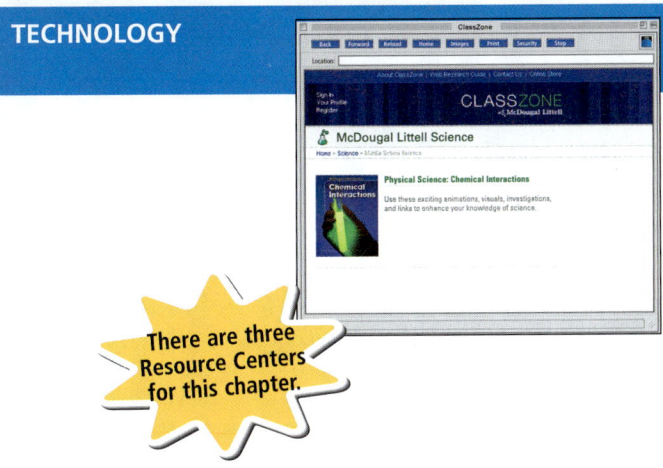
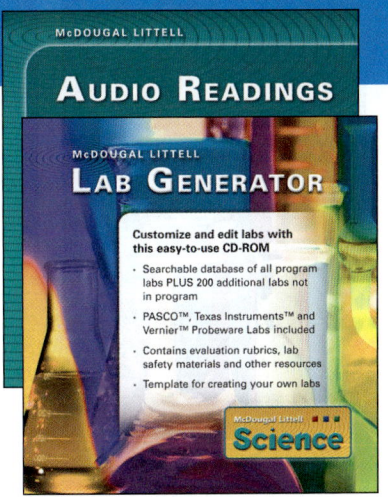
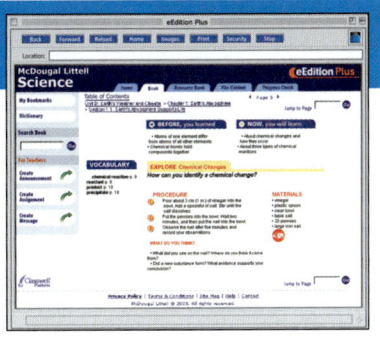

There are three Resource Centers for this chapter.

CLASSZONE.COM   **CD/CD-ROMS**   **CLASSZONE.COM**

VISUAL CONTENT

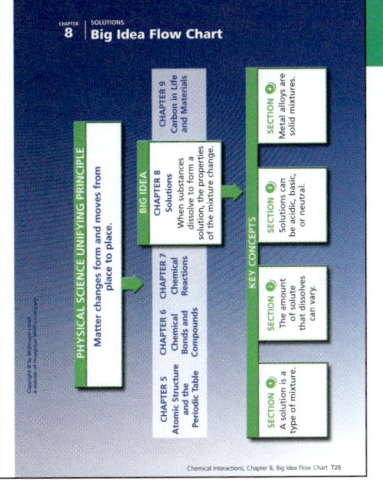
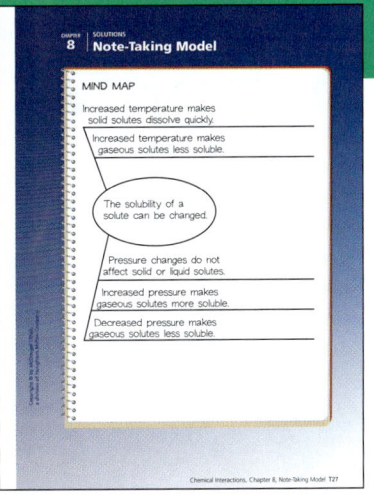

UNIT TRANSPARENCY BOOK, p. T25   p. T27   p. T30

MORE SUPPORT

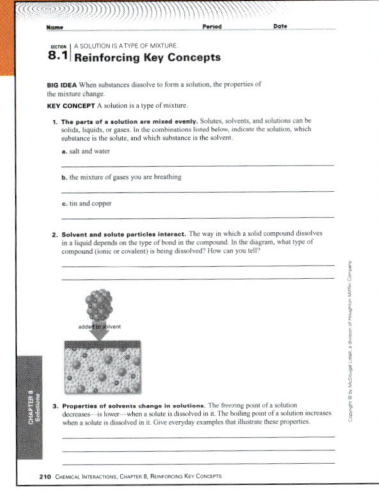
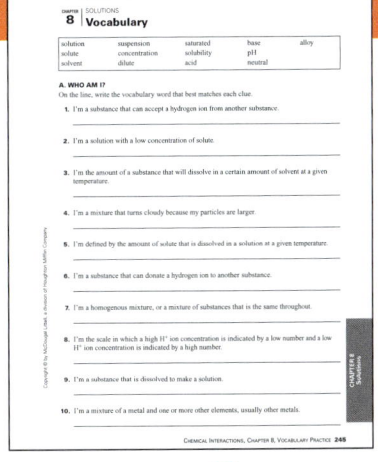
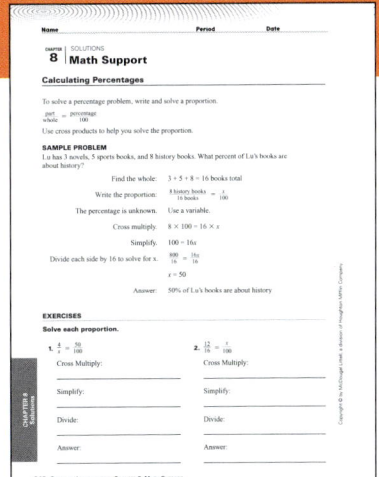

Reinforcing Key Concepts for each section

UNIT RESOURCE BOOK, p. 210   pp. 245–246   p. 248

Chapter 8: **Solutions** 235H

CHAPTER 8 Solutions

INTRODUCE

Have students look at the photograph of the seafloor and sunken boat and discuss how the question in the box links to the Big Idea.

- What substances might be dissolved in seawater?
- Why might the various substances and objects on the seafloor not dissolve?
- How might the properties of water change when substances are dissolved in it?

National Science Education Standards

Content

B.1.a A substance has characteristic properties, such as solubility, which are independent of the amount of the sample. A mixture of substances often can be separated into the original substances using one or more of the characteristic properties.

B.1.c Chemical elements do not break down during normal laboratory reactions involving such treatments as heating, exposure to electric current, or reaction with acids.

Process

A.1–8 Identify questions that can be answered through scientific investigations; design and conduct an investigation; use tools; use evidence; think critically between evidence and explanation; recognize different explanations and predictions; communicate procedures and explanations; use mathematics.

A.9.a–g Understand scientific inquiry by using different investigations, methods, mathematics, technology, explanations based on logic, evidence, and skepticism. Data often results in new investigations.

E.1–5 Identify a problem; design, implement, evaluate a solution or product; communicate technological design.

236 Unit 2: Chemical Interactions

CHAPTER 8 Solutions

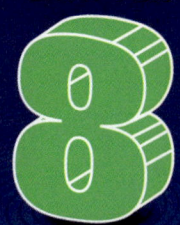

When substances dissolve to form a solution, the properties of the mixture change.

Why might some substances dissolve in the seawater in this photograph, but others do not?

Key Concepts

SECTION 1 A solution is a type of mixture.
Learn how solutions differ from other types of mixtures.

SECTION 2 The amount of solute that dissolves can vary.
Learn how solutions can contain different amounts of dissolved substances.

SECTION 3 Solutions can be acidic, basic, or neutral.
Learn about acids and bases and where they are found.

SECTION 4 Metal alloys are solid mixtures.
Learn about alloys and how they are used.

Internet Preview

CLASSZONE.COM
Chapter 8 online resources: Content Review, Simulation, Visualization, three Resource Centers, Math Tutorial, Test Practice

236 Unit 2: Chemical Interactions

INTERNET PREVIEW

CLASSZONE.COM For student use with the following pages:

Review and Practice
- Content Review, pp. 238, 268
- Math Tutorial: Understanding Percents, p. 267
- Test Practice, p. 271

Activities and Resources
- Internet Activity, p. 237
- Visualization: Supersaturated Solutions and Precipitation, p. 246
- Resource Centers: Aquifers and Purification, p. 252; Acids and Bases, p. 254; Alloys, p. 264

Solutions Code: MDL025

EXPLORE the BIG idea

Does It Dissolve?
Pour water into four small clear cups. Add a teaspoon of each of the following: in cup 1, powdered drink mix; in cup 2, vinegar; in cup 3, milk; in cup 4, sand. Stir briefly. Observe the contents of all four cups for five minutes.

Observe and Think Do all of the substances dissolve in water? How can you tell?

Acid Test
Rub a radish on three blank index cards until the marks on the cards become dark pink. Use cotton swabs to wipe lemon juice onto the mark on the first card, tap water onto the mark on the second card, and soda water onto the mark on the third card. Observe the color of the radish mark on each index card.

Observe and Think What happened to the color on each index card? How might the three liquids that you tested differ?

Internet Activity: Alloys
Go to ClassZone.com to investigate alloys. Explore the production of different varieties of an alloy by changing the percentages of the metals used to make them. Find out how different alloys have different properties.

Observe and Think How does changing the composition of an alloy change its properties? Why?

NSTA SCLINKS
scilinks.org
Solutions Code: MDL025

Chapter 8: Solutions 237

EXPLORE the BIG idea

These inquiry-based activities are appropriate for use at home or as a supplement to classroom instruction.

Does It Dissolve?
PURPOSE To observe differences between solutions and mixtures. Students observe different substances in water.

TIP *10 min.* Glass jars can be used instead of plastic cups.

Answer: The drink mix and vinegar dissolve; the milk and sand do not. The drink mix and vinegar are not distinct from the water; the milk and sand are.

REVISIT after p. 240.

Acid Test
PURPOSE To observe a pH indicator test. Students use a radish as an indicator.

TIP *10 min.* Cut cotton swabs in half. Vinegar can be used instead of lemon juice.

Answer: The pink color changes on the index card when exposed to an acid. The change is most evident with lemon juice because it is the most acidic.

REVISIT after p. 257.

Internet Activity: Alloys
PURPOSE To investigate and change virtual alloys.

TIP *20 min.* Emphasize that an alloy changes when the types and amounts of metals in it are changed.

Answer: Changing the materials or percentages of materials in an alloy can make the alloy stronger, lighter, or otherwise physically different, because the mixture is altered.

REVISIT after p. 263.

Chapter 8 237

TEACHING WITH TECHNOLOGY

CBL and Probeware Students can use a pH probe in the Chapter Investigation, pp. 260–261.

Spreadsheet Have students use a spreadsheet to record their data and do the calculations in "Investigate Alloys" on p. 265.

PREPARE

CONCEPT REVIEW

Activate Prior Knowledge

Add table salt to a small amount of water to make a saltwater solution. Tell students what is in the solution.

- Heat the saltwater solution until the water evaporates. Ask: Have physical changes or chemical changes taken place? *physical*
- Ask: Why do you think the changes are physical? *The salt and water have not changed into other substances. Only their physical properties changed.*

TAKING NOTES

Mind Map

Students can include as many lines of information as they want with their diagrams. If students have trouble remembering what they have written, they may be including too much detail.

Choose Your Own Strategy

Allow students to choose the vocabulary strategy that works best for them.

Vocabulary and Note-Taking Resources

- Vocabulary Practice, pp. 245–246
- Decoding Support, p. 247

- Daily Vocabulary Scaffolding, p. T26
- Note-Taking Model, p. T27

- Choose Your Own Strategy, B18–27
- Mind Map, C40–41
- Daily Vocabulary Scaffolding, H1–8

238 Unit 2: Chemical Interactions

CHAPTER 8
Getting Ready to Learn

CONCEPT REVIEW
- Matter can change from one physical state to another.
- A mixture is a blend of substances that do not react chemically.
- Particles can have electrical charges.

VOCABULARY REVIEW
proton p. 139
ion p. 142
molecule p. 179
chemical reaction p. 197
mixture See Glossary.

CONTENT REVIEW
CLASSZONE.COM
Review concepts and vocabulary.

TAKING NOTES

MIND MAP

Write each main idea, or blue heading, in an oval; then write details that relate to each other and to the main idea. Organize the details so that each line of the map has a note about one part of the main idea.

CHOOSE YOUR OWN STRATEGY

For each new vocabulary term, take notes by choosing one of the strategies from earlier chapters—**frame game**, **description wheel**, or **four square** diagram. You can also use other vocabulary strategies that you might already know.

See the Note-Taking Handbook on pages R45–R51.

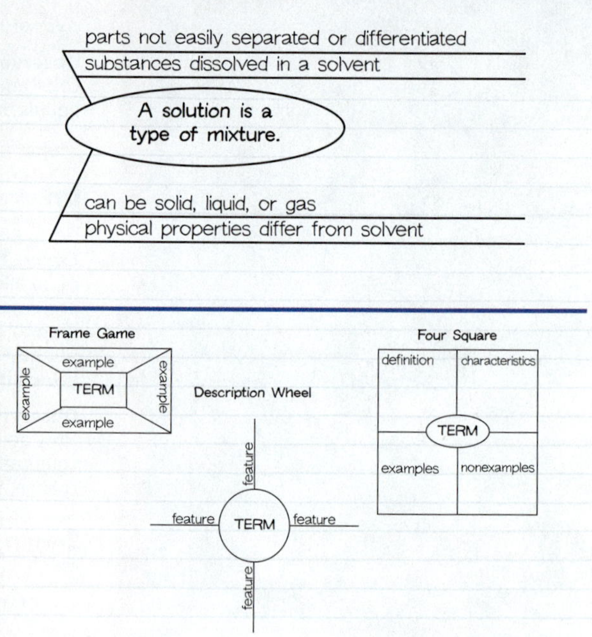

238 Unit 2: Chemical Interactions

CHECK READINESS

Administer the Diagnostic Test to determine students' readiness for new science content and their mastery of requisite math skills.

 Diagnostic Test, pp. 59–60

Technology Resources

Students needing content and math skills should visit **ClassZone.com**.

- CONTENT REVIEW
- MATH TUTORIAL

 CONTENT REVIEW CD-ROM

KEY CONCEPT

A solution is a type of mixture.

◀ **BEFORE, you learned**
- Ionic or covalent bonds hold a compound together
- Chemical reactions produce chemical changes
- Chemical reactions alter the arrangements of atoms

▶ **NOW, you will learn**
- How a solution differs from other types of mixtures
- About the parts of a solution
- How properties of solutions differ from properties of their separate components

VOCABULARY
solution p. 239
solute p. 240
solvent p. 240
suspension p. 241

EXPLORE Mixtures

Which substances dissolve in water?

PROCEDURE
1. Pour equal amounts of water into each cup.
2. Pour one spoonful of table salt into one of the cups. Stir.
3. Pour one spoonful of flour into the other cup. Stir.
4. Record your observations.

WHAT DO YOU THINK?
- Did the salt dissolve? Did the flour dissolve?
- How can you tell?

MATERIALS
- tap water
- 2 clear plastic cups
- plastic spoon
- table salt
- flour

VOCABULARY
Remember to use the strategy of your choice. You might use a four square diagram for *solution*.

The parts of a solution are mixed evenly.

A mixture is a combination of substances, such as a fruit salad. The ingredients of any mixture can be physically separated from each other because they are not chemically changed—they are still the same substances. Sometimes, however, a mixture is so completely blended that its ingredients cannot be identified as different substances. A **solution** is a type of mixture, called a homogeneous mixture, that is the same throughout. A solution can be physically separated, but all portions of a solution have the same properties.

If you stir sand into a glass of water, you can identify the sand as a separate substance that falls to the bottom of the glass. Sand in water is a mixture that is not a solution. If you stir sugar into a glass of water, you cannot identify the sugar as a separate substance. Sugar in water is a common solution, as are examples such as seawater, gasoline, and the liquid part of your blood.

Chapter 8: **Solutions** 239

8.1 INSTRUCT

Teach from Visuals

To help students interpret the visual showing types of solutions, have them read each block of text in the photograph. Ask: What do all three solutions have in common? *Each contains substances dissolved in another substance.*

EXPLORE the BIG idea

Revisit "Does It Dissolve?" on p. 237. Have students explain their results.

Develop Critical Thinking

ANALYZE Have students analyze the atmosphere as a solution. Ask:

- Is Earth's atmosphere a solution? Why? *No; because Earth's atmosphere is constantly in motion and changing, every portion of it will not be the same as all other portions. Thus, the atmosphere as a whole is not a solution.*

- If you took a sample of Earth's atmosphere and placed it in a container, would the sample be a solution? Why? *Yes; all parts of the sample are the same, so the sample is a solution.*

Ongoing Assessment

Name the different parts of a solution.

Ask: What are the two components of all solutions? *solute and solvent*

CHECK YOUR READING Answer: A solute is the substance that is dissolved; a solvent dissolves a solute.

CHECK YOUR READING Answer: The solvent is the substance that is present in the greatest amount.

READING TIP
The words *solute* and *solvent* are both related to the Latin word *solvere*, which means "to loosen."

Solutes and Solvents

Like other mixtures, a solution has definite components. A **solute** (SAHL-yoot) is a substance that is dissolved to make a solution. When a solute dissolves, it separates into individual particles. A **solvent** is a substance that dissolves a solute. Because a solute dissolves into individual particles in a solvent, it is not possible to identify the solute and solvent as different substances when they form a solution.

In a solution of table salt and water, the salt is the solute and the water is the solvent. In the cells of your body, substances such as calcium ions and sugar are solutes, and water is the solvent. Water is the most common and important solvent, but other substances can also be solvents. For example, if you have ever used an oil-based paint you know that water will not clean the paintbrushes. Instead, a solvent like turpentine must be used.

CHECK YOUR READING What is the difference between a solute and a solvent?

Types of Solutions

Many solutions are made of solids dissolved in liquids. However, solutes, solvents, and solutions can be gases, liquids, or solids. For example, oxygen, a gas, is dissolved in seawater. The bubbles in carbonated drinks come from the release of carbon dioxide gas that was dissolved in the drink.

In some solutions, both the solute and the solvent are in the same physical state. Vinegar, for example, is a solution of acetic acid in water. In a solution of different liquids, it may be difficult to say which substance is the solute and which is the solvent. In general, the substance present in the greater amount is the solvent. Since there is more water than acetic acid in vinegar, water is the solvent and acetic acid is the solute.

Although you may usually think of a solution as a liquid, solid solutions also exist. For example, bronze is a solid solution in which tin is the solute and copper is the solvent. Solid solutions are not formed as solids. Instead, the solvent metal is heated until it melts and becomes a liquid. Then the solute is added, and the substances are thoroughly mixed together. When the mixture cools, it is a solid solution.

Solutions made of combinations of gases are also common. The air you breathe is a solution. Because nitrogen makes up the largest portion of air, it is the solvent. Other gases present, such as oxygen and carbon dioxide, are solutes.

Gas Solution Air is oxygen and other gases dissolved in nitrogen.

Solid Solution Bronze consists of tin dissolved in copper.

Liquid Solution Water often contains many dissolved substances.

CHECK YOUR READING When substances in a solution are in the same physical state, which is the solvent?

DIFFERENTIATE INSTRUCTION

 **More Reading Support**

A What is the most common solvent? *water*

B What are many solutions made of? *solids dissolved in liquids*

English Learners Words with multiple meanings may confuse English learners. For example, the term *solution*, introduced on p. 239, has another common use that English learners may be more familiar with (as in a solution to a problem).

Below Level The terms *solution, solute,* and *solvent* look and sound similar. Have students write the definition for each term on an index card. They should keep the cards available for quick reference.

INVESTIGATE Solutions

How can you separate the parts of a solution?

PROCEDURE

1. Draw a solid black circular region 6 cm in diameter around the point of the filter.
2. Place the filter, point up, over the top of the bottle.
3. Squeeze several drops of water onto the point of the filter.
4. Observe the filter once every minute for 10 minutes. Record your observations.

WHAT DO YOU THINK?

- What happened to the ink on the filter?
- Identify, in general, the solutes and the solution in this investigation.

CHALLENGE Relate your observations of the ink and water on the coffee filter to the properties of solutions.

SKILL FOCUS
Observing

MATERIALS
- black marker
- coffee filter
- plastic bottle
- eyedropper
- tap water
- stopwatch

TIME
15 minutes

Suspensions

When you add flour to water, the mixture turns cloudy, and you cannot see through it. This mixture is not a solution but a suspension. In a **suspension,** the particles are larger than those found in a solution. Instead of dissolving, these larger particles turn the liquid cloudy. Sometimes you can separate the components of a suspension by filtering the mixture.

Solution Dissolved particles cannot be identified as a substance different from the solvent.

Suspension Particles that do not dissolve make a suspension look cloudy.

Chapter 8: **Solutions** 241

INVESTIGATE Solutions

PURPOSE To separate the parts of a solution

TIP *15 min.* Use a cone-shaped coffee filter for best results. The marker must have water-soluble ink.

WHAT DO YOU THINK? *The black ink separated into several colors. The solutes are the different-colored substances, and the solution is the black ink.*

CHALLENGE *Substances of different colors are dissolved in the ink, and these substances can be separated.*

Datasheet, Solutions, p. 209

Technology Resources

Customize this student lab as needed or look for an alternative. Print rubrics to assess student lab reports.

Lab Generator CD-ROM

Develop Critical Thinking

COMPARE A solution is a homogeneous mixture; a suspension is a heterogeneous mixture. Ask: How do the terms *homogeneous* and *heterogeneous* describe the different types of mixtures? *A homogeneous mixture is the same throughout; a heterogeneous mixture is different throughout.*

Teach from Visuals

To help students interpret the illustration comparing solutions and suspensions, ask: How are the appearances of the mixtures in the photographs related to the blow-up illustrations? *The larger particle size in the suspension makes the mixture appear cloudy.*

DIFFERENTIATE INSTRUCTION

More Reading Support

C How does the particle size compare in a solution and a suspension? *It is larger in a suspension.*

Alternative Assessment Have students answer the questions in "Investigate Solutions" by drawing a diagram.

Chapter 8 **241**

Teach from Visuals

To help students interpret the diagrams showing how solutes dissolve, ask:

- How do the solvent molecules interact with the solute particles. *The solvent molecules surround each solute particle, dissolving and evenly distributing the solute.*
- Identify the difference between the dissolved ionic compound and the dissolved covalent compound. *The ions separate from one another; each molecule of the covalent compound separates from each other, but the covalent bonds within the molecules remain intact.*

Address Misconceptions

IDENTIFY Ask: Why doesn't sand dissolve in water? If students suggest that it doesn't dissolve because of physical properties such as density, hardness, or roughness, they may hold a misconception about why some substances dissolve but others do not.

CORRECT Have students observe the physical characteristics of salt or granulated sugar, sand, and flour, but do not tell the students what the substances are. Have students predict, based on their observations, which of the substances will dissolve. Add the substances to water and have the students observe which substance dissolves. Explain that substances dissolve when the interaction between solute and solvent particles is greater than the interaction between the solute or solvent particles alone.

REASSESS Ask students again why sand does not dissolve in water. *The forces holding the particles of sand together are stronger than the force of water trying to pull them apart.*

Technology Resources

Visit **ClassZone.com** for background on common student misconceptions.

 **MISCONCEPTION DATABASE**

Ongoing Assessment

 *Answer: An ionic compound dissociates into individual ions; a covalent compound dissociates into individual molecules.*

242 Unit 2: Chemical Interactions

Solvent and solute particles interact.

The parts of a solution—that is, the solute and the solvent—can be physically separated because they are not changed into new substances. However, individual particles of solute and solvent do interact. When a solid dissolves in a liquid, the particles of the solute are surrounded by particles of the liquid. The solute particles become evenly distributed throughout the solvent.

The way in which a solid compound dissolves in a liquid depends on the type of bonds in the compound. Ionic compounds, such as table salt (NaCl), split apart into individual ions. When table salt dissolves in water, the sodium and chloride ions separate, and each ion is surrounded by water molecules. When a covalent compound, such as table sugar ($C_{12}H_{22}O_{11}$), dissolves, each molecule stays together and is surrounded by solvent molecules. The general processes that take place when ionic compounds dissolve and when covalent compounds dissolve are shown below.

How Solutes Dissolve

Ionic compounds separate into ions. Covalent compounds separate into individual molecules.

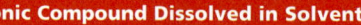
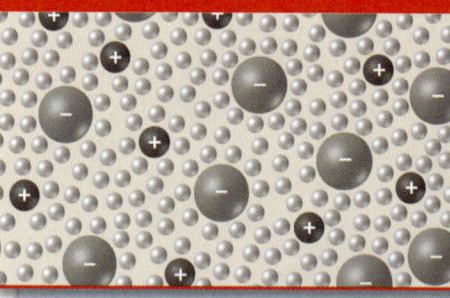
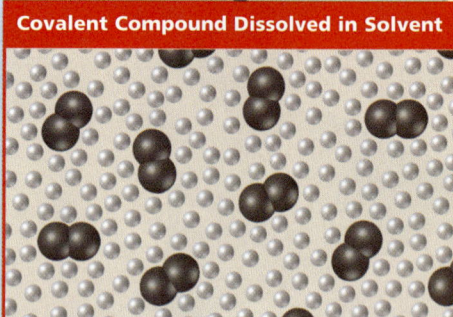

READING VISUALS What difference between the two illustrations tells you whether a compound is ionic or covalent?

242 Unit 2: Chemical Interactions

DIFFERENTIATE INSTRUCTION

 **More Reading Support**

D What determines the way a solid dissolves in a liquid? *the type of bonds in the solid*

English Learners To help English learners recognize cause-and-effect relationships, have them make a two-column Cause-and-Effect chart and put each part of a sentence where it belongs, as in the example. Tell students to look for introductory phrases that set up cause-and-effect sentences.

Cause	Effect
When you add flour to water,	the mixture turns cloudy, and you cannot see through it.

Properties of solvents change in solutions.

In every solution—solid, liquid, and gas—solutes change the physical properties of a solvent. Therefore, a solution's physical properties differ from the physical properties of the pure solvent. The amount of solute in the solution determines how much the physical properties of the solvent are changed.

Lowering the Freezing Point

Recall that the freezing point is the temperature at which a liquid becomes a solid. The freezing point of a liquid solvent decreases—becomes lower—when a solute is dissolved in it. For example, pure water freezes at 0°C (32°F) under normal conditions. When a solute is dissolved in water, the resulting solution has a freezing point below 0°C.

Lowering the freezing point of water can be very useful in winter. Road crews spread salt on streets and highways during snowstorms because salt lowers the freezing point of water. When snow mixes with salt on the roads, a saltwater solution that does not freeze at 0°C is formed. The more salt that is used, the lower the freezing point of the solution.

Since salt dissolves in the small amount of water usually present on the surface of ice, it helps to melt any ice already present on the roads. However, there is a limit to salt's effectiveness because there is a limit to how much will dissolve. No matter how much salt is used, once the temperature goes below –21°C (–6°F), the melted ice will freeze again.

> **REMINDER**
> In temperature measurements, *C* stands for "Celsius" and *F* stands for "Fahrenheit."

CHECK YOUR READING How does the freezing point of a solvent change when a solute is dissolved in it?

Making ice cream also depends on lowering the freezing point of a solvent. Most hand-cranked ice cream makers hold the liquid ice cream ingredients in a canister surrounded by a mixture of salt and ice. The salt added to the ice lowers the freezing point of this mixture. This causes the ice to melt—absorbing heat from its surroundings, including the ice cream ingredients. The ice cream mix is chilled while its ingredients are constantly stirred. As a result, tiny ice crystals form all at once in the ice cream mixture instead of a few crystals forming and growing larger as the mix freezes. This whole process helps to make ice cream that is smooth and creamy.

Adding salt to lower the freezing point of ice helps to make ice cream.

DIFFERENTIATE INSTRUCTION

More Reading Support
E What changes the physical properties of a solvent when it is in a solution? *the solute*

Advanced Not only does the melting point (same as freezing point) of a solvent decrease after a solute is added, but in some cases it stops being an actual point. Copper melts at 1083.4°C (1982.12°F). However, brass (zinc dissolved in copper) melts somewhere between 900°C and 1000°C. Brass may be a either a solid or a liquid in that temperature range.

Challenge and Extension, p. 208

Real World Example

Calcium chloride ($CaCl_2$) is better than sodium chloride (NaCl) for melting ice and snow on roads. When calcium chloride dissolves in water, it separates into three ions (one calcium ion and two chloride ions), while sodium chloride separates into two ions. The greater number of dissolved ions causes a greater decrease in the freezing point of water.

Teacher Demo

To demonstrate freezing-point depression, perform this demonstration with the help of one or two students. Fill two beakers with crushed ice and add 50 milliliters of cold water to each. Stir each beaker with a separate stirring rod until the temperature stabilizes. Read and record the temperature in each beaker. Add about 75 grams of rock salt or kosher salt to one of the beakers, and continue stirring both beakers. When the temperature in each beaker is stabilized, read and record the temperatures. The freezing point in the beaker containing salt will be depressed by about 5°C.

Address Misconceptions

IDENTIFY Ask students how much mass a liter of a saturated sugar-water solution has. If they answer that it would have a mass of one kilogram, they may hold the misconception that when the sugar dissolves to make a solution, it does not contribute to the solution's mass.

CORRECT Using a balance, find the mass of a liter of water. Next, find the mass of 400 to 500 mL of sugar. Place both on the balance at the same time, if possible. Pour the sugar into the water and stir. Draw attention to the mass of the solution.

REASSESS Ask students how much mass a liter of water with 300 mL of salt dissolved in it would have. *1.3 kilograms*

Technology Resources
Visit **ClassZone.com** for background on common student misconceptions.

MISCONCEPTION DATABASE

Ongoing Assessment

CHECK YOUR READING Answer: It decreases.

Chapter 8 **243**

Ongoing Assessment

Distinguish how properties of solutions differ from properties of their original components.

Ask: What determines how much the physical properties of a solvent change when you add a solute? *the amount of the solute in the solution*

PHOTO CAPTION Answer: *The antifreeze would increase the boiling point of water, thus keeping it liquid at higher temperatures.*

 Answer: *The more solute that is added, the greater the increase in the boiling point.*

Reinforce

Have students relate the section to the Big Idea.

 Reinforcing Key Concepts, p. 210

8.1 ASSESS & RETEACH

Assess
 Section 8.1 Quiz, p. 61

Reteach
Have students write a short paragraph describing the dissolving of an ionic compound in water, from the point of view of an ion in the compound. *Answers should describe how the solvent molecules are attracted to the ion, pull it out of the compound, and surround it.*

Technology Resources
Have students visit **ClassZone.com** for reteaching of Key Concepts.

 CONTENT REVIEW

CONTENT REVIEW CD-ROM

Raising the Boiling Point

The boiling point of a liquid is the temperature at which the liquid forms bubbles in its interior and becomes a gas. Under normal conditions, a substance cannot exist as a liquid at a temperature greater than its boiling point. However, the boiling point of a solution is higher than the boiling point of the pure solvent. Therefore, a solution can remain a liquid at a higher temperature than its pure solvent.

For example, the boiling point of pure water is 100°C (212°F) under normal conditions. Saltwater, however, can be a liquid at temperatures above 100°C because salt raises the boiling point of water. The amount of salt in the water determines how much the boiling point is increased. The more solute that is dissolved in a solution, the greater the increase in boiling point.

APPLY Why might the addition of antifreeze to the water in this car's radiator have prevented the car from overheating?

 How does the boiling point of a solution depend on the amount of solute in it?

A solute lowers the freezing point and raises the boiling point of the solvent in the solution. The result is that the solute extends the temperature range in which the solvent remains a liquid. One way in which both a decrease in freezing point and an increase in boiling point can be useful in the same solution involves a car's radiator. Antifreeze, which is mostly a chemical called ethylene glycol, is often added to the water in the radiator. This solution prevents the water from freezing in the winter and also keeps it from boiling in the summer.

8.1 Review

KEY CONCEPTS
1. How is a solution different from other mixtures?
2. Describe the two parts of a solution. How can you tell them apart?
3. How does the boiling point of a solvent change when a solute is dissolved in it? How does the freezing point change?

CRITICAL THINKING
4. **Contrast** Contrast the way in which an ionic compound, such as table salt, dissolves with the way in which a covalent compound, such as sugar, dissolves.
5. **Infer** Pure water freezes at 0°C and boils at 100°C. Would tap water likely freeze and boil at those exact temperatures? Why or why not?

CHALLENGE
6. **Synthesize** People often sprinkle salt on icy driveways and sidewalks. Would a substance like flour have a similar effect on the ice? Explain.

244 Unit 2: Chemical Interactions

ANSWERS

1. All of a solution appears the same, and the components of a solution are evenly distributed, unlike a typical mixture.

2. The solute is the substance that dissolves. The solvent dissolves the solute. The substance present in the greatest amount is the solvent.

3. Boiling point increases; freezing point decreases.

4. Ionic compounds separate into individual ions, and covalent compounds split into individual molecules.

5. No; tap water contains dissolved substances.

6. No; the salt lowers the freezing point of water because it makes a salt solution. Flour does not make a solution, so the freezing point will not decrease and the ice will not melt.

KEY CONCEPT
8.2 The amount of solute that dissolves can vary.

BEFORE, you learned
- Solutions are a type of mixture
- A solution is made when a solute is dissolved in a solvent
- Solutes change the properties of solvents

NOW, you will learn
- About the concentration of a solution
- How a solute's solubility can be changed
- How solubility depends on molecular structure

VOCABULARY
concentration p. 245
dilute p. 246
saturated p. 246
solubility p. 247

EXPLORE Solutions and Temperature
How does temperature affect a solution?

PROCEDURE
1. Pour cold soda water into one cup and warm soda water into another cup. Record your observations.
2. After 5 minutes, observe both cups of soda water. Record your observations.

WHAT DO YOU THINK?
- Which solution bubbled more at first?
- Which solution bubbled for a longer period of time?

MATERIALS
- soda water
- 2 clear plastic cups

MIND MAP Remember to use a mind map to take notes on the concentration of a solution.

A solution with a high concentration contains a large amount of solute.

Think of water from the ocean and drinking water from a well. Water from the ocean tastes salty, but water from a well does not. The well water does contain salt, but in a concentration so low that you cannot taste it. A solution's **concentration** depends on the amount of solute dissolved in a solvent at a particular temperature. A solution with only a small amount of dissolved solute, such as the salt dissolved in well water, is said to have a low concentration. As more solute is dissolved, the concentration gets higher.

If you have ever used a powdered mix to make lemonade, you probably know that you can change the concentration of the drink by varying the amount of mix you put into a certain amount of water. Two scoops of mix in a pitcher of water makes the lemonade stronger than just one scoop. The lemonade with two scoops of mix has a higher concentration of the mix than the lemonade made with one scoop.

Chapter 8: Solutions 245

8.2 INSTRUCT

Teach from Visuals

To help students interpret the graphic of dilute and concentrated solutions, ask:

- How can you make a solution more concentrated? *by adding more solute*
- What is the difference between the dilute solution and the concentrated solution, the amount of solute particles or the amount of solvent particles? *the amount of solute particles in relation to the amount of solvent*

Integrate the Sciences

The concentration of salt among bodies of water varies. Fresh water is usually defined as water containing less than 1% total dissolved solute concentration and less than 0.2% salt. The average concentration of salt across all of Earth's oceans is approximately 3.5%. The Great Salt Lake in Utah has a much higher concentration of salt. The southern end of the lake has a salt concentration of approximately 15% and the northern end has a salt concentration of approximately 27%.

Teacher Demo

To demonstrate how solutions can become supersaturated, dissolve 2 cups of sugar in 1 cup of boiling water. Carefully pour it into a clean jar. Dip a piece of string into the solution, stretch it out on a piece of wax paper, and let it dry overnight. Place the dried string in the jar and let the jar stand for 7 days. Eventually, rock candy will form on the string. The solution becomes more concentrated as the water evaporates and then becomes supersaturated.

Ongoing Assessment

CHECK YOUR READING Answer: A dilute solution contains a low concentration of solute. A saturated solution contains the highest concentration of solute that can dissolve in that solvent at that temperature.

READING TIP
The word *dilute* can be used as either an adjective or a verb. A dilute solution has a low concentration of solute. To dilute a solution is to add more solvent to it, thus lowering the concentration of the solution.

Degrees of Concentration

A solution that has a low concentration of solute is called a **dilute** solution. Salt dissolved in the drinking water from a well is a dilute solution. The concentration of a solution can be even further reduced, or diluted, by adding more solvent. On the other hand, as more solute is added to a solution, the solution becomes more concentrated. A concentrated solution has a large amount of solute.

Less solute is dissolved in a dilute solution.

More solute is dissolved in a concentrated solution.

Have you ever wondered how much sugar can be dissolved in a glass of iced tea? If you keep adding sugar to the tea, eventually no more sugar will dissolve. The tea will contain as much dissolved sugar as it can hold at that temperature. Such a solution is called a **saturated** solution because it contains the maximum amount of solute that can be dissolved in the solvent at a given temperature. If a solution contains less solute than this maximum amount, it is an unsaturated solution.

 CHECK YOUR READING How are the terms *dilute* and *saturated* related to the concept of concentration?

Explore supersaturated solutions and precipitation.

Supersaturated Solutions

Sometimes, a solution contains more dissolved solute than is normally possible. This type of solution is said to be supersaturated. A saturated solution can become supersaturated if more solute is added while the temperature is raised. Then if this solution is slowly cooled, the solute can remain dissolved. This type of solution is very unstable, though. If the solution is disturbed, or more solute is added in the form of a crystal, the excess solute will quickly solidify and form a precipitate. This process is shown in the photographs on the top of page 247.

246 Unit 2: Chemical Interactions

DIFFERENTIATE INSTRUCTION

More Reading Support

A What do we call a solution with a low concentration of solute? *dilute*

B What is a solution with the maximum amount of solute? *saturated*

English Learners Tell English learners that *given* (p. 247) is often used as an adjective meaning "specified" or "certain." The phrase "said to be" is used to introduce unfamiliar expressions or a description. Have students make note cards that list definitions of *solute, solvent,* and *solubility.* If students have a hard time comprehending *soluble,* the adjective form of *solubility,* tell them it means "able to dissolve."

1. A supersaturated solution contains more dissolved solute than is normally possible.

2. After a crystal of solute is added, or the solution is disturbed, a precipitate forms.

REMINDER
A precipitate is a solid substance that comes out of a solution.

One example of a supersaturated solution is a chemical heat pack that contains sodium acetate and water. The pack contains more sodium acetate than can normally dissolve at room temperature, but when the pack is heated in a microwave oven, all of the sodium acetate dissolves. The solution inside the pack is supersaturated. The heat pack is activated by bending it. This disturbs the solution, solidifying the sodium acetate and releasing a large amount of heat over a long period of time.

Solubility

The **solubility** (SAHL-yuh-BIHL-ih-tee) of a substance is the amount of that substance that will dissolve in a certain amount of solvent at a given temperature. For example, consider household ammonia used for cleaning. This ammonia is not pure ammonia—it is a solution of ammonia in water.

Because a large amount of ammonia can dissolve in water, ammonia is said to have a high solubility in water. However, other substances do not dissolve in such large amounts in water. Only a small amount of carbon dioxide will dissolve in water, so carbon dioxide has a low solubility in water. Oils do not dissolve at all in water, so oils are said to be insoluble in water.

READING TIP
The word *solubility* is related to the words *solute* and *solvent*, and means "ability to be dissolved." A substance that is insoluble will not dissolve.

The amount of solute needed to make a saturated solution depends on the solubility of a solute in a particular solvent.

- If the solute is highly soluble, a saturated solution will be very concentrated.
- If the solute has a low solubility, the saturated solution will be dilute.

In other words, a saturated solution can be either dilute or concentrated, depending on the solubility of a solute in a particular solvent.

CHECK YOUR READING How does solubility affect a solution?

Chapter 8: **Solutions** 247

DIFFERENTIATE INSTRUCTION

More Reading Support

C What do you call the amount of a substance that will dissolve in a certain amount of solvent at a certain temperature?
solubility

Below Level To teach the concept of concentration, provide students with marbles (or another object) in a box. A dilute solution has few marbles in the box; a concentrated solution has many. A saturated solution has a completely filled layer of marbles in the bottom of the box with no room to add more. A supersaturated solution has a filled layer of marbles with additional marbles resting on top of the layer.

Teach Difficult Concepts

Students often confuse a concentrated solution with a saturated solution. Ask students how these two concepts differ. *A concentrated solution holds a large amount of solute per unit volume of solvent. A saturated solution holds as much solute as possible at a given temperature. A concentrated solution may or may not be saturated.* To help students understand solubility, you might try the following demonstration.

Teacher Demo

To demonstrate the solubility of Styrofoam in acetone (nail polish remover) in a dramatic way, pour about 400 mL of acetone into a 1 L beaker. Add foam packing peanuts, one at a time at first, then several at a time. Stir with a glass stirring rod. The peanuts will dissolve so quickly that they will appear to melt. Although the resulting solution is concentrated, it is not saturated. Caution: Acetone is flammable, and you should avoid prolonged exposure to its fumes. Let most of the solution evaporate outdoors before properly disposing of the residue in a chemical waste container.

Ongoing Assessment

Explain how the concentration of a solution varies.

Ask: Why is a supersaturated solution unstable? *It holds more dissolved solute than is normally possible at that temperature. Any disturbance will cause the excess solute to precipitate out of the solution.*

CHECK YOUR READING Answer: The more soluble a substance is, the greater the amount that will dissolve and the greater its concentration before the solution becomes saturated.

INVESTIGATE Solubility

PURPOSE To design an experiment to demonstrate the effect of temperature on solubility

TIPS 20 min. Students can bring many of the materials—salt, cups, spoon—from home. For best results, an ice bath could be used instead of a cold-water bath.

WHAT DO YOU THINK? *The variable being changed should involve heating or cooling water. The amount of water should stay the same. An increase in water temperature increases the solubility of salt; a decrease in water temperature decreases the solubility of salt.*

 Datasheet, Solubility, p. 220

Technology Resources

Customize this student lab as needed or look for an alternative. Print rubrics to assess student lab reports.

 Lab Generator CD-ROM

Metacognitive Strategy

Ask students to write a short paragraph discussing whether they find it difficult to design an experiment. What parts of the process do they find most challenging? What parts are easy for them?

Ongoing Assessment

CHECK YOUR READING *Answer: An increase in temperature increases the solubility of most solid solutes. An increase in temperature decreases the solubility of gases.*

The solubility of a solute can be changed.

 The solubility of a solute can be changed in two ways. Raising the temperature is one way to change the solubility of the solute, because most solids are more soluble at higher temperatures. Another way to change solubility when the solute is a gas is to change the pressure. The solubility of gases in a liquid solvent increases at high pressure.

Temperature and Solubility

REMINDER
An increase in temperature means an increase in particle movement.

An increase in temperature has two effects on most solid solutes—they dissolve more quickly, and a greater amount of the solid dissolves in a given amount of solvent. In general, solids are more soluble at higher temperatures, and they dissolve faster.

 The opposite is true of all gases—an increase in temperature makes a gas less soluble in water. You can see this by warming tap water in a pan. As the water approaches its boiling point, any air that is dissolved in the water comes out of solution. The air forms tiny bubbles that rise to the surface.

CHECK YOUR READING What effect does temperature have on most solid solutes? on gaseous solutes?

INVESTIGATE Solubility

How can you change solubility?

Use what you know about solubility to design an experiment that shows how a change in temperature can change the amount of table salt that will dissolve in water.

PROCEDURE

1. Use the materials in the list to identify the relationship between temperature and solubility.
2. Write your procedure, identifying the constants and variables.
3. Perform your experiment and record your results.

WHAT DO YOU THINK?
- Which variable did you change? What were your constants? Why?
- How do your results demonstrate the effect of temperature on solubility?

SKILL FOCUS
Designing experiments

MATERIALS
- clear plastic cups
- thermometer
- tap water
- table salt
- balance
- plastic spoon
- hot-water bath
- cold-water bath

TIME
20 minutes

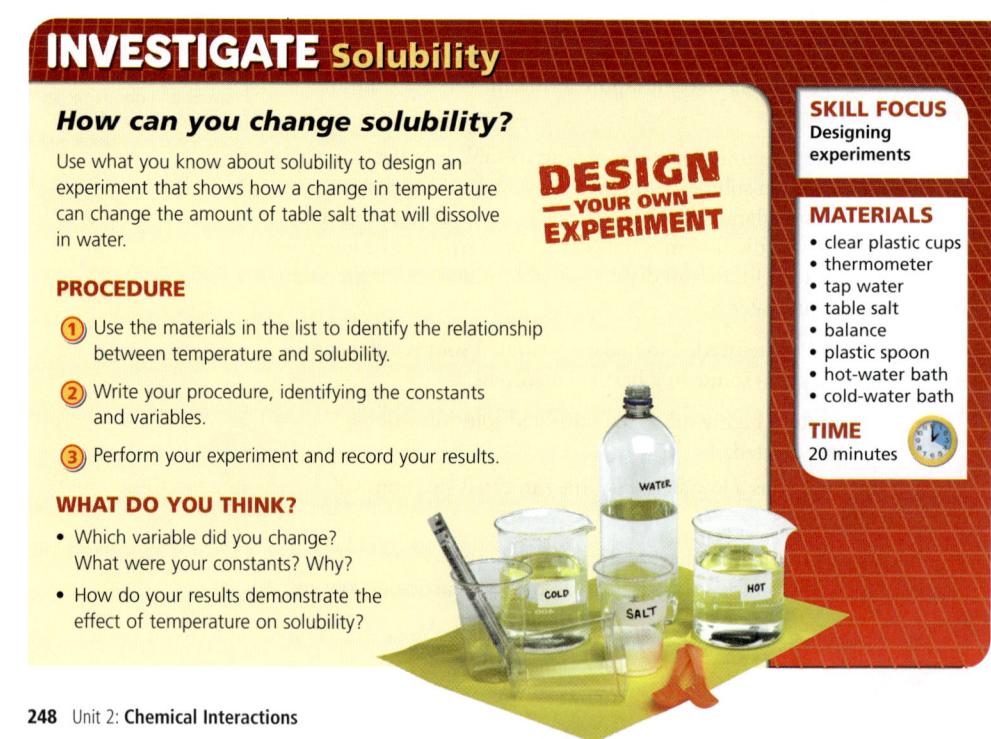

248 Unit 2: Chemical Interactions

DIFFERENTIATE INSTRUCTION

 **More Reading Support**

D Are most solid solutes more soluble in warm or cool solvents? *in warm solvent*

 Are gases more soluble in warm or in cool solvents? *in cool solvent*

Additional Investigation To reinforce Section 8.2 learning goals, use the following full-period investigation:

Additional INVESTIGATION, Rates of Solution, A, B, & C, pp. 259–267, 329–330
(Advanced students should complete Levels B and C.)

Alternative Assessment Have each group give an oral report to the class describing their experimental procedures in the investigation. The class should then critique each group's procedure. Students should discuss what was good about each experimental design as well as what was incorrect or unclear.

Think back to the earlier discussion of supersaturated solutions. One way in which a solution can become supersaturated is through a change in temperature. For example, suppose that a solution is saturated at 50°C (122°F), and is then allowed to cool slowly. The solid is less soluble in the cooler solution, but the excess solute may not form a precipitate. As a result, the solution contains more of the dissolved solute than would be possible under normal conditions because of the change in temperature.

Temperature and Solubility		
Solute	Increased Temperature	Decreased Temperature
Solid	increase in solubility	decrease in solubility
Gas	decrease in solubility	increase in solubility

A change in temperature can produce changes in solutions in the environment. For example, a factory located on the shore of a lake may use the lake water as a coolant and then return heated water to the lake. This increase in temperature decreases the solubility of oxygen in the lake water. As a result, less oxygen will remain dissolved in the water. A decrease in the oxygen concentration can harm plant and animal life in the lake.

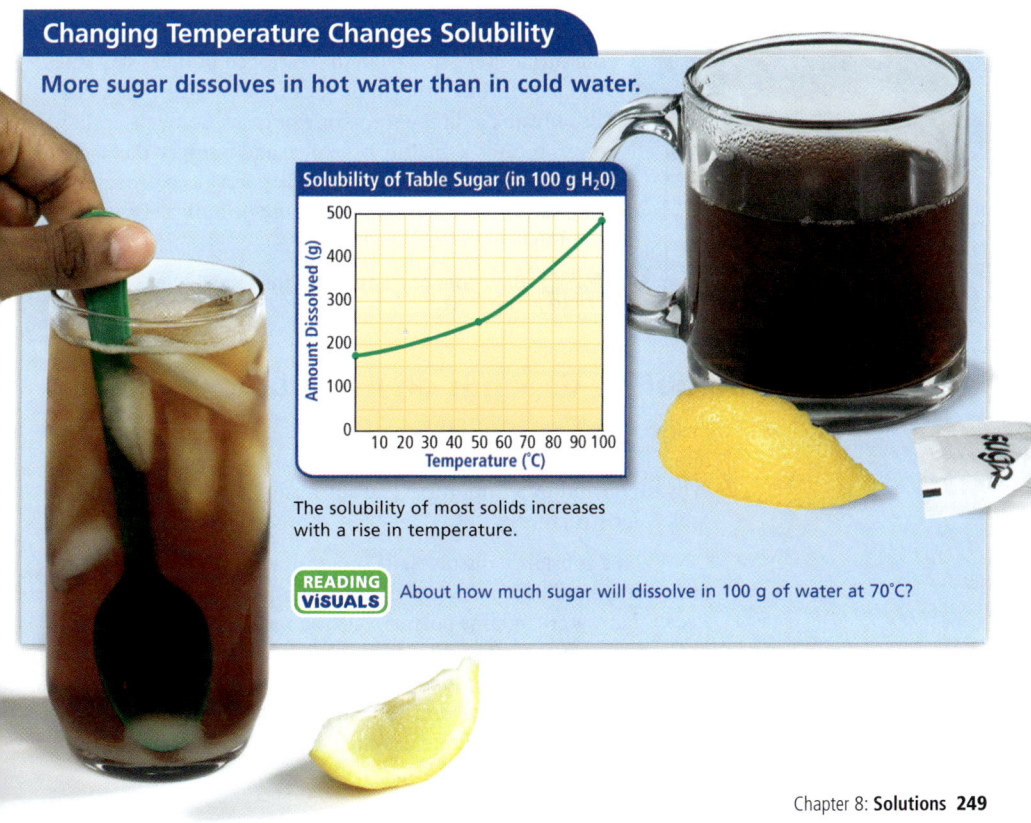

Changing Temperature Changes Solubility
More sugar dissolves in hot water than in cold water.

Solubility of Table Sugar (in 100 g H_2O)

The solubility of most solids increases with a rise in temperature.

READING VISUALS About how much sugar will dissolve in 100 g of water at 70°C?

Chapter 8: **Solutions** 249

DIFFERENTIATE INSTRUCTION

Advanced Have students repeat the investigation on p. 248, using sodium sulfate (Na_2SO_4) instead of table salt. This solid substance is less soluble at higher temperatures. Ask them how temperature can be used to make a supersaturated solution of sodium sulfate? *Make a saturated solution, cool it, and dissolve more solute. Then allow the temperature to slowly increase.*

 Challenge and Extension, p. 219

Teach from Visuals
To help students interpret the graph of solubility of table sugar (sucrose) versus temperature, ask:

- Can you dissolve any sugar in iced tea? Explain. *Yes; even at almost-freezing temperatures, sugar is soluble in water.*
- What would the temperature of 100 g of tea have to be for 200 g of sugar to dissolve in it? *at least 20°C*

Integrate the Sciences
Thermal pollution occurs when warm wastewater is dumped into a body of water. This causes the temperature of the water to increase above its normal level. When the water temperature raises, it can harm animals and plants that live in the water. Fish can die from the quick change in temperature, and algae in the water grow more rapidly, blocking the sunlight from other plant life in the water. One of the main sources of thermal pollution is factories or power plants that use water to cool equipment or to produce steam and then discharge the water into a nearby river, lake, or ocean. The Environmental Protection Agency (EPA) has regulations for discharging wastewater. In the United States, many factories try to reduce thermal pollution by cooling the water before it is released so that the heat escapes through the air.

Ongoing Assessment
Describe how a solute's solubility can be changed.
Ask: How could a soft-drink manufacturer increase the amount of dissolved carbon dioxide to make the drink fizzier? *Cool the drink before adding carbon dioxide.*

 Answer: about 340 g

Chapter 8 **249**

History Connection

Three workers involved in the building of the Brooklyn Bridge, which opened in 1883, died from the bends. The disorder was called caisson disease because workers were susceptible to it while working underwater in a caisson, or airlock, on the riverbed.

Teacher Demo

Remind students of the Teacher Demo on p. 247. Repeat the demonstration using 100 milliliters of acetone and starch-based packing peanuts. These peanuts will not dissolve in acetone. Dissolve the peanuts in water. Point out that the solubility of the two kinds of peanuts is different because the molecular structure of the peanuts is different. Both starch and water are polar. Polystyrene and acetone are nonpolar.

Integrate the Sciences

Many vitamins are fat soluble but not water soluble. Because vitamin molecules are nonpolar they are stored in a person's body fat. Vitamin C and the B-complex vitamins are exceptions—they are water soluble, and so are not stored in the body for a long period of time.

Ongoing Assessment

CHECK YOUR READING *Answer: Solid and liquid solutes are not affected by pressure. An increase in pressure increases solubility of gases.*

PHOTO CAPTION Answer: *The divers need to know their depth so they will know how slowly to return to the surface to allow nitrogen to come out of their blood safely.*

Pressure and Solubility

A change in pressure does not usually change the solubility of solid or liquid solutes. However, the solubility of any gas increases at higher pressures and decreases at lower pressures.

When manufacturers make carbonated beverages, such as soda, they add carbon dioxide gas at a pressure slightly greater than normal air pressure. When you open the can or bottle, the pressure decreases and the carbon dioxide bubbles out of solution with a fizz.

Another example is shown in the photograph on the left. When a diver's tank contains regular air, about 79 percent of the air is nitrogen. People breathe air like this all the time without any problem, but the pressure underwater is much greater than on Earth's surface. The higher pressure increases the solubility of nitrogen in the diver's blood.

When a diver heads up to the surface too fast, the pressure decreases, and so does the solubility of the nitrogen. The nitrogen comes out of solution, forming bubbles in the diver's blood vessels. These bubbles can cause a painful and sometimes fatal condition called the bends.

Divers can avoid the bends in two ways. They can rise to the surface very slowly, so that nitrogen bubbles stay small and pass through the bloodstream more easily. They can also breathe a different mixture of gases. Some professional divers breathe a mixture of oxygen and nitrogen that contains only about 66 percent nitrogen. For very deep dives, the mixture can also include helium because helium is less soluble in blood than nitrogen.

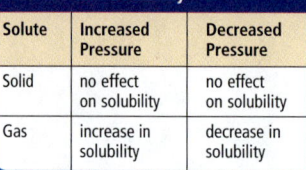

INFER If these divers are breathing regular air, why might they be looking at their depth gauges?

Pressure and Solubility

Solute	Increased Pressure	Decreased Pressure
Solid	no effect on solubility	no effect on solubility
Gas	increase in solubility	decrease in solubility

CHECK YOUR READING How does pressure affect the solubility of solids? of gases?

Solubility depends on molecular structure.

Everyone knows that oil and water do not mix. When a tanker spills oil near shore, the oil floats on the water and pollutes the beaches. Why do oil and water not mix? The answer involves their different molecular structures.

When a substance dissolves, its molecules or ions separate from one another and become evenly mixed with molecules of the solvent. Recall that water contains polar covalent bonds. As a result, water molecules have a negative region and a positive region. Water molecules are said to be polar. The molecules of an oil are nonpolar—the molecules do not have positive and negative regions. This difference makes oil insoluble in water.

DIFFERENTIATE INSTRUCTION

More Reading Support

F What type of solute is more soluble at higher pressures? *gas*

G What type of bonds does a water molecule contain? *polar covalent bonds*

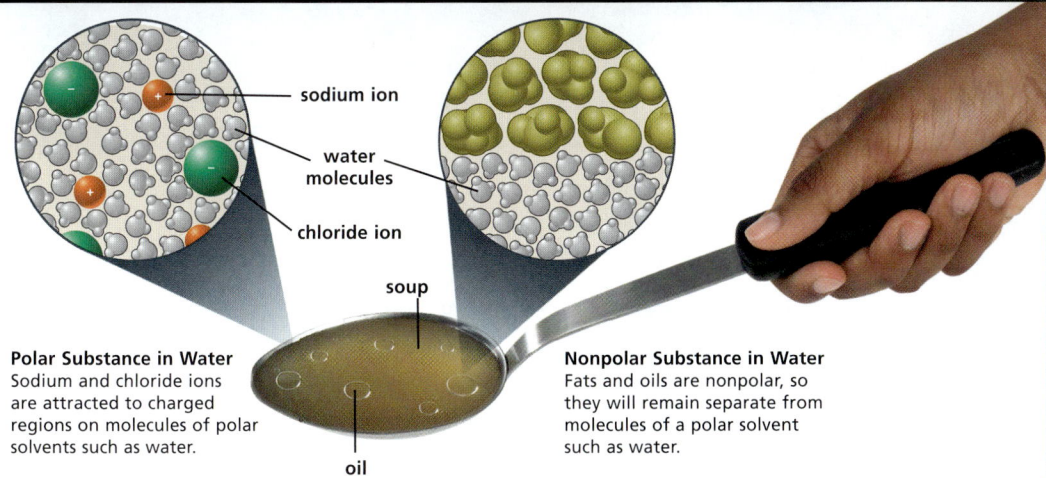

Polar Substance in Water
Sodium and chloride ions are attracted to charged regions on molecules of polar solvents such as water.

Nonpolar Substance in Water
Fats and oils are nonpolar, so they will remain separate from molecules of a polar solvent such as water.

Because water is polar and oil is nonpolar, their molecules are not attracted to each other. The molecules of a polar solvent like water are attracted to other polar molecules, such as those of sugar. This explains why sugar has such a high solubility in water. Ionic compounds, such as sodium chloride, are also highly soluble in water. Because water molecules are polar, they interact with the sodium and chloride ions. In general, polar solvents dissolve polar solutes, and nonpolar solvents dissolve nonpolar solutes. This concept is often expressed as "Like dissolves like."

So many substances dissolve in water that it is sometimes called the universal solvent. Water is considered to be essential for life because it can carry so many different ions and molecules—just about anything the body needs or needs to get rid of—through the body.

 Why will a nonpolar substance not dissolve in a polar substance?

8.2 Review

KEY CONCEPTS
1. How can a solution be made more concentrated? less concentrated?
2. What two factors can change the solubility of a gas?
3. Are nonpolar compounds highly soluble in water? Why or why not?

CRITICAL THINKING
4. **Predict** Suppose you stir sugar into ice water. Some sugar remains on the bottom of the glass. After the glass sits out for an hour, you stir it again. What will happen? Why?
5. **Infer** A powder dissolves easily in water but not in oil. Are the molecules in the powder probably polar or nonpolar? Explain.

CHALLENGE
6. **Synthesize** If mixing a substance with water forms a suspension, does the substance have a high or a low solubility in water? Explain.

Chapter 8: **Solutions** 251

ANSWERS

1. Add more solute, keeping the solvent constant; add more solvent, keeping the solute constant.
2. temperature and pressure
3. No; water is polar, and nonpolar substances are not highly soluble in polar solvents.
4. More of the sugar will dissolve as the water's temperature increases.
5. They are probably polar. They dissolve well in water, which is polar, but not in oil, which is nonpolar.
6. It has a low solubility because little if any of the substance dissolves.

Ongoing Assessment
Recognize that solubility depends on molecular structure.

Ask: What must happen between molecules for a solute to dissolve? *Solute and solvent particles must attract each other.*

 Answer: Nonpolar solutes do not have charged regions that would be attracted to charged regions of polar solvents.

Reinforce
Have students relate the section to the Big Idea.

 Reinforcing Key Concepts, p. 221

8.2 ASSESS & RETEACH

Assess
Section 8.2 Quiz, p. 62

Reteach
Discuss with students the types of solutions that have high solubility and low solubility. For example, ammonia has high solubility because a large amount of it is dissolved in water. Remind students that the amount of solute to make a saturated solution depends on its solubility. Ask students what happens to a saturated solution when a solute is highly soluble. What if it has low solubility? *When a solute is highly soluble, a saturated solution will be very concentrated; with low solubility, the solution will be dilute.*

Technology Resources
Have students visit **ClassZone.com** for reteaching of Key Concepts.

 CONTENT REVIEW

 CONTENT REVIEW CD-ROM

Chapter 8 **251**

CONNECTING SCIENCES
Integration of Sciences

Set Learning Goal
To understand that drinking water and groundwater are solutions

Present the Science
About two-thirds of the water drawn from aquifers in the United States is used for irrigation. Many aquifers are being drawn down below their natural recharge rates, resulting in subsidence and changes in water quality.

Some minerals that dissolve in groundwater are annoying and others are harmful. For example, well water that contains a large amount of sulfur smells like rotten eggs. Also, some minerals contain arsenic, which is a poison.

Discussion Questions
- Ask: Where do solutes in groundwater come from? *soil, rocks, rain, wastewater*
- Ask: How do the solutes in water change underground? *They may be trapped on clay or removed in chemical reactions with the soil and rocks.*
- Ask: What might be some sources of water pollution in our area? *Answers might include pesticide and fertilizer from lawns and fields, underground tanks, byproducts of manufacturing.*

DIFFERENTIATION TIP Demonstrate the difference between hard water and soft water. Pour equal amounts of hard and soft water into two jars. Add the same amount of liquid soap to each jar, shake them, and have students observe the different amounts of suds produced and the formation of scum or insoluble particulates.

Close
Ask: How could you soften hard water? *Sample answer: By adding a chemical that would cause solutes to precipitate out of the solution; physical filtering can't do it alone, because the minerals are dissolved.*

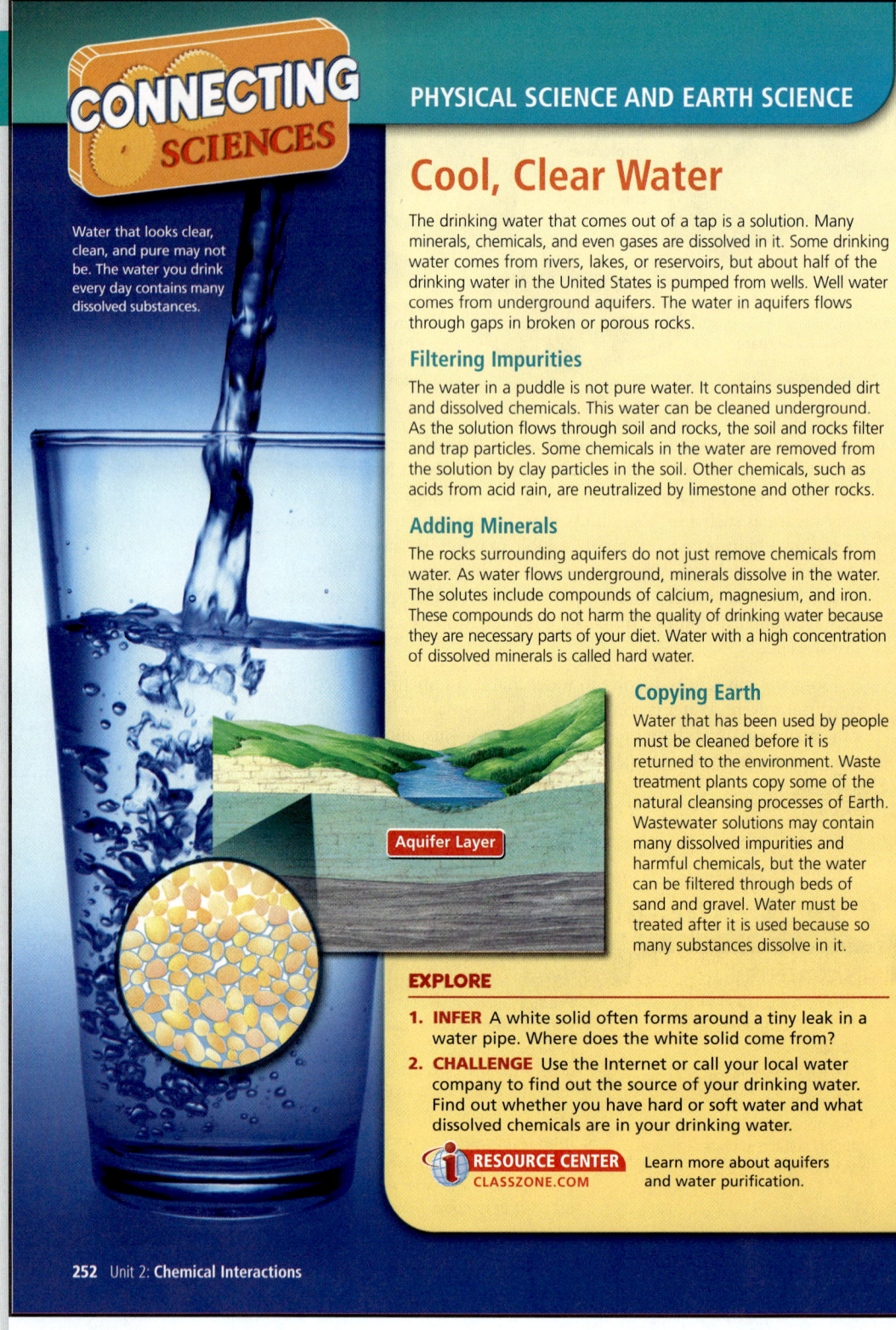

CONNECTING SCIENCES
PHYSICAL SCIENCE AND EARTH SCIENCE

Cool, Clear Water

The drinking water that comes out of a tap is a solution. Many minerals, chemicals, and even gases are dissolved in it. Some drinking water comes from rivers, lakes, or reservoirs, but about half of the drinking water in the United States is pumped from wells. Well water comes from underground aquifers. The water in aquifers flows through gaps in broken or porous rocks.

Filtering Impurities
The water in a puddle is not pure water. It contains suspended dirt and dissolved chemicals. This water can be cleaned underground. As the solution flows through soil and rocks, the soil and rocks filter and trap particles. Some chemicals in the water are removed from the solution by clay particles in the soil. Other chemicals, such as acids from acid rain, are neutralized by limestone and other rocks.

Adding Minerals
The rocks surrounding aquifers do not just remove chemicals from water. As water flows underground, minerals dissolve in the water. The solutes include compounds of calcium, magnesium, and iron. These compounds do not harm the quality of drinking water because they are necessary parts of your diet. Water with a high concentration of dissolved minerals is called hard water.

Copying Earth
Water that has been used by people must be cleaned before it is returned to the environment. Waste treatment plants copy some of the natural cleansing processes of Earth. Wastewater solutions may contain many dissolved impurities and harmful chemicals, but the water can be filtered through beds of sand and gravel. Water must be treated after it is used because so many substances dissolve in it.

Water that looks clear, clean, and pure may not be. The water you drink every day contains many dissolved substances.

EXPLORE

1. **INFER** A white solid often forms around a tiny leak in a water pipe. Where does the white solid come from?
2. **CHALLENGE** Use the Internet or call your local water company to find out the source of your drinking water. Find out whether you have hard or soft water and what dissolved chemicals are in your drinking water.

RESOURCE CENTER CLASSZONE.COM Learn more about aquifers and water purification.

EXPLORE

1. **INFER** Leaking water evaporates, leaving the solutes.
2. **CHALLENGE** Hard water usually contains relatively high concentrations of calcium, magnesium, or iron. Soft water usually has small quantities of these (and other) elements.

KEY CONCEPT
8.3 Solutions can be acidic, basic, or neutral.

◀ **BEFORE, you learned**
- Substances dissolved in solutions can break apart into ions
- Concentration is the amount of a substance dissolved in a solution
- Water is a common solvent

▶ **NOW, you will learn**
- What acids and bases are
- How to determine if a solution is acidic or basic
- How acids and bases react with each other

VOCABULARY
acid p. 254
base p. 254
pH p. 257
neutral p. 257

EXPLORE Acids and Bases

What happens when an antacid mixes with an acid?

PROCEDURE
 Fill the cup halfway with vinegar.
② Observe the vinegar in the cup. Record your observations.
③ Crush two antacid tablets and place them in the vinegar.
④ Observe the contents of the cup for 5 minutes. Record your observations.

WHAT DO YOU THINK?
- What did you observe before adding the antacid tablets?
- What happened after you added the tablets?

MATERIALS
- clear plastic cup
- vinegar
- 2 antacid tablets

Acids and bases have distinct properties.

Many solutions have certain properties that make us call them acids or bases. Acids are found in many foods, such as orange juice, tomatoes, and vinegar. They taste slightly sour when dissolved in water and produce a burning or itchy feeling on the skin. Strong acids should never be tasted or touched—these solutions are used in manufacturing and are dangerous chemicals.

READING TiP
The prefix *ant-* means "against," so an antacid is a substance that works against an acid.

Bases are the chemical opposite of acids. They tend to taste bitter rather than sour and often feel slippery to the touch. Bases are also found in common products around the home, including soap, ammonia, and antacids. Strong bases, like the lye used for unclogging drains, are also dangerous chemicals.

Chapter 8: **Solutions** 253

RESOURCES FOR DIFFERENTIATED INSTRUCTION

Below Level
UNIT RESOURCE BOOK
- Reading Study Guide A, pp. 224–225
- Decoding Support, p. 247

 **AUDIO CDS**

Advanced
UNIT RESOURCE BOOK
- Challenge and Extension, p. 230
- Challenge Reading, pp. 243–244

English Learners
UNIT RESOURCE BOOK
Spanish Reading Study Guide, pp. 228–229

AUDIO CDS
- Audio Readings in Spanish
- Audio Readings (English)

8.3 FOCUS

◉ **Set Learning Goals**
Students will
- Explain what acids and bases are.
- Determine if a solution is acidic or basic.
- Describe how acids and bases react with each other.

◉ **3-Minute Warm-Up**
Display Transparency 29 or copy this exercise on the board:

Look at the illustration of the dilute solution on p. 246. Draw diagrams that show this solution as more dilute and as more concentrated. *A more dilute solution should have fewer solute particles and the same number of solvent particles, or the same number of solute particles and more solvent particles. A more concentrated solution should have more solute particles and the same number of solvent particles, or the same number of solute particles and fewer solvent particles.*

T 3-Minute Warm-Up, p. T29

8.3 MOTIVATE

EXPLORE Acids and Bases
PURPOSE To observe the chemical reaction between an acid and a base

TIP 10 min. The antacid used must contain a carbonate. Check the label.

WHAT DO YOU THINK? *The vinegar looked like water but had a strong, sour smell. White foamy bubbles appeared and made a fizzing sound. The vinegar odor was not as strong.*

Chapter 8 253

8.3 INSTRUCT

Teach from Visuals

To help students interpret atomic diagrams of an acid and a base dissolving in water, ask:

- What in the diagrams indicates that the acid and base are dissolved in water? *the H₂O shown above the arrows*

- How does the size of a hydrogen ion compare with the size of other ions? *It is the smallest.*

- Why do you think this is so? *Hydrogen has only one electron to begin with. When hydrogen loses its only electron to become a hydrogen ion, it is a bare hydrogen nucleus, or a proton.*

History of Science

The definitions of acids and bases have changed over time. The first generally accepted theory was the Arrhenius model of acids and bases, which states that an acid contains hydrogen and produces hydrogen ions in solution. A base contains a hydroxide group and produces hydroxide ions in solution. Currently, acids and bases are defined by the Brønsted-Lowry theory. This model states that acids are hydrogen-ion donors and bases are hydrogen-ion acceptors. The definitions used in this book are based on the Brønsted-Lowry theory.

Ongoing Assessment

Explain what acids and bases are.

Ask: What happens to the hydrogen and hydroxide ions that are released from acids and bases? *They are free to combine with other substances in the solution.*

 *Answer: Acids donate a proton; bases accept a proton.*

Find out more about acids and bases.

Acids, Bases, and Ions

Generally, a compound that is an acid or a base acts as an acid or a base only when it is dissolved in water. In a water-based solution, these compounds produce ions. Recall that an ion is a charged particle. For example, if a hydrogen atom, which consists of one proton and one electron, loses its electron, it becomes a hydrogen ion. The hydrogen ion is simply a proton and has a positive charge.

An **acid** can be defined as a substance that can donate a hydrogen ion—that is, a proton—to another substance. The diagram below shows what happens when the compound hydrogen chloride (HCl) is dissolved in water. The compound separates into hydrogen ions (H^+) and chloride ions (Cl^-). Hydrogen ions are free to react with other substances, so the solution is an acid. When hydrogen chloride is dissolved in water, the solution is called hydrochloric acid.

READING TIP
The H₂O above the arrow means the substance on the left is added to water and the substances on the right are dissolved in the water.

Acid

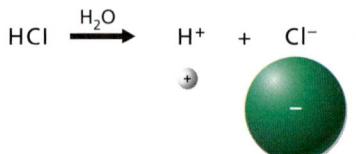

In water, acids release a proton (H^+) into the solution.

A **base** can be defined as a substance that can accept a hydrogen ion from another substance. The diagram below shows what happens when the compound sodium hydroxide (NaOH) is dissolved in water. The compound separates into sodium ions (Na^+) and hydroxide ions (OH^-). The hydroxide ions are free to accept protons from other substances, so the solution is a base. The solution that results when NaOH is dissolved in water is called sodium hydroxide.

Base

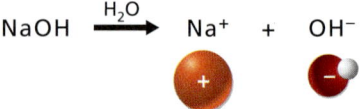

In water, many bases release a hydroxide ion (OH^-), which can accept a proton.

On the atomic level, the difference between acids and bases is that acids donate protons and bases accept protons. When a proton—a hydrogen ion—from an acid is accepted by a hydroxide ion from a base, the two ions join together and form a molecule of water. This simple transfer of protons between substances is involved in a great many useful and important chemical reactions.

CHECK YOUR READING How are protons related to acids and bases?

254 Unit 2: Chemical Interactions

DIFFERENTIATE INSTRUCTION

 **More Reading Support**

A What type of substance can donate a hydrogen ion? *an acid*

B What type of substance can accept a hydrogen ion? *a base*

English Learners The many word forms of *acid* and *base* in this section may confuse English learners. *Acid* and *acidity* are nouns, while *acidic* is an adjective. *Base* and *basicity* are nouns, while *basic* is an adjective. Help English learners use the correct word form when they are writing.

Characteristics of Acids

As you read earlier, acids in foods taste sour and produce a burning or prickling feeling on the skin. However, since tasting or touching an unknown chemical is extremely dangerous, other methods are needed to tell whether a solution is an acid.

One safe way to test for an acid is to place a few drops of a solution on a compound that contains a carbonate (CO_3). For example, limestone is a rock that contains calcium carbonate ($CaCO_3$). When an acid touches a piece of limestone, a reaction occurs that produces carbon dioxide gas.

Acids also react with most metals. The reaction produces hydrogen gas, which you can see as bubbles in the photograph on the right. Such a reaction is characteristic of acids.

The feature of acids most often used to identify them is their ability to change the colors of certain compounds known as acid-base indicators. One common indicator is litmus, which is often prepared on slips of paper. When a drop of an acid is placed on litmus paper, the paper turns red.

Acids react with some metals, such as zinc, and release hydrogen gas.
$2HCl + Zn \rightarrow H_2 + ZnCl_2$

CHECK YOUR READING What are three safe methods to test for an acid?

Characteristics of Bases

Bases also have certain common characteristics. Mild bases in foods taste bitter and feel slippery, but as with acids, tasting and touching are not safe ways of testing whether a solution is a base. In fact, some strong bases can burn the skin as badly as strong acids.

Bases feel soapy or slippery because they react with acidic molecules in your skin called fatty acids. In fact, this is exactly how soap is made. Mixing a base—usually sodium hydroxide—with fatty acids produces soap. So, when a base touches your skin, the combination of the base with your own fatty acids actually makes a small amount of soap.

Like acids, bases change the colors of acid-base indicators, but the colors they produce are different. Bases turn litmus paper blue. A base will counteract the effect that an acid has on an acid-base indicator. You might put a few drops of acid on litmus paper to make it turn red. If you put a few drops of a base on the red litmus paper, the litmus paper will change colors again.

CHECK YOUR READING How do the characteristics of bases differ from those of acids?

Bases are found in many cleaning agents, including soap.

Chapter 8: **Solutions** 255

DIFFERENTIATE INSTRUCTION

More Reading Support

C What happens when an acid reacts with a carbonate or a metal? *It releases a gas.*

D How does a base feel? *slippery or soapy*

Alternative Assessment Have students make a two-column checklist that they can use to identify unknown substances for characteristics of acids and bases.

Acids	Bases

Address Misconceptions

IDENTIFY Ask students what actions they would take if they were to spill a strong base on exposed skin. If they reply that they would need to take no actions or that bases are not harmful, they may hold the misconception that acids are bad and bases are good.

CORRECT Ask students if they think drain or oven cleaners are safe chemicals. Present labels from such products and draw attention to words such as *danger* and *caustic* on them. Explain that *caustic* usually refers to a chemical that is a strong base.

REASSESS Ask students again if a base can be as dangerous as an acid. *It can.* Ask them what information they would put on the label of a product that contained a strong base. *Keep out of reach of children. Warning: can irritate skin.*

Technology Resources
Visit **ClassZone.com** for background on common student misconceptions.
MISCONCEPTION DATABASE

Real World Example

Saponification is the process that makes soap. Fats, which contain fatty acids, react with a strong base such as sodium hydroxide to form glycerol and a soap. Soaps are the sodium salts of fatty acids. They have a polar end and a nonpolar end. The nonpolar end can bond to nonpolar dirt and oils, and the polar end is soluble in water. Dirt can then be rinsed away.

Ongoing Assessment

Determine if a solution is acidic or basic.

Ask: What colors do acids and bases turn litmus paper? *Acids turn litmus paper red; bases turn it blue.*

CHECK YOUR READING Answer: Look for a reaction with a carbonate, a metal, or an indicator such as litmus.

CHECK YOUR READING Answer: Bases taste bitter (not sour, like acids) and feel slippery or soapy. Bases turn litmus blue, rather than red.

Chapter 8 **255**

Teach from Visuals

To help students interpret the molecular depiction of strong and weak acids, ask:

- Are more ions present in the solution of a strong acid or a weak acid? *strong acid*
- Which solution contains intact acid molecules? *the weak acid*
- In which solution are more hydrogen ions available to be donated to other substances? *the strong acid*

Health Connection

Stomach acid, which is mainly HCl, is a strong acid that can seriously burn skin. Why doesn't stomach acid burn the lining of the stomach? The inner surface of the stomach is covered with a protective coating of mucus. If a break develops in this protective coating, the acid begins to burn the cells of the stomach's inner surface, and an ulcer forms. Medical research suggests that acid-resistant bacteria can make holes in the mucus and contribute to ulcer formation.

Develop Critical Thinking

PREDICT Tell students that when ions are present in a solution, the solution can conduct electricity. The more ions present, the stronger the electric current that will be conducted. Ask: What can you predict about the conductivity of a solution containing a weak acid? *The solution does not conduct electricity very well, if at all.*

Art Connection

Hydrofluoric acid (HF) is a weak but extremely dangerous acid that is used to decorate and etch glass. Hydrofluoric acid may be used to give glass a frosted appearance. Designs can be etched in glass by coating the glass with wax and then cutting the pattern to be etched through the wax layer to the glass. The acid will etch the uncovered glass, but will not harm the wax-covered areas.

MIND MAP Remember to use a mind map to take notes about acid and base strength.

The strengths of acids and bases can be measured.

Battery fluid and many juices contain acids. Many people drink some type of juice every morning, but you would not want to drink, or even touch, the liquid in a car battery. Similarly, you probably wash your hands with soap several times a day, but you would not want to touch the liquid used to unclog drains. Both soap and drain cleaners are bases. Clearly, some acids and bases are stronger than others.

Acid and Base Strength

Strong acids break apart completely into ions. For example, when hydrogen chloride (HCl) dissolves in water to form hydrochloric acid, it breaks down into hydrogen ions and chloride ions. No hydrogen chloride remains in the solution. Because all of the hydrogen chloride forms separate ions, hydrochloric acid is a strong acid.

A weak acid does not form many ions in solution. When acetic acid ($HC_2H_3O_2$), which is the acid in vinegar, dissolves in water, only about 1 percent of the acetic acid breaks up into hydrogen ions and acetate ions. The other 99 percent of the acetic acid remains unchanged. Therefore, acetic acid is a weak acid.

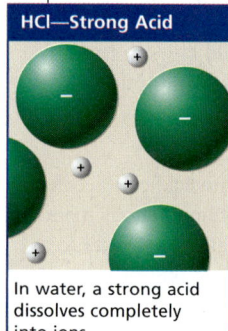
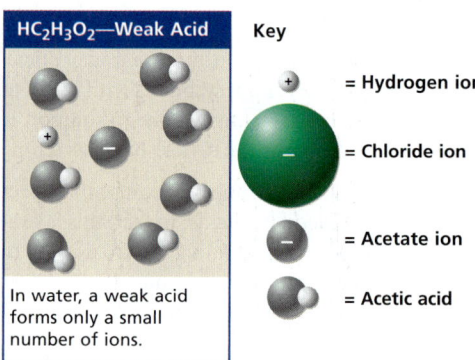

HCl—Strong Acid. In water, a strong acid dissolves completely into ions.

$HC_2H_3O_2$—Weak Acid. In water, a weak acid forms only a small number of ions.

Key:
+ = Hydrogen ion
− = Chloride ion
− = Acetate ion
= Acetic acid

Bases also can be strong or weak. When sodium hydroxide (NaOH) dissolves in water, it forms sodium ions (Na^+) and hydroxide ions (OH^-). None of the original NaOH remains in the solution, so sodium hydroxide is a strong base. However, when ammonia (NH_3) dissolves in water, only about 1 percent of the ammonia reacts with water to form OH^- ions.

$$NH_3 + H_2O \rightarrow NH_4^+ + OH^-$$

The other 99 percent of the ammonia remains unchanged, so ammonia is a weak base. The ions formed when NaOH or NH_3 is dissolved in water are shown on the top of page 257.

DIFFERENTIATE INSTRUCTION

 **More Reading Support**

E What happens to strong acids and bases when they dissolve? *They break apart completely into ions.*

Advanced Students may notice that acid and base molecules, such as HCl or NH_3, are covalent compounds rather than ionic compounds, yet dissociate into ions in solution. These substances are exceptions to the information presented earlier in the chapter. The covalent bond that holds HCl together is very polar, and is intermediate between a covalent bond and an ionic bond.

 Challenge Reading, pp. 243–244

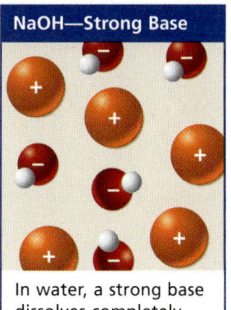

In water, a strong base dissolves completely into ions.

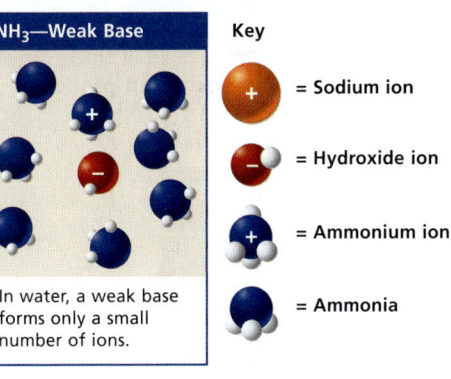

In water, a weak base forms only a small number of ions.

Key
- = Sodium ion
- = Hydroxide ion
- = Ammonium ion
- = Ammonia

READING TiP
Look at the reaction on the bottom of page 256 for help with the illustration of NH_3 in water.

Note that the strength of an acid or base is not the same as its concentration. Dilute hydrochloric acid is still strong and can burn holes in your clothing, whereas acetic acid cannot. The strengths of acids and bases depend on the percentage of the substance that forms ions.

 What determines acid and base strength?

Measuring Acidity

The acidity of a solution depends on the concentration of H^+ ions in the solution. This concentration is often measured on the **pH** scale. In this scale, a high H^+ concentration is indicated by a low number, and a low H^+ concentration is indicated by a high number. The numbers of the pH scale usually range from 0 to 14, but numbers outside this range are possible. The middle number, 7, represents a neutral solution. A **neutral** substance is neither an acid nor a base. Pure water has a pH of 7.

Numbers below 7 indicate acidic solutions. A concentrated strong acid has a low pH value—the pH of concentrated hydrochloric acid, for example, is less than 0. Numbers above 7 indicate a basic solution. A concentrated strong base has a high pH value—the pH of concentrated sodium hydroxide, for example, is greater than 14. The illustration on page 258 shows the pH values of some common acids and bases.

Today, electronic pH meters are commonly used to measure pH. A probe is placed in a solution, and the pH value is indicated by the meter. An older method of measuring pH is to use an acid-base indicator. You read earlier that acids turn litmus paper red and bases turn litmus paper blue. Other acid-base indicators, such as a universal pH indicator, show a variety of colors at different pH values.

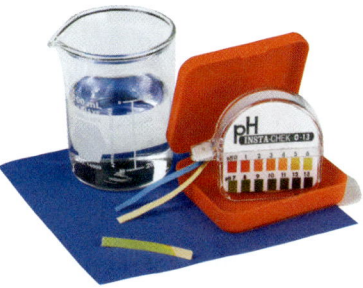

The strip of universal indicator paper in the bottom front of the photograph shows a nearly neutral pH.

 Is the pH of a base higher or lower than the pH of an acid?

Chapter 8: **Solutions** 257

DIFFERENTIATE INSTRUCTION

More Reading Support

F What does the pH scale measure? *concentration of hydrogen ions*

G What does a pH below 7 mean? *The solution is acidic.*

Inclusion Print these formulas on cardboard: HCl, NaOH, NH_3, and $HC_2H_3O_2$. Cut apart the H and Cl and the Na and OH, like jigsaw puzzle pieces. Leave the other two formulas intact. Students with cognitive disabilities will benefit by manipulating the "molecules" and separating the strong acid and base into ions. They will see that the weak acid and base cannot be separated.

Teach from Visuals

To help students interpret the pH chart, ask:

- Would you expect fatty acids to be weak or strong acids? Explain. *Weak; they make milk only slightly acidic.*
- Why is the hydrogen ion concentration equal to the hydroxide ion concentration in pure water? *A water molecule dissociates into one hydrogen ion and one hydroxide ion.*

 This transparency is also available as T30 in the Unit Transparency Book.

Mathematics Connection

The pH scale is based on a negative logarithmic scale that measures the concentration of hydrogen ions. Therefore, a pH of 0 is 1×10^0, or 1.0, while a pH of 14 represents a hydrogen ion concentration of 1×10^{-14}, or 0.00000000000001. Ask students how many times greater the hydrogen ion concentration is if the pH of a solution decreases by one unit, as from a pH of 4 to a pH of 3. *ten times*

Teacher Demo

To make an indicator solution that will identify the pH of substances, place three or four chopped-up, fresh, red cabbage leaves in a plastic bottle and fill the bottle halfway with hot tap water. Screw the top on tightly, and shake for several minutes until the water turns deep purple. Cool to room temperature. Strain the indicator solution, and add water to make a final volume of one liter. Place a small amount of each liquid to be tested in a plastic cup. Fill the cup halfway with indicator solution, and stir. The indicator solution will turn color ranging from cherry red for very acidic solutions through purple (neutral), blue, green, and yellow (strongly basic).

Ongoing Assessment

 Answer: The strong acids are at the low end of the pH scale; the strong bases are at the high end. The hydrogen ion concentration decreases as pH increases.

258 Unit 2: **Chemical Interactions**

Common Acids and Bases

Dilute acids and bases are found in many common products.

low H⁺ concentration

pH 14, 13, 12, 11, 10, 9, 8, 7, 6, 5, 4, 3, 2, 1, pH 0

high H⁺ concentration

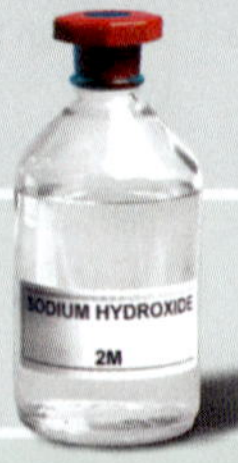

sodium hydroxide (NaOH)—pH > 14
Concentrated NaOH has a pH greater than 14 because it has a very low H⁺ concentration. Drain openers usually contain concentrated NaOH.

milk—pH 6.5
Milk contains molecules called fatty acids, which make milk slightly acidic.

lemon—pH 2
Lemons and other types of citrus fruit contain citric acid.

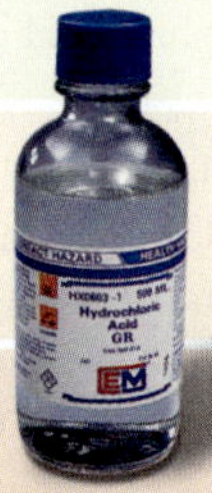

soap—pH 10
Soap is commonly made by mixing fats with NaOH. There is a relatively low concentration of NaOH in soap.

pure water (H₂O)—pH 7
In pure water, the H⁺ concentration is equal to the OH⁻ concentration. Pure water has a pH of 7 and is neutral.

hydrochloric acid (HCl)—pH < 0
Concentrated HCl has a pH lower than 0 because it has a very high H⁺ concentration. HCl is used in many processes, including refining sugar from sugar cane.

READING VISUALS Where are the strong acids on the chart? Where are the strong bases? How does the concentration of hydrogen ions change?

258 Unit 2: **Chemical Interactions**

DIFFERENTIATE INSTRUCTION

Below Level Students who have difficulty reading can give an oral report summarizing the main science concepts represented in the chart. Reports should include the meaning of pH and identification of the nature of substances at various pH points on the chart.

Advanced

 Challenge and Extension, p. 230

Acids and bases neutralize each other.

Acids donate hydrogen ions, and bases accept hydrogen ions. Therefore, it is not surprising that acids and bases react when they come into contact with each other. Recall that when a hydrogen ion (H^+) from an acid collides with a hydroxide ion (OH^-) from a base, the two ions join to form a molecule of water (H_2O).

The negative ion of an acid (Cl^-) joins with the positive ion of a base (Na^+) to form a substance called a salt. Since both the salt and water are neutral, an acid-base reaction is called a neutralization (NOO-truh-lih-ZAY-shuhn) reaction. The reactants are an acid and a base, and the products are a salt and water.

READING TIP
The salt produced by a neutralization reaction is not necessarily table salt.

A common example of a neutralization reaction occurs when you swallow an antacid tablet to relieve an upset stomach. The acid in your stomach has a pH of about 1.5, due mostly to hydrochloric acid produced by the stomach lining. If your stomach produces more acid than is needed, you may feel a burning sensation. An antacid tablet contains a base, such as sodium bicarbonate, magnesium hydroxide, or calcium carbonate. The base reacts with the stomach acid and produces a salt and water. This reaction lowers the acidity—and raises the pH—to its normal value.

Acid rain forms when certain gases in the atmosphere dissolve in water vapor, forming acidic solutions. During rainstorms these acids fall to Earth. They can harm forests by making soil acidic and harm aquatic life by making lakes acidic. Acid rain can also dissolve marble and limestone in buildings and statues, because both marble and limestone contain calcium carbonate, which is a base.

 How is neutralization an example of a chemical reaction?

8.3 Review

KEY CONCEPTS
1. Use the concept of ions to explain the difference between an acid and a base.
2. How do the properties of an acid differ from the properties of a base?
3. What happens when an acid and a base react with each other?

CRITICAL THINKING
4. **Infer** When an acid reacts with a metal, such as zinc, what is released? Where does that product come from?
5. **Infer** Suppose that you have 1 L of an acid solution with a pH of 2. You add 1 L of pure water. What happens to the pH of the solution? Explain.

CHALLENGE
6. **Synthesize** Suppose that equal amounts of solutions of HCl and NaOH with the same concentration are mixed together. What will the pH of the new solution be? What are the products of this reaction?

Chapter 8: **Solutions** 259

ANSWERS

1. An acid is a substance that can give up a proton (a hydrogen ion). A base is a substance that can accept a proton.
2. taste, feel, reactions with metals and carbonates, color change in indicators
3. A neutralization reaction occurs, forming a salt and water.
4. Hydrogen gas is released; it comes from the acid.
5. Adding water dilutes the solution. The concentration of hydrogen ions decreases, so the pH goes up.
6. The pH will move toward 7 (neutral). The products are water and table salt (NaCl).

CHAPTER INVESTIGATION

Focus

PURPOSE To test and classify common substances as acidic or basic

OVERVIEW Students will test various household substances to determine whether they are acidic or basic. Students should find that:

- fruit juice, soda water, and vinegar are acidic
- baking soda, shampoo, and detergent powder are basic
- table salt is neutral

Lab Preparation

- Remind students to measure to the bottom of the meniscus in the graduated cylinder.
- Use a shampoo that is not deeply colored. The color could interfere with the testing. Not all shampoos are basic.
- Prior to the investigation, have students read through the investigation and prepare their data tables. Or you may wish to copy and distribute datasheets and rubrics.

 UNIT RESOURCE BOOK, pp. 250–258

 SCIENCE TOOLKIT, F15

Lab Management

- This lab cannot use litmus paper; it requires universal indicator paper that detects a wide pH range.
- Clear film canisters can be used in place of plastic cups.
- You could divide the class into seven groups, with each group testing a different substance.

Teaching with Technology

Students can use a probeware system with a pH probe to measure the pH of the substances.

CHAPTER INVESTIGATION

Acids and Bases

OVERVIEW AND PURPOSE Acids and bases are very common. For example, the limestone formations in the cave shown on the left are made of a substance that is a base when it is dissolved in water. In this activity you will use what you have learned about solutions, acids, and bases to

- test various household substances and place them in categories according to their pH values
- investigate the properties of common acids and bases

Procedure

1. Make a data table like the one shown on the sample notebook page.

2. Set out 7 cups in your work area. Collect the substances that you will be testing: baking soda, fruit juice, shampoo, soda water, table salt, laundry detergent, and vinegar.

3. Label each cup. Be sure to wear goggles when pouring the substances that you will be testing. Pour 30 mL of each liquid substance into a separate cup. Dissolve 1 tsp of each solid substance in 30 mL of distilled water in a separate cup. To avoid contaminating the test solutions, wash and dry your measuring tools and hands between measurements.

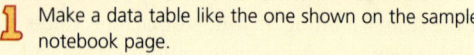 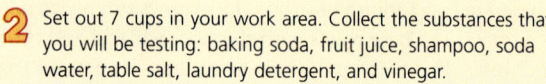

MATERIALS
- plastic cups
- baking soda
- fruit juice
- shampoo
- soda water
- table salt
- detergent powder
- vinegar
- masking tape
- marking pen
- measuring spoons
- graduated cylinder
- distilled water
- paper towels
- pH indicator paper

260 Unit 2: Chemical Interactions

INVESTIGATION RESOURCES

 CHAPTER INVESTIGATION, Acids and Bases
- Level A, pp. 250–253
- Level B, pp. 254–257
- Level C, p. 258

Advanced students should complete Levels B & C.

 Writing a Lab Report, D12–13

Technology Resources

Customize this student lab as needed or look for an alternative. Print rubrics to assess student lab reports.

 Lab Generator CD-ROM

4. Dip a piece of indicator paper into each solution. Compare the color of the test strip with the colors in the chart included in the package. Record the indicator color and the approximate pH number for each solution.

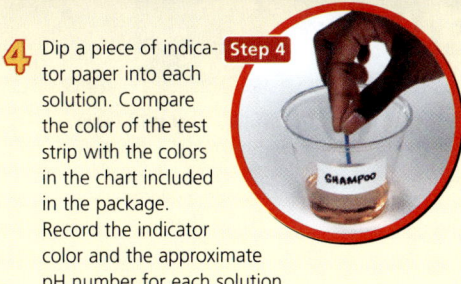
Step 4

5. After you have tested all of the solutions, arrange the cups in order of their pH values.

Observe and Analyze *Write It Up*

1. **RECORD DATA** Check to be sure that your data table is complete.
2. **ANALYZE DATA** What color range did the substances show when tested with the indicator paper? What do your results tell you about the pH of each substance you tested?
3. **CLASSIFY** Look for patterns in the pH values. Use your test results to place each household substance in one of three groups—acids, bases, or neutral.
4. **MODEL** Draw a diagram of the pH scale from 0 to 14. Use arrows and labels to show where the substances you tested fall on this scale.

Conclude *Write It Up*

1. **GENERALIZE** What general conclusions can you draw about the hydrogen ion concentration in many acids and bases found in the home? Are the hydrogen ion concentrations very high or very low? How do you know?
2. **EVALUATE** What limitations or difficulties did you experience in interpreting the results of your tests or other observations?
3. **APPLY** Antacid tablets react with stomach acid containing hydrochloric acid. What is this type of reaction called? What are the products of this type of reaction?

INVESTIGATE Further

CHALLENGE Repeat the experiment, changing one variable. You might change the concentrations of the solutions you are testing or see what happens when you mix an acidic solution with a basic solution. Get your teacher's approval of your plan before proceeding. How does changing one particular variable affect the pH of the solutions?

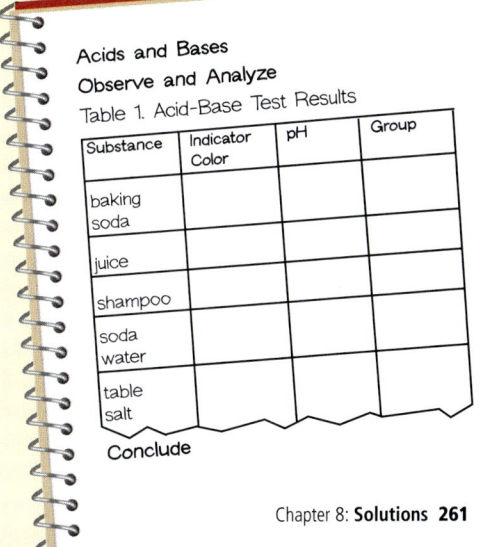

Acids and Bases
Observe and Analyze
Table 1. Acid-Base Test Results

Substance	Indicator Color	pH	Group
baking soda			
juice			
shampoo			
soda water			
table salt			

Conclude

Chapter 8: **Solutions** 261

Observe and Analyze *Write It Up*

1. Sample data: baking soda, pH 8; detergent powder, pH 10; fruit juice, pH 4; shampoo, pH 5; soda water, pH 5; table salt, pH 7; vinegar, pH 2
2. The range of indicator colors and pH should vary between relatively weak acids and relatively weak bases.
3. The placement of substances on the pH scale will vary with observations and the particular products tested. Baking soda, detergents, and some shampoos are basic. Soda water, vinegar, fruit juices, and some shampoos are acidic. Table salt (dissolved in distilled water) should be neutral.
4. See students' diagrams, which should properly place their test results on a pH scale.

Conclude *Write It Up*

1. In general, the hydrogen ion concentrations of many household products is neither very high nor very low. They are often in a middle range, between a pH of 2 and a pH of 12 as indicated by the sample of substances tested.
2. Answers will vary, but may indicate pH tests that do not correspond exactly to the color standards.
3. A neutralization reaction; water and a salt

INVESTIGATE Further

CHALLENGE Changing the concentrations changes the pH slightly but does not make an acidic substance basic, or vice versa.

Post-Lab Discussion

- Ask: Why might it be important to test the pH of the distilled water used to dissolve the solids? *If the pH of the water is not neutral, it will affect the pH of the solution being tested.*
- Discuss why it is important for manufacturers and water-treatment plants to regulate the pH of their products. Lead the discussion to include the dangers of extreme pH to plants and animals.

Chapter 8 **261**

8.4 FOCUS

◉ Set Learning Goals

Students will
- Describe how metal alloys are made.
- Identify how a variety of alloys are used in modern society.
- Explain why different alloys have different uses.
- Differentiate between a pure metal and its alloy by observing their properties in an experiment.

◉ 3-Minute Warm-Up

Display Transparency 29 or copy this exercise on the board:

Match the definition to the correct term.

Definitions

1. amount of a substance that will dissolve in a certain amount of solvent at a certain temperature **e**
2. describes a solution that can hold no more of a solute at a particular temperature **b**
3. amount of dissolved solute in a solution **a**

Terms

a. concentration   d. solution
b. saturated   e. solubility
c. dilute

 3-Minute Warm-Up, p. T29

8.4 MOTIVATE

THINK ABOUT

PURPOSE To examine why mixing metals might be desirable

DISCUSS Brainstorm possible reasons why goldsmiths might want to add other metals to pure gold. *to make the gold harder and more durable, to change its color*

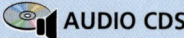 *Answer: by melting and mixing the metals, then waiting for the alloy to cool and solidify*

262 Unit 2: Chemical Interactions

KEY CONCEPT

8.4 Metal alloys are solid mixtures.

◀ **BEFORE, you learned**
- A solution can be a solid
- Solutes change the properties of solvents
- The concentration of a solution can vary

▶ **NOW, you will learn**
- How metal alloys are made
- How a variety of alloys are used in modern society
- Why different alloys have different uses

VOCABULARY
alloy p. 262

THINK ABOUT

If gold jewelry is not pure gold, what is it?

People have prized gold since ancient times—archaeologists have found gold jewelry that was made thousands of years ago. Gold is a very soft metal, and jewelry made of pure gold bends very easily. Today, most gold jewelry is about 75 percent gold and 25 percent other metals. Why might these metals be mixed in?

VOCABULARY
Remember to use the strategy of your choice. You might use a description wheel diagram for *alloy*.

Humans have made alloys for thousands of years.

The gold used in jewelry is an example of an alloy. An **alloy** is a mixture of a metal and one or more other elements, usually metals as well. The gold alloys used in jewelry contain silver and copper in various amounts.

Many alloys are made by melting the metals and mixing them in the liquid state to form a solution. For example, bronze is made by melting and mixing copper and tin and then letting the solution cool. Bronze is not difficult to make, because both copper and tin melt at relatively low temperatures. Bronze was probably the first alloy made in ancient times—historians say it was discovered about 3800 B.C.

 How is an alloy usually made?

262 Unit 2: Chemical Interactions

RESOURCES FOR DIFFERENTIATED INSTRUCTION

Below Level
UNIT RESOURCE BOOK
- Reading Study Guide A, pp. 234–235
- Decoding Support, p. 247

🎵 **AUDIO CDS**

Advanced
UNIT RESOURCE BOOK
Challenge and Extension, p. 240

English Learners
UNIT RESOURCE BOOK
Spanish Reading Study Guide, pp. 238–239

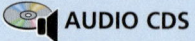 **AUDIO CDS**

- Audio Readings in Spanish
- Audio Readings (English)

Recall that the addition of a solute changes the properties of a solvent. The alloy bronze is harder than either copper or tin alone. This hardness made bronze a better material than stones or animal bones for making tools. The transition from the Stone Age to the Bronze Age, when humans first began to use metals, was an important period in human history.

Even though alloys have been made for thousands of years, new alloys with new properties are still being developed. One alloy with a very interesting property is nitinol, which is made of nickel and titanium. Nitinol is called a memory alloy because it can be given a particular shape and then reshaped. What makes nitinol unusual is that it will return to its original shape after being heated. Because of this property, nitinol is used in several common products, including eyeglass frames.

A short list of useful alloys is given in the table below. The percentages shown in the table are those for only one type of each alloy.

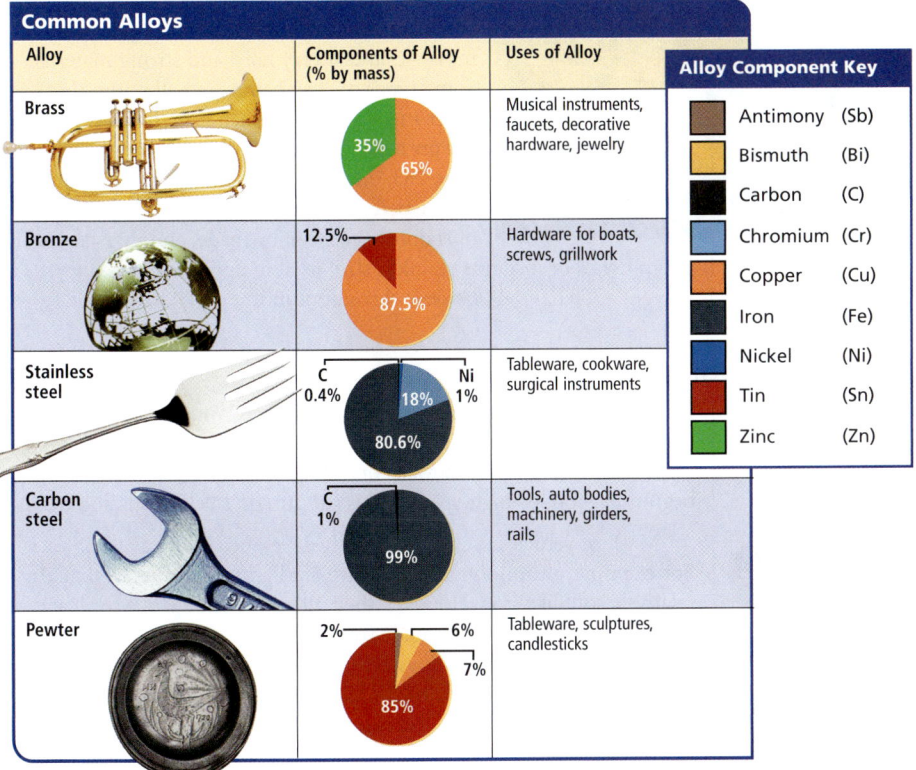

READING VISUALS How are brass and bronze different from each other? How are stainless steel and carbon steel different from each other?

Chapter 8: **Solutions** 263

History of Science

Sir Henry Bessemer developed the method of making steel by blasting compressed air through molten iron. The oxygen in the air combines with excess carbon and other impurities to form oxides. The heat generated by this process raises the temperature and keeps the mass of iron molten. Large batches of steel can be made in this way. The Bessemer process has been replaced by even more efficient methods in most of the industrialized world.

Develop Critical Thinking

ANALYZE Discuss qualities of an alloy that would be useful in an airplane engine. *lightweight, heat resistance, freedom from rust, high strength*
Ask: Would steel be the best alloy to use in an airplane engine? *No; it is not lightweight, and it will rust.* What alloys would be better to use? *aluminum, titanium, because they are lighter*

Ongoing Assessment

Explain why different alloys have different uses.
Ask: Why would an alloy used for a racing bicycle be unsuitable for the framework of a building? *Racing bikes must be lightweight for maximum speed. The steel used in the framework of buildings must be strong; weight is not important.*

 Answer: Steel is used in ships and railroads. Aluminum alloys are used in aircraft, high-speed ferries, and cars. Titanium alloys are also used in aircraft.

Alloys have many uses in modern life.

Explore alloys and their uses.

The advances in materials science that began with bronze almost 6000 years ago continue today. Modern industry uses many different alloys. Some alloys, based on lightweight metals such as aluminum and titanium, are relatively recent developments. However, the most important alloy used today—steel—has been around for many years.

A major advance in technology occurred in the 1850s with the development of the Bessemer process. This process made it possible to manufacture large amounts of steel in a short time. Until then, steel could be made only in batches of less than 100 pounds. The Bessemer process made it possible to produce up to 30 tons of steel in about 20 minutes. Since it began to be mass-produced, steel has been used in everything from bridges to cars to spoons.

Steel is the main material used in the structure of this sphere at Epcot Center in Florida.

Most steel used in construction is an alloy of iron and carbon. Iron is too soft to be a good building material by itself, but adding only a small amount of carbon—about 1 percent by mass—makes a very hard and strong material. Some types of steel contain small amounts of other metals as well, which give the alloys different properties. As you can see on the chart on page 263, one type of stainless steel contains only 1 percent nickel. However, different types of stainless steel can be made, and they have different uses. For instance, stainless steel used in appliances has 8 to 10 percent nickel and 18 percent chromium in it.

Alloys in Transportation

Different forms of transportation rely on steel. Wooden sailing ships were replaced by steel ships in the late 1800s. Today, steel cargo ships carry steel containers. Railroads depended on steel from their very beginning. Today's high-speed trains still run on steel wheels and tracks.

Modern vehicles use more recently developed alloys as well. For example, aluminum and titanium are lightweight metals that are relatively soft, like iron. However, their alloys are strong, like steel, and light. Airplane engines are made from aluminum alloys, and both aluminum and titanium alloys are used in aircraft bodies. Aluminum alloys are also commonly used in high-speed passenger ferries and in the bodies of cars. Because the alloys are light, they help to improve the fuel efficiency of these vehicles.

 How are alloys used in transportation?

264 Unit 2: Chemical Interactions

DIFFERENTIATE INSTRUCTION

 More Reading Support
B What is the most important alloy used today? *steel*
C What makes aluminum alloys useful? *They are strong and light.*

Advanced Have students research the economic advantages of using aluminum alloys in automobiles. Have them make a table comparing the properties of the structural materials used in cars.

R Challenge and Extension, p. 240

Alloys in Medicine

You may have noticed that most medical equipment is shiny and silver-colored. This equipment is made of stainless steel, which contains nickel and chromium in addition to iron and carbon. Surgical instruments are often made of stainless steel because it can be honed to a very sharp edge and is also rust resistant.

Cobalt and titanium alloys are also widely used in medicine because they do not easily react with substances in the body, such as blood and digestive juices. These alloys can be surgically placed inside the body with a minimum of harm to either the body or the metal. The photographs on the right show one use of alloys—making artificial joints.

Memory alloys similar to the nitinol alloy described earlier also have a wide range of medical uses. These alloys are used in braces for teeth, and as implants that hold open blocked arteries or correct a curve in the spine. Medical devices made of memory alloys can be made in a particular shape and then reshaped for implantation. After the device is in place, the person's body heat causes it to return to its original shape.

 What properties make alloys useful in medicine?

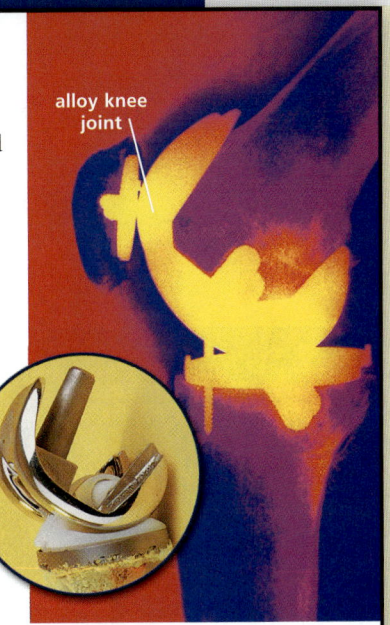

alloy knee joint

Artificial knee joints are often made of a titanium alloy. The x-ray image shows the device in place.

INVESTIGATE Alloys

How is a pure metal different from its alloy?

PROCEDURE

1. Examine the iron nails and the alloy (steel or stainless steel) nails. Record your observations.
2. Find and record the mass of the three iron nails. Repeat with the three alloy nails.
3. Find the volume of the nails by displacement, as follows: Into the empty graduated cylinder, pour water to a height that is higher than the nails are long. Note the water level. Add the iron nails and record the change in water level. Repeat this step with the alloy nails.
4. Calculate the density of each type of nail. $\text{Density} = \frac{\text{mass}}{\text{Volume}}$

WHAT DO YOU THINK?
- Compare your observations of the metals contained in the nails.
- Which metal has the greater density? How might a metal's density be important in how it is used?

CHALLENGE How can you identify different alloys of a metal?

SKILL FOCUS
Observing

MATERIALS
- 3 iron nails
- 3 steel nails or 3 stainless steel nails
- balance
- graduated cylinder
- water

TIME
30 minutes

Chapter 8: Solutions 265

DIFFERENTIATE INSTRUCTION

More Reading Support

D What are surgical instruments usually made of? <u>stainless steel</u>

Below Level Students may have a difficult time understanding why volume can be determined by measuring water displacement. Remind them that when a solid object is immersed in water, it displaces the same amount of water that it occupies as a solid object, its volume.

INVESTIGATE Alloys

PURPOSE To differentiate between a pure metal and its alloy by observing their properties

TIPS 30 min.
- To save time, each student group should examine two of the three types of nails. The groups should combine their data so all students will have data for all three metals.
- The nails must be completely submerged in water.

WHAT DO YOU THINK? *Iron has the dullest color, steel is shinier, and stainless steel is the shiniest. Steel has the highest density, and it has many structural uses.*

CHALLENGE *by their physical and chemical properties*

 Datasheet, Alloys, p. 241

Technology Resources

Customize this student lab as needed or look for an alternative. Print rubrics to assess student lab reports.

Lab Generator CD-ROM

Teaching with Technology

If a spreadsheet program is available, students can use it to record their data and do the calculations.

Metacognitive Strategy

Have students write a short paragraph examining whether their measuring techniques were precise enough to calculate accurate densities. If they could repeat the experiment, how would they improve their techniques?

Ongoing Assessment

CHECK YOUR READING Answer: *Stainless steel is used in surgery because it can be sharpened and is rust-resistant. Cobalt and titanium alloys are implanted because they do not easily react with substances in the body. Memory alloys are used in braces and implants.*

Ongoing Assessment

 Answer: New alloys can be developed in microgravity, which cannot be done on Earth.

Reinforce

Have students relate the section to the Big Idea.

 Reinforcing Key Concepts, p. 242

8.4 ASSESS & RETEACH

Assess

 Section 8.4 Quiz, p. 64

Reteach

Ask students to write a short paragraph explaining why this lesson on alloys is included in a chapter on solutions. *Alloys are solid mixtures that have many of the properties of solutions. One metal is dissolved in another metal, and the properties of the alloy differ from the properties of the components in the alloy.*

Technology Resources

Have students visit ClassZone.com for reteaching of Key Concepts.

- CONTENT REVIEW
- CONTENT REVIEW CD-ROM

Alloys in Space Flight

The aerospace industry develops and uses some of the newest and most advanced alloys. The same qualities that make titanium and aluminum alloys useful in airplanes—lightness, strength, and heat resistance—also make them useful in spacecraft. Titanium alloys were used in the Gemini space program of the 1960s. Large portions of the wings of today's space shuttle are made of aluminum alloys.

For more than 20 years, the heat shield on the shuttle's belly has been made from ceramic tiles. However, engineers have experimented with a titanium heat shield as well.

Construction of the International Space Station, which is shown in the photograph on the left, began in 1998. Alloys are a major part of the space station's structure. More important, research on the space station may lead to the development of new alloys.

Research on the International Space Station may lead to the development of new alloys.

One of the goals of research on the space station is to make alloys in a microgravity environment, which cannot be done on Earth. For example, astronauts have experimented with thick liquids, made with iron, that harden or change shape when a magnet is placed nearby, and then return to their previous shapes when the magnet is removed. These liquid alloys may be useful in robots or in artificial organs for humans.

 Why is research into new alloys on the International Space Station important?

8.4 Review

KEY CONCEPTS

1. How can one metal be made to dissolve in another metal?
2. Name three metal alloys and a use for each one.
3. Why are alloys of cobalt or titanium, instead of pure iron, used for medical devices that are implanted inside people?

CRITICAL THINKING

4. **Infer** In industry, all titanium alloys are simply called titanium. What might this tell you about the use of pure titanium?
5. **Compare and Contrast** How are modern alloys similar to alloys made hundreds or thousands of years ago? How are they different?

CHALLENGE

6. **Synthesize** The melting point of copper is 1083°C. Tin is dissolved in copper to make bronze. Will bronze have a melting point of 1083°C? Why or why not?

266 Unit 2: Chemical Interactions

ANSWERS

1. by melting both, mixing the two together, and cooling the solution into a solid
2. Sample answer: Stainless steel: medical equipment; Aluminum alloys: airplane engines; Titanium alloys: artificial joints
3. The alloys do not react with substances within the body, and they are light but strong.
4. It is not used.
5. Making an alloy still involves melting and mixing different substances. Modern alloys use more complex mixtures, with carefully measured amounts of materials for specific purposes.
6. No; adding a solute changes the properties of a solvent, so copper and bronze will not have the same melting point.

MATH in SCIENCE

SKILL: CALCULATING PERCENTAGES

The Mixtures in Alloys

An alloy is a mixture of a metal with other substances. Because even a small change in the percentages of materials in an alloy can change its properties, alloys are made according to strict specifications. For example, steel is an alloy of iron and carbon. Steel that contains 0.6 percent carbon by mass is used in steel beams, whereas steel that contains 1.0 percent carbon by mass, which makes the steel harder, is used to make tools and springs. How can the percentages of materials in an alloy be calculated?

Example

Calculate the percentage of nickel in an alloy if a small portion of the alloy has 10 atoms, 3 of which are nickel.

(1) Convert the number of atoms into a fraction.

3 of 10 atoms in the alloy are nickel = $\frac{3}{10}$

(2) To calculate a percentage, first find an equivalent fraction that has a denominator of 100. Use x as the numerator.

$\frac{3}{10} = \frac{x}{100}$

(3) Convert the fraction into a percentage by using cross products

$3 \cdot 100 = 10 \cdot x$

$300 = 10x$

$30 = x$

ANSWER The percentage of nickel atoms in the alloy is 30%.

Answer the following questions.

1. A sample of an alloy contains 4 iron atoms, 3 zinc atoms, 2 aluminum atoms, and 1 copper atom.
   a. What percentage of the alloy is aluminum by number of atoms?
   b. What percentage is zinc by number of atoms?

2. A sample of an alloy contains 12 titanium atoms, 4 niobium atoms, and 4 aluminum atoms.
   a. What percentage of the alloy is titanium by number of atoms?
   b. What percentage is niobium by number of atoms?

CHALLENGE Suppose there is an alloy in which 2 of every 3 atoms are silver atoms, 1 of every 4 atoms is a copper atom, and 1 of every 12 atoms is a tin atom. What are the percentages of each metal in the alloy by number of atoms?

Chapter 8: **Solutions** 267

Click on Math Tutorial for more help understanding percents.

The steel in girders like these contains iron and 0.6 percent carbon by mass.

ANSWERS

1a. 2/10 = x/100; 10x = 200; x = 20%
1b. 3/10 = x/100; 10x = 300; x = 30%
2a. 12/20 = x/100; 20x = 1200; x = 60%
2b. 4/20 = x/100; 20x = 400; x = 20%
CHALLENGE 2/3 = x/100; 3x = 200; x = 66.67; 67% silver,
1/4 = x/100; 4x = 100; x = 25; 25% copper,
1/12 = x/100; 12x = 100; x = 8.33; 8% tin

MATH IN SCIENCE
Math Skills Practice for Science

Set Learning Goal
To calculate the percentage of a metal in an alloy

Present the Science
Steel contains materials other than carbon and iron. The steel-making process introduces traces of various elements. Some metals are deliberately added. For example, adding more than 10.5% of chromium creates stainless steel. Typically, when percentages of components of an alloy are given, the percentage is in terms of mass, not the number of atoms. So, if an alloy contains 10.5% chromium, it means that 10.5% of the alloy's mass is from chromium, not that 10.5% of the atoms are chromium atoms.

Develop Algebra Skills
- Point out that whenever you look for a percentage, one side of the cross-products equation will be x over 100.
- Ask: If you knew that 4 percent of the atoms in the sample of an alloy were zinc and wanted to find out how many atoms of zinc would be in 50 atoms of alloy, what would your cross product look like? *x/50 = 4/100*

DIFFERENTIATION TIP Students may find it helpful to represent atoms in different-colored disks or other distinctive small objects to model the word problems.

Close
Ask students to think of other situations where cross products would be useful. *everyday situations such as scaling a recipe up or down, calculating percentages of other types of mixtures*

 • Math Support, p. 248
• Math Practice, p. 249

Technology Resources
Students can visit **ClassZone.com** for practice in understanding percents.

 MATH TUTORIAL

Chapter 8 **267**

CHAPTER 8 • REVIEW

BACK TO

Give students the following list of properties and ask them to pick out any properties of a solvent that do not change when a solute dissolves in the solvent: density, boiling point, freezing point, chemical reactivity, physical state. *Dissolving is a physical process that changes only the physical properties of a solvent. All properties listed are physical properties except chemical reactivity, which does not change.*

KEY CONCEPTS SUMMARY

SECTION 8.1
Ask: What is happening in the diagram? *An ionic solute breaks up in a solvent to form individual ions. Solvent molecules surround each ion.*

SECTION 8.2
Ask: Explain why some solutes cannot form a concentrated solution. *If a solute is only slightly soluble in a solvent, not enough of the solute will dissolve to form a concentrated solution.*

SECTION 8.3
Ask: What is the relationship between hydrogen ions and whether a substance is an acid or a base? *An acid donates hydrogen ions; a base (through, for example, a hydroxide ion) can accept hydrogen ions.*

SECTION 8.4
Ask: What structures in the photograph are most likely made of alloys? *the sphere, the monorail cars, and the tracks*

Review Concepts

- Big Idea Flow Chart, p. T25
- Chapter Outline, pp. T31–T32

---

8 Chapter Review

the BIG idea
When substances dissolve to form a solution, the properties of the mixture change.

 CONTENT REVIEW
CLASSZONE.COM

KEY CONCEPTS SUMMARY

1 A solution is a type of mixture.
- A solution is a mixture in which one or more solutes are dissolved in a solvent.
- A solution is a homogeneous mixture.

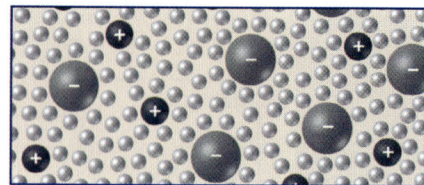
Ionic compound dissolved in solvent

VOCABULARY
solution p. 239
solute p. 240
solvent p. 240
suspension p. 241

2 The amount of solute that dissolves can vary.
- The amount of dissolved solute determines a solution's concentration.
- The more soluble a substance is, the more of it will dissolve in a solution.

Dilute   Concentrated

VOCABULARY
concentration p. 245
dilute p. 246
saturated p. 246
solubility p. 247

3 Solutions can be acidic, basic, or neutral.
- Acids donate protons (H+) in solutions, and bases accept protons in solutions.
- Acidity is measured by the H+ concentration on the pH scale.

Acid   HCl $\xrightarrow{H_2O}$ H$^+$ + Cl$^-$

Base   NaOH $\xrightarrow{H_2O}$ Na$^+$ + OH$^-$

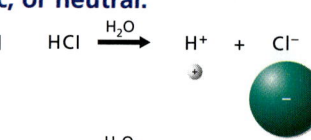

VOCABULARY
acid p. 254
base p. 254
pH p. 257
neutral p. 257

4 Metal alloys are solid mixtures.
- Many of the metals used in modern transportation and medicine are alloys.
- The properties of a metal can be changed by adding one or more substances to produce a more useful material.

VOCABULARY
alloy p. 262

Technology Resources

Have students visit **ClassZone.com** or use the CD-ROM for a cumulative review of concepts.

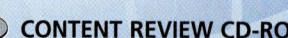 CONTENT REVIEW

CONTENT REVIEW CD-ROM

Engage students in a whole-class interactive review of Key Concepts. Edit content as you wish.

 POWER PRESENTATIONS

Reviewing Vocabulary

Draw a diagram similar to the example shown below to connect and organize the concepts of related vocabulary terms. After you have completed your diagram, explain in two or three sentences why you organized the terms in that way. Underline each of the terms in your explanation.

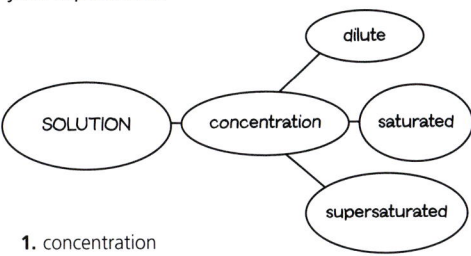

1. concentration
2. acid
3. base
4. neutral
5. pH

Latin Roots Several of the vocabulary terms in this chapter come from the Latin word *solvere*, which means "to loosen." Describe how each of the following terms is related to the Latin word.

6. solution
7. solute
8. solvent
9. solubility

Reviewing Key Concepts

Multiple Choice *Choose the letter of the best answer.*

10. What makes a solution different from other types of mixtures?
    a. Its parts can be separated.
    b. It is the same throughout.
    c. Its parts can be seen.
    d. It is a liquid.

11. When a solute is dissolved in a solvent, the solvent's
    a. boiling point decreases
    b. boiling point decreases and its freezing point increases
    c. freezing point increases
    d. freezing point decreases and its boiling point increases

12. When a compound held together by ionic bonds dissolves, the compound
    a. releases molecules into the solution
    b. forms a suspension
    c. releases ions into the solution
    d. becomes nonpolar

13. Water is called the universal solvent because it
    a. dissolves many substances
    b. dissolves very dense substances
    c. has no charged regions
    d. is nonpolar

14. How does an increase in temperature affect the solubility of solids and gases?
    a. It increases solubility of most solids and decreases the solubility of gases.
    b. It decreases solubility of most solids and gases.
    c. It increases solubility of gases and decreases the solubility of most solids.
    d. It increases solubility of both solids and gases.

15. A solution with a very high H^+ concentration has a
    a. very high pH   c. pH close to 5
    b. very low pH   d. pH close to 7

16. Why are oils insoluble in water?
    a. They are acids.   c. They are bases.
    b. They are polar.   d. They are nonpolar.

Short Answer *Write a short answer to each question.*

17. Describe the reaction that occurs when a strong acid reacts with a strong base.

18. How might an alloy be changed for different uses? Explain.

Chapter 8: **Solutions** 269

Reviewing Vocabulary

1–5. Answers should indicate that concentration is the amount of solute dissolved. Answers should indicate differences between acids, bases, and neutral solutions in pH, and that the three are closely related due to hydrogen-ion concentrations in the different solutions.

6. A solution is a mixture of substances whose bonds have been "loosened."

7. A solute is the substance that is "loosened," or dispersed, in the solvent.

8. A solvent is the substance that "loosens," or disperses, the solute.

9. Solubility is the degree to which a solute can be "loosened," or dissolved, by a given amount of a particular solvent.

Reviewing Key Concepts

10. b
11. d
12. c
13. a
14. a
15. b
16. d

17. The hydrogen ion of the acid combines with the hydroxide ion of the base to form water. The negative ion of the acid combines with the positive ion of the base to form a neutral salt. The resulting solution's pH is close to 7 if equal amounts of acid and base react.

18. Different substances, or differing concentrations of substances, can be mixed with the primary metal in the alloy to make a new alloy with different properties. Examples include differing carbon concentrations in steel for different applications.

ASSESSMENT RESOURCES

UNIT ASSESSMENT BOOK
- Chapter Test A, pp. 65–68
- Chapter Test B, pp. 69–72
- Chapter Test C, pp. 73–76
- Alternative Assessment, 77–78

SPANISH ASSESSMENT BOOK
Spanish Chapter Test, pp. 245–248

Technology Resources

Edit test items and answer choices.

 Test Generator CD-ROM

Visit **ClassZone.com** to extend test practice.

 Test Practice

Chapter 8 **269**

Thinking Critically

19. Acids: strips A & D; Bases: strips B & C

20. strip D; because the litmus paper is dark red, which indicates the lowest pH

21. The acid and the base would neutralize each other, and form a salt and water.

22. It will be orange; the base on strip C is not concentrated, so it will not neutralize all of the strong acid on strip D.

23. As the solution cooled, the solubility of the solute decreased. Some of it fell out of the solution onto the bottom of the beaker.

24. No; iron is relatively soft. It would not have the strength to support a bridge.

25. The properties depend on the amount of the solute. Bronze has different melting points, depending on the amount of tin in the alloy. Gold alloys differ in hardness depending on the amount of other metals dissolved in the gold.

Using Math Skills in Science

26. It increases; it decreases

27. 23 g; 63 g

28. A solid; solubility of a gas decreases as the temperature increases.

the BIG idea

29. Answers will vary.

30. Both dissolve in water. Table salt forms separate sodium and chloride ions, while sugar forms individual sugar molecules. Both will decrease freezing point and increase boiling point because the change in these properties depends on the amount of the substance that is dissolved rather than the identity of the substance that is dissolved.

UNIT PROJECTS

Students should have begun designing their models or presentations by this time. Encourage them to try different solutions to the problems they encounter.

 Unit Projects, pp. 5–10

Thinking Critically

The illustration below shows the results of pH tests of four different solutions. Assume the solutions are made with strong acids or strong bases. Use the diagram to answer the next four questions.

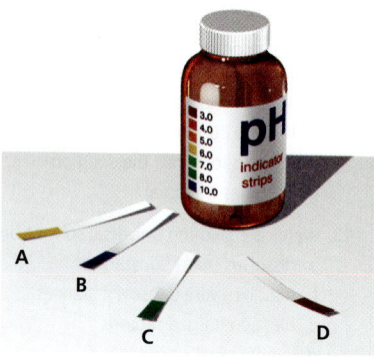

19. **OBSERVE** Which of the indicator strips show an acidic solution? Which show a basic solution?

20. **INFER** Which strip of indicator paper detected the highest concentration of H^+ ions? How do you know?

21. **PREDICT** What would happen if you mixed together equal amounts of the solutions that produced the results of strip B and strip D?

22. **INFER** Suppose you mix together equal amounts of the solutions that produced the results of strip C and strip D, then test the pH of this new solution. What color will the indicator paper be? Explain.

23. **CAUSE AND EFFECT** Suppose that you place a beaker containing a solution in a refrigerator. An hour later there is a white solid on the bottom of the beaker. What happened? Why?

24. **INFER** Do you think iron by itself would be a good material to use in the frame of a bridge? Why or why not?

25. **SYNTHESIZE** How might the concentration of a solute in an alloy be related to the properties of the alloy? Explain.

270 Unit 2: Chemical Interactions

Using Math Skills in Science

Use the graph below to answer the next three questions.

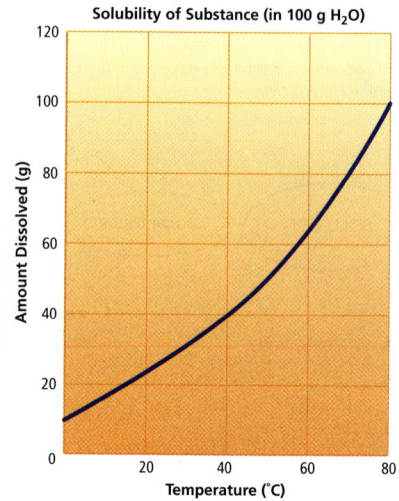

26. What happens to the solubility of the substance as the temperature increases? decreases?

27. Approximately how many grams of the substance dissolve at 20°C? 60°C?

28. Is the substance a solid or a gas? Explain.

the BIG idea

29. **APPLY** Look back at pages 236–237. Think about the answer you gave to the question about the photograph. How has your understanding of solutions and their properties changed?

30. **COMPARE** Describe the similarities and differences between solutions of table salt (NaCl) in water and sugar in water. Do both solutes have similar effects on the properties of the solvent? Explain.

UNIT PROJECTS

Check your schedule for your unit project. How are you doing? Be sure that you have placed data or notes from your research in your project folder.

MONITOR AND RETEACH

If students have trouble connecting the properties of an alloy to its composition in items 24 and 25, suggest that they review the material in Section 8.4. Students should make a table summarizing the use and properties of various alloys in everyday life, transportation, medicine, and space flight.

Students may benefit from summarizing one or more sections of the chapter.

 Summarizing the Chapter, pp. 268–269

Standardized Test Practice

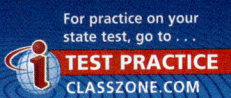

For practice on your state test, go to...
TEST PRACTICE
CLASSZONE.COM

Interpreting Graphs

Use the information in the paragraph and the graph to answer the questions.

Acid rain is an environmental concern in the United States and in other countries. Acid rain is produced when the burning of fuels releases certain chemicals into the air. These chemicals can react with water vapor in Earth's atmosphere to form acids. The acids then fall back to the ground in either rain or snow. The acids can damage plants, animals, and buildings. Normally, rain has a pH of about 5.6, which is slightly acidic. But rain in some areas of the United States has a pH that is lower than 4.0. The graph shows the pH of water in several lakes.

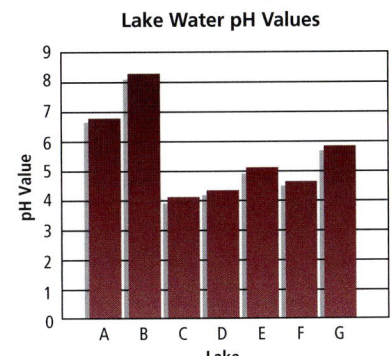

1. Which lake is the most acidic?
   a. Lake A   c. Lake C
   b. Lake B   d. Lake D

2. Which lake is the least acidic?
   a. Lake A   c. Lake C
   b. Lake B   d. Lake D

3. Which lake has water the closest to neutral?
   a. Lake A   c. Lake E
   b. Lake B   d. Lake G

4. Lakes that form on a bed of limestone are less likely to suffer from high acidity. The limestone reacts with acids to neutralize them. Which of the following lakes is most likely to have a limestone bed?
   a. Lake C   c. Lake F
   b. Lake D   d. Lake G

5. Lake trout are fish that live in many freshwater lakes. When the pH of the water in a lake drops below 5.5, this species of fish can no longer reproduce, because its eggs cannot hatch. Which of the following statements is most likely true?
   a. Lake trout have probably stopped reproducing in all the lakes.
   b. In terms of reproducing, lake trout are not in danger in any of the lakes.
   c. Lake trout will probably be able to reproduce in lakes A, B, and G but not in the others.
   d. Lake trout have probably stopped reproducing only in lakes C, D, and F.

Extended Response

Answer the following two questions in detail. Include some of the terms from the list in the box. Underline each term you use in your answers.

| concentration | solute | solubility |
| polar | solution | solvent |

6. Suppose you are trying to make two solutions. One contains water and salt. The other contains water and oil. What do you think will happen in both cases? How might charges on particles affect your results?

7. Explain why some substances dissolve more easily than others. How can this characteristic of a solute be changed by changing the temperature or pressure of a solution?

Chapter 8: Solutions 271

Interpreting Graphs
1. c   4. d
2. b   5. c
3. a

Extended Response

6. RUBRIC
4 points for a response that correctly uses each of the following terms to answer the question:
- polar
- solution
- solute
- solvent
- solubility

Sample answer: Salt has high <u>solubility</u> in water because sodium and chloride ions are charged and water molecules are <u>polar</u>. The <u>solute</u> salt and the <u>solvent</u> water form a <u>solution</u> as the sodium and chloride ions separate and become surrounded by water molecules. Oil is insoluble in water because its molecules are nonpolar and water is polar. Oil and water do not form a solution.

3 points for a response that correctly uses four terms
2 points for a response that correctly uses three terms
1 point for a response that correctly uses one or two terms

7. RUBRIC
4 points for a response that correctly describes the dissolving process using the following terms:
- solute
- solvent
- solubility
- concentration

Sample: Each <u>solute</u> has a unique <u>solubility</u> that depends on the characteristics of the solute and the <u>solvent</u>. The higher a solute's solubility, the higher the <u>concentration</u> can be. The solubility of most solids can be increased by increasing the temperature; the solubility of gases can be increased by lowering the temperature or by increasing the pressure.

3 points for a response that correctly uses three terms
2 points for a response that correctly uses two terms
1 point for a response that correctly uses one term

METACOGNITIVE ACTIVITY

Have students answer the following questions in their **Science Notebook:**
1. Why do you think it is important for you to learn about acids and bases?
2. Which topics in this chapter would you like to learn more about?
3. What have you learned from your research on your Unit Project?

CHAPTER 9
Carbon in Life and Materials

Physical Science
UNIFYING PRINCIPLES

PRINCIPLE 1
Matter is made of particles too small to see.

PRINCIPLE 2
Matter changes form and moves from place to place.

PRINCIPLE 3
Energy changes from one form to another, but it cannot be created or destroyed.

PRINCIPLE 4
Physical forces affect the movement of all matter on Earth and throughout the universe.

Unit 2: Chemical Interactions
BIG IDEAS

**CHAPTER 5
Atomic Structure and the Periodic Table**
A substance's atomic structure determines its physical and chemical properties.

**CHAPTER 6
Chemical Bonds and Compounds**
The properties of compounds depend on their atoms and chemical bonds.

**CHAPTER 7
Chemical Reactions**
Chemical reactions form new substances by breaking and making chemical bonds.

**CHAPTER 8
Solutions**
When substances dissolve to form a solution, the properties of the mixture change.

**CHAPTER 9
Carbon in Life and Materials**
Carbon is essential to living things and to modern materials.

CHAPTER 9
KEY CONCEPTS

SECTION 1

Carbon-based molecules have many structures.
1. Living and nonliving things contain carbon.
2. Carbon forms many different compounds.

SECTION 2

Carbon-based molecules are life's building blocks.
1. Carbon-based molecules have many functions in living things.
2. Living things contain four major types of carbon-based molecules.

SECTION 3

Carbon-based molecules are in many materials.
1. Carbon-based compounds from ancient organisms are used to make new materials.
2. Polymers contain repeating carbon-based units.

 The Big Idea Flow Chart is available on p. T33 in the **UNIT TRANSPARENCY BOOK**.

Previewing Content

SECTION 1
Carbon-based molecules have many structures. pp. 275–281

1. **Living and nonliving things contain carbon.**
   All **organic compounds** contain carbon and are the basis of all living things on Earth. There are different definitions of *organic* because it is an arbitrary classification system, and not all carbon compounds are considered to be organic. Compounds such as carbon dioxide, as well as those that contain cyanides (a CN^- group) or carbonates (a CO_3^{2-} group), are not considered to be organic and are called **inorganic compounds**. Also, all compounds that do not contain carbon are considered to be inorganic.

2. **Carbon forms many different compounds.**
   Carbon can form millions of different compounds because a carbon atom forms four covalent bonds with other atoms. In addition, two carbon atoms can form one, two, or three bonds with each other, as the diagram below shows.

Single Bond	Double Bond	Triple Bond
	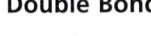	
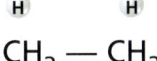	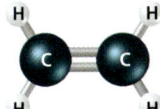	

   - Carbon atoms can bond together to form long chains. The chains can be straight or branched.
   - Carbon atoms also form rings. Benzene is an important carbon ring. It has six carbon atoms with alternating double and single bonds.
   - Compounds that contain the same types and numbers of atoms are called **isomers**. Isomers can have very different properties because their structures are different.

   $$CH_3 - CH_2 - CH_2 - CH_3 \qquad \begin{matrix} & & CH_3 & & \\ & & | & & \\ CH_3 & - & CH & - & CH_3 \end{matrix}$$

   Isobutane

SECTION 2
Carbon-based molecules are life's building blocks. pp. 282–290

1. **Carbon-based molecules have many functions in living things.**
   The many carbon-based molecules found in living things have different structures and different functions but work together to fulfill all life processes.

2. **Living things contain four major types of carbon-based molecules.**
   Organic molecules in living things comprise four groups.
   - **Carbohydrates** include sugars, starches, and cellulose and are used primarily for energy and for cell structure. Glucose ($C_6H_{12}O_6$) is a sugar used as a source of energy by cells of most living things. Starch is a macromolecule that stores glucose; it is made of many glucose molecules linked together. Cellulose is similar to starch but is used by plants to build cell walls. Cellulose is made of linked glucose molecules, but the bonds between each glucose subunit give cellulose a different structure than starch.
   - **Lipids** include fats and oils that are used primarily for energy and for cell structure. Lipids typically contain up to three carbon chains called fatty acids. When all of the carbon-carbon bonds in the fatty acids are single bonds, the lipid is a saturated fat. If one or more of the bonds are double bonds, it is an unsaturated fat. Phospholipids are structural lipids that contain two fatty acid chains and a phosphate group, and are a major part of cell membranes.
   - **Proteins** are macromolecules made of linked units called amino acids. The order of amino acids gives a protein its structure and its function. If the order of amino acids changes, the structure and function of the protein changes. Proteins have many roles in living things, including cell and tissue structure, transport, and immunity. **Enzymes** are proteins that are catalysts for chemical reactions within cells.
   - **Nucleic acids** carry an organism's genetic code and assemble proteins from that code. DNA (deoxyribonucleic acid) carries the genetic code. The backbone of DNA is made of deoxyribose sugar molecules and phosphate groups. The genetic information of DNA is carried by four molecules called bases. The sequence of DNA bases directs the production of proteins. Several types of RNA (ribonucleic acid) read DNA and assemble proteins.

Common Misconceptions

PROTEINS FOR ENERGY Students may think that protein cannot be used by the body to supply energy. In fact, the body breaks down proteins and uses them as an energy source if carbohydrates or lipids are not available. The body does this only as a last resort.

 MISCONCEPTION DATABASE
CLASSZONE.COM Background on student misconceptions

 This misconception is addressed on p. 287.

Previewing Content

SECTION 3
Carbon-based molecules are in many materials. pp. 291–299

1. **Carbon-based compounds from ancient organisms are used to make new materials.**
   Carbon moves through the environment in the carbon cycle. Carbon dioxide in the atmosphere is absorbed by plants during photosynthesis. This carbon becomes a part of sugars, starches, and cellulose. Animals absorb carbon from the foods they eat. Some of this carbon is used to build the cells of the animal and some of it is returned to the atmosphere as carbon dioxide. When plants or animals die, they decompose and carbon returns to the environment. In some cases, carbon can fall out of the carbon cycle if the decaying organisms are trapped in mud or sediment. Carbon that fell out of the carbon cycle millions of years ago is the source of hydrocarbons used in today's world. Thus, carbon cycles through the environment, as shown in the diagram below.

   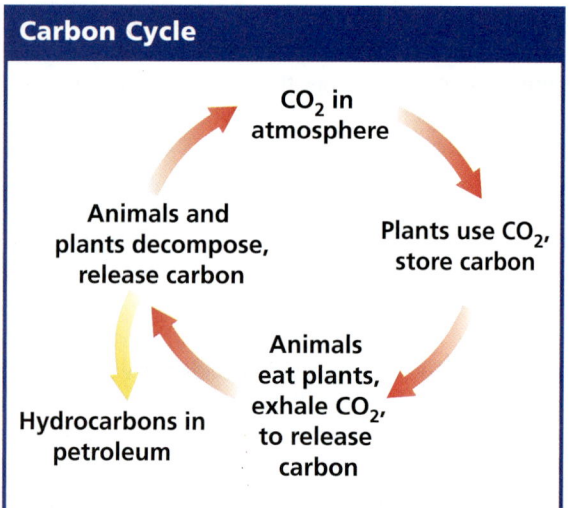

   Hydrocarbons are molecules of carbon and hydrogen that are found in petroleum. The many hydrocarbons in petroleum can be separated according to differences in their boiling points through a process called distillation. Each fraction, such as lubricating oil or gasoline, is used for a different purpose.

2. **Polymers contain repeating carbon-based units.**
   Polymers are very large carbon-based molecules made by linking together smaller repeating units called **monomers.** Polymers can be made by synthesis reactions that break bonds within two monomers and re-form to link the monomers together. The two types of synthesis reactions typically used to make polymers are called addition reactions and condensation reactions. The properties of a polymer are determined by its size and structure. The figure below shows how polymers are made.

   Monomer
   $$CH_2 = CH - CH_3$$

   Monomers Are Linked Together
   $$CH_2 = CH - CH_3 \quad CH_2 = CH - CH_3 \quad CH_2 = CH - CH_3$$

   Polymer
   $$CH_2 - CH - CH_2 - CH - CH_2 - CH ---$$
   $$\quad\quad\quad | \quad\quad\quad\quad | \quad\quad\quad\quad |$$
   $$\quad\quad CH_3 \quad\quad CH_3 \quad\quad CH_3$$

   — = double bond changed to single bond
   — = new bond formed between monomers

   - Some useful polymers are **plastics.** Thousands of plastics with different structures and functions have been created.
   - Chemists have developed polymers for specific functions. Nylon, Teflon, Kevlar, and Nomex are a few of these polymers.

Previewing Labs

EXPLORE the BIG idea

Structure and Function, p. 273
Students observe that structure influences function of a rubber ball.

TIME 10 minutes
MATERIALS hollow rubber ball, hacksaw, glue

Sweet Crackers, p. 273
Students observe that crackers become sweet when chewed for a long time.

TIME 10 minutes
MATERIALS unsalted cracker

Internet Activity: Polymers, p. 273
Students investigate how changes in the structures of virtual polymers affect their properties.

TIME 20 minutes
MATERIALS computer with Internet access

SECTION 1

INVESTIGATE Carbon Bonding, p. 277
Students use foam balls and toothpicks to model the different numbers of bonds that can be formed between carbon atoms.

TIME 10 minutes
MATERIALS marking pen, 2 large foam balls, 6 small foam balls, 7 toothpicks

SECTION 2

EXPLORE Carbon in Food, p. 282
Students burn food samples and infer that they contain carbon.

TIME 10 minutes
MATERIALS aluminum pie plate, candle, wooden matches, tongs, small marshmallow, piece of carrot

INVESTIGATE Organic Molecules, p. 286
Students test food samples to infer which ones contain starch.

TIME 20 minutes
MATERIALS 4 small jar lids, 3 eyedroppers, cornstarch solution, liquid gelatin, iodine solution, bread, tofu, stopwatch

SECTION 3

**CHAPTER INVESTIGATION
Polymers,** pp. 298–299
Students make a polymer and test its physical properties.

TIME 40 minutes
MATERIALS measuring spoons, 2 plastic containers, tap water, white glue, food coloring, borax, jar with lid, plastic spoon, zip-top plastic bags, scissors, 2 L plastic bottle with cap, ring stand with ring, stopwatch, straws

R Additional **INVESTIGATION,** Testing Simple Sugars, A, B, & C, pp. 318–326; Teacher Instructions, pp. 329–330

Chapter 9: **Carbon in Life and Materials** 271D

Previewing Chapter Resources

	INTEGRATED TECHNOLOGY	LABS AND ACTIVITIES
CHAPTER 9 **Carbon in Life and Materials**	**CLASSZONE.COM** • eEdition Plus • EasyPlanner Plus • Misconception Database • Content Review • Test Practice • Simulation • Visualization • Resource Centers • Internet Activity: Polymers • Math Tutorial **SCILINKS.ORG** **CD-ROMS** • eEdition • EasyPlanner • Power Presentations • Content Review • Lab Generator • Test Generator **AUDIO CDS** • Audio Readings • Audio Readings in Spanish	EXPLORE the Big Idea, p. 273 • Structure and Function • Sweet Crackers • Internet Activity: Polymers **UNIT RESOURCE BOOK** Unit Projects, pp. 5–10 **Lab Generator CD-ROM** Generate customized labs.
SECTION 1 **Carbon-based molecules have many structures.** pp. 275–281 Time: 2 periods (1 block) Lesson Plan, pp. 270–271	• **SIMULATION**, 3-D Molecules • **RESOURCE CENTER**, Nanotubes **UNIT TRANSPARENCY BOOK** • Big Idea Flow Chart, p. T33 • Daily Vocabulary Scaffolding, p. T34 • Note-Taking Model, p. T35 • 3-Minute Warm-Up, p. T36 • "Carbon Chains and Carbon Rings" Visual, p. T38	• INVESTIGATE Carbon Bonding, p. 277 • Extreme Science, p. 281 **UNIT RESOURCE BOOK** • Datasheet, Carbon Bonding, p. 279
SECTION 2 **Carbon-based molecules are life's building blocks.** pp. 282–290 Time: 2 periods (1 block) Lesson Plan, pp. 281–282	• **RESOURCE CENTER**, Carbohydrates, Lipids, Proteins, and Nucleic Acids • **MATH TUTORIAL** **UNIT TRANSPARENCY BOOK** • Daily Vocabulary Scaffolding, p. T34 • 3-Minute Warm-Up, p. T36	• EXPLORE Carbon in Food, p. 282 • INVESTIGATE Organic Molecules, p. 286 • Math in Science, p. 290 **UNIT RESOURCE BOOK** • Datasheet, Organic Molecules, p. 290 • Math Support, p. 307 • Math Practice, p. 308 • Additional INVESTIGATION, Testing Simple Sugars, A, B, & C, pp. 318–326
SECTION 3 **Carbon-based molecules are in many materials.** pp. 291–299 Time: 4 periods (2 blocks) Lesson Plan, pp. 292–293	• **RESOURCE CENTER**, Petroleum and Hydrocarbons • **VISUALIZATION**, Petroleum Distillation **UNIT TRANSPARENCY BOOK** • Big Idea Flow Chart, p. T33 • Daily Vocabulary Scaffolding, p. T34 • 3-Minute Warm-Up, p. T37 • Chapter Outline, pp. T39–T40	CHAPTER INVESTIGATION, Polymers, pp. 298–299 **UNIT RESOURCE BOOK** CHAPTER INVESTIGATION, Polymers, A, B, & C, pp. 309–317

KEY TO ICONS	CD/CD-ROM	Teacher Edition	T UNIT TRANSPARENCY BOOK	 SPANISH ASSESSMENT BOOK
 INTERNET	PE Pupil Edition	R UNIT RESOURCE BOOK	A UNIT ASSESSMENT BOOK	SCIENCE TOOLKIT

READING AND REINFORCEMENT

ASSESSMENT

STANDARDS

- Magnet Word Diagram, B24–25
- Supporting Main Ideas, C42
- Daily Vocabulary Scaffolding, H1–8

 UNIT RESOURCE BOOK
- Vocabulary Practice, pp. 304–305
- Decoding Support, p. 306
- Summarizing the Chapter, pp. 327–328

Audio Readings CD
Listen to Pupil Edition.

Audio Readings in Spanish CD
Listen to Pupil Edition in Spanish.

PE
- Chapter Review, pp. 301–302
- Standardized Test Practice, p. 303

A **UNIT ASSESSMENT BOOK**
- Diagnostic Test, pp. 79–80
- Chapter Test, A, B, & C, pp. 84–95
- Alternative Assessment, pp. 96–97
- Unit Test, pp. 98–109
- Spanish Chapter Test, pp. 249–252
- Spanish Unit Test, pp. 253–256

Test Generator CD-ROM
Generate customized tests.

Lab Generator CD-ROM
Rubrics for Labs

National Standards
A.1–8, A.9.a–c, A.9.e–f, B.1.c, C.1.a

See p. 272 for the standards.

 UNIT RESOURCE BOOK
- Reading Study Guide, A & B, pp. 272–275
- Spanish Reading Study Guide, pp. 276–277
- Challenge and Extension, p. 278
- Reinforcing Key Concepts, p. 280

TE Ongoing Assessment, pp. 275–276, 278, 280

PE Section 9.1 Review, p. 280

A **UNIT ASSESSMENT BOOK**
Section 9.1 Quiz, p. 81

National Standards
A.2–7, A.9.a–b, A.9.e–f, B.1.c

 UNIT RESOURCE BOOK
- Reading Study Guide, A & B, pp. 283–286
- Spanish Reading Study Guide, pp. 287–288
- Challenge and Extension, p. 289
- Reinforcing Key Concepts, p. 291

TE Ongoing Assessment, pp. 284–285, 287–289

PE Section 9.2 Review, p. 289

A **UNIT ASSESSMENT BOOK**
Section 9.2 Quiz, p. 82

National Standards
A.2–8, A.9.a–c, A.9.e–f, C.1.a

 UNIT RESOURCE BOOK
- Reading Study Guide, A & B, pp. 294–297
- Spanish Reading Study Guide, pp. 298–299
- Challenge and Extension, p. 300
- Reinforcing Key Concepts, p. 301
- Challenge Reading, pp. 302–303

TE Ongoing Assessment, pp. 292, 294–297

PE Section 9.3 Review, p. 297

A **UNIT ASSESSMENT BOOK**
Section 9.3 Quiz, p. 83

National Standards
A.1–7, A.9.a–b, A.9.e–f, B.1.c

Chapter 9: **Carbon in Life and Materials** 271F

Previewing Resources for Differentiated Instruction

CHAPTER INVESTIGATION

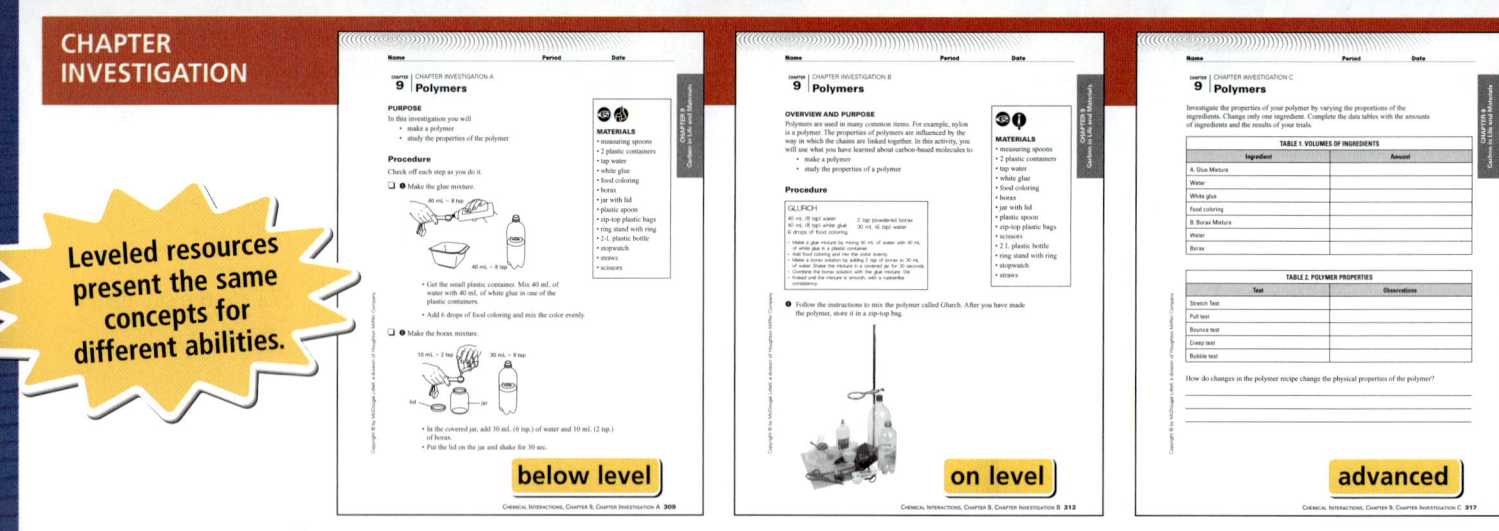

Leveled resources present the same concepts for different abilities.

UNIT RESOURCE BOOK, pp. 309–312 | pp. 313–316 | pp. 313–317

READING STUDY GUIDE

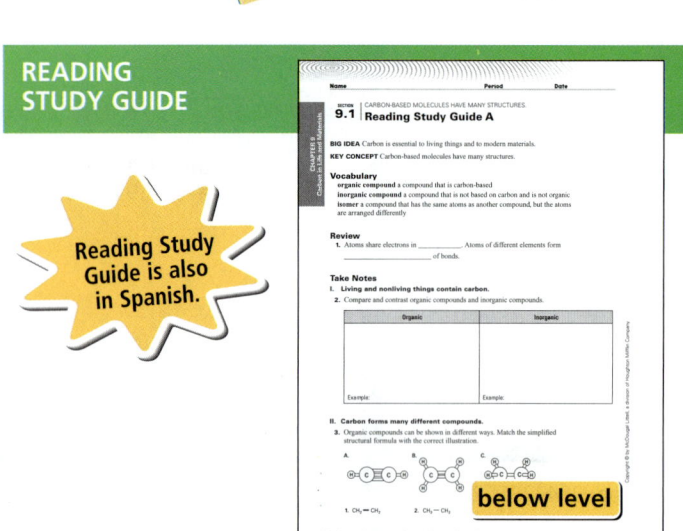
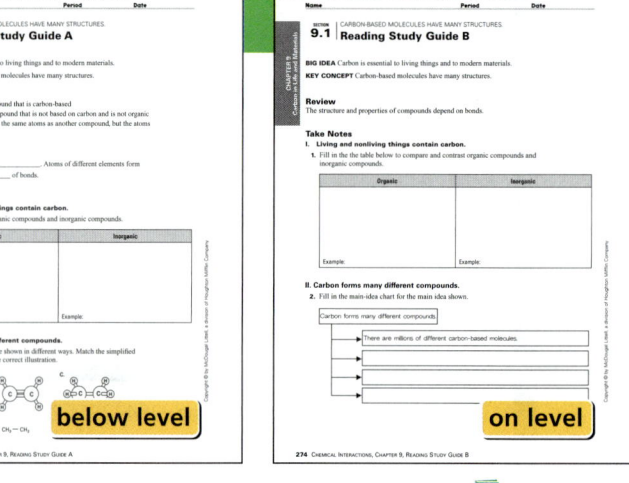
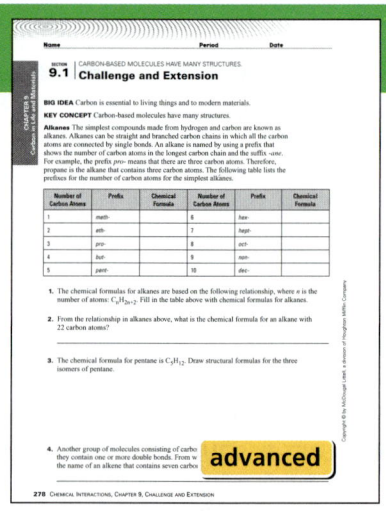

Reading Study Guide is also in Spanish.

UNIT RESOURCE BOOK, pp. 272–273 | pp. 274–275 | p. 278

CHAPTER TEST

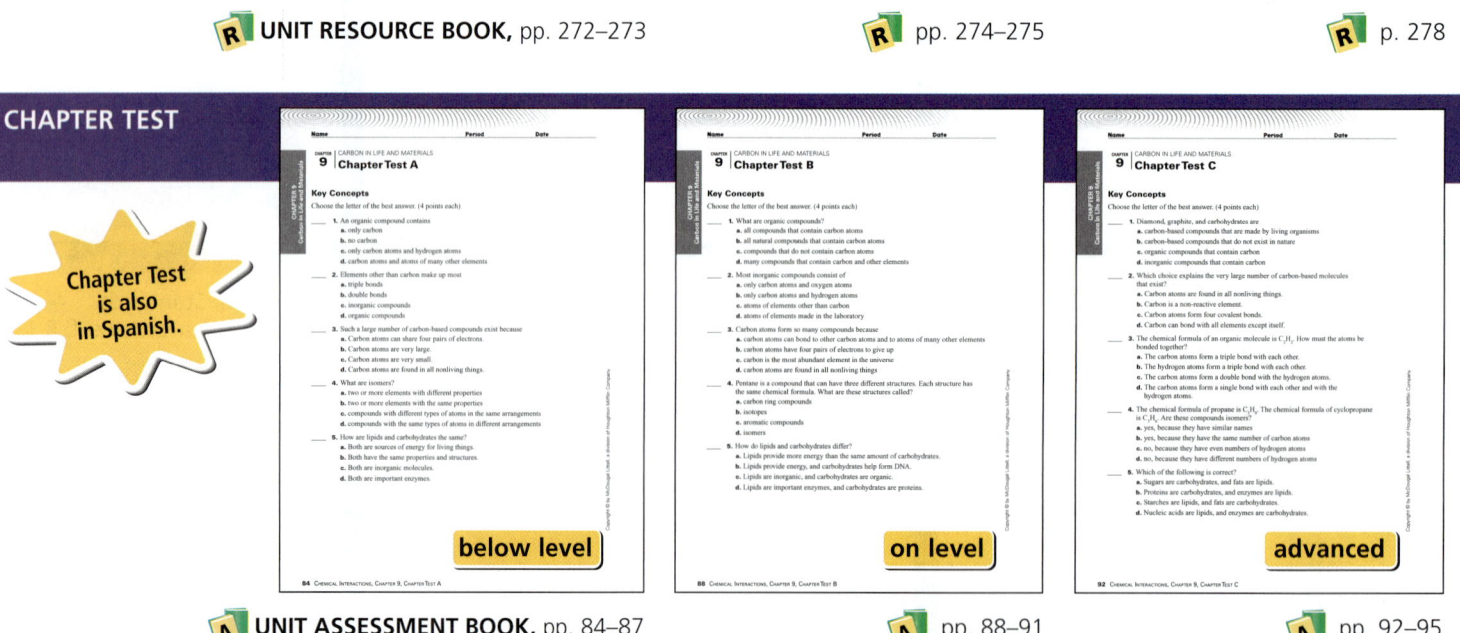

Chapter Test is also in Spanish.

UNIT ASSESSMENT BOOK, pp. 84–87 | pp. 88–91 | pp. 92–95

271G Unit 2: **Chemical Interactions**

TECHNOLOGY

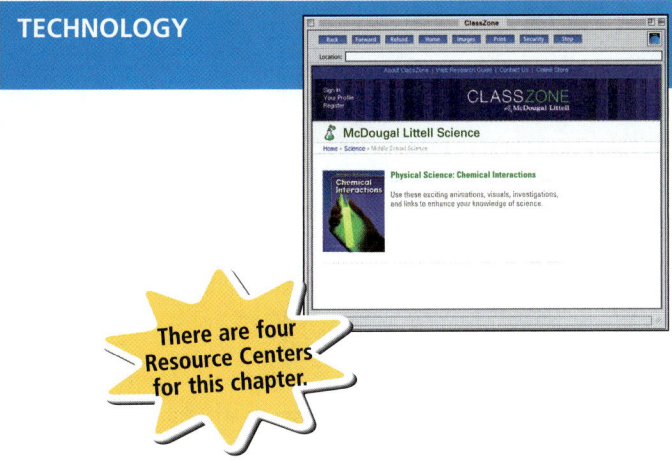
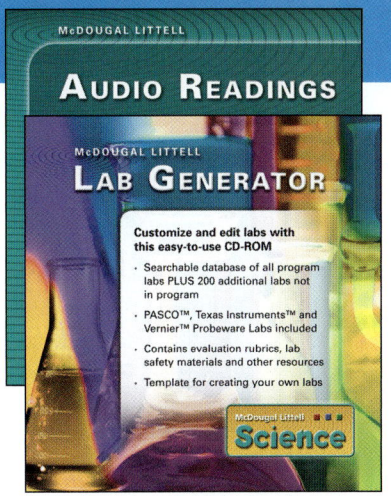
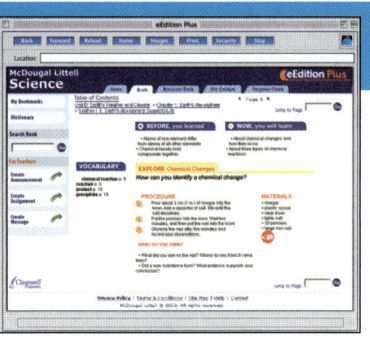

There are four Resource Centers for this chapter.

CLASSZONE.COM   **CD/CD-ROMS**   **CLASSZONE.COM**

VISUAL CONTENT

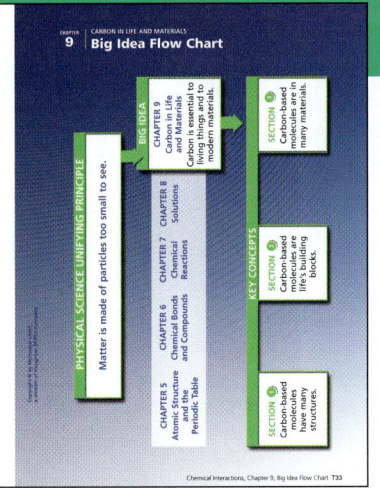
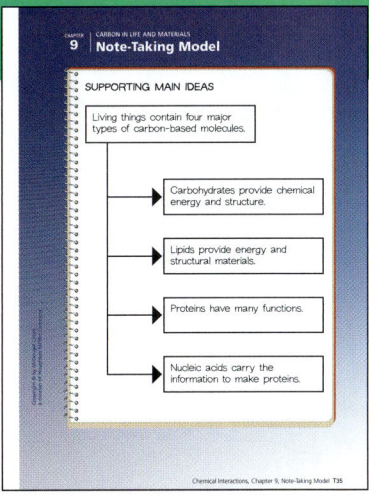

UNIT TRANSPARENCY BOOK, p. T33   p. T35   p. T38

MORE SUPPORT

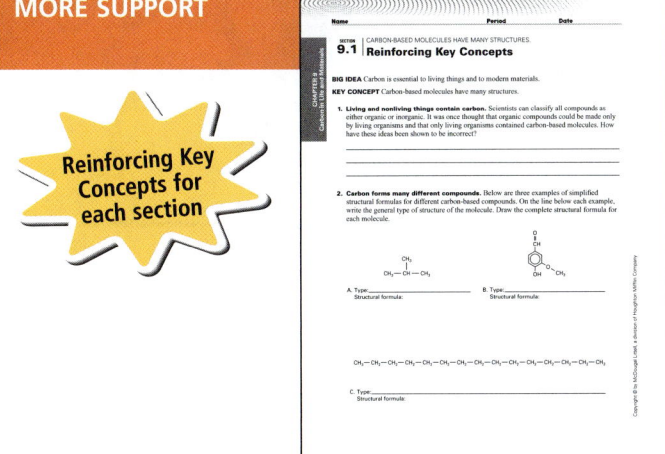
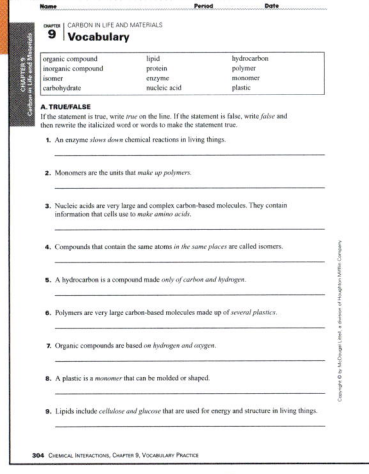
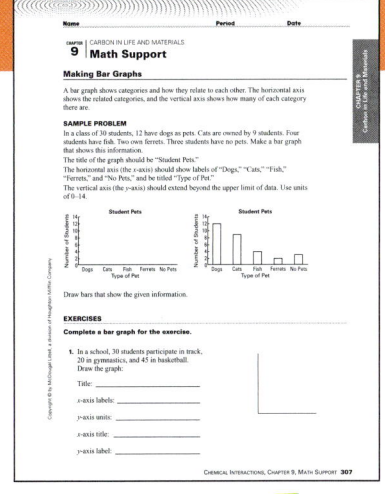

Reinforcing Key Concepts for each section

UNIT RESOURCE BOOK, p. 280   pp. 304–305   p. 307

Chapter 9: **Carbon in Life and Materials** 271H

CHAPTER

9 Carbon in Life and Materials

INTRODUCE

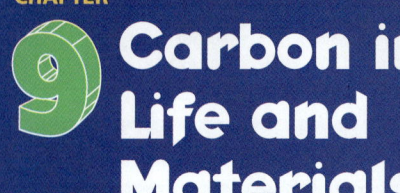

Have students look at the photograph of the race car and pit crew and discuss how the question in the box links to the Big Idea:

- What do you think the clothing worn by the pit crew is made of?
- What are the car tires made of?
- What else shown in the photograph contains carbon?

National Science Education Standards

Content

B.1.c There are more than 100 known elements that combine in a multitude of ways to produce compounds, which account for the living and nonliving substances that we encounter.

C.1.a Living systems at all levels of organization demonstrate the complementary nature of structure and function. Important levels of organization for structure and function include cells, organs, tissues, organ systems, whole organisms, and ecosystems.

Process

A.1–8 Identify questions that can be answered through scientific investigation; design and conduct an investigation; use tools to gather and interpret data; use evidence to describe, predict, explain, model; think critically to make relationships between evidence and explanation; recognize different explanations and predictions; communicate scientific procedures and explanations; use mathematics.

A.9.a–c, A.9.e–f Understand scientific inquiry by using different investigations, methods, and explanations based on logic, evidence, and skepticism.

272 Unit 2: **Chemical Interactions**

CHAPTER

9 Carbon in Life and Materials

Carbon is essential to living things and to modern materials.

Where in this photograph might you find carbon-based molecules?

Key Concepts

SECTION 1 Carbon-based molecules have many structures.
Learn why carbon forms many different compounds.

SECTION 2 Carbon-based molecules are life's building blocks.
Learn about the four main types of carbon-based molecules in living things.

SECTION 3 Carbon-based molecules are in many materials.
Learn how common materials are made from carbon-based molecules.

Internet Preview

CLASSZONE.COM
Chapter 9 online resources: Content Review, Simulation, Visualization, four Resource Centers, Math Tutorial, Test Practice

272 Unit 2: **Chemical Interactions**

INTERNET PREVIEW

CLASSZONE.COM For student use with the following pages:

Review and Practice
- Content Review, pp. 274, 300
- Math Tutorial: Bar Graphs, p. 290
- Test Practice, p. 303

Activities and Resources
- Internet Activity, p. 273
- Simulation, p. 278
- Visualization, p. 292
- Resource Centers: Nanotubes, p. 281; Carbohydrates, Lipids, Proteins, and Nucleic Acids, p. 289; Petroleum and Hydrocarbons, p. 291

Organic Compounds
Code: MDL026

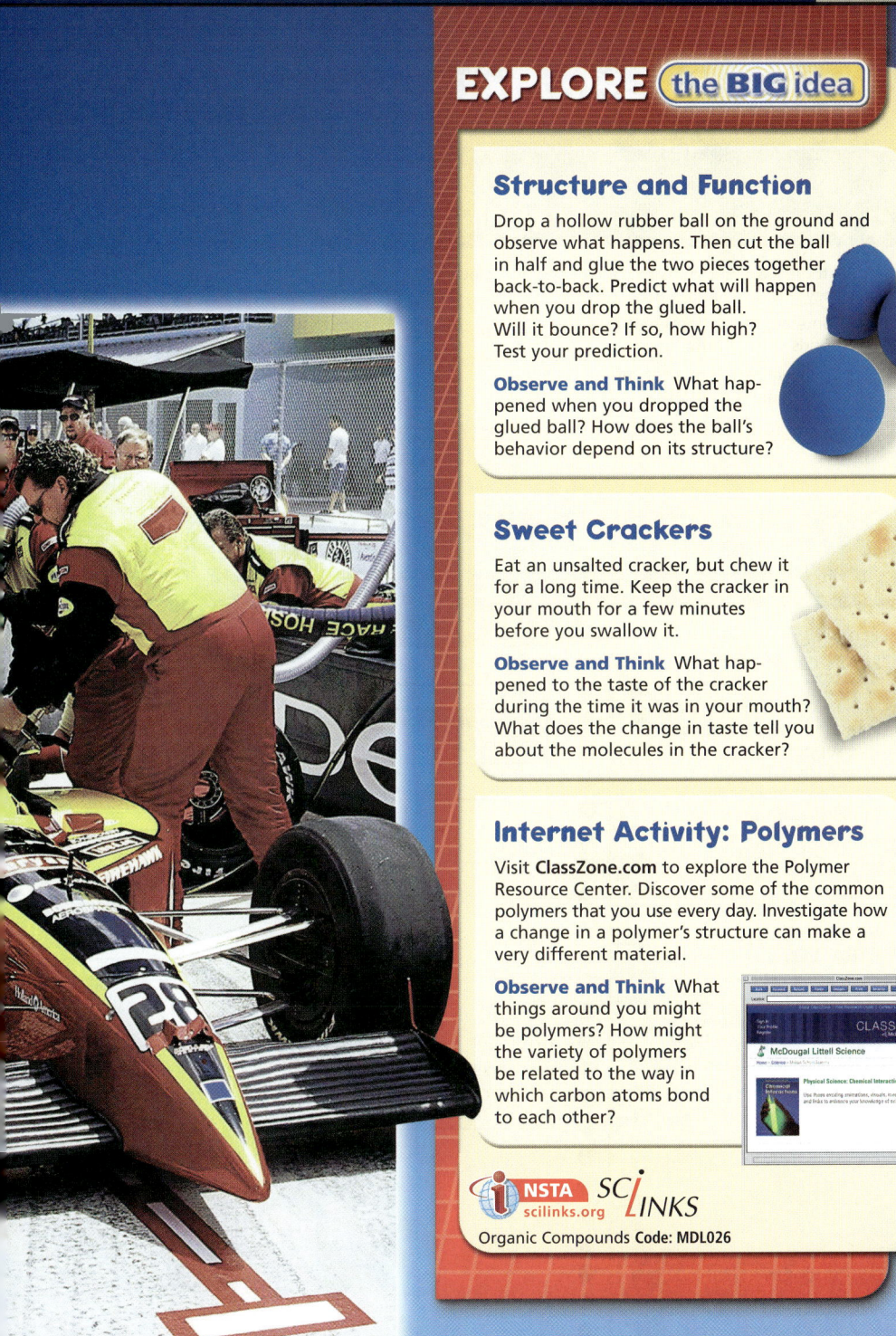

EXPLORE the BIG idea

Structure and Function

Drop a hollow rubber ball on the ground and observe what happens. Then cut the ball in half and glue the two pieces together back-to-back. Predict what will happen when you drop the glued ball. Will it bounce? If so, how high? Test your prediction.

Observe and Think What happened when you dropped the glued ball? How does the ball's behavior depend on its structure?

Sweet Crackers

Eat an unsalted cracker, but chew it for a long time. Keep the cracker in your mouth for a few minutes before you swallow it.

Observe and Think What happened to the taste of the cracker during the time it was in your mouth? What does the change in taste tell you about the molecules in the cracker?

Internet Activity: Polymers

Visit ClassZone.com to explore the Polymer Resource Center. Discover some of the common polymers that you use every day. Investigate how a change in a polymer's structure can make a very different material.

Observe and Think What things around you might be polymers? How might the variety of polymers be related to the way in which carbon atoms bond to each other?

NSTA SCLINKS
scilinks.org
Organic Compounds Code: MDL026

Chapter 9: Carbon in Life and Materials 273

TEACHING WITH TECHNOLOGY

Digital Camera In "Investigate Organic Molecules" on p. 286, students could photograph a positive reaction when they test cornstarch, so they can compare the color when testing other substances.

Video Camera You may wish to videotape parts of the Chapter Investigation on pp. 298–299. Ask students to narrate the procedures as you tape them.

EXPLORE the BIG idea

These inquiry-based activities are appropriate for use at home or as a supplement to classroom instruction.

Structure and Function

PURPOSE To observe that structure influences function. Students observe a rubber ball's behavior before and after they cut it in half.

TIP *10 min.* Use a racquetball; an adult should cut the ball in half carefully with a hacksaw.

Answer: The glued ball should barely bounce, if at all. A change in the ball's structure changes its function completely.

REVISIT after p. 280.

Sweet Crackers

PURPOSE To observe that crackers contain sugar. Students observe that crackers begin to taste sweet when chewed for a long time.

TIP *10 min.* Unsalted crackers must be used. Oyster crackers work best.

Answer: It became sweet. Starch in the crackers is broken down into sugar.

REVISIT after p. 283.

Internet Activity: Polymers

PURPOSE To investigate polymers in common items.

TIP *20 min.* Students should realize that a polymer changes when its structure changes.

Answer: Living things, plastics, and fabrics are made of polymers. Because carbon atoms can form different numbers of bonds with each other and carbon-based molecules can include long chains of carbon atoms or carbon-based rings, a very large number of different polymers are possible.

REVISIT after p. 294.

PREPARE

CONCEPT REVIEW

Activate Prior Knowledge

- Draw a diagram of a carbon atom. With an atomic number of 6, carbon has two electrons in its inner shell and four in its outer shell.
- Ask: How many electrons are available to form bonds in carbon atoms? *four*
- Ask: What type of bonds do carbon atoms form? *covalent*

TAKING NOTES

Supporting Main Ideas

Students will find these charts analogous to an outline because of the way they organize main points and supporting information. The chart provides a meaningful way to organize information, especially for visual learners.

Vocabulary Strategy

Making side-by-side magnet word diagrams for two terms that can be compared, such as *organic compound* and *inorganic compound*, can be a valuable study tool.

Vocabulary and Note-Taking Resources

R
- Vocabulary Practice, pp. 304–305
- Decoding Support, p. 306

T
- Daily Vocabulary Scaffolding, p. T34
- Note-Taking Model, p. T35

- Magnet Word Diagram, B24–25
- Supporting Main Ideas, C42
- Daily Vocabulary Scaffolding, H1–8

CHAPTER 9

Getting Ready to Learn

CONCEPT REVIEW

- Atoms share electrons when they form covalent bonds.
- Some atoms can form multiple bonds with another atom.
- Chemical reactions alter the arrangement of atoms.

VOCABULARY REVIEW

electron p. 139
covalent bond p. 178
chemical reaction p. 197
catalyst p. 204

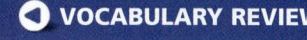

CONTENT REVIEW
CLASSZONE.COM
Review concepts and vocabulary.

TAKING NOTES

SUPPORTING MAIN IDEAS

Make a chart to show main ideas and the information that supports them. Copy each blue heading. Below each heading, add supporting information, such as reasons, explanations, and examples.

VOCABULARY STRATEGY

Think about a vocabulary term as a **magnet word** diagram. Write the other terms or ideas related to that term around it.

See the Note-Taking Handbook on pages R45–R51.

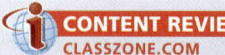

SCIENCE NOTEBOOK

Living and nonliving things contain carbon.
- All life on Earth is based on carbon.
- All organic compounds contain carbon.
- Compounds that do not contain carbon are inorganic.

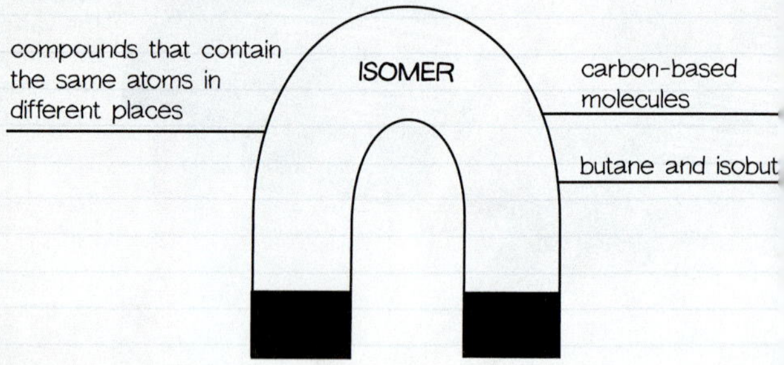

CHECK READINESS

Administer the Diagnostic Test to determine students' readiness for new science content and their mastery of requisite math skills.

A Diagnostic Test, pp. 79–80

Technology Resources

Students needing content and math skills should visit **ClassZone.com**.

- CONTENT REVIEW
- MATH TUTORIAL

CONTENT REVIEW CD-ROM

KEY CONCEPT

Carbon-based molecules have many structures.

▶ **BEFORE, you learned**
- Atoms of one element differ from atoms of other elements
- The structure and properties of compounds depend on bonds
- Atoms of different elements can form different numbers of bonds

▶ **NOW, you will learn**
- About the importance of carbon in living things
- Why carbon can form many different compounds
- About different structures of carbon-based molecules

VOCABULARY
organic compound p. 275
inorganic compound p. 276
isomer p. 280

THINK ABOUT

Where can you find carbon?

The wood of a pencil consists of carbon-based molecules. These molecules are considered to be organic. The graphite in the center of the pencil is also made of carbon. In fact, graphite is pure carbon, but it is not considered to be organic. What makes the carbon in wood different from the carbon in graphite?

Living and nonliving things contain carbon.

Just about every substance that makes up living things contains carbon atoms. In fact, carbon is the most important element for life. Molecules containing carbon atoms were originally called organic because a large number of carbon-based molecules were found in living organisms. Sugars are organic. They are formed by plants, which are living organisms, and they contain carbon. Notice that the term *organic* is closely related to the term *organism*.

Organic compounds are based on carbon. Besides carbon, organic compounds often contain atoms of the elements hydrogen and oxygen, but they can also contain atoms of nitrogen, sulfur, and phosphorus. Scientists once thought that organic compounds could be made only in living organisms by an organism's life processes. Then an organic compound was made in a laboratory. This discovery showed that organic substances were not unique to living things. Instead, organic compounds could be made in a laboratory just like all other chemical compounds.

VOCABULARY
Remember to make a magnet word diagram for *organic compound* and for other vocabulary terms.

 Why were carbon compounds called organic compounds?

Chapter 9: **Carbon in Life and Materials** 275

RESOURCES FOR DIFFERENTIATED INSTRUCTION

Below Level
UNIT RESOURCE BOOK
- Reading Study Guide A, pp. 272–273
- Decoding Support, p. 306

 **AUDIO CDS**

Advanced
UNIT RESOURCE BOOK
Challenge and Extension, p. 278

English Learners
UNIT RESOURCE BOOK
Spanish Reading Study Guide, pp. 276–277

 **AUDIO CDS**

- Audio Readings in Spanish
- Audio Readings (English)

 FOCUS

▶ **Set Learning Goals**
Students will
- Recognize the importance of carbon in living things.
- Describe how carbon can form many different compounds.
- Identify different structures of carbon-based molecules.
- Make experimental models to demonstrate how two carbon atoms can form different numbers of bonds.

◀ **3-Minute Warm-Up**

Display Transparency 36 or copy this exercise on the board:

Draw and label two diagrams, one of an ionic compound such as sodium chloride (NaCl) and one of a covalent compound such as methane (CH_4). Identify the difference in what happens to electrons in the two types of bonds. *Electrons are transferred from one atom to another in ionic bonds; pairs of electrons are shared by atoms in covalent bonds.*

 3-Minute Warm-Up, p. T36

MOTIVATE

THINK ABOUT

PURPOSE To identify common objects that contain carbon-based molecules and that may be either organic or inorganic

DISCUSS Have students identify classroom items that contain carbon-based molecules. Compile a list on the board. Have students identify items that are organic and items that are inorganic.

Answer: The structure of carbon in wood is different from that of graphite.

Ongoing Assessment

 *Answer: They were thought to be found only in living organisms.*

Chapter 9 **275**

9.1 INSTRUCT

Teach Difficult Concepts
Explain that the definitions of *organic* and *inorganic* are difficult because they have arbitrary boundaries. The concepts of organic and inorganic arose when carbon-based molecules were believed to be formed by the life force of a living thing. Today, organic chemistry typically refers to the study of hydrocarbon compounds and their derivatives.

History of Science
The first organic compound to be made outside a living organism was urea, a waste product formed from the breakdown of proteins in the body. Kidneys filter urea out of the blood. In 1828, Friedrich Wöhler was trying to synthesize ammonium cyanate. The compound he made turned out to be identical to urea. Amazed, he wrote to a colleague, "I must tell you that I can make urea without the use of kidneys, either man or dog. Ammonium cyanate is urea."

Teach from Visuals
To help students interpret the bonding diagram, ask: How does the number of hydrogen atoms in a molecule change when two carbon atoms form a single, a double, or a triple bond? *Each carbon atom shares four pairs of electrons. The more pairs that are shared by the two carbon atoms, the fewer that can be shared with other atoms.*

Ongoing Assessment
Recognize that carbon is the basis of life.
Ask: Where do you find carbon in nature? *in diamond, graphite, cyanides, carbonates, and carbon dioxide, and mostly in every organism*

CHECK YOUR READING — Answer: one, two, or three

Sugar, shown here as cubes, is organic and contains carbon atoms. It is made by plants from inorganic substances.

Carbon dioxide, shown here as dry ice, is inorganic even though it contains carbon atoms. It is used by plants to make sugars.

READING TiP
The prefix *in-* means "not," so *inorganic* means "not organic."

There are several exceptions to the rule that carbon-based molecules are organic. These include diamond and graphite, which are made entirely of carbon but are not considered to be organic. The same is true of other compounds, such as cyanides (which contain a CN^- group), carbonates (which contain a CO_3^{2-} group), and carbon dioxide (CO_2). These carbon-containing compounds, among others, and all compounds without carbon are called **inorganic compounds.**

Carbon forms many different compounds.

Millions of different carbon-based molecules exist. Consider the number of molecules that make up living things and all of the processes that occur in living things. Carbon-based molecules are vital for all of them.

SUPPORTING MAIN IDEAS
Make a chart about how carbon forms many different compounds.

The large variety of carbon-based molecules results from the number of bonds that each carbon atom forms in a molecule and from a carbon atom's ability to form bonds with atoms of many different elements. In compounds, carbon atoms always share four pairs of electrons in four covalent bonds. This means that one carbon atom can form single bonds with up to four other atoms. Carbon atoms can also form multiple bonds—the atoms can share more than one pair of electrons—with other atoms including, most importantly, other carbon atoms. Different ways of showing the same carbon-based molecules are illustrated below and on page 277.

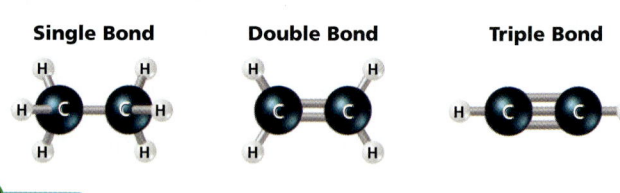

Single Bond   Double Bond   Triple Bond

CHECK YOUR READING How many bonds can one carbon atom form with another?

276 Unit 2: **Chemical Interactions**

DIFFERENTIATE INSTRUCTION

More Reading Support

A How many pairs of electrons does a carbon atom share in its bonds? *four*

English Learners Encourage students to be aware of words or phrases that make generalizations such as "Just about every substance that makes up living things contains carbon atoms" and "Besides carbon, organic compounds often contain atoms of the elements hydrogen and oxygen." "Just about" implies that most, but not all, of the substances that make up living things contain carbon. "Often" implies that organic compounds sometimes contain hydrogen and oxygen, but not always.

As you can see in the compounds shown, two carbon atoms can form single, double, or even triple bonds with one another. The compounds have different numbers of hydrogen atoms and different numbers of bonds between their carbon atoms. Count the bonds for each carbon atom. Each carbon atom makes a total of four bonds and always makes just one bond with each hydrogen atom.

Organic molecules are often shown in a simplified way. Instead of models that include all of a molecule's atoms and bonds, structural formulas—such as those shown below—can be used.

> **REMINDER**
> One pair of electrons is shared in a single covalent bond.

B

Full Structural Formulas

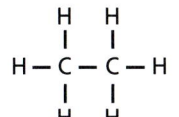 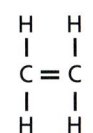 H—C≡C—H

Simplified Structural Formulas

$CH_3 — CH_3$ $CH_2 = CH_2$ $CH ≡ CH$

Carbon-based molecules can have many different structures. Some of the most important structures are molecules shaped like chains and molecules shaped like rings.

INVESTIGATE Carbon Bonding

How do carbon-based molecules depend on the number of bonds between carbon atoms?

PROCEDURE

1. Label the large foam balls "C" for carbon, and label the small foam balls "H" for hydrogen.
2. Using a toothpick to represent a bond, construct a model of a molecule with two carbons, six hydrogens, and seven toothpicks. Carbon has four bonds and hydrogen has one.
3. Make a new model, using two carbons, two hydrogens, and five toothpicks.

WHAT DO YOU THINK?
- How many bonds are there between carbon atoms in the first model? in the second model?
- Which molecule might be more tightly held together? Why?

CHALLENGE In the model on the right, would it be possible for an additional hydrogen atom to bond to each carbon atom? Why or why not?

SKILL FOCUS
Modeling

MATERIALS
- marking pen
- 2 large foam balls
- 6 small foam balls
- toothpicks

TIME
10 minutes

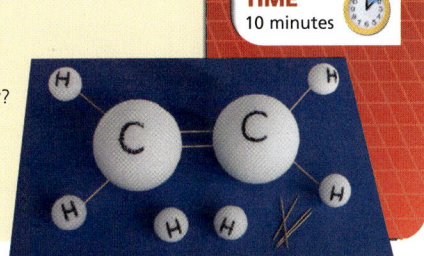

Chapter 9: **Carbon in Life and Materials** 277

DIFFERENTIATE INSTRUCTION

? More Reading Support

B What is a simplified way of showing organic molecules? *structural formulas*

Inclusion "Investigate Carbon Bonding" is a good activity for students with visual impairments and tactile learners. Ask students to rephrase each direction in their own words to demonstrate their comprehension.

Carbon Chains

Observe and rotate three-dimensional models of carbon-based molecules.

Unlike atoms of other elements, carbon atoms have the unusual property of being able to bond to each other to form very long chains. One carbon chain might have hundreds of carbon atoms bonded together. A carbon chain can be straight or branched.

Straight Chain

$CH_3 — CH_2 — CH_2 — CH_2 — CH_2 — CH_3$

Branched Chain

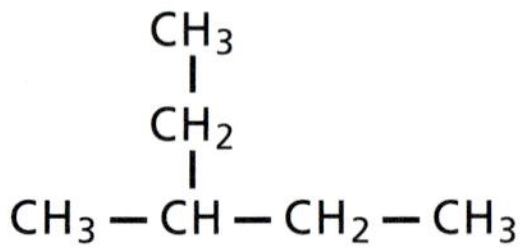

$$\begin{array}{c} CH_3 \\ | \\ CH_2 \\ | \\ CH_3 — CH — CH_2 — CH_3 \end{array}$$

In a branched carbon chain, additional carbon atoms, or even other carbon chains, can bond to carbon atoms in the main carbon chain. Straight chains and branched chains are both results of carbon's ability to form four bonds.

 How is it possible for carbon atoms to form both straight and branched chains?

Carbon Rings

Carbon-based molecules also can be shaped like rings. Carbon rings containing either 5 or 6 carbon atoms are the most common ones, and carbon rings containing more than 20 carbon atoms do not occur naturally.

Just as there are different types of carbon chains, there are different types of carbon ring molecules. One of the most important carbon-based ring molecules is a molecule called benzene (BEHN–ZEEN). Benzene contains six carbon atoms and six hydrogen atoms. Benzene differs from other carbon-based rings because it contains alternating single and double bonds between carbon atoms, as shown below. The benzene molecule is often shown as a circle inside a hexagon.

Benzene Ring

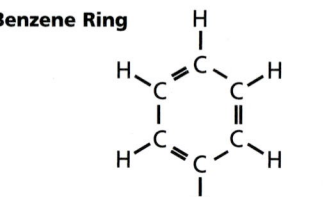

Simplified Benzene Ring

Many compounds are based on benzene's ring structure. These carbon-based molecules often have very strong smells, or aromas, and so are called aromatic compounds. One aromatic compound that contains a benzene ring is a molecule called vanillin. Vanillin is the molecule that gives vanilla its distinctive smell.

278 Unit 2: Chemical Interactions

Carbon Chains and Carbon Rings

Carbon-based molecules shaped like chains or rings are found in the world around you.

Carbon Chains

One of the carbon chains in the diesel fuel for this locomotive has the formula $C_{15}H_{32}$. It contains 13 CH_2 groups between the CH_3 groups that are on both ends of the molecule. This molecule can be written as $CH_3(CH_2)_{13}CH_3$.

$CH_3 — CH_2 — CH_2 — CH_2 — CH_2 — CH_2 — CH_2 — CH_2 — CH_2 — CH_2 — CH_2 — CH_2 — CH_2 — CH_2 — CH_3$

Carbon Rings

Vanilla ice cream gets its flavor from vanilla, which is also used to enhance other flavors. The molecule that gives vanilla its strong smell is based on the benzene carbon ring.

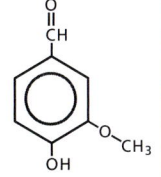

Carbon Chains and Rings

The molecules in polystyrene, which make up this foam container, contain carbon rings attached to a long carbon chain. The dashed lines at both ends of the structural formula tell you that the molecule continues in both directions.

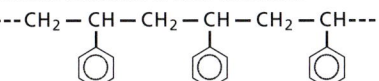

Chapter 9: **Carbon in Life and Materials** 279

Teach from Visuals

To help students interpret the structural formulas on the page, ask:

- Is the structure of the carbon chain that is shown for diesel fuel a straight chain or a branched chain? *a straight chain*

- Do you think it is possible for that carbon chain to be branched? Why or why not? *Yes; carbon chains can be straight or branched by changing where carbon atoms bond to other carbon atoms in the molecule. A carbon atom can replace a hydrogen atom to form a branch off the main part of the chain.*

- Why do some of the carbon atoms in the vanillin structure (vanilla) seem to have only three bonds? *They actually have four bonds, but to save space the hydrogen atoms are not shown sticking out from the carbon. A CH in a structure represents a bond between carbon and hydrogen.*

- What do the dotted lines at both ends of the polystyrene structure (at bottom) indicate? *The molecule is much longer than shown. The chain continues in both directions.*

 This visual is also available as T38 in the Unit Transparency Book.

History of Science

In the mid-1800s, chemists were unable to identify a structure for benzene that had the correct number of carbon and hydrogen atoms and also accounted for benzene's unusual properties. A German chemist, Friedrich Kekulé, solved the mystery when he dreamed about a dancing snake that formed a ring by biting its own tail. Kekulé realized that benzene had a ring structure.

DIFFERENTIATE INSTRUCTION

Advanced Have interested students investigate how hydrocarbons are named. *Hydrocarbons with only single bonds end in –ane (for example, ethane). Hydrocarbons with at least one double bond end in –ene (for example, ethene). Hydrocarbons with at least one triple bond end in –yne (for example, ethyne).*

 Challenge and Extension, p. 278

Chapter 9 **279**

Ongoing Assessment

Identify different carbon-based molecules.

Ask: Can you know what the structure of an organic molecule is from its chemical formula? Explain. *No; the formula for both butane and isobutane is C_4H_{10}. You would have to see the structural formula to know how the molecule is arranged.*

 Answer: *They are each made up of the same atoms, but the atoms are arranged differently. The isomers have different properties.*

EXPLORE the BIG idea

Revisit "Structure and Function" on p. 273. Have students explain their results.

Reinforce the BIG idea

Have students relate the section to the Big Idea.

R Reinforcing Key Concepts, p. 280

9.1 ASSESS & RETEACH

Assess

A Section 9.1 Quiz, p. 81

Reteach

Have students write a short summary of the section. They should use heads, topic sentences, and vocabulary terms for guidance.

Technology Resources

Have students visit ClassZone.com for reteaching of Key Concepts.

 CONTENT REVIEW

 CONTENT REVIEW CD-ROM

Isomers

Another reason there is such a large number of carbon-based molecules is that carbon can form different molecules with the same atoms. The atoms in these molecules are in different places, and the molecules have different structures. Because the atoms are arranged differently, they are actually two different substances. Compounds that contain the same atoms, but in different places, are called **isomers.**

READING TIP
The prefix *iso-* means "equal," and the root *mer-* means "part."

The formulas below show a pair of compounds—butane and isobutane—that are isomers. Both molecules contain four carbon atoms and ten hydrogen atoms. However, butane molecules are straight chains of carbon atoms. Isobutane molecules are branched chains of carbon atoms. Even though both butane and isobutane contain the same atoms, the structures of the molecules are different, so they are isomers.

Butane

$$CH_3 - CH_2 - CH_2 - CH_3$$

Butane contains four carbon atoms and ten hydrogen atoms. It has a straight chain structure.

Isobutane

$$\begin{array}{c} CH_3 \\ | \\ CH_3 - CH - CH_3 \end{array}$$

Isobutane also contains four carbon atoms and ten hydrogen atoms. It has a branched chain structure.

Some carbon-based molecules can shift from one isomer to another, and then back to the original structure. For example, isomers of a molecule called retinal are necessary for your eyesight. When light strikes retinal, its structure changes from one isomer to another. The new isomer of retinal starts a process that sends a signal from the eye to the brain. After the retinal isomer starts the signaling process, the molecule shifts back to its original structure.

 If two substances are isomers of each other, how are they the same? different?

9.1 Review

KEY CONCEPTS

1. Why were carbon-based compounds first called organic? How has the understanding of organic compounds changed?
2. How is the way in which carbon atoms bond to each other important for the number of carbon-based compounds?
3. Describe three structures of carbon-based molecules.

CRITICAL THINKING

4. **Infer** Could the last carbon atom in a carbon chain make bonds with four hydrogen atoms? Why or why not?
5. **Synthesize** Do you think molecules based on carbon rings can have isomers? Why or why not?

CHALLENGE

6. **Communicate** A molecule called naphthalene consists of ten carbon atoms and eight hydrogen atoms in two linked benzene rings. Draw a diagram of a molecule that could be naphthalene. Be sure to include the atoms and the bonds between the atoms.

280 Unit 2: Chemical Interactions

ANSWERS

1. They were thought to be found only in organisms. Some carbon compounds are inorganic, and organic compounds can be made in a laboratory.

2. Two carbon atoms can form multiple bonds, making a great variety of molecules.

3. Possible answers: chains (carbon atoms bonded one after another), rings (carbon atoms on the ends of a chain are bonded), chains and rings (rings attached to a chain), isomers (same atoms, different structures)

4. No; it must make at least one bond with a carbon atom.

5. Yes; the isomers would include atoms bonded to the ring in different places.

6. 2 carbon rings joined at 2 carbons that share a double bond; 8 hydrogens at the other 8 carbons

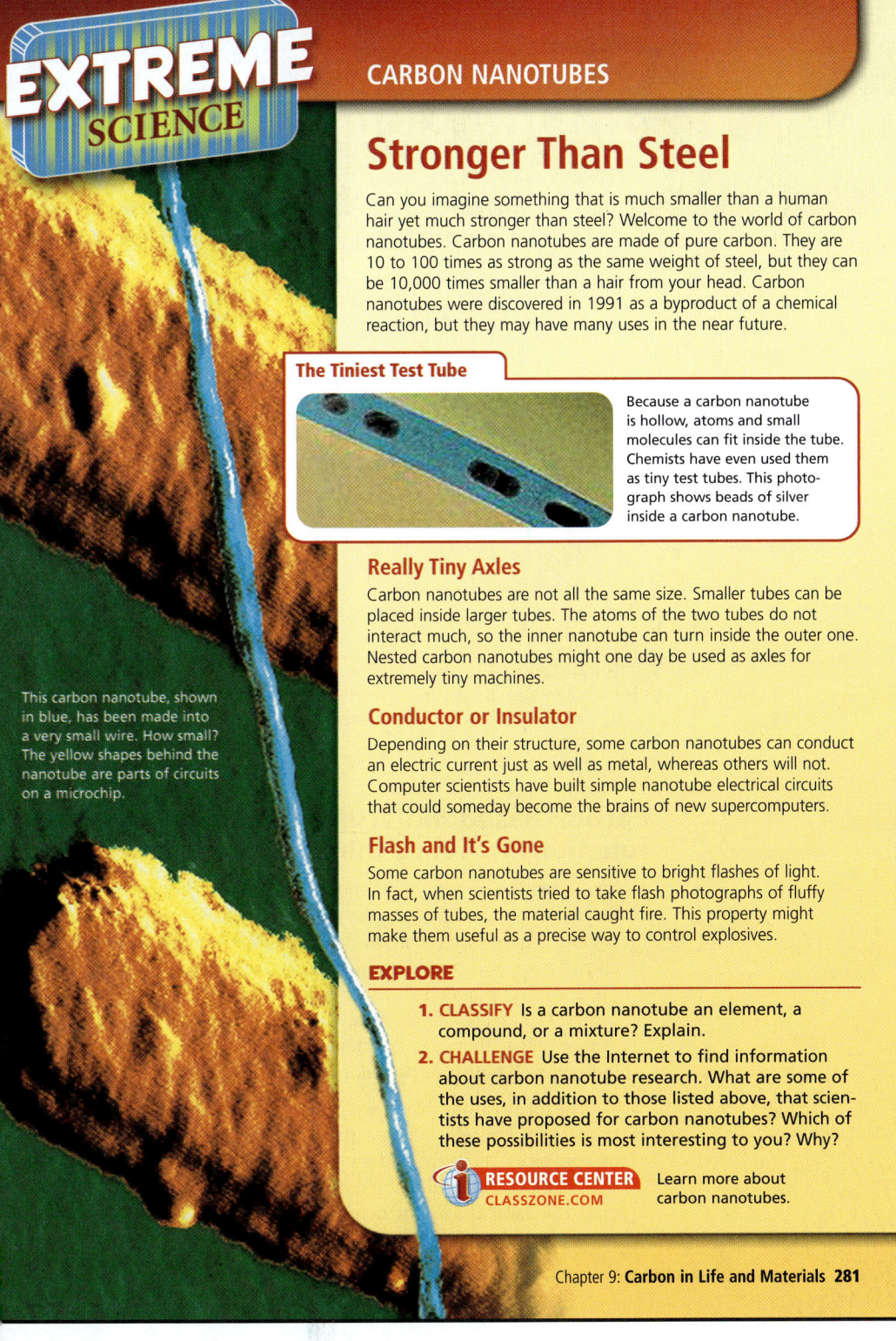

Extreme Science

CARBON NANOTUBES

Stronger Than Steel

Can you imagine something that is much smaller than a human hair yet much stronger than steel? Welcome to the world of carbon nanotubes. Carbon nanotubes are made of pure carbon. They are 10 to 100 times as strong as the same weight of steel, but they can be 10,000 times smaller than a hair from your head. Carbon nanotubes were discovered in 1991 as a byproduct of a chemical reaction, but they may have many uses in the near future.

The Tiniest Test Tube

Because a carbon nanotube is hollow, atoms and small molecules can fit inside the tube. Chemists have even used them as tiny test tubes. This photograph shows beads of silver inside a carbon nanotube.

Really Tiny Axles
Carbon nanotubes are not all the same size. Smaller tubes can be placed inside larger tubes. The atoms of the two tubes do not interact much, so the inner nanotube can turn inside the outer one. Nested carbon nanotubes might one day be used as axles for extremely tiny machines.

Conductor or Insulator
Depending on their structure, some carbon nanotubes can conduct an electric current just as well as metal, whereas others will not. Computer scientists have built simple nanotube electrical circuits that could someday become the brains of new supercomputers.

Flash and It's Gone
Some carbon nanotubes are sensitive to bright flashes of light. In fact, when scientists tried to take flash photographs of fluffy masses of tubes, the material caught fire. This property might make them useful as a precise way to control explosives.

EXPLORE

1. **CLASSIFY** Is a carbon nanotube an element, a compound, or a mixture? Explain.
2. **CHALLENGE** Use the Internet to find information about carbon nanotube research. What are some of the uses, in addition to those listed above, that scientists have proposed for carbon nanotubes? Which of these possibilities is most interesting to you? Why?

RESOURCE CENTER CLASSZONE.COM Learn more about carbon nanotubes.

This carbon nanotube, shown in blue, has been made into a very small wire. How small? The yellow shapes behind the nanotube are parts of circuits on a microchip.

EXTREME SCIENCE
Fun and Motivating Science

Set Learning Goal
To learn about carbon nanotubes and their possible uses

Present the Science
Carbon nanotubes were discovered accidentally as a byproduct of making fullerenes (also called buckyballs), which are C_{60} molecules shaped like soccer balls. A carbon nanotube can be thought of as a single sheet of graphite that has been rolled into a tube shape. Therefore, the walls of the tube are one atom thick. Today, carbon nanotubes are made purposely, although it is very difficult for chemists to make them the size they want. NASA expects to use carbon nanotubes in space exploration in applications such as energy storage, life-support systems, electronics, sensors, and biomedicine.

Discussion Questions
- Why do you think these carbon tubes are called nanotubes? *They are only a few nanometers (one-billionth of a meter) in diameter. They can be very long compared with their diameter, however.*
- Why might carbon nanotubes be combined with fibers? What would the advantage of these fibers be? *Nanotubes could be woven together with fibers to strengthen them. The fibers would probably look like ordinary fibers but be extremely strong.*

Close
Ask: Why are carbon nanotubes likely to be an important part of future technology? *Electronic devices, aerospace equipment, and computers are becoming smaller and smaller. Nanotechnology can contribute to miniaturization.*

EXPLORE

1. **CLASSIFY** It is an element. It does not contain atoms of other elements, so it cannot be a compound, and it is not a mixture for similar reasons.
2. **CHALLENGE** Answers will vary depending on each student's interests. Check students' research on nanotubes.

9.2 FOCUS

► Set Learning Goals
Students will
- Describe the functions of carbohydrates and lipids in living things.
- Describe how protein structure determines protein function.
- Recognize that nucleic acids carry instructions for building proteins.
- Infer from an experiment how starches can be detected in samples of food.

► 3-Minute Warm-Up
Display Transparency 36 or copy this exercise on the board:

Decide if these statements are true. If not true, correct them.

1. Carbon atoms can form only one bond with each other. *one, two, or three bonds*
2. Carbon chains are always branched. *They can also be straight.*
3. Two isomers contain the same kind and number of atoms arranged in different ways. *true*

 3-Minute Warm-Up, p. T36

9.2 MOTIVATE

EXPLORE Carbon in Food
PURPOSE To test foods for the presence of carbon

TIP *10 min.* Samples should be held in the blue part closest to the wick because it is the hottest part of the flame.

WHAT DO YOU THINK? *The food samples turned black; combustion.*

KEY CONCEPT
9.2 Carbon-based molecules are life's building blocks.

◄ BEFORE, you learned
- Carbon is the basis of life on Earth
- Carbon atoms can form multiple bonds
- Carbon can form molecules shaped like chains or rings

► NOW, you will learn
- About the functions of carbohydrates and lipids in living things
- About structures and functions of proteins
- How nucleic acids carry instructions for building proteins

VOCABULARY
carbohydrate p. 283
lipid p. 284
protein p. 286
enzyme p. 287
nucleic acid p. 289

EXPLORE Carbon in Food
How can you see the carbon in food?

PROCEDURE
1. Place the candle in the pie plate and light the candle.
2. Use the tongs to hold each food sample in the candle flame for 20 seconds. Record your observations.

WHAT DO YOU THINK?
- What changes did you observe in the samples?
- What type of chemical reaction might have caused these changes?

MATERIALS
- aluminum pie plate
- candle
- wooden matches
- tongs
- small marshmallow
- piece of carrot

Carbon-based molecules have many functions in living things.

You depend on carbon-based molecules for all of the activities in your life. For example, when you play softball, you need energy to swing the bat and run the bases. Carbon-based molecules are the source of the chemical energy needed by your muscle cells. Carbon-based molecules make up your muscle cells and provide those cells with the ability to contract and relax. Carbon-based molecules carry oxygen to your muscle cells so that your muscles can function properly. Carbon-based molecules even provide the information for building new molecules.

READING TIP
The prefix *macro-* means "large," so a macromolecule is a large molecule.

The many carbon-based molecules in all living things have certain similarities. They all contain carbon and elements such as hydrogen, oxygen, nitrogen, sulfur, and phosphorus. Many of the molecules are also very large molecules called macromolecules. However, these molecules have different structures and different functions.

282 Unit 2: Chemical Interactions

RESOURCES FOR DIFFERENTIATED INSTRUCTION

Below Level
UNIT RESOURCE BOOK
- Reading Study Guide A, pp. 283–284
- Decoding Support, p. 306

 AUDIO CDS

R Additional INVESTIGATION,
Testing Simple Sugars, A, B, & C, pp. 318–326; Teacher Instructions, pp. 329–330

Advanced
UNIT RESOURCE BOOK
Challenge and Extension, p. 289

English Learners
UNIT RESOURCE BOOK
Spanish Reading Study Guide, pp. 287–288

 AUDIO CDS

- Audio Readings in Spanish
- Audio Readings (English)

Living things contain four major types of carbon-based molecules.

The organic molecules found in living things are classified into four major groups—carbohydrates, lipids, proteins, and nucleic acids. You may already be familiar with these types of molecules and their functions in living things.

Carbohydrates include sugars and starches found in foods such as bread and pasta. Many lipids are fats or oils. Proteins are necessary for many functions in the body, including the formation of muscle tissue. Nucleic acids are the molecules that carry the genetic code for all living things. As you read about each of these types of molecules, look for ways in which the molecule's function depends on its structure.

Carbohydrates

Carbohydrates (KAHR-boh-HY-DRAYTZ) include sugars, starches, and cellulose, and contain atoms of three elements—carbon, hydrogen, and oxygen. They serve two main functions. Carbohydrates are a source of chemical energy for cells in many living things. They are also part of the structural materials of plants.

One important carbohydrate is the sugar glucose, which has the chemical formula $C_6H_{12}O_6$. Cells in both plants and animals break down glucose for energy. In plants glucose molecules also can be joined together to form more complex carbohydrates, such as starch and cellulose. Starch is a macromolecule that consists of many glucose molecules, or units, bonded together. Many foods, such as pasta, contain starch. When starch is broken back down into individual glucose molecules, those glucose molecules can be used as an energy source by cells.

Modeling Glucose

The glucose molecule can be represented by a hexagon. The red O shows that an oxygen atom is in the ring.

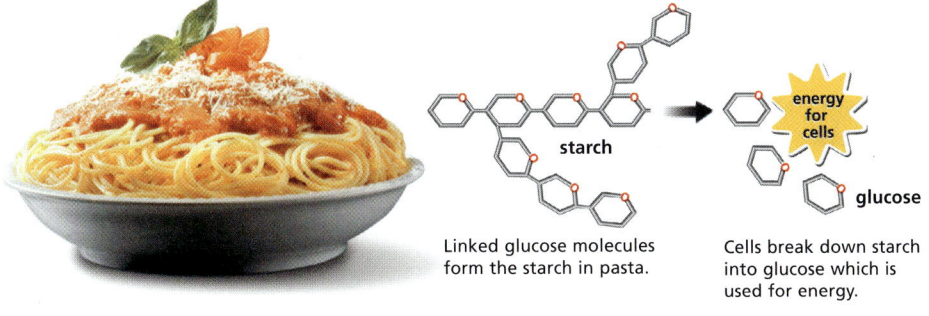

Linked glucose molecules form the starch in pasta.

Cells break down starch into glucose which is used for energy.

Chapter 9: Carbon in Life and Materials 283

DIFFERENTIATE INSTRUCTION

More Reading Support

 Which major groups of organic molecules are found in living things? *carbohydrates, lipids, proteins, and nucleic acids*

English Learners Point out the word *macromolecule* on p. 283. Ask students what they think the prefix *macro* means. Guide them to use the context of the sentence to find the answer. Then have students look up *macro* in the dictionary to find that it means "large."

Additional Investigation To reinforce Section 9.2 learning goals, use the following full-period investigation:

Additional INVESTIGATION, Testing Simple Sugars, A, B, & C, pp. 318–326, 329–330

9.2 INSTRUCT

Develop Critical Thinking

INFER Ask: Why do athletes eat large amounts of pasta or other starches when they are in training, a process called carbo-loading? *They need large amounts of energy to train. Pasta, which is rich in carbohydrates, provides that energy.*

EXPLORE the BIG idea

Revisit "Sweet Crackers" on p. 273. Have students explain their results.

Integrate the Sciences

Animals, as well as plants, store glucose in a macromolecule. The macromolecule in animals is glycogen, which is also called animal starch. In glycogen, glucose molecules are bonded together in a highly branched arrangement. The liver and muscles store glycogen. Glycogen can be broken down into glucose molecules when cells need energy. It is also important to note that the glucose molecule is not the direct source of energy for cells. Through the process of cellular respiration, glucose is broken down to produce ATP (adenosine triphosphate), which is the molecule that provides energy.

Teach from Visuals

To help students interpret the diagrams of glucose and starch, ask:

- How is the hexagon that represents glucose different from the hexagon that represents benzene? *There is an oxygen atom in the glucose ring; there is no circle inside the ring to represent alternating double and single bonds.*

- Where is the energy in pasta stored? *in the glucose molecules that make up the starch in pasta*

- Why does starch have to be broken down into glucose before energy can be released? *Glucose, not starch, is broken down in the reactions that provide energy for cells.*

Chapter 9 283

Teach from Visuals

To help students interpret the picture of the structure of cellulose, ask:

- How is the structure of cellulose different from the structure of starch as shown on p. 283? *The glucose molecules in cellulose are linked in a long chain, whereas the glucose molecules in starch are linked in branches.*

- How is the structure of cellulose similar to the structure of starch? *They both contain glucose molecules.*

Real World Example

Lipids are found in soaps and detergents. Many substances that need to be cleaned from clothes and skin, such as soil, grass, and grease, are nonpolar and organic. These substances are not easily removed by water alone because they do not dissolve in water, which is polar.

Teach from Visuals

To help students interpret the model of a fatty acid molecule, ask:

- What is the basic structure of a fatty acid? *It is a carbon chain.*

- What does the break in the middle of the model of the structure represent? Why? *Not all carbon atoms are shown in the chain because a fatty acid can be a very large molecule.*

Ongoing Assessment

Recognize that carbohydrates and lipids have similar functions.

Ask: Why are lipids better energy storage molecules than carbohydrates? *One gram of fat contains approximately twice as much energy as one gram of carbohydrate or protein.*

CHECK YOUR READING Answer: to supply chemical energy; to supply chemical energy and structure

---

Plants make their own glucose through a process called photosynthesis, which you read about in Chapter 7. Some of the glucose made during photosynthesis is used to make the complex carbohydrate molecules that form a plant's structure.

Moss Leaf Cells

Cellulose

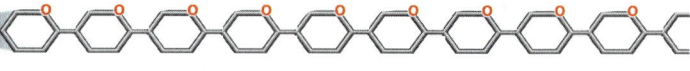

Cellulose is a long chain-like molecule that forms part of a plant's structure.

Unlike animal cells, plant cells have a tough, protective layer outside the cell membrane called the cell wall. Cellulose (SEHL-yuh-LOHS) is a macromolecule found in plant cell walls, and it is a large part of vegetables such as lettuce and celery. The illustration shows moss leaf cells with their cell walls, and a diagram of part of a cellulose molecule.

Cellulose and starch are both carbohydrates composed of glucose molecules, but the glucose molecules that make up these larger macromolecules are linked in different ways. Because of their different structures, starch and cellulose have different functions. In fact, this structural difference also prevents your body from breaking down and using cellulose as it would starch.

CHECK YOUR READING What are some functions of carbohydrates in animals? in plants?

VOCABULARY Make a magnet word diagram for *lipid* and for other vocabulary terms.

Lipids

Lipids include fats and oils and are used mainly for energy and as structural materials in living things. Like carbohydrates, most lipids are made of carbon, hydrogen, and oxygen. Even though lipids and carbohydrates have many similarities, they have different structures and properties.

Animals store chemical energy in fat. Plants store chemical energy in oils, such as olive oil and peanut oil. Fats and oils store energy very efficiently—one gram of fat contains about twice as much energy as one gram of carbohydrate or protein. Fats and oils contain three carbon chains called fatty acids. The illustration below shows the general structure of a fatty acid.

Modeling Fatty Acids

$$CH_3 - CH_2 - CH_2 \{ \} CH_2 - CH_2 - CH_2 - COOH =$$

The carbon chains in lipids are called fatty acids. A carbon atom is at each bend of the zig-zag model above. The break in the middle of the chain shows that some carbon atoms have been left out.

DIFFERENTIATE INSTRUCTION

More Reading Support

B Where is cellulose found? *plant cell walls*

C What are the main functions of lipids? *energy storage and as structural materials*

English Learners Help English learners understand how prepositions are used in phrasal verbs. The sentence below is an example—note the verb phrase *breaking down*.

"In fact, this structural difference also prevents your body from breaking down and using cellulose as it would starch."

Have students read this sentence and point out the verb phrase—be sure they do not interpret "down" as a literal direction.

You may have heard the terms *saturated* and *unsaturated* in relation to fats. If all of the bonds between carbon atoms in the fatty acids are single bonds, the lipid is a saturated fat. If one or more of these bonds is a double bond, the lipid is an unsaturated fat. Most animal fats are saturated, and most oils from plants are unsaturated. Diets high in saturated fats have been linked to heart disease. Lipids in the butter in the photograph on the right are saturated fats.

Fat Structure

CHECK YOUR READING What is the difference between a saturated fat and an unsaturated fat?

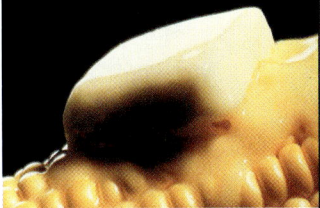

Fats in butter contain three fatty acids and are used for energy. Butter contains saturated fats.

Some lipids are important parts of cell structure. Structural lipids often contain the element phosphorus and are called phospholipids. Phospholipids are a significant part of cell membranes such as the one shown in the photograph of the nerve cell on the right.

Phospholipid Structure

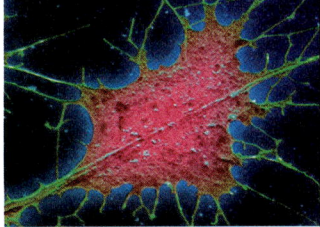

Some lipids in this nerve cell's membrane have two fatty acids and one phosphate group. These lipids are called phospholipids.

Another lipid involved in cell structure is cholesterol, which is a part of cell membranes. Cholesterol has other functions as well. It is necessary to make substances called hormones. Hormones, such as adrenaline, are chemical messengers in your body.

Your body makes some of the cholesterol that it needs, but it also uses cholesterol from foods you eat. Cholesterol is found in many foods that come from animals, such as meat and eggs. Even some plant products, such as coconut oil, can increase the amount of cholesterol in your body. Although you need cholesterol, eating too much of it—just like eating too much saturated fat—can lead to heart disease.

Chapter 9: **Carbon in Life and Materials** 285

Integrating the Sciences

A very important fat in the human nervous system is myelin. Myelin forms a sheath that covers many nerve cells, which increases the speed of transmission of nerve signals. Without myelin, nerves cannot transmit signals. In the disease multiple sclerosis, the body's own immune system destroys the myelin sheath that covers nerve cells.

Language Arts Connection

Many lipids are based on fatty acids that are linked to a molecule called glycerol. The fat illustrated in butter is called a triglyceride; the phospholipid is called a diglyceride. Ask: What does this difference tell you about the structure of a lipid molecule? (If necessary, instruct students to look up the prefixes *tri-* and *di-* in a dictionary.) *A triglyceride has three fatty acids, whereas a diglyceride has two fatty acids.*

Teach from Visuals

To help students interpret the diagrams of different kinds of fats, ask: Where is the phosphate group in a phospholipid? *It takes the place of one fatty acid.*

Ongoing Assessment

CHECK YOUR READING *Answer: saturated fat—all bonds between carbon atoms in fatty acids are single bonds; unsaturated fat—one or more bonds between carbon atoms are double bonds.*

DIFFERENTIATE INSTRUCTION

D Where are phospholipids in the body? *in cell membranes*

E Why is cholesterol important? *for cell membrane structure and in making hormones*

Advanced Students could extend their knowledge of phospholipids by researching how they participate in the structure of cell membranes. The fluid mosaic model of membrane structure is not difficult to understand and will enhance students' understanding of phospholipids.

 Challenge and Extension, p. 289

INVESTIGATE Organic Molecules

PURPOSE To discover what foods contain starch by testing them with iodine

TIP 20 min. Use plain gelatin. The liquid gelatin and tofu are included as substances that do not contain starch. They are both proteins.

WHAT DO YOU THINK? *Iodine turned blue-black with cornstarch but not with gelatin. The bread contains starch but the tofu does not, as shown by a color change with bread but not with tofu.*

CHALLENGE *crust and sauce*

 Datasheet, Organic Molecules, p. 290

Technology Resources

Customize this student lab as needed or look for an alternative. Print rubrics to assess student lab reports.

 Lab Generator CD-ROM

Teaching with Technology

Students may want to photograph a positive reaction when testing cornstarch, so they can compare the color when testing other substances.

Real World Example

A change of amino acids in hemoglobin, the protein responsible for carrying oxygen in the blood, changes the shape of the protein. Sickle-cell anemia is a disease that results from this kind of change in protein structure. The change in the protein from hemoglobin A to hemoglobin S changes the shape of red blood cells and leads to many health problems.

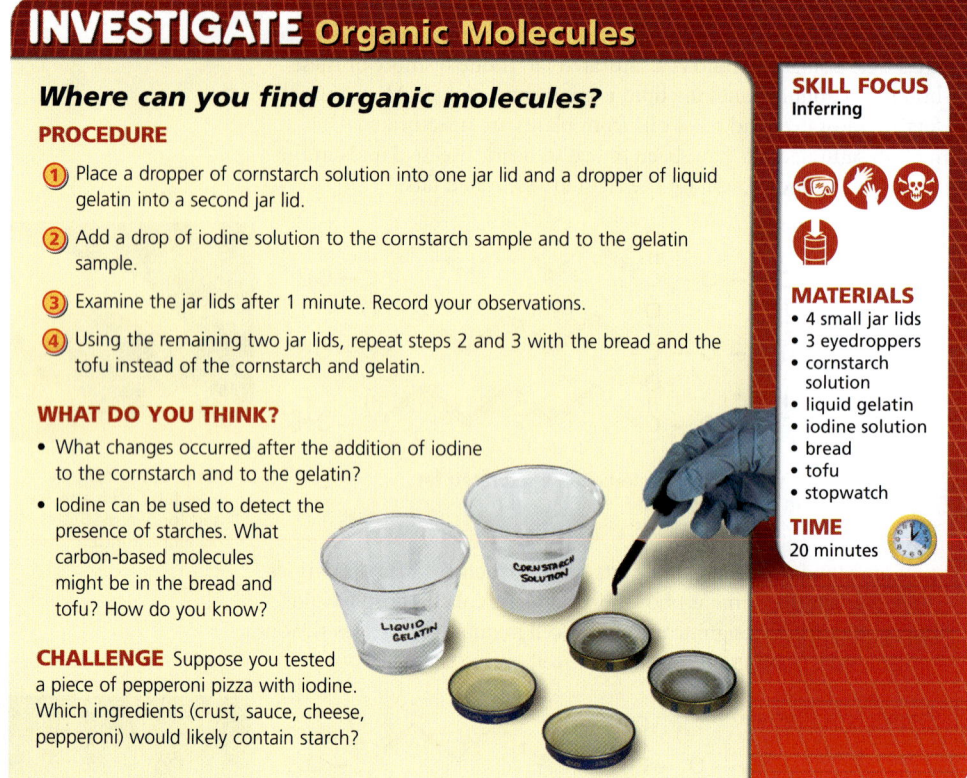

INVESTIGATE Organic Molecules

Where can you find organic molecules?

PROCEDURE

1. Place a dropper of cornstarch solution into one jar lid and a dropper of liquid gelatin into a second jar lid.
2. Add a drop of iodine solution to the cornstarch sample and to the gelatin sample.
3. Examine the jar lids after 1 minute. Record your observations.
4. Using the remaining two jar lids, repeat steps 2 and 3 with the bread and the tofu instead of the cornstarch and gelatin.

WHAT DO YOU THINK?
- What changes occurred after the addition of iodine to the cornstarch and to the gelatin?
- Iodine can be used to detect the presence of starches. What carbon-based molecules might be in the bread and tofu? How do you know?

CHALLENGE Suppose you tested a piece of pepperoni pizza with iodine. Which ingredients (crust, sauce, cheese, pepperoni) would likely contain starch?

SKILL FOCUS Inferring

MATERIALS
- 4 small jar lids
- 3 eyedroppers
- cornstarch solution
- liquid gelatin
- iodine solution
- bread
- tofu
- stopwatch

TIME 20 minutes

Proteins

 Proteins are macromolecules that are made of smaller molecules called amino acids. Proteins, like carbohydrates and lipids, contain carbon, hydrogen, and oxygen. However, proteins differ from carbohydrates and lipids in that they also contain nitrogen, sulfur, and other elements. Unlike carbohydrates and lipids, which are used primarily for energy and structure, proteins have many different functions.

Think of a protein as being like a word, with amino acids as the letters in that word. The meaning of a word depends on the order of letters in the word. For example, rearranging the letters in the word "eat" makes different words with different meanings. Similarly, proteins depend on the order of their amino acids.

Linked Amino Acids

tyrosine   lysine   cysteine   serine   leucine

DIFFERENTIATE INSTRUCTION

 **More Reading Support**

F Which small molecules make up a protein? *amino acids*

Alternative Assessment Have students make a poster with colored pictures showing their results in the investigation. They could extend the activity by including a section with pictures of other foods and their predictions of the results when these foods are tested with iodine. Students may want to test these foods after they make their predictions.

Just as 26 letters of the alphabet make up all words in the English language, 20 amino acids make up all of the proteins in your body. The structure of a protein is determined by the order of its amino acids. If two amino acids change places, the entire protein changes.

The function of a protein depends on its structure. There are at least 100,000 proteins in your body, each with a different structure that gives it a specific function. Some proteins are structural materials, some control chemical reactions, and others transport substances within cells and through the body. Still others are a part of the immune system, which protects you from infections.

CHECK YOUR READING How does the function of a protein depend on its structure?

Proteins that are part of the structure of living things are often shaped like coils. One coil-shaped protein, keratin, is part of human hair as shown on the left below. Proteins called actin and myosin are coil-shaped proteins that help your muscles contract.

Other types of proteins have coiled regions but curl up into shapes like balls. One example is hemoglobin, shown on the right below. Hemoglobin is a transport protein that carries oxygen in the blood.

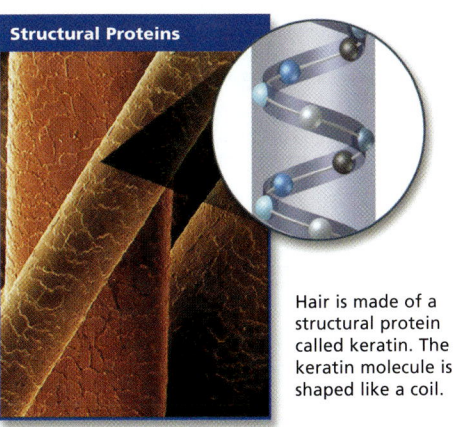

Structural Proteins

Hair is made of a structural protein called keratin. The keratin molecule is shaped like a coil.

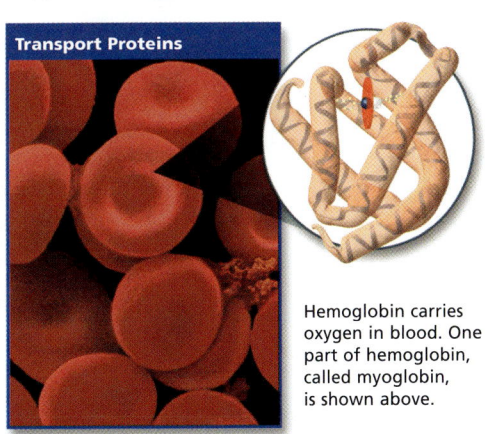

Transport Proteins

Hemoglobin carries oxygen in blood. One part of hemoglobin, called myoglobin, is shown above.

Some proteins that curl up into a shape like a ball are enzymes. An **enzyme** (EHN-zym) is a catalyst for a chemical reaction in living things. Catalysts increase the rate of chemical reactions. Enzymes are necessary for many chemical reactions in your body. Without enzymes, these reactions would occur too slowly to keep you alive.

It is important to have proteins in your diet so that your body can make its own proteins. Proteins in foods such as meats, soybeans, and nuts are broken down into amino acids by your body. These amino acids are then used by your cells to make new proteins.

Chapter 9: **Carbon in Life and Materials** 287

DIFFERENTIATE INSTRUCTION

More Reading Support

G What are enzymes? *catalysts for chemical reactions in living things*

Below Level To help students understand the three-dimensional structure of proteins, provide a string of large beads (pop beads are good for this purpose) and some two-sided adhesive tape. Students can model a three-dimensional molecule by creating "attractive forces" between the beads with the tape.

Teach Difficult Concepts

Students often have trouble visualizing how a chain of amino acids can form a three-dimensional structure. Explain that the polarity of amino acids can either attract or repel other amino acids. These attractive and repulsive forces cause the chain to fold into a specific three-dimensional structure.

Address Misconceptions

IDENTIFY Ask: What are energy sources for your cells? If students answer carbohydrates and lipids, they may think that proteins cannot be used for energy.

CORRECT Have students examine a nutrition label that lists Calories per gram. (Not all labels list this information.) Proteins contain 4 Calories per gram, the same number of calories as carbohydrates.

REASSESS Ask: How can the body get energy if carbohydrates and lipids are not available? *It can break down proteins for energy, but usually only as a last resort.*

Technology Resources

Visit **ClassZone.com** for background on common student misconceptions.

MISCEPTION DATABASE

Ongoing Assessment

Describe how a protein's structure determines its function.

Ask: What determines the structure and function of a protein? *the order of the amino acids in the molecule*

CHECK YOUR READING Answer: *The order of amino acids gives a protein a specific structure, which also gives it a specific function.*

Chapter 9 **287**

Teach from Visuals

To help students interpret the visual of the structure of DNA, ask:

- Which molecules make up the sides of the "ladder"? *alternating 5-carbon sugar molecules and phosphate groups*
- Which molecules make up the ladder's rungs? *the four bases (A, T, G, and C)*
- Which bases are always paired with each other? *A (adenine) always pairs with T (thymine); C (cytosine) always pairs with G (guanine).*
- Which part of DNA contains the code for an amino acid? *a sequence of three DNA bases*

History of Science

James Watson and Francis Crick discovered the double-helix structure and bonding of base pairs in the DNA molecule in 1953. The story behind the discovery and a personal look at the scientific process is described in the book *The Double Helix*, written by James Watson.

Ongoing Assessment

Explain how proteins are put together from the information contained in nucleic acid molecules.

Ask: How does the fact that DNA is a long chain of subunits help to create a protein molecule? *A protein molecule also is a long chain of subunits. The process is linear, with one sequence of three bases coding for an amino acid.*

READING VISUALS *Answer: It provides the code for correctly assembling proteins.*

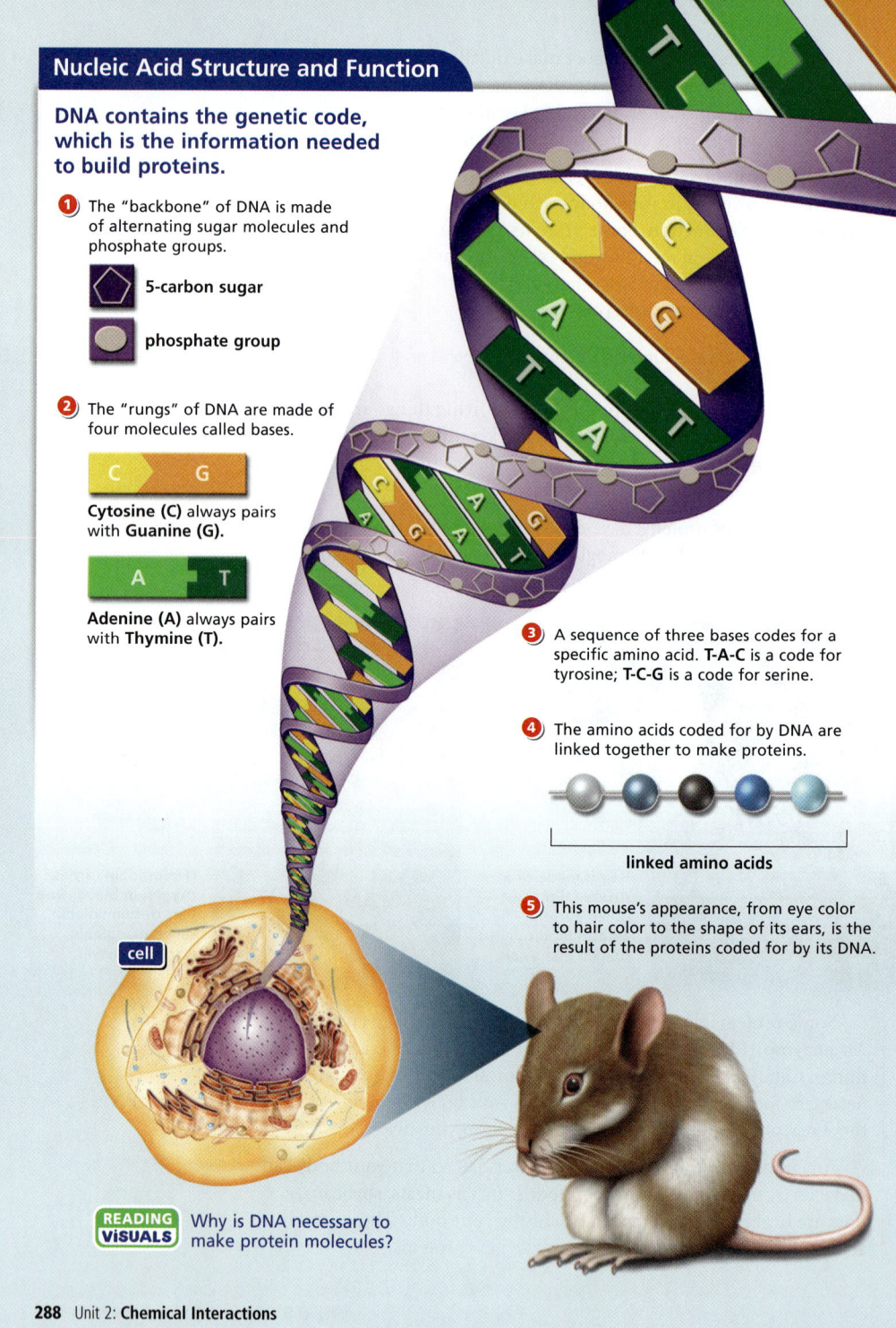

Nucleic Acid Structure and Function

DNA contains the genetic code, which is the information needed to build proteins.

1. The "backbone" of DNA is made of alternating sugar molecules and phosphate groups.
   - 5-carbon sugar
   - phosphate group

2. The "rungs" of DNA are made of four molecules called bases.
   - Cytosine (C) always pairs with Guanine (G).
   - Adenine (A) always pairs with Thymine (T).

3. A sequence of three bases codes for a specific amino acid. **T-A-C** is a code for tyrosine; **T-C-G** is a code for serine.

4. The amino acids coded for by DNA are linked together to make proteins.

   linked amino acids

5. This mouse's appearance, from eye color to hair color to the shape of its ears, is the result of the proteins coded for by its DNA.

READING VISUALS Why is DNA necessary to make protein molecules?

288 Unit 2: Chemical Interactions

DIFFERENTIATE INSTRUCTION

Inclusion Students with visual impairments may better understand how the DNA molecule is constructed if you let them handle a zipper. The sides of the zipper represent the sugar-phosphate backbones of the DNA molecule. The zipper's teeth represent the bases. When the zipper is closed, hydrogen bonds have formed between the bases to hold the two halves of the DNA molecule together. Twisting the zipper into a helix also helps students visualize the molecule's structure.

Nucleic Acids

Nucleic acids (noo-KLEE-ihk AS-ihdz) are huge, complex carbon-based molecules that contain the information that cells use to make proteins. These macromolecules are made of carbon, hydrogen, and oxygen, as well as nitrogen and phosphorus. Each of the cells in your body contains a complete set of nucleic acids. This means that each cell has all of the instructions necessary for making any protein in your body.

The illustration on page 288 shows part of a nucleic acid molecule called DNA, which looks like a twisted ladder. The sides of the ladder are made of sugar molecules and phosphate groups. Each rung of the ladder is composed of two nitrogen-containing molecules called bases. DNA has four types of bases, represented by the letters A, C, T, and G. The order of the bases in a DNA molecule is the way in which DNA stores the instructions for making proteins. How do just four molecules—A, C, T, and G—carry all of this important information?

READING TIP
The *NA* in DNA stands for nucleic acid. The *D* stands for deoxyribose, which is the type of sugar in the molecule.

Recall that a protein is composed of amino acids that have to be linked in a certain order. Each of the 20 amino acids is represented by a particular series of three DNA bases. For example, the sequence T–A–C corresponds to—or is a code for—the amino acid tyrosine. There are 64 different three-base sequences in DNA, all of which have a specific meaning. This genetic code works in the same way in every living thing on Earth. It provides a complete set of instructions for linking amino acids in the right order to make each specific protein molecule. The DNA code is only one part of making proteins, though. Other types of nucleic acids, called RNA, are responsible for reading the code and assembling a protein with the correct amino acids.

RESOURCE CENTER CLASSZONE.COM
Find out more about carbohydrates, lipids, proteins, and nucleic acids.

 How many different types of bases make up the genetic code in DNA?

9.2 Review

KEY CONCEPTS
1. How does the function of a lipid depend on its structure?
2. What determines the structure of a protein?
3. What role does DNA perform in the making of proteins?

CRITICAL THINKING
4. **Synthesize** Give two examples of carbon-based molecules in living things that are based on a chain structure. Explain.
5. **Compare and Contrast** How are carbohydrates and lipids similar? How are they different?

CHALLENGE
6. **Infer** Suppose the order of bases in a DNA molecule is changed. What do you think will happen to the structure of the protein that is coded for by that region of DNA? Why?

Chapter 9: Carbon in Life and Materials 289

ANSWERS

1. Sample answer: A lipid with a phosphate group is used for cell structure.
2. The order of amino acids in a protein gives the protein its structure and function.
3. DNA carries instructions for lining up amino acids in a protein.
4. Starch and cellulose are chains of glucose; fatty acids in lipids contain chains; proteins are long chains of amino acids.
5. They are both organic; contain carbon, hydrogen, and oxygen; are based on carbon chains; are used for energy and structure. However, lipids include fats and oils, and carbohydrates include sugars and starches; lipids can also contain other elements.
6. The protein would change because the code for amino acids is changed.

Ongoing Assessment

Answer: four

Integrate the Sciences
DNA is one of two nucleic acids. DNA contains the genetic code, but a different type of nucleic acid, called RNA (ribonucleic acid), is necessary for making a protein. There are several kinds of RNA. Unlike DNA, which is double-stranded, RNA molecules are single-stranded. Also, RNA molecules contain the base uracil (U) instead of thymine (T).

Reinforce the BIG idea
Have students relate the section to the Big Idea.

 Reinforcing Key Concepts, p. 291

9.2 ASSESS & RETEACH

Assess
 Section 9.2 Quiz, p. 82

Reteach
Have students examine nutrition labels on food products at home for information about carbohydrates, lipids (fats), and proteins. Have students describe the general structures of these organic molecules in the food. Students should identify the difference between sugar and fiber (cellulose) and between saturated and unsaturated fats.

Technology Resources
Have students visit ClassZone.com for reteaching of Key Concepts.

 CONTENT REVIEW

 CONTENT REVIEW CD-ROM

Chapter 9 **289**

MATH IN SCIENCE
Math Skills Practice for Science

Set Learning Goal
To make a bar graph that shows the daily dietary recommendations for healthful nutrition

Present the Science
The data in the table are based on the U.S. Department of Agriculture's (USDA) food guide pyramid. The USDA compiled the pyramid from research on what foods Americans eat, which nutrients are in these foods, and how Americans should make the best food choices to promote good health. Although it outlines what Americans should eat every day, the pyramid is a guideline rather than a rigid prescription.

Develop Graphing Skills
- Explain that a bar graph is the best choice of graphs to represent data that are not continuously changing.
- The independent variable is usually plotted on the *x*-axis. The dependent variable is usually plotted on the *y*-axis.

DIFFERENTIATION TIP Review independent and dependent variables with students. Be sure they understand why the axes are labeled as they are in the bar graph.

Close
Which type of organic molecule (carbohydrates, lipids, or proteins) accounts for the majority of recommended servings in a healthy diet? How do you know?
Carbohydrates; grains, vegetables, and fruits make up more of a healthy diet than dairy products, meats, and beans.

- Math Support, p. 307
- Math Practice, p. 308

Technology Resources
Students can visit ClassZone.com for practice making bar graphs.

 MATH TUTORIAL

290 Unit 2: **Chemical Interactions**

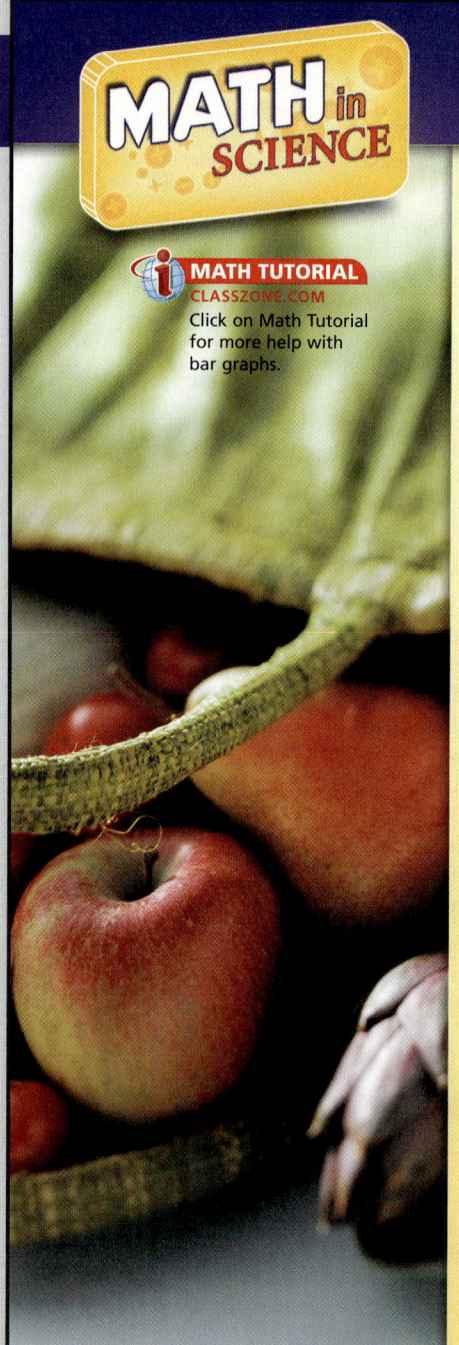

290 Unit 2: Chemical Interactions

MATH in SCIENCE

MATH TUTORIAL
CLASSZONE.COM
Click on Math Tutorial for more help with bar graphs.

SKILL: MAKING BAR GRAPHS

Graphing Good Food

People need to eat carbohydrates, proteins, and lipids to have a healthy diet. Different amounts of each type of organic molecule are recommended for different groups of people. In general, grains, vegetables, and fruits contain carbohydrates. Dairy products, meats, and beans contain proteins and lipids. The table on the right shows dietary recommendations. The information could also be shown in a bar graph.

Recommended Servings

Food group	Young children	Teen girls	Teen boys
Grains	6	9	11
Vegetables	3	4	5
Fruits	2	3	4
Dairy	3	3	3
Meats, beans	2	2	3

SOURCE: U.S. Department of Agriculture, Home and Garden Bulletin Number 252, 1996

Example
Create a bar graph that shows the dietary recommendation of grains for each group.
(1) Use the height of the bar to indicate the numerical value of a piece of data.
(2) Show the number of servings on the vertical axis. Label each group of bars on the horizontal axis.
(3) Use a different color for each group.

ANSWER

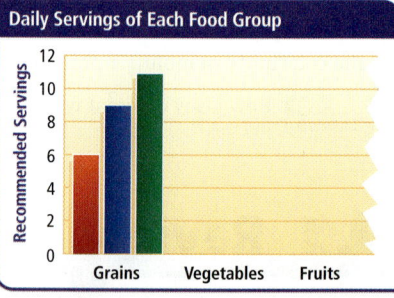

Use the Recommended Servings table above to answer the following questions.

1. Copy and complete the bar graph to show the dietary recommendations for the other four food groups.

2. Which group has the tallest bars on the graph? the shortest?

CHALLENGE Choose one group of people and make a pie graph showing recommendations for them. (Hint: First convert the numbers of servings into fractions of the whole diet.)

ANSWERS

1. See students' graphs.
2. tallest: teen boys; shortest: young children

CHALLENGE Students' pie charts will vary with the age group chosen. The fractions should add up to one.

KEY CONCEPT
9.3 Carbon-based molecules are in many materials.

BEFORE, you learned
- Organic compounds are based on carbon
- Carbon can form molecules shaped like chains or rings
- Four types of carbon-based compounds are common in living things

NOW, you will learn
- How carbon-based molecules are obtained from petroleum
- How carbon-based molecules are designed for specific uses
- How a material's properties depend on its molecular structure

VOCABULARY
hydrocarbon p. 291
polymer p. 294
monomer p. 294
plastic p. 295

THINK ABOUT
What do windbreakers and motor oil have in common?

Motor oil and windbreakers are both made of carbon-based molecules. The motor oil is composed mostly of carbon and hydrogen. The nylon windbreaker is also composed mostly of carbon and hydrogen. How can two materials that are so different be made of similar molecules?

Carbon-based compounds from ancient organisms are used to make new materials.

Many of the things you see around you every day contain carbon-based molecules. Some, such as people, plants, and animals, are easy to spot. Others are not so easy to identify. These objects include clothing, furniture, packing materials, sports equipment, and more. You have read that a large number of substances that make up living things are based on carbon. Where do we get carbon-based molecules that we use to make modern materials?

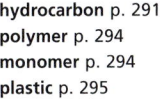

RESOURCE CENTER
CLASSZONE.COM
Find out more about petroleum and hydrocarbons.

The carbon-based compounds that are the basis of many materials are called hydrocarbons. A **hydrocarbon** is simply a compound made of only carbon and hydrogen. Many different hydrocarbons are found in large deposits underground and under the sea. The story of how they got there began a long time ago and is related to the way carbon moves through the environment in a cycle.

Chapter 9: Carbon in Life and Materials 291

9.3 FOCUS

● Set Learning Goals
Students will
- Recognize how carbon-based molecules are obtained from petroleum.
- Explain how carbon-based molecules are designed for specific uses.
- Describe how a material's properties depend on its molecular structure.

● 3-Minute Warm-Up
Display Transparency 37 or copy this exercise on the board:

Match the definition to the correct term.
Definitions
1. type of molecule made of linked units called amino acids **d**
2. type of molecule that contains carbon chains called fatty acids **c**
3. a class of compounds based on carbon **a**

Terms
a. organic compound
b. inorganic compound
c. lipid
d. protein
e. carbohydrate

 3-Minute Warm-Up, p. T37

9.3 MOTIVATE

THINK ABOUT
PURPOSE To introduce the concept of hydrocarbons as the basis for many materials

DEMONSTRATE To demonstrate the importance of petroleum-based materials in modern life, have students take five minutes to list as many items that are made of petroleum-based materials as they can.

Sample answer: Different materials of similar molecules probably have different molecular structures.

RESOURCES FOR DIFFERENTIATED INSTRUCTION

Below Level
UNIT RESOURCE BOOK
- Reading Study Guide A, pp. 294–295
- Decoding Support, p. 306

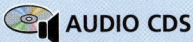 **AUDIO CDS**

Advanced
UNIT RESOURCE BOOK
- Challenge and Extension, p. 300
- Challenge Reading, pp. 302–303

English Learners
UNIT RESOURCE BOOK
Spanish Reading Study Guide, pp. 298–299

 **AUDIO CDS**
- Audio Readings in Spanish
- Audio Readings (English)

Chapter 9 **291**

9.3 INSTRUCT

Teach from Visuals

To help students interpret the diagram of the carbon cycle, ask:

- What type of organic molecule is made during the part of the cycle labeled "Plants use CO_2"? *carbohydrate*
- In which two ways does carbon return to the atmosphere? *exhalation of carbon dioxide by animals, decomposition of plants and animals*
- How is carbon removed from the carbon cycle? *Decaying organisms are trapped in the ground, where their carbon-based molecules become the hydrocarbons in petroleum.*

Teach Difficult Concepts

Students may have trouble understanding how distillation works. Remind them that steam forms when a kettle of water boils. Tell them that if the steam can be captured in a container and cooled, it becomes liquid water again. This process is called distillation. Ask whether distillation involves a physical or chemical change. *physical* To help students understand, you might try the following demonstration.

Teacher Demo

Boil some water in a beaker. After it begins to boil, place a cool glass plate over the top of the beaker. When the glass is covered with condensed water, lift it off the beaker while using thermal gloves, and drain the condensed water into another beaker.

Ongoing Assessment

Recognize why many items used in modern life contain carbon.

Ask: Which natural resource is the source of modern carbon-based materials? *petroleum or crude oil*

CHECK YOUR READING Answer: Hydrocarbons are separated by using differences in their boiling points.

SUPPORTING MAIN IDEAS Make a chart about the carbon-based molecules in modern materials.

READING TIP As you read the numbered steps, follow the process shown on page 293.

VISUALIZATION CLASSZONE.COM Observe the process involved in the separation of the hydrocarbons in petroleum.

In the carbon cycle, plants use carbon dioxide from the air to make carbohydrates. Animals eat plants and absorb carbon, and then release carbon dioxide into the air when they exhale. When animals and plants die, they decompose and carbon returns to the environment. Most carbon returns to the atmosphere as part of the carbon cycle, but some does not. This carbon is the source of the carbon-based compounds that are so important for modern life.

Carbon Cycle

- CO_2 in atmosphere
- Plants use CO_2 and store carbon
- Animals eat plants, exhale CO_2, releasing carbon
- Hydrocarbons in petroleum
- Animals and plants decompose, release carbon

① **Obtaining Petroleum** Some living things that died hundreds of millions of years ago fell into mud or sediment. Instead of returning to the atmosphere, the carbon-based molecules from these organisms became trapped in the ground. Over time, and through a process of chemical changes, some of this organic material became petroleum, which is a mixture of hundreds of different hydrocarbons. People pump petroleum from underground and undersea deposits. Liquid petroleum is called crude oil.

② **Refining Petroleum** In its raw form, petroleum is not a useful substance. However, when it is processed at a refinery, it is separated into many useful parts.

③ **Using Products Made from Petroleum** Many products, including gasoline, plastics, and fibers such as nylon are made from the separated parts of petroleum.

The refining of petroleum is an example of the separation of a mixture based on physical properties. Each type of hydrocarbon in petroleum has a different boiling point. In general, each boiling point depends on the number and arrangement of carbon atoms in the molecule. For example, lubricating oil contains long carbon chains and boils at temperatures above 350°C. The hydrocarbons that make up gasoline are smaller molecules, and they boil between 35°C and 220°C.

At a refinery, petroleum is heated until all but the largest of the hydrocarbons are in gaseous form. This gaseous petroleum is released into a distillation tower. As the gases rise in the tower, they gradually cool. When each specific hydrocarbon cools to its boiling point, it condenses back into a liquid. Thus, lubricating oil cools to its boiling point quickly and is collected from a low level in the tower. Hydrocarbons in gasoline take longer to become liquids and are collected higher in the tower.

CHECK YOUR READING How are hydrocarbons in petroleum separated from each other?

292 Unit 2: Chemical Interactions

DIFFERENTIATE INSTRUCTION

More Reading Support

A Is petroleum formed by physical changes or chemical changes? *chemical changes*

English Learners Place the terms *hydrocarbon, polymer,* and *plastic* on the classroom's Science Word Wall with a brief definition for each. English learners may not have prior knowledge of windbreakers on p. 291, Teflon on p. 296, and the practice of using police dogs shown on p. 297.

Using Petroleum

Carbon-based compounds in petroleum are used to make a wide range of products.

① Obtaining Petroleum

Petroleum is trapped underground between rock layers that it cannot move through. People have pumped petroleum out of the ground since the 1850s.

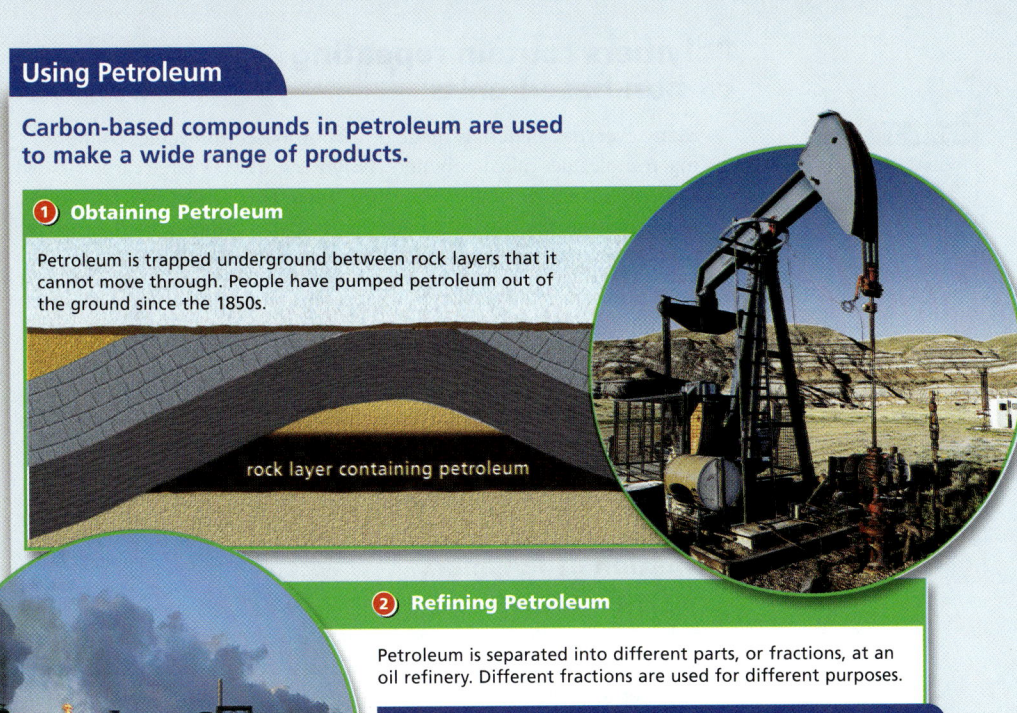

② Refining Petroleum

Petroleum is separated into different parts, or fractions, at an oil refinery. Different fractions are used for different purposes.

Petroleum Products

Petroleum Fraction	Number of Carbon Atoms per Molecule	Uses
Gases	1 to 4	Cooking, heating, manufacturing
Gasoline	5 to 12	Automobile fuel
Kerosene	12 to 16	Airplane fuel
Fuel oil	15 to 18	Diesel fuel, heating oil
Greases	16 to 20	Lubrication

SOURCE: Mortimer, *Chemistry*, 6th edition

③ Using Products Made from Petroleum

The gas fraction of petroleum is often used to make such products as fibers and plastics. The gasoline fraction is often used as a fuel for cars.

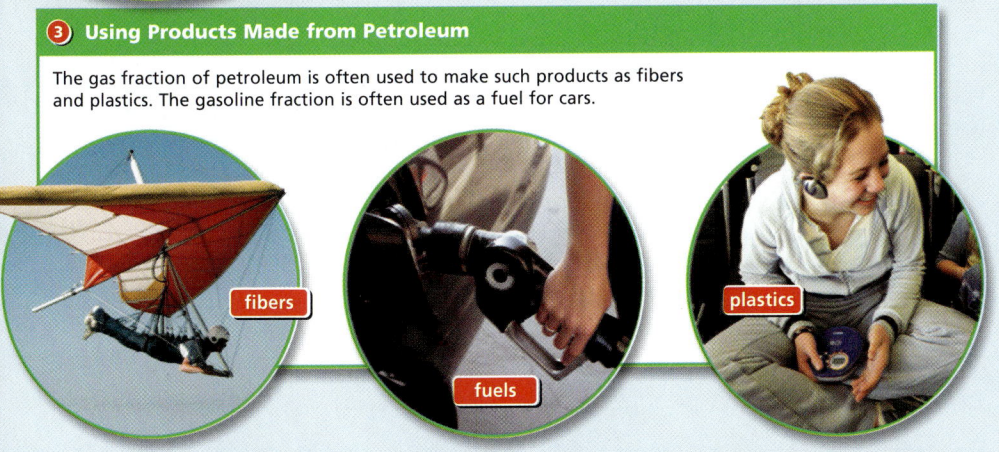

Chapter 9: **Carbon in Life and Materials** 293

Teach from Visuals

To help students interpret the visuals showing how petroleum is processed and used, ask:

- Where are oil deposits found? *trapped between rock layers through which it cannot move*
- Why must the different compounds in petroleum be separated? *They each have different uses, based on their properties. The original mixture of compounds is not a useful product.*

Teach Difficult Concepts

The many hydrocarbons in petroleum can be separated by simple distillation only if their boiling points differ by 50°C or more. If two compounds have similar boiling points, the distillate will contain a mixture of the two. To separate these compounds, the mixture is redistilled over and over in a fractionating tower. The condensed liquid is boiled and recondensed several times. These are all physical changes; no chemical changes are involved.

Social Studies Connection

Recent estimates indicate the world's petroleum reserves amount to approximately 1 trillion barrels (1 barrel = 42 gallons). An even larger quantity may be available from a different source—oil shale. Oil shale is a type of rock that contains a relatively large amount of organic material, from which oil and gas can be extracted. It has been estimated that there could be 2.6 trillion barrels of oil that could be extracted from oil shale. However, due to the higher cost of mining and refining oil shale, only a few countries currently obtain oil from it.

DIFFERENTIATE INSTRUCTION

Advanced Students might want to learn more about where crude oil deposits are found on Earth. If you can provide students with an outline of a world map, they can conduct research and color a copy of the map in to show the oil-rich regions.

 Challenge and Extension, p. 300

Chapter 9 **293**

EXPLORE the BIG idea

Revisit "Internet Activity: Polymers" on p. 273. Have students explain how changes in a polymer's structure alter the material.

Develop Critical Thinking

ANALYZE Simple sugars, such as glucose, are called monosaccharides, and complex carbohydrates, such as starch, are called polysaccharides. Ask: In terms of monomers and polymers, what is the relationship between simple sugars and complex carbohydrates? *Simple sugars are monomers and complex carbohydrates are polymers made by linking simple sugars.*

Ongoing Assessment

 *Answer: They are both polymers that contain repeating, smaller units.*

 *Answer: Polypropylene is a polymer that is a strong, solid plastic, but the monomer propylene is a gas.*

Polymers contain repeating carbon-based units.

READING TIP
The prefix *mono-* means "one," and the prefix *poly-* means "many."

B

Many everyday materials made of carbon-based molecules contain macromolecules called polymers. **Polymers** are very large carbon-based molecules made of smaller, repeating units. These small, repeating units, called **monomers**, are linked together one after another. By themselves, monomers are also carbon-based molecules.

Some of the carbon-based molecules that you read about in the previous section are polymers. For example, both cellulose and starch are polymers. They are chains of linked glucose units. The glucose units are the monomers. Many common materials that are manufactured for specific purposes are polymers. Plastics and fibers are two examples of these kinds of polymers.

 What do starch and plastic have in common?

Formation of Polymers

The properties of a polymer depend on the size and structure of the polymer molecule. The size and structure of a polymer depend both on its particular monomers and how many monomers are added together to make the final product.

C

The process of making a polymer involves chemical reactions that bond monomers together. Think back to the different types of reactions described in Chapter 7. The process of making a polymer is a synthesis reaction that yields a more complex product from simpler reactants.

The diagram on the top of page 295 shows one way in which a polymer can be made. The monomer that is the building block of the polymer in the illustration is called propylene (PROH-puh-LEEN). The propylene molecule consists of three carbon atoms and six hydrogen atoms. By itself, propylene is a gas. Notice that propylene has a double bond between two of its carbon atoms.

During the reaction that links the monomers, one of the bonds that makes up the double bond is broken. When that bond is broken, a new bond can form between two of the monomer units. A large number of the propylene monomers bonded together form a polymer called polypropylene. Polypropylene is a strong, solid plastic used to make such items as plastic crates, toys, bicycle helmets, and even indoor-outdoor carpeting.

 How do the properties of polypropylene differ from those of propylene?

294 Unit 2: Chemical Interactions

DIFFERENTIATE INSTRUCTION

More Reading Support

B What are polymers made of? *repeating monomers*

C What type of chemical reaction creates polymers? *a synthesis reaction*

Below Level Students can put together pop beads to model how a polymer is made out of monomers. As an alternative, they can use marshmallows or gumdrops and toothpicks to model the production of polymers.

294 Unit 2: **Chemical Interactions**

Building Polymers

Polymers such as polypropylene are made by linking many monomers together.

① Propylene (C_3H_6) can be used as a monomer.

Monomer
$CH_2 = CH - CH_3$

② Propylene monomers are linked together.

Monomers Are Linked Together
$CH_2 = CH - CH_3$ $CH_2 = CH - CH_3$ $CH_2 = CH - CH_3$

③ Linked propylene monomers make polypropylene.

Polymer
$CH_2 - CH - CH_2 - CH - CH_2 - CH ---$
         | | |
        CH_3 CH_3 CH_3

— = double bond changed to single bond
— = new bond formed between monomers

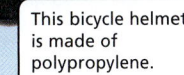
This bicycle helmet is made of polypropylene.

Polymers may be composed of more than one type of monomer. Polyester fabric is an example of a polymer that contains two different monomers. Protein is another example. In fact, as you read earlier, proteins in living things contain several different monomers. The monomers in proteins are amino acids.

Plastics

Polypropylene is one of many polymers that are called plastics. As an adjective, *plastic* means "capable of being molded or shaped." A **plastic** is a polymer that can be molded or shaped. If you look around, you can see how common plastics are in everyday life.

The first plastic made by chemists was celluloid, which was patented in 1870. It was based on cellulose molecules from cotton plants and was used to make such things as billiard balls and movie film. Celluloid is different from many of the plastics that are made today. It was made by chemically changing an existing, naturally occurring polymer—cellulose.

Many of today's plastics are made artificially, by building polymers from monomers. The first completely artificial polymer made by scientists was a plastic called Bakelite, which was invented in 1907. Chemists made Bakelite by linking individual monomers together. Because Bakelite is moldable and nonflammable, it used for many household items such as pot handles, jewelry, lamps, buttons, and radio cases.

 How does the term *plastic* describe a polymer's properties?

DIFFERENTIATE INSTRUCTION

D How was the first artificial plastic made?
by linking individual monomers

Inclusion To demonstrate the formation of a polymer for students with visual impairments and tactile learners, create a chain of paper clips. Adding paper clips to the chain one by one is similar to the synthesis reaction that produces a polymer. Have students feel the chain and ask students what represents the monomer and what represents the polymer. *a single paper clip; the chain of paper clips*

Teach from Visuals

To help students interpret the steps in building polymers, ask:

- What does the name *polypropylene* mean? *many propylene molecules*
- Which carbon atoms in propylene are linked together to make polypropylene? *The middle one is linked to the first carbon of the next monomer.*
- How many propylene monomers were joined to make the section of polymer shown in step 3? *three*
- What happens to the double bond in each monomer? *One of the bonds is broken so one monomer can bond to another.*

Integrating the Sciences

Celluloid was produced by treating nitrocellulose molecules from cotton plants with camphor. That discovery began the era of plastics. Even though celluloid is closely linked with the cinema and the film industry, it is at least partly responsible for helping to save African elephants. The ivory of elephant tusks was used to make products such as billiard balls and piano keys, and the killing of elephants for their tusks dramatically decreased their numbers. The use of celluloid as a substitute for ivory in billiard balls and piano keys decreased the hunting of elephants for those purposes.

Ongoing Assessment

Explain how carbon-based molecules are designed for specific uses.

Ask: What properties would you want a plastic to have if it were to be used for cookware handles? *nonflammable, heat-resistant, lightweight*

 *Answer: The polymer can be molded and shaped.*

Teach from Visuals

To help students interpret the table of plastics, make a recycling display in your classroom. Have students bring in samples of each kind of plastic so they can examine them. Have students identify the monomers in each type of plastic.

Integrating the Sciences

In 1998, Americans recycled 1.45 billion pounds of plastic bottles. At least 94 percent of this recycled plastic was PET and HDPE, types 1 and 2, respectively. Recycled plastics can be used to make thousands of products. However, each time a plastic is recycled, it loses some of its strength. Often, after a plastic has been recycled about five times, it is of such poor quality that it must be discarded. Disposal of this old plastic is difficult.

Teacher Demo

Create a polymer gel that climbs the side of a beaker. Mix 20–25 mL of methyl or ethyl alcohol with 3–4 g of polyethylene oxide in a clean, dry 600 mL beaker. Swirl the mixture to completely wet it with the alcohol. Add 350–400 mL of tap water to the mixture all at once. Stir until the polymer has disappeared and the mixture is blended and thick. Pour the gel into a second 600 mL beaker and then pour it back and forth between the two beakers. The gel can be made to siphon "uphill" out of a beaker and against gravity. To start the process, raise the beaker with the gel above an empty beaker. Once the gel starts to pour, turn the raised beaker upright again. The gel will move up the sides of the raised beaker as a thin film and then form thick strands as it falls. This process can be repeated indefinitely.

Ongoing Assessment

Describe how a material's properties depend on its molecular structure.

Ask: Why do isomers have different properties? *Their structure is different.*

Recycling Plastics

Code	Chemical Name	Monomers	Properties	Uses
1	Polyethylene terephthalate (PET or PETE)	$C_2H_6O_2$ and $C_8H_6O_4$	Transparent, high strength, does not stretch	Clothing, soft-drink bottles, audiotapes, videotapes
2	High Density Polyethylene (HDPE)	C_2H_4	Similar to LDPE (code 4) but denser, tougher, more rigid	Milk and water jugs, gasoline tanks, cups
3	Polyvinyl chloride (PVC)	C_2H_3Cl	Rigid, transparent, high strength	Shampoo bottles, garden hoses, plumbing pipes
4	Low Density Polyethylene (LDPE)	C_2H_4	White, soft, subject to cracking	Plastic bags, toys, electrical insulation
5	Polypropylene (PP)	C_3H_6	High strength and rigidity, impermeable to liquids and gases	Battery cases, indoor-outdoor carpeting, bottle caps, auto trim
6	Polystyrene (PS)	C_8H_8	Glassy, rigid, brittle	Insulation, drinking cups, packing materials

SOURCE: *American Chemical Society*

The chart above lists some common plastics and their uses. You may have noticed the symbols shown in the first column of the chart on plastic bottles and containers that you have around your home. The numbers stand for different types of plastic, with different uses. After a plastic has been used in a certain way, such as in soft drink bottles, it can recycled and used again. When a plastic is recycled it can be made into a new product that has a different use. For example, recycled soft drink bottles can be made into fibers for carpeting.

Designing Materials

Chemists have been designing and making polymers for many years. However, new polymers are always being developed. One way in which scientists make new polymers is by chemically changing an original monomer. When scientists change a monomer and then link the monomers together, a new material is produced.

Teflon is a common polymer that is made by chemically changing a hydrocarbon monomer. Chemists replace the hydrogen atoms in the monomer with fluorine atoms and link the monomers together. You have probably seen Teflon as a nonstick coating on pots and pans. Teflon is also very strong, and it was used as a part of the structure of the stadium's dome in the photograph on the left.

Teflon is very strong and light in weight. It was used to make the roof of this stadium in Minneapolis.

$--- CF_2 — CF_2 — CF_2 — CF_2 ---$

DIFFERENTIATE INSTRUCTION

More Reading Support

 How can a new polymer be developed? *by chemically changing an original monomer*

Alternative Assessment Students who have difficulty reading can make a poster that summarizes the main ideas of the section. Students could draw or cut out pictures from magazines to illustrate the parts of the carbon cycle and how carbon that was removed from the cycle is used in the world.

Advanced Have students who are interested in molecules read the following article:

R Challenge Reading, pp. 302–303

Nomex is used to make fireproof clothing worn by firefighters.

Kevlar is used in bulletproof vests worn by police officers and police dogs.

Chemists have developed several other materials by changing the monomers in nylon, a polymer that is often used in clothing. By adding a carbon-based ring to the nylon monomer, chemists made Nomex, which is used in fireproof clothing. Then scientists changed the placement of this ring on the monomer. This change resulted in the polymer called Kevlar, which is used in bulletproof vests.

Nomex and Kevlar are isomers. The monomers that are the basis of each contain the same atoms but have different structures. As a result, the polymers have different properties and uses. The structure of the polymer in Nomex gives the fibers flexibility along with fire resistance. As a result, Nomex can be made into relatively comfortable fireproof clothing for firefighters and race car drivers. Kevlar, however, is very rigid because of its structure and is the strongest known fiber. In fact, Kevlar is five times stronger than an equal amount of steel, which helps explain why Kevlar is used in bulletproof vests.

 Why are Nomex and Kevlar isomers?

9.3 Review

KEY CONCEPTS
1. What physical property allows the hydrocarbons in petroleum to be separated? Explain.
2. What are monomers? How are monomers related to polymers?
3. How are polymers such as Kevlar and Nomex similar to each other? How are they different?

CRITICAL THINKING
4. **Synthesize** What general type of chemical reaction makes polymers from monomers? Explain.
5. **Compare and Contrast** How are plastics such as polypropylene similar to celluloid, the first plastic? How are they different?

CHALLENGE
6. **Synthesize** A petroleum deposit is full of carbon compounds. How did that carbon get out of the atmosphere and into the petroleum?

Chapter 9: **Carbon in Life and Materials** 297

ANSWERS

1. boiling point; larger molecules have higher boiling points
2. small carbon-based molecules; linked to make polymers.
3. They are both based on nylon; they are isomers because their carbon rings are in different positions.
4. synthesis reactions; a more complex molecule is made by combining simpler molecules
5. They are organic, and they are polymers. Celluloid is based on cellulose, a natural material, but modern plastics are artificial.
6. Plants removed carbon dioxide from the air during photosynthesis, and animals ate the plants. Petroleum was formed from the remains of the plants and animals.

CHAPTER INVESTIGATION

Focus

PURPOSE To make a polymer and observe its properties

OVERVIEW Students will make a polymer by using white glue and borax and will test the polymer's properties. Students should find that their polymer

- is very stretchable and feels like both a solid and a liquid
- stretches when pulled slowly but breaks when pulled quickly
- does not bounce
- flows slowly and
- can be filled with air to make a bubble.

Lab Preparation

- Students can bring in many of the materials from home.
- Prior to the investigation, have students read through the investigation and prepare their data tables. You may wish to copy and distribute datasheets and rubrics.

 UNIT RESOURCE BOOK, pp. 309–317

 SCIENCE TOOLKIT, F15

Lab Management

- The creep test can be done as a demonstration that students observe periodically during the class period.
- Do not allow students to take their polymers out of the classroom.
- Warn students not to eat their polymer or put it into their mouths.

Teaching with Technology

If a video camera is available, students may want to tape this lab and narrate their discoveries.

CHAPTER INVESTIGATION

Polymers

OVERVIEW AND PURPOSE Polymers are used in many common items. For example, the substance that is being pulled out of the beaker in the photograph on the left is raw nylon, which is a polymer. The properties of polymers are influenced by the way in which the chains are linked together. In this activity, you will use what you have learned about carbon-based molecules to
- make a polymer
- study the properties of a polymer

▶ Procedure

1. Create a data table like the one shown on the sample notebook page.

2. Follow the instructions to mix the polymer called Glurch. After you have made the polymer, store it in a zip-top bag.

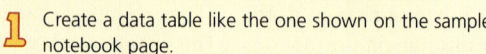

GLURCH

40 mL (8 tsp) water
40 mL (8 tsp) white glue
6 drops of food coloring
2 tsp powdered borax
30 mL (6 tsp) water

- Make a glue mixture by mixing 40 mL of water with 40 mL of white glue in a plastic container.
- Add food coloring and mix the color evenly.
- Make a borax solution by adding 2 tsp of borax to 30 mL of water. Shake the mixture in a covered jar for 30 seconds.
- Combine the borax solution with the glue mixture. Stir.
- Knead until the mixture is smooth, with a rubberlike consistency.

MATERIALS
- measuring spoons
- 2 plastic containers
- tap water
- white glue
- food coloring
- borax
- jar with lid
- plastic spoon
- zip-top plastic bags
- scissors
- 2 L plastic bottle
- ring stand with ring
- stopwatch
- straws

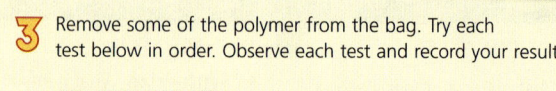

3. Remove some of the polymer from the bag. Try each test below in order. Observe each test and record your results.

4. **SQUEEZE TEST** Put some of the polymer in your hand. Squeeze the polymer to test its shape and its feel. Is it a solid, a liquid, or a little like both? Record your observations.

5. **PULL TEST** Hold the polymer between your hands and pull it apart slowly. Try again, and pull it apart very quickly. What happens to the polymer? Record the results of this test.

298 Unit 2: Chemical Interactions

INVESTIGATION RESOURCES

 CHAPTER INVESTIGATION, Polymers
- Level A, pp. 309–312
- Level B, pp. 313–316
- Level C, p. 317

Advanced students should complete Levels B & C.

 Writing a Lab Report, D12–13

Technology Resources

Customize this student lab as needed or look for an alternative. Print rubrics to assess student lab reports.

 Lab Generator CD-ROM

6. **BOUNCE TEST** Roll some of the polymer into a ball between your palms. Test whether the polymer ball will bounce. Record your observations about the polymer's behavior.

7. **CREEP TEST**
   Setup Cut the top off a 2 L bottle. Keep the bottle cap on. Set up a ring stand. To use the bottle top as a funnel, place it upside down in the ring. Put a plastic container under the funnel.

   Trials Place approximately 100 mL of the polymer in the funnel. Remove the bottle cap and time how long it takes for the polymer to flow completely through the funnel. Record the time. If time allows, conduct one or two more trials.

8. **BUBBLE TEST** Take a small amount of the polymer and roll it into a ball around the end of a straw. Pinch the polymer closed around the straw. Hold the ball in one hand as you gently blow into the other end of the straw. Try to make a bubble by filling the polymer with air. Record your observations.

Observe and Analyze

1. **RECORD OBSERVATIONS** Be sure that your data table is complete. Describe how the polymer feels, as well as its state, shape, and behavior.

2. **COMMUNICATE** Include drawings of any observations for which a picture is helpful in understanding your results.

3. **INTERPRET DATA** Make a list of the polymer's physical properties. Which test was most helpful in identifying these properties? Which test was the least helpful?

Conclude

1. **INFER** The more complex a polymer is, the more rigid it is. Do you think that the polymer you made contains molecules with extremely long or complex carbon chains? Why or why not? What properties of your polymer provide evidence for your answer?

2. **EVALUATE** What limitations or difficulties did you experience in interpreting the results of your tests or other observations?

3. **APPLY** Based upon your results, what uses could you suggest for the polymer? What further tests would you need to do to make sure it would stand up to the demands of that use?

INVESTIGATE Further

CHALLENGE Investigate the properties of your polymer by varying the proportions of the ingredients. Change only one ingredient. Be sure to record the change you made in the polymer. Make a new data table. Record the results of the experimental tests. How do changes in the polymer recipe change the physical properties of the polymer?

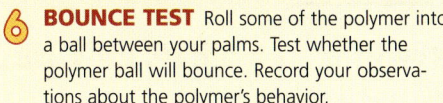

Polymers
Observe and Analyze
Table 1. Polymer Properties

Test	Observations
Squeeze test	
Pull test	
Bounce test	
Creep test	Trial 1 (time) / Trial 2 (time) / Trial 3 (time)
Bubble test	

Conclude

Observe and Analyze

1. The polymer should be somewhat sticky and slimy and very malleable.
2. The diagram most likely to be helpful would show the flow of the polymer in the creep test.
3. The polymer should be sticky, slimy, fluid, and malleable. The stretch test, pull test, and creep test should be most helpful; the bounce test and bubble test the least helpful.

Conclude

1. No; the polymer is not rigid but is instead very malleable and somewhat fluid, as shown by the test results.
2. Answers will vary but could include difficulties using subjective rather than objective observations for most of the tests, changes in the polymer properties over the duration of the investigation, and problems associated with making an error while making the polymer.
3. Sample answer: Possible uses could be as a putty or a sealer. It could be used as a toy or as bubble gum if it is tested and found to be nontoxic and safe for use by children.

INVESTIGATE Further

CHALLENGE Answers will depend on the proportions that are used and the ingredient that is changed. Changing the recipe will most likely change the polymer's properties and various test results.

Post Lab Discussion

- Ask: Why was it important to follow the recipe exactly? *The recipe was developed to produce a certain polymer. Changes in the recipe would change the properties of the polymer.*
- Describe how the testing of a polymer's properties might differ if the polymer was designed for a specific function or if it was discovered by accident. *If the polymer was designed for a particular function, tests would be carried out to see how well it performed that function. If the polymer was discovered by chance, tests would be carried out to see what it could be used for.*

CHAPTER 9 • REVIEW

BACK TO

Have students discuss the following questions:
- Atoms of which element are the basis of all life on Earth? *carbon*
- How is carbon from living things used to make many modern materials? *Hydrocarbons from petroleum, formed from the carbon-based molecules of living things from hundreds of millions of years ago, are refined to make materials such as fibers and plastics.*

◀ KEY CONCEPTS SUMMARY

SECTION 9.1
Ask: Why can carbon atoms form a large number of molecules with different structures such as chains, rings, and isomers? *Carbon atoms form four bonds, including single, double, and triple bonds, with other atoms, including other carbon atoms.*

SECTION 9.2
Ask: Give an example of how each of the four carbon-based macromolecules is used in the body. *Sample answer: Carbohydrates are a source of chemical energy for cells; lipids are a part of cell membranes; proteins make up muscle tissue; nucleic acids carry genetic information.*

SECTION 9.3
Ask: How are polymers made? *A polymer is made from small repeating monomers. As in all chemical reactions, bonds within the reactants (the monomers) are broken and new bonds form in the products (the polymer).*

Review Concepts

- Big Idea Flow Chart, p. T33
- Chapter Outline, pp. T39–T40

 Chapter Review

the BIG idea

Carbon is essential to living things and to modern materials.

CONTENT REVIEW
CLASSZONE.COM

◀ KEY CONCEPTS SUMMARY

1. Carbon-based molecules have many structures.

Carbon forms a large number of different compounds because of the number of bonds it can make with other atoms.

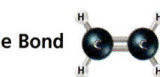

Single Bond

Double Bond

Triple Bond

Carbon can form chains and rings.

Hexane
$CH_3 — CH_2 — CH_2 — CH_2 — CH_2 — CH_3$

Vanillin

VOCABULARY
organic compound p. 275
inorganic compound p. 276
isomer p. 280

2. Carbon-based molecules are life's building blocks.

There are four main types of carbon-based molecules in living things.

Carbon-Based Molecules			
Carbohydrates	Lipids	Proteins	Nucleic Acids
• include sugars and starches	• include fats and oils	• function depends on order of amino acids	• DNA
• energy for cells	• energy for cells	• structure, transport, immune system, enzymes	• carries genetic code
• plant cell walls	• cell membranes		• sequence of three DNA bases is the code for an amino acid

VOCABULARY
carbohydrate p. 283
lipid p. 284
protein p. 286
enzyme p. 287
nucleic acid p. 289

3. Carbon-based molecules are in many materials.

Carbon from ancient organisms is used to make many common items, such as clothing and plastics. These items are based on polymers.

Monomer $CH_2 = CH — CH_3$

Polymer $CH_2 — CH — CH_2 — CH — CH_2 — CH — — —$
$\qquad\qquad\quad\; |\qquad\qquad\;\, |\qquad\qquad\;\, |$
$\qquad\qquad\; CH_3\qquad\; CH_3\qquad\; CH_3$

VOCABULARY
hydrocarbon p. 291
polymer p. 294
monomer p. 294
plastic p. 295

Technology Resources

Have students visit ClassZone.com or use the CD-ROM for a cumulative review of concepts.

 CONTENT REVIEW

 CONTENT REVIEW CD-ROM

Engage students in a whole-class interactive review of Key Concepts. Edit content as you wish.

 POWER PRESENTATIONS

Reviewing Vocabulary

Copy and complete the chart below. Fill in the blanks with the missing term, example, or function. See the example in the chart.

Term	Example	Function
inorganic compound	carbon dioxide	used by plants to make glucose
1. organic compound	glucose	
2. carbohydrate	sugar	
3.	fat	stores chemical energy
4.	keratin	found in hair and feathers
5. nucleic acid		instructions for proteins
6. plastic	polypropylene	

Greek Roots Describe how each of the following terms is related to one or more of the following Greek roots.

iso- means "equal" *mono-* means "one"
-mer means "part" *poly-* means "many"

7. isomer
8. polymer
9. monomer
10. polyunsaturated

Reviewing Key Concepts

Multiple Choice *Choose the letter of the best answer.*

11. All life on Earth is based on atoms of which element?
    a. oxygen
    b. nitrogen
    c. carbon
    d. hydrogen

12. One reason that carbon atoms can form large numbers of compounds is that a carbon atom forms
    a. two bonds with a hydrogen atom
    b. four bonds in its compounds
    c. ionic bonds in its compounds
    d. bonds with up to five hydrogen atoms

13. Which of the following is not found in living things?
    a. proteins   c. lipids
    b. petroleum   d. carbohydrates

14. What functions do carbohydrates and lipids perform in living things?
    a. They provide energy and instructions.
    b. They provide water and oxygen.
    c. They provide water and immunity.
    d. They provide energy and structure.

15. The molecules that carry instructions to make other molecules are called
    a. nucleic acids   c. carbohydrates
    b. proteins   d. lipids

16. Which kinds of molecules are best for storing chemical energy in living things?
    a. enzymes   c. lipids
    b. proteins   d. nucleic acids

17. The properties of artificial polymers are determined by
    a. the structure of the molecule
    b. the reaction used to make the polymer
    c. the time it took to make the polymer
    d. a series of DNA bases

Short Answer *Write a short answer to each question.*

18. Explain how carbon's ability to form isomers is related to the large number of carbon-based molecules that exist.

19. Describe the movement of carbon through the environment in a cycle. How does a break in the cycle provide carbon for modern materials?

Reviewing Vocabulary

1. provides energy for cells
2. provides energy in most living things
3. lipid
4. protein
5. DNA
6. used to make products such as containers, toys, and indoor-outdoor carpeting
7. Equal parts: isomers have the same kind and number of atoms.
8. Many parts: polymers contain many monomers.
9. One part: monomers are one part of a polymer.
10. many (more than one) double bonds in the fatty acids of a lipid

Reviewing Key Concepts

11. c
12. b
13. b
14. d
15. a
16. c
17. a
18. Because carbon can form molecules with the same atoms but in different arrangements, the number of possible compounds increases greatly.
19. In the carbon cycle, plants use carbon dioxide from the atmosphere to create food; animals eat plants and exhale carbon dioxide; animals and plants decompose and release carbon into the environment. Petroleum comes from living things that died hundreds of millions of years ago. Petroleum can be separated into different parts that can be used to make many things, including plastics and fabrics.

ASSESSMENT RESOURCES

UNIT ASSESSMENT BOOK
- Chapter Test A, pp. 84–87
- Chapter Test B, pp. 88–91
- Chapter Test C, pp. 92–95
- Alternative Assessment, pp. 96–97
- Unit Test, pp. 98–109

SPANISH ASSESSMENT BOOK
- Spanish Chapter Test, pp. 249–252
- Spanish Unit Test, pp. 253–256

Technology Resources

Edit test items and answer choices.

 Test Generator CD-ROM

Visit **ClassZone.com** to extend test practice.

 Test Practice

Thinking Critically

20. Amino acids could be thought of as monomers, which are linked to form a protein.

21. The sequence of bases in a DNA molecule codes for a particular sequence of amino acids.

22. No, because the order of amino acids gives a protein its structure, which, in turn, gives the protein its function.

23. Sample answer: structural; an enzyme

24. Chains and rings: both contain carbon and are found in living things and in modern products; they differ in structure, bonding, and properties. Proteins and lipids: both contribute to the structure of living things; they differ in that proteins are not typically used for energy, as are lipids, and have many more functions than lipids. Glucose and amino acids: both are found in living things and are monomers; they contain different elements and form different polymers.

Using Math Skills in Science

25. approximately 53 from fats, 88 from carbohydrates, and 9 from proteins

26. Check students' charts; the portions of the pie chart should show 211° of the circle as carbohydrate, 127° as fat, and 22° as protein.

27. It is relatively close, but not exact—59% carbohydrates, 35% fats, and 6% protein. To be the recommended balance, it should have more protein and slightly less carbohydrates and fats.

28. Answers will vary.
29. Answers will vary.

UNIT PROJECTS

Have students present their projects. Use the appropriate rubrics from the URB to evaluate their work.

 Unit Projects, pp. 5–10

302 Unit 2: **Chemical Interactions**

Thinking Critically

The illustration below models linked amino acids. Use the illustration to answer the next four questions.

20. **SYNTHESIZE** Why can the model shown by the illustration be considered to be a polymer?

21. **CONCLUDE** What would cause the amino acids in the illustration to be placed in that particular order? Explain.

22. **APPLY** If the order of amino acids shown in the illustration changes, would the protein formed likely still have the same function? Why or why not?

23. **PREDICT** Suppose the protein formed by the amino acids has a coiled shape. What might be the general function of that protein? What if the protein is coiled but also curls up into a ball?

24. **COMPARE AND CONTRAST** Copy and complete the chart below. Provide two similarities and two differences for each pair of items.

Items	Similarities	Differences
starch/cellulose	both carbohydrates; both polymers	starch used for energy, cellulose for structure; starch molecule branched, cellulose molecule straight
carbon chains/carbon rings		
proteins/lipids		
glucose/amino acids		

Using Math Skills in Science

The nutrition label below shows the Calories and the amount of fat, carbohydrates, and protein in a type of cracker. Use the information on the label to answer the following three questions.

Nutrition Facts

Servings Per Container about 15

Amount Per Serving

Calories 150

Total Fat 6g
Total Carbohydrates 20g
Protein 2g

25. Fats contain about twice as many Calories per gram as carbohydrates and proteins. Assume that all of the Calories on the label come from the carbohydrates, fats, and proteins. About how many Calories come from each substance?

26. Make a pie chart that compares the number of Calories from carbohydrates, fats, and proteins contained in this food.

27. Adult athletes are recommended to eat a diet that provides 15% of its Calories from protein, 30% from fats, and 55% from carbohydrates. Does this food have the recommended balance of nutrients? Why or why not?

the BIG idea

28. **DRAW CONCLUSIONS** Look at the photographs on pages 272–273. Describe three ways in which carbon is important in the activities taking place.

29. **SYNTHESIZE** Write one or more paragraphs describing how plants, animals, and plastics are related to each other.

UNIT PROJECTS

Evaluate all the data, results, and information from your project folder. Prepare to present your project.

302 Unit 2: Chemical Interactions

MONITOR AND RETEACH

If students have trouble applying the concept of polymer formation as a chemical reaction in items 20–23, review chemical reactions in general and synthesis reactions in particular. Refer students to the top of p. 295. Use ball-and-stick or gumdrop-and-toothpick models to demonstrate the process.

Students may benefit from summarizing one or more sections of the chapter.

 Summarizing the Chapter, pp. 327–328

Standardized Test Practice

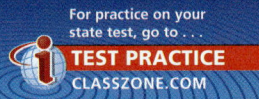

For practice on your state test, go to...
TEST PRACTICE
CLASSZONE.COM

Interpreting Tables

The following table contains information about some of the different products that can be separated from petroleum. Use the information in the table to answer questions 1–5.

Characteristics of Petroleum Products

Product	Number of Carbon Atoms per Molecule	Boiling Point (°C)
Natural gas	1 to 4	lower than 20
Gasoline	5 to 12	35 to 220
Kerosene	12 to 16	200 to 315
Jet fuel	12 to 16	200 to 315
Diesel fuel	15 to 18	250 to 375
Heating oil	15 to 18	250 to 375
Lubricating oil	16 to 20	350 and higher
Asphalt	More than 25	600 and higher

SOURCE: *Mortimer, Chemistry, 6th edition*

1. Which petroleum product has the lowest boiling point?
   a. diesel fuel
   b. gasoline
   c. kerosene
   d. natural gas

2. Which petroleum product has the highest boiling point?
   a. asphalt
   b. heating oil
   c. jet fuel
   d. kerosene

3. Petroleum is heated and turned into gas. The gas rises in a distillation tower. The lightest gases—those with the smallest molecules—rise highest. The heaviest gases—those with the largest molecules—stay lowest. Which of the following products would be found lowest in the tower?
   a. diesel fuel
   b. kerosene
   c. lubricating oil
   d. natural gas

4. Petroleum is split into fractions. Each fraction includes all the products that have the same boiling point. Which of the following pairs of products are in the same fraction?
   a. gasoline and natural gas
   b. jet fuel and kerosene
   c. lubricating oil and diesel fuel
   d. natural gas and asphalt

5. What might be the boiling point of a petroleum product that contains 22 carbon atoms?
   a. 100°C
   b. 300°C
   c. 500°C
   d. 700°C

Extended Response

Answer the following two questions in detail. Include some of the terms from the list in the box at right. Underline each term that you use in your answers.

atoms	carbon chains	carbon rings
molecules	properties	structure
function	monomer	

6. How are polymers made? Give examples of a natural polymer and an artificial polymer.

7. Carbohydrates, lipids, and proteins are all carbon-based molecules. How are they similar? How are they different?

Interpreting Tables

1. d   2. a   3. c   4. b   5. c

Extended Response

6. RUBRIC
4 points for a response that correctly answers the question, gives two correct examples, and uses the following terms accurately:
- carbon chains
- structure
- carbon rings
- monomer
- molecules

Sample: Polymers are large molecules that are made of smaller monomers linked together. A polymer can have a structure made of carbon chains, carbon rings, or a combination of the two. Cellulose, proteins, and starches are natural polymers; plastics and fibers are artificial polymers.

3 points for a response that correctly answers the question, gives two correct examples, and uses at least three terms correctly

2 points for a response that correctly answers the question, gives two correct examples, and uses at least two terms correctly

1 point for a response that correctly answers the question and either gives one correct example or uses one term correctly

7. RUBRIC
4 points for a response that correctly answers both questions and uses the following terms accurately:
- atoms
- structure
- molecules
- function
- properties

Sample: Carbohydrates, lipids, and proteins are similar in that they all are large molecules that contain carbon atoms. They are different in that they have different structures, properties, and functions.

3 points for a response that correctly answers both questions and uses at least three terms correctly

2 points for a response that correctly answers both questions and uses at least one term correctly

1 point for a response that correctly answers one question and uses at least one term correctly

METACOGNITIVE ACTIVITY

Have students answer the following questions in their **Science Notebook:**

1. Think of questions to address what you found most challenging to understand about carbon-based molecules. How can you answer these questions?
2. Which topics in this chapter would you like to learn more about?
3. What have you learned from your research on your Unit Project?

McDougal Littell Science

Motion and Forces

$F=ma$

GRAVITY

VELOCITY

Motion and Forces
Contents Overview

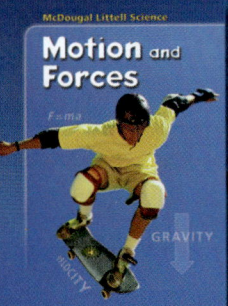

Unit Features
FRONTIERS IN SCIENCE Robots on Mars — 306
TIMELINES IN SCIENCE Understanding Forces — 412

10 Motion — 310
the BIG idea
The motion of an object can be described and predicted.

11 Forces — 342
the BIG idea
Forces change the motion of objects in predictable ways.

12 Gravity, Friction, and Pressure — 378
the BIG idea
Newton's laws apply to all forces.

13 Work and Energy — 416
the BIG idea
Energy is transferred when a force moves an object.

14 Machines — 446
the BIG idea
Machines help people do work by changing the force applied to an object.

FRONTIERS in Science

VIDEO SUMMARY

SCIENTIFIC AMERICAN FRONTIERS

TEETERING TO VICTORY This 10-minute video documents an exciting annual contest held at MIT—Massachusetts Institute of Technology—in which students build machines using principles of force and motion. Their devices compete against an opponent's machine to tilt their end of a teeter-totter beam—and they have 45 seconds to defeat that opponent's machine. Students design their own technology with very specific constraints: they are given identical kits of parts, each machine can weigh no more than 10 pounds, and it must fit back into the box the parts came in. The top contenders are carpet grabbers, bulldozers, and mobile jacks. As different competitors eliminate each other, viewers get caught up in the contest while learning about technological design.

National Science Education Standards

A.9.a–d Understandings About Scientific Inquiry

E.6.a–f Understandings About Science and Technology

F.5.a–e Science and Technology in Society

G.1.a–b Science as a Human Endeavor

G.2.a Nature of Science

FRONTIERS in Science

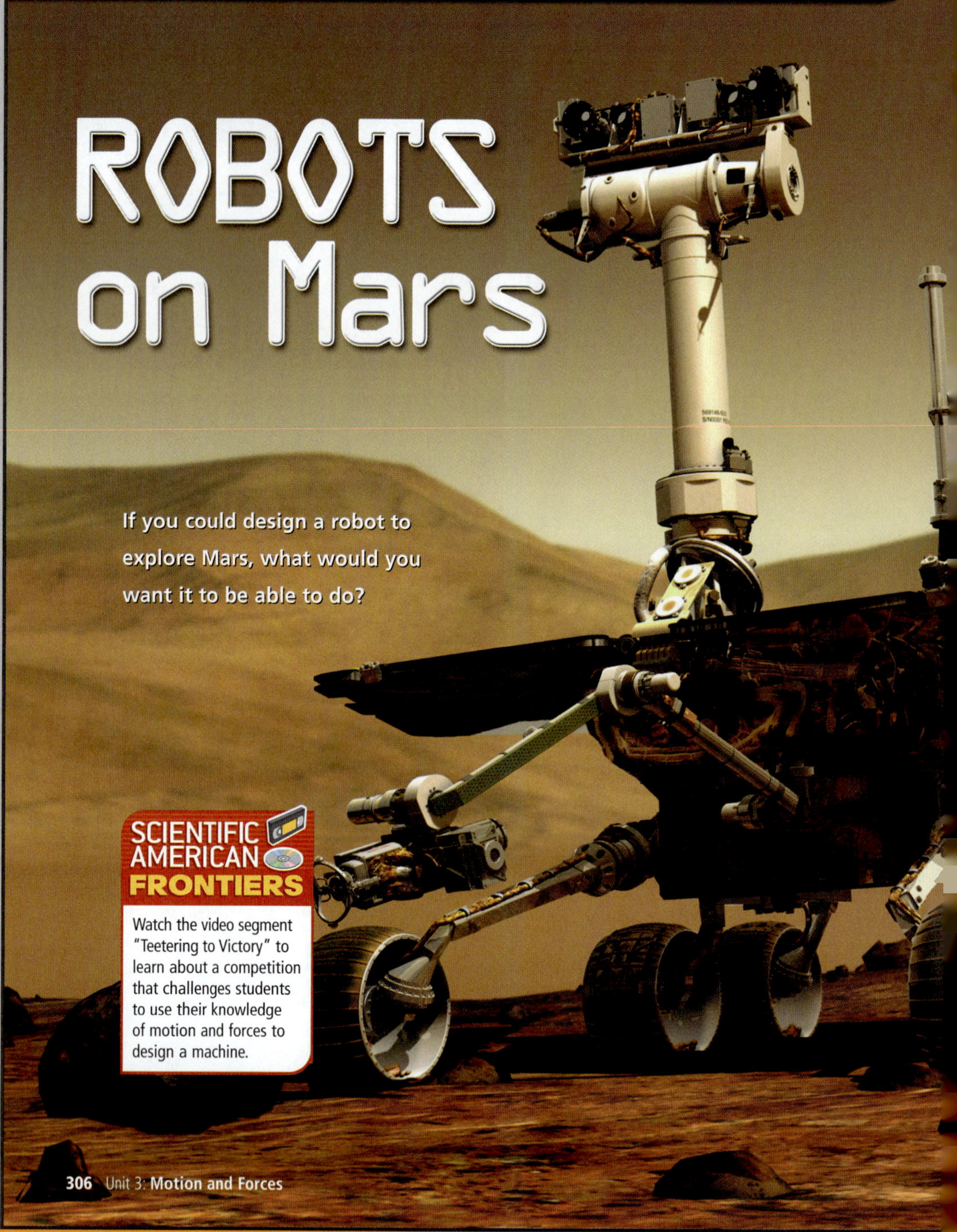

ROBOTS on Mars

If you could design a robot to explore Mars, what would you want it to be able to do?

SCIENTIFIC AMERICAN FRONTIERS
Watch the video segment "Teetering to Victory" to learn about a competition that challenges students to use their knowledge of motion and forces to design a machine.

ADDITIONAL RESOURCES

Technology Resources

 Scientific American Frontiers Video: *Teetering to Victory:* 10-minute video segment that introduces the unit

 ClassZone.com
CAREER LINK: physicists, mechanical engineer

Guide student viewing and comprehension of the video:

 Frontiers in Science Teaching Guide, pp. 1–2; Viewing Guide, p. 3, Video Wrap-Up, p. 4

Scientific American Frontiers Video Guide, pp. 9–12

Unit projects procedures and rubrics:

 Unit Projects, pp. 5–10

The surface of Mars looks rocky and barren today, but scientists have long wondered if life might have existed on Mars long ago. That would have been possible only if Mars once had water, which is necessary for all forms of life.

The Design Challenge

It's still not possible to send scientists to Mars to search for signs of water, but in 1999 a team of scientists and engineers began to design two robots for NASA's 2004 mission to Mars. As the team worked, they relied on their scientific understanding of motion, forces, and machines to create and test a successful design.

To identify their goals, the team started by thinking about what scientists would want to do if they could go to Mars. First they would want to look around the landscape to find good areas to study. Then they would need to travel to those areas and analyze rock samples. Finally they would use a variety of tools to analyze the rocks, interpret their data, and communicate their findings back to Earth. Those goals set the basic plan for the Mars Exploration Rovers (MERs).

As you can see in the photograph, the MER team designed a rover with cameras for viewing the surface, wheels for moving around the landscape, and an extendable arm in front equipped with tools for drilling into, observing, and identifying rocks. The rover also has a computer to process information, an antenna for radio communication with Earth, and batteries and solar panels to provide energy for everything.

As in any technology project, the MER team had to work within specific constraints, or limits. The most basic constraints were time and money. They had to design rovers that could be built within NASA's budget and that would be ready in time for launch in 2003. But the team also faced some more challenging

NASA's Mars Exploration Rover (MER) shown in a computer-simulated Martian landscape

Technology Design

Sharing results and learning from the past help scientists design better technology. Ask students what design change to *Sojourner* allows a MER to make more useful visual observations. *Sojourner was very close to the ground. A MER is larger and has cameras on top of a mast that give it a view similar to what a person would see standing on the surface of Mars.*

Scientific Process

The MER team built and used models such as FIDO to conduct testing. Ask students what the purpose of their testing models was. *to make sure all the parts worked* Then ask students to brainstorm why scientists used models instead of a completed MER. *Sample answers: cost, might want to make sure an individual part worked, no need to use whole robot to test one part*

Members of the project team stand with a MER and a replica of the much smaller *Sojourner*.

surface of Mars for 12 weeks in 1997. At the left you see one of the MERs next to a replica of *Sojourner,* which was only about 28 centimeters (about 11 in) tall. MER's mast rises up to 1.4 meters (almost 5 ft), giving the cameras, which can be angled up or down, a view similar to what a person would see when standing on the surface of Mars.

Testing the Model

Every part of the MER had to be tested to be sure it would work properly in the harsh conditions on Mars. For example, consider the Rock Abrasion Tool (RAT) at the end of the rover's extendable arm. The RAT is designed to grind off the weathered surface of rock, exposing a fresh surface for examination. Tests with the RAT showed that it worked fine on hard rocks, but its diamond-tipped grinding wheel became clogged with pieces of soft rock. The solution: Add brushes to clean the RAT automatically after each use.

D

Scientists were also concerned that the RAT's diamond grinding wheel might wear out if it had to grind a lot of hard rocks. An entry from the design team's status report explains why that turned out not to be a problem:

C Scientists built on some valuable lessons learned from an earlier robot, *Sojourner,* which explored the

View the "Teetering to Victory" segment of your Scientific American Frontiers video to learn how some students solved a much simpler design challenge.

IN THIS SCENE FROM THE VIDEO ▶
MIT students prepare to test their machines.

BATTLE OF MACHINES Each year more than 100 engineering students at the Massachusetts Institute of Technology (MIT) compete in a contest to see who can design and build the best machine. The challenge this time is to build a machine that

starts out sitting on a teeter-totter beam and within 45 seconds manages to tilt its end down against an opponent trying to do the same thing.

Just as the Mars rover designers had to consider the constraints of space travel and Mars' harsh environment, the students had constraints on their designs. They all started with the same kit of materials, and their finished machines had to weigh less than 10 pounds as well as fit inside the box the materials came in. Within these constraints, the student designers came up with an amazing variety of solutions.

308 Unit 3: Motion and Forces

DIFFERENTIATE INSTRUCTION

 More Reading Support

C What earlier robot explored Mars? *Sojourner*

D What parts of MER had to be tested to make sure they worked? *all parts*

Below Level Students may have trouble with the word *constraint.* Make sure they understand that a constraint is a limit. Have students list constraints the MER team faced. *time, money, surviving a rocket launch from Earth and a landing on Mars, space travel, harsh environment of Mars* Then have students list the constraints the MIT students had. *same materials, build machine less than 10 pounds that fit inside box*

The big question, of course, was how things would work under the very cold, dry, low-pressure atmospheric conditions on Mars. We put a RAT into a test chamber recently, took it to real Martian conditions for the first time, and got a very pleasant surprise. The rate at which our diamond studded teeth wear away slowed way down! We're still figuring out why, but it turns out that when you put this Martian RAT into its natural environment, its teeth don't wear down nearly as fast.

Engineers also needed to test the system by which scientists on Earth would communicate with and control the rovers on Mars. For this purpose, they built a smaller version of the real robot, nicknamed FIDO. In tests FIDO successfully traveled to several locations, dug trenches, and observed and measured rock samples.

Goals of the Mission

Technology like the Mars Exploration Rovers extends the power of scientists to gather data and answer questions about our solar system. One main goal of the MER missions is to study different kinds of rock and soils that might indicate whether water was ever present on Mars. From the data gathered by the MERs, scientists hope to find out what factors shaped the Martian landscape. They also hope to check out areas that have been studied only from far away so that the scientists can confirm their hypotheses about Mars.

UNANSWERED Questions

As scientists learn more and more about Mars, new questions always arise.

- What role, if any, did water, wind, or volcanoes play in shaping the landscape of Mars?
- Were the conditions necessary to support life ever present on Mars?
- Could there be bacteria-like life forms surviving below the surface of Mars today?

UNIT PROJECTS

As you study this unit, work alone or with a group on one of these projects.

Build a Mechanical Arm

Design and build a mechanical arm to perform a simple task.

- Plan and sketch an arm that could lift a pencil from the floor at a distance of one meter.
- Collect materials and assemble your arm.
- Conduct trials and improve your design.

Multimedia Presentation

Create an informative program on the forces involved in remote exploration.

- Collect information about the Galileo mission to Jupiter or a similar expedition.
- Learn how engineers use air resistance, gravity, and rocket thrusters to maneuver the orbiter close to the planet and its moons.
- Give a presentation describing what you learned using mixed media, such as a computer slide show and a model.

Design an Experiment

Design an experiment to determine the pressure needed to crush a small object.

- Select a small object, such as a vitamin C tablet, to use in your experiment.
- Collect other materials of your choosing.
- Plan and conduct a procedure to test the pressure required to crush the object. Vary the procedure until you can crush the object using the least amount of force.

CAREER CENTER
CLASSZONE.COM
Learn more about careers in physics and engineering.

Frontiers in Science 309

DIFFERENTIATE INSTRUCTION

More Reading Support

E What will the MER study that might indicate whether water was ever present? *rocks and soil*

Differentiate Unit Projects Projects are appropriate for varying abilities. Allow students to choose the ones that interest them most. Encourage them to vary the products they produce throughout the year. Below-level students might try "Multimedia Presentation." Challenge advanced students to try "Design an Experiment."

UNANSWERED Questions

Have students read the questions and think of some of their own. Remind them that scientists always end up with more questions—that inquiry is the driving force of science.

- With the class, generate on the board a list of new questions.
- Students can add to the list after they watch the *Scientific American Frontiers* Video.
- Students can use the list as a springboard for choosing their Unit Projects.

UNIT PROJECTS

Encourage students to pick the project that most appeals to them. Point out that each is long-term and will take several weeks to complete. You might group or pair students to work on projects, and in some cases guide student choice. Some of the projects have student choice built into them. Each project has two worksheet pages, including a rubric. Use the pages to guide students through criteria, process, and schedule.

 Unit Projects, pp. 5–10

Technology Resources

Visit **ClassZone.com** for project procedures and for science career direction.

 RESOURCE CENTER, Unit Projects

REVISIT concepts introduced in this article:

Chapter 11, Forces change motion, pp. 345–351

Chapter 12, Gravity is a force exerted by masses, pp. 381–387

Chapter 13, Work is the use of force to move an object, pp. 419–423

Chapter 14, Machines help people do work, pp. 449–456; Six simple machines have many uses, pp. 458–466; Modern technology uses compound machines, pp. 468–473

CHAPTER 10 Motion

Physical Science
UNIFYING PRINCIPLES

PRINCIPLE 1
Matter is made of particles too small to see.

PRINCIPLE 2
Matter changes form and moves from place to place.

PRINCIPLE 3
Energy changes from one form to another, but it cannot be created or destroyed.

PRINCIPLE 4
Physical forces affect the movement of all matter on Earth and throughout the universe.

Unit 3: Motion and Forces
BIG IDEAS

CHAPTER 10 Motion
The motion of an object can be described and predicted.

CHAPTER 11 Forces
Forces change the motion of objects in predictable ways.

CHAPTER 12 Gravity, Friction, and Pressure
Newton's laws apply to all forces.

CHAPTER 13 Work and Energy
Energy is transferred when a force moves an object.

CHAPTER 14 Machines
Machines help people do work by changing the force applied to an object.

CHAPTER 10 KEY CONCEPTS

SECTION 1

An object in motion changes position.
1. Position describes the location of an object.
2. Motion is a change in position.

SECTION 2

Speed measures how fast position changes.
1. Position can change at different rates.
2. Velocity includes speed and direction.

SECTION 3

Acceleration measures how fast velocity changes.
1. Speed and direction can change with time.
2. Acceleration can be calculated from velocity and time.

The Big Idea Flow Chart is available on p. T1 in the **UNIT TRANSPARENCY BOOK**.

Previewing Content

SECTION

 An object in motion changes position. pp. 313–319

1. **Position describes the location of an object.**
   The **position**, or location, of an object is described relative to a **reference point**. The choice of reference point affects how the position is described. For example, a city can be located by measuring its direction and distance from another city, or by using a grid system such as the longitude-latitude system.

   There are two ways to measure the distance an object has traveled. One is to measure the length of the path the object followed. Another is to measure the straight-line distance of an object from its starting point. This straight-line distance is called the displacement of the object.

2. **Motion is a change in position.**
   Motion is a change in position over time. How quickly or slowly the position changes depends on the object's speed.

   How motion is observed depends upon the observer's point of view. The observed motion of an object is measured by comparing the object's motion relative to the observer's frame of reference. Suppose a person throws a ball forward on a moving train. The motion of the ball is measured differently by observers on the train and by observers on the ground outside. An observer on the ground would measure the motion of the ball as being faster than the motion of the train, as shown in the diagram below.

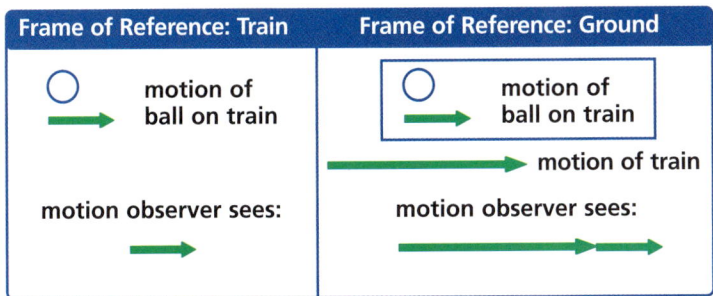

If the ball is thrown backward on the train, an observer on the ground outside would measure the motion of the ball as being slower than the motion of the train.

SECTION

 Speed measures how fast position changes. pp. 320–328

1. **Position can change at different rates.**
   Speed is a measure of how fast something moves through a particular distance over a given amount of time.

   $$\text{Speed} = \frac{\text{distance}}{\text{time}}, \text{ or } S = \frac{d}{t}$$

   Average speed is the average of several instantaneous speeds whose measurements are taken over a specific period of time. A distance-time graph shows how both distance and speed change with time. You can use these graphs to determine the speed of an object by calculating the slope of the line. A positive slope means the object is moving away from its starting point. A negative slope means an object is moving back toward its starting point.

   $$\text{slope} = \frac{\text{change in distance}}{\text{change in time}} = \text{speed}$$

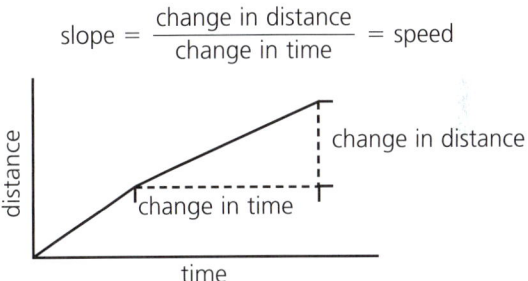

2. **Velocity includes speed and direction.**
   Velocity is speed in a specific direction. Velocity is an example of a vector. A **vector** is a quantity that has both size and direction. Vectors are shown by arrows. The longer the arrow, the faster the speed. The direction of the arrow indicates the direction of motion.

   Speed and velocity are not the same. If two runners run at the same speed in opposite directions, they will have identical speed but different velocities.

Previewing Content

SECTION

 Acceleration measures how fast velocity changes. pp. 329–337

1. **Speed and direction can change with time.**
   Acceleration is the rate at which velocity changes with time. Contrary to a popular misconception, acceleration is not limited to increases in velocity but includes *any* change in velocity. The following are examples of acceleration:
   - speed increases
   - speed decreases
   - direction changes (regardless of speed)

2. **Acceleration can be calculated from velocity and time.**
   You determine acceleration from the change in velocity and how long the change took. The formula for calculating acceleration is shown below.

   $$a = \frac{v_{final} - v_{initial}}{t}$$

   Negative acceleration is a decrease in velocity during a specific period of time. The acceleration formula yields a negative result when the final velocity is less than the initial velocity. A velocity-time graph shows how both velocity and acceleration change with time. The graph on the right below is a velocity-time graph; compare it with the distance-time graph for the same set of data, which is shown below. The graphs show a boy (1) starting and speeding up on his scooter, (2) coasting (velocity is constant), and (3) slowing to a stop.

Distance-Time Graph

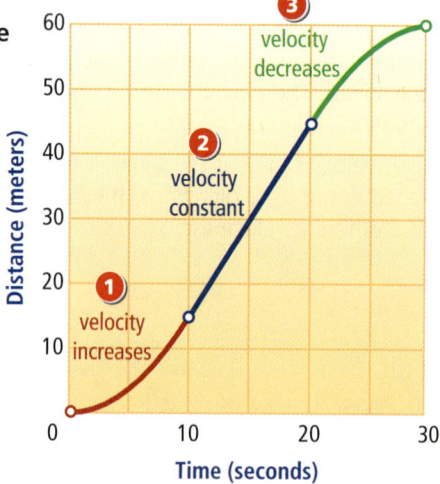

Velocity-Time Graph

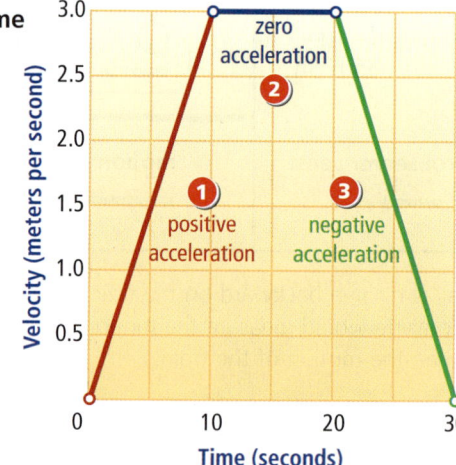

Common Misconceptions

ACCELERATION EQUATED WITH SPEEDING UP Acceleration describes *any* change in velocity. However, students may hold the misconception that acceleration means only an increase in velocity.

 This misconception is addressed on p. 330.

MISCONCEPTION DATABASE
CLASSZONE.COM Background on student misconceptions

NEGATIVE ACCELERATION The change in velocity that occurs during a slowing down is described by the term *negative acceleration*. Students may confuse negative acceleration with negative direction, which involves reversing direction.

 This misconception is addressed on p. 333.

309C   Unit 3: Motion and Forces

Previewing Labs

EXPLORE the BIG idea

Off the Wall, p. 311
Students time a rolling ball to understand that speed is related to time and distance.

TIME 10 minutes
MATERIALS rubber ball, stopwatch

Rolling Along, p. 311
Students roll a marble on a ramp to observe that speed can change.

TIME 10 minutes
MATERIALS hardbound books, marble

Internet Activity: Relative Motion, p. 311
Students are introduced to relative motion.

TIME 20 minutes
MATERIALS computer with Internet access

SECTION 1

EXPLORE Location, p. 313
Students describe the location of an object by giving directions.

TIME 10 minutes
MATERIALS none

INVESTIGATE Changing Positions, p. 316
Students observe motion from varying vantage points.

TIME 20 minutes
MATERIALS small ball, paper, pencil

SECTION 2

EXPLORE Speed, p. 320
Students time a tennis ball rolled at different speeds.

TIME 10 minutes
MATERIALS 20 cm masking tape, meter stick, tennis ball, stopwatch

INVESTIGATE Speed and Distance, p. 323
Students design a car to discover how shape affects speed.

TIME 20 minutes
MATERIALS clay, film container lids, 4 toothpicks, beam balance, board (1 m in length), 2–3 small books, 3 m string, straw, scissors, stopwatch

SECTION 3

INVESTIGATE Acceleration, p. 331
Students measure the acceleration that occurs in different types of movements.
 Template for Tool, p. 42

TIME 30 minutes
MATERIALS Template for Tool, cardboard (8.5 x 11 in), scissors, glue, a 25 cm piece of string, weight (such as a washer)

CHAPTER INVESTIGATION
Acceleration and Slope, pp. 336–337
Students investigate how steepness of slope affects acceleration of a marble.

TIME 40 minutes
MATERIALS 2 meter sticks, 50 cm masking tape, marble, 2 paperback books, metric ruler, stopwatch, calculator

 Additional INVESTIGATION, On the Move, A, B, & C, pp. 65–73; Teacher Instructions, pp. 346–347

Previewing Chapter Resources

	INTEGRATED TECHNOLOGY	LABS AND ACTIVITIES
CHAPTER 10 **Motion**	**CLASSZONE.COM** • eEdition Plus • EasyPlanner Plus • Misconception Database • Content Review • Test Practice • Visualization • Simulation • Resource Centers • Internet Activity: Relative Motion • Math Tutorial **SCILINKS.ORG** SCILINKS	 **CD-ROMS** • eEdition • EasyPlanner • Power Presentations • Content Review • Lab Generator • Test Generator **AUDIO CDS** • Audio Readings • Audio Readings in Spanish	EXPLORE the Big Idea, p. 311 • Off the Wall • Rolling Along • Internet Activity: Relative Motion **UNIT RESOURCE BOOK** • Family Letter, p. ix • Spanish Family Letter, p. x • Unit Projects, pp. 5–10 **Lab Generator CD-ROM** Generate customized labs.
SECTION 1 **An object in motion changes position.** pp. 313–319 Time: 2 periods (1 block) Lesson Plan, pp. 11–12	**RESOURCE CENTER,** Finding Position **UNIT TRANSPARENCY BOOK** • Big Idea Flow Chart, p. T1 • Daily Vocabulary Scaffolding, p. T2 • Note-Taking Model, p. T3 • 3-Minute Warm-Up, p. T4	• EXPLORE Location, p. 313 • INVESTIGATE Changing Positions, p. 316 • Science on the Job, p. 319 **UNIT RESOURCE BOOK** Datasheet, Changing Positions, p. 20
SECTION 2 **Speed measures how fast position changes.** pp. 320–328 Time: 2 periods (1 block) Lesson Plan, pp. 22–23	**MATH TUTORIAL** **UNIT TRANSPARENCY BOOK** • Daily Vocabulary Scaffolding, p. T2 • 3-Minute Warm-Up, p. T4 • "Distance Time Graph," Visual, p. T6	• EXPLORE Speed, p. 320 • INVESTIGATE Speed and Distance, p. 323 • Math in Science, p. 328 **UNIT RESOURCE BOOK** • Datasheet, Speed and Distance, p. 31 • Math Support, pp. 50, 54 • Math Practice, pp. 51, 55
SECTION 3 **Acceleration measures how fast velocity changes.** pp. 329–337 Time: 4 periods (2 blocks) Lesson Plan, pp. 33–34	• **RESOURCE CENTER,** Acceleration • **SIMULATION,** Changing Acceleration **UNIT TRANSPARENCY BOOK** • Big Idea Flow Chart, p. T1 • Daily Vocabulary Scaffolding, p. T2 • 3-Minute Warm-Up, p. T5 • Chapter Outline, pp. T7–T8	• THINK ABOUT How does velocity change? p. 329 • INVESTIGATE Acceleration, p. 331 • CHAPTER INVESTIGATION, Acceleration and Slope, pp. 336–337 **UNIT RESOURCE BOOK** • Template for Tool, p. 42 • Datasheet, Acceleration, p. 43 • Math Support and Practice, pp. 52–53 • CHAPTER INVESTIGATION, Acceleration and Slope, A, B, & C, pp. 56–64 • Additional INVESTIGATION, On the Move, A, B, & C, pp. 65–73

KEY TO ICONS 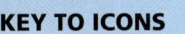 CD/CD-ROM Teacher Edition UNIT TRANSPARENCY BOOK  SPANISH ASSESSMENT BOOK
 INTERNET Pupil Edition UNIT RESOURCE BOOK UNIT ASSESSMENT BOOK SCIENCE TOOLKIT

READING AND REINFORCEMENT

ASSESSMENT

STANDARDS

- Description Wheel, B20–21
- Outline, C43
- Daily Vocabulary Scaffolding, H1–8

 UNIT RESOURCE BOOK
- Vocabulary Practice, pp. 47–48
- Decoding Support, p. 49
- Summarizing the Chapter, pp. 74–75

- Chapter Review, pp. 339–340
- Standardized Test Practice, p. 341

 UNIT ASSESSMENT BOOK
- Diagnostic Test, pp. 1–2
- Chapter Test, A, B, & C, pp. 6–17
- Alternative Assessment, pp. 18–19

Spanish Chapter Test, pp. 257–260

National Standards
A.2–8, A.9.a, A.9.c–e, B.2.a, E.2–5, E.6.d–f, G.1.b

See p. 310 for the standards.

Audio Readings CD
Listen to Pupil Edition.

Audio Readings in Spanish CD
Listen to Pupil Edition in Spanish.

Test Generator CD-ROM
Generate customized tests.

Lab Generator CD-ROM
Rubrics for Labs

 UNIT RESOURCE BOOK
- Reading Study Guide, A & B, pp. 13–16
- Spanish Reading Study Guide, pp. 17–18
- Challenge and Extension, p. 19
- Reinforcing Key Concepts, p. 21

 Ongoing Assessment, pp. 313, 314, 317, 318

 Section 10.1 Review, p. 318

 UNIT ASSESSMENT BOOK
Section 10.1 Quiz, p. 3

National Standards
A.2–7, A.9.a–b, A.9.d–f, B.2.a, E.6.d, E.6.f, G.1.b

 UNIT RESOURCE BOOK
- Reading Study Guide, A & B, pp. 24–27
- Spanish Reading Study Guide, pp. 28–29
- Challenge and Extension, p. 30
- Reinforcing Key Concepts, p. 32

 Ongoing Assessment, pp. 320–322, 324–327

 Section 10.2 Review, p. 327

 UNIT ASSESSMENT BOOK
Section 10.2 Quiz, p. 4

National Standards
A.2–8, A.9.a–f, B.2.a, E.2–5, G.1.b

 UNIT RESOURCE BOOK
- Reading Study Guide, A & B, pp. 35–38
- Spanish Reading Study Guide, pp. 39–40
- Challenge and Extension, p. 41
- Reinforcing Key Concepts, p. 44
- Challenge Reading, pp. 45–46

 Ongoing Assessment, pp. 329, 330, 332–335

 Section 10.3 Review, p. 335

 UNIT ASSESSMENT BOOK
Section 10.3 Quiz, p. 5

National Standards
A.2–8, A.9.a–f, B.2.a, E.6.e, G.1.b

Chapter 10: **Motion 309F**

Previewing Resources for Differentiated Instruction

CHAPTER INVESTIGATION

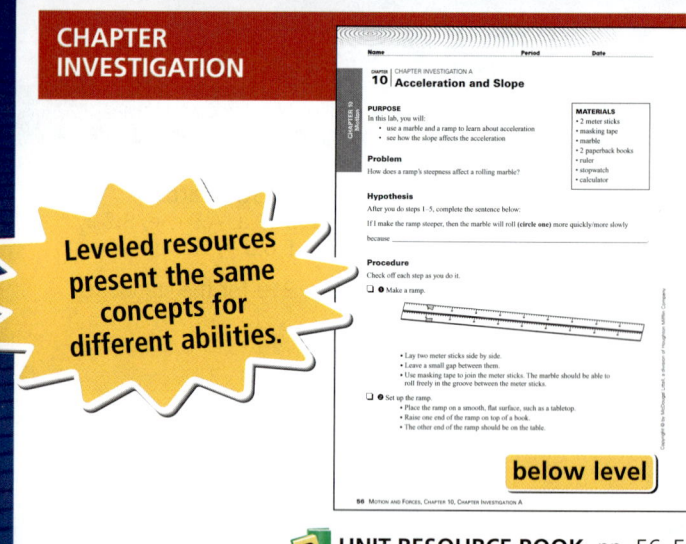 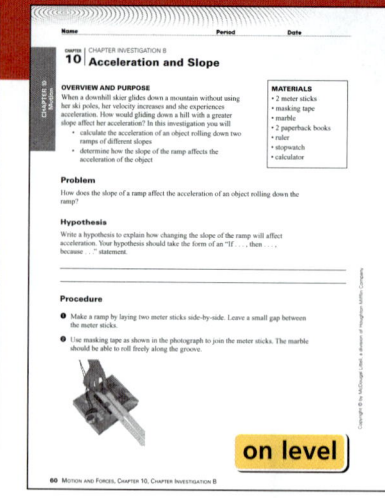 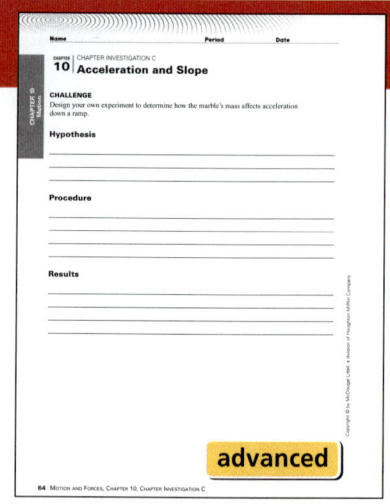

Leveled resources present the same concepts for different abilities.

R UNIT RESOURCE BOOK, pp. 56–59   **R** pp. 60–63   **R** pp. 60–64

READING STUDY GUIDE

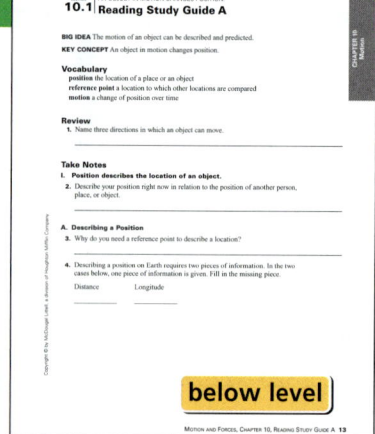 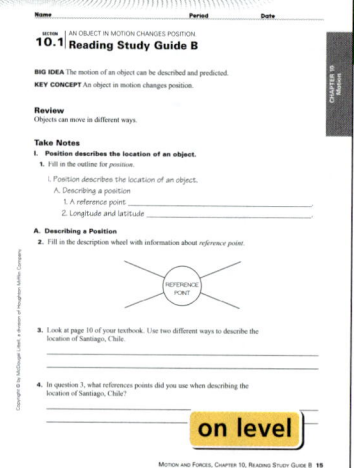 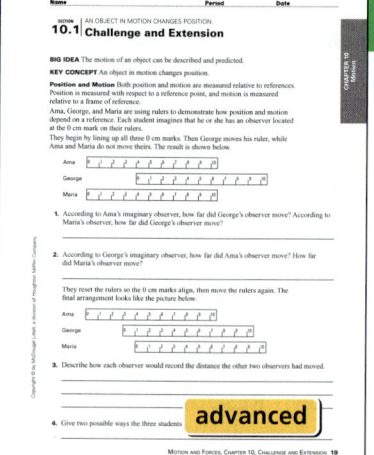

Reading Study Guide is also in Spanish.

R UNIT RESOURCE BOOK, pp. 13–14   **R** pp. 15–16   **R** p. 19

CHAPTER TEST

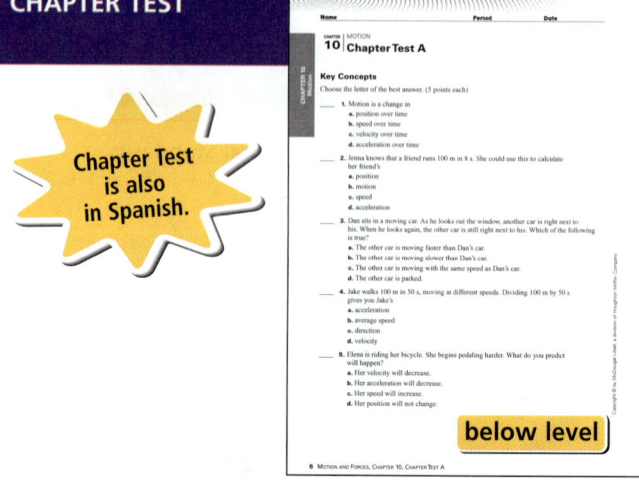 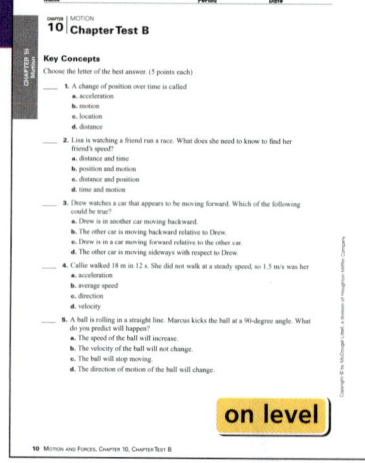 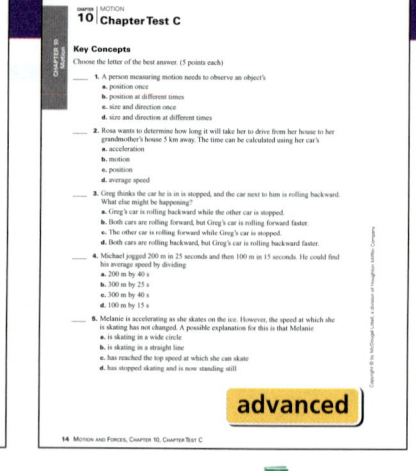

Chapter Test is also in Spanish.

A UNIT ASSESSMENT BOOK, pp. 6–9   **A** pp. 10–13   **A** pp. 14–17

309G Unit 3: **Motion and Forces**

TECHNOLOGY

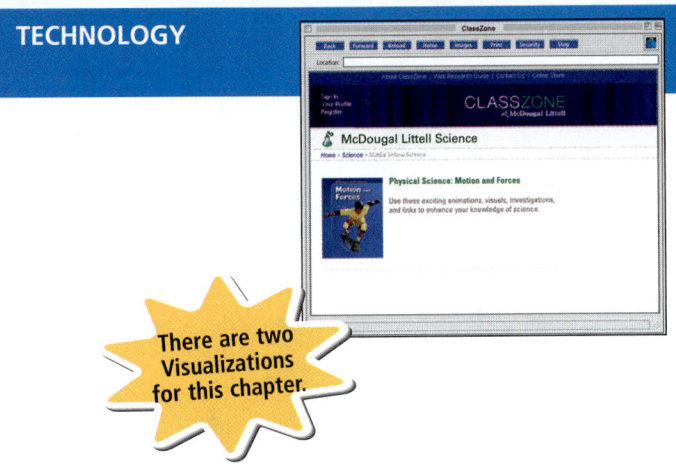

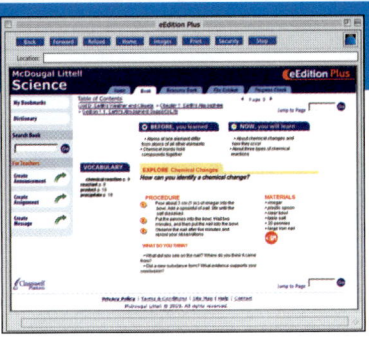

There are two Visualizations for this chapter.

CLASSZONE.COM   CD/CD-ROMS   CLASSZONE.COM

VISUAL CONTENT

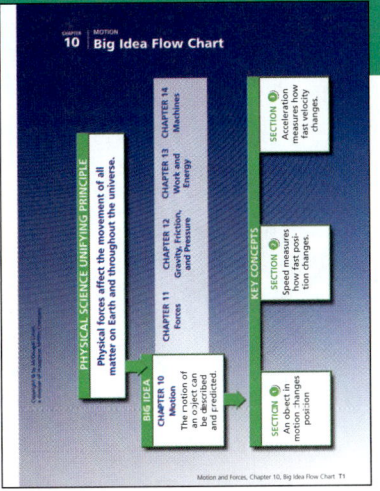
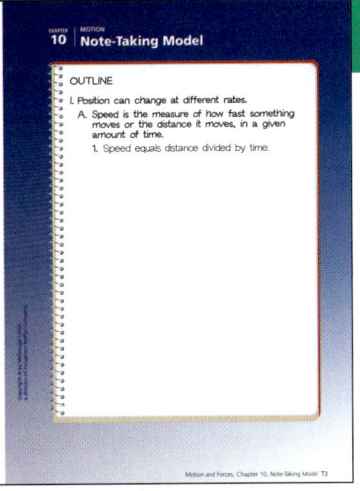
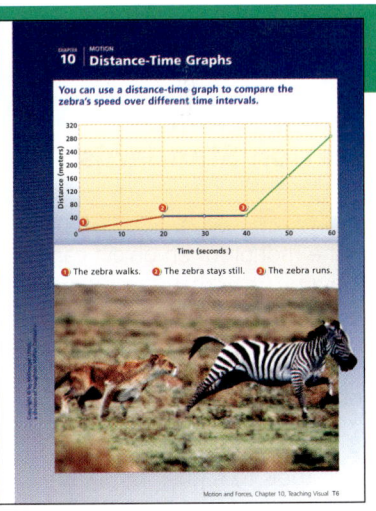

UNIT TRANSPARENCY BOOK, p. T1   p. T3   p. T6

MORE SUPPORT

Reinforcing Key Concepts for each section

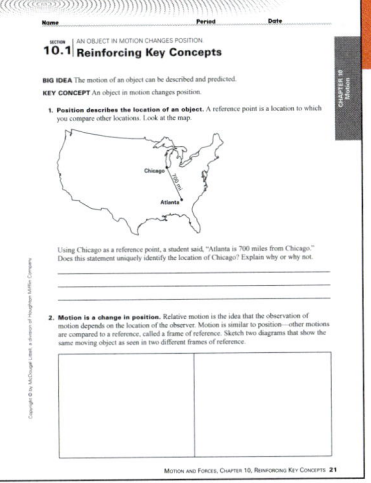
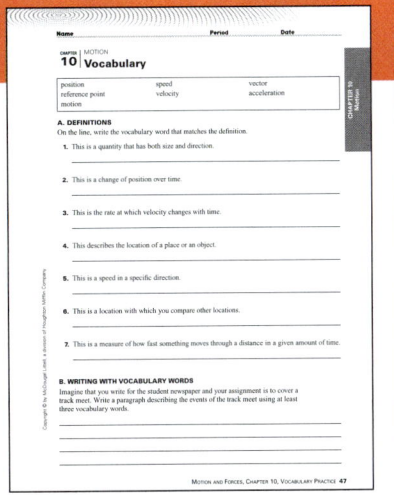
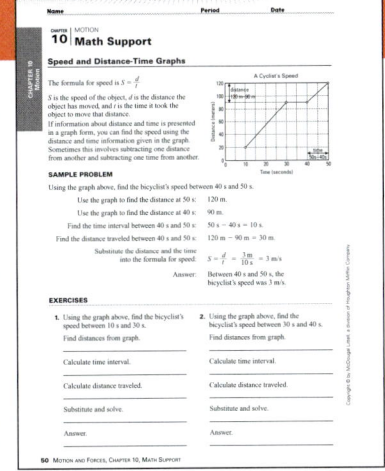

UNIT RESOURCE BOOK, p. 21   pp. 47–48   p. 50

Chapter 10: **Motion** 309H

CHAPTER 10: Motion

INTRODUCE the BIG idea

Have students look at the photograph of the roller coaster and discuss how the question in the box links to the Big Idea:

- Do you expect that the speed of the car on the roller coaster will change from time to time? Describe how it might change.
- Will the direction of the track change?
- How does the motion depicted here differ from other familiar motions, such as walking or riding in a car?

National Science Education Standards

Content

B.2.a The motion of an object can be described by its position, direction of motion, and speed. That motion can be measured and represented on a graph.

Process

A.2–8 Design and conduct an investigation; use tools to gather and interpret data; use evidence to describe, predict, explain, model; think critically to make relationships between evidence and explanation; recognize different explanations and predictions; communicate scientific procedures and explanations; use mathematics.

A.9.a–f Understand scientific inquiry by using different investigations, methods, mathematics, technology, and explanations based on logic, evidence, and skepticism.

E.2–5 Design, implement, and evaluate a solution or product; communicate technological design.

E.6.d–f Understandings about science and technology

G.1.b Science as human endeavor

310 Unit 3: **Motion and Forces**

CHAPTER 10: Motion

the BIG idea

The motion of an object can be described and predicted.

Where will these people be in a few seconds? How do you know?

Key Concepts

SECTION 1 — An object in motion changes position.
Learn about measuring position from reference points, and about relative motion.

SECTION 2 — Speed measures how fast position changes.
Learn to calculate speed and how velocity depends on speed and direction.

SECTION 3 — Acceleration measures how fast velocity changes.
Learn about acceleration and how to calculate it.

Internet Preview

CLASSZONE.COM
Chapter 10 online resources: Content Review, Visualization, Simulation, two Resource Centers, Math Tutorial, Test Practice

310 Unit 3: **Motion and Forces**

INTERNET PREVIEW

CLASSZONE.COM For student use with the following pages:

Review and Practice
- Content Review, pp. 312, 338
- Math Tutorial: Units and Rates, p. 328
- Test Practice, p. 341

Activities and Resources
- Internet Activity: Relative Motion, p. 311
- Resource Centers: Finding Position, p. 314; Acceleration, p. 333
- Simulation: Changing Acceleration, p. 335

Velocity **Code: MDL004**

EXPLORE the BIG idea

Off the Wall
Roll a rubber ball toward a wall. Record the time from the starting point to the wall. Change the distance between the wall and the starting point. Adjust the speed at which you roll the ball until it takes the same amount of time to hit the wall as before.

Observe and Think How did the speed of the ball over the longer distance compare with the speed over the shorter distance?

Rolling Along
Make a ramp by leaning the edge of one book on two other books. Roll a marble up the ramp. Repeat several times and notice what happens each time.

Observe and Think How does the speed of the marble change? At what point does its direction of motion change?

Internet Activity: Relative Motion
Go to ClassZone.com to examine motion from different points of view. Learn how your motion makes a difference in what you observe.

Observe and Think How does the way you see motion depend on your point of view?

NSTA scilinks.org SCLINKS
Velocity Code: MDL004

Chapter 10: **Motion** 311

EXPLORE the BIG idea

These inquiry-based activities are appropriate for use at home or as a supplement to classroom instruction.

Off the Wall
PURPOSE To introduce students to the idea that speed is related to time and distance.

TIP *10 min.* Remind students to study their data for patterns as they contemplate the questions.

Answer: The speed over the longer distance was higher than the speed over the shorter distance.

REVISIT after p. 321.

Rolling Along
PURPOSE To introduce students to the idea that speed can change.

TIP *10 min.* Use a hardbound book so there is no bow or dip in the ramp.

Answer: The marble loses speed while it is rolling up. It changes direction after it stops on its way up the ramp. After it stops, it rolls back down.

REVISIT after p. 330.

Internet Activity: Relative Motion
PURPOSE To introduce students to the idea that how motion is perceived depends on the observer's reference point.

TIP *20 min.* Be sure students understand the difference between a reference point and a frame of reference.

Answer: The way you perceive motion depends on your location and whether you are in motion.

REVISIT after p. 318.

TEACHING WITH TECHNOLOGY

CBL and Probeware If students have probeware, have them use a motion sensor as they push various objects. Motion is introduced on p. 315.

Video Camera You might want to film short clips of students performing variations of the investigation on p. 316. Use them to reinforce the concept that change in position depends on the perspective of the observer.

Chapter 10 **311**

PREPARE

◐ Concept Review
Activate Prior Knowledge

- Have students read the concept review at the top of the page.
- Using a battery-operated toy vehicle or a wind-up toy, demonstrate speed and direction. Have students change the direction of the moving toy. Have them speculate how fast the toy is moving.
- Start the toy again and have someone hold it back. Ask how the speed of the toy is affected. Challenge students to speed up the toy.
- Ask students how this activity demonstrates the principles in the concept review.

▶ Taking Notes

Outline
An outline helps students organize their ideas as they would in writing a paragraph by proceeding from main topic to details.

Vocabulary Strategy
Description wheels help students focus on all the parts of a complex definition. Point out that students can fill in as few or as many of the spokes as appropriate.

Vocabulary and Note-Taking Resources

- Vocabulary Practice, pp. 47–48
- Decoding Support, p. 49

- Daily Vocabulary Scaffolding, p. T2
- Note-Taking Model, p. T3

- Description Wheel, B20–21
- Outline, C43
- Daily Vocabulary Scaffolding, H1–8

CHAPTER 10
Getting Ready to Learn

◐ CONCEPT REVIEW
- Objects can move at different speeds and in different directions.
- Pushing or pulling on an object will change how it moves.

◐ VOCABULARY REVIEW
See Glossary for definitions.
- horizontal
- meter
- second
- vertical

CONTENT REVIEW
CLASSZONE.COM
Review concepts and vocabulary.

▶ TAKING NOTES

OUTLINE
As you read, copy the headings onto your paper in the form of an outline. Then add notes in your own words that summarize what you read.

VOCABULARY STRATEGY
Place each new vocabulary term at the center of a **description wheel** diagram. As you read about the term, write some words on the spokes describing the term.

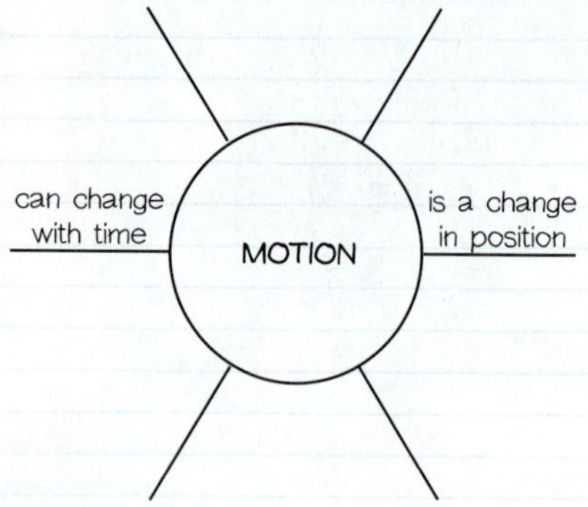

See the Note-Taking Handbook on pages R45–R51.

312 Unit 3: Motion and Forces

SCIENCE NOTEBOOK

OUTLINE
I. Position describes the location of an object.
  A. Describing a position
    1. A position is compared to a reference point.
    2. Position can be described using distance and direction.

can change with time — MOTION — is a change in position

CHECK READINESS

Administer the Diagnostic Test to determine students' readiness for new science content and their mastery of requisite math skills.

 Diagnostic Test, pp. 1–2

Technology Resources
Students needing content and math skills should visit ClassZone.com.

- CONTENT REVIEW
- MATH TUTORIAL

 CONTENT REVIEW CD-ROM

KEY CONCEPT

10.1 An object in motion changes position.

◀ **BEFORE, you learned**
- Objects can move in different ways
- An object's position can change

▶ **NOW, you will learn**
- How to describe an object's position
- How to describe an object's motion

VOCABULARY

position p. 313
reference point p. 314
motion p. 315

EXPLORE Location

How do you describe the location of an object?

PROCEDURE

1. Choose an object in the classroom that is easy to see.
2. Without pointing to, describing, or naming the object, give directions to a classmate for finding it.
3. Ask your classmate to identify the object using your directions. If your classmate does not correctly identify the object, try giving directions in a different way. Continue until your classmate has located the object.

WHAT DO YOU THINK?
What kinds of information must you give another person when you are trying to describe a location?

Position describes the location of an object.

VOCABULARY
Make a description wheel in your notebook for *position*.

Have you ever gotten lost while looking for a specific place? If so, you probably know that accurately describing where a place is can be very important. The **position** of a place or an object is the location of that place or object. Often you describe where something is by comparing its position with where you currently are. You might say, for example, that a classmate sitting next to you is about a meter to your right, or that a mailbox is two blocks south of where you live. Each time you identify the position of an object, you are comparing the location of the object with the location of another object or place.

 Why do you need to discuss two locations to describe the position of an object?

Chapter 10: **Motion** 313

10.1 FOCUS

▶ Set Learning Goals
Students will
- Describe an object's position.
- Describe an object's motion.
- Observe changes in position through experimentation.

◉ 3-Minute Warm-Up
Display Transparency 4 or copy this exercise on the board:

Draw pictures to represent the motion described in these two scenarios.

1. An ant crawls across the top of your shoe, from left to right. *short series of pictures showing ant's movement*
2. A hiker walks from the beginning to the end of a hiking path. *short series of pictures showing hiker's movement*

 3-Minute Warm-Up, p. T4

10.1 MOTIVATE

EXPLORE Location
PURPOSE To consider how to identify a location

TIP *10 min.* Have several students try choosing and describing an object. After the activity, have the class discuss how much and what type of information was needed.

WHAT DO YOU THINK? *Sample answer: I had my partner count a specific number of desks to the front and to the right so she could locate the object.*

RESOURCES FOR DIFFERENTIATED INSTRUCTION

Below Level
UNIT RESOURCE BOOK
- Reading Study Guide A, pp. 13–14
- Decoding Support, p. 49

 **AUDIO CDS**

Advanced
UNIT RESOURCE BOOK
- Challenge and Extension, p. 19

English Learners
UNIT RESOURCE BOOK
Spanish Reading Study Guide, pp. 17–18

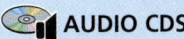 **AUDIO CDS**
- Audio Readings in Spanish
- Audio Readings (English)

Ongoing Assessment
 *Answer: You need to compare the location of the object with the location of another object or place.*

Chapter 10 **313**

10.1 INSTRUCT

Teach from Visuals

To point out different ways to describe a location, use the "Describing Position" visual and ask:

- What does the map on the left show? *using Brasília as a reference point for finding Santiago*
- What does the map on the right show? *using latitude and longitude, a grid system, to locate Santiago*

Teacher Demo

Make a tube out of graph paper and tape it so it will stay closed. Draw a point on the tube. Ask students how they could use the graph paper squares to locate the point. List the different suggestions on the board, and discuss the similarities and differences in the methods. Point out how two reference lines, one vertical and one horizontal, are needed to describe the location. Discuss how longitude and latitude are like the lines on the tube.

Ongoing Assessment

Describe an object's position.

Ask: If you describe positions on a map by comparing them with the position of landmark Q, what is Q called? *a reference point*

 *Answer: The left-hand map uses a distance and a direction from Brasília to describe Santiago's location. The right-hand map uses the number of degrees from the equator and the prime meridian to describe Santiago's location.*

 **RESOURCE CENTER**
CLASSZONE.COM
Learn more about how people find and describe position.

Describing a Position

You might describe the position of a city based on the location of another city. A location to which you compare other locations is called a **reference point**. You can describe where Santiago, Chile, is from the reference point of the city Brasília, Brazil, by saying that Santiago is about 3000 kilometers (1860 mi) southwest of Brasília.

You can also describe a position using a method that is similar to describing where a point on a graph is located. For example, in the longitude and latitude system, locations are given by two numbers—longitude and latitude. Longitude describes how many degrees east or west a location is from the prime meridian, an imaginary line running north-south through Greenwich, England. Latitude describes how many degrees north or south a location is from the equator, the imaginary circle that divides the northern and southern hemispheres. Having a standard way of describing location, such as longitude and latitude, makes it easier for people to compare locations.

Describing Position

There are several different ways to describe a position. The way you choose may depend on your reference point.

① Reference Point: Brasília

To describe where Santiago is, using Brasília as a reference point, you would need to know how far Santiago is from Brasília and in what direction it is.

② Reference Point: 0° longitude, 0° latitude

In the longitude and latitude system, a location is described by how many degrees north or south it is from the equator and how many degrees east or west it is from the prime meridian.

READING VISUALS Compare and contrast the two ways of describing the location of Santiago as shown here.

314 Unit 3: Motion and Forces

DIFFERENTIATE INSTRUCTION

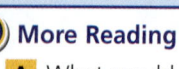 **More Reading Support**

A What would you call a location with which other locations can be compared? *a reference point*

English Learners English learners may need help understanding sentences that imply *if/then* construction, such as *If you were to travel from Brasília to Santiago, you would end up about 3000 kilometers from where you started* (p. 315). This sentence begins with *If* but does not contain *then*, and therefore requires a reader to infer the cause-and-effect relationship. Point out other examples of this construction and make sure English learners recognize that *then* is implied.

Measuring Distance

If you were to travel from Brasília to Santiago, you would end up about 3000 kilometers from where you started. The actual distance you traveled, however, would depend on the exact path you took. If you took a route that had many curves, the distance you traveled would be greater than 3000 kilometers.

The way you measure distance depends on the information you want. Sometimes you want to know the straight-line distance between two positions. Sometimes, however, you might need to know the total length of a certain path between those positions. During a hike, you are probably more interested in how far you have walked than in how far you are from your starting point.

When measuring either the straight-line distance between two points or the length of a path between those points, scientists use a standard unit of measurement. The standard unit of length is the meter (m), which is 3.3 feet. Longer distances can be measured in kilometers (km), and shorter distances in centimeters (cm).

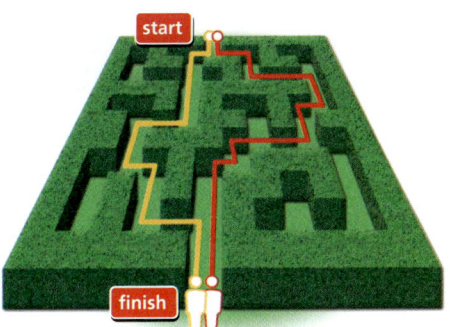

COMPARE How does the distance each person has walked compare with the distance each is from the start of the maze?

Motion is a change in position.

The illustration below shows an athlete at several positions during a long jump. If you were to watch her jump, you would see that she is in motion. **Motion** is the change of position over time. As she jumps, both her horizontal and vertical positions change. If you missed the motion of the jump, you would still know that motion occurred because of the distance between her starting and ending positions. A change in position is evidence that motion happened.

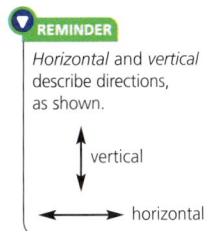

REMINDER

Horizontal and *vertical* describe directions, as shown.

vertical
horizontal

starting position
ending position

Chapter 10: **Motion** 315

DIFFERENTIATE INSTRUCTION

More Reading Support

B List two ways to measure distance. *measure a straight-line distance between two positions; measure the total length of a path between two positions*

Advanced Have students refer to the map on page 314 that shows a connecting line between Santiago and Brasília. Ask: How could you estimate the distance of this diagonal line using grid units—that is, the distance south and the distance west? *You could measure the vertical distance and the horizontal distance; then use the Pythagorean theorem to determine the length of the hypotenuse.*

 Challenge and Extension, p. 19

History of Science

In eighteenth-century France, some 2000 different units of measurement were used across the country because different locales had their own systems. The French Revolution (1789–1799) set the stage for a new, universal system of measurement. A commission decided on a basic unit of measurement, the meter. They designed a decimal system that uses base names (such as *meter* and *gram*) and affixes standard prefixes to indicate fractional and multiple units (such as *milligram* and *kilogram*). In 1795 the French government adopted the new metric system.

Teach from Visuals

Direct students' attention to the time-exposure illustration at the bottom of the page, and then ask:

- How does the picture show time passing? *It shows the jumper in a number of different positions between the start and finish of her long jump.*
- How is the picture different from a snapshot? *A snapshot freezes a single moment in time.*

Teaching with Technology

If students have probeware, encourage them to use a motion sensor as they push various classroom objects across a flat, smooth surface.

Chapter 10 **315**

INVESTIGATE
Changing Positions

PURPOSE To explore how change in position depends on the perspective of the observer

TIPS 20 min.
- Use tennis balls or rubber balls of about the same diameter.
- Model the walking/ball-tossing activity. Then encourage volunteers to try it.
- Check that students, when sketching their own ball tosses, aren't adding their motion to what they see but are recording only what they observe.

WHAT DO YOU THINK? *The path of the ball looked straight up and down when I threw it; when I watched another student throwing the ball, it looked curving. The same motion can look different to two people who are in different locations relative to the motion.*

CHALLENGE *as though it were moving straight up and down*

 Datasheet, Changing Positions, p. 20

Technology Resources
Customize this student lab as needed or look for an alternative. Print rubrics to assess student lab reports.

 Lab Generator CD-ROM

Metacognitive Strategy
Ask students if they would have accepted the conclusions of the investigation without actually participating in it. Have students write a paragraph explaining the importance of observations.

Teaching with Technology
As students perform the ball-tossing activity, videotape them from various perspectives, such as coming toward, going away from, moving parallel to, and so forth. Have participants label each clip. Have groups view the videos and discuss the change in position of the ball in regard to motion and perspective.

316 Unit 3: Motion and Forces

INVESTIGATE Changing Position

How are changes in position observed?
PROCEDURE

① Begin walking while tossing a ball straight up and catching it as it falls back down toward your hand. Observe the changes in the position of the ball as you toss it while walking a distance of about 4 m.

② Make a sketch showing how the position of the ball changed as you walked. Use your own position as a reference point for the ball's position.

③ Watch while a classmate walks and tosses the ball. Observe the changes in the position of the ball using your own position as a reference point. Make a sketch showing how the ball moved based on your new point of view.

WHAT DO YOU THINK?
- Compare your two sketches. How was the change in position of the ball you tossed different from the change in position of the ball that your partner tossed?
- How did your change in viewpoint affect what you observed? Explain.

CHALLENGE How would the change in position of the ball appear to a person standing 4 m directly in front of you?

SKILL FOCUS
Observing

MATERIALS
- small ball
- paper
- pencil

TIME
20 minutes

Describing Motion

A change in an object's position tells you that motion took place, but it does not tell you how quickly the object changed position. The speed of a moving object is a measure of how quickly or slowly the object changes position. A faster object moves farther than a slower moving object would in the same amount of time.

The way in which an object moves can change. As a raft moves along a river, its speed changes as the speed of the river changes. When the raft reaches a calm area of the river, it slows down. When the raft reaches rapids, it speeds up. The rafters can also change the motion of the raft by using paddles. You will learn more about speed and changing speed in the following sections.

APPLY Describe the different directions in which the raft is moving.

316 Unit 3: **Motion and Forces**

DIFFERENTIATE INSTRUCTION

 More Reading Support

C What determines how quickly or slowly a moving object changes position?
the speed of the object

Alternative Assessment Have students write a paragraph explaining the differences between the perspectives of two people viewing a moving bicycle rider, where one observer is in a car keeping pace with the cyclist, and the other observer is standing at the side of a bicycle path as the cyclist whizzes by.

Relative Motion

If you sit still in a chair, you are not moving. Or are you? The answer depends on the position and motion of the person observing you. You do not notice your position changing compared with the room and the objects in it. But if an observer could leave Earth and look at you from outer space, he could see that you are moving along with Earth as it travels around the Sun. How an observer sees your motion depends on how it compares with his own motion. Just as position is described by using a reference point, motion is described by using a frame of reference. You can think of a frame of reference as the location of an observer, who may be in motion.

Consider a student sitting behind the driver of a moving bus. The bus passes another student waiting at a street sign to cross the street.

① To the observer on the bus, the driver is not changing his position compared with the inside of the bus. The street sign, however, moves past the observer's window. From this observer's point of view, the driver is not moving, but the street sign is.

② To the observer on the sidewalk, the driver is changing position along with the bus. The street sign, on the other hand, is not changing position. From this observer's point of view, the street sign is not moving, but the driver is.

OUTLINE
Add relative motion to your outline, along with supporting details.

I. Main idea
   A. Supporting idea
      1. Detail
      2. Detail
   B. Supporting idea

Relative Motion

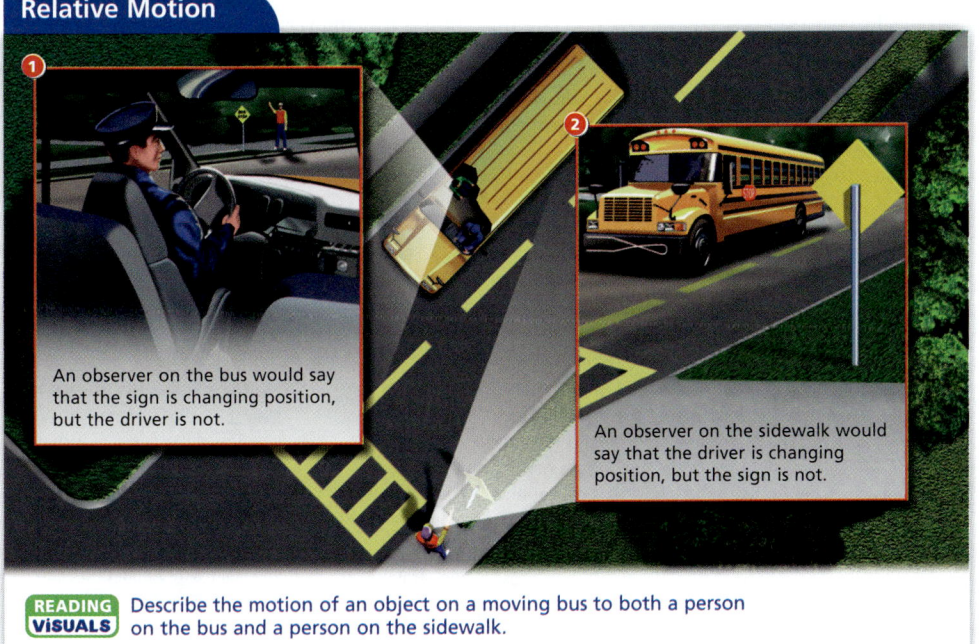

① An observer on the bus would say that the sign is changing position, but the driver is not.

② An observer on the sidewalk would say that the driver is changing position, but the sign is not.

READING VISUALS Describe the motion of an object on a moving bus to both a person on the bus and a person on the sidewalk.

Chapter 10: **Motion** 317

DIFFERENTIATE INSTRUCTION

More Reading Support

 One observer may see a motion differently than another observer. What idea does this statement express? *relative motion*

Inclusion Adapt the relative-motion examples on this page for students with vision impairments. Prompt students to imagine that a person standing on a sidewalk would feel and hear a bus whiz by. To a person on the bus, however, there might be no more sensation of movement than some seat vibrations. These two observers would have completely different perspectives on the motion of the bus.

Teach Difficult Concepts

Students may have a hard time understanding that all motion is measured relative to an observer's frame of reference. Explain that an object that is not moving in one frame of reference will be moving in another.

Have students think about sitting on an airplane that is in the air. Discuss whether or not the seat is moving. Have students consider the airplane and Earth as frames of reference. Encourage students to think about other frames of reference, such as one in which Earth is moving.

Point out that you can always find a frame of reference in which an object is still and others in which the object moves. There is no correct frame of reference—they are all equally valid.

Develop Critical Thinking

APPLY Describe a puppet show that calls for the puppets to sit on a moving train. The stage set consists of a board with cutouts for windows that is placed behind the puppets.

Ask: How could you convince the audience that the train is moving? *Sample answer: You could paint scenery on a long strip of paper and pull it through the stage set behind the window cutouts. The motion of the pictures would look like scenery passing, because of the reference point of the puppet "observers" inside the train.*

Ongoing Assessment

Describe a frame of reference.

Ask: What is a frame of reference? *the location of an observer of a motion*

READING VISUALS *Answer: To an observer on the bus, an object on the bus appears to be still. The same object will appear to be traveling at the same speed as the bus to an observer on the sidewalk.*

Chapter 10 **317**

Ongoing Assessment

 Sample answer: You observe motion relative to your own position. If you are on a train, for example, you see the ground outside the train moving past you.

EXPLORE
Revisit "Internet Activity: Relative Motion" on p. 311. Have students explain the reasons for their results.

Reinforce
Have students relate the section to the Big Idea.

 Reinforcing Key Concepts, p. 21

10.1 ASSESS & RETEACH

Assess
 Section 10.1 Quiz, p. 3

Reteach
Put two marbles randomly on a checkerboard. Have students describe the positions, and then roll the two marbles at different speeds. Emphasize that a good description of motion includes speed. Finally, have students view the rolling of a marble from very different positions. Solicit students' observations. Discuss relative motion.

Technology Resources
Have students visit ClassZone.com for reteaching of Key Concepts.
 CONTENT REVIEW
CONTENT REVIEW CD-ROM

When you ride in a train, a bus, or an airplane, you think of yourself as moving and the ground as standing still. That is, you usually consider the ground as the frame of reference for your motion. If you traveled between two cities, you would say that you had moved, not that the ground had moved under you in the opposite direction.

If you cannot see the ground or objects on it, it is sometimes difficult to tell if a train you are riding in is moving. If the ride is very smooth and you do not look out the window at the scenery, you might never realize you are moving at all.

Suppose you are in a train, and you cannot tell if you are stopped or moving. Outside the window, another train is slowly moving forward. Could you tell which of the following situations is happening?

- Your train is stopped, and the other train is moving slowly forward.
- The other train is stopped, and your train is moving slowly backward.
- Both trains are moving forward, with the other train moving a little faster.
- Your train is moving very slowly backward, and the other train is moving very slowly forward.

Actually, all four of these possibilities would look exactly the same to you. Unless you compared the motion to the motion of something outside the train, such as the ground, you could not tell the difference between these situations.

APPLY In the top picture, the train is moving compared with the camera and the ground. Describe the relative motion of the train, camera, and ground in the bottom picture.

How does your observation of motion depend on your own motion?

10.1 Review

KEY CONCEPTS
1. What information do you need to describe an object's location?
2. Describe how your position changes as you jump over an object.
3. Give an example of how the apparent motion of an object depends on the observer's motion.

CRITICAL THINKING
4. **Infer** Kyle walks 3 blocks south from his home to school, and Jana walks 2 blocks north from her home to Kyle's home. How far and in what direction is the school from Jana's home?
5. **Predict** If you sit on a moving bus and toss a coin straight up into the air, where will it land?

CHALLENGE
6. **Infer** Jamal is in a car going north. He looks out his window and thinks that the northbound traffic is moving very slowly. Ellen is in a car going south. She thinks the northbound traffic is moving quickly. Explain why Jamal and Ellen have different ideas about the motion of the traffic.

ANSWERS

1. a reference point

2. As a person jumps over an object, both his horizontal and vertical positions change.

3. Sample answer: A person in an airplane will think of her or his seat as not moving, but an observer on the ground will think the seats are moving with the airplane.

4. one block south

5. It should land back in your hand (or directly beneath where you threw it).

6. Jamal and Ellen have different ideas about motion because both compare the northbound traffic with their own motion. From Jamal's point of view, traffic is going in the same direction as he is; therefore, traffic seems to be moving slowly. Ellen sees oncoming cars and thinks they are moving quickly.

SCIENCE on the JOB

COAST GUARD RESCUE

Physics for Rescuers

Performing a rescue operation is often difficult and risky because the person in trouble is in a dangerous situation. Coast Guard Search and Rescue Teams have an especially difficult problem to deal with. As a rescue ship or helicopter approaches a stranded boat, the team must get close enough to help but avoid making the problem worse by colliding with the boat. At the same time, wind, waves, and currents cause changes in the motion of both crafts.

Finding the Problem

A stranded boater fires a flare to indicate his location. The observer on the Coast Guard ship tracks the motion of the flare to its source.

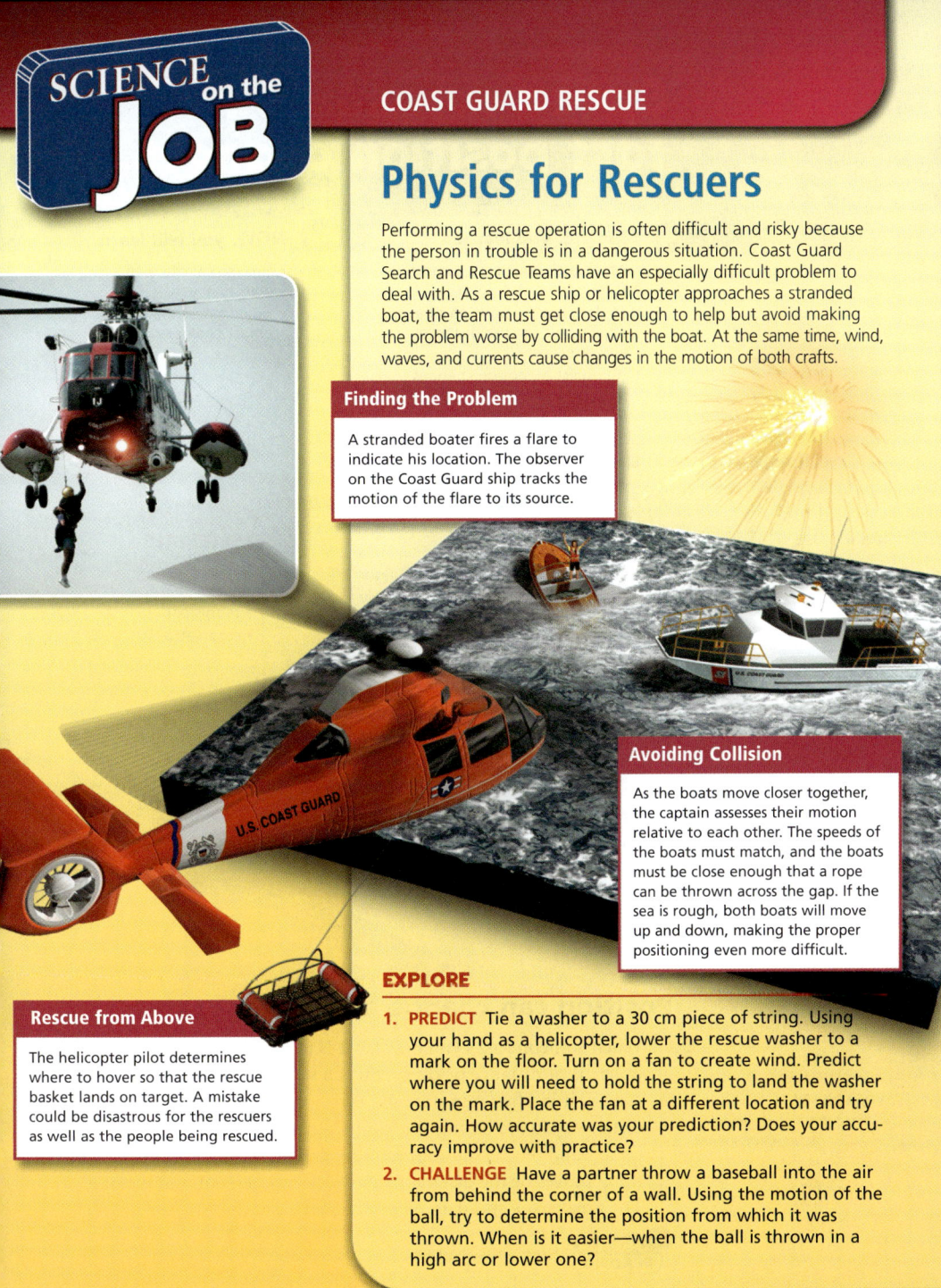

Avoiding Collision

As the boats move closer together, the captain assesses their motion relative to each other. The speeds of the boats must match, and the boats must be close enough that a rope can be thrown across the gap. If the sea is rough, both boats will move up and down, making the proper positioning even more difficult.

Rescue from Above

The helicopter pilot determines where to hover so that the rescue basket lands on target. A mistake could be disastrous for the rescuers as well as the people being rescued.

EXPLORE

1. **PREDICT** Tie a washer to a 30 cm piece of string. Using your hand as a helicopter, lower the rescue washer to a mark on the floor. Turn on a fan to create wind. Predict where you will need to hold the string to land the washer on the mark. Place the fan at a different location and try again. How accurate was your prediction? Does your accuracy improve with practice?

2. **CHALLENGE** Have a partner throw a baseball into the air from behind the corner of a wall. Using the motion of the ball, try to determine the position from which it was thrown. When is it easier—when the ball is thrown in a high arc or lower one?

SCIENCE ON THE JOB
Relevance of Science to Non-science Jobs

Set Learning Goal

To understand why rescuers rely on principles of physics to do their job

Present the Science

FINDING POSITIONS Many boats carry a Global Positioning System (GPS) device that enables rescue workers to locate the boat. The GPS device works by transmitting a signal to satellites in orbit around Earth. Each satellite measures a distance between it and the boat. By comparing the distances provided by three or more satellites in different locations, rescuers can determine the boat's position.

HOVERING A helicopter, unlike an airplane, has the ability to hover in place above a target. In order for a helicopter to remain above a moving target, it must match the target's motion.

Discussion Questions

Ask: What are some of the dangers faced by rescuers at sea? *Wind and waves can add forces that make it difficult to predict how a boat will move. Rescuers in helicopters must maintain a balance of forces during the hovering maneuver. There is always the danger of a collision.*

Ask: How does relative motion contribute to these hazards? *Rescuers can adjust for constant relative motion, but unexpected changes in speed make the results unpredictable and increase the possibility of collision.*

Close

Ask: Why does a knowledge of physical science provide a good background for rescuers? *Rescuers need to know about forces and motion, which are explored in physical science.*

EXPLORE

PREDICT Students should improve their accuracy with practice.
CHALLENGE thrown in a high arc

10.2 FOCUS

▶ Set Learning Goals

Students will
- Calculate an object's speed.
- Describe an object's velocity.
- Observe through experimentation the relationship between speed and distance.

◀ 3-Minute Warm-Up

Display Transparency 4 or copy this exercise on the board:

Suppose you pass a table on which a ball is sitting near the end of a cardboard tube. After a few minutes, you pass the table again. The ball is now near the other end of the tube. What can you say about the motion of the ball between those two times? What can't you say about the motion? *You can say that the ball moved from one end of the tube to another. You can't say anything about the path. The ball may have gone through the tube, or it may have been moved around the tube.*

 3-Minute Warm-Up, p. T4

10.2 MOTIVATE

EXPLORE Speed

PURPOSE To introduce the relationship among speed, distance, and time

TIP 10 min. Select a flat, level area without carpeting.

WHAT DO YOU THINK? *I pushed the ball harder to decrease the time and less hard to increase it. If the time was shorter, the ball had to travel the same distance faster.*

Ongoing Assessment

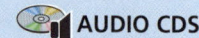 Answer: *They are related by time: speed is a measure of how quickly an object changes position.*

320 Unit 3: Motion and Forces

KEY CONCEPT

10.2 Speed measures how fast position changes.

◀ BEFORE, you learned
- An object's position is measured from a reference point
- To describe the position of an object, you can use distance and direction
- An object in motion changes position with time

▶ NOW, you will learn
- How to calculate an object's speed
- How to describe an object's velocity

VOCABULARY

speed p. 320
velocity p. 326
vector p. 326

EXPLORE Speed

How can you measure speed?

PROCEDURE

1. Place a piece of tape on the floor. Measure a distance on the floor 2 m away from the tape. Mark this distance with a second piece of tape.
2. Roll a tennis ball from one piece of tape to the other, timing how long it takes to travel the 2 m.
3. Roll the ball again so that it travels the same distance in less time. Then roll the ball so that it takes more time to travel that distance than it did the first time.

MATERIALS
- tape
- meter stick
- tennis ball
- stopwatch

WHAT DO YOU THINK?
- How did you change the time it took the ball to travel 2 m?
- How did changing the time affect the motion of the ball?

VOCABULARY
Make a description wheel in your notebook for *speed*.

Position can change at different rates.

When someone asks you how far it is to the library, you can answer in terms of distance or time. You can say it is several blocks, or you can say it is a five-minute walk. When you give a time instead of a distance, you are basing your time estimate on the distance to the library and the person's speed. **Speed** is a measure of how fast something moves or the distance it moves, in a given amount of time. The greater the speed an object has, the faster it changes position.

 How are speed and position related?

320 Unit 3: Motion and Forces

RESOURCES FOR DIFFERENTIATED INSTRUCTION

Below Level
UNIT RESOURCE BOOK
- Reading Study Guide A, pp. 24–25
- Decoding Support, p. 49

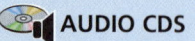 **AUDIO CDS**

Advanced
UNIT RESOURCE BOOK
- Challenge and Extension, p. 30

English Learners
UNIT RESOURCE BOOK
Spanish Reading Study Guide, pp. 28–29

AUDIO CDS
- Audio Readings in Spanish
- Audio Readings (English)

The way in which one quantity changes compared to another quantity is called a rate. Speed is the rate at which the distance an object moves changes compared to time. If you are riding a bike to a movie, and you think you might be late, you increase the rate at which your distance changes by pedaling harder. In other words, you increase your speed.

Calculating Speed

To calculate speed, you need to know both distance and time measurements. Consider the two bike riders below.

① The two bikes pass the same point at the same time.

② After one second, the first bike has traveled four meters, while the second has traveled only two meters. Because the first bike has traveled four meters in one second, it has a speed of four meters per second. The second bike has a speed of two meters per second.

③ If each bike continues moving at the same speed as before, then after two seconds the first rider will have traveled eight meters, while the second one will have traveled only four meters.

Comparing Speed

Objects that travel at different speeds move different distances in the same amount of time.

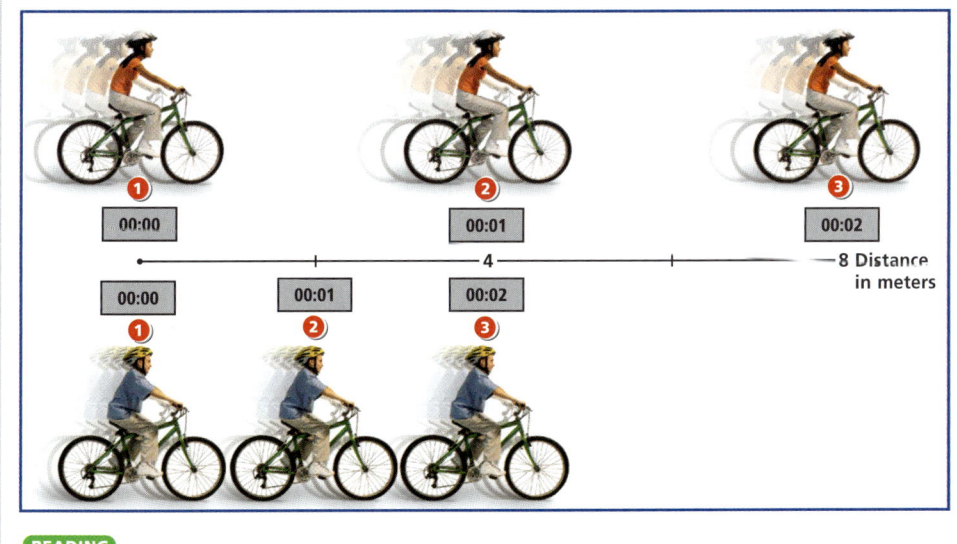

 How far will each rider travel in five seconds?

Chapter 10: **Motion** 321

DIFFERENTIATE INSTRUCTION

More Reading Support

A Which measurements do you need to calculate speed? *distance and time*

English Learners Students may have difficulty using the words *affect* and *effect* correctly. Explain that *affect* is a verb and *effect* is a noun. A common trick for remembering the difference is that *affect* begins with the letter *a*. A verb is an action, which also begins with the letter *a*. *Affect* is a verb, or a word that denotes an action.

10.2 INSTRUCT

Teach from Visuals

Help students identify the distance lines for the two bikes. To help students interpret the visual, ask:

- What does each group of numbers in a box represent? *timers that show minutes and seconds*
- How can you tell at a glance which cyclist is pedaling faster? *by observing which bike went farther in the given time (2 seconds)*

Develop Estimation Skills

Make sure students understand how the distance is calculated in step 3. Point out that because the bikes travel at constant speeds, we can sample the speeds in a unit of time, such as one second, and then multiply the base speed by the total number of seconds.

Develop Critical Thinking

PROVIDE EXAMPLES Speed is a rate, that is, a measure of how one quantity (distance) changes compared with another (time). Ask students to give two examples of everyday measures that are rates. *Examples will vary. Heart rate or pulse is a measure of the number of heartbeats per minute, fuel efficiency of cars is measured in miles per gallon, electric power is measured in kilowatts per hour.*

EXPLORE the BIG idea

Revisit "Off the Wall" on p. 311. Have students explain their results.

Ongoing Assessment

Answer: The faster rider will travel 20 meters; the slower rider will travel 10 meters.

Chapter 10 **321**

Integrate the Sciences

The fastest-running mammal is the cheetah, a large cat native to Africa. The cheetah can reach a speed of 110 kilometers per hour (about 70 miles per hour) when chasing prey. By contrast, the fastest Olympic runner can reach a speed of about 37 kilometers per hour (about 23 miles per hour). Neither the cheetah nor the runner, however, can maintain that speed for very long.

Ongoing Assessment

Calculate an object's speed.

Ask: Suppose a race is 50 meters, and it takes an athlete 15 seconds to run it. Is that enough information to calculate the runner's speed? Explain your answer.
Yes; the formula for speed is distance divided by time, and both of these measurements are given.

 *The runner with the shortest time ran the fastest.*

Practice the Math

Answers

1. $S = \dfrac{d}{t} = \dfrac{200 \text{ m}}{25 \text{ s}} = 8 \text{ m/s}$

2. $S = \dfrac{d}{t} = \dfrac{100 \text{ m}}{50 \text{ s}} = 2 \text{ m/s}$

Racing wheelchairs are specially designed to reach higher speeds than regular wheelchairs.

Speed can be calculated by dividing the distance an object travels by the time it takes to cover the distance. The formula for finding speed is

$$\text{Speed} = \dfrac{\text{distance}}{\text{time}} \qquad S = \dfrac{d}{t}$$

Speed is shown in the formula as the letter S, distance as the letter d, and time as the letter t. The formula shows how distance, time, and speed are related. If two objects travel the same distance, the object that took a shorter amount of time will have the greater speed. Similarly, an object with a greater speed will travel a longer distance in the same amount of time than an object with a lower speed will.

The standard unit for speed is meters per second (m/s). Speed is also given in kilometers per hour (km/h). In the United States, where the English system of measurement is still used, speeds are often given in miles per hour (mi/h or mph). One mile per hour is equal to 0.45 m/s.

The man participating in the wheelchair race, at left, will win if his speed is greater than the speed of the other racers. You can use the formula to calculate his speed.

CHECK YOUR READING If two runners cover the same distance in different amounts of time, how do their speeds compare?

Calculating Speed

Sample Problem

A wheelchair racer completes a 100-meter course in 20 seconds. What is his speed?

What do you know?	distance = 100 m, time = 20 s
What do you want to find out?	speed
Write the formula:	$S = \dfrac{d}{t}$
Substitute into the formula:	$S = \dfrac{100 \text{ m}}{20 \text{ s}}$
Calculate and simplify:	$S = 5$ m/s
Check that your units agree:	Unit is m/s. Unit of speed is m/s. Units agree.
Answer:	$S = 5$ m/s

Practice the Math

1. A man runs 200 m in 25 s. What is his speed?
2. If you travel 100 m in 50 s, what is your speed?

322 Unit 3: Motion and Forces

DIFFERENTIATE INSTRUCTION

More Reading Support

B What is the formula for calculating speed? *speed = distance ÷ time*

C What is the standard unit for speed? *meters per second*

Inclusion If you have a student who uses a wheelchair, ask him or her to make a "run" of a predetermined course. Record the time, and measure the course distance. Then ask the student to plug these values into the speed formula introduced on this page to calculate the speed.

Average Speed

Speed is not constant. When you run, you might slow down to pace yourself, or speed up to win a race. At each point as you are running, you have a specific speed. This moment-to-moment speed is called your instantaneous speed. Your instantaneous speed can be difficult to measure; however, it is easier to calculate your average speed over a distance.

READING TIP
The root of *instantaneous* is *instant*, meaning "moment."

In a long race, runners often want to know their times for each lap so that they can pace themselves. For example, an excellent middle school runner might have the following times for the four laps of a 1600-meter race: 83 seconds, 81 seconds, 79 seconds, 77 seconds. The lap times show the runner is gradually increasing her speed throughout the race.

The total time for the four laps can be used to calculate the runner's average speed for the entire race. The total time is 320 seconds (5 min 20 s) for the entire distance of 1600 meters. The runner's average speed is 1600 meters divided by 320 seconds, or 5.0 meters per second.

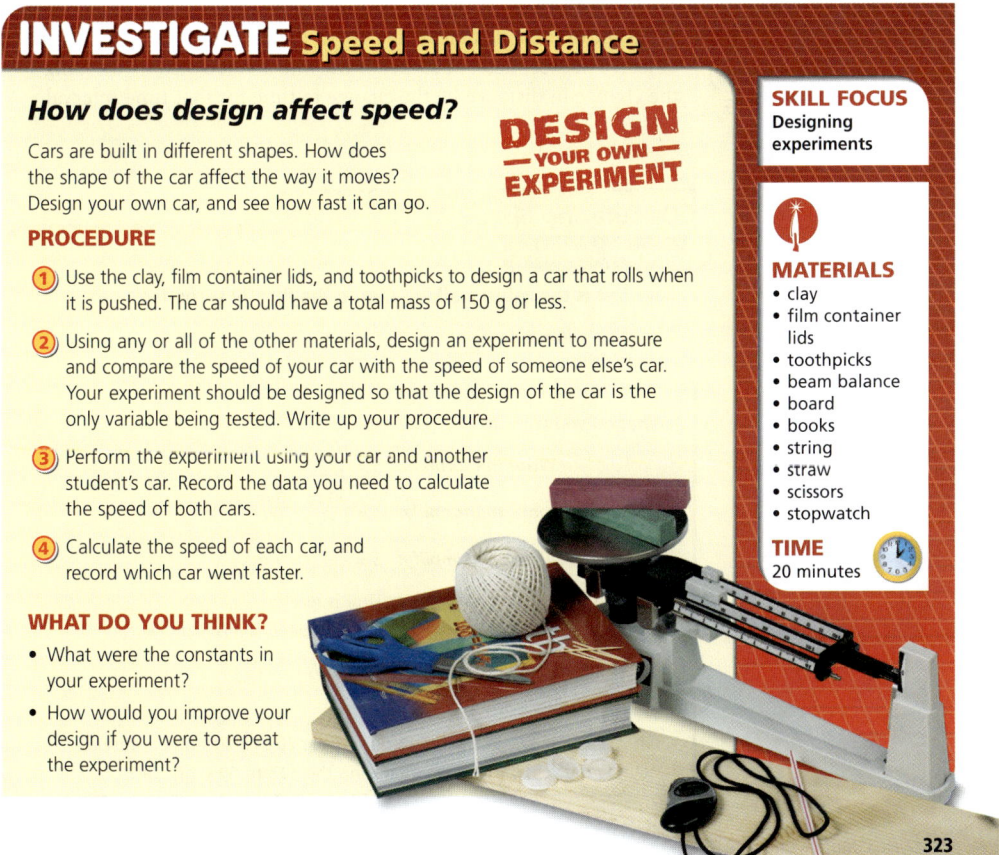

INVESTIGATE Speed and Distance

How does design affect speed?

Cars are built in different shapes. How does the shape of the car affect the way it moves? Design your own car, and see how fast it can go.

DESIGN YOUR OWN EXPERIMENT

PROCEDURE

1. Use the clay, film container lids, and toothpicks to design a car that rolls when it is pushed. The car should have a total mass of 150 g or less.
2. Using any or all of the other materials, design an experiment to measure and compare the speed of your car with the speed of someone else's car. Your experiment should be designed so that the design of the car is the only variable being tested. Write up your procedure.
3. Perform the experiment using your car and another student's car. Record the data you need to calculate the speed of both cars.
4. Calculate the speed of each car, and record which car went faster.

WHAT DO YOU THINK?
- What were the constants in your experiment?
- How would you improve your design if you were to repeat the experiment?

SKILL FOCUS
Designing experiments

MATERIALS
- clay
- film container lids
- toothpicks
- beam balance
- board
- books
- string
- straw
- scissors
- stopwatch

TIME 20 minutes

INVESTIGATE Speed and Distance

PURPOSE To design a car and an experiment to determine how the car's shape affects the speed at which it moves

TIPS 20 min.
- To save time, use a kitchen scale to measure the mass of the car. Kitchen scales are an affordable alternative for measuring mass in increments of 10 grams.
- For best comparisons of car design, the masses of the two cars should be as close to each other as possible.
- Tape can be used to mark the end of the race course. Choose a distance from the bottom of the ramp, such as 25 cm, that will make calculations easy.

WHAT DO YOU THINK? *Constants should include mass of car, height of ramp, design of car.*

CHALLENGE *Answers will vary. Improvements might include making the wheels turn more easily, lowering the center of gravity of the car, or changing the mass of the car.*

Datasheet, Speed and Distance, p. 31

Technology Resources

Customize this student lab as needed or look for an alternative. Print rubrics to assess student lab reports.

Lab Generator CD-ROM

Real World Example

Japan and many countries in Europe have high-speed passenger trains whose top speeds are advertised to entice travelers. This speed is usually the fastest the train can travel on the best track in open country. It is an instantaneous speed. The train schedules, however, reflect the average speed of the train.

DIFFERENTIATE INSTRUCTION

 **More Reading Support**

D What is instantaneous speed? *moment-by-moment speed*

E How can you calculate average speed? *Divide the total distance by total time.*

Chapter 10 **323**

Develop Graphing Skills

Speed is measured by the steepness, or slope, of a line. In mathematics, slope is defined as the change in *y*-values divided by the change in *x*-values. Here, slope is calculated by dividing the change in distance by the change in time for a given interval.

- A rising line, or positive slope, indicates that the distance an object travels from its starting point is increasing with time.
- A horizontal line, or 0 slope, indicates that the speed is zero meters per second.

- Math Support, pp. 50
- Math Practice, pp. 51

Ongoing Assessment

▶ **Practice the Math**

Answers

1. $S = \dfrac{d}{t} = \dfrac{40\ m - 40\ m}{40\ s - 20\ s} = \dfrac{0\ m}{20\ s} = 0\ m/s$

2. $S = \dfrac{d}{t} = \dfrac{280\ m - 40\ m}{60\ s - 40\ s} = \dfrac{240\ m}{20\ s} = 12\ m/s$

▼ **REMINDER**
The *x*-axis and *y*-axis are arranged as shown:

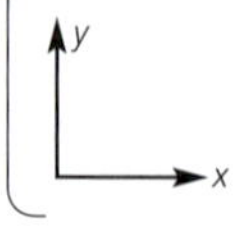

Distance-Time Graphs

A convenient way to show the motion of an object is by using a graph that plots the distance the object has traveled against time. This type of graph, called a distance-time graph, shows how speed relates to distance and time. You can use a distance-time graph to see how both distance and speed change with time.

The distance-time graph on page 325 tracks the changing motion of a zebra. At first the zebra looks for a spot to graze. Its meal is interrupted by a lion, and the zebra starts running to escape.

In a distance-time graph, time is on the horizontal axis, or *x*-axis, and distance is on the vertical axis, or *y*-axis.

① As an object moves, the distance it travels increases with time. This can be seen as a climbing, or rising, line on the graph.

② A flat, or horizontal, line shows an interval of time where the speed is zero meters per second.

③ Steeper lines show intervals where the speed is greater than intervals with less steep lines.

You can use a distance-time graph to determine the speed of an object. The steepness, or slope, of the line is calculated by dividing the change in distance by the change in time for that time interval.

Calculating Speed from a Graph

▶ **Sample Problem**

How fast is the zebra walking during the first 20 seconds?

What do you know? Reading from the graph:
At time = 0 s, distance = 0 m.
At time = 20 s, distance = 40 m.

What do you want to find out? speed

Write the formula: $S = \dfrac{d}{t}$

Substitute into the formula: $S = \dfrac{40\ m - 0\ m}{20\ s - 0\ s}$

Calculate and simplify: $S = \dfrac{40\ m}{20\ s} = 2\ m/s$

Check that your units agree: Unit is m/s.
Unit of speed is m/s. Units agree.

Answer: $S = 2\ m/s$

▶ **Practice the Math**

1. What is the speed of the zebra during the 20 s to 40 s time interval?
2. What is the speed of the zebra during the 40 s to 60 s interval?

---

324 Unit 3: Motion and Forces

DIFFERENTIATE INSTRUCTION

 More Reading Support

F What kind of graph shows how both distance and speed change with time? *a distance-time graph*

G What is the slope of a line? *its steepness*

Advanced Point out that the accuracy of a distance-time graph depends on how frequent the sampling is. Have students describe a way to compile data for a more accurate graph.
Sample answer: sample more frequently, perhaps with the help of technology

 Challenge and Extension, p. 30

Distance-Time Graph

A zebra's speed will change throughout the day, especially if a hungry lion is nearby. You can use a distance-time graph to compare the zebra's speed over different time intervals.

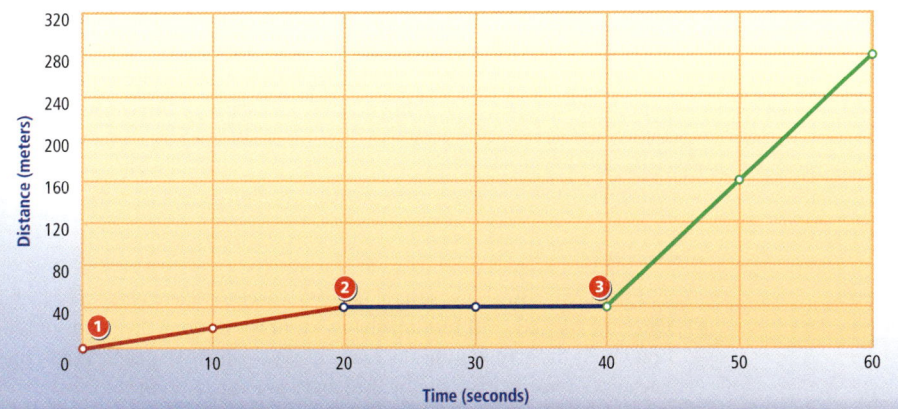

① When the zebra is walking, its distance from its starting point increases. You can see this motion on the graph as a climbing line.

② When the zebra stops to graze, it no longer changes its distance from the starting point. Time, however, continues to pass. Therefore, the graph shows a flat, or horizontal, line.

③ As soon as the zebra notices the lion, it stops grazing and starts to run for its life. The zebra is covering a greater distance in each time interval than it was before the chase started, so the line is steeper.

READING VISUALS How do the distances change over each 10-second time interval?

Chapter 10: **Motion** 325

DIFFERENTIATE INSTRUCTION

Below Level Draw attention to the numbered circles in the visual. Ask: What are these numbers used for? *to show order and represent stages in the scenario* Point out that the numbered text tells a story about the zebra. The numbers show the order in which events happen. Demonstrate how the numbers on the graph match up with the numbers in the story.

Teach from Visuals

Have students identify the *x*-axis and *y*-axis and the line plot on the distance-time graph, then ask:

- How does each circled number in the graph relate to the number beside each text block? *The text describes what happened at the corresponding point in the graph.*

- Would average speed give an accurate picture of the zebra's motion during this minute? *no*

 This visual is also available as T6 in the Unit Transparency Book.

Teach Difficult Concepts

A distance-time graph shows how the position of an object changes over time. However, students may think that the path the object takes is the same as the lines shown on the object's distance-time graph. To help students understand how the graph relates to the path of the zebra, try the teacher demo below.

Teacher Demo

Draw the axes of a distance-time graph on the board. Cut out a piece of paper to represent the zebra. Have a student move the paper zebra slowly up the *y*-axis, stop briefly, and then continue at a faster speed. During this process, create the distance-time graph by drawing a line that continually matches the height of the zebra on the *y*-axis as you move your hand horizontally at a constant rate. Compare the distance-time graph to the actual motion of the paper zebra.

Ongoing Assessment

READING VISUALS *Answer: increases, increases, stays the same, stays the same, increases sharply, increases sharply*

Teach Difficult Concepts

The term *vector* may be an entirely new concept to students. Emphasize practical reasons for the distinction between speed and velocity, which is an example of a vector, with the example below.

Your dog Sam often runs away from home. You know that he averages 3 miles per hour on these adventures. Ask: Is that enough information to determine his location when he has been gone for 20 minutes? *no*

A neighbor calls to tell you that she saw Sam making a beeline north. Now do you have enough information to determine his location? *yes, if he hasn't changed direction since then*

Point out that in the first case, Sam could be anywhere within a circle with a radius of one mile from your house. In the second case, you could search along just one straight line north from the neighbor's house to find him.

Ongoing Assessment

Describe an object's velocity.

Ask: If two scooters are moving at the same speed but in opposite directions, is their velocity the same? Explain. *no; they have different directions*

CHECK YOUR READING *Answer: Velocity is speed in a specific direction. Students' examples should include both speed and direction.*

CAPTION The velocity of the ant on the right is greater than that of the ant moving upward and less than the velocity of the ant moving downward.

Velocity includes speed and direction.

Sometimes the direction of motion is as important as its speed. In large crowds, for example, you probably always try to walk in the same direction the crowd is moving and at the same speed. If you walk in even a slightly different direction, you can bump into other people. In a crowd, in other words, you try to walk with the same velocity as the people around you. **Velocity** is a speed in a specific direction. If you say you are walking east at a speed of three meters per second, you are describing your velocity. A person walking north with a speed of three meters per second would have the same speed as you do, but not the same velocity.

CHECK YOUR READING What is velocity? Give an example of a velocity.

Velocity

The picture below shows several ants as they carry leaves along a branch. Each ant's direction of motion changes as it walks along the bends of the branch. As the arrows indicate, each ant is moving in a specific direction. Each ant's velocity is shown by the length and direction of the arrow. A longer arrow means a greater speed in the direction the arrow is pointing. In this picture, for example, the ant moving up the branch is traveling more slowly than the ant moving down the branch.

To determine the velocity of an ant as it carries a leaf, you need to know both its speed and its direction. A change in either speed or direction results in a change in velocity. For example, the velocity of an ant changes if it slows down but continues moving in the same direction. Velocity also changes if the ant continues moving at the same speed but changes direction.

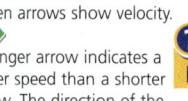

READING TIP Green arrows show velocity. A longer arrow indicates a faster speed than a shorter arrow. The direction of the arrow indicates the direction of motion.

Velocity is an example of a vector. A **vector** is a quantity that has both size and direction. Speed is not a vector because speed is a measure of how fast or slow an object moves, not which direction it moves in. Velocity, however, has a size—the speed—and a direction, so it is a vector quantity.

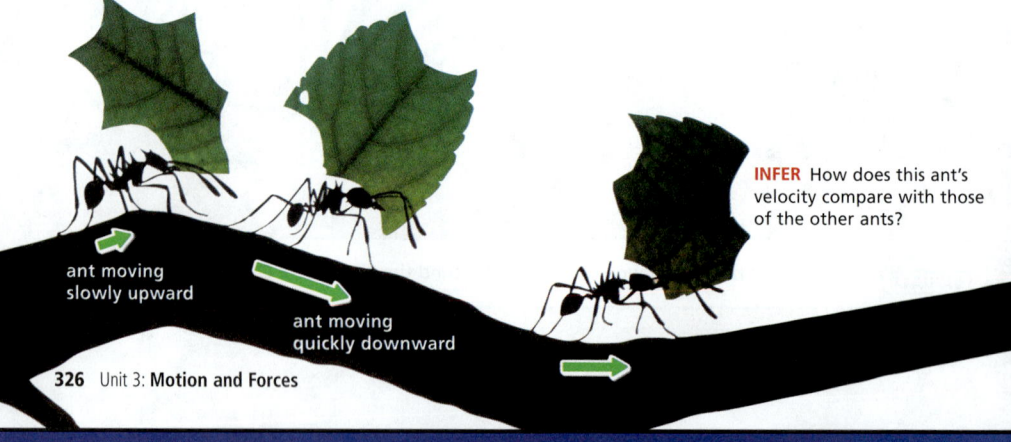

INFER How does this ant's velocity compare with those of the other ants?

ant moving slowly upward

ant moving quickly downward

DIFFERENTIATE INSTRUCTION

More Reading Support

H What does velocity have that speed does not have? *a specific direction*

I A vector has a direction. What else does it have? *size*

Velocity Versus Speed

Because velocity includes direction, it is possible for two objects to have the same speed but different velocities. If you traveled by train to visit a friend, you might go 30 kilometers per hour (km/h) north on the way there and 30 km/h south on the way back. Your speed is the same both going and coming back, but your velocity is different because your direction of motion has changed.

Another difference between speed and velocity is the way the average is calculated. Your average speed depends on the total distance you have traveled. The average velocity depends on the total distance you are from where you started. Going north, your average speed would be 30 km/h, and your average velocity would be 30 km/h north. After the round-trip ride, your average traveling speed would still be 30 km/h. Your average velocity, however, would be 0 km/h because you ended up exactly where you started.

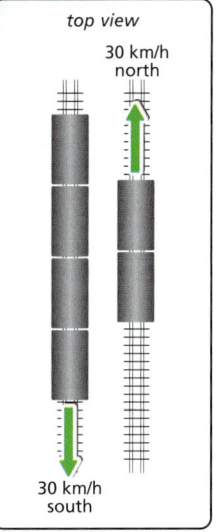

INFER How do the speeds and velocities of these trains compare?

 Use a Venn diagram to compare and contrast speed and velocity.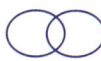

10.2 Review

KEY CONCEPTS

1. How is speed related to distance and time?
2. How would decreasing the time it takes you to run a certain distance affect your speed?
3. What two things do you need to know to describe the velocity of an object?

CRITICAL THINKING

4. **Compare** Amy and Ellie left school at the same time. Amy lives farther away than Ellie, but she and Ellie arrived at their homes at the same time. Compare the girls' speeds.
5. **Calculate** Carlos lives 100 m away from his friend's home. What is his average speed if he reaches his friend's home in 50 s?

CHALLENGE

6. **Synthesize** If you watch a train go by at 20 m/s, at what speed will the people sitting on the train be moving relative to you? Would someone walking toward the back of the train have a greater or lesser speed relative to you? Explain.

Chapter 10: **Motion** 327

ANSWERS

1. Speed is distance divided by time.

2. Your speed would increase.

3. speed and direction of motion

4. Amy traveled faster than Ellie.

5. $S = \dfrac{d}{t} = \dfrac{100\ m}{50\ s} = 2\ m/s$

6. 20 m/s; lesser speed because of the frame of reference

MATH IN SCIENCE
Math Skills Practice for Science

Set Learning Goal
To use units appropriately when performing calculations

Present the Science
An instructive example of not paying attention to units is the failure of the *Mars Climate Orbiter* spacecraft. Because the measurements were not converted from English units into metric units, the spacecraft went too close to the planet and probably burned up in the Martian atmosphere. It never had a chance to enter its observation orbit.

Develop Algebra Skills
Point out the fractional expression in the denominator of a fraction on this page. Emphasize that division by a fraction is equivalent to multiplication by the inverse of the fraction. Present some examples on the board if students aren't following the math on the page.

DIFFERENTIATION TIP Prepare students who have cognitive disabilities to consider units in math formulas by counting different quantities. You could discuss the value of attaching units to types of drinks, foods in packages, sports statistics, and so forth.

Close
Ask: If you were a construction worker, what might happen if you measured your work in the wrong units? *You would probably cause a flaw in construction that either would have to be repaired right away or could cause serious problems after the structure was finished.*

- Math Support, p. 54
- Math Practice, p. 55

Technology Resources
Students can visit ClassZone.com for practice with calculations using units.

 MATH TUTORIAL

A cheetah can reach a speed of 30 meters per second, but only in short bursts.

328 Unit 3: Motion and Forces

SKILL: WORKING WITH UNITS

Time, Distance, and Speed

If someone tells you the store is "five" from the school, you would probably ask, "Five what? Five meters? Five blocks?" You typically describe a distance using standard units of measurement, such as meters, miles, or kilometers. By using units, you help other people understand exactly what your measurement means.

When you work with a formula, the numbers that you substitute into the formula have units. When you calculate with a number, you also calculate with the unit associated with that number.

Example
A cheetah runs at a speed of 30 meters per second. How long does the cheetah take to run 90 meters?

The formula for time in terms of speed and distance is

$$\text{time} = \frac{\text{distance}}{\text{Speed}} \qquad t = \frac{d}{s}$$

(1) Start by substituting the numbers into the formula. Include the units with the numbers.

$$t = \frac{90 \text{ m}}{30 \text{ m/s}}$$

(2) When the units or calculations include fractions, write out the units as fractions as well:

$$t = \frac{90 \text{ m}}{\frac{30 \text{ m}}{s}}$$

(3) Do the calculation and simplify the units by cancellation:

$$t = 90 \text{ m} \cdot \frac{s}{30 \text{ m}} = \frac{90}{30} \cdot \frac{\text{m} \cdot s}{\text{m}} = 3 \cdot \frac{\cancel{\text{m}} \cdot s}{\cancel{\text{m}}} = 3 \text{ s}$$

ANSWER 3 seconds

Note that the answer has a unit of time. Use the units to check that your answer is reasonable. An answer that is supposed to have a unit of time, for example, should not have a unit of distance.

Answer the following questions.

1. How long would it take an object traveling 12 m/s to go 60 m? What unit of time is your answer in?

2. If a car travels 60 km/h, how long would it take the car to travel 300 km? What unit of time is your answer in?

3. If a man walks 3 miles in 1 hour, what is his speed? What unit of speed is your answer in? (Use the formula on page 322.)

CHALLENGE Show that the formula *distance = speed · time* has a unit for distance on both sides of the equal sign.

ANSWERS

1. $t = d/S = 60 \text{ m}/12 \text{ m/s} = 5$ seconds

2. $t = d/S = 300 \text{ km}/60 \text{ km/h} = 5$ hours

3. 3 miles per hour

CHALLENGE Distance has units of length, for example, meters. Speed has units of length per time interval, such as meters per second.

Distance (m) = $\frac{\text{distance (m)}}{\cancel{\text{time (s)}}} \cdot \cancel{\text{time (s)}}$ = distance (m). Both sides have units of distance.

KEY CONCEPT

10.3 Acceleration measures how fast velocity changes.

BEFORE, you learned

- Speed describes how far an object travels in a given time
- Velocity is a measure of the speed and direction of motion

NOW, you will learn

- How acceleration is related to velocity
- How to calculate acceleration

VOCABULARY

acceleration p. 329

THINK ABOUT

How does velocity change?

The photograph at right shows the path that a bouncing ball takes. The time between each image of the ball is the same during the entire bounce. Is the ball moving the same distance in each time interval? Is the ball moving the same direction in each time interval?

OUTLINE

Remember to use the blue and red headings in this chapter to help you make notes on acceleration.

I. Main idea
   A. Supporting idea
      1. Detail
      2. Detail
   B. Supporting idea

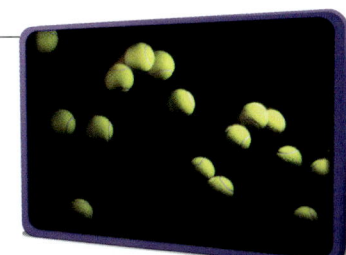

Speed and direction can change with time.

When you throw a ball into the air, it leaves your hand at a certain speed. As the ball rises, it slows down. Then, as the ball falls back toward the ground, it speeds up again. When the ball hits the ground, its direction of motion changes and it bounces back up into the air. The speed and direction of the ball do not stay the same as the ball moves. The ball's velocity keeps changing.

You can find out how much an object's position changes during a certain amount of time if you know its velocity. In a similar way, you can measure how an object's velocity changes with time. The rate at which velocity changes with time is called **acceleration.** Acceleration is a measure of how quickly the velocity is changing. If velocity does not change, there is no acceleration.

CHECK YOUR READING What is the relationship between velocity and acceleration?

10.3 FOCUS

Set Learning Goals

Students will

- Explain how acceleration is related to velocity.
- Calculate acceleration.
- Measure acceleration through an experiment.

3-Minute Warm-Up

Display Transparency 5 or copy this exercise on the board:

Decide if these statements are true. If they are not true, correct them.

1. A distance-time graph shows how speed changes with time. *true*
2. Speed is a vector. *Velocity is a vector.*
3. Average speed is total distance multiplied by total time. *Average speed is total distance divided by total time.*

3-Minute Warm-Up, p. T5

10.3 MOTIVATE

THINK ABOUT

PURPOSE To examine the path, velocity, and direction of a bouncing ball

DISCUSS Ask students how the distance the ball travels between time intervals relates to speed. Discuss how speed and direction are changing as the ball bounces. Have students describe situations in which velocity changes. *Examples: a person stopping to open a door; a roller-coaster car moving through a loop*

Answers: No, it does not move the same distance in each time interval; no, it is not moving in the same direction in each time interval.

Ongoing Assessment

CHECK YOUR READING *Answer: Acceleration is the change in velocity over time.*

RESOURCES FOR DIFFERENTIATED INSTRUCTION

Below Level

UNIT RESOURCE BOOK
- Reading Study Guide A, pp. 35–36
- Decoding Support, p. 49

AUDIO CDS

Additional INVESTIGATION, On the Move, A, B, & C, pp. 65–73; Teacher Instructions, pp. 346–347

Advanced

UNIT RESOURCE BOOK
- Challenge and Extension, p. 41
- Challenge Reading, pp. 45–46

English Learners

UNIT RESOURCE BOOK
Spanish Reading Study Guide, pp. 39–40

AUDIO CDS
- Audio Readings in Spanish
- Audio Readings (English)

10.3 INSTRUCT

Address Misconceptions

IDENTIFY Ask: If you ride in a car during acceleration, what happens? If students say "the car speeds up," they may hold the misconception that acceleration only means speeding up, although it means any change in speed or direction.

CORRECT Review the first paragraph on this page. Emphasize that *any* change in velocity is acceleration. Remind students that velocity includes the speed of an object *and* its direction. Mention that "speeding up" is the meaning in English but not the meaning in physics.

REASSESS Ask: Which of the following is an example of acceleration? *all of them*

- a car slowing down from 50 miles per hour to 40 miles per hour
- a car turning a corner
- a car starting up again after stopping

Technology Resources

Visit **ClassZone.com** for background on common student misconceptions.

 MISCONCEPTION DATABASE

Integrate the Sciences

Some animals that travel in groups exhibit a very striking form of acceleration: they suddenly change direction as a group. An example includes flocks of birds that suddenly shift direction, totally in sync with each other. This behavior occurs without the guidance of any leader. Computer scientists have studied this behavior and have made computer models of it.

EXPLORE the BIG idea

Revisit "Rolling Along" on p. 311. Have students explain their results.

Ongoing Assessment

Explain how acceleration affects velocity.

Ask: Suppose velocity remains steady. Will there be any acceleration? Explain. *No; acceleration is a change in velocity.*

CHECK YOUR READING *Answer: When an object accelerates, velocity can increase, decrease, or change direction.*

330 Unit 3: Motion and Forces

A

The word *acceleration* is commonly used to mean "speeding up." In physics, however, acceleration refers to any change in velocity. A driver slowing down to stop at a light is accelerating. A runner turning a corner at a constant speed is also accelerating because the direction of her velocity is changing as she turns.

Like velocity, acceleration is a vector, which means it has both size and direction. The direction of the acceleration determines whether an object will slow down, speed up, or turn.

READING TIP
Orange arrows are used to show acceleration.

Remember that green arrows show velocity.

A longer arrow means greater acceleration or velocity.

① **Acceleration in the Same Direction as Motion** When the acceleration is in the same direction as the object is moving, the speed of the object increases. The car speeds up.

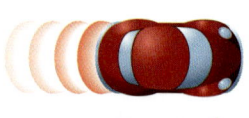

② **Acceleration in the Opposite Direction of Motion** When the acceleration is opposite to the motion, the speed of the object decreases. The car slows down. Slowing down is also called negative acceleration.

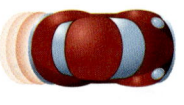

③ **Acceleration at a Right Angle to Motion** When the acceleration is at a right angle to the motion, the direction of motion changes. The car changes the direction in which it is moving by some angle, but its speed does not change.

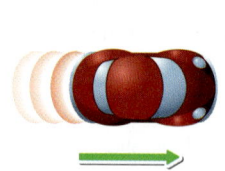

CHECK YOUR READING How does acceleration affect velocity? Give examples.

330 Unit 3: Motion and Forces

DIFFERENTIATE INSTRUCTION

 More Reading Support

A Does *acceleration* mean "speeding up," or does it refer to any possible change in velocity? *any change in velocity*

English Learners English learners may not be familiar with the mathematical concept of right angles on this page. Also, notice the terms *speeding up* and *slowing down* on this page. These idioms may be confusing to English learners who take them literally—in terms of direction (*up* and *down*) instead of acceleration. Explain that the terms refer to the change in velocity.

INVESTIGATE Acceleration

When does an object accelerate?

PROCEDURE

1. Use the template and materials to construct an acceleration measuring tool.
2. Hold the tool in your right hand so that the string falls over the 0 m/s² mark. Move the tool in the direction of the arrow. Try to produce both positive and negative acceleration without changing the direction of motion.
3. With the arrow pointing ahead of you, start to walk. Observe the motion of the string while you increase your speed.
4. Repeat step 3, but this time observe the string while slowing down.
5. Repeat step 3 again, but observe the string while walking at a steady speed.

WHAT DO YOU THINK?
- When could you measure an acceleration?
- What was the largest acceleration (positive or negative) that you measured?

CHALLENGE If you moved the acceleration measuring tool backward, how would the measuring scale change?

SKILL FOCUS
Measuring

MATERIALS
- template for tool
- cardboard
- scissors
- glue
- piece of string
- weight

TIME
30 minutes

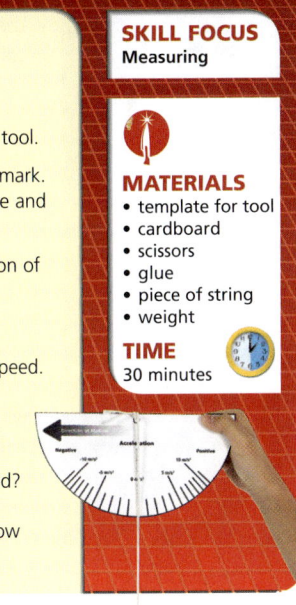

Acceleration can be calculated from velocity and time.

Suppose you are racing a classmate. In one second, you go from standing still to running at six meters per second. In the same time, your classmate goes from standing still to running at three meters per second. How does your acceleration compare with your classmate's acceleration? To measure acceleration, you need to know how velocity changes with time.

- The change in velocity can be found by comparing the initial velocity and the final velocity of the moving object.
- The time interval over which the velocity changed can be measured.

In one second, you increase your velocity by six meters per second, and your friend increases her velocity by three meters per second. Because your velocity changes more, you have a greater acceleration during that second of time than your friend does. Remember that acceleration measures the change in velocity, not velocity itself. As long as your classmate increases her current velocity by three meters per second, her acceleration will be the same whether she is going from zero to three meters per second or from three to six meters per second.

Chapter 10: **Motion** 331

Teach Difficult Concepts

Remind students that any value times itself is the value squared. On the board, draw a square with each side labeled x. Ask: What is the area of this square? *x times x, or x^2*

Have a volunteer read the paragraph immediately following the acceleration formula on this page. Help students make the connection between the x^2 for area of a square and the unit of acceleration: m/s^2.

Develop Mathematics Skills

- Math Support, p. 52
- Math Practice, p. 53

Mathematics Connection

A common variation on the acceleration formula is $a = \dfrac{(v_2 - v_1)}{t}$, where v_2 replaces v_{final} and v_1 replaces $v_{initial}$.

Ongoing Assessment

Calculate acceleration.

Ask: Suppose you know the initial velocity of a toy airplane taking off and the final velocity when it is cruising high up in the air. Could you calculate the acceleration? Explain why or why not. *No; you also need the time interval during which the airplane changed velocity.*

▶ **Practice the Math**

Answers

1. $a = \dfrac{v_{final} - v_{initial}}{t} =$

   $\dfrac{0.6 \text{ m/s} - 0.5 \text{ m/s}}{1 \text{ s}} = 0.1 \text{ m/s}^2$

2. $a = \dfrac{v_{final} - v_{initial}}{t} =$

   $\dfrac{0 \text{ m/s} - 10 \text{ m/s}}{20 \text{ s}} = -0.5 \text{ m/s}^2$

Calculating Acceleration

If you know the starting velocity of an object, the final velocity, and the time interval during which the object changed velocity, you can calculate the acceleration of the object. The formula for acceleration is shown below.

$$\text{acceleration} = \frac{\text{final velocity} - \text{initial velocity}}{\text{time}}$$

$$a = \frac{v_{final} - v_{initial}}{t}$$

Remember that velocity is expressed in units of meters per second. The standard units for acceleration, therefore, are meters per second over time, or meters per second per second. This is simplified to meters per second squared, which is written as m/s^2.

As the girl in the photograph at left sleds down the sandy hill, what happens to her velocity? At the bottom of the hill, her velocity will be greater than it was at the top. You can calculate her average acceleration down the hill if you know her starting and ending velocities and how long it took her to get to the bottom. This calculation is shown in the sample problem below.

REMINDER Remember that velocity is the speed of the object in a particular direction.

Calculating Acceleration

▶ **Sample Problem**

Ama starts sliding with a velocity of 1 m/s. After 3 s, her velocity is 7 m/s. What is Ama's acceleration?

What do you know?	initial velocity = 1 m/s, final velocity = 7 m/s, time = 3 s
What do you want to find out?	acceleration
Write the formula:	$a = \dfrac{v_{final} - v_{initial}}{t}$
Substitute into the formula:	$a = \dfrac{7 \text{ m/s} - 1 \text{ m/s}}{3 \text{ s}}$
Calculate and simplify:	$a = \dfrac{6 \text{ m/s}}{3 \text{ s}} = 2\dfrac{\text{m/s}}{\text{s}} = 2 \text{ m/s}^2$
Check that your units agree:	$\dfrac{\text{m/s}}{\text{s}} = \dfrac{\text{m}}{\text{s}} \cdot \dfrac{1}{\text{s}} = \dfrac{\text{m}}{\text{s}^2}$

Unit of acceleration is m/s^2. Units agree.

Answer: $a = 2 \text{ m/s}^2$

▶ **Practice the Math**

1. A man walking at 0.5 m/s accelerates to a velocity of 0.6 m/s in 1 s. What is his acceleration?

2. A train traveling at 10 m/s slows down to a complete stop in 20 s. What is the acceleration of the train?

DIFFERENTIATE INSTRUCTION

? More Reading Support

C What values must you plug into the acceleration formula to calculate acceleration? *final velocity, initial velocity, and time*

Below Level Help students understand the expression for acceleration units. On the board write "m/s = velocity," and read it as "meters per second." Write "velocity/s = acceleration," and read it as "velocity per second."

Point out that, because velocity is in units of meters per second, you can substitute those words for velocity in the acceleration expression, and write "meters per second per second = acceleration."

The sledder's final velocity was greater than her initial velocity. If an object is slowing down, on the other hand, the final velocity is less than the initial velocity. Suppose a car going 10 meters per second takes 2 seconds to stop for a red light. In this case, the initial velocity is 10 m/s and the final velocity is 0 m/s. The formula for acceleration gives a negative answer, -5 m/s^2. The negative sign indicates a negative acceleration—that is, an acceleration that decreases the velocity.

RESOURCE CENTER
CLASSZONE.COM
Learn more about acceleration.

 What would be true of the values for initial velocity and final velocity if the acceleration were zero?

Acceleration over Time

Even a very small positive acceleration can lead to great speeds if an object accelerates for a long enough period. In 1998, NASA launched the *Deep Space 1* spacecraft. This spacecraft tested a new type of engine—one that gave the spacecraft an extremely small acceleration. The new engine required less fuel than previous spacecraft engines. However, the spacecraft needed a great deal of time to reach its target velocity.

The acceleration of the *Deep Space 1* spacecraft is less than 2/10,000 of a meter per second per second (0.0002 m/s^2). That may not seem like much, but over 20 months, the spacecraft could increase its speed by 4500 meters per second (10,000 mi/h).

By carefully adjusting both the amount and the direction of the acceleration of *Deep Space 1*, scientists were able to control its flight path. In 2001, the spacecraft successfully flew by a comet, sending back images from about 230 million kilometers (140 million mi) away.

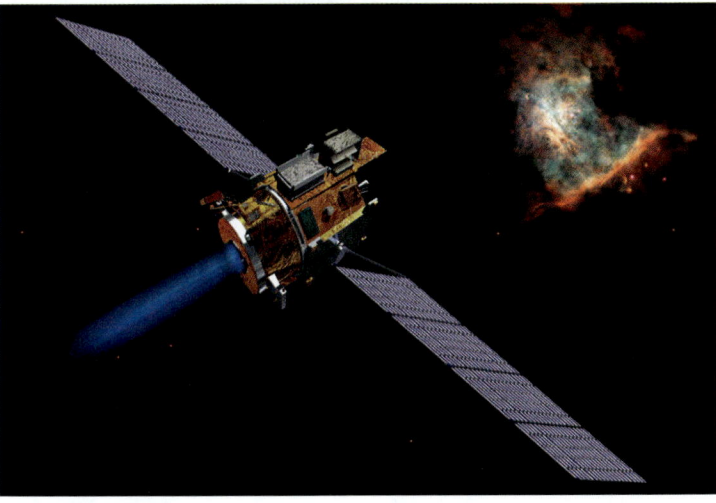

APPLY What makes the new engine technology used by *Deep Space 1* more useful for long-term missions than for short-term ones?

Chapter 10: **Motion** 333

DIFFERENTIATE INSTRUCTION

 **More Reading Support**

D What happens if an object positively accelerates a little over a long time? *After time has passed, the object will be going very fast.*

Advanced Ask students to imagine riding on a roller coaster. Ask how acceleration would change throughout the ride (through negative, positive, or vector acceleration). Challenge students to draw cartoons of at least three places in a roller coaster ride that show different kinds of acceleration. Have them label each cartoon to describe briefly what is happening in terms of acceleration.

Challenge and Extension, p. 41

Address Misconceptions

IDENTIFY Ask: What does negative acceleration mean to you? If students answer that it means going backward, then they are confusing negative acceleration with reversing direction.

CORRECT Stage a modified form of the Teacher Demo on page 331: roll one car at a steady speed and make the other car slow down as it rolls. Ask: Which car is demonstrating acceleration? *The car that is slowing down.* Ask: Is the same car demonstrating negative acceleration? *Yes; its velocity is decreasing while it is still going forward.*

REASSESS Write the following scenarios on the board. Say that all demonstrate kinds of acceleration. Ask students which demonstrates negative acceleration.

- a bird shifts direction in flight
- an arrow shoots out of a bow
- an out-of-gas car rolls to a stop

the last one, because the velocity is decreasing

Technology Resources

Visit **ClassZone.com** for background on common student misconceptions.

 MISCONCEPTION DATABASE

History of Science

NASA, the space administration agency of the United States, launched *Deep Space 1* (*DS1*) in October 1998. It was powered by ion propulsion. An ion propulsion engine uses a stream of electrically charged particles to move the spacecraft forward in a way similar to that of a jet engine. An ion propulsion engine builds speed by accelerating slowly and steadily. *DS1* flew by an asteroid called Braille in July 1999 and a comet called Borelly in September 2001. The *DS1* mission ended in late 2001.

Ongoing Assessment

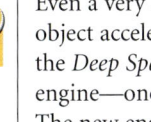 *Answer: The values for initial velocity and final velocity would be the same.*

Chapter 10 **333**

Teach from Visuals

Make sure students understand how the parts of the velocity-time and distance-time graphs fit together, and then ask:

- Do the graphs represent the same data, different data, or related data? *related data*
- Why does distance change at zero acceleration? *Velocity continues and the boy moves.*

Teach Difficult Concepts

On the velocity-time graph, students see the line fall when velocity slows. They may expect to see a similar drop on the distance-time graph. Point out that the line on a distance-time graph can level out but doesn't fall because it shows the distance already traveled, even if the person in motion slows or stops.

Real World Example

An arrow fired from a bow has a distinctive velocity-time graph shaped like a post. When the arrow leaves the bow, it goes from zero to high velocity in a split second. As the arrow travels through air, its velocity stays the same or very gradually decreases. When the arrow hits a target, its velocity goes from high to zero in a split second.

Develop Graphing Skills

When reading a graph, students often need to estimate intermediate values on one or both axes. Have students scan the distance values in the bottom graph on p. 334. Ask:

- What is the range of numbers? *0 to 60* How much distance is represented by the space between the lines marked 0 and 10? *10 m*
- What is half of 10? *5*
- Where does 5 fall on the y-axis? *halfway between the tick marks for 0 and 10*

Ongoing Assessment

 Answer: 1.5 m/s; about 4 m

334 Unit 3: **Motion and Forces**

Velocity-Time Graphs

Velocity-time graphs and distance-time graphs are related. This is because the distance an object travels depends on its velocity. Compare the velocity-time graph on the right with the distance-time graph below it.

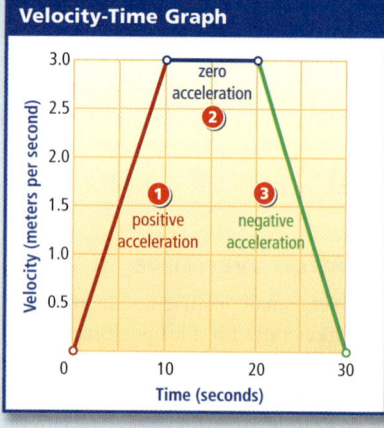

① As the student starts to push the scooter, his velocity increases. His acceleration is positive, so he moves forward a greater distance with each second that passes.

② He coasts at a constant velocity. Because his velocity does not change, he has no acceleration, and he continues to move forward the same distance each second.

③ As he slows down, his velocity decreases. His acceleration is negative, and he moves forward a smaller distance with each passing second until he finally stops.

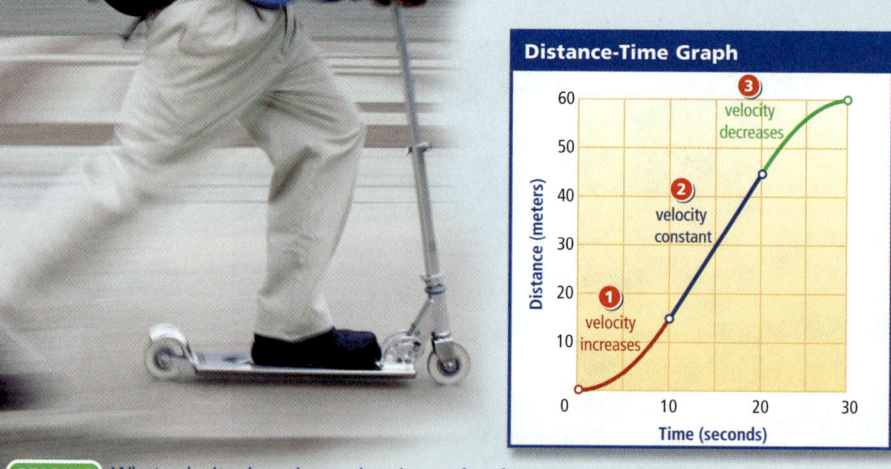

READING VISUALS What velocity does the student have after five seconds? About how far has he moved in that time?

334 Unit 3: Motion and Forces

DIFFERENTIATE INSTRUCTION

Below Level Introduce the visual with the following summary.

All the parts of the page are about the motion of the young man on the scooter. He speeds up, holds this speed, slows down, and stops. The picture tells the story in one way, and the words beside the numbers tell it in another way. The two graphs tell his story in yet another way. They help us analyze acceleration in the motion of the young man and his scooter.

Velocity-Time Graphs

Acceleration, like position and velocity, can change with time. Just as you can use a distance-time graph to understand velocity, you can use a velocity-time graph to understand acceleration. Both graphs tell you how something is changing over time. In a velocity-time graph, time is on the horizontal axis, or *x*-axis, and velocity is on the vertical axis, or *y*-axis.

Explore how changing the acceleration of an object changes its motion.

The two graphs on page 334 show a velocity-time graph and a distance-time graph of a student riding on a scooter. He first starts moving and speeds up. He coasts, and then he slows down to a stop.

❶ The rising line on the velocity-time graph shows where the acceleration is positive. The steeper the line, the greater the acceleration. The distance-time graph for the same interval is curving upward more and more steeply as the velocity increases.

❷ The flat line on the velocity-time graph shows an interval of no acceleration. The distance-time graph has a straight line during this time, since the velocity is not changing.

❸ The falling line on the velocity-time graph shows where the acceleration is negative. The same interval on the distance-time graph shows a curve that becomes less and less steep as the velocity decreases. Notice that the overall distance still increases.

Velocity-time graphs and distance-time graphs can provide useful information. For example, scientists who study earthquakes create these graphs in order to study the up-and-down and side-to-side movement of the ground during an earthquake. They produce the graphs from instruments that measure the acceleration of the ground.

 What does a flat line on a velocity-time graph represent?

10.3 Review

KEY CONCEPTS
1. What measurements or observations tell you that a car is accelerating?
2. If an object accelerates in the same direction in which it is moving, how is its speed affected?
3. What measurements do you need in order to calculate acceleration?

CRITICAL THINKING
4. **Calculate** A car goes from 20 m/s to 30 m/s in 10 seconds. What is its acceleration?
5. **Infer** Two runners start a race. After 2 seconds, they both have the same velocity. If they both started at the same time, how do their average accelerations compare?

CHALLENGE
6. **Analyze** Is it possible for an object that has a constant negative acceleration to change the direction in which it is moving? Explain why or why not.

Chapter 10: **Motion** 335

Develop Critical Thinking

APPLY Suppose you viewed velocity-time graphs for two cyclists in a race. Because you saw the race, you know that one cyclist built speed rapidly and then coasted to the finish. The other built speed gradually throughout the race. Have students apply their knowledge of graphs and slope to match each cyclist's racing strategy with an appropriate graph. *The graph of the first cyclist would have a steep rise and then a plateau. The graph of the second would show a smoothly rising line.*

Ongoing Assessment

 Answer: A flat line on a velocity-time graph represents an interval of no acceleration.

Reinforce the BIG idea

Have students relate the section to the Big Idea.

 Reinforcing Key Concepts, p. 44

10.3 ASSESS & RETEACH

Assess
 Section 10.3 Quiz, p. 5

Reteach
Have students give a real-world example of each type of acceleration:
- positive (speeding up)
- negative (slowing down)
- direction change (changing direction)

Have students review p. 332 and explain why the unit for acceleration is meters per second squared. Students should include the formula for acceleration in their explanation.

Technology Resources
Have students visit ClassZone.com for reteaching of Key Concepts.

 CONTENT REVIEW

 CONTENT REVIEW CD-ROM

ANSWERS

1. The velocity is changing.
2. The speed increases.
3. starting velocity of an object, final velocity of an object, and time interval during which the object changed velocity

4. $a = \dfrac{v_{final} - v_{initial}}{t}$

   $= \dfrac{30 \text{ m/s} - 20 \text{ m/s}}{10 \text{s}}$

   $= \dfrac{10 \text{ m/s}}{10 \text{s}}$

   $= 10 \text{ m/s}^2$

5. They are the same.
6. Yes; if the object is still accelerating when the speed reaches 0 m/s, it will start moving in the opposite direction. Once the direction changes, the object will positively accelerate.

CHAPTER INVESTIGATION

Focus

PURPOSE Students will investigate how the steepness of a slope affects acceleration of a marble.

OVERVIEW Students will record the time it takes for a marble to roll down a slope of one book's thickness in multiple trials. They will

- average the times for all the runs
- repeat the trials for a slope of two books' thickness
- use their averaged data to calculate acceleration of the marble on each slope

Lab Preparation

- As an alternative to taping two meter sticks together, students could use a ruler that has a central groove.
- Prior to the investigation, have students read through the investigation, write their hypothesis, and prepare their data tables. Or you may wish to copy and distribute datasheets and rubrics.

 UNIT RESOURCE BOOK, pp. 56–64

 SCIENCE TOOLKIT, F14

Lab Management

- Have one student roll the marble and a partner record the times. Tell students to reverse roles after setting up the ramp on two books.
- Students should release—not push—the marble.
- Make sure students understand that they will have to calculate average times for all the trial data in both columns to complete their data tables. If they need a refresher, review how to calculate an average.
- Verify that students are calculating v_{final} correctly before they attempt to calculate acceleration.

INCLUSION Encourage students with visual impairments to perform tactile tasks, such as rolling the marble.

336 Unit 3: **Motion and Forces**

CHAPTER INVESTIGATION

Acceleration and Slope

OVERVIEW AND PURPOSE When a downhill skier glides down a mountain without using her ski poles, her velocity increases and she experiences acceleration. How would gliding down a hill with a greater slope affect her acceleration? In this investigation you will

- calculate the acceleration of an object rolling down two ramps of different slopes
- determine how the slope of the ramp affects the acceleration of the object

 Problem

How does the slope of a ramp affect the acceleration of an object rolling down the ramp?

Hypothesize

Write a hypothesis to explain how changing the slope of the ramp will affect acceleration. Your hypothesis should take the form of an "If . . . , then . . . , because . . ." statement.

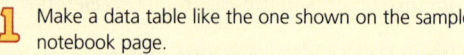 Procedure

MATERIALS
- 2 meter sticks
- masking tape
- marble
- 2 paperback books
- ruler
- stopwatch
- calculator

1. Make a data table like the one shown on the sample notebook page.

2. Make a ramp by laying two meter sticks side by side. Leave a small gap between the meter sticks.

3. Use masking tape as shown in the photograph to join the meter sticks. The marble should be able to roll freely along the groove.

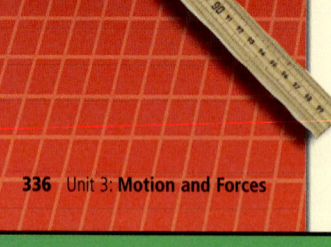

4. Set up your ramp on a smooth, even surface, such as a tabletop. Raise one end of the ramp on top of one of the books. The other end of the ramp should remain on the table.

5. Make a finish line by putting a piece of tape on the tabletop 30 cm from the bottom of the ramp. Place a ruler just beyond the finish line to keep your marble from rolling beyond your work area.

336 Unit 3: Motion and Forces

INVESTIGATION RESOURCES

 CHAPTER INVESTIGATION, Acceleration and Slope
- Level A, pp. 56–59
- Level B, pp. 60–63
- Level C, p. 64

Advanced students should complete Levels B & C.

 Writing a Lab Report, D12–13

Technology Resources

Customize this student lab as needed or look for an alternative. Print rubrics to assess student lab reports.

 Lab Generator CD-ROM

6. Test your ramp by releasing the marble from the top of the ramp. Make sure that the marble rolls freely. Do not push on the marble.

7. Release the marble and measure the time it takes for it to roll from the release point to the end of the ramp. Record this time under Column A for trial 1.

8. Release the marble again from the same point, and record the time it takes the marble to roll from the end of the ramp to the finish line. Record this time in Column B for trial 1. Repeat and record three more trials.

9. Raise the height of the ramp by propping it up with both paperback books. Repeat steps 7 and 8.

Observe and Analyze

1. **RECORD OBSERVATIONS** Draw the setup of your procedures. Be sure your data table is complete.

2. **IDENTIFY VARIABLES AND CONSTANTS** Identify the variables and constants in the experiment. List them in your notebook.

3. **CALCULATE**

   Average Time For ramps 1 and 2, calculate and record the average time it took for the marble to travel from the end of the ramp to the finish line.

   Final Velocity For ramps 1 and 2, calculate and record v_{final} using the formula below.

   $$v_{final} = \frac{\text{distance from end of ramp to finish line}}{\text{average time from end of ramp to finish line}}$$

   Acceleration For ramps 1 and 2, calculate and record acceleration using the formula below. (Hint: Speed at the release of the marble is 0 m/s.)

   $$a = \frac{v_{final} - v_{initial} \text{ (speed at release)}}{\text{average time from release to bottom of ramp}}$$

Conclude

1. **COMPARE** How did the acceleration of the marble on ramp 1 compare with the acceleration of the marble on ramp 2?

2. **INTERPRET** Answer the question posed in the problem.

3. **ANALYZE** Compare your results with your hypothesis. Do your data support your hypothesis?

4. **EVALUATE** Why was it necessary to measure how fast the marble traveled from the end of the ramp to the finish line?

5. **IDENTIFY LIMITS** What possible limitations or sources of error could have affected your results? Why was it important to perform four trials for each measurement of speed?

INVESTIGATE Further

CHALLENGE Design your own experiment to determine how the marble's mass affects its acceleration down a ramp.

Acceleration and Slope

Problem How does the slope of a ramp affect the acceleration of an object rolling down the ramp?

Hypothesize

Observe and Analyze

Table 1. Times for Marble to Travel down Ramp

Height of Ramp (cm)	Trial Number	Column A Time from release to end of ramp	Column B Time from end of ramp to finish line
Ramp 1	1		
	2		
	3		
	4		
	Totals	Average	Average

Chapter 10: **Motion** 337

Observe and Analyze

SAMPLE DATA With ramp height of one book (3 cm):

$$v_{final} = \frac{0.3 \text{ m}}{2 \text{ s}} = 0.15 \text{ m/s};$$

$$\text{Acceleration} = \frac{0.15 \text{ m/s} - 0 \text{ m/s}}{4.5 \text{ s}} = 0.03 \text{ m/s}^2.$$

With ramp height of two books (6 cm):

$$v_{final} = \frac{0.3 \text{ m}}{1.5 \text{ s}} = 0.2 \text{ m/s};$$

$$\text{Acceleration} = \frac{0.2 \text{ m/s} - 0 \text{ m/s}}{3.5 \text{ s}} = 0.06 \text{ m/s}^2.$$

1. See students' drawings and tables.
2. Variable: steepness of ramp; constants: marble, length of ramp, distance from the top of the ramp to the finish line
3. See students' data.

Conclude

1. The higher ramp produced greater acceleration.
2. A steeper slope causes greater acceleration.
3. Students' answers will vary.
4. It allows you to calculate the final velocity.
5. Sample answer: Limitations were possible inaccuracy of time measurements and failure to let the marble roll without pushing it. Averaging a number of trials is a way to minimize the effect of errors.

INVESTIGATE Further

CHALLENGE Students' designs will vary.

Post-Lab Discussion

- Prompt students to think of ways they might increase the accuracy of their data. *Sample answer: Increase the number of trial runs and discard the time measurement that was most different from the others.*

- Ask students what effect adding a second finish line two meters beyond the existing finish line and running more trials would have on their observations about acceleration. *The marble would exhibit negative acceleration between the first and second finish lines.*

CHAPTER 10 • REVIEW

BACK TO

Have students list and explain three ways they have learned to describe motion. *Sample answer: by calculating speed, by describing velocity, and by recognizing and calculating acceleration*

◐ KEY CONCEPTS SUMMARY

SECTION 10.1
Ask: How could you describe the change of position of the jumper shown in the visual? *The jumper starts at point A and stops at point B. You could also measure the distance of her jump in meters.*

SECTION 10.2
Ask: What can you tell about speed from the visual if the bike moves a distance of 3 m? *You could calculate speed from the given data.*

Ask: What can you tell about velocity from the picture if the bike moves a distance of 3 m? *You can calculate speed and observe the bike's direction; that's enough information to figure out velocity.*

SECTION 10.3
Ask: Explain why slowing down is an example of acceleration. *Slowing down is a change in velocity, so it fits the definition of acceleration.*

Review Concepts

- Big Idea Flow Chart, p. T1
- Chapter Outline, pp. T7–T8

---

10 Chapter Review

the BIG idea

The motion of an object can be described and predicted.

CONTENT REVIEW
CLASSZONE.COM

◁ **KEY CONCEPTS SUMMARY**

 An object in motion changes position.

Position is measured from a reference point.   Motion is measured relative to an observer.

start — finish

VOCABULARY
position p. 313
reference point p. 314
motion p. 315

 Speed measures how fast position changes.
- Speed is how fast positions change with time.
- Velocity is speed in a specific direction.

00:00   Speed = $\frac{\text{distance}}{\text{time}}$ 00:02 time

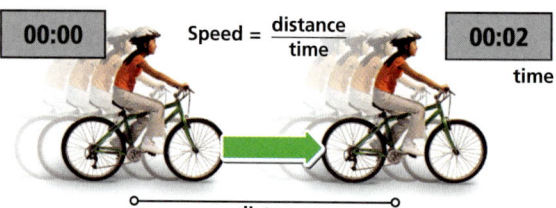

distance

VOCABULARY
speed p. 320
velocity p. 326
vector p. 326

 Acceleration measures how fast velocity changes.

$$\text{acceleration} = \frac{\text{final velocity} - \text{initial velocity}}{\text{time}}$$

initial velocity   acceleration   final velocity

VOCABULARY
acceleration p. 329

338 Unit 3: Motion and Forces

Technology Resources

Have students visit **ClassZone.com** or use the CD-ROM for a cumulative review of concepts.

 CONTENT REVIEW

 CONTENT REVIEW CD-ROM

Engage students in a whole-class interactive review of Key Concepts. Edit content as you wish.

 POWER PRESENTATIONS

338 Unit 3: Motion and Forces

Reviewing Vocabulary

Copy and complete the chart below. If the left column is blank, give the correct term. If the right column is blank, give a brief description.

Term	Description
1.	speed in a specific direction
2.	a change of position over time
3. speed	
4.	an object's location
5. reference point	
6.	the rate at which velocity changes over time
7.	a quantity that has both size and direction

Reviewing Key Concepts

Multiple Choice *Choose the letter of the best answer.*

8. A position describes an object's location compared to
   a. its motion
   b. a reference point
   c. its speed
   d. a vector

9. Maria walked 2 km in half an hour. What was her average speed during her walk?
   a. 1 km/h
   b. 2 km/h
   c. 4 km/h
   d. 6 km/h

10. A vector is a quantity that has
    a. speed
    b. acceleration
    c. size and direction
    d. position and distance

11. Mary and Keisha run with the same constant speed but in opposite directions. The girls have
    a. the same position
    b. different accelerations
    c. different speeds
    d. different velocities

12. A swimmer increases her speed as she approaches the end of the pool. Her acceleration is
    a. in the same direction as her motion
    b. in the opposite direction of her motion
    c. at right angles to her motion
    d. zero

13. A cheetah can go from 0 m/s to 20 m/s in 2 s. What is the cheetah's acceleration?
    a. 5 m/s^2
    b. 10 m/s^2
    c. 20 m/s^2
    d. 40 m/s^2

14. Jon walks for a few minutes, then runs for a few minutes. During this time, his average speed is
    a. the same as his final speed
    b. greater than his final speed
    c. less than his final speed
    d. zero

15. A car traveling at 40 m/s slows down to 20 m/s. During this time, the car has
    a. no acceleration
    b. positive acceleration
    c. negative acceleration
    d. constant velocity

Short Answer *Write a short answer to each question.*

16. Suppose you are biking with a friend. How would your friend describe your relative motion as he passes you?

17. Describe a situation where an object has a changing velocity but constant speed.

18. Give two examples of an accelerating object.

Chapter 10: **Motion** 339

Reviewing Vocabulary

1. velocity
2. motion
3. the rate that an object's position changes or the distance it moves in a given amount of time
4. position
5. a location that other locations are compared with
6. acceleration
7. vector

Reviewing Key Concepts

8. b
9. c
10. c
11. d
12. a
13. b
14. c
15. c
16. He would say that you were moving backward compared with him.
17. Sample answer: A woman runs around a corner without changing speed.
18. Sample answer: A bike turning a corner is accelerating. A car coming to a stop at a light is also accelerating.

ASSESSMENT RESOURCES

UNIT ASSESSMENT BOOK
- Chapter Test A, pp. 6–9
- Chapter Test B, pp. 10–13
- Chapter Test C, pp. 14–17
- Alternative Assessment, pp. 18–19

SPANISH ASSESSMENT BOOK
Spanish Chapter Test, pp. 257–260

Technology Resources

Edit test items and answer choices.

 Test Generator CD-ROM

Visit **ClassZone.com** to extend test practice.

 Test Practice

Thinking Critically

19. Students' answers will vary.
20. See students' drawings.
21. object moving from point A to point C
22. The hare lost the race because its average speed was less than that of the tortoise.
23. Tortoise graph: straight line for the tortoise climbing from 0 to 100 meters over the 40 minutes. Hare graph: steeper slope for part of the time, then a flat line, and then a steep line that climbs to just under 100 meters at the 40-minute mark.
24. Its velocity would be changing constantly.
25. He could time how long it takes the stick to move a certain distance to find its speed. Because the stick and water have the same relative motion, the speed of the stick is the same as the speed of the river.
26. Students' answers will vary.

Using Math Skills in Science

27. $S = \dfrac{d}{t} = \dfrac{50 \text{ m}}{10 \text{ s}} = 5 \text{ m/s}$

28. $S = \dfrac{d}{t} = \dfrac{10 \text{ m}}{5 \text{ s}} = 2 \text{ cm/s}$

29. $a = \dfrac{v_{final} - v_{initial}}{t}$

    $= \dfrac{2 \text{ m/s} - 7 \text{ m/s}}{5 \text{ s}}$

    $= \dfrac{-5 \text{ m/s}}{5 \text{ s}} = -1 \text{ m/s}^2$

the BIG idea

30. Velocity will increase.
31. Assumptions should include statements about whether the average velocity will change in the future. If velocity does not change, the car will be 40 km farther east after one hour.

UNIT PROJECTS

Give students the appropriate Unit Project worksheets from the URB for their projects. Both directions and rubrics can be used as a guide.

Unit Projects, pp. 5–10

340 Unit 3: **Motion and Forces**

Thinking Critically

Use the following graph to answer the next three questions.

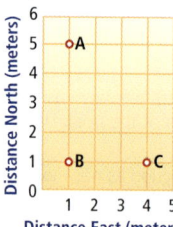

19. **OBSERVE** Describe the location of point A. Explain what you used as a reference point for your location.

20. **COMPARE** Copy the graph into your notebook. Draw two different paths an object could take when moving from point B to point C. How do the lengths of these two paths compare?

21. **ANALYZE** An object moves from point A to point C in the same amount of time that another object moves from point B to point C. If both objects traveled in a straight line, which one had the greater speed?

Read the following paragraph and use the information to answer the next three questions.

In Aesop's fable of the tortoise and the hare, a slow-moving tortoise races a fast-moving hare. The hare, certain it can win, stops to take a long nap. Meanwhile, the tortoise continues to move toward the finish line at a slow but steady speed. When the hare wakes up, it runs as fast as it can. Just as the hare is about to catch up to the tortoise, however, the tortoise wins the race.

22. **ANALYZE** How does the race between the tortoise and the hare show the difference between average speed and instantaneous speed?

23. **MODEL** Assume the racetrack was 100 meters long and the race took 40 minutes. Create a possible distance-time graph for both the tortoise and the hare.

24. **COMPARE** If the racetrack were circular, how would the tortoise's speed be different from its velocity?

340 Unit 3: Motion and Forces

25. **APPLY** How might a person use a floating stick to measure the speed at which a river flows?

26. **CONNECT** Describe a frame of reference other than the ground that you might use to measure motion. When would you use it?

Using Math Skills in Science

27. José skated 50 m in 10 s. What was his speed?

28. Use the information in the photograph below to calculate the speed of the ant as it moves down the branch.

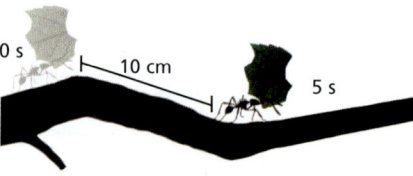

29. While riding her bicycle, Jamie accelerated from 7 m/s to 2 m/s in 5 s. What was her acceleration?

the BIG idea

30. **PREDICT** Look back at the picture at the beginning of the chapter on pages 310–311. Predict how the velocity of the roller coaster will change in the next moment.

31. **WRITE** A car is traveling east at 40 km/h. Use this information to predict where the car will be in one hour. Discuss the assumptions you made to reach your conclusion and the factors that might affect it.

UNIT PROJECTS

If you are doing a unit project, make a folder for your project. Include in your folder a list of the resources you will need, the date on which the project is due, and a schedule to keep track of your progress. Begin gathering data.

MONITOR AND RETEACH

If students have trouble applying the concepts in items 22–24, discuss what a distance-time graph of the race looks like. Use the graph of the tortoise-and-hare race. Draw a possible answer on the board. Have students calculate the speed of the tortoise for the whole race. Help them calculate the acceleration of the hare in its final spurt in the race. Calculate the hare's speed at the end by taking measurement estimates from the graph. The hare's starting speed after his nap would be 0 m/s. Students may benefit from summarizing sections of the chapter.

Summarizing the Chapter, pp. 74–75

Standardized Test Practice

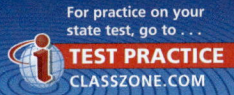

For practice on your state test, go to...
TEST PRACTICE
CLASSZONE.COM

Interpreting Graphs

The graph below is a distance-time graph showing a 50-meter race.

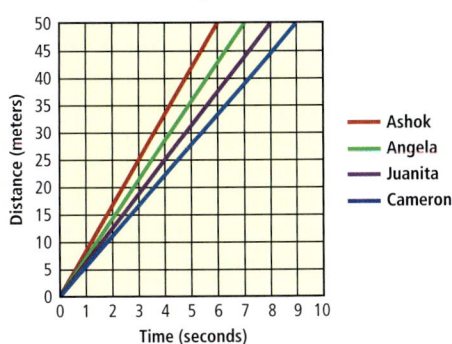

Study the graph and then answer the questions that follow.

1. Which runner reached the finish line first?
 a. Ashok **c.** Juanita
 b. Angela **d.** Cameron

2. How far did Juanita run in the first 4 seconds of the race?
 a. 5 m **c.** 25 m
 b. 15 m **d.** 35 m

3. How much time passed between the time Angela finished the race and Cameron finished the race?
 a. 1 s **c.** 3 s
 b. 2 s **d.** 4 s

4. Which of the following setups would you use to calculate Angela's average speed during the race?
 a. $\frac{7 \text{ m}}{50 \text{ s}}$ **c.** $\frac{50 \text{ m}}{6 \text{ s}}$
 b. $\frac{7 \text{ s}}{50 \text{ m}}$ **d.** $\frac{50 \text{ m}}{7 \text{ s}}$

5. What can you say about the speed of all of the runners?
 a. They ran at the same speed.
 b. They ran at a steady pace but at different speeds.
 c. They sped up as they reached the finish line.
 d. They slowed down as they reached the finish line.

Extended Response

Answer the two questions below in detail.

6. Suppose you are biking. What is the difference between your speed at any given moment during your bike ride and your average speed for the entire ride? Which is easier to measure? Why?

7. Suppose you are riding your bike along a path that is also used by in-line skaters. You pass a skater, and another biker passes you, both going in the same direction you're going. You pass a family having a picnic on the grass. Describe your motion from the points of view of the skater, the other biker, and the family.

Chapter 10: **Motion** 341

METACOGNITIVE ACTIVITY

Have students answer the following questions in their **Science Notebook:**
1. What do you think is the most important concept in this chapter? Why?
2. What questions do you still have about motion?
3. Did this chapter change or influence your idea for your Unit Project? How?

Interpreting Graphs

1. a 4. d
2. c 5. b
3. b

Extended Response

6. RUBRIC
4 points for a response that correctly answers both questions and uses the following terms accurately:
- distance
- speed
- average speed

The speed at any given moment during the bike ride would be the very short distance traveled divided by a very short moment in time, or S = d/t. The average speed for the entire race is the entire distance divided by the total time. It is easier to calculate an average speed over a distance because it is easier to measure longer distances and longer times.

3 points for a response that uses two terms accurately
2 points for a response that correctly answers the question and uses one term accurately
1 point for a response that correctly answers the question, but doesn't use the terms

7. RUBRIC
4 points for a response that answers the question and uses the following terms accurately:
- motion
- relative
- frame of reference

My motion would be relative to the position and motion of the people observing me. Motion is described by a frame of reference to the location of the observer of the motion. The skater would think I am fast, the other biker would think I am slow, and the family would think we are all going fast.

3 points for a response that correctly answers the question and uses 2 terms accurately
2 points for a response that correctly answers the question and uses 1 term accurately
1 point for a response that correctly answers the question but doesn't use the terms

Chapter 10 **341**

CHAPTER 11 Forces

Physical Science
UNIFYING PRINCIPLES

PRINCIPLE 1
Matter is made of particles too small to see.

PRINCIPLE 2
Matter changes form and moves from place to place.

PRINCIPLE 3
Energy changes from one form to another, but it cannot be created or destroyed.

PRINCIPLE 4
Physical forces affect the movement of all matter on Earth and throughout the universe.

Unit 3: Motion and Forces
BIG IDEAS

CHAPTER 10
Motion
The motion of an object can be described and predicted.

CHAPTER 11
Forces
Forces change the motion of objects in predictable ways.

CHAPTER 12
Gravity, Friction, and Pressure
Newton's laws apply to all forces.

CHAPTER 13
Work and Energy
Energy is transferred when a force moves an object.

CHAPTER 14
Machines
Machines help people do work by changing the force applied to an object.

CHAPTER 11
KEY CONCEPTS

SECTION 1
Forces change motion.
1. A force is a push or a pull.
2. Newton's first law relates force and motion.

SECTION 2
Force and mass determine acceleration.
1. Newton's second law relates force, mass, and acceleration.
2. Forces can change the direction of motion.

SECTION 3
Forces act in pairs.
1. Newton's third law relates action and reaction forces.
2. Newton's three laws describe and predict motion.

SECTION 4
Forces transfer momentum.
1. Objects in motion have momentum.
2. Momentum can be transferred from one object to another.
3. Momentum is conserved.

The Big Idea Flow Chart is available on p. T9 in the UNIT TRANSPARENCY BOOK.

Previewing Content

SECTION Forces change motion. pp. 345–352

1. A force is a push or a pull.

Force in physics is defined as "a push or a pull." Some forces
- require contact between objects, such as friction; and
- act at a distance, such as gravity and electromagnetic forces.

Net force is the total force that affects an object when multiple forces are combined. The net force depends on both the direction and the size of the individual forces.

To show visually how to measure net force, use the following:

Measuring Net Force

Identify forces to combine.	Put tail of second force arrow to tip of first. Maintain length (size) and direction.	Measure from tail of first force to tip of second force arrow.

Combining forces in the same direction

Combining forces in opposite directions

2. Newton's first law relates force and motion.

The key points of Newton's first law are
- objects with no net force acting on them have either constant or zero velocity; and
- force is needed to start or change motion.

Inertia is the resistance of an object to a change in its motion; it is directly proportional to the object's mass.

SECTION Force and mass determine acceleration. pp. 353–360

1. Newton's second law relates force, mass, and acceleration.

The key points of **Newton's second law** are that the acceleration of an object is
- directly proportional to the force acting on the object;
- inversely proportional to the mass of the object; and
- in the same direction as the net force acting on the object.

Newton's second law is summed up by the equation Force = mass · acceleration, or $F = ma$.

Sample problems show students how to solve for each variable in the equation.

Calculating Mass
Sample Problem

A model rocket is accelerating at 2 m/s². The force on it is 1 N. What is the mass of the rocket?

What do you know? acceleration = 2 m/s², force = 1 N
What do you want to find out? mass
Rearrange the formula: $m = \dfrac{F}{a}$
Substitute into the formula: $m = \dfrac{1 \text{ N}}{2 \text{ m/s}^2}$
Calculate and simplify: $m = \dfrac{1 \text{ N}}{2 \text{ m/s}^2} = \dfrac{1 \text{ kg} \cdot \text{m/s}^2}{2 \text{ m/s}^2} = 0.5 \text{ kg}$

2. Forces can change the direction of motion.

Force can change the direction of an object without changing its speed if the force acts at right angles to the motion. A force that continuously acts at right angles to an object's motion will pull the object into circular motion. Any force that keeps an object moving in a circle at a constant speed is called a centripetal force. The centripetal force needed to keep an object moving in a circle depends on the mass of the object, the speed of the object, and the radius of the circle.

$$\text{centripetal force} = \frac{(\text{mass} \cdot \text{speed}^2)}{\text{radius}}$$

Common Misconceptions

PASSIVE FORCES Many students consider something a force only if there is an action associated with it. Passive forces, such as the force of a table resisting the push from a person, are not seen as force because the table does not move.

 This misconception is addressed on p. 347.

MISCONCEPTION DATABASE
CLASSZONE.COM Background on student misconceptions

FRICTION Students commonly think that if there is no force on an object in motion, it will slow down. In fact, a force is needed to slow the object down. Friction usually slows down moving objects.

 This misconception is addressed in the Teacher Demo on p. 348.

Previewing Content

SECTION 3 Forces act in pairs. pp. 361–367

1. Newton's third law relates action and reaction forces.
The key points to **Newton's third law** are that when objects A and B interact,
• the force of A on B equals the force of B on A; and
• the forces are opposite in direction.

In **action/reaction pairs** either force can be considered the action force or the reaction force. The two forces occur simultaneously.

Example: When you push down on a table, the force from the table's resistance increases instantly to match your force.

Action/reaction force pairs occur when any two objects interact, not just through contact forces.

Example: The pull of Earth on a falling baseball is exactly that of the baseball on Earth. Earth is so much more massive, however, that Earth's acceleration from the pull is nearly nothing. The acceleration of the baseball is quite noticeable.

2. Newton's three laws describe and predict motion.
Newton's laws work together to explain changes in the motion of objects, such as a squid moving forward when squirting water backward, or a bird flying higher or changing direction. Newton's laws are also useful in calculating how objects move under the conditions found in everyday life. Scientists such as Albert Einstein have added to our understanding of motion since Newton's time. Under certain conditions, such as extreme speed or extreme gravity, Newton's laws need to be adjusted.

Common Misconceptions

ACTION/REACTION PAIRS Action/reaction pairs can be confused with balanced and unbalanced forces. Students may not understand that action/reaction forces act on different objects.

This misconception is addressed on p. 363.

SECTION 4 Forces transfer momentum. pp. 368–373

1. Objects in motion have momentum.
Momentum can be thought of as inertia for moving objects. It is the tendency of a moving object to keep moving at a constant velocity, and it depends on the mass and velocity of the object.

$$\text{momentum} = \text{mass} \cdot \text{velocity}, \text{ or } p = mv$$

• Momentum, like velocity, is a vector, so it has both size and direction.
• Adding the momentum of two objects is similar to adding net forces.

A force on an object changes the object's momentum. The change in momentum is equal to the force on the object multiplied by the time over which the force is acting.

2. Momentum can be transferred from one object to another.
Momentum is transferred during a **collision.** Colliding objects exert equal and opposite forces on each other while they are in contact. The forces in the collision will change the velocity of each object involved.

3. Momentum is conserved.
In any case where no outside forces are acting on a system, the total momentum of the system will not change, even if the momentum of individual parts of the system changes. This conservation of momentum is most easily seen in collisions. The forces acting are equal and opposite, and they act over the same time period. Therefore, the change in momentum for two colliding objects is equal and opposite, and the total change in momentum is zero.

In the following example, as the ball that is released strikes the line of balls, momentum transfers to the last ball, causing it to swing out.

MISCONCEPTION DATABASE
CLASSZONE.COM Background on student misconceptions

MOMENTUM Some students may think that momentum is the same thing as force. While a moving object can apply a force to another object, that force is not the momentum itself.

This misconception is addressed on p. 371.

Previewing Labs

Lab Generator CD-ROM Edit these Pupil Edition labs and generate alternative labs.

EXPLORE the BIG idea

Popping Ping-Pong Balls, p. 343
Students compare the effects of varying force, mass, and acceleration on two objects.
TIME 10 minutes
MATERIALS Ping-Pong ball, flexible ruler, heavier ball

Take Off! p. 343
Students use a model to learn about force pairs.
TIME 10 minutes
MATERIALS long balloon, toy car, 50 cm tape

Internet Activity: Forces, p. 343
Students predict direction and amount of motion.
TIME 20 minutes
MATERIALS computer with Internet access

SECTION 1

EXPLORE Changing Motion, p. 345
Students experiment with changing the motion of different objects.
TIME 10 minutes
MATERIALS quarter, book, tennis ball, cup, feather

INVESTIGATE Inertia, p. 350
Students design an experiment to determine the inertia of two balls.
TIME 30 minutes
MATERIALS 2 balls of unknown masses, 1 m string, block, meter stick

SECTION 2

EXPLORE Acceleration, p. 353
Students relate the force of gravity on a paper clip to the paper clip's acceleration.
TIME 10 minutes
MATERIALS paper clips, 40 cm string

INVESTIGATE Motion and Force, p. 358
Students hypothesize about the motion of a marble traveling in a circular path when the force is removed.
TIME 15 minutes
MATERIALS newspaper, paper plate, marble, scissors, poster paint, paintbrush

SECTION 3

INVESTIGATE Newton's Third Law, p. 362
Students observe action and reaction forces on a spring scale.
TIME 15 minutes
MATERIALS 2 spring scales

CHAPTER INVESTIGATION
Newton's Laws of Motion, pp. 366–367
Students build a straw bottle rocket and use Newton's laws to improve the rocket's performance.
TIME 40 minutes
MATERIALS 2 straws with different diameters, several plastic bottles (in different sizes), modeling clay, scissors, construction paper, meter stick, 10 cm tape

SECTION 4

EXPLORE Collisions, p. 368
Students observe what happens when two balls collide.
TIME 10 minutes
MATERIALS 2 balls of different masses

INVESTIGATE Momentum, p. 370
Students observe changes in momentum when marbles collide.
TIME 20 minutes
MATERIALS 2 rulers, 8 marbles

R **Additional INVESTIGATION,** Newton's First Law, A, B, & C, pp. 138–146; Teacher Instructions, pp. 346–347

Previewing Chapter Resources

	INTEGRATED TECHNOLOGY	LABS AND ACTIVITIES

CHAPTER 11
Forces

 CLASSZONE.COM
- eEdition Plus
- EasyPlanner Plus
- Misconception Database
- Content Review
- Test Practice
- Simulations
- Resource Centers
- Internet Activity: Forces
- Math Tutorial

 SCILINKS.ORG

 **CD-ROMS**
- eEdition
- EasyPlanner
- Power Presentations
- Content Review
- Lab Generator
- Test Generator

 AUDIO CDS
- Audio Readings
- Audio Readings in Spanish

 EXPLORE the Big Idea, p. 343
- Popping Ping-Pong Balls
- Take Off!
- Internet Activity: Forces

 UNIT RESOURCE BOOK
Unit Projects, pp. 5–10

Lab Generator CD-ROM
Generate customized labs.

SECTION 1
Forces change motion.
pp. 345–352

Time: 2 periods (1 block)

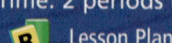 Lesson Plan, pp. 76–77

 RESOURCE CENTERS, Inertia; Moving Rocks

UNIT TRANSPARENCY BOOK
- Big Idea Flow Chart, p. T9
- Daily Vocabulary Scaffolding, p. T10
- Note-Taking Model, p. T11
- 3-Minute Warm-Up, p. T12

 • EXPLORE Changing Motion, p. 345
- INVESTIGATE Inertia, p. 350
- Think Science, p. 352

UNIT RESOURCE BOOK
- Datasheet, Inertia, p. 85
- Additional INVESTIGATION, Newton's First Law, A, B, & C, pp. 138–146

SECTION 2
Force and mass determine acceleration.
pp. 353–360

Time: 2 periods (1 block)

Lesson Plan, pp. 87–88

 • **SIMULATION,** Newton's Second Law
- **MATH TUTORIAL**

UNIT TRANSPARENCY BOOK
- Daily Vocabulary Scaffolding, p. T10
- 3-Minute Warm-Up, p. T12

 • EXPLORE Acceleration, p. 353
- INVESTIGATE Motion and Force, p. 358
- Math in Science, p. 360

UNIT RESOURCE BOOK
- Datasheet, Motion and Force, p. 96
- Math Support and Practice, pp. 125–128

SECTION 3
Forces act in pairs.
pp. 361–367

Time: 3 periods (1.5 block)

 Lesson Plan, pp. 98–99

 RESOURCE CENTER, Newton's Laws of Motion

 UNIT TRANSPARENCY BOOK
- Daily Vocabulary Scaffolding, p. T10
- 3-Minute Warm-Up, p. T13
- "Newton's Three Laws of Motion" Visual, p. T14

 • INVESTIGATE Newton's Third Law, p. 362
- CHAPTER INVESTIGATION, Newton's Laws of Motion, pp. 366–367

 UNIT RESOURCE BOOK
- Datasheet, Newton's Third Law, p. 107
- CHAPTER INVESTIGATION, Newton's Laws of Motion, A, B, & C, pp. 129–137

SECTION 4
Forces transfer momentum.
pp. 368–373

Time: 3 periods (1.5 block)

 Lesson Plan, pp. 109–110

 RESOURCE CENTER, Momentum

UNIT TRANSPARENCY BOOK
- Big Idea Flow Chart, p. T9
- Daily Vocabulary Scaffolding, p. T10
- 3-Minute Warm-Up, p. T13
- Chapter Outline, pp. T15–T16

 • EXPLORE Collisions, p. 368
- INVESTIGATE Momentum, p. 370

 UNIT RESOURCE BOOK
Datasheet, Momentum, p. 118

KEY TO ICONS CD/CD-ROM 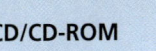 Teacher Edition   UNIT TRANSPARENCY BOOK 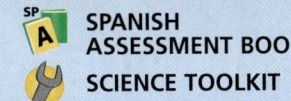 SPANISH ASSESSMENT BOOK

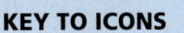 INTERNET PE Pupil Edition R UNIT RESOURCE BOOK A UNIT ASSESSMENT BOOK SCIENCE TOOLKIT

READING AND REINFORCEMENT

- Magnet Words, B24–25
- Combination Notes, C36
- Daily Vocabulary Scaffolding, H1–8

R UNIT RESOURCE BOOK
- Vocabulary Practice, pp. 122–123
- Decoding Support, p. 124
- Summarizing the Chapter, pp. 147–148

 Audio Readings CD
Listen to Pupil Edition.

 Audio Readings in Spanish CD
Listen to Pupil Edition in Spanish.

R UNIT RESOURCE BOOK
- Reading Study Guide, A & B, pp. 78–81
- Spanish Reading Study Guide, pp. 82–83
- Challenge and Extension, p. 84
- Reinforcing Key Concepts, p. 86

R UNIT RESOURCE BOOK
- Reading Study Guide, A & B, pp. 89–92
- Spanish Reading Study Guide, pp. 93–94
- Challenge and Extension, p. 95
- Reinforcing Key Concepts, p. 97
- Challenge Reading, pp. 120–121

R UNIT RESOURCE BOOK
- Reading Study Guide, A & B, pp. 100–103
- Spanish Reading Study Guide, pp. 104–105
- Challenge and Extension, p. 106
- Reinforcing Key Concepts, p. 108

R UNIT RESOURCE BOOK
- Reading Study Guide, A & B, pp. 111–114
- Spanish Reading Study Guide, pp. 115–116
- Challenge and Extension, p. 117
- Reinforcing Key Concepts, p. 119

ASSESSMENT

- Chapter Review, pp. 375–376
- Standardized Test Practice, p. 377

 UNIT ASSESSMENT BOOK
- Diagnostic Test, pp. 20–21
- Chapter Test, A, B, & C, pp. 26–37
- Alternative Assessment, pp. 38–39

 Spanish Chapter Test, pp. 261–264

 Test Generator CD-ROM
Generate customized tests.

 Lab Generator CD-ROM
Rubrics for Labs

 Ongoing Assessment, pp. 346–351

PE Section 11.1 Review, p. 351

A **UNIT ASSESSMENT BOOK**
Section 11.1 Quiz, p. 22

 Ongoing Assessment, pp. 353–359

 Section 11.2 Review, p. 359

A **UNIT ASSESSMENT BOOK**
Section 11.2 Quiz, p. 23

 Ongoing Assessment, pp. 361–365

 Section 11.3 Review, p. 365

A **UNIT ASSESSMENT BOOK**
Section 11.3 Quiz, p. 24

 Ongoing Assessment, pp. 369–373

 Section 11.4 Review, p. 373

A **UNIT ASSESSMENT BOOK**
Section 11.4 Quiz, p. 25

STANDARDS

National Standards
A.2–8, A.9.a–c, A.9.e–f, B.2.b–c, E.2–5

See p. 342 for the standards.

National Standards
A.2–8, A.9.a–c, A.9.e–f, B.2.b, E.2–5

National Standards
A.2–8, A.9.a–c, A.9.e–f

National Standards
A.2–8, A.9.a–c, A.9.e–f, B.2.c

National Standards
A.2–8, A.9.a–c, A.9.e–f

Chapter 11: **Forces** 341F

Previewing Resources for Differentiated Instruction

CHAPTER INVESTIGATION

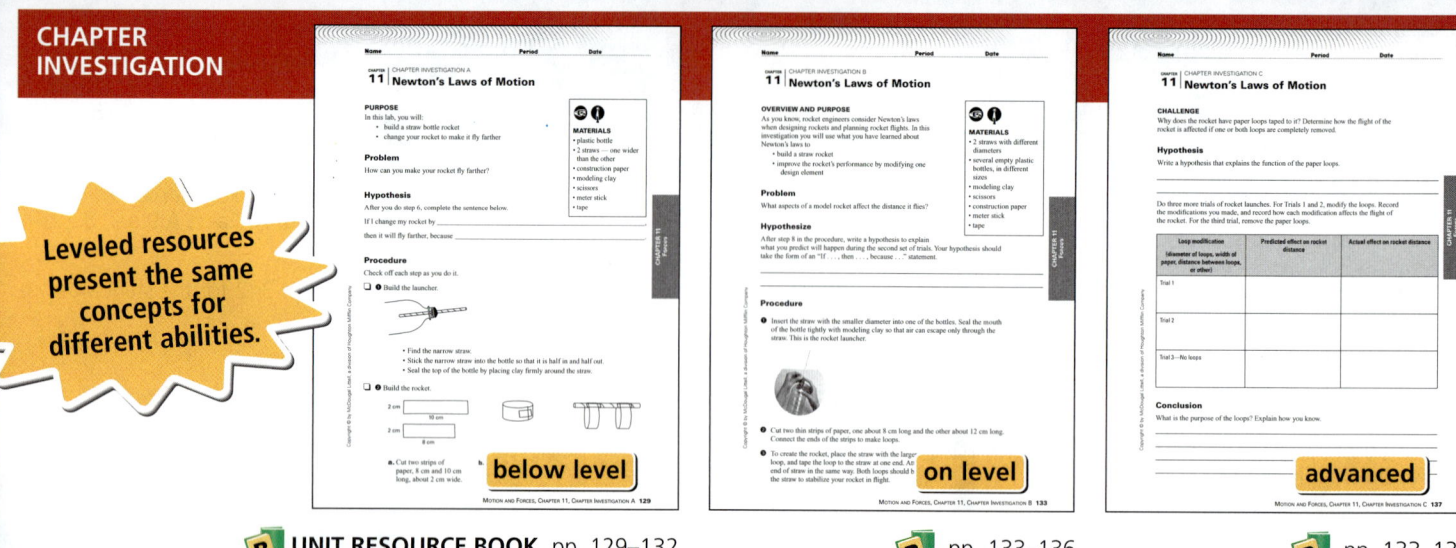

Leveled resources present the same concepts for different abilities.

R UNIT RESOURCE BOOK, pp. 129–132 **R** pp. 133–136 **R** pp. 133–137

READING STUDY GUIDE

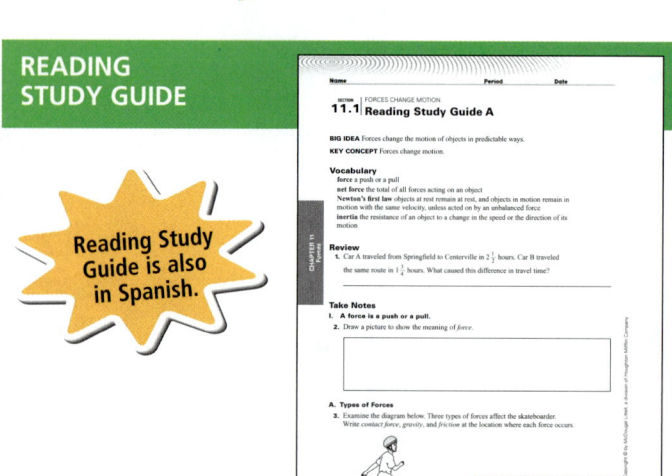
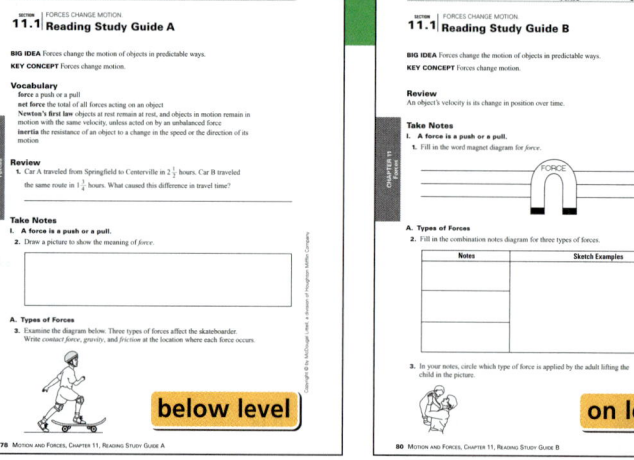
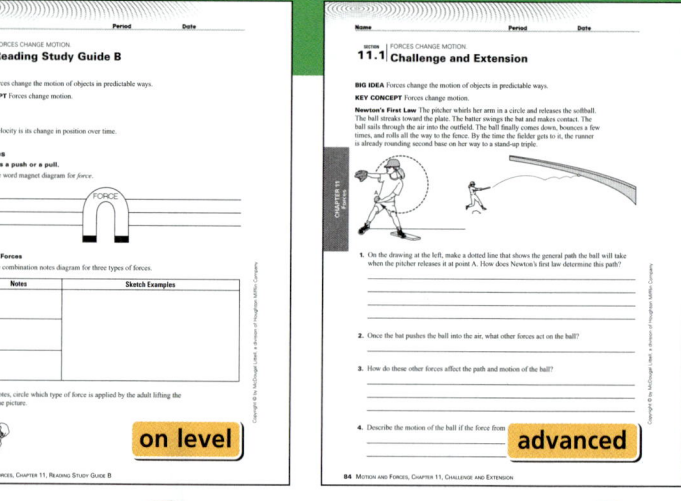

Reading Study Guide is also in Spanish.

R UNIT RESOURCE BOOK, pp. 78–79 **R** pp. 80–81 **R** p. 84

CHAPTER TEST

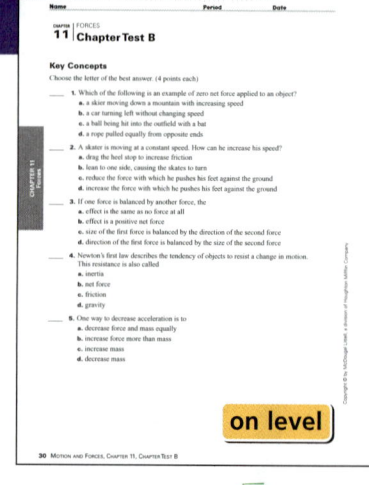
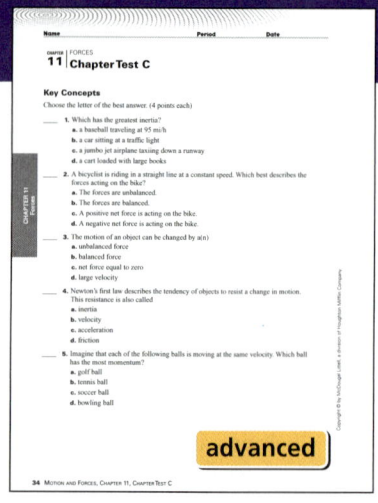

Chapter Test is also in Spanish.

A UNIT ASSESSMENT BOOK, pp. 26–29 **A** pp. 30–33 **A** pp. 34–37

341G   Unit 3: Motion and Forces

TECHNOLOGY

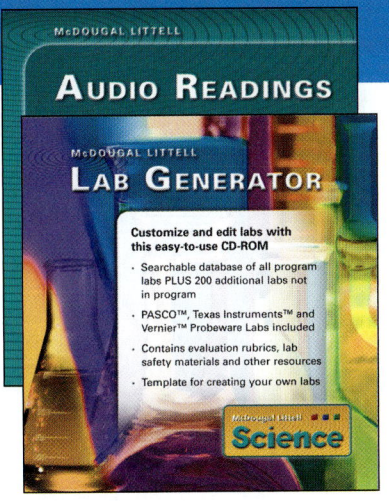
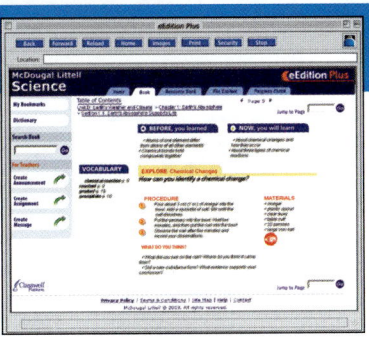

There are two Simulations for this chapter.

 CLASSZONE.COM    CD/CD-ROMS    CLASSZONE.COM

VISUAL CONTENT

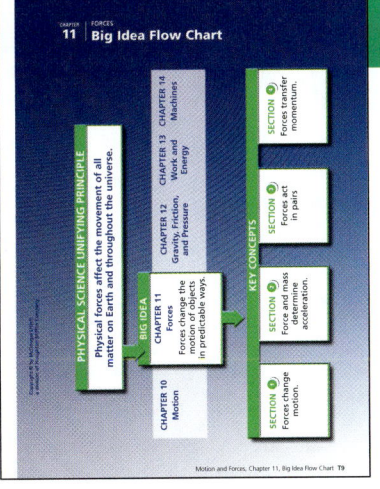
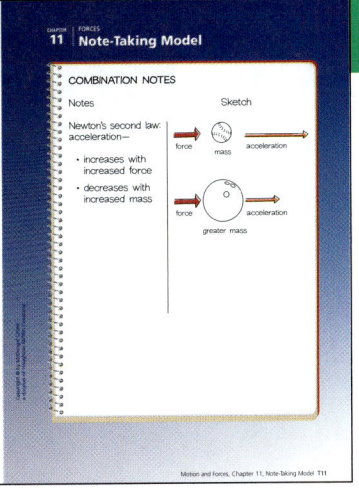

UNIT TRANSPARENCY BOOK, p. T9    p. T11   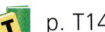 p. T14

MORE SUPPORT

Reinforcing Key Concepts for each section

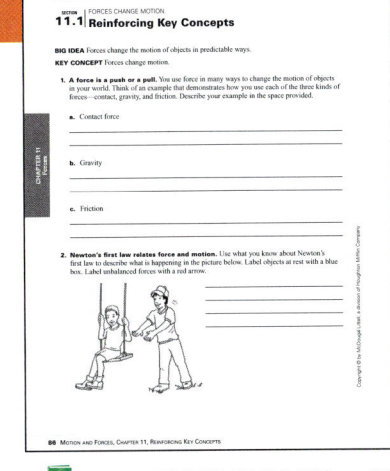
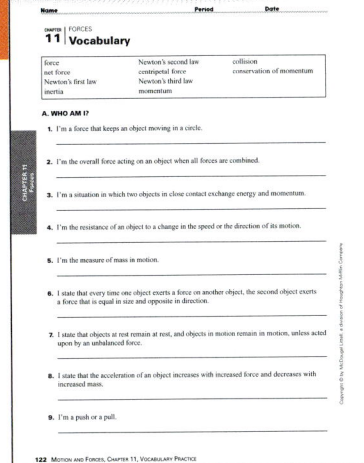
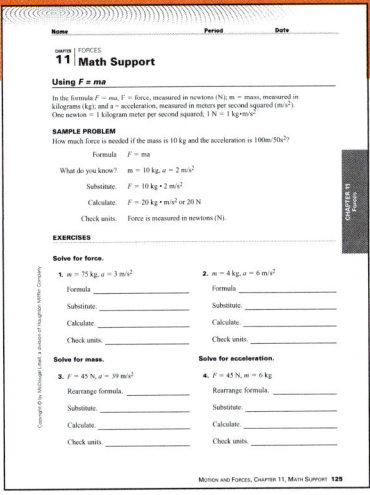

UNIT RESOURCE BOOK, p. 86   pp. 122–123   p. 125

Chapter 11: **Forces** 341H

CHAPTER 11 Forces

INTRODUCE

the BIG idea

Have students look at the photograph of the tug of war. Discuss how the question in the box links to the Big Idea:

- Why might adding more students to one team make winning easier?
- How do you know one team will move forward and not sideways?
- What do you think of when you hear the word *force*?
- What role does force play in the picture?

National Science Education Standards

Content

B.2.b An object that is not being subjected to a force will continue to move at a constant speed in a straight line.

B.2.c If more than one force acts on an object along a straight line, then the forces will reinforce or cancel one another, depending on their direction and magnitude. Unbalanced forces will cause changes in the speed or direction of an object's motion.

Process

A.2–8 Design and conduct an investigation; use tools to gather and interpret data; use evidence to describe, predict, explain, model; think critically to make relationships between evidence and explanation; recognize different explanations and predictions; communicate scientific procedures and explanations; use mathematics.

A.9.a–c, A.9.e–f Understand scientific inquiry by using different investigations, methods, mathematics, and explanations based on logic, evidence, and skepticism.

E.2–5 Design, implement, and evaluate a product or solution; communicate technological design.

342 Unit 3: **Motion and Forces**

CHAPTER 11 Forces

the BIG idea

Forces change the motion of objects in predictable ways.

What must happen for a team to win this tug of war?

Key Concepts

SECTION 1 Forces change motion.
Learn about inertia and Newton's first law of motion.

SECTION 2 Force and mass determine acceleration.
Learn to calculate force through Newton's second law of motion.

SECTION 3 Forces act in pairs.
Learn about action forces and reaction forces through Newton's third law of motion.

SECTION 4 Forces transfer momentum.
Learn about momentum and how it is affected in collisions.

Internet Preview

CLASSZONE.COM
Chapter 11 online resources: Content Review, two Simulations, four Resource Centers, Math Tutorial, Test Practice

342 Unit 3: **Motion and Forces**

INTERNET PREVIEW

CLASSZONE.COM For student use with the following pages:

Review and Practice
- Content Review, pp. 344, 374
- Math Tutorial: Rounding Decimals, p. 360
- Test Practice, p. 377

Activities and Resources
- Internet Activity: Forces, p. 343
- Resource Centers: Inertia, p. 351; Moving Rocks, p. 352; Newton's Laws of Motion, p. 365; Momentum, p. 369
- Simulation: Newton's Second Law, p. 354

NSTA scilinks.org
Forces Code: MDL005

EXPLORE the BIG idea

Popping Ping-Pong Balls
Place a Ping-Pong ball in front of a flexible ruler. Carefully bend the ruler back and then release it. Repeat with a golf ball or another heavier ball. Be sure to bend the ruler back to the same spot each time. Predict which ball will go farther.

Observe and Think Which ball went farther? Why?

Take Off!
Blow up a balloon and hold the end closed. Tape the balloon to the top of a small model car. (Put the tape around the car and the balloon.) Predict what will happen to the car when you set it down and let go of the balloon. Will the car move? If so, in what direction? How far?

Observe and Think What happened to the car? If you try it again, will you get the same results? What do you think explains the motion of the car?

Internet Activity: Forces
Go to **ClassZone.com** to change the sizes and directions of forces on an object. Predict how the object will move, and then run the simulation to see if you were right.

Observe and Think What happens if two forces are applied to the object in the same direction? in opposite directions? Why?

NSTA scilinks.org SciLINKS
Forces Code: MDL005

Chapter 11: Forces 343

EXPLORE the BIG idea

These inquiry-based activities are appropriate for use at home or as a supplement to classroom instruction.

Popping Ping-Pong Balls
PURPOSE To introduce students to the relationship of force to mass and acceleration. Students observe that the same force causes objects with different masses to accelerate differently.

TIP *10 min.* Remind students that plastic rulers can break; they should bend the ruler only about an inch.

Answer: the ball with less mass; for a given force, the smaller the mass, the greater the acceleration

REVISIT after p. 357.

Take Off!
PURPOSE To introduce students to the concept of action/reaction force pairs. Students observe the action force, which is the balloon pushing air out, and the reaction force, which is the air pushing on the balloon, moving the car forward.

TIP *10 min.* Students can use different-sized balloons and note differences in speed.

Answer: The car moved in the direction opposite the outflowing air; yes; the force from the air leaving the balloon.

REVISIT after p. 363.

Internet Activity: Forces
PURPOSE To introduce students to the effects of forces of differing size and direction.

TIP *20 min.* Students might try predicting the change in the object's motion before they change the forces.

Answer: The object moves in that direction; the object moves in the direction of the greater force; forces are combined using both size and direction.

REVISIT after p. 349.

TEACHING WITH TECHNOLOGY

Spreadsheet Several experiments in this chapter lend themselves to analyzing data entered into spreadsheets. See the investigations on pp. 350 and 353. Formulas can be entered into spreadsheets and used to solve problems such as those on pp. 355 and 356.

CBL and Probeware If students have probeware, encourage them to try using a force sensor and a motion detector for "Investigate Inertia" on p. 350.

PREPARE

◉ CONCEPT REVIEW

Activate Prior Knowledge

- Make a transparency of a piece of graph paper and display it on an overhead projector. Place a marble or a Superball on the transparency.
- Show the marble or ball in motion.
- Ask students to describe how the action demonstrates each principle listed in the concept review.

◉ TAKING NOTES

Combination Notes

Combining pictures with notes will help students connect abstract concepts with concrete examples. The two-column format allows students to write their notes in one column and draw their pictures in the second.

Vocabulary Strategy

Students might think that there must be an attraction between the magnet word and the words around it. Emphasize to students that the magnet shows a connection, but attraction is not a requirement.

Vocabulary and Note-Taking Resources

- Vocabulary Practice, pp. 122–123
- Decoding Support, p. 124

- Daily Vocabulary Scaffolding, p. T10
- Note-Taking Model, p. T11

- Magnet Words, B24–25
- Combination Notes, C36
- Daily Vocabulary Scaffolding, H1–8

CHAPTER 11
Getting Ready to Learn

◉ CONCEPT REVIEW

- All motion is relative to the position and motion of an observer.
- An object's motion is described by position, direction, speed, and acceleration.
- Velocity and acceleration can be measured.

◉ VOCABULARY REVIEW

velocity p. 326
vector p. 326
acceleration p. 329
mass See Glossary.

CONTENT REVIEW
CLASSZONE.COM
Review concepts and vocabulary.

▶ TAKING NOTES

COMBINATION NOTES

When you read about a concept for the first time, take notes in two ways. First, make an outline of the information. Then make a sketch to help you understand and remember the concept. Use arrows to show the direction of forces.

VOCABULARY STRATEGY

Think about a vocabulary term as a **magnet word** diagram. Write the other terms or ideas related to that term around it.

See the Note-Taking Handbook on pages R45–R51.

344 Unit 3: Motion and Forces

CHECK READINESS

Administer the Diagnostic Test to determine students' readiness for new science content and their mastery of requisite math skills.

 Diagnostic Test, pp. 20–21

Technology Resources

Students needing content and math skills should visit **ClassZone.com**.

- CONTENT REVIEW
- MATH TUTORIAL

 CONTENT REVIEW CD-ROM

11.1 KEY CONCEPT
Forces change motion.

> **BEFORE, you learned**
> - The velocity of an object is its change in position over time
> - The acceleration of an object is its change in velocity over time

> **NOW, you will learn**
> - What a force is
> - How unbalanced forces change an object's motion
> - How Newton's first law allows you to predict motion

VOCABULARY
force p. 345
net force p. 347
Newton's first law p. 349
inertia p. 350

EXPLORE Changing Motion

How can you change an object's motion?

PROCEDURE

1. Choose an object from the materials list and change its motion in several ways, from
   - not moving to moving
   - moving to not moving
   - moving to moving faster
   - moving to moving in a different direction
2. Describe the actions used to change the motion.
3. Experiment again with another object. First, decide what you will do; then predict how the motion of the object will change.

MATERIALS
- quarter
- book
- tennis ball
- cup
- feather

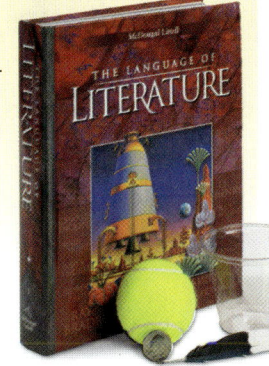

WHAT DO YOU THINK?
In step 3, how were you able to predict the motion of the object?

A force is a push or a pull.

> REMINDER
> Motion is a change in position over time.

Think about what happens during an exciting moment at the ballpark. The pitcher throws the ball across the plate, and the batter hits it high up into the stands. A fan in the stands catches the home-run ball. In this example, the pitcher sets the ball in motion, the batter changes the direction of the ball's motion, and the fan stops the ball's motion. To do so, each must use a **force**, or a push or a pull.

You use forces all day long to change the motion of objects in your world. You use a force to pick up your backpack, to open or close a car door, and even to move a pencil across your desktop. Any time you change the motion of an object, you use a force.

Chapter 11: **Forces** 345

RESOURCES FOR DIFFERENTIATED INSTRUCTION

Below Level
UNIT RESOURCE BOOK
- Reading Study Guide A, pp. 78–79
- Decoding Support, p. 124

 **AUDIO CDS**

R Additional INVESTIGATION,
Newton's First Law, A, B, & C, pp. 138–146;
Teacher Instructions, pp. 346–347

Advanced
UNIT RESOURCE BOOK
Challenge and Extension, p. 84

English Learners
UNIT RESOURCE BOOK
Spanish Reading Study Guide, pp. 82–83

 **AUDIO CDS**

- Audio Readings in Spanish
- Audio Readings (English)

11.1 FOCUS

▶ Set Learning Goals
Students will
- Describe forces and how unbalanced forces change an object's motion.
- Explain how Newton's first law allows them to predict motion.
- Explain how the inertia of an object affects its motion.
- Design an experiment to investigate inertia.

● 3-Minute Warm-Up

Display Transparency 12 or copy this exercise on the board:

Decide if these statements are true. If they are not true, correct them.

1. Speed includes direction, while velocity does not. *Velocity includes direction, while speed does not.*
2. A moving object covers the same distance in less time if its velocity is greater. *true*
3. Acceleration measures only change in speed. *Acceleration measures change in velocity over time.*

 3-Minute Warm-Up, p. T12

11.1 MOTIVATE

EXPLORE Changing Motion

PURPOSE To introduce the concept that force is needed to change motion

TIP *10 min.* Have groups compare two or three objects of their choice.

WHAT DO YOU THINK? *The force and direction with which you push determine the speed and direction of the object's movement.*

Chapter 11 **345**

11.1 INSTRUCT

Teach from Visuals

Remind students that the length of the arrows shows the size of the force. To help students interpret the visual of the skater, ask:

- What do the red arrows represent in the picture of the skater? *a force in action*
- What objects are gravity, friction, and contact forces acting upon? *Gravity is acting upon on the skater; friction, on the wheels and ground; contact force, on the wheels and ground. Some students might mention friction between the skater and the air.*
- Would the forces shown be similar or different for a person walking? *similar*

Develop Critical Thinking

APPLY Have students discuss examples of contact forces in the following situations:

- turning a page
- pulling a chair
- brushing hair

For each example, ask them to visualize, demonstrate, or explain the size and direction of the contact forces.

Sample answer: hand applying a contact force to the page; hand applying contact force to the chair and contact force between the ground and the chair legs; brush applying contact force to the hair

Ongoing Assessment

CHECK YOUR READING *Answer: It is when one object pushes or pulls another object by touching it; the force your shoe and the ground exert on each other when you walk.*

Types of Forces

A variety of forces are always affecting the motion of objects around you. For example, take a look at how three kinds of forces affect the skater in the photograph on the left.

① The ground produces a **contact force** on the skater as she pushes against the ground.

② **Gravity** pulls the skater toward the ground.

③ There is **friction** between the wheels and the ground.

❶ **Contact Force** When one object pushes or pulls another object by touching it, the first object is applying a contact force to the second. The skater applies a contact force as she pushes against the ground. The ground applies a contact force that pushes the skater forward.

❷ **Gravity** Gravity is the force of attraction between two masses. Earth's gravity is pulling on the skater, holding her to the ground. The strength of the gravitational force between two objects depends on their masses. For example, the pull between you and Earth is much greater than the pull between you and a book.

❸ **Friction** Friction is a force that resists motion between two surfaces that are pressed together. Friction between the surface of the ground and the wheels of the skates exerts a force that resists the skater's forward motion.

You will learn more about gravity and friction in Chapter 12. In this chapter, most of the examples involve contact forces. You use contact forces constantly. Turning a page, pulling a chair, using a pencil to write, pushing your hair away from your eyes—all involve contact forces.

CHECK YOUR READING What is a contact force? Give an example of a contact force.

Size and Direction of Forces

Like velocity, force is a vector. That means that force has both size and direction. For example, think about what happens when you try to make a shot in basketball. To get the ball through the hoop, you must apply the right amount of force to the ball and aim the force in the right direction. If you use too little force, the ball will not reach the basket. If you use too much force, the ball may bounce off the backboard and into your opponent's hands.

In the illustrations in this book, red arrows represent forces. The direction of an arrow shows the direction of the force, and the length of the arrow indicates the amount, or size, of the force. A blue box represents mass.

READING TIP
Red arrows are used to show force.

Blue boxes show mass.

DIFFERENTIATE INSTRUCTION

More Reading Support

A What does it mean to say that friction resists motion? *It slows motion.*

B Force has size and what else? *direction*

English Learners Some students may lack background knowledge of the baseball and basketball terminology on pp. 345 and 346.

Balanced and Unbalanced Forces

Considering the size and the direction of all the forces acting on an object allows you to predict changes in the object's motion. The overall force acting on an object when all the forces are combined is called the **net force.**

If the net force on an object is zero, the forces acting on the object are balanced. Balanced forces have the same effect as no force at all. That is, the motion of the object does not change. For example, think about the forces on the basketball when one player attempts a shot and another blocks it. In the photograph below on the left, the players are pushing on the ball with equal force but from opposite directions. The forces on the ball are balanced, and so the ball does not move.

Only an unbalanced force can change the motion of an object. If one of the basketball players pushes with greater force than the other player, the ball will move in the direction that player is pushing. The motion of the ball changes because the forces on the ball become unbalanced.

It does not matter whether the ball started at rest or was already moving. Only an unbalanced force will change the ball's motion.

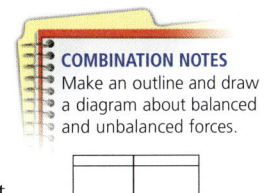

COMBINATION NOTES
Make an outline and draw a diagram about balanced and unbalanced forces.

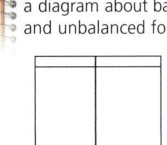

balanced forces

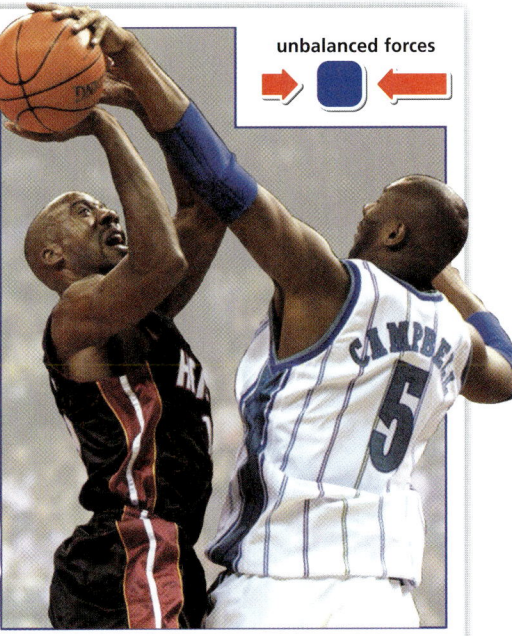
unbalanced forces

READING VISUALS **COMPARE** Compare the net force on the balls in these two photographs. Which photograph shows a net force of zero?

Chapter 11: **Forces** 347

DIFFERENTIATE INSTRUCTION

More Reading Support

C If forces on an object are balanced, what is the net force? *zero*

D What kind of force changes the motion of an object? *unbalanced*

Advanced Have students predict the angle at which a ball at rest will move when pushed with equal force from two directions. Ask what happens if equal forces on the ball are at right angles. *Equal forces send the object moving at a 45-degree angle.* Have students experiment with different angles. Challenge them to draw diagrams showing the different results.

 Challenge and Extension, p. 84

Address Misconceptions

IDENTIFY Ask: Does an object always move when a force acts on it? If students answer yes, they may hold the misconception that movement always accompanies a force.

CORRECT Place a book on a desk. Ask students what forces are acting on it. Explain that an upward force from the table balances the downward pull of gravity. Even though the book does not move, there are forces acting on it.

REASSESS Ask: If you are holding a book so that it does not move, what can be said about the force of gravity on the book and the force of your hand on the book? *The forces are present but balanced.*

Technology Resources

Visit **ClassZone.com** for background on common student misconceptions.

 MISCONCEPTION DATABASE

Teach from Visuals

Students can add diagrams of shooting a basketball to their notes.

- Encourage students to add the direction of force. Ask what happens if you push the ball with the right amount of force but in the wrong direction. *The ball misses the basket.*
- Challenge students to sketch other examples of direction and size of forces, such as force on a bowling ball resulting in a gutter ball, a strike, or a split.

Ongoing Assessment

Describe how unbalanced forces change an object's motion.

Ask: When you lift and turn a page, how do unbalanced forces change its motion? *To lift the page, you apply an unbalanced force upward. When you let it go, gravity becomes the unbalanced force pushing downward.*

 *Answer: the left-hand picture*

Chapter 11 **347**

Teach Difficult Concepts

Because friction slows down moving objects, students may think that a continuous force is needed to keep an object moving. To help students understand that a force is needed to stop a moving object, you might try the following demonstration.

Teacher Demo

This demonstration can be used to address the misconception cited on p. 341B.
- Spin a wheel of any type.
- Ask: What keeps the wheel in motion after you take your hand away? *No force has made it stop moving.*
- Ask: What will stop the wheel? *a force, probably friction*

History of Science

Galileo developed hypotheses about events that were impossible to observe in nature; he applied knowledge from related observable events. For example, he thought that if you started a ball rolling, it would move forever if no friction existed. By observing how a ball rolled along a series of ramps, he was able to deduce that without a force such as friction, a rolling ball would roll forever. The ability to hypothesize about what cannot be observed using knowledge of what can be observed enables scientists like Galileo and Newton to describe unobservable events in nature accurately.

Ongoing Assessment

CHECK YOUR READING Answer: The object continues moving in the same direction with the same speed; first sentence of paragraph 2.

Forces on Moving Objects

An object with forces acting on it can be moving at a constant velocity as long as those forces are balanced. For example, if you ride a bike straight ahead at a constant speed, the force moving the bike forward exactly balances the forces of friction that would slow the bike down. If you stop pedaling, the forces are no longer balanced, and frictional forces slow you down until you eventually stop.

Balanced forces cannot change an object's speed or its direction. An unbalanced force is needed to change an object's motion.

- To increase the speed of your bike, you may exert more forward force by pedaling harder or changing gears. The net force moves the bike ahead faster.
- To turn your bike, you apply an unbalanced force by leaning to one side and turning the handlebars.
- To stop the bike, you use the extra force of friction that your bike brakes provide.

CHECK YOUR READING What happens to a moving object if all the forces on it are balanced? Which sentence above tells you?

Newton's first law relates force and motion.

In the mid-1600s, the English scientist Sir Isaac Newton studied the effects of forces on objects. He formulated three laws of motion that are still helping people describe and predict the motions of objects today. Newton's ideas were built on those of other scientists, in particular the Italian scientist Galileo Galilei (gal-uh-LEE-oh gal-uh-LAY). Both Galileo and Newton overturned thinking that had been accepted since the times of the ancient Greek philosophers.

The ancient Greeks had concluded that it was necessary to apply a continuous force to keep an object in motion. For example, if you set a book on a table and give the book a quick push, the book slides a short way and then stops. To keep the book moving, you need to keep pushing it. The Greeks reasoned that the book stops moving because you stop pushing it.

Galileo's Thought Experiment

In the early 1600s, Galileo suggested a different way of interpreting such observations. He imagined a world without friction and conducted a thought experiment in this ideal world. He concluded that, in the absence of friction, a moving object will continue moving even if there is no force acting on it. In other words, it does not take a force to keep an object moving; it takes a force—friction—to stop an object that is already moving.

READING TIP Contrast the last sentence of this paragraph with the last sentence of the previous paragraph.

348 Unit 3: Motion and Forces

DIFFERENTIATE INSTRUCTION

 More Reading Support

E What happens to a moving object if balanced forces act on it? What will it do if there is no force? *In both cases, it keeps moving with same velocity.*

Below Level Use the table to help students understand the conflicting ideas about force and motion.

Greeks	Galileo
Force keeps an object in motion.	Force is needed to change motion.
Force causes continuing movement.	Force is not required to keep an object moving.

Objects at rest and objects in motion both resist changes in motion. That is, objects at rest tend to stay at rest, and objects that are moving tend to continue moving unless a force acts on them. Galileo reasoned there was no real difference between an object that is moving at a constant velocity and an object that is standing still. An object at rest is simply an object with zero velocity.

 How were Galileo's ideas about objects in motion different from the ideas of the ancient Greeks?

Newton's First Law

 Newton restated Galileo's conclusions as his first law of motion. **Newton's first law** states that objects at rest remain at rest, and objects in motion remain in motion with the same velocity, unless acted upon by an unbalanced force. You can easily observe the effects of unbalanced forces, both on the ball at rest and the ball in motion, in the pictures below.

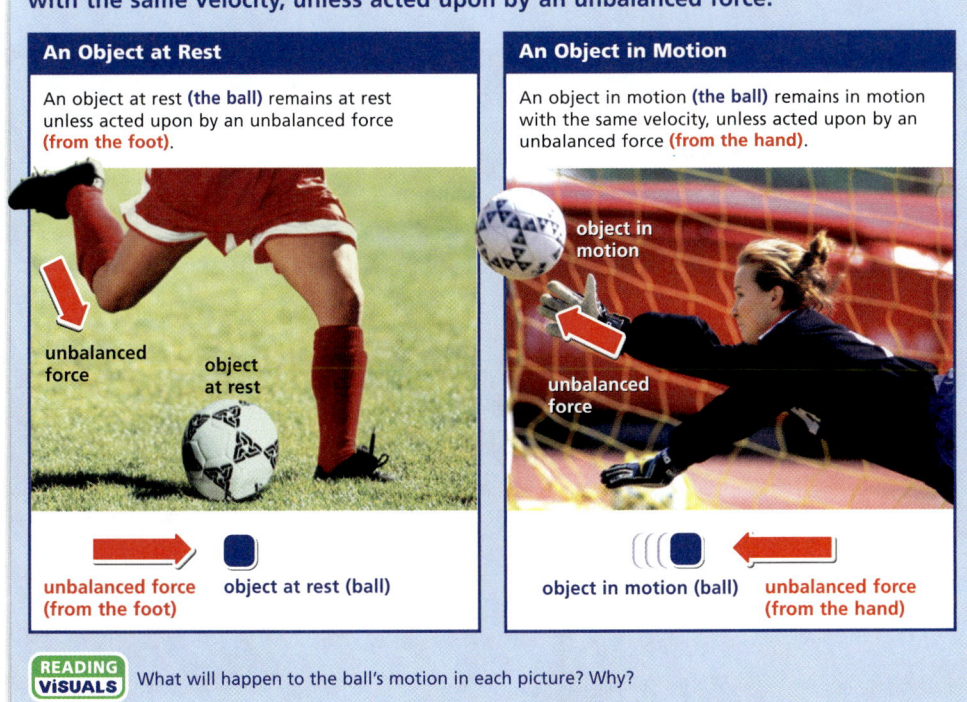

Newton's First Law

Objects at rest remain at rest, and objects in motion remain in motion with the same velocity, unless acted upon by an unbalanced force.

An Object at Rest
An object at rest (the ball) remains at rest unless acted upon by an unbalanced force (from the foot).

unbalanced force • object at rest
unbalanced force (from the foot) • object at rest (ball)

An Object in Motion
An object in motion (the ball) remains in motion with the same velocity, unless acted upon by an unbalanced force (from the hand).

object in motion • unbalanced force
object in motion (ball) • unbalanced force (from the hand)

What will happen to the ball's motion in each picture? Why?

Chapter 11: **Forces** 349

DIFFERENTIATE INSTRUCTION

 More Reading Support

F State Newton's first law in your own words.
Answer: Unmoving objects stay still. A moving object moves in the same direction unless a force changes its motion.

Additional Investigation To reinforce Section 11.1 learning goals, use the following full-period investigation:

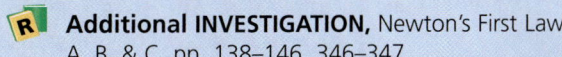 Additional INVESTIGATION, Newton's First Law, A, B, & C, pp. 138–146, 346–347

Advanced Have students research Galileo's experiments with inclined planes and inertia. Students should then design a recreation of Galileo's inclined plane experiment, or design another experiment that demonstrates the same principle.

Teach from Visuals

To help students interpret the visuals of kids playing soccer, ask:

- What symbol is used to show an object in motion? *a blue box with motion lines to one side of it*
- How might the symbol be different in a third picture after the goalie hits the ball? *The motion lines would be drawn on the right side of the box instead of on the left.*

Real World Example

Consider this dramatic example of a force changing the motion of a 10,000 kg satellite. On Earth, any force that an astronaut could apply by pushing on the satellite would be balanced by the force of friction. In space, however, there is no friction to balance the push. Even a small unbalanced force on the satellite can cause it to start moving or change its motion, although the change would be extremely small due to the satellite's large mass.

EXPLORE the BIG idea

Revisit "Internet Activity: Forces" on p. 343. Have students explain their results.

Ongoing Assessment

Explain how Newton's first law allows you to predict motion.

Ask: What unbalanced forces change the motion of a volleyball that is hit hard over the net? How will its velocity change? *The contact force of a hand changes the ball's direction, and may increase its velocity.*

CHECK YOUR READING Answer: Galileo: friction slows down motion; neither objects at rest nor objects with constant velocity are being acted upon by a net force; it takes force to change velocity. Greeks: an object stays in motion only if force is continuously applied; no motion means no force is present.

READING VISUALS Answer: The ball's motion will change. In the picture on the left, it will start moving. In the picture on the right, it will probably change both speed and direction.

Chapter 11 **349**

INVESTIGATE Inertia

PURPOSE To design an experiment to determine the inertia of two objects

TIPS 30 min. Allow students a few minutes to explore, then suggest the following:

- Think of ways to apply equal forces to both balls.
- Change the velocity of the ball from both rest and motion.

WHAT DO YOU THINK? *The ball with greater mass has greater inertia. The variable is the mass of the balls. Constants should include the amount of force applied and may include the standard of measuring change in motion. The ball with greater mass has greater inertia, and it is more difficult to change its motion.*

 Datasheet, Inertia, p. 85

Technology Resources

Customize this student lab as needed or look for an alternative. Print rubrics to assess student lab reports.

 Lab Generator CD-ROM

Metacognitive Strategy

Ask students to write a paragraph about one thing that posed a problem while they were designing the procedure. Have them describe their solution to this problem.

Teaching with Technology

If students have probeware, encourage them to use a force sensor and motion detector in their experiments.

Ongoing Assessment

Explain how the inertia of an object affects its motion.

Ask: How would the inertia of each object used in the Explore on p. 345 affect its motion? *the greater the mass, the more difficult it is to change its motion*

You will find many examples of Newton's first law around you. For instance, if you throw a stick for a dog to catch, you are changing the motion of the stick. The dog changes the motion of the stick by catching it and by dropping it at your feet. You change the motion of a volleyball when you spike it, a tennis racket when you swing it, a paintbrush when you make a brush stroke, and an oboe when you pick it up to play or set it down after playing. In each of these examples, you apply a force that changes the motion of the object.

Inertia

 VOCABULARY Make a magnet word diagram for *inertia* in your notebook.

Inertia (ih-NUR-shuh) is the resistance of an object to a change in the speed or the direction of its motion. Newton's first law, which describes the tendency of objects to resist changes in motion, is also called the law of inertia. Inertia is closely related to mass. When you measure the mass of an object, you are also measuring its inertia. You know from experience that it is easier to push or pull an empty box than it is to push or pull the same box when it is full of books. Likewise, it is easier to stop or to turn an empty wagon than to stop or turn a wagon full of sand. In both of these cases, it is harder to change the motion of the object that has more mass.

INVESTIGATE Inertia

Which ball has more inertia?

Two balls have different masses and therefore different amounts of inertia. Use what you know about force and inertia to design an experiment that shows which ball has more inertia. Your procedure cannot include lifting the balls, weighing the balls, or touching the balls with your hands.

DESIGN YOUR OWN EXPERIMENT

PROCEDURE

1. Figure out how to use the meter stick or other materials to compare the inertia of the two balls.
2. Write up your procedure.
3. Test your procedure.

WHAT DO YOU THINK?
- What were the results of your experiment? Did it work? Why or why not?
- What was the variable? What were the constants?
- How does your experiment demonstrate the property of inertia?

SKILL FOCUS Designing experiments

MATERIALS
- 2 balls of unknown masses
- string
- block
- meter stick

TIME 30 minutes

350 Unit 3: Motion and Forces

DIFFERENTIATE INSTRUCTION

 More Reading Support

G What is Newton's first law also called? *the law of inertia* How do you measure inertia? *by measuring the mass of an object*

English Learners Help English learners understand that on p. 350, *resist* and *resistance* are verb and noun forms of the same word. English learners may also be confused by the ways in which certain English words are used in different contexts, as in, "it is harder to change the motion of the object that has more mass" (p. 350). *Harder* describes the degree of difficulty, not how firm or solid an object is. Help students recognize when a tactile word is being used to describe something abstract.

Inertia is the reason that people in cars need to wear seat belts. A moving car has inertia, and so do the riders inside it. When the driver applies the brakes, an unbalanced force is applied to the car. Normally, the bottom of the seat applies an unbalanced force—friction—which slows the riders down as the car slows. If the driver stops the car suddenly, however, this force is not exerted over enough time to stop the motion of the riders. Instead, the riders continue moving forward with most of their original speed because of their inertia.

RESOURCE CENTER
CLASSZONE.COM
Find out more about inertia.

① As a car moves forward, the driver—shown here as a crash-test dummy—moves forward with the same velocity as the car.

② When the driver hits the brakes, the car stops. If the stop is sudden and the driver is not wearing a seat belt, the driver keeps moving forward.

③ Finally, the windshield applies an unbalanced force that stops the driver's forward motion.

If the driver is wearing a seat belt, the seat belt rather than the windshield applies the unbalanced force that stops the driver's forward motion. The force from the seat belt is applied over a longer time, so the force causes less damage. In a collision, seat belts alone are sometimes not enough to stop the motion of drivers or passengers. Air bags further cushion people from the effects of inertia in an accident.

CHECK YOUR READING If a car makes a sudden stop, what happens to a passenger riding in the back seat who is not wearing a seat belt?

11.1 Review

KEY CONCEPTS
1. Explain the difference between balanced and unbalanced forces.
2. What is the relationship between force and motion described by Newton's first law?
3. What is inertia? How is the inertia of an object related to its mass?

CRITICAL THINKING
4. **Infer** Once a baseball has been hit into the air, what forces are acting upon it? How can you tell that any forces are acting upon the ball?
5. **Predict** A ball is at rest on the floor of a car moving at a constant velocity. What will happen to the ball if the car swerves suddenly to the left?

CHALLENGE
6. **Synthesize** What can the changes in an object's position tell you about the forces acting on that object? Describe an example from everyday life that shows how forces affect the position of an object.

Chapter 11: **Forces** 351

ANSWERS

1. Balanced forces do not change an object's motion; unbalanced forces exert a net force and can change an object's motion.

2. An object's state of motion does not change unless acted upon by an unbalanced force.

3. an object's resistance to having its state of motion changed; the greater its mass, the greater its inertia

4. gravity (friction with the air may also be mentioned), as shown by change in speed and direction

5. It will continue straight ahead (to the right side of the car).

6. If changes in an object's position demonstrate a change in speed or direction, the object has an unbalanced force acting upon it.

THINK SCIENCE
Scientific Methods of Thinking

Set Learning Goal
To evaluate hypotheses by checking them against observations

Present the Science
The sliding rock phenomenon on this desert floor has been observed since the early 1900s, but no one has ever seen the rocks move. Ask students to discuss what the evidence of sliding is. *Rocks are found in new locations; tracks in the clay show movement.*

Guide the Activity
- Remind students that to evaluate means to judge a statement based on criteria.
- Students should determine whether each observation supports each hypothesis.
- Point out that if even one observation does not support the hypothesis, students should recheck the observation or revise the hypothesis.
- Remind students to use visual clues.

COOPERATIVE LEARNING STRATEGY
Divide the class into groups of three to six students. In each group, assign a facilitator, a recorder, and a reporter. Assign each group one hypothesis to evaluate. The facilitator ensures that everyone has a chance to respond. The recorder writes the group's consensus. The reporter presents each observation to the class.

Close
Ask: Why does a hypothesis have to be checked against each observation? *One observation can disprove the entire hypothesis.*

Technology Resources
Students can visit ClassZone.com for links to Racetrack Playa pictures, animations, and more information.

 RESOURCE CENTER

352 Unit 3: **Motion and Forces**

A playa was once a shallow lake. The water in it evaporated, leaving a dry lakebed.

SKILL: EVALUATING HYPOTHESES

Why Do These Rocks Slide?
In Death Valley, California, there is a dry lakebed known as Racetrack Playa. Rocks are mysteriously moving across the ground there, leaving tracks in the clay. These rocks can have masses as great as 320 kilograms (corresponding to 700 lb). No one has ever observed the rocks sliding, even though scientists have studied their tracks for more than 50 years. What force moves these rocks? Scientists do not yet know.

◯ Observations
Scientists made these observations.

> a. Some rocks left trails that are almost parallel.
> b. Some rocks left trails that took abrupt turns.
> c. Sometimes a small rock moved while a larger rock did not.
> d. Most of the trails are on level surfaces. Some trails run slightly uphill.
> e. The temperature in that area sometimes drops below freezing.

This rock made a U-turn.

◯ Hypotheses
Scientists formed these hypotheses about how the rocks move.

> - When the lakebed gets wet, it becomes so slippery that gravity causes the rocks to slide.
> - When the lakebed gets wet, it becomes so slippery that strong winds can move the rocks.
> - When the lakebed gets wet and cold, a sheet of ice forms and traps the rocks. Strong winds move both the ice sheet and the trapped rocks.

◯ Evaluate Each Hypothesis
On Your Own Think about whether all the observations support each hypothesis. Some facts may rule out some hypotheses. Some facts may neither support nor contradict a particular hypothesis.

As a Group Decide which hypotheses are reasonable. Discuss your thinking and conclusions in a small group, and list the reasonable hypotheses.

CHALLENGE What further observations would you make to test any of these hypotheses? What information would each observation add?

 Learn more about the moving rocks.

352 Unit 3: Motion and Forces

ANSWERS

Hypothesis 1 is not reasonable and is not supported by observations a, b, and d. Gravity does not cause rocks to slide in parallel lines, turn, or move uphill.
Hypothesis 2 is reasonable. Observation a does not support or weaken it, and b–e support it: winds can change direction, move smaller rocks, cause rocks to move uphill, and move rocks on ice.

Hypothesis 3 is reasonable and supported by all observations: if frozen in ice, rocks can move together; winds can make rocks change direction, move small rocks, move rocks uphill; ice will form when temperature is below freezing.
CHALLENGE Sample answer: record movement and temperatures; this might prove a relationship between movement and freezing temperatures

11.2 KEY CONCEPT
Force and mass determine acceleration.

BEFORE, you learned
- Mass is a measure of inertia
- The motion of an object will not change unless the object is acted upon by an unbalanced force

NOW, you will learn
- How Newton's second law relates force, mass, and acceleration
- How force works in circular motion

VOCABULARY
Newton's second law p. 354
centripetal force p. 358

EXPLORE Acceleration
How are force and acceleration related?

PROCEDURE
1. Tie a paper clip to each end of a long string. Hook two more paper clips to one end.
2. Hold the single paper clip in the middle of a smooth table; hang the other end of the string over the edge. Let go and observe.
3. Add one more paper clip to the hanging end and repeat the experiment. Observe what happens. Repeat.

MATERIALS
- paper clips
- string

WHAT DO YOU THINK?
- What happened each time that you let go of the single paper clip?
- Explain the relationship between the number of hanging paper clips and the motion of the paper clip on the table.

Newton's second law relates force, mass, and acceleration.

Suppose you are eating lunch with a friend and she asks you to pass the milk container. You decide to slide it across the table to her. How much force would you use to get the container moving? You would probably use a different force if the container were full than if the container were empty.

If you want to give two objects with different masses the same acceleration, you have to apply different forces to them. You must push a full milk container harder than an empty one to slide it over to your friend in the same amount of time.

REMINDER
Acceleration is a change in velocity over time.

CHECK YOUR READING What three concepts are involved in Newton's second law?

Chapter 11: Forces 353

RESOURCES FOR DIFFERENTIATED INSTRUCTION

Below Level
UNIT RESOURCE BOOK
- Reading Study Guide A, pp. 89–90
- Decoding Support, p. 124

🔘 **AUDIO CDS**

Advanced
UNIT RESOURCE BOOK
- Challenge and Extension, p. 95
- Challenge Reading, pp. 120–121

English Learners
UNIT RESOURCE BOOK
Spanish Reading Study Guide, pp. 93–94

🔘 **AUDIO CDS**
- Audio Readings in Spanish
- Audio Readings (English)

11.2 FOCUS

◗ Set Learning Goals
Students will
- Explain how Newton's second law relates force, mass, and acceleration.
- Describe how force works in circular motion.
- Hypothesize about how circular motion is affected by force.

◗ 3-Minute Warm-Up
Display Transparency 12 or copy this exercise on the board:

Draw a force/mass diagram for the following information:

Two identical disks are on a table. Disk A is pushed from the left with a small force. Disk B is pushed from the left with a force twice as large as disk A and pushed from the right with a force the same size as disk A. How does the motion of disk A compare to the motion of disk B? *It is the same.*

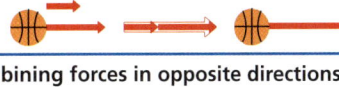

T 3-Minute Warm-Up, p. T12

11.2 MOTIVATE

EXPLORE Acceleration
PURPOSE To introduce the concept that force and acceleration are interrelated

TIP *10 min.* The paper clips must be the same size, so that the only independent variable is the number of paper clips.

WHAT DO YOU THINK? *The more paper clips on the other end of the thread, the faster the motion of the paper clip on the table.*

Ongoing Assessment
CHECK YOUR READING *Answer: force, mass, acceleration*

Chapter 11 353

11.2 INSTRUCT

Teach from Visuals

To help students interpret the visuals depicting Newton's Second Law, ask:

- In the picture on the left, what stays constant? What changes? *Mass stays constant; force and acceleration change.*

- In the picture on the right, what stays constant? What changes? *Force stays constant; mass and acceleration change.*

Ongoing Assessment

Explain how Newton's second law relates force, mass, and acceleration.

Ask: An apple and a bowling ball are pushed with the same force. Which one will accelerate more? Why? *the apple, because it has less mass*

READING VISUALS *Answer: The upper arrows show size and direction of force, and the bottom arrows show size and direction of acceleration.*

Newton's Second Law

Explore Newton's second law.

Newton studied how objects move, and he noticed some patterns. He observed that the acceleration of an object depends on the mass of the object and the size of the force applied to it. **Newton's second law** states that the acceleration of an object increases with increased force and decreases with increased mass. The law also states that the direction in which an object accelerates is the same as the direction of the force.

The photographs below show Newton's second law at work in a supermarket. The acceleration of each shopping cart depends upon two things:

- the size of the force applied to the shopping cart
- the mass of the shopping cart

In the left-hand photograph, the force on the cart changes, while the mass of the cart stays the same. In the right-hand photograph, the force on the cart stays the same, while the mass of the cart varies. Notice how mass and force affect acceleration.

Newton's Second Law

The acceleration of an object increases with increased force, decreases with increased mass, and is in the same direction as the force.

Increasing Force Increases Acceleration

small force — larger force
acceleration — acceleration

The force exerted on the cart by the man is greater than the force exerted on the same cart by the boy, so the acceleration is greater.

Increasing Mass Decreases Acceleration

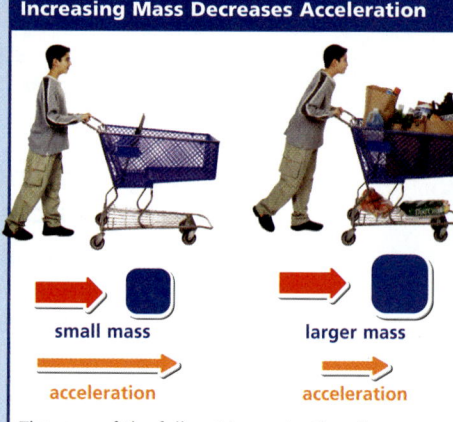

small mass — larger mass
acceleration — acceleration

The mass of the full cart is greater than the mass of the empty cart, and the boy is pushing with the same force, so the acceleration is less.

READING VISUALS What do the arrows in these diagrams show?

DIFFERENTIATE INSTRUCTION

 More Reading Support

A What happens to the acceleration of an object when the force on it increases? *It increases.*

English Learners English learners may have difficulty distinguishing between comparative (*-er*) and superlative (*-est*) adjectives. When an adjective ends in *-er*, it is comparing two people, places, things, or ideas (as *greater* is in the captions on this page). When an adjective ends in *-est*, it is comparing three or more people, places, things, or ideas.

Force Equals Mass Times Acceleration

Newton was able to describe the relationship of force, mass, and acceleration mathematically. You can calculate the force, the mass, or the acceleration if you know two of the three factors. The mathematical form of Newton's second law, stated as a formula, is

$$\text{Force} = \text{mass} \cdot \text{acceleration}$$
$$F = ma$$

To use this formula, you need to understand the unit used to measure force. In honor of Newton's contribution to our understanding of force and motion, the standard unit of force is called the newton (N). Because force equals mass times acceleration, force is measured in units of mass (kilograms) times units of acceleration (meters per second per second). A newton is defined as the amount of force that it takes to accelerate one kilogram (1 kg) of mass one meter per second per second (1 m/s^2). So 1 N is the same as 1 kg · m/s^2.

REMINDER
Meters per second per second is the same as m/s^2, which can be read "meters per second squared."

CHECK YOUR READING If the same force is applied to two objects of different mass, which object will have the greater acceleration?

The mathematical relationship of force, mass, and acceleration allow you to solve problems about how objects move. If you know the mass of an object and the acceleration you want to achieve, you can use the formula to find the force you need to exert to produce that acceleration. Use Newton's second law to find the force that is needed to accelerate the shopping cart in the sample problem.

Calculating Force

Sample Problem

What force is needed to accelerate a 10 kg shopping cart 3 m/s^2?

What do you know?	mass = 10 kg, acceleration = 3 m/s^2
What do you want to find out?	Force
Write the formula:	$F = ma$
Substitute into the formula:	$F = 10 \text{ kg} \cdot 3 \text{ m/s}^2$
Calculate and simplify:	$F = 10 \text{ kg} \cdot \frac{3m}{s^2} = 30 \text{ kg} \cdot \text{m/s}^2$
Check that your units agree:	Unit is kg · m/s^2. Unit of force is newton, which is also kg · m/s^2. Units agree.
Answer:	$F = 30$ N

Practice the Math

1. If a 5 kg ball is accelerating 1.2 m/s^2, what is the force on it?
2. A person on a scooter is accelerating 2 m/s^2. If the person has a mass of 50 kg, how much force is acting on that person?

Integrate the Sciences

Many athletes train with weights to improve their performance. Strengthening their muscles allows athletes to apply more force to objects they use in their sports. Increased force means increased acceleration. A stronger baseball player can throw and hit the ball farther, a stronger swimmer can move through the water more quickly, and a stronger discus thrower can throw the discus farther.

Develop Algebra Skills

- Math Support, p. 125
- Math Practice, p. 126

Ongoing Assessment

CHECK YOUR READING Answer: the object with less mass

Practice the Math Answers:

1. $F = ma = 5 \text{ kg} \cdot 1.2 \text{ m/s}^2$
   $= 6 \text{ kg} \cdot \text{m/s}^2 = 6$ N

2. $F = ma = 50 \text{ kg} \cdot 2 \text{ m/s}^2$
   $= 100 \text{ kg} \cdot \text{m/s}^2 = 100$ N

DIFFERENTIATE INSTRUCTION

More Reading Support

B What is the standard unit of force? **newton**

C What unit is used for mass when calculating force or acceleration? **kilogram**

Advanced Have students describe a scenario that involves force, mass, and acceleration. Using this scenario, have them write related additional problems to solve using $F = ma$. Each set of problems should include at least one problem for each variable. Review how to rearrange the equation to solve for any of the variables. Have students exchange problems and solve.

Challenge and Extension, p. 95

Develop Algebra Skills

Remind students that formulas can be rearranged to find any variable in the formula.

- Isolate the desired variable on one side of the equation.
- To isolate the desired variable, "undo" any process done to the variable in the formula. Multiplication and division are opposite processes, as are addition and subtraction.
- To solve for C in the formula $F = (9C/5) + 32$, subtract 32 from both sides of the equation. Divide both sides by 9, then multiply by 5. The formula for C is $5(F - 32)/9$.

Teacher Demo

Use a toy with wheels to demonstrate the difference between velocity and acceleration. Pull the toy at a steady speed for 6 m while a student measures the amount of time it takes to pull the toy over each 2 m section. Ask students to calculate the speed of the toy in each section. These values should agree closely. Ask students how much the speed changed from one section to another; in other words, what was the acceleration? Students should be able to see that the acceleration of the toy is zero, even though it moves constantly.

Teach from Visuals

To help students interpret the visual of people pulling a plane and the information in the caption, ask:

- What was the average velocity of the plane while it was pulled? *v = d/t = 3.7 m/6.74 s = 0.55 m/s*
- If the people pulled a car with the same amount of force they used on the plane, how would the car's acceleration compare with the plane's? Why? *It would be greater because its mass is less.*

Ongoing Assessment

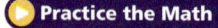 **Practice the Math** Answers:

1. $a = F/m = 4500 N/30,000 kg = 0.15 m/s^2$
2. $a = F/m = 3N/6 kg = 0.5 m/s^2$

This team of 20 people pulled a 72,000-kilogram (159,000 lb) Boeing 727 airplane 3.7 meters (12 ft) in 6.74 seconds.

The photograph above shows people who are combining forces to pull an airplane. Suppose you knew the mass of the plane and how hard the people were pulling. How much would the plane accelerate? The sample problem below shows how Newton's second law helps you calculate the acceleration.

Calculating Acceleration

Sample Problem

If a team pulls with a combined force of 9000 N on an airplane with a mass of 30,000 kg, what is the acceleration of the airplane?

What do you know? mass = 30,000 kg, force = 9000 N

What do you want to find out? acceleration

Rearrange the formula: $a = \dfrac{F}{m}$

Substitute into the formula: $a = \dfrac{9000 \text{ N}}{30,000 \text{ kg}}$

Calculate and simplify: $a = \dfrac{9000 \text{ N}}{30,000 \text{ kg}} = \dfrac{9000 \text{ kg} \cdot \text{m/s}^2}{30,000 \text{ kg}} = 0.3 \text{ m/s}^2$

Check that your units agree: Unit is m/s^2. Unit for acceleration is m/s^2. Units agree.

Answer: $a = 0.3 \text{ m/s}^2$

Practice the Math

1. Half the people on the team decide not to pull the airplane. The combined force of those left is 4500 N, while the airplane's mass is still 30,000 kg. What will be the acceleration?
2. A girl pulls a wheeled backpack with a force of 3 N. If the backpack has a mass of 6 kg, what is its acceleration?

DIFFERENTIATE INSTRUCTION

More Reading Support

D What formula is used to calculate acceleration? $a = \dfrac{F}{m}$

E A mass is 2 kg. What other information do you need to calculate acceleration? *force*

Below Level Have students draw a graphic organizer that shows the steps used to solve problems for each form of $F = ma$. The graphic organizer should show what formula is used to solve for each variable and a sample problem of each type. Have students use their organizers to solve the practice problems on pp. 356 and 357.

Mass and Acceleration

Mass is also a variable in Newton's second law. If the same force acts on two objects, the object with less mass will have the greater acceleration. For instance, if you push a soccer ball and a bowling ball with equal force, the soccer ball will have a greater acceleration.

If objects lose mass, they can gain acceleration if the force remains the same. When a rocket is first launched, most of its mass is the fuel it carries. As the rocket burns fuel, it loses mass. As the mass continually decreases, the acceleration continually increases.

APPLY This NASA launch rocket accelerates with enough force to lift about 45 cars off the ground. As the rocket loses fuel, will it accelerate more or less? Why?

Calculating Mass

Sample Problem

A model rocket is accelerating at 2 m/s². The force on it is 1 N. What is the mass of the rocket?

What do you know? acceleration = 2 m/s², force = 1 N
What do you want to find out? mass
Rearrange the formula: $m = \dfrac{F}{a}$
Substitute into the formula: $m = \dfrac{1\ N}{2\ m/s^2}$
Calculate and simplify: $m = \dfrac{1\ N}{2\ m/s^2} = \dfrac{1\ kg \cdot m/s^2}{2\ m/s^2} = 0.5\ kg$
Check that your units agree: Unit is kg. Unit of mass is kg. Units agree.
Answer: $m = 0.5\ kg$

Practice the Math

1. Another model rocket is accelerating at a rate of 3 m/s² with a force of 1 N. What is the mass of the rocket?
2. A boy pushes a shopping cart with a force of 10 N, and the cart accelerates 1 m/s². What is the mass of the cart?

Forces can change the direction of motion.

Usually, we think of a force as either speeding up or slowing down the motion of an object, but force can also make an object change direction. If an object changes direction, it is accelerating. Newton's second law says that if you apply a force to an object, the direction in which the object accelerates is the same as the direction of the force. You can change the direction of an object without changing its speed. For example, a good soccer player can control the motion of a soccer ball by applying a force that changes the ball's direction but not its speed.

CHECK YOUR READING How can an object accelerate when it does not change speed?

Chapter 11: Forces 357

DIFFERENTIATE INSTRUCTION

More Reading Support

F If an object moves at a constant speed, but it accelerates, what changes? *direction*

Inclusion Students with learning disabilities might have difficulty rearranging formulas to solve for all possible variables. For these students, list all possible forms of a formula, so that they can choose the one needed rather than having to derive it. For example, for the force formula, list $F = ma$, $a = \dfrac{F}{m}$, and $m = \dfrac{F}{a}$. Be sure students understand that all of these formulas present the same information.

Real World Example

A fully loaded tractor-trailer and a passenger car are going 55 miles per hour. If both drivers apply their brakes at the same time, the truck will travel farther than the car before it stops. While the truck's brakes apply about 16 times the force of the car's brakes, the truck is also about 27 times as massive as the car. Therefore, the truck's acceleration when braking is only about 60% of the car's acceleration. This is why truck drivers are advised to keep a greater following distance than passenger car drivers are.

EXPLORE the BIG idea

Revisit "Popping Ping-Pong Balls" on p. 343. Have students explain their results.

Ongoing Assessment

CHECK YOUR READING Answer: It can change direction.

PHOTO CAPTION Answer: It will accelerate more because mass becomes less.

Practice the Math Answers:

1. $m = F/a = 1N/3\ m/s^2 = 1/3\ kg = 0.3\ kg$
2. $m = F/a = 10N/1\ m/s^2 = 10\ kg$

Chapter 11 357

INVESTIGATE Motion and Force

PURPOSE To hypothesize about the circular motion of a ball when the force on it changes

TIPS 15 min.

- Have water and paper towels on hand for cleaning up paint.
- To anchor a lightweight plate, place an object in the center of the plate. Make sure that the object will not interfere with the motion of the ball.
- Revise any hypotheses that are not supported by experimental results, then repeat the experiment.

WHAT DO YOU THINK? *Students should determine if observations supported their hypotheses. The marble moved in a straight line in the direction it was moving when it left the plate; the marble was affected by friction.*

CHALLENGE *The marble will roll in the same direction, will leave the plate at a different speed, and will roll a different distance before it stops.*

 Datasheet, Motion and Force, p. 96

Technology Resources

Customize this student lab as needed or look for an alternative. Print rubrics to assess student lab reports.

 Lab Generator CD-ROM

Metacognitive Strategy

Ask students to discuss with a partner any additions or modifications they made to the procedure of the lab.

Teaching with Technology

If students have probeware, they may wish to use a motion detector for this activity.

Ongoing Assessment

 *Answer: It consistently changes its direction.*

INVESTIGATE Motion and Force

What affects circular motion?

PROCEDURE

1. Spread newspaper over your work surface. Place the paper plate down on the newspaper.
2. Practice rolling the marble around the edge of the plate until you can roll it around completely at least once.
3. Cut out a one-quarter slice of the paper plate. Put a dab of paint on the edge of the plate where the marble will leave it. Place the plate back down on the newspaper.
4. Hypothesize: How will the marble move once it rolls off the plate? Why?
5. Roll the marble all the way around the paper plate into the cut-away section and observe the resulting motion as shown by the trail of paint.

WHAT DO YOU THINK?
- Did your observations support your hypothesis?
- What forces affected the marble's motion after it left the plate?

CHALLENGE How will changing the speed at which you roll the marble change your results? Repeat the activity to test your prediction.

SKILL FOCUS
Hypothesizing

MATERIALS
- newspaper
- paper plate
- marble
- scissors
- poster paint
- paintbrush

TIME
15 minutes

Centripetal Force

When you were younger, you may have experimented with using force to change motion. Perhaps you and a friend took turns swinging each other in a circle. If you remember this game, you may also remember that your arms got tired because they were constantly pulling your friend as your friend spun around. It took force to change the direction of your friend's motion. Without that force, your friend could not have kept moving in a circle.

Any force that keeps an object moving in a circle is known as a **centripetal force** (sehn-TRIHP-ih-tuhl). This force points toward the center of the circle. Without the centripetal force, the object would go flying off in a straight line. When you whirl a ball on a string, what keeps the ball moving in a circle? The force of the string turns the ball, changing the ball's direction of motion. When the string turns, so does the ball. As the string changes direction, the force from the string also changes direction. The force is always pointing along the string toward your hand, the center of the circle. The centripetal force on the whirling ball is the pull from the string. If you let go of the string, the ball would fly off in the direction it was headed when you let go.

 VOCABULARY Remember to make a magnet word diagram for *centripetal force.*

 How does centripetal force change the motion of an object?

358 Unit 3: Motion and Forces

DIFFERENTIATE INSTRUCTION

 More Reading Support

G In what direction does centripetal force point? *toward the center of the circle*

Alternative Assessment Have students prepare diagrams that show how centripetal force affects their daily lives. Each diagram should show motion in a circle and arrows indicating force. Examples include a car on a curved ramp and amusement park rides that spin.

Advanced Have students who are interested in learning how forces affect the motion of a boomerang read:

Challenge Reading, pp. 120–121

top view
Centripetal force
The force that keeps the female skater moving in a circle is the pull exerted by her partner. The diagram shows the direction of the centripetal force.

Circular Motion and Newton's Second Law

Suppose the male skater shown above spins his partner faster. Her direction changes more quickly than before, so she accelerates more. To get more acceleration, he must apply more force. The same idea holds for a ball you whirl on a string. You have to pull harder on the string when you whirl the ball faster, because it takes more centripetal force to keep the ball moving at the greater speed.

You can apply the formula for Newton's second law even to an object moving in a circle. If you know the size of the centripetal force acting upon the object, you can find its acceleration. A greater acceleration requires a greater centripetal force. A more massive object requires a greater centripetal force to have the same circular speed as a less massive object. But no matter what the mass of an object is, if it moves in a circle, its force and acceleration are directed toward the center of the circle.

 How does increasing the centripetal force on an object affect its acceleration?

11.2 Review

KEY CONCEPTS
1. If the force acting upon an object is increased, what happens to the object's acceleration?
2. How does the mass of an object affect its acceleration?
3. What force keeps an object moving in a circle? In what direction does this force act?

CRITICAL THINKING
4. **Infer** Use Newton's second law to determine how much force is being applied to an object that is traveling at a constant velocity.
5. **Calculate** What force is needed to accelerate an object 5 m/s² if the object has a mass of 10 kg?

CHALLENGE
6. **Synthesize** Carlos pushes a 3 kg box with a force of 9 N. The force of friction on the box is 3 N in the opposite direction. What is the acceleration of the box? *Hint:* Combine forces to find the net force.

Chapter 11: **Forces** 359

ANSWERS
1. Acceleration increases.
2. Assuming force is constant, the greater the mass, the less the acceleration.
3. centripetal force; toward the center of the circle
4. No net force is applied. If a force were applied, the object would change velocity, and thus change acceleration.
5. F = ma = 10 kg · 5 m/s² = 50 N
6. net force = 9N − 3N = 6N
   a = F/m = 6N/3 kg = 2 m/s²

Real World Example

If possible, borrow a centrifuge from a local medical facility to show students. Explain that a tube in a centrifuge can spin several thousand times a minute. The motion separates the contents of the tube according to their density. Ask students to predict where the parts of blood end up in the tube after it is placed in a centrifuge. The denser parts—red and white blood cells—move to the outer part of the circle. Plasma is in the inner part because it is less dense.

Ongoing Assessment

Describe how force works in circular motion.

Ask: What is the centripetal force that keeps the Moon in orbit around Earth? *gravity*

 *Answer: Its acceleration increases.*

Reinforce the BIG idea

Have students relate the section to the Big Idea.

 Reinforcing Key Concepts, p. 97

11.2 ASSESS & RETEACH

Assess
 Section 11.2 Quiz, p. 23

Reteach
Tie a heavy cord about 1 m long to a bucket. Place an inch of water in the bucket. Swing it around in a circle. Ask students why the water remains in the bucket. *Centripetal force acts on the water and keeps it in the bucket.*

Technology Resources
Have students visit **ClassZone.com** for reteaching of Key Concepts.

 CONTENT REVIEW

 CONTENT REVIEW CD-ROM

Chapter 11 **359**

MATH IN SCIENCE
Math Skills Practice for Science

Set Learning Goal
To analyze the number of significant figures in sets of data and in calculations using these data

Present the Science
Significant figures apply to measurements only, not to counting numbers. For example, 35 cm has two significant figures, but significant figures are not considered with a counted amount, such as 35 coins. Thus, the product of a measurement and a counted number has the same number of significant figures as the measurement factor. For example, the mass of 12 buttons, each of which has a mass of 5.43 g, would be 65.2 g.

Develop Skills in Estimation
Provide students with several measuring devices. Examples might be meter sticks or rulers, balances, and measuring cups or other graduated containers. Tell students that significant measurements can be made by estimating one place farther than the smallest measurement on the instrument. For example, if a meter stick is calibrated so that the smallest unit on it is centimeters, length can be measured to millimeters by estimating between the centimeter units. Have pairs of students use the instruments to measure several objects.

Close
Ask: A rectangular garden is 2.5 m by 4.23 m. If the area of the garden is found by multiplying these figures together, how many significant figures will be in the area? *two*

- Math Support, p. 127
- Math Practice, p. 128

Technology Resources
Students can visit **ClassZone.com** for practice working with rounding decimals.

MATH TUTORIAL

Math in Science

MATH TUTORIAL
CLASSZONE.COM
Click on Math Tutorial for more help with rounding decimals.

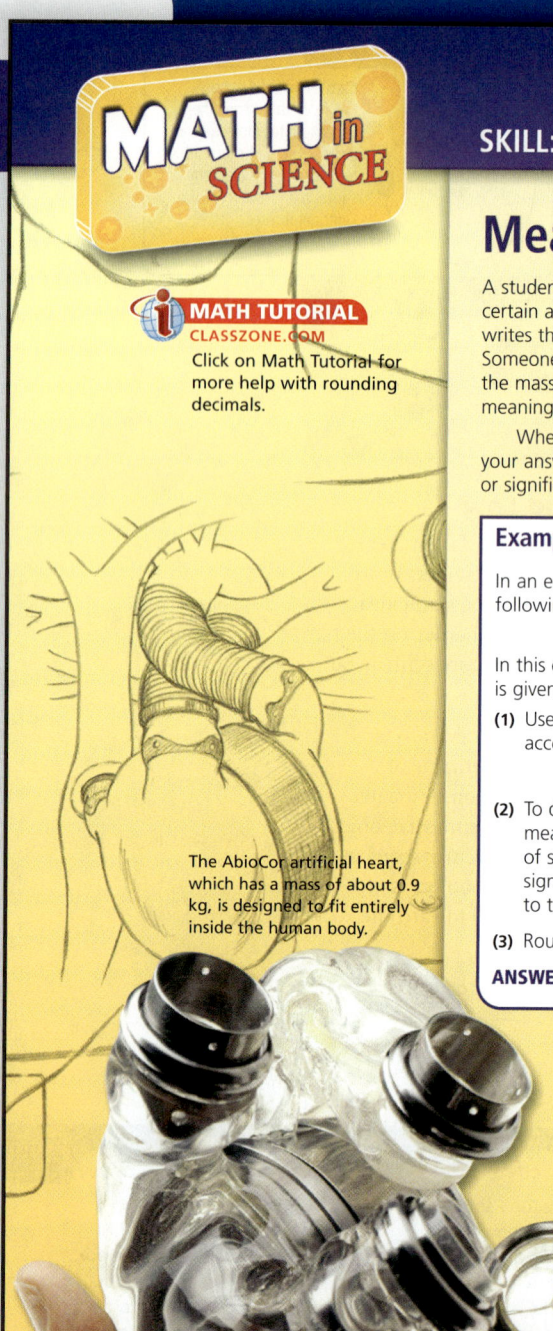

The AbioCor artificial heart, which has a mass of about 0.9 kg, is designed to fit entirely inside the human body.

SKILL: USING SIGNIFICANT FIGURES

Meaningful Numbers

A student doing a science report on artificial hearts reads that a certain artificial heart weighs about 2 pounds. The student then writes that the mass of the artificial heart is 0.907185 kilograms. Someone reading this report might think that the student knows the mass to a high precision, when actually he knows it only to one meaningful number.

When you make calculations, the number of digits to include in your answer depends in part on the number of meaningful digits, or significant figures, in the numbers you are working with.

Example
In an experiment to find acceleration, a scientist might record the following data.

Force = 3.1 N   mass = 1.450 kg

In this example, force is given to two significant figures, and mass is given to four significant figures.

(1) Use a calculator and the formula $a = F/m$ to find the acceleration. The display on the calculator shows

2.1379310345

(2) To determine how many of the digits in this answer are really meaningful, look at the measurement with the least number of significant figures. In this example, force is given to two significant figures. Therefore, the answer is meaningful only to two significant figures.

(3) Round the calculated number to two digits.

ANSWER acceleration = 2.1 m/s^2

Answer the following questions.
For each pair of measurements, calculate the acceleration to the appropriate number of digits.

1. Force = 3.100 N   mass = 3.1 kg
2. Force = 2 N   mass = 4.2 kg
3. Force = 1.21 N   mass = 1.1000 kg

CHALLENGE Suppose a scientist measures a force of 3.25 N and a mass of 3.3 kg. She could round the force to two significant figures and then divide, or she could divide and then round the answer. Compare these two methods. Which method do you think is more accurate?

360 Unit 3: Motion and Forces

ANSWERS

1. $a = F/m = 3.100 \text{ N}/3.1 \text{ kg} = 1.000 \text{ N/kg} = 1.0 \text{ m/s}^2$
2. $a = F/m = 2 \text{ N}/4.2 \text{ kg} = 0.5 \text{ N/kg} = 0.5 \text{ m/s}^2$
3. $a = F/m = 1.21 \text{ N}/1.1000 \text{ kg} = 1.10 \text{ N/kg} = 1.10 \text{ m/s}^2$

CHALLENGE Using 3.25 N: $a = F/m = 3.25 \text{ N}/3.3 \text{ kg} = 0.98 \text{ m/s}^2$.
Using 3.3 N: $a = F/m = 3.3 \text{ N}/3.3 \text{ kg} = 1.0 \text{ m/s}^2$. In general, the solution rounded off after dividing is more accurate.

KEY CONCEPT

Forces act in pairs.

BEFORE, you learned
- A force is a push or a pull
- Increasing the force on an object increases the acceleration
- The acceleration of an object depends on its mass and the force applied to it

NOW, you will learn
- How Newton's third law relates action/reaction pairs of forces
- How Newton's laws work together

VOCABULARY
Newton's third law p. 361

THINK ABOUT

How do jellyfish move?

Jellyfish do not have much control over their movements. They drift with the current in the ocean. However, jellyfish do have some control over their up-and-down motion. By squeezing water out of its umbrella-like body, the jellyfish shown here applies a force in one direction to move in the opposite direction. If the water is forced downward, the jellyfish moves upward. How can a person or an object move in one direction by exerting a force in the opposite direction?

Newton's third law relates action and reaction forces.

COMBINATION NOTES
In your notebook, make an outline and draw a diagram about Newton's third law.

Newton made an important observation that explains the motion of the jellyfish. He noticed that forces always act in pairs. **Newton's third law** states that every time one object exerts a force on another object, the second object exerts a force that is equal in size and opposite in direction back on the first object. As the jellyfish contracts its body, it applies a downward force on the water. The water applies an equal force back on the jellyfish. It is this equal and opposite force on the jellyfish that pushes it up. This is similar to what happens when a blown-up balloon is released. The balloon pushes air out the end, and the air pushes back on the balloon and moves it forward.

 What moves the jellyfish through the water?

Chapter 11: Forces 361

11.3 FOCUS

◆ Set Learning Goals
Students will
- Explain how Newton's third law relates action/reaction pairs of forces.
- Describe how Newton's laws work together.
- Investigate how action and reaction forces compare.

◆ 3-Minute Warm-Up
Display Transparency 13 or copy this exercise on the board:

A worker pushes a 5-kilogram box with a force of 10 N. What is the acceleration of the box? Use the formula $F = ma$ to find the answer. $a = F/m = 10 \text{ N}/5 \text{ kg} = 2 \text{ m/s}^2$

 3-Minute Warm-Up, p. T13

11.3 MOTIVATE

THINK ABOUT

PURPOSE To understand action/reaction forces as a way of causing motion

DISCUSS Point out that the movement of the jellyfish is in the opposite direction of the force it exerts. Have students give parallel examples based on human movement, such as a strong sneeze forcing a person's head back.

Ongoing Assessment

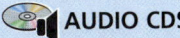 Answer: As the jellyfish applies a downward force on the water, the water applies an equal force on the jellyfish.

RESOURCES FOR DIFFERENTIATED INSTRUCTION

Below Level
UNIT RESOURCE BOOK
- Reading Study Guide A, pp. 100–101
- Decoding Support, p. 124

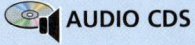 **AUDIO CDS**

Advanced
UNIT RESOURCE BOOK
Challenge and Extension, p. 106

English Learners
UNIT RESOURCE BOOK
Spanish Reading Study Guide, pp. 104–105

🎧 **AUDIO CDS**
- Audio Readings in Spanish
- Audio Readings (English)

Chapter 11 **361**

11.3 INSTRUCT

INVESTIGATE Newton's Third Law

PURPOSE To observe pairs of action and reaction forces

TIP *15 min.* Hold the scales securely and pull only hard enough to provide a reasonable reading.

WHAT DO YOU THINK? *Whether one partner pulled or both partners pulled, the force was the same on both spring scales. The scales show equal and opposite action and reaction.*

CHALLENGE *Sample answer: First law: fasten a spring scale to an object; pull on the object so that its speed or direction changes; the force needed for this motion can be read on the scale. Second law: fasten a spring scale to an object; pull the object by the scale, noting that, as force increases, acceleration increases.*

 Datasheet, Newton's Third Law, p. 107

Technology Resources

Customize this student lab as needed or look for an alternative. Print rubrics to assess student lab reports.

 Lab Generator CD-ROM

Metacognitive Strategy

Ask students to explain what they would do differently if they repeated the investigation.

Ongoing Assessment

 *Answer: the rocket's engine pushes exhaust downward/exhaust pushes back on rocket; force of toe on table/force of table on toe; force of hand on table/force of table on hand*

Action and Reaction Pairs

The force that is exerted on an object and the force that the object exerts back are known together as an action/reaction force pair. One force in the pair is called the action force, and the other is called the reaction force. For instance, if the jellyfish pushing on the water is the action force, the water pushing back on the jellyfish is the reaction force. Likewise, if the balloon pushing the air backward is the action force, the air pushing the balloon forward is the reaction force.

You can see many examples of action and reaction forces in the world around you. Here are three:

- You may have watched the liftoffs of the space shuttle on television. When the booster rockets carrying the space shuttle take off, their engines push fuel exhaust downward. The exhaust pushes back on the rockets, sending them upward.
- When you bang your toe into the leg of a table, the same amount of force that you exert on the table is exerted back on your toe.
- Action and reaction forces do not always result in motion. For example, if you press down on a table, the table resists the push with the same amount of force, even though nothing moves.

CHECK YOUR READING Identify the action/reaction forces in each example described above.

INVESTIGATE Newton's Third Law

How do action and reaction forces compare?
PROCEDURE

1. With a partner, hook the two spring scales together.
2. Pull gently on your spring scale while your partner holds but does not pull on the other scale.
3. Observe and record the amount of force that is shown on your scale and on your partner's scale.
4. Both of you pull together. Observe the force shown on each scale.

WHAT DO YOU THINK?
- What happened to your partner's force as your force increased?
- What happened when you both pulled?
- Explain why you think what you observed in each case happened.

CHALLENGE Can you think of a way to use the scales to show Newton's first or second law?

SKILL FOCUS Observing

MATERIALS 2 spring scales

TIME 15 minutes

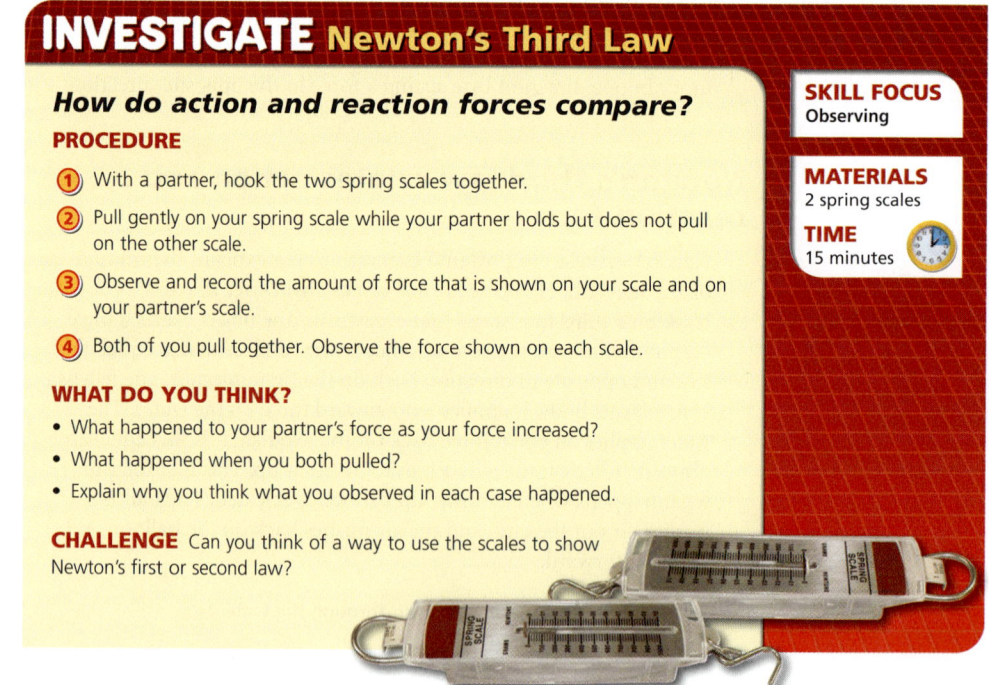

362 Unit 3: Motion and Forces

DIFFERENTIATE INSTRUCTION

 More Reading Support

A If the action force is the force of scissors on paper, what is the reaction force? *the force of paper on scissors*

English Learners English learners might not recognize sentences beginning with *If* that do not also contain *then*. Point out the sentence on p. 362 that begins with *If*. Explain that *then* is implied and that a cause-and-effect relationship is at work.

Action and Reaction Forces Versus Balanced Forces

Because action and reaction forces are equal and opposite, they may be confused with balanced forces. Keep in mind that balanced forces act on a single object, while action and reaction forces act on different objects.

Balanced Forces If you and a friend pull on opposite sides of a backpack with the same amount of force, the backpack doesn't move, because the forces acting on it are balanced. In this case, both forces are exerted on one object—the backpack.

Action and Reaction As you drag a heavy backpack across a floor, you can feel the backpack pulling on you with an equal amount of force. The action force and the reaction force are acting on two different things—one is acting on the backpack, and the other is acting on you.

The illustration below summarizes Newton's third law. The girl exerts an action force on the boy by pushing him. Even though the boy is not trying to push the girl, an equal and opposite reaction force acts upon the girl, causing her to move as well.

Newton's Third Law
When one object exerts a force on another object, the second object exerts an equal and opposite force on the first object.

1 One Skater Pushes

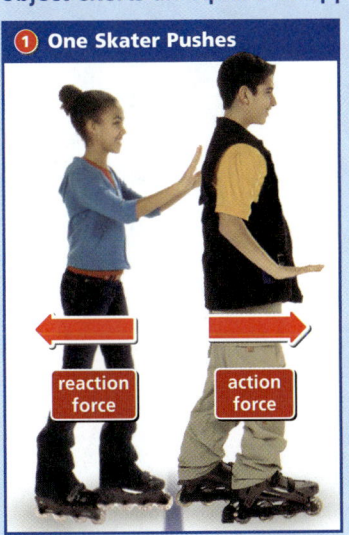

The action force from the girl sets the boy in motion.

2 Both Skaters Move

Even though the boy does not do anything, the reaction force from him sets the girl in motion as well.

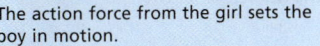 How does the direction of the force on the girl relate to her motion?

Chapter 11: **Forces** 363

DIFFERENTIATE INSTRUCTION

More Reading Support

B What type of force pair acts on only one object? *balanced*

C What type of force pair acts on different objects? *action/reaction*

Advanced

 Challenge and Extension, p. 106

Address Misconceptions

IDENTIFY Ask: If one object has two equal but opposite forces acting on it, what type of forces are they? If students answer that the forces are action/reaction pairs, they may hold the misconception that action/reaction forces act on a single object.

CORRECT Make two lists on the board. Label one "Balanced forces" and the other "Action/reaction." Ask students to give examples of force pairs. List each in the correct column after students agree whether or not the forces act on a single object.

REASSESS Ask: What type of force pair is present when someone steps from a boat onto a dock, and the boat moves away from the dock? Explain your answer. *An action/reaction force pair; the force on the boat is from the shoe, the force on the shoe is from the boat.*

Technology Resources
Visit **ClassZone.com** for background on common student misconceptions.

 MISCONCEPTION DATABASE

EXPLORE the BIG idea
Revisit "Take Off!" on p. 343. Have students explain their results.

Ongoing Assessment
Explain how Newton's third law relates action/reaction pairs of forces.

Ask: If a reaction force is 5 N, what is the action force? *5 N*

Answer: The girl's motion is in the same direction as the force acting on her. This force is equal and opposite to the direction of the force she applied.

Teach from Visuals

To help students understand the visual demonstrating Newton's three laws of motion, ask:

- Would a lighter animal, such as a cat, require as much force to jump as high? Explain your answer in terms of Newton's first law. *No; less mass means less inertia to overcome.*
- Would a dog be able to leap 30 ft, as a kangaroo can? Explain your answer in terms of Newton's third law. *No; a dog does not have legs as powerful as those of a kangaroo. A dog could not produce as much of an action force, so the reaction force would also be less.*

T The visual "Newton's Three Laws of Motion" is available as T14 in the Unit Transparency Book.

Real World Example

Have students apply Newton's three laws of motion in comparing how they jump with how a kangaroo jumps. Gravity acts on the students as it does on the kangaroo, or their inertia would keep them rising upward after they jumped. Even though a student's mass is less than that of a kangaroo, a student's acceleration after jumping would be less because the force applied by the kangaroo is much greater. Because the action force that the student applies on the ground is much less than the force a kangaroo applies, the reaction force is also much less, so the kangaroo jumps much farther.

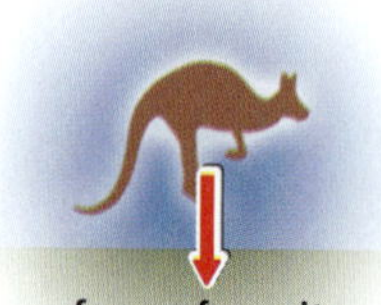

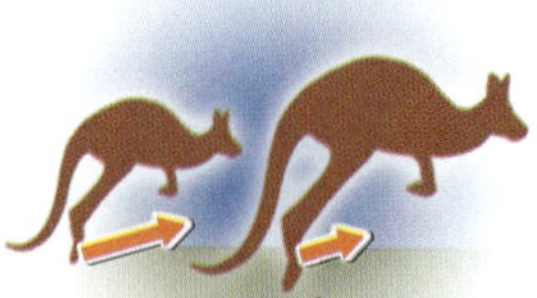

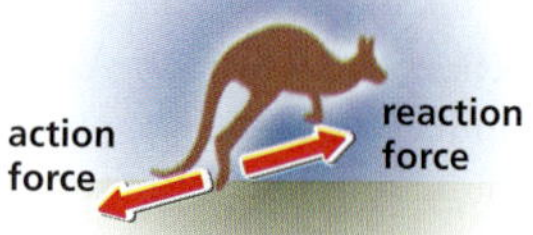

Ongoing Assessment

READING VISUALS *Answer: gravity on the kangaroo; force of the kangaroo on the ground; force of the ground on the kangaroo*

Newton's Three Laws of Motion

All three of Newton's laws work together to help describe how an object will move.

Newton's First Law

This kangaroo has jumped, setting itself in motion. If no other forces acted on it, the kangaroo would continue to move through the air with the same motion. Instead, the force of gravity will bring this kangaroo back to the ground.

Newton's Second Law

The large kangaroo does not have as much acceleration as a less massive kangaroo would if it used the same force to jump. However, the more massive kangaroo can increase its acceleration by increasing the force of its jump.

Newton's Third Law

A kangaroo applies an action force on the ground with its powerful back legs. The reaction force from the ground can send the kangaroo as far as 8 meters (26 ft) through the air.

? D

? E

READING VISUALS What forces are involved in a kangaroo jump?

Common Name: Red kangaroo
Scientific Name: *Macropus rufus*
Home: Australia
Top Speed: 65 km/h (40 mi/h)
Maximum Leap: 8 m (26 ft)

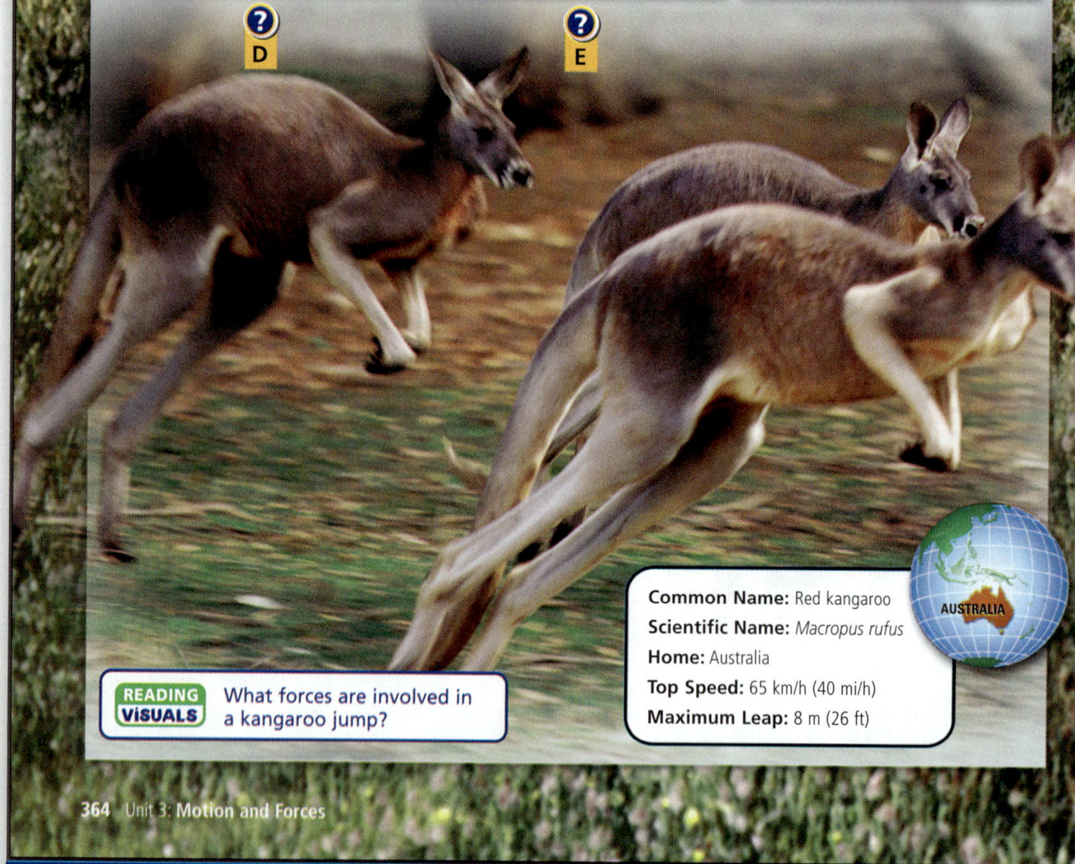

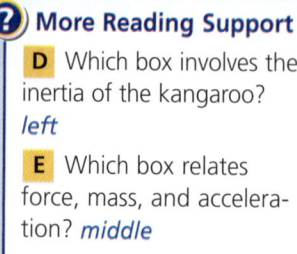

DIFFERENTIATE INSTRUCTION

? More Reading Support

D Which box involves the inertia of the kangaroo? *left*

E Which box relates force, mass, and acceleration? *middle*

Newton's three laws describe and predict motion.

Newton's three laws can explain the motion of almost any object, including the motion of animals. The illustrations on page 364 show how all three of Newton's laws can be used to describe how kangaroos move. The three laws are not independent of one another; they are used together to explain the motion of objects.

You can use the laws of motion to explain how other animals move as well. For example, Newton's laws explain why a squid moves forward while squirting water out behind it. These laws also explain that a bird is exerting force when it speeds up to fly away or when it changes its direction in the air.

You can also use Newton's laws to make predictions about motion. If you know the force acting upon an object, then you can predict how that object's motion will change. For example, if you want to send a spacecraft to Mars, you must be able to predict exactly where Mars will be by the time the spacecraft reaches it. You must also be able to control the force on your spacecraft so that it will arrive at the right place at the right time.

Knowing how Newton's three laws work together can also help you win a canoe race. In order to start the canoe moving, you need to apply a force to overcome its inertia. Newton's second law might affect your choice of canoes, because a less massive canoe is easier to accelerate than a more massive one. You can also predict the best position for your paddle in the water. If you want to move straight ahead, you push backward on the paddle so that the canoe moves forward. Together, Newton's laws can help you explain and predict how the canoe, or any object, will move.

Find out more about Newton's laws of motion.

COMBINATION NOTES
Make an outline and draw a diagram showing how all three of Newton's laws apply to the motion of one object.

11.3 Review

KEY CONCEPTS
1. Identify the action/reaction force pair involved when you catch a ball.
2. Explain the difference between balanced forces and action/reaction forces.
3. How do Newton's laws of motion apply to the motion of an animal, such as a cat that is running?

CRITICAL THINKING
4. **Apply** A man pushes on a wall with a force of 50 N. What are the size and the direction of the force that the wall exerts on the man?
5. **Evaluate** Jim will not help push a heavy box. He says, "My force will produce an opposite force and cancel my effort." Evaluate Jim's statement.

CHALLENGE
6. **Calculate** Suppose you are holding a basketball while standing still on a skateboard. You and the skateboard have a mass of 50 kg. You throw the basketball with a force of 10 N. What is your acceleration before and after you throw the ball?

Chapter 11: Forces 365

Ongoing Assessment

Describe how Newton's laws work together.

Ask: Use Newton's three laws to explain how you take a step. *Sample answer: Force is needed to overcome your inertia. Applying force accelerates your foot. The action force of the foot on the ground equals the reaction force of the ground on the foot.*

Reinforce the BIG idea

Have students relate the section to the Big Idea.

 Reinforcing Key Concepts, p. 108

11.3 ASSESS & RETEACH

Assess
 Section 11.3 Quiz, p. 24

Reteach
Stand on a skateboard or wear a pair of roller skates. Have students hypothesize how you could move the skateboard without touching any part of the room or any student. *Sample answer: Throw an object in the direction opposite the direction you want to move.*

Technology Resources
Have students visit ClassZone.com for reteaching of Key Concepts.

 CONTENT REVIEW
 CONTENT REVIEW CD-ROM

ANSWERS

1. force of the ball on your hand, force of your hand on the ball

2. Balanced forces act on one object, and each cancels the effect of the other. Action and reaction forces act on two different objects.

3. force exerted by cat overcomes cat's inertia; force cat needs to accelerate depends on its mass; when running, cat applies backward force on ground, ground applies forward force on cat

4. 50 N in direction opposite to his force on the wall

5. It is incorrect; the reaction force doesn't act on the box, it acts on Jim.

6. before: no change in velocity = 0 m/s^2; after: a = F/m = 10 N/50 kg = 0.2 m/s^2

CHAPTER INVESTIGATION

Focus

PURPOSE To learn how Newton's laws can be applied to make rockets fly farther

OVERVIEW Students create a straw bottle rocket and modify it to test how the modification affects flight. Students will find that the distance of flight increases

- as the size of the bottle increases;
- as the mass of the straws decreases;
- as the amount of clay decreases; and
- as the size of the paper loops increases.

Lab Preparation

- Have students cut strips in advance to allow more time to investigate.
- Have extra plastic bottles in a variety of sizes on hand in case cracks develop from squeezing.
- Prior to the investigation, have students read through the investigation and prepare their data tables. Or you may wish to copy and distribute datasheets and rubrics.

 UNIT RESOURCE BOOK, pp. 129–137

 SCIENCE TOOLKIT, F14

Lab Management

- Have different groups of students try different modifications, so the class can address all the ways in which a rocket's flight could be affected.
- Students can work in pairs and take turns launching the rocket and recording the distance it flies. Remind students to exert the same force in order to achieve consistent results.
- Remind students to measure the distance the rocket flies consistently. For example, always measure from the launching point (tip of the straw) to the place where the rocket lands (tip of the straw).

SAFETY Emphasize that students should always point projectiles away from other students.

366 Unit 3: **Motion and Forces**

CHAPTER INVESTIGATION

Newton's Laws of Motion

OVERVIEW AND PURPOSE As you know, rocket engineers consider Newton's laws when designing rockets and planning rocket flights. In this investigation you will use what you have learned about Newton's laws to
- build a straw rocket
- improve the rocket's performance by modifying one design element

 Problem

What aspects of a model rocket affect the distance it flies?

 Hypothesize

After step 8 in the procedure, write a hypothesis to explain what you predict will happen during the second set of trials. Your hypothesis should take the form of an "If . . . , then . . . , because . . ." statement.

MATERIALS
- 2 straws with different diameters
- several plastic bottles, in different sizes
- modeling clay
- scissors
- construction paper
- meter stick
- tape

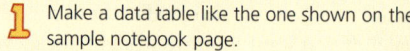 Procedure

1. Make a data table like the one shown on the sample notebook page.

2. Insert the straw with the smaller diameter into one of the bottles. Seal the mouth of the bottle tightly with modeling clay so that air can escape only through the straw. This is the rocket launcher.

3. Cut two thin strips of paper, one about 8 cm long and the other about 12 cm long. Connect the ends of the strips to make loops.

4. To create the rocket, place the straw with the larger diameter through the smaller loop and tape the loop to the straw at one end. Attach the other loop to the other end of the straw in the same way. Both loops should be attached to the same side of the straw to stabilize your rocket in flight.

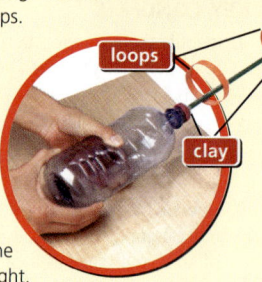

366 Unit 3: **Motion and Forces**

INVESTIGATION RESOURCES

 CHAPTER INVESTIGATION, Newton's Laws of Motion
- Level A, pp. 129–132
- Level B, pp. 133–136
- Level C, p. 137

Advanced students should complete Levels B & C.

 Writing a Lab Report, D12–13

Technology Resources

Customize this student lab as needed or look for an alternative. Print rubrics to assess student lab reports.

 Lab Generator CD-ROM

5. Use a small ball of modeling clay to seal the end of the straw near the smaller loop.

6. Slide the open end of the rocket over the straw on the launcher. Place the bottle on the edge of a table so that the rocket is pointing away from the table.

7. Test launch your rocket by holding the bottle with two hands and squeezing it quickly. Measure the distance the rocket lands from the edge of the table. Practice the launch several times. Remember to squeeze with equal force each time.

8. Launch the rocket four times. Keep the amount of force you use constant. Measure the distance the rocket travels each time, and record the results in your data table.

9. List all the variables that may affect the distance your rocket flies. Change the rocket or launcher to alter one variable. Launch the rocket and measure the distance it flies. Repeat three more times, and record the results in your data table.

Observe and Analyze

1. **RECORD OBSERVATIONS** Draw a diagram of both of your bottle rockets. Make sure your data table is complete.

2. **IDENTIFY VARIABLES** What variables did you identify, and what variable did you modify?

Conclude

1. **COMPARE** How did the flight distances of the original rocket compare with those of the modified rocket?

2. **ANALYZE** Compare your results with your hypothesis. Do the results support your hypothesis?

3. **IDENTIFY LIMITS** What possible limitations or errors did you experience or could you have experienced?

4. **APPLY** Use Newton's laws to explain why the rocket flies.

5. **APPLY** What other real-life example can you think of that demonstrates Newton's laws?

INVESTIGATE Further

CHALLENGE Why does the rocket have paper loops taped to it? Determine how the flight of the rocket is affected if one or both loops are completely removed. Hypothesize about the function of the paper loops and design an experiment to test your hypothesis.

Newton's Laws of Motion

Problem What aspects of a model rocket affect the distance it flies?

Hypothesize

Observe and Analyze

Table 1. Flight Distances of Original and Modified Rocket

Trial Number	Original Rocket Distance Rocket Flew (cm)	Modified Rocket Distance Rocket Flew (cm)
1		
2		
3		
4		

Conclude

Chapter 11: **Forces** 367

Observe and Analyze

SAMPLE DATA Original rocket: 200 cm, 175 cm, 185 cm, 195 cm; modified rocket with larger bottle: 250 cm, 225 cm, 230 cm, 240 cm

1. See students' diagrams.

2. Variables include the size of the bottle, the length and diameter of the straws, the amount of modeling clay, the size of the loops, and the distance between the loops.

Conclude

1. Student answers will vary.

2. Student answers will vary, depending on students' results and original hypotheses.

3. Possible limits and errors include inconsistent force, inconsistent measurements, and changing more than one variable.

4. Newton's first law: The unbalanced force of the air pushing on the straw changes the straw's motion. Newton's second law: The acceleration of the straw should be greater with a larger bottle because it produces more force; a straw with smaller mass or less clay accelerates more easily than a straw with greater mass or more clay. Newton's third law: As the straw forces air backward, air forces the straw forward.

5. Sample answer: rowing a boat or using a bow and arrow

INVESTIGATE Further

CHALLENGE The loops stabilize the rocket. An experiment might include adding additional loops and then removing the loops one at a time and observing the results.

Post-Lab Discussion

- On the board, list the different modifications made. Have groups of students write whether each modification made the rocket fly farther, the same distance, or a shorter distance. Keep a tally from period to period to show that larger data samples show trends more accurately.

- Ask students to work in groups and have each group come to a consensus on the questions. Then have the class as a whole come to a consensus.

Chapter 11 **367**

11.4 FOCUS

▶ Set Learning Goals
Students will
- Calculate momentum.
- Explain how momentum is affected by collisions.
- Investigate what happens to momentum when objects collide.

◯ 3-Minute Warm-Up
Display Transparency 13 or copy this exercise on the board:

Match each definition with the correct term.

Definitions
1. resistance of an object to a change in its speed or direction **b**
2. a force that is exerted on an object and the force that the object exerts back **c**
3. a push or a pull **d**

Terms
a. acceleration
b. inertia
c. action and reaction force pair
d. force

 3-Minute Warm-Up, p. T13

11.4 MOTIVATE

EXPLORE Collisions
PURPOSE To observe that energy and momentum are transferred during a collision

TIP *10 min.* For easily observed results, use balls that vary considerably in mass.

WHAT DO YOU THINK? *Greater speeds before the collision yielded greater speeds and more motion after the collision; a ball at rest moved after the collision, and the other ball moved more slowly; motion after the collision depended on the mass of the balls.*

368 Unit 3: Motion and Forces

KEY CONCEPT

11.4 Forces transfer momentum.

◀ **BEFORE, you learned**
- A force is a push or a pull
- Newton's laws help to describe and predict motion

▶ **NOW, you will learn**
- What momentum is
- How to calculate momentum
- How momentum is affected by collisions

VOCABULARY
momentum p. 368
collision p. 370
conservation of momentum p. 371

EXPLORE Collisions
What happens when objects collide?
PROCEDURE
1. Roll the two balls toward each other on a flat surface. Try to roll them at the same speed. Observe what happens. Experiment by changing the speeds of the two balls.
2. Leave one ball at rest, and roll the other ball so that it hits the first ball. Observe what happens. Then repeat the experiment with the balls switched.

MATERIALS
2 balls of different masses

WHAT DO YOU THINK?
- How did varying the speed of the balls affect the motion of the balls after the collision?
- What happened when one ball was at rest? Why did switching the two balls affect the outcome?

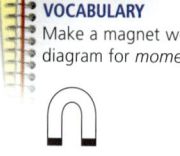
VOCABULARY
Make a magnet word diagram for *momentum*.

Objects in motion have momentum.

If you throw a tennis ball at a wall, it will bounce back toward you. What would happen if you could throw a wrecking ball at the wall at the same speed that you threw the tennis ball? The wall would most likely break apart. Why would a wrecking ball have a different effect on the wall than the tennis ball?

A moving object has a property that is called momentum. **Momentum** (moh-MEHN-tuhm) is a measure of mass in motion; the momentum of an object is the product of its mass and its velocity. At the same velocity, the wrecking ball has more momentum than the tennis ball because the wrecking ball has more mass. However, you could increase the momentum of the tennis ball by throwing it faster.

368 Unit 3: Motion and Forces

RESOURCES FOR DIFFERENTIATED INSTRUCTION

Below Level
UNIT RESOURCE BOOK
- Reading Study Guide A, pp. 111–112
- Decoding Support, p. 124

 **AUDIO CDS**

Advanced
UNIT RESOURCE BOOK
Challenge and Extension, p. 117

English Learners
UNIT RESOURCE BOOK
Spanish Reading Study Guide, pp. 115–116

 **AUDIO CDS**
- Audio Readings in Spanish
- Audio Readings (English)

Momentum is similar to inertia. Like inertia, the momentum of an object depends on its mass. Unlike inertia, however, momentum takes into account how fast the object is moving. A wrecking ball that is moving very slowly, for example, has less momentum than a fast-moving wrecking ball. With less momentum, the slower-moving wrecking ball would not be able to do as much damage to the wall.

To calculate an object's momentum, you can use the following formula:

momentum = mass · velocity
$p = mv$

In this formula, p stands for momentum, m for mass, and v for velocity. In standard units, the mass of an object is given in kilograms (kg), and velocity is given in meters per second (m/s). Therefore, the unit of momentum is the kilogram-meter per second (kg · m/s). Notice that the unit of momentum combines mass, length, and time.

Like force, velocity, and acceleration, momentum is a vector—it has both a size and a direction. The direction of an object's momentum is the same as the direction of its velocity. You can use speed instead of velocity in the formula as long as you do not need to know the direction of motion. As you will read later, it is important to know the direction of the momentum when you are working with more than one object.

REMINDER
Inertia is the resistance of an object to changes in its motion.

Explore momentum.

CHECK YOUR READING — How do an object's mass and velocity affect its momentum?

Calculating Momentum
Sample Problem

What is the momentum of a 1.5 kg ball moving at 2 m/s?

What do you know?	mass = 1.5 kg, velocity = 2 m/s
What do you want to find out?	momentum
Write the formula:	$p = mv$
Substitute into the formula:	$p = 1.5$ kg · 2 m/s
Calculate and simplify:	$p = 3$ kg · m/s
Check that your units agree:	Unit is kg · m/s. Unit of momentum is kg · m/s. Units agree.
Answer:	$p = 3$ kg · m/s

Practice the Math
1. A 3 kg ball is moving with a velocity of 1 m/s. What is the ball's momentum?
2. What is the momentum of a 0.5 kg ball moving 0.5 m/s?

Chapter 11: **Forces** 369

DIFFERENTIATE INSTRUCTION

More Reading Support

A Compare and contrast the inertia and the momentum of an object. *Both depend on mass, but momentum depends on velocity, while inertia does not.*

English Learners English learners often employ memorization as a tool in learning new concepts. When using definitions, formulas, or laws, be sure the language is always consistent. This will help students remember key ideas and important vocabulary. Remind students of the difference between *affect* and *effect*. *Affect* is a verb, as in, "the speed of the balls affects the motion of the balls" (in the Explore on p. 368). *Effect* is a noun, as in "a different effect."

11.4 INSTRUCT

History of Science
René Descartes (1596–1650), a French mathematician and philosopher, first used the term *momentum* to mean "the amount of motion."

- Through experimental observations, Descartes discovered that this amount of motion could be calculated by multiplying the mass of an object and its speed.

- Descartes thought that momentum is always positive. His theory could not explain how momentum is conserved when two objects with equal momentum moving from opposite directions collide and stop moving. The Dutch scientist Christiaan Huygens (1629–1695) solved this problem by stating that the "amount of motion" can be either positive or negative when two objects are moving relative to each other. If an object is moving in the opposite direction, the "amount of motion," or momentum, is considered to be negative.

Ongoing Assessment
Describe how forces act in collisions.
Ask: In terms of forces, what happens when a tennis ball collides with a racket? *The ball and the racket exert equal and opposite forces on each other.*

Define and calculate momentum.
Ask: What is the momentum of a 2 kg rock moving at 3 m/s? $p = mv$ = 2 kg · 3 m/s = 6 kg m/s

CHECK YOUR READING — Answer: An increase in either mass or velocity increases momentum; a decrease in either mass or velocity decreases momentum.

Practice the Math Answers:
1. $p = mv = 3$ kg · 1 m/s = 3 kg m/s
2. $p = mv = 0.5$ kg · 0.5 m/s = 0.25 kg m/s

Chapter 11 **369**

INVESTIGATE Momentum

PURPOSE To observe what happens when objects collide

TIPS 20 min. Allow students a few minutes to explore, then suggest the following:

- If the marbles do not roll easily, try another ruler or use the groove in the ruler.
- The setup should be far enough from the edge of the table that marbles do not roll onto the floor.
- Make sure you work on a flat, level table.

WHAT DO YOU THINK? *If one marble collides with the row of marbles, one marble moves away from the row. Equal numbers of marbles move for two and three marbles, also. Momentum transfers to the last marbles in the line.*

CHALLENGE *Sample hypothesis: The number of marbles that collide with the stationary marbles equals the number of marbles that move from the end of the row because the marbles are the same mass. Designs might include a similar experiment using different sizes of marbles.*

Datasheet, Momentum, p. 118

Technology Resources
Customize this student lab as needed or look for an alternative. Print rubrics to assess student lab reports.

Lab Generator CD-ROM

Metacognitive Strategy
Ask students to explain what in the procedure or in the results surprised them about the investigation.

Ongoing Assessment
 *Answer: When two objects collide, they exchange energy and transfer momentum.*

370 Unit 3: **Motion and Forces**

INVESTIGATE Momentum

What happens when objects collide?

PROCEDURE

1. Set up two parallel rulers separated by one centimeter. Place a line of five marbles, each touching the next, in the groove between the rulers.
2. Roll a marble down the groove so that it collides with the line of marbles, and observe the results.
3. Repeat your experiment by rolling two and then three marbles at the line of marbles. Observe the results.

WHAT DO YOU THINK?
- What did you observe when you rolled the marbles?
- Why do you think the marbles moved the way they did?

CHALLENGE Use your answers to write a hypothesis explaining your observations. Design your own marble experiment to test this hypothesis. Do your results support your hypothesis?

SKILL FOCUS
Observing

MATERIALS
- 2 rulers
- 8 marbles

TIME
20 minutes

Momentum can be transferred from one object to another.

If you have ever ridden in a bumper car, you have experienced collisions. A **collision** is a situation in which two objects in close contact exchange energy and momentum. As another car bumps into the back of yours, the force pushes your car forward. Some of the momentum of the car behind you is transferred to your car. At the same time, the car behind you slows because of the reaction force from your car. You gain momentum from the collision, and the other car loses momentum. The action and reaction forces in collisions are one way in which objects transfer momentum.

If two objects involved in a collision have very different masses, the one with less mass has a greater change in velocity. For example, consider what happens if you roll a tennis ball and a bowling ball toward each other so that they collide. Not only will the speed of the tennis ball change, but the direction of its motion will change as it bounces back. The bowling ball, however, will simply slow down. Even though the forces acting on the two balls are the same, the tennis ball will be accelerated more during the collision because it has less mass.

 How can a collision affect the momentum of an object?

370 Unit 3: Motion and Forces

DIFFERENTIATE INSTRUCTION

 More Reading Support

B If a bowling ball and a tennis ball collide, which ball will have the greater change in velocity? *the tennis ball*

Below Level Have students model transferring momentum. Have several student volunteers stand in a line with each student facing the back of the student in front of him. Each student places his right hand on the right shoulder of the person in front of him with his elbow locked in place. Have the student in the back of the line gently push forward on the shoulder of the student in front of him, and observe how far along the line the push could be felt. Repeat the activity with different amounts of force to the push. Caution students to push gently.

Momentum is conserved.

During a collision between two objects, each object exerts a force on the other. The colliding objects make up a system—a collection of objects that affect one another. As the two objects collide, the velocity and the momentum of each object change. However, as no other forces are acting on the objects, the total momentum of both objects is unchanged by the collision. This is due to the conservation of momentum. The principle of **conservation of momentum** states that the total momentum of a system of objects does not change, as long as no outside forces are acting on that system.

READING TIP
A light blue-green arrow shows the momentum of an individual object.

A dark blue-green arrow shows the total momentum.

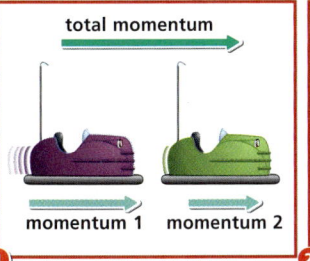
① Before the collision The momentum of the first car is greater than the momentum of the second car. Their combined momentum is the total momentum of the system.

② During the collision The forces on the two cars are equal and opposite, as described by Newton's third law. Momentum is transferred from one car to the other during the collision.

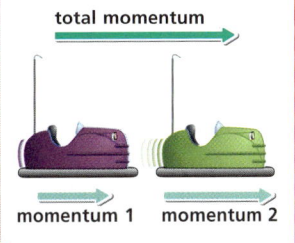
③ After the collision The momentum lost by one car was gained by the other car. The total momentum of the system remains the same as it was before the collision.

How much an object's momentum changes when a force is applied depends on the size of the force and how long that force is applied. Remember Newton's third law—during a collision, two objects are acted upon by equal and opposite forces for the same length of time. This means that the objects receive equal and opposite changes in momentum, and the total momentum does not change.

You can find the total momentum of a system of objects before a collision by combining the momenta of the objects. Because momentum is a vector, like force, the direction of motion is important. To find the total momentum of objects moving in the same direction, add the momenta of the objects. For two objects traveling in opposite directions, subtract one momentum from the other. Then use the principle of conservation of momentum and the formula for momentum to predict how the objects will move after they collide.

READING TIP
The plural of *momentum* is *momenta*.

 What is meant by "conservation of momentum"? What questions do you have about the application of this principle?

Chapter 11: **Forces** 371

DIFFERENTIATE INSTRUCTION

More Reading Support

C If the momentum of a system before a collision is 5 kg m/s, what is the momentum of the system after the collision? *5 kg m/s*

Advanced Have students relate common uses of the word *conservation*. Examples of uses of this term include environmental conservation; conservation of works of art; and other scientific uses, such as conservation of mass or energy. In each case, what is conserved is not wasted or used up.

 Challenge and Extension, p. 117

Address Misconceptions

IDENTIFY Ask: Is there any difference between force and momentum? If students answer no, they hold the misconception that momentum is the same thing as force.

CORRECT Move a toy car through the air to demonstrate that momentum is not the same as force. Ask if the car applies any forces. Students may suggest a force on the air or your hand. Discuss the force exerted on surrounding air particles. Ask if the car would apply any force if it were moving by itself in empty space where there is nothing for the car to hit. Help students realize that the moving car applies a force only when it interacts with another object, such as an air particle; it does not apply a force simply because it is moving. However, the car will have momentum because of its motion.

REASSESS Ask: What measurements are necessary to calculate force? to calculate momentum? *mass and acceleration; mass and velocity*

Technology Resources
Visit **ClassZone.com** for background on common student misconceptions.
MISCONCEPTION DATABASE

Develop Critical Thinking

APPLY Ask: What is the overall momentum of a system made up of a 1 kg ball moving south at 2 m/s and a 1.5 kg ball moving north at the same speed? *1 kg · 2 m/s = 2 kg · m/s south; 1.5 kg · 2 m/s = 3 kg m/s north; opposite, so subtract: 3 kg · m/s − 2 kg m/s = 1 kg m/s north*

Ongoing Assessment

Explain how momentum is affected by collisions.

Ask: What happens to the momentum of a bowling ball when it strikes the pins? *some momentum transfers to pins, but total momentum remains the same*

 Answer: The amount of momentum a system of objects has does not change as long as there are no outside forces acting on the system.

Chapter 11 **371**

Teach from Visuals

To help students understand the visual of a crash test, ask:

- In addition to the bending metal, what else uses some of the energy in the collision? *Sample answer: thermal energy caused by friction between parts of the cars or between the cars and the pavement*
- What role does friction between the pavement and the cars play in the conservation of momentum in this crash? *Because friction acts as an outside force on the cars and slows their velocity, it reduces the amount of momentum the two cars have after the crash.*

Real World Example

In most situations students are familiar with, momentum does not appear to be conserved. Outside forces such as friction transfer momentum to Earth or other objects that do not move noticeably due to their large mass. In some systems, such as balls in a game of pool, this loss of momentum is not very noticeable. If a pool ball hits a ball at rest, the initial forward momentum is shared by the two balls after the collision. Momentum is conserved not only in the forward direction, but also in the sideways direction. The two will move to opposite sides of the table. Ultimately, the momentum of each ball is completely transferred to the table by friction, and the balls come to a stop.

Ongoing Assessment

 *Answer: In the two types of collisions, movement is different but momentum is conserved.*

Two Types of Collisions

When bumper cars collide, they bounce off each other. Most of the force goes into changing the motion of the cars. The two bumper cars travel separately after the collision, just as they did before the collision. The combined momentum of both cars after the collision is the same as the combined momentum of both cars before the collision.

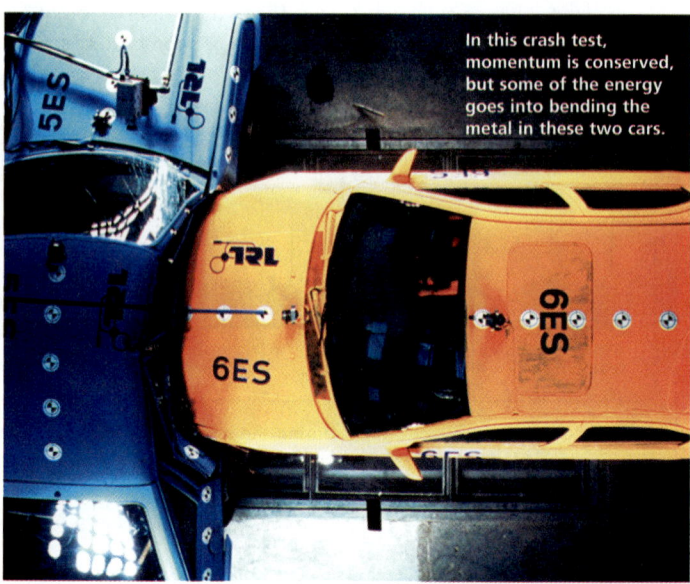

In this crash test, momentum is conserved, but some of the energy goes into bending the metal in these two cars.

When two cars collide during a crash test, momentum is also conserved during the collision. Unlike the bumper cars, however, which separate, the two cars shown in the photograph above stick and move together after the collision. Even in this case, the total momentum of both cars together is the same as the total momentum of both cars before the collision. Before the crash shown in the photograph, the yellow car had a certain momentum, and the blue car had no momentum. After the crash, the two cars move together with a combined momentum equal to the momentum the yellow car had before the collision.

 Compare collisions in which objects separate with collisions in which objects stick together.

Momentum and Newton's Third Law

Collisions are not the only events in which momentum is conserved. In fact, momentum is conserved whenever the only forces acting on objects are action/reaction force pairs. Conservation of momentum is really just another way of looking at Newton's third law.

372 Unit 3: Motion and Forces

DIFFERENTIATE INSTRUCTION

More Reading Support

D Is momentum conserved in a collision where the objects stick together? *yes*

Below Level Have students working alone or in pairs use the note-taking strategy explained on p. 344 to summarize what they know about momentum. Remind them that the heads in the student text can be part of their outlines. Diagrams should include arrows to represent momentum before and after collisions.

When a firefighter turns on a hose, water comes out of the nozzle in one direction, and the hose moves back in the opposite direction. You can explain why by using Newton's third law. The water is forced out of the hose. A reaction force pushes the hose backward. You can also use the principle of conservation of momentum to explain why the hose moves backward:

- Before the firefighter turns on the water, the hose and the water are not in motion, so the hose/water system has no momentum.
- Once the water is turned on, the water has momentum in the forward direction.
- For the total momentum of the hose and the water to stay the same, the hose must have an equal amount of momentum in the opposite direction. The hose moves backward.

Firefighters must apply a force to the water hose to prevent it from flying backward when the water comes out.

If the hose and the water are not acted on by any other forces, momentum is conserved. Water is pushed forward, and the hose is pushed backward. However, the action and reaction force pair acting on the hose and the water are not usually the only forces acting on the hose/water system, as shown in the photograph above. There the firefighters are holding the hose steady.

The force the firefighters apply is called an outside force because it is not being applied by the hose or the water. When there is an outside force on a system, momentum is not conserved. Because the firefighters hold the hose, the hose does not move backward, even though the water has a forward momentum.

 Under what condition is momentum not conserved? What part of the paragraph above tells you?

11.4 Review

KEY CONCEPTS
1. How does increasing the speed of an object change its momentum?
2. A car and a truck are traveling at the same speed. Which has more momentum? Why?
3. Give two examples showing the conservation of momentum. Give one example where momentum is not conserved.

CRITICAL THINKING
4. **Predict** A performing dolphin speeds through the water and hits a rubber ball originally at rest. Describe what happens to the velocities of the dolphin and the ball.
5. **Calculate** A 50 kg person is running at 2 m/s. What is the person's momentum?

CHALLENGE
6. **Apply** A moving train car bumps into another train car with the same mass. After the collision, the two cars are coupled and move off together. How does the final speed of the two train cars compare with the initial speed of the moving train cars before the collision?

Chapter 11: Forces 373

Ongoing Assessment

 Answer: According to the second sentence, momentum is not conserved if outside forces act on the system.

Reinforce the BIG idea
Have students relate the section to the Big Idea.

 Reinforcing Key Concepts, p. 119

11.4 ASSESS & RETEACH

Assess
A Section 11.4 Quiz, p. 25

Reteach
Use this demonstration to emphasize the importance of outside forces on the conservation of momentum. Place a long piece of waxed paper on a desk. Roll two tennis balls at the same speed so that they collide on the waxed paper. Have students observe that the speed of the balls after the collision is nearly the same as their speed before the collision. Roll the balls again, so that they collide on sandpaper or a piece of textured fabric. The resulting speed will be less because of increased friction.

Technology Resources
Have students visit **ClassZone.com** for reteaching of Key Concepts.

 CONTENT REVIEW

 CONTENT REVIEW CD-ROM

ANSWERS

1. Momentum increases.

2. The truck has more momentum because it has more mass.

3. Sample answer: Momentum is conserved when a bat hits a ball or when two cars collide. Momentum is not conserved when an inflated balloon releases air but is held in place.

4. The dolphin loses momentum and velocity; the ball gains momentum and velocity.

5. $p = mv = 50$ kg $\cdot$ 2 m/s = 100 kg $\cdot$ m/s

6. The total momentum is conserved. The mass of the two cars together is twice the mass of the original moving car, so the velocity will be half the original velocity.

Chapter 11 373

CHAPTER 11 • REVIEW

BACK TO

Have students explain why each of the following words in the Big Idea statement is important: *change, motion,* and *predictable*. **Answer: Change implies that a force alters motion; changing motion is an important result of forces acting on an object; predictable indicates that forces always change motion in the same way if under the same conditions.**

◀ KEY CONCEPTS SUMMARY

SECTION 11.1
Ask: In the picture on the left, in which direction will the ball accelerate? *to the right*

Ask: In the second picture, what would you need to do to stop the blue box from accelerating? *Place a force on the box that pushes to the right and is equal to the force pushing the box to the left.*

SECTION 11.2
Ask: If the box has a mass of 20 kg and a force of 10 N acting on it, what is the box's acceleration? *a = F/m = 10 N/20 kg = 0.5 m/s²*

Ask: How could you modify the force or the mass to make the box accelerate faster? *decrease box's mass or increase force*

SECTION 11.3
Ask: If the girl pushes on the boy with a force of 5 N, with what force does the boy push back on her? *5 N*

Ask: If the girl were pushing against a wall instead, why wouldn't the wall move? *Forces from ground and wall prevent its moving.*

SECTION 11.4
A 1 kg ball moving at a speed of 3 m/s hits a 2 kg ball at rest. Ask: If they stick together, at what speed will they move? *1 m/s*

Review Concepts

- Big Idea Flow Chart, p. T9
- Chapter Outline, pp. T15–T16

374 Unit 3: **Motion and Forces**

---

11 Chapter Review

 the BIG idea

Forces change the motion of objects in predictable ways.

◀ KEY CONCEPTS SUMMARY

1 Forces change motion.

Newton's first law
Objects at rest remain at rest, and objects in motion remain in motion with the same velocity, unless acted upon by an unbalanced force.

VOCABULARY
force p. 345
net force p. 347
Newton's first law p. 349
inertia p. 350

2 Force and mass determine acceleration.

Newton's second law
The acceleration of an object increases with increased force and decreases with increased mass, and is in the same direction as the force.

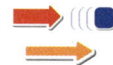   

same mass, larger force = increased acceleration   larger mass, same force = decreased acceleration

VOCABULARY
Newton's second law p. 354
centripetal force p. 358

3 Forces act in pairs.

Newton's third law
When one object exerts a force on another object, the second object exerts an equal and opposite force on the first object.

VOCABULARY
Newton's third law p. 361

4 Forces transfer momentum.

- Momentum is a property of a moving object.
- Forces in collisions are equal and opposite.
- Momentum is conserved in collisions.

VOCABULARY
momentum p. 368
collision p. 370
conservation of momentum p. 371

374 Unit 3: Motion and Forces

Technology Resources

Have students visit **ClassZone.com** or use the CD-ROM for a cumulative review of concepts.

 CONTENT REVIEW

 CONTENT REVIEW CD-ROM

Engage students in a whole-class interactive review of Key Concepts. Edit content as you wish.

 POWER PRESENTATIONS

Reviewing Vocabulary

Copy and complete the chart below. If the left column is blank, give the correct term. If the right column is blank, give an example from real life.

Term	Example from Real Life
1. acceleration	
2. centripetal force	
3.	The pull of a handle on a wagon
4. inertia	
5. mass	
6. net force	
7. Newton's first law	
8. Newton's second law	
9.	When you're walking, you push backward on the ground, and the ground pushes you forward with equal force.
10. momentum	

Reviewing Key Concepts

Multiple Choice *Choose the letter of the best answer.*

11. Newton's second law states that to increase acceleration, you
    a. increase force
    b. decrease force
    c. increase mass
    d. increase inertia

12. What units are used to measure force?
    a. kilograms
    b. meters
    c. newtons
    d. seconds

13. A wagon is pulled down a hill with a constant velocity. All the forces on the wagon are
    a. balanced
    b. unbalanced
    c. increasing
    d. decreasing

14. An action force and its reaction force are
    a. equal in size and direction
    b. equal in size and opposite in direction
    c. different in size but in the same direction
    d. different in size and in direction

15. John pulls a box with a force of 4 N, and Jason pulls the box from the opposite side with a force of 3 N. Ignore friction. Which of the following statements is true?
    a. The box moves toward John.
    b. The box moves toward Jason.
    c. The box does not move.
    d. There is not enough information to determine if the box moves.

16. A more massive marble collides with a less massive one that is not moving. The total momentum after the collision is equal to
    a. zero
    b. the original momentum of the more massive marble
    c. the original momentum of the less massive marble
    d. twice the original momentum of the more massive marble

Short Answer *Write a short answer to each question.*

17. List the following objects in order, from the object with the least inertia to the object with the most inertia: feather, large rock, pencil, book. Explain your reasoning.

18. During a race, you double your velocity. How does that change your momentum?

19. Explain how an object can have forces acting on it but not be accelerating.

20. A sea scallop moves by shooting jets of water out of its shell. Explain how this works.

Chapter 11: **Forces** 375

Reviewing Vocabulary

Sample answers:

1. a ball speeding up as it falls to the ground
2. the pull of a string on a yo-yo as the yo-yo spins in a circle
3. force
4. the difficulty experienced moving a heavy table
5. a brick
6. the combined force of two people pushing on a box
7. a still ball moves when kicked
8. pulling harder to accelerate a full wagon
9. Newton's third law of motion
10. the mass and velocity of an automobile

Reviewing Key Concepts

11. a
12. c
13. a
14. b
15. a
16. b
17. Feather, pencil, book, large rock; the more mass an object has, the more inertia it will have.
18. It also doubles.
19. The forces are balanced.
20. According to Newton's third law, the scallop pushes water out of its shell in one direction (the action force) and the water pushes on the shell in the opposite direction (the reaction force) to move the animal backward.

ASSESSMENT RESOURCES

UNIT ASSESSMENT BOOK
- Chapter Test A, pp. 26–29
- Chapter Test B, pp. 30–33
- Chapter Test C, pp. 34–37
- Alternative Assessment, pp. 38–39

SPANISH ASSESSMENT BOOK
Spanish Chapter Test, pp. 261–264

Technology Resources

Edit test items and answer choices.

 Test Generator CD-ROM

Visit **ClassZone.com** to extend test practice.

 Test Practice

Chapter 11 375

Thinking Critically

21. The forces are balanced because the ball is not moving.
22. Student diagrams should show balanced forces; the downward force of gravity balances an upward force from the string.
23. When ball 1 hits ball 2, ball 2 exerts a force on ball 1, stopping its motion.
24. The velocity of the first ball became zero. The momentum from the first ball was transferred from the first ball down the balls to the last ball.
25. no change in motion
26. change in motion
27. no change in motion
28. The net force on the baseball must be three times the net force on the tennis ball.

Using Math Skills in Science

29. 5 kg · 2 m/s² = 10 N
30. 10 N/5 m/s² = 2 kg
31. 5 N/10 kg = 0.5 m/s²
32. 40 kg · 0.5 m/s = 20 kg · m/s

the BIG idea

33. Sample answer: You need to know the mass of the people on both sides of the rope and the force with which they can pull. Newton's first law states that the rope will not move unless the forces on it are unbalanced. If the force is unbalanced, the rope will accelerate toward the greater force.
34. Student answers will vary.
35. Student answers will vary.

UNIT PROJECTS

Students should have begun designing their models or multimedia presentations by this time. Remind them to continue researching as needed. Encourage them to try different solutions to problems they encounter.

 Unit Projects, pp. 5–10

376 Unit 3: **Motion and Forces**

Thinking Critically

Use the information in the photographs below to answer the next four questions.

The photographs above show a toy called Newton's Cradle. In the first picture (1), ball 1 is lifted and is being held in place.

21. Are the forces on ball 1 balanced? How do you know?
22. Draw a diagram showing the forces acting on ball 2. Are these forces balanced?

In the second picture (2), ball 1 has been let go.

23. Ball 1 swung down, hit ball 2, and stopped. Use Newton's laws to explain why ball 1 stopped.
24. Use the principle of conservation of momentum to explain why ball 5 swung into the air.

Copy the chart below. Write what will happen to the object in each case.

Cause	Effect
25. Balanced forces act on an object.	
26. Unbalanced forces act on an object.	
27. No force acts on an object.	

28. **INFER** A baseball is three times more massive than a tennis ball. If the baseball and the tennis ball are accelerating equally, what can you determine about the net force on each?

Using Math Skills in Science

Complete the following calculations.

29. What force should Lori apply to a 5 kg box to give it an acceleration of 2 m/s²?
30. If a 10 N force accelerates an object 5 m/s², how massive is the object?
31. Ravi applies a force of 5 N to a wagon with a mass of 10 kg. What is the wagon's acceleration?
32. Use the information in the photograph on the right to calculate the momentum of the shopping cart.

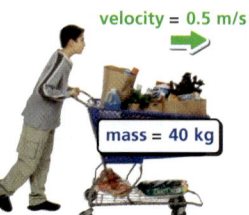

the BIG idea

33. **PREDICT** Look again at the tug of war pictured on pages 342–343. Describe what information you need to know to predict the outcome of the game. How would you use that information and Newton's laws to make your prediction?
34. **WRITE** Pick an activity you enjoy, such as running or riding a scooter, and describe how Newton's laws apply to that activity.
35. **SYNTHESIZE** Think of a question you have about Newton's laws that is still unanswered. What information do you need in order to answer the question? How might you find the information?

UNIT PROJECTS

If you need to do an experiment for your unit project, gather the materials. Be sure to allow enough time to observe results before the project is due.

MONITOR AND RETEACH

If students have trouble applying the concepts in items 21–24, they should review the diagram on p. 364 showing Newton's three laws in relation to a kangaroo jump. They can create a similar diagram for the canoe example on p. 365. **Part 1** should show an unbalanced force applied to the canoe. **Part 2** should show how an increase in mass or force affects acceleration (include a formula). **Part 3** should show equal and opposite forces on you and the paddle.

Students may benefit from summarizing sections of the chapter.

 Summarizing the Chapter, pp. 147–148

Standardized Test Practice

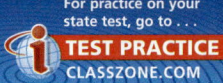

For practice on your state test, go to...
TEST PRACTICE
CLASSZONE.COM

Analyzing Data

To test Newton's second law, Jodie accelerates blocks of ice across a smooth, flat surface. The table shows her results. (For this experiment, you can ignore the effects of friction.)

Accelerating Blocks of Ice

Mass (kg)	1.0	1.5	2.0	2.5	3.0	3.5	4.0
Acceleration (m/s^2)	4.0	2.7	2.0	1.6	1.3	1.1	1.0

Study the data table and then answer the questions that follow.

1. The data show that as mass becomes greater, acceleration
   a. increases
   b. decreases
   c. stays the same
   d. cannot be predicted

2. From the data, you can tell that Jodie was applying a force of
   a. 1 N
   b. 2 N
   c. 3 N
   d. 4 N

3. If Jodie applied less force to the ice blocks, the accelerations would be
   a. greater
   b. less
   c. the same
   d. inconsistent

4. If Jodie applied a force of 6 N to the 2 kg block of ice, the acceleration would be
   a. 2 m/s^2
   b. 4 m/s^2
   c. 3 m/s^2
   d. 5 m/s^2

5. The average mass of the ice blocks she pushed was
   a. 1.5 kg
   b. 2.5 kg
   c. 3 kg
   d. 4 kg

6. If Jodie used a 3.25 kg block in her experiment, the force would accelerate the block somewhere between
   a. 1.0 and 1.1 m/s^2
   b. 1.1 and 1.3 m/s^2
   c. 1.3 and 1.6 m/s^2
   d. 1.6 and 2.0 m/s^2

Extended Response

Answer the two questions in detail. Include some of the terms shown in the word box. Underline each term you use in your answer.

Newton's second law	velocity
mass	inertia
gravity	balanced forces
centripetal force	unbalanced forces

7. Tracy ties a ball to a string and starts to swing the ball around her head. What forces are acting on the ball? What happens if the string breaks?

8. Luis is trying to pull a wagon loaded with rocks. What can he do to increase the wagon's acceleration?

Chapter 11: **Forces** 377

METACOGNITIVE ACTIVITY

Have students answer the following questions in their **Science Notebooks**:
1. What about forces did you find most challenging to understand?
2. What questions do you still have about force and motion?
3. How have you solved a problem while working on your Unit Project?

Analyzing Data
1. b   4. c
2. d   5. b
3. b   6. b

Extended Response

7. RUBRIC
4 points for a response that correctly answers both questions and uses the following terms accurately:
- centripetal force
- inertia
- velocity
- unbalanced force(s)

Sample answer: As Tracy spins the string, the centripetal force from the string acts on the ball to pull it toward the center of the circle. This unbalanced force continually changes the velocity of the ball by changing its direction. If the string were to break, the ball would fly off in a straight line because its inertia would resist change in velocity. (Students may also mention gravity.)

3 points correctly answers both questions and uses three terms accurately
2 points correctly answers one question and uses two terms accurately
1 point correctly answers one question or uses one term accurately

8. RUBRIC
4 points for a response that uses the following terms accurately:
- unbalanced force(s)
- mass
- Newton's second law
- acceleration

Sample answer: According to Newton's second law, decreasing mass will increase acceleration for the same force. To decrease the mass, Luis can remove rocks. Applying a greater unbalanced force will also increase the wagon's acceleration. To increase the force, Luis can pull harder or ask a friend to help pull.

3 points uses three terms accurately
2 points uses two terms accurately
1 point uses one term accurately

Gravity, Friction, and Pressure

Physical Science
UNIFYING PRINCIPLES

PRINCIPLE 1
Matter is made of particles too small to see.

PRINCIPLE 2
Matter changes form and moves from place to place.

PRINCIPLE 3
Energy changes from one form to another, but it cannot be created or destroyed.

PRINCIPLE 4
Physical forces affect the movement of all matter on Earth and throughout the universe.

Unit 3: Motion and Forces
BIG IDEAS

CHAPTER 10
Motion
The motion of an object can be described and predicted.

CHAPTER 11
Forces
Forces change the motion of objects in predictable ways.

CHAPTER 12
Gravity, Friction, and Pressure
Newton's laws apply to all forces.

CHAPTER 13
Work and Energy
Energy is transferred when a force moves an object.

CHAPTER 14
Machines
Machines help people do work by changing the force applied to an object.

CHAPTER 12
KEY CONCEPTS

SECTION 1
Gravity is a force exerted by masses.
1. Masses attract each other.
2. Gravity keeps objects in orbit.

SECTION 2
Friction is a force that opposes motion.
1. Friction occurs when surfaces slide against each other.
2. Motion through fluids produces friction.

SECTION 3
Pressure depends on force and area.
1. Pressure describes how a force is spread over an area.
2. Pressure acts in all directions in fluids.
3. Pressure in fluids depends on depth.

SECTION 4
Fluids can exert a force on objects.
1. Fluids can exert an upward force on objects.
2. The motion of a fluid affects its pressure.
3. Forces can be transmitted through fluids.

 The Big Idea Flow Chart is available on p. T17 in the **UNIT TRANSPARENCY BOOK.**

377A Unit 3: Motion and Forces

Previewing Content

SECTION

Gravity is a force exerted by masses. pp. 381–388

1. Masses attract each other.
Gravity is the force objects exert on each other because of their mass. It attracts any two masses anywhere in the universe. The strength of the gravitational force is proportional to the product of the masses divided by the distance between them squared.

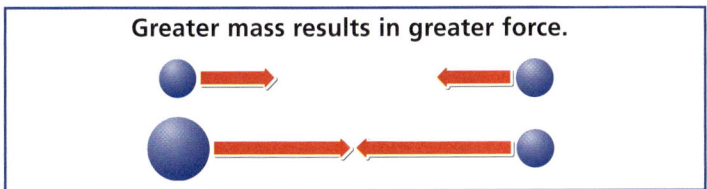

Greater mass results in greater force.

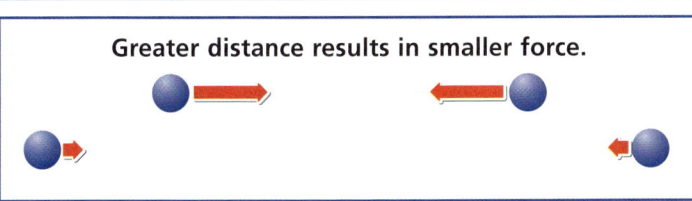

Greater distance results in smaller force.

- Gravitational acceleration is symbolized by g and equals 9.8 m/s^2 at Earth's surface. Any object falling in a vacuum, no matter how massive, has this acceleration. The force of gravity, F, equals mg at Earth's surface.
- **Mass** and **weight** are not synonymous. Mass is the amount of matter something contains. Weight is the effect of gravity on the object.

2. Gravity keeps objects in orbit.
An **orbit** is an elliptical path that one object takes around another object. An orbital path is the result of the speed of the orbiting body and the gravitational pull between the two objects.

The speed an object must have to escape the gravitational pull of another body, such as a spacecraft leaving a planet, is called escape velocity. Speeds lower than the escape velocity will result in an orbit.

A spacecraft and its contents in orbit are in free fall. The environment is such that an astronaut can't feel gravity.

SECTION

Friction is a force that opposes motion. pp. 389–394

1. Friction occurs when surfaces slide against each other.
Friction is a force that resists the movement of two surfaces that are in contact with each other. Several factors determine the amount of friction between two surfaces.

- The type of surface determines the amount of friction. Generally, smooth surfaces have less friction than rough surfaces.
- The motion of the surfaces affects friction. It takes more force to start an object moving (static friction) than it does to keep one moving (sliding friction).
- As the force pressing the surfaces together increases, friction increases. This force is often called the normal force because it is perpendicular, or normal, to the surface.

Friction between surfaces produces heat.

2. Motion through fluids produces friction.
A **fluid** is a substance that flows easily, such as liquids and gases. As an object moves through a fluid, its surface moves against particles in the fluid, causing friction.
When the fluid is air, the friction caused by a moving object is called **air resistance**.

- The amount of air resistance is based on the surface area of the object and the speed at which it moves.
- When an object falls through air at a speed at which air resistance balances gravity, the object reaches its maximum speed, called terminal velocity.

Common Misconceptions

MISCONCEPTION DATABASE
CLASSZONE.COM Background on student misconceptions

WEIGHT AND MASS Students frequently think that *weight* and *mass* are terms that can be used interchangeably. In fact, mass is the amount of matter an object contains, and it remains the same no matter where the object is. Weight depends on the force of gravity exerted upon an object.

 This misconception is addressed on p. 384.

FRICTION AND SURFACES Because students generally observe that rougher surfaces have greater friction, students may think that roughness is the sole cause of friction. In fact, friction is more complicated than just roughness, and is due to the interaction between surfaces.

 This misconception is addressed in Teach Difficult Concepts on p. 390.

Chapter 12: **Gravity, Friction, and Pressure** 377B

Previewing Content

SECTION 3 — Pressure depends on force and area. pp. 395–401

1. Pressure describes how a force is spread over an area.
Pressure measures how much force is acting on a certain area.
- It increases when force stays the same but acts on a smaller area.
- It increases when area stays the same but force increases.

The equation $P = F/A$, where force is in newtons and area is in square meters, can be used to find pressure, which is in units of **pascals**, Pa. See the sample problem below.

> A winter hiker weighing 500 N is wearing snowshoes that cover an area of 0.2 m². What pressure does the hiker exert on the snow?
> What do you know? Area = 0.2 m², Force = 500 N
> What do you want to find out? Pressure
>
> Write the formula: $P = \dfrac{F}{A}$
>
> Substitute into the formula: $P = \dfrac{500 \text{ N}}{0.2 \text{ m}^2}$
>
> Calculate and simplify: $P = 2500 \, \dfrac{\text{N}}{\text{m}^2} = 2500 \text{ N/m}^2$

2. Pressure acts in all directions in fluids.
The particles in a fluid move constantly and rapidly. They collide with objects that come in contact with the fluid, applying pressure to the surface of the object. The amount of pressure exerted depends on the density and the depth of the fluid. Air exerts pressure on all objects in air. It is more dense at lower elevations and less dense at higher elevations. The denser the air, the more pressure it exerts.
Because water is denser than air, it exerts more pressure on objects in it.

3. Pressure in fluids depends on depth.
The pressure that a fluid exerts depends on depth and density of the fluid. At sea level, air exerts a pressure called atmospheric pressure. Air has weight.
- The more air above you, the greater the weight of that air.
- Air at higher elevations weighs less.
- Air at lower elevations is more compressed, therefore denser, and weighs more.

Water has a greater density than air, and therefore exerts more pressure on objects than air.

Common Misconceptions

BUOYANCY Students might think that ships and boats float because the materials in them are less dense than water. The overall density of the ship or boat is less than that of water only if you include the air it contains.

This misconception is addressed on p. 403.

SECTION 4 — Fluids can exert a force on objects. pp. 402–407

1. Fluids can exert an upward force on objects.
On Earth, objects are subject to forces from all directions, but these forces might not be balanced. The difference in water pressure at different depths produces an upward force, called **buoyant force,** which is illustrated below.

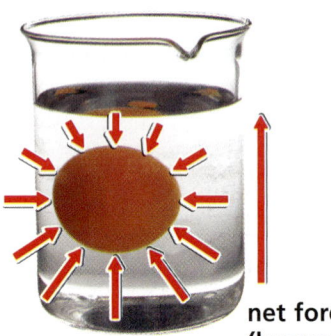

net force
(buoyant force)

For a particular object, this force directly relates to the amount of fluid the object replaces.

Density is the amount of matter per unit of volume, $D = m/V$, where mass is commonly in grams and volume is commonly in cubic centimeters.

Because of buoyancy, a less dense material will float on another, denser material.

2. The motion of a fluid affects its pressure.
Bernoulli's principle states that, as speed of a fluid increases, the pressure inside the fluid decreases.

3. Forces can be transmitted through fluids.
Pascal's principle states that, when outside pressure is applied to a fluid in a container, that pressure is transmitted equally throughout the entire fluid.
Hydraulic machines use liquids to transmit forces. Gases would be less effective because they change volume when force is applied.

MISCONCEPTION DATABASE
CLASSZONE.COM Background on student misconceptions

Previewing Labs

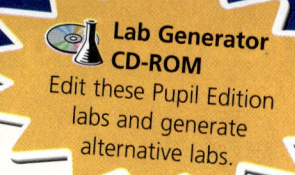

EXPLORE the BIG idea

Let It Slide, p. 379
Students examine the effect of friction on motion by using a ramp with various surfaces.

TIME 10 minutes
MATERIALS board, books, small object, materials of different textures to place on the ramp, such as sandpaper or wax paper

Under Pressure, p. 379
Students are introduced to the relationship of pressure to the amount of gas. They compare bottles of carbonated drinks.

TIME 10 minutes
MATERIALS 2 plastic bottles of carbonated soft drink

Internet Activity: Gravity, p. 379
Students are introduced to the gravitational attraction of masses.

TIME 20 minutes
MATERIALS computer with Internet access

SECTION 1

EXPLORE Downward Acceleration, p. 381
Students predict and compare the acceleration of different falling objects.

TIME 10 minutes
MATERIALS golf ball, Ping-Pong ball

INVESTIGATE Gravity, p. 386
Students predict how gravity affects falling objects and test their ideas with cups of water.

TIME 15 minutes
MATERIALS pencil, paper cup, water, large dishpan

SECTION 2

INVESTIGATE Friction in Air, p. 392
Students design an experiment to show how the shape of an object affects how it falls.

TIME 30 minutes
MATERIALS 3 identical sheets of paper

SECTION 3

EXPLORE Pressure, p. 395
Students observe imprints on Styrofoam to find out how surface area affects pressure.

TIME 10 minutes
MATERIALS sharpened pencil, Styrofoam board, book

CHAPTER INVESTIGATION
Pressure in Fluids, pp. 400–401
Students vary depth and volume of water to determine what factors affect pressure.

TIME 40 minutes
MATERIALS nail; 2 plastic bottles, small and large with tops cut off; ruler; plastic container; meter stick; coffee can; water

SECTION 4

EXPLORE Forces in Liquid, p. 402
Students observe water exerting a force on paper clips.

TIME 10 minutes
MATERIALS 3 pieces of string, pencil, 8 paper clips, cup full of water

INVESTIGATE Bernoulli's Principle, p. 404
Students observe how the speed of air affects air pressure.

TIME 15 minutes
MATERIALS pen, ruler, 2 clear straws, clear plastic cup filled with water, food coloring

 Additional INVESTIGATION, What Floats Your Boat? A, B, & C, pp. 210–218; Teacher Instructions, pp. 346–347

Chapter 12: **Gravity, Friction, and Pressure** 377D

Previewing Chapter Resources

	INTEGRATED TECHNOLOGY	LABS AND ACTIVITIES
CHAPTER 12 **Gravity, Friction, and Pressure**	**CLASSZONE.COM** • eEdition Plus • EasyPlanner Plus • Misconception Database • Content Review • Test Practice • Visualization • Simulation • Resource Centers • Internet Activity: Gravity • Math Tutorial **SCILINKS.ORG**	EXPLORE the Big Idea, p. 379 • Let It Slide • Under Pressure • Internet Activity: Gravity **UNIT RESOURCE BOOK** Unit Projects, pp. 5–10
	CD-ROMS • eEdition • EasyPlanner • Power Presentations • Content Review • Lab Generator • Test Generator  **AUDIO CDS** • Audio Readings • Audio Readings in Spanish	**Lab Generator CD-ROM** Generate customized labs.
SECTION 1  **Gravity is a force exerted by masses.** pp. 381–388 Time: 2 periods (1 block) Lesson Plan, pp. 149–150	• **RESOURCE CENTER,** Gravitational Lenses • **VISUALIZATION,** Gravity in a Vacuum **UNIT TRANSPARENCY BOOK** • Big Idea Flow Chart, p. T17 • Daily Vocabulary Scaffolding, p. T18 • Note-Taking Model, p. T19 • 3-Minute Warm-Up, p. T20 • "Orbits" Visual, p. T22	• EXPLORE Downward Acceleration, p. 381 • INVESTIGATE Gravity, p. 386 • Extreme Science, p. 388 **UNIT RESOURCE BOOK** Datasheet, Gravity, p. 158
SECTION 2 **Friction is a force that opposes motion.** pp. 389–394 Time: 2 periods (1 block) Lesson Plan, pp. 160–161	• **RESOURCE CENTER,** Friction, Forces, and Surfaces • **MATH TUTORIAL** **UNIT TRANSPARENCY BOOK** • Daily Vocabulary Scaffolding, p. T18 • 3-Minute Warm-Up, p. T20	• INVESTIGATE Friction in Air, p. 392 • Math in Science, p. 394 **UNIT RESOURCE BOOK** • Datasheet, Friction in Air, p. 169 • Math Support, p. 199 • Math Practice, p. 200
SECTION 3 **Pressure depends on force and area.** pp. 395–401 Time: 3 periods (1.5 blocks) Lesson Plan, pp. 171–172	**SIMULATION,** Fluids and Pressure **UNIT TRANSPARENCY BOOK** • Daily Vocabulary Scaffolding, p. T18 • 3-Minute Warm-Up, p. T21	• EXPLORE Pressure, p. 395 • CHAPTER INVESTIGATION, Pressure in Fluids, pp. 400–401 **UNIT RESOURCE BOOK** • Math Support & Practice, pp. 197–198 • CHAPTER INVESTIGATION, Pressure in Fluids, A, B, & C, pp. 201–209
SECTION 4 **Fluids can exert a force on objects.** pp. 402–407 Time: 3 periods (1.5 blocks) Lesson Plan, pp. 181–182	**UNIT TRANSPARENCY BOOK** • Big Idea Flow Chart, p. T17 • Daily Vocabulary Scaffolding, p. T18 • 3-Minute Warm-Up, p. T21 • Chapter Outline, pp. T23–T24	• EXPLORE Forces in Liquid, p. 402 • INVESTIGATE Bernoulli's Principle, p. 404 **UNIT RESOURCE BOOK** • Datasheet, Bernoulli's Principle, p. 190 • Additional INVESTIGATION, What Floats Your Boat?, A, B, & C, pp. 210–218

KEY TO ICONS CD/CD-ROM Teacher Edition   T UNIT TRANSPARENCY BOOK   SPANISH ASSESSMENT BOOK
INTERNET   PE Pupil Edition   R UNIT RESOURCE BOOK   A UNIT ASSESSMENT BOOK   SCIENCE TOOLKIT

READING AND REINFORCEMENT

- Four Square, B22–23
- Supporting Main Ideas, C42
- Daily Vocabulary Scaffolding, H1–8

 UNIT RESOURCE BOOK
- Vocabulary Practice, pp. 194–195
- Decoding Support, p. 196
- Summarizing the Chapter, pp. 219–220

Audio Readings CD
Listen to Pupil Edition.

Audio Readings in Spanish CD
Listen to Pupil Edition in Spanish.

 UNIT RESOURCE BOOK
- Reading Study Guide, A & B, pp. 151–154
- Spanish Reading Study Guide, pp. 155–156
- Challenge and Extension, p. 157
- Reinforcing Key Concepts, p. 159

 UNIT RESOURCE BOOK
- Reading Study Guide, A & B, pp. 162–165
- Spanish Reading Study Guide, pp. 166–167
- Challenge and Extension, p. 168
- Reinforcing Key Concepts, p. 170

 UNIT RESOURCE BOOK
- Reading Study Guide, A & B, pp. 173–176
- Spanish Reading Study Guide, pp. 177–178
- Challenge and Extension, p. 179
- Reinforcing Key Concepts, p. 180

 UNIT RESOURCE BOOK
- Reading Study Guide, A & B, pp. 183–186
- Spanish Reading Study Guide, pp. 187–188
- Challenge and Extension, p. 189
- Reinforcing Key Concepts, p. 191
- Challenge Reading, pp. 192–193

ASSESSMENT

- Chapter Review, pp. 409–410
- Standardized Test Practice, p. 411

 UNIT ASSESSMENT BOOK
- Diagnostic Test, pp. 40–41
- Chapter Test, A, B, & C, pp. 46–57
- Alternative Assessment, pp. 58–59

 Spanish Chapter Test, pp. 265–268

 Test Generator CD-ROM
Generate customized tests.

Lab Generator CD-ROM
Rubrics for Labs

 Ongoing Assessment, pp. 381–387

 Section 12.1 Review, p. 387

 UNIT ASSESSMENT BOOK
Section 12.1 Quiz, p. 42

 Ongoing Assessment, pp. 389, 391, 393

 Section 12.2 Review, p. 393

UNIT ASSESSMENT BOOK
Section 12.2 Quiz, p. 43

 Ongoing Assessment, pp. 396–397, 399

 Section 12.3 Review, p. 399

 UNIT ASSESSMENT BOOK
Section 12.3 Quiz, p. 44

 Ongoing Assessment, pp. 403–406

 Section 12.4 Review, p. 407

 UNIT ASSESSMENT BOOK
Section 12.4 Quiz, p. 45

STANDARDS

National Standards
A.2–8, A.9.a–c, A.9.e–f, B.1.a, D.3.c, E.2–5, G.1.a–b

See p. 378 for the standards.

National Standards
A.2–8, A.9.a–c, A.9.e–f, D.3.c, G.1.b

National Standards
A.2–8, A.9.a–c, A.9.e–f, E.2–5, G.1.b

National Standards
A.2–8, A.9.a–c, A.9.e–f, G.1.b

National Standards
A.2–8, A.9.a–c, A.9.e, B.1.a, G.1.a–b

Chapter 12: **Gravity, Friction, and Pressure** 377F

Previewing Resources for Differentiated Instruction

CHAPTER INVESTIGATION

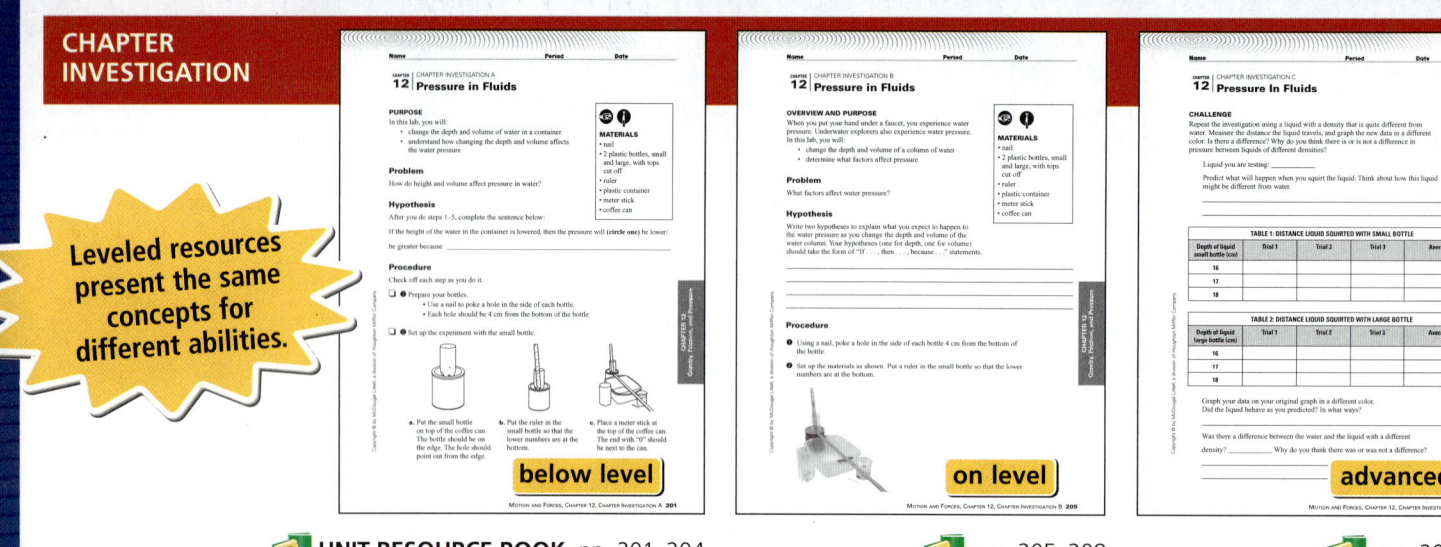

Leveled resources present the same concepts for different abilities.

UNIT RESOURCE BOOK, pp. 201–204   pp. 205–208   pp. 205–209

READING STUDY GUIDE

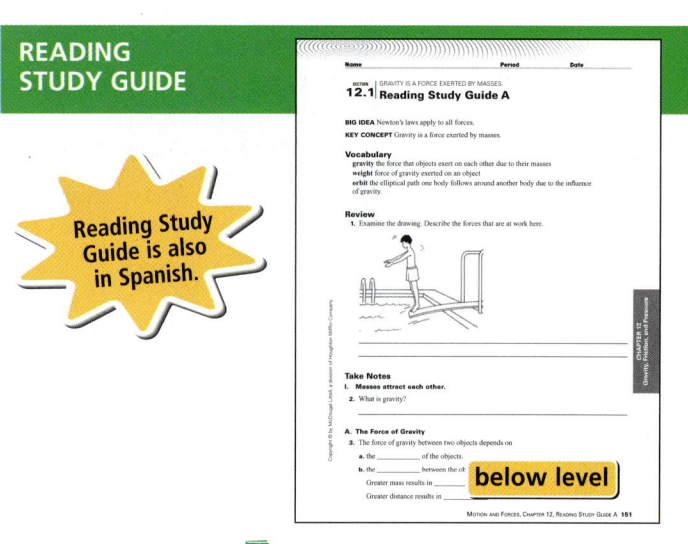
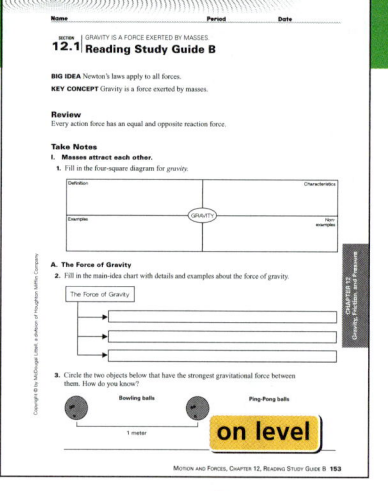
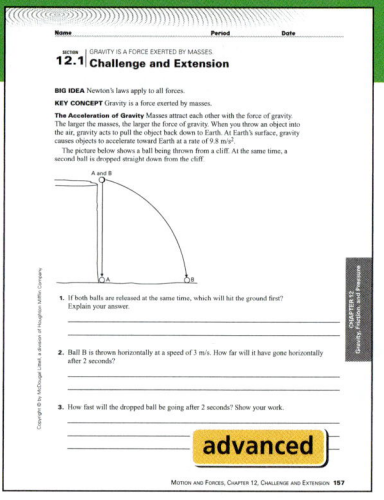

Reading Study Guide is also in Spanish.

UNIT RESOURCE BOOK, pp. 151–152   pp. 153–154   p. 157

CHAPTER TEST

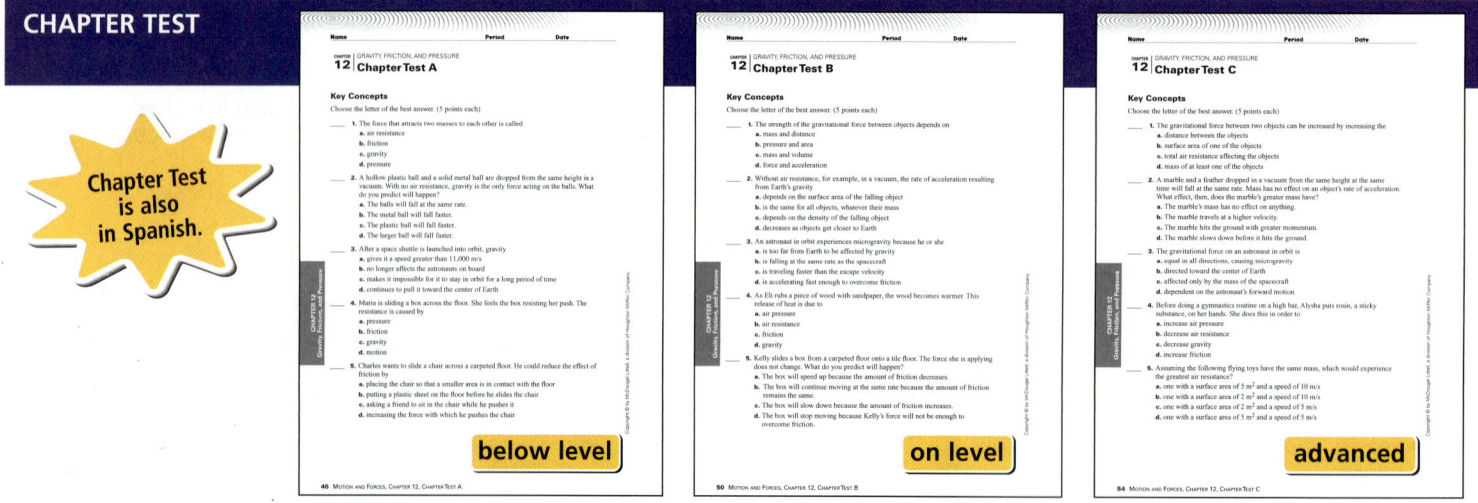

Chapter Test is also in Spanish.

UNIT ASSESSMENT BOOK, pp. 46–49   pp. 50–53   pp. 54–57

377G   Unit 3: Motion and Forces

TECHNOLOGY

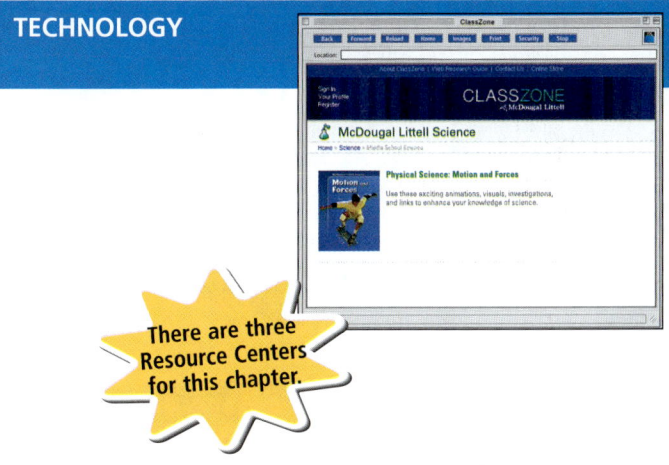
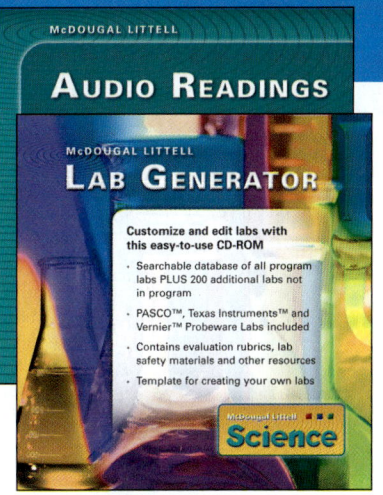
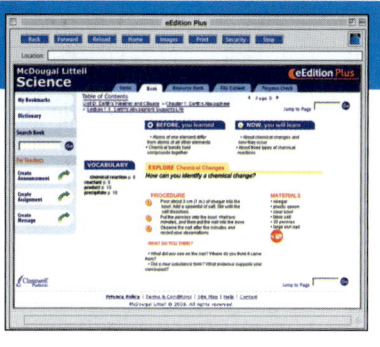

There are three Resource Centers for this chapter.

CLASSZONE.COM   CD/CD-ROMS   CLASSZONE.COM

VISUAL CONTENT

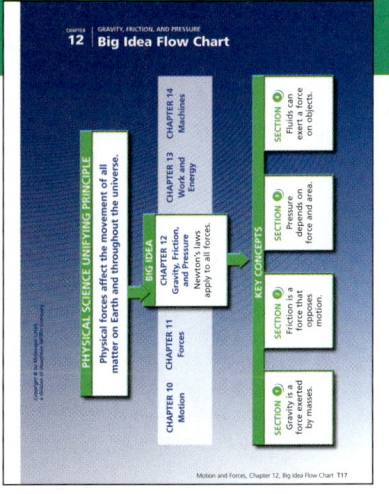
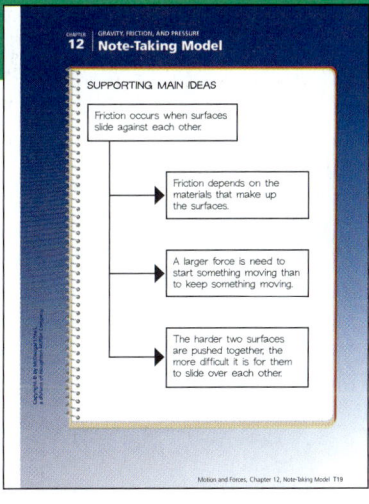
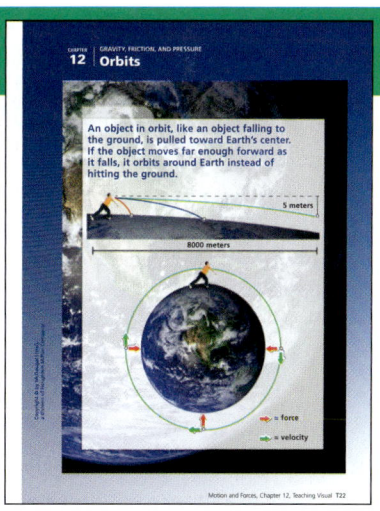

UNIT TRANSPARENCY BOOK, p. T17   p. T19   p. T22

MORE SUPPORT

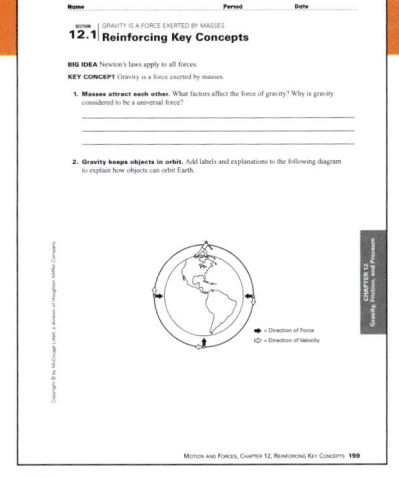
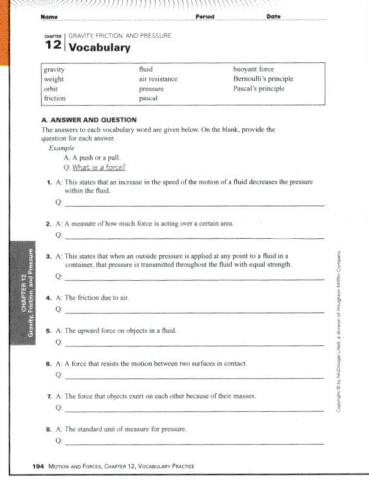
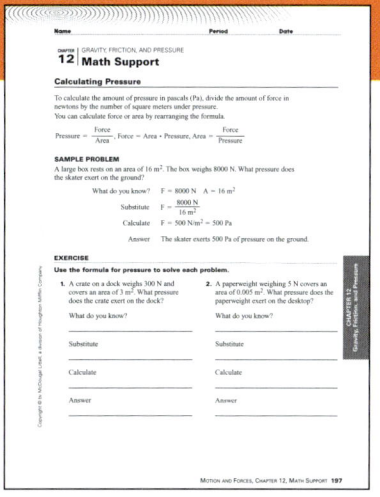

Reinforcing Key Concepts for each section

UNIT RESOURCE BOOK, p. 159   pp. 194–195   p. 197

Chapter 12: **Gravity, Friction, and Pressure** 377H

CHAPTER 12
Gravity, Friction, and Pressure

INTRODUCE

Have students look at the photograph of the snowboarder and describe the scene. Have them discuss how the question in the box on p. 379 links to the Big Idea: What effect do each of the forces acting on the snowboarder have on his motion?

National Science Education Standards

Content

B.1.a Substances have certain properties, including density.

D.3.c Gravity is the force that keeps planets in orbit around the Sun and governs the rest of the motion in the solar system. Gravity alone holds us to Earth's surface and explains the phenomena of the tides.

Process

A.2–8 Design and conduct an investigation; use tools to gather and interpret data; use evidence to describe, predict, explain, model; think critically to make relationships between evidence and explanation; recognize different explanations and predictions; communicate scientific procedures and explanations; use mathematics.

A.9.a–c, A.9.e–f Understand scientific inquiry by using different investigations, methods, mathematics, and explanations based on logic, evidence and skepticism.

E.2–5 Design, implement, and evaluate a solution; communicate technological design.

G.1.a–b Science as human endeavor

378 Unit 3: **Motion and Forces**

CHAPTER 12
Gravity, Friction, and Pressure

the BIG idea
Newton's laws apply to all forces.

Key Concepts

SECTION 1 **Gravity is a force exerted by masses.**
Learn about gravity, weight, and orbits.

SECTION 2 **Friction is a force that opposes motion.**
Learn about friction and air resistance.

SECTION 3 **Pressure depends on force and area.**
Learn about pressure and how forces act on objects in fluids.

SECTION 4 **Fluids can exert a force on objects.**
Learn how fluids apply forces to objects and how forces are transmitted through fluids.

Internet Preview
CLASSZONE.COM
Chapter 12 online resources: Content Review, Simulation, two Visualizations, three Resource Centers, Math Tutorial, Test Practice

378 Unit 3: **Motion and Forces**

 INTERNET PREVIEW

CLASSZONE.COM For student use with the following pages:

Review and Practice
- Content Review, pp. 380, 408
- Math Tutorial: Creating a Line Graph, p. 394
- Test Practice, 411

Activities and Resources
- Internet Activity: Gravity, p. 379
- Visualization, p. 383
- Simulation, p. 397
- Resource Centers: Gravitational Lenses, p. 388; Friction, Forces, and Surfaces, p. 390

Pressure Code: MDL006

EXPLORE the BIG idea

What forces are acting on this snowboarder? What forces are acting on the snow?

Let It Slide
Make a ramp using a board and some books. Slide an object down the ramp. Change the surface of the ramp using various materials such as sandpaper.

Observe and Think What effects did different surfaces have on the motion of the object? What may have caused these effects?

Under Pressure
Take two never-opened plastic soft-drink bottles. Open and reseal one of them. Squeeze each bottle.

Observe and Think How did the fluid inside each bottle react to your force? What may have caused the difference in the way the bottles felt?

Internet Activity: Gravity
Go to **ClassZone.com** to explore gravity. Learn more about the force of gravity and its effect on you, objects on Earth, and orbits of planets and satellites. Explore how gravity determines weight, and find out how your weight would be different on other planets.

Observe and Think What would you weigh on Mars? What would you weigh on Neptune?

NSTA SciLinks
scilinks.org
Pressure Code: MDL006

Chapter 12: **Gravity, Friction, and Pressure** 379

EXPLORE the BIG idea

These inquiry-based activities are appropriate for use at home or as a supplement to classroom instruction.

Let It Slide
PURPOSE To introduce students to the effect of friction on motion. Students slide an object down a ramp a few times, changing the surface of the ramp each time, to see the effects of friction.

TIP *10 min.* One surface should provide a lot of friction and one a little friction, such as waxed paper. The object should slide, not roll, down the ramp.

Answer: The rougher the surface, the more the motion slowed. A rough surface "holds back" motion of the object.

REVISIT after p. 390.

Under Pressure
PURPOSE To introduce students to the relationship of pressure to amount of gas. Students compare closed and opened bottles of carbonated drinks.

TIP *10 min.* Check that the cap is tightly fastened on the bottle that has been opened to avoid spills from squeezing the bottle.

Answer: The liquid did not change in volume, but the gas is compressed more in the closed bottle. There was less gas in the opened bottle, so the molecules could be pushed closer together.

REVISIT after p. 397.

Internet Activity: Gravity
PURPOSE To introduce students to the effect of mass on gravitational attraction. Students choose masses and see how they interact.

TIP *20 min.* Students can predict the gravitational attraction of two masses before they try the activity to determine it.

REVISIT after p. 382.

TEACHING WITH TECHNOLOGY

CBL and Probeware Use an accelerometer probe to measure the acceleration of the paper falling in the Investigate on p. 392. Students should compare their qualitative and quantitative results.

Video Camera Students can film the investigations on pp. 386 and 392 that involve falling objects. Playing the videotape in slow motion will help students analyze their observations.

PREPARE

◉ CONCEPT REVIEW

Activate Prior Knowledge

- Ask students to describe a situation that illustrates each of Newton's three laws.
- Have students use each law to explain the importance of using restraints on amusement-park rides.

◉ TAKING NOTES

Supporting Main Ideas

Students will find these charts analogous to an outline because of the way they organize main points and supporting information. The chart provides a meaningful way to organize information, especially for visual learners.

Vocabulary Strategy

As students start the chapter, have each student write a four square diagram for gravity. Use their individual diagrams to compile a class diagram for the concept. Discuss why individual diagrams contain different information.

Vocabulary and Note-Taking Resources

- Vocabulary Practice, pp. 194–195
- Decoding Support, p. 196

- Daily Vocabulary Scaffolding, p. T18
- Note-Taking Model, p. T19

- Four Square, B22–23
- Supporting Main Ideas, C42
- Daily Vocabulary Scaffolding, H1–8

CHAPTER 12
Getting Ready to Learn

◉ CONCEPT REVIEW

- The motion of an object will not change unless acted upon by an unbalanced force.
- The acceleration of an object depends on force and mass.
- For every action force there is an equal and opposite reaction.

◉ VOCABULARY REVIEW

force p. 345
Newton's first law p. 349
Newton's second law p. 354
Newton's third law p. 361
density See Glossary.

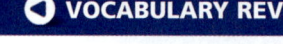
Review concepts and vocabulary.

◉ TAKING NOTES

SUPPORTING MAIN IDEAS

Make a chart to show main ideas and the information that supports them. Copy the main ideas. Below each main idea, add supporting information, such as reasons, explanations, and examples.

VOCABULARY STRATEGY

Write each new vocabulary term in the center of a **four square** diagram. Write notes in the squares around each term. Include a definition, some characteristics, and some examples of the term. If possible, write some things that are not examples of the term.

See the Note-Taking Handbook on pages R45–R51.

SCIENCE NOTEBOOK

Force of gravity depends on mass and distance.
→ More mass = more gravitational force
→ More distance = less gravitational force

Definition	Characteristics
force of gravity acting on an object	• changes if gravity changes • measured in newtons

WEIGHT

Examples	Nonexamples
A 4 kg bowling ball weighs 39 N.	Mass in kg is not a weight.

380 Unit 3: Motion and Forces

CHECK READINESS

Administer the Diagnostic Test to determine students' readiness for new science content and their mastery of requisite math skills.

 Diagnostic Test, pp. 40–41

Technology Resources

Students needing content and math skills should visit ClassZone.com.

- CONTENT REVIEW
- MATH TUTORIAL

 CONTENT REVIEW CD-ROM

380 Unit 3: **Motion and Forces**

KEY CONCEPT

Gravity is a force exerted by masses.

◀ **BEFORE, you learned**
- Every action force has an equal and opposite reaction force
- Newton's laws are used to describe the motions of objects
- Mass is the amount of matter an object contains

▶ **NOW, you will learn**
- How mass and distance affect gravity
- What keeps objects in orbit

VOCABULARY
gravity p. 381
weight p. 383
orbit p. 384

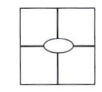
VOCABULARY
Create a four square diagram for *gravity* in your notebook.

EXPLORE Downward Acceleration

How do the accelerations of two falling objects compare?

PROCEDURE

1. Make a prediction: Which ball will fall faster?
2. Drop both balls from the same height at the same time.
3. Observe the balls as they hit the ground.

WHAT DO YOU THINK?
- Were the results what you had expected?
- How did the times it took the two balls to hit the ground compare?

MATERIALS
- golf ball
- Ping-Pong ball

Masses attract each other.

When you drop any object—such as a pen, a book, or a football—it falls to the ground. As the object falls, it moves faster and faster. The fact that the object accelerates means there must be a force acting on it. The downward pull on the object is due to gravity. **Gravity** is the force that objects exert on each other because of their masses. You are familiar with the force of gravity between Earth and objects on Earth.

Gravity is present not only between objects and Earth, however. Gravity is considered a universal force because it acts between any two masses anywhere in the universe. For example, there is a gravitational pull between the Sun and the Moon. Even small masses attract each other. The force of gravity between dust and gas particles in space helped form the solar system.

 Why is gravity considered a universal force?

Chapter 12: **Gravity, Friction, and Pressure** 381

RESOURCES FOR DIFFERENTIATED INSTRUCTION

Below Level
UNIT RESOURCE BOOK
- Reading Study Guide A, pp. 151–152
- Decoding Support, p. 196

 **AUDIO CDS**

Advanced
UNIT RESOURCE BOOK
Challenge and Extension, p. 157

English Learners
UNIT RESOURCE BOOK
Spanish Reading Study Guide, pp. 155–156

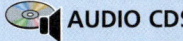 **AUDIO CDS**
- Audio Readings in Spanish
- Audio Readings (English)

12.1 FOCUS

▶ **Set Learning Goals**

Students will
- Describe how mass and distance affect gravity.
- Explain what keeps objects in orbit.
- Investigate through experimentation how gravity affects falling objects.

▶ **3-Minute Warm-Up**

Display Transparency 20 or copy this exercise on the board:

Match each definition with a term.

Definitions
1. the rate at which velocity changes with time *b*
2. a measure of mass in motion *e*
3. the force that keeps an object moving in a circle *a*

Terms
a. centripetal force   d. contact force
b. acceleration   e. momentum
c. mass

 3-Minute Warm-Up, p. T20

12.1 MOTIVATE

EXPLORE Downward Acceleration

PURPOSE To introduce the relationship between gravity and mass

TIP *10 min.* If students have difficulty seeing which ball hits first, have them listen to the balls hitting the floor.

WHAT DO YOU THINK? *Both balls will hit the floor at the same time. Gravity accelerates all masses equally.*

Ongoing Assessment

 *Answer: Gravity is present everywhere in the universe.*

Chapter 12 **381**

12.1 INSTRUCT

Real World Example

Although building codes and architects seek to ensure that buildings are stable, some basic designs are more stable than others. One of the most stable structures is the geodesic dome, like the one at the Epcot Center in Florida. Its rounded shape excels at resisting damage from strong winds and heavy snows. One of its greatest advantages is that its shape spreads the force of gravity down the sides. The compression that gravity would otherwise cause is evenly distributed. Another example of a stable dome is the igloo, used as a temporary dwelling by the Inuit people.

Teach Difficult Concepts

If all objects were single points, there would be no difficulty finding the distance between any two of them. The center of mass of an object is the point in space where an object (or system of objects) behaves as if all the mass were concentrated at that point. For example, a large sphere can be treated like it is a point-sized mass located at the center of the sphere. When finding the gravitational force between two objects, the distance between them is the distance between each object's center of mass.

EXPLORE the BIG idea

Revisit "Internet Activity: Gravity" on p. 379. Have students explain their results.

Ongoing Assessment

Describe how mass and distance affect gravity.

Ask: Which has more gravitational attraction, a pair of students standing one meter apart or the same students standing three meters apart? *those standing one meter apart*

 Answer: *As mass increases, gravity increases. As distance increases, gravity decreases.*

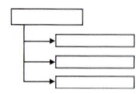

SUPPORTING MAIN IDEAS Support the main ideas about the force of gravity with details and examples.

The Force of Gravity

If there is a force between all masses, why are you not pulled toward your desk by the desk's gravity when you walk away from it? Remember that the net force on you determines how your motion changes. The force of gravity between you and the desk is extremely small compared with other forces constantly acting on you, such as friction, the force from your muscles, Earth's gravity, and the gravitational pull from many other objects. The strength of the gravitational force between two objects depends on two factors, mass and distance.

The Mass of the Objects The more mass two objects have, the greater the force of gravity the masses exert on each other. If one of the masses is doubled, the force of gravity between the objects is doubled.

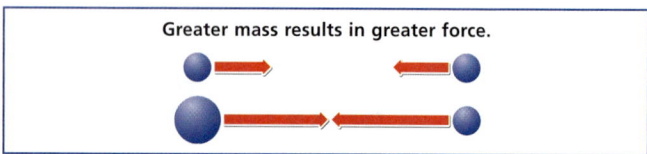

Greater mass results in greater force.

The Distance Between the Objects As distance between the objects increases, the force of gravity decreases. If the distance is doubled, the force of gravity is one-fourth as strong as before.

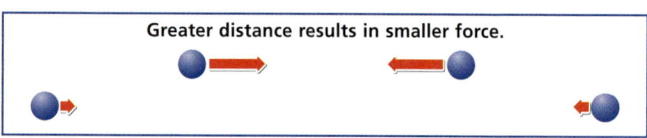

Greater distance results in smaller force.

 How do mass and distance affect the force of gravity?

Gravity on Earth

The force of gravity acts on both masses equally, even though the effects on both masses may be very different. Earth's gravity exerts a downward pull on a dropped coin. Remember that every action force has an equal and opposite reaction force. The coin exerts an equal upward force on Earth. Because the coin has an extremely small mass compared with Earth, the coin can be easily accelerated. Earth's acceleration due to the force of the coin is far too small to notice because of Earth's large mass.

The acceleration due to Earth's gravity is called g and is equal to 9.8 m/s^2 at Earth's surface. You can calculate the force of gravity on an object using the object's mass and this acceleration. The formula that expresses Newton's second law is $F = ma$. If you use g as the acceleration, the formula for calculating the force due to gravity on a mass close to Earth's surface becomes $F = mg$.

DIFFERENTIATE INSTRUCTION

More Reading Support

A Two objects are exerting force on each other. If one of the masses is doubled, what happens to the force of gravity between the objects? *It is also doubled.*

English Learners This chapter contains many hypothetical sentences that start with *if* and *when* phrases, such as, "When you drop any object . . . it falls," (p. 381). Help students understand these abstract ideas by eliminating *when* and separating the sentence into two separate parts. ("You drop an object. It falls.") Point out the cause and effect between the parts of the original sentence.

Acceleration Due to Gravity

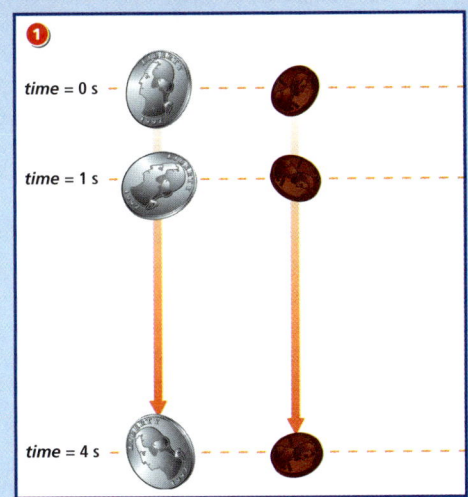

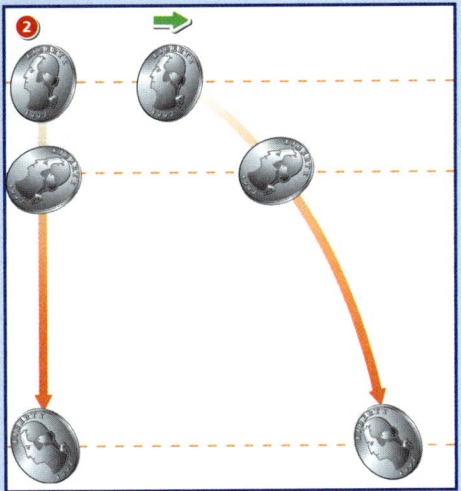

If any two objects are dropped from the same height in a vacuum, they fall at the same rate even if they have different masses.

If an object has a velocity in the horizontal direction when it falls, the horizontal velocity does not change its downward acceleration.

In a vacuum—that is, where there is no air—all falling objects have the same acceleration.

① The quarter falls at the same rate as the penny when they are dropped together. Because the quarter has more mass, gravity exerts more force on it. But greater mass also means more inertia, so the greater force does not produce a larger acceleration. Objects with different masses fall with the same acceleration.

② A coin that is dropped falls at the same rate as one that is thrown forward. Horizontal velocity does not affect acceleration due to gravity. Because gravity is directed downward, it changes only the downward velocity of the coin, not its forward velocity.

VISUALIZATION CLASSZONE.COM
Explore how objects fall at the same rate in a vacuum.

CHECK YOUR READING Compare the times it takes two objects with different masses to fall from the same height.

Weight and Mass

While weight and mass are related, they are not the same properties. Mass is a measure of how much matter an object contains. **Weight** is the force of gravity on an object. Mass is a property that an object has no matter where it is located. Weight, on the other hand, depends on the force of gravity acting on that object.

Chapter 12: **Gravity, Friction, and Pressure** 383

Address Misconceptions

IDENTIFY Ask: If a student reading a beam balance determines that a rock is 0.5 kg, what is the student measuring? If students answer weight, they may hold the misconception that mass and weight can be used interchangeably.

CORRECT Explain to students that kilograms are commonly used to describe weight because most measurements are taken on Earth. Ask students what would happen to the weight of the rock if it were taken to the Moon, which has 1/6 of Earth's gravity. *It would weigh less.* Ask them if the amount of matter—its mass—would change. *no*

REASSESS Ask: On Earth, a person who weighs 300 N has a mass of about 31 kg. What would that person's weight be on the Moon? *50 N* What would her mass be? *31 kg*

Technology Resources
Visit **ClassZone.com** for background on common student misconceptions.

  MISCONCEPTION DATABASE

History of Science

By the middle 1500s, scientific observations were changing the way people understood astronomical orbits. In Denmark, Tycho Brahe made the most accurate observations of the stars and planets up to that time. The German astronomer Johannes Kepler used Brahe's data to show that the planets don't travel in perfect circles but in ellipses. In the 1600s, Galileo turned his telescope toward the sky. His observations, including observations of moons orbiting Jupiter, led him to champion the theory that Earth orbits the Sun. Regardless of the evidence Galileo offered, many people still did not accept his ideas.

Ongoing Assessment

Explain what keeps objects in orbit.

Ask: What two factors keep an object in orbit? *its speed and gravity*

384 Unit 3: Motion and Forces

On Earth
Mass = 50 kg
Weight = 490 N

On the Moon
Mass = 50 kg
Weight = 82 N

When you use a balance, you are measuring the mass of an object. A person with a mass of 50 kilograms will balance another mass of 50 kilograms whether she is on Earth or on the Moon. Traveling to the Moon would not change how much matter a person is made of. When you use a spring scale, such as a bathroom scale, to measure the weight of an object, however, you are measuring how hard gravity is pulling on an object. The Moon is less massive than Earth, and its gravitational pull is one-sixth that of Earth's. A spring scale would show that a person who has a weight of 490 newtons (110 lb) on Earth would have a weight of 82 newtons (18 lb) on the Moon.

Gravity keeps objects in orbit.

Sir Isaac Newton hypothesized that the force that pulls objects to the ground—gravity—also pulls the Moon in its orbit around Earth. An **orbit** is the elliptical path one body, such as the Moon, follows around another body, such as Earth, due to the influence of gravity. The centripetal force keeping one object in orbit around another object is due to the gravitational pull between the two objects. In the case of the Moon's orbit, the centripetal force is the gravitational pull between the Moon and Earth. Similarly, Earth is pulled around the Sun by the gravitational force between Earth and the Sun.

READING TIP
An ellipse is shaped as shown below. A circle is a special type of ellipse.

You can think of an object orbiting Earth as an object that is falling around Earth rather than falling to the ground. Consider what happens to the ball in the illustration on page 385. A dropped ball will fall about five meters during the first second it falls. Throwing the ball straight ahead will not change that falling time. What happens as you throw faster and faster?

Earth is curved. This fact is noticeable only over very long distances. For every 8000 meters you travel, Earth curves downward about 5 meters. If you could throw a ball at 8000 meters per second, it would fall to Earth in such a way that its path would curve the same amount that Earth curves. Since the ball would fall along the curve of Earth, the ball would never actually land on the ground. The ball would be in orbit.

384 Unit 3: Motion and Forces

DIFFERENTIATE INSTRUCTION

More Reading Support

C Does a spring scale measure mass or weight? *weight*

D What is the centripetal force of the Moon's orbit? *the gravitational attraction of Earth*

Inclusion Tie a metal paper clip to one end of a 30-cm piece of string. Tape the other end of the string to a desk. Have students hold the paper clip straight up in the air. Bring a magnet close to the paper clip, so that it is not touching the paper clip but suspends the clip in the air. Point out that the force of the magnet is stronger than the force of gravity on the paper clip. This activity is suitable for any student; students with a visual impairment can do the activity using touch.

Orbits

An object in orbit, like an object falling to the ground, is pulled toward Earth's center. If the object moves far enough forward as it falls, it orbits around Earth instead of hitting the ground.

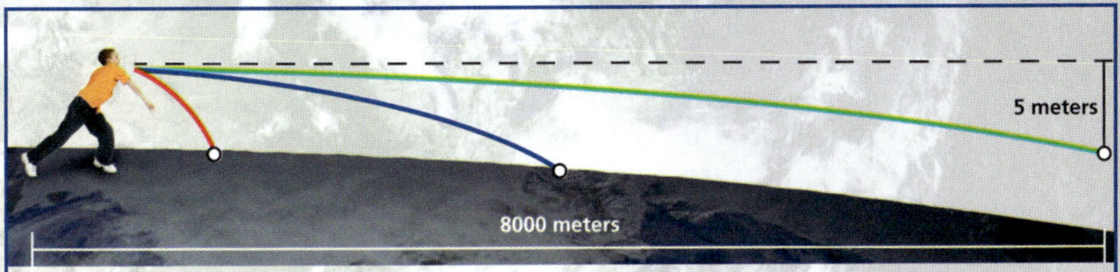

5 meters

8000 meters

If a ball is thrown straight ahead from a 5-meter height, it will drop 5 meters in the first second it falls. At low speeds, the ball will hit the ground after 1 second.

If the ball is going fast enough, the curvature of Earth becomes important. While the ball still drops 5 meters in the first second, it must fall farther than 5 meters to hit the ground.

If the ball is going fast enough to travel 8000 meters forward as it drops downward 5 meters, it follows the curvature of Earth. The ball will fall around Earth, not into it.

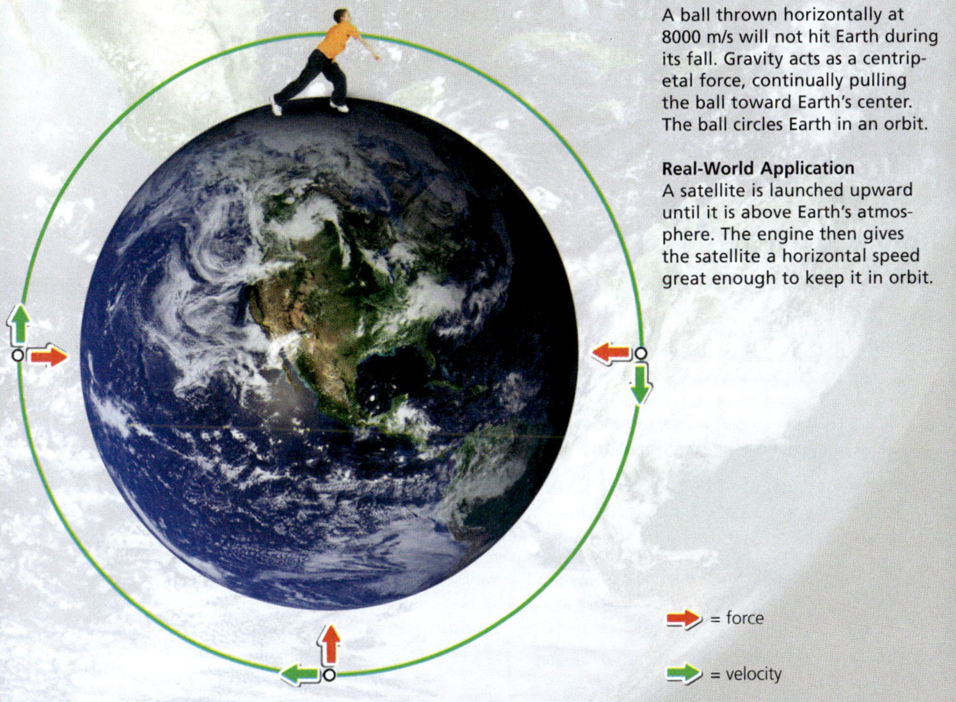

A ball thrown horizontally at 8000 m/s will not hit Earth during its fall. Gravity acts as a centripetal force, continually pulling the ball toward Earth's center. The ball circles Earth in an orbit.

Real-World Application
A satellite is launched upward until it is above Earth's atmosphere. The engine then gives the satellite a horizontal speed great enough to keep it in orbit.

 = force
 = velocity

READING VISUALS Compare the direction of the velocity with the direction of the force for an object in a circular orbit.

Chapter 12: Gravity, Friction, and Pressure **385**

Teach from Visuals

Explain to students that the visual "Orbits" represents a thought experiment. While it is not possible for a person to throw a ball at the speeds described, students can use what they know about throwing a ball to imagine the results if a ball could be thrown at extremely high speeds. Another imaginary factor in the visual is the size of the boy. People are not five meters high. Five meters is closer to the height of a single-story building. Students also may need to be told that the image of the boy is not shown at the same scale as the image of Earth in either picture.

T The visual "Orbits" is available as T22 in the Unit Transparency Book.

Teach Difficult Concepts

You may need to spend extra time on the idea that the velocity of an object in a circular orbit and the force acting on it have different directions. Emphasize that the motion of the object is a combination of its velocity and the centripetal force from gravity.

Ongoing Assessment

READING VISUALS *Answer: The force and the velocity are at right angles to each other.*

DIFFERENTIATE INSTRUCTION

Advanced Have students design and perform an experiment that shows the effects of horizontal velocity on the falling time of an object. Students should include a discussion of which variables need to be held constant and which will change.

Chapter 12 **385**

INVESTIGATE Gravity

PURPOSE Predict how gravity affects falling objects and check the prediction

TIPS 15 min.
- Have paper towels available to clean up spills immediately.
- Students should hold the cup straight when they drop it.
- Step 4 can be repeated if needed.

WHAT DO YOU THINK? *In step 3, the water came out the hole in a horizontal stream that fell into the pan. In step 5, all the water in the cup fell with the cup and none came out the hole. The cup and water fell at the same rate.*

CHALLENGE *The first time, the cup was not falling. Gravity pulled on the water. The second time both were falling—the cup could not produce a reaction force on water since the water was not applying a force to the falling cup. Water does apply a force to a still cup.*

 Datasheet, Gravity, p. 158

Technology Resources
Customize this student lab as needed or look for an alternative. Print rubrics to assess student lab reports.

 Lab Generator CD-ROM

Metacognitive Strategy
Ask students to write a paragraph about how working with a partner might help them complete the activity.

Ongoing Assessment

CHECK YOUR READING *Answer: Answers might include that gravity on a spacecraft in low orbit is so close to what it is on Earth's surface and that once outside the pull of Earth's gravity, a spacecraft is still subject to gravity—of the Sun.*

Spacecraft in Orbit

The minimum speed needed to send an object into orbit is approximately 8000 meters per second. At this speed, the path of a falling object matches the curve of Earth's surface. If you launch a spacecraft or a satellite at a slower speed, it will eventually fall to the ground.

A spacecraft launched at a greater speed can reach a higher orbit than one launched at a lower speed. The higher the orbit, the weaker the force from Earth's gravity. The force of gravity is still very strong, however. If a craft is in a low orbit—about 300 kilometers (190 mi)—Earth's gravitational pull is about 91 percent of what it is at Earth's surface. The extra distance makes a difference in the force of only about 9 percent.

If a spacecraft is launched with a speed of 11,000 meters per second or more, it is moving too fast to go into an orbit. Instead, the spacecraft will ultimately escape the pull of Earth's gravity altogether. The speed that a spacecraft needs to escape the gravitational pull of an object such as a planet or a star is called the escape velocity. A spacecraft that escapes Earth's gravity will go into orbit around the Sun unless it is also going fast enough to escape the Sun's gravity.

 Did any facts in the text above surprise you? If so, which surprised you and why?

INVESTIGATE Gravity

How does gravity affect falling objects?
PROCEDURE

1. Carefully use the pencil to punch a hole that is the width of the pencil in the side of the cup, about one-third of the way up from the bottom.
2. Holding your finger over the hole, fill the cup three-fourths full of water.
3. Hold the cup above the dishpan. Predict what will happen if you remove your finger from the hole. Remove your finger and observe what happens.
4. With your finger over the hole, refill the cup to the same level as in step 2. Predict how the water will move if you hold the cup 50 cm above the dishpan and drop the cup and its contents straight down into the pan.
5. Drop the cup and observe what happens to the water while the cup is falling.

WHAT DO YOU THINK?
- What happened to the water in step 3? in step 5?
- How did gravity affect the water when you dropped the cup?

CHALLENGE Why did the water behave differently the second time?

SKILL FOCUS Predicting

MATERIALS
- pencil
- paper cup
- water
- dishpan

TIME 15 minutes

386 Unit 3: Motion and Forces

DIFFERENTIATE INSTRUCTION

 More Reading Support

E Will a launched spacecraft always go into orbit? *No; if the speed is great enough, it will escape Earth's gravity.*

Alternative Assessment Have students make a poster that shows time-lapse drawings of what happens to the water in steps 3 and 5 of the Investigate.

People in Orbit

When an elevator you are riding in accelerates downward, you may feel lighter for a short time. If you were standing on a scale during the downward acceleration, the scale would show that you weighed less than usual. Your mass would not have changed, nor would the pull of gravity. What would cause the apparent weight loss?

When the elevator is still, the entire force of your weight presses against the scale. When the elevator accelerates downward, you are not pressing as hard on the scale, because the scale is also moving downward. Since the scale measures how hard you are pushing on it, you appear to weigh less. If you and the scale were in free fall—a fall due entirely to gravity—the scale would fall as fast as you did. You would not press against the scale at all, so you would appear to be weightless.

A spacecraft in orbit is in free fall. Gravity is acting on the astronauts and on the ship—without gravity, there could be no orbit. However, the ship and the astronauts are falling around Earth at the same rate. While astronauts are in orbit, their weight does not press against the floor of the spacecraft. The result is an environment, called a microgravity environment, in which objects behave as if there were no gravity. People and objects simply float as if they were weightless.

Astronaut Mae Jemison is shown here working in a microgravity environment.

 Why do astronauts float when they are in orbit?

12.1 Review

KEY CONCEPTS

1. What effect would increasing the mass of two objects have on the gravitational attraction between them?
2. What effect would decreasing the distance between objects have on their gravitational attraction to each other?
3. How does gravity keep the Moon in orbit around Earth?

CRITICAL THINKING

4. **Compare** How does the size of the force exerted by Earth's gravity on a car compare with the size of the force the car exerts on Earth?
5. **Apply** What would be the effect on the mass and the weight of an object if the object were taken to a planet with twice the gravity of Earth?

CHALLENGE

6. **Synthesize** Precision measurements of the acceleration due to gravity show that the acceleration is slightly different in different locations on Earth. Explain why the force of gravity is not exactly the same everywhere on Earth's surface. *Hint:* Think about the details of Earth's surface.

Chapter 12: **Gravity, Friction, and Pressure** 387

Ongoing Assessment

 *Answer: The astronauts and the spaceship are falling at the same rate. They are in free fall.*

Reinforce the BIG idea

Have students relate the section to the Big Idea.

 Reinforcing Key Concepts, p. 159

12.1 ASSESS & RETEACH

Assess

 Section 12.1 Quiz, p. 42

Reteach

Have students list on the board twenty classroom objects of different masses. Assume each of the items is positioned one meter from another item. Have students sequence the items from greatest to smallest amount of gravitational attraction exerted.

Technology Resources

Have students visit ClassZone.com for reteaching of Key Concepts.

 CONTENT REVIEW

CONTENT REVIEW CD-ROM

ANSWERS

1. The gravitational attraction would increase.

2. The gravitational attraction would increase.

3. Gravity acts as a centripetal force. A combination of this centripetal force and the velocity of the Moon keep the Moon in orbit.

4. They are equal and opposite.

5. Its weight would be twice as much, but its mass would remain the same.

6. Places that have more mass between the object and the center of Earth, such as a mountain, would have slightly greater gravity.

EXTREME SCIENCE
Fun and Motivating Science

Set Learning Goal
To understand that light can be bent by extremely massive objects

Present the Science
The bending of light from a distant, bright object by a massive object is called gravitational lensing because the intervening object acts as a lens, focusing the image of the distant, bright object to new locations. If the bright object, the massive object, and Earth are not in a straight line, the light paths travel different distances around the massive object. Because the distances from all objects is so great in space, the size of the massive object and that of the bright object can be considered to be points in space. If the distant object varies in brightness, the brightness of the different images will change at different times. Astronomers can use the time differences to calculate the differences in path lengths. The distance to the bright object can then be calculated.

Discussion Questions
Ask: Why do you think that the bending of light shown here is called gravitational lensing? *Lenses bend light. In this concept, gravity of an extremely massive object bends light.*

Ask: What is the importance of Einstein's prediction? *Sample answer: After Einstein predicted this bending of light, scientists were aware of the concept and recognized it when they observed it.*

Close
Ask: Would it be accurate to state that every very large object could bend light? *No; a large object might not have a large mass, and gravity depends on mass.*

Technology Resources
Students can visit **ClassZone.com** to find out more about gravitational lenses.

 RESOURCE CENTER

EXTREME SCIENCE — GRAVITY IN THE EXTREME

Bending Light

You know that gravity can pull objects toward each other, but did you know that gravity can also affect light? Very extreme sources of gravity cause the normally straight path of a light beam to bend.

Going in Circles
Although Earth is massive, the effects of its gravity on light are not noticeable. However, scientists can model what a familiar scene might look like with an extreme source of gravity nearby. The image to the left shows how the light from the Seattle Space Needle could be bent almost into circles if an extremely small yet extremely massive object, such as a black hole, were in front of it.

Seeing Behind Galaxies
How do we know that gravity can bend light? Astronomers, who study space, have seen the phenomenon in action. If a very bright but distant object is behind a very massive one, such as a large galaxy, the mass of the galaxy bends the light coming from the distant object. This effect, called gravitational lensing, can produce multiple images of the bright object along a ring around the massive galaxy. Astronomers have observed gravitational lensing in their images.

Facts About Bending Light
- Gravitational lensing was predicted by Albert Einstein in the early 1900s, but the first example was not observed until 1979.
- The masses of distant galaxies can be found by observing their effect on light.

Seeing Quadruple
This gravitational lens is called the Einstein Cross. The four bright objects that ring the central galaxy are all images of the same very bright yet very distant object that is located 20 times farther away than the central galaxy.

EXPLORE
1. **INFER** Why are you unable to notice the gravitational bending of light by an object such as a large rock?
2. **CHALLENGE** Look at the photographs in the Resource Center. Find the multiple images of the distant objects and the more massive object bending the light from them.

 **RESOURCE CENTER** CLASSZONE.COM — Find out more information about gravitational lenses.

EXPLORE
INFER *The large rock does not have enough mass to produce noticeable bending of light.*

12.2 KEY CONCEPT
Friction is a force that opposes motion.

BEFORE, you learned
- Gravity is the attractive force masses exert on each other
- Gravity increases with greater mass and decreases with greater distance
- Gravity is the centripetal force keeping objects in orbit

NOW, you will learn
- How friction affects motion
- About factors that affect friction
- About air resistance

VOCABULARY
friction p. 389
fluid p. 392
air resistance p. 393

THINK ABOUT
What forces help you to walk?

As a person walks, she exerts a backward force on the ground. A reaction force moves her forward. But some surfaces are harder to walk on than others. Ice, for example, is harder to walk on than a dry surface because ice is slippery. How can different surfaces affect your ability to walk?

Friction occurs when surfaces slide against each other.

Have you ever pushed a heavy box across the floor? You probably noticed that it is easier to push the box over some surfaces than over others. You must apply a certain amount of force to the box to keep it moving. The force that acts against your pushing force is called friction. **Friction** is a force that resists the motion between two surfaces in contact.

When you try to slide two surfaces across each other, the force of friction resists the sliding motion. If there were no friction, the box would move as soon as you applied any force to it. Although friction can make some tasks more difficult, most activities, including walking, would be impossible without it. Friction between your feet and the ground is what provides the action and reaction forces that enable you to walk.

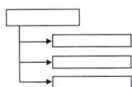
SUPPORTING MAIN IDEAS
Take notes about friction, including details and examples.

Chapter 12: **Gravity, Friction, and Pressure** 389

12.2 FOCUS

Set Learning Goals
Students will
- Describe how friction affects motion.
- List the factors that affect friction.
- Explain air resistance.
- Design an experiment to investigate how the shape of an object affects how it falls.

3-Minute Warm-Up
Display Transparency 20 or copy this exercise on the board:

Gravity is pulling the Moon toward the center of Earth. Write a brief paragraph explaining why the Moon does not crash into Earth. *Gravity is pulling at right angles to the motion of the Moon. The force changes the direction in which the Moon is moving, rather than pulling the Moon downward to Earth's surface. The Moon is in orbit.*

 3-Minute Warm-Up, p. T20

12.2 MOTIVATE

THINK ABOUT

PURPOSE To introduce the concept of friction

DISCUSS Ask students to list previous experiences they have had walking on different surfaces. List them on the board and ask students to group the experiences according to ease of walking.

Examples: On slick surfaces, such as ice, it is more difficult to exert a backward force on the ground. Thus, the reaction force that moves you forward is also less. It is easier to exert a backward force on rougher surfaces.

Ongoing Assessment
Describe how friction affects motion.
Ask: Is it more difficult to move a box across a tile floor or across carpet? *across carpet*

Chapter 12 **389**

RESOURCES FOR DIFFERENTIATED INSTRUCTION

Below Level
UNIT RESOURCE BOOK
- Reading Study Guide A, pp. 162–163
- Decoding Support, p. 196

 AUDIO CDS

Advanced
UNIT RESOURCE BOOK
Challenge and Extension, p. 168

English Learners
UNIT RESOURCE BOOK
Spanish Reading Study Guide, pp. 166–167

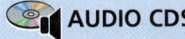 AUDIO CDS
- Audio Readings in Spanish
- Audio Readings (English)

12.2 INSTRUCT

Teach Difficult Concepts

Because friction is generally greater between rough surfaces, students may not realize that friction is complicated by more factors than surface roughness. Friction is produced by the interaction of atoms or molecules on surfaces as they resist sliding over each other. In some cases, smoothing two surfaces actually produces greater friction between them.

Real World Example

Friction can have both positive and negative effects in machines. If a moving part of a machine rubs against another part of the machine or against something existing in the environment, the resulting friction can cause damage. For example, an electric drill can overheat because of friction between motor parts. Drill bits can become so hot from the friction between the bit and the material it is drilling through that it burns the user's skin. In a sander, the friction is necessary for the machine to smooth a surface and, in fact, to work at all.

EXPLORE

Revisit "Let It Slide" on p. 379. Have students explain the reasons for their results.

RESOURCE CENTER
CLASSZONE.COM
Learn more about friction, forces, and surfaces.

REMINDER
Remember that balanced forces on an object do not change the object's motion.

Forces and Surfaces

If you look down from a great height, such as from the window of an airplane, a flat field appears to be smooth. If you were to walk in the field, however, you would see that the ground has many bumps and holes. In the same way, a flat surface such as a piece of plastic may look and feel smooth. However, if you look at the plastic through a strong microscope, you see that it has tiny bumps and ridges. Friction depends on how these bumps and ridges on one surface interact with and stick to the bumps and ridges on other surfaces. There are several factors that determine the friction between two surfaces.

Types of Surfaces Friction between two surfaces depends on the materials that make up the surfaces. Different combinations of surfaces produce different frictional forces. A rubber hockey puck sliding across ice has a smaller frictional force on it than the same puck sliding across a wooden floor. The friction between rubber and ice is less than the friction between rubber and wood.

Motion of the Surfaces You need a larger force to start something moving than you do to keep something moving. If you have ever tried to push a heavy chair, you may have noticed that you had to push harder and harder until the chair suddenly accelerated forward.

As you apply a force to push a chair or any other object that is not moving, the frictional force keeping it from sliding increases so the forces stay balanced. However, the frictional force has a limit to how

Friction and Motion

Before Object Moves

When an object is standing still, there is a maximum force needed to overcome friction and start it moving. Any force less than this will be exactly balanced by the force of friction, and the object will not move.

While Object Moves

Once the object is moving, the frictional force remains constant. This constant force is less than the maximum force needed to start the object moving.

390 Unit 3: Motion and Forces

DIFFERENTIATE INSTRUCTION

 More Reading Support

A Why might a wooden hockey puck on a wooden floor have a different frictional force than a rubber puck? *Different surface combinations produce different frictional forces.*

English Learners Help students with the complex sentences in this section by breaking each down into smaller sentences and ideas. Then help students make the connections between the phrases in the more complex sentence.

large it can be. When your force is greater than this limit, the forces on the chair are no longer balanced, and the chair moves. The frictional force remains at a new lower level once the chair is moving.

Force Pressing the Surfaces Together The harder two surfaces are pushed together, the more difficult it is for the surfaces to slide over each other. When an object is placed on a surface, the weight of the object presses on that surface. The surface exerts an equal and opposite reaction force on the object. This reaction force is one of the factors that determines how much friction there is.

If you push a chair across the floor, there will be a certain amount of friction between the chair and the floor. Increasing the weight of the chair increases the force pushing the surfaces together. The force of friction between the chair and the floor is greater when a person is sitting in it than when the chair was empty.

Friction depends on the total force pressing the surfaces together, not on how much area this force acts over. Consider a rectangular cardboard box. It can rest with its smaller or larger side on the floor. The box will have the same force from friction regardless of which side sits on the floor. The larger side has more area in contact with the floor than the smaller side, but the weight of the box is more spread out on the larger side.

CHECK YOUR READING What factors influence frictional force? Give two examples.

Friction and Weight

Less Weight — The force of friction depends on the total force pushing the surfaces together. Here the weight of the chair is the force pressing the surfaces together.

More Weight — The weight of the chair increases when someone sits in it. The force of friction is now greater than when the chair was empty.

Chapter 12: **Gravity, Friction, and Pressure** 391

DIFFERENTIATE INSTRUCTION

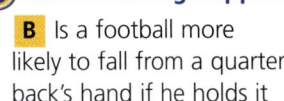

More Reading Support

B Is a football more likely to fall from a quarterback's hand if he holds it tightly or loosely? *loosely*

Below Level Have students make a ramp using a sturdy binder or a board and a stack of textbooks. Have them lay a large hardware nut or washer at the top of the ramp and adjust the height until the nut slides down. Have them place several other materials on the surface of the ramp, such as waxed paper, sandpaper, or cloth, and again observe what happens when the nut or washer is placed at the top. Ask students to explain their observations, which should include that the object will slide more easily on some surfaces because friction is less.

Teach from Visuals

To help students interpret the visual on friction and weight, ask:

How does increasing the weight in the chair influence force? *Increasing the weight of the chair increases the force of friction between the chair and the floor.*

Develop Critical Thinking

CONNECT To completely understand friction, students should relate the concepts to practical situations.

- Ask: What are some everyday examples illustrating that friction increases because surfaces press together with greater force? *pressing down on a piece of sandpaper that is used to sand wood, filling tractor tires with water or lime to add weight for extra traction, or using a finger to hold down strings while tying a knot*

- Ask: What are some everyday examples illustrating that friction decreases because the texture of the surfaces changes? *tires wearing down, ice forming on a roadway or sidewalk, or using polished metal or plastic to make a slide*

Ongoing Assessment

List the factors that affect friction.

Ask: How could you decrease friction between a dishcloth and a plate? *by changing the surface texture or the force pressing the surfaces together*

CHECK YOUR READING Answer: types of surface, motion of the surfaces, force pressing the surfaces together; examples will vary

Chapter 12 **391**

INVESTIGATE Friction in Air

PURPOSE Design an experiment to determine the relationship between the shape of an object and how it falls.

TIPS 30 min.

- Emphasize that the pieces of paper must be identical.
- Students should write a procedure and have it approved before they follow it.

WHAT DO YOU THINK? *Paper that has been crumpled will fall more quickly than paper that has not been crumpled. The more tightly it is crumpled, the faster it will fall. Students should explain if results supported their hypothesis. A small, round shape has less air resistance than a flat shape has.*

CHALLENGE *Answers might include air currents in the room or the humidity of the air. Check students' plans for testing.*

 Datasheet, Friction in Air, p. 169

Technology Resources

Customize this student lab as needed or look for an alternative. Print rubrics to assess student lab reports.

 Lab Generator CD-ROM

Integrate the Sciences

Some scientists study how much friction and heat earthquakes produce. During an earthquake, large moving pieces that form Earth's crust, called tectonic plates, collide, move apart, or slide past each other. The friction from this sliding should produce a large amount of heat. However, in many cases, scientists do not see the increases in temperature that they expect based on their current understanding of friction.

Friction and Heat

Friction between surfaces produces heat. You feel heat produced by friction when you rub your hands together. As you rub, friction causes the individual molecules on the surface of your hands to move faster. As the individual molecules in an object move faster, the temperature of the object increases. The increased speed of the molecules on the surface of your hands produces the warmth that you feel.

The heat produced by friction can be intense. The friction that results from striking a match against a rough surface produces enough heat to ignite the flammable substance on the head of the match. In some machines, such as a car engine, too much heat from friction can cause serious damage. Substances such as oil are often used to reduce friction between moving parts in machines. Without motor oil, a car's engine parts would overheat and stop working.

Friction produces sparks between a match head and a rough surface. The heat from friction eventually lights the match.

Motion through fluids produces friction.

As you have seen, two objects falling in a vacuum fall with the same acceleration. Objects falling through air, however, have different accelerations. This difference occurs because air is a fluid. A **fluid** is a substance that can flow easily. Gases and liquids are fluids.

INVESTIGATE Friction in Air

How does the shape of an object affect how it falls?

DESIGN YOUR OWN EXPERIMENT

Write a hypothesis that explains how shape affects the speed of falling objects. Design an experiment that tests your hypothesis.

PROCEDURE

1. Figure out how you can use the three sheets of paper to test your hypothesis. Remember to control all other variables, including the mass of the paper.
2. Write up your procedure.
3. Conduct your experiment.

WHAT DO YOU THINK?

- What were the results of your experiment?
- Did the results support your hypothesis? Explain your answer.
- Write a statement that summarizes your findings.

CHALLENGE What other variable might affect falling time? How could you test it?

SKILL FOCUS
Designing experiments

MATERIALS
3 identical sheets of paper

TIME
30 minutes

DIFFERENTIATE INSTRUCTION

 **More Reading Support**

C How does friction affect temperature? *Temperature increases.*

D Is the amount of heat produced by friction always the same? *no*

Advanced Vehicle tires are designed to increase friction between the tire and the surface over which it moves. Have students investigate different materials, tread depths, and tread patterns used in tires to increase friction. Challenge students to explain the advantages and disadvantages of each tread choice.

 Challenge and Extension, p. 168

When an object moves through a fluid, it pushes the molecules of the fluid out of the way. At the same time, the molecules of the fluid exert an equal and opposite force on the object that slows it down. This force resisting motion through a fluid is a type of friction that is often called drag. Friction in fluids depends on the shape of the moving object. Objects can be designed either to increase or reduce the friction caused by a fluid. Airplane designs, for example, improve as engineers find ways to reduce drag.

The friction due to air is often called **air resistance**. Air resistance differs from the friction between solid surfaces. Air resistance depends on surface area and the speed of an object in the following ways:

- An object with a larger surface area comes into contact with more molecules as it moves than an object with a smaller surface area. This increases the air resistance.
- The faster an object moves through air, the more molecules it comes into contact with in a given amount of time. As the speed of the object increases, air resistance increases.

When a skydiver jumps out of a plane, gravity causes the skydiver to accelerate toward the ground. As the skydiver falls, his body pushes against the air. The air pushes back—with the force of air resistance. As the skydiver's speed increases, his air resistance increases. Eventually, air resistance balances gravity, and the skydiver reaches terminal velocity, which is the final, maximum velocity of a falling object. When the skydiver opens his parachute, air resistance increases still further, and he reaches a new, slower terminal velocity that enables him to land safely.

When the force of air resistance equals the force from gravity, a skydiver falls at a constant speed.

 How do speed and surface area affect air resistance?

12.2 Review

KEY CONCEPTS
1. How does friction affect forward motion? Give an example.
2. Describe two ways to change the frictional force between two solid surfaces.
3. How does air resistance affect the velocity of a falling object?

CRITICAL THINKING
4. **Infer** What two sources of friction do you have to overcome when you are walking?
5. **Synthesize** If you push a chair across the floor at a constant velocity, how does the force of friction compare with the force you exert? Explain.

CHALLENGE
6. **Synthesize** If you push a book against a wall hard enough, it will not slide down even though gravity is pulling it. Use what you know about friction and Newton's laws of motion to explain why the book does not fall.

Chapter 12: Gravity, Friction, and Pressure 393

ANSWERS
1. It opposes forward motion. According to Newton's first law, a moving bicycle would continue to move forward without being pedaled if friction did not stop the motion.
2. Answers might include changing the amount of force, pressing the surfaces together, and changing the textures of the surfaces.
3. Air resistance increases until it balances gravity. At that point, an object reaches its maximum velocity.
4. You must overcome friction between your feet and the ground and air resistance.
5. The force will be equal to the force of friction because the forces are balanced (constant velocity).
6. The hand causes force that increases the force of friction between the book and the wall. Friction balances gravity.

MATH IN SCIENCE
Math Skills Practice for Science

Set Learning Goal
To use data and graphs to relate terminal velocity to time and mass

Present the Science
Smoke jumpers are highly skilled firefighters who parachute into areas surrounding forest fires in remote places that are not otherwise accessible.

A parachuter or skydiver has a terminal velocity based on the amount of surface area exposed, and the mass.

To maximize terminal velocity, the skydiver would minimize surface area by keeping arms close to the body and legs close together, aiming the body slightly downward. To minimize terminal velocity, the skydiver would spread out arms and legs. A smoke jumper would probably want to minimize terminal velocity so as to have better control over the landing site.

Develop Graphing Skills
It is standard to plot the independent variable on the horizontal axis of a graph and the dependent variable on the vertical axis.

Have students interpret the graph in the Example. *The graph shows that velocity remained constant after 10 seconds. Therefore, the diver reached terminal velocity at 10 seconds.*

Close
Ask: Which of the data will you graph on the horizontal axis? on the vertical axis? *extra mass; terminal velocity*

- Math Support, p. 199
- Math Practice, p. 200

Technology Resources
Students can visit ClassZone.com for practice in graphing.

 MATH TUTORIAL

SKILL: CREATING A LINE GRAPH

Smoke Jumpers in Action

Scientists often use graphs as a way to present data. Sometimes information is easier to understand when it is presented in graphic form.

Example
Smoke jumpers are firefighters who parachute down into a forest that is on fire. Suppose you measured how the velocity of a smoke jumper changed as he was free-falling, and recorded the following data:

Time (s)	0	2	4	6	8	10	12	14	16	18
Velocity (m/s)	0	18	29	33	35	36	36	36	36	36

Follow these steps to make a line graph of the data in the table.

(1) For both variables, decide the scale that each box on your graph will represent and what range you will show for each variable. For the above time data you might choose a range of 0 to 18 s, with each interval representing 2 s. For velocity, a range of 0 to 40 m/s with intervals of 5 m/s each is reasonable.

(2) Determine the dependent and independent variables. In this example, the velocity depends on the falling time, so velocity is the dependent variable.

(3) Plot the independent variable along the horizontal axis, or *x*-axis. Plot the dependent variable along the vertical axis, or *y*-axis. Connect the points with a smooth line.

Use the data below to answer the following questions.

Suppose a smoke jumper varied the mass of his equipment over 5 jumps, and you measured his different terminal velocities as follows:

Extra Mass (kg)	0	5	10	15	20
Terminal Velocity (m/s)	36	37	38	39	40

1. Identify the independent and dependent variables.
2. Choose the scales and intervals you would use to graph the data. **Hint:** Your velocity range does not have to start at 0 m/s.
3. Plot your graph.

CHALLENGE How do different scales give different impressions of the data? Try comparing several different scales for the same data.

ANSWERS

1. The independent variable is extra mass, and the dependent variable is terminal velocity.
2. Scales and intervals will vary, but intervals for each axis should be equal.
3. The graph will be a straight line going from (0, 36) to (20, 40).

CHALLENGE Different scales can make the line look more or less steep.

KEY CONCEPT
12.3 Pressure depends on force and area.

 BEFORE, you learned
- Frictional forces oppose motion when surfaces resist sliding
- Frictional force depends on the surface types and the total force pushing them together
- Air resistance is a type of friction on objects moving through air

 NOW, you will learn
- How pressure is determined
- How forces act on objects in fluids
- How pressure changes in fluids

VOCABULARY
pressure p. 395
pascal p. 396

EXPLORE Pressure

How does surface area affect pressure?

PROCEDURE

1. Place the pencil flat on the Styrofoam board. Balance the book on top of the pencil. After 5 seconds, remove the book and the pencil. Observe the Styrofoam.

2. Balance the book on top of the pencil in an upright position as shown. After 5 seconds, remove the book and the pencil. Observe the Styrofoam.

WHAT DO YOU THINK?
- How did the effect on the Styrofoam change from step 1 to step 2?
- What do you think accounts for any differences you noted?

MATERIALS
- sharpened pencil
- Styrofoam board
- book

VOCABULARY
Create a four square diagram for *pressure* in your notebook.

Pressure describes how a force is spread over an area.

Pressure is a measure of how much force is acting on a certain area. In other words, pressure describes how concentrated a force is. When a cat lies down on your lap, all the force of the cat's weight is spread out over a large area of your lap. If the cat stands up, however, all the force from the cat's weight is concentrated into its paws. The pressure the cat exerts on you increases when the cat stands up in your lap.

While the increased pressure may make you feel as if there is more force on you, the force is actually the same. The cat's weight is simply pressing on a smaller area. How you feel a force when it is pressing on you depends on both the force and the area over which it is applied.

Chapter 12: **Gravity, Friction, and Pressure** 395

RESOURCES FOR DIFFERENTIATED INSTRUCTION

Below Level
UNIT RESOURCE BOOK
- Reading Study Guide A, pp. 173–174
- Decoding Support, p. 196

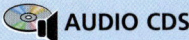 **AUDIO CDS**

Advanced
UNIT RESOURCE BOOK
Challenge and Extension, p. 179

English Learners
UNIT RESOURCE BOOK
Spanish Reading Study Guide, pp. 177–178

 **AUDIO CDS**
- Audio Readings in Spanish
- Audio Readings (English)

12.3 FOCUS

▶ Set Learning Goals
Students will
- Explain how pressure is determined.
- Describe how forces act on objects in fluids.
- Describe pressure changes in fluids.

▶ 3-Minute Warm-Up
Display Transparency 21 or copy this exercise on the board:

Write a paragraph about what happens when you try to walk on ice. Compare walking on ice to walking on a sidewalk in the summer. *Students' paragraphs should discuss the role that friction between surfaces plays in walking.*

[T] 3-Minute Warm-Up, p. T21

12.3 MOTIVATE

EXPLORE Pressure
PURPOSE To introduce how surface area affects pressure

TIP *10 min.* A small piece of Styrofoam of about five square centimeters is adequate. Students should balance the book with their hand and not press down on it.

WHAT DO YOU THINK? *The total force remained the same. The effect was greater in step 2 because the force was exerted over a smaller area.*

Chapter 12 **395**

12.3 INSTRUCT

Teacher Demo

Use shoes with different sized heels to demonstrate how pressure changes when area changes and force stays constant. Wear shoes such as athletic shoes and stand on a piece of soft wood, Styrofoam, or corrugated cardboard. Switch to shoes with increasingly narrower heels to show how pressure increases, as shown by increased indentations, as the area of the heel decreases. You can use a student volunteer, but it is important that one person performs the entire activity so that force remains constant throughout. You must use a new piece of Styrofoam or cardboard each time.

Develop Algebra Skills

Review with students the importance of using the correct formula and correct units when solving problems.

- Show students how to use the pressure formula to solve for force or area. Remind them that multiplication and division are opposite operations, and they "undo" each other. Emphasize that an operation must be done to both sides of the equation.

- Units can be especially tricky when students cannot easily see their relationship within the problem. The relationship among square meters, newtons, and pascals is not obvious. Remind students that area must be in square meters for these problems.

- Math Support, p. 197
- Math Practice, p. 198

Ongoing Assessment

Explain how to determine pressure.

Ask: What two quantities do you need to know to calculate pressure? *force and area*

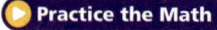 Answers:

1. $P = \dfrac{F}{A} = \dfrac{500\text{ N}}{0.075\text{ m}^2} = 6670\text{ Pa}$

2. $F = PA = 2000\,\dfrac{\text{N}}{\text{m}^2} \cdot 20\text{ m}^2 = 40{,}000\text{ N}$

396 Unit 3: **Motion and Forces**

READING TIP
Notice that when a unit, such as pascal or newton, is named for a person, the unit is not capitalized but its abbreviation is.

One way to increase pressure is to increase force. If you press a wall with your finger, the harder you press, the more pressure you put on the wall. But you can also increase the pressure by decreasing the area. When you push a thumbtack into a wall, you apply a force to the thumbtack. The small area of the sharp point of the thumbtack produces a much larger pressure on the wall than the area of your finger does. The greater pressure from the thumbtack can pierce the wall, while the pressure from your finger alone cannot.

The following formula shows exactly how pressure depends on force and area:

$$\text{Pressure} = \dfrac{\text{Force}}{\text{Area}} \qquad P = \dfrac{F}{A}$$

In this formula, P is the pressure, F is the force in newtons, and A is the area over which the force is exerted, measured in square meters (m^2). The unit for pressure is the **pascal** (Pa). One pascal is the pressure exerted by one newton (1 N) of force on an area of one square meter (1 m^2). That is, one pascal is equivalent to one N/m^2.

Sometimes knowing pressure is more useful than knowing force. For example, many surfaces will break or crack if the pressure on them is too great. A person with snowshoes can walk on top of snow, while a person in hiking boots will sink into the snow.

COMPARE How does the pressure from her snowshoes compare to the pressure from her boots?

Calculating Pressure

▶ **Sample Problem**

A winter hiker weighing 500 N is wearing snowshoes that cover an area of 0.2 m^2. What pressure does the hiker exert on the snow?

What do you know? Area = 0.2 m^2, Force = 500 N

What do you want to find out? Pressure

Write the formula: $P = \dfrac{F}{A}$

Substitute into the formula: $P = \dfrac{500\text{ N}}{0.2\text{ m}^2}$

Calculate and simplify: $P = 2500\,\dfrac{\text{N}}{\text{m}^2} = 2500\text{ N/m}^2$

Check that your units agree: Unit is N/m^2.
Unit of pressure is Pa, which is also N/m^2. Units agree.

Answer: $P = 2500$ Pa

▶ **Practice the Math**

1. If a winter hiker weighing 500 N is wearing boots that have an area of 0.075 m^2, how much pressure is exerted on the snow?
2. A pressure of 2000 Pa is exerted on a surface with an area of 20 m^2. What is the total force exerted on the surface?

DIFFERENTIATE INSTRUCTION

More Reading Support

A If force increases, what happens to pressure? *It increases.*

B What unit is used for pressure? *pascal*

English Learners English learners may not have prior knowledge of the snowshoes mentioned on this page, elevation on p. 398, and ice skating on p. 399. The Chapter Investigation on p. 400 asks students to write hypotheses in the form of "If . . . then . . . because . . ." statements. This concept should be taught directly to English learners. Offer examples to illustrate how the sentence structure works. For example, "If you climb a mountain, then the air pressure will decrease, because air is less dense at higher elevations."

Pressure acts in all directions in fluids.

Fluids are made of loosely connected particles that are too small to see. These particles are in constant, rapid motion. The motion is random, which means particles are equally likely to move in any direction. Particles collide with—or crash into—one another and into the walls of a container holding the fluid. The particles also collide with any objects in the fluid.

Explore how a fluid produces pressure.

As particles collide with an object in the fluid, they apply a constant force to the surfaces of the object. This force produces a pressure against the surfaces that the particles come in contact with. A fluid contains many particles, each moving in a different direction, and the force from each particle can be exerted in any direction. Therefore, the pressure exerted by the fluid acts on an object from all directions.

The diver in the picture below experiences a constant pressure from the particles—or molecules—in the water. Water molecules are constantly hitting her body from all directions. The collisions on all parts of her body produce a net force on the surface of her body.

CHECK YOUR READING How does understanding particle motion help you understand fluid pressure?

Pressure in Fluids

Randomly moving water molecules collide with a diver. The net force from the many collisions produces the pressure on the diver.

net force (arm)

READING VISUALS How are the water molecules exerting pressure on the diver?

Chapter 12: **Gravity, Friction, and Pressure** 397

DIFFERENTIATE INSTRUCTION

 **More Reading Support**

C What is the result of collisions of particles with an object? *pressure on the object*

D In which direction does pressure act on an object in a fluid? *in all directions*

Alternative Assessment Have students make a diagram of the heart or the ear and show where and why pressure increases or decreases.

Integrate the Sciences

Pressure exerted by fluids has many biological implications.

Blood exerts pressure against the walls of blood vessels. The pressure in arteries can be determined by using a blood pressure cuff and a stethoscope. Blood pressure is reported as a fraction. The top number is the pressure of blood when the heart is beating. The lower number measures the pressure of blood when the heart is resting.

Differences in air pressure and the pressure of air in the middle ear can cause ear pain. This pressure difference occurs when the eustachian tube does not open enough to equalize the pressures. This problem most often occurs when air pressure is much less than usual, such as in an airplane.

EXPLORE the BIG idea

Revisit "Under Pressure" on p. 379. Have students explain the reasons for their results.

Ongoing Assessment

Describe how forces act on objects in fluids.

Ask: A balloon is floating in the air. In which direction is pressure acting on the balloon? *in all directions*

CHECK YOUR READING Answer: A fluid contains many particles, and the forces from each particle can be exerted in any direction. Therefore, fluid pressure acts on an object from all directions.

READING VISUALS Answer: The water molecules are hitting the diver from all directions. The collisions produce a net force which produces pressure on the diver.

Chapter 12 **397**

Develop Critical Thinking

APPLY One practical use of air pressure is scuba diving. Pressurized gases are placed into tanks that divers use as a source of air for breathing when diving.

- Remind students that pressure is caused by collisions with an object, such as the walls of a container. Ask: What happens to the pressure of gases as they are forced into the tanks? *Pressure increases because the more particles, the more collisions. In this case, the gas particles hit the container more frequently.*

- Certain parts of the body are compressible. That is, these parts become smaller in volume when pressure is increased, such as when a diver goes deeper into water. These parts are the middle ear, the sinuses, and the lungs. Ask: What do these body parts have in common that would make them affected by increased pressure? *They all contain some air.*

- The air in a scuba tank exerts a pressure that is about 200 times greater than normal atmospheric pressure. Ask: Why does a scuba tank need a regulator to control the pressure of the air that is breathed? *If the pressure were not reduced to an appropriate level, it might damage lung tissue.*

Teach Difficult Concepts

Relate friction and pressure to an everyday example. Ask: If you are going on a long road trip, why might the tires on your car have a greater pressure when you reach your destination than they did when you began your journey? *Friction between the tires and the road heats the tires, raising the pressure.*

Pressure in fluids depends on depth.

The pressure that a fluid exerts depends on the density and the depth of the fluid. Imagine that you have a tall cylinder sitting on the palm of your hand. As you fill the cylinder with water, the force of the water's weight exerts more and more pressure on your hand. The force of the water's weight increases as you put in more water.

Suppose you had two identical cylinders of water sitting on your hand. The cylinders would push with twice the weight of a single cylinder, but the force would be spread over twice the area. Therefore, the pressure would still be the same. The pressure does not depend on the total volume of the fluid, only on the depth and density.

Pressure in Air

Although you do not notice the weight of air, air exerts pressure on you at all times. At sea level, air exerts a pressure on you equal to about 100,000 pascals. This pressure is called atmospheric pressure and is referred to as one atmosphere. At this pressure, every square centimeter of your body experiences a force of ten newtons (2.2 lb). You do not notice it pushing your body inward, however, because the materials in your body provide an equal outward pressure that balances the air pressure.

Changing Elevation Air has weight. The more air there is above you, the greater the weight of that air. As you climb a mountain, the column of air above you is shorter and weighs less, so the pressure of air on you at higher elevations is less than one atmosphere.

Changing Density The air at the top of a column presses down on the air below it. The farther down the column, the more weight there is above to press downward. Air at lower elevations is more compressed, and therefore denser, than air at higher elevations.

Effects on Pressure Pressure is exerted by individual molecules colliding with an object. In denser air, there are more molecules—and therefore more collisions. An increase in the number of collisions results in an increase in the force, and therefore pressure, exerted by the air.

As you travel up a mountain, the air pressure on you decreases. For a short time, the pressure on the inside surface of your eardrum may continue to push out with the same force that balanced the air pressure at a lower elevation. The eardrum is pushed outward, and you may feel pain until your internal pressure adjusts to the new air pressure.

A person at an altitude of 2000 meters experiences approximately 20 percent less atmospheric pressure than a person at sea level.

DIFFERENTIATE INSTRUCTION

 More Reading Support

E Will the pressure at the top of a mountain be greater than one atmosphere or less than one atmosphere? *less*

Advanced The fact that pressure depends on the depth of a fluid, not the total volume, can be difficult for students to accept. Have advanced students create a visual that will help convince other students that pressure depends on depth.

R Challenge and Extension, p. 179

Pressure in Water

Unlike air molecules, water molecules are already very close together. The density of water does not change very much with depth. However, the deeper you go underwater, the more water there is above you. The weight of that water above you produces the water pressure acting on your body. Just as air pressure increases at lower elevations, water pressure increases with greater water depth.

Water exerts more pressure on you than air does because water has a greater density than air. Therefore, the change in weight of the column of water above you as you dive is greater for each meter that you descend than it is in air. There is a greater difference in pressure if you dive ten meters farther down in the ocean than if you walked ten meters down a mountain. In fact, ten meters of water above you applies about as much pressure on you as the entire atmosphere does.

If you were to dive 1000 meters (3300 ft) below the surface of the ocean, the pressure would be nearly 100 times greater than pressure from the atmosphere. The force of this pressure would collapse your lungs unless you were protected by special deep-sea diving equipment. As scientists explore the ocean to greater depths, new underwater vehicles are designed that can withstand the increase in water pressure. Some whales, however, can dive to a depth of 1000 meters without being injured. As these whales dive to great depths, their lungs are almost completely collapsed by the pressure. However, the whales have adapted to the collapse—they store most of their oxygen intake in their muscles and blood instead of within their lungs.

A deep-diving whale at 1000 meters below the surface experiences about 34 times more pressure than a turtle diving to a depth of 20 meters (65 ft).

 Why is water pressure greater than air pressure?

12.3 Review

KEY CONCEPTS
1. How is pressure related to force and surface area?
2. Describe the way in which a fluid exerts pressure on an object immersed in it.
3. How does changing elevation affect air pressure? How does changing depth affect water pressure?

CRITICAL THINKING
4. **Calculate** If a board with an area of 3 m² has a 12 N force exerted on it, what is the pressure on the board?
5. **Infer** What might cause a balloon blown up at a low altitude to burst if it is taken to a higher altitude?

CHALLENGE
6. **Synthesize** During cold winters, ice can form on small lakes and ponds. Many people enjoy skating on the ice. Occasionally, a person skates on thin ice and breaks through it. Why do rescue workers lie flat on the ice instead of walking upright when reaching out to help rescue a skater?

ANSWERS
1. Pressure describes how force is spread over an area.
2. Pressure is exerted in all directions.
3. Increasing elevation decreases air pressure. As water becomes deeper, its pressure increases.
4. P = F/A = 12 N/ 3 m² = 4 Pa
5. As the balloon is taken to a higher altitude, outside pressure decreases. The balloon expands because the inside pressure becomes greater than the outside air pressure. If the balloon expands enough, it will burst.
6. The weight (force) of the person causes less pressure if exerted over a larger area. The area over which the force is exerted is much greater for a person lying on the ice than for the same person standing up on it.

CHAPTER INVESTIGATION

Focus

PURPOSE Students will learn how water pressure changes when depth and volume of the water change.

OVERVIEW Students will determine how much pressure is produced by varying volumes and depths of water. Students will determine that

- Pressure is the same for a larger volume
- Pressure is greater for a greater depth

Lab Preparation

- Ask students to bring plastic bottles of different sizes from home several days before doing the lab. For consistency, use only bottles with smooth sides.
- To save class time and for student safety, carefully cut the tops off the bottles ahead of time with scissors or a sharp knife.
- Prior to the investigation, have students read through the investigation and prepare their data tables. Or you may wish to copy and distribute datasheets and rubrics.

 UNIT RESOURCE BOOK, pp. 201–209

 SCIENCE TOOLKIT, F14

Lab Management

- Advise students to allow for all depths down to four centimeters when making their data tables.
- Warn students not to squeeze the bottles when they put their finger over the hole. Squeezing the bottle will give a volume reading that is too high.
- Have rags available for cleaning up any spills.

SAFETY Students should use caution in cutting the bottles and making the holes. Clean up any spills immediately.

INCLUSION Use colored tape to mark off the meter stick in measurements of 10 cm to help students see the numbers.

400 Unit 3: **Motion and Forces**

CHAPTER INVESTIGATION

Pressure in Fluids

OVERVIEW AND PURPOSE When you put your hand under a faucet, you experience water pressure. Underwater explorers also experience water pressure. In this investigation you will
- change the depth and volume of a column of water
- determine what factors affect pressure

 **Problem**

What factors affect water pressure?

 **Hypothesize**

Write two hypotheses to explain what you expect to happen to the water pressure as you change the depth and volume of the water column. Your hypotheses (one for depth, one for volume) should take the form of "If . . . , then . . . , because . . ." statements.

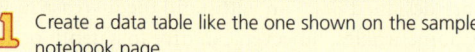

MATERIALS
- nail
- 2 plastic bottles, small and large, with tops cut off
- ruler
- plastic container
- meter stick
- coffee can
- water

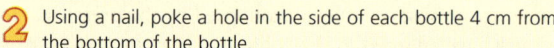 **Procedure**

1. Create a data table like the one shown on the sample notebook page.

2. Using a nail, poke a hole in the side of each bottle 4 cm from the bottom of the bottle.

3. Set up the materials as shown on the left. Put a ruler in the small bottle so that the lower numbers are at the bottom.

4. Put your finger over the hole so no water will squirt out. Add or remove water (by lifting your finger off the hole) so that the water level is exactly at the 12 cm mark.

5. Release your finger from the hole, while your partner reads the exact mark where the water hits the meter stick. Cover the hole immediately after your partner reads the distance the water squirted. Record the distance on the line for this depth in your table.

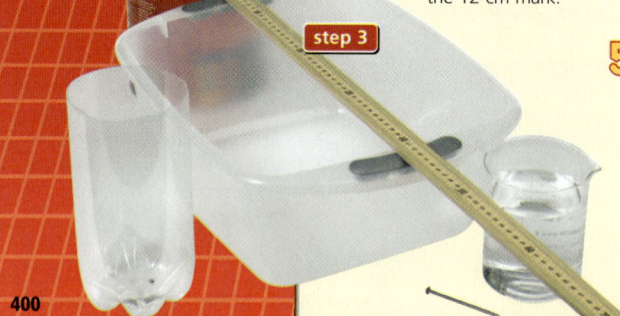

INVESTIGATION RESOURCES

 CHAPTER INVESTIGATION, Pressure in Fluids
- Level A, pp. 201–204
- Level B, pp. 205–208
- Level C, p. 209

Advanced students should complete Levels B & C.

 Writing a Lab Report, D12–13

Technology Resources

Customize this student lab as needed or look for an alternative. Print rubrics to assess student lab reports.

 Lab Generator CD-ROM

6. Add or remove water so that the water level is now exactly at the 11 cm mark. Repeat step 5.

7. Continue adding, removing, and squirting water at each whole centimeter mark until no more water squirts from the bottle.

8. Repeat steps 4–7 two more times for a total of three trials.

9. Repeat steps 4–8 using the large bottle.

Observe and Analyze

1. **RECORD OBSERVATIONS** Be sure that your data table is complete.
2. **GRAPH** Construct a graph showing distance versus depth. Draw two curves, one for the small bottle and one for the large bottle. Use different colors for the two curves.
3. **IDENTIFY VARIABLES AND CONSTANTS** List the variables and constants for the experiment using the small bottle and the experiment using the large bottle.
4. **ANALYZE** Is the depth greater when the bottle is more full or more empty? When did the water squirt farther, when the bottle was more full or more empty?
5. **ANALYZE** Did the water squirt farther when you used the small or the large bottle?

Conclude

1. **INTERPRET** Answer the question posed in the problem.
2. **ANALYZE** Examine your graph and compare your results with your hypotheses. Do your results support your hypotheses?
3. **INFER** How does depth affect pressure? How does volume affect pressure?

4. **IDENTIFY LIMITS** What possible limitations or errors did you experience or could you have experienced with this investigation?
5. **APPLY** Dams store water for irrigation, home use, and hydroelectric power. Explain why dams must be constructed so that they are much thicker at the bottom than at the top.
6. **APPLY** Have you ever dived to the bottom of a swimming pool to pick up a coin? Describe what you felt as you swam toward the bottom.

INVESTIGATE Further

CHALLENGE Repeat the investigation using a liquid with a density that is quite different from water. Measure the distance the liquid travels, and graph the new data in a different color. Is there a difference? Why do you think there is or is not a difference in pressure between liquids of different densities?

Observe and Analyze

SAMPLE DATA Depth of Water, Small Bottle, 11 cm; Distance, 12 cm, 11.5 cm, 14 cm; Distance Average, 12.5 cm; Depth of Water, Large Bottle, 11 cm; Distance, 11 cm, 12.5 cm, 11.5 cm; Distance Average, 11.2 cm

2. Graphs should show depth as the independent variable on the horizontal axis and distance on the vertical axis. The curve will be the same for both bottles.

3. For both, the independent variable is depth, and the dependent variable is distance. Volume at the same depth is the independent variable. Constants include water temperature, height of the bottle, location of the meter stick, and fluid used.

4. When the bottle was more full, the water squirted farther and the depth was greater.

5. The water squirted the same distance from the larger bottle.

Conclude

1. Depth affects water pressure.
2. Student answers will vary.
3. Greater depth results in greater pressure. Volume does not affect pressure.
4. Sample answers: distance on the meter stick could be difficult to determine; placement of the bottles on the can was not the same.
5. Water pressure is greater at the bottom.
6. Pressure increases as you get closer to the bottom.

INVESTIGATE Further

SAFETY Do not let students use liquids that are flammable or toxic, or have hazardous vapors.

CHALLENGE Students' results will depend on the viscosity of the liquid they choose. However, if the hole is large enough, the results should be similar to the original experiment.

Post-Lab Discussion

- Ask students to compare their results to those of others. They should note that the curves produced are similar but might not be exactly the same. Ask them to compare the results with the results attained when different bottles were used.
- Discuss how the results of this investigation could be used in designing a swimming pool.

12.4 FOCUS

◗ Set Learning Goals
Students will
- Explain how fluids apply forces to objects.
- Describe how the motion of a fluid affects the pressure it exerts.
- Explain how forces are transmitted through fluids.
- Observe through experimentation how the speed of air affects air pressure.

◗ 3-Minute Warm-Up
Display Transparency 21 or copy this exercise on the board:

Decide if these statements are true. If not true, correct them.

1. A person exerts the same force on a floor whether she is lying on it or standing on it. *true*
2. A force is applied over two square centimeters. The same force is applied over four square centimeters. The amount of force per square centimeter is the same for both. *The amount of force per square centimeter differs.*
3. If $F = mg$, then m can be found by multiplying g by F. *If $F = mg$, then m can be found by dividing F by g.*

3-Minute Warm-Up, p. T21

12.4 MOTIVATE

EXPLORE Forces in Liquid
PURPOSE To observe how water applies a force on objects

TIP 10 min. Use large paper clips so that students can easily tie string to them.

WHAT DO YOU THINK? *The paper clips in water seemed lighter, and they seemed out of balance. The water was applying an upward force on them.*

KEY CONCEPT
12.4 Fluids can exert a force on objects.

◁ **BEFORE, you learned**
- Pressure depends on force and area
- Pressure acts in all directions in fluids
- Density is mass divided by volume

▶ **NOW, you will learn**
- How fluids apply forces to objects
- How the motion of a fluid affects the pressure it exerts
- How forces are transmitted through fluids

VOCABULARY
buoyant force p. 402
Bernoulli's principle p. 404
Pascal's principle p. 406

EXPLORE Forces in Liquid
How does water affect weight?

PROCEDURE
1. Tie a piece of string to the middle of the pencil. Tie 4 paper clips to each end of the pencil as shown.
2. Move the middle string along the pencil until the paper clips are balanced and the pencil hangs flat.
3. While keeping the pencil balanced, slowly lower the paper clips on one end of the pencil into the water. Observe what happens.

WHAT DO YOU THINK?
- How did the water affect the balance between the two sets of paper clips?
- Did the water exert a force on the paper clips? Explain.

MATERIALS
- 3 pieces of string
- pencil
- 8 paper clips
- cup full of water

Fluids can exert an upward force on objects.

If you drop an ice cube in air, it falls to the floor. If you drop the ice cube into water, it may sink a little at first, but the cube quickly rises upward until it floats. You know that gravity is pulling downward on the ice, even when it is in the water. If the ice cube is not sinking, there must be some force balancing gravity that is pushing upward on it.

The upward force on objects in a fluid is called **buoyant force**, or buoyancy. Buoyancy is why ice floats in water. Because of buoyant force, objects seem lighter in water. For example, it is easier to lift a heavy rock in water than on land because the buoyant force pushes upward on the rock, reducing the net force you need to lift it.

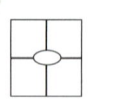
VOCABULARY
Create a four square diagram for *buoyant force.*

402 Unit 3: Motion and Forces

RESOURCES FOR DIFFERENTIATED INSTRUCTION

Below Level
UNIT RESOURCE BOOK
- Reading Study Guide A, pp. 183–184
- Decoding Support, p. 196

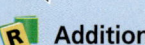 AUDIO CDS

Additional INVESTIGATION,
What Floats Your Boat?, A, B, & C, pp. 210–218;
Teacher Instructions, pp. 346–347

Advanced
UNIT RESOURCE BOOK
- Challenge and Extension, p. 189
- Challenge Reading, pp. 192–193

English Learners
UNIT RESOURCE BOOK
Spanish Reading Study Guide, pp. 187–188

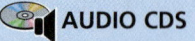 AUDIO CDS
- Audio Readings in Spanish
- Audio Readings (English)

Buoyancy

The photograph on the right shows a balloon that has been pushed into a beaker of water. Remember that in a fluid, pressure increases with depth. This means that there is greater pressure acting on the bottom of the balloon than on the top of it. The pressure difference between the top and bottom of the balloon produces a net force that is pushing the balloon upward.

When you push a balloon underwater, the water level rises because the water and the balloon cannot be in the same place at the same time. The volume of the water has not changed, but some of the water has been displaced, or moved, by the balloon. The volume of the displaced water is equal to the volume of the balloon. The buoyant force on the balloon is equal to the weight of the displaced water. A deflated balloon would displace less water and would therefore have a smaller buoyant force on it.

net force

CHECK YOUR READING Why does increasing the volume of an object increase the buoyant force on it when it is in a fluid?

Density and Buoyancy

Whether or not an object floats in a fluid depends on the densities of both the object and the fluid. Density is a measure of the amount of matter packed into a unit volume. The density of an object is equal to its mass divided by its volume, and is commonly measured in grams per cubic centimeter (g/cm^3).

If an object is less dense than the fluid it is in, the fluid the object displaces can weigh more than the object. A wooden ball that is pushed underwater, as in the beaker below and on the left, rises to the top and floats. An object rising in a liquid has a buoyant force acting upon it that is greater than its own weight. If an object is floating in a liquid, the buoyant force is balancing the weight.

READING TIP
Remember that both air and water are fluids, and water has a greater density than air. Therefore, water has a greater buoyant force.

If the object is more dense than the fluid it is in, the object weighs more than the fluid it displaces. A glass marble placed in the beaker on the far right sinks to the bottom because glass is denser than water. The weight of the water the marble displaces is less than the weight of the marble. A sinking object has a weight that is greater than the buoyant force on it.

weight — buoyant force — no net force

weight — buoyant force — net force

Chapter 12: Gravity, Friction, and Pressure 403

INVESTIGATE
Bernoulli's Principle

PURPOSE Observe how the speed of air affects air pressure

TIPS 15 min.

- The marks on the straw should be straight and narrow.
- Practice blowing straight across the top of the straw before recording observations. Students should be careful not to blow downward into the marked straw.

WHAT DO YOU THINK? *The water rose in the marked straw. When air was blown softly, water rose in the straw, but not as much as when air was blown with greater intensity.*

CHALLENGE *The air blown across the top of the tube would not change the pressure of the air in the tube.*

 Datasheet, Bernoulli's Principle, p. 190

Technology Resources

Customize this student lab as needed or look for an alternative. Print rubrics to assess student lab reports.

 Lab Generator CD-ROM

Ongoing Assessment

CHECK YOUR READING Answer: *The faster the fluid moves, the less pressure it exerts on surfaces or openings over which it flows.*

The motion of a fluid affects its pressure.

The motion of a fluid affects the amount of pressure it exerts. A faster-moving fluid exerts less pressure as it flows over the surface of an object than a slower moving fluid. For example, wind blowing over a chimney top decreases the pressure at the top of the chimney. The faster air has less pressure than the slower-moving air in the fireplace. The increased pressure difference more effectively pulls the smoke from a fire out of the fireplace and up the chimney.

Bernoulli's Principle

Bernoulli's principle, named after Daniel Bernoulli (buhr-NOO-lee), a Swiss mathematician who lived in the 1700s, describes the effects of fluid motion on pressure. In general, **Bernoulli's principle** says that an increase in the speed of the motion of a fluid decreases the pressure within the fluid. The faster a fluid moves, the less pressure it exerts on surfaces or openings it flows over.

 What is the relationship between the speed of a fluid and the pressure that the fluid exerts?

INVESTIGATE Bernoulli's Principle

How does the speed of air affect air pressure?
PROCEDURE

1. Use the pen to mark off intervals of 1 cm along the length of one of the straws.
2. Put a drop of food coloring in the cup of water and stir it. Place the marked straw into the cup and hold it upright so that the water level in the straw is at one of the marks. The straw should not touch the bottom of the cup.
3. Position the second straw as shown. Blow across the open end of the marked straw. Observe the level of the water in the marked straw as you blow.
4. Blow harder and then softer. Observe the water level as you change the speed of the air.

WHAT DO YOU THINK?
- What happened to the water in the straw as you blew?
- How did the speed of the air relate to the changes you observed?

CHALLENGE What results would you expect if you blew over the top of a tube with a closed bottom instead of the straw? Explain.

SKILL FOCUS Observing

MATERIALS
- pen
- ruler
- two clear straws
- clear plastic cup filled with water
- food coloring

TIME 15 minutes

404 Unit 3: Motion and Forces

DIFFERENTIATE INSTRUCTION

 **More Reading Support**

C If a moving fluid slows down, what happens to its pressure? *pressure increases*

English Learners English learners may have a difficult time recognizing cause-and-effect relationships when sentences beginning with *If* do not contain clauses in which *then* is stated directly. Copy the following chart on the board and ask students to model the examples provided (from p. 403).

Cause	Effect
If an object is floating in a liquid,	the buoyant force is balancing the weight.
If the object is more dense than the fluid it is in,	the object weighs more than the fluid it displaces.

404 Unit 3: **Motion and Forces**

Applying Bernoulli's Principle

Bernoulli's principle has many applications. One important application is used in airplanes. Airplane wings can be shaped to take advantage of Bernoulli's principle. Certain wing shapes cause the air flowing over the top of the wing to move faster than the air flowing under the wing. Such a design improves the lifting force on a flying airplane.

Many racecars, however, have a device on the rear of the car that has the reverse effect. The device is designed like an upside-down airplane wing. This shape increases the pressure on the top of the car. The car is pressed downward on the road, which increases friction between the tires and the road. With more friction, the car is less likely to skid as it goes around curves at high speeds.

A prairie-dog colony also shows Bernoulli's principle in action. The mounds that prairie dogs build over some entrances to their burrows help to keep the burrows well-ventilated.

1. Air closer to the ground tends to move at slower speeds than air higher up. The air over an entrance at ground level generally moves slower than the air over an entrance in a raised mound.
2. The increased speed of the air over a raised mound entrance decreases the pressure over that opening.
3. The greater air pressure over a ground-level entrance produces an unbalanced force that pushes air through the tunnels and out the higher mound entrance.

Bernoulli's Principle in Nature

Bernoulli's principle explains why having two entrances at different heights helps ventilate a prairie-dog burrow.

1. Air moves more slowly near the ground.
2. The air over the raised entrance moves faster and has less pressure than the slower-moving air near the ground.
3. The pressure difference between the two entrances moves air through the tunnel.

Chapter 12: Gravity, Friction, and Pressure **405**

Teach Difficult Concepts

Students may have previously been taught that airplanes fly "because of Bernoulli's principle." Many physicists prefer to explain airplane flight using Newton's third law—the wings push the air down, and the air pushes the wings up. The roles of both Bernoulli's principle and Newton's laws in flight are still being debated among scientists. Encourage interested students to research this debate on the Internet.

It is true that wings can be designed to improve lift by forcing the air flowing over the wing to move faster than the air flowing under the wing. Contrary to what students may have learned, however, the air does not go faster over the longer top side because it is forced to "meet up" at the back of the wing. Wind tunnel experiments, in fact, show that the air does not meet up again.

Ongoing Assessment

Describe how the motion of a fluid affects the pressure it exerts.

Ask: Which exerts more pressure, the water in rapids or water in a slow-moving stream? *water in a slow-moving stream*

DIFFERENTIATE INSTRUCTION

 More Reading Support

D Why does air flow from a ground-level entrance to a higher entrance? *The pressure is greater at the lower entrance.*

Alternative Assessment Fluids forced through narrow spaces flow faster. This effect, called the Venturi effect, can be used to demonstrate Bernoulli's principle. Have students design an experiment using a stream table to show that water flows faster through narrow channels.

Advanced Have students who are interested in how pressure affects the motion of fluids read the following article:

Challenge Reading, pp. 192–193

Chapter 12 **405**

Real World Example

Squeeze a tube of toothpaste at one end and watch the toothpaste squirt out the other end. Apply pressure to one end of a container of caulk, and the caulk flows out the top. In both instances, pressure applied to one part of the fluid is transmitted through the fluid. Other examples include squeezing a plastic container of ketchup or mustard.

The amount of pressure is reflected in the results of the application. If you apply a lot of pressure to a tube or bottle, then a lot of fluid comes out quickly. A small amount of pressure releases a small amount of fluid.

Mathematics Connection

Although Pascal was a scientist, he is primarily known as a mathematician. A triangle containing a classic numeric pattern is named after him. He worked extensively in the areas of geometry and probability.

Develop Critical Thinking

APPLY Air bags can be used to lift large weights. They can be used when basements are installed under an existing house. Have students use Pascal's principle to devise a plan to move a house using air bags. *Sample answer: Excavate the land around the base of the house, and install beams under the house. Gradually work the air bag under the house, and pump air into it. The house will rise by small amounts as the pressure from the air is transmitted throughout the air bag.*

Ongoing Assessment

Explain how forces are transmitted through fluids.

Ask: Why does toothpaste come out of the tube when you squeeze it? *When you increase pressure on the fluid toothpaste, pressure increases all through the tube, and the fluid finds and takes the path of least resistance, through the opening.*

Forces can be transmitted through fluids.

Imagine you have a bottle full of water. You place the bottle cap on it, but you do not tighten the cap. You give the bottle a hard squeeze and the cap falls off. How was the force you put on the bottle transferred to the bottle cap?

Pascal's Principle

In the 1600s Blaise Pascal (pa-SKAL), a French scientist for whom the unit of measure called the pascal was named, experimented with fluids in containers. One of his key discoveries is called Pascal's principle. **Pascal's principle** states that when an outside pressure is applied at any point to a fluid in a container, that pressure is transmitted throughout the fluid with equal strength.

You can use Pascal's principle to transmit a force through a fluid. Some car jacks lift cars using Pascal's principle. These jacks contain liquids that transmit and increase the force that you apply.

① The part of the jack that moves down and pushes on the liquid is called a piston. As you push down on the piston, you increase the pressure on the liquid.

② The increase in pressure is equal to your applied force divided by the area of the downward-pushing piston. This increase in pressure is transmitted throughout the liquid.

Pascal's Principle

The pressure from the smaller piston is equal to the pressure pushing up the larger one. The large piston can exert more force because of its greater area.

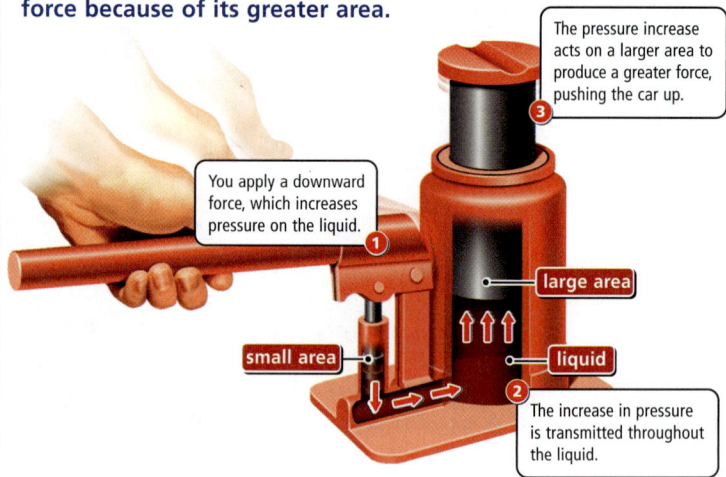

DIFFERENTIATE INSTRUCTION

 More Reading Support

E What is Pascal's principle? *If pressure is increased at one point in a fluid, it increases by the same amount everywhere in the fluid.*

Advanced In hydraulics, pressure is applied to a small piston that transfers this pressure to a larger piston, which multiplies the force. Have students use the pressure equation to find the amount of force produced when a 400 N force is applied to a 4 cm² piston, which transfers this pressure to a large piston with an area of 40 cm². *400 N/4 cm² = x/40 cm². The resulting force of the large piston is 4000 N.*

 Challenge and Extension, p. 189

The increased pressure pushes upward on another piston, which raises the car. This piston has a large area compared with the first piston, so the upward force is greater than the downward force. A large enough area produces the force needed to lift a car. However, the larger piston does not move upward as far as the smaller one moved downward.

 Describe how pressure is transmitted through a fluid.

Hydraulics

Machines that use liquids to transmit or increase a force are called hydraulic (hy-DRAW-lihk) machines. The advantage to using a liquid instead of a gas is that when you squeeze a liquid, its volume does not change much. The molecules in a liquid are so close together that it is hard to push the molecules any closer. Gas molecules, however, have a lot of space between them. If you apply pressure to a gas, you decrease its volume.

The hydraulic arm on the garbage truck lifts and empties trash cans.

Although hydraulic systems are used in large machines such as garbage trucks, research is being done on using hydraulics on a much smaller scale. Researchers are developing a storage chip similar to a computer chip that uses hydraulics rather than electronics. This chip uses pipes and pumps to move fluid into specific chambers on a rubber chip. Researchers hope that a hydraulic chip system will eventually allow scientists to use a single hand-held device to perform chemical experiments with over a thousand different liquids.

12.4 Review

KEY CONCEPTS

1. Why is there an upward force on objects in water?
2. How does changing the speed of a fluid affect its pressure?
3. If you push a cork into the neck of a bottle filled with air, what happens to the pressure inside the bottle?

CRITICAL THINKING

4. **Infer** Ebony is a dark wood that has a density of 1.2 g/cm³. Water has a density of 1.0 g/cm³. Will a block of ebony float in water? Explain.
5. **Analyze** When you use a spray bottle, you force air over a small tube inside the bottle. Explain why the liquid inside the bottle comes out.

CHALLENGE

6. **Synthesize** If you apply a force of 20 N downward on a car jack piston with an area of 2.5 cm², what force will be applied to the upward piston if it has an area of 400 cm²? Hint: Remember that pressure equals force divided by area.

Chapter 12: **Gravity, Friction, and Pressure** 407

ANSWERS

1. The pressure in a fluid increases with depth. The pressure acting on the lower side of an object in a fluid is greater than the pressure on the upper side.

2. A fluid that moves fast exerts less pressure than one that moves more slowly.

3. The pressure increases equally throughout the fluid.

4. No; the density of the ebony wood is greater than the density of water.

5. The moving air over the tube has less pressure than the air in the bottle, so water is pushed up and out of the tube.

6. Find the increase in pressure, then multiply by the area of the large piston.

$$P = \frac{F}{A} = \frac{20\ N}{2.5\ cm^2} = 8\ N/cm^2$$

$$F = PA = 8\ N/cm^2 \cdot 400\ cm^2 = 3200\ N$$

CHAPTER 12 • REVIEW

BACK TO

Have students use information from this chapter to explain how each of the following terms relates to force: gravity, friction, pressure, fluid. *Sample answer: Gravity is an attractive force of one mass to another mass, and friction is a force that opposes motion. Pressure is not itself a force but describes how force spreads out over an area. A fluid exerts force from all directions upon an object in it.*

◉ KEY CONCEPTS SUMMARY

SECTION 12.1
Ask: In the bottom set of masses, what changes would occur in the arrows if the masses were moved closer together? *They would become larger.*

Ask: If other masses were added to the right of the masses shown, how would the existing arrows change? *Other arrows would be added, but current arrows would not change.*

SECTION 12.2
Ask: How does the force that is needed to start the chair moving compare with the force needed to keep the chair moving? *It is greater.*

Ask: Is air resistance a noticeable force in moving the chair? *no*

SECTION 12.3
Ask: What is the pressure if 50 N of force is applied over 10 m²? *5 Pa*

Ask: Describe the forces applied by the water on a scuba diver. *Forces are applied by the water in all directions.*

SECTION 12.4
Ask: If a diver displaces water with a weight of 523 N, what is the buoyant force on the diver? *523 N*

Ask: Why might strong winds blowing by a building cause a window to pop out? *The wind creates an area of pressure that is less than the pressure inside the building.*

Review Concepts

- Big Idea Flow Chart, p. T17
- Chapter Outline, pp. T23–T24

408 Unit 3: **Motion and Forces**

---

12 Chapter Review

the BIG idea
Newton's laws apply to all forces.

CONTENT REVIEW
CLASSZONE.COM

◉ KEY CONCEPTS SUMMARY

 Gravity is a force exerted by masses.

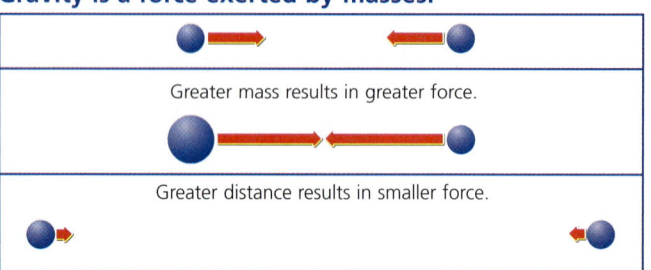

Greater mass results in greater force.

Greater distance results in smaller force.

VOCABULARY
gravity p. 381
weight p. 383
orbit p. 384

② **Friction is a force that opposes motion.**
Frictional force depends on—
- types of surfaces
- motion of surfaces
- force pressing surfaces together

Air resistance is a type of friction.

friction

VOCABULARY
friction p. 389
fluid p. 392
air resistance p. 393

③ **Pressure depends on force and area.**

Pressure = Force / Area

Pressure in a fluid acts in all directions.

VOCABULARY
pressure p. 395
pascal p. 396

④ **Fluids can exert a force on objects.**
- Buoyant force is equal to the weight of the displaced fluid.
- A faster-moving fluid produces less pressure than a slower-moving one.
- Pressure is transmitted through fluids.

VOCABULARY
buoyant force p. 402
Bernoulli's principle p. 404
Pascal's principle p. 406

408 Unit 3: Motion and Forces

Technology Resources

Have students visit **ClassZone.com** or use the CD-ROM for a cumulative review of concepts.

 CONTENT REVIEW

 CONTENT REVIEW CD-ROM

Engage students in a whole-class interactive review of Key Concepts. Edit content as you wish.

 POWER PRESENTATIONS

Reviewing Vocabulary

Write a sentence describing the relationship between each pair of terms.

1. gravity, weight
2. gravity, orbit
3. pressure, pascal
4. fluid, friction
5. density, buoyant force
6. fluid, Bernoulli's principle

Reviewing Key Concepts

Multiple Choice *Choose the letter of the best answer.*

7. Which force keeps Venus in orbit around the Sun?
   - a. gravity
   - b. friction
   - c. hydraulic
   - d. buoyancy

8. You and a classmate are one meter apart. If you move farther away, how does the gravitational force between you and your classmate change?
   - a. It increases.
   - b. It decreases.
   - c. It stays the same.
   - d. It disappears.

9. You kick a ball on a level sidewalk. It rolls to a stop because
   - a. there is no force on the ball
   - b. gravity slows the ball down
   - c. air pressure is pushing down on the ball
   - d. friction slows the ball down

10. You push a chair at a constant velocity using a force of 5 N to overcome friction. You stop to rest, then push again. To start the chair moving again, you must use a force that is
    - a. greater than 5 N
    - b. equal to 5 N
    - c. greater than 0 N but less than 5 N
    - d. 0 N

11. How could you place an empty bottle on a table so that it produces the greatest amount of pressure on the table?

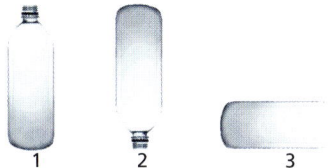

   - a. position 1
   - b. position 2
   - c. position 3
   - d. All positions produce the same pressure.

12. As you climb up a mountain, air pressure
    - a. increases
    - b. decreases
    - c. stays the same
    - d. changes unpredictably

13. If you squeeze a balloon in the middle, what happens to the air pressure inside the balloon?
    - a. It increases only in the middle.
    - b. It decreases only in the middle.
    - c. It increases throughout.
    - d. It decreases throughout.

Short Answer *Write a short answer to each question.*

14. How does the force of attraction between large masses compare with the force of attraction between small masses at the same distance?

15. Explain why a satellite in orbit around Earth does not crash into Earth.

16. You are pushing a dresser with drawers filled with clothing. What could you do to reduce the friction between the dresser and the floor?

17. Why is water pressure greater at a depth of 20 feet than it is at a depth of 10 feet?

18. If you blow over the top of a small strip of paper, the paper bends upward. Why?

Chapter 12: **Gravity, Friction, and Pressure** 409

Reviewing Vocabulary

1. Weight is the force of gravity acting on a mass.
2. Gravity is the centripetal force that keeps objects in orbit.
3. Pascal is the unit of pressure.
4. Objects moving in a fluid have a frictional force acting upon them.
5. The density of a liquid determines the buoyant force upon it. The greater the density, the greater the force.
6. Bernoulli's principle says that an increase in the speed of the motion of a fluid decreases the pressure within the fluid.

Reviewing Key Concepts

7. a
8. b
9. d
10. a
11. b
12. b
13. c

14. The force between the larger masses is greater.

15. The speed of the satellite is great enough to cause the satellite to orbit around Earth instead of crashing to Earth. Gravity acts as a centripetal force.

16. Reduce weight by removing the drawers and clothes, or place a smooth surface under the dresser to reduce friction.

17. More water is above at 20 feet than at 10 feet, and the increased amount of water applies a greater force.

18. The pressure of the moving air on the top of the paper is less than the pressure of the still air under the paper.

ASSESSMENT RESOURCES

UNIT ASSESSMENT BOOK
- Chapter Test A, pp. 46–49
- Chapter Test B, pp. 50–53
- Chapter Test C, pp. 54–57
- Alternative Assessment, pp. 58–59

SPANISH ASSESSMENT BOOK
Spanish Chapter Test, pp. 265–268

Technology Resources

Edit test items and answer choices.

 Test Generator CD-ROM

Visit **ClassZone.com** to extend test practice.

 Test Practice

Thinking Critically

19. The boat is shaped so that it displaces more liquid than the weight of the materials that it is made of. The volume of the boat contains iron and air, and the overall density is less than that of water.
20. Solid surface friction does not depend on speed and surface area, while friction between a moving object and fluid does.
21. Rubbing produces friction, and friction produces heat.
22. The gravity is gradually decreasing because gravity decreases with increased distance.
23. You need less initial speed on the Moon because it has less gravity.
24. The arrow for air resistance would be greater than that for gravity.
25. The buoyant force will increase because the diver is increasing volume but not weight.
26. No; without an atmosphere, there would be no air resistance to slow down the skydiver.
27. The density of oil is less than the density of water.
28. The pressure at the bottom of each flask would be the same because the water levels are the same.

Using Math Skills in Science

29. $F = mg = 10 \text{ kg} \cdot 98 \text{ m/s}^2 = 98 \text{ N}$
30. $P = FA = 50 \text{ N}/0.5 \text{ m}^2 = 100 \text{ Pa}$

the BIG idea

31. Sample answer: Gravity, friction with the snowboard, and air resistance act on the snowboarder. The weight of the snowboarder and the snowboard, and friction with the snowboard, act on the ground. Gravity is greater than friction, so it causes the snowboarder to change motion and accelerate.
32. Student answers will vary.

UNIT PROJECTS

Collect schedules, materials lists, and questions. Be sure dates and materials are obtainable, and questions are focused.

 Unit Projects, pp. 5–10

410 Unit 3: **Motion and Forces**

Thinking Critically

19. **APPLY** Explain why an iron boat can float in water, while an iron cube cannot.
20. **COMPARE** How does the friction between solid surfaces compare with the friction between a moving object and a fluid?
21. **APPLY** Explain why a block of wood gets warm when it is rubbed with sandpaper.
22. **PREDICT** The Moon's orbit is gradually increasing. Each year the Moon is about 3.8 cm farther from Earth than the year before. How does this change affect the force of gravity between Earth and the Moon?
23. **APPLY** The Moon has one-sixth the gravity of Earth. Why would it be easier to launch spacecraft into orbit around the Moon than around Earth?

Use the photograph below to answer the next three questions.

24. **APPLY** A skydiver jumps out of a plane. After he reaches terminal velocity, he opens his parachute. Draw a sketch showing the forces of air resistance and gravity on the skydiver after the parachute opens. Use a longer arrow for a greater force.
25. **SYNTHESIZE** Air is a fluid, which produces a small buoyant force on the skydiver. How does this buoyant force change after he opens his parachute? Why?
26. **INFER** The Moon has no atmosphere. Would it be safe to skydive on the Moon? Why or why not?

410 Unit 3: Motion and Forces

27. **INFER** When oil and water are mixed together, the two substances separate and the oil floats to the top. How does the density of oil compare with the density of water?
28. **COMPARE** Three flasks are filled with colored water as shown below. How does the water pressure at the bottom of each flask compare with the water pressure at the bottom of the other two?

1   2   3

Using Math Skills in Science

Complete the following calculations.

29. How much force does a 10 kg marble exert on the ground?
30. A force of 50 N is applied on a piece of wood with an area of 0.5 m². What is the pressure on the wood?

the BIG idea

31. **ANALYZE** Look again at the picture on pages 378–379. What forces are acting on the snowboarder? on the snow? Use Newton's laws to explain how these forces enable the snowboarder to move down the hill.
32. **SYNTHESIZE** Choose two concepts discussed in this chapter, and describe how Newton's laws relate to those concepts.

UNIT PROJECTS

Check your schedule for your unit project. How are you doing? Be sure that you have placed data or notes from your research into your project folder.

MONITOR AND RETEACH

If students have trouble applying the concepts in items 24–26, watching a videotape of a skydiver can help them. Have them watch the tape without interruption. Then replay the tape, pausing whenever necessary to discuss what forces are acting on the skydiver both before and after the parachute opens. Specifically, discuss gravity, terminal velocity, buoyant force, and air resistance.

Students may benefit from summarizing one or more sections of the chapter.

 Summarizing the Chapter, pp. 219–220

Standardized Test Practice

For practice on your state test, go to...
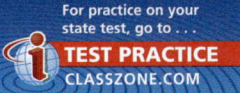
TEST PRACTICE
CLASSZONE.COM

Interpreting Diagrams

Study the diagram and then answer the questions that follow.

Bernoulli's principle states that an increase in the speed of the motion of a fluid decreases the pressure exerted by the fluid. The diagram below relates the movement of a curve ball in baseball to this principle. The ball is shown from above.

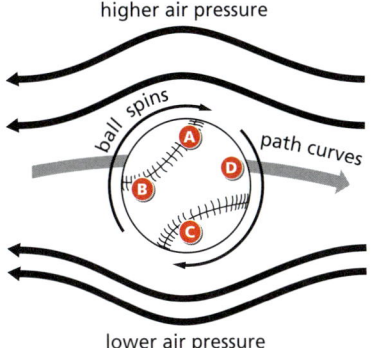

1. To which of these properties does Bernoulli's principle apply?
   a. air pressure
   b. temperature
   c. air resistance
   d. density

2. Where is the air moving fastest in the diagram?
   a. region A
   b. region B
   c. region C
   d. region D

3. Because the ball is spinning, the air on one side is moving faster than on the other side. This causes the ball to curve due to the
   a. air molecules moving slowly and evenly around the ball
   b. forward motion of the ball
   c. difference in air pressure on the ball
   d. changing air temperature around the ball

4. If the baseball were spinning as it moved forward underwater, instead of through the air, how would the pressure of the fluid act on the ball?
   a. The water pressure would be the same on all sides.
   b. The water pressure would vary as air pressure does.
   c. The water pressure would be greatest on the side where air pressure was least.
   d. The water pressure would prevent the ball from spinning.

Extended Response

Answer the two questions below in detail. Include some of the terms from the word box. Underline each term you use in your answer.

acceleration	air resistance	density
fluid	friction	gravity
mass	pressure	velocity

5. If a feather and a bowling ball are dropped from the same height, will they fall at the same rate? Explain.

6. A balloon filled with helium or hot air can float in the atmosphere. A balloon filled with air from your lungs falls to the ground when it is released. Why do these balloons behave differently?

Interpreting Diagrams
1. a
2. c
3. c
4. c

Extended Response

5. RUBRIC
4 points for a response that correctly answers the question and uses the following terms accurately:
- gravity
- mass
- acceleration

The feather and bowling ball fall at the same rate. The force of <u>gravity</u> acts on both <u>masses</u> equally. Because the bowling ball has more mass, gravity will exert more force on it. However, the greater force does not produce greater <u>acceleration</u> due to inertia. Both fall with the same acceleration.

3 points for a response that correctly answers the question and uses 2 terms accurately
2 points for a response that correctly answers the question and uses 1 term accurately
1 point for a response that correctly answers the question, but doesn't use the terms

6. RUBRIC
4 points for a response that correctly answers the question and uses the following terms accurately:
- fluid
- density

Air and gases, like water, are <u>fluids</u>. Both balloons are in a fluid yet behave differently because of <u>density</u>. The balloon filled with helium or hot air is less dense than the air in the atmosphere. An object that is less dense than the fluid will float. The balloon filled with air from my lungs falls to the ground slowly because the balloon is denser than the air.

3 points for a response that correctly answers the question and uses one term accurately
2 points for a response that correctly answers the question, but doesn't use the terms

Chapter 12: **Gravity, Friction, and Pressure** 411

METACOGNITIVE ACTIVITY

Have students answer the following questions in their **Science Notebook:**
1. What did you find the most challenging to understand about gravity, friction, and pressure?
2. What questions do you still have about these concepts?
3. How have you solved a problem while working on your Unit Project?

Chapter 12 **411**

TIMELINES in Science

FOCUS

▶ Set Learning Goals
Students will
- Compare ancient and modern ideas of force and motion.
- Observe how progress in science aided progress in technology and vice versa.
- Examine the development of technological design and its limits.

National Science Education Standards
A.9.a–g Understandings About Scientific Inquiry

E.6.a–c Understandings About Science and Technology

F.5.a–e, F.5.g Science and Technology In Society

G.1.a–b Science as a Human Endeavor

G.2.a Nature of Science

G.3.a–c History of Science

INSTRUCT

The timeline shows major developments in science and the years in which they occurred. The bottom half addresses developments in technology based on the scientific discoveries in the top half. Gaps in the timeline represent blocks of time that have been omitted.

Social Studies Connection
350 B.C. Ancient philosophers studied a broad range of topics—including the sciences. Philosophers talked and wrote about everything from politics to how objects move. Have students notice how ancient Greeks used forces to achieve speed, move water, and balance weight.

Technology
CATAPULTS were instruments of war, and technology has often been developed for the purpose of improving war weaponry. Point out how catapults, a concept developed by ancient civilizations, are still used today.

412 Unit 3: **Motion and Forces**

TIMELINES in Science

UNDERSTANDING FORCES

In ancient times, people thought that an object would not move unless it was pushed. Scientists came up with ingenious ways to explain how objects like arrows stayed in motion. Over time, they came to understand that all motion could be described by three basic laws. Modern achievements such as suspension bridges and space exploration are possible because of the experiments with motion and forces performed by scientists and philosophers over hundreds of years.

This timeline shows just a few of the many steps on the path toward understanding forces. Notice how scientists used the observations and ideas of previous thinkers as a springboard for developing new theories. The boxes below the timeline show how technology has led to new insights and to applications of those ideas.

350 B.C.
Aristotle Discusses Motion
The Greek philosopher Aristotle states that the natural condition of an object is to be at rest. A force is necessary to keep the object in motion. The greater the force, the faster the object moves.

EVENTS

400 B.C.   350 B.C.   300 B.C.

APPLICATIONS AND TECHNOLOGY

TECHNOLOGY
Catapulting into History
As early as 400 B.C., armies were using objects in motion to do work. Catapults, or machines for hurling stones and spears, were used as military weapons. Five hundred years later, the Roman army used catapults mounted on wheels. In the Middle Ages, young trees were sometimes bent back, loaded with an object, and then released like a large slingshot. Today catapult technology is used to launch airplanes from aircraft carriers. A piston powered by steam propels the plane along the deck of the aircraft carrier until it reaches takeoff speed.

412

DIFFERENTIATE INSTRUCTION

Below Level To give students a better idea of the amount of time that passed between discoveries, draw a long line across the blackboard. Label the left end 350 B.C., the middle A.D. 750, and the right end 2000. Mark off other year divisions. As you discuss the timeline with students, point to the section of the blackboard timeline in which that event took place.

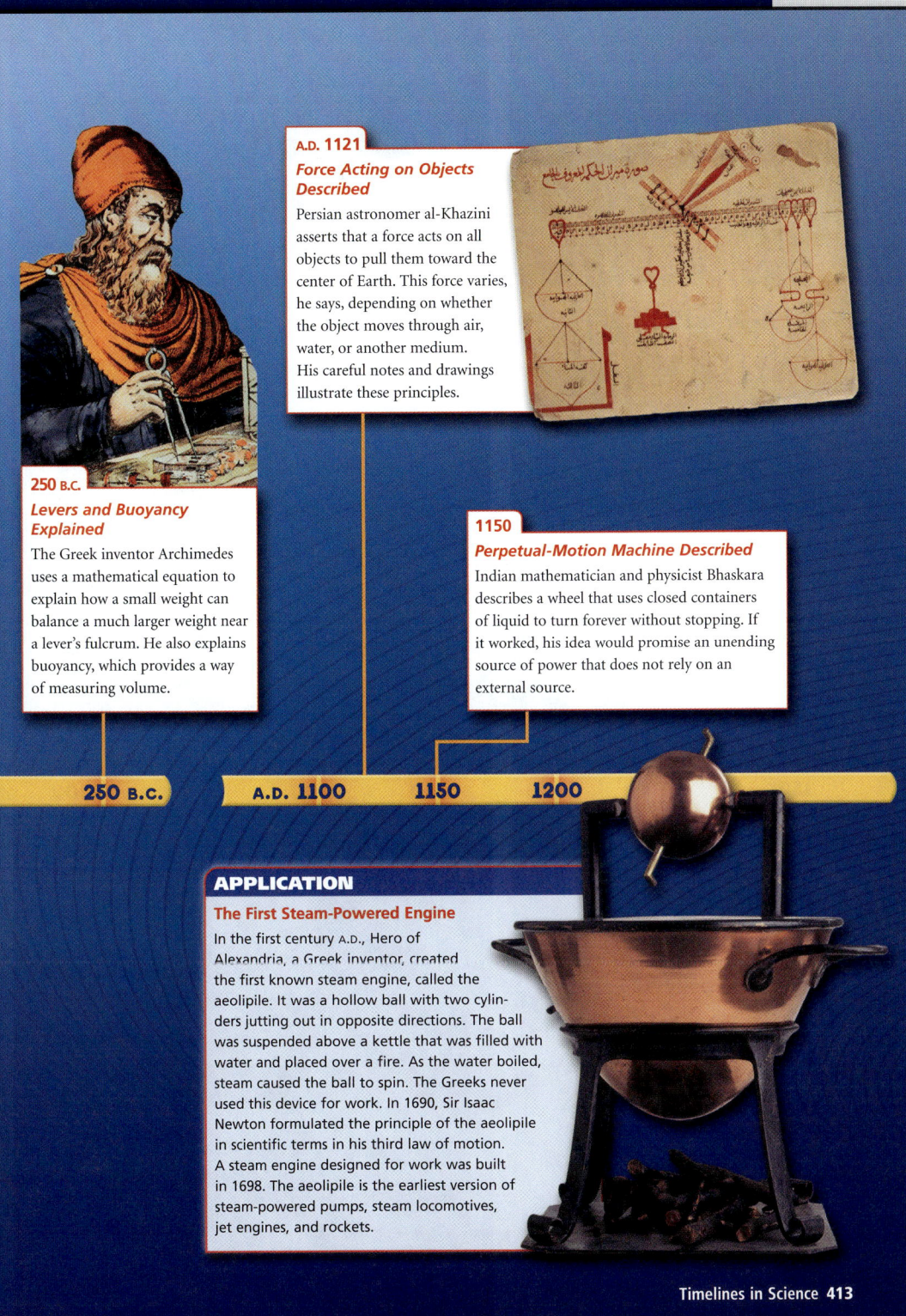

A.D. 1121
Force Acting on Objects Described
Persian astronomer al-Khazini asserts that a force acts on all objects to pull them toward the center of Earth. This force varies, he says, depending on whether the object moves through air, water, or another medium. His careful notes and drawings illustrate these principles.

250 B.C.
Levers and Buoyancy Explained
The Greek inventor Archimedes uses a mathematical equation to explain how a small weight can balance a much larger weight near a lever's fulcrum. He also explains buoyancy, which provides a way of measuring volume.

1150
Perpetual-Motion Machine Described
Indian mathematician and physicist Bhaskara describes a wheel that uses closed containers of liquid to turn forever without stopping. If it worked, his idea would promise an unending source of power that does not rely on an external source.

APPLICATION
The First Steam-Powered Engine
In the first century A.D., Hero of Alexandria, a Greek inventor, created the first known steam engine, called the aeolipile. It was a hollow ball with two cylinders jutting out in opposite directions. The ball was suspended above a kettle that was filled with water and placed over a fire. As the water boiled, steam caused the ball to spin. The Greeks never used this device for work. In 1690, Sir Isaac Newton formulated the principle of the aeolipile in scientific terms in his third law of motion. A steam engine designed for work was built in 1698. The aeolipile is the earliest version of steam-powered pumps, steam locomotives, jet engines, and rockets.

Timelines in Science 413

DIFFERENTIATE INSTRUCTION

Advanced Encourage students to trace the development of ideas from Aristotle to Leonardo to Newton to Einstein. Students might create a visual that represents each new idea as "building on" or "knocking down" the previous idea.

Scientific Process
Stress to students that we should not think of the science of the past as being wrong or of the people of the past as being less intelligent. The ideas they formed were based on the observations available to them at that time. Throughout history, people have tried to explain how the natural world worked; their explanations were simply different from the ones we have today. As important as any discovery was the development of scientific methods of thinking.

Social Studies Connection
A.D. 800 TO 1300 Present-day Iran was once the heart of the Persian Empire. Have students find Iran on a world map. Point out that al-Khazini was an astronomer and physician who lived in the Persian Empire. Emphasize that from about the 800s to the 1300s, some of the world's most innovative science was being done in this region. Ask how geographical features might have helped this civilization advance. *(Ideas from Greece, Egypt, China, and India spread throughout the Persian Empire via sea, river, and overland trade routes.)*

Application
AEOLIPILE Help students make a connection between the simple device shown on page 413 and Watt's steam engine on page 414—and with modern-day steam locomotives and rockets. The aeolipile (EE-uh-lih-PYL) showed the effects produced by steam under pressure. A steam engine converts thermal energy from steam into mechanical energy by allowing the steam to expand and cool. A rocket engine burns fuel, which comes out of the rocket at high speed, creating the thrust needed to propel the rocket.

Timelines in Science 413

Teach from Visuals

1494 This drawing by Leonardo shows the impossibility of perpetual motion. The wheel spins because gravity pulls down on the weights placed around its rim. While it seems that the wheel should spin constantly, eventually friction will stop it. Have students draw the wheel on a sheet of paper and note the forces acting on it.

Scientific Process

1687 Isaac Newton's theories differed from others. Newton was the first to say that there was an attraction (gravity) between all objects, not just between Earth and other things. Earth attracts a rock, and the rock attracts Earth.

Arts Connection

1600s At about the same time that Galileo and Newton were changing the way we think about motion, Shakespeare wrote the plays *Antony and Cleopatra* (1607) and *The Winter's Tale* (1611). In 1640, Rembrandt painted *The Night Watch.* Stress to students that works of art and literature reflect the scientific beliefs of the time.

Application

STEAM ENGINE James Watt's achievements provide one of the best examples of how advances in scientific knowledge can be applied to improve technology. Watt knew that cooling steam required a great amount of energy. Watt determined that, if he cooled steam outside the cylinder of the engine in a unit called a condenser, he would save a lot of energy. Another important improvement Watt made to the steam engine was finding a new way to change the up-and-down motion of the engine into rotary motion. You may have students suggest ways of changing up-and-down motion to circular motion using gears, levers, and other simple machines.

1638
Objects Need No Force to Keep Moving
Italian astronomer Galileo Galilei says that an object's natural state is either in constant motion or at rest. Having observed the motion of objects on ramps, he concludes that an object in motion will slow down or speed up only if a force is exerted on it. He also claims that all objects dropped near the surface of Earth fall with the same acceleration due to the force of gravity.

1494
Perpetual-Motion Machine Impossible
Italian painter and engineer Leonardo da Vinci proves that it is impossible to build a perpetual-motion machine that works. He states that the force of friction keeps a wheel from turning forever without more force being applied.

1687
An Object's Motion Can Be Predicted
English scientist Sir Isaac Newton publishes his three laws of motion, which use Galileo's ideas as a foundation. He concludes that Earth exerts a gravitational force on objects on its surface and that Earth's gravity keeps the Moon in orbit.

APPLICATION
A New and Improved Steam Engine
Scottish scientist James Watt designed steam engines that were much more efficient, and much smaller, than older models. About 500 of Watt's engines were in use by 1800. His pump engines drew water out of coal mines, and his rotating engines were used in factories and cotton mills. Watt's steam engines opened the way to the Industrial Revolution. They were used in major industries such as textile manufacturing, railroad transportation, and mining. Watt's steam technology also opened up new areas of research in heat, kinetic energy, and motion.

DIFFERENTIATE INSTRUCTION

Below Level Explain to students that a perpetual-motion machine is one that continues working forever without added force. Remind students that they have read about Galileo and Newton in Chapter 11, "Forces."

Advanced Galileo thought about what would happen if he could do his experiments under impossible conditions. Have students drop same-sized solid and hollow metal balls at the same time in a tall container of oil. Observe the difference in falling times. Repeat using water and then air in the container. Ask students to speculate what the time difference would be if there were no fluid at all.

1919
Gravity Bends Light
A solar eclipse confirms German-American physicist Albert Einstein's modification of Newton's laws. Einstein's theory states that the path of a light beam will be affected by nearby massive objects. During the eclipse, the stars appear to shift slightly away from one another because their light has been bent by the Sun's gravity.

2001
Supercomputers Model Strong Force
Scientists have been using supercomputers to model the force that holds particles in the nucleus of an atom together. This force, called the strong force, cannot be measured directly in the same way that gravity and other forces can. Instead, computer models allow scientists to make predictions that are then compared with experimental results.

 RESOURCE CENTER
CLASSZONE.COM
Get current research on force and motion.

1850 1900 1950 2000

INTO THE FUTURE

Since ancient times, scientists and philosophers have tried to explain how forces move objects. We now know that the laws of gravity and motion extend beyond Earth. Engineers have designed powerful spacecraft that can carry robots—and eventually people—to Mars and beyond. Rockets using new technology travel farther on less fuel than liquid-fueled rockets do.

Space travel and related research will continue to unravel the mysteries of forces in the universe. For example, recent observations of outer space provide evidence of an unidentified force causing the universe to expand rapidly. As people venture beyond Earth, we may learn new and unexpected things about the forces we have come to understand so far. The timeline shown here is just the beginning of our knowledge of forces.

ACTIVITIES

Reliving History
Bhaskara's design for a perpetual-motion machine involved a wheel with containers of mercury around the rim. As the wheel turned, the mercury would move in such a way that the wheel would always be heavier on one side—and stay in motion. Now we know that this theory goes against the laws of physics. Observe a wheel, a pendulum, or a swing. Think about why it cannot stay in motion forever.

Writing About Science
Suppose you won a trip to outer space. Write a letter accepting or refusing the prize. Give your reasons.

TECHNOLOGY

Science Propels Exploration of Outer Space
An increased understanding of forces made space exploration possible. In 1926 American scientist Robert H. Goddard constructed and tested the first liquid-propelled rocket. A replica of Goddard's rocket can be seen at the National Air and Space Museum in Washington, D.C. In 1929 Goddard launched a rocket that carried the first scientific payload, a barometer and a camera.

Many later achievements—including the 1969 walk on the Moon—are a direct result of Goddard's trail-blazing space research.

Technology
1960s ONWARD The space program has made countless contributions to scientific knowledge. Lunar rocks gathered during the Apollo missions have provided much information about how the Moon—and even Earth—formed billions of years ago. One astronaut dropped a hammer and a feather on the Moon to prove Galileo's claim that objects always fall at the same rate when there is no air resistance.

INTO THE FUTURE

Have students read the passage. With the class, generate a list of questions on the board that students might have about force. To get students thinking, ask: *Why would a better understanding of force be useful in space travel? What more could we know about the force of gravity? What more might we be able to do with a better understanding of force?*

ACTIVITIES

Reliving History
Using a model would help students understand the principles behind Bhaskara's machine. Encourage students to design a model of such a machine and experiment with keeping it in motion.

Writing Project: The Story Behind the News
Point out that the timeline is written as short newspaper articles, as if the events being reported happened recently. Have students imitate the style: punchy headlines; journalistic reporting of who, what, when, where, and why at the beginning of the article; and details coming later in the report.

Technology Resources
Students can visit **ClassZone.com** for current news about forces.

DIFFERENTIATE INSTRUCTION

Below Level Point out that the timeline comes up to the present, including rockets and space travel. The ideas of the Greeks have been added to and perfected by subsequent thinkers. Stress how much time—nearly 2500 years—the timeline covers.

CHAPTER 13: Work and Energy

Physical Science
UNIFYING PRINCIPLES

PRINCIPLE 1
Matter is made of particles too small to see.

PRINCIPLE 2
Matter changes form and moves from place to place.

PRINCIPLE 3
Energy changes from one form to another, but it cannot be created or destroyed.

PRINCIPLE 4
Physical forces affect the movement of all matter on Earth and throughout the universe.

Unit 3: Motion and Forces
BIG IDEAS

CHAPTER 10 Motion
The motion of an object can be described and predicted.

CHAPTER 11 Forces
Forces change the motion of objects in predictable ways.

CHAPTER 12 Gravity, Friction, and Pressure
Newton's laws apply to all forces.

CHAPTER 13 Work and Energy
Energy is transferred when a force moves an object.

CHAPTER 14 Machines
Machines help people do work by changing the force applied to an object.

CHAPTER 13 KEY CONCEPTS

SECTION 1

Work is the use of force to move an object.
1. Force is necessary to do work.
2. Objects that are moving can do work.

SECTION 2

Energy is transferred when work is done.
1. Work transfers energy.
2. Work changes potential and kinetic energy.
3. The total amount of energy is constant.

SECTION 3

Power is the rate at which work is done.
1. Power can be calculated from work and time.
2. Power can be calculated from energy and time.

 The Big Idea Flow Chart is available on p. T25 in the **UNIT TRANSPARENCY BOOK**.

Previewing Content

SECTION Work is the use of force to move an object. pp. 419–424

1. Force is necessary to do work.
To do **work** on an object, a force must be applied to the object, and the object must move in the direction of the force, as the first diagram below shows. Work is done only by the component of the force that acts in the same direction as the movement of the object, as shown in the second diagram.

Work is done by force that acts in the same direction as the motion of an object.

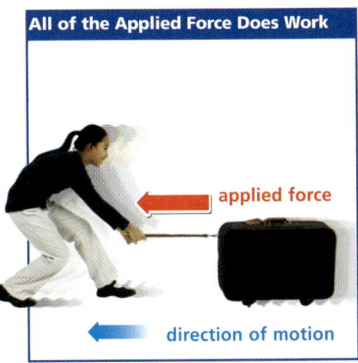 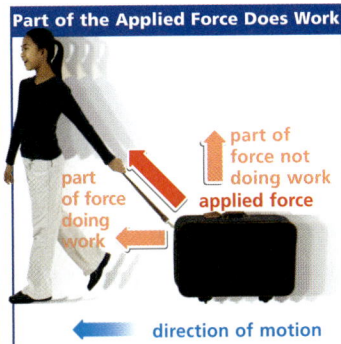

Work can be calculated by multiplying the force applied to an object by the distance the object moves while that force is being applied.

$W = F \cdot d$

The standard unit of measurement of work is the newton-meter, also called a **joule**.

2. Objects that are moving can do work.
Moving objects can do work.
- The gravitational force of Earth does work on water and other natural materials.
- People use moving objects to help them do work.

SECTION Energy is transferred when work is done. pp. 425–433

1. Work transfers energy.
When work is done on an object, energy is transferred from whatever is exerting the force to the object.

2. Work changes potential and kinetic energy.
All forms of energy can be considered in terms of either potential energy or kinetic energy.
- An object has **potential energy** due to its position or shape. Potential energy due to gravity is called gravitational potential energy (GPE). The GPE of an object can be found by multiplying the object's mass by the acceleration due to Earth's gravity and by the object's height above the ground.

  $GPE = mgh$

- An object has **kinetic energy** when it is moving. Kinetic energy can be calculated by the formula

  $KE = \frac{1}{2} mv^2$

Mechanical energy is an object's combined potential energy and kinetic energy. An object with mechanical energy can do work on another object.

3. The total amount of energy is constant.
The law of **conservation of energy** states that energy is neither created nor destroyed, although it can change into another form. Common forms of energy are mechanical, thermal, chemical, nuclear, and electromagnetic energy.

As a ball rolls down a ramp, the amounts of potential energy and kinetic energy change, but the total energy is the same.

Common Misconceptions

WORK REQUIRES A FORCE Students might think that work continues even after a force ceases to be applied. In fact, an object can continue to move after the force is removed, but work is no longer being done.

 This misconception is addressed on p. 421.

MISCONCEPTION DATABASE
CLASSZONE.COM Background on student misconceptions

FORCE AND ENERGY Students may think that force and energy are the same or that energy is a type of force. Actually, force and energy are two different phenomena that are related through the concept of work—the means of transferring energy from one object to another using a force.

 This misconception is addressed on p. 428.

Previewing Content

SECTION

 Power is the rate at which work is done. pp. 434–441

1. **Power can be calculated from work and time.**
   Power is the rate at which work is done. When the power of an object increases, work is done faster. Power can be calculated from work and time.

   $$P = \frac{W}{t} \text{ or } P = \frac{F \cdot d}{t}$$

   - The unit of measurement for power is the **watt,** equal to one joule of work done in one second.
   - Another unit of power is **horsepower,** which is based on how much work a horse can do in one minute. It is used primarily to describe engines and motors. One horsepower equals 745 watts.

2. **Power can be calculated from energy and time.**
   Power can be thought of as the rate at which energy is transferred over a certain period of time. Power can be calculated from energy as well as from work. The formula is

   $$P = \frac{E}{t}$$

 MISCONCEPTION DATABASE
CLASSZONE.COM Background on student misconceptions

Common Misconceptions

THE WORD POWER The word *power* has many meanings in everyday language. Students often confuse the common meanings of the word for the physical meaning—that of a rate of work or energy transfer.

 This misconception is addressed on p. 435.

Previewing Labs

Lab Generator CD-ROM — Edit these Pupil Edition labs and generate alternative labs.

EXPLORE the BIG idea

Bouncing Ball, p. 417
Students will observe that mechanical energy is lost when a bouncing ball loses height with each bounce.

TIME 10 minutes
MATERIALS large ball; hard, flat floor

Power Climbing, p. 417
Students will vary their power as they walk and run up a flight of stairs.

TIME 10 minutes
MATERIALS backpack, flight of stairs

Internet Activity: Work, p. 417
Students will manipulate a computer model to determine how varying force and distance affects the amount of work done.

TIME 20 minutes
MATERIALS computer with Internet access

SECTION 1

EXPLORE Work, p. 419
Students compare the work done by lifting a book and by holding it without moving it.

TIME 5 minutes
MATERIALS book

INVESTIGATE Work, p. 422
Students determine the amount of work done in lifting a notebook by measuring the force applied and the distance the notebook is moved.

TIME 20 minutes
MATERIALS meter stick, spiral notebook, spring scale

SECTION 2

INVESTIGATE Mechanical Energy, p. 429
Students calculate the potential, kinetic, and mechanical energy of a ball as it rolls down a ramp.

TIME 20 minutes
MATERIALS ball, balance, board (60–100 cm long), several books, ruler, 15 cm masking tape, stopwatch, calculator

SECTION 3

EXPLORE Power, p. 434
Students explore how time affects work by comparing work done in an initial time with that same work done in half the time.

TIME 10 minutes
MATERIALS 2 plastic cups, 10 marbles, stopwatch

INVESTIGATE Power, p. 437
Students calculate the power it takes to pull an object over a given distance by measuring the force and the time needed.

TIME 15 minutes
MATERIALS meter stick, 30 cm masking tape, 100 g object, spring scale, 60 cm string, stopwatch

**CHAPTER INVESTIGATION
Work and Power,** pp. 440–441
Students compare the amount of work and power needed to lift an object straight up with the amount needed to move it up a ramp.

TIME 40 minutes
MATERIALS board (60–100 cm long), chair, meter stick, 60 cm string, small wheeled object, spring scale, stopwatch

 Additional INVESTIGATION, Ramp It Up, A, B, & C, pp. 276–284; Teacher Instructions, pp. 346–347

Chapter 13: **Work and Energy** 415D

Previewing Chapter Resources

	INTEGRATED TECHNOLOGY	LABS AND ACTIVITIES
CHAPTER 13 **Work and Energy**	**CLASSZONE.COM** • eEdition Plus • EasyPlanner Plus • Misconception Database • Content Review • Test Practice • Visualization • Resource Centers • Internet Activity: Work • Math Tutorial **CD-ROMS** • eEdition • EasyPlanner • Power Presentations • Content Review • Lab Generator • Test Generator  **AUDIO CDS** • Audio Readings • Audio Readings in Spanish **SCILINKS.ORG**	EXPLORE the Big Idea, p. 417 • Bouncing Ball • Power Climbing • Internet Activity: Work **UNIT RESOURCE BOOK** Unit Projects, pp. 5–10 **Lab Generator CD-ROM** Generate customized labs.
SECTION 1 **Work is the use of force to move an object.** pp. 419–424 Time: 2 periods (1 block) Lesson Plan, pp. 221–222	• RESOURCE CENTER, Work • MATH TUTORIAL  **UNIT TRANSPARENCY BOOK** • Big Idea Flow Chart, p. T25 • Daily Vocabulary Scaffolding, p. T26 • Note-Taking Model, p. T27 • 3-Minute Warm-Up, p. T28	• EXPLORE Work, p. 419 • INVESTIGATE Work, p. 422 • Math in Science, p. 424 **UNIT RESOURCE BOOK** • Datasheet, Work, p. 230 • Additional INVESTIGATION, Ramp It Up, A, B, & C, pp. 276–284 • Math Support, pp. 259, 265 • Math Practice, pp. 260, 266
SECTION 2 **Energy is transferred when work is done.** pp. 425–433 Time: 2 periods (1 block) Lesson Plan, pp. 232–233	VISUALIZATION, Transfer of Potential and Kinetic Energy 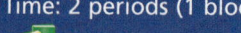 **UNIT TRANSPARENCY BOOK** • Daily Vocabulary Scaffolding, p. T26 • 3-Minute Warm-Up, p. T28 • "Conserving Mechanical Energy" Visual, p. T30	• INVESTIGATE Mechanical Energy, p. 429 • Think Science, p. 433 **UNIT RESOURCE BOOK** • Datasheet, Mechanical Energy, p. 241 • Math Support, p. 261 • Math Practice, p. 262
SECTION 3 **Power is the rate at which work is done.** pp. 434–441 Time: 4 periods (2 blocks) Lesson Plan, pp. 243–244	RESOURCE CENTER, Power **UNIT TRANSPARENCY BOOK** • Big Idea Flow Chart, p. T25 • Daily Vocabulary Scaffolding, p. T26 • 3-Minute Warm-Up, p. T29 • Chapter Outline, pp. T31–T32	• EXPLORE Power, p. 434 • INVESTIGATE Power, p. 437 • CHAPTER INVESTIGATION, Work and Power, pp. 440–441 **UNIT RESOURCE BOOK** • Datasheet, Power, p. 252 • Math Support, p. 263 • Math Practice, p. 264 • CHAPTER INVESTIGATION, Work and Power, A, B, & C, pp. 267–275

KEY TO ICONS CD/CD-ROM  Teacher Edition T UNIT TRANSPARENCY BOOK SP/A SPANISH ASSESSMENT BOOK

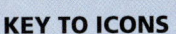 INTERNET PE Pupil Edition R UNIT RESOURCE BOOK A UNIT ASSESSMENT BOOK 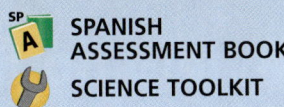 SCIENCE TOOLKIT

READING AND REINFORCEMENT

ASSESSMENT

STANDARDS

- Choose Your Own Strategy, B20–25
- Main Idea Web, C38–39
- Daily Vocabulary Scaffolding, H1–8

 UNIT RESOURCE BOOK
- Vocabulary Practice, pp. 256–257
- Decoding Support, p. 258
- Summarizing the Chapter, pp. 285–286

- Chapter Review, pp. 443–444
- Standardized Test Practice, p. 445

 UNIT ASSESSMENT BOOK
- Diagnostic Test, pp. 60–61
- Chapter Test, A, B, & C, pp. 65–76
- Alternative Assessment, pp. 77–78

 Spanish Chapter Test, pp. 269–272

National Standards
A.2–8, A.9.a–c, A.9.e–f, B.2.b, B.3.a, G.1.b

See p. 416 for the standards.

Audio Readings CD
Listen to Pupil Edition.

Audio Readings in Spanish CD
Listen to Pupil Edition in Spanish.

 Test Generator CD-ROM
Generate customized tests.

 Lab Generator CD-ROM
Rubrics for Labs

 UNIT RESOURCE BOOK
- Reading Study Guide, A & B, pp. 223–226
- Spanish Reading Study Guide, pp. 227–228
- Challenge and Extension, p. 229
- Reinforcing Key Concepts, p. 231

 Ongoing Assessment, pp. 419–421, 423

 Section 13.1 Review, p. 423

 UNIT ASSESSMENT BOOK
Section 13.1 Quiz, p. 62

National Standards
A.2–8, A.9.a–c, A.9.e–f, G.1.b

 UNIT RESOURCE BOOK
- Reading Study Guide, A & B, pp. 234–237
- Spanish Reading Study Guide, pp. 238–239
- Challenge and Extension, p. 240
- Reinforcing Key Concepts, p. 242
- Challenge Reading, pp. 254–255

 Ongoing Assessment, pp. 425, 427–431

Section 13.2 Review, p. 432

 UNIT ASSESSMENT BOOK
Section 13.2 Quiz, p. 63

National Standards
A.2–8, A.9.a–c, A.9.e–f, B.3.a, G.1.b

 UNIT RESOURCE BOOK
- Reading Study Guide, A & B, pp. 245–248
- Spanish Reading Study Guide, pp. 249–250
- Challenge and Extension, p. 251
- Reinforcing Key Concepts, p. 253

 Ongoing Assessment, pp. 435–436, 438–439

Section 13.3 Review, p. 439

 UNIT ASSESSMENT BOOK
Section 13.3 Quiz, p. 64

National Standards
A.2–8, A.9.a–c, A.9.e–f, G.1.b

Chapter 13: **Work and Energy** 415F

Previewing Resources for Differentiated Instruction

CHAPTER INVESTIGATION

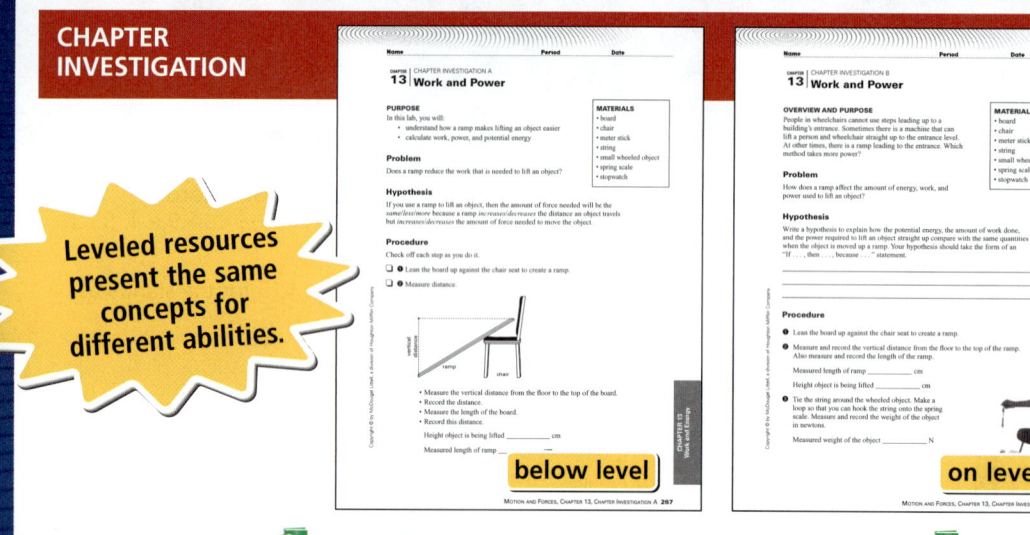
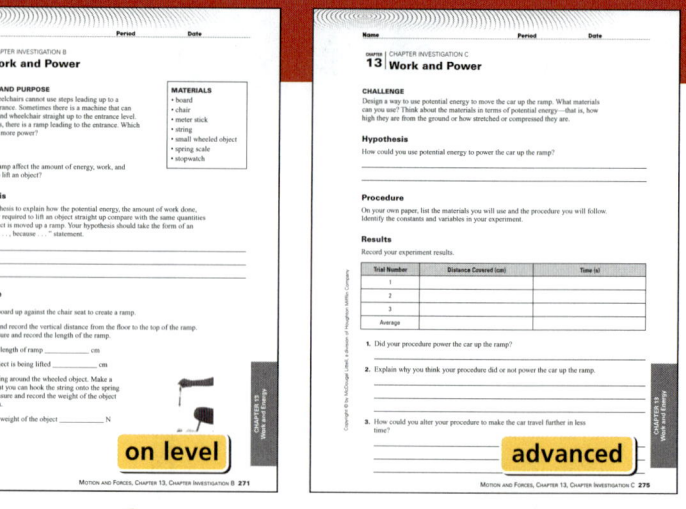

Leveled resources present the same concepts for different abilities.

UNIT RESOURCE BOOK, pp. 267–270 | pp. 271–274 | pp. 271–275

READING STUDY GUIDE

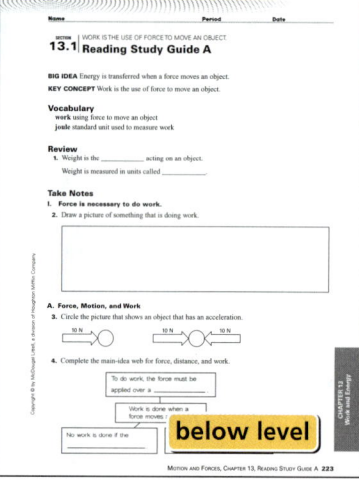
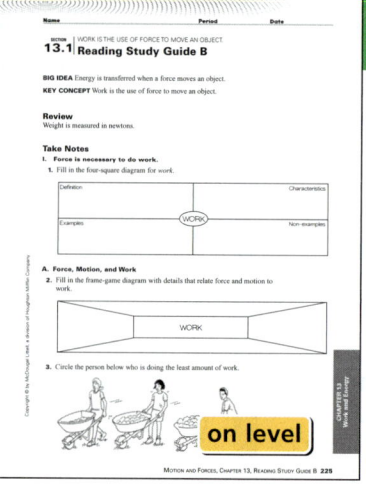
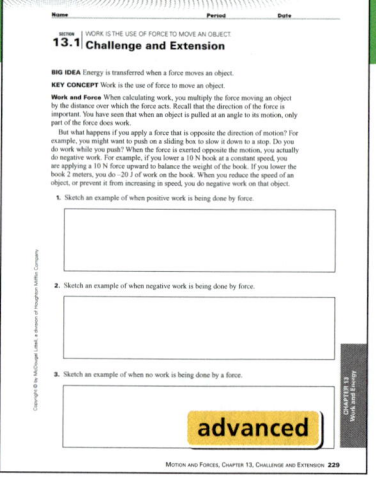

Reading Study Guide is also in Spanish.

UNIT RESOURCE BOOK, pp. 223–224 | pp. 225–226 | p. 229

CHAPTER TEST

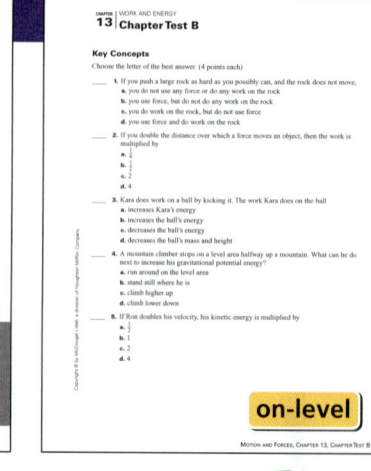
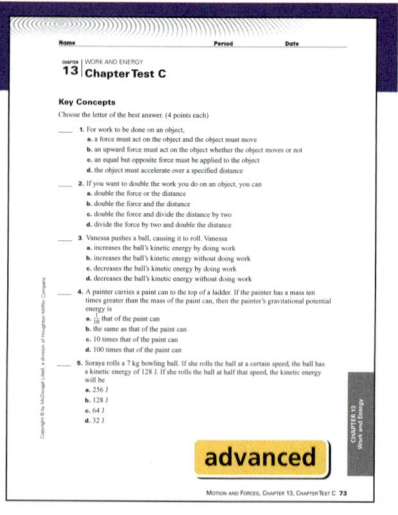

Chapter Test is also in Spanish.

UNIT ASSESSMENT BOOK, pp. 65–68 | pp. 69–72 | pp. 73–76

415G Unit 3: Motion and Forces

TECHNOLOGY

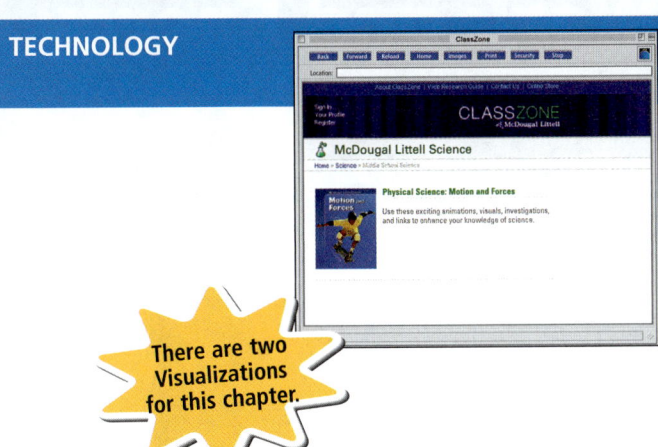

There are two Visualizations for this chapter.

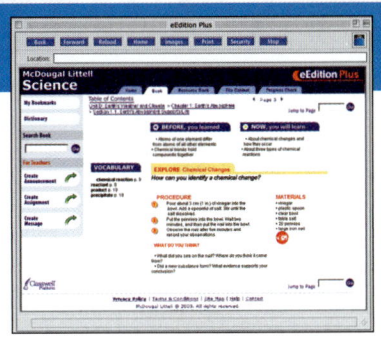

CLASSZONE.COM   CD/CD-ROMS   CLASSZONE.COM

VISUAL CONTENT

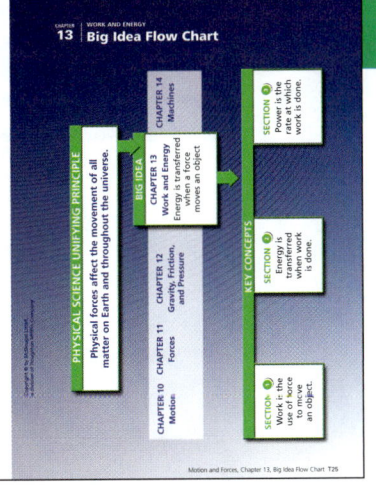

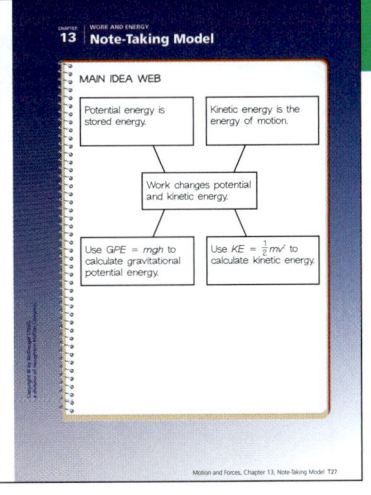

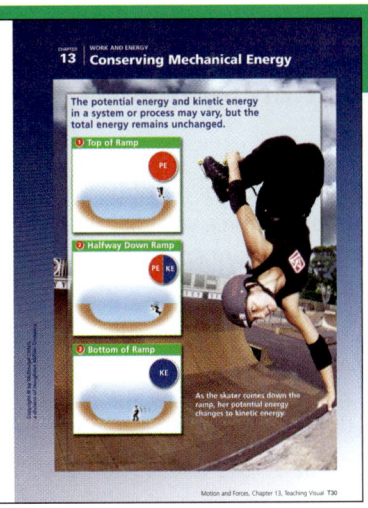

 UNIT TRANSPARENCY BOOK, p. T25    p. T27    p. T30

MORE SUPPORT

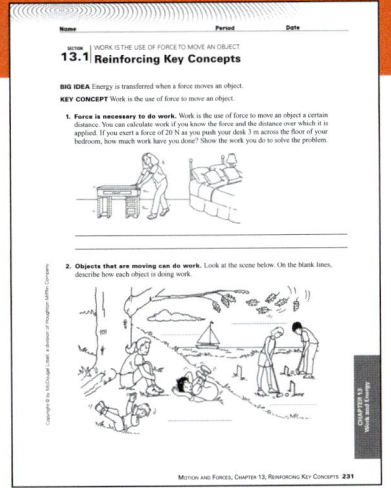

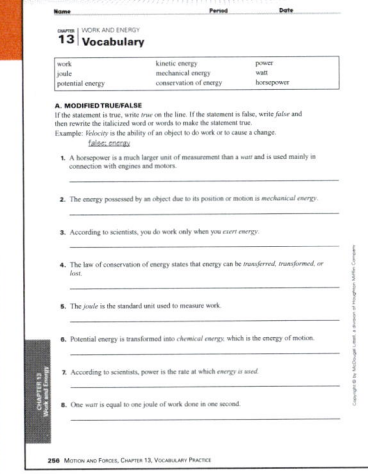

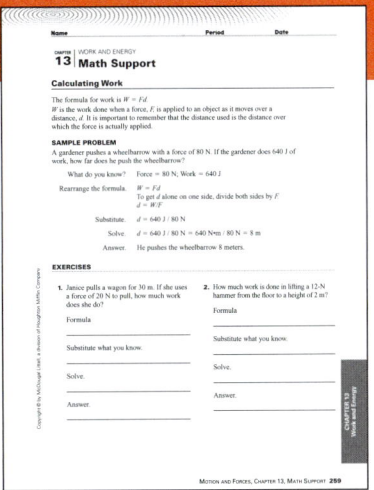

Reinforcing Key Concepts for each section

UNIT RESOURCE BOOK, p. 231   pp. 256–257   p. 259

Chapter 13: **Work and Energy** 415H

CHAPTER 13 Work and Energy

INTRODUCE the BIG idea

Have students look at the photograph of the young woman carrying a box and discuss how the question in the blue box links to the Big Idea:

- In what way is the person in the photograph doing work?
- What is a force?
- Did the person in the photograph apply force at any time but not do any work?

National Science Education Standards

Content

B.2.b An object that is not being subjected to a force will continue to move at a constant speed and in a straight line.

B.3.a Energy is a property of many substances and is associated with heat, light, electricity, mechanical motion, sound, nuclei, and the nature of a chemical. Energy is transferred in many ways.

Process

A.2–8 Design and conduct an investigation; use tools to gather and interpret data; use evidence to describe, predict, explain, model; think critically to make relationships between evidence and explanation; recognize different explanations and predictions; communicate scientific procedures and explanations; use mathematics.

A.9.a–c, A.9.e–f Understand scientific inquiry by using different investigations, methods, mathematics, and explanations based on logic, evidence, and skepticism.

G.1.b Science requires different abilities

CHAPTER 13 Work and Energy

the BIG idea

Energy is transferred when a force moves an object.

Key Concepts

SECTION 1 — Work is the use of force to move an object.
Learn about the relationship between force and work.

SECTION 2 — Energy is transferred when work is done.
Learn how energy is related to work.

SECTION 3 — Power is the rate at which work is done.
Learn to calculate power from work and energy.

Which takes more work, lifting a box or holding a box? Why?

Internet Preview

CLASSZONE.COM
Chapter 13 online resources: Content Review, Simulation, Visualization, two Resource Centers, Math Tutorial, Test Practice

INTERNET PREVIEW

CLASSZONE.COM For student use with the following pages:

Review and Practice
- Content Review, pp. 418, 442
- Math Tutorial: Finding the Mean, p. 424
- Test Practice, p. 445

Activities and Resources
- Internet Activity: Work, p. 417
- Resource Centers: Work, p. 420; Power, p. 436
- Visualization: Transfer of Potential & Kinetic Energy, p. 430

Potential and Kinetic Energy
Code: MDL007

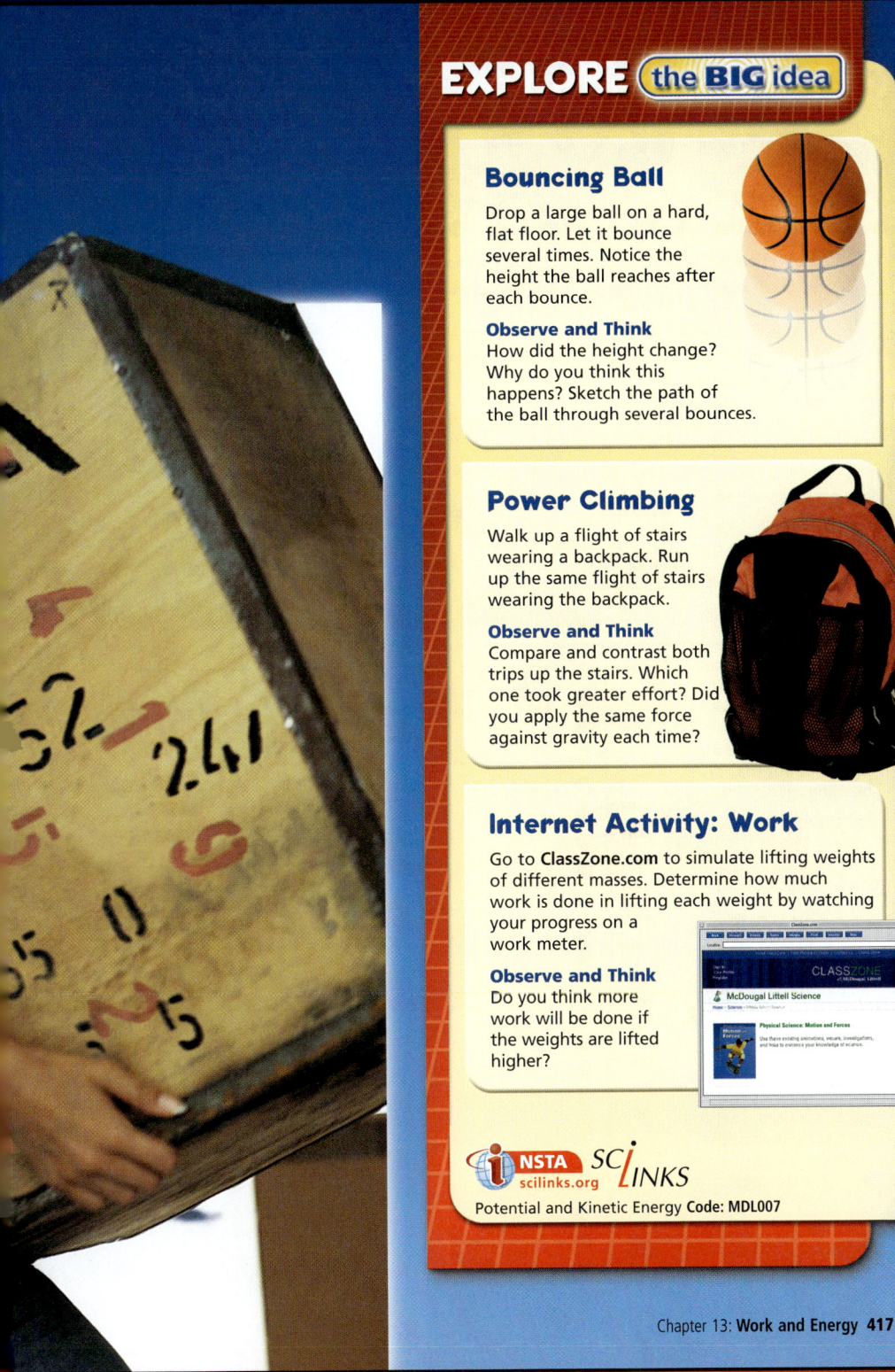

EXPLORE the BIG idea

Bouncing Ball
Drop a large ball on a hard, flat floor. Let it bounce several times. Notice the height the ball reaches after each bounce.

Observe and Think
How did the height change? Why do you think this happens? Sketch the path of the ball through several bounces.

Power Climbing
Walk up a flight of stairs wearing a backpack. Run up the same flight of stairs wearing the backpack.

Observe and Think
Compare and contrast both trips up the stairs. Which one took greater effort? Did you apply the same force against gravity each time?

Internet Activity: Work
Go to **ClassZone.com** to simulate lifting weights of different masses. Determine how much work is done in lifting each weight by watching your progress on a work meter.

Observe and Think
Do you think more work will be done if the weights are lifted higher?

NSTA SCLINKS
scilinks.org
Potential and Kinetic Energy **Code: MDL007**

Chapter 13: **Work and Energy** 417

EXPLORE the BIG idea

These inquiry-based activities are appropriate for use at home or as a supplement to classroom instruction.

Bouncing Ball
PURPOSE To observe a decrease in mechanical energy. Students see that a ball loses height as it bounces.

TIP *10 min.* Students should think about what happens to the ball's energy as it bounces.

Answer: The height of the ball decreases with each bounce. Some of the ball's energy of motion is converted to other forms of energy as the ball moves through the air.

REVISIT after p. 430.

Power Climbing
PURPOSE To perform work using different amounts of power

TIP *10 min.* Have students think about how their results would change if they carried a heavier backpack.

Answer: Both trips up the stairs took the same amount of work, but running used more effort because it took less time to climb the stairs. The same force against gravity was applied each time.

REVISIT after p. 435.

Internet Activity: Work
PURPOSE To see how much work is done when applying force to an object

TIP *20 min.* Assign different distances to student groups. Have the class graph distance versus work.

Answer: Yes, more work will be done if the weights are lifted higher. To lift the weights higher, more energy must be used.

REVISIT after p. 422.

TEACHING WITH TECHNOLOGY

Spreadsheet Have students use a spreadsheet program to record their data and do the calculations for "Investigate Mechanical Energy" on p. 429, and the Chapter Investigation, pp. 440–441.

Video Camera Students can use a video camera to tape "Investigate Power" on p. 437. They then can view the tape to make sure they are pulling the object across the floor while using a constant force.

Chapter 13 **417**

PREPARE

◀ CONCEPT REVIEW

Activate Prior Knowledge

- Set a toy car on a table, then give the car a push. Have students describe what they observe in terms of the force applied, the change in the car's position, its velocity, and its acceleration.
- Ask students to identify correct units for velocity, speed, and acceleration.
- Ask students to define *force* in their own words.

▶ TAKING NOTES

Main Idea Web

Writing notes around each heading is similar to making an outline of the major concepts in the chapter. Summarizing the most important details of a concept in this way will help students learn by organizing new material.

Vocabulary Strategy

Having students choose a note-taking strategy allows them to use the strategy that works best for a particular topic. It is also a good review of the strategies already presented: description wheel, magnet words, and four square.

Vocabulary and Note-Taking Resources

- Vocabulary Practice, pp. 256–257
- Decoding Support, p. 258

- Daily Vocabulary Scaffolding, p. T26
- Note-Taking Model, p. T27

- Choose Your Own Strategy, B20–25
- Main Idea Web, C38–39
- Daily Vocabulary Scaffolding, H1–8

CHAPTER 13
Getting Ready to Learn

◀ CONCEPT REVIEW

- Forces change the motion of objects in predictable ways.
- Velocity is a measure of the speed and direction of an object.
- An unbalanced force produces acceleration.

◀ VOCABULARY REVIEW

velocity p. 326
force p. 345

See Glossary for definitions.
energy, mass

Review concepts and vocabulary.

▷ TAKING NOTES

MAIN IDEA WEB

Write each new blue heading in a box. Then write notes in boxes around it that give important terms and details about that blue heading.

SCIENCE NOTEBOOK

- Work is the use of force to move an object.
- Work = Force · distance
- Force is necessary to do work.
- Joule is the unit for measuring work.
- Work depends on force and distance.

CHOOSE YOUR OWN STRATEGY

Take notes about new vocabulary terms using one or more of the strategies from earlier chapters—**description wheel, magnet words,** or **four square.** Feel free to mix and match the strategies or use a different strategy.

Description Wheel / Four Square / Magnet Word

See the Note-Taking Handbook on pages R45–R51.

418 Unit 3: Motion and Forces

CHECK READINESS

Administer the Diagnostic Test to determine students' readiness for new science content and their mastery of requisite math skills.

 Diagnostic Test, pp. 60–61

Technology Resources

Students needing content and math skills should visit ClassZone.com.

- CONTENT REVIEW
- MATH TUTORIAL

 CONTENT REVIEW CD-ROM

KEY CONCEPT

Work is the use of force to move an object.

BEFORE, you learned
- An unbalanced force produces acceleration
- Weight is measured in newtons

NOW, you will learn
- How force and work are related
- How moving objects do work

VOCABULARY

work p. 419
joule p. 421

EXPLORE Work

How do you work?

PROCEDURE

1. Lift a book from the floor to your desktop. Try to move the book at a constant speed.
2. Now lift the book again, but stop about halfway up and hold the book still for about 30 seconds. Then continue lifting the book to the desktop.

WHAT DO YOU THINK?
- Do you think you did more work the first time you lifted the book or the second time you lifted the book?
- What do you think *work* means?

MATERIALS
book

Force is necessary to do work.

VOCABULARY
You might want to make a description wheel diagram in your notebook for *work*.

What comes to mind when you think of work? Most people say they are working when they do anything that requires a physical or mental effort. But in physical science, **work** is the use of force to move an object some distance. In scientific terms, you do work only when you exert a force on an object and move it. According to this definition of work, reading this page is not doing work. Turning the page, however, would be work because you are lifting the page.

Solving a math problem in your head is not doing work. Writing the answer is work because you are moving the pencil across the paper. If you want to do work, you have to use force to move something.

 How does the scientific definition of work differ from the familiar definition?

Chapter 13: Work and Energy 419

13.1 FOCUS

▶ Set Learning Goals

Students will
- Recognize how force and work are related.
- Identify how moving objects do work.
- Determine through an experiment how much work is done when lifting an object.

◀ 3-Minute Warm-Up

Display Transparency 28 or copy this exercise on the board:

Decide whether these statements are true. If they are not true, correct them.

1. An object has acceleration if its velocity is changing. *true*
2. Force is measured in joules. *Force is measured in newtons.*
3. Gravity is a force. *true*

 T 3-Minute Warm-Up, p. T28

13.1 MOTIVATE

EXPLORE Work

PURPOSE To explore the scientific definition of work

TIP *5 min.* Help students understand that work is done only when an object is moving. Ask if work would be done if the book were replaced by a barbell that was too heavy to be lifted. *Work is not done if the barbell does not move.*

WHAT DO YOU THINK? *Many students will say that they did more work the second time. Work is done only when the book is moving.*

Ongoing Assessment

 *Answer: The scientific definition of work involves the use of force to move an object over a distance. The ordinary definition involves making a mental or a physical effort.*

Chapter 13 **419**

RESOURCES FOR DIFFERENTIATED INSTRUCTION

Below Level
UNIT RESOURCE BOOK
- Reading Study Guide A, pp. 223–224
- Decoding Support, p. 258

 **AUDIO CDS**

 R **Additional INVESTIGATION,**
Ramp It Up, A, B, & C, pp. 276–284;
Teacher Instructions, pp. 346–347

Advanced
UNIT RESOURCE BOOK
Challenge and Extension, p. 229

English Learners
UNIT RESOURCE BOOK
Spanish Reading Study Guide, pp. 227–228

 AUDIO CDS

- Audio Readings in Spanish
- Audio Readings (English)

13.1 INSTRUCT

Teach Difficult Concepts

Students may have a difficult time adopting the scientific definition of work. Tell them to imagine a waiter with a tray of food. Ask:

- Does the waiter do work to get the tray up to shoulder height? Why or why not? *Yes; force is applied in the same direction as movement.*

- Is the force the waiter is using to hold up the tray doing work? Why? *No; the force he exerts to hold up the tray does not change its position.*

Teach from Visuals

To help students interpret the "Work" visual, ask:

- Is the same amount of work done when you pull the suitcase with the handle in a horizontal position as when you pull it at an angled position? *No; if you use the same force, less of that force does work when you pull the handle at an angle.*

- If you walk while carrying the suitcase by its small top handle, is the force that you are using to hold up the suitcase doing work? Why? *No; the suitcase is moving forward and you are applying the force upward.*

Ongoing Assessment

Recognize how force and work are related.

Ask: Is work being done if you hold a trumpet? Why? *No; you are not moving it.* Is work being done if you carry a trumpet while marching up the stairs? Why? *Yes; both the force on the trumpet and its motion are in the same direction, so work is being done.*

CHECK YOUR READING *Answer: when the object is not moving and when the force is not acting in the same direction as the motion of the object*

READING VISUALS *Answer: It changes the amount of the applied force that does work.*

420 Unit 3: Motion and Forces

RESOURCE CENTER
CLASSZONE.COM
Learn more about work.

Force, Motion, and Work

Work is done only when an object that is being pushed or pulled actually moves. If you lift a book, you exert a force and do work. What if you simply hold the book out in front of you? No matter how tired your muscles may become from holding the book still, you are not doing work unless you move the book.

The work done by a force is related to the size of the force and the distance over which the force is applied. How much work does it take to push a grocery cart down an aisle? The answer depends on how hard you push the cart and the length of the aisle. If you use the same amount of force, you do more work pushing a cart down a long aisle than a short aisle.

Work is done only by the part of the applied force that acts in the same direction as the motion of an object. Suppose you need to pull a heavy suitcase on wheels. You pull the handle up at an angle as you pull the suitcase forward. Only the part of the force pulling the suitcase forward is doing work. The force with which you pull upward on the handle is not doing work because the suitcase is not moving upward—unless you are going uphill.

CHECK YOUR READING Give two examples of when you are applying a force but not doing work.

Work

Work is done by force that acts in the same direction as the motion of an object.

All of the Applied Force Does Work

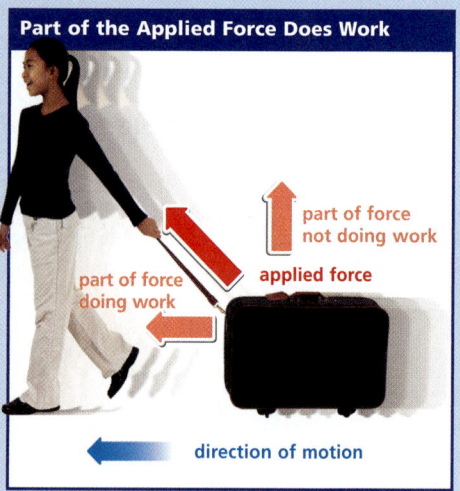
Part of the Applied Force Does Work

READING VISUALS How does changing the direction of the applied force change the amount of the force that is doing work?

DIFFERENTIATE INSTRUCTION

? More Reading Support

A Which two things determine how much work is done? *size of the force, distance over which it is applied*

English Learners English learners may have difficulty distinguishing between nouns and verbs when they are used in different contexts. For example, the following sentences use the word *work* in two different ways: *He works all day. He does his work all day.* In the first sentence, *work* is a verb. In the second sentence, *work* is a noun. Throughout this chapter, the word *work* is most often a noun; "Work is the use of force to move an object." Make sure students are reading nouns and verbs correctly.

Calculating Work

Work is a measure of how much force is applied over a certain distance. You can calculate the work a force does if you know the size of the force applied to an object and the distance over which the force acts. The distance involved is the distance the object moved in the direction of that force. The calculation for work is shown in the following formula:

Work = Force · distance
$W = Fd$

This man is doing work when he applies force to lift his body.

You read in previous chapters that you can measure force in newtons. You also know that you can measure distance in meters. When you multiply a force in newtons times a distance in meters, the product is a measurement called the newton-meter (N·m), or the **joule** (jool).

The joule (J) is the standard unit used to measure work. One joule of work is done when a force of one newton moves an object one meter. To get an idea of how much a joule of work is, lift an apple (which weighs about one newton) from your foot to your waist (about one meter).

Use the formula for work to solve the problem below.

Calculating Work

Sample Problem

How much work is done if a person lifts a barbell weighing 450 N to a height of 2 m?

What do you know?	force needed to lift = 450 N, distance = 2 m
What do you want to find out?	Work
Write the formula:	$W = Fd$
Substitute into the formula:	$W = 450\ N \cdot 2\ m$
Calculate and simplify:	$W = 900\ N \cdot m$
Check that your units agree:	Unit is newton-meter (N·m). Unit of work is joule, which is N·m. Units agree.
Answer:	$W = 900\ J$

Practice the Math

1. If you push a cart with a force of 70 N for 2 m, how much work is done?
2. If you did 200 J of work pushing a box with a force of 40 N, how far did you push the box?

 REMINDER
You know that $W = Fd$. You can manipulate the formula to find force or distance.
$d = \dfrac{W}{F}$ and $F = \dfrac{W}{d}$

Chapter 13: **Work and Energy** 421

DIFFERENTIATE INSTRUCTION

 More Reading Support

B How do you calculate work? *Multiply the force on an object by the distance the object moves in the direction of the force.*

Additional Investigation To reinforce Section 13.1 learning goals, use the following full-period investigation:

Additional INVESTIGATION, Ramp It Up, A, B, & C, pp. 276–284, 346–347
(Advanced students should complete Levels B and C.)

English Learners English learners may not be familiar with the following words and phrases: *hit a baseball, swim a lap, tap a keyboard, bowling alley* (p. 422), and *escalator* on p. 424. Make sure English learners have sufficient background knowledge.

Teach from Visuals

Remind students that work equals force times distance. Ask: In what two ways could the man in the photograph increase the amount of work he does? *He could increase the force with which he pushes against the floor or increase the distance that he raises his body.*

Address Misconceptions

IDENTIFY Ask: If you shove a ball with a force of 50 newtons and it rolls 3 meters across the floor, how much work have you done? If students answer 150 joules, they may hold the misconception that work is done on the ball even while it rolls.

CORRECT Remind students that work is done only while a force is being applied to an object. For example, when you throw a ball, no work is done after the ball leaves your hand, because the forward force is no longer being applied.

REASSESS Ask students when someone does work while skateboarding. *while the skateboarder is pushing on the ground with his or her foot*

Technology Resources

Visit **ClassZone.com** for background on common student misconceptions.

MISCONCEPTION DATABASE

Develop Mathematics Skills

- Math Support, p. 259
- Math Practice, p. 260

History of Science

The joule is named for James Prescott Joule (1818–1889), a British physicist who established the mechanical theory of heat and the law of conservation of energy.

Ongoing Assessment

Practice the Math   *Answers:*

1. $W = F \cdot d = 70\ N \cdot 2\ m = 140\ N \cdot m$
   $W = 140\ J$

2. $d = \dfrac{W}{F} = \dfrac{200\ J}{40\ N} = 5\ m$

Chapter 13   **421**

INVESTIGATE Work

PURPOSE To show the relationship between work, force, and distance by finding the work done in lifting a notebook

TIP 20 min. Have one student in each group measure the force of all the group members so measurements are consistent.

WHAT DO YOU THINK? *Answers will vary. You will do less work if you are shorter and more work if you are taller. No work is done if you stop moving the book.*

CHALLENGE *The work done would equal students' results times 10, times the number of days in the school year (180 days).*

 Datasheet, Work, p. 230

Technology Resources
Customize this student lab as needed or look for an alternative. Print rubrics to assess student lab reports.

 Lab Generator CD-ROM

Metacognitive Strategy
Ask students if they had misconceptions about the concepts that "Investigate Work" illustrated. For example, did they think the weight of the notebook would increase when a taller person lifted it? Have them write about what changed their ideas.

EXPLORE the BIG idea
Revisit "Internet Activity: Work" on p. 417. Have students explain their results.

MAIN IDEA WEB Remember to organize your notes in a web as you read.

Objects that are moving can do work.

You do work when you pick up your books, hit a baseball, swim a lap, or tap a keyboard. These examples show that you do work on objects, but objects can also do work.

For example, in a bowling alley, the bowling balls do work on the pins they hit. Outdoors, the moving air particles in a gust of wind do work that lifts a leaf off the ground. Moving water, such as the water in a river, also does work. If the windblown leaf lands in the water, it might be carried downstream by the current. As the leaf travels downstream, it might go over the edge of a waterfall. In that case, the gravitational force of Earth would pull the leaf and water down.

You can say that an object or person does work on an object, or that the force the object or person is exerting does work. For example, you could say that Earth (an object) does work on the falling water, or that gravity (a force) does work on the water.

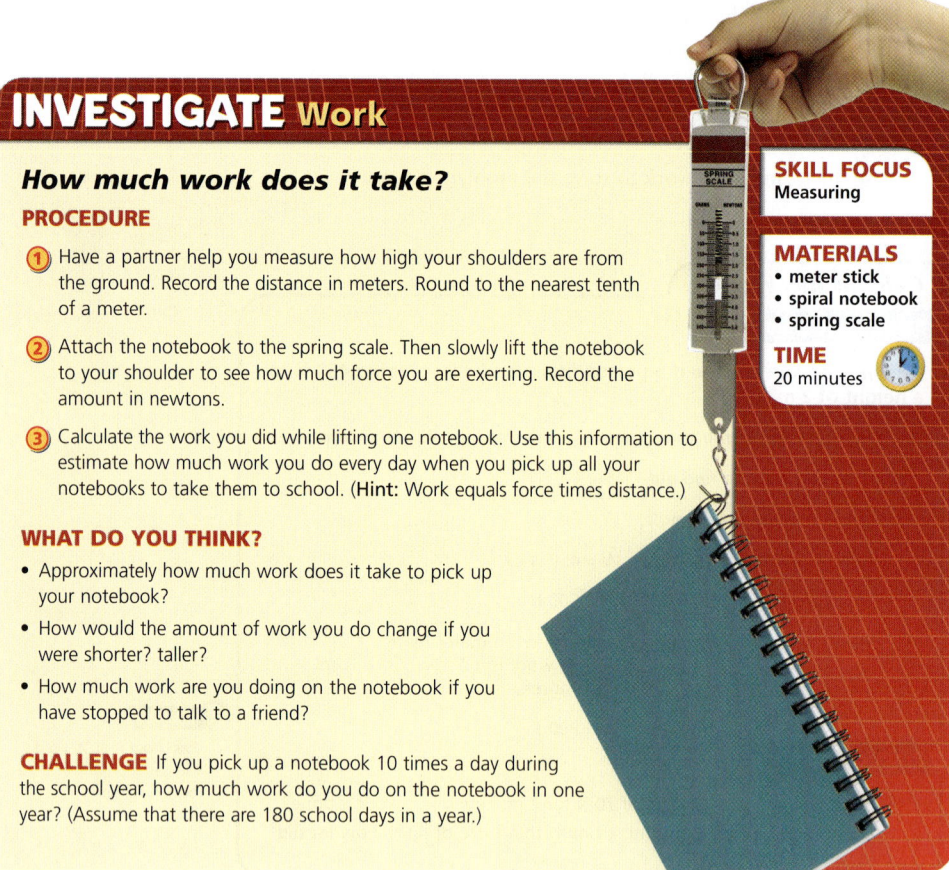

INVESTIGATE Work

How much work does it take?

PROCEDURE

1. Have a partner help you measure how high your shoulders are from the ground. Record the distance in meters. Round to the nearest tenth of a meter.
2. Attach the notebook to the spring scale. Then slowly lift the notebook to your shoulder to see how much force you are exerting. Record the amount in newtons.
3. Calculate the work you did while lifting one notebook. Use this information to estimate how much work you do every day when you pick up all your notebooks to take them to school. (Hint: Work equals force times distance.)

WHAT DO YOU THINK?
- Approximately how much work does it take to pick up your notebook?
- How would the amount of work you do change if you were shorter? taller?
- How much work are you doing on the notebook if you have stopped to talk to a friend?

CHALLENGE If you pick up a notebook 10 times a day during the school year, how much work do you do on the notebook in one year? (Assume that there are 180 school days in a year.)

SKILL FOCUS Measuring

MATERIALS
- meter stick
- spiral notebook
- spring scale

TIME 20 minutes

422 Unit 3: Motion and Forces

DIFFERENTIATE INSTRUCTION

 More Reading Support

C How can a bowling ball do work? *by exerting a force on bowling pins when it hits them*

Advanced Challenge students to compare the amount of work done while lifting a notebook on Earth and when standing on the Moon. Students should conduct research about the Moon to find that the force of gravity is one-sixth of that on Earth. *Since the weight of the notebook on the Moon is only one-sixth of its weight on Earth, only one-sixth of the amount of work would be done when lifting the notebook on the Moon.*

 Challenge and Extension, p. 229

APPLY How could you increase the work done by this water wheel?

Throughout history, people have taken advantage of the capability of objects in motion to do work. Many early cultures built machines such as water wheels to use the force exerted by falling water, and windmills to use the force exerted by moving air. In a water wheel like the one in the photograph, gravity does work on the water. As the water falls, it also can do work on any object that is put in its path. Falling water can turn a water wheel or the turbine of an electric generator.

The water wheel shown above uses the work done by water to turn gears that run a mill and grind grain. In the same way, windmills take advantage of the force of moving air particles. The wind causes the sails of a windmill to turn. The turning sails do work to run machinery or an irrigation system.

 Describe how a water wheel does work.

13.1 Review

KEY CONCEPTS

1. If you push very hard on an object but it does not move, have you done work? Explain.
2. What two factors do you need to know to calculate how much work was done in any situation?
3. Was work done on a book that fell from a desk to the floor? If so, what force was involved?

CRITICAL THINKING

4. **Synthesize** Work is done on a ball when a soccer player kicks it. Is the player still doing work on the ball as it rolls across the ground? Explain.
5. **Calculate** Tina lifted a box 0.5 m. The box weighed 25 N. How much work did Tina do on the box?

CHALLENGE

6. **Analyze** Ben and Andy each pushed an empty grocery cart. Ben used twice the force, but they both did the same amount of work. Explain.

Chapter 13: **Work and Energy** 423

ANSWERS

1. No; the object must move for work to be done.
2. force and distance
3. yes; the force of gravity
4. No; the player is no longer exerting a force on the ball.
5. $W = F \cdot d$
   $= 25 \text{ N} \cdot 0.5 \text{ m}$
   $W = 12.5 \text{ J}$
6. Ben used twice the force, but his cart moved only half as far as Andy's cart.

MATH IN SCIENCE
Math Skills Practice for Science

Set Learning Goal
To learn how extreme values (outliers) in a data set can affect the mean of the data set

Present the Science
Ask students if they have ridden on an escalator (a moving staircase between floors of a building). Tell them that an escalator is like a large conveyor belt set on an incline. The steps are pulled along tracks by chains that move around gears at the top and bottom of the staircase. A typical escalator uses a 100 horsepower motor—about half the power of a large automobile engine—to turn the gears. Discuss an escalator in terms of *Work = Force times distance.*

Develop Algebra Skills
- Remind students to divide the total by the correct number of values after they drop outliers.
- Ask: What is another term for *mean*? *average*

DIFFERENTIATION TIP Below level: If students have trouble understanding the concept of outliers, have them show the eight data entries on a number line. The high outlier, 4850 J, will be obvious.

Close
Ask students to give an example of how their school lives are affected by means. *Their course grades are means of test scores, homework scores, and other scores.*

- Math Support, p. 265
- Math Practice, p. 266

Technology Resources
Students can visit **ClassZone.com** for practice in finding the mean of a data set.

 MATH TUTORIAL

424 Unit 3: Motion and Forces

MATH TUTORIAL CLASSZONE.COM
Click on Math Tutorial for more help with finding the mean.

SKILL: WORKING WITH AVERAGES

Eliminating Extreme Values

A value that is far from most others in a set of data is called an outlier. Outliers make it difficult to find a value that might be considered average. Extremely high or extremely low values can throw off the mean. That is why the highest and lowest figures are ignored in some situations.

Example
The data set below shows the work an escalator does to move 8 people of different weights 5 meters. The work was calculated by multiplying the force needed to move each person by a distance of 5 meters.

4850 J   1600 J   3400 J   2750 J
2950 J   1750 J   3350 J   3800 J

The mean amount of work done is 3056 J.

(1) To calculate an adjusted mean, begin by identifying a high outlier in the data set.

High outlier: 4850

(2) Discard this value and find the new mean.

1600 J + 3400 J + 2750 J + 2950 J + 1750 J + 3350 J + 3800 J = 19,600 J

Mean = $\frac{19,600 \text{ J}}{7}$ = 2800 J

ANSWER The mean amount of work done for this new data set is 2800 J.

Answer the following questions.

1. After ignoring the high outlier in the data set, does this new mean show a more typical level of work for the data set? Why or why not?

2. Do you think the lowest value in the data set is an outlier? Remove it and calculate the new average. How did this affect the results?

3. Suppose the heaviest person in the original data set were replaced by a person weighing the same as the lightest person. What would be the new mean for the data set?

CHALLENGE The median of a data set is the middle value when the values are written in numerical order. Find the median of the adjusted data set (without the high outlier). Compare it with the original and adjusted means. Why do you think it is closer to one than the other?

ANSWERS

1. Yes; the new mean is not distorted by a very large or a very small value in the data set.

2. The new average to the nearest whole number is 3000 J. The mean is less than the mean in the original set of data.

3. After replacing 4850 J with 1600 J, the new mean for the data set would be 2650 J.

CHALLENGE Median: 1600 1750 2750 ⓿2950 3350 3400 3800
The median is closer to the adjusted mean because both calculations have been done without the high outlier.

13.2 Energy is transferred when work is done.

KEY CONCEPT

BEFORE, you learned
- Work is the use of force to move an object
- Work can be calculated

NOW, you will learn
- How work and energy are related
- How to calculate mechanical, kinetic, and potential energy
- What the conservation of energy means

VOCABULARY

potential energy p. 426
kinetic energy p. 426
mechanical energy p. 429
conservation of energy p. 430

THINK ABOUT

How is energy transferred?

School carnivals sometimes include dunk tanks. The goal is to hit a target with a ball, causing a person sitting over a tank of water to fall into the water. You do work on the ball as you throw with your arm. If your aim is good, the ball does work on the target. How do you transfer your energy to the ball?

Work transfers energy.

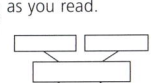

MAIN IDEA WEB
Remember to add boxes to your main idea web as you read.

When you change the position and speed of the ball in the carnival game, you transfer energy to the ball. Energy is the ability of a person or an object to do work or to cause a change. When you do work on an object, some of your energy is transferred to the object. You can think of work as the transfer of energy. In fact, both work and energy are measured in the same unit, the joule.

The man in the photograph above converts one form of energy into another form when he uses his muscles to toss the ball. You can think of the man and the ball as a system, or a group of objects that affect one another. Energy can be transferred from the man to the ball, but the total amount of energy in the system does not change.

 How are work and energy related?

Chapter 13: **Work and Energy** 425

13.2 FOCUS

▶ Set Learning Goals
Students will
- Recognize how work and energy are related.
- Demonstrate how to calculate mechanical, kinetic, and potential energy.
- Explain the law of conservation of energy.
- Analyze data through experimentation to determine energy changes in a rolling ball.

▶ 3-Minute Warm-Up
Display Transparency 28 or copy this exercise on the board:

Draw a picture of yourself pushing or pulling an object. Add arrows to show the direction of the motion and the applied force. *Refer students to the photographs on p. 420, if needed.* Exchange your drawing with a partner and indicate whether all of the applied force in your partner's picture is doing work.

 3-Minute Warm-Up, p. T28

13.2 MOTIVATE

THINK ABOUT

PURPOSE To have students think about how energy is transferred

DISCUSS Have students look at the photograph. Ask:
- What is the source of the energy that allows the thrower to fling the ball toward the target? *the muscles in the thrower's arm*
- What change of energy occurs when the ball is thrown? *Energy is transferred from the man to the ball.*

Answer: You do work to change the ball's speed and position.

Ongoing Assessment

 *Answer: When work is done, energy is transferred.*

Chapter 13 **425**

RESOURCES FOR DIFFERENTIATED INSTRUCTION

Below Level
UNIT RESOURCE BOOK
- Reading Study Guide A, pp. 234–235
- Decoding Support, p. 258

 **AUDIO CDS**

Advanced
UNIT RESOURCE BOOK
- Challenge and Extension, p. 240
- Challenge Reading, pp. 254–255

English Learners
UNIT RESOURCE BOOK
Spanish Reading Study Guide, pp. 238–239

 **AUDIO CDS**
- Audio Readings in Spanish
- Audio Readings (English)

13.2 INSTRUCT

Develop Critical Thinking

APPLY Have students apply their knowledge of potential energy to answer the questions below about a person using a bow and arrow.

- When the person pulls back on the bowstring, what happens to the energy of the bow? *Its potential energy increases.*
- What kind of potential energy does the bow have? *elastic potential energy*
- What happens to the bow's potential energy when the arrow is released? *It is transferred to the arrow as kinetic energy.*
- What determines how far the arrow will travel? *the amount of work that was done on the bow*

Teach from Visuals

To help students interpret the visuals of potential and kinetic energy, ask:

- In which picture is the boy's potential energy at a maximum? *the first picture*
- In which picture does the boy have the most kinetic energy? *the second picture*
- What kind of energy does the trampoline have when the boy lands on it? *elastic potential energy*

READING TIP
The word *potential* comes from the Latin word *potentia*, which means "power." The word *kinetic* comes from the Greek word *kinetos*, which means "moving."

Work changes potential and kinetic energy.

When you throw a ball, you transfer energy to it and it moves. By doing work on the ball, you can give it **kinetic energy** (kuh-NEHT-ihk), which is the energy of motion. Any moving object has some kinetic energy. The faster an object moves, the more kinetic energy it has.

When you do work to lift a ball from the ground, you give the ball a different type of energy, called potential energy. **Potential energy** is stored energy, or the energy an object has due to its position or its shape. The ball's position in your hand above the ground means that it has the potential to fall to the ground. The higher you lift the ball, the more work you do, and the more potential energy the ball has.

You can also give some objects potential energy by changing their shape. For example, if you are holding a spring, you can do work on the spring by squeezing it. After you do the work, the spring has potential energy because it is compressed. This type of potential energy is called elastic potential energy. Just as position gives the spring the potential to fall, compression gives the spring the potential to expand.

Potential and Kinetic Energy

Potential Energy
The boy has potential energy based on his position because gravity will pull him back down.

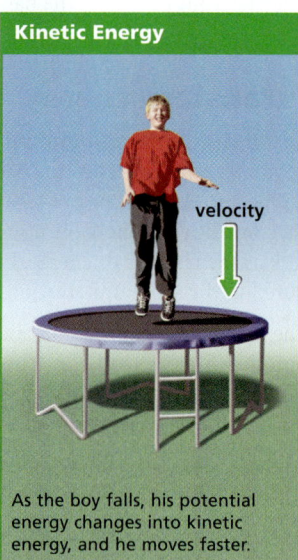

Kinetic Energy
As the boy falls, his potential energy changes into kinetic energy, and he moves faster.

Potential Energy
The trampoline has potential energy because it is stretched.

DIFFERENTIATE INSTRUCTION

More Reading Support

A What is potential energy? *energy stored in an object because of its position or shape*

B What is kinetic energy? *energy that an object has due to its motion*

English Learners English learners may not have prior knowledge of *carnivals* on p. 425, *divers* on p. 427, *in-line skating* on p. 431, and *treadmills* on p. 433. You may also want to call their attention to the phrase "due to" on pp. 426, 427, 429, and explain that "due to" often means "because of."

Calculating Gravitational Potential Energy

Potential energy caused by gravity is called gravitational potential energy. Scientists must take gravitational potential energy into account when launching a spacecraft. Designers of roller coasters must make sure that roller-coaster cars have enough potential energy at the top of a hill to reach the top of the next hill. You can use the following formula to calculate the gravitational potential energy of an object:

Gravitational Potential Energy = mass · gravitational acceleration · height

$$GPE = mgh$$

Recall that g is the acceleration due to Earth's gravity. It is equal to 9.8 m/s^2 at Earth's surface.

The diver in the photograph below has given herself gravitational potential energy by climbing to the diving board. If you know her mass and the height of the board, you can calculate her potential energy.

Calculating Potential Energy

Sample Problem

What is the gravitational potential energy of a girl who has a mass of 40 kg and is standing on the edge of a diving board that is 5 m above the water?

What do you know?	mass = 40 kg, gravitational acceleration = 9.8 m/s^2, height = 5 m
What do you want to find out?	Gravitational Potential Energy
Write the formula:	GPE = mgh
Substitute into the formula:	GPE = 40 kg · 9.8 m/s^2 · 5 m
Calculate and simplify:	GPE = 1960 kg m^2/s^2
Check that your units agree:	kg m^2/s^2 = kg · m/s^2 · m = N·m = J
	Unit of energy is J. Units agree.
Answer:	GPE = 1960 J

Practice the Math

1. An apple with a mass of 0.1 kg is attached to a branch of an apple tree 4 m from the ground. How much gravitational potential energy does the apple have?
2. If you lift a 2 kg box of toys to the top shelf of a closet, which is 3 m high, how much gravitational potential energy will the box of toys have?

 REMINDER A newton (N) is a kg · m/s^2, and a joule (J) is a N·m.

The formula for gravitational potential energy is similar to the formula for work $(W = Fd)$. The formula for GPE also has a force (mg) multiplied by a distance (h). To understand why mg is a force, remember two things: force equals mass times acceleration, and g is the acceleration due to Earth's gravity.

Chapter 13: Work and Energy 427

Develop Algebra Skills

Students must be careful to check whether a problem gives mass or weight. In the formula $GPE = mgh$, mass is multiplied by gravity and height. Because weight is defined as mass times gravity, g drops out when the problem gives weight.

Real World Example

Juggling is a good example of the conversion of gravitational potential energy and kinetic energy. The juggler's hand does work when it is tossing the ball upward to give the ball its initial kinetic energy. After the ball leaves the juggler's hand, the force of gravity acts on it. Because gravity acts to pull the ball downward, the ball loses kinetic energy and slows to a stop at its highest point. When the ball begins to move downward, gravity increases the ball's kinetic energy.

Develop Mathematics Skills

- Math Support, p. 261
- Math Practice, p. 262

Ongoing Assessment

Practice the Math Answers:

1. GPE = mgh
  = 0.1 kg · 9.8 m/s^2 · 4 m
  GPE = 3.92 J
2. GPE = mgh
  = 2 kg · 9.8 m/s^2 · 3 m
  GPE = 58.8 J

DIFFERENTIATE INSTRUCTION

More Reading Support

C What is gravitational potential energy? *potential energy that is caused by gravity*

Below Level If students are having difficulty with calculations, the value for g in the formula for gravitational potential energy can be rounded to 10 m/s^2. This will make calculations easier.

Address Misconceptions

IDENTIFY Ask: If a space shuttle is moving in a straight line through space at a constant speed, what can you say about its energy and any force exerted on it? If students respond that the shuttle has both force and energy, they may not fully understand that force and energy are two different phenomena.

CORRECT Ask if the space shuttle has energy. *Yes, it has kinetic energy due to its motion through space.* Ask if force is being exerted on the space shuttle. *No force is being exerted on the shuttle once it has been set in motion.*

REASSESS Ask students to explain the relationship between force and energy in the example of a book being pushed over the floor. *The force of the push, exerted over a distance, provides the book with kinetic energy.*

Technology Resources
Visit **ClassZone.com** for background on common student misconceptions.

 MISCONCEPTION DATABASE

Integrate the Sciences

All molecules have thermal energy because their atoms are in constant motion. The higher the temperature, the faster the molecules move, and the more thermal energy they have. This concept is crucial in chemical and biochemical reactions because molecules must have a certain amount of energy to react with each other. In industry, a reaction often can be made to occur by heating the reactants. In biological systems, high temperatures can damage the cells of a living organism, but enzymes can lower the amount of energy the reactants need to react with each other.

Ongoing Assessment

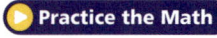 Answers:

1. $KE = \frac{1}{2}mv^2$
   $= \frac{1}{2} \cdot 0.002 \text{ kg} \cdot (15 \text{ m/s})^2$
   $= \frac{1}{2} \cdot 0.002 \text{ kg} \cdot 225 \text{ m}^2/\text{s}^2$
   $KE = 0.225 \text{ J}$

2. the car

428 Unit 3: **Motion and Forces**

Calculating Kinetic Energy

The girl on the swing at left has kinetic energy. To find out how much kinetic energy she has at the bottom of the swing's arc, you must know her mass and her velocity. Kinetic energy can be calculated using the following formula:

$$\text{Kinetic Energy} = \frac{\text{mass} \cdot \text{velocity}^2}{2}$$

$$KE = \frac{1}{2}mv^2$$

Notice that velocity is squared while mass is not. Increasing the velocity of an object has a greater effect on the object's kinetic energy than increasing the mass of the object. If you double the mass of an object, you double its kinetic energy. Because velocity is squared, if you double the object's velocity, its kinetic energy is four times greater.

Calculating Kinetic Energy

Sample Problem

What is the kinetic energy of a girl who has a mass of 40 kg and a velocity of 3 m/s?

What do you know? mass = 40 kg, velocity = 3 m/s

What do you want to find out? Kinetic Energy

Write the formula: $KE = \frac{1}{2}mv^2$

Substitute into the formula: $KE = \frac{1}{2} \cdot 40 \text{ kg} \cdot (3 \text{ m/s})^2$

Calculate and simplify: $KE = \frac{1}{2} \cdot 40 \text{ kg} \cdot \frac{9 \text{ m}^2}{\text{s}^2}$

$$= \frac{360 \text{ kg} \cdot \text{m}^2}{2 \text{ s}^2}$$

$$= 180 \text{ kg} \cdot \text{m}^2/\text{s}^2$$

Check that your units agree: $\frac{\text{kg} \cdot \text{m}^2}{\text{s}^2} = \frac{\text{kg} \cdot \text{m}}{\text{s}^2} \cdot \text{m} = \text{N} \cdot \text{m} = \text{J}$

Unit of energy is J. Units agree.

Answer: $KE = 180 \text{ J}$

Practice the Math

1. A grasshopper with a mass of 0.002 kg jumps up at a speed of 15 m/s. What is the kinetic energy of the grasshopper?
2. A truck with a mass of 6000 kg is traveling north on a highway at a speed of 17 m/s. A car with a mass of 2000 kg is traveling south on the same highway at a speed of 30 m/s. Which vehicle has more kinetic energy?

428 Unit 3: **Motion and Forces**

DIFFERENTIATE INSTRUCTION

 More Reading Support

D How do you calculate kinetic energy? *multiply an object's mass by the square of its velocity and divide by two*

Advanced Have students graph a linear relationship (kinetic energy versus mass) and a nonlinear relationship (kinetic energy versus the velocity). The first graph will be a straight line, and the second graph will be a steep curve. The differences between these two graphs will show students that the kinetic energy of an object is affected much more by a given percentage change in velocity than by the same percentage change in mass.

 Challenge and Extension, p. 240

Calculating Mechanical Energy

Mechanical energy is the energy possessed by an object due to its motion or position—in other words, it is the object's combined potential energy and kinetic energy. A thrown baseball has mechanical energy as a result of both its motion (kinetic energy) and its position above the ground (gravitational potential energy). Any object that has mechanical energy can do work on another object.

Once you calculate an object's kinetic and potential energy, you can add the two values together to find the object's mechanical energy.

Mechanical Energy = Potential Energy + Kinetic Energy

$$ME = PE + KE$$

For example, a skateboarder has a potential energy of 200 joules due to his position at the top of a hill and a kinetic energy of 100 joules due to his motion. His total mechanical energy is 300 joules.

 How is mechanical energy related to kinetic and potential energy?

VOCABULARY Use a vocabulary strategy to help you remember *mechanical energy*.

INVESTIGATE Mechanical Energy

How does mechanical energy change?
PROCEDURE

1. Find and record the mass of the ball.
2. Build a ramp with the board and books. Measure and record the height of the ramp. You will place the ball at the top of the ramp, so calculate the ball's potential energy at the top of the ramp using mass and height.
3. Mark a line on the floor with tape 30 cm from the bottom of the ramp.
4. Place the ball at the top of the ramp and release it without pushing. Time how long the ball takes to travel from the end of the ramp to the tape.
5. Calculate the ball's speed using the time you measured in step 4. Use this speed to calculate the ball's kinetic energy after it rolled down the ramp.

WHAT DO YOU THINK?
- At the top of the ramp, how much potential energy did the ball have? kinetic energy? mechanical energy?
- Compare the ball's mechanical energy at the top of the ramp with its mechanical energy at the bottom of the ramp. Are they the same? Why or why not?

CHALLENGE Other than gravity, what forces could have affected the movement of the ball?

SKILL FOCUS Analyzing data

MATERIALS
- ball
- balance
- board
- books
- ruler
- tape
- stopwatch
- calculator

TIME 20 minutes

Real World Example

The first hill of a roller coaster is always the highest. A roller-coaster car has maximum potential energy and minimum kinetic energy at the top of the first hill. This potential energy changes to kinetic energy when the car begins to move downhill. Because some energy is lost to friction, the car could not climb the second hill if it were as high as the first hill. Each hill must be lower than the previous hill.

EXPLORE the BIG idea

Revisit "Bouncing Ball" on p. 417. Have students explain their results.

Ongoing Assessment

Explain the law of conservation of energy.

Ask: How can energy be added to an object and still follow the law of conservation of energy? *Another object in the system must lose energy.*

PHOTO CAPTION Answer: Tell students that an anchor attached to the pendulum nudges the pendulum in the right direction each time it swings. This is the energy the pendulum needs to overcome friction and keep swinging. Some clocks have a key-wound spring inside the clock.

VISUALIZATION
CLASSZONE.COM
Observe how potential and kinetic energy are transferred on an amusement park ride.

F

The total amount of energy is constant.

You know that energy is transferred when work is done. No matter how energy is transferred or transformed, all of the energy is still present somewhere in one form or another. This is known as the **law of conservation of energy.** As long as you account for all the different forms of energy involved in any process, you will find that the total amount of energy never changes.

Conserving Mechanical Energy

Look at the photograph of the in-line skater on page 431. As she rolls down the ramp, the amounts of kinetic energy and potential energy change. However, the total—or the mechanical energy—stays the same. In this example, energy lost to friction is ignored.

① At the top of the ramp, the skater has potential energy because gravity can pull her downward. She has no velocity; therefore, she has no kinetic energy.

② As the skater rolls down the ramp, her potential energy decreases because the elevation decreases. Her kinetic energy increases because her velocity increases. The potential energy lost as the skater gets closer to the ground is converted into kinetic energy. Halfway down the ramp, half of her potential energy has been converted to kinetic energy.

③ At the bottom of the ramp, all of the skater's energy is kinetic. Gravity cannot pull her down any farther, so she has no more gravitational potential energy. Her mechanical energy—the total of her potential and kinetic energy—stays the same throughout.

APPLY Energy must occasionally be added to a pendulum to keep it swinging. What keeps a grandfather clock's pendulum swinging regularly?

Losing Mechanical Energy

A pendulum is an object that is suspended from a fixed support so that it swings freely back and forth under the influence of gravity. As a pendulum swings, its potential energy is converted into kinetic energy and then back to potential energy in a continuous cycle. Ideally, the potential energy at the top of each swing would be the same as it was the previous time. However, the height of the pendulum's swing actually decreases slightly each time, until finally the pendulum stops altogether.

In most energy transformations, some of the energy is transformed into heat. In the case of the pendulum, there is friction between the string and the support, as well as air resistance from the air around the pendulum. The mechanical energy is used to do work against friction and air resistance. This process transforms the mechanical energy into heat. The mechanical energy has not been destroyed; it has simply changed form and been transferred from the pendulum.

430   Unit 3: Motion and Forces

DIFFERENTIATE INSTRUCTION

 **More Reading Support**

F What is the law of conservation of energy? *Energy cannot be created or destroyed.*

English Learners English learners may be unfamiliar with some informal writing styles. Writers often use sentence fragments and leave readers to substitute the remainder of the sentence themselves. For example, in "Investigate Mechanical Energy" on p. 429, ". . . how much potential energy did the ball have? Kinetic energy? Mechanical energy?" readers are expected to substitute the terms into the initial question:" . . . how much kinetic energy did the ball have?" Be aware of informal writing styles and assist English learners in understanding them.

Conserving Mechanical Energy

The potential energy and kinetic energy in a system or process may vary, but the total energy remains unchanged.

① Top of Ramp

At the top of the ramp, the skater's mechanical energy is equal to her potential energy because she has no velocity.

100% PE

② Halfway Down Ramp

As the skater goes down the ramp, she loses height but gains speed. The potential energy she loses is equal to the kinetic energy she gains.

50% PE | 50% KE

③ Bottom of Ramp

As the skater speeds along the bottom of the ramp, all of the potential energy has changed to kinetic energy. Her mechanical energy remains unchanged.

100% KE

Fabiola da Silva is a professional in-line skater who was born in Brazil but now lives in California.

READING VISUALS How do the skater's kinetic and potential energy change as she skates up and down the ramp? (Assume she won't lose any energy to friction.)

Chapter 13: **Work and Energy** 431

Teach from Visuals

To help students interpret the "Conserving Mechanical Energy" visual, ask:

- Why does the skater have no kinetic energy at the top of the ramp? *She is momentarily at rest.*
- Why does the skater have no potential energy at the bottom of the ramp? *The bottom of the ramp is the lowest height.*

 This visual is also available as T30 in the Unit Transparency Book.

Teach Difficult Concepts

Students may have a difficult time understanding that work must be done for an object's total energy to increase. Explain that an object's energy cannot increase unless additional energy comes from somewhere. To help students understand, you might try the following demonstration.

Teacher Demo

With a sharp knife, carefully cut a racquetball in half. Trim one of the halves so that it is slightly smaller than a hemisphere. Turn it inside out and drop it, bulge side up, on a hard surface. The ball will snap and rebound to a height much greater than that from which it was dropped. Ask students how the ball can bounce higher than its original height. *The work required to turn the hemisphere inside out is stored as potential energy. As the dropped ball hits the hard surface, the potential energy is released and converted to kinetic energy, which allows the ball to rebound to a greater height.*

Ongoing Assessment

READING VISUALS *Answer: As the skater goes down the ramp, kinetic and potential energy become equal. At the bottom of the ramp, all of the potential energy has changed to kinetic energy. As the skater goes up the ramp, the opposite happens. At the top of the ramp, all the kinetic energy has changed to potential energy.*

Chapter 13 **431**

DIFFERENTIATE INSTRUCTION

Below Level Have students give an oral summary of the energy changes that take place in the visual. The changes can be displayed graphically as well.

Advanced Have students interested in finding out about how pole vaulting works read the following article:

 Challenge Reading, pp. 254–255

Develop Critical Thinking

PROVIDE EXAMPLES Have students make a set of four flash cards, one for each form of energy mentioned in the text. Students should write the energy form on one side of a card and list examples on the other side. Encourage students to apply their knowledge of the forms of energy by providing examples that are not in the text.

Integrate the Sciences

Organisms are continually transforming energy from one type to another. A plant transforms electromagnetic energy (light) to chemical energy (sugar). Chemical energy fuels muscles, which can transform it to mechanical energy (climbing and sliding down a slide). Shivering converts chemical energy to thermal energy.

Reinforce the BIG idea

Have students relate the section to the Big Idea.

 Reinforcing Key Concepts, p. 242

13.2 ASSESS & RETEACH

Assess
 Section 13.2 Quiz, p. 63

Reteach
Have students draw a picture and label the energy exchanges that take place when a skier rides a ski lift to the top of a slope and then skis down the slope. Students should realize that work is done on the skier by the lift and that the energy needed to do that work comes from the fuel used to run the lift.

Technology Resources
Have students visit ClassZone.com for reteaching of Key Concepts.

 CONTENT REVIEW

 CONTENT REVIEW CD-ROM

432 Unit 3: Motion and Forces

MAIN IDEA WEB Include common forms of energy in your web.

Forms of Energy

As you have seen, mechanical energy is a combination of kinetic energy and potential energy. Other common forms of energy are discussed below. Each of these forms of energy is also a combination of kinetic energy and potential energy. Chemical energy, for example, is potential energy when it is stored in bonds.

Thermal energy is the energy an object has due to the motion of its molecules. The faster the molecules in an object move, the more thermal energy the object has.

Chemical energy is the energy stored in chemical bonds that hold chemical compounds together. If a molecule's bonds are broken or rearranged, energy is released or absorbed. Chemical energy is used to light up fireworks displays. It is also stored in food and in matches.

Nuclear energy is the potential energy stored in the nucleus of an atom. In a nuclear reaction, a tiny portion of an atom's mass is turned into energy. The source of the Sun's energy is nuclear energy. Nuclear energy can be used to run power plants that provide electricity.

Electromagnetic energy is the energy associated with electrical and magnetic interactions. Energy that is transferred by electric charges or current is often called electrical energy. Another type of electromagnetic energy is radiant energy, the energy carried by light, infrared waves, and x-rays.

It is possible to transfer, or convert, one energy form into one or more other forms. For example, when you rub your hands together on a cold day, you convert mechanical energy to thermal energy. Your body converts chemical energy stored in food to thermal and mechanical energy (muscle movement).

13.2 Review

KEY CONCEPTS
1. Explain the relationship between work and energy.
2. How are potential energy and kinetic energy related to mechanical energy?
3. When one form of energy changes into one or more other forms of energy, what happens to the total amount of energy?

CRITICAL THINKING
4. **Infer** Debra used 250 J of energy to roll a bowling ball. When the ball arrived at the end of the lane, it had only 200 J of energy. What happened to the other 50 J?
5. **Calculate** A satellite falling to Earth has a kinetic energy of 182.2 billion J and a potential energy of 1.6 billion J. What is its mechanical energy?

CHALLENGE
6. **Apply** At what point in its motion is the kinetic energy of the end of a pendulum greatest? At what point is its potential energy greatest? When its kinetic energy is half its greatest value, how much potential energy did it gain?

432 Unit 3: Motion and Forces

ANSWERS

1. When work is done, energy is transferred.

2. Mechanical energy is the total potential and kinetic energy that an object has.

3. The total amount of energy stays the same.

4. The rest of the energy was lost to friction.

5. ME = PE + KE
   = 182.2 billion J
   + 1.6 billion J
   ME = 183.8 billion J

6. A pendulum's kinetic energy is greatest at the bottom of its swing. Its potential energy is greatest at the top of its swing. When its kinetic energy is half its greatest value, the potential energy gained is equal to half the kinetic energy.

Think SCIENCE

SKILL: ISOLATING VARIABLES

How Do They Do It?

Some women in Kenya and other African countries walk many miles every day carrying heavy loads on their heads without an increase in their heart rate. Most have done it since they were children. Scientists have studied African women to learn how they do this.

▶ Variables

In scientific research, variables must be chosen and tested. Variables are usually compared with a control group—that is, a group for whom all potential variables are held constant. Scientists first asked several Kenyan women to walk on a treadmill. The scientists measured the women's heart rate and how much oxygen they used while carrying different weights on their heads. They found that the women could carry as much as 20 percent of their own body weight without using extra oxygen or increasing their heart rate.

The same scientists asked subjects in a control group in the United States to walk on a treadmill. The people in this group wore helmets lined with different amounts of lead. Even the lightest load caused their heart rate and oxygen consumption to increase.

If you were studying the way these African women carry loads, what variables would you choose to isolate? What control group would you use? Here are some variables and controls to consider:

- carrying the load on the head compared with carrying it on the back
- weight of the load
- women compared with men
- African women compared with other women
- method of walking

▶ Isolate the Variables

On Your Own Design an experiment that could test one of the variables without interference from other variables. Can each variable be tested independently?

As a Group Discuss each variable and see if the group agrees that it can be tested independently. Can you eliminate any of the variables based on information on this page?

CHALLENGE How would you measure the amount of energy used for the variable you chose?

Women in many countries, like this woman from Abidjan, Ivory Coast, balance heavy loads as they walk.

Chapter 13: **Work and Energy** 433

THINK SCIENCE
Scientific Methods of Thinking

Set Learning Goal
To isolate variables when designing an experiment to learn why some African women can carry large loads without increasing their heart rate

Present the Science
In a recent study, two European researchers learned that some African women unconsciously modify their gait when carrying large loads on their heads and thereby use less energy. The energy they save is applied to carrying the weight.

Guide the Activity
- Students should understand how a treadmill works before they begin to consider variables.
- Ask students if they can think of other variables to test.
- Have students compare a walking human to an upside-down pendulum in terms of potential and kinetic energy.

COOPERATIVE LEARNING STRATEGY
Have groups discuss why they think the women can carry so much weight. The group should brainstorm the variables they might test, choose one, and design an experiment to test it.

If you want students to design an experiment that tests a variable, display the following resources to help them along.

- Identifying Variables and Constants, A25–26
- Setting Up Experimental Groups and Controls, A27–28

Close
Ask: Humans transfer potential and kinetic energy when they walk, but only about 65 percent of the energy is actually transferred. Where does the remaining 35 percent of the energy for walking come from? *the muscles*

ANSWERS

See students' plans. The researchers did not test the women by having them carry the loads on their backs, nor did they compare women with men. These variables can be eliminated based on information on the page.

CHALLENGE Measure test subjects' heart rates and oxygen consumption.

Chapter 13 **433**

13.3 FOCUS

▶ Set Learning Goals

Students will
- Explain how power relates to work and time.
- Explain how power relates to energy and time.
- Describe some common uses of power.
- Measure the power needed to pull an object.

⏱ 3-Minute Warm-Up

Display Transparency 29 or copy this exercise on the board:

Match the correct term to each definition.

Definitions
1. stored energy *b*
2. the use of force to move an object a certain distance *d*
3. the energy of motion *c*

Terms

a. mechanical energy   c. kinetic energy
b. potential energy   d. work

[T] 3-Minute Warm-Up, p. T29

13.3 MOTIVATE

EXPLORE Power

PURPOSE To investigate whether time affects the amount of work done

TIP *10 min.* Have a partner set the timer and record the times.

WHAT DO YOU THINK? *The same amount of work was done both times. The amount of work done is independent of the time needed to do the work. Answers will vary.*

KEY CONCEPT
13.3 Power is the rate at which work is done.

◀ BEFORE, you learned	▶ NOW, you will learn
• Mechanical energy is a combination of kinetic energy and potential energy	• How power is related to work and time
• Mechanical energy can be calculated	• How power is related to energy and time
• Work transfers energy	• About common uses of power

VOCABULARY

power p. 434
watt p. 435
horsepower p. 436

EXPLORE Power

How does time affect work?

PROCEDURE

1. Place the cups side by side. Put all of the marbles in one cup.
2. Place each marble, one by one, into the other cup. Time how long it takes to do this.
3. Set the timer for half that amount of time. Then repeat step 2 in that time.

WHAT DO YOU THINK?
- Did you do more work the first time or the second time? Why?
- What differences did you notice between the two tries?

MATERIALS
- 2 plastic cups
- 10 marbles
- stopwatch

 VOCABULARY Use a vocabulary strategy to help you remember the meaning of *power*.

Power can be calculated from work and time.

If you lift a book one meter, you do the same amount of work whether you lift the book quickly or slowly. However, when you lift the book quickly, you increase your **power**—the rate at which you do work. A cook increases his power when he beats eggs rapidly instead of stirring them slowly. A runner increases her power when she breaks into a sprint to reach the finish line.

The word *power* has different common meanings. It is used to mean a source of energy, as in a power plant, or strength, as in a powerful engine. When you talk about a powerful swimmer, for example, you would probably say that the swimmer is very strong or very fast. If you use the scientific definition of power, you would instead say that a powerful swimmer is one who does the work of moving herself through the water in a short time.

RESOURCES FOR DIFFERENTIATED INSTRUCTION

Below Level
UNIT RESOURCE BOOK
- Reading Study Guide A, pp. 245–246
- Decoding Support, p. 258

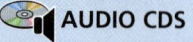 AUDIO CDS

Advanced
UNIT RESOURCE BOOK
Challenge and Extension, p. 251

English Learners
UNIT RESOURCE BOOK
Spanish Reading Study Guide, pp. 249–250

🎧 AUDIO CDS
- Audio Readings in Spanish
- Audio Readings (English)

Each of the swimmers shown in the photograph above is doing work—that is, she is using a certain force to move a certain distance. It takes time to cover that distance. The power a swimmer uses depends on the force, the distance, and the time it takes to cover that distance. The more force the swimmer uses, the more power she has. Also, the faster she goes, the more power she has because she is covering the same distance in a shorter time. Swimmers often increase their speed toward the end of a race, which increases their power, making it possible for them to reach the end of the pool in less time.

 Summarize in your own words the difference between work and power.

Calculating Power from Work

 You know that a given amount of work can be done by a slow-moving swimmer over a long period of time or by a fast-moving swimmer in a short time. Likewise, a given amount of work can be done by a low-powered motor over a long period of time or by a high-powered motor in a short time.

Because power is a measurement of how much work is done in a given time, power can be calculated based on work and time. To find power, divide the amount of work by the time it takes to do the work.

$$\text{Power} = \frac{\text{Work}}{\text{time}} \qquad P = \frac{W}{t}$$

READING TIP
W (in italicized type) is the letter that represents the variable *Work*. W, not italicized, is the abbreviation for watt.

Remember that work is measured in joules. Power is often measured in joules of work per second. The unit of measurement for power is the **watt** (W). One watt is equal to one joule of work done in one second. If an object does a large amount of work, its power is usually measured in units of 1000 watts, or kilowatts.

Chapter 13: **Work and Energy** 435

DIFFERENTIATE INSTRUCTION

 More Reading Support

A How do you calculate power if you know the time and the amount of work done? *Power is work divided by time.*

English Learners Place the words *power, watt,* and *horsepower* on the classroom's Science Word Wall with abbreviated definitions for quick reference. English learners may not have prior knowledge of *conveyor belt* on p. 436 (under "Practice the Math"), and may be confused by the phrase "beats eggs rapidly" on p. 434. Explain that a conveyer belt is a mechanical piece of equipment that moves items on an assembly line and that beating eggs means stirring them quickly.

History of Science

James Watt did not invent the steam engine. However, the improvements he made to an engine invented by Thomas Newcomen made Watt's engine the first economically feasible engine, which contributed to the Industrial Revolution. Watt defined 1 horsepower as 1 horse lifting 33,000 pounds (14,968 kg) a distance of 1 foot in 1 minute. One horsepower is actually about 50 percent more than the rate at which an average horse can work.

Develop Algebra Skills

In question 2 of Practice the Math, students should note that the elevator takes 8 seconds to go up 2 floors, but the height of only a single floor is given.

- Math Support, p. 263
- Math Practice, p. 264

Ongoing Assessment

Practice the Math Answer:

1. $P = \dfrac{W}{t}$

   $\dfrac{10 \text{ J}}{20 \text{ s}} = 0.5 \text{ J/s}$

   $P = 0.5 \text{ W}$

2. $P = \dfrac{W}{t}$, $W = F \cdot d$

   $P = \dfrac{F \cdot d}{t} = \dfrac{1710 \text{ N} \cdot 8 \text{ m}}{8 \text{ s}}$

   $P = 1710 \text{ N} \cdot \text{m/s} = 1710 \text{ J/s}$
   $= 1710 \text{ W}$

RESOURCE CENTER
CLASSZONE.COM
Find out more about power.

Calculating Power from Work

Sample Problem

An Antarctic explorer uses 6000 J of work to pull his sled for 60 s. What power does he need?

What do you know?	Work = 6000 J, time = 60 s
What do you want to find out?	Power
Write the formula:	$P = \dfrac{W}{t}$
Substitute into the formula:	$P = \dfrac{6000 \text{ J}}{60 \text{ s}}$
Calculate and simplify:	$P = 100$ J/s = 100 W
Check that your units agree:	$\dfrac{\text{J}}{\text{s}} = \text{W}$
	Unit of power is W. Units agree.
Answer:	$P = 100$ W

Practice the Math

1. If a conveyor belt uses 10 J to move a piece of candy a distance of 3 m in 20 s, what is the conveyor belt's power?
2. An elevator uses a force of 1710 N to lift 3 people up 1 floor. Each floor is 4 m high. The elevator takes 8 s to lift the 3 people up 2 floors. What is the elevator's power?

Horsepower

Both the horse and the tractor use power to pull objects around a farm.

James Watt, the Scottish engineer for whom the watt is named, improved the power of the steam engine in the mid-1700s. Watt also developed a unit of measurement for power called the horsepower.

Horsepower is based on what it sounds like—the amount of work a horse can do in a minute. In Watt's time, people used horses to do many different types of work. For example, horses were used on farms to pull plows and wagons.

Watt wanted to explain to people how powerful his steam engine was compared with horses. After observing several horses doing work, Watt concluded that an average horse could move 150 pounds a distance of 220 feet in 1 minute. Watt called this amount of power 1 horsepower. A single horsepower is equal to 745 watts. Therefore, a horsepower is a much larger unit of measurement than a watt.

Today horsepower is used primarily in connection with engines and motors. For example, you may see a car advertised as having a 150-horsepower engine. The power of a motorboat, lawn mower, tractor, or motorcycle engine is also referred to as horsepower.

436 Unit 3: Motion and Forces

DIFFERENTIATE INSTRUCTION

 More Reading Support

B What is horsepower based on? *the amount of work a horse can do in one minute*

Advanced To give students practice in converting units, ask them to estimate how many 75-watt engines it would take to equal the power of a 100-horsepower engine. *Since 1 horsepower is equal to 745 W, 100 hp = 74,500 W. Approximately 1000 75-watt engines equal a 100-horsepower engine.*

 Challenge and Extension, p. 251

INVESTIGATE Power

How much power do you have?

PROCEDURE

1. Measure a length of 5 meters on the floor. Mark the beginning and the end of the 5 meters with masking tape.
2. Attach the object to the spring scale with a piece of string. Slowly pull the object across the floor using a steady amount of force. Record the force and the time it takes you to pull the object.

WHAT DO YOU THINK?
- How much power did you use to pull the object 5 meters?
- How do you think you could increase the power you used? decrease the power?

CHALLENGE How quickly would you have to drag the object along the floor to produce 40 watts of power?

SKILL FOCUS
Measuring

MATERIALS
- meter stick
- masking tape
- 100 g object
- spring scale
- string
- stopwatch

TIME
15 minutes

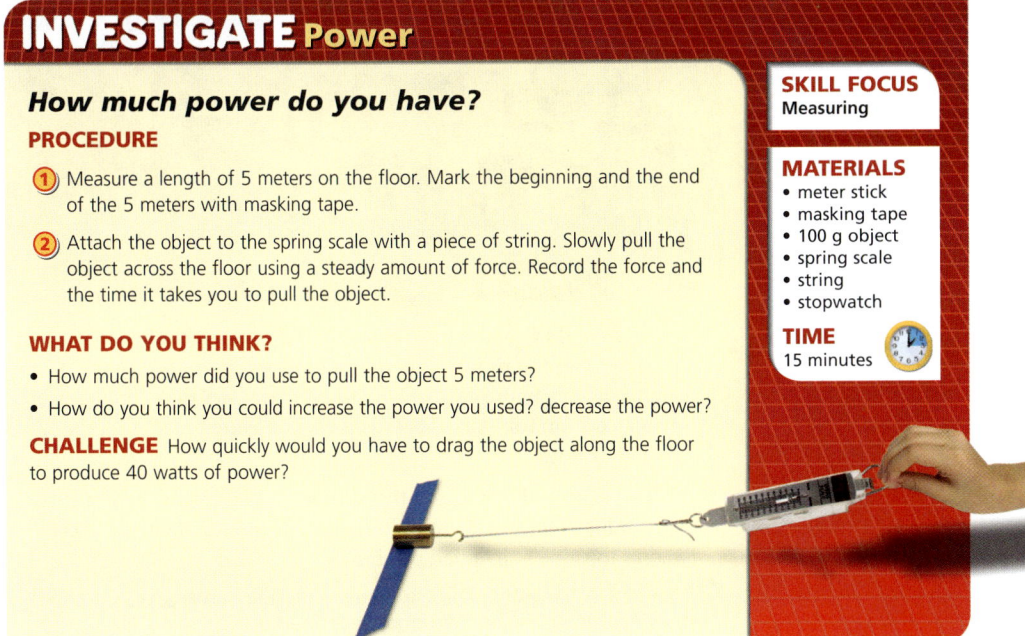

Power can be calculated from energy and time.

Sometimes you may know that energy is being transferred, but you cannot directly measure the work done by the forces involved. For example, you know that a television uses power. But there is no way to measure all the work every part of the television does in terms of forces and distance. Because work measures the transfer of energy, you can also think of power as the amount of energy transferred over a period of time.

Calculating Power from Energy

When you turn on a television, it starts using energy. Each second the television is on, a certain amount of electrical energy is transferred from a local power plant to your television. If you measure how much energy your television uses during a given time period, you can find out how much power it needs by using the following formula:

$$\text{Power} = \frac{\text{Energy}}{\text{time}} \qquad P = \frac{E}{t}$$

This formula should look familiar to you because it is very similar to the formula used to calculate power from work.

Chapter 13: **Work and Energy** 437

DIFFERENTIATE INSTRUCTION

 More Reading Support

C How do you calculate power if you know the amount of energy and the time? *Power is energy divided by time.*

Inclusion A spring scale with large numerals will be helpful to students with visual impairments while they are performing "Investigate Power." Students with physical ailments can do the timing.

Alternative Assessment Have students write a brochure that a tractor manufacturer could give to customers. It should explain the concept of power and describe the power of the engine in terms of horsepower.

INVESTIGATE Power

PURPOSE To measure the work used to pull an object and to calculate power

TIPS *15 min.* Allow students a few minutes to explore, and then suggest the following:

- If students need help in reading spring scales, refer them to p. R16 in the Lab Handbook at the end of their textbook.
- Any object can be used as long as the force needed to pull it is easy to measure. A small sack of beans is a good choice.
- A 100 g object weighs about one-fourth of a pound.

WHAT DO YOU THINK? *Students who pull faster should record more power used. Increase the power by pulling the object faster; decrease the power by pulling the object more slowly.*

CHALLENGE *Answers will depend on the friction between the object and the floor.*

 Datasheet, Power, p. 252

Technology Resources

Customize this student lab as needed or look for an alternative. Print rubrics to assess student lab reports.

 Lab Generator CD-ROM

Metacognitive Strategy

Have students identify content that challenges their prior understandings about power. Ask: How is the scientific definition of power different from the way you use the word in everyday conversation? What surprised you about the scientific meaning of power?

Teaching with Technology

If you have a video camera, have students videotape when they pull the object along the floor so that they can see if they are using a steady amount of force.

Chapter 13 **437**

Ongoing Assessment

Explain how power relates to energy and time.

Ask: What is the relationship between power, energy, and time? *Power is directly related to energy and inversely related to time. It is the rate at which energy is transferred.*

CHECK YOUR READING Answer: Calculate power from energy and time when you cannot measure the work used to transfer the energy, as a television set.

Practice the Math Answers:

1. $P = \dfrac{E}{t}$

    $= \dfrac{100 \text{ J}}{2 \text{ s}}$

    $P = 50 \text{ J/s} = 50 \text{ W}$

2. $E = P \cdot t$

    $= 1.1 \text{ W} \cdot 10 \text{ s}$

    $E = 11 \text{ W} \cdot \text{s} = 11 \text{ J}$

The photograph shows Hong Kong, China, at night. Every second, the city uses more than 4 billion joules of electrical energy!

You can think about power as any kind of transfer of energy in a certain amount of time. It is useful to think of power in this way if you cannot directly figure out the work used to transfer the energy. Power calculated from transferred energy is also measured in joules per second, or watts.

You have probably heard the term *watt* used in connection with light bulbs. A 60-watt light bulb requires 60 joules of energy every second to shine at its rated brightness.

CHECK YOUR READING In what situations is it useful to think of power as the transfer of energy in a certain amount of time?

REMINDER Remember that energy and work are both measured in joules.

Calculating Power from Energy

Sample Problem

A light bulb used 600 J of energy in 6 s. What is the power of the light bulb?

What do you know?	Energy = 600 J, time = 6 s
What do you want to find out?	Power
Write the formula:	$P = \dfrac{E}{t}$
Substitute into the formula:	$P = \dfrac{600 \text{ J}}{6 \text{ s}}$
Calculate and simplify:	$P = 100$ J/s
Check that your units agree:	Unit is J/s. Unit for power is W, which is also J/s. Units agree.
Answer:	$P = 100$ W

Practice the Math

1. A laptop computer uses 100 J every 2 seconds. How much power is needed to run the computer?
2. The power needed to pump blood through your body is about 1.1 W. How much energy does your body use when pumping blood for 10 seconds?

438 Unit 3: Motion and Forces

DIFFERENTIATE INSTRUCTION

More Reading Support

D When is it useful to calculate power from energy rather than from work? *when you cannot figure out the amount of work used to transfer the energy*

Below Level Have students write the formulas for calculating power from work and power from energy. If they see the formulas side by side, they will realize how similar the formulas are.

438 Unit 3: **Motion and Forces**

Everyday Power

Many appliances in your home rely on electricity for energy. Each appliance requires a certain number of joules per second, the power it needs to run properly. An electric hair dryer uses energy. For example, a 600-watt hair dryer needs 600 joules per second. The wattage of the hair dryer indicates how much energy per second it needs to operate.

The dryer works by speeding up the evaporation of water on the surface of hair. It needs only two main parts to do this: a heating coil and a fan turned by a motor.

① When the hair dryer is plugged into an outlet and the switch is turned on, electrical energy moves electrons in the wires, creating a current.

② This current runs an electric motor that turns the fan blades. Air is drawn into the hair dryer through small holes in the casing. The turning fan blades push the air over the coil.

③ The current also makes the heating coil become hot.

④ The fan pushes heated air out of the dryer.

Most hair dryers have high and low settings. At the high power setting, the temperature is increased, more air is pushed through the dryer, and the dryer does its work faster. Some dryers have safety switches that shut off the motor when the temperature rises to a level that could burn your scalp. Insulation keeps the outside of the dryer from becoming hot to the touch.

Many other appliances, from air conditioners to washing machines to blenders, need electrical energy to do their work. Take a look around you at all the appliances that help you during a typical day.

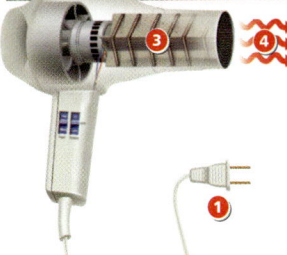

13.3 Review

KEY CONCEPTS
1. How is power related to work?
2. Name two units used for power, and give examples of when each unit might be used.
3. What do you need to know to calculate how much energy a light bulb uses?

CRITICAL THINKING
4. **Apply** Discuss different ways in which a swimmer can increase her power.
5. **Calculate** Which takes more power: using 15 N to lift a ball 2 m in 5 seconds or using 100 N to push a box 2 m in 1 minute?

CHALLENGE
6. **Analyze** A friend tells you that you can calculate power by using a different formula from the one given in this book. The formula your friend gives you is as follows:
   Power = force • speed
   Do you think this is a valid formula for power? Explain.

Chapter 13: **Work and Energy** 439

ANSWERS

1. Power is the rate at which work is done. The faster you do work, the greater your power.
2. Power can be measured in joules per second (watts) or in horsepower. Examples will vary but might include light bulbs for watts and cars for horsepower.
3. how many watts it needs and how long it is on
4. by adding force and increasing speed
5. using 15 N to lift a ball 2 m in 5 seconds
6. Yes; speed is distance divided by time, so power equals force times distance divided by time. Since work is force times distance, the formula can be simplified to work divided by time.

CHAPTER INVESTIGATION

Focus

PURPOSE Students will relate work done to the potential energy gained, and power to the work and the time.

OVERVIEW Students will calculate the potential energy, the work done, and the power needed to lift a wheeled object straight up and to raise it to the same height using a ramp. Students should find that

- the work done equals or exceeds the gain in potential energy as the car moves up the ramp.
- power depends on the time it takes the student to move the car. The longer the time taken to move the car, the less power the car has.

Lab Preparation

- If appropriate, have students bring in small wheeled objects from home. A toy car or truck is a good choice.
- Review how to use and read a spring scale. Remind students that a spring scale measures force in newtons.
- Prior to the investigation, have students read through the investigation, write their hypothesis, and prepare their data tables. Or you may wish to copy and distribute datasheets and rubrics.

 UNIT RESOURCE BOOK, pp. 267–275

 SCIENCE TOOLKIT, F14

Lab Management

If necessary, substitute a wristwatch for a stopwatch.

INCLUSION Spring scales with large numbers are useful if you have students with visual impairments. Spring scales that are easy to hold are useful if you have physically challenged students.

Teaching with Technology

Students can use spreadsheet software to record their data and calculate their results. Spreadsheets will simplify number manipulation.

440 Unit 3: **Motion and Forces**

CHAPTER INVESTIGATION

Work and Power

OVERVIEW AND PURPOSE People in wheelchairs cannot use steps leading up to a building's entrance. Sometimes there is a machine that can lift a person and wheelchair straight up to the entrance level. At other times, there is a ramp leading to the entrance. Which method takes more power?

▶ Problem

How does a ramp affect the amount of energy, work, and power used to lift an object?

▶ Hypothesize

Write a hypothesis to explain how the potential energy, the amount of work done, and the power required to lift an object straight up compare with the same quantities when the object is moved up a ramp. Your hypothesis should take the form of an "If . . . , then . . . , because . . ." statement.

▶ Procedure

MATERIALS
- board
- chair
- meter stick
- string
- small wheeled object
- spring scale
- stopwatch

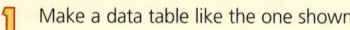

1. Make a data table like the one shown.

2. Lean the board up against the chair seat to create a ramp.

3. Measure and record the vertical distance from the floor to the top of the ramp. Also measure and record the length of the ramp.

4. Tie the string around the wheeled object. Make a loop so that you can hook the string onto the spring scale. Measure and record the weight of the object in newtons.

5. Lift the object straight up to the top of the ramp without using the ramp, as pictured.

440 Unit 3: **Motion and Forces**

INVESTIGATION RESOURCES

 CHAPTER INVESTIGATION, Work and Power
- Level A, pp. 267–270
- Level B, pp. 271–274
- Level C, p. 275

Advanced students should complete Levels B & C.

 Writing a Lab Report, D12–13

Technology Resources

Customize this student lab as needed or look for an alternative. Print rubrics to assess student lab reports.

 Lab Generator CD-ROM

6. On the spring scale, read and record the newtons of force needed to lift the object. Time how long it takes to lift the object from the floor to the top of the ramp. Conduct three trials and average your results. Record your measurements in the data table.

7. Drag the object from the bottom of the ramp to the top of the ramp with the spring scale, and record the newtons of force that were needed to move the object and the time it took. Conduct three trials and average your results.

Observe and Analyze

1. **RECORD OBSERVATIONS** Draw the setup of the procedure. Be sure your data table is complete.

2. **IDENTIFY VARIABLES AND CONSTANTS** List the variables and constants in your notebook.

3. **CALCULATE**
   Potential Energy Convert centimeters to meters. Then calculate the gravitational potential energy (GPE) of the object at the top of the ramp. (Recall that weight equals mass times gravitational acceleration.)

   Gravitational Potential Energy = weight · height

   Work Calculate the work done, first when the object was lifted and then when it was pulled. Use the appropriate distance.

   Work = Force · distance

   Power Calculate the power involved in both situations.

   Power = Work / time

Conclude

1. **COMPARE** How did the distance through which the object moved when it was pulled up the ramp differ from the distance when it was lifted straight up? How did the amount of force required differ in the two situations?

2. **COMPARE** How does your calculated value for potential energy compare with the values you obtained for work done?

3. **INTERPRET** Answer the question posed in the problem.

4. **ANALYZE** Compare your results with your hypothesis. Did your results support your hypothesis?

5. **IDENTIFY LIMITS** What possible limitations or sources of error could you have experienced?

6. **APPLY** A road going up a hill usually winds back and forth instead of heading straight to the top. How does this affect the work a car does to get to the top? How does it affect the power involved?

INVESTIGATE Further

CHALLENGE Design a way to use potential energy to move the car up the ramp. What materials can you use? Think about the materials in terms of potential energy—that is, how high they are from the ground or how stretched or compressed they are.

Observe and Analyze

SAMPLE DATA Weight of object: 0.75 N; Height of object being lifted, 48 cm; Length of ramp, 68 cm; Force (3 trials), 0.7 N, 0.75 N, 0.75 N; Time, 1 s, 0.5 s, 0.5 s; Force (3 trials), 0.55 N, 0.5 N, 0.5 N; Time, 6 s, 5 s, 4 s.

1. See students' diagrams.

2. Variables include distance, force, and time. Constants include mass of the object, force of gravity, and vertical height of the chair seat.

3. See students' data tables.

Conclude

1. The ramp distance was greater than the distance straight up. The amount of force required to move the object up the ramp was less than the amount of force required to lift it straight up. If more work was done in moving the car up the ramp than in moving it straight up, it was due to friction on the ramp.

2. Answers will vary.

3. A ramp can decrease the amount of force needed to move an object, but the amount of work is the same. For a given speed, power will be less when using a ramp.

4. Students' answers will vary.

5. Sources of error might include not pulling the object at a constant force, not measuring to the nearest centimeter, and not reading the scale correctly.

6. The work that a car does is the same as one heading straight to the top. The power may be less if the car takes longer to get there.

INVESTIGATE Further

CHALLENGE Sample answer: Attach the car to a heavy object with a string. Place the object on the chair, then drop it to the floor. As it falls, the car will be pulled up the ramp.

Post-Lab Discussion

- Discuss the variables and constants in the lab. Students should understand that the gravitational potential energy is the same when lifting something straight up and when using a ramp because mass, gravitational acceleration, and height are constants. Only distance, force, and time—the factors used when calculating work and power—vary.

- Movers' trucks usually have ramps that workers use to load and unload heavy objects such as furniture. Ask students what advantages a ramp provides.

CHAPTER 13 • REVIEW

BACK TO

This demonstration illustrates that energy is transferred when a force moves an object. You may want to use a Newton's cradle if one is available. Tie two steel balls to an overhead bar. Pull one ball to the side, then release it. It will hit the second ball and move it. Ask students to describe the force and the energy transfer and explain why the second ball moves. *A force is applied to the first ball when it is pulled. When the ball is released, its gravitational potential energy changes to kinetic energy, which is transferred to the second ball during the collision.*

◐ KEY CONCEPTS SUMMARY

SECTION 13.1
Ask: In which diagram is more work done if the distance is the same? *the left-hand diagram*

Ask: Why is less work done in the right-hand picture? *Part of the force does no work because it is not applied in the same direction as the motion.*

SECTION 13.2
Ask: Which form of energy does the skater have at the top of the ramp? *gravitational potential energy*

Ask: What happens to this potential energy as the skater travels down the ramp? *It changes to kinetic energy.*

SECTION 13.3
Ask: What can you infer about the power of the leading swimmer? *She has more power than the other swimmers.*

Ask: What can you infer about the leading swimmer's time? *She is covering the distance in less time than the other swimmers.*

Review Concepts

- Big Idea Flow Chart, p. T25
- Chapter Outline, pp. T31–T32

---

13 Chapter Review

the BIG idea
Energy is transferred when a force moves an object.

CONTENT REVIEW
CLASSZONE.COM

◐ KEY CONCEPTS SUMMARY

① Work is the use of force to move an object.
Work is done by a force that acts in the same direction as the motion of an object.
Work = Force • distance

VOCABULARY
work p. 419
joule p. 421

② Energy is transferred when work is done.
The amounts of potential energy and kinetic energy in a system or process may vary, but the total amount of energy remains unchanged.

$GPE = mgh$

$KE = \frac{1}{2}mv^2$

$ME = PE + KE$

VOCABULARY
potential energy p. 426
kinetic energy p. 426
mechanical energy p. 429
conservation of energy p. 430

③ Power is the rate at which work is done.
Power can be calculated from work and time.

$$Power = \frac{Work}{time}$$

Power can be calculated from energy and time.

$$Power = \frac{Energy}{time}$$

Power is measured in watts (W) and sometimes horsepower (hp).

VOCABULARY
power p. 434
watt p. 435
horsepower p. 436

442 Unit 3: Motion and Forces

Technology Resources

Have students visit ClassZone.com or use the CD-ROM for a cumulative review of concepts.

 CONTENT REVIEW

 CONTENT REVIEW CD-ROM

Engage students in a whole-class interactive review of Key Concepts. Edit content as you wish.

 POWER PRESENTATIONS

Reviewing Vocabulary

Make a four square diagram for each of the terms listed below. Write the term in the center. Define it in one square. Write characteristics, examples, and formulas (if appropriate) in the other squares. A sample is shown below.

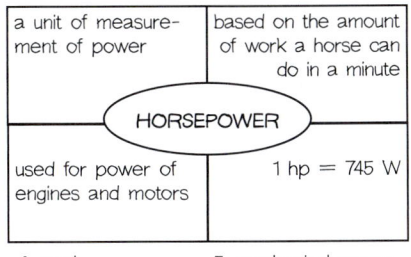

1. work
2. joule
3. potential energy
4. kinetic energy
5. mechanical energy
6. power
7. watt

Reviewing Key Concepts

Multiple Choice Choose the letter of the best answer.

8. Work can be calculated from
   a. force and speed
   b. force and distance
   c. energy and time
   d. energy and distance

9. If you balance a book on your head, you are not doing work on the book because
   a. doing work requires moving an object
   b. you are not applying any force to the book
   c. the book is doing work on you
   d. the book has potential energy

10. Energy that an object has because of its position or shape is called
    a. potential energy c. thermal energy
    b. kinetic energy d. chemical energy

11. Suppose you are pushing a child on a swing. During what space of time are you doing work on the swing?
    a. while you hold it back before letting go
    b. while your hands are in contact with the swing and pushing forward
    c. after you let go of the swing and it continues to move forward
    d. all the time the swing is in motion

12. A falling ball has a potential energy of 5 J and a kinetic energy of 10 J. What is the ball's mechanical energy?
    a. 5 J   c. 15 J
    b. 10 J   d. 50 J

13. The unit that measures one joule of work done in one second is called a
    a. meter   c. newton-meter
    b. watt   d. newton

14. By increasing the speed at which you do work, you increase your
    a. force   c. energy
    b. work   d. power

15. A ball kicked into the air will have the greatest gravitational potential energy
    a. as it is being kicked
    b. as it starts rising
    c. at its highest point
    d. as it hits the ground

Short Answer Answer each of the following questions in a sentence or two.

16. How can you tell if a force you exert is doing work?
17. How does a water wheel do work?
18. State the law of conservation of energy. How does it affect the total amount of energy in any process?
19. Explain why a swing will not stay in motion forever after you have given it a push. What happens to its mechanical energy?
20. What are two ways to calculate power?
21. Why did James Watt invent a unit of measurement based on the work of horses?

Chapter 13: **Work and Energy** 443

ASSESSMENT RESOURCES

UNIT ASSESSMENT BOOK
- Chapter Test A, pp. 65–68
- Chapter Test B, pp. 69–72
- Chapter Test C, pp. 73–76
- Alternative Assessment, pp. 77–78

SPANISH ASSESSMENT BOOK
Spanish Chapter Test, pp. 269–272

Technology Resources

Edit test items and answer choices.

 Test Generator CD-ROM

Visit ClassZone.com to extend test practice.

 Test Practice

Reviewing Vocabulary

Sample answers:

1. work: the use of force to move an object a certain distance; W = F · d; example: turning a page; nonexample: pushing an immovable object
2. joule: unit for measuring work; same as newton-meter; a force in newtons times a distance in meters; 1 J = force of 1 N moving an object 1 m
3. potential energy: energy due to an object's position or shape; stored energy; example: a person at the top of a diving board; GPE = mgh
4. kinetic energy: energy due to an object's motion; most kinetic energy when object moves fastest; example: moving car; KE = $\frac{1}{2}$ mv^2
5. mechanical energy: energy due to an object's position or motion; any object with mechanical energy can do work on another object; example: thrown ball; ME = PE + KE
6. power: rate at which work is done; to increase power, do activity faster; P = W/t; P = E/t
7. watt: unit of measurement for power; 1 W = 1 J of work done in 1 s; kilowatt = 1000 W

Reviewing Key Concepts

8. b   12. c
9. a   13. b
10. a   14. d
11. b   15. c

16. It moves an object.
17. Falling water works on gears moving the wheel. The wheel grinds grain.
18. No matter how energy is transferred or transformed, all of it is still present in one form or another. The total amount of energy in a process never changes.
19. The ME goes into heating the chain through friction, moving air molecules the swing hits, and creating sound. The swing eventually converts all of its ME and stops.
20. by dividing the amount of work done by the time it takes to do it; by dividing energy used in a given period by time
21. to show people how powerful his engine was by comparing it with the more familiar work of horses

Chapter 13 **443**

Thinking Critically

22. The barbell has potential energy when it is resting on the ground. The weightlifter gives the barbell mechanical energy by doing work on it. As it goes up, it has both kinetic energy and gravitational potential energy.
23. Winding up a car gives it potential energy. When released, it becomes kinetic energy.
24. No; motion in the direction of the force is necessary to do work.
25. Power increases as the chair moves faster because the time is less. Work increases with distance.
26. It became thermal energy due to friction between the chair and the floor.
27. As the ball falls, gravitational potential energy changes to kinetic energy. Some energy changes to thermal energy as the ball hits the floor.
28. from chemical energy in the muscles, which transfer it to an object

Using Math Skills in Science

29. 225 J 32. 120 J
30. 9 m   33. 25 W
31. 4.9 J 34. 2400 J

the BIG idea

35. The young woman lifting the box does work because she is using force to hold the box. The box has potential energy, and the woman has kinetic energy if she is walking. Power is the rate at which the work of lifting and carrying the box is done.
36. Answers should include force applied over a distance (for example, work) and should trace the energy transfers.

UNIT PROJECTS

Students should have begun designing their models or presentations by this time. Remind them to continue researching as needed. Encourage them to try different solutions to problems.

 Unit Projects, pp. 5–10

Thinking Critically

22. **SYNTHESIZE** A weightlifter holds a barbell above his head. How do the barbell's potential energy, kinetic energy, and mechanical energy change as it is lifted and then lowered to the ground?
23. **SYNTHESIZE** What happens when you wind up a toy car and release it? Describe the events in terms of energy.

Use the photograph below to answer the next three questions.

24. **APPLY** When the boy first pushes on the chair, the chair does not move due to friction. Is the boy doing work? Why or why not?
25. **ANALYZE** For the first two seconds, the boy pushes the chair slowly at a steady speed. After that, he pushes the chair at a faster speed. How does his power change if he is using the same force at both speeds? How does his work change?
26. **SYNTHESIZE** As the boy pushes the chair, he does work. However, when he stops pushing, the chair stops moving and does not have any additional kinetic or potential energy. What happened to the energy he transferred by doing work on the chair?
27. **APPLY** A bouncing ball has mechanical energy. Each bounce, however, reaches a lower height than the last. Describe what happens to the mechanical, potential, and kinetic energy of the ball as it bounces several times.
28. **CONNECT** When you do work, you transfer energy. Where does the energy you transfer come from?

444 Unit 3: Motion and Forces

Using Math Skills in Science

Complete the following calculations.

29. Use the information in the photograph below to calculate the work the person does in lifting the box.

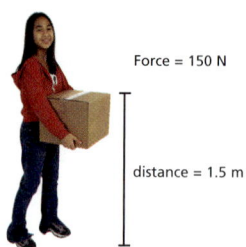

Force = 150 N
distance = 1.5 m

30. If you did 225 J of work to pull a wagon with a force of 25 N, how far did you pull it?
31. A kite with a mass of 0.05 kg is caught on the roof of a house. The house is 10 m high. What is the kite's gravitational potential energy? (Recall that $g = 9.8$ m/s^2.)
32. A baseball with a mass of 0.15 kg leaves a pitcher's hand traveling 40 m/s toward the batter. What is the baseball's kinetic energy?
33. Suppose it takes 150 J of force to push a cart 10 m in 60 s. Calculate the power.
34. If an electric hair dryer uses 1200 W, how much energy does it need to run for 2 s?

the BIG idea

35. **SYNTHESIZE** Look back at the photograph of the person lifting a box on pages 416–417. Describe the picture in terms of work, potential energy, kinetic energy, and power.
36. **WRITE** Think of an activity that involves work. Write a paragraph explaining how the work is transferring energy and where the transferred energy goes.

UNIT PROJECTS

If you need to create graphs or other visuals for your project, be sure you have grid paper, poster board, markers, or other supplies.

MONITOR AND RETEACH

If students have trouble applying the concepts in questions 24–26, have volunteers take turns reenacting the scenario in the photograph. As they push the chair, they can describe for the class what is happening in terms of force, work, speed, friction, and energy.

Students may benefit from summarizing one or more sections of the chapter.

 Summarizing the Chapter, pp. 285–286

Standardized Test Practice

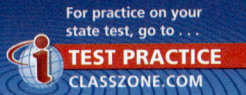
For practice on your state test, go to...
TEST PRACTICE
CLASSZONE.COM

Understanding Experiments

Read the following description of an experiment. Then answer the questions that follow.

James Prescott Joule is well known for a paddle-wheel experiment he conducted in the mid-1800s. He placed a paddle wheel in a bucket of water. Then he set up two weights on either side of the bucket. As the weights fell, they turned the paddle wheel. Joule recorded the temperature of the water before and after the paddle wheel began turning. He found that the water temperature increased as the paddle wheel turned.

Based on this experiment, Joule concluded that the falling weights released mechanical energy, which was converted into heat by the turning wheel. He was convinced that whenever mechanical force is exerted, heat is produced.

1. Which principle did Joule demonstrate with this experiment?
   a. When energy is converted from one form to another, some energy is lost.
   b. The amount of momentum in a system does not change as long as there are no outside forces acting on the system.
   c. One form of energy can be converted into another form of energy.
   d. When one object exerts a force on another object, the second object exerts an equal and opposite force on the first object.

2. Which form of energy was released by the weights in Joule's experiment?
   a. electrical
   b. mechanical
   c. nuclear
   d. heat

3. Which form of energy was produced in the water?
   a. chemical
   b. electrical
   c. nuclear
   d. heat

4. Based on Joule's finding that movement causes temperature changes in water, which of the following would be a logical prediction?
   a. Water held in a container should increase in temperature.
   b. Water at the base of a waterfall should be warmer than water at the top.
   c. Water with strong waves should be colder than calm water.
   d. Water should increase in temperature with depth.

Extended Response

Answer the two questions below in detail. Include some of the terms from the word box. Underline each term you use in your answer.

| potential energy | conservation of energy | force |
| kinetic energy | power | work |

5. A sledder has the greatest potential energy at the top of a hill. She has the least amount of potential energy at the bottom of a hill. She has the greatest kinetic energy when she moves the fastest. Where on the hill does the sledder move the fastest? State the relationship between kinetic energy and potential energy in this situation.

6. Andre and Jon are moving boxes of books from the floor to a shelf in the school library. Each box weighs 15 lb. Andre lifts 5 boxes in one minute. Jon lifts 5 boxes in 30 seconds. Which person does more work? Which person applies more force? Which person has the greater power? Explain your answers.

Chapter 13: **Work and Energy** 445

Understanding Experiments
1. c   3. d
2. b   4. b

Extended Response

5. RUBRIC
4 points for a response that correctly answers the question and uses the following terms accurately:
- potential energy
- kinetic energy

At the top of the hill, the sledder has <u>potential energy</u> but no <u>kinetic energy</u>. As the sledder moves down the hill, her potential energy decreases because the elevation decreases. Her kinetic energy increases because her velocity increases. Halfway down the hill, the sledder's potential energy is equal to her kinetic energy. Therefore, the sledder moves the fastest at the bottom of the hill.

3 points for a response that correctly answers the question and uses one term accurately

2 points for a response that correctly answers the question but does not use the terms accurately

6. RUBRIC
4 points for a response that correctly answers all the questions and uses the following terms accurately:
- energy
- work
- power

Jon and Andre both did the same amount of <u>work</u> lifting the boxes, since the potential <u>energy</u> they gave each box was the same. <u>Power</u> is the rate at which work is done. Jon has the greater power because he lifted the same weight of boxes the same distance in half the time.

3 points for a response that correctly answers two questions and uses two terms accurately

2 points for a response that correctly answers one question and uses one term accurately

1 point for a response that correctly answers the questions, but does not use the terms

---

METACOGNITIVE ACTIVITY

Have students answer the following questions in their **Science Notebook:**
1. Which concepts about work and energy did you find to be the most challenging?
2. Predict the content of the next chapter.
3. What information are you having a difficult time finding that is needed to complete your Unit Project?

Chapter 13 **445**

CHAPTER 14: Machines

Physical Science
UNIFYING PRINCIPLES

PRINCIPLE 1
Matter is made of particles too small to see.

PRINCIPLE 2
Matter changes form and moves from place to place.

PRINCIPLE 3
Energy changes from one form to another, but it cannot be created or destroyed.

PRINCIPLE 4
Physical forces affect the movement of all matter on Earth and throughout the universe.

Unit 3: Motion and Forces
BIG IDEAS

CHAPTER 10 Motion
The motion of an object can be described and predicted.

CHAPTER 11 Forces
Forces change the motion of objects in predictable ways.

CHAPTER 12 Gravity, Friction, and Pressure
Newton's laws apply to all forces.

CHAPTER 13 Work and Energy
Energy is transferred when a force moves an object.

CHAPTER 14 Machines
Machines help people do work by changing the force applied to an object.

CHAPTER 14 KEY CONCEPTS

SECTION 1
Machines help people do work.
1. Machines change the way force is applied.
2. Work transfers energy.
3. Output work is always less than input work.

SECTION 2
Six simple machines have many uses.
1. There are six simple machines.
2. The mechanical advantage of a machine can be calculated.

SECTION 3
Modern technology uses compound machines.
1. Compound machines are combinations of simple machines.
2. Modern technology creates new uses for machines.

 The Big Idea Flow Chart is available on p. T33 in the **UNIT TRANSPARENCY BOOK**.

Previewing Content

SECTION

Machines help people do work.
pp. 449–457

1. **Machines change the way force is applied.**
   A **machine** is a device that helps people do work. It does not change the amount of work done.
   - If a machine decreases the amount of force needed to do the work, the distance over which that force must be applied increases.
   - A machine can change the direction of an applied force.

   Input force is the force exerted on a machine. Output force is the force exerted on an object by a machine. The number of times a machine multiplies the input force is the machine's **mechanical advantage.**

2. **Work transfers energy.**
   A machine increases the potential or kinetic energy of an object by doing work on it. For a certain amount of work, if distance increases, force decreases, as shown in the figure below.

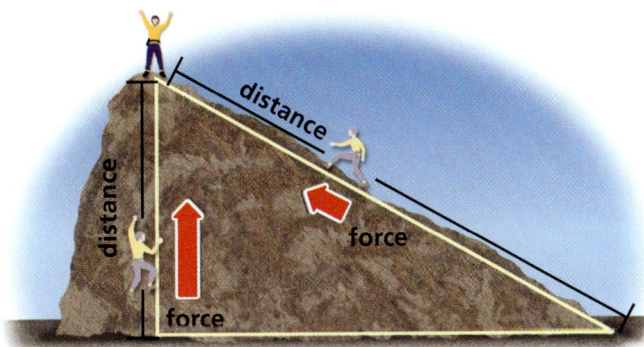

3. **Output work is always less than input work.**
   Efficiency is the ratio of a machine's output work to the input work.

   Efficiency (%) = Output work/Input work · 100

   No real machine is 100 percent efficient. Machines lose energy to friction, which is why we lubricate moving parts. Another source of loss of efficiency is air resistance, which is the reason for streamlined designs for vehicles and cyclists' helmets.

Common Misconceptions

WORK Students may think that machines reduce work and energy. In fact, machines reduce the amount of effort required to do work by changing the size or the direction of the force. Because the machine must transfer a certain amount of energy, it must do an equivalent amount of work.

 This misconception is addressed on p. 452.

SECTION

Six simple machines have many uses. pp. 458–467

1. **There are six simple machines.**
   The lever and the inclined plane are the two main types of **simple machines.** Other simple machines are based on these two.
   - A **lever** is a solid bar that rotates on a fixed point called a **fulcrum.** There are three classes of levers based on the relative locations of the input force, the output force, and the fulcrum.
   - A **wheel and axle** is a wheel attached to a shaft. It acts like a rotating collection of levers. The input force can be applied to either part, which transfers force to the other part.
   - A **pulley** is a wheel with an axle and a grooved rim. A rope or a cable moves in the groove. Pulleys can be either fixed or movable. A combination of the two types is called a block and tackle.
   - An **inclined plane** is a sloping surface that supports the weight of an object while the object moves from one level to another.
   - A **wedge** has a thick end and a thin end. A wedge can be used to cut, split, pierce objects or to hold objects together.
   - A **screw** is an inclined plane wrapped around a cylinder or a cone to form a spiral. Screws can be used to hold things together or to raise and lower objects.

2. **The mechanical advantage of a machine can be calculated.**
   If a machine were 100 percent efficient, its ideal mechanical advantage would be output force/input force, or

   $MA = \dfrac{F_{out}}{F_{in}}$

   - For an inclined plane, divide the length of the incline by the height of the incline.
   - For a wheel and axle, divide the radius where the input force is applied by the radius where the output force is applied.
   - For a lever, calculate this by dividing distance from input force to fulcrum by the distance from output force to fulcrum.
   - For pulleys, the mechanical advantage is equal to the number of ropes that support the weight.

MISCONCEPTION DATABASE
CLASSZONE.COM Background on student misconceptions

EFFICIENCY Students might think that machines can be 100 percent efficient. In reality, any machine that has a moving part loses some energy, and thus efficiency, to friction. Only ideal machines have 100 percent efficiency.

 This misconception is addressed on p. 454.

Chapter 14: **Machines** 445B

Previewing Content

SECTION
 Modern technology uses compound machines. pp. 468–475

1. **Compound machines are combinations of simple machines.**
   A machine that is made of two or more simple machines is a **compound machine.** Compound machines often have many moving parts and must overcome more friction than simple machines.

   The mechanical advantage of a compound machine equals the product of the mechanical advantages of all the simple machines that make up the compound machine.
   For example, if a lever with a *MA* of 2 acts in series with a lever with a *MA* of 3, the mechanical advantage of the lever combination will be 2 · 3, or 6.
   - The mechanical advantage of a gear system comprising two wheel-and-axle systems is found by dividing the number of teeth on the output wheel by the number of teeth on the input wheel. For example, a wheel with 16 teeth turns another wheel with 24 teeth. The wheel with 16 teeth is the input wheel and the wheel with 24 teeth is the output wheel.

   $MA = \frac{24}{16} = 1.5$

   Thus, 1.5 is the mechanical advantage.
   - For these two gears, the smaller input gear has half as many teeth as the output gear. The mechanical advantage is 2.

2. **Modern technology creates new uses for machines.**
   Sophisticated machines are often based on or contain several simple machines.
   - Machines built from individual atoms and molecules of material are the result of **nanotechnology.** Most nanomachines are still in the experimental stage.
   - **Robots** are machines that work automatically or by remote control. They do jobs in places where it is difficult or dangerous for people to work.

Previewing Labs

Lab Generator CD-ROM — Edit these Pupil Edition labs and generate alternative labs.

EXPLORE the BIG idea

Changing Direction, p. 447
Students examine a window blind to learn that machines can change the direction of a force.
- **TIME** 10 minutes
- **MATERIALS** window blind

Shut the Door! p. 447
Students experiment with a door to test the relationship between force and the length of a lever arm.
- **TIME** 10 minutes
- **MATERIALS** a door on hinges

Internet Activity: Machines, p. 447
Students analyze tools to learn about different machines.
- **TIME** 20 minutes
- **MATERIALS** computer with Internet access

SECTION 1

EXPLORE Machines, p. 449
Students examine small machines to learn how they help people work.
- **TIME** 15 minutes
- **MATERIALS** various small machines

INVESTIGATE Efficiency, p. 455
Students collect and analyze data for a block moving on a ramp and use the results to calculate efficiency.
- **TIME** 20 minutes
- **MATERIALS** board, books, meter stick, wooden block with eye hook, spring scale, sandpaper

SECTION 2

EXPLORE Changing Forces, p. 458
Students adjust the fulcrum of a lever to determine how the input force changes.
- **TIME** 15 minutes
- **MATERIALS** 2 pencils, small book

INVESTIGATE Pulleys, p. 461
Students create a block-and-tackle pulley system, calculate mechanical advantage, and infer how the input and output forces vary.
- **TIME** 20 minutes
- **MATERIALS** 100 g mass, spring scale, 2 pulleys with rope, ring stand with ring or clamp

SECTION 3

CHAPTER INVESTIGATION Design a Machine, pp. 474–475
Students design a machine, build it, test it, and calculate its mechanical advantage and its efficiency.
- **TIME** 40 minutes
- **MATERIALS** 500 g object; 100 g object; meter stick; spring scale; single, double, or triple pulleys with rope; board; stick or pole

 Additional INVESTIGATION, Levers and Fulcrums, A, B, & C, pp. 335–343; Teacher Instructions, pp. 346–347

Previewing Chapter Resources

	INTEGRATED TECHNOLOGY	LABS AND ACTIVITIES
CHAPTER 14 **Machines**	**CLASSZONE.COM** • eEdition Plus • EasyPlanner Plus • Misconception Database • Content Review • Test Practice • Resource Centers • Simulation • Internet Activity: Machines • Math Tutorial  **CD-ROMS** • eEdition • EasyPlanner • Power Presentations • Content Review • Lab Generator • Test Generator **AUDIO CDS** • Audio Readings • Audio Readings in Spanish **SCILINKS.ORG**	EXPLORE the Big Idea, p. 447 • Changing Direction • Shut the Door! • Internet Activity: Machines **UNIT RESOURCE BOOK** Unit Projects, pp. 5–10 **Lab Generator CD-ROM** Generate customized labs.
SECTION 1 **Machines help people do work.** pp. 449–457 Time: 2 periods (1 block) Lesson Plan, pp. 287–288	**MATH TUTORIAL** **UNIT TRANSPARENCY BOOK** • Big Idea Flow Chart, p. T33 • Daily Vocabulary Scaffolding, p. T34 • Note-Taking Model, p. T35 • 3-Minute Warm-Up, p. T36	• EXPLORE Machines, p. 449 • INVESTIGATE Efficiency, p. 455 • Math in Science, p. 457 **UNIT RESOURCE BOOK** • Datasheet, Efficiency, p. 296 • Math Support, p. 324 • Math Practice, p. 325
SECTION 2 **Six simple machines have many uses.** pp. 458–467 Time: 2 periods (1 block) Lesson Plan, pp. 298–299	• **SIMULATION,** Mechanical Advantage • **RESOURCE CENTER,** Artificial Limbs **UNIT TRANSPARENCY BOOK** • Daily Vocabulary Scaffolding, p. T34 • 3-Minute Warm-Up, p. T36	• EXPLORE Changing Forces, p. 458 • INVESTIGATE Pulleys, p. 461 • Connecting Sciences, p. 467 **UNIT RESOURCE BOOK** • Datasheet, Pulleys, p. 307 • Additional INVESTIGATION, Levers and Fulcrums, A, B, & C, pp. 335–343
SECTION 3 **Modern technology uses compound machines.** pp. 468–475 Time: 4 periods (2 blocks) Lesson Plan, pp. 309–310	**RESOURCE CENTERS,** Nanomachines, Robots **UNIT TRANSPARENCY BOOK** • Big Idea Flow Chart, p. T33 • Daily Vocabulary Scaffolding, p. T34 • 3-Minute Warm-Up, p. T37 • "A Robot at Work" Visual, p. T38 • Chapter Outline, pp. T39–T40	CHAPTER INVESTIGATION, Design a Machine, pp. 474–475 **UNIT RESOURCE BOOK** CHAPTER INVESTIGATION, Design a Machine, A, B, & C, pp. 326–334

445E Unit 3: **Motion and Forces**

KEY TO ICONS CD/CD-ROM Teacher Edition UNIT TRANSPARENCY BOOK 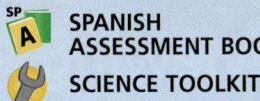 SPANISH ASSESSMENT BOOK
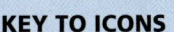 INTERNET Pupil Edition UNIT RESOURCE BOOK UNIT ASSESSMENT BOOK SCIENCE TOOLKIT

READING AND REINFORCEMENT

- Word Triangle, B18–19
- Choose Your Own Strategy, C36, C38–39, C42, C43
- Daily Vocabulary Scaffolding, H1–8

 UNIT RESOURCE BOOK
- Vocabulary Practice, pp. 321–322
- Decoding Support, p. 323
- Summarizing the Chapter, pp. 344–345

 Audio Readings CD
Listen to Pupil Edition.

 Audio Readings in Spanish CD
Listen to Pupil Edition in Spanish.

 UNIT RESOURCE BOOK
- Reading Study Guide, A & B, pp. 289–292
- Spanish Reading Study Guide, pp. 293–294
- Challenge and Extension, p. 295
- Reinforcing Key Concepts, p. 297

 UNIT RESOURCE BOOK
- Reading Study Guide, A & B, pp. 300–303
- Spanish Reading Study Guide, pp. 304–305
- Challenge and Extension, p. 306
- Reinforcing Key Concepts, p. 308

 UNIT RESOURCE BOOK
- Reading Study Guide, A & B, pp. 311–314
- Spanish Reading Study Guide, pp. 315–316
- Challenge and Extension, p. 317
- Reinforcing Key Concepts, p. 318
- Challenge Reading, pp. 319–320

ASSESSMENT

- Chapter Review, pp. 477–478
- Standardized Test Practice, p. 479

 UNIT ASSESSMENT BOOK
- Diagnostic Test, pp. 79–80
- Chapter Test, A, B, & C, pp. 84–95
- Alternative Assessment, pp. 96–97
- Unit Test, A, B, & C, pp. 98–109

- Spanish Chapter Test, pp. 225–228
- Spanish Unit Test, pp. 277–280

 Test Generator CD-ROM
Generate customized tests.

 Lab Generator CD-ROM
Rubrics for Labs

 Ongoing Assessment, pp. 450–451, 453–456

 Section 14.1 Review, p. 456

 UNIT ASSESSMENT BOOK
Section 14.1 Quiz, p. 81

 Ongoing Assessment, pp. 459–463, 465

 Section 14.2 Review, p. 466

 UNIT ASSESSMENT BOOK
Section 14.2 Quiz, p. 82

 Ongoing Assessment, pp. 468–469, 471–473

 Section 14.3 Review, p. 473

 UNIT ASSESSMENT BOOK
Section 14.3 Quiz, p. 83

STANDARDS

National Standards
A.1–8, A.9.a–g, E.2–5, E.6.c–e, F.5.a–c, F.5.e, G.1.b

See p. 446 for the standards.

National Standards
A.2–8, A.9.a–c, A.9.e–f, G.1.b

National Standards
A.2–8, A.9.a–c, A.9.e–f, G.1.b

National Standards
A.1–8, A.9.a–g, E.2–5, E.6.c–e, F.5.a–c, F.5.e, G.1.b

Chapter 14: **Machines** 445F

Previewing Resources for Differentiated Instruction

CHAPTER INVESTIGATION

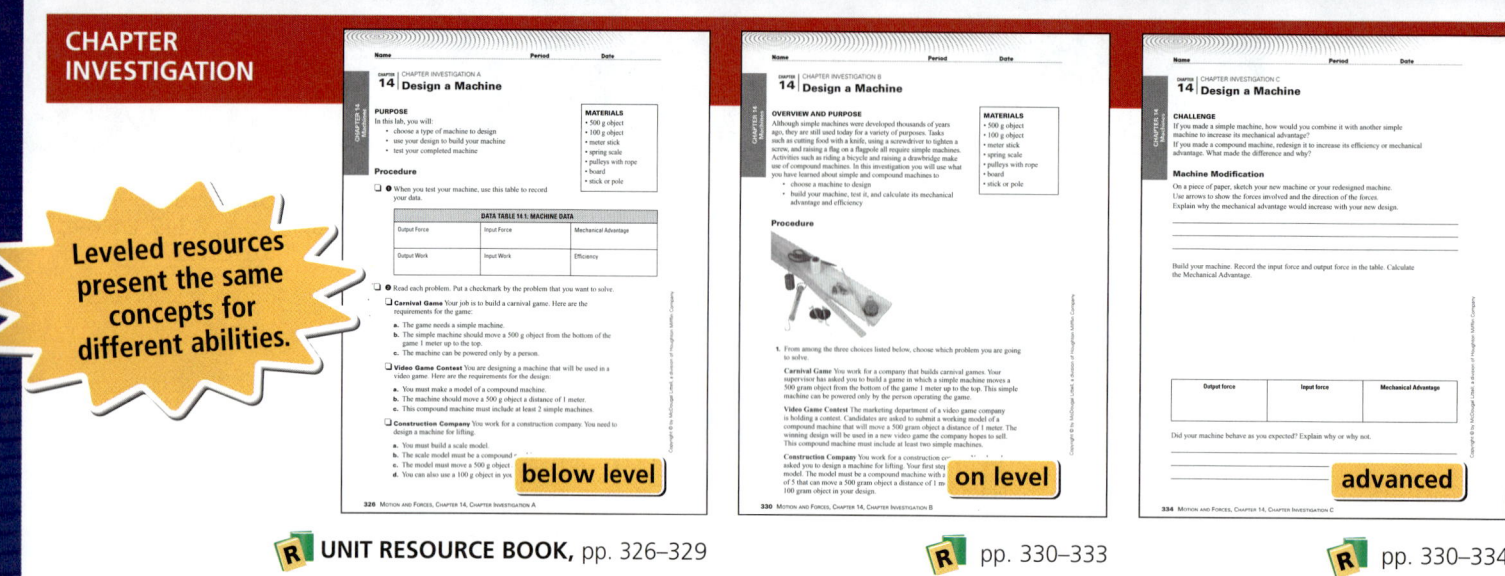

Leveled resources present the same concepts for different abilities.

UNIT RESOURCE BOOK, pp. 326–329 | pp. 330–333 | pp. 330–334

READING STUDY GUIDE

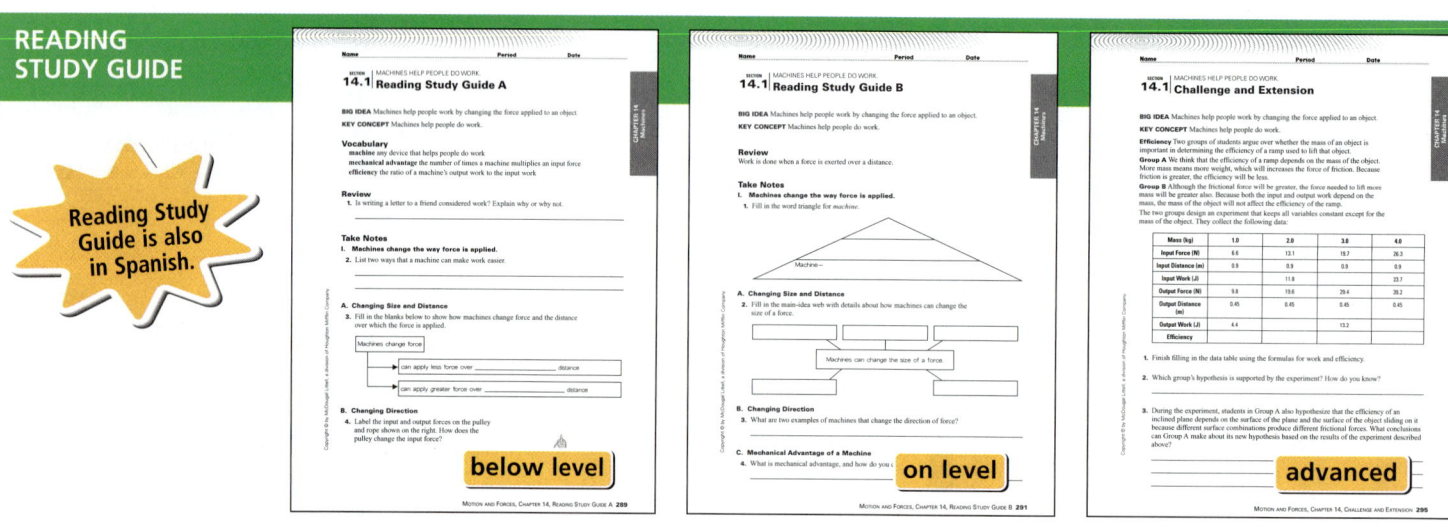

Reading Study Guide is also in Spanish.

UNIT RESOURCE BOOK, pp. 289–290 | pp. 291–292 | p. 295

CHAPTER TEST

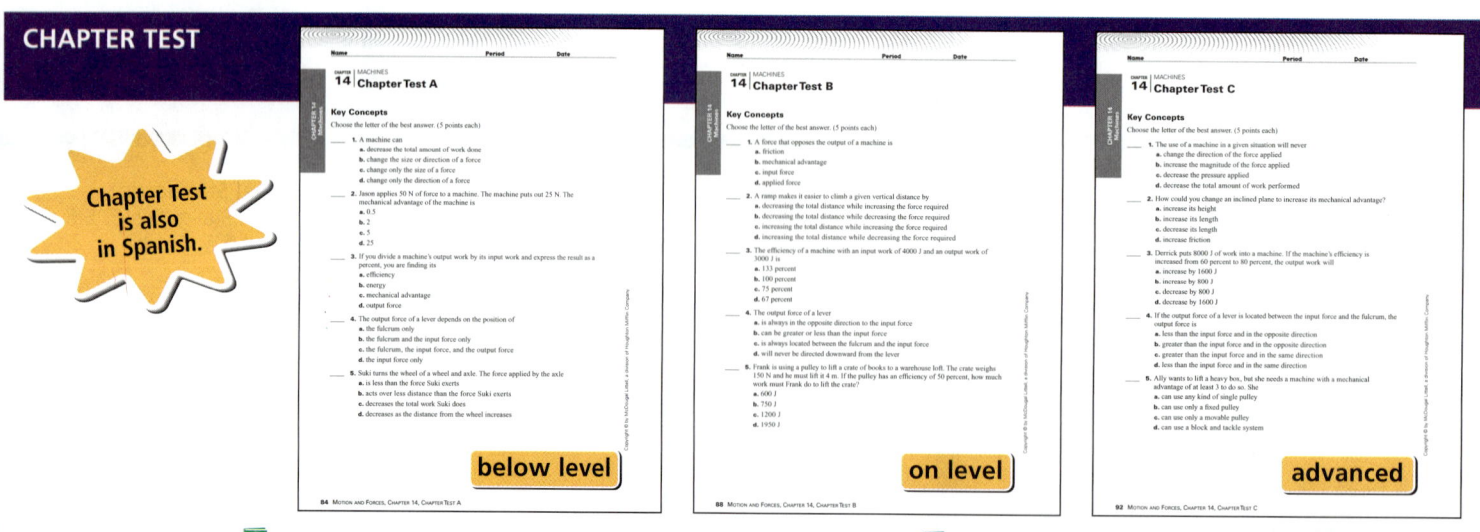

Chapter Test is also in Spanish.

UNIT ASSESSMENT BOOK, pp. 84–87 | pp. 88–91 | pp. 92–95

445G Unit 3: Motion and Forces

TECHNOLOGY

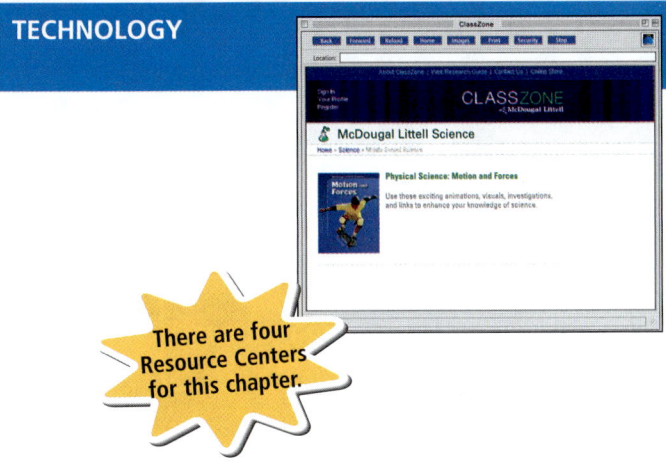
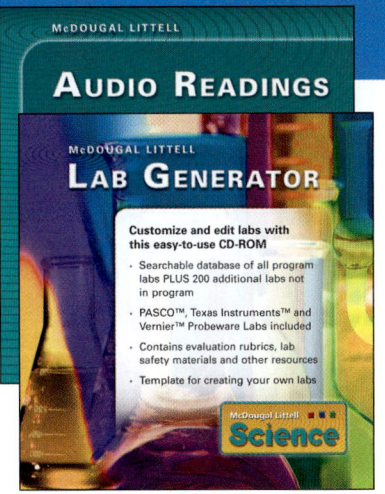
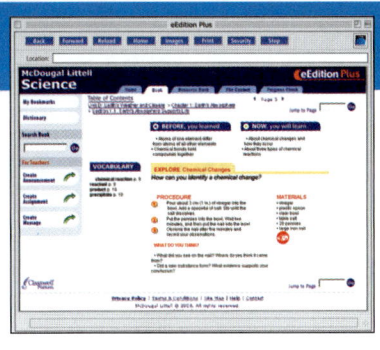

There are four Resource Centers for this chapter.

 CLASSZONE.COM    CD/CD-ROMS    CLASSZONE.COM

VISUAL CONTENT

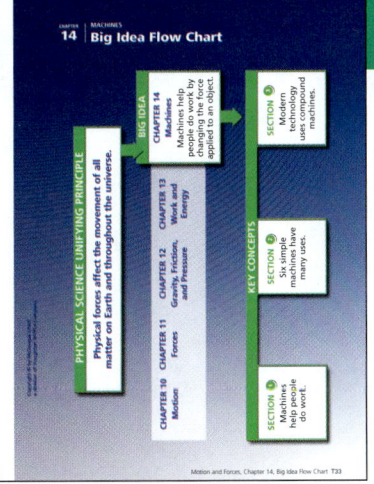
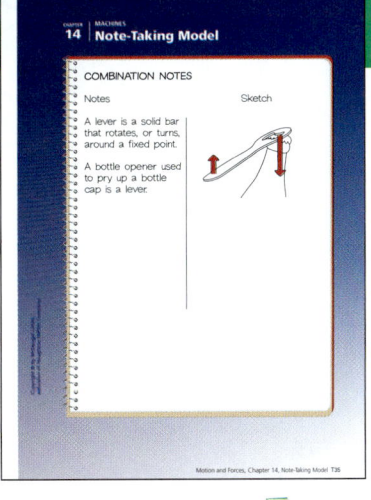
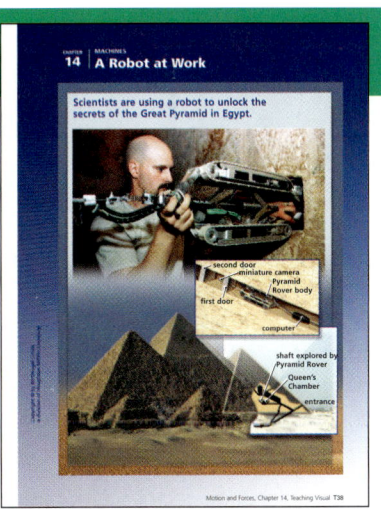

UNIT TRANSPARENCY BOOK, p. T33   p. T35   p. T38

MORE SUPPORT

Reinforcing Key Concepts for each section

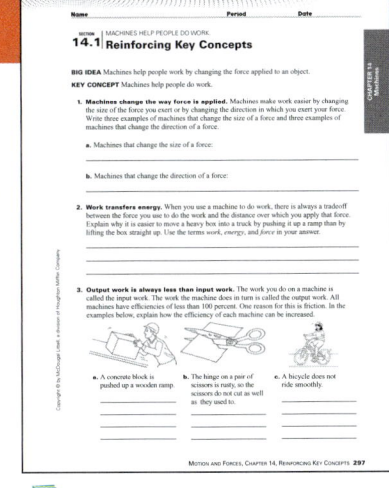
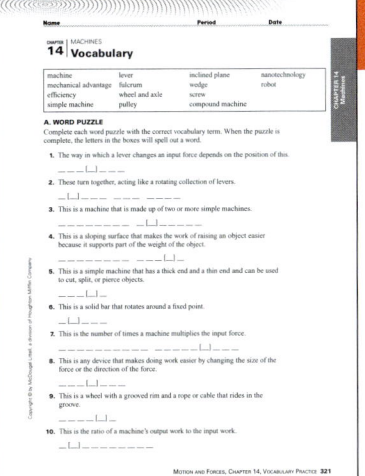
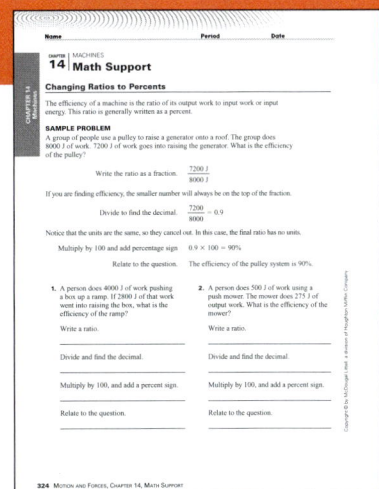

UNIT RESOURCE BOOK, p. 297   pp. 321–322   p. 324

Chapter 14: **Machines** 445H

CHAPTER 14 Machines

INTRODUCE

Have students look at the photograph of the sculpture and discuss how the question in the box links to the Big Idea:

- What work is this machine doing?
- Can you find places where something changes the direction of a force?
- What types of machines do you see in the sculpture?

National Science Education Standards

Process

A.1–8 Identify questions that can be answered through scientific investigations; design and conduct an investigation; use tools to gather and interpret data; use evidence to describe, predict, explain, model; think critically to make relationships between evidence and explanation; recognize different explanations and predictions; communicate scientific procedures and explanations; use mathematics.

A.9.a–g Understand scientific inquiry by using different investigations, methods, mathematics, technology, explanations based on logic, evidence, and skepticism. Data often results in new investigations.

E.2–5 Design, implement, and evaluate a solution or product; communicate technological design.

E.6.c–e Science drives technology and technology drives science; perfectly designed solutions don't exist, all technology has tradeoffs; all designs have limits.

F.5.a–c, F.5.e Science influences society; societal challenges inspire scientific research; technology influences society; scientists work in different settings.

G.1.b Science requires different abilities.

446 Unit 3: Motion and Forces

CHAPTER 14 Machines

the BIG idea

Machines help people do work by changing the force applied to an object.

Balls move through this sculpture. What do you think keeps the balls in motion?

Key Concepts

SECTION 1 Machines help people do work.
Learn about machines and how they are used to do work.

SECTION 2 Six simple machines have many uses.
Learn about levers and inclined planes and the other simple machines that are related to them.

SECTION 3 Modern technology uses compound machines.
Learn how scientists are using nanotechnology and robots to create new ways for machines to do work.

Internet Preview

CLASSZONE.COM
Chapter 14 online resources: Content Review, Simulation, four Resource Centers, Math Tutorial, Test Practice

446 Unit 3: Motion and Forces

INTERNET PREVIEW

CLASSZONE.COM For student use with the following pages:

Review and Practice
- Content Review, pp. 448, 476
- Math Tutorial: Percents and Fractions, p. 457
- Test Practice, p. 479

Activities and Resources
- Internet Activity: Machines, p. 447
- Simulation: Mechanical Advantage, p. 465
- Resource Centers: Artificial Limbs, p. 467; Nanomachines, p. 471; Robots, p. 473

Simple Machines
Code: MDL008

EXPLORE the BIG idea

Changing Direction
Observe how a window blind works. Notice how you use a downward force to pull the blind up. Look around you for other examples.

Observe and Think Why does changing the direction of a force make work easier?

Shut the Door!
Find a door that swings freely on its hinges. Stand on the side where you can push the door to close it. Open the door. Push the door closed several times, placing your hand closer to or farther from the hinge each time.

Observe and Think Which hand placement made it easiest to shut the door? Why do you think that is so?

Internet Activity: Machines
Go to ClassZone.com to learn more about the simple machines in everyday objects. Select an item and think about how it moves and does its job. Then test your knowledge of simple machines.

Observe and Think What other objects contain simple machines?

NSTA scilinks.org SCLINKS
Simple Machines Code: MDL008

Chapter 14: **Machines** 447

EXPLORE the BIG idea

These inquiry-based activities are appropriate for use at home or as a supplement to classroom instruction.

Changing Direction
PURPOSE To show that machines can change the direction of force. Students observe that a machine can change not only the size but also the direction of a force.

TIP *10 min.* Be sure the blind is firmly attached so that it does not fall when force is applied. Instruct students in how to use the blind before beginning the activity.

Answer: It is easier for people to pull down rather than up.

REVISIT after p. 451.

Shut the Door!
PURPOSE To learn about the relationship between force and the length of a lever. Students will observe that the length of the lever arm affects the amount of effort required.

TIP *10 min.* Students also could use a book cover to do this activity.

Answer: It is easiest to close when you push the edge farthest from the hinge.

REVISIT after p. 465.

Internet Activity: Machines
PURPOSE To introduce students to different machines. Students will examine different tools and relate them to simple machines.

TIP *20 min.* Students might want to have sketches of each simple machine available when they examine the tools.

Sample answers: doorknobs, cars, elevators

REVISIT after p. 466.

TEACHING WITH TECHNOLOGY

Video Camera You might want to tape the movement of parts of simple and compound machines pictured in "Explore Machines" on p. 449. Clips could be shown at regular speed or in slow motion to help students examine how the machines work.

Digital Camera Have students photograph their examples of compound machines from the Chapter Investigation on pp. 474–475. They can classify the different machines according to the simple machines they contain.

Chapter 14 **447**

PREPARE

CONCEPT REVIEW
Activate Prior Knowledge
- Have a student lift a stack of books straight up from a desk.
- Ask students to list all the energy transformations that take place when this work is done. *chemical energy to kinetic energy in the arm; potential energy to kinetic energy of the books*

TAKING NOTES

Choose Your Own Strategy
Having tried different note-taking techniques, students can choose the strategies that best fit their individual learning styles.

Vocabulary Strategy
The word triangle helps tie concepts to concrete objects. Drawings in word triangles are especially useful because they present information visually. Tell students to make drawings that help them remember what the terms mean. Often, the drawings will not look like physical objects. They may wish to use symbols in their drawings, such as arrows, to represent motion and direction.

Vocabulary and Note-Taking Resources

- Vocabulary Practice, pp. 321–322
- Decoding Support, p. 323

- Daily Vocabulary Scaffolding, p. T34
- Note-Taking Model, p. T35

- Word Triangle, B18–19
- Combination Notes, C36
- Main Idea Web, C38–39
- Supporting Main Ideas, C42
- Outline, C43
- Daily Vocabulary Scaffolding, H1–8

448 Unit 3: **Motion and Forces**

CHAPTER 14
Getting Ready to Learn

 CONCEPT REVIEW
- Work is done when a force moves an object over a distance.
- Energy can be converted from one form to another.
- Energy is transferred when work is done.

 VOCABULARY REVIEW
work p. 419
mechanical energy p. 429
power p. 434

See Glossary for definitions.
energy, technology

CONTENT REVIEW
CLASSZONE.COM
Review concepts and vocabulary.

TAKING NOTES

CHOOSE YOUR OWN STRATEGY
Take notes using one or more of the strategies from earlier chapters—**outline, combination notes, supporting main ideas,** and **main idea web.** Feel free to mix and match the strategies, or use an entirely different note-taking strategy.

VOCABULARY STRATEGY
Draw a **word triangle** diagram for each new vocabulary term. On the bottom line, write and define the term. Above that, write a sentence that uses the term correctly. At the top, draw a small picture to show what the term looks like.

See the Note-Taking Handbook on pages R45–R51.

SCIENCE NOTEBOOK

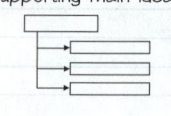
Outline
I. Main idea
  A. Supporting idea
   1. Detail
   2. Detail
  B. Supporting idea

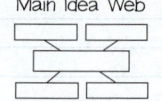
Combination Notes

Supporting Main Ideas

Main Idea Web

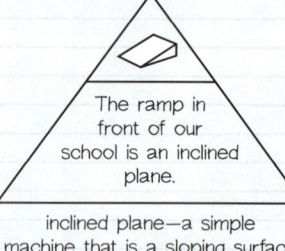
The ramp in front of our school is an inclined plane.

inclined plane—a simple machine that is a sloping surface

448 Unit 3: **Motion and Forces**

CHECK READINESS

Administer the Diagnostic Test to determine students' readiness for new science content and their mastery of requisite math skills.

 Diagnostic Test, pp. 79–80

Technology Resources
Students needing content and math skills should visit **ClassZone.com**.

- CONTENT REVIEW
- MATH TUTORIAL

 CONTENT REVIEW CD-ROM

14.1 KEY CONCEPT
Machines help people do work.

◀ **BEFORE, you learned**
- Work is done when a force is exerted over a distance
- Some work can be converted to heat or sound energy

▶ **NOW, you will learn**
- How machines help you do work
- How to calculate a machine's efficiency

VOCABULARY
machine p. 449
mechanical advantage p. 451
efficiency p. 454

EXPLORE Machines

How do machines help you work?

PROCEDURE

1. Look at one of the machines closely. Carefully operate the machine and notice how each part moves.
2. Sketch a diagram of the machine. Try to show all of the working parts. Add arrows and labels to show the direction of motion for each part.

WHAT DO YOU THINK?
- What is the function of the machine?
- How many moving parts does it have?
- How do the parts work together?
- How does this machine make work easier?

MATERIALS
various small machines

Machines change the way force is applied.

For thousands of years, humans have been improving their lives with technology. Technology is the use of knowledge to create products or tools that make life easier. The simplest machine is an example of technology.

A **machine** is any device that helps people do work. A machine does not decrease the amount of work that is done. Instead, a machine changes the way in which work is done. Recall that work is the use of force to move an object. If, for example, you have to lift a heavy box, you can use a ramp to make the work easier. Moving the box up a ramp—which is a machine—helps you do the work by reducing the force you need to lift the box.

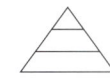
VOCABULARY Make a word triangle diagram in your notebook for *machine*.

Chapter 14: **Machines** 449

RESOURCES FOR DIFFERENTIATED INSTRUCTION

Below Level
UNIT RESOURCE BOOK
- Reading Study Guide A, pp. 289–290
- Decoding Support, p. 323

 **AUDIO CDS**

Advanced
UNIT RESOURCE BOOK
Challenge and Extension, p. 295

English Learners
UNIT RESOURCE BOOK
Spanish Reading Study Guide, pp. 293–294

 **AUDIO CDS**
- Audio Readings in Spanish
- Audio Readings (English)

14.1 FOCUS

▶ **Set Learning Goals**

Students will
- Explain how machines help people do work.
- Calculate a machine's efficiency.
- Analyze data from an experiment investigating the efficiency of a ramp.

◀ **3-Minute Warm-Up**

Display Transparency 36 or copy this exercise on the board:

Write a short paragraph describing a situation in which you are doing work on an object. What type of energy does the object gain? How do you know?

Examples should include some use of force to move an object, such as kicking a ball or lifting a box. If the object's velocity increases, the object gains kinetic energy. If the object's height increases, the object gains potential energy.

 3-Minute Warm-Up, p. T36

14.1 MOTIVATE

EXPLORE Machines

PURPOSE To learn how machines make work easier

TIP 15 min. The machines could include a nutcracker, an eggbeater, a bottle opener, a screwdriver, pliers, and scissors.

WHAT DO YOU THINK? *Sample answer: Pliers grip something tightly. They have two moving parts screwed together that come together as the handles are squeezed. Work is easier because the pliers apply lots of pressure to a small area more easily than someone could without them.*

Teaching with Technology

Videotape some of the machines from "Explore Machines" while they are in use. Show the tape in class—first at regular speed and then in slow motion—so students can see the different parts involved.

Chapter 14 **449**

14.1 INSTRUCT

Teach from Visuals

To help students interpret the visual of the boy raking leaves, ask:

- What do the arrows tell you about the size of the force the boy's hand applies to the rake and the size of the force the rake applies to the leaves? *The hand applies more force to the rake than the rake applies to the leaves.*

- If the boy pulls the rake until it is straight up and down, how does the distance the bottom of the rake moves compare with the distance his lower hand moves? *The rake bottom moves a larger distance than the hand.*

Ongoing Assessment

 *Answer: The rake exerts an output force on the leaves.*

If machines do not reduce the amount of work required, how do they help people do work? Machines make work easier by changing

- the size of the force needed to do the work and the distance over which the force is applied
- the direction in which the force is exerted

Machines can be powered by different types of energy. Electronic machines, such as computers, use electrical energy. Mechanical machines, such as a rake, use mechanical energy. Often this mechanical energy is supplied by the person who is using the machine.

Changing Size and Distance

Some machines help you do work by changing the size of the force needed. Have you ever tried to open a door by turning the doorknob's shaft instead of the handle? This is not easy to do. It takes less force to turn the handle of the doorknob than it does to turn the shaft. Turning the handle makes opening the door easier, even though you must turn it through a greater distance.

If a machine—such as a doorknob attached to a shaft—allows you to exert less force, you must apply that force over a greater distance. The total amount of work remains the same whether it is done with a machine or not. You can think of this in terms of the formula for calculating work—work is force times distance. Because a machine does not decrease the amount of work to be done, less force must mean greater distance.

A doorknob allows you to apply a smaller force over a greater distance. Some machines allow you to apply a greater input force over a shorter distance. Look at the boy using a rake, which is a machine. The boy moves his hands a short distance to move the end of the rake a large distance, allowing him to rake up more leaves.

Input force is the force exerted on a machine. Output force is the force that a machine exerts on an object. The boy in the photograph is exerting an input force on the rake. As a result, the rake exerts an output force on the leaves. The work the boy puts into the rake is the same as the work he gets out of the rake. However, the force he applies is greater than the force the rake can apply to the leaves. The output force is less than the input force, but it acts over a longer distance.

A rake is a machine that changes a large force over a short distance to a smaller force over a larger distance.

 How can a rake help you do work? Use the word *force* in your answer.

450 Unit 3: **Motion and Forces**

DIFFERENTIATE INSTRUCTION

? More Reading Support

A What is work? *force times distance*

English Learners English learners may be unfamiliar with the use of dashes in writing. A dash can be used to show a sudden break in a sentence, such as a change in thought or an interjection. Use the following example from the middle of this page: *You can think of this in terms of the formula for calculating work—work is force times distance.*

Changing Direction

Machines also can help you work by changing the direction of a force. Think of raising a flag on a flagpole. You pull down on the rope, and the flag moves up. The rope system is a machine that changes the direction in which you exert your force. The rope system does not change the size of the force, however. The force pulling the flag upward is equal to your downward pull.

A shovel is a machine that can help you dig a hole. Once you have the shovel in the ground, you push down on the handle to lift the dirt up. You can use some of the weight of your body as part of your input force. That would not be possible if you were lifting the dirt by using only your hands. A shovel also changes the size of the force you apply, so you need less force to lift the dirt.

Mechanical Advantage of a Machine

When machines help you work, there is an advantage—or benefit—to using them. The number of times a machine multiplies the input force is called the machine's **mechanical advantage** (MA). To find a machine's mechanical advantage, divide the output force by the input force.

$$\text{Mechanical Advantage} = \frac{\text{Output Force}}{\text{Input Force}}$$

For machines that allow you to apply less force over a greater distance—such as a doorknob—the output force is greater than the input force. Therefore, the mechanical advantage of this type of machine is greater than 1. For example, if the input force is 10 newtons and the output force is 40 newtons, the mechanical advantage is 40 N divided by 10 N, or 4.

For machines that allow you to apply greater force over a shorter distance—such as a rake—the output force is less than the input force. In this case, the mechanical advantage is less than 1. If the input force is 10 newtons and the output force is 5 newtons, the mechanical advantage is 0.5. However, such a machine allows you to move an object a greater distance.

Sometimes changing the direction of the force is more useful than decreasing the force or the distance. For machines that change only the direction of a force—such as the rope system on a flagpole—the input force and output force are the same. Therefore, the mechanical advantage of the machine is 1.

APPLY How does the rope system help the man raise the flag?

Chapter 14: **Machines** 451

DIFFERENTIATE INSTRUCTION

? More Reading Support

B How can using a rope system to open or close curtains make the work easier? *It changes the direction of the applied force.*

Below Level Have students describe what is meant by the word *advantage*. Ask questions that lead to concrete examples, such as, What advantage does a track team with faster runners have over another team? Responses should include the concept that if you have a greater advantage, the results are more favorable. Compare the responses with the concept that increased mechanical advantage results in a more favorable output force compared with input force.

EXPLORE the BIG idea

Revisit "Changing Direction" on p. 447. Have students explain their results.

Teach Difficult Concepts

Provide some simple mechanical-advantage problems to help students learn how to solve them. Review how to rearrange the variables in an equation to isolate the one you are trying to find. Use these sample problems:

- The output force of a machine is 600 N, and the input force is 200 N. What is the mechanical advantage of the machine?
$$MA = \frac{F_{out}}{F_{in}} = \frac{600 \text{ N}}{200 \text{ N}} = 3$$

- A machine has an input force of 150 N and a mechanical advantage of 0.5. What is the output force?
$$F_{out} = MA \cdot F_{in} = 0.5 \cdot 150 \text{ N} = 75 \text{ N}$$

- The output force of a machine is 135 N, and the mechanical advantage is 2.5. What is the input force?
$$F_{in} = \frac{F_{out}}{MA} = \frac{135 \text{ N}}{2.5} = 54 \text{ N}$$

Teach from Visuals

Have students look at the visual on p. 450. Ask: Is the mechanical advantage of the rake greater than 1 or less than 1? How do you know? *The mechanical advantage is less than 1 because the input force is greater than the output force.*

Ongoing Assessment

Explain how machines make work easier.

Ask: Is it easier to lift a heavy box or to push it up a ramp? Why? *easier to push it up a ramp; the ramp changes the size of the force needed to move the box.*

PHOTO CAPTION Answer: *The rope system changes the direction of the force that he must exert. The input force and output force are the same, however.*

Address Misconceptions

IDENTIFY Ask: How does a machine affect the amount of work done, and how does this affect energy? If students say that machines reduce the amount of work and less energy is expended, they may hold the misconception that machines reduce the amount of work and energy needed.

CORRECT Place a pencil under a meter stick at the 20 cm mark. Place or tape a 100 g mass at the 0 cm mark. Place a 200 g mass (weighing 1.9 N) on the meter stick so that it just pushes up the 100 g mass. Remove the 200 g mass so the meter stick returns to its original position, and measure the distance the 200 g mass moved through (the height). Repeat with a 50 g (0.49 N) mass. Using the weights as the force, have students calculate and compare the work done in both cases.

REASSESS How did the forces compare in the two examples? How did the work compare? *The second force was less, the work was the same.*

Technology Resources
Visit **ClassZone.com** for background on common student misconceptions.

 MISCONCEPTION DATABASE

Teach Difficult Concepts

Refer students to the formula for gravitational potential energy, $GPE = mgh$, where g, the gravitational acceleration, is 9.8 m/s^2. Ask the following questions:

- A girl with a mass of 50 kg starts at the bottom of a cliff that is 30 m high. After she has climbed to the top, what is her gravitational potential energy? *$GPE = mgh = 50 \text{ kg} \cdot 9.8 \text{ m/s}^2 \cdot 30 \text{ m} = 14,700 \text{ J}$*

- Does her gravitational potential energy at the top depend on her path or the way she climbed up the cliff? *no*

- Where does this potential energy come from? *the work the girl does climbing*

- How much work must the girl do to get to the top of the cliff? *$W = F \cdot d = ma \cdot d = 50 \text{ kg} \cdot 9.8 \text{ m/s}^2 \cdot 30 \text{ m} = 14,700 \text{ J}$*

452 Unit 3: **Motion and Forces**

NOTE-TAKING STRATEGY
Remember to organize your notes in a chart or web as you read.

Work transfers energy.

Machines transfer energy to objects on which they do work. Every time you open a door, the doorknob is transferring mechanical energy to the shaft. A machine that lifts an object gives it potential energy. A machine that causes an object to start moving, such as a baseball bat hitting a ball, gives the object kinetic energy.

Energy

When you lift an object, you transfer energy to it in the form of gravitational potential energy—that is, potential energy caused by gravity. The higher you lift an object, the more work you must do and the more energy you give to the object. This is also true if a machine lifts an object. The gravitational potential energy of an object depends on its height above Earth's surface, and it equals the work required to lift the object to that height.

Recall that gravitational potential energy is the product of an object's mass, gravitational acceleration, and height ($GPE = mgh$). In the diagram on page 453, the climber wants to reach the top of the hill. The higher she climbs, the greater her potential energy. This energy comes from the work the climber does. The potential energy she gains equals the amount of work she does.

Work

As you have seen, when you use a machine to do work, there is always an exchange, or tradeoff, between the force you use to do the work and the distance over which you apply that force. You apply less force over a longer distance or greater force over a shorter distance.

To reach the top of the hill, the climber must do work. Because she needs to increase her potential energy by a certain amount, she must do the same amount of work to reach the top of the hill whether she climbs a steep slope or a gentle slope.

The sloping surface of the hill acts like a ramp, which is a simple machine called an inclined plane. You know that machines make work easier by changing the size or direction of a force. How does this machine make the climber's work easier?

As the climber goes up the hill, she is doing work against gravity.

❶ One side of the hill is a very steep slope—almost straight up. If the climber takes the steep slope, she climbs a shorter distance, but she must use more force.

❷ Another side of the hill is a long, gentle slope. Here the climber travels a greater distance but uses much less effort.

452 Unit 3: **Motion and Forces**

DIFFERENTIATE INSTRUCTION

 More Reading Support

C How can a machine increase the amount of energy an object has? *by doing work on the object*

Advanced Have students design a physical model that shows how, for a given amount of work, there must be a trade-off between force and distance. Have students present their models to the class. *Example: Students can use blocks to represent a unit of work. The student can arrange a set number of blocks into different-shaped rectangles, with one side representing force and the other side representing distance. This is also a good activity for students who have physical disabilities, particularly vision impairments.*

 Challenge and Extension, p. 295

If the climber uses the steep slope, she must lift almost her entire weight. The inclined plane allows her to exert her input force over a longer distance; therefore, she can use just enough force to overcome the net force pulling her down the inclined plane. This force is less than her weight. In many cases, it is easier for people to use less force over a longer distance than it is for them to use more force over a shorter distance.

Energy and Work

To reach the top of the hill, the climber must do at least as much work as the amount of potential energy she needs to gain.

① The Short Route
By climbing straight up the steep slope, the climber covers a shorter distance but must apply more force against gravity.

② The Long Route
By climbing the gentle slope, the climber covers more distance but uses less force. The work does not decrease even though the force does.

READING VISUALS What combination of forces makes it more difficult to climb a steep slope? How might climbers try to overcome this problem?

Chapter 14: **Machines** 453

Teach from Visuals

To help students interpret the visual of the rock climber, ask:

- Will more work be done in climbing the face of the steep slope or in going up the gentle slope? *The work will be the same.*

- Will the distance the person has to walk be greater or less if the gentle slope is used? *The distance will be greater.*

- Will the force applied be greater or less if the gentle slope is used? *The force will be less.*

Develop Number Sense

Remind students that units that look different are not necessarily unrelated. Show them that gravitational potential energy (discussed on p. 452) equals the work done in the visual.

$F = m \cdot a$ and $W = F \cdot d$, so $W = m \cdot a \cdot d$ (mass times acceleration times distance)

Gravitational potential energy equals mgh (mass times gravitational acceleration times height [distance]). So when you find gravitational potential energy, you also have found the amount of work it takes to climb to the given height.

Ongoing Assessment

READING VISUALS *Answer: Gravity makes it more difficult to climb a steep slope. Climbers must lift almost their entire weight and use enough force to overcome the net force pulling them down the steep slope. They could overcome the problem by using a harness and other climbing equipment.*

DIFFERENTIATE INSTRUCTION

? More Reading Support

D What happens when someone is climbing straight up a steep slope? *They cover a shorter distance, but use more force*

Below Level Ask students to quickly answer the question, Which would be easier to climb: a set of steps or a telephone pole of the same height? *The steps would be easier to climb.* Have them relate their conclusions to the amount of work done. *The amount of work done in climbing the stairs is the same as the amount required to climb a pole, though less force is required.*

Chapter 14 **453**

Address Misconceptions

IDENTIFY Ask: What is the maximum efficiency of a real machine? If students answer "100 percent," they hold the misconception that machines can be 100 percent efficient.

CORRECT Have students conduct the Investigation on p. 455 while using materials that will minimize friction. They could cover the ramp with waxed paper or oil. No matter how little friction is present, the ramp will not be 100 percent efficient.

REASSESS Ask: Electric motors are quite efficient. How do you know that they are not 100 percent efficient? *Machines containing electric motors become warm, showing a transformation of input energy to heat.*

Technology Resources

Visit **ClassZone.com** for background on common student misconceptions.

MISCONCEPTION DATABASE

Develop Number Sense

Students might have a difficult time remembering whether to divide output work by input work or vice versa to calculate efficiency.

- Remind students that some friction is present in all real machines.
- Because friction is present, efficiency is always less than 100 percent. Since output work is always less than input work, output work must be divided by input work in order for efficiency to be less than 100%.
- If students still have difficulty after they have heard this reasoning, tell them that they can find efficiency by remembering the simple mnemonic **DOBI**, which stands for **D**ivide **O**utput work **B**y **I**nput work.

Ongoing Assessment

CHECK YOUR READING *Answer: A machine's efficiency is the ratio of its output work to the input work.*

PHOTO CAPTION *Answer: 30 percent*

454 Unit 3: **Motion and Forces**

VOCABULARY Write your own definition of *efficiency* in a word triangle.

Output work is always less than input work.

The work you do on a machine is called the input work, and the work the machine does in turn is called the output work. A machine's **efficiency** is the ratio of its output work to the input work. An ideal machine would be 100 percent efficient. All of the input work would be converted to output work. Actual machines lose some input work to friction.

You can calculate the efficiency of a machine by dividing the machine's output work by its input work and multiplying that number by 100.

$$\text{Efficiency (\%)} = \frac{\text{Output work}}{\text{Input work}} \cdot 100$$

Recall that work is measured in joules. Suppose you do 600 J of work in using a rope system to lift a box. The work done on the box is 540 J. You would calculate the efficiency of the rope system as follows:

$$\text{Efficiency} = \frac{540 \text{ J}}{600 \text{ J}} \cdot 100 = 90\%$$

CHECK YOUR READING What is a machine's efficiency? How does it affect the amount of work a machine can do?

APPLY The mail carrier is riding a motorized human transport machine. Suppose the machine has an efficiency of 70 percent. How much work is lost in overcoming friction on the sidewalk and in the motor?

Efficiency
The work you put into a machine will always be greater than the work done by the machine. Some input work is always lost in overcoming friction.

454 Unit 3: **Motion and Forces**

DIFFERENTIATE INSTRUCTION

More Reading Support

E Which is greater—a machine's output work or its input work? *input*

F If a machine loses 10 percent of the input work to friction, what is its efficiency? *90 percent*

Efficiency and Energy

You know that work transfers energy and that machines make work easier. The more mechanical energy is lost in the transfer to other forms of energy, the less efficient the machine. Machines lose some energy in the form of heat due to friction. The more moving parts a machine has, the more energy it loses to friction because the parts rub together. Machines can lose energy to other processes as well.

For example, a car engine has an efficiency of only about 25 percent. It loses much of the energy supplied by its fuel to heat from combustion. By comparison, a typical electric motor has more than an 80 percent efficiency. That means the motor converts more than 80 percent of the input energy into mechanical energy, or motion.

Many appliances come with energy guides that can help a buyer compare the energy efficiency of different models. A washing machine with the highest energy rating may not always save the most energy, however, because users may have to run those machines more often.

INVESTIGATE Efficiency

What is the efficiency of a ramp?
PROCEDURE

1. Build a ramp as shown. Measure the vertical height of the ramp and the length of the ramp in centimeters. Convert these distances to meters and record.
2. Attach the block to the spring scale and measure the force in newtons needed to lift the block straight up. Record this force as the output force. Multiply the output force by the height of the ramp in meters to get the output work. Record the output work.
3. Use the spring scale to pull the block up the ramp with a constant force. Record the force measured on the spring scale as the input force. Multiply the input force by the length of the ramp in meters to get the input work. Record the input work.
4. Use the input work and output work from steps 2 and 3 to calculate the efficiency of the ramp. Record your results.

WHAT DO YOU THINK?
- How did your input work compare with your output work?
- What could you do to increase the efficiency of the ramp?

CHALLENGE Would adding sandpaper on the surface of the ramp increase or decrease the efficiency of the ramp? Why? Test your hypothesis.

SKILL FOCUS Analyzing data

MATERIALS
- board
- books
- meter stick
- wooden block with eye hook
- spring scale
for Challenge:
- sandpaper

TIME 20 minutes

Chapter 14: **Machines** 455

INVESTIGATE Efficiency

PURPOSE To determine the efficiency of a ramp

TIP *20 min.* If necessary, point out that the length of the ramp is not equal to the horizontal distance along the desktop.

WHAT DO YOU THINK? *Output work should be less than input work. One way to increase efficiency is to reduce the friction between the board and the block.*

CHALLENGE *Adding sandpaper would decrease efficiency because it would increase friction.*

R Datasheet, Efficiency, p. 296

Technology Resources
Customize this student lab as needed or look for an alternative. Print rubrics to assess student lab reports.

Lab Generator CD-ROM

Ongoing Assessment
Calculate a machine's efficiency.

Ask: If someone does 500 joules of work on a pair of pliers and the pliers do 300 joules of work on a wire, what is the efficiency of the pliers?
Input work = 500 J
Output work = 300 J
$E = \frac{300 \text{ J}}{500 \text{ J}} \cdot 100 = 60\%$

DIFFERENTIATE INSTRUCTION

More Reading Support

G Which is more efficient—a car engine or an electric motor? *electric motor*

H What does an appliance's energy rating reflect? *the energy efficiency of the machine*

Inclusion For students who are visual and kinesthetic learners, supply mathematical models that they can use to determine the relationship between efficiency and the energy lost to friction. A ten-by-ten grid (or graph paper) can be a model. Students can shade in the efficiency percentage and find the amount of energy lost to friction in the unshaded part.

Chapter 14 **455**

Ongoing Assessment

 **Answer:** reduce friction by using oil or grease

Reinforce the BIG idea

Have students relate the section to the Big Idea.

 Reinforcing Key Concepts, p. 297

14.1 ASSESS & RETEACH

Assess

 Section 14.1 Quiz, p. 81

Reteach

No real machine is 100 percent efficient. The law of conservation of energy states that, under normal circumstances, energy is conserved. Ask students to explain how both of these statements can be true. *Some energy that is put into the machine is transformed into other forms of energy, such as heat from friction. The total amount of energy in the system is conserved.*

Technology Resources

Have students visit ClassZone.com for reteaching of Key Concepts.

 CONTENT REVIEW

 CONTENT REVIEW CD-ROM

Proper maintenance can help keep a bicycle running as efficiently as possible.

Increasing Efficiency

Because all machines lose input work to friction, one way to improve the efficiency of a machine is by reducing friction. Oil is used to reduce friction between the moving parts of car engines. The use of oil makes engines more efficient.

Another machine that loses input work is a bicycle. Bicycles lose energy to friction and to air resistance. Friction losses result from the meeting of the gears, from the action of the chain on the sprocket, and from the tires changing shape against the pavement. A bicycle with poorly greased parts or other signs of poor maintenance requires more force to move. For a mountain bike that has had little maintenance, as much as 15 percent of the total work may be lost to friction. A well-maintained Olympic track bike, on the other hand, might lose only 0.5 percent.

 What is a common way to increase a machine's efficiency?

14.1 Review

KEY CONCEPTS

1. In what ways can a machine change a force?
2. How is a machine's efficiency calculated?
3. Why is a machine's actual output work always less than its input work?

CRITICAL THINKING

4. **Apply** How would the input force needed to push a wheelchair up a ramp change if you increased the height of the ramp but not its length?
5. **Compare** What is the difference between mechanical advantage and efficiency?

CHALLENGE

6. **Apply** Draw and label a diagram to show how to pull down on a rope to raise a load of construction materials.

456 Unit 3: Motion and Forces

ANSWERS

1. by changing the size of a force, changing its direction, or both

2. Divide the output work by the input work, and multiply by 100.

3. Some input work is always lost to friction.

4. More input force would be needed.

5. Mechanical advantage is the number of times a machine multiplies the input force. Efficiency is the ratio of a machine's output work to input work.

6. Students' diagrams should show that pulling down on a rope helps to raise the load by changing the direction of the force.

MATH IN SCIENCE

SKILL: CHANGING RATIOS TO PERCENTS

Click on Math Tutorial for more help with percents and fractions.

No machine, no matter how large or small, is 100 percent efficient. Some of the input energy is lost to sound, heat, or other products.

How Efficient Are Machines?

A hammer is used to pound in nails. It can also be used to pry nails out of wood. When used to pry nails, a hammer is a machine called a lever. Like all machines, the hammer is not 100 percent efficient.

Efficiency is the amount of work a machine does divided by the amount of work that is done on the machine. To calculate efficiency, you must first find the ratio of the machine's output work to the input work done on the machine. A ratio is the comparison of two numbers by means of division. You convert the ratio to a decimal by dividing. Then convert the decimal to a percent.

Example

A person is doing 1000 joules of work on a hammer to pry up a nail. The hammer does 925 joules of work on the nail to pull it out of the wood.

(1) Find the ratio of output work to input work.

$$\frac{\text{Output work}}{\text{Input work}} = \frac{925 \text{ J}}{1000 \text{ J}} = 0.925$$

(2) To convert the decimal to a percent, multiply 0.925 by 100 and add a percent sign.

$$0.925 \cdot 100 = 92.5\%$$

ANSWER The efficiency of the hammer is 92.5 percent. This means that the hammer loses 7.5 percent of the input work to friction and other products.

Answer the following questions.

1. A construction worker does 1000 J of work in pulling down on a rope to lift a weight tied to the other end. If the output work of the rope system is 550 J, what is the ratio of output work to input work? What is the efficiency of the rope system?

2. If a machine takes in 20,000 J and puts out 5000 J, what is its efficiency?

3. You do 6000 J of work to pull a sled up a ramp. After you reach the top, you discover that the sled had 3600 J of work done on it. What is the efficiency of the ramp?

CHALLENGE If you put 7000 J of work into a machine with an efficiency of 50 percent, how much work will you get out?

Chapter 14: **Machines** 457

MATH IN SCIENCE
Math Skills Practice for Science

Set Learning Goal
To calculate the efficiency of a machine by changing ratios to percents

Present the Science
The efficiency of a machine is the ratio of its output work to the input work. Output work is defined as work done by the machine on something else. Input work is work done on the machine. Some input work is lost to undesired work, such as work done against friction. Such work is not considered output work.

Develop Number Sense
Students have to know how to write a ratio that compares output work to input work and be able to change this ratio to a percent.

- If students have difficulty identifying work as either output or input, they should remember that output work is always smaller than input work.
- Remind students that energy is conserved. If they find that the efficiency of a machine is 74 percent, for example, they should keep in mind that 26 percent of the energy input is lost to friction or other unwanted products, such as sound.

Close
Ask: What is the input work if the output work of a machine is 500 joules and the efficiency is 49 percent?

$$W_{in} = \frac{W_{out}}{E} = \frac{500 \text{ J}}{.49} = 1020 \text{ J}$$

- Math Support, p. 324
- Math Practice, p. 325

Technology Resources
Students can visit **ClassZone.com** for practice working with ratios and percents.

MATH TUTORIAL

ANSWERS

1. 550 J; 1000 J; $E = \frac{550 \text{ J}}{1000 \text{ J}} \cdot 100 = 55\%$

2. $E = \frac{5000 \text{ J}}{20,000 \text{ J}} \cdot 100 = 25\%$

3. $E = \frac{3600 \text{ J}}{6000 \text{ J}} \cdot 100 = 60\%$

CHALLENGE $W_{out} = E \cdot W_{in} = 0.5 \cdot 7000 \text{ J} = 3500 \text{ J}$

Chapter 14 **457**

14.2 FOCUS

▶ Set Learning Goals
Students will
- Describe how six simple machines change the size or direction of a force.
- Calculate mechanical advantage.
- Infer through experimentation the mechanical advantage of a pulley system.

◀ 3-Minute Warm-Up
Display Transparency 36 or copy this exercise on the board:

Think about all the chores a landscaping crew must do to get a yard or park in shape in the spring. They must mow, weed, and trim. They might have to plant flowers and grass seed and to water the plants. List the machines needed for landscaping. Explain how each machine helps the workers do work. *Sample answer: A hoe helps workers by cutting into the ground and pulling apart compacted soil.*

 3-Minute Warm-Up, p. T36

14.2 MOTIVATE

EXPLORE Changing Forces
PURPOSE To change a force applied to an object

TIP *15 min.* A hexagonal pencil will stay in place better than a round pencil.

WHAT DO YOU THINK? *Moving the bottom pencil closer to the book requires someone to use less force to lift the book; moving the pencil farther from the book requires more force. It is easier to lift the book when the bottom pencil is closer to the book and harder when it is farther away.*

KEY CONCEPT
14.2 Six simple machines have many uses.

 BEFORE, you learned
- Machines help you work by changing the size or direction of a force
- The number of times a machine multiplies the input force is the machine's mechanical advantage

▶ **NOW, you will learn**
- How six simple machines change the size or direction of a force
- How to calculate mechanical advantage

VOCABULARY
simple machine p. 458
lever p. 459
fulcrum p. 459
wheel and axle p. 460
pulley p. 460
inclined plane p. 462
wedge p. 462
screw p. 463

EXPLORE Changing Forces
How can you change a force?
PROCEDURE
1. Lay one pencil on a flat surface. Place the other pencil on top of the first pencil and perpendicular to it, as shown. Place the book on one end of the top pencil.
2. Push down on the free end of the top pencil to raise the book.
3. Change the position of the bottom pencil so that it is closer to the book and repeat step 2. Then move the bottom pencil closer to the end of the pencil you are pushing on and repeat step 2.

MATERIALS
- 2 pencils
- small book

WHAT DO YOU THINK?
- How did changing the position of the bottom pencil affect how much force you needed to lift the book?
- At which position is it easiest to lift the book? most difficult?

There are six simple machines.
You have read about how a ramp and a shovel can help you do work. A ramp is a type of inclined plane, and a shovel is a type of lever. An inclined plane and a lever are both simple machines. **Simple machines** are the six machines on which all other mechanical machines are based. In addition to the inclined plane and the lever, simple machines include the wheel and axle, pulley, wedge, and screw. As you will see, the wheel and axle and pulley are related to the lever, and the wedge and screw are related to the inclined plane. You will read about each of the six simple machines in detail in this section.

NOTE-TAKING STRATEGY
As you read, remember to take notes about the main ideas and supporting details.

458 Unit 3: Motion and Forces

RESOURCES FOR DIFFERENTIATED INSTRUCTION

Below Level
UNIT RESOURCE BOOK
- Reading Study Guide A, pp. 300–301
- Decoding Support, p. 323

 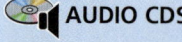 AUDIO CDS

Additional INVESTIGATION, Levers and Fulcrums, A, B, & C, pp. 335–343; Teacher Instructions, pp. 346–347

Advanced
UNIT RESOURCE BOOK
Challenge and Extension, p. 306

English Learners
UNIT RESOURCE BOOK
Spanish Reading Study Guide, pp. 304–305

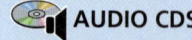 AUDIO CDS
- Audio Readings in Spanish
- Audio Readings (English)

Lever

A **lever** is a solid bar that rotates, or turns, around a fixed point. The bar can be straight or curved. The fixed point is called the **fulcrum.** A lever can multiply the input force. It can also change the direction of the input force. If you apply a force downward on one end of a lever, the other end can lift a load.

The way in which a lever changes an input force depends on the positions of the fulcrum, the input force, and the output force in relation to one another. Levers with different arrangements have different uses. Sometimes a greater output force is needed, such as when you want to pry up a bottle cap. At other times you use a greater input force on one end to get a higher speed at the other end, such as when you swing a baseball bat. The three different arrangements, sometimes called the three classes of levers, are shown in the diagram below.

CHECK YOUR READING What two parts are needed to make a lever?

Levers
Levers can be classified according to where the fulcrum is.

First-Class Lever

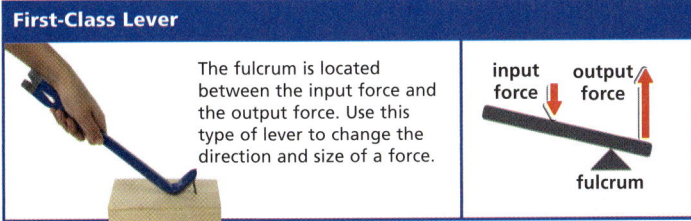

The fulcrum is located between the input force and the output force. Use this type of lever to change the direction and size of a force.

READING TiP
The lengths of the arrows in the diagram represent the size of the force.

Second-Class Lever

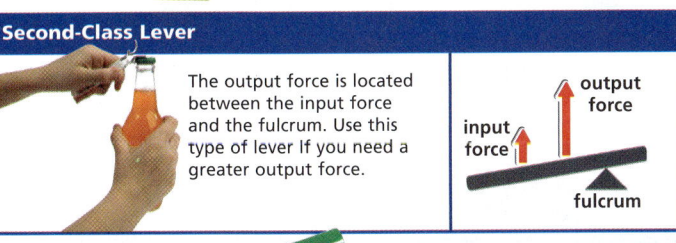

The output force is located between the input force and the fulcrum. Use this type of lever if you need a greater output force.

Third-Class Lever

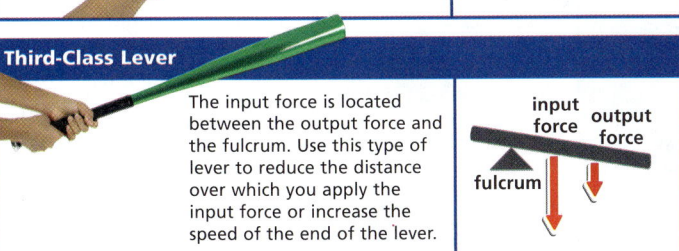

The input force is located between the output force and the fulcrum. Use this type of lever to reduce the distance over which you apply the input force or increase the speed of the end of the lever.

Chapter 14: **Machines** 459

Develop Critical Thinking

APPLY A screwdriver is a type of wheel and axle. Have students apply their knowledge of a wheel and axle to describe what type of screwdriver they would use to apply a large force, such as one required to put a screw into a hard piece of wood. *one with a large-diameter handle*

Teacher Demo

Provide groups of students with old doorknobs that have been taken apart so students can view their operation. While students are examining their doorknobs, point out the various parts of the wheel and axle that they contain. Elicit from students that the knob is the wheel, and the shaft is the axle. Have them describe the output force of the axle compared with the input force of the wheel in a doorknob. *The output force acts over a shorter distance than the input force.*

Ongoing Assessment

CHECK YOUR READING Answer: Force on the axle increased distance and decreased force from the wheel. Force on the wheel results in decreased distance and increased force from the axle.

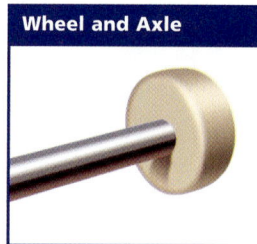
Wheel and Axle

Wheel and Axle

A **wheel and axle** is a simple machine made of a wheel attached to a shaft, or axle. The wheels of most means of transportation—such as a bicycle and a car—are attached to an axle. The wheel and axle act like a rotating collection of levers. The axle at the wheel's center is like a fulcrum. Other examples of wheels and axles are screwdrivers, steering wheels, doorknobs, and electric fans.

Depending on your purpose for using a wheel and axle, you might apply a force to turn the wheel or the axle. If you turn the wheel, your input force is transferred to the axle. Because the axle is smaller than the wheel, the output force acts over a shorter distance than the input force. A driver applies less force to a steering wheel to get a greater turning force from the axle, or steering column. This makes it easier to steer the car.

If, instead, you turn the axle, your force is transferred to the wheel. Because the wheel is larger than the axle, the force acts over a longer distance. A car also contains this use of a wheel and axle. The engine turns the drive axles, which turn the wheels.

**CHECK YOUR READING** Compare the results of putting force on the axle with putting force on the wheel.

Pulley

A **pulley** is a wheel with a grooved rim and a rope or cable that rides in the groove. As you pull on the rope, the wheel turns.

A pulley that is attached to something that holds it steady is called a fixed pulley. An object attached to the rope on one side of the wheel rises as you pull down on the rope on the other side of the wheel. The fixed pulley makes work easier by changing the direction of the force. You must apply enough force to overcome the weight of the load and any friction in the pulley system.

Fixed Pulley

A fixed pulley allows you to take advantage of the downward pull of your weight to move a load upward. It does not, however, reduce the force you need to lift the load. Also, the distance you pull the rope through is the same distance that the object is lifted. To lift a load two meters using a fixed pulley, you must pull down two meters of rope.

DIFFERENTIATE INSTRUCTION

 More Reading Support

C A wheel and axle is a form of what other type of simple machine? *lever*

D What is a pulley that is attached to something that holds it steady called? *a fixed pulley*

Advanced

Challenge and Extension, p. 306

460 Unit 3: Motion and Forces

In a movable pulley setup, one end of the rope is fixed, but the wheel can move. The load is attached to the wheel. The person pulling the rope provides the output force that lifts the load. A single movable pulley does not change the direction of the force. Instead, it multiplies the force. Because the load is supported by two sections of rope, you need only half the force you would use with a fixed pulley to lift it. However, you must pull the rope through twice the distance.

Movable Pulley

CHECK YOUR READING How does a single fixed pulley differ from a single movable pulley?

A combination of fixed and movable pulleys is a pulley system called a block and tackle. A block and tackle is used to haul and lift very heavy objects. By combining fixed and movable pulleys, you can use more rope sections to support the weight of an object. This reduces the force you need to lift the object. The mechanical advantage of a single pulley can never be greater than 2. If engineers need a pulley system with a mechanical advantage greater than 2, they often use a block-and-tackle system.

INVESTIGATE Pulleys

What is the mechanical advantage of a pulley system?

PROCEDURE

1. Hang the mass on the spring scale to find its weight in newtons. Record this weight as your output force.
2. Tie the top of one pulley to the ring stand.
3. Attach the mass to the second pulley.
4. Attach one end of the second pulley's rope to the bottom of the first pulley. Then thread the free end of the rope through the second pulley. Loop the rope up and over the first pulley, as shown.
5. Attach the spring scale to the free end of the rope. Pull down to lift the mass. Record the force you used as your input force. Calculate the mechanical advantage of this pulley system.
   Hint: The mechanical advantage can be calculated by dividing the output force by the input force.

WHAT DO YOU THINK?
- How did your input force compare with your output force?
- What caused the results you observed?

CHALLENGE Explain what the mechanical advantage would be for a pulley system that includes another movable pulley.

SKILL FOCUS
Inferring

MATERIALS
- 100 g mass
- spring scale
- 2 pulleys with rope
- ring stand

TIME
20 minutes

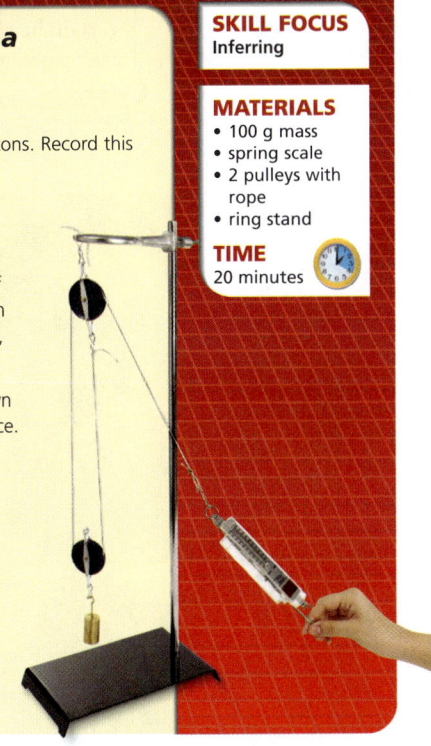

Chapter 14: **Machines** 461

INVESTIGATE Pulleys

PURPOSE To infer the mechanical advantage of a pulley system

TIPS 20 min. Use a clamp or a ring on the ring stand to hold the pulleys.

WHAT DO YOU THINK? *Students should observe that the input force is about half of the output force. The force must be applied over a greater distance (more rope is pulled).*

CHALLENGE *Because the mechanical advantage of a single movable pulley is 2, the mechanical advantage of the system with two such pulleys would be 4.*

R Datasheet, Pulleys, p. 307

Technology Resources

Customize this student lab as needed or look for an alternative. Print rubrics to assess student lab reports.

Lab Generator CD-ROM

Metacognitive Strategy

Ask students to write a paragraph identifying specific steps in the procedure that confused them. Ask them to describe how the picture in the investigation helped them perform any troublesome steps of the procedure.

Ongoing Assessment

CHECK YOUR READING *Answer: A fixed pulley changes the direction of force; its mechanical advantage is 1. A movable pulley decreases the size of the force and increases its distance; its mechanical advantage is 2.*

DIFFERENTIATE INSTRUCTION

More Reading Support

E What is in a fixed position in a movable pulley? *one end of the rope*

F Where is the load attached on a movable pulley? *to the wheel*

Alternative Assessment Have interested students work in groups to brainstorm limitations to pulley systems. Would there be a situation in which a pulley system could not work to lift an object? *Answers might include a weight so heavy that the output force would break the rope or an object placed in a location where no pulley could be set up.*

Chapter 14 **461**

Real World Example

Anyone who has driven over mountains has observed that the roads curve and do not go straight up and down. Because a mountain road is an inclined plane, increasing its length by zigzagging decreases the steepness of the incline. A less steep slope decreases the amount of force needed to get to the top of the mountain. Thus, a heavy truck can drive up a winding road to the top of a mountain because the engine has to exert less force. That same truck has less trouble going down a winding road because the upward force from the incline reduces the net downward force and makes it easier to control its speed.

Integrate the Sciences

The teeth of different animals indicate the differences in their diets.

- Carnivores, such as wolves, have sharp, wedgelike teeth with small angles. These teeth apply great force to tear apart meat.
- Some herbivores, such as many types of rodents, have wedgelike teeth in front, which are useful for gnawing.

Ongoing Assessment

CHECK YOUR READING *Answer: Inclined planes allow you to exert less force over a greater distance. They help support the weight of the object being raised.*

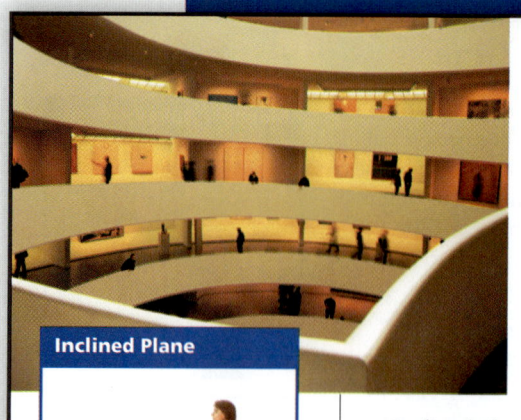

Inclined Plane

Inclined Plane

Recall that it is difficult to lift a heavy object straight up because you must apply a force great enough to overcome the downward pull of the force of gravity. For this reason people often use ramps. A ramp is an **inclined plane,** a simple machine that is a sloping surface. The photograph at the left shows the interior of the Guggenheim Museum in New York City. The levels of the art museum are actually one continuous inclined plane.

Inclined planes make the work of raising an object easier because they support part of the weight of the object while it is being moved from one level to another. The surface of an inclined plane applies a reaction force on the object resting on it. This extra force on the object helps to act against gravity. If you are pushing an object up a ramp, you have to push with only enough force to overcome the smaller net force that pulls the object down parallel to the incline.

The less steep an inclined plane is, the less force you need to push or pull an object on the plane. This is because a less steep plane supports more of an object's weight than a steeper plane. However, the less steep an inclined plane is, the farther you must go to reach a certain height. While you use less force, you must apply that force over a greater distance.

CHECK YOUR READING How do inclined planes help people do work? Your answer should mention force.

Wedge

A **wedge** is a simple machine that has a thick end and a thin end. Wedges are used to cut, split, or pierce objects—or to hold objects together. A wedge is a type of inclined plane, but inclined planes are stationary, while wedges often move to do work.

Some wedges are single, movable inclined planes, such as a doorstop, a chisel, or an ice scraper. Another kind of wedge is made of two back-to-back inclined planes. Examples include the blade of an axe or a knife. In the photograph at the left, a sculptor is using a chisel to shape stone. The sculptor applies an input force on the chisel by tapping its thicker end with a mallet. That force pushes the thinner end of the chisel into the stone. As a result, the sides of the thinner end exert an output force that separates the stone.

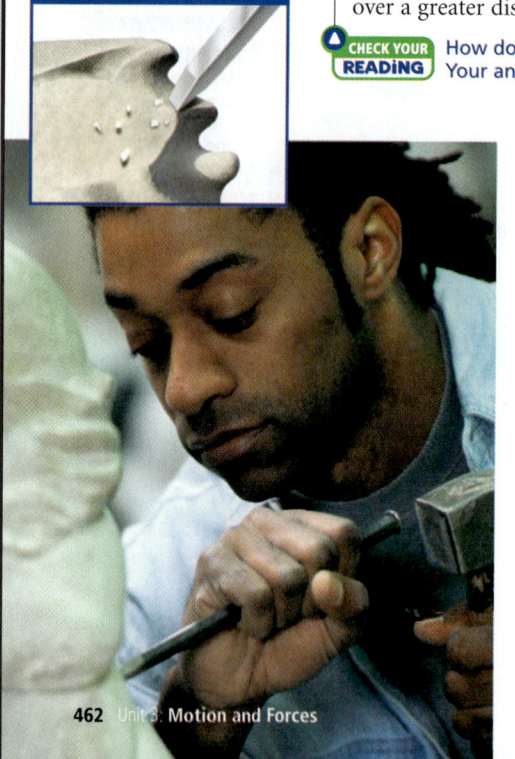

DIFFERENTIATE INSTRUCTION

? More Reading Support

G What is an inclined plane? *a simple machine that is a sloping surface*

The angle of the cutting edge determines how easily a wedge can cut through an object. Thin wedges have small angles and need less input force to cut than do thick wedges with large angles. That is why a sharp knife blade cuts more easily than a dull one.

You also can think of a wedge that cuts objects in terms of how it changes the pressure on a surface. The thin edges of a wedge provide a smaller surface area for the input force to act on. This greater pressure makes it easier to break through the surface of an object. A sharp knife can cut through an apple skin, and a sharp chisel can apply enough pressure to chip stone.

A doorstop is a wedge that is used to hold objects together. To do its job, a doorstop is pressed tip-first under a door. As the doorstop is moved into position, it lifts the door slightly and applies a force to the bottom of the door. In return, the door applies pressure to the doorstop and causes the doorstop to press against the floor with enough force to keep the doorstop—and the door—from moving.

Screw

A **screw** is an inclined plane wrapped around a cylinder or cone to form a spiral. A screw is a simple machine that can be used to raise and lower weights as well as to fasten objects. Examples of screws include drills, jar lids, screw clamps, and nuts and bolts. The spiraling inclined plane that sticks out from the body of the screw forms the threads of the screw.

In the photograph at right, a person is using a screwdriver, which is a wheel and axle, to drive a screw into a piece of wood. Each turn of the screwdriver pushes the screw farther into the wood. As the screw is turned, the threads act like wedges, exerting an output force on the wood. If the threads are very close together, the force must be applied over a greater distance—that is, the screw must be turned many times—but less force is needed.

The advantage of using a screw instead of a nail to hold things together is the large amount of friction that keeps the screw from turning and becoming loose. Think of pulling a nail out of a piece of wood compared with pulling a screw from the same piece of wood. The nail can be pulled straight out. The screw must be turned through a greater distance to remove it from the wood.

Notice that the interior of the Guggenheim Museum shown on page 462 is not only an inclined plane. It is also an example of a screw. The inclined plane is wrapped around the museum's atrium, which is an open area in the center.

CHECK YOUR READING Explain how a screw moves deeper into the wood as it is turned.

Screw

Chapter 14: Machines 463

DIFFERENTIATE INSTRUCTION

More Reading Support

H What does the tip of a wedge apply to a surface? *greater pressure*

I What is the inclined plane on a screw called? *the thread*

Below Level Have students use a table to summarize the effect on force of the six simple machines. Have them create a table with three columns and label them "Simple Machine," "Changes Direction of Force," and "Changes Size of Force." They should draw diagrams of all six simple machines and decide how they change force.

Teacher Demo

This demo may help students understand the relationship between a wedge and a screw. Cut a piece of paper into a right triangle. Darken the long edge (the hypotenuse) with a marker or pen. Show students how this resembles an inclined plane. Now place one of the short edges of the triangle against a pencil so it runs along and parallel to the pencil. Wrap the triangular piece of paper tightly around the pencil. Point out how the darkened edge now resembles the spiral of a screw, which can be seen as one inclined ramp wrapped around a wedge.

Ongoing Assessment

Describe how six simple machines change the size or direction of a force.

Ask: Explain how a pulley changes the direction or size of a force. *A fixed pulley changes the direction of a force by using the downward pull of your weight to move a load upward; a movable pulley multiplies the force but does not change the direction of force.*

CHECK YOUR READING *Answer: As the screw moves deeper into the wood, the threads act like wedges, exerting an output force on the wood. The force is applied over a greater distance if the threads are very close together, so less force is needed.*

Chapter 14 463

Real World Example

The force required for everyday tasks can sometimes be reduced by using simple machines. For a person in a wheelchair, going up and over a curb or up stairs requires a great amount of force. Ramps allow people in wheelchairs to apply less force over a greater distance. Pulleys allow people who are weak or have limited use of their arms or legs to be more mobile. Suspended pulleys might help these people get in and out of bed, a chair, a bathtub, or a vehicle.

The mechanical advantage of a machine can be calculated.

Recall that the number of times a machine multiplies the input force is the machine's mechanical advantage. You can calculate a machine's mechanical advantage using this formula:

$$\text{Mechanical Advantage} = \frac{\text{Output Force}}{\text{Input Force}}$$

$$MA = \frac{F_{out}}{F_{in}}$$

This formula works for all machines, regardless of whether they are simple machines or more complicated machines.

If a machine decreases the force you use to do work, the distance over which you have to apply that force increases. It is possible to use this idea to calculate the mechanical advantage of a simple machine without knowing what the input and output forces are. To make this calculation, however, you must assume that your machine is not losing any work to friction. In other words, you must assume that your machine is 100 percent efficient. The mechanical advantage that you calculate when making this assumption is called the ideal mechanical advantage.

READING TIP
Scientists often consider the way in which an object will behave under ideal conditions, such as when there is no friction.

Inclined Plane You can calculate the ideal mechanical advantage of an inclined plane by dividing its length by its height.

$$\text{Ideal Mechanical Advantage} = \frac{\text{length of incline}}{\text{height of incline}}$$

$$IMA = \frac{l}{h}$$

464 Unit 3: Motion and Forces

DIFFERENTIATE INSTRUCTION

? More Reading Support

J How does ideal mechanical advantage differ from actual mechanical advantage? *Ideal mechanical advantage assumes no loss of work to friction.*

Inclusion Allow students with learning disabilities to use calculators to help with mechanical-advantage calculations. Remind them that although efficiency is always less than 1 (100 percent), mechanical advantage can be greater than, less than, or equal to 1.

464 Unit 3: **Motion and Forces**

Be sure to use the length of the incline in your calculation, as shown in the diagram, and not the length of the base. If the mover in the photograph on page 464 increased the length of the ramp, he would increase the ramp's mechanical advantage. However, he would also increase the distance over which he had to carry the box.

Wheel and Axle To calculate the ideal mechanical advantage of a wheel and axle, use the following formula:

$$\text{Ideal Mechanical Advantage} = \frac{\text{Radius of input}}{\text{Radius of output}}$$

$$IMA = \frac{R_{in}}{R_{out}}$$

Explore the mechanical advantage of an inclined plane.

The radius is the distance from the center of the wheel or axle to any point on its circumference.

The Ferris wheel below is a giant wheel and axle. A motor applies an input force to the Ferris wheel's axle, which turns the wheel. In this example, the input force is applied to the axle, so the radius of the axle is the input radius in the formula above. The output force is applied by the wheel, so the radius of the wheel is the output radius.

For a Ferris wheel, the input force is greater than the output force. The axle turns through a shorter distance than the wheel does. The ideal mechanical advantage of this type of wheel and axle is less than 1.

Sometimes, as with a steering wheel, the input force is applied to turn the wheel instead of the axle. Then the input radius is the wheel's radius, and the output radius is the axle's radius. In this case, the input force on the wheel is less than the output force applied by the axle. The ideal mechanical advantage of this type of wheel and axle is greater than 1.

DIFFERENTIATE INSTRUCTION

K What is the ideal mechanical advantage of a wheel and axle in which the radius of input is 12 centimeters and the radius of output is 2 centimeters? **6**

Advanced Have students pick two simple machines and show mathematically the relationship between the ideal mechanical advantage and the shape of the machine. Remind students that for an ideal machine, output work equals input work.

Example: For an ideal inclined plane, input work equals input force times the length of the plane. Output work equals output force times height of plane. For an ideal machine, output work equals input work, so $F_{out} \cdot \text{height} = F_{in} \cdot \text{length}$ Rearranging gives $F_{out}/F_{in} = \text{length/height}$.

Teacher Demo

Demonstrate that beams of different length on a lever need different amounts of force. Turn a broom upside down. Have two students tightly hold the broom handle just below the brush. The handle should be off the floor. Have another student sit on the floor near the broom handle. Have the student on the floor touch the handle near its end with one finger. Ask students to explain how the seated student so easily made the broom handle move. *The students' hands acted as a fulcrum. The long lever beam of the handle multiplied the small force applied at its end.*

EXPLORE the BIG idea

Revisit "Shut the Door!" on p. 447. Have students explain their results.

Ongoing Assessment

Calculate mechanical advantage.

Ask: What is the mechanical advantage if the output force is 60 N and the input force is 15 N?

$MA = \dfrac{F_{out}}{F_{in}} = 60 \text{ N}/15 \text{ N} = 4$

EXPLORE

Revisit "Internet Activity: Machines" on p. 447. Ask students to name more machines that contain simple machines.

Reinforce

Have students relate the section to the Big Idea.

R Reinforcing Key Concepts, p. 308

Assess
A Section 14.2 Quiz, p. 82

Reteach
Have pairs of students make up questions about force and simple machines based on the photograph on p. 450. Have them trade questions and answer them for review. Questions might include the following:

- How do you know that the efficiency of the rake is less than 100 percent? *It is a real machine.*
- Which simple machine is used in the photograph? *a lever*
- How would you calculate the mechanical advantage of the rake? *by dividing the distance from the input force to the point where the rake prongs connect to the handle (fulcrum) by the distance from the output force to the fulcrum.*

Technology Resources
Have students visit **ClassZone.com** for reteaching of Key Concepts.

 CONTENT REVIEW

 CONTENT REVIEW CD-ROM

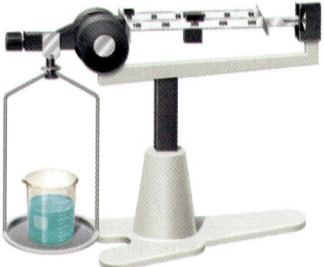 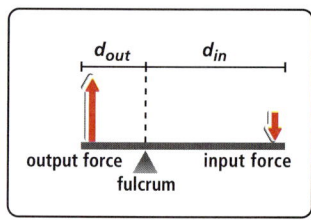

Lever The beam balance above is a lever. The beam is the solid bar that turns on a fixed point, or fulcrum. The fulcrum is the beam's balance point. When you slide the weight across the beam, you are changing the distance between the input force and the fulcrum. The mechanical advantage depends on the distances of the input force and output force from the fulcrum. The output force is applied to balance the beaker.

To calculate the ideal mechanical advantage of a lever, use the following formula:

$$\text{Ideal Mechanical Advantage} = \frac{\text{distance from input force to fulcrum}}{\text{distance from output force to fulcrum}}$$

$$IMA = \frac{d_{in}}{d_{out}}$$

This formula applies to all three arrangements of levers. If the distance from the input force to the fulcrum is greater than the distance from the output force to the fulcrum, the ideal mechanical advantage is greater than 1. The beam balance is an example of this type of lever.

14.2 Review

KEY CONCEPTS
1. Name the six simple machines and give an example of each.
2. Explain how a screw changes the size of the force needed to push it into wood.
3. To calculate mechanical advantage, what two things do you need to know?

CRITICAL THINKING
4. **Synthesize** How is a pulley similar to a wheel and axle?
5. **Calculate** What is the ideal mechanical advantage of a wheel with a diameter of 30 cm fixed to an axle with a diameter of 4 cm if the axle is turned?

⬥ CHALLENGE
6. **Infer** How can you increase a wedge's mechanical advantage? Draw a diagram to show your idea.

466 Unit 3: Motion and Forces

ANSWERS

1. Sample answer: lever, bottle opener; wheel and axle, doorknob; pulley, flagpole system; inclined plane, ramp; wedge, chisel; screw, jar lid

2. A small input force is applied over a long distance.

3. output force and input force

4. A pulley contains a wheel that turns on an axle.

5. MA = $\frac{4 \text{ cm}}{30 \text{ cm}}$ = 0.13

6. Make the wedge longer and thinner.

Connecting Sciences

PHYSICAL SCIENCE AND LIFE SCIENCE

A Running Machine

Marlon Shirley, who lives in Colorado, lost his lower left leg due to an accident at the age of five. He is a champion sprinter who achieved his running records while using a prosthesis (prahs-THEE-sihs), or a device used to replace a body part. Like his right leg, his prosthetic leg is a combination of simple machines that convert the energy from muscles in his body to move him forward. The mechanical system is designed to match the forces of his right leg.

Legs as Levers

Compare Marlon Shirley's artificial leg with his right leg. Both legs have long rods—one made of bone and the other of metal—that provide a strong frame. These rods act as levers. At the knee and ankle, movable joints act as fulcrums for these levers to transfer energy between the runner's body and the ground.

How Does It Work?

1. As the foot—real or artificial—strikes the ground, the leg stops moving forward and downward and absorbs the energy of the change in motion. The joints in the ankle and knee act as fulcrums as the levers transfer the energy to the muscle in the upper leg. This muscle acts like a spring to store the energy.

2. When the runner begins the next step, the energy is transferred back into the leg from the upper leg muscle. The levers in the leg convert the energy into forward motion of the runner's body.

The people who design prosthetic legs study the natural motion of a runner to learn exactly how energy is distributed and converted to motion so that they can build an artificial leg that works well with the real leg.

EXPLORE

1. **VISUALIZE** Run across a room, paying close attention to the position of one of your ankles and knees as you move. Determine where the input force, output force, and fulcrum are in the lever formed by your lower leg.

2. **CHALLENGE** Use the library or the Internet to learn more about mechanical legs used in building robots that walk. How do the leg motions of these robots resemble your walking motions? How are they different?

RESOURCE CENTER
CLASSZONE.COM
Find out more about artificial limbs.

Other parts of the human body can act like simple machines. For example, teeth work like wedges.

Chapter 14: **Machines** 467

Connecting Sciences
Integration of Sciences

Set Learning Goal
To understand how parts of a human leg act as levers

Integrate the Sciences
Several types of levers are present in the human body. For example, when you stand on your toes, your foot is a lever. The fulcrum is at the ankle joint. The output force is at the arch area, and the input force is the tendon at the back of the heel.

A lever system is formed by the head and the neck when the head is lowered toward the chest. The neck muscles provide the input force, and the weight of the head supplies the output force. The fulcrum is between these two forces.

Discussion Questions
Ask: Name all the levers in a leg. *thigh, lower leg, foot, toes*

Ask: Where are the fulcrums in the system of levers that is a leg? *hip, knee, ankle, toe joints*

Ask: What part of the human leg would be hardest to simulate? Why? *Sample answer: the muscles, because of their elasticity and self-contained energy*

Close
Ask: Which joint in the arm acts as a fulcrum for the lever formed by the bones in the lower arm? *the elbow*

Technology Resources
Have students visit **ClassZone.com** to find out more about artificial limbs
 RESOURCE CENTER, Artificial Limbs

EXPLORE

1. **VISUALIZE** *Input force comes from the knee area, and the output force comes from the foot. The ankle serves as the fulcrum.*

2. **CHALLENGE** *Answers will vary, but should reflect that different machines in the mechanical legs correspond to human body parts (such as movable joints that function as fulcrums) and that these machines work together to closely resemble a person's walking motion.*

Chapter 14 **467**

14.3 FOCUS

▶ Set Learning Goals
Students will
- Recognize how simple machines can be combined.
- Describe how scientists have developed extremely small machines.
- Explain how robots are used.

◀ 3-Minute Warm-Up
Display Transparency 37 or copy this exercise on the board:

All machines are based on six simple machines. Draw a picture of each of the following machines.

lever
inclined plane
wedge
screw
pulley
wheel and axle

 3-Minute Warm-Up, p. T37

14.3 MOTIVATE

THINK ABOUT
PURPOSE To introduce the concept that compound machines are made up of simple machines

DISCUSS Discuss with students how tow trucks for cars and light trucks would differ from tow trucks used to pull heavy trucks, such as tractor-trailers.
In the picture, students might recognize a pulley, a wheel and axle, a wedge, and an inclined plane.

Ongoing Assessment
 Answer: Compound machines are made of two or more simple machines.

KEY CONCEPT
14.3 Modern technology uses compound machines.

◀ **BEFORE, you learned**
- Simple machines change the size or direction of a force
- All machines have an ideal and an actual mechanical advantage

▶ **NOW, you will learn**
- How simple machines can be combined
- How scientists have developed extremely small machines
- How robots are used

VOCABULARY
compound machine p. 468
nanotechnology p. 471
robot p. 473

THINK ABOUT
How does a tow truck do work?
When a car is wrecked or disabled, the owner might call a towing service. The service sends a tow truck to take the car to be repaired. Tow trucks usually are equipped with a mechanism for freeing stuck vehicles and towing, or pulling, them. Look at the tow truck in the photograph at the right. What simple machines do you recognize?

Compound machines are combinations of simple machines.

Like the tow truck pictured above, many of the more complex devices that you see or use every day are combinations of simple machines. For example, a pair of scissors is a combination of two levers. The cutting edges of those levers are wedges. A fishing rod is a lever with the fishing line wound around a wheel and axle, the reel. A machine that is made of two or more simple machines is called a **compound machine**.

In a very complex compound machine, such as a car, the simple machines may not be obvious at first. However, if you look carefully at a compound machine, you should be able to identify forms of levers, pulleys, and wheels and axles.

 **VOCABULARY** Remember to write a definition for *compound machine* in a word triangle.

 How are simple machines related to compound machines?

468 Unit 3: Motion and Forces

RESOURCES FOR DIFFERENTIATED INSTRUCTION

Below Level
UNIT RESOURCE BOOK
- Reading Study Guide A, pp. 311–312
- Decoding Support, p. 323

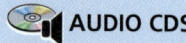 AUDIO CDS

Advanced
UNIT RESOURCE BOOK
- Challenge and Extension, p. 317
- Challenge Reading, pp. 319–320

English Learners
UNIT RESOURCE BOOK
Spanish Reading Study Guide, pp. 315–316

 AUDIO CDS
- Audio Readings in Spanish
- Audio Readings (English)

468 Unit 3: Motion and Forces

The gears in the photograph and diagram are spur gears, the most common type of gear.

Gears

Gears are based on the wheel and axle. Gears have teeth on the edge of the wheel that allow one gear to turn another. A set of gears forms a compound machine in which one wheel and axle is linked to another.

Two linked gears that are the same size and have the same number of teeth will turn at the same speed. They will move in opposite directions. In order to make them move in the same direction, a third gear must be added between them. The gear that turns another gear applies the input force; the gear that is turned exerts the output force. A difference in speed between two gears—caused by a difference in size and the distance each turns through—produces a change in force.

 How do gears form a compound machine?

Mechanical Advantage of Compound Machines

The mechanical advantage of any compound machine is equal to the product of the mechanical advantages of all the simple machines that make up the compound machine. For example, the ideal mechanical advantage of a pair of scissors would be the product of the ideal mechanical advantages of its two levers and two wedges.

The mechanical advantage of a pair of gears with different diameters can be found by counting the teeth on the gears. The mechanical advantage is the ratio of the number of teeth on the output gear to the number of teeth on the input gear. If there are more than two gears, count only the number of teeth on the first and last gears in the system. This ratio is the mechanical advantage of the whole gear system.

Compound machines typically must overcome more friction than simple machines because they tend to have many moving parts. Scissors, for example, have a lower efficiency than one lever because there is friction at the point where the two levers are connected. There is also friction between the blades of the scissors as they close.

Chapter 14: **Machines** 469

14.3 INSTRUCT

Develop Algebra Skills

To clarify the procedure for calculating mechanical advantage, provide students with practice problems. Sample problems:

- A compound machine contains two simple machines, one with a mechanical advantage of 3 and another with a mechanical advantage of 2. What is the mechanical advantage of the compound machine? $MA = 2 \cdot 3 = 6$

- A gear with 15 teeth turns another gear with 20 teeth. What is the mechanical advantage of the gear system?

$MA = \dfrac{20}{15} = 1.3$

Ongoing Assessment

 One wheel and axle turns another wheel and axle.

DIFFERENTIATE INSTRUCTION

More Reading Support

A How does a gear differ from a simple wheel and axle? *It has teeth on the edge of the wheel.*

English Learners Be aware that English learners do not always have the same background knowledge as the rest of the class. Certain technical terms mentioned in this chapter may be new to English Learners, such as *prosthesis* (p. 467), *artery* (p. 470), *Jaws of Life* (p. 470), *remote control* (p. 472), and *fiber optic cable* (p. 472).

Chapter 14 469

Teach from Visuals

Remind students that hydraulics can produce great force. In a hydraulic system, fluid is contained in two connected chambers, each of which contains a free-moving piston. The force applied to the smaller piston causes the larger piston to exert a greater force.

Integrate the Sciences

Some scientists working with nanotechnology base their work on cells, proteins, and molecules in the human body. For example, one group of researchers manipulated strands of DNA molecules to produce nano-sized tweezers. Two strands of DNA form the tweezers, while a third strand provides the fuel to close or open the arms. Such tweezers could be used to build other nanomachines or to manipulate the materials needed to build nanocircuits.

Ongoing Assessment

PHOTO CAPTION Answer: levers and wedges are some simple machines in the Jaws of Life tool.

APPLY What simple machines do you see in this Jaws of Life cutting tool?

Modern technology creates new uses for machines.

Sophisticated modern machinery is often based on or contains simple machines. Consider Jaws of Life tools, which are used to help rescue people who have been in accidents. These cutters, spreaders, and rams are powered by hydraulics, the use of fluids to transmit force. When every second counts, these powerful machines can be used to pry open metal vehicles or collapsed concrete structures quickly and safely. The cutters are a compound machine made up of two levers—much like a pair of scissors. Their edges are wedges.

Contrast this equipment with a drill-like machine so small that it can be pushed easily through human arteries. Physicians attach the tiny drill to a thin, flexible rod and push the rod through a patient's artery to an area that is blocked. The tip rotates at extremely high speeds to break down the blockage. The tiny drill is a type of wheel and axle.

Microtechnology and Nanotechnology

Manufacturers make machines of all sizes by shaping and arranging pieces of metal, plastic, and other materials. Scientists have used technology to create very small machines through miniaturization—the making of smaller and smaller, or miniature, parts. Micromachines are too small to be seen by the naked eye but are visible under a microscope. There is a limit, however, to how far micromachines can be shrunk.

To develop even tinier machines, scientists needed a new approach. Scientists have used processes within the human body as their model. For example, inside the body a protein molecule carries materials back and forth within a cell on regular paths that are similar to little train tracks. The natural machines in the human body inspired scientists to develop machines that could be 1000 times smaller than the diameter of a human hair.

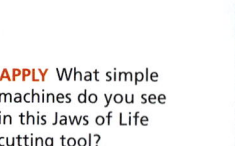

READING TIP
*Micro-*means "one-millionth." For example, a microsecond is one-millionth of a second. *Nano-* means "one-billionth." A nanosecond is one-billionth of a second.

470   Unit 3: Motion and Forces

DIFFERENTIATE INSTRUCTION

More Reading Support

B How is technology involved in miniaturization? *It allows scientists to create machines with miniature parts.*

Alternative Assessment American cartoonist Rube Goldberg (1883–1970) was famous for his cartoons of humorous and complicated machines. Today any device that is more complicated than practical is called a "Rube Goldberg machine." Show students a few examples of a Rube Goldberg machine. Ask students to design their own Rube Goldberg machine that uses the principles they have learned from the chapter.

470   Unit 3: **Motion and Forces**

These extremely tiny machines are products of **nanotechnology**, the science and technology of building electronic circuits and devices from single atoms and molecules. Scientists say that they create these machines, called nanomachines, from the bottom up. Instead of shaping already formed material—such as metal and plastic—they guide individual atoms of material to arrange themselves into the shapes needed for the machine parts.

Tools enable scientists to see and manipulate single molecules and atoms. The scanning tunneling microscope can create pictures of individual atoms. To manipulate atoms, special tools are needed to guide them into place. Moving and shaping such small units presents problems, however. Atoms tend to attach themselves to other atoms, and the tools themselves are also made of atoms. Thus it is difficult to pick up an atom and place it in another position using a tool because the atom might attach itself to the tool.

RESOURCE CENTER
CLASSZONE.COM
Learn more about nanomachines.

 Compare the way in which nanomachines are constructed with the way in which larger machines are built.

Nanomachines are still mostly in the experimental stage. Scientists have many plans for nanotechnology, including protecting computers from hackers and performing operations inside the body. For example, a nanomachine could be injected into a person's bloodstream, where it could patrol and search out infections before they become serious problems. When the machine had completed its work, it could switch itself off and be passed out of the body. Similar nanomachines could carry anti-cancer drugs to specific cells in the body.

Nanotechnology could also be used to develop materials that repel water and dirt and make cleaning jobs easy. Nanoscale biosensors could be used to detect harmful substances in the environment. Another possible use for nanotechnology is in military uniforms that can change color—the perfect camouflage.

In the future, nanotechnology may change the way almost everything is designed and constructed. As with any new technology, it will be important to weigh both the potential risks and benefits.

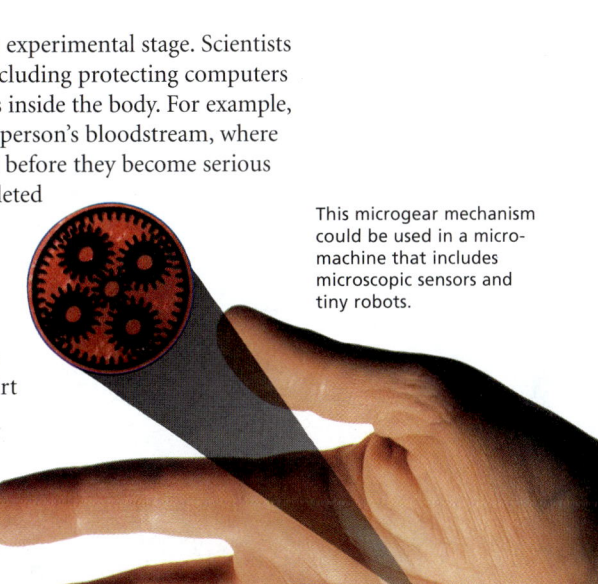

This microgear mechanism could be used in a micromachine that includes microscopic sensors and tiny robots.

Chapter 14: Machines 471

Real World Example

Ask students: When machines perform tasks, what happens to the people who formerly were doing those tasks? New processes have always made old processes obsolete. In some instances, new jobs are created by new technology. After all, someone needs to build and maintain robots, for example. However, these jobs often require skills that the workers might not have.

Ongoing Assessment

Describe how modern technology has enabled scientists to create extremely small machines.

Ask: How did scientists learn how to build a nanomachine? *They studied processes that build natural machines in the human body.*

Point out to students that these processes are common to nearly all life forms on Earth. Much nano research is based on bacteria.

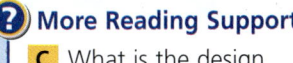 *Answer: Larger machines are constructed by shaping and arranging already formed pieces of material. Nanomachines are constructed from individual atoms of material that arrange themselves into the shape that is needed.*

DIFFERENTIATE INSTRUCTION

? More Reading Support

C What is the design and building of very tiny machines called?
nanotechnology

Alternative Assessment Have students write a short story or create a comic book about a way in which they think microtechnology or nanotechnology could be used in the future. Encourage creativity based on accurate science. Allow class time for students to share their products.

Chapter 14 **471**

Teach from Visuals

To help students interpret the visual "A Robot at Work," ask:

- Which tasks did the Pyramid Rover perform? *climbing a ramp, drilling, collecting and sending information, sensing conditions*
- Where else would a similar robot be useful? *Sample answers: cave exploration, looking for people in a collapsed mine or building*

 This visual is also available as T38 in the Unit Transparency Book.

Social Studies Connection

The Great Pyramid of Egypt is one of dozens of large pyramids built by ancient Egyptians to serve as burial places for their kings and queens. It is unknown exactly how workers lifted 1 million stones with an average weight of 2.5 tons to form this pyramid. One theory is that the Egyptians used ramps lubricated with mud. Another is that they used levers to raise each block a bit at a time.

Real World Example

A robot helped astronauts build the International Space Station. The space station includes a robotic arm, a 58-foot crane known as Canadarm 2. This robot has more dexterity than a human arm and will eventually have its own robot "hand."

Ongoing Assessment

READING VISUALS *Sample answer: wheels and axles to turn the treads, a screw for the drill, and levers to help it expand in size*

A Robot at Work

Scientists are using a robot to unlock the secrets of the Great Pyramid in Egypt.

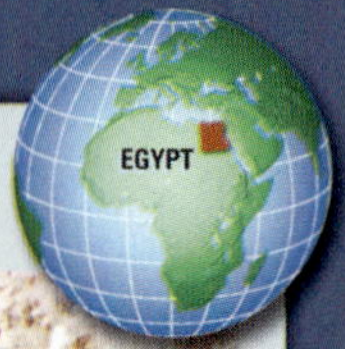

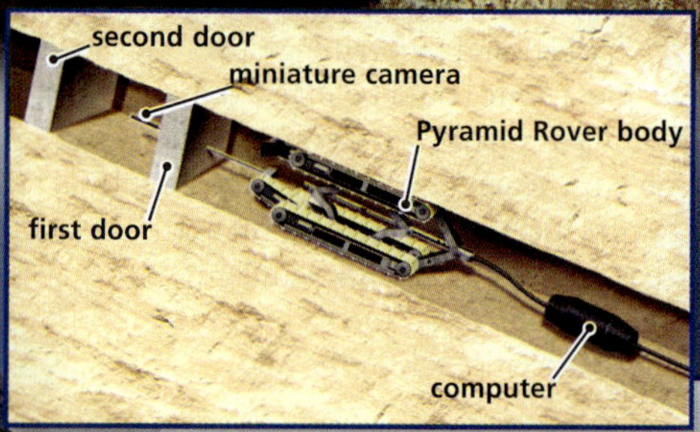

The frame of the Pyramid Rover is 12 centimeters (about 5 in.) wide and 30 centimeters (about 1 ft) long. As it moves, it uses two sets of flexible treads to grip the top and bottom of the narrow shafts inside the pyramid. The robot is linked to a computer by a fiber-optic cable.

READING VISUALS What simple machines do you think might be part of the Pyramid Rover?

472 Unit 3: Motion and Forces

DIFFERENTIATE INSTRUCTION

Advanced Have students use the Internet to find information about the Pyramid Rover or other robots. Designate a classroom bulletin board to which students can add information as it is acquired. Ask them to explain how other robots they learn about are used.

 Challenge and Extension, p. 317

Have students who are interested in learning more about how modern technology creates new uses for machines read the following article:

 Challenge Reading, pp. 319–320

472 Unit 3: **Motion and Forces**

Robots

Humans have always taken risks to do jobs in places that are dangerous or difficult to get to. More and more often, robots can be used to do these jobs. A **robot** is a machine that works automatically or by remote control. When many people hear the word *robot*, they think of a machine that looks or moves like a person. However, most robots do not resemble humans at all. That is because they are built to do things humans cannot do or to go places where it is difficult for humans to go.

Find out more about the Pyramid Rover and other robots.

The Pyramid Rover, shown on page 472, is an example of a robot developed to go where people cannot. After a camera revealed a door at the end of an eight-inch-square shaft inside the Great Pyramid, the Pyramid Rover was sent through the shaft to explore the area. While researchers remained in the Queen's Chamber in the center of the pyramid, the robot climbed the shaft until it came to a door. Using ultrasound equipment mounted on the robot, researchers determined that the door was three inches thick. The robot drilled a hole in the door for a tiny camera and a light to pass through. The camera then revealed another sealed door!

Many companies use robots to manufacture goods quickly and efficiently. Robots are widely used for jobs such as welding, painting, and assembling products. Robots do some repetitive work better than humans, because robots do not get tired or bored. Also, they do the task in exactly the same way each time. Robots are very important to the automobile and computer industries.

 How are robots better than humans at some jobs?

14.3 Review

KEY CONCEPTS

1. How do you estimate the mechanical advantage of a compound machine?
2. What are some uses of nanotechnology? Can you think of other possible uses for nanomachines?
3. What are three types of jobs that robots can do?

CRITICAL THINKING

4. **Synthesize** What factors might limit how large or how small a machine can be?
5. **Infer** How do you think the size of a gear compared with other gears in the same system affects the speed of its rotation?

CHALLENGE

6. **Apply** Robots might be put to use replacing humans in firefighting and other dangerous jobs. Describe a job that is dangerous. Tell what a robot must be able to do and what dangers it must be able to withstand to accomplish the required tasks.

Chapter 14: **Machines** 473

ANSWERS

1. You multiply the mechanical advantages of all the simple machines that make up the compound machine.
2. protecting computers from hackers, environmental monitoring, medicine
3. Sample answers: exploring dangerous areas, exploring distant places, and repetitive work in manufacturing
4. the space in which it works; it cannot be smaller than atoms
5. the larger the gear, the slower its rotation
6. Sample answer: Demolition: a robot could place explosives, set detonators, and relay information in buildings that are unsafe; it must be able to travel over unstable surfaces.

CHAPTER INVESTIGATION

Focus

PURPOSE To build and use a compound machine made from simple machines

OVERVIEW Students will design one of three types of machine. They will
- build the machine
- test it to make sure it will move a 500-gram object 1 meter
- calculate its mechanical advantage
- calculate its efficiency

Lab Preparation

- Have students read the lab for homework and choose a machine to build.
- Tell students that they can bring in additional materials but that you have to approve them beforehand.
- Have students read through the investigation and prepare their data tables. Or you may wish to copy and distribute datasheets and rubrics.

 UNIT RESOURCE BOOK, pp. 326–334

 SCIENCE TOOLKIT, F13

Lab Management

- Have students individually decide what type of machine they want to build. Then group students according to what machine they chose.
- If enough equipment is available, students can work in groups of two or three.
- Show students how to thread the pulley.

SAFETY You should preapprove materials that students want to bring from home.

INCLUSION Some students may have difficulty calculating the mechanical advantage and efficiency of the machine. Review how to make the calculations before beginning the investigation.

Teaching with Technology

Use a digital camera to photograph students' machines. Display images and have students identify the simple machines they contain.

474 Unit 3: **Motion and Forces**

CHAPTER INVESTIGATION

Design a Machine

OVERVIEW AND PURPOSE
Although simple machines were developed thousands of years ago, they are still used today for a variety of purposes. Tasks such as cutting food with a knife, using a screwdriver to tighten a screw, and raising a flag on a flagpole all require simple machines. Activities such as riding a bicycle and raising a drawbridge make use of compound machines. In this investigation you will use what you have learned about simple and compound machines to
- choose a machine to design
- build your machine, test it, and calculate its mechanical advantage and efficiency

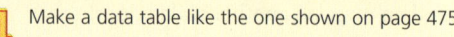 Procedure

MATERIALS
- 500 g object
- 100 g object
- meter stick
- spring scale
- pulleys with rope
- board
- stick or pole

1. Make a data table like the one shown on page 475.

2. From among the three choices listed below, choose which problem you are going to solve.

Carnival Game You work for a company that builds carnival games. Your supervisor has asked you to build a game in which a simple machine moves a 500-gram object from the bottom of the game 1 meter up to the top. This simple machine can be powered only by the person operating the game.

Video Game Contest The marketing department of a video game company is holding a contest. Candidates are asked to submit a working model of a compound machine that will move a 500-gram object a distance of 1 meter. The winning design will be used in a new video game the company hopes to sell. This compound machine must include at least 2 simple machines.

Construction Company You work for a construction company. Your boss has asked you to design a machine for lifting. Your first step is to build a scale model. The model must be a compound machine with a mechanical advantage of 5 that can move a 500-gram object a distance of 1 meter. You also can use a 100-gram object in your design.

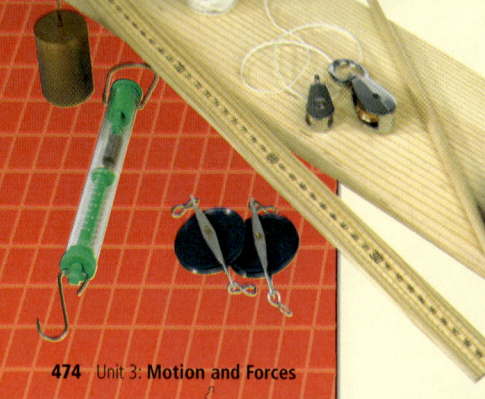

474   Unit 3: **Motion and Forces**

INVESTIGATION RESOURCES

 CHAPTER INVESTIGATION, Design a Machine
- Level A, pp. 326–329
- Level B, pp. 330–333
- Level C, p. 334

Advanced students should complete Levels B & C.

 Writing a Lab Report, D12–13

Technology Resources

Customize this student lab as needed or look for an alternative. Print rubrics to assess student lab reports.

 Lab Generator CD-ROM

3. Brainstorm design ideas on paper. Think of different types of machines you might want to build. Choose one machine to build.

4. Build your machine. Use your machine to perform the task of moving a 500-gram object a distance of 1 meter.

   If you chose the third problem, test your compound machine to determine if it has a mechanical advantage of 5. If not, modify your machine and retest it.

5. Record all measurements in your data table.

Observe and Analyze

1. **RECORD OBSERVATIONS** Make a sketch of your machine.

2. **CALCULATE** Use your data to calculate the mechanical advantage and efficiency of your machine. Use the formulas below.

   $$\text{Mechanical Advantage} = \frac{\text{Output Force}}{\text{Input Force}}$$

   $$\text{Efficiency (\%)} = \frac{\text{Output work}}{\text{Input work}} \cdot 100$$

3. **ANALYZE**

   Carnival Game Add arrows to the drawing of your machine to show the forces involved and the direction of those forces. If your goal was to move the ball from the top of the game to the bottom at a constant speed, how would your machine and diagram have to be changed?

   Video Game Contest Does your machine change the size of the force, the direction of the force, or both? If you used a pulley system (two or more pulleys working together), describe the advantages of using such a system.

   Construction Company Determine whether force or distance is changed by each simple machine in your compound machine. In what ways might you improve your machine to increase its efficiency?

Conclude

1. **INFER** How might changing the arrangement of the parts in your machine affect the machine's mechanical advantage?

2. **IDENTIFY LIMITS** What was the hardest part about designing and constructing your machine?

3. **APPLY** If you needed to lift a large rock from a hole at a construction site, which type of simple machine would you use and why? Which type of compound machine would be useful?

INVESTIGATE Further

CHALLENGE If you made a simple machine, how would you combine it with another simple machine to increase its mechanical advantage?

If you made a compound machine, redesign it to increase its efficiency or mechanical advantage. What made the difference and why?

Draw a plan for the new machine. Circle the parts that were changed. If you have time, build your new machine.

Design a Machine
Observe and Analyze
Table 1. Machine Data

Output force	Input force	Mechanical Advantage
Output work	Input work	Efficiency

Sketch

Chapter 14: **Machines** 475

Observe and Analyze

1. See students' drawings.

2. Mechanical advantage should use force as measured by the spring scale. Work done can be determined by force and distance.

3. Sample answers: Carnival game: The input and output would be reversed. Video game contest: A pulley system multiplies force. Construction company: Increase the efficiency by reducing friction.

Conclude

1. Students should specify whether they think the mechanical advantage will increase, decrease, or stay the same. Students should explain their answers.

2. Have students identify specific problems and difficulties in designing and constructing their designs.

3. Sample answer: A lever could be placed under the edge of the rock, and you could increase the force by controlling the location of the fulcrum. A compound machine could use a lever to pry the rock out of the ground and a pulley to raise it.

INVESTIGATE Further

CHALLENGE Combine the first simple machine with another simple machine that has a mechanical advantage greater than 1. For a compound machine, decrease friction, perhaps by oiling the machine, to increase efficiency. Increase its mechanical advantage by increasing the mechanical advantage of the simple machines in it. Check students' plans for new machines.

Post-Lab Discussion

• Have each lab group demonstrate their machine for the rest of the class. For each machine, identify appropriate problems for technological design, design solutions, and implement a proposed design to improve the machine.

• Make a table to tally the number of times each type of simple machine was used in the compound machines.

CHAPTER 14 • REVIEW

BACK TO

Have each student list five machines they have used today.
- For each, have them describe whether it is a simple or a compound machine.
- For compound machines, have students name the simple machines that are included in it.
- Invite students to share their lists with the rest of the class.

KEY CONCEPTS SUMMARY

SECTION 14.1
Ask: If the slope of the inclined plane were made steeper, what would happen to the size of the force arrow? *It would increase.*

Ask: If the person climbed straight up to the top position, would she do more or less work than if she walked up the slope? *The amount of work would be the same.*

SECTION 14.2
Have students sketch the first two simple machines shown with force arrows. Label arrows as input force or output force. Check students' drawings.
Pulley—input force: person pulling rope; output force: lifts the load. Wheel and axle—input force: turning the wheel; output force: turning force of the axle.

SECTION 14.3
Have students describe the flow of force through each simple machine shown.
The lever is turned and that applies a force to the wheel and axle.

Review Concepts

- Big Idea Flow Chart, p. T33
- Chapter Outline, pp. T39–T40

---

14 Chapter Review

the BIG idea
Machines help people do work by changing the force applied to an object.

 KEY CONCEPTS SUMMARY

1 Machines help people do work.

When you use a machine to do work, there is always an exchange, or tradeoff, between the force you use and the distance over which you apply that force. You can use less force over a greater distance or a greater force over a shorter distance to do the same amount of work.

VOCABULARY
machine p. 449
mechanical advantage p. 451
efficiency p. 454

 Six simple machines have many uses.

Simple machines change the size and/or direction of a force.

   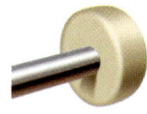   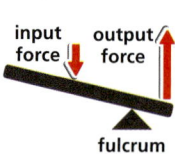

changes direction   changes size   changes both

VOCABULARY
simple machine p. 458
lever p. 459
fulcrum p. 459
wheel and axle p. 460
pulley p. 460
inclined plane p. 462
wedge p. 462
screw p. 463

3 Modern technology uses compound machines.
- Compound machines are combinations of simple machines.

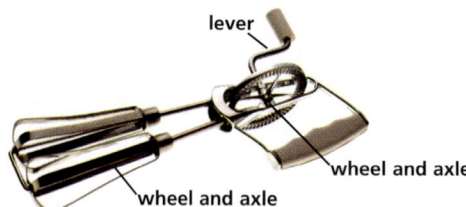

- Modern technology creates new uses for machines.
  —Microtechnology and nanotechnology
  —Robots

VOCABULARY
compound machine p. 468
nanotechnology p. 471
robot p. 473

476 Unit 3: Motion and Forces

Technology Resources

Have students visit **ClassZone.com** or use the CD-ROM for a cumulative review of concepts.

 CONTENT REVIEW

CONTENT REVIEW CD-ROM

Engage students in a whole-class interactive review of Key Concepts. Edit content as you wish.

 POWER PRESENTATIONS

Reviewing Vocabulary

Write the name of the simple machine shown in each illustration. Give an example from real life for each one.

1.

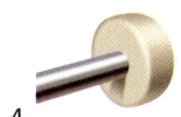
4.

2.

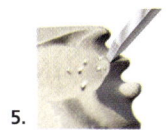
5.

3.

6.

Copy the chart below, and write the definition for each term in your own words. Use the meaning of the term's root to help you.

Term	Root Meaning	Definition
7. machine	having power	
8. nanotechnology	one-billionth	
9. simple machine	basic	
10. efficiency	to accomplish	
11. compound machine	put together	
12. robot	work	
13. fulcrum	to support	

Reviewing Key Concepts

Multiple Choice *Choose the letter of the best answer.*

14. Machines help you work by
    a. decreasing the amount of work that must be done
    b. changing the size and/or direction of a force
    c. decreasing friction
    d. conserving energy

15. To calculate mechanical advantage, you need to know
    a. time and energy
    b. input force and output force
    c. distance and work
    d. size and direction of a force

16. A machine in which the input force is equal to the output force has a mechanical advantage of
    a. 0   c. 1
    b. between 0 and 1   d. more than 1

17. You can increase a machine's efficiency by
    a. increasing force   c. increasing distance
    b. reducing work   d. reducing friction

18. Levers turn around a
    a. fixed point called a fulcrum
    b. solid bar that rotates
    c. wheel attached to an axle
    d. sloping surface called an inclined plane

19. When you bite into an apple, your teeth act as what kind of simple machine?
    a. lever   c. wedge
    b. pulley   d. screw

Short Answer *Answer each of the following questions in a sentence or two.*

20. Describe the simple machines that make up scissors.

21. How do you calculate the mechanical advantage of a compound machine?

22. How did scientists use processes inside the human body as a model for making nanomachines?

Chapter 14: **Machines** 477

Reviewing Vocabulary

Sample answers

1. lever, crowbar
2. screw, jar lid
3. pulley, system for raising a flag
4. wheel and axle, doorknob
5. wedge, doorstop
6. inclined plane, ramp
7. any device that helps you do work
8. the science and technology of building tiny devices from single atoms and molecules
9. a basic machine on which all other machines are based
10. the percentage of the input work that a machine can return in output work
11. a machine that is made up of two or more simple machines
12. a machine that works automatically or by remote control
13. a fixed point on which a lever rotates

Reviewing Key Concepts

14. b
15. b
16. c
17. d
18. a
19. c
20. A pair of scissors is made up of two levers with cutting edges that are wedges.
21. Multiply the mechanical advantages of all the simple machines in it.
22. Scientists noticed that molecules in the body act as natural machines and learned how they are built.

ASSESSMENT RESOURCES

UNIT ASSESSMENT BOOK
- Chapter Test A, pp. 84–87
- Chapter Test B, pp. 88–91
- Chapter Test C, pp. 92–95
- Alternative Assessment, pp. 96–97
- Unit Test, A, B, & C, pp. 98–109

SPANISH ASSESSMENT BOOK
- Spanish Chapter Test, pp. 273–276
- Spanish Unit Test, pp. 277–280

Technology Resources

Edit test items and answer choices.

 Test Generator CD-ROM

Visit **ClassZone.com** to extend test practice.

 Test Practice

Thinking Critically

23. A screw is an inclined plane wrapped around a cylinder.

24. Sample answer: Use a block and tackle. The fixed and movable pulleys increase the mechanical advantage of the machine.

25. The amount of work would be the same because each person adds the same amount of potential energy. The person on the shorter path must use more force.

26. The MA of the board is less, but the amount of work will not change.

27. fixed pulley changes the direction of force and its MA is 1; movable pulley decreases the size of the force and increases its distance; its MA is 2

28. 2.67; 2.67

29. The mechanical advantage would increase and this would require the man to exert less input force.

30. The input force would increase.

Using Math Skills in Science

31. MA = 5 N/10 N = 0.5
32. E = 90,000 J/125,000 J · 100 = 72%
33. 80%
34. MA = 21 cm/3 cm = 7
35. MA = 24/24 = 1

the BIG idea

36. wheel and axle, pulley, inclined plane; the balls move down the inclined plane and continue down the tracks, which are moved by the wheels and the pulley system to help the balls complete their paths.

37. Answers will vary depending on the machine students choose.

38. Answers should include the concept that work will be done on a smaller scale.

UNIT PROJECTS

Have students present their projects. Use the appropriate rubrics from the URB to evaluate their work.

 Unit Projects, pp. 5–10

Thinking Critically

23. **SYNTHESIZE** How is a screw related to an inclined plane?

24. **INFER** Which simple machine would you use to raise a very heavy load to the top of a building? Why?

25. **APPLY** If you reached the top of a hill by using a path that wound around the hill, would you do more work than someone who climbed a shorter path? Why or why not? Who would use more force?

26. **APPLY** You are using a board to pry a large rock out of the ground when the board suddenly breaks apart in the middle. You pick up half of the board and use it to continue prying up the rock. The fulcrum stays in the same position. How has the mechanical advantage of the board changed? How does it change your work?

27. **SYNTHESIZE** What is the difference between a single fixed pulley and a single movable pulley? Draw a diagram to illustrate the difference.

Use the information in the diagram below to answer the next three questions.

28. **SYNTHESIZE** What is the mechanical advantage of the ramp? By how many times does the ramp multiply the man's input force?

29. **SYNTHESIZE** If the ramp's length were longer, what effect would this have on its mechanical advantage? Would this require the man to exert more or less input force?

30. **INFER** If the ramp's length stayed the same but the height was raised, how would this change the input force required?

Using Math Skills in Science

Complete the following calculations.

31. You swing a hockey stick with a force of 10 N. The stick applies 5 N of force on the puck. What is the mechanical advantage of the hockey stick?

32. Your input work on a manual lawn mower is 125,000 J. The output work is 90,000 J. What is the efficiency of the lawn mower?

33. If a car engine has a 20 percent efficiency, what percentage of the input work is lost?

34. A steering wheel has a radius of 21 cm. The steering column on which it turns has a radius of 3 cm. What is the mechanical advantage of this wheel and axle?

35. Two gears with the same diameter form a gear system. Each gear has 24 teeth. What is the mechanical advantage of this gear system?

the BIG idea

36. **DRAW CONCLUSIONS** Look back at the photograph on pages 446–447. Name the simple machines you see in the photograph. How do you think they work together to move balls through the sculpture? How has your understanding changed as to the way in which machines help people work?

37. **SYNTHESIZE** Think of a compound machine you have used recently. Explain which simple machines it includes and how they helped you do work.

38. **PREDICT** How do you think nanotechnology will be useful in the future? Give several examples.

UNIT PROJECTS

Evaluate all of the data, results, and information from your project folder. Prepare to present your project to the class. Be ready to answer questions posed by your classmates about your results.

MONITOR AND RETEACH

If students have trouble applying the concepts in items 28–30, have them model the scenario using a ramp, a mass, and a spring scale. Ask:
1. What distances do you measure to determine mechanical advantage of an inclined plane? *ramp length and height* 2. How does increasing the length of a ramp affect the amount of force used? *It decreases it.*
3. Can you use this model to answer items 28–30? Explain. *In theory, yes, by using similar reasoning; but the values would be different.*
Students may benefit from summarizing sections of the chapter.

 Summarizing the Chapter, pp. 344–345

Standardized Test Practice

For practice on your state test, go to...
TEST PRACTICE
CLASSZONE.COM

Analyzing Graphics

The Archimedean screw is a mechanical device first used more than 2000 years ago. It consists of a screw inside a cylinder. One end of the device is placed in water. As the screw is turned with a handle, its threads carry water upward. The Archimedean screw is still used in some parts of the world to pump water for irrigating fields. It can also be used to move grain in mills.

Study the illustration of an Archimedean screw. Then answer the questions that follow.

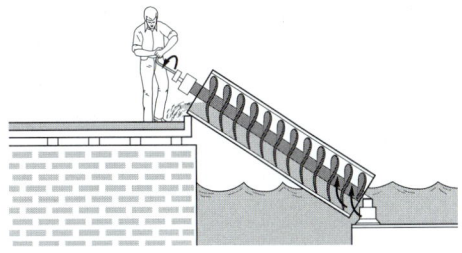

1. Which type of simple machine moves water in the cylinder?
   a. block and tackle   c. screw
   b. pulley   d. wedge

2. Which type of simple machine is the handle?
   a. wheel and axle   c. pulley
   b. inclined plane   d. wedge

3. What is the energy source for the Archimedean screw?
   a. the water pressure inside the screw
   b. the person who is turning the handle
   c. falling water that is turning the screw
   d. electrical energy

4. How is the Archimedean screw helping the person in the illustration do work?
   a. by decreasing the input force needed to lift the water
   b. by decreasing the work needed to lift the water
   c. by decreasing the distance over which the input force is applied
   d. by keeping the water from overflowing its banks

5. If the threads on the Archimedean screw are closer together, the input force must be applied over a greater distance. This means that the person using it must turn the handle
   a. with more force
   b. fewer times but faster
   c. in the opposite direction
   d. more times with less effort

Extended Response

Answer the two questions below in detail.

6. A playground seesaw is an example of a lever. The fulcrum is located at the center of the board. People seated at either end take turns applying the force needed to move the other person. If one person weighs more than the other, how can they operate the seesaw? Consider several possibilities in your answer.

7. Picture two gears of different sizes turning together. Suppose you can apply a force to turn the larger gear or the smaller gear, and it will turn the other. Discuss what difference it would make whether you turned the larger or smaller gear. Describe the input work you would do on the gear you are turning and the output work that gear would do on the other gear.

Chapter 14: **Machines** 479

Analyzing Graphics

1. c   4. a
2. a   5. d
3. b

Extended Response

6. RUBRIC
4 points for a response that correctly answers the question and gives 3 or more correct and varied examples.

Sample answer: Assuming the seesaw (the lever) cannot be moved, there are several possibilities: 1. The heavier person can sit closer to the fulcrum. 2. The heavier person can stay seated and the lighter person can be positioned farther away from the fulcrum. 3. Both people move at the same time. In all cases, they try to balance the board first.

3 points correctly answers the question and gives 2 or more correct and varied examples

2 points correctly answers the question and gives 1 or more correct and varied examples

1 point correctly answers the question

7. RUBRIC
4 points for a response that correctly describes the situation and covers the following key concepts accurately:
- compound machine
- input force
- output force
- mechanical advantage

Sample answer: A set of gears forms a <u>compound machine</u>. The gear that turns another gear applies the <u>input force</u>; the gear that is turned exerts the <u>output force</u>. One turn of the larger gear will turn the smaller gear several times. You will need to turn the smaller gear several times in order to make the larger gear turn once. The <u>mechanical advantage</u> is greater when the smaller gear turns the larger gear.

3 points for a response that covers 3 key concepts accurately
2 points for a response that covers 2 key concepts accurately
1 point for a response that covers 1 key concept accurately

METACOGNITIVE ACTIVITY

Have students answer the following questions in their **Science Notebook:**

1. How can you tell when you have made a mistake in doing calculations?
2. What constraint did you experience when building your machine as part of the Chapter Investigation?
3. Now that you have completed the chapters on forces, motion, and machines, what would you have done differently with your Unit Project? Refer back to the formula for efficiency on p. 454.

Chapter 14   **479**

McDougal Littell Science

Waves, Sound, and Light

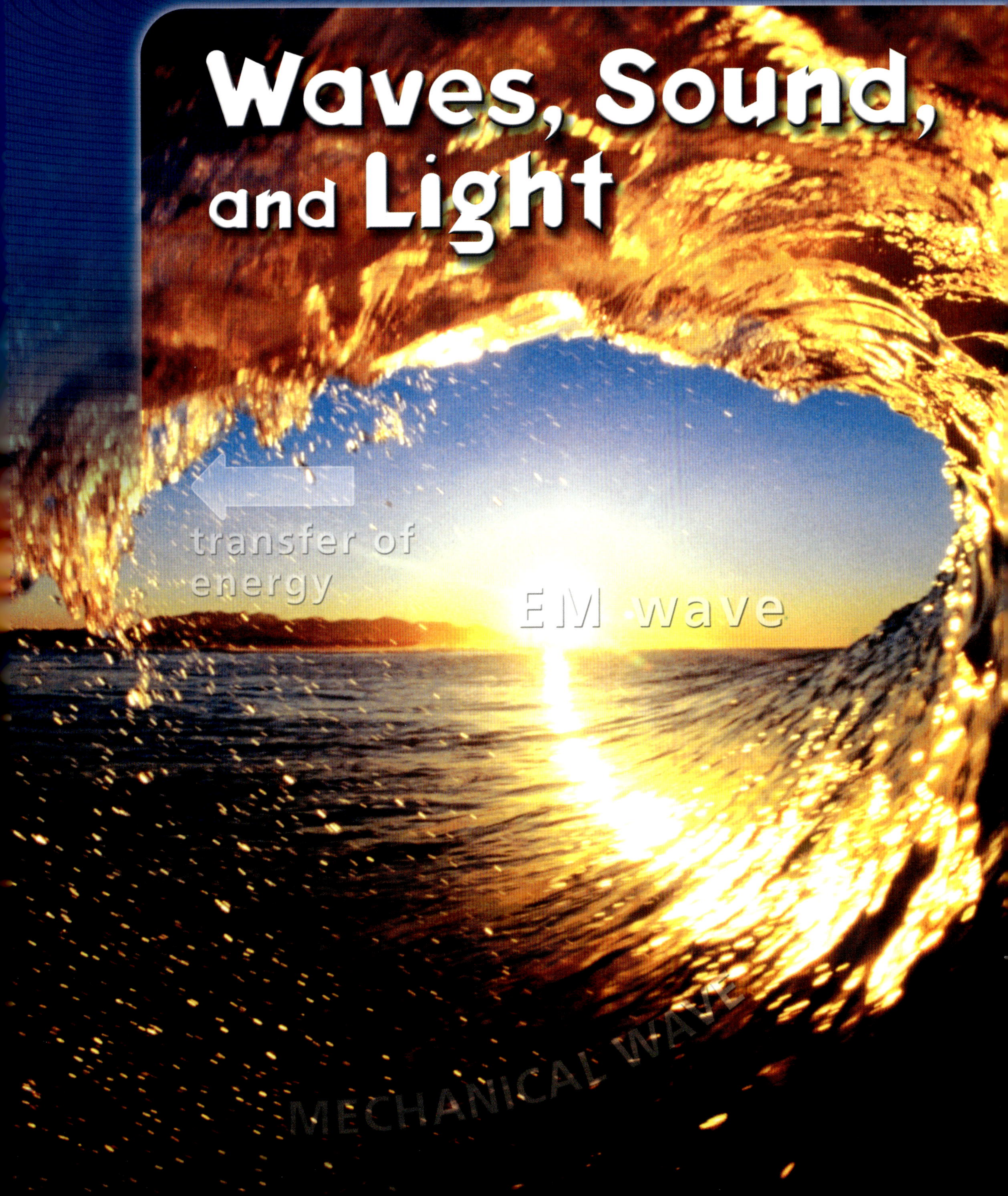

transfer of energy

EM wave

MECHANICAL WAVE

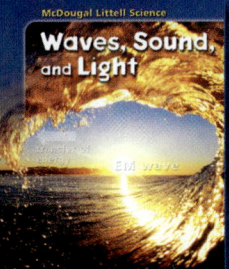

Waves, Sound, and Light
Contents Overview

Unit Features
FRONTIERS IN SCIENCE Sound Medicine 482
TIMELINES IN SCIENCE The Story of Light 586

15 Waves   486
the BIG idea
Waves transfer energy and interact in predictable ways.

16 Sound   514
the BIG idea
Sound waves transfer energy through vibrations.

17 Electromagnetic Waves   550
the BIG idea
Electromagnetic waves transfer energy through radiation.

18 Light and Optics   590
the BIG idea
Optical tools depend on the wave behavior of light.

Contents Overview 481

FRONTIERS in Science

VIDEO SUMMARY

SCIENTIFIC AMERICAN FRONTIERS

EACH SOUND IS A PRESENT "Each Sound Is a Present" is a segment of the Scientific American Frontiers series that aired on PBS stations. This segment focuses on Kelley Flynn, who suffered severe hearing damage from an infection. At seven, Kelley's hearing is becoming worse, and she will have cochlear implant surgery. The goal of the implant is to compensate for hair cells destroyed by Kelley's infection.

The human ear contains the cochlea, a spiral bone lined with thousands of tiny hairs that bend from sound vibrations. This movement triggers electrical signals along nerves to the brain, which receives and processes these signals as sound. Damaged hairs do not recover.

Kelley's surgeons replace cochlear hairs with electrodes connected to a magnet and an antenna implanted in her skull. After surgery, a transmitter is attached to the magnet inside her head. The transmitter is attached to a small computer that converts sounds collected by a microphone to electrical signals that are sent to the brain.

National Science Education Standards

A.9.a–d Understandings About Scientific Inquiry

E.6.a–f Understandings About Science and Technology

F.5.a–e Science and Technology in Society

G.1.a–b Science as a Human Endeavor

G.2.a Nature of science

FRONTIERS in Science

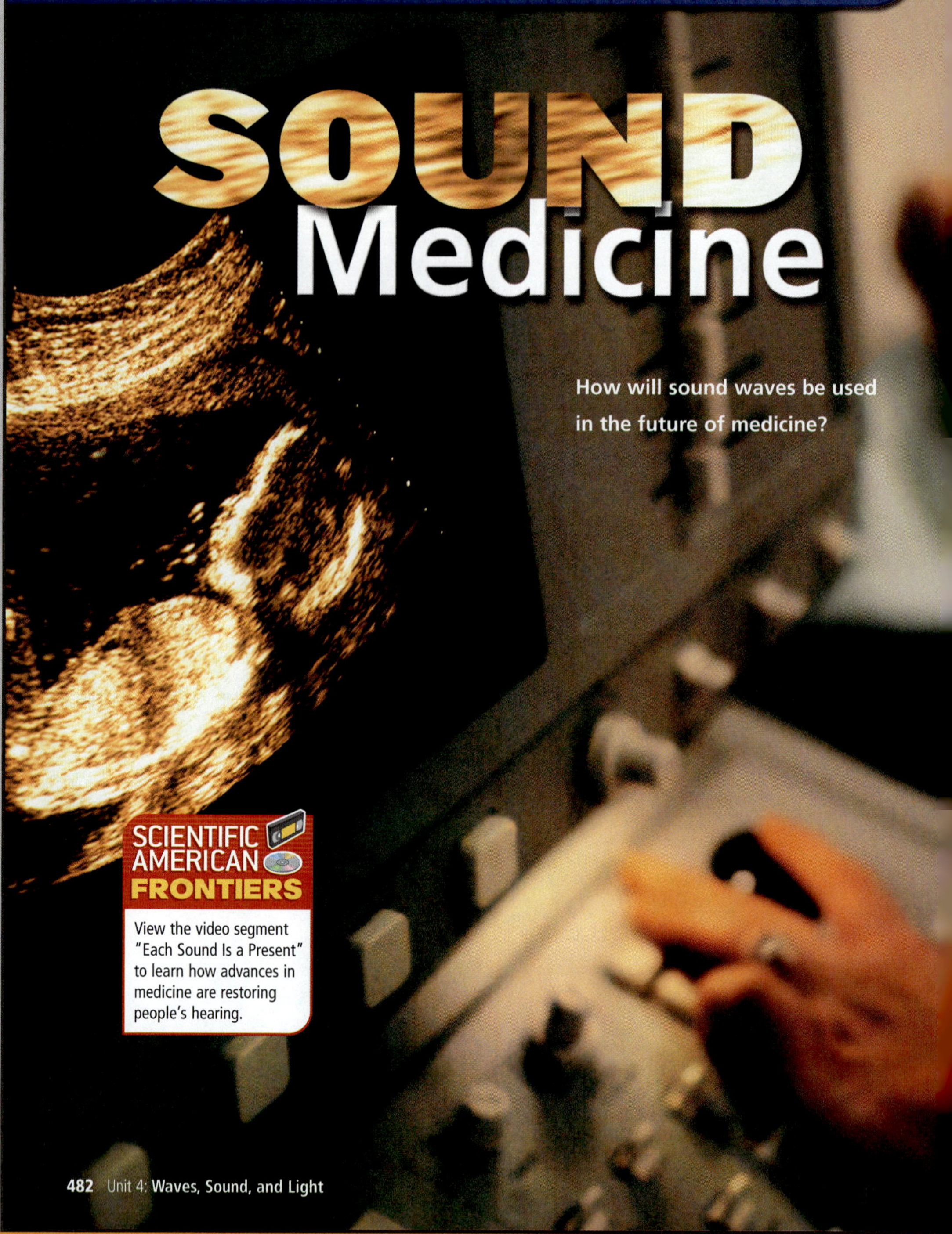

SOUND Medicine

How will sound waves be used in the future of medicine?

SCIENTIFIC AMERICAN FRONTIERS

View the video segment "Each Sound Is a Present" to learn how advances in medicine are restoring people's hearing.

482 Unit 4: Waves, Sound, and Light

ADDITIONAL RESOURCES

Technology Resources

 Scientific American Frontiers Video: *Each Sound Is a Present:* 7-minute video segment introduces the unit.

 ClassZone.com
CAREER LINK, careers in audiology

Guide student viewing and comprehension of the video:

 Frontiers in Science Teaching Guide, pp. 1–2; Viewing Guide, p. 3, Video Wrap-Up, p. 4

Scientific American Frontiers Video Guide, pp. 51–54

Unit project procedures and rubrics:

 Unit Projects, pp. 5–10

482 Unit 4: **Waves, Sound, and Light**

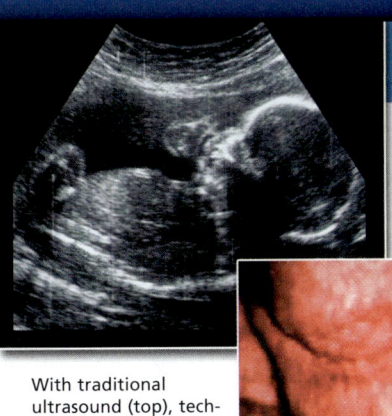

With traditional ultrasound (top), technicians interpret the image of the fetus. With the newer three-dimensional ultrasound (right), the image is much clearer.

Seeing Inside the Body

Have you ever wondered what the inside of your body looks like? Doctors have tried for many years to find ways of seeing what goes on inside a person's body that makes that person sick. Around 100 years ago, scientists found that a kind of wave called x-rays could be used to make images of the bones inside a person. This common method of seeing inside a body, is used mainly to show bones and teeth. However, repeated exposure to x-rays can be damaging to body cells. In the 1960s doctors started using a different kind of wave called ultrasound to make images of the organs inside the body.

Waves are now used in many medical applications. For example, cochlear implants use radio waves to help people hear. Ultrasound now has many new medical applications, from breaking up kidney stones to monitoring the flow of blood in the body.

Sound and Ultrasound

Sound is a type of wave, a vibration in the air. Humans can hear a wide range of different sounds, from very low pitches to very high. Sounds that are higher in pitch than humans can hear are referred to as ultrasound. They are no different from sounds we can hear, except they vibrate much faster than human ears can detect. Many animals can detect ultrasound; for example, dog whistles are in the ultrasound range.

FOCUS

▸ Set Learning Goals

Students will

- Observe practical uses of sound waves in medicine
- Compare technological uses of waves to similar uses in nature
- Design and produce a product that involves uses of waves

Remind students that frontiers are not totally unexplored areas; they are areas that are currently being explored and developed. Use the video segment "Each Sound Is a Present" to show that areas of science can have practical technologies yet still have new developments to come. Have students look at the ultrasound photographs and compare the effectiveness of the results shown.

INSTRUCT

Teach from Visuals

Have students examine the two ultrasound photographs and identify the heads and arms of the fetuses. Ask students if they know anyone who has had ultrasound tests or treatments. Emphasize that ultrasound is used for diagnosis of many diseases and disorders, including the presence and location of certain tumors.

Sharing Results

Ask: Why is it important that developments in medical research be shared among medical personnel? *Such developments are necessary for diagnosis and treatment of many diseases and disorders. The research that must be done is quite expensive and time-consuming, and specialized equipment is necessary. If the results of such research are not shared, the health of many people can be negatively affected.*

DIFFERENTIATE INSTRUCTION

More Reading Support

A What type of wave is used to make images of bones inside a human body? *X-rays*

B Why can't humans hear ultrasound? *Its pitch is too high.*

Advanced Show students a copy of the electromagnetic spectrum. Point out the different types of electromagnetic waves. Ask: Why aren't ultrasound waves listed on the spectrum? *Ultrasound waves are sound waves, not electromagnetic waves.*

Teach from Visuals

Have students look at the figure of the dolphin and the sound waves reflecting off a fish, ask:

- Why do you think the process shown in this figure is called echolocation? *Sample answer: Dolphins use echoes to locate objects.*
- For what purposes other than finding food might a dolphin or bat use echolocation? *Sample answer: locate objects in its path*

Scientific Process

Emphasize to students that observations of wave behavior in nature were the bases for hypotheses regarding practical applications of waves. For example, observations of echolocation led to use of sound waves in ultrasound applications. By observing the results of these applications, further hypotheses can be made and conclusions can be drawn.

Asking a Question

Ask: In developing the technology that is used to help Kelley Flynn hear better, what questions might researchers have asked? *Sample answers: What part of the ear was damaged? What technology can duplicate the function of the damaged part of the ear?*

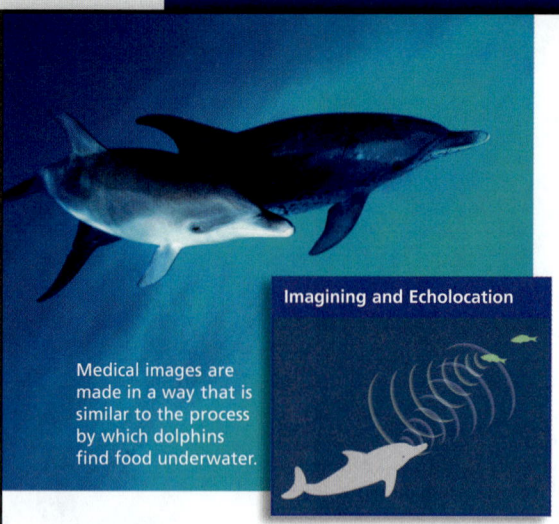

Imagining and Echolocation

Medical images are made in a way that is similar to the process by which dolphins find food underwater.

 C The technology of ultrasound in medicine is based upon a process similar to that used by bats and dolphins to find food, a process called echolocation. The animal emits an ultrasound click or chirp and then listens for an echo. The echo indicates that an object has reflected the sound back to the animal. Over time, these animals have evolved the ability to judge the distance of the object by noting the time required for the sound to travel to the object and return. Echolocation enables bats to capture flying insects at night and dolphins to catch fish in the ocean depths, where light doesn't penetrate.

Similarly, in ultrasound imaging, a machine sends a beam of ultrasound into a person's body and detects any echoes. The waves reflect whenever they strike a boundary between two objects with different densities. A computer measures the time required for the wave to travel to the boundary and reflect back; this information is used to determine the location and shape of the organ. The computer can then generate a live image of the organ inside the body.

Ultrasound imaging has been used most often to monitor the development of a fetus inside its mother and to observe the valves of the heart. Blood flow can be color coded with faster flow in one color and slower flow in another color. The colors make it easier to see the location of blockages affecting the rate of flow in the blood vessels. This helps doctors detect blockages and diagnose heart problems.

View the "Each Sound Is a Present" segment of your *Scientific American Frontiers* video to learn how a cochlear implant restores hearing to a young girl.

IN THIS SCENE FROM THE VIDEO
A young girl's cochlear implant is turned on for the first time.

HEARING IS A GIFT A recent development in technology is about to give seven-year-old Kelley Flynn something she has always wanted—better hearing. Kelley has been almost completely deaf since she was two years old, and now she is losing the little hearing she does have. The development is a device called a cochlear implant. Cochlear implants work inside the ear, stimulating the brain when a sound is detected.

Normally, sound travels as vibrations from the outer ear, through the middle ear to the inner ear, where thousands of tiny cells—called hair cells—register the quality of the sound and send a signal to the brain. In a cochlear implant, tiny electrical sensors, or electrodes, mimic the hair cells by registering the sound and sending a signal to the brain. The signals get to the electrodes through a system including a computer, microphone, and radio transmitter and receiver. Using this system, people with little or no hearing are able to sense sounds.

484 Unit 4: Waves, Sound, and Light

DIFFERENTIATE INSTRUCTION

 More Reading Support

C By what process do dolphins and bats locate food? *echolocation*

D What are two common medical uses of ultrasound? *studying a fetus and the heart*

Below Level Have each student write a short story about a bat on its nightly hunt for food. Stories should include how the bat uses echolocation to find food.

484 Unit 4: **Waves, Sound, and Light**

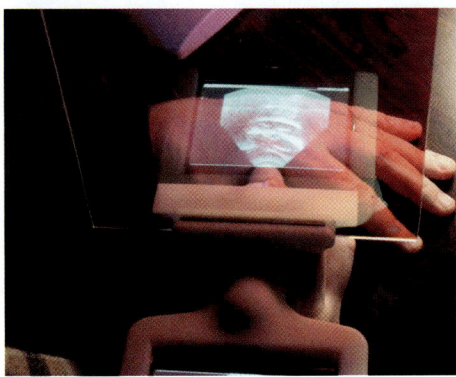

Recent advances in ultrasound technology include the development of portable devices that display images of the body, such as this hand-held device.

Advances in Ultrasound

Waves, including ultrasound, transfer energy. Physical therapists often use this fact when applying ultrasound to sore joints, heating the muscles and ligaments so they can move more freely. If the ultrasound waves are given stronger intensity and sharper focus, they can transfer enough energy to break up kidney stones in the body. The use of focused sound waves is now being tested for its ability to treat other problems, such as foot injuries.

Other recent advances in medical ultrasound include the development of devices that produce clearer images and use equipment that is smaller in size. In the late 1990's portable ultrasound devices were developed that allow the technology to be brought to the patient.

UNANSWERED Questions

As scientists learn more about the use of sound and other types of waves, new questions will arise.

- Will new methods of imaging the body change the way diseases are diagnosed?
- How closely do sounds heard using a cochlear implant resemble sounds heard by the ear?

UNIT PROJECTS

As you study this unit, work alone or with a group on one of these projects.

Magazine Article

Write a magazine article about the medical uses of ultrasound.

- Collect information about medical ultrasound and take notes about applications that interest you.
- If possible, conduct an interview with a medical practitioner who uses ultrasound.
- Read over all your notes and decide what information to include in your article.

Make a Music Video

Make a music video for a song of your choice, and explain how the video uses sound waves and light waves.

- Plan the sound portion of the video, including how the music will be played and amplified.
- For the lighting, use colored cellophane or gels to mix different colors of light. Explain your choices.
- Rehearse the video. Record the video and present it to the class.

Design a Demonstration

Design a hands-on demonstration of echolocation.

- Research the use of echolocation by animals.
- Design a demonstration of echolocation using a tennis ball and an obstacle.
- Present your demonstration to the class.

 CAREER CENTER
CLASSZONE.COM

Learn more about careers in audiology.

Frontiers in Science 485

DIFFERENTIATE INSTRUCTION

More Reading Support

E Why can ultrasound be used to break kidney stones? *It transfers energy.*

F What are two recent advances in ultrasound? *clearer images and smaller equipment*

Differentiate Unit Projects Projects are appropriate for varying abilities. Allow students to choose the ones that interest them most. Encourage them to vary the products they produce throughout the year. Encourage below-level students to try "Design a Demonstration." Challenge advanced students to complete the "Magazine Article."

? UNANSWERED Questions

Have students read the questions and think of some of their own. Remind them that scientists always end up with more questions—that inquiry is the driving force of science.

- With the class, generate on the board a list of new questions.
- Students can add to the list after they watch the *Scientific American Frontiers* Video.
- Students can use the list as a springboard for choosing their Unit Projects.

UNIT PROJECTS

Encourage students to pick the project that most appeals to them. Point out that each is long-term and will take several weeks to complete. You might group or pair students to work on projects and in some cases guide student choice.

Each project has two worksheet pages, including a rubric. Use the pages to guide students through criteria, process, and schedule.

R Unit Projects, pp. 5–10

Technology Resources

Visit **ClassZone.com** for project procedures and for science career direction.

RESOURCE CENTER, Unit Projects

REVISIT concepts introduced in this article:

Chapter 15
- Properties of waves, pp. 496–503

Chapter 16
- Sound is a wave, pp. 517–523
- Uses of sound, pp. 538–543

Chapter 17
- Uses of electromagnetic waves, pp. 559–566

CHAPTER 15 Waves

Physical Science
UNIFYING PRINCIPLES

PRINCIPLE 1
Matter is made of particles too small to see.

PRINCIPLE 2
Matter changes form and moves from place to place.

PRINCIPLE 3
Energy changes from one form to another, but it cannot be created or destroyed.

PRINCIPLE 4
Physical forces affect the movement of all matter on Earth and throughout the universe.

Unit 4: Waves, Sound, and Light
BIG IDEAS

**CHAPTER 15
Waves**
Waves transfer energy and interact in predictable ways.

**CHAPTER 16
Sound**
Sound waves transfer energy through vibrations.

**CHAPTER 17
Electromagnetic Waves**
Electromagnetic waves transfer energy through radiation.

**CHAPTER 18
Light and Optics**
Optical tools depend on the wave behavior of light.

CHAPTER 15 KEY CONCEPTS

SECTION 1
Waves transfer energy.
1. A wave is a disturbance.
2. Waves can be classified by how they move.

SECTION 2
Waves have measurable properties.
1. Waves have amplitude, wavelength, and frequency.
2. Wave speed can be measured.

SECTION 3
Waves behave in predictable ways.
1. Waves interact with materials.
2. Waves interact with other waves.

The Big Idea Flow Chart is available on p. T1 in the **UNIT TRANSPARENCY BOOK**.

485A   Unit 4: **Waves, Sound, and Light**

Previewing Content

SECTION

 Waves transfer energy. pp. 489–495

1. A wave is a disturbance.
A **wave** is a disturbance that transfers energy from one place to another. **Mechanical waves** travel through a material, called a **medium,** transferring energy.
When a mechanical wave travels through a medium, such as water, ground, or air, the medium moves as the wave passes through it, but is not permanently moved. After the wave has passed, the medium returns to its former state.

2. Waves can be classified by how they move.
A **transverse wave** travels in the direction perpendicular to the disturbance that caused it. If you thrust your fist into a tub of water, waves travel out from the disturbance along the water's surface. These waves move at right angles to the downward force of your fist.
A **longitudinal wave** travels in the same direction as the disturbance that caused it. If you lay a spring toy on its side and push sharply on one end, waves will travel through the coils along the length of the spring toy. In this example, the disturbance—the push of your hand—is in the same direction in which the wave moves down the spring toy.

SECTION

 Waves have measurable properties. pp. 496–503

1. Waves have amplitude, wavelength, and frequency.
A wave has repeating **crests** and **troughs,** which alternate in a wave. **Amplitude** is either how high a wave peaks above level (at its crests) or how low it dips below level (at its troughs).
Wavelength is the distance from trough to trough or crest to crest. Wavelength can be measured from any part of one wave to the corresponding part on the next wave.
In a longitudinal wave such as in a spring toy, wavelength is the distance between compressions or rarefactions. Rarefactions are the spaces between compressions where the medium is spread out. Amplitude describes how tightly bunched the spring coils are in the wave.
Frequency is the number of wavelengths that pass a fixed point in a period of time—usually one second.
The graph below shows how wavelength, amplitude, and frequency are measured on a wave.

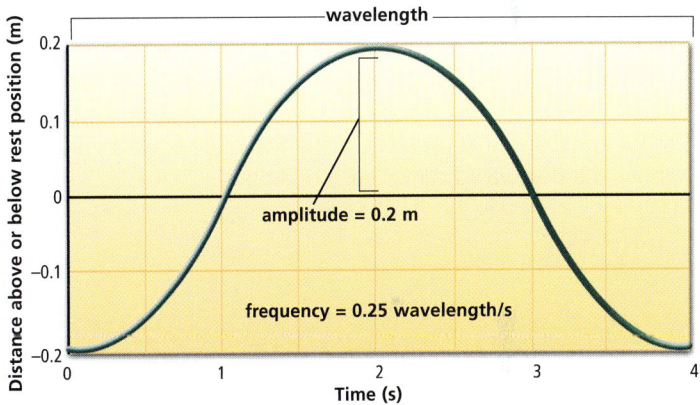

2. Wave speed can be measured.
The formula for calculating the speed of a wave is
$$S = \lambda \cdot f,$$
where S is speed, λ (lambda) is wavelength, and f is frequency.

Common Misconceptions

DISPLACEMENT OF MATTER Students may conceive of waves as the motion of matter from one place to another. Although matter can move in a wave, it is not permanently displaced. Rather, it is energy that is transferred in a wave.

 This misconception is addressed on p. 492.

MISCONCEPTION DATABASE
CLASSZONE.COM Background on student misconceptions

Chapter 15: **Waves** 485B

Previewing Content

SECTION

 Waves behave in predictable ways.
pp. 504–509

1. **Waves interact with materials.**
   Waves behave predictably when they interact with barriers or other obstacles. Waves can undergo reflection, refraction, or diffraction.
   - In **reflection,** waves meet a solid barrier and bounce back. For example, an echo occurs when a sound wave meets a wall and bounces back to the source of the sound.
   - In **refraction,** waves move from one medium to another and bend, or refract. An example is a glass of water with a straw. Where the straw passes into the water, it looks broken. But the break is an illusion caused by refraction of light waves as they pass from air to water.
   - In **diffraction,** waves interact with a partial barrier and a portion of the waves pass through and spread out. An example is the way sound waves spread around corners.

2. **Waves interact with other waves.**
   In **constructive interference,** two waves combine in phase, so that a crest meets a crest or a trough meets a trough. In **destructive interference,** two waves of the same frequency meet up such that the trough of one wave joins with the crests of the other. If the amplitudes of the two original waves are equal, the two waves cancel each other out.

The following diagrams show how wave amplitudes can be added and subtracted as the waves interfere.

Constructive Interference   **Destructive Interference**

Previewing Labs

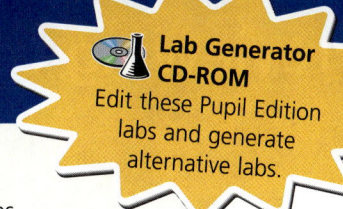

Lab Generator CD-ROM Edit these Pupil Edition labs and generate alternative labs.

EXPLORE the BIG idea

How Can Energy Be Passed Along? p. 487 Students observe a domino effect and learn that energy can be transferred.	**TIME** 10 minutes **MATERIALS** 4 video cassettes
How Can You Change a Wave? p. 487 Students make waves in a bowl and observe wave properties.	**TIME** 10 minutes **MATERIALS** large bowl, half-full of water; pencil
Internet Activity: Waves, p. 487 Students find out how different forces start waves.	**TIME** 20 minutes **MATERIALS** computer with Internet access

SECTION 1

EXPLORE Waves, p. 489 Students use a rope to find out how a wave travels.	**TIME** 5 minutes **MATERIALS** 20 cm ribbon, 2 m rope, chair
INVESTIGATE Wave Types, p. 493 Students observe transverse and longitudinal waves in a spring toy.	**TIME** 10 minutes **MATERIALS** spring toy

SECTION 2

INVESTIGATE Frequency, p. 500 Students vary the length of a pendulum to find out how length affects its frequency.	**TIME** 30 minutes **MATERIALS** 3 metal washers, 60 cm string, 5 cm tape, stopwatch
CHAPTER INVESTIGATION Wavelength, pp. 502–503 Students vary the length of a pendulum to find out how it affects wavelength.	**TIME** 40 minutes **MATERIALS** 1/2 sheet white paper, 16 cm tape, scissors, 80 cm string, meter stick, 40 mL fine sand, graduated cylinder, 2 sheets colored construction paper

SECTION 3

EXPLORE Reflection, p. 504 Students make ripples in water in a pan to find out how waves reflect.	**TIME** 10 minutes **MATERIALS** wide, shallow pan, half-full of water; 3 drops food coloring; pencil
INVESTIGATE Diffraction, p. 506 Students manipulate water waves to go around an obstacle to learn about diffraction.	**TIME** 20 minutes **MATERIALS** wide, shallow pan, half-full of water; 3 drops food coloring; plastic ruler; wooden block; sealable sandwich bag; 1–2 cups sand

R Additional **INVESTIGATION,** Tracking the Path of Light, A, B, & C, pp. 62–70; Teacher Instructions, pp. 284–285

Chapter 15: **Waves** 485D

Previewing Chapter Resources

	INTEGRATED TECHNOLOGY	LABS AND ACTIVITIES

CHAPTER 15
 Waves
	CLASSZONE.COM
	• eEdition Plus
	• EasyPlanner Plus
	• Misconception Database
	• Content Review
	• Test Practice
	• Visualization
	• Simulation
	• Resource Centers
	• Internet Activity: Waves
	• Math Tutorial

	  **CD-ROMS**
	• eEdition
	• EasyPlanner
	• Power Presentations
	• Content Review
	• Lab Generator
	• Test Generator
	
	  AUDIO CDS
	• Audio Readings
	• Audio Readings in Spanish
	
	  SCILINKS.ORG
		EXPLORE the Big Idea, p. 487
		• How Can Energy Be Passed Along?
		• How Can You Change a Wave?
		• Internet Activity: Waves
		
		  UNIT RESOURCE BOOK
		• Family Letter, p. vii
		• Spanish Family Letter, p. viii
		• Unit Projects, pp. 5–10
		
		  Lab Generator CD-ROM
		 Generate customized lab.

SECTION 1
 Waves transfer energy.
 pp. 489–495
 	
 Time: 2 periods (1 block)
  Lesson Plan, pp. 11–12
	• **RESOURCE CENTER,** Waves
	• **MATH TUTORIAL**
	
	  UNIT TRANSPARENCY BOOK
	• Big Idea Flow Chart, p. T1
	• Daily Vocabulary Scaffolding, p. T2
	• Note-Taking Model, p. T3
	• 3-Minute Warm-Up, p. T4
		• EXPLORE Waves, p. 489
		• INVESTIGATE Wave Types, p. 493
		• Math in Science, p. 495
		
		  UNIT RESOURCE BOOK
		• Datasheet, Wave Types, p. 20
		• Math Support, p. 49
		• Math Practice, p. 50

SECTION 2
 Waves have measurable properties.
 pp. 496–503
 	
 Time: 3 periods (1.5 blocks)
  Lesson Plan, pp. 22–23
	• **VISUALIZATION,** Wave Graphing
	• **RESOURCE CENTER,** Wave Speed
	
	 UNIT TRANSPARENCY BOOK
	• Daily Vocabulary Scaffolding, p. T2
	• 3-Minute Warm-Up, p. T4
	• "Graphing a Wave" Visual, p. T6
		• INVESTIGATE Frequency, p. 500
		• CHAPTER INVESTIGATION, Wavelength, pp. 502–503
		
		  UNIT RESOURCE BOOK
		• Datasheet, Frequency, p. 31
		• Math Support & Practice, pp. 51–52
		• CHAPTER INVESTIGATION, Wavelength, A, B, & C, pp. 53–61

SECTION 3
 Waves behave in predictable ways.
 pp. 504–509
 	
 Time: 3 periods (1.5 blocks)
  Lesson Plan, pp. 33–34
	UNIT TRANSPARENCY BOOK
	• Big Idea Flow Chart, p. T1
	• Daily Vocabulary Scaffolding, p. T2
	• 3-Minute Warm-Up, p. T5
	• Chapter Outline, pp. T7–T8
		• EXPLORE Reflection, p. 504
		• INVESTIGATE Diffraction, p. 506
		• Connecting Sciences, p. 509
		
		  UNIT RESOURCE BOOK
		• Datasheet, Diffraction, p. 42
		• Additional INVESTIGATION, Tracking the Path of Light, A, B, & C, pp. 62–70

KEY TO ICONS	CD/CD-ROM	 Teacher Edition	UNIT TRANSPARENCY BOOK	SPANISH ASSESSMENT BOOK
 INTERNET	Pupil Edition	R UNIT RESOURCE BOOK	A UNIT ASSESSMENT BOOK	 SCIENCE TOOLKIT

READING AND REINFORCEMENT | ASSESSMENT | STANDARDS

- Four Square, B22–23
- Combination Notes, C36
- Daily Vocabulary Scaffolding, H1–8

 UNIT RESOURCE BOOK
- Vocabulary Practice, pp. 46–47
- Decoding Support, p. 48
- Summarizing the Chapter, pp. 71–72

Audio Readings CD
Listen to Pupil Edition.

Audio Readings in Spanish CD
Listen to Pupil Edition in Spanish.

- Chapter Review, pp. 511–512
- Standardized Test Practice, p. 513

UNIT ASSESSMENT BOOK
- Diagnostic Test, pp. 1–2
- Chapter Test, A, B, & C, pp. 6–17
- Alternative Assessment, pp. 18–19

Spanish Chapter Test, pp. 281–284

Test Generator CD-ROM
Generate customized tests.

Lab Generator CD-ROM
Rubrics for Labs

National Standards
A.2–8, A.9.a–c, A.9.e–f, B.3.a, G.1.b

See p. 486 for the standards.

 UNIT RESOURCE BOOK
- Reading Study Guide, A & B, pp. 13–16
- Spanish Reading Study Guide, pp. 17–18
- Challenge and Extension, p. 19
- Reinforcing Key Concepts, p. 21
- Challenge Reading, pp. 44–45

 Ongoing Assessment, pp. 489–494

 Section 15.1 Review, p. 494

UNIT ASSESSMENT BOOK
Section 15.1 Quiz, p. 3

National Standards
A.2–8, A.9.a–c, A.9.e–f, B.3.a, G.1.b

 UNIT RESOURCE BOOK
- Reading Study Guide, A & B, pp. 24–27
- Spanish Reading Study Guide, pp. 28–29
- Challenge and Extension, p. 30
- Reinforcing Key Concepts, p. 32

 Ongoing Assessment, pp. 496–501

 Section 15.2 Review, p. 501

 UNIT ASSESSMENT BOOK
Section 15.2 Quiz, p. 4

National Standards
A.2–8, A.9.a–c, A.9.e–f, G.1.b

 UNIT RESOURCE BOOK
- Reading Study Guide, A & B, pp. 35–38
- Spanish Reading Study Guide, pp. 39–40
- Challenge and Extension, p. 41
- Reinforcing Key Concepts, p. 43

 Ongoing Assessment, pp. 504–505, 507–508

 Section 15.3 Review, p. 508

 UNIT ASSESSMENT BOOK
Section 15.3 Quiz, p. 5

National Standards
A.2–8, A.9.a–c, A.9.e–f, G.1.b

Previewing Resources for Differentiated Instruction

CHAPTER INVESTIGATION

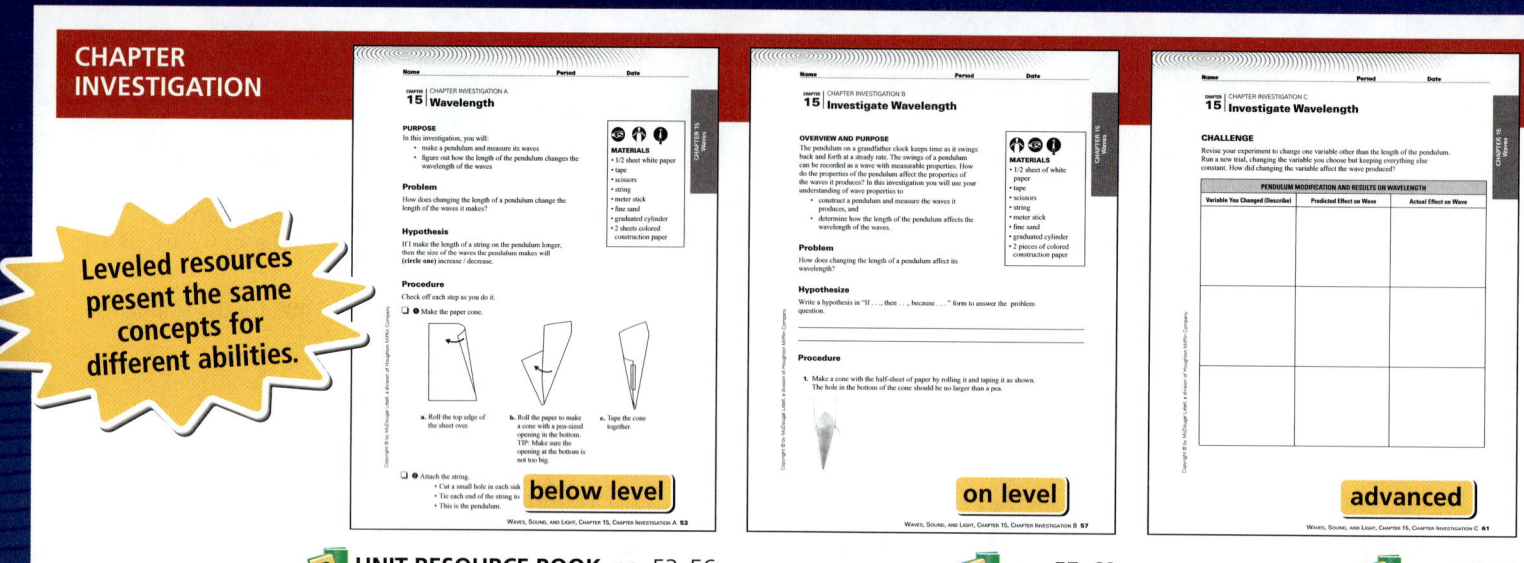

Leveled resources present the same concepts for different abilities.

UNIT RESOURCE BOOK, pp. 53–56 | pp. 57–60 | pp. 57–61

READING STUDY GUIDE

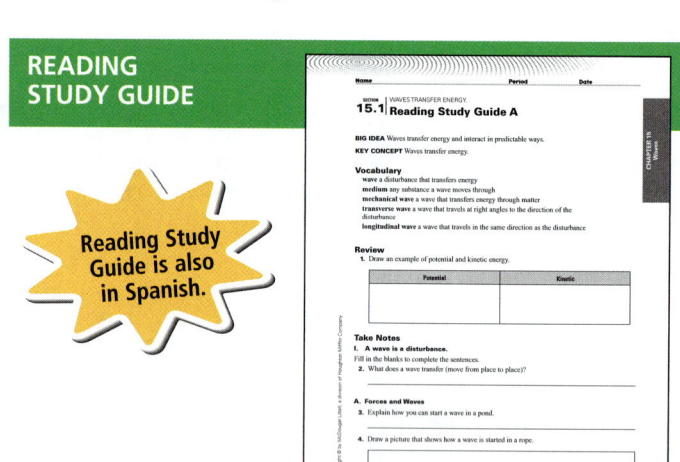
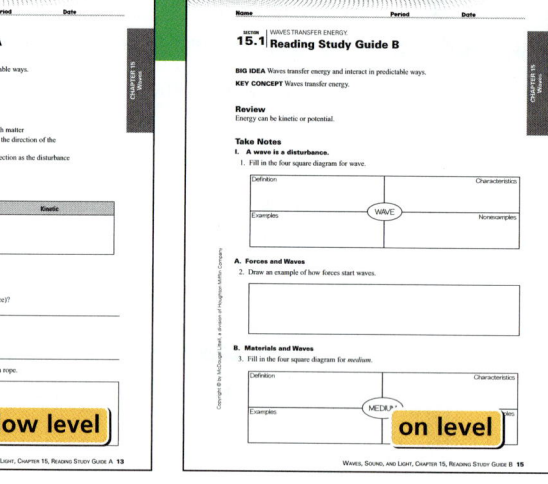
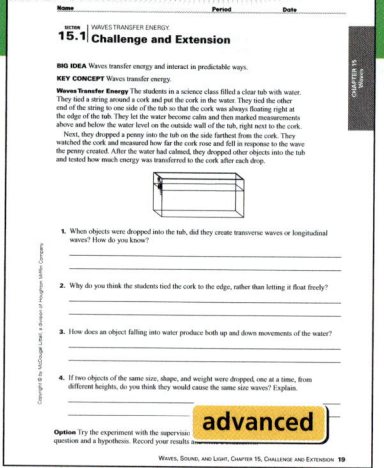

Reading Study Guide is also in Spanish.

UNIT RESOURCE BOOK, pp. 13–14 | pp. 15–16 | p. 19

CHAPTER TEST

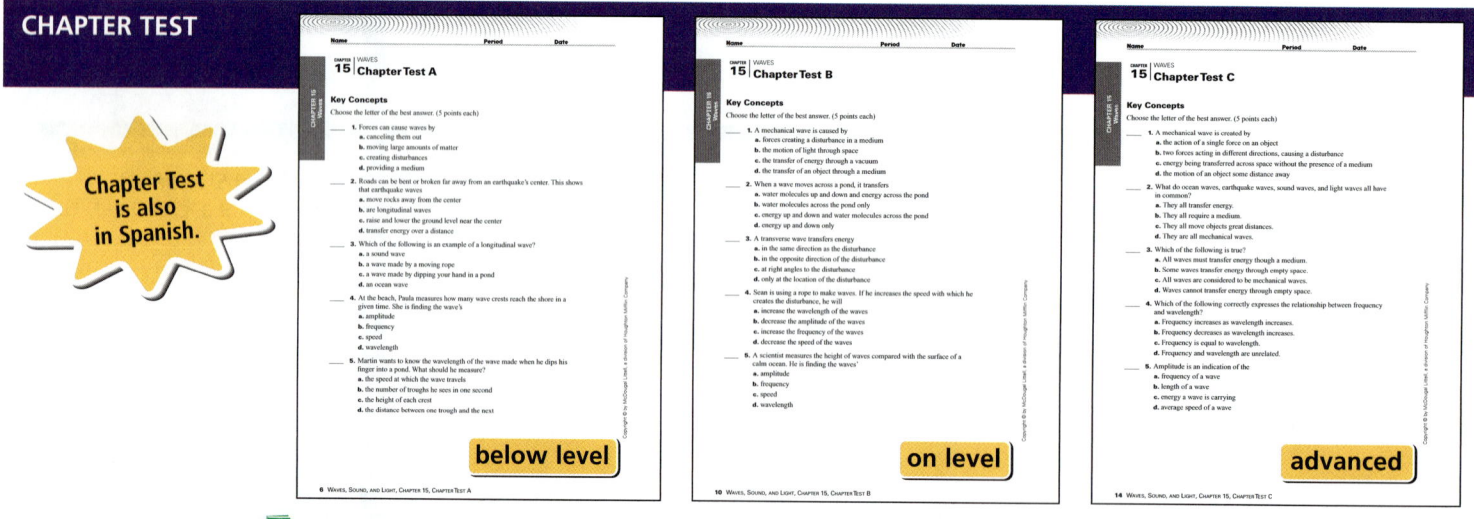

Chapter Test is also in Spanish.

UNIT ASSESSMENT BOOK, pp. 6–9 | pp. 10–13 | pp. 14–17

485G Unit 4: Waves, Sound, and Light

TECHNOLOGY

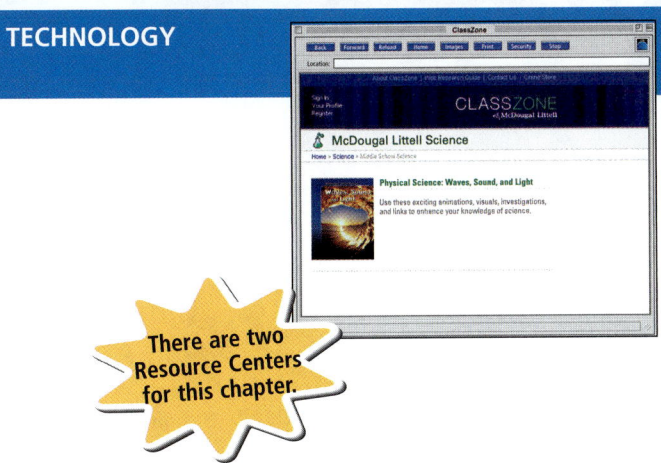

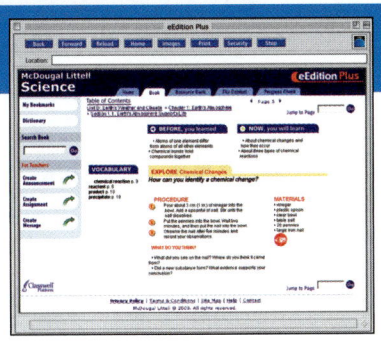

There are two Resource Centers for this chapter.

 CLASSZONE.COM    CD/CD-ROMS    CLASSZONE.COM

VISUAL CONTENT

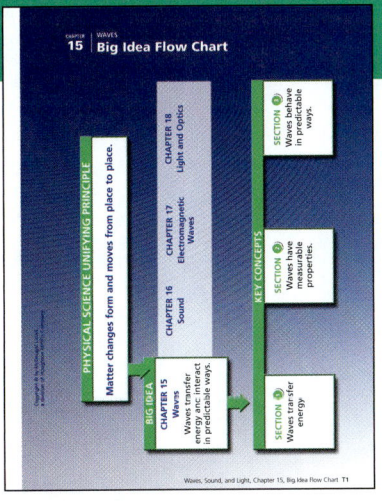
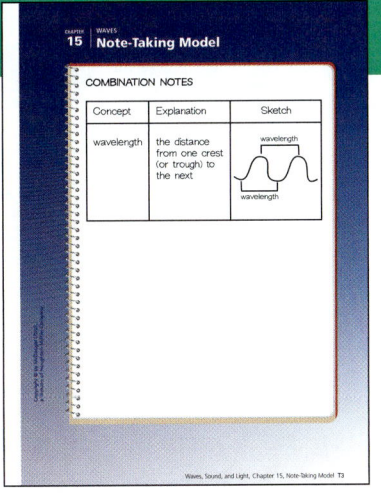
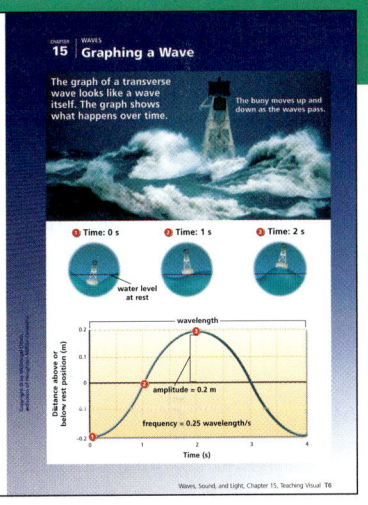

UNIT TRANSPARENCY BOOK, p. T1   p. T3   p. T6

MORE SUPPORT

Reinforcing Key Concepts for each section

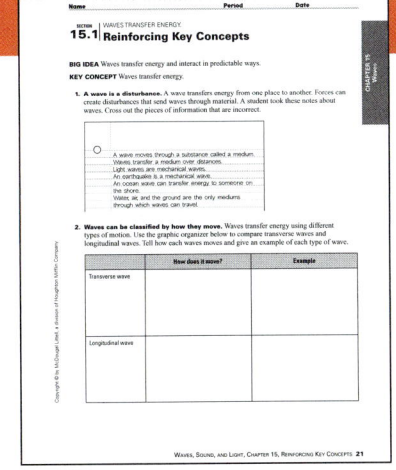
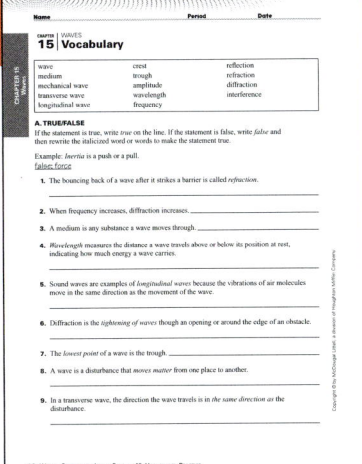
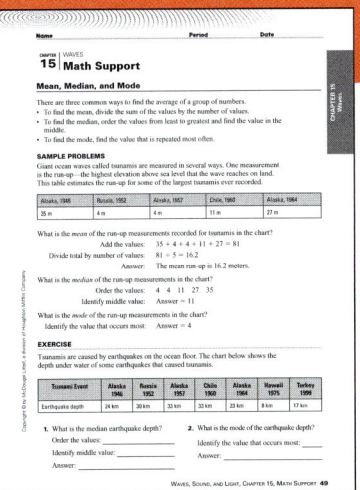

UNIT RESOURCE BOOK, p. 21   pp. 46–47   p. 49

Chapter 15: **Waves** 485H

CHAPTER 15 Waves

INTRODUCE
the BIG idea

Have students look at the photograph of the surfers riding the waves and discuss how the question in the box links to the Big Idea:

- What clues can you find that the wave carries energy?
- What parts of the wave can you see?
- What other kinds of waves can you think of?
- How do waves move from one place to another?

National Science Education Standards

Content

B.3.a Energy is a property of many substances and is associated with heat, light, electricity, mechanical motion, sound, nuclei, and the nature of a chemical. Energy is transferred in many ways.

Process

A.2–8 Design and conduct an investigation; use tools to gather and interpret data; use evidence to describe, predict, explain, model; think critically to make relationships between evidence and explanation; recognize different explanations and predictions; communicate scientific procedures and explanations; use mathematics.

A.9.a, A.9.c, A.9.e Understand scientific inquiry by using different investigations, methods, mathematics, and explanations based on logic, evidence, and skepticism.

G.1.b Science requires different abilities.

CHAPTER 15 Waves

the BIG idea

Waves transfer energy and interact in predictable ways.

What is moving these surfers?

Key Concepts

SECTION 1 — Waves transfer energy.
Learn about forces and energy in wave motion.

SECTION 2 — Waves have measurable properties.
Learn how the amplitude, wavelength, and frequency of a wave are measured.

SECTION 3 — Waves behave in predictable ways.
Learn about reflection, refraction, diffraction, and interference.

Internet Preview

CLASSZONE.COM
Chapter 15 online resources: Content Review, Simulation, Visualization, two Resource Centers, Math Tutorial, Test Practice

486 Unit 4: Waves, Sound, and Light

INTERNET PREVIEW

CLASSZONE.COM For student use with the following pages:

Review and Practice
- Content Review, pp. 488, 510
- Math Tutorial: Finding the Mean, Median, and Mode, p. 495
- Test Practice, p. 513

Activities and Resources
- Internet Activity: Waves, p. 487
- Resource Centers: Waves, p. 494; Wave Speed, p. 501
- Visualization: Wave Graphing, p. 498

Seismic Waves **Code: MDL027**

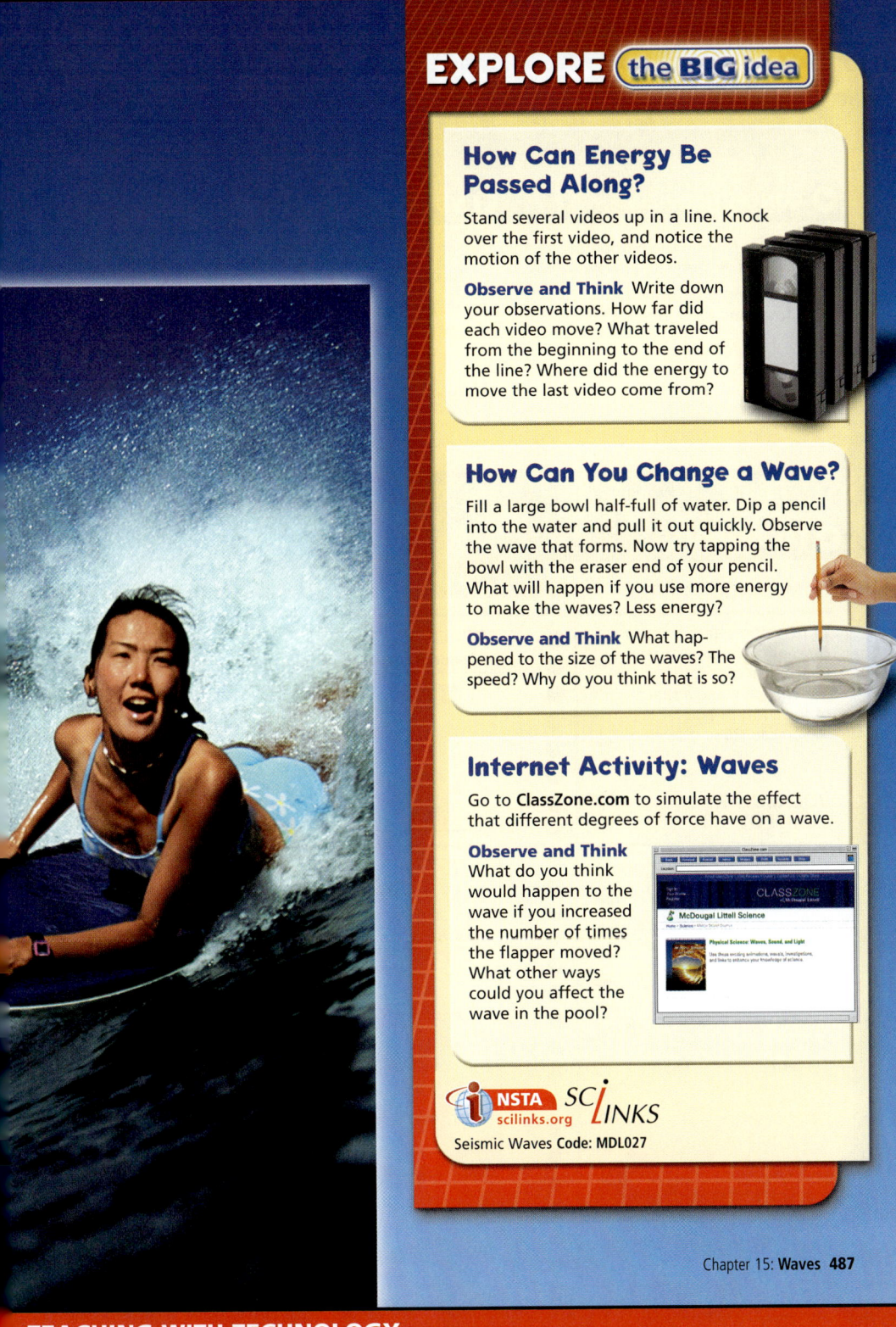

EXPLORE the BIG idea

How Can Energy Be Passed Along?

Stand several videos up in a line. Knock over the first video, and notice the motion of the other videos.

Observe and Think Write down your observations. How far did each video move? What traveled from the beginning to the end of the line? Where did the energy to move the last video come from?

How Can You Change a Wave?

Fill a large bowl half-full of water. Dip a pencil into the water and pull it out quickly. Observe the wave that forms. Now try tapping the bowl with the eraser end of your pencil. What will happen if you use more energy to make the waves? Less energy?

Observe and Think What happened to the size of the waves? The speed? Why do you think that is so?

Internet Activity: Waves

Go to **ClassZone.com** to simulate the effect that different degrees of force have on a wave.

Observe and Think What do you think would happen to the wave if you increased the number of times the flapper moved? What other ways could you affect the wave in the pool?

NSTA SCLINKS
scilinks.org
Seismic Waves Code: MDL027

Chapter 15: Waves 487

EXPLORE the BIG idea

These inquiry-based activities are appropriate for use at home or as a supplement to classroom instruction.

How Can Energy Be Passed Along?

PURPOSE To introduce students to the idea that energy can be transferred. Students set up a row of video cassettes, push the first one, and observe as the whole row falls over.

TIP *10 min.* Students may use dominoes as an alternative to the video cassettes.

Answer: each video moved only to the next video; energy traveled from the beginning to the end of the line; the original source of energy could be the push, the first cassette falling, or the next to last cassette falling

REVISIT after p. 492.

How Can You Change a Wave?

PURPOSE To introduce students to wave properties such as amplitude and speed. Students generate and observe waves in a bowl.

TIP *10 min.* Only a small motion of the pencil is needed.

Answer: More energy produced larger waves; less energy produced smaller waves. The speed of the waves remained the same. Energy affects size of waves, but some other factor must affect speed of waves.

REVISIT after p. 501.

Internet Activity: Waves

PURPOSE To show how forces are involved in waves.

TIP *20 min.* Students observe waves produced by varying forces.

Answer: The waves would be produced at a higher rate if you increased the number of times the flapper moved. You could also affect the wave by moving the flapper slowly, or changing the amount of force applied by the flapper.

REVISIT after p. 490.

Chapter 15 487

TEACHING WITH TECHNOLOGY

Computer Software and Overhead Projector Use a computer-generated wave to illustrate the form and motion of a transverse wave on p. 493. Help students identify crest, trough, amplitude, frequency, and wavelength in the wave.

Graphing Calculator Use a graphing calculator on p. 498 to graph sine and cosine functions. Graph $y = \sin x$ and $y = \cos x$, then point out to students that the graphs form a shape of a wave. Challenge students to alter the equations and report their findings. Ask them how the amplitude and wavelength vary.

PREPARE

◀ CONCEPT REVIEW

Activate Prior Knowledge

Put two marbles on a flat surface. Flick one marble so that it strikes the other one. The first marble must move forcefully enough to move the second marble as well.

- Ask: How did force change the motion of the first marble? *The first marble went from rest to motion.*
- Ask: How was energy transferred to the second marble? *Energy was transferred from the first marble to the second marble when they hit.*

▶ TAKING NOTES

Combination Notes

Combining pictures with notes will help students connect abstract concepts with concrete examples. The three-column format allows students to write their notes in the first and second columns and draw their pictures in the third column.

Vocabulary Strategy

The four square diagram helps students organize complex information in a user-friendly, visual way. The format also prompts students to process more information for a concept than they might otherwise do.

Vocabulary and Note-Taking Resources

- Vocabulary Practice, pp. 46–47
- Decoding Support, p. 48

- Daily Vocabulary Scaffolding, p. T2
- Note-Taking Model, p. T3

- Four Square, B22–23
- Combination Notes, C36
- Daily Vocabulary Scaffolding, H1–8

488 Unit 4: **Waves, Sound, and Light**

CHAPTER 15
Getting Ready to Learn

◀ CONCEPT REVIEW
- Forces change the motion of objects in predictable ways.
- Energy can be transferred from one place to another.

◀ VOCABULARY REVIEW
See Glossary for definitions.
force
kinetic energy
potential energy

CONTENT REVIEW
CLASSZONE.COM
Review concepts and vocabulary.

▶ TAKING NOTES

COMBINATION NOTES

To take notes about a new concept, write an explanation of the concept in a table. Then make a sketch of the concept and label it so you can study it later.

VOCABULARY STRATEGY

Write each new vocabulary term in the center of a **four square** diagram. Write notes in the squares around each term. Include a definition, some characteristics, and some examples of the term. If possible, write some things that are not examples of the term.

See the Note-Taking Handbook on pages R45–R51.

SCIENCE NOTEBOOK

Concept	Explanation	Sketch
Forces and waves	Forces move a medium up and down or back and forth. A wave moves forward.	(direction of force; direction of wave)

Definition	Characteristics
A disturbance that transfers energy from one place to another	Matter moves in place. Energy travels entire distance.

WAVE

Examples	Nonexamples
Water wave Sound wave	Ball rolling Water rushing downstream

488 Unit 4: Waves, Sound, and Light

CHECK READINESS

Administer the Diagnostic Test to determine students' readiness for new science content and their mastery of requisite math skills.

 Diagnostic Test, pp. 1–2

Technology Resources

Students needing content and math skills should visit **ClassZone.com**.

- **CONTENT REVIEW**
- **MATH TUTORIAL**

 CONTENT REVIEW CD-ROM

KEY CONCEPT
Waves transfer energy.

◁ BEFORE, you learned
- Forces can change an object's motion
- Energy can be kinetic or potential

▷ NOW, you will learn
- How forces cause waves
- How waves transfer energy
- How waves are classified

VOCABULARY
wave p. 489
medium p. 491
mechanical wave p. 491
transverse wave p. 493
longitudinal wave p. 494

EXPLORE Waves

How will the rope move?

PROCEDURE
1. Tie a ribbon in the middle of a rope. Then tie one end of the rope to a chair.
2. Holding the loose end of the rope in your hand, stand far enough away from the chair that the rope is fairly straight.
3. Flick the rope by moving your hand up and down quickly. Observe what happens.

WHAT DO YOU THINK?
- How did the rope move? How did the ribbon move?
- What do you think starts a wave, and what keeps it going?

MATERIALS
- ribbon
- rope
- chair

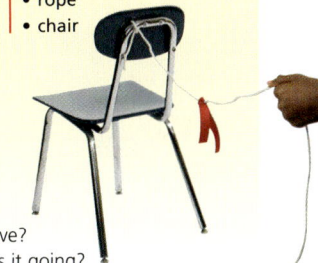

A wave is a disturbance.

You experience the effects of waves every day. Every sound you hear depends on sound waves. Every sight you see depends on light waves. A tiny wave can travel across the water in a glass, and a huge wave can travel across the ocean. Sound waves, light waves, and water waves seem very different from one another. So what, exactly, is a wave?

READING TiP
To *disturb* means to agitate or unsettle.

A **wave** is a disturbance that transfers energy from one place to another. Waves can transfer energy over distance without moving matter the entire distance. For example, an ocean wave can travel many kilometers without the water itself moving many kilometers. The water moves up and down—a motion known as a disturbance. It is the disturbance that travels in a wave, transferring energy.

 How does an ocean wave transfer energy across the ocean?

Chapter 15: **Waves** 489

RESOURCES FOR DIFFERENTIATED INSTRUCTION

Below Level
UNIT RESOURCE BOOK
- Reading Study Guide A, pp. 13–14
- Decoding Support, p. 48

🔵 **AUDIO CDS**

Advanced
UNIT RESOURCE BOOK
- Challenge and Extension, p. 19
- Challenge Reading, pp. 44–45

English Learners
UNIT RESOURCE BOOK
Spanish Reading Study Guide, pp. 17–18

🔵 **AUDIO CDS**
- Audio Readings in Spanish
- Audio Readings (English)

15.1 FOCUS

▸ Set Learning Goals
Students will
- Explain how forces cause waves.
- Explain how waves transfer energy.
- Classify wave types.
- Compare and contrast different wave types in an experiment.

◂ 3-Minute Warm-Up
Display Transparency 4 or copy this exercise on the board:

1. Name two ways you can apply force to a soccer ball. *kicking with feet and hitting with hands*

2. Name two ways the force you apply can change the motion of the soccer ball. *The force changes the ball's speed and direction*

T 3-Minute Warm-Up, p. T4

15.1 MOTIVATE

EXPLORE Waves
PURPOSE To think of how wave motion starts and how a wave moves through a medium

TIP *5 min.* Jump ropes work well.

WHAT DO YOU THINK? *A wave moved through the rope; the ribbon moved up and down. Forces start a wave and keep it going through the material.*

Ongoing Assessment

 *Answer: through a moving disturbance, which we see as a moving wave*

Chapter 15 489

15.1 INSTRUCT

Teach from Visuals

To help students interpret the rope wave visual, ask:

- What represents the forces? *the up and down arrows*
- What produces the forces? *the person's hand and arm moving up and down*
- What is the result of the force? *a wave traveling down the rope*

Ask similar questions for the other visuals on the page.

Real World Example

A telephone cord wave can occur when you stretch out the cord and shake one end of the cord. The wave moves along the cord and reaches the handset.

EXPLORE the BIG idea

Revisit "Internet Activity: Waves" on p. 487. Have students explain the reasons for their results.

Ongoing Assessment

Explain how forces cause waves.

When a diver hits the smooth surface of water in a swimming pool, series of waves spread in all directions. Ask: How do forces make this happen? *The force of the diver striking the surface pushes water briefly out of the way; then the water rushes back in. These movements in the water set off the series of ripples, or waves, across the pool.*

490 Unit 4: Waves, Sound, and Light

Forces and Waves

READING TIP
As you read each example, think of how it is similar to and different from the other examples.

You know that a force is required to change the motion of an object. Forces can also start a disturbance, sending a wave through a material. The following examples describe how forces cause waves.

Example 1 Rope Wave Think of a rope that is tied to a doorknob. You apply one force to the rope by flicking it upward and an opposite force when you snap it back down. This sends a wave through the rope. Both forces—the one that moves the rope up and the one that moves the rope down—are required to start a wave.

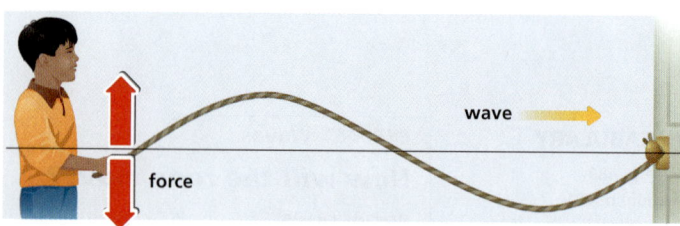

Example 2 Water Wave Forces are also required to start a wave in water. Think of a calm pool of water. What happens if you apply a force to the water by dipping your finger into it? The water rushes back after you remove your finger. The force of your finger and the force of the water rushing back send waves across the pool.

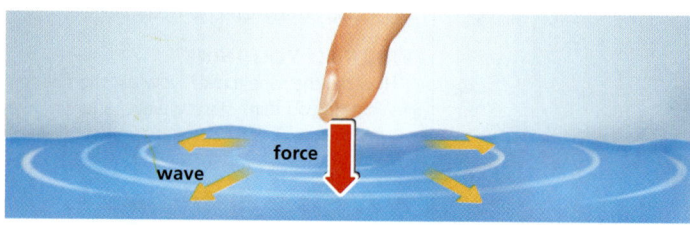

Example 3 Earthquake Wave An earthquake is a sudden release of energy that has built up in rock as a result of the surrounding rock pushing and pulling on it. When these two forces cause the rock to suddenly break away and move, the energy is transferred as a wave through the ground.

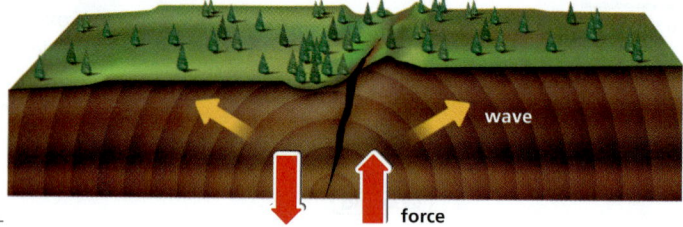

490 Unit 4: Waves, Sound, and Light

DIFFERENTIATE INSTRUCTION

 More Reading Support

A What is required to make a disturbance that will set off a wave? *forces*

English Learners English learners may not always understand certain abbreviated instructions. For example, when a student is asked to "study a sketch," the word *study* is vague to an English learner. Use precise instructions like *examine*, *analyze*, or *compare*, and make sure students know the exact meaning of these instructions.

Materials and Waves

A rope tied to a doorknob, water, and the ground all have something in common. They are all materials through which waves move. A **medium** is any substance that a wave moves through. Water is the medium for an ocean wave; the ground is the medium for an earthquake wave; the rope is the medium for the rope wave. In the next chapter, you will learn that sound waves can move through many mediums, including air.

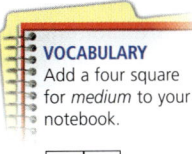

VOCABULARY
Add a four square for *medium* to your notebook.

Waves that transfer energy through matter are known as **mechanical waves.** All of the waves you have read about so far, even sound waves, are mechanical waves. Water, the ground, a rope, and the air are all made up of matter. Later, you will learn about waves that can transfer energy through empty space. Light is an example of a wave that transfers energy through empty space.

 How are all mechanical waves similar?

Energy and Waves

The waves caused by an earthquake are good examples of energy transfer. The disturbed ground shakes from side to side and up and down as the waves move through it. Such waves can travel kilometers away from their source. The ground does not travel kilometers away from where it began; it is the energy that travels in a wave. In the case of an earthquake, it is kinetic energy, or the energy of motion, that is transferred.

This photograph was taken after a 1995 earthquake in Japan. A seismic wave transferred enough energy through the ground to bend the railroad tracks, leaving them in the shape of a wave.

Develop Critical Thinking

CLASSIFY Write the following choices on the board:
- air
- water
- rocks and soil

State that these can all be mediums for different kinds of waves. Have students identify the medium for each of the following waves:
- ocean wave *water*
- seismic wave in an earthquake *rocks and soil*
- pulsating sound from a bell *air*

Ongoing Assessment

 Answer: *All mechanical waves transfer energy through matter.*

DIFFERENTIATE INSTRUCTION

More Reading Support
B What is the medium for an ocean wave? *water*
C Does a mechanical wave transfer material or energy? *energy*

Below Level Students may find the term *medium* confusing in the context of wave science. Students are likely to be familiar with *medium* meaning "halfway" or "in between."
Write the following sentences on the board:
- I like my steak medium rare.
- Water is the medium for an ocean wave . . . (p. 491).

Ask: Which of these sentences involves the scientific definition of *medium*? *the second sentence*

Address Misconceptions

IDENTIFY Ask students to imagine a wave in water. Ask: What moves from the beginning to the end of the wave? If students say water (or other matter), they may hold the misconception that matter is transferred in a wave.

CORRECT Have several students stand in a row. Have the first student tap the second on the shoulder, who in turn taps the third student, and so on. Notice that energy is transferred to the end of the row while each student stays in place.

REASSESS Ask: Why don't ocean waves that move toward the shore empty out the ocean? *Because waves transfer energy, not matter.*

Technology Resources
Visit **ClassZone.com** for background on common student misconceptions.

 MISCONCEPTION DATABASE

EXPLORE the BIG idea
Revisit "How Can Energy Be Passed Along?" on p. 487. Have students explain the reasons for their results.

Integrate the Sciences
Although ocean waves do not pile up water onshore, their energy dramatically shapes the coast. Examples of wave erosion on seacoasts include the formation of broad sandy beaches, sand spits and barrier islands, and stacks (rocky columns isolated in the water near the shoreline) or coves in stony coastlines.

Ongoing Assessment

Classify waves by how they move.
Ask: Name three directions waves can move. *up and down, side to side, or forward and backward*

READING VISUALS *Answer: The people move up and down. The wave moves around the stadium.*

CHECK YOUR READING *Answer: In an ocean wave, one part of the water pushes on the next. In the stadium wave, the people do not push on each other. Thus, the stadium wave is not a real wave because the energy is not transferred through a medium.*

492 Unit 4: **Waves, Sound, and Light**

A Wave Model

When these fans do "the wave" in a stadium, they are modeling the way a disturbance travels through a medium.

Each person only moves up and down.

The wave can move all the way around the stadium.

READING VISUALS In which direction do people move when doing the stadium wave? In which direction does the wave move?

Look at the illustration of people modeling a wave in a stadium. In this model, the crowd of people represents a wave medium. The people moving up and down represent the disturbance. The transfer of the disturbance around the stadium represents a wave. Each person only moves up and down, while the disturbance can move all the way around the stadium.

Ocean waves are another good example of energy transfer. Ocean waves travel to the shore, one after another. Instead of piling up all the ocean water on the shore, however, the waves transfer energy. A big ocean wave transfers enough kinetic energy to knock someone down.

CHECK YOUR READING How does the stadium wave differ from a real ocean wave?

Waves can be classified by how they move.

 As you have seen, one way to classify waves is according to the medium through which they travel. Another way to classify waves is by how they move. You have read that some waves transfer an up-and-down or a side-to-side motion. Other waves transfer a forward-and-backward motion.

492 Unit 4: Waves, Sound, and Light

DIFFERENTIATE INSTRUCTION

More Reading Support

D What does an ocean wave transfer? *energy*

E What are two ways to classify waves? *by medium and by how the wave moves*

 **Advanced** Have students who are interested in learning about harnessing the energy of ocean waves read the following article:

 Challenge Reading, pp. 44–45

Transverse Waves

Think again about snapping the rope with your hand. The action of your hand causes a vertical, or up-and-down, disturbance in the rope. However, the wave it sets off is horizontal, or forward. This type of wave is known as a transverse wave. In a **transverse wave,** the direction in which the wave travels is perpendicular, or at right angles, to the direction of the disturbance. *Transverse* means "across" or "crosswise." The wave itself moves crosswise as compared with the vertical motion of the medium.

READING TIP
Perpendicular means at a 90° angle.
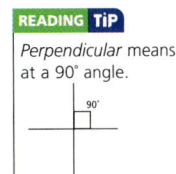

Transverse Wave

direction of disturbance   direction of wave

Water waves are also transverse. The up-and-down motion of the water is the disturbance. The wave travels in a direction that is perpendicular to the direction of the disturbance. The medium is the water, and energy is transferred outward in all directions from the source.

 What is a transverse wave? Find two examples in the paragraphs above.

INVESTIGATE Wave Types

How do waves compare?

PROCEDURE

1. Place the spring toy on the floor on its side. Stretch out the spring. To start a disturbance in the spring, take one end and move it from side to side. Observe the movement in the spring. Remember that a transverse wave travels at right angles to the disturbance.

2. Put the spring toy on the floor in the same position as before. Think about how you could make a different kind of disturbance to produce a different kind of wave. (Hint: Suppose you push the spring in the direction of the wave you expect to make.) Observe the movement in the spring.

WHAT DO YOU THINK?
- Compare the waves you made. How are they alike? How are they different?
- What kind of wave did you produce by moving the spring from side to side?

CHALLENGE Can you think of a third way to make a wave travel through a spring?

SKILL FOCUS Comparing

MATERIALS spring toy

TIME 10 minutes

Chapter 15: **Waves** 493

INVESTIGATE Wave Types

PURPOSE To observe a spring and explore the differences between transverse waves and longitudinal waves

TIPS *10 min.* Suggest the following:
- In step 1, make the shape of the spring toy look like a wavy line.
- In step 2, concentrate on what is happening inside the spring coils instead of the overall shape of the spring toy.

WHAT DO YOU THINK? *Both types travel from one end of the spring to the other. Transverse waves move the spring from side to side; longitudinal waves move the spring forward and backward.*

CHALLENGE *pinching together a bunch of coils and letting them go; moving the spring up and down*

Datasheet, Wave Types, p. 20

Technology Resources

Customize this student lab as needed or look for an alternative. Print rubrics to assess student lab reports.

Lab Generator CD-ROM

Teaching with Technology

Use a computer-generated sine wave to illustrate the form and motion of a transverse wave. Use an overhead projector and ask students to identify the parts and properties of the wave.

Teach Difficult Concepts

Some students may have difficulty with the concept of a right angle in a three-dimensional context. Place a box on a tabletop. Help students identify the right angle between the vertical side of the box and the table surface. Have them think of other familiar examples.

Ongoing Assessment

 *Answer: a wave that moves perpendicular to the direction of the disturbance; water waves and rope waves*

Chapter 15 **493**

DIFFERENTIATE INSTRUCTION

F What does transverse mean? *"across" or "crosswise"*

Inclusion Offer a wave model that is tailored to students with visual impairments. Ask students to imagine they are floating on an inner tube on a lake in which the water's surface is disturbed by waves. Ask how they would move with the waves. *They would bob up and down.* What types of waves are involved in this scenario? How do you know? *transverse; bobbing up and down is disturbance in a direction perpendicular to the direction of the wave.*

Longitudinal Waves

READING TIP
The word *long* can help you remember longitudinal waves. The disturbance moves along the length of the spring.

Another type of wave is a longitudinal wave. In a **longitudinal wave** (LAHN-jih-TOOD-n-uhl), the wave travels in the same direction as the disturbance. A longitudinal wave can be started in a spring by moving it forward and backward. The coils of the spring move forward and bunch up and then move backward and spread out. This forward and backward motion is the disturbance. Longitudinal waves are sometimes called compressional waves because the bunched-up area is known as a compression. How is a longitudinal wave similar to a transverse wave? How is it different?

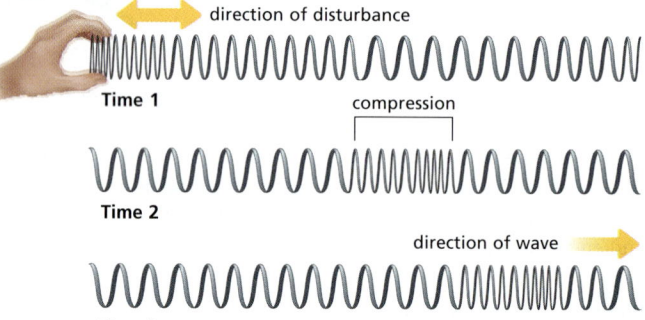

Sound waves are examples of longitudinal waves. Imagine a bell ringing. The clapper inside the bell strikes the side and makes it vibrate, or move back and forth rapidly. The vibrating bell pushes and pulls on nearby air molecules, causing them to move forward and backward. These air molecules, in turn, set more air molecules into motion. A sound wave pushes forward. In sound waves, the vibrations of the air molecules are in the same direction as the movement of the wave.

RESOURCE CENTER
CLASSZONE.COM
Learn more about waves.

15.1 Review

KEY CONCEPTS
1. Describe how forces start waves.
2. Explain how a wave can travel through a medium and yet the medium stays in place. Use the term *energy* in your answer.
3. Describe two ways in which waves travel, and give an example of each.

CRITICAL THINKING
4. **Analyze** Does water moving through a hose qualify as a wave? Explain why or why not.
5. **Classify** Suppose you drop a cookie crumb in your milk. At once, you see ripples spreading across the surface of the milk. What type of waves are these? What is the disturbance?

CHALLENGE
6. **Predict** Suppose you had a rope long enough to extend several blocks down the street. If you were to start a wave in the rope, do you think it would continue all the way to the other end of the street? Explain why or why not.

494 Unit 4: Waves, Sound, and Light

ANSWERS

1. Forces start a disturbance that travels through a medium.
2. Energy travels through the medium, leaving the matter in place.
3. Transverse waves travel at right angles to the disturbance. Longitudinal waves travel in the same direction as the disturbance. Examples are ocean waves and sound waves.
4. No; the water travels from one end to the other end of the hose. In a wave, the disturbance moves, but the medium does not.
5. Transverse waves; the falling crumb
6. A rope wave would probably not continue all the way down the street. Gravity would be pulling down on the rope along the way, eventually stopping it.

MATH in SCIENCE

SKILL: MEAN, MEDIAN, AND MODE

MATH TUTORIAL
CLASSZONE.COM
Click on Math Tutorial for more help with finding the mean, median, and mode.

Before going out on the water, boaters can check reports on wave conditions in their area.

Wave Heights

Tracking stations throughout the world's oceans measure and record the height of water waves that pass beneath them. The data recorded by the stations can be summarized as average wave heights over one hour or one day.

How would you summarize the typical wave heights over one week? There are a few different ways in which data can be summarized. Three common ways are finding the mean, median, and mode.

Example

Wave height data for one week are shown below.

| 1.2 m | 1.5 m | 1.4 m | 1.7 m | 2.0 m | 1.4 m | 1.3 m |

(1) **Mean** To find the mean of the data, divide the sum of the values by the number of values.

$$\text{Mean} = \frac{1.2 + 1.5 + 1.4 + 1.7 + 2.0 + 1.4 + 1.3}{7} = 1.5 \text{ m}$$

ANSWER The mean wave height is 1.5 m.

(2) **Median** To find the median of the data, write the values in order from least to greatest. The value in the middle is the median.

1.2 m 1.3 m 1.4 m (1.4 m) 1.5 m 1.7 m 2.0 m

ANSWER The median wave height is 1.4 m.

(3) **Mode** The mode is the number that occurs most often.

ANSWER The mode for the data is also 1.4 m.

Use the data to answer the following questions.

The data below show wave heights taken from a station off the coast of Florida over two weeks.

| Wk 1 | 1.2 m | 1.1 m | 1.1 m | 1.5 m | 4.7 m | 1.2 m | 1.1 m |
| Wk 2 | 0.7 m | 0.8 m | 0.9 m | 0.8 m | 1.0 m | 1.1 m | 0.8 m |

1. Find the mean, median, and mode of the data for Week 1.
2. Find the mean, median, and mode of the data for Week 2.

CHALLENGE A storm carrying strong winds caused high waves on the fifth day of the data shown above for Week 1. Which of the following was most affected by the high value—the mean, median, or mode?

Chapter 15: **Waves** 495

MATH IN SCIENCE
Math Skills Practice for Science

Set Learning Goal
To learn how to calculate three kinds of averages: mean, median, and mode

Present the Science
Point out that wave height measures from trough to crest.

Develop Estimation Skills
Students may wonder how to calculate median for an even number of data values. Inform students that they would find the two center values and calculate their mean value.

Make up a row of data with an even number of values and have students calculate the median.

Close
Present the following scenario: You are collecting and analyzing test scores for all sixth-grade students in the Centerville school system. What special insight would each of the three kinds of averages give you about students' test performance? *Sample answer: The mean will give an idea of the overall success of all the classes; the median will show approximately what the average student's score was; the mode will show where scores clustered.*

- Math Support, p. 49
- Math Practice, p. 50

Technology Resources
Students can visit **ClassZone.com** for practice finding mean, median, and mode.

MATH TUTORIAL

ANSWERS

1. mean (1.2 + 1.1 + 1.1 + 1.5 + 4.7 + 1.2 + 1.1) ÷ 7 = 1.7 m; mean = 1.7 m
   median 1.1 m; 1.1 m; 1.1 m; (1.2 m); 1.2 m; 1.5 m; 4.7 m; median = 1.2 m;
   mode = 1.1 m

2. mean (0.7 + 0.8 + 0.9 + 0.8 + 1.0 + 1.1 + 0.8) ÷ 7 = 0.9 m; mean = 0.9 m
   median 0.7 m; 0.8 m; 0.8 m; (0.8 m); 0.9 m; 1.0 m; 1.1 m; median = 0.8 m;
   mode = 0.8 m

CHALLENGE the mean

Chapter 15 **495**

15.2 FOCUS

▶ Set Learning Goals

Students will
- Learn how to measure amplitude, wavelength, and frequency.
- Calculate a wave's speed.
- Collect data to investigate how to change frequency in an experiment.

◯ 3-Minute Warm-Up

Display Transparency 4 or copy this exercise on the board:

How could you measure each of these things? What problems might you encounter in doing so?

1. width of a door opening
2. volume of liquid
3. length of time

Sample answers:

1. *with measuring tape; keeping the tension in the tape across the door opening to get an accurate measurement*
2. *with a measuring cup; making sure liquid is stable*
3. *with a stopwatch; determining start and end time and variations in timing*

T 3-Minute Warm-Up, p. T4

15.2 MOTIVATE

THINK ABOUT

PURPOSE To think about different ways a wave can be measured

DISCUSS Have students look at the photograph and describe the scene. Solicit ideas for ways in which waves can be measured.

Ongoing Assessment

 *Answer: amplitude, frequency, and wavelength*

496 Unit 4: **Waves, Sound, and Light**

KEY CONCEPT
15.2 Waves have measurable properties.

◀ BEFORE, you learned
- Forces cause waves
- Waves transfer energy
- Waves can be transverse or longitudinal

▶ NOW, you will learn
- How amplitude, wavelength, and frequency are measured
- How to find a wave's speed

VOCABULARY

crest p. 497
trough p. 497
amplitude p. 497
wavelength p. 497
frequency p. 497

THINK ABOUT

How can a wave be measured?

This enormous wave moves the water high above sea level as it comes crashing through. How could you find out how high a water wave actually goes? How could you find out how fast it is traveling? In what other ways do you think a wave can be measured? Read on to find out.

 **COMBINATION NOTES**
Use combination notes in your notebook to describe how waves can be measured.

Waves have amplitude, wavelength, and frequency.

The tallest ocean wave ever recorded was measured from the deck of a ship during a storm. An officer on the ship saw a wave reach a height that was level with a point high on the ship, more than 30 meters (100 ft)! Height is a property of all waves—from ripples in a glass of water to gigantic waves at surfing beaches—and it can be measured.

The speed of a water wave is another property that can be measured—by finding the time it takes for one wave peak to travel a set distance. Other properties of a wave that can be measured include the time between waves and the length of a single wave. Scientists use the terms *amplitude*, *wavelength*, and *frequency* to refer to some commonly measured properties of waves.

 What are three properties of a wave that can be measured?

496 Unit 4: **Waves, Sound, and Light**

RESOURCES FOR DIFFERENTIATED INSTRUCTION

Below Level
UNIT RESOURCE BOOK
- Reading Study Guide A, pp. 24–25
- Decoding Support, p. 48

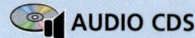 **AUDIO CDS**

Advanced
UNIT RESOURCE BOOK
Challenge and Extension, p. 30

English Learners
UNIT RESOURCE BOOK
Spanish Reading Study Guide, pp. 28–29

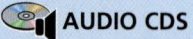 **AUDIO CDS**

- Audio Readings in Spanish
- Audio Readings (English)

Measuring Wave Properties

A **crest** is the highest point, or peak, of a wave. A **trough** is the lowest point, or valley, of a wave. Suppose you are riding on a boat in rough water. When the boat points upward and rises, it is climbing to the crest of a wave. When it points downward and sinks, the boat is falling to the trough of the wave.

❶ **Amplitude** for a transverse wave is the distance between a line through the middle of a wave and a crest or trough. In an ocean wave, amplitude measures how far the wave rises above, or dips below, its original position, or rest position.

Amplitude is an important measurement, because it indicates how much energy a wave is carrying. The bigger the amplitude, the more energy the wave has. Find amplitude on the diagram below.

❷ The distance from one wave crest to the very next crest is called the **wavelength**. Wavelength can also be measured from trough to trough. Find wavelength on the diagram below.

❸ The number of waves passing a fixed point in a certain amount of time is called the **frequency**. The word *frequent* means "often," so frequency measures how often a wave occurs. Frequency is often measured by counting the number of crests or troughs that pass by a given point in one second. Find frequency on the diagram below.

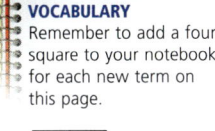

VOCABULARY
Remember to add a four square to your notebook for each new term on this page.

 How is amplitude related to energy?

Wave Properties

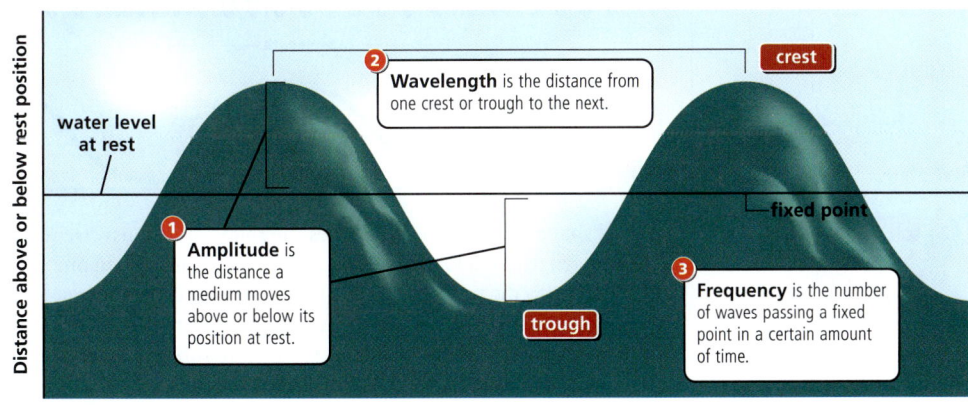

 How many wavelengths are shown in this diagram? How do you know?

Chapter 15: **Waves** 497

15.2 INSTRUCT

Develop Critical Thinking

EVALUATE Instruct students to think about two waves having equal frequencies and wavelengths. Ask them if that means the waves are identical. Have them draw a diagram to explain their answer. *Two waves can have the same frequency and wavelength without being identical if they have different amplitudes.*

Ongoing Assessment

Learn how to measure frequency.

Ask: How is frequency measured? *Frequency is measured by counting the number of crests or troughs that pass by a fixed point in one second.*

 Answer: The larger the amplitude, the more energy a wave carries.

READING VISUALS Answer: two wavelengths, shown from trough to trough

---

DIFFERENTIATE INSTRUCTION

More Reading Support

A What is the crest of a wave? *the highest point, or peak*

B What is the trough of a wave? *the lowest point, or valley*

English Learners Be aware that English learners do not always have the same background knowledge as the rest of the class. For example, this section's Investigate refers to small, metal rings called *washers*. English learners most likely won't connect the term *washer* to the metal rings in front of them. You may also want to point out the comparative structure of sentences such as: The bigger the amplitude, the more energy the wave has (p. 497).

Chapter 15 **497**

Teach Difficult Concepts

Students may have trouble with the concept of wave frequency. Ask students to brainstorm examples of repetitive events. Students might think of natural cycles such as the sun rising and setting each day. Point out that the patterns change repeatedly with a particular frequency, or repeating time period. For example, the sun rises every 24 hours.

Relate examples to frequency in wave motion: in a transverse wave, the pattern is repeating crests or troughs; in a longitudinal wave, the pattern is repeating bunched-up areas. Emphasize that frequency describes *regular* repeating patterns.

Teach from Visuals

Draw attention to the visual of the spring toy. Ask:

- What repeating pattern do you observe? *bunching up/ spreading out*
- What part of the spring coil corresponds to the wave crest? *where the coils are spread out*
- What part corresponds to the wave trough? *where the coils are bunched up*

Teaching with Technology

On a graphing calculator, have students graph $y = \sin x$ and $y = \cos x$. Point out that the graphs form a shape of a wave. Ask students to alter the equations (for example, $y = 3 \sin x$, $y = \sin 2x$) and have them compare the different wavelengths and amplitudes.

Ongoing Assessment

 Answer: For a longitudinal wave, wavelength is a measure of the distance between compressions. Amplitude is a measure of how compressed the medium gets. Frequency is the number of compressions that occur within a certain time.

498 Unit 4: **Waves, Sound, and Light**

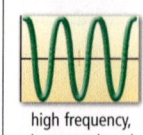

low frequency, long wavelength

high frequency, short wavelength

REMINDER
Frequency is the number of waves that pass a given point in a certain amount of time.

VISUALIZATION
CLASSZONE.COM
Watch the graph of a wave form.

How Frequency and Wavelength Are Related

The frequency and wavelength of a wave are related. When frequency increases more wave crests pass a fixed point each second. That means the wavelength shortens. So, as frequency increases, wavelength decreases. The opposite is also true—as frequency decreases, wavelength increases.

Suppose you are making waves in a rope. If you make one wave crest every second, the frequency is one wave per second (1/s). Now suppose you want to increase the frequency to more than one wave per second. You flick the rope up and down faster. The wave crests are now closer together. In other words, their wavelengths have decreased.

Graphing Wave Properties

The graph of a transverse wave looks much like a wave itself. The illustration on page 499 shows the graph of an ocean wave. The measurements for the graph come from a float, or buoy (BOO-ee), that keeps track of how high or low the water goes. The graph shows the position of the buoy at three different points in time. These points are numbered. Since the graph shows what happens over time, you can see the frequency of the waves.

Unlike transverse waves, longitudinal waves look different from their graphs. The graph of a longitudinal wave in a spring is drawn below. The coils of the spring get closer and then farther apart as the wave moves through them.

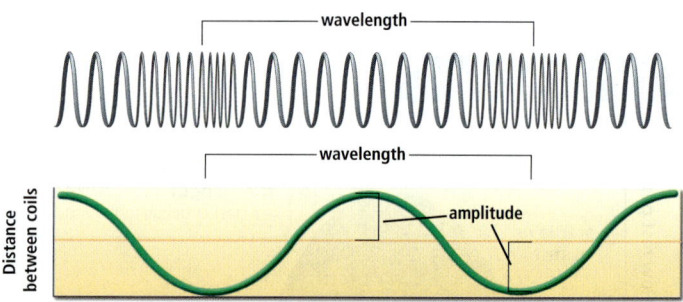

The shape of the graph resembles the shape of a transverse wave. The wavelength on a longitudinal wave is the distance from one compression to the next. The amplitude of a longitudinal wave measures how compressed the medium gets. Just as in a transverse wave, frequency in a longitudinal wave is the number of waves passing a fixed point in a certain amount of time.

 How are longitudinal waves measured?

498 Unit 4: Waves, Sound, and Light

DIFFERENTIATE INSTRUCTION

More Reading Support

C Explain how frequency and wavelength of a wave are related. *If frequency increases, wavelength decreases. If frequency decreases, wavelength increases.*

Below Level Draw two identical rectangular boxes far apart on the board, each about 65 cm wide and 25 cm deep. Ask two volunteers to each draw waves in one of the boxes. Have one student draw lazy, slow waves and the other fast-moving waves.

Ask: Which box has the most waves? Which box has the longest wavelengths? *Students should see that more waves mean shorter wavelengths (as in the box with fast-moving waves) and that fewer waves mean longer wavelengths (as in the box with slow waves).*

Graphing a Wave

The graph of a transverse wave looks like a wave itself. The graph shows what happens over time.

The buoy moves up and down as the waves pass.

① **Time: 0 s** The buoy is below the rest position.

② **Time: 1 s** The buoy is equal with the rest position.

③ **Time: 2 s** The buoy is above the rest position.

water level at rest

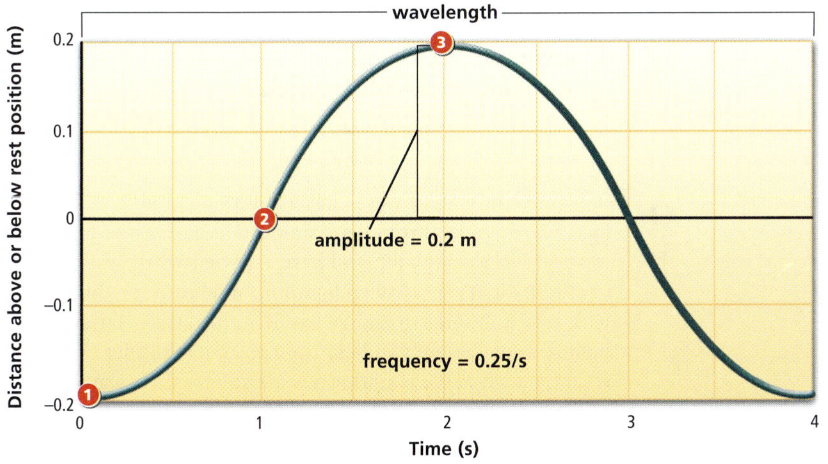

wavelength
amplitude = 0.2 m
frequency = 0.25/s

Distance above or below rest position (m)
Time (s)

 How many seconds does it take for one wave to pass? How much of the wave passes in one second?

Chapter 15: **Waves** 499

DIFFERENTIATE INSTRUCTION

 More Reading Support

D Which type of wave has a graph that looks like the real wave—transverse or longitudinal? *transverse*

Advanced Instruct students to use the data in the graph on this page. Have them make a graph in which the frequency is doubled (0.5 wavelengths/second).

Have students write a sentence or two comparing their modified graph to the printed one.

 Challenge and Extension, p. 30

Teach from Visuals

To help students interpret the "Graphing a Wave" visual, ask:

- What are the different parts of the visual on this page? *a photo, three diagrams, and a graph*
- What does the curved line on the graph represent? *the wave in the photo*
- What do the *x*-axis and the *y*-axis represent? *time in seconds, and distance (amplitude) in meters*
- What do the bubble pictures above the graph show? Why are they important? *The buoy bobs up and down as a wave passes underneath; it is the fixed point from which frequency and other wave measurements can be taken.*

 The visual "Graphing a Wave" is available as T6 in the Unit Transparency Book.

Teacher Demo

Demonstrate wavelength and frequency in a wave. Tie a cord to a fixed object such as a doorknob; holding the other end, move back until the cord is taut. Pull up and down on the cord to set off waves, and then have students identify crests and troughs. Ask students how they could measure wavelength. Measure distance from one crest or trough to the next.

Place an object under the cord between you and the tied end. Prompt students to count waves passing this reference point as you call time. Say "start" when you set off the rope wave, time three seconds, and then say "stop." Get students' wave counts. Have students discuss how they counted the waves and how they could use their data to determine frequency.

Ongoing Assessment

Answer: 4 seconds; one-fourth of the wave

Chapter 15 **499**

INVESTIGATE Frequency

PURPOSE To investigate how changing the length of a pendulum affects wave frequency

TIPS 30 min. If students have trouble with the technique, here are some suggestions.

- Tie the washers tightly together so that they will not shift weight.
- Make sure the washers swing freely, without bumping anything.
- Count one full swing each time the pendulum returns to the start position.

WHAT DO YOU THINK? *The longer the string, the lower the frequency. The swinging string is similar because it has frequency and amplitude. It is different because it does not transfer energy.*

CHALLENGE *Pulling the washers back farther would change the amplitude. Changing the amplitude does not change the frequency.*

 Datasheet, Frequency, p. 31

Technology Resources
Customize this student lab as needed or look for an alternative. Print rubrics to assess student lab reports.

 Lab Generator CD-ROM

History of Science
Scientists are continually refining measurement of the speed of sound. The standard speed of sound in air is measured at sea level at 0°C. In 1738, French scientists determined the speed of sound in air to be 332 m/s. In 1942, scientists made a more precise measurement: 331.45 m/s. As recently as 1986, scientists further refined the measurement to 331.29 m/s.

Ongoing Assessment
Calculate a wave's speed.
Ask: What measurements do you need to calculate a wave's speed? *wavelength and frequency*

INVESTIGATE Frequency

How can you change frequency?

PROCEDURE

1. Tie 3 washers to a string. Tape the string to the side of your desk so that it can swing freely. The swinging washers can model wave action.
2. Pull the washers slightly to the side and let go. Find the frequency by counting the number of complete swings that occur in 1 minute.
3. Make a table in your notebook to record both the length of the string and the frequency.
4. Shorten the string by moving and retaping it. Repeat for 5 different lengths. Keep the distance you pull the washers the same each time.

WHAT DO YOU THINK?
- How did changing the length of the string affect the frequency?
- How does this model represent a wave? How does it differ from a wave?

CHALLENGE How could you vary the amplitude of this model? Predict how changing the amplitude would affect the frequency.

SKILL FOCUS Collecting data

MATERIALS
- 3 metal washers
- piece of string
- tape
- stopwatch
- meter stick

TIME 30 minutes

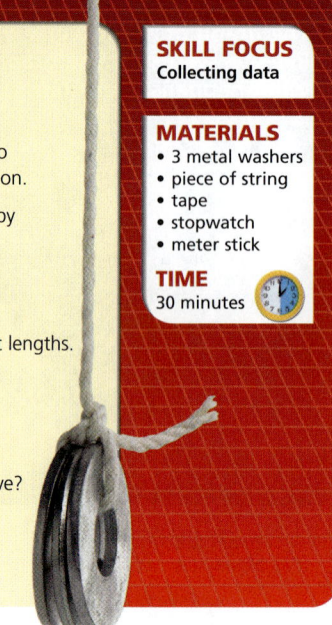

Wave speed can be measured.

In addition to amplitude, wavelength, and frequency, a wave's speed can be measured. One way to find the speed of a wave is to time how long it takes for a wave to get from one point to another. Another way to find the speed of a wave is to calculate it. The speed of any wave can be determined when both the frequency and the wavelength are known, using the following formula:

REMINDER
The symbol λ represents wavelength.

$$\text{Speed} = \text{wavelength} \cdot \text{frequency}$$
$$S = \lambda f$$

Different types of waves travel at very different speeds. For example, light waves travel through air almost a million times faster than sound waves travel through air. You have experienced the difference in wave speeds if you have ever seen lightning and heard the thunder that comes with it in a thunderstorm. When lightning strikes far away, you see the light seconds before you hear the clap of its thunder. The light waves reach you while the sound waves are still on their way.

How fast do you think water waves can travel? Water waves travel at different speeds. You can calculate the speed using wavelength and frequency.

DIFFERENTIATE INSTRUCTION

 More Reading Support

E Wavelength times frequency is the formula for which wave measurement? *wave speed*

F Do all kinds of waves travel at the same speed? *no*

Below Level Give this analogy for the formula for wave speed: To find the frequency of cars on a moving train, you could watch a moving train and count the number of railroad cars that pass in a certain length of time, such as 10 seconds, using a stopwatch. Wavelength is like the length of a railroad car. Frequency is the number of cars that pass in a certain length of time.

Suppose you wish to calculate the speed of an ocean wave with a wavelength of 16 meters and a frequency of 0.31 wave per second. When working through the problem in the example below, it is helpful to think of the frequency as

$$f = 0.31 \text{ (wave)/s}$$

even though the units for frequency are just 1/second. You can think of wavelengths as "meters per wave," or

$$\lambda = 16 \text{ m/(wave)}$$

RESOURCE CENTER
CLASSZONE.COM
Find out more about wave speed.

Calculating Wave Speed

Sample Problem

An ocean wave has a wavelength of 16 meters and a frequency of 0.31 wave per second. What is the speed of the wave?

What do you know?	wavelength = 16 m, frequency = 0.31 (wave)/s
What do you want to find out?	Speed
Write the formula:	$S = \lambda f$
Substitute into the formula:	$S = 16 \frac{m}{(wave)} \cdot 0.31 \frac{(wave)}{s}$
Calculate and simplify:	$16 \frac{m}{(wave)} \cdot 0.31 \frac{(wave)}{s} = 5 \frac{m}{s}$
Check that your units agree:	Unit is m/s. Unit for speed is m/s. Units agree.
Answer:	$S = 5$ m/s

Practice the Math

1. In a stormy sea, 2 waves pass a fixed point every second, and the waves are 10 m apart. What is the speed of the waves?
2. In a ripple tank, the wavelength is 0.1 cm, and 10 waves occur each second. What is the speed of the waves (in cm/s)?

15.2 Review

KEY CONCEPTS

1. Make a simple diagram of a wave, labeling amplitude, frequency, and wavelength. For frequency, you will need to indicate a span of time, such as one second.
2. What two measurements of a wave do you need to calculate its speed?

CRITICAL THINKING

3. **Observe** Suppose you are watching water waves pass under the end of a pier. How can you figure out their frequency?
4. **Calculate** A wave has a speed of 3 m/s and a frequency of 6 (waves)/s. What is its wavelength?

CHALLENGE

5. **Apply** Imagine you are on a boat in the middle of the sea. You are in charge of recording the properties of passing ocean waves into the ship's logbook. What types of information could you record? How would this information be useful? Explain your answer.

Chapter 15: **Waves** 501

ANSWERS

1. See students' diagrams.
2. wavelength and frequency
3. Sample answer: Look at a fixed point below, and time how many waves pass that point within a unit of time.
4. $S = \lambda \cdot f$
   $\lambda = f \div s$
   $\lambda = 6 \frac{(wave)}{s} \div 3 \text{ m/s}$
   $= 0.5 \text{ m}$
5. Sample answer: You could record the amplitude, wavelength, and frequency of waves at different times during the day. Changes in these measures could help indicate the approach of a storm.

Ongoing Assessment

CHECK YOUR READING Answer: measure the speed of sound traveling through rock

▶ **Practice the Math**

1. $S = \lambda \cdot f$
   $S = 10 \frac{m}{(wave)} \cdot 2 \frac{(wave)}{s}$
   $= 20 \text{ m/s}$

2. $S = \lambda \cdot f$
   $S = 0.1 \frac{cm}{(wave)} \cdot 10 \frac{(wave)}{s}$
   $= 1 \text{ cm/s}$

 Math Support, p. 51
Math Practice, p. 52

EXPLORE the BIG idea

Revisit "How Can You Change Waves?" on p. 487. Have students explain the reasons for their results.

Reinforce the BIG idea

Have students relate the section to the Big Idea.

 Reinforcing Key Concepts, p. 32

15.2 ASSESS & RETEACH

Assess

A Section 15.2 Quiz, p. 4

Reteach

Have students make the following drawings to illustrate the main concepts.
1. A sketch of an ocean wave (transverse), with wavelength and amplitude clearly marked, and a dotted or dashed line to show level.
2. A sketch of a wave in a spring toy (longitudinal wave), illustrating regions of compression and wavelength.

Technology Resources

Have students visit ClassZone.com for reteaching of Key Concepts.

 CONTENT REVIEW

 CONTENT REVIEW CD-ROM

Chapter 15 **501**

CHAPTER INVESTIGATION

Focus

PURPOSE Students will learn how to measure waves produced by a pendulum and will investigate how the length of the pendulum affects wavelength.

OVERVIEW Students will:
- Make a pendulum from which sand drains.
- Record the pendulum's wave pattern with sand on construction paper.
- Repeat the activity with varying pendulum lengths.
- Evaluate the different waves produced.

Lab Preparation

- Students can prepare the paper cones ahead of time. Be sure students make the hole no larger than a pea. Have them make extra cones in case some perform poorly.
- For homework the night before, have students read the investigation, write their hypothesis, and draw their data table. Or you may wish to copy and distribute datasheets and rubrics.

 UNIT RESOURCE BOOK, pp. 53–61

 SCIENCE TOOLKIT, F14

Lab Management

- Pair students. Have students choose roles: one partner will manipulate the pendulum, while the other will fill the pendulum with sand and then pull the paper under the swinging pendulum.
- The waves may not look like those earlier in the text, but should have clear crests and troughs.

INCLUSION Encourage students working together to discuss in advance which tasks each will perform. Help students identify tasks that they can do well or alternate approaches that suit their abilities.

502 Unit 4: **Waves, Sound, and Light**

CHAPTER INVESTIGATION

Wavelength

OVERVIEW AND PURPOSE The pendulum on a grandfather clock keeps time as it swings back and forth at a steady rate. The swings of a pendulum can be recorded as a wave with measurable properties. How do the properties of the pendulum affect the properties of the waves it produces? In this investigation you will use your understanding of wave properties to
- construct a pendulum and measure the waves it produces, and
- determine how the length of the pendulum affects the wavelength of the waves.

 Problem

How does changing the length of a pendulum affect the wavelength?

Hypothesize

Write a hypothesis in "If . . . , then . . . , because . . ." form to answer the problem question.

MATERIALS
- 1/2 sheet white paper
- tape
- scissors
- string
- meter stick
- fine sand
- graduated cylinder
- 2 sheets colored construction paper

Procedure

1. Make a data table like the one shown on the sample notebook page.

2. Make a cone with the half-sheet of paper by rolling it and taping it as shown. The hole in the bottom of the cone should be no larger than a pea.

3. Cut a hole in each side of the cone and tie the ends of the string to the cone to make a pendulum.

4. Hold the string on the pendulum so that the distance from your fingers holding the string to the bottom of the cone is 20 cm.

5. Cover the bottom of the cone with your fingertip. While you hold the cone, have your partner pour about 40 mL of sand into the cone.

502 Unit 4: **Waves, Sound, and Light**

INVESTIGATION RESOURCES

 CHAPTER INVESTIGATION, Wavelength
- Level A, pp. 53–56
- Level B, pp. 57–60
- Level C, p. 61

Advanced students should complete Levels B & C.

 Writing a Lab Report, D12–13

Technology Resources

Customize this student lab as needed or look for an alternative. Print rubrics to assess student lab reports.

 Lab Generator CD-ROM

6. Hold the pendulum about 5 cm above the construction paper as shown. Pull the pendulum from the bottom to one side of the construction paper. Be careful not to move the pendulum at the top, or to pull the pendulum over the edge of the paper.

7. Let the pendulum go while your partner gently pulls the paper forward so that the sand makes waves on the paper. Be sure to pull the paper at a steady rate. Let the remaining sand pile up on the end of the paper.

8. Measure the wavelength from crest to crest or trough to trough. Record the wavelength in your table.

9. Run two more trials, repeating steps 5–8. Be sure to pull the paper at the same speed for each trial. Calculate the average wavelength over all three trials, and record it in your table.

10. Repeat steps 4–8, changing the length of the pendulum to 30 cm and then to 40 cm.

Observe and Analyze *Write It Up*

1. **RECORD OBSERVATIONS** Draw the setup of your procedure. Be sure your data table is complete.
2. **IDENTIFY VARIABLES AND CONSTANTS** Identify the variables and constants that affected the wave produced by the moving pendulum. List them in your notebook.
3. **ANALYZE** What patterns can you find in your data? For example, do the numbers increase or decrease as you read down each column?

Conclude *Write It Up*

1. **INFER** Answer your problem question.
2. **INTERPRET** Compare your results with your hypothesis. Do your data support your hypothesis?
3. **IDENTIFY LIMITS** What possible limitations or sources of error could have affected your results?
4. **APPLY** Suppose you were examining the tracing made by a seismograph, a machine that records an earthquake wave. What would happen if you increased the speed at which the paper ran through the machine? What do you think the amplitude of the tracing represents?

INVESTIGATE Further

CHALLENGE Revise your experiment to change one variable other than the length of the pendulum. Run a new trial, changing the variable you choose but keeping everything else constant. How did changing the variable affect the wave produced?

Wavelength

Problem How does changing the length of a pendulum affect the wavelength?

Hypothesize

Observe and Analyze

Table 1. Wavelengths Produced by Pendulums

Pendulum Length (cm)	Trial 1	Trial 2	Trial 3	Average Wavelength (cm)
20				
30				
40				

Conclude

Chapter 15: **Waves** 503

Observe and Analyze *Write It Up*

SAMPLE DATA wavelength with 20-cm string: 3.5 cm; wavelength with 30-cm string: 5 cm; wavelength with 40-cm string: 8 cm

1. See students' diagrams. See students' data tables.
2. The variable is the length of the pendulum. Ideally, constants will include the speed of the paper as the partner pulls it forward, the height of the pendulum above the table, the amount the pendulum is pulled back before letting go, and the amount of sand used in each trial.
3. Sample answer: Most of the numbers increase as you read down the columns.

Conclude *Write It Up*

1. Changing the length of the pendulum changes the wavelength of waves it produces.
2. Student answers will vary, depending on students' original hypotheses.
3. Sample answer: The speed at which the paper is pulled each time may have varied, affecting the results.
4. If you increase the speed of paper that runs through a seismograph, you would increase the wavelength. The amplitude represents the amount of energy carried by a seismic wave.

INVESTIGATE Further

CHALLENGE Students could choose to vary the weight of the pendulum, the size of the cone, the speed at which the paper is pulled under the pendulum, or the height of the pendulum above the paper. Any of these changes could affect the wave produced by the pendulum.

Post-Lab Discussion

- Discuss with students how the activity enabled them to graph the movement of a pendulum.
- Point out that almost any motion that is regular and repeating can be graphed as a wave. Challenge students to describe how the movement of a clock's minute hand could be interpreted and graphed as wave motion. You could graph the 12 o'clock position as the crest of the wave and the 6 o'clock position as the trough.

15.3 FOCUS

▶ Set Learning Goals
Students will
- Describe how waves change as they encounter a barrier.
- Explain what happens when waves enter a new medium.
- Identify ways in which waves interact with one another.
- Investigate in an experiment how waves behave when they meet a barrier.

◉ 3-Minute Warm-Up
Display Transparency 5 or copy this exercise on the board:

Draw a diagram that shows how a duck floats on waves. Use arrows to show how the waves move and how the duck moves. *Arrows for the duck should show it staying in the same position but bobbing up and down vertically; arrows for waves should point in a horizontal direction.*

 3-Minute Warm-Up, p. T5

15.3 MOTIVATE

EXPLORE Reflection
PURPOSE To introduce the concept that waves reflect off a barrier

TIP 10 min. The waves will be circular.

WHAT DO YOU THINK? *The ripples travel back in the opposite direction after they encounter the side of the pan. Waves encounter a medium that they cannot travel through.*

Ongoing Assessment
 Answer: reflection, refraction, diffraction

---

KEY CONCEPT
15.3 Waves behave in predictable ways.

 BEFORE, you learned
- Waves transfer energy
- Amplitude, wavelength, and frequency can be measured

 NOW, you will learn
- How waves change as they encounter a barrier
- What happens when waves enter a new medium
- How waves interact with other waves

VOCABULARY
reflection p. 505
refraction p. 505
diffraction p. 506
interference p. 507

EXPLORE Reflection
How do ripples reflect?
PROCEDURE

1. Put a few drops of food coloring into the pan of water.
2. Dip the pencil in the water at one end of the pan to make ripples in the water.
3. Observe the ripples as they reflect off the side of the pan. Draw a sketch of the waves reflecting.

WHAT DO YOU THINK?
- What happens when the waves reach the side of the pan?
- Why do you think the waves behave as they do?

MATERIALS
- wide pan, half full of water
- food coloring
- pencil

COMBINATION NOTES
Use combination notes in your notebook to describe how waves interact with materials.

Waves interact with materials.

You have read that mechanical waves travel through a medium like air, water, or the ground. In this section, you will read how the motion of waves changes when they encounter a new medium. For instance, when an ocean wave rolls into a ship or a sound wave strikes a solid wall, the wave encounters a new medium.

When waves interact with materials in these ways, they behave predictably. All waves, from water waves to sound waves and even light waves, show the behaviors that you will learn about next. Scientists call these behaviors reflection, refraction, and diffraction.

 What behaviors do all waves have in common?

504 Unit 4: Waves, Sound, and Light

RESOURCES FOR DIFFERENTIATED INSTRUCTION

Below Level
UNIT RESOURCE BOOK
- Reading Study Guide A, pp. 35–36
- Decoding Support, p. 48

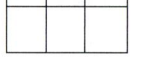 **AUDIO CDS**

 **Additional INVESTIGATION,**
Tracking the Path of Light, A, B, & C, pp. 62–70;
Teacher Instructions, pp. 284–285

Advanced
UNIT RESOURCE BOOK
Challenge and Extension, p. 41

English Learners
UNIT RESOURCE BOOK
Spanish Reading Study Guide, pp. 39–40

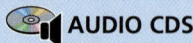 **AUDIO CDS**
- Audio Readings in Spanish
- Audio Readings (English)

Reflection

What happens to water waves at the end of a swimming pool? The waves cannot travel through the wall of the pool. Instead, the waves bounce off the pool wall. The bouncing back of a wave after it strikes a barrier is called **reflection.**

Remember what you have learned about forces. A water wave, like all waves, transfers energy. When the water wave meets the wall of the pool, it pushes against the wall. The wall applies an equal and opposite force on the water, sending the wave back in another direction. In the illustration on the right, you can see water waves reflecting off a barrier.

Sound and light waves reflect too. Sound waves reflecting off the walls of a canyon produce an echo. Light waves reflecting off smooth metal behind glass let you see an image of yourself in the mirror. The light waves bounce off the metal just as the water waves bounce off the pool wall. You will learn more about how sound and light waves reflect in the next chapters.

Reflection Water waves move in predictable ways. Here waves are shown from above as they reflect off a barrier.

How would you define *reflection* in your own words?

Refraction

Sometimes, a wave does not bounce back when it encounters a new medium. Instead, the wave continues moving forward. When a wave enters a new medium at an angle, it bends, or refracts. **Refraction** is the bending of a wave as it enters a new medium at an angle other than 90 degrees. Refraction occurs because waves travel at different speeds in different mediums. Because the wave enters the new medium at an angle, one side of the wave enters the new medium before the rest of the wave. When one side of a wave speeds up or slows down before the other side, it causes the wave to bend.

You have probably noticed the refraction of light waves in water. Objects half-in and half-out of water look broken or split. Look at the photograph of the straw in the glass. What your eyes suggest—that the straw is split—is not real, is it? You are seeing the refraction of light waves caused by the change of medium from air to water. You will learn more about the refraction of light waves in Chapter 18.

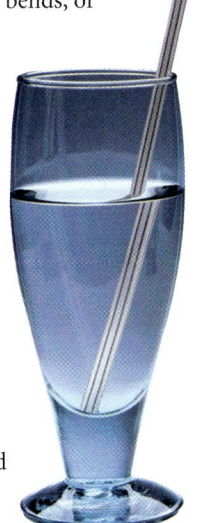

Refraction Light waves refract as they pass from air to water, making this straw look split.

Chapter 15: **Waves** 505

15.3 INSTRUCT

Real World Example
Bands sometimes play on stages surrounded by a large curved backdrop. This curved backdrop, or shell, reflects sound waves out to the audience. Without the band shell, sound waves produced by the performers would shoot out in all directions in the open air, lost to listeners, and the music would sound faint and dull.

Integrate the Sciences
Seismologists—scientists who study earthquakes—measure seismic waves all over Earth. These waves, set off by earthquakes in Earth's crust, travel in all directions and eventually reach the surface. Surface stations make precise measurements of the seismic waves. By studying how these waves travel and are refracted by different materials, seismologists have learned much about the density and composition of Earth's core and mantle.

Ongoing Assessment
Describe how waves change as they encounter a barrier.

Ask: What happens when sound waves strike solid rock? Give an example. *They reflect from the rock, as in an echo.*

Explain what happens when waves enter a new medium.

Ask: Why do you see distorted shapes when you look into the water in a swimming pool? *Light waves bend, or undergo refraction, when they pass from the air into the water. This refraction distorts underwater objects.*

Sample answer: waves bouncing off a barrier

DIFFERENTIATE INSTRUCTION

More Reading Support

A What happens to a wave when it meets the wall of a pool? *It reflects.*

B What describes a wave moving into a new medium at an angle? *refraction*

Additional Investigation To reinforce Section 15.3 learning goals, use the following full-period investigation:

Additional INVESTIGATION, Tracking the Path of Light, A, B, & C, pp. 62–70, 284–285
(Advanced students should complete Levels B and C.)

English Learners Providing models is an effective way to help English learners produce work that is representative of their abilities. For example, if a student is asked to write an explanatory paragraph, provide an appropriate model of one.

Chapter 15 **505**

INVESTIGATE Diffraction

PURPOSE To investigate how waves behave when they meet a partial barrier

TIPS *20 min.* Allow students a few minutes to explore, then suggest the following:

- Make sure the block sticks out of the water.
- Use a gentle push on the ruler to create waves.

WHAT DO YOU THINK? *by putting a partial barrier in their path; students' answers will vary depending on their predictions.*

CHALLENGE *Sample answer: You could try blocks with different sizes and shapes to better diffract the waves.*

 Datasheet, Diffraction, p. 42

Technology Resources

Customize this student lab as needed or look for an alternative. Print rubrics to assess student lab reports.

 Lab Generator CD-ROM

Metacognitive Strategy

Ask students to write a paragraph describing the reasoning behind their prediction about what would happen when the waves hit the barrier in the pan.

Teach from Visuals

To help students interpret the visual of diffraction, ask:

- Through what medium are the waves moving? *water*
- From what perspective are you viewing the waves? *from above*
- What happens to the waves as they go through the opening? *The waves spread out.*

Diffraction

You have seen how waves reflect off a barrier. For example, water waves bounce off the side of a pool. But what if the side of the pool had an opening in it? Sometimes, waves interact with a partial barrier, such as a wall with an opening. As the waves pass through the opening, they spread out, or diffract. **Diffraction** is the spreading out of waves through an opening or around the edge of an obstacle. Diffraction occurs with all types of waves.

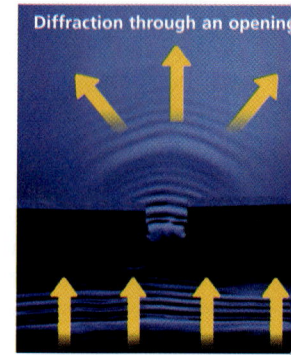

Diffraction through an opening

Look at the photograph on the right. It shows water waves diffracting as they pass through a small gap in a barrier. In the real world, ocean waves diffract through openings in cliffs or rock formations.

Similarly, sound waves diffract as they pass through an open doorway. Turn on a TV or stereo, and walk into another room. Listen to the sound with the door closed and then open. Then try moving around the room. You can hear the sound wherever you stand because the waves spread out, or diffract, through the doorway and reflect from the walls.

INVESTIGATE Diffraction

How can you make a wave diffract?

PROCEDURE

1. Put a few drops of food coloring into the container of water.
2. Experiment with quick motions of the ruler to set off waves in the container.
3. Place the block on its side in the center of the container. Set the bag of sand on the block to hold it down. Predict how the waves will interact with the barrier you have added.
4. Make another set of waves, and observe how they interact with the barrier.

WHAT DO YOU THINK?
- How did you make the waves diffract?
- How did your observations compare with your prediction?

CHALLENGE How could you change the experiment to make the effect of the diffraction more obvious?

SKILL FOCUS
Predicting

MATERIALS
- wide pan of water
- food coloring
- ruler
- wooden block
- bag of sand

TIME
20 minutes

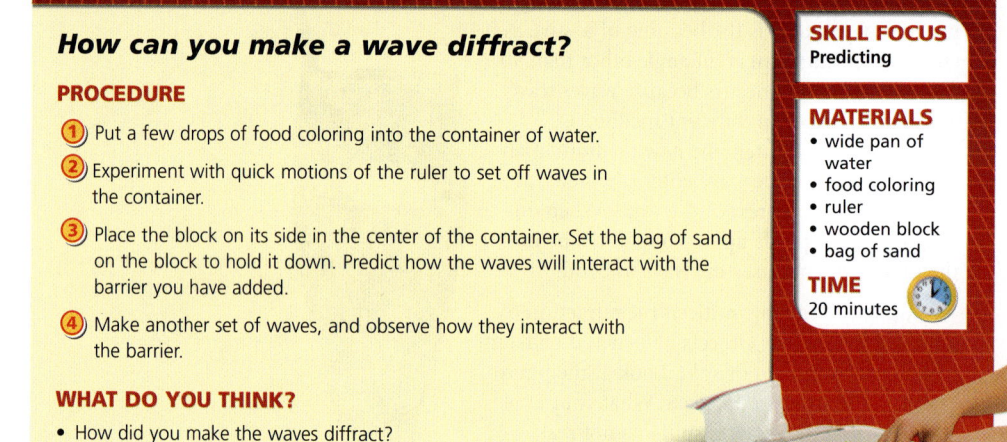

DIFFERENTIATE INSTRUCTION

More Reading Support

C What do waves do when they pass through an opening in a barrier? *They diffract.*

Below Level Students may have difficulty with the similar-sounding vocabulary in this lesson. Write "reflection," "refraction," and "diffraction" on the board, dividing them into syllables. Pronounce each word. Ask students to visually scan each word and find similarities and differences among them. *Reflection and refraction have identical prefixes and suffixes but different roots. Refraction and diffraction have identical roots and suffixes but different prefixes.*

Diffraction also occurs as waves pass the edge of an obstacle. The photograph at the right shows water waves diffracting as they pass an obstacle. Ocean waves also diffract in this way as they pass large rocks in the water.

Light waves diffract around the edge of an obstacle too. The edges of a shadow appear fuzzy because of diffraction. The light waves spread out, or diffract, around the object that is making the shadow.

Diffraction around an obstacle

 Describe what happens when waves diffract.

Waves interact with other waves.

Just as waves sometimes interact with new mediums, they can also interact with other waves. Two waves can add energy to or take away energy from each other in the place where they meet. **Interference** is the meeting and combining of waves.

Waves Adding Together

Suppose two identical waves coming from opposite directions come together at one point. The waves' crests and troughs are aligned briefly, which means they join up exactly. When the two waves merge into a temporary, larger wave, their amplitudes are added together. When the waves separate again, they have their original amplitudes and continue in their original directions.

Constructive Interference

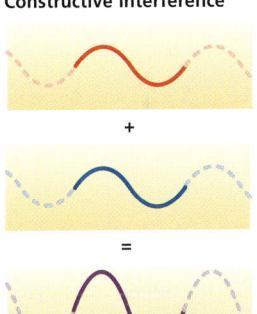

When two wave crests with amplitudes of 1 m each combine, a wave with an amplitude of 2 m is formed.

The adding of two waves is called constructive interference. It builds up, or constructs, a larger wave out of two smaller ones. Look at the diagram at the right to see what happens in constructive interference.

Because the waves in the example joined together perfectly, the amplitude of the new wave equals the combined amplitudes of the 2 original waves. For example, if the crest of a water wave with an amplitude of 1 meter (3.3 ft) met up with the crest of another wave with an amplitude of 1 meter (3.3 ft), there would be a 2 meter (6.6 ft) crest in the spot where they met.

Chapter 15: **Waves** 507

Ongoing Assessment

 Sample answer: The amplitudes of waves can add or subtract when two waves with the same frequency meet.

Reinforce

Have students relate the section to the Big Idea.

 Reinforcing Key Concepts, p. 43

15.3 ASSESS & RETEACH

Assess
Section 15.3 Quiz, p. 5

Reteach
Present these four wave scenarios:
- You shout into a cave and hear an echo.
- Two people in a choir are singing slightly off-key, and their voices combine to produce loud, unpleasant beats.
- From shore, it looks like all of a bridge's pilings are broken at the water level, but trucks are safely driving over it.
- Before you reach the corner of a huge stone building, you hear a noisy parade approaching down the other street.

Have each student choose a scenario and find the appropriate presentation for that topic in the lesson. Have students diagram the wave scenario and write a scientific explanation for it.

Technology Resources
Have students visit ClassZone.com for reteaching of Key Concepts.

 CONTENT REVIEW

 CONTENT REVIEW CD-ROM

Waves Canceling Each Other Out

Imagine again that two very similar waves come together. This time, however, the crest of one wave joins briefly with the trough of the other. The energy of one wave is subtracted from the energy of the other. The new wave is therefore smaller than the original wave. This process is called destructive interference. Look at the diagram below to see what happens in destructive interference.

For example, if a 2-meter (6.6 ft) crest met up with a 1-meter (3.3 ft) trough, there would be a temporary crest of only 1 meter (3.3 ft) where they met. If the amplitudes of the two original waves are identical, the two waves can cancel each other out completely!

When identical waves meet, they are usually not aligned. Instead, the crests meet up with crests in some places and troughs in others. As a result, the waves add in some places and subtract in others. The photograph on the left shows a pattern resulting from waves both adding and subtracting on the surface of a pond. Have you ever listened to music on stereo speakers that were placed at a distance from each other? The music may have sounded loud in some places and soft in others, as the sound waves from the two speakers interfered with each other.

Wave interference produces this pattern on a pond as two sets of waves interact.

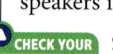 Summarize in your own words what happens during interference.

Destructive Interference

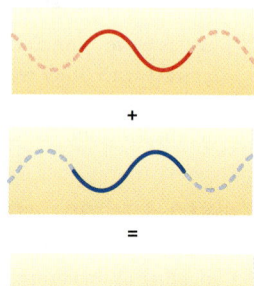

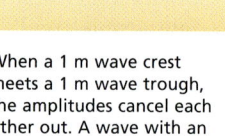

When a 1 m wave crest meets a 1 m wave trough, the amplitudes cancel each other out. A wave with an amplitude of 0 m is formed where they meet.

15.3 Review

KEY CONCEPTS
1. Explain what happens when waves encounter a medium that they cannot travel through.
2. Describe a situation in which waves would diffract.
3. Describe two ways that waves are affected by interference.

CRITICAL THINKING
4. **Synthesize** Explain how reflection and diffraction can happen at the same time in a wave.
5. **Compare** How is interference similar to net force? How do you think the two concepts might be related? **Hint:** Think about how forces are involved in wave motion.

⬤ CHALLENGE
6. **Predict** Imagine that you make gelatin in a long, shallow pan. Then you scoop the gelatin out of one end of the pan and add icy cold water to the exact same depth as the gelatin. Now suppose you set off waves at the water end. What do you think will happen when the waves meet the gelatin?

508 Unit 4: Waves, Sound, and Light

ANSWERS

1. Waves reflect.
2. Sample answer: Ocean waves hit a spot of land.
3. Amplitudes can add up or cancel each other out.
4. When a wave hits a partial barrier, the part of the wave that hits the barrier reflects into the oncoming waves. The part of the wave that passes through the gap in the barrier diffracts.
5. Forces are responsible for moving a wave medium up and down as a wave passes through it. Forces can be added and subtracted on a wave medium just as they can on any object.
6. Answers could describe refraction, as waves meet and enter a new medium, or reflection, as waves encounter a barrier.

CONNECTING SCIENCES

PHYSICAL SCIENCE AND EARTH SCIENCE

Tsunamis!

Tsunamis (tsu-NAH-mees) are among the most powerful waves on Earth. They can travel fast enough to cross the Pacific Ocean in less than a day! When they reach shore, these powerful waves strike with enough force to destroy whole communities.

What Causes Tsunamis?

Tsunamis are caused by an undersea volcanic eruption, an earthquake, or even a landslide. This deep-sea event sends out a series of waves. Surprisingly, if you were out at sea, you would not even notice these powerful waves. The reason has to do with the physics of waves—their velocity, wavelength, and amplitude.

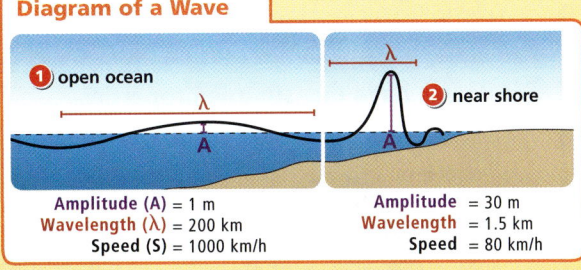

Diagram of a Wave

① open ocean
- Amplitude (A) = 1 m
- Wavelength (λ) = 200 km
- Speed (S) = 1000 km/h

② near shore
- Amplitude = 30 m
- Wavelength = 1.5 km
- Speed = 80 km/h

The Changing Wave

① On the open ocean, the waves of a tsunami are barely visible. The amplitude of the waves is less than a few meters, but the energy of the waves extends to the sea floor. The tsunami's wavelength is extremely long—up to 200 kilometers (120 mi). These long, low waves can travel as fast as a jet—almost 1000 kilometers per hour (600 mi/h).

② Near shore, the waves slow down as they approach shallow water. As their velocity drops, their wavelengths get shorter, but their amplitude gets bigger. All the energy that was spread out over a long wave in deep water is now compressed into a huge wave that can reach a height of more than 30 meters (100 ft).

Individual tsunami waves may arrive more than an hour apart. Many people have lost their lives returning home between waves, making the fatal mistake of thinking the danger was over.

EXPLORE

1. **VISUALIZE** Look at ② on the diagram. How tall is 30 meters (100 ft)? Find a 100-foot building or structure near you to visualize the shore height of a tsunami.
2. **CHALLENGE** Use library or Internet resources to prepare a chart on the causes and effects of a major tsunami event.

Chapter 15: **Waves** 509

A tsunami generated by a powerful earthquake struck Japan in 1983. The photograph above shows a scene before the tsunami struck. What changes do you see in the picture below showing the scene after the tsunami struck?

CONNECTING SCIENCES
Integration of Sciences

Set Learning Goal
To understand how the physics of waves applies to tsunamis

Present the Science
Share the following facts with students:
- The word *tsunami* is a Japanese word meaning "harbor wave."
- The most devastating tsunami occurred in Papua New Guinea in 1998.
- The states of Alaska and Hawaii have frequently felt tsunamis hitting their shores.
- Tsunamis are often confused with tidal waves, which are caused by the gravitational attraction of the Sun and Moon.
- Tsunamis are often called "seismic sea waves" because they are usually the result of "underwater earthquakes."

Discussion Questions
Ask: Why does the amplitude of the wave go up in shallow water? *It has nowhere else to go.*

Ask: Where will the energy of the wave go when it hits shore? *It will strike the shoreline with the force of the wave.*

Ask: How is the cause of a tsunami different from the cause of regular waves? *Regular waves are formed from wind and weather, while tsunamis develop from underwater volcanic eruptions or underwater earthquakes.*

Ask: Why do you think the waves slow down when they reach water that is more shallow? *They are slowed down by friction with the ocean floor.*

Close
Ask: How do tsunamis show that waves carry energy? *by the destruction they cause*

EXPLORE

1. **VISUALIZE** Discuss with students the impact that 30 meters of water might have.
2. **CHALLENGE** While many pictures and Internet sites show the devastation caused by tsunamis, there are very few pictures of a tsunami in action. Artists have attempted to depict the phenomenon. Students should have no trouble finding information on tsunamis.

PHOTO CAPTION Answer: There is a significant amount of water on the shore, the wall surrounding the water is destroyed, and the objects near the shore are pulled into the water by the force of the tsunami hitting the land.

Chapter 15 **509**

CHAPTER 15 • REVIEW

BACK TO

Ask students to describe a demonstration they could present to show that waves transfer energy. *Sample answer: You could go to the beach and put a plastic bucket in the sand a few centimeters out in the surf. The incoming waves would push the bucket, showing the transfer of energy.*

KEY CONCEPTS SUMMARY

SECTION 15.1
For the picture on the left, have students describe the direction of the disturbance compared to the direction of the wave. *It is at right angles with the direction of the wave.* For the picture on the right, have students describe the direction of the disturbance compared to the direction of the wave. *They are both in the same direction.*

SECTION 15.2
Ask: What wave properties are identified in the picture? Which property indicates the amount of energy the wave has? *The wave properties are amplitude, wavelength, and frequency. Amplitude indicates the energy in the wave.*

SECTION 15.3
Have students describe the three wave behaviors pictured here. *In reflection, waves bounce off a solid barrier. In refraction, waves bend as they pass from one medium into another. In diffraction, waves pass by a barrier and spread out.*

Review Concepts

- Big Idea Flow Chart, p. T1
- Chapter Outline, pp. T7–T8

---

15 Chapter Review

the BIG idea
Waves transfer energy and interact in predictable ways.

CONTENT REVIEW
CLASSZONE.COM

KEY CONCEPTS SUMMARY

1 Waves transfer energy.

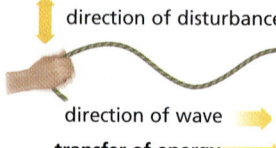
Transverse Wave
direction of disturbance
direction of wave
transfer of energy

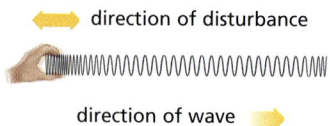
Longitudinal Wave
direction of disturbance
direction of wave
transfer of energy

VOCABULARY
wave p. 489
medium p. 491
mechanical wave p. 491
transverse wave p. 493
longitudinal wave p. 494

2 Waves have measurable properties.

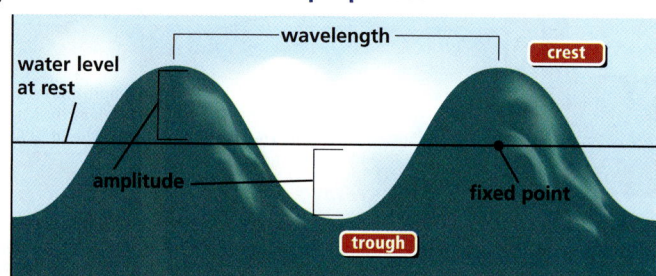

Frequency is the number of waves passing a fixed point in a certain amount of time.

VOCABULARY
crest p. 497
trough p. 497
amplitude p. 497
wavelength p. 497
frequency p. 497

3 Waves behave in predictable ways.

Reflection   Refraction   Diffraction

 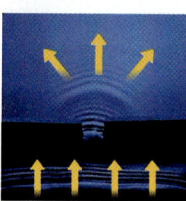

VOCABULARY
reflection p. 505
refraction p. 505
diffraction p. 506
interference p. 507

510 Unit 4: Waves, Sound, and Light

Technology Resources

Have students visit **ClassZone.com** or use the CD-ROM for a cumulative review of concepts.

 CONTENT REVIEW

 CONTENT REVIEW CD-ROM

Engage students in a whole-class interactive review of Key Concepts. Edit content as you wish.

 POWER PRESENTATIONS

Reviewing Vocabulary

Draw a word triangle for each of the terms below. On the bottom row, write the term and your own definition of it. Above that, write a sentence in which you use the term correctly. At the top, draw a small picture to show what the term looks like. A sample is completed for you.

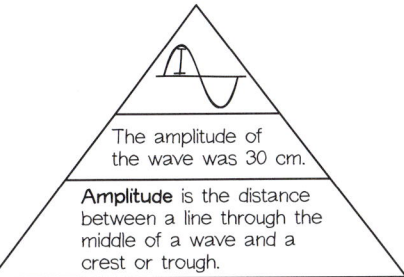

1. transverse wave
2. diffraction
3. frequency
4. medium
5. crest
6. interference
7. reflection
8. trough
9. refraction
10. wavelength

Reviewing Key Concepts

Multiple Choice *Choose the letter of the best answer.*

11. The direction in which a transverse wave travels is
    a. the same direction as the disturbance
    b. toward the disturbance
    c. from the disturbance downward
    d. at right angles to the disturbance

12. An example of a longitudinal wave is a
    a. water wave
    b. stadium wave
    c. sound wave
    d. rope wave

13. Which statement best defines a wave medium?
    a. the material through which a wave travels
    b. a point halfway between the crest and trough of a wave
    c. the distance from one wave crest to the next
    d. the speed at which waves travel in water

14. As you increase the amplitude of a wave, you also increase the
    a. frequency
    b. wavelength
    c. speed
    d. energy

15. To identify the amplitude in a longitudinal wave, you would measure areas of
    a. reflection
    b. compression
    c. crests
    d. refraction

16. Which statement describes the relationship between frequency and wavelength?
    a. When frequency increases, wavelength increases.
    b. When frequency increases, wavelength decreases.
    c. When frequency increases, wavelength remains constant.
    d. When frequency increases, wavelength varies unpredictably.

17. For wave refraction to take place, a wave must
    a. increase in velocity
    b. enter a new medium
    c. increase in frequency
    d. merge with another wave

18. Which setup in a wave tank would best enable you to demonstrate diffraction?
    a. water only
    b. water and sand
    c. water and food coloring
    d. water and a barrier with a small gap

19. Two waves come together and interact to form a new, smaller wave. This process is called
    a. destructive interference
    b. constructive interference
    c. reflective interference
    d. positive interference

Chapter 15: **Waves** 511

Reviewing Vocabulary

Sample definitions are given below.

1. Amplitude is how high or low a wave is from its test position.
2. Diffraction is the spreading of waves through a hole.
3. Frequency is the number of waves passing a fixed point in a certain time.
4. A medium is anything a wave travels through.
5. A crest is the highest point of a wave.
6. Interference is the meeting of two waves.
7. Reflection is the bouncing back of a wave after it meets a barrier.
8. A trough is the lowest point of a wave.
9. Refraction is the bending of a wave as it moves from one medium into another.
10. Wavelength is the distance from crest to crest.

Reviewing Key Concepts

11. d
12. c
13. a
14. d
15. b
16. b
17. b
18. d
19. a

ASSESSMENT RESOURCES

UNIT ASSESSMENT BOOK
- Chapter Test A, pp. 6–9
- Chapter Test B, pp. 10–13
- Chapter Test C, pp. 14–17
- Alternative Assessment, pp. 18–19

SPANISH ASSESSMENT BOOK
Spanish Chapter Test, pp. 281–284

Technology Resources

Edit test items and answer choices.

 Test Generator CD-ROM

Visit **ClassZone.com** to extend test practice.

 Test Practice

Chapter 15 **511**

Thinking Critically

20. a and b measure amplitude
21. wavelength
22. 3 waves
23. frequency
24. 3 wavelengths/s
25. No, it could be a liquid or gas.
26. By drawing the pendulum back farther; The swinging motion has amplitude, frequency, and wavelength.
27. It might diffract through the gap.
28. Sample answer: Yes, in each instance one wave meets another and changes it in some way.

Using Math in Science

29. $S = \lambda \cdot f$

    $S = 1.2 \dfrac{m}{(wave)} \cdot 2 \dfrac{(wave)}{s}$

    $= 2.4$ m/s

30. $S = \lambda \cdot f$

    $S = 9 \dfrac{m}{(wave)} \cdot 0.42 \dfrac{(wave)}{s}$

    $= 3.78$ m/s

31. $S = \lambda \cdot f; \lambda = s \div f$

    $\lambda = 340$ m/s $\div 10{,}000 \dfrac{(wave)}{s}$

    $= 0.034$ m, or 3.4 cm

32. $S = \lambda \cdot f; f = s \div \lambda$

    $f = 2.5$ m/s $\div 4 \dfrac{m}{(wave)}$

    $= 0.625$, round to 0.63 $\dfrac{(wave)}{s}$

the BIG idea

33. Sample answer: The wave has transferred energy to a surfer.
34. Sample answer: (1) Sound in an empty room. (2) Ripples in a pond. (3) Waves in a swimming pool.
35. Students' paragraphs should demonstrate an understanding of the Big Idea.

UNIT PROJECTS

Give students the appropriate Unit Project worksheets from the URB for their projects. Both directions and rubrics can be used as a guide.

 Unit Projects, pp. 5–10

Thinking Critically

Use the diagram below to answer the next two questions.

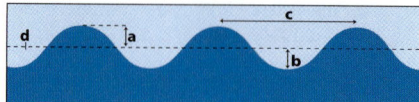

20. What two letters in the diagram measure the same thing? What do they both measure?

21. In the diagram above, what does the letter c measure?

Use the diagram below to answer the next three questions. The diagram shows waves passing a fixed point.

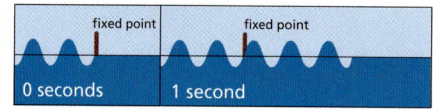

22. At 0 seconds, no waves have passed. How many waves have passed after 1 second?

23. What is being measured in the diagram?

24. How would you write the measurement taken in the diagram?

25. **EVALUATE** Do you think the following is an accurate definition of medium? Explain your answer.

    A **medium** is any solid through which waves travel.

26. **APPLY** Picture a pendulum. The pendulum is swinging back and forth at a steady rate. How could you make it swing higher? How is swinging a pendulum like making a wave?

27. **PREDICT** What might happen to an ocean wave that encounters a gap or hole in a cliff along the shore?

28. **EVALUATE** Do you think *interference* is an appropriate name for the types of wave interaction you read about in Section 15.3? Explain your answer.

Using Math in Science

29. At what speed is the wave below traveling if it has a frequency of 2/s?

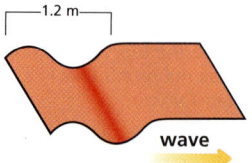

30. An ocean wave has a wavelength of 9 m and a frequency of 0.42/s. What is the wave's speed?

31. Suppose a sound wave has a frequency of 10,000/s. The wave's speed is 340 m/s. Calculate the wavelength of this sound wave.

32. A water wave is traveling at a speed of 2.5 m/s. The wave has a wavelength of 4 m. Calculate the frequency of this water wave.

the BIG idea

33. **INTERPRET** Look back at the photograph at the start of the chapter on pages 486–487. How does this photograph illustrate a transfer of energy?

34. **SYNTHESIZE** Describe three situations in which you can predict the behavior of waves.

35. **SUMMARIZE** Write a paragraph summarizing this chapter. Use the big idea from page 486 as the topic sentence. Then write an example from each of the key concepts listed under the big idea.

UNIT PROJECTS

If you are doing a unit project, make a folder for your project. Include in your folder a list of the resources you will need, the date on which the project is due, and a schedule to track your progress. Begin gathering data.

MONITOR AND RETEACH

If students have difficulty answering questions 20 and 21, make flash cards for all the vocabulary words in the chapter. Draw a wave diagram on the board. Have students play a flash-card game. When a word and definition apply to some part of the diagram, have students identify it. For vocabulary words that are illustrated in the chapter, have students find a visual that depicts the vocabulary word. Students may benefit from summarizing one or more sections of the chapter.

 Summarizing the Chapter, pp. 71–72

Standardized Test Practice

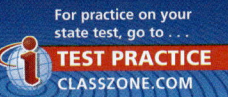

For practice on your state test, go to...
TEST PRACTICE
CLASSZONE.COM

Interpreting Diagrams

Study the illustration below and then answer the questions.

The illustration below shows a wave channel, a way of making and studying water waves. The motor moves the rod, which moves the paddle back and forth. The movement of the paddle makes waves, which move down the length of the channel. The material behind the paddle absorbs the waves generated in that direction.

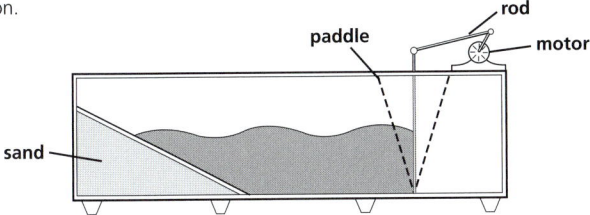

1. An experimenter can adjust the position of the rod on the arm of the motor. Placing it closer to the motor makes shallower waves. Placing it farther from the motor makes deeper waves. What property of waves does this affect?
   a. amplitude
   b. direction
   c. frequency
   d. wavelength

2. By changing motor speeds, an experimenter can make the paddle move faster or slower. What property of waves does this affect?
   a. amplitude
   b. direction
   c. trough depth
   d. wavelength

3. Sand is piled up in the channel at the end of the tank opposite the motor. When waves pass over this sand, their wavelengths shorten. Assuming that the speed of the waves stays the same, their frequency
   a. stays the same
   b. increases
   c. decreases
   d. cannot be predicted

4. Suppose there was no sand at the end of the tank opposite the paddle. In that case, the waves would hit the glass wall. What would they do then?
   a. stop
   b. reflect
   c. refract
   d. diffract

Extended Response

Answer the two questions below in detail.

5. Suppose temperatures in one 10-day period were as follows: 94°, 96°, 95°, 97°, 95°, 98°, 99°, 97°, 99°, and 98°. Make a simple line graph of the data. In what ways is the series of temperatures similar to a wave, and in what ways does it differ?

6. Lydia and Bill each drop a ball of the same size into the same tank of water but at two different spots. Both balls produce waves that spread across the surface of the water. As the two sets of waves cross each other, the water forms high crests in some places. What can you say about both waves? Explain your answer.

Chapter 15: **Waves** 513

Interpreting Diagrams

1. a
2. d
3. c
4. b

Extended Response

5. RUBRIC
4 points for a response that correctly answers the question and uses the following terms accurately:
- amplitude
- frequency
- wavelength

Sample: The series of high temperatures is similar to a wave in that its graph has amplitude, frequency, and wavelength, but it is different in that energy is not transferred from one place to another.

3 points for a response that correctly answers the question and uses two terms accurately
2 points for a response that correctly uses one term accurately
1 point for a response that correctly answers the question but doesn't use the terms

6. RUBRIC
4 points for a response that correctly answers the question and uses the following terms accurately:
- amplitude
- crests
- trough

Sample: Both waves have the same amplitude and cancel each other out because the crests and troughs were matched exactly. This is an example of destructive interference showing that when the two waves meet, the trough of one wave joins with the crest of the other.

3 points for a response that correctly answers the question and uses two terms accurately
2 points for a response that correctly uses one term accurately
1 point for a response that correctly answers the question but doesn't use the terms

METACOGNITIVE ACTIVITY

Have students answer the following questions in their **Science Notebook:**
1. What did you find most surprising about how waves behave?
2. What questions do you still have about the ways waves interact?
3. What did you learn about waves that can be applied to your Unit Project?

CHAPTER 16 Sound

Physical Science
UNIFYING PRINCIPLES

PRINCIPLE 1
Matter is made of particles too small to see.

PRINCIPLE 2
Matter changes form and moves from place to place.

PRINCIPLE 3
Energy changes from one form to another, but it cannot be created or destroyed.

PRINCIPLE 4
Physical forces affect the movement of all matter on Earth and throughout the universe.

Unit 4: Waves, Sound, and Light
BIG IDEAS

CHAPTER 15
Waves
Waves transfer energy and interact in predictable ways.

CHAPTER 16
Sound
Sound waves transfer energy through vibrations.

CHAPTER 17
Electromagnetic Waves
Electromagnetic waves transfer energy through radiation.

CHAPTER 18
Light and Optics
Optical tools depend on the wave behavior of light.

CHAPTER 16
KEY CONCEPTS

SECTION 1
Sound is a wave.
1. Sound is a type of mechanical wave.
2. Sound waves vibrate particles.
3. The speed of sound depends on its medium.

SECTION 2
Frequency determines pitch.
1. Pitch depends on the frequency of a sound wave.
2. The motion of the source of a sound affects its pitch.

SECTION 3
Intensity determines loudness.
1. Intensity depends on the amplitude of a sound wave.
2. The intensity of sound can be controlled.
3. Intense sound can damage hearing.

SECTION 4
Sound has many uses.
1. Ultrasound waves are used to detect objects.
2. Sound waves can produce music.
3. Sound can be recorded and reproduced.

 The Big Idea Flow Chart is available on p. T9 in the **UNIT TRANSPARENCY BOOK**.

Previewing Content

SECTION 1 — Sound is a wave. pp. 517–524

1. Sound is a type of mechanical wave.
Sound is a longitudinal wave. **Vibrations** in the wave move in the same direction as the wave. Because sound is a mechanical wave, it must travel through a medium.

Humans detect sound because of vibrations in the ear caused by sound waves.

2. Sound waves vibrate particles.
As sound waves push against molecules in the medium, they compress the molecules, creating bands of high and low pressure. These bands of pressure push and pull on the surrounding air, which then pushes and pulls on the air around that and so on. This creates a sound wave travelling through the air.

Materials and Sound Speeds		
Medium	State	Speed of Sound
Air (20°C)	Gas	344 m/s (769 mi/h)
Water (20°C)	Liquid	1,400 m/s (3,130 mi/h)
Steel (20°C)	Solid	5,000 m/s (11,200 mi/h)

Temperature and Sound Speeds		
Medium	Temperature	Speed of Sound
Air	0°C (32°F)	331 m/s (741 mi/h)
Air	100°C (212°F)	386 m/s (864 mi/h)

Sound waves can travel through mediums that are made up of particles, but sound waves cannot travel through a vacuum.

3. The speed of sound depends on its medium.
The speed of sound depends on the state and the temperature of the medium.
- Sound usually travels most quickly through a solid and most slowly through a gas.
- Sound travels more quickly through a specific medium at higher temperatures.

SECTION 2 — Frequency determines pitch. pp. 525–531

1. Pitch depends on the frequency of a sound wave.
Pitch is an indication of how high or how low a sound is. A high-frequency wave has a short wavelength and produces a high pitch. A low-frequency wave has a long wavelength and produces a low pitch.

Hertz is the unit used to measure frequency and therefore pitch. One hertz is one wavelength per second.

All objects have a natural frequency of vibrations. When a sound wave is produced that matches an object's natural frequency, its waves combine to create sound with a larger amplitude. This increase is **resonance.**

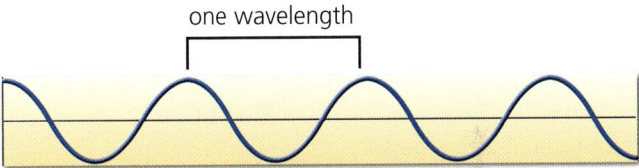
Low-frequency, low-pitched sound wave

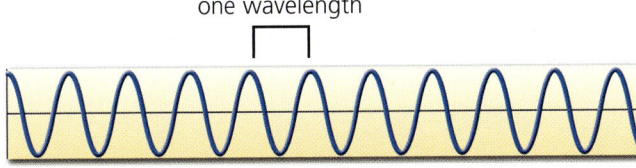
High-frequency, high-pitched sound wave

Timbre, or sound quality, is affected by
- the combination of waves produced by an object and
- how the sound starts and stops.

2. The motion of the source of a sound affects its pitch.
The **Doppler effect** is a change in pitch that occurs because the source or receiver of a sound is moving. Because the sound source is a little closer to the receiver each time it vibrates, it takes less time for the compression to reach the receiver. The decrease in distance makes the wavelength shorter, and the pitch rises.

Common Misconceptions

TYPES OF WAVES Students might think that all waves are the same. They should be aware that waves are classified according to whether they need a medium to travel or not. Electromagnetic waves do not need a medium, and mechanical waves do.

This misconception is addressed on p. 518.

MISCONCEPTION DATABASE
CLASSZONE.COM Background on student misconceptions

SPEED OF SOUND The phrase "the speed of sound" might lead students to assume that sound always travels at the same speed. Mechanical waves, such as sound, travel at a speed that depends on the nature and temperature of the medium.

This misconception is addressed on p. 522.

Chapter 16: **Sound** 513B

Previewing Content

SECTION

 Intensity determines loudness. pp. 532–537

1. **Intensity depends on the amplitude of a sound wave.**
   Intensity is the amount of energy a sound wave has, measured in **decibels** (dB). Low-intensity sound waves are heard as quiet sounds. Louder sounds are produced by high-intensity sound waves.

2. **The intensity of sound can be controlled.**
   Changing the amount of energy in a sound wave changes the sound's intensity without changing its pitch or quality.
   - A muffler decreases intensity.
   - An **amplifier** increases intensity.

3. **Intense sound can damage hearing.**
   The hair cells in the cochlea in the ear are easily damaged by loud sounds. Long-term exposure to sounds of 90 dB or more can damage human hearing. Even short bursts of very intense sound can deafen a person.

SECTION

 Sound has many uses. pp. 538–545

1. **Ultrasound waves are used to detect objects.**
   Reflected ultrasound waves are used to detect the presence and location of objects.
   - Some animals, such as bats, use **echolocation,** which involves sending out ultrasound signals and interpreting the returning sound echoes.
   - Humans use **sonar,** a form of echolocation, to locate objects underwater.
   - In medicine, **ultrasound** is used to treat stones that form in the human body and to scan internal organs.

2. **Sound waves can produce music.**
   Noise is sound with no pattern. Music is sound with clear patterns of pitch and rhythm. Stringed, wind, and percussion instruments all produce vibrations in different ways, which accounts for their distinctive timbres.

3. **Sound can be recorded and reproduced.**
   Vibrations can be changed to other types of signals or stored as reproducible information.
   - Some methods of communication, such as the telephone, change sound waves into electrical signals. These signals travel to a receiver that changes them back into sound.
   - Sound can be recorded as physical grooves (records) or pits (CDs) or as magnetic information (tapes) that can be changed back to sound waves.

Common Misconceptions

HEARING DAMAGE Students commonly assume that any hearing damage resulting from loud noises is temporary. Noises greater than 90 dB can cause permanent hearing damage.

 This misconception is addressed on p. 535.

 MISCONCEPTION DATABASE
CLASSZONE.COM Background on student misconceptions

Previewing Labs

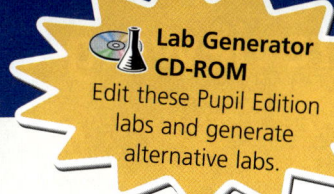

EXPLORE the BIG idea

What Gives a Sound Its Qualities? p. 515 Students will explore sound to discover its properties.	**TIME** 5 minutes **MATERIALS** table
How Does Size Affect Sound? p. 515 Students test three nails to find that the size of a sample affects its pitch.	**TIME** 10 minutes **MATERIALS** 3 different-sized nails of the same material, string (at least 1 m), scissors, metal spoon
Internet Activity: Sound, p. 515 Students discover how air particles move as sound travels through air.	**TIME** 20 minutes **MATERIALS** computer with Internet access

SECTION 1

EXPLORE Sound, p. 517 Students listen to sounds traveling via string to understand that sound travels through a medium.	**TIME** 10 minutes **MATERIALS** 75 cm of string; large, metal spoon
INVESTIGATE Sound Energy, p. 521 Students observe sound waves moving salt to find out that sound transfers energy.	**TIME** 10 minutes **MATERIALS** clean jar, a pinch of table salt, balloon, scissors, rubber band, pencil with good eraser end

SECTION 2

EXPLORE Pitch, p. 525 Students observe sounds to find out what affects pitch.	**TIME** 5 minutes **MATERIALS** ruler
INVESTIGATE Sound Frequency, p. 528 Students listen to rubber bands at differing tensions and infer the relationship between frequency and pitch.	**TIME** 20 minutes **MATERIALS** two rubber bands of different sizes; small, open box; 16 cm tape

SECTION 3

INVESTIGATE Loudness, p. 533 Students pluck a rubber band to observe the relationship between amplitude and loudness.	**TIME** 15 minutes **MATERIALS** piece of cardboard, 25 cm long; scissors; large rubber band; two pencils; ruler

SECTION 4

EXPLORE Echoes, p. 538 Students use sound to detect an object.	**TIME** 10 minutes **MATERIALS** two cardboard tubes, 10 cm tape, book
CHAPTER INVESTIGATION **Build a Stringed Instrument,** pp. 544–545 Students make a simple stringed instrument and find out how it can produce different pitches.	**TIME** 40 minutes **MATERIALS** book, 3–5 rubber bands, two pencils, ruler, shoebox, scissors

R **Additional INVESTIGATION,** Exploring Resonance, A, B, & C, pp. 132–140; Teacher Instructions, pp. 284–285

Chapter 16: **Sound** 513D

Previewing Chapter Resources

	INTEGRATED TECHNOLOGY		LABS AND ACTIVITIES

CHAPTER 16
Sound

 CLASSZONE.COM
- eEdition Plus
- EasyPlanner Plus
- Misconception Database
- Content Review
- Test Practice
- Visualizations
- Resource Centers
- Internet Activity: Sound
- Math Tutorial

 CD-ROMS
- eEdition
- EasyPlanner
- Power Presentations
- Content Review
- Lab Generator
- Test Generator

 AUDIO CDS
- Audio Readings
- Audio Readings in Spanish

 SCILINKS.ORG

 EXPLORE the Big Idea, p. 515
- What Gives a Sound Its Qualities?
- How Does Size Affect Sound?
- Internet Activity: Sound

 UNIT RESOURCE BOOK
Unit Projects, pp. 5–10

 Lab Generator CD-ROM
Generate customized labs.

SECTION 1
Sound is a wave.
pp. 517–524

Time: 2 periods (1 block)
 Lesson Plan, pp. 73–74

 RESOURCE CENTER, Supersonic Aircraft

UNIT TRANSPARENCY BOOK
- Big Idea Flow Chart, p. T9
- Daily Vocabulary Scaffolding, p. T10
- Note-Taking Model, p. T11
- 3-Minute Warm-Up, p. T12

- EXPLORE Sound, p. 517
- INVESTIGATE Sound Energy, p. 521
- Extreme Science, p. 524

 UNIT RESOURCE BOOK
Datasheet, Sound Energy, p. 82

SECTION 2
Frequency determines pitch.
pp. 525–531

Time: 2 periods (1 block)
 Lesson Plan, pp. 84–85

 VISUALIZATION, Doppler Effect

UNIT TRANSPARENCY BOOK
- Daily Vocabulary Scaffolding, p. T10
- 3-Minute Warm-Up, p. T12
- "Sound Frequencies Heard by Animals" Visual, p. T14

- EXPLORE Pitch, p. 525
- INVESTIGATE Sound Frequency, p. 528

 UNIT RESOURCE BOOK
- Datasheet, Sound Frequency, p. 93
- Additional INVESTIGATION, Exploring Resonance, A, B, & C, pp. 132–140

SECTION 3
Intensity determines loudness.
pp. 532–537

Time: 2 periods (1 block)
 Lesson Plan, pp. 95–96

 RESOURCE CENTER, Sound Safety
MATH TUTORIAL

 UNIT TRANSPARENCY BOOK
- Daily Vocabulary Scaffolding, p. T10
- 3-Minute Warm-Up, p. T13

- INVESTIGATE Loudness, p. 533
- Math in Science, p. 537

 UNIT RESOURCE BOOK
- Datasheet, Loudness, p. 104
- Math Support, p. 121
- Math Practice, p. 122

SECTION 4
Sound has many uses.
pp. 538–545

Time: 4 periods (2 blocks)
 Lesson Plan, pp. 106–107

 RESOURCE CENTER, Musical Instruments

 UNIT TRANSPARENCY BOOK
- Big Idea Flow Chart, p. T9
- Daily Vocabulary Scaffolding, p. T10
- 3-Minute Warm-Up, p. T13
- Chapter Outline, pp. T15–16

- EXPLORE Echoes, p. 538
- CHAPTER INVESTIGATION, Build a Stringed Instrument, pp. 544–545

 UNIT RESOURCE BOOK
CHAPTER INVESTIGATION, Build a Stringed Instrument, A, B, & C, pp. 123–131

KEY TO ICONS
- CD/CD-ROM
- Teacher Edition
- UNIT TRANSPARENCY BOOK
- 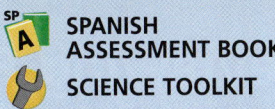 SPANISH ASSESSMENT BOOK
-  INTERNET
- Pupil Edition
- UNIT RESOURCE BOOK
- UNIT ASSESSMENT BOOK
- SCIENCE TOOLKIT

READING AND REINFORCEMENT

- Description Wheel, B20–21
- Outline, C43
- Daily Vocabulary Scaffolding, H1–8

UNIT RESOURCE BOOK
- Vocabulary Practice, pp. 118–119
- Decoding Support, p. 120
- Summarizing the Chapter, pp. 141–142

Audio Readings CD
Listen to Pupil Edition.

Audio Readings in Spanish CD
Listen to Pupil Edition in Spanish

UNIT RESOURCE BOOK
- Reading Study Guide, A & B, pp. 75–78
- Spanish Reading Study Guide, pp. 79–80
- Challenge and Extension, p. 81
- Reinforcing Key Concepts, p. 83

UNIT RESOURCE BOOK
- Reading Study Guide, A & B, pp. 86–89
- Spanish Reading Study Guide, pp. 90–91
- Challenge and Extension, p. 92
- Reinforcing Key Concepts, p. 94
- Challenge Reading, pp. 116–117

UNIT RESOURCE BOOK
- Reading Study Guide, A & B, pp. 97–100
- Spanish Reading Study Guide, pp. 101–102
- Challenge and Extension, p. 103
- Reinforcing Key Concepts, p. 105

UNIT RESOURCE BOOK
- Reading Study Guide, A & B, pp. 108–111
- Spanish Reading Study Guide, pp. 112–113
- Challenge and Extension, p. 114
- Reinforcing Key Concepts, p. 115

ASSESSMENT

- Chapter Review, pp. 547–548
- Standardized Test Practice, p. 549

UNIT ASSESSMENT BOOK
- Diagnostic Test, pp. 20–21
- Chapter Test, A, B, & C, pp. 26–37
- Alternative Assessment, pp. 38–39

Spanish Chapter Test, pp. 285–288

Test Generator CD-ROM
Generate customized tests.

Lab Generator CD-ROM
Rubrics for Labs

Ongoing Assessment, pp. 517–523

Section 16.1 Review, p. 523

UNIT ASSESSMENT BOOK
Section 16.1 Quiz, p. 22

Ongoing Assessment, pp. 525–531

Section 16.2 Review, p. 531

UNIT ASSESSMENT BOOK
Section 16.2 Quiz, p. 23

Ongoing Assessment, pp. 532–536

Section 16.3 Review, p. 536

UNIT ASSESSMENT BOOK
Section 16.3 Quiz, p. 24

Ongoing Assessment, pp. 538, 540–543

Section 16.4 Review, p. 543

UNIT ASSESSMENT BOOK
Section 16.4 Quiz, p. 25

STANDARDS

National Standards
A.1–8, A.9.a–g, E.2–5, F.5.a–d

See p. 514 for the standards.

National Standards
A.2–8, A.9.a–c, A.9.e–f, F.5.d

National Standards
A.2–8, A.9.a–f, F.5.b

National Standards
A.2–8, A.9.a–f, F.5.a, F.5.c

National Standards
A.1–7, A.9.a–b, A.9.d–g, E.2–5, F.5.a–c

Chapter 16: **Sound** 513F

Previewing Resources for Differentiated Instruction

CHAPTER INVESTIGATION

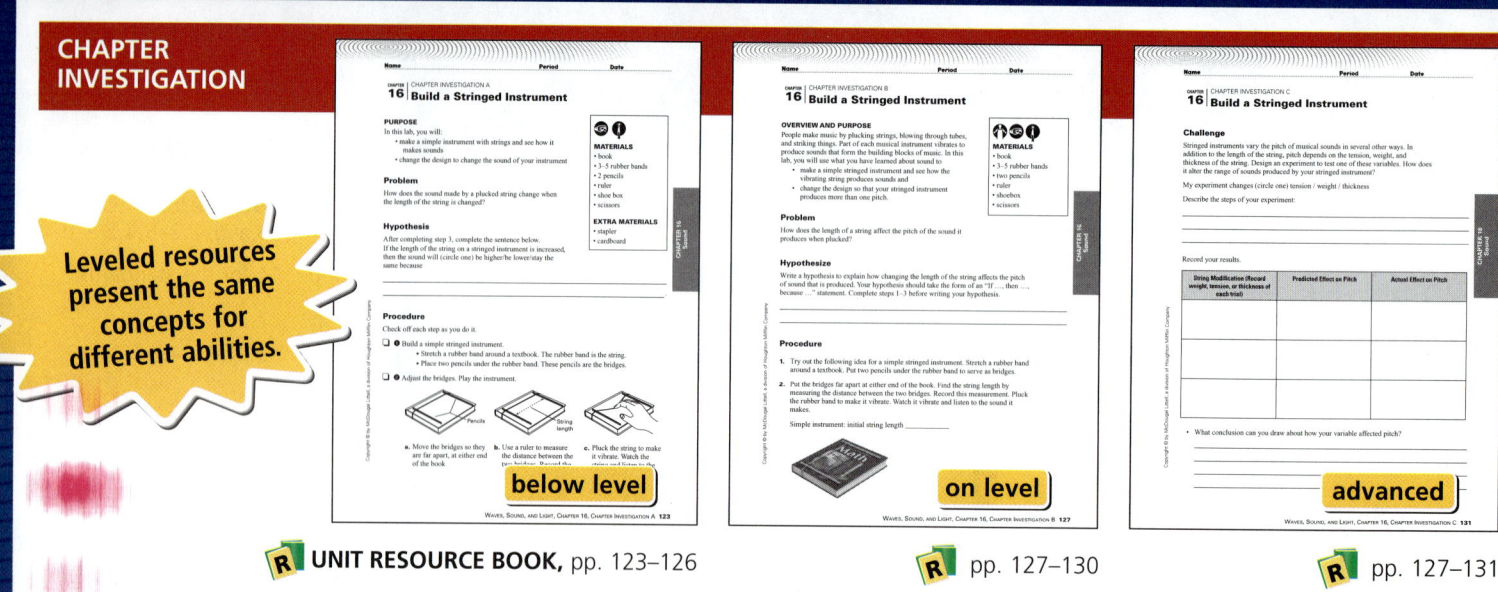

Leveled resources present the same concepts for different abilities.

UNIT RESOURCE BOOK, pp. 123–126   pp. 127–130   pp. 127–131

READING STUDY GUIDE

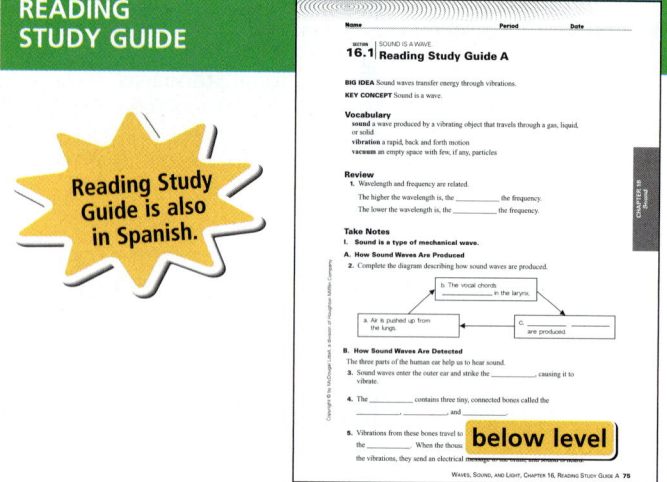
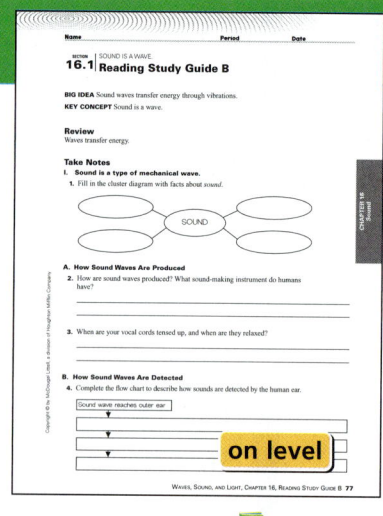
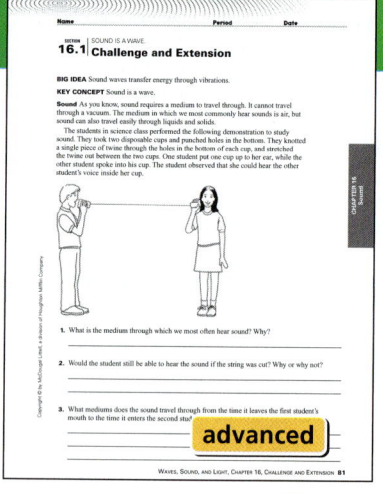

Reading Study Guide is also in Spanish.

UNIT RESOURCE BOOK, pp. 75–76   pp. 77–78   p. 81

CHAPTER TEST

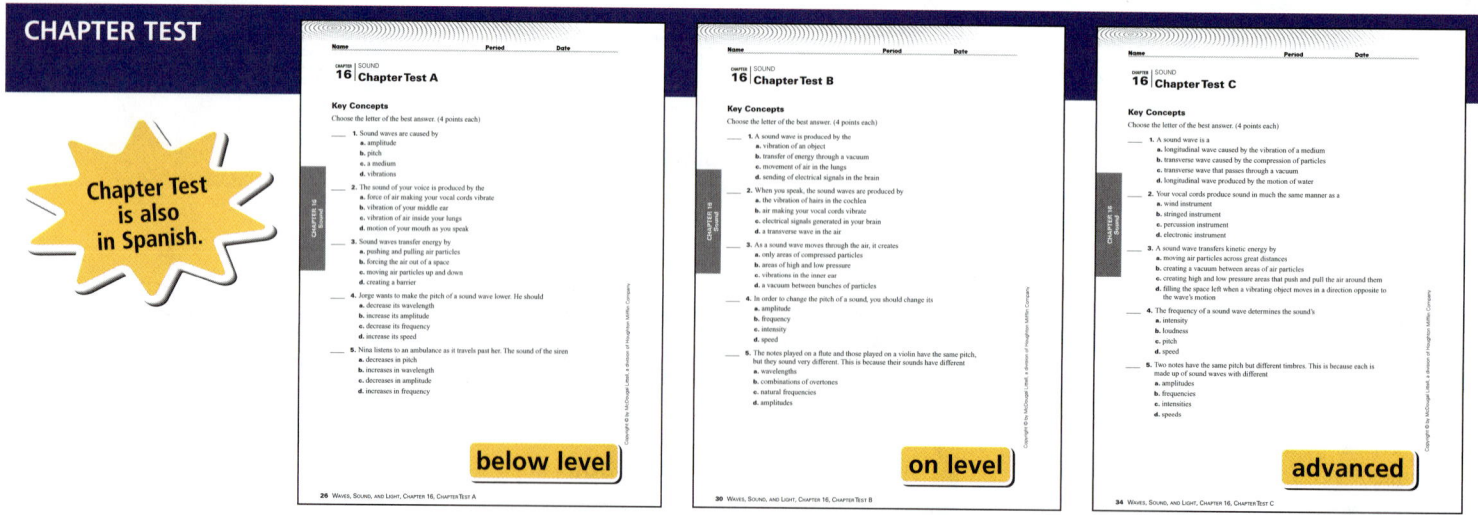

Chapter Test is also in Spanish.

UNIT ASSESSMENT BOOK, pp. 26–29   pp. 30–33   pp. 34–37

Unit 4: Waves, Sound, and Light

TECHNOLOGY

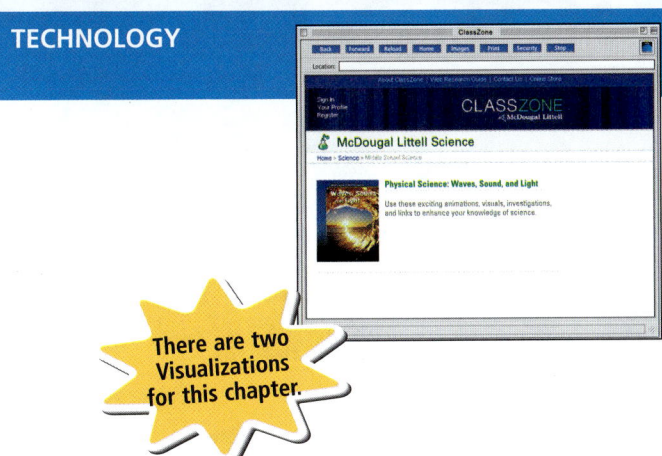
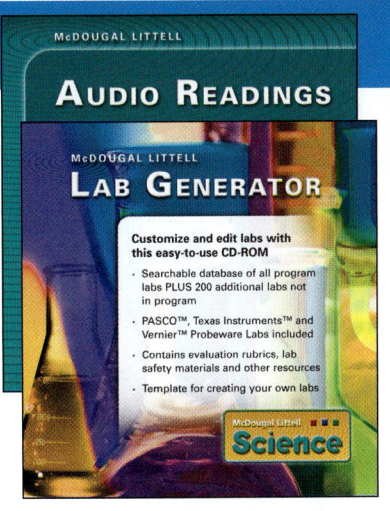
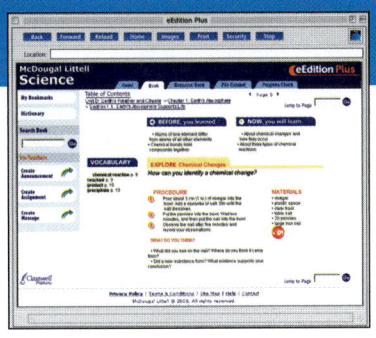

There are two Visualizations for this chapter.

CLASSZONE.COM   **CD/CD-ROMS**   **CLASSZONE.COM**

VISUAL CONTENT

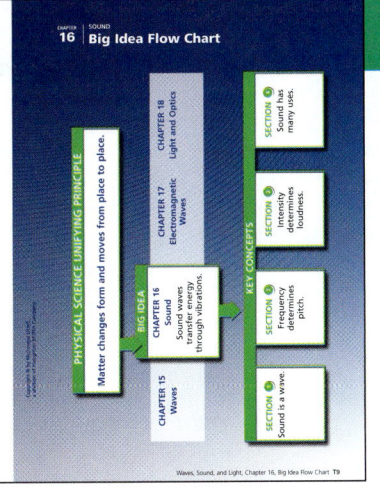
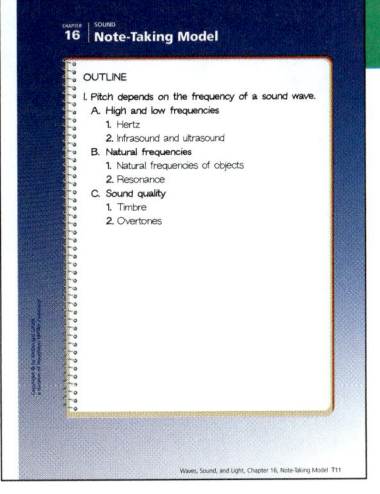
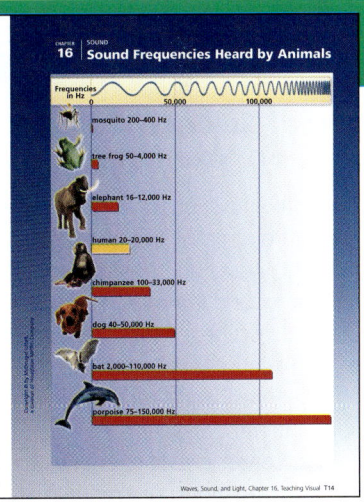

UNIT TRANSPARENCY BOOK, p. T9   p. T11   p. T14

MORE SUPPORT

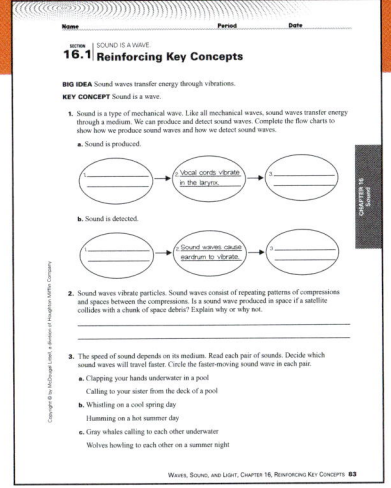
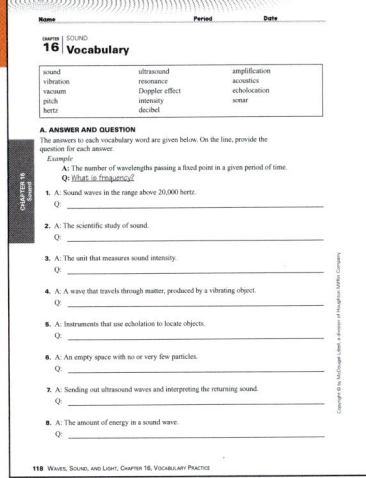
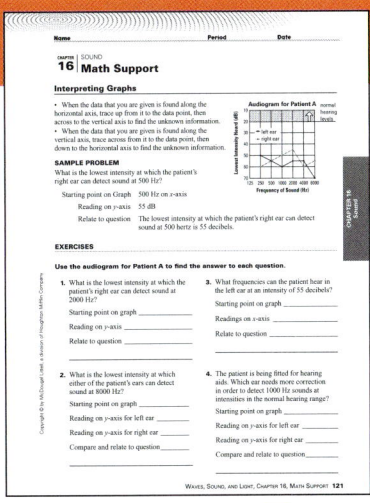

Reinforcing Key Concepts for each section

UNIT RESOURCE BOOK, p. 83   pp. 118–119   p. 121

Chapter 16: **Sound** 513H

CHAPTER 16 Sound

INTRODUCE

Have students look at the photograph of the guitar player and discuss how the question in the box links to the Big Idea:

- What role do guitar strings play in producing vibrations?
- What role does the body of the guitar play in producing sound?
- What part of the human body receives the vibrations from the guitar?
- How are the vibrations from the guitar perceived as sound?

National Science Education Standards

A.1–8 Identify questions that can be answered through scientific investigations; design and conduct an investigation; use tools to gather and interpret data; use evidence to describe, predict, explain, model; think critically to make relationships between evidence and explanation; recognize different explanations and predictions; communicate scientific procedures and explanations; use mathematics.

A.9.a–g Understand scientific inquiry by using different investigations, methods, mathematics, technology, and explanations based on logic, evidence, and skepticism. Data often results in new investigations.

E.2-5 Design, implement, evaluate a solution or product; communicate technological design.

F.5.a–d Science and technology in society

CHAPTER 16 Sound

the BIG idea

Sound waves transfer energy through vibrations.

How is this guitar player producing sound?

Key Concepts

SECTION 1 Sound is a wave.
Learn how sound waves are produced and detected.

SECTION 2 Frequency determines pitch.
Learn about the relationship between the frequency of a sound wave and its pitch.

SECTION 3 Intensity determines loudness.
Learn how the energy of a sound wave relates to its loudness.

SECTION 4 Sound has many uses.
Learn how sound waves are used to detect objects and to make music.

Internet Preview

CLASSZONE.COM
Chapter 16 online resources: Content Review, two Visualizations, three Resource Centers, Math Tutorial, Test Practice

514 Unit 4: Waves, Sound, and Light

INTERNET PREVIEW

CLASSZONE.COM For student use with the following pages:

Review and Practice
- Content Review, pp. 516, 546
- Math Tutorial: Interpreting Line Graphs, p. 537
- Test Practice, p. 549

Activities and Resources
- Internet Activity, p. 515
- Visualization: Doppler Effect, p. 531
- Resource Centers: Supersonic Aircraft, p. 524; Sound Safety, p. 536; Musical Instruments, p. 540

What is Sound?
Code: MDL028

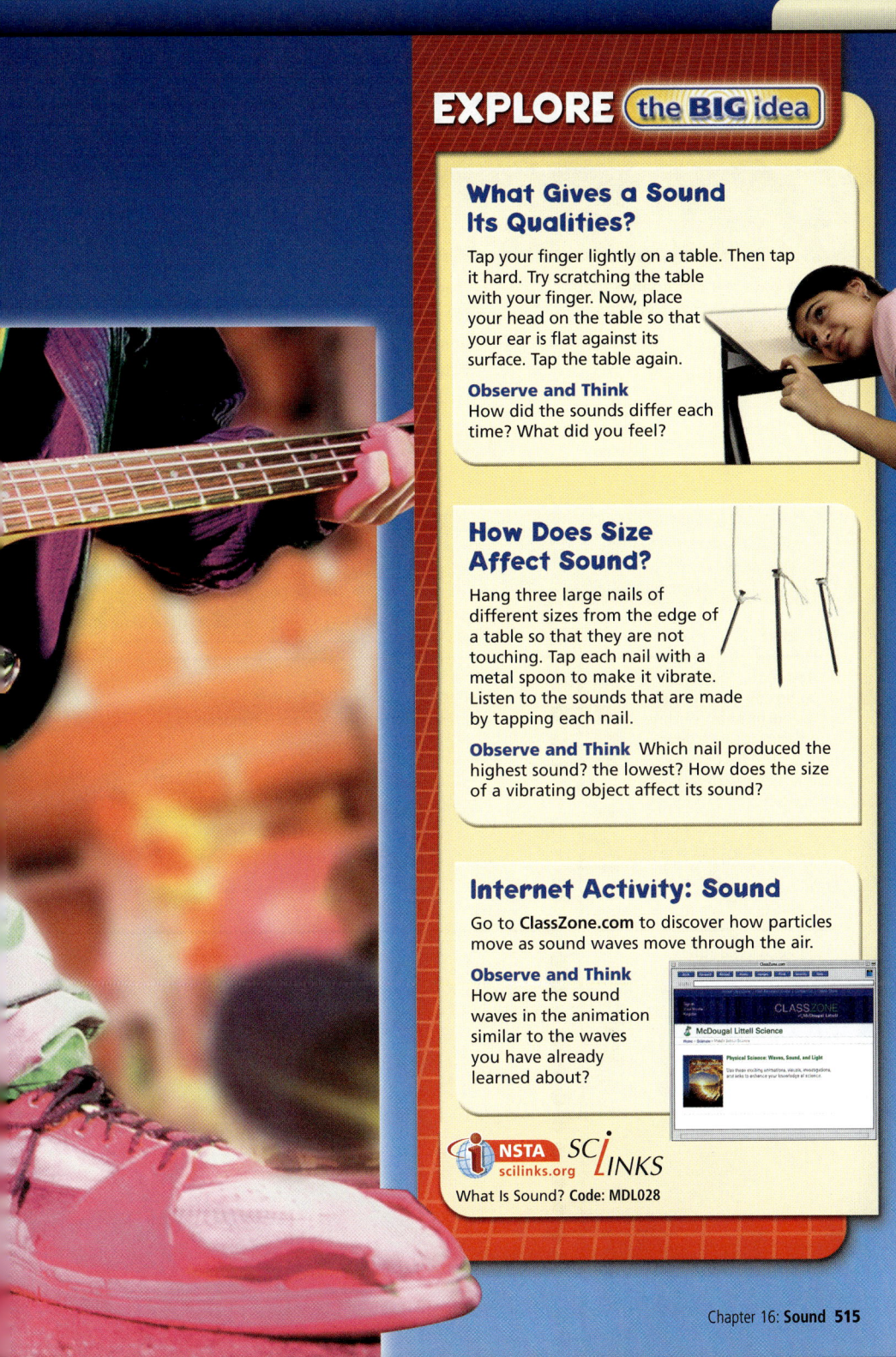

EXPLORE the BIG idea

What Gives a Sound Its Qualities?

Tap your finger lightly on a table. Then tap it hard. Try scratching the table with your finger. Now, place your head on the table so that your ear is flat against its surface. Tap the table again.

Observe and Think How did the sounds differ each time? What did you feel?

How Does Size Affect Sound?

Hang three large nails of different sizes from the edge of a table so that they are not touching. Tap each nail with a metal spoon to make it vibrate. Listen to the sounds that are made by tapping each nail.

Observe and Think Which nail produced the highest sound? the lowest? How does the size of a vibrating object affect its sound?

Internet Activity: Sound

Go to ClassZone.com to discover how particles move as sound waves move through the air.

Observe and Think How are the sound waves in the animation similar to the waves you have already learned about?

NSTA SCILINKS
scilinks.org
What Is Sound? Code: MDL028

Chapter 16: **Sound** 515

TEACHING WITH TECHNOLOGY

Tape Recorder Use a tape recorder to record the sounds of the stringed instruments the students build in the Chapter Investigation on pp. 544–545. Have students listen to the sounds so they can hear the differences in pitch between the different instrument designs.

CBL and Probeware If students have probeware, you might encourage them to use a microphone during activities and demonstrations throughout the chapter.

EXPLORE the BIG idea

These inquiry-based activities are appropriate for use at home or as a supplement to classroom instruction.

What Gives a Sound Its Qualities?

PURPOSE To introduce students to sound properties such as loudness, pitch, and general sound quality.

TIP *10 min.* Adapt the activity for students who might be hearing impaired. Depending on the degree of impairment, students might tap with an object that makes more noise than their fingernail.

Answer: The sounds each had a different quality. Students should feel the vibrations in the table.

REVISIT after p. 529.

How Does Size Affect Sound?

PURPOSE To show that the size of a nail affects the pitch produced by striking it. Students observe that the size and shape of an object affects the frequency of the vibration produced by the object.

TIP *10 min.* All nails must be made of the same material, so that comparison involves only the size and not the type of material.

Answer: The smallest nail produced the highest sound. The largest nail produced the lowest sound. The size of an object affects how high or low its sound is.

REVISIT after p. 541.

Internet Activity: Sound

PURPOSE To help students visualize sound moving through air as longitudinal waves.

TIP *20 min.* Ask students to predict the difference in the sound waves produced by a jet engine and those produced by a whisper. Have students keep their predictions for evaluation at the end of Section 3.

Answer: Accept any of the following: The sound waves in the animation have amplitude, frequency, and wavelength; transfer energy; are longitudinal waves.

REVISIT after p. 521.

Chapter 16 **515**

PREPARE

◐ CONCEPT REVIEW

Activate Prior Knowledge

- Ask students to list examples of how waves transfer energy from one place to another. Examples include electromagnetic waves from the Sun warming Earth, and water waves moving a boat.
- Ask students to explain what a medium is.
- Review the concept of matter and that matter is present in a medium.

◐ TAKING NOTES

Outline

Outlining the chapter will help students pull together their ideas about sound and waves. Using the headings as a skeleton helps them identify the important points in the chapter.

Vocabulary Strategy

Students can use the description wheels not only to describe terms but also to differentiate between them.

Vocabulary and Note-Taking Resources

- Vocabulary Practice, pp. 118–119
- Decoding Support, p. 120

- Daily Vocabulary Scaffolding, p. T10
- Note-Taking Model, p. T11

- Description Wheel, B20–21
- Outline, C43
- Daily Vocabulary Scaffolding, H1–8

CHAPTER 16
Getting Ready to Learn

◐ CONCEPT REVIEW
- A wave is a disturbance that transfers energy from one place to another.
- Mechanical waves are waves that travel through matter.

◐ VOCABULARY REVIEW
medium p. 491
longitudinal wave p. 494
amplitude p. 497
wavelength p. 497
frequency p. 497

CONTENT REVIEW
CLASSZONE.COM
Review concepts and vocabulary.

▶ TAKING NOTES

OUTLINE

As you read, copy the headings on your paper in the form of an outline. Then add notes in your own words that summarize what you have read.

VOCABULARY STRATEGY

Place each vocabulary term at the center of a **description wheel** diagram. Write some words on the spokes describing it.

See the Note-Taking Handbook on pages R45–R51.

SCIENCE NOTEBOOK

I. Sound is a type of mechanical wave.
   A. How sound waves are produced
      1.
      2.
      3.
   B. How sound waves are detected
      1.
      2.
      3.

rapid back-and-forth motion / *can produce a sound* / **VIBRATION** / *usually too small to see* / *can make with vocal cords*

516 Unit 4: Waves, Sound, and Light

CHECK READINESS

Administer the Diagnostic Test to determine students' readiness for new science content and their mastery of requisite math skills.

 Diagnostic Test, pp. 20–21

Technology Resources

Students needing content and math skills should visit **ClassZone.com**.

- **CONTENT REVIEW**
- **MATH TUTORIAL**

 CONTENT REVIEW CD-ROM

KEY CONCEPT
Sound is a wave.

BEFORE, you learned
- Waves transfer energy
- Waves have wavelength, amplitude, and frequency

NOW, you will learn
- How sound waves are produced and detected
- How sound waves transfer energy
- What affects the speed of sound waves

VOCABULARY
sound p. 517
vibration p. 517
vacuum p. 521

EXPLORE Sound

What is sound?

PROCEDURE

1. Tie the middle of the string to the spoon handle.
2. Wrap the string ends around your left and right index fingers. Put the tips of these fingers gently in your ears and hold them there.
3. Stand over your desk so that the spoon dangles without touching your body or the desk. Then move a little to make the spoon tap the desk lightly. Listen to the sound.

MATERIALS
- piece of string
- large metal spoon

WHAT DO YOU THINK?
- What did you hear when the spoon tapped the desk?
- How did sound travel from the spoon to your ears?

Sound is a type of mechanical wave.

In the last chapter, you read that a mechanical wave travels through a material medium. Such mediums include air, water, and solid materials. Sound is an example of a mechanical wave. **Sound** is a wave that is produced by a vibrating object and travels through matter.

The disturbances that travel in a sound wave are vibrations. A **vibration** is a rapid, back-and-forth motion. Because the medium vibrates back and forth in the same direction as the wave travels, sound is a longitudinal wave. Like all mechanical waves, sound waves transfer energy through a medium.

 What do sound waves have in common with other mechanical waves? Your answer should include the word *energy*.

OUTLINE
Start an outline for this heading. Remember to leave room for details.

I. Main idea
  A. Supporting idea
    1. Detail
    2. Detail
  B. Supporting idea

Chapter 16: **Sound** 517

RESOURCES FOR DIFFERENTIATED INSTRUCTION

Below Level
UNIT RESOURCE BOOK
- Reading Study Guide A, pp. 75–76
- Decoding Support, p. 120

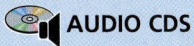 **AUDIO CDS**

Advanced
UNIT RESOURCE BOOK
Challenge and Extension, p. 81

English Learners
UNIT RESOURCE BOOK
Spanish Reading Study Guide, pp. 79–80

 **AUDIO CDS**
- Audio Readings in Spanish
- Audio Readings (English)

16.1 FOCUS

▶ Set Learning Goals
Students will
- Explain how sound waves are produced and detected.
- Explain how sound waves transfer energy.
- Describe what affects the speed of sound waves.
- Observe through experimentation that sound transfers energy.

◉ 3-Minute Warm-Up
Display Transparency 12 or copy this exercise on the board:

In each situation below, what might happen to show that the waves transfer energy?

1. a seaside beach in a storm *waves in the water eroding the beach*
2. an earthquake *waves in the earth shaking buildings*
3. movement of coils *a wave travelling from one end to the other*

 3-Minute Warm-Up, p. T12

16.1 MOTIVATE

EXPLORE Sound
PURPOSE To introduce the concept that sound travels through a medium

TIP *10 min.* If metal spoons are not available, use another metal object, such as a metal coat hanger.

WHAT DO YOU THINK? *A loud, ringing sound; the sound traveled through the string*

Ongoing Assessment

 *Answer: Sound waves transfer energy.*

Chapter 16 **517**

16.1 INSTRUCT

Address Misconceptions

IDENTIFY Ask: Do all waves have the same traits, or are there different types of waves? If students answer that all waves have the same traits, they hold the misconception that all waves are the same.

CORRECT Place a small amount of water in a flask. Attach a bell to a solid stopper with a wire and a thumbtack, so that it will hang in the middle of the flask when you insert the stopper. Shake the flask and listen to the bell. Shine a light through the flask against a dark surface.

Remove the stopper and heat the water to boiling. Immediately replace the stopper and allow the flask to cool. Shake the flask again, and note that the sound is much less. Shine a light through the flask again, and note that the intensity of the light is the same.

REASSESS Ask students to explain why sound decreased in intensity and light did not. *Sound is a mechanical wave and needs a medium. Heating the water causes the gases in the flask to expand. Cooling creates a partial vacuum, decreasing the amount of medium. Light is an electromagnetic wave that does not need a medium, so the partial vacuum does not affect its intensity.*

Technology Resources
Visit **ClassZone.com** for background on common student misconceptions.

MISCONCEPTION DATABASE

Ongoing Assessment

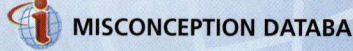 *Answer: The vocal cords vibrate, producing sound waves.*

Answer: The vibrations start when air from the lungs passes through the vocal cords.

READING TIP
When you see the word *push* or *pull*, think of force.

How Sound Waves Are Produced

The disturbances in a sound wave are vibrations that are usually too small to see. Vibrations are also required to start sound waves. A vibrating object pushes and pulls on the medium around it and sends out waves in all directions.

You have a sound-making instrument within your own body. It is the set of vocal cords within the voice box, or larynx, in your throat. Put several of your fingers against the front of your throat. Now hum. Do you feel the vibrations of your vocal cords?

Your vocal cords relax when you breathe to allow air to pass in and out of your windpipe. Your vocal cords tense up and draw close together when you are about to speak or sing. The illustration below shows how sound waves are produced by the human vocal cords.

① Your muscles push air up from your lungs and through the narrow opening between the vocal cords.

② The force of the air causes the vocal cords to vibrate.

③ The vibrating vocal cords produce sound waves.

CHECK YOUR READING How do human vocal cords produce sound waves?

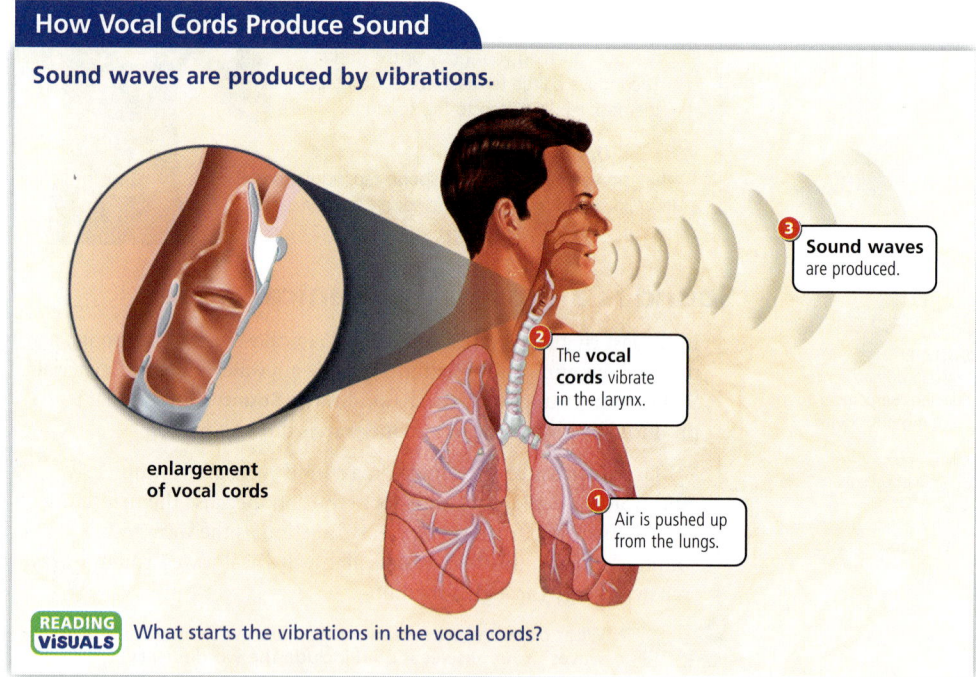

How Vocal Cords Produce Sound
Sound waves are produced by vibrations.

enlargement of vocal cords

① Air is pushed up from the lungs.
② The **vocal cords** vibrate in the larynx.
③ Sound waves are produced.

READING VISUALS What starts the vibrations in the vocal cords?

518 Unit 4: Waves, Sound, and Light

DIFFERENTIATE INSTRUCTION

 More Reading Support

A What makes sounds in your throat? *the vibrations of vocal cords*

English Learners Students new to English may be confused about what is required in review items, such as those on p. 523. For instructions such as "describe and explain," tell students exactly what each direction asks them to do.

- *describe:* Write as if drawing a picture. Give physical details.
- *explain:* Write as if listing steps in a process.

Students can practice both types of answers with simple questions, such as, "Describe and explain what happens in your classroom." It is also helpful to provide model answers.

How Sound Waves Are Detected

The shape of a human ear helps it collect sound waves. Picture a satellite dish. It collects radio waves from satellites. Your ear works in much the same way. Actually, what we typically call the ear is only the outer section of the ear. The illustration below shows the main parts of the human ear.

① Your outer ear collects sound waves and reflects them into a tiny tube called the ear canal. At the end of the ear canal is a thin, skin-like membrane stretched tightly over the opening, called the eardrum. When sound waves strike the eardrum, they make it vibrate.

② The middle ear contains three tiny, connected bones called the hammer, anvil, and stirrup. These bones carry vibrations from the eardrum to the inner ear.

③ One of the main parts of the inner ear, the cochlea (KAWK-lee-uh), contains about 30,000 hair cells. Each of these cells has tiny hairs on its surface. The hairs bend as a result of the vibrations. This movement triggers changes that cause the cell to send electrical signals along nerves to your brain. Only when your brain receives and processes these signals do you actually hear a sound.

READING TIP
As you read each numbered description here, match it to the number on the illustration below.

How the Ear Detects Sound

Sound waves are detected in the human ear, beginning with vibrations of the eardrum.

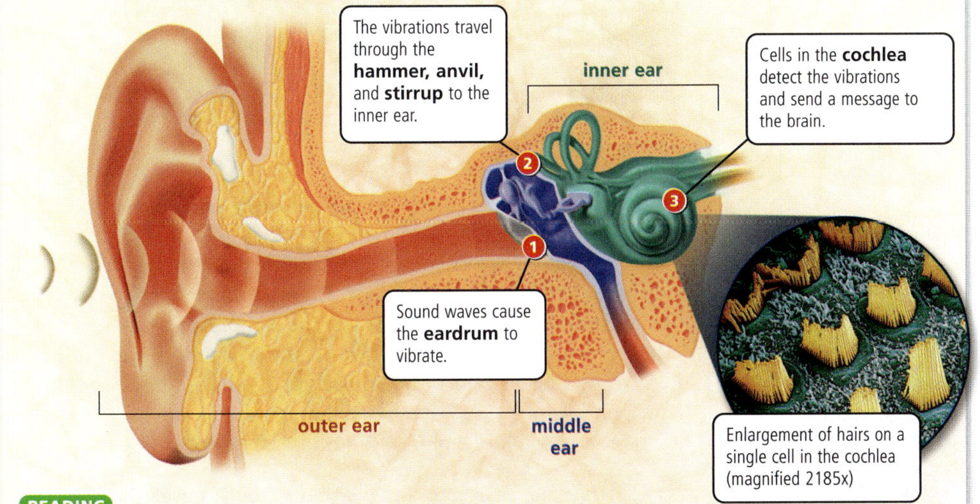

- The vibrations travel through the **hammer, anvil,** and **stirrup** to the inner ear.
- Cells in the **cochlea** detect the vibrations and send a message to the brain.
- Sound waves cause the **eardrum** to vibrate.

outer ear | middle ear | inner ear

Enlargement of hairs on a single cell in the cochlea (magnified 2185x)

How do vibrations get from the eardrum to the cochlea?

Chapter 16: **Sound** 519

DIFFERENTIATE INSTRUCTION

 **More Reading Support**

B What happens when sound hits the eardrum? *The eardrum vibrates.*

Advanced

Challenge and Extension, p. 81

Integrate the Sciences

Although the ears detect sound and change it to electrical signals, the brain interprets the signals sent to it. One important function of the brain is to sort out unneeded noise, focusing on important or unusual sounds. This filtering occurs in a network of nerve cells in the brain stem, known as the reticular activating system (RAS). The action of the RAS enables you to study with the radio on or hear the sound of an announcer over the noise of a crowd.

Teach from Visuals

To help students interpret the visual of the ear, ask:

- What causes the eardrum to vibrate? *sound waves striking the eardrum*

- What effect would an inner ear infection, when the inner ear fills up with fluid, have on hearing? What might happen? *Students may infer that sound is blocked or it changes the perception of sounds. In fact, most ear infections block some vibrations from passing through the inner ear.*

Ongoing Assessment

Explain how sound waves are produced and detected.

Ask: If two people talk, how is sound produced and detected? *Air pushes between vocal cords to produce sound. The ear detects vibrations that enter it and interprets them as sound.*

READING VISUALS *Answer: The vibrations get to the cochlea by passing through the hammer, anvil, and stirrup.*

Chapter 16 **519**

Ongoing Assessment

Explain how sound waves transfer energy.

Ask: What happens to the particles in a medium when sound waves pass through it? *The particles vibrate.*

CHECK YOUR READING *Sample answer: Sound travels as compressions in the particles that make up the air.*

Sound waves vibrate particles.

You can see the motion of waves in water. You can even ride them with a surfboard. But you cannot see air. How, then, can you picture sound waves moving through air? Sound waves transfer the motion of particles too small to see from one place to another.

For example, think about a drum that has been struck. What happens between the time the drum is struck and the sound is heard?

- The drum skin vibrates rapidly. It pushes out and then in, over and over again. Of course, this happens very, very fast. The vibrating drum skin pushes against nearby particles in the air. The particles in the air become bunched together, or compressed.
- When the drum skin pushes the opposite way, a space opens up between the drum's surface and the particles. The particles rush back in to fill the space.
- The back-and-forth movement, or vibration, of the particles is the disturbance that travels to the listener. Both the bunched up areas, or compressions, and the spaces between the compressions are parts of the wave.

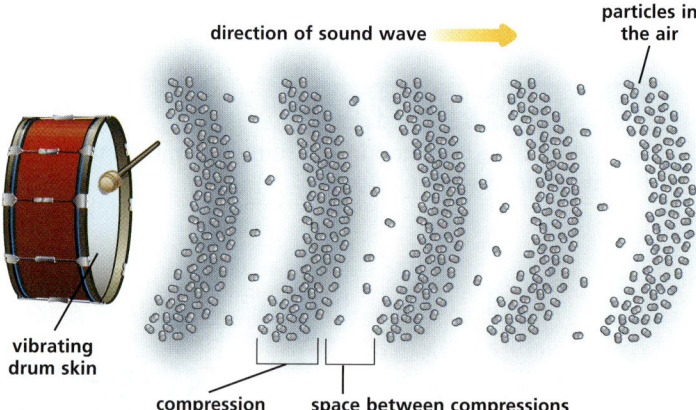

Notice that the waves consist of repeating patterns of compressions and spaces between the compressions. The compressions are areas of high air pressure. The spaces between the compressions are areas of low air pressure. The high- and low-pressure air pushes and pulls on the surrounding air, which then pushes and pulls on the air around that. Soon a sound wave has traveled through the air and has transferred kinetic energy from one place to another.

REMINDER Kinetic energy is the energy of motion.

CHECK YOUR READING Summarize in your own words how sound travels through air.

520 Unit 4: Waves, Sound, and Light

DIFFERENTIATE INSTRUCTION

 **More Reading Support**

C What is the name for air particles bunching up in a sound wave? *compression*

Below Level Have two students model how a sound wave travels. Have them place a spring toy on the floor and stretch it between them until it is approximately 2 meters long. Have one student squeeze together about 20 coils on his or her end. They should see that the other coils become farther apart. When they release the coils, the compression travels down the spring.

520 Unit 4: **Waves, Sound, and Light**

In the middle 1600s, scientists began to do experiments to learn more about air. They used pumps to force the air out of enclosed spaces to produce a vacuum. A **vacuum** is empty space. It has no particles—or very, very few of them. Robert Boyle, a British scientist, designed an experiment to find out if sound moves through a vacuum.

Boyle put a ticking clock in a sealed jar. He pumped some air out of the jar and still heard the clock ticking. Then he pumped more air out. The ticking grew quieter. Finally, when Boyle had pumped out almost all the air, he could hear no ticking at all. Boyle's experiment demonstrated that sound does not travel through a vacuum.

The photograph at the right shows equipment that is set up to perform an experiment similar to Boyle's. A bell is placed in a sealed jar and powered through the electrical connections at the top. The sound of the loudly ringing bell becomes quieter as air is pumped out through the vacuum plate.

Sound is a mechanical wave. It can move only through a medium that is made up of matter. Sound waves can travel through air, solid materials, and liquids, such as water, because all of these mediums are made up of particles. Sound waves cannot travel through a vacuum.

Sound Experiment
- connections
- sealed jar
- bell
- vacuum plate

INFER As air is pumped out of the jar, the sound of the bell becomes quieter. Why do you think the bell is suspended?

 How did Boyle's experiment show that sound cannot travel through a vacuum?

INVESTIGATE Sound Energy

How does sound transfer energy?
PROCEDURE
1. Sprinkle a few grains of salt into the jar. Put the jar on a flat surface in a well-lit place.
2. Cut off the neck of the balloon with the scissors.
3. Stretch the balloon over the mouth of the jar and pull the sides down past the rim of the jar's mouth. Use a rubber band to make a tight fit.
4. Tap the balloon with the eraser end of the pencil. Observe what happens to the salt on the bottom of the jar.

WHAT DO YOU THINK?
- What happens to the salt?
- How can you explain what you observed?

CHALLENGE Suppose you could pump all the air out of the jar and could leave the salt grains in the jar and the tight rubber cover on top. If you repeated the experiment, do you think the results would be different? Explain your answer.

SKILL FOCUS Observing

MATERIALS
- clean jar
- table salt
- balloon
- scissors
- rubber band
- pencil with good eraser end

TIME 10 minutes

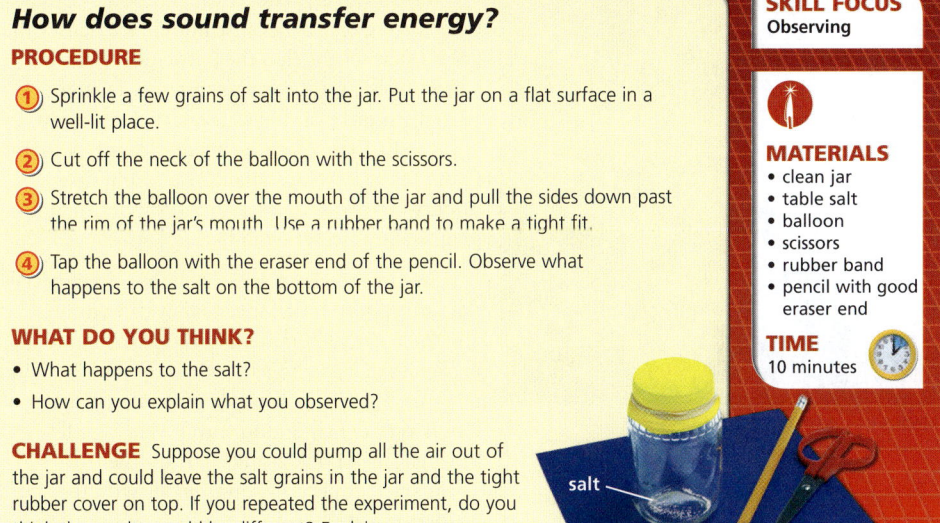

salt

Chapter 16: Sound 521

Address Misconceptions

IDENTIFY Ask: How fast does sound travel? If students answer with a specific speed, they may hold the misconception that sound always travels at the same speed.

CORRECT Elicit from students that sound will travel faster when particles are able to quickly pass a vibration to another particle. Have students draw molecular models of warm air and cold air. Also have them draw molecular models of solids and gases.

REASSESS Ask students to use their models to explain why sound travels more quickly at increased temperature in the same medium and more quickly in a solid than in a gas. *Particles in warm gas move more quickly than particles in a cooler gas, so they collide more often and with more energy, quickly moving the sound wave. Particles in a solid are closer than in a gas; thus, they pass vibrations more quickly from one particle to another.*

Technology Resources
Visit **ClassZone.com** for background on common student misconceptions.

MISCONCEPTION DATABASE

Ongoing Assessment

Describe what affects the speed of sound waves.

Ask: How does increasing temperature affect the speed of sound? *Sound travels more quickly as temperature rises.*

 Answer: The material and temperature of the medium affect the speed of sound.

The speed of sound depends on its medium.

Suppose you are in the baseball stands during an exciting game. A pitch flies from the mound toward home plate, and you see the batter draw back, swing, and hit the ball high. A split second later you hear the crack of the bat meeting the ball. You notice that the sound of the hit comes later than the sight. Just how fast does sound travel?

 Sound travels more slowly than light, and it does not always travel at the same speed. Two main factors affect the speed of sound: the material that makes up the medium—such as air or water—and the temperature. If we know the medium and the temperature, however, we can predict the speed of sound.

CHECK YOUR READING Which two factors affect the speed of sound?

The Effect of the Material

You have probably heard sounds in more than one medium. Think about the medium in which you most often hear sound—air. You listen to a radio or a compact disk player. You hear the siren of a fire truck. These sound waves travel through air, a mixture of gases.

Now think about going swimming. You dip below the water's surface briefly. Someone jumps into the water nearby and splashes water against the pool wall. You hear strange underwater sounds. These sound waves travel through water, a liquid.

Sound travels faster through liquids than it does through gases because liquids are denser than gases. That means that the particles are packed closer together. It takes less time for a water particle to push on the water particles around it because the particles are already closer together than are the particles in air. As a result, divers underwater would hear a sound sooner than people above water would.

Sound can also travel through solid materials that are elastic, which means they can vibrate back and forth. In solid materials, the particles are packed even closer together than they are in liquids or gases. Steel is an example of an elastic material that is very dense. Sound travels very rapidly through steel. Look at the chart on the left. Compare the speed of sound in air with the speed of sound in steel.

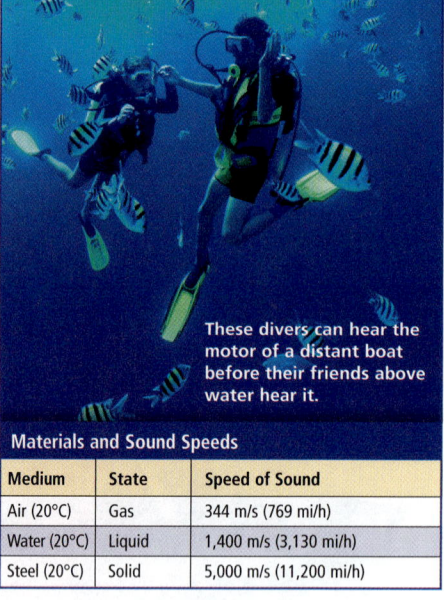

These divers can hear the motor of a distant boat before their friends above water hear it.

Materials and Sound Speeds

Medium	State	Speed of Sound
Air (20°C)	Gas	344 m/s (769 mi/h)
Water (20°C)	Liquid	1,400 m/s (3,130 mi/h)
Steel (20°C)	Solid	5,000 m/s (11,200 mi/h)

522 Unit 4: Waves, Sound, and Light

DIFFERENTIATE INSTRUCTION

 More Reading Support

F Which moves faster, light waves or sound waves? *light*

G Does sound travel faster through a gas or a liquid? *a liquid*

Advanced
- Ask: what might prevent you from performing an experiment in class to measure the speed of sound in a medium? *The speed is too great to measure without specialized equipment.*
- Ask: What requirements do you think are needed for the equipment that is used to measure the speed of sound in a medium? *Answers might include the ability to detect small vibrations and measure extremely small periods of time.*

The Effect of Temperature

Sound also travels faster through a medium at higher temperatures than at lower ones. Consider the medium of air, a mixture of gases. Gas particles are not held tightly together as are particles in solids. Instead, the gas particles bounce all around. The higher the temperature, the more the gas particles wiggle and bounce. It takes less time for particles that are already moving quickly to push against the particles around them than it takes particles that are moving slowly. Sound, therefore, travels faster in hot air than in cold air.

Look at the picture of the snowboarders. The sound waves they make by yelling will travel more slowly through air than similar sounds made on a hot day. If you could bear to stand in air at a temperature of 100°C (212°F—the boiling point of water) and listen to the same person yelling, you might notice that the sound of the person's voice reaches you faster.

The chart on the right shows the speed of sound in air at two different temperatures. Compare the speed of sound at the temperature at which water freezes with the speed of sound at the temperature at which water boils. Sound travels about 17 percent faster in air at 100°C than in air at 0°C.

These snowboarders' shouts reach their friends more slowly in this cold air than they would in hot air.

Temperature and Sound Speeds

Medium	Temperature	Speed of Sound
Air	0°C (32°F)	331 m/s (741 mi/h)
Air	100°C (212°F)	386 m/s (864 mi/h)

 What is the difference between the speed of sound in air at 0°C and at 100°C?

16.1 Review

KEY CONCEPTS
1. Describe how sound waves are produced.
2. Describe how particles move as energy is transferred through a sound wave.
3. Explain how temperature affects the speed of sound.

CRITICAL THINKING
4. **Predict** Would the sound from a distant train travel faster through air or through steel train tracks? Explain.
5. **Evaluate** Suppose an audience watching a science fiction movie hears a loud roar as a spaceship explodes in outer space. Why is this scene unrealistic?

CHALLENGE
6. **Evaluate** A famous riddle asks this question: If a tree falls in the forest and there is no one there to hear it, is there any sound? What do you think? Give reasons for your answer.

Chapter 16: **Sound** 523

ANSWERS

1. Sound waves are produced when an object vibrates.
2. Particles compress and then spread out as a sound wave passes through them.
3. the higher the temperature, the faster the speed of sound
4. The sound would travel faster through steel train tracks than through air because steel is a denser material than air.
5. Sound must travel through a material medium such as a gas, liquid, or solid. Outer space is a vacuum, and so the sound of the explosion would not be heard.
6. Accept either of these answers if well-defended: The sole criterion for sound is the production of sound waves. The sound waves must be detected by some receiver to qualify as sound.

Ongoing Assessment

 Answer: 55m/s

Reinforce the BIG idea
Have students relate the section to the Big Idea.

R Reinforcing Key Concepts, p. 83

16.1 ASSESS & RETEACH

Assess
 Section 16.1 Quiz, p. 22

Reteach
Have students perform the following activity:

- Remove both the top and the bottom of a coffee can or an oatmeal box.
- Stretch a balloon tightly over one end and secure it with a rubber band.
- Glue a small mirror to the center of the balloon.
- Lay the can on its side on a desk.
- Shine a flashlight on the mirror at a 45° angle so that the reflection is on a white wall or screen.
- Yell into the open end and explain what happens. *The sound waves cause the balloon to vibrate, which causes the mirror to vibrate. These vibrations can be seen in the reflection of the flashlight on the wall or screen.*

Technology Resources
Have students visit ClassZone.com for reteaching of Key Concepts.

 CONTENT REVIEW

 CONTENT REVIEW CD-ROM

Chapter 16 523

EXTREME SCIENCE
Fun and Motivating Science

Set Learning Goal
To find out more about supersonic aircraft and the sonic booms they produce

Present the Science
A sonic boom is caused by an extremely high-pressure wave that is produced as an object accelerates to a speed faster than its sound waves and breaks through the pressure barrier.

The pressure from a sonic boom normally causes no damage on Earth. The energy range of a sonic boom is less than that of most industrial noise. Occasionally, minor damage such as broken glass results from a sonic boom.

Discussion Questions
Ask: How is the atmosphere different at the height of an airplane flying compared to close to Earth? *Air at the height of the plane is colder and less dense.*

Ask: Based on your answer to the first question, would the speed of sound be greater or less at Earth's surface? *greater*

Close
Ask: How do the sound waves produced by an airplane compare to the waves produced by the front of a ship as it moves through water? *The waves are similar because the moving object generates them. They collect at the front of the object, and the object passes through them.*

Technology Resources
Students can visit **ClassZone.com** to find out more about supersonic aircraft.

 RESOURCE CENTER

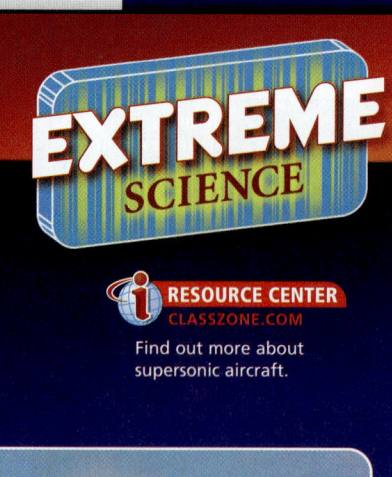

RESOURCE CENTER
CLASSZONE.COM
Find out more about supersonic aircraft.

This photograph may actually show the wake of a sonic boom. It was taken on a very humid day, and water vapor may have condensed in the low-pressure part of the sound wave.

Boom Notes
- The pilot of an airplane cannot hear the sonic boom because the sound waves are behind the plane.
- Lightning heats particles in the air so rapidly that they move faster than the speed of sound and cause a shock wave, which is what makes the boom of thunder. If a lightning strike is very close, you will hear a sharp crack.
- Large meteors enter the atmosphere fast enough to make a sonic boom.

524 Unit 4: Waves, Sound, and Light

SURPASSING THE SPEED OF SOUND

Sonic Booms
Airplanes traveling faster than the speed of sound can produce an incredibly loud sound called a sonic boom. The sonic boom from a low-flying airplane can rattle and even break windows!

How It Works

Breaking the Barrier

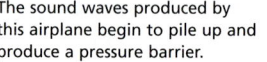

The sound waves produced by this airplane begin to pile up and produce a pressure barrier.

This airplane has broken through the pressure barrier and has produced a loud boom.

When an airplane reaches extremely high speeds, it actually catches up to its own sound waves. The waves start to pile up and form a high-pressure area in front of the plane. If the airplane has enough acceleration, it breaks through the barrier, making a sonic boom. The airplane gets ahead of both the pressure barrier and the sound waves and is said to be traveling at supersonic speeds—speeds faster than the speed of sound.

Boom and It's Gone
If an airplane that produces a boom is flying very high, it may be out of sight by the time the sonic boom reaches a hearer on the ground. To make a sonic boom, a plane must be traveling faster than about 1240 kilometers per hour (769 mi/h)! The sound does not last very long—about one-tenth of a second for a small fighter plane to one-half second for a supersonic passenger plane.

EXPLORE

1. **PREDICT** Specially designed cars have traveled faster than the speed of sound. Would you expect them to produce a sonic boom?
2. **CHALLENGE** The space shuttles produce sonic booms when they are taking off and landing, but not while they are orbiting Earth, even though they are moving much faster than 1240 km/h. Can you explain why?

EXPLORE
1. **PREDICT** *Yes, a car traveling faster than the speed of sound would produce a sonic boom.*
2. **CHALLENGE** *Sonic waves would not be produced in space because there is no medium in which the sound can travel.*

16.2 KEY CONCEPT
Frequency determines pitch.

BEFORE, you learned
- Sound waves are produced by vibrations
- Frequency measures the number of waves passing a fixed point per second

NOW, you will learn
- How the frequency of a wave affects the way it sounds
- How sound quality differs from pitch
- How the Doppler effect works

VOCABULARY
pitch p. 525
hertz p. 526
ultrasound p. 526
resonance p. 528
Doppler effect p. 530

EXPLORE Pitch
Why does the sound change?

PROCEDURE
1. Hold the ruler flat on the edge of a desk so that it sticks out about 25 centimeters beyond the edge.
2. With your free hand, push the tip of the ruler down and then let it go. As the ruler vibrates, slide it back onto the desk. Listen to the sounds the ruler makes.

MATERIALS
ruler

WHAT DO YOU THINK?
- What happened to the sound as you slid the ruler back onto the desk?
- Describe the motion of the ruler.

Pitch depends on the frequency of a sound wave.

VOCABULARY
Remember to add a description wheel in your notebook for each new term.

When you listen to music, you hear both high and low sounds. The characteristic of highness or lowness of a sound is called **pitch**. The frequency of a sound wave determines the pitch of the sound you hear. Remember that frequency is the number of waves passing a fixed point in a given period of time. A high-frequency wave with short wavelengths, such as that produced by a tiny flute, makes a high-pitched sound. A low-frequency wave with long wavelengths, such as the one produced by the deep croak of a tuba, makes a low-pitched sound. An object vibrating very fast produces a high-pitched sound, while an object vibrating slower produces a lower-pitched sound.

CHECK YOUR READING How is frequency related to pitch?

Chapter 16: Sound 525

16.2 FOCUS

Set Learning Goals
Students will
- Describe how the frequency of a wave affects the way it sounds.
- Describe how sound quality differs from pitch.
- Learn about the Doppler effect.
- Discover through an experiment how frequency and pitch are related.

3-Minute Warm-Up
Display Transparency 12 or copy this exercise on the board:

Decide if these statements are true. If not true, correct them.

1. In a longitudinal wave, the vibrations move perpendicular to the direction of the wave. *In a longitudinal wave, the vibrations move in the same direction as the wave.*
2. Sound is a type of electromagnetic wave. *Sound is a type of mechanical wave.*
3. Vibrations pass through many parts of the ear, not just the eardrum. *True*

3-Minute Warm-Up, p. T12

16.2 MOTIVATE

EXPLORE Pitch

PURPOSE To examine factors that affect the pitch of a sound

TIP 10 min. Experiment with available rulers before class begins. Use those that produce the best results. Do not use plastic rulers that might break.

WHAT DO YOU THINK? *The sound became higher. The ruler moved up and down a greater distance when the ruler extended farther than when it was pulled back.*

Ongoing Assessment
CHECK YOUR READING *Answer: The higher the frequency of the sound wave, the higher pitched the sound.*

Chapter 16 **525**

RESOURCES FOR DIFFERENTIATED INSTRUCTION

Below Level
UNIT RESOURCE BOOK
- Reading Study Guide A, pp. 86–87
- Decoding Support, p. 120

AUDIO CDS

Additional INVESTIGATION, Exploring Resonance, A, B, & C, pp. 132–140; Teacher Instructions, pp. 284–285

Advanced
UNIT RESOURCE BOOK
- Challenge and Extension, p. 92
- Challenge Reading, pp. 116–117

English Learners
UNIT RESOURCE BOOK
Spanish Reading Study Guide, pp. 90–91

AUDIO CDS
- Audio Readings in Spanish
- Audio Readings (English)

16.2 INSTRUCT

Teach from Visuals

To help students interpret the visual on frequency and pitch, have pairs of students prepare a series of flash cards, each of which contains a wave of a different wavelength. Have students work together, choosing two cards at a time and deciding which wave has a lower pitch. Have them identify the wavelength of each wave and compare their frequencies. You may want to remind students that wavelength and frequency are inversely related—the higher the frequency, the shorter the wavelength.

Develop Critical Thinking

APPLY Have students apply their knowledge of pitch by having them compare the length of vocal cords, based on the pitch of voices. Have them use the categories of male child, female child, male adult, and female adult. *In general, male adult vocal cords are longest, as indicated by the lower pitches of adult male voices. Female adult vocal cords are the next longest. The lengths of the vocal cords of a male and female child are about the same and are shorter than the vocal cords of a female adult.*

Ongoing Assessment

Describe the effect of frequency on how a wave sounds.

Ask: Does a wave with a high frequency have a high pitch or a low pitch? *a high pitch*

CHECK YOUR READING Answer: Humans can hear frequencies between 20 hertz and 20,000 hertz.

High and Low Frequencies

Frequency is a measure of how often a wave passes a fixed point. One complete wave can also be called a cycle. The unit for measuring frequency, and also pitch, is the hertz. A **hertz** (Hz) is one complete wave, or cycle, per second. For example, a wave with a frequency of 20 hertz has 20 cycles per second. In a wave with a frequency of 100 hertz, 100 waves pass a given point every second. The diagram below shows how frequency and pitch are related.

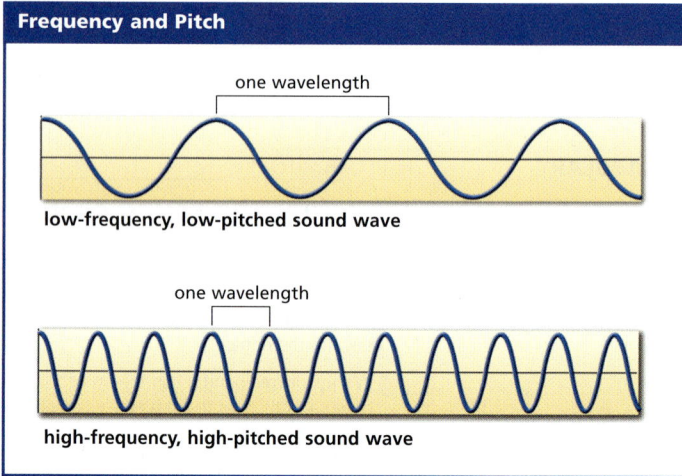

Frequency and Pitch

one wavelength

low-frequency, low-pitched sound wave

one wavelength

high-frequency, high-pitched sound wave

Human ears can hear a wide range of pitches. Most people with good hearing can hear sounds in the range of 20 hertz to 20,000 hertz. The note of middle C on a piano, for example, has a frequency of 262 hertz.

Sound waves with wavelengths below 20 hertz are called infrasound. People cannot hear sounds in this range. Infrasound waves have a very long wavelength and can travel great distances without losing much energy. Elephants may use infrasound to communicate over long distances. Some of the waves that elephants use travel through the ground instead of the air, and they may be detected by another elephant up to 32 kilometers (about 20 miles) away.

The highest frequency that humans can hear is 20,000 hertz. Sound waves in the range above 20,000 hertz are called **ultrasound.** Though people cannot hear ultrasound, it is very useful. Later in this chapter, you will learn about some of the uses of ultrasound. Many animals can hear sound waves in the ultrasound range. The chart on page 527 shows the hearing ranges of some animals.

READING TIP The prefix *infra* means "below," and the prefix *ultra* means "beyond."

CHECK YOUR READING What is the range of frequencies that humans can hear?

DIFFERENTIATE INSTRUCTION

More Reading Support

A If a wave has a frequency of 16 Hz, how many wavelengths per second does it have? *16*

B What are sound waves above 20,000 Hz called? *ultrasound*

Inclusion If you have students in class who have visual impairments, sketch the waves in the figure on this page and glue yarn on the waves. Have students feel the difference in the high-frequency wave and the low-frequency wave.

English Learners Be aware that English learners do not always have necessary background knowledge. For example, English learners may not be familiar with some musical terminology, such as *cymbals* and *clarinet* (p. 529), and *middle C* and *piano* (above).

Sound Frequencies Heard by Animals

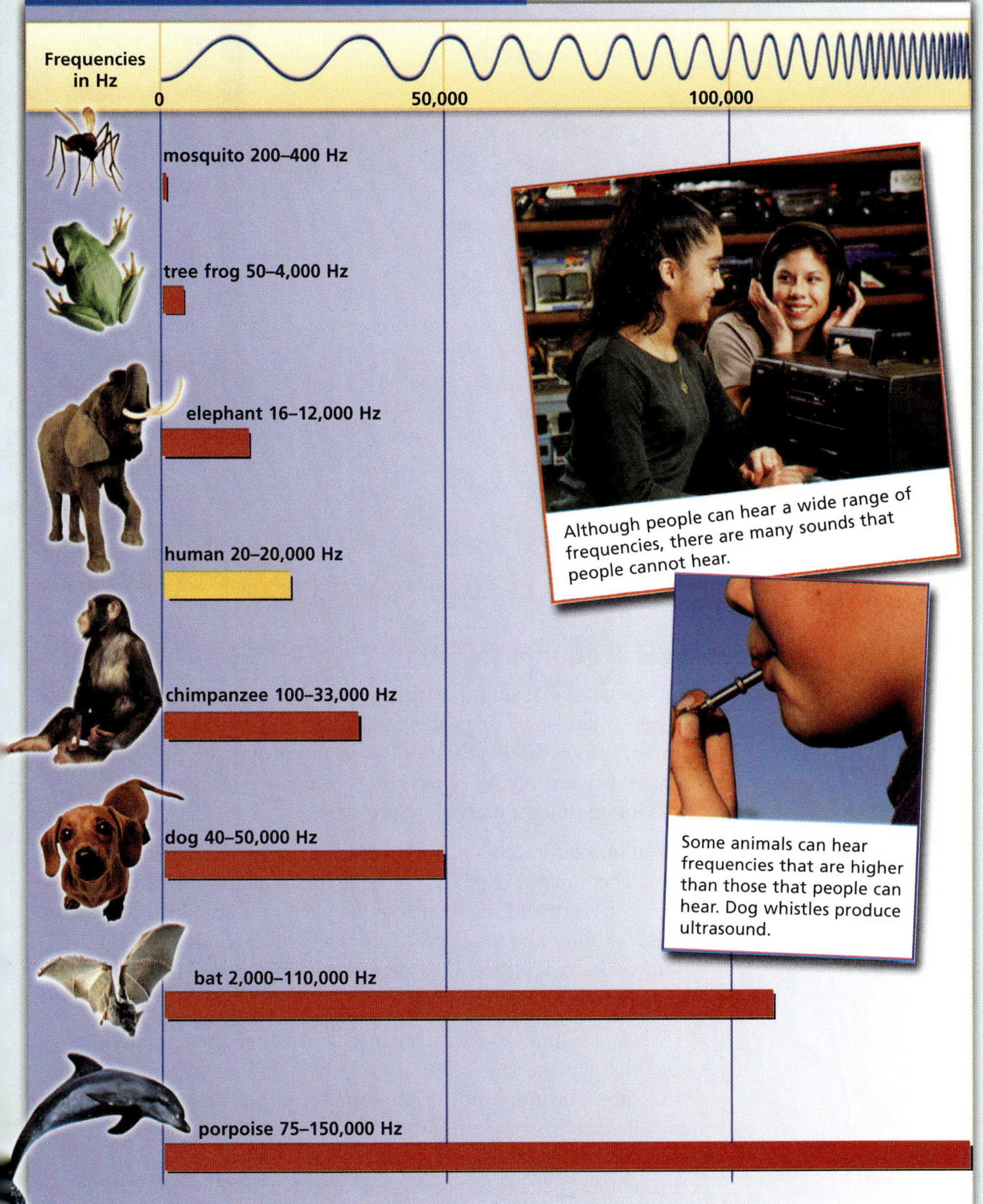

Frequencies in Hz: 0, 50,000, 100,000

- mosquito 200–400 Hz
- tree frog 50–4,000 Hz
- elephant 16–12,000 Hz
- human 20–20,000 Hz
- chimpanzee 100–33,000 Hz
- dog 40–50,000 Hz
- bat 2,000–110,000 Hz
- porpoise 75–150,000 Hz

Although people can hear a wide range of frequencies, there are many sounds that people cannot hear.

Some animals can hear frequencies that are higher than those that people can hear. Dog whistles produce ultrasound.

 Which animals on this chart can hear frequencies above those that humans can hear?

Chapter 16: **Sound** 527

DIFFERENTIATE INSTRUCTION

 More Reading Support

C Which animals on the chart hear frequencies below those that humans can hear? *elephant*

Inclusion Have a group of students make a collage that represents the wavelengths heard by different animals. Have students use a variety of materials: yarn, cord, ribbon, paper, aluminum foil, etc. It should have enough texture so that students with visual impairments can feel the difference in ranges of frequencies.

Advanced

 Challenge Reading, pp. 116–117

Teach from Visuals

To help students interpret the sound frequency visual, ask:

- Why are devices that send out high-frequency sounds sometimes used as repellents for pests such as mice? (A mouse can hear frequencies from 1,000 to 90,000 hertz.) *Frequencies too high for human hearing can be heard by mice. Broadcasting upper frequencies that are uncomfortable for mice could repel them.*

- Why can't people hear the sound produced by a dog whistle? *The whistle sends out sound between 20,000 and 50,000 hertz. Dogs hear it, but it is barely audible to humans.*

- Cats have a hearing range from approximately 100 to 60,000 hertz. Where would cats be placed on the diagram on this page? *between dogs and bats*

 This visual is also available as T14 in the Unit Transparency Book.

Real World Example

Hearing aids amplify vibrations so that people with hearing loss can detect sound. However, hearing aids amplify all frequencies of sound. Very few people have equal hearing loss at all frequency levels. Some people have difficulty wearing hearing aids because, to make certain frequencies loud enough to hear, other frequencies become too loud.

Ongoing Assessment

Answer: chimpanzee, dog, bat, and porpoise

Chapter 16 **527**

INVESTIGATE Sound Frequency

PURPOSE To discover how frequency relates to pitch

TIP 20 min. Students can use two identical rubber bands, pulling one tighter than the other, to show that the difference in pitch is from a difference in frequency, not a difference in rubber bands. Students may need to use tape to hold one or both of the rubber bands in place.

WHAT DO YOU THINK? *The tighter rubber band produces a higher pitch. The higher the frequency, the higher the pitch.*

CHALLENGE *To make a guitar string sound higher in pitch, tighten the string. A tighter string has a higher frequency and therefore higher pitch.*

 Datasheet, Sound Frequency, p. 93

Technology Resources

Customize this student lab as needed or look for an alternative. Print rubrics to assess student lab reports.

 Lab Generator CD-ROM

Ongoing Assessment

Discover how frequency relates to pitch.

Ask: Does the tighter rubber band vibrate at a higher or lower frequency? *higher*

CHECK YOUR READING *Answer: Resonance is the adding of a sound wave with an object's natural frequency of vibration.*

INVESTIGATE Sound Frequency

How is frequency related to pitch?

PROCEDURE

1. Stretch the rubber bands around the open box.
2. Pull one of the rubber bands tightly across the open part of the box so that it vibrates with a higher frequency than the looser rubber band. Tape the rubber band in place.
3. Pluck each rubber band and listen to the sound it makes.

WHAT DO YOU THINK?
- Which rubber band produces a sound wave with a higher pitch?
- How is frequency related to pitch?

CHALLENGE Suppose you are tuning a guitar and want to make one of the strings sound higher in pitch. Do you tighten or loosen the string? Explain your answer.

SKILL FOCUS Inferring

MATERIALS
- 2 rubber bands of different sizes
- small open box
- tape

TIME 20 minutes

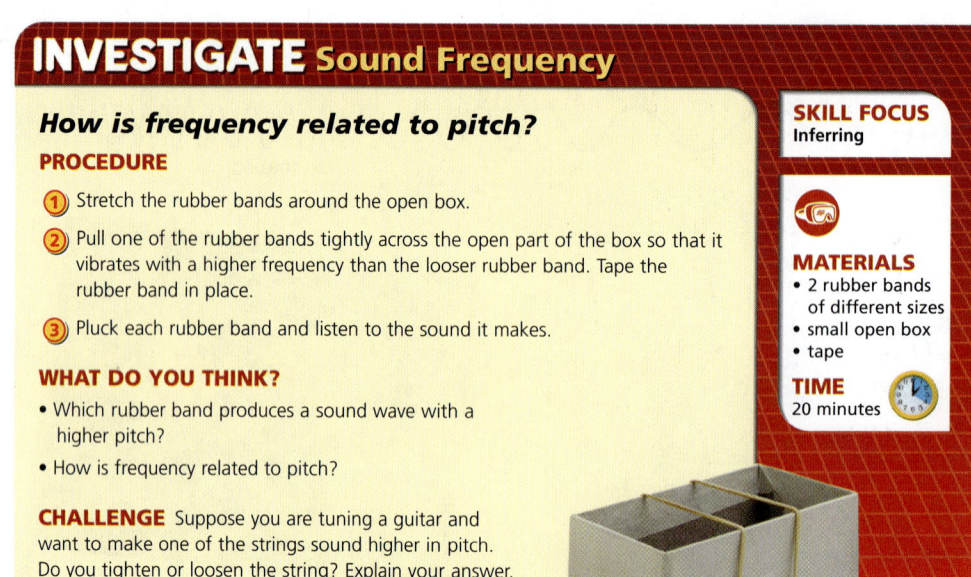

Natural Frequencies

You have read that sound waves are produced by vibrating objects. Sound waves also cause particles in the air to vibrate as they travel through the air. These vibrations have a frequency, or a number of cycles per second. All objects have a frequency at which they vibrate called a natural frequency.

You may have seen a piano tuner tap a tuning fork against another object. The tuner does this to make the fork vibrate at its natural frequency. He or she then listens to the pitch produced by the tuning fork's vibrations and tunes the piano string to match it. Different tuning forks have different frequencies and can be used to tune instruments to different pitches.

When a sound wave with a particular frequency encounters an object that has the same natural frequency, constructive interference takes place. The amplitude of the sound from the vibrating object adds together with the amplitude of the initial sound wave. The strengthening of a sound wave in this way is called **resonance.** When a tuning fork is struck, a nearby tuning fork with the same natural frequency will also begin to vibrate because of resonance.

 How is natural frequency related to resonance?

528 Unit 4: Waves, Sound, and Light

DIFFERENTIATE INSTRUCTION

 More Reading Support

D What is produced when a sound wave combines with a natural vibration? *resonance*

Additional Investigation To reinforce Section 16.2 learning goals, use the following full-period investigation:

 Additional INVESTIGATION, Exploring Resonance, A, B, & C, pp. 132–140, 284–285
(Advanced students should complete Levels B and C.)

Below Level Make sure students understand how frequency is represented in the visuals *Frequency and Pitch* (p. 526) and *Sound Frequencies Heard by Animals* (p. 527).

528 Unit 4: **Waves, Sound, and Light**

Sound Quality

Have you ever noticed that two singers can sing exactly the same note, or pitch, and yet sound very different? The singers produce sound waves with their vocal cords. They stretch their vocal cords in just the right way to produce sound waves with a certain frequency. That frequency produces the pitch that the note of music calls for. Why, then, don't the singers sound exactly the same?

Each musical instrument and each human voice has its own particular sound, which is sometimes called the sound quality. Another word for sound quality is timbre (TAM-buhr). Timbre can be explained by the fact that most sounds are not single waves but are actually combinations of waves. The pitch that you hear is called the fundamental tone. Other, higher-frequency pitches are called overtones. The combination of pitches is the main factor affecting the quality of a sound.

Another factor in sound quality is the way in which a sound starts and stops. Think about a musician who is crashing cymbals. The cymbals' sound blasts out suddenly. A sound produced by the human voice, on the other hand, starts much more gently.

CHECK YOUR READING What are two factors that affect sound quality? Which sentences above tell you?

The illustration below shows oscilloscope (uh-SIHL-uh-SKOHP) screens. An oscilloscope is a scientific instrument that tracks an electrical signal. The energy of a sound wave is converted into a signal and displayed on an oscilloscope screen. The screens below show sound wave diagrams made by musicians playing a piano and a clarinet. Both of these musical instruments are producing the same note, or pitch. Notice that the diagrams look slightly different from each other. Each has a different combination of overtones, producing a unique sound quality.

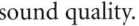

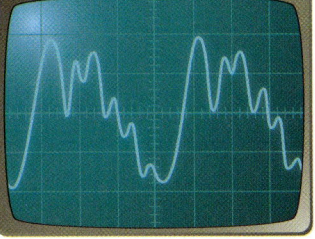
piano

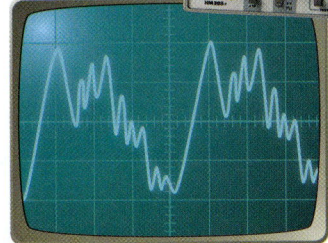
clarinet

Both oscilloscope images at left show diagrams of sound waves of the same pitch produced on two different instruments. The waves, however, have different sound qualities.

Chapter 16: **Sound** 529

Integrate the Sciences

Because the Doppler effect applies to all waves, astronomers can use it to determine the speed and direction of a galaxy's movement. If the galaxy is getting nearer, the light it generates will shift toward blue (shorter) wavelengths. If it is moving away, its light will shift toward red (longer) wavelengths.

Teach Difficult Concepts

Some students may have a hard time understanding the pattern of waves in the Doppler effect. To clarify the concept, have them visualize or recall the pattern of waves that surround a moving boat. Waves to the front of the boat are close together. To the back of the boat, the waves are farther apart.

Ongoing Assessment

Explain how the Doppler effect works.

Ask: As a siren moves away from you, does the pitch become higher or lower?
lower

CHECK YOUR READING Answer: *If a sound moves toward the listener, the pitch rises. If it moves away from the listener, the pitch lowers.*

The motion of the source of a sound affects its pitch.

Sometimes in traffic, a screeching siren announces that an ambulance must pass through traffic. Drivers slow down and pull over to the side, leaving room for the ambulance to speed by. Suppose you are a passenger in one of these cars. What do you hear?

When the ambulance whizzes past you, the pitch suddenly seems to drop. The siren on the ambulance blasts the same pitches again and again. What has made the difference in what you hear is the rapid motion of the vehicle toward you and then away from you. The motion of the source of a sound affects its pitch.

The Doppler Effect

In the 1800s an Austrian scientist named Christian Doppler hypothesized about sound waves. He published a scientific paper about his work. In it, he described how pitch changes when a sound source moves rapidly toward and then away from a listener. Doppler described the scientific principle we notice when a siren speeds by. The **Doppler effect** is the change in perceived pitch that occurs when the source or the receiver of a sound is moving.

Before long, a Dutch scientist learned of Doppler's work. In 1845 he staged an experiment to test the hypothesis that Doppler described. In the experiment, a group of trumpet players were put on a train car. Other musicians were seated beside the railroad track. Those musicians had perfect pitch—that is, the ability to identify a pitch just by listening to it. The train passed by the musicians while the trumpeters on the train played their instruments. The musicians recorded the pitches they heard from one moment to the next. At the end of the demonstration, the musicians reported that they had heard the pitch of the trumpets fall as the train passed. Their experiment showed that the Doppler effect exists.

DESCRIPTION WHEEL Make a description wheel in your notebook for the Doppler effect.

CHECK YOUR READING How does the motion of a sound's source affect its pitch?

To listeners outside a train, the sound made by the train seems higher in pitch while it approaches them than while it speeds away.

530 Unit 4: Waves, Sound, and Light

DIFFERENTIATE INSTRUCTION

More Reading Support

G When a siren approaches you, what happens to its pitch? *The pitch seems higher.*

English Learners English learners may have difficulty using the words *affect* and *effect* correctly. Explain that *affect* is a verb and *effect* is a noun. Compare the following two sentences from this page. *The motion of the source of a sound affects its pitch. The Doppler effect is the change in perceived pitch that occurs when the source or receiver of a sound is moving.* The first sentence uses the verb *affect*. The second sentence uses the noun *effect*.

The Doppler Effect

The perceived pitch of a sound changes as the source of the sound moves toward or away from the hearer.

Sound waves arrive at these people farther apart, so the frequency is lower.

Sounds waves arrive at these people closer together, so the frequency is higher.

 Which people hear a higher pitch?

Frequency and Pitch

Again imagine sitting in a car as an ambulance approaches. The siren on the ambulance continually sends out sound waves. As the ambulance pulls closer to you, it catches up with the sound waves it is sending out. As a result, the sound waves that reach your ears are spaced closer together. The frequency, and therefore the pitch, is higher when it reaches you. As the ambulance continues, it gets farther and farther away from you, while the sound waves still move toward you. Now the waves arrive farther and farther apart. As the frequency decreases, you hear a lower pitch.

Explore the Doppler effect.

16.2 Review

KEY CONCEPTS

1. Describe what is different about the sound waves produced by a low note and a high note on a musical instrument.
2. Explain why two people singing the same pitch do not sound exactly the same.
3. How does perceived pitch change as a sound source passes a listener?

CRITICAL THINKING

4. **Apply** How could you produce vibrations in a tuning fork without touching it? Explain your answer.
5. **Predict** Suppose you could view the waves produced by a high-pitched and a low-pitched voice. Which wave would display the greater number of compressions in 1 s? Why?

CHALLENGE

6. **Infer** Offer a possible explanation for why no one noticed the Doppler effect before the 1800s.

Chapter 16: Sound 531

Ongoing Assessment

 Answer: the people on the left

Reinforce the BIG idea

Have students relate the section to the Big Idea.

Reinforcing Key Concepts, p. 94

16.2 ASSESS & RETEACH

Assess
Section 16.2 Quiz, p. 23

Reteach

Have students try the following activity:

- Tightly stretch a thread or light string about 50 cm long between two supports, parallel to the floor. There should be at least 25 cm of space beneath the string.
- Tie a piece of string to each of seven identical metal washers. Three pieces of string should be 20 cm long, two should be 15 cm, one 10 cm, and one 5 cm. Tie the strings evenly spaced on the long thread.
- Start swinging one washer. Notice that other washers on the same length of string will also swing because they have the same natural frequency. The other washers will not move.
- Repeat with each different length of string.

Technology Resources

Have students visit ClassZone.com for reteaching of Key Concepts.

 CONTENT REVIEW

 CONTENT REVIEW CD-ROM

ANSWERS

1. The sound waves have different frequencies—high frequency for the high note and low frequency for the low note.
2. The quality, or timbre, of the sounds made by the voices is different, even though the pitch is the same.
3. The frequency changes as the source of the sound moves past a listener, changing the pitch.
4. by striking an identical tuning fork nearby; Resonance would cause the tuning fork to vibrate.
5. the high-pitched voice because the sound waves have higher frequency and thus more waves per unit of time
6. None of the modes of transportation went fast enough for the Doppler effect to happen.

Chapter 16 531

16.3 FOCUS

▶ Set Learning Goals

Students will
- Explain how the intensity of a wave affects its loudness.
- Describe how sound intensity can be controlled.
- Explain how loudness can affect hearing.
- Observe through an experiment how amplitude relates to loudness.

◀ 3-Minute Warm-Up

Display Transparency 13 or copy this exercise on the board:

Match each of the definitions in the first column to one of the terms in the second column.

Definitions
1. sound waves with frequency greater than 20,000 hertz *c*
2. the measure of the height of a wave's crest *b*
3. how high or low a sound is *a*

Terms
a. pitch
b. amplitude
c. ultrasound

 3-Minute Warm-Up, p. T13

16.3 MOTIVATE

THINK ABOUT

PURPOSE To understand how to produce different types of sound

DISCUSS Ask: Which part of the drum vibrates? *all of it (especially the drum head)*

Answers: drumstick moving up and down; louder: move drumsticks with more energy; softer: with less energy

Ongoing Assessment

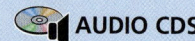 *Answer: the more energy, the louder the sound*

532 Unit 4: Waves, Sound, and Light

16.3 KEY CONCEPT
Intensity determines loudness.

◀ BEFORE, you learned
- Sound waves are produced by vibrations
- Frequency determines the pitch of a sound
- Amplitude is a measure of the height of a wave crest

▶ NOW, you will learn
- How the intensity of a wave affects its loudness
- How sound intensity can be controlled
- How loudness can affect hearing

VOCABULARY
intensity p. 532
decibel p. 532
amplification p. 535
acoustics p. 535

THINK ABOUT

What makes a sound louder?

A drum player has to play softly at some times and loudly at others. Think about what the drummer must do to produce each type of sound. If you could watch the drummer in the photograph in action, what would you see? How would the drummer change the way he moves the drumsticks to make a loud, crashing sound? What might he do to make a very soft sound?

Intensity depends on the amplitude of a sound wave.

OUTLINE
Make an outline for this heading. Remember to include main ideas and details.

I. Main idea
  A. Supporting idea
    1. Detail
    2. Detail
  B. Supporting idea

Earlier you read that all waves carry energy. The more energy a sound wave carries, the more intense it is and the louder it will sound to listeners. The **intensity** of a sound is the amount of energy its sound wave has. A unit called the **decibel** (dB) is used to measure sound intensity. The faint rustling of tree leaves on a quiet summer day can hardly be heard. Some of the softest sounds measure less than 10 decibels. On the other hand, the noise from a jet taking off or the volume of a TV set turned all the way up can hurt your ears. Very loud sounds measure more than 100 decibels. Remember that amplitude is related to wave energy. The greater the amplitude, the more intensity a sound wave has and the louder the sound will be.

 How is energy related to loudness?

532 Unit 4: Waves, Sound, and Light

RESOURCES FOR DIFFERENTIATED INSTRUCTION

Below Level
UNIT RESOURCE BOOK
- Reading Study Guide A, pp. 97–98
- Decoding Support, p. 120

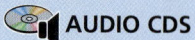 **AUDIO CDS**

Advanced
UNIT RESOURCE BOOK
Challenge and Extension, p. 103

English Learners
UNIT RESOURCE BOOK
Spanish Reading Study Guide, pp. 101–102

 AUDIO CDS
- Audio Readings in Spanish
- Audio Readings (English)

INVESTIGATE Loudness

How is amplitude related to loudness?

PROCEDURE

1. Cut a notch in the middle of both ends of the cardboard. Stretch the rubber band around the cardboard so that it fits into the notches as shown.
2. Mark lines on the cardboard at one and four centimeters away from the rubber band.
3. Slide the pencils under the rubber band at each end.
4. Pull the rubber band to the one-centimeter line and let it go so that it vibrates with a low amplitude. Notice the sound it makes. Pull the rubber band to the four-centimeter line and let it go again. This time the amplitude is higher. Notice the sound it makes this time.

WHAT DO YOU THINK?
- How did the loudness of the sounds compare?
- How is amplitude related to loudness?

CHALLENGE Using what you learned from experimenting with the rubber band, explain why swinging a drumstick harder on a drum would make a louder sound than swinging a drumstick lightly.

SKILL FOCUS
Observing

MATERIALS
- piece of cardboard
- scissors
- large rubber band
- 2 pencils
- ruler

TIME
15 minutes

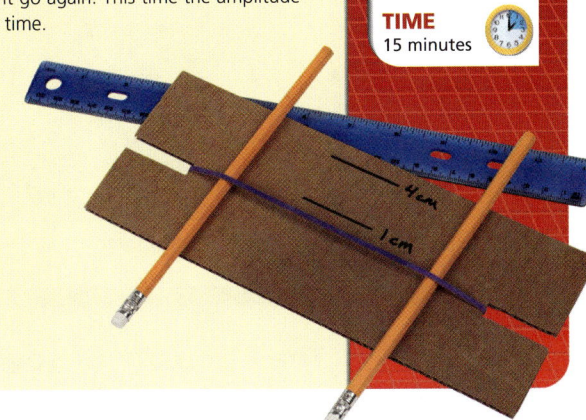

A

The drummer varies the loudness of a sound by varying the energy with which he hits the drum. Loudness is also affected by the distance between the source and the listener.

Have you ever wondered why sound gradually dies out over distance? Think about someone walking away from you with a radio. When the radio is close, the radio seems loud. As the person walks away, the sound grows fainter and fainter. Sound waves travel in all directions from their source. As the waves travel farther from the radio, their energy is spread out over a greater area. This means that their intensity is decreased. The sound waves with lower intensities are heard as quieter sounds.

Other forces can take energy away from sound waves, too. Forces can act within the medium of a sound wave to decrease the intensity of the waves. This effect on sound is probably a good thing. Imagine what the world would be like if every sound wave continued forever!

Chapter 16: Sound 533

16.3 INSTRUCT

INVESTIGATE Loudness

PURPOSE To observe how amplitude relates to loudness

TIPS 15 min.

- The cardboard must be thick. It should remain flat when the rubber band is stretched on it.
- Emphasize safety. The notch should be narrow and deep enough that the rubber band stays in the notch when stretched.
- It might be easier to use a knife to notch the cardboard before the lab.
- For accurate observations, students should pull the rubber bands from the middle.

WHAT DO YOU THINK? *The sound was louder when the rubber band was pulled back 4 cm than when it was pulled back 1 cm. The greater the amplitude, the louder the sound.*

CHALLENGE *Swinging a drumstick harder would make a louder sound because the drum skin would vibrate with greater amplitude.*

R Datasheet, Loudness, p. 104

Technology Resources
Customize this student lab as needed or look for an alternative. Print rubrics to assess student lab reports.

Lab Generator CD-ROM

Ongoing Assessment

Explain the effect of intensity of a wave on its loudness.

Ask: Which sound will have greater intensity, a whisper or a yell? *a yell*

Observe how amplitude relates to loudness.

Ask: How can you make a sound louder? *by increasing the amplitude of the sound wave*

DIFFERENTIATE INSTRUCTION

More Reading Support

A How does distance affect intensity? *the less distance, the more intensity*

English Learners Often readers are asked to imagine a situation and consider its implications. Consider the example from this page: *Have you ever wondered why sound gradually dies out over distance? Think about someone walking away from you with a radio.* These sentences require the reader to imagine a hypothetical scenario. When this occurs explain to English learners that they should imagine the situation. Also, tell students that the phrasal verb *dies out* means "fades."

Chapter 16 533

History of Science

Galileo, a famous physicist, studied resonance in the 1600s. Galileo noted that the swings of a pendulum increasingly grow with repeated, timed applications of a small force. When the frequency of an applied force matches the natural frequency of a system, large-amplitude vibrations result in what's called resonance. Resonance explains why a glass shatters at a pitch that matches its natural frequency.

Teaching with Technology

If you have a tape recorder, you might want to record various sounds and play them back for student analysis of pitch, intensity, and quality. Examples might include birdcalls or musical instruments.

Ongoing Assessment

Describe how to control sound intensity.

Ask: How does a muffler affect the intensity of sound? *It absorbs energy from the sound wave, decreasing the intensity.*

READING VISUALS *Answer: The sound of the jet taking off is the most intense; the rustling of leaves is the least intense.*

CHECK YOUR READING *Answer: Change its amplitude but not its frequency.*

Approximate Sound Intensities

dB	Examples
10	leaves rustling
20	light rainfall
30	whisper
50	conversation
60	dog barking
70	traffic
90	lawn mower
100	motorcycle
120	amplified music
140	firecrackers
150	airplane taking off

20 dB light rainfall
150 dB airplane taking off nearby
90 dB lawn mower
60 dB dog barking
10 dB leaves rustling in gentle breeze

READING VISUALS What is the source of the most intense sound in this picture? the least intense?

The intensity of sound can be controlled.

REMINDER Remember, amplitude is related to wave energy.

Over time and distance, a sound wave gets weaker and weaker until the sound becomes undetectable. The pitch, however, does not typically change as the sound grows weaker. In other words, even as the amplitude decreases, the frequency stays the same.

Sometimes it is desirable to change sound intensity without changing the pitch and quality of a sound. We can do this by adding energy to or taking energy away from a sound wave. As you have already seen, intensity is the amount of energy in a sound wave. Changing the intensity of a sound wave changes its amplitude.

B
C

Sound intensity can be controlled in many ways. Mufflers on cars and trucks reduce engine noise. Have you ever heard a car with a broken muffler? You were probably surprised at how loud it was. Burning fuel in an engine produces hot gases that expand and make a very loud noise. A muffler is designed to absorb some of the energy of the sound waves and so decrease their amplitude. As a result, the intensity of the sound you hear is much lower than it would be without the muffler.

CHECK YOUR READING How could you change the intensity of a sound without changing the pitch?

534 Unit 4: Waves, Sound, and Light

DIFFERENTIATE INSTRUCTION

More Reading Support

B Changing the intensity of sound also changes what else? *amplitude*

C What does a muffler in a car do? *reduces the sound of the engine*

Below Level Ask students what properties they think would be necessary for a device that could be worn over the ears to control sound intensity. *Sample answer: being made of dense material that would either absorb sound or keep vibrations from reaching the eardrums.* If possible, show students examples of such devices, such as earplugs or the devices used by people who work with loud industrial machinery or near airplanes at airports.

Amplification

In addition to being reduced, as they are in a muffler, sound waves can be amplified. The word *amplify* may remind you of *amplitude*, the measure of the height of a wave's crest. These words are related. To amplify something means to make it bigger. **Amplification** is the increasing of the strength of an electrical signal. It is often used to increase the intensity of a sound wave.

When you listen to a stereo, you experience the effects of amplification. Sound input to the stereo is in the form of weak electrical signals from a microphone. Transistors in an electronic circuit amplify the signals. The electrical signals are converted into vibrations in a coil in your stereo's speaker. The coil is attached to a cone, which also vibrates and sends out sound waves. You can control the intensity of the sound waves by adjusting your stereo's volume.

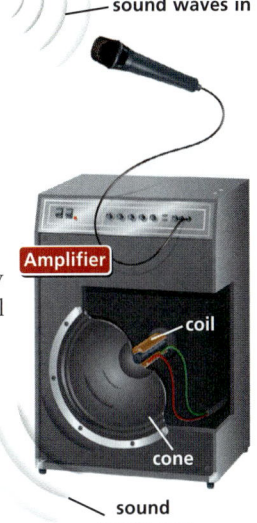

Acoustics

The scientific study of sound is called **acoustics** (uh-KOO-stihks). Acoustics involves both how sound is produced and how it is received and heard by humans and animals.

Acoustics also refers to the way sound waves behave inside a space. Experts called acoustical engineers help design buildings to reduce unwanted echoes. An echo is simply a reflected sound wave. To control sound intensity, engineers design walls and ceilings with acoustical tiles. The shapes and surfaces of acoustical tiles are designed to absorb or redirect some of the energy of sound waves.

The pointed tiles in this sound-testing room are designed to absorb sound waves and prevent any echoes.

The shapes and surfaces in this concert hall direct sound waves to the audience.

READING VISUALS COMPARE AND CONTRAST Imagine sound waves reflecting off the surfaces in the two photographs above. How do the reflections differ?

Chapter 16: **Sound** 535

Real World Example

Here are a few branches of acoustics.

- Communications acoustics incorporates radio and other sound reproduction.
- Architectural acoustics is the control of sound waves inside buildings.
- Environmental acoustics applies sound theories to control noise pollution.

Integrate the Sciences

Physiological acoustics integrates the physics of sound with its biological application to human hearing. In the 1800s, German physicist Georg Ohm stated that the human ear is sensitive to the amplitude of sound waves. In 1863, Hermann von Helmholtz later expanded upon Ohm's theory by relating the physics of sound and music.

Address Misconceptions

IDENTIFY Ask: If sound damages your ears, how long does the damage last? If student answers indicate that any damage is not permanent, they hold the misconception that any hearing damage resulting from loud noises is temporary.

CORRECT Make two lists on the board. Label one "Temporary damage" and the other one "Permanent damage." Ask students to give instances when permanent physical damage occurs, such as some heart attacks, and instances of temporary damage, such as a cut finger.

REASSESS Ask: When delicate cells like hair cells in the ear are damaged, do you think the damage is permanent or temporary? *If the damage is slight, injured cells might be repaired, but such delicate cells could be irreversibly damaged.*

Technology Resources

Visit **ClassZone.com** for background on common student misconceptions.

 MISCONCEPTION DATABASE

Ongoing Assessment

 Answer: There is more absorption than reflection of sound waves in the sound-testing room, but more reflection in the concert hall.

Chapter 16 **535**

DIFFERENTIATE INSTRUCTION

? More Reading Support

D When sound is amplified, what happens to it? *It becomes bigger, or louder.*

E What is the study of sound called? *acoustics*

Alternative Assessment Have students sketch a room interior. Then have them draw arrows showing how sound reflects off surfaces in the room. Ask: How would the addition of sound-absorbing materials affect your drawing? *It would reduce reflected sound.*

Ongoing Assessment

Explain how loudness can affect hearing.

Ask: What cells in the ear are most easily damaged by loud noises? *hair cells in the inner ear*

 *Answer: High-intensity sounds damage the hair cells of the inner ear.*

Reinforce the BIG idea

Have students relate the section to the Big Idea.

 Reinforcing Key Concepts, p. 105

16.3 ASSESS & RETEACH

Assess

 Section 16.3 Quiz, p. 24

Reteach

Have groups of students design a device that will reduce the intensity of sound reaching their ears. It can reduce sound at the source or at the receiver (ear). Supply students with materials such as plastic foam or cotton, or have them provide their own materials. Allow class time for students to demonstrate their inventions and compare the effectiveness of each. To review main ideas and vocabulary, write an outline on the board, using blue heads for main topics and red heads and vocabulary terms for subtopics. Leave operative words blank, and invite students to come to the board to fill in the holes.

Technology Resources

Have students visit ClassZone.com for reteaching of Key Concepts.

 CONTENT REVIEW

 CONTENT REVIEW CD-ROM

536 Unit 4: Waves, Sound, and Light

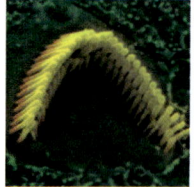
healthy hair cells

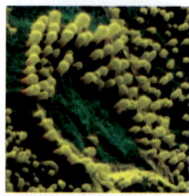
damaged hair cells

RESOURCE CENTER
CLASSZONE.COM
Find out more about sound and protecting your hearing.

Intense sound can damage hearing.

When a train screeches to a stop in a subway station, the sound of the squealing brakes echoes off the tunnel walls. Without thinking about it, you cover your ears with your hands. This response helps protect your ears from possible damage.

In the first section of this chapter, you read about the main parts of the human ear. The part of the inner ear called the cochlea is lined with special cells called hair cells. As you have seen, these cells are necessary for hearing.

The hair cells are extremely sensitive. This sensitivity makes hearing possible, but it also makes the cells easy to damage. Continual exposure to sounds of 90 dB or louder can damage or destroy the cells. This is one reason why being exposed to very loud noises, especially for more than a short time, is harmful to hearing.

 How do high-intensity sounds damage hearing?

Using earplugs can prevent damage from too much exposure to high-intensity sounds such as amplified music. The intensity at a rock concert is between 85 and 120 dB. Ear protection can also protect the hearing of employees in factories and other noisy work sites. In the United States, there are laws that require employers to reduce sounds at work sites to below 90 dB or to provide workers with ear protection.

Even a brief, one-time exposure to an extremely loud noise can destroy hair cells. Noises above 130 dB are especially dangerous. Noises above 140 dB are even painful. It is best to avoid such noises altogether. If you find yourself exposed suddenly to such a noise, covering your ears with your hands may be the best protection.

16.3 Review

KEY CONCEPTS

1. Explain how the terms *intensity*, *decibel*, and *amplitude* are related.
2. Describe one way in which sound intensity can be controlled.
3. How do loud sounds cause damage to hearing?

CRITICAL THINKING

4. **Synthesize** A wind chime produces both soft and loud sounds. If you could see the waves, how would they differ?
5. **Design an Experiment** How could you demonstrate that sound dies away over distance? Suppose you could use three volunteers, a radio, and a tape recorder.

CHALLENGE

6. **Apply** Which of these acoustical designs would be best for a concert hall? Why?
   a. bare room with hard walls, floor, and ceiling
   b. room padded with sound-absorbing materials such as acoustical tile
   c. room with some hard surfaces and some sound padding

536 Unit 4: Waves, Sound, and Light

ANSWERS

1. The greater the amplitude, the more intensity the sound wave has, so it will have more decibels.
2. Sample answer: Sound intensities can be controlled with an amplifier.
3. Loud sounds damage the hair cells of the inner ear which are necessary for hearing.
4. Sound waves of the soft sounds would have a low amplitude, and sound waves of the loud sounds would have a high amplitude.
5. One person could play the radio. Another person could go a certain distance away and record the sound with a tape recorder. The third person could do the same farther away.
6. c; design a would lead to an "echoey" room, and design b would deaden the sound too much. Design c is a good compromise.

MATH in SCIENCE

SKILL: INTERPRETING GRAPHS

Measuring Hearing Loss

An audiogram is a graph that can be used to determine if a patient has hearing loss. The vertical axis shows the lowest intensity, in decibels, that the patient can hear for each frequency tested. Notice that intensity is numbered from top to bottom on an audiogram.

To determine the lowest intensity heard at a given frequency, find the frequency on the horizontal axis. Follow the line straight up until you see the data points, shown as ✳ for the right ear and ● for the left ear. Look to the left to find the intensity. For example, the lowest intensity heard in both ears at 250 Hz is 10 dB.

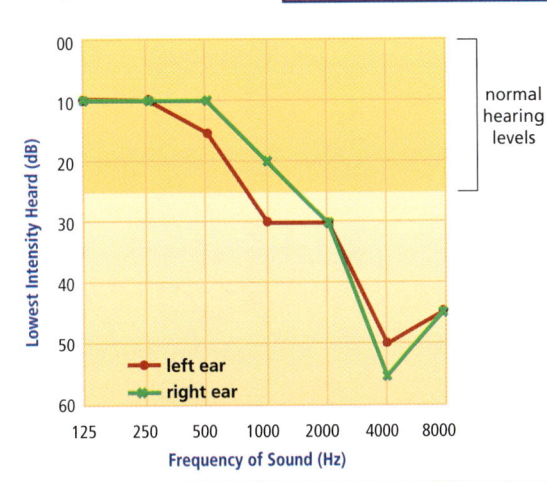

Audiogram for Patient A

Use the graph to answer the following questions.

1. What is the lowest intensity heard in the patient's left ear at 1000 Hz? the right ear at the same frequency?

2. At which frequencies are the data points for both ears within normal hearing levels?

3. Data points outside the normal hearing levels indicate hearing loss. At which frequencies are the data points for both ears outside the normal levels?

CHALLENGE A dip in the graph at 3000 to 4000 Hz is a sign that the hearing loss was caused by exposure to loud noises. The patient is referred to a specialist for further testing. Should Patient A get further testing? Why or why not?

Chapter 16: **Sound** 537

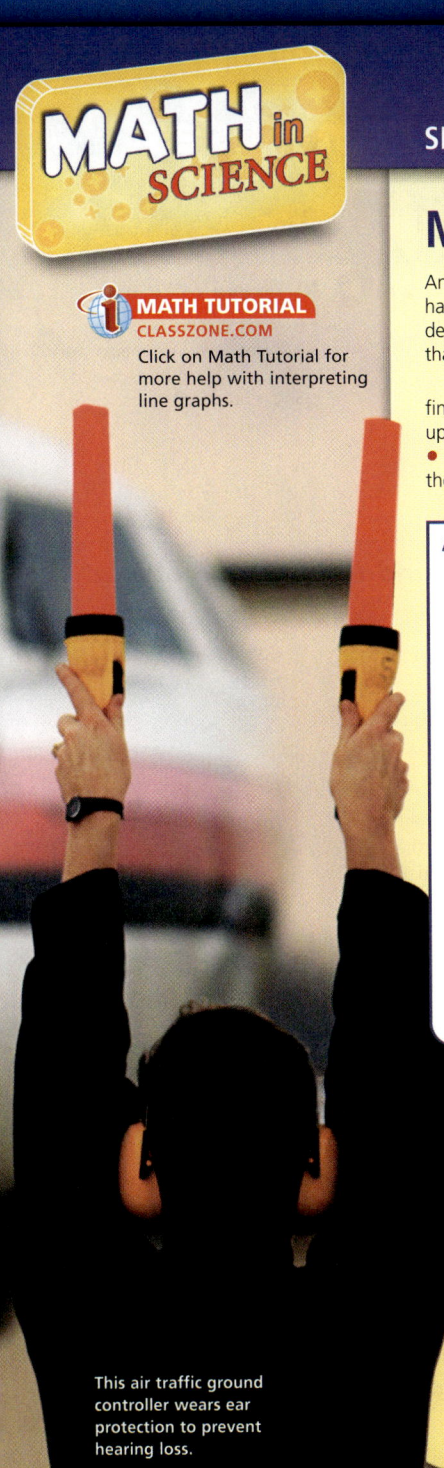

MATH TUTORIAL
CLASSZONE.COM

Click on Math Tutorial for more help with interpreting line graphs.

This air traffic ground controller wears ear protection to prevent hearing loss.

MATH IN SCIENCE
Math Skills Practice for Science

Set Learning Goal
To interpret a graph that relates intensity heard to frequency of sound

Present the Science
Few people with hearing difficulties lose the same amount of hearing at all frequencies. If the hearing loss is a consequence of exposure to loud noises, the frequencies that show greatest loss depend on the frequency of the noise that caused the damage. Hair cells that are permanently damaged by noise of certain frequencies might never again respond to sounds of that frequency.

Develop Graphing Skills
The vertical axis of the graph is labeled in an unconventional manner that should be explained. Ask students how many examples they can think of where lower is better. *Examples might include a game of Crazy 8s or miniature golf scores.*

In the audiogram, the greater the intensity necessary for hearing, the more hearing loss is present. The scale produces a graph that gives the correct impression—patient A has lost hearing at high frequencies in both ears.

Close
Ask: Why might an audiogram show quite different hearing results for the right and left ear of a patient? *Answers might include that the patient was consistently exposed to different intensities of noise in different ears.*

 • Math Support, p. 121
• Math Practice, p. 122

Technology Resources
Students can visit **ClassZone.com** for practice interpreting graphs.

 MATH TUTORIAL

ANSWERS

1. 30 dB, 20 dB
2. from 125 Hz to about 750 Hz
3. 1500 (also accept 2000) to 8000 Hz

CHALLENGE Yes; patient A should get further testing because a dip in this audiogram occurs between 2000 and 4000 Hz.

Chapter 16 **537**

16.4 FOCUS

● Set Learning Goals
Students will
- Describe how ultrasound is used.
- Observe how musical instruments work.
- Explain how sound can be recorded and reproduced.
- Build a stringed instrument in an experiment.

● 3-Minute Warm-Up
Display Transparency 13 or copy this exercise on the board:

You own a movie theater. Explain how you could control the loudness of the sound of movies. How would you eliminate as much audience noise as possible?

The intensity of the sound from the movie should be measured so that it is loud enough to be heard but not loud enough to damage hearing. Because sound reflects, using sound-absorbing materials would eliminate echoing and minimize audience noise.

 3-Minute Warm-Up, p. T13

16.4 MOTIVATE

EXPLORE Echoes
PURPOSE To introduce the concept that sound reflects from an object

TIP 10 min. Have students trade places so both partners have the opportunity to whisper and to listen.

WHAT DO YOU THINK? *The sound was louder with the book than without the book. An echo can be used to detect an object by reflecting off the object. If there is no object to reflect off, there would be no echo.*

Ongoing Assessment
 *Acceptable answers include detecting objects, finding food, imaging the body.*

538 Unit 4: Waves, Sound, and Light

KEY CONCEPT
16.4 Sound has many uses.

 BEFORE, you learned
- Sound waves are produced by vibrations
- Sound waves have amplitude, frequency, and wavelength

 **NOW, you will learn**
- How ultrasound is used
- How musical instruments work
- How sound can be recorded and reproduced

VOCABULARY
echolocation p. 539
sonar p. 539

EXPLORE Echoes
How can you use sound to detect an object?

PROCEDURE
1. Tape the two cardboard tubes onto your desk at a right angle as shown.
2. Put your ear up to the end of one of the tubes. Cover your other ear with your hand.
3. Listen as your partner whispers into the outside end of the other tube.
4. Stand the book upright where the tubes meet. Repeat steps 2 and 3.

MATERIALS
- 2 cardboard tubes
- tape
- book

WHAT DO YOU THINK?
- How did the sound change when you added the book?
- How can an echo be used to detect an object?

Ultrasound waves are used to detect objects.

A ringing telephone, a honking horn, and the sound of a friend's voice are all reminders of how important sound is. But sound has uses that go beyond communication. For example, some animals and people use reflected ultrasound waves to detect objects. Some animals, such as bats, use the echoes of ultrasound waves to find food. People use ultrasound echoes to detect objects underwater or even to produce images of the inside of the body.

 Other than communication, what are three uses of sound?

538 Unit 4: Waves, Sound, and Light

RESOURCES FOR DIFFERENTIATED INSTRUCTION

Below Level
UNIT RESOURCE BOOK
- Reading Study Guide A, pp. 108–109
- Decoding Support, p. 120

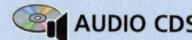 AUDIO CDS

Advanced
UNIT RESOURCE BOOK
Challenge and Extension, p. 114

English Learners
UNIT RESOURCE BOOK
Spanish Reading Study Guide, pp. 112–113

 AUDIO CDS
- Audio Readings in Spanish
- Audio Readings (English)

Echolocation

Sending out ultrasound waves and interpreting the returning sound echoes is called **echolocation** (*echo* + *location*). Bats flying at night find their meals of flying insects by using echolocation. They send out as many as 200 ultrasound squeaks per second. By receiving the returning echoes, they can tell where prey is and how it is moving. They can also veer away from walls, trees, and other big objects.

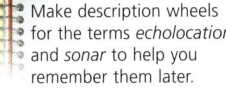

VOCABULARY
Make description wheels for the terms *echolocation* and *sonar* to help you remember them later.

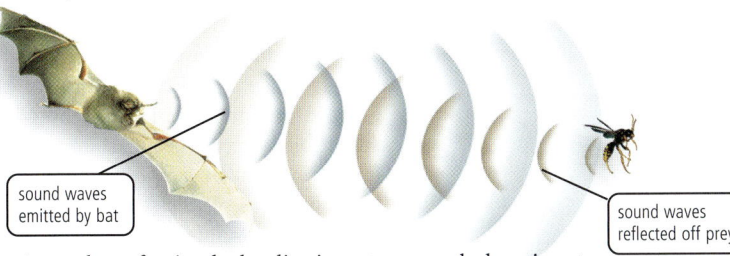

sound waves emitted by bat

sound waves reflected off prey

A number of animals that live in water use echolocation, too. Dolphins, toothed whales, and porpoises produce ultrasound squeaks or clicks. They listen to the returning echo patterns to find fish and other food in the water.

Sonar

People use the principles of echolocation to locate objects underwater. During World War I (1914–1918), scientists developed instruments that used sound waves to locate enemy submarines. Instruments that use echolocation to locate objects are known as **sonar**. Sonar stands for "sound navigation and ranging." The sonar machines could detect sounds coming from submarine propellers. Sonar devices could also send out ultrasound waves and then use the echoes to locate underwater objects. The information from the echoes could then be used to form an image on a screen.

Later, people found many other uses for sonar. Fishing boats use sonar to find schools of fish. Oceanographers—scientists who study the ocean—use it to map the sea floor. People have even used sonar to find ancient sunken ships in deep water.

This woman is using sonar to monitor for submarines.

Sonar is used to locate sunken ships. The image of the sunken ship above was produced on the basis of information from sonar.

Chapter 16: **Sound** 539

Teach from Visuals

Have students examine the photograph of the ultrasound image and share what they see. Ask them to identify the three fetuses and any features, such as the heads, that they can identify. If possible, make a transparency of the photograph so various features can be pointed out on an overhead projector.

Integrate the Sciences

Show students a tessellation to explain the difference between noise and music. A tessellation is a pattern formed by regular-shaped pieces, such as equilateral triangles, with no gaps or overlaps. Examples can be found in many algebra or geometry books or on the Internet. Show students that tessellations produce a nonrandom pattern. Then show students that some shapes, such as pentagons, will not form a regular pattern and are analogous to noise.

Ongoing Assessment

Describe how ultrasound is used.
Ask: How might ultrasound be used to examine a human liver? *Ultrasound waves bounce off the liver, producing an image.*

CHECK YOUR READING *Answer: Both use the reflection of ultrasound waves to detect objects.*

Medical Uses of Ultrasound

Ultrasound has many uses in medicine. Because ultrasound waves are not heard by humans, ultrasound can be used at very high intensities. For example, high-intensity vibrations from ultrasound waves are used to safely break up kidney stones in patients. The energy transferred by ultrasound waves is also used to clean medical equipment.

One of the most important medical uses of ultrasound is the ultrasound scanner. This device relies on the same scientific principle as sonar. It sends sound waves into a human body and then records the waves that are reflected from inside the body. Information from these echoes forms a picture on a screen. The ultrasound scanner is used to examine internal organs such as the heart, pancreas, bladder, ovaries, and brain. Doppler ultrasound is a technology that can detect the movement of fluids through the body and is used to examine blood flow.

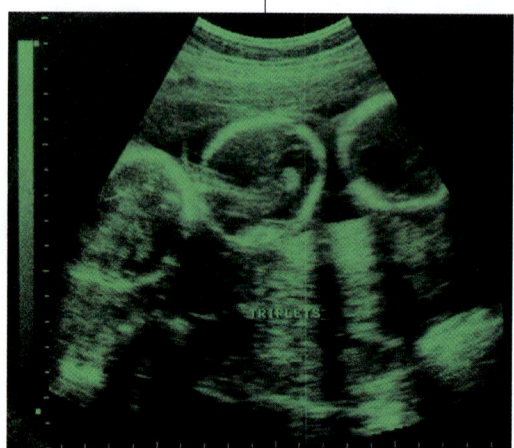
The image of these triplets was produced by reflected ultrasound waves.

 How is an ultrasound scanner similar to sonar?

One of the most well-known uses of ultrasound is to check on the health of a fetus during pregnancy. Problems that are discovered may possibly be treated early. The scan can also reveal the age and gender of the fetus and let the expecting parents know if they will be having twins or triplets. Ultrasound is safer than other imaging methods, such as the x-ray, which might harm the development of the fetus.

Sound waves can produce music.

Why are some sounds considered noise and other sounds considered music? Music is sound with clear pitches or rhythms. Noise is random sound; that means it has no intended pattern.

Explore musical instruments from around the world.

Musical instruments produce pitches and rhythms when made to vibrate at their natural frequencies. Some musical instruments have parts that vibrate at different frequencies to make different pitches. All of the pitches, together with the resonance of the instrument itself, produce its characteristic sound. The three main types of musical instruments are stringed, wind, and percussion. Some describe electronic instruments as a fourth type of musical instrument. Look at the illustration on the next page to learn more about how each type of musical instrument works.

DIFFERENTIATE INSTRUCTION

More Reading Support

C What type of sound waves are used to check on the health of a fetus? *ultrasound*

D If sound is random, is it noise or music? *noise*

English Learners Discuss these words and their meanings with students: *scanner, fetus, expecting,* and *electronics.* Medical terms are often difficult for English learners because they usually are considerably different from one language to another. These terms also are not used frequently in everyday conversation. Use a bilingual dictionary to make a small medical dictionary of terms that might clarify the medical uses of ultrasound for English learners.

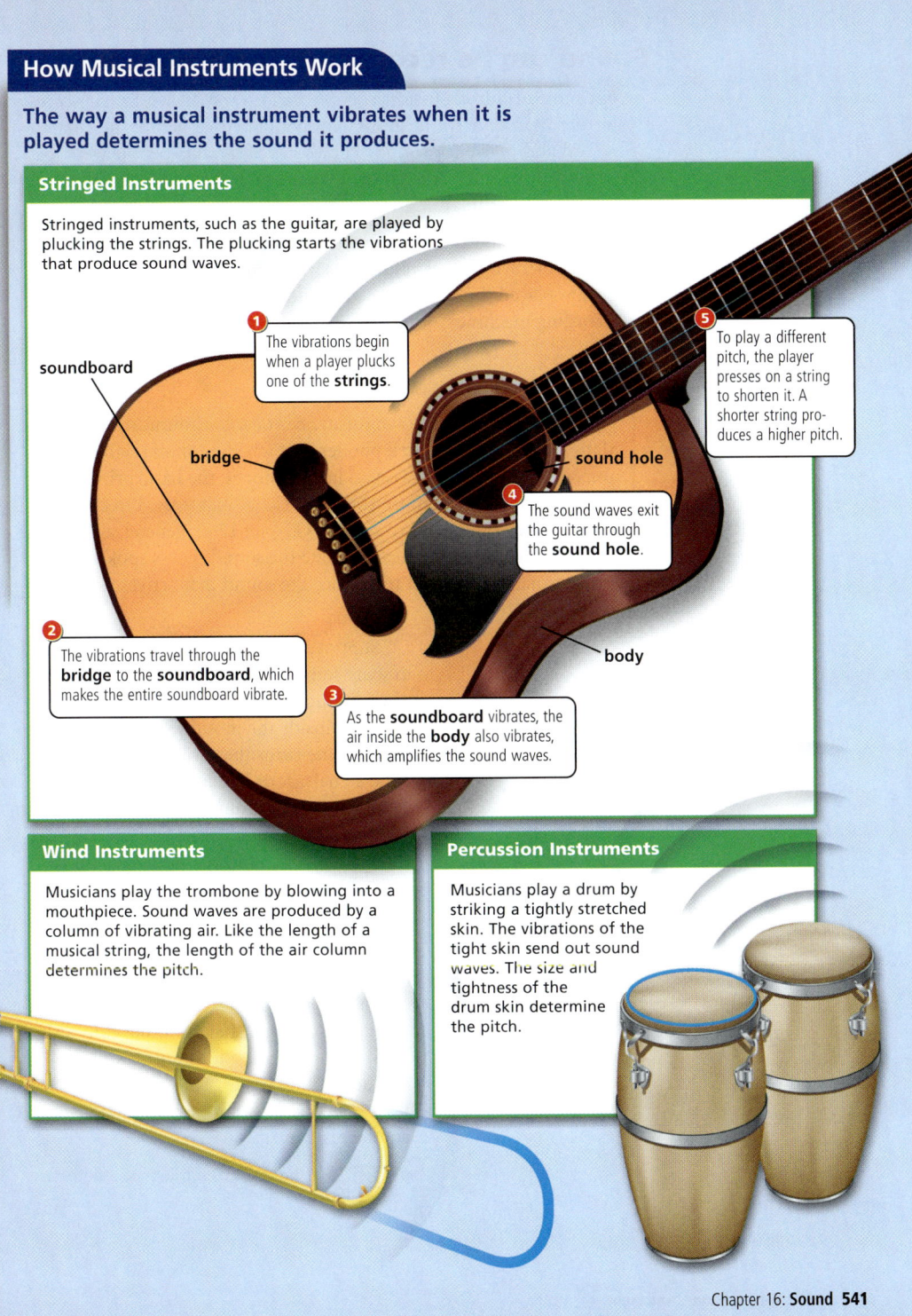

How Musical Instruments Work

The way a musical instrument vibrates when it is played determines the sound it produces.

Stringed Instruments

Stringed instruments, such as the guitar, are played by plucking the strings. The plucking starts the vibrations that produce sound waves.

soundboard

bridge

sound hole

body

1 The vibrations begin when a player plucks one of the **strings**.

2 The vibrations travel through the **bridge** to the **soundboard**, which makes the entire soundboard vibrate.

3 As the **soundboard** vibrates, the air inside the **body** also vibrates, which amplifies the sound waves.

4 The sound waves exit the guitar through the **sound hole**.

5 To play a different pitch, the player presses on a string to shorten it. A shorter string produces a higher pitch.

Wind Instruments

Musicians play the trombone by blowing into a mouthpiece. Sound waves are produced by a column of vibrating air. Like the length of a musical string, the length of the air column determines the pitch.

Percussion Instruments

Musicians play a drum by striking a tightly stretched skin. The vibrations of the tight skin send out sound waves. The size and tightness of the drum skin determine the pitch.

Chapter 16: **Sound** 541

Teach from Visuals

Have students examine the guitar in the visual. Explain that this acoustic guitar differs from an electric guitar. Show students an electric guitar or a picture of one.

- Ask them to predict the loudness of the electric guitar if the strings are plucked when it is not plugged in. *It will have a soft sound.*
- Ask students why an acoustic guitar is louder than the sound from an unamplified electric guitar. *It is designed to amplify the sound of the strings just the way it is.*

Teacher Demo

Use identical bottles, such as 1-liter or smaller transparent soft drink bottles, to make a wind instrument. Add different amounts of water to each bottle so that one bottle is nearly empty, one bottle is almost full, and the other bottles contain varying amounts of water. Blow across the mouth of each bottle, and ask students to explain their observations.

The pitch of the sound is lower as the amount of water decreases. The highest pitch comes from the bottle with the most water. Students should relate the pitch to the size of the column of air above the water.

EXPLORE the BIG idea

Revisit "How Does Size Affect Sound?" on p. 515. Have students explain their results.

Ongoing Assessment

Observe how musical instruments work.

Ask: What purpose does the bridge perform in a guitar? *It carries vibrations to the soundboard.*

DIFFERENTIATE INSTRUCTION

Alternative Assessment Have students label each of three pieces of paper with the name of a type of musical instrument. On half of the appropriate piece of paper, have them sketch an example of that type of instrument. Sketches should emphasize what part of the instrument is vibrating and producing sound. On the other half of the paper, have students list the characteristics and features of that type of instrument, and speculate as to how they determine pitch, quality, and intensity of sound.

Chapter 16 **541**

Real World Example

Ask students to list as many examples as they can of sound being recorded and reproduced. Compile a class list so students can see how many ways sound reproduction is incorporated into daily life.

Teacher Demo

Have someone bring in an old phone that is no longer operating. Take the phone apart so that students can observe the different parts. Ask students to distinguish between the functions of the microphone and the diaphragm. *The microphone changes vibrations to electrical signals, and the diaphragm changes electrical signals into sound.*

If students have difficulty distinguishing between these roles, remind them that they speak into the microphone and hear sound from the diaphragm.

Ongoing Assessment

Explain how sound can be recorded and reproduced.

Ask: How are electrical signals related to sound waves? *Sound can be changed into electrical signals. These signals can be sent to other locations, where they are changed back into sound waves.*

 *Answer: the microphone (or mouthpiece)*

Sound can be recorded and reproduced.

For most of human history, people had no way to send their voices farther than they could shout. Nor could people before the 1800s record and play back sound. The voices of famous people were lost when they died. Imagine having a tape or a compact disk recording of George Washington giving a speech!

Then in the late 1800s, two inventions changed the world of sound. In 1876, the telephone was invented. And in 1877, Thomas Edison played the first recorded sound on a phonograph, or sound-recording machine.

READING TIP
The prefix *phono* means "sound," and the suffix *graph* means "writing."

The Telephone

The telephone has made long-distance voice communication possible. Many people today use cell phones. But whether phone signals travel over wires or by microwaves, as in cell phones, the basic principles are similar. You will learn more about the signal that is used in cell phones when you read about microwaves in Chapter 17. In general, a telephone must do two things. It must translate the sound that is spoken into it into a signal, and it must reproduce the sound that arrives as a signal from somewhere else.

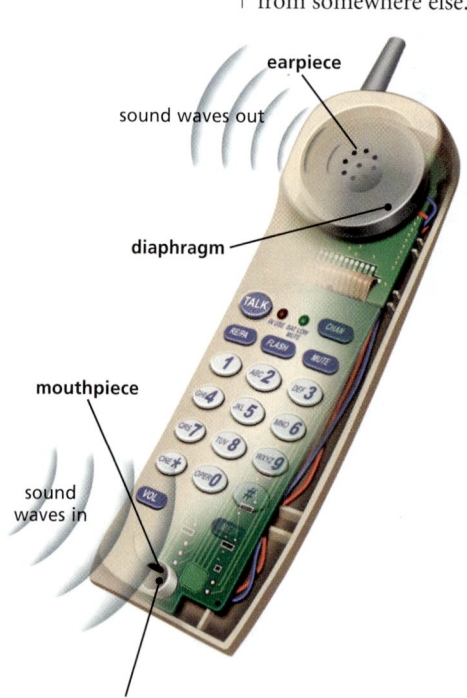

Suppose you are phoning your best friend to share some news. You speak into the mouthpiece. Sound waves from your voice cause a thin disk inside the mouthpiece to vibrate. A microphone turns these vibrations into electrical signals. Your handset sends these signals over wire to a switching station. Computers in the switching station connect phone callers and keep them connected until they finish their conversation.

Your friend receives the news by listening to the earpiece on his handset. There the process is more or less reversed. The electrical signals that arrive in the earpiece are turned into vibrations that shake another thin disk called a diaphragm. The vibrating diaphragm produces sound waves. The sound your friend hears is a copy of your voice, though it sounds like the real you.

 What part of a telephone detects sound waves?

542 Unit 4: Waves, Sound, and Light

DIFFERENTIATE INSTRUCTION

More Reading Support

E What machine first recorded sound? *the phonograph*

F What in a telephone changes vibrations into electrical signals? *a microphone*

Advanced Have students make a Venn diagram that shows the similarities and differences between how sound travels through a telephone and how sound travels from one place to another in the human body. *In both cases, vibrations change into electrical signals. A telephone changes electrical signals back into sound. In the human body, however, the electrical signals travel to the brain, which interprets them.*

R Challenge and Extension, p. 114

Recorded Sound

Sound occurs in real time, which means it is here for a moment and then gone. That is why Thomas Edison's invention of the phonograph—a way to preserve sound—was so important.

Edison's phonograph had a needle connected to a diaphragm that could pick up sound waves. The vibrations transferred by the sound waves were sent to a needle that cut into a piece of foil. The sound waves were translated into bumps along the grooves cut into the foil. These grooves contained all the information that was needed to reproduce the sound waves. Look at the image on top at the right to view an enlargement of record grooves. To play back the sound, Edison used another needle to track along the grooves etched in the foil. Later, phonographs were developed that changed sound waves into electrical signals that could be amplified.

Most people today listen to music on audio tapes or CDs. Tape consists of thin strips of plastic coated with a material that can be magnetized. Sounds that have been turned into electrical signals are stored on the tape as magnetic information. A CD is a hard plastic disc that has millions of microscopic pits arranged in a spiral. The bottom photograph at the right shows an enlargement of pits on the surface of a CD. These pits contain the information that a CD player can change into electrical signals, which are then turned into sound waves.

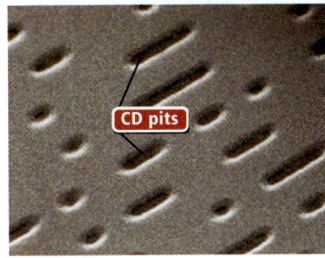

The images above were taken by a scanning electron micrograph (SEM). Both the record grooves (top) and CD pits (bottom) store all of the information needed to reproduce sound.

 Describe three devices on which sound is recorded.

16.4 Review

KEY CONCEPTS
1. Describe one medical use of ultrasound.
2. How are vibrations produced by each of the three main types of musical instruments?
3. How does a telephone record and reproduce sound?

CRITICAL THINKING
4. **Model** Draw a simple diagram to show how telephone communication works. Begin your diagram with the mouthpiece and end with the earpiece.
5. **Classify** The pitch of a musical instrument is changed by shortening the length of a vibrating column of air. What type of instrument is it?

CHALLENGE
6. **Synthesize** How is the earpiece of a telephone similar to the amplifier you read about in Section 3? Look again at the diagram of the amplifier on page 535 to help you find similarities.

Chapter 16: **Sound** 543

ANSWERS

1. Sample answer: to detect the health of a fetus
2. Strings: by plucking or bowing the strings; Winds: by blowing air into a column; Percussion: by striking a part of the instrument
3. The microphone changes the vibrations to electrical signals that travel to another phone. The other phone changes the signals back into vibrations.
4. Diagrams should include sound waves entering the mouthpiece and being converted into electrical signals; electrical signals traveling to switching station; electrical signals traveling to listener's end; electrical signals being converted into sound waves in listener's earpiece.
5. a wind instrument
6. In both, electrical signals are converted into vibrations that produce sound waves.

Ongoing Assessment

CHECK YOUR READING Answer: Records store sound information in grooves, cassette tapes store information as magnetic information, and CDs store information in pits on the surface.

Reinforce the BIG idea

Have students relate the section to the Big Idea.

 Reinforcing Key Concepts, p. 115

16.4 ASSESS & RETEACH

Assess
 Section 16.4 Quiz, p. 25

Reteach
Conduct a survey of students in the class, and find out which musical instruments they play. Classify each instrument according to the way it produces sound. Have students demonstrate each type of instrument by sketching and emphasizing the source of sound for the instrument.

Technology Resources

Have students visit ClassZone.com for reteaching of Key Concepts.

CONTENT REVIEW

CONTENT REVIEW CD-ROM

Chapter 16 **543**

CHAPTER INVESTIGATION

Focus

PURPOSE Students will make a stringed instrument and adjust it, so that changes in vibration produce two pitches.

OVERVIEW Students will observe how vibrations produce sound. They will build a stringed instrument and will find that

- the location of bridges on the instrument affects the pitch of its sound;
- cutting a hole in the instrument affects sound quality.

Lab Preparation

- Several days before performing the activity, have students bring appropriate boxes from home.
- Check rubber bands to be sure they are identical so that a difference in type or length of rubber band is not a variable.
- Prior to the investigation, have students read through the investigation, write their hypothesis, and prepare their data tables. Or you may wish to copy and distribute datasheets and rubrics.

 UNIT RESOURCE BOOK, pp. 123–131

 SCIENCE TOOLKIT, F14

Lab Management

SAFETY Emphasize the importance of using the rubber bands for their intended purpose only. Everyone in the classroom should wear safety goggles during the investigation.

INCLUSION Be sure any students who have hearing impairments are working with students who can describe the results to them. Have these students hold the sides of the box when the strings are plucked and note any differences in the vibrations they feel.

Teaching with Technology

Use a tape recorder to record the sounds of students' stringed instruments. Then play the tape back and ask students to recall what each pitch suggests about the instrument that made it.

544 Unit 4: **Waves, Sound, and Light**

CHAPTER INVESTIGATION

Build a Stringed Instrument

OVERVIEW AND PURPOSE

People make music by plucking strings, blowing through tubes, and striking things. Part of each musical instrument vibrates to produce sounds that form the building blocks of music. In this lab, you will use what you have learned about sound to

- make a simple stringed instrument and see how the vibrating string produces sounds and
- change the design so that your stringed instrument produces more than one pitch.

Problem

How does the length of a string affect the pitch of the sound it produces when plucked?

Hypothesize

Write a hypothesis to explain how changing the length of the string affects the pitch of sound that is produced. Your hypothesis should take the form of an "If . . . , then . . . , because . . ." statement. Complete steps 1–3 before writing your hypothesis.

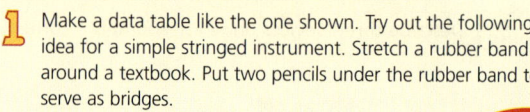

MATERIALS
- book
- 3–5 rubber bands
- 2 pencils
- ruler
- shoebox
- scissors

Procedure

1. Make a data table like the one shown. Try out the following idea for a simple stringed instrument. Stretch a rubber band around a textbook. Put two pencils under the rubber band to serve as bridges.

2. Put the bridges far apart at either end of the book. Find the string length by measuring the distance between the two bridges. Record this measurement in your **Science Notebook.** Pluck the rubber band to make it vibrate. Watch it vibrate and listen to the sound it makes.

3. Move the bridges closer together. What effect does this have on the length of the string? Measure and record the new length. How does this affect the tone that is produced? Record your observations.

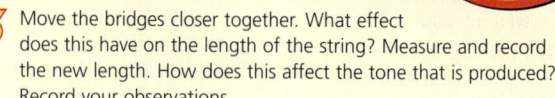

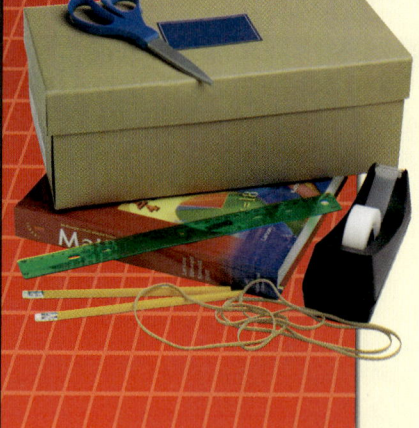

544 Unit 4: **Waves, Sound, and Light**

INVESTIGATION RESOURCES

 CHAPTER INVESTIGATION, Build a Stringed Instrument
- Level A, pp. 123–126
- Level B, pp. 127–130
- Level C, p. 131

Advanced students should complete Levels B & C.

 Writing a Lab Report, D12–13

Technology Resources

Customize this student lab as needed or look for an alternative. Print rubrics to assess student lab reports.

 Lab Generator CD-ROM

4. Make a musical instrument based on the principles you just identified. Begin by stretching rubber bands of the same weight or thickness over the box.

5. If necessary, reinforce the box with an extra layer of cardboard or braces so that it can withstand the tension of the rubber bands without collapsing.

6. Place pencils under the rubber bands at each end of the box. Arrange one pencil at an angle so that each string is a different length. Record the length of each string and your observations of the sounds produced. Experiment with the placement of the bridges.

7. You might also try putting one bridge at the center of the box and plucking on either side of it. How does this affect the range of pitches your instrument produces?

8. Experiment with the working model to see how you can vary the sounds. Try this variation: cut a hole in the center of the box lid. Put the lid back on the box. Replace the rubber bands and bridges. How does the hole change the sound quality?

Observe and Analyze Write It Up

1. **RECORD OBSERVATIONS** Draw a picture of your completed instrument design. Be sure your data table is complete.

2. **ANALYZE** Explain what effect moving the bridges farther apart or closer together has on the vibrating string.

3. **SYNTHESIZE** Using what you have learned from this chapter, write a paragraph that explains how your instrument works. Be sure to describe how sound waves of different frequencies and different intensities can be produced on your instrument.

Conclude Write It Up

1. **INTERPRET** Answer the question posed in the problem.

2. **ANALYZE** Compare your results with your hypothesis. Did your results support your hypothesis?

3. **EVALUATE** Describe any difficulties with or limitations of the materials that you encountered as you made your instrument.

4. **APPLY** Based on your experiences, how would you explain the difference between music and noise?

INVESTIGATE Further

CHALLENGE Stringed instruments vary the pitch of musical sounds in several other ways. In addition to the length of the string, pitch depends on the tension, weight, and thickness of the string. Design an experiment to test one of these variables. How does it alter the range of sounds produced by your stringed instrument?

Build a Stringed Instrument
Problem How does the length of a string affect the pitch of the sound it produces when plucked?
Hypothesize
Observe and Analyze
Simple instrument: initial string length _____
Simple instrument: new string length _____
Table 1. Stringed Instrument Sound Observations

Stringed Instrument Designs	Length of Strings (cm)	Observations About Pitch and Sound Quality
Bridges at each end		
Bridge in middle		
After adding sound hole		

Conclude

Chapter 16: **Sound** 545

Observe and Analyze Write It Up

SAMPLE DATA Initial string length: 22 cm; New string length: 18 cm; String length with bridges at each end: 30 cm; Observations: low pitch; String length with bridge in middle: 15 cm; Observations: higher pitch; Observations after adding sound hole: improved quality

1. See students' diagrams. See students' data tables.

2. The closer the bridges, the shorter the length of the vibrating band and the higher the pitch.

3. Sound waves of different frequencies can be produced by changing the length or tightness of the vibrating string. Sound waves of different intensities can be produced by varying the amplitude (or energy) with which the strings are plucked.

Conclude Write It Up

1. The longer the string is, the lower the pitch is.

2. Student answers will vary.

3. Answers might include incompatibility of the length of the rubber band and the size of the box.

4. Music is intended to include certain pitches and intensities; noise is random sound.

INVESTIGATE Further

CHALLENGE Student results should include one of the following: tighter strings produce higher pitch, heavier and thicker strings produce lower pitch.

Post-Lab Discussion

- From the student instruments, choose one or two that have unique features. Discuss with the class the effect the features have on pitch and quality.
- Have students make a conclusion about the relationships between string length and pitch and about factors that affect sound quality.
- Ask students how they might revise their designs if they were to do a follow-up experiment to test another variable.

Chapter 16 **545**

CHAPTER 16 • REVIEW

BACK TO

Have students describe a situation that demonstrates the transfer of energy by a sound wave. *Students could use investigations in this chapter, the effect of vibrations on the human ear, or another example of how sound waves affect the medium they travel in.*

◯ KEY CONCEPTS SUMMARY

SECTION 16.1
Ask: If the drum were in a vacuum, would sound be produced when it was struck? *No; sound needs a medium, and a vacuum has no medium.*

Ask: What part of the drum vibrates, producing sound? *the drum skin*

SECTION 16.2
Ask: If the frequency of the top wave is 200 hertz, what is the frequency of the bottom wave? *600 Hz*

SECTION 16.3
The waves shown were originally identical, but one of the waves has been amplified. Ask: Which wave was amplified? How do you know? *The bottom wave was amplified; its amplitude is greater.*

Ask: If energy is removed from the top wave, will it be more similar to the bottom wave or more different from it? *different since amplitude will be less*

SECTION 16.4
Ask: How is sound being used in the picture on the left? *Sound bounces off an object and is used to determine its location.*

Ask: What is the term for this practice? *echolocation*

Review Concepts

- Big Idea Flow Chart, p. T9
- Chapter Outline, p. T15–T16

---

16 Chapter Review

the BIG idea
Sound waves transfer energy through vibrations.

 CONTENT REVIEW
CLASSZONE.COM

◀ **KEY CONCEPTS SUMMARY**

1 Sound is a wave.

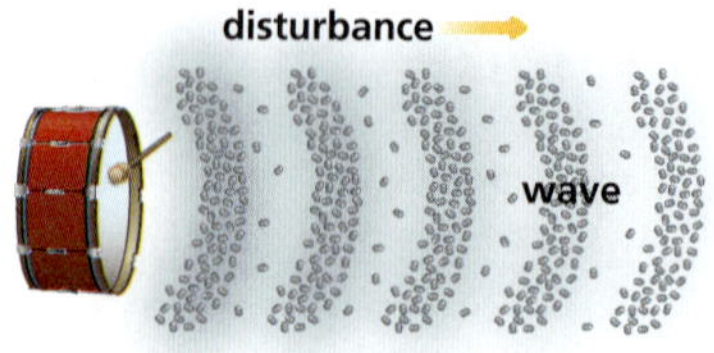

Sound is a longitudinal wave that travels through a material medium, such as air.

VOCABULARY
sound p. 517
vibration p. 517
vacuum p. 521

2 Frequency determines pitch.

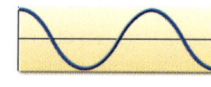
A sound wave with a lower frequency and longer wavelength is perceived to have a lower pitch.

A sound wave with a higher frequency and shorter wavelength is perceived to have a higher pitch.

VOCABULARY
pitch p. 525
hertz p. 526
ultrasound p. 526
resonance p. 528
Doppler effect p. 530

3 Intensity determines loudness.

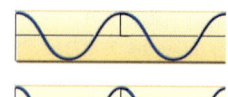
A sound wave with a lower amplitude and energy is perceived as a softer sound.

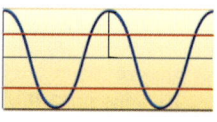
A sound wave with a higher amplitude and energy is perceived as a louder sound.

VOCABULARY
intensity p. 532
decibel p. 532
amplification p. 535
acoustics p. 535

4 Sound has many uses.

Human uses of sound:
sonar
ultrasound
music
telephone
recording

Bats use sound to locate objects.

VOCABULARY
echolocation p. 539
sonar p. 539

546 Unit 4: Waves, Sound, and Light

Technology Resources

Have students visit ClassZone.com or use the CD-ROM for a cumulative review of concepts.

 CONTENT REVIEW

 CONTENT REVIEW CD-ROM

Engage students in a whole-class interactive review of Key Concepts. Edit content as you wish.

 POWER PRESENTATIONS

Reviewing Vocabulary

Copy and complete the chart below by using vocabulary terms from this chapter.

Property of Wave	Unit of Measurement	Characteristic of Sound
Frequency	1.	2.
3.	4.	loudness

Make a frame for each of the vocabulary words listed below. Write the word in the center. Decide what information to frame it with. Use definitions, examples, descriptions, parts, or pictures. An example is shown.

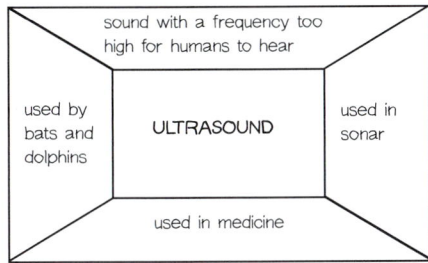

5. resonance
6. Doppler effect
7. amplification
8. acoustics
9. echolocation
10. sonar

Reviewing Key Concepts

Multiple Choice *Choose the letter of the best answer.*

11. Sound is a mechanical wave, so it always
    a. travels through a vacuum
    b. has the same amplitude
    c. is made by a machine
    d. travels through matter

12. Which unit is a measure of sound frequency?
    a. hertz
    b. decibel
    c. amp
    d. meter

13. In which of the following materials would sound waves move fastest?
    a. water
    b. cool air
    c. hot air
    d. steel

14. Which of the following effects is caused by amplification?
    a. wavelength increases
    b. amplitude increases
    c. frequency decreases
    d. decibel measure decreases

15. The frequency of a sound wave determines its
    a. pitch
    b. loudness
    c. amplitude
    d. intensity

16. As sound waves travel away from their source, their
    a. intensity increases
    b. energy increases
    c. intensity decreases
    d. frequency decreases

17. A telephone mouthpiece changes sound waves into
    a. electric signals
    b. vibrations
    c. CD pits
    d. grooves on a cylinder

Short Answer *Look at the diagrams of waves below. For the next two items, choose the wave diagram that best fits the description, and explain your choice.*

a.   b.   c.

18. the sound of a basketball coach blowing a whistle during practice
19. the sound of a cow mooing in a pasture

Chapter 16: **Sound** 547

ASSESSMENT RESOURCES

UNIT ASSESSMENT BOOK
- Chapter Test A, pp. 26–29
- Chapter Test B, pp. 30–33
- Chapter Test C, pp. 34–37
- Alternative Assessment, pp. 38–39

SPANISH ASSESSMENT BOOK
Spanish Chapter Test, pp. 285–288

Technology Resources

Edit test items and answer choices.

 Test Generator CD-ROM

Visit **ClassZone.com** to extend test practice.

 Test Practice

Reviewing Vocabulary

1. hertz
2. pitch
3. intensity
4. decibel

Sample answers:

5. resonance: sound wave has the same frequency as an object's natural frequency; constructive interference; amplitudes combine with each other, sound wave is stronger
6. Doppler effect: lower pitch as source moves away; higher pitch as source approaches; pitch changes with movement of source; discovered by Christian Doppler
7. amplification: louder, greater intensity; greater height of sound wave; effect of an amplifier; used in TV, radio, stereo
8. acoustics: scientific study; study of sound; study of how sound is produced; study of how sound is detected
9. echolocation: use of sound; locates objects by reflection; used by bats; used by dolphins
10. sonar: used by humans to locate objects; used underwater; used in submarines, sound navigation, and mapping the sea floor

Reviewing Key Concepts

11. d
12. a
13. d
14. b
15. a
16. c
17. a
18. c; high frequency, pitch, and amplitude
19. a; low frequency, pitch, and amplitude

Thinking Critically

20. By plucking the strings, which causes them to vibrate
21. by plucking the strings harder or more softly
22. The sound quality is different.
23. The order should be c, a, d, b.
24. Frequency and amplitude are both measures of a sound wave; frequency determines pitch, while amplitude determines loudness. Intensity and amplitude both relate to loudness of sound; intensity relates to amount of energy, while amplitude relates to the measure of wave energy. Pitch and quality concern an aspect of sound that we hear; pitch relates to the highness or lowness, while quality concerns other aspects of the sound. Fundamentals and overtones are pitches in a musical tone; the fundamental is the basic pitch we hear, while overtones are higher, fainter pitches that mix into the sound.

Using Math in Science

25. 7:45 A.M. to 8:00 A.M.
26. 103 dB; allow ±3 dB variance
27. yes, from about 7:30 A.M. to about 8:30 A.M.
28. You could use a bar to represent the noise-level "snapshot" at each quarter hour or half hour. The graph would not be as informative, because noise measures for times between would not be shown.

the BIG idea

29. by plucking the strings on the guitar; vibrations magnified by the amplifier; sound waves coming from the boom box; and sound caused by the shoes hitting the ground
30. Sample answer: Sound waves transfer energy through vibrations. Sound is a longitudinal wave that requires a medium. As frequency increases, pitch is higher. More intense sounds are louder.

UNIT PROJECTS

Collect schedules, materials lists, and questions. Be sure dates and materials are obtainable, and questions are focused.

 Unit Projects, pp. 5–10

548 Unit 4: **Waves, Sound, and Light**

Thinking Critically

Look at the photograph of an instrument above. Write a short answer to the next two questions.

20. **HYPOTHESIZE** How might sound waves be produced using the instrument in the photograph?
21. **APPLY** How might a person playing the instrument in the photograph vary the intensity?
22. **COMMUNICATE** Two people are singing at the same pitch, yet they sound different. Explain why.
23. **SEQUENCE** Copy the following sequence chart on your paper. Write the events in the correct sequence on the chart.

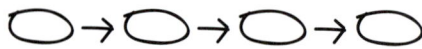

Events
a. Sound waves race out from the wind chime.
b. Forces in air gradually weaken the chime sound.
c. A breeze makes a wind chime vibrate.
d. A person nearby hears the wind chime.

24. **COMPARE AND CONTRAST** Write a description of the similarities and differences between each of the following pairs of terms: frequency—amplitude; intensity—amplitude; pitch—quality; fundamental tone—overtones.

Using Math in Science

Read the line graph below showing freeway noise levels at a toll collector's booth. Use the data in the graph to answer the next four questions.

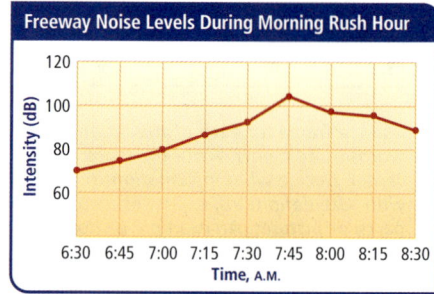

25. Which is the noisiest quarter-hour?
26. Estimate the loudest level of sound that the toll collector is exposed to.
27. If ear protection should be worn for a sound level above 90 dB, should the toll collector wear hearing protection? If so, during which times?
28. Describe how you could turn the line graph into a bar graph. Would the bar graph be as informative? Explain your answer.

the BIG idea

29. **ANALYZE** Look back at the picture at the start of the chapter on pages 514–515. How are sound waves being produced?
30. **SUMMARIZE** Write a paragraph summarizing this chapter. Use the Big Idea on page 514 as your topic sentence. Write examples of each key concept listed on page 514.

UNIT PROJECTS

Check your schedule for your unit project. How are you doing? Be sure that you've placed data or notes from your research in your project folder.

548 Unit 4: Waves, Sound, and Light

MONITOR AND RETEACH

If students have trouble applying the concepts in items 25–28, have them do the following activities:
- Make a bar graph as in problem 28 and compare the information.
- Trace the graph on a piece of paper. Use a ruler to carefully sketch grid lines on the graph, so that the numbers can be easily read.
- Make up additional questions about the graph. Trade questions, and answer someone else's questions.

Students may benefit from summarizing one or more sections of the chapter.

 Summarizing the Chapter, pp. 141–142

Standardized Test Practice

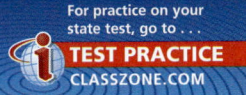

For practice on your state test, go to...
TEST PRACTICE
CLASSZONE.COM

Analyzing Experiments

Read the following description of the way scientists study animals' hearing. Then answer the questions below.

Scientists test the hearing ranges of a human by making a sound and asking the person to say whether it was heard. This cannot be done with animals. Scientists use different methods to find animals' hearing ranges. In some experiments, they train animals—by rewarding them with food or water—to make specific behaviors when they hear a sound. Another method is to study an animal's nervous system for electrical reactions to sounds.

Researchers have found that dogs and cats can hear a wide range of sounds. Both dogs and cats can hear much higher frequencies than humans can. Lizards and frogs can only hear sounds in a much narrower range than humans can. Elephants can hear a wider range than lizards and frogs but not as wide a range as dogs and cats. Elephants can hear the lowest frequency sounds of all these animals.

1. What type of behavior would be best for scientists to train animals to make as a signal that they hear a sound?
   a. a typical motion that the animal makes frequently
   b. a motion that is difficult for the animal to make
   c. a motion the animal makes rarely but does make naturally
   d. a complicated motion of several steps

2. According to the passage, which animals can hear sounds with the highest frequencies?
   a. cats
   b. elephants
   c. frogs
   d. lizards

3. The high-pitched sounds of car brakes are sometimes more bothersome to pet dogs than they are to their owners. Based on the experimental findings, what is the best explanation for that observation?
   a. The dogs hear high-intensity sounds that their owners cannot hear.
   b. The dogs hear low-intensity sounds that their owners cannot hear.
   c. The dogs hear low-frequency sounds that their owners cannot hear.
   d. The dogs hear high-frequency sounds that their owners cannot hear.

4. Which animal hears sounds with the longest wavelengths?
   a. cat
   b. dog
   c. elephant
   d. frog

Extended Response

Answer the two questions below in detail. Include some of the terms from the word box in your answer. Underline each term you use in your answer.

| amplitude | distance | Doppler effect |
| frequency | pitch | wavelength |

5. Suppose you are riding in a car down the street and pass a building where a fire alarm is sounding. Will the sound you hear change as you move up to, alongside, and past the building? Why or why not?

6. Marvin had six glass bottles that held different amounts of water. He blew air into each bottle, producing a sound. How would the sounds produced by each of the six bottles compare to the others? Why?

Chapter 16: **Sound** 549

Analyzing Experiments
1. c
2. a
3. d
4. c

Extended Response

5. RUBRIC
4 points for a response that correctly answers the question and uses the following terms accurately:
• pitch • wavelength • distance

Sample: The sound is higher in pitch *as the car moves closer to the alarm and becomes lower in pitch as it moves farther away. This is because sound changes with* distance. *When the distance decreases, the* wavelength *is shorter and the pitch is higher. When the distance increases, the wavelength is longer and the pitch lowers. A change in pitch occurs when either the source or the receiver of the sound is moving. This is known as the* Doppler effect.

3 points for a response that correctly answers the question and uses two terms accurately
2 points for a response that correctly answers the question and uses one term accurately
1 point for a response that correctly answers the question but does not use the terms

6. RUBRIC
4 points for a response that correctly answers the question and uses the following terms accurately:
• pitch • frequency • distance

Sample: The pitch, *or* frequency, *increases as the amount of water increases. So the bottles with more water would have a higher pitch than the bottles with less water. The reason for this is that the sound is traveling through a smaller* distance *since there is a smaller amount of air.*

3 points for a response that correctly answers the question and uses two terms accurately
2 points for a response that correctly answers the question and uses one term accurately
1 point for a response that correctly answers the question but does not use the terms

METACOGNITIVE ACTIVITY

Have students answer the following questions in their **Science Notebook:**

1. Was there a quality of sound that was new to you? If so, what?
2. What questions that you had about sound were answered in this chapter? What questions do you still have about sound?
3. Do the concepts in this chapter relate to your Unit Project? If so, how? If not, how might you revise your project to include sound?

CHAPTER 17 Electromagnetic Waves

Physical Science
UNIFYING PRINCIPLES

PRINCIPLE 1
Matter is made of particles too small to see.

PRINCIPLE 2
Matter changes form and moves from place to place.

PRINCIPLE 3
Energy changes from one form to another, but it cannot be created or destroyed.

PRINCIPLE 4
Physical forces affect the movement of all matter on Earth and throughout the universe.

Unit 4: Waves, Sound, and Light
BIG IDEAS

CHAPTER 15
Waves
Waves transfer energy and interact in predictable ways.

CHAPTER 16
Sound
Sound waves transfer energy through vibrations.

CHAPTER 17
Electromagnetic Waves
Electromagnetic waves transfer energy through radiation.

CHAPTER 18
Light and Optics
Optical tools depend on the wave behavior of light.

CHAPTER 17 KEY CONCEPTS

 SECTION 1
Electromagnetic waves have unique traits.
1. An electromagnetic (EM) wave is a disturbance in a field.
2. EM waves can travel in a vacuum.
3. EM waves can interact with a material medium.

 **SECTION 2**
Electromagnetic waves have many uses.
1. EM waves have different frequencies.
2. Long length, low frequency (radio waves, microwaves)
3. Mid-range length and frequency (infrared, visible and ultraviolet light)
4. Short length, high-frequency (x-rays, gamma rays)

 SECTION 3
The Sun is the source of most visible light.
1. Light comes from the Sun and other natural sources.
2. Some living things produce visible light.
3. Human technologies produce visible light.

 SECTION 4
Light waves interact with materials.
1. Light can be reflected, transmitted, or absorbed.
2. Wavelength determines color.

 The Big Idea Flow Chart is available on p. T17 in the **UNIT TRANSPARENCY BOOK**.

Previewing Content

SECTION

 Electromagnetic waves have unique traits. pp. 553–558

1. **An electromagnetic wave is a disturbance in a field.**
   An **electromagnetic wave** is a disturbance that transfers energy through a field.
   A **field** is the area around an object where the object applies force on another object without touching it. The two fields of an EM wave—electric and magnetic—vibrate at right angles to each other and are perpendicular to the direction the wave is moving (as illustrated in the visual below).

   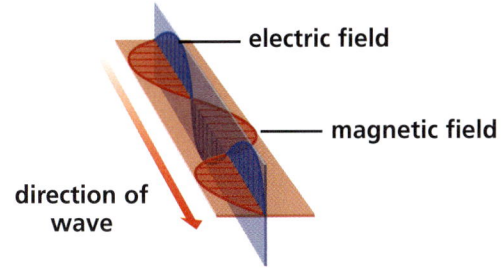

   An EM wave is emitted whenever a charged atomic particle accelerates. The Sun and human technology are the two main sources of EM waves.

2. **Electromagnetic waves can travel in a vacuum.**
   Once EM waves are produced, they travel on their own, independent of the source that emitted them. They don't need a medium and can travel in a vacuum at about 300,000 kilometers per second.
   Radiation is the transfer of energy in the form of EM waves. EM waves do not lose energy as they travel in a vacuum. EM radiation from the Sun travels in a straight line through the vacuum of outer space.

3. **Electromagnetic waves can interact with a material medium.**
   When EM waves encounter a material medium, they may transfer energy to it. Different mediums interact differently with EM waves, and can change the direction of the wave and affect energy transfer.
   - In a vacuum, EM waves transfer energy by moving potential energy from one place to another.
   - In a medium, an EM wave's potential energy can be converted into other forms, such as heat.

Common Misconceptions

WAVE TRANSMISSION Students may think that EM waves must have a medium, or matter, to travel. EM waves can travel through matter, but do not need matter to travel.

 This misconception is addressed on p. 555.

SECTION

 Electromagnetic waves have many uses. pp. 559–567

1. **EM waves have different frequencies.**
   An EM wave's frequency determines the wave's characteristics. The higher the frequency, the more energy the wave carries. The **electromagnetic spectrum** is a continuum of waves from the lowest-frequency radio waves to the highest-frequency gamma waves.

2. **Radio waves and microwaves have long wavelengths and low frequencies.**
   Radio waves are long, low-energy EM waves. They can be modified and converted into the sound and pictures of radios and TVs. **Microwaves** have more energy and shorter wavelengths than radio waves.
   - In radar, microwaves are reflected off an object and returned to their source as a way of locating the object.
   - Cell phone technology is like radio transmission but uses microwaves. A system of towers connects cell phones to each other and to the regular phone system.

3. **Infrared, visible, and ultraviolet light have mid-range wavelengths and frequencies.**
   The range of frequencies that humans can see is just a tiny part of the EM spectrum.
   - **Infrared waves** lie between visible light and microwaves. They are emitted by warm objects. Infrared technology is used to cook food, detect warm objects, and provide heat.
   - **Ultraviolet light** carries more energy than visible light and can damage human tissue. It is used to sterilize medical equipment and kill bacteria in food.

4. **X-rays and gamma rays have short wavelengths and high frequencies.**
   Because of their high frequencies, x-rays and gamma rays carry very high energies. They are naturally produced by stars.
   - **X-rays** can penetrate soft tissues but not hard tissues of the body, making these waves useful for medical imaging.
   - **Gamma rays** can penetrate all the tissues of the body, killing normal cells and causing cancer cells to grow.

MISCONCEPTION DATABASE
CLASSZONE.COM Background on student misconceptions

INFRARED LIGHT Students may think infrared light is part of the visible spectrum. Infrared light, however, is below the visible range and cannot be detected by the human eye.

 This misconception is addressed on p. 565.

Chapter 17: **Electromagnetic Waves** 549B

Previewing Content

SECTION

3 The Sun is the source of most visible light. pp. 568–572

1. Light comes from the Sun and other natural sources.
Almost all organisms depend on light for survival. Virtually all light on Earth initiates in sunlight. Green plants use sunlight to synthesize food that both plants and animals depend on for energy. The Sun's intense heat produces light through **incandescence**. This light is the ultimate source of almost all energy on Earth.

2. Some living things produce visible light.
Chemical reactions in some living organisms produce **bioluminescence**. Unlike incandescence, luminescence produces light without the high temperatures that could harm organisms.

3. Human technologies produce visible light.
The discovery of electricity has led to several artificial lighting technologies.

- Most incandescent light bulbs use tungsten filaments and produce light and heat.
- Halogen lighting also produces lots of heat, but the tungsten filament lasts longer than in ordinary incandescent light bulbs and produces more light.
- Fluorescent lighting is cool and efficient. The bulb is coated with a phosphor, which glows when it absorbs the UV waves generated within the bulb.
- LEDs are semiconductors that produce light when electricity passes through. They are cool, efficient, and long-lasting. Light produced by LEDs has many advantages over other forms of lighting.

The visual below shows the different parts of incandescent, halogen, and fluorescent bulbs.

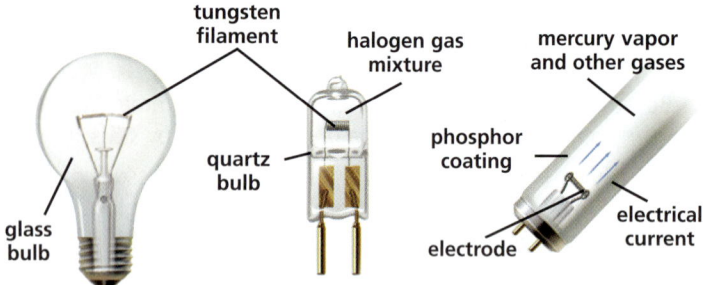

SECTION

4 Light waves interact with materials. pp. 573–581

1. Light can be reflected, transmitted, or absorbed.
EM waves can interact with a material medium in the same ways that mechanical waves do. The medium can reflect, transmit, or absorb the waves. Most objects are visible because they reflect light. **Transmission** and **absorption** affect how objects look.

- Objects that transmit most of the light that strikes them appear transparent.
- Objects that transmit some of the light that strikes them but cause it to scatter appear translucent.
- Opaque objects do not transmit light.

Scattering from fine particles in a material sends light in all directions and creates diffuse light. **Polarization** reduces glare. When all of the electric fields of a group of light waves vibrate in the same direction, the light is polarized.

2. Wavelength determines color.
Visible light is a spectrum that is usually divided into seven colors. Visible light reflected from an object gives it color; a green leaf reflects green wavelengths and absorbs all other visible wavelengths.

The three **primary colors** are light of different wavelengths that produce white light when mixed equally. They are red, green, and blue.

The **primary pigments** reflect wavelengths of cyan, yellow, and magenta. When you mix pigments, the mixture absorbs more colors, and reflects fewer wavelengths. The visual below shows primary pigments.

Common Misconceptions

BIOLUMINESCENCE Students commonly think that bioluminescence is an electrical process that occurs within an organism. In truth, bioluminescence is the result of chemical reactions that produce energy in the form of light.

 This misconception is addressed on p. 569.

MISCONCEPTION DATABASE
CLASSZONE.COM Background on student misconceptions

THE SKY'S COLOR It is commonly thought that the sky is blue because of the reflection of blue light from Earth's oceans. In fact, particles in the atmosphere scatter the blue wavelengths of sunlight more than they scatter other wavelengths, making the sky appear blue.

 This misconception is addressed on p. 575.

549C Unit 4: Waves, Sound, and Light

Previewing Labs

EXPLORE the BIG idea

What Melts the Ice Cubes? p. 551 Students will observe ice cubes melting to find out that black and white materials absorb different quantities of energy from light.	**TIME** 10 minutes **MATERIALS** 2 ice cubes, 2 sandwich bags, sheet of white paper, sheet of black paper
What Is White Light Made Of? p. 551 Students will use a CD as a prism to find out that white light can separate into several colors.	**TIME** 10 minutes **MATERIALS** compact disc, sheet of white paper, flashlight
Internet Activity: Electromagnetic Waves, p. 551 Students learn that the Sun emits different wavelengths.	**TIME** 20 minutes **MATERIALS** computer with Internet access

SECTION 1

EXPLORE Electromagnetic Waves, p. 553 Students use a mirror to show that EM waves can be reflected.	**TIME** 10 minutes **MATERIALS** TV with remote control unit, mirror with stand
INVESTIGATE Wave Behavior, p. 556 Students design an experiment to determine what makes the vanes of a radiometer move.	**TIME** 30 minutes **MATERIALS** radiometer

SECTION 2

EXPLORE Radio Waves, p. 559 Students explore how radio waves form and how they are detected.	**TIME** 10 minutes **MATERIALS** 25 cm copper wire (2 pieces), C or D battery, 5 cm electrical tape, metal fork, portable radio
INVESTIGATE The Electromagnetic Spectrum, p. 564 Students draw conclusions about the existence of invisible EM waves by measuring their temperature.	**TIME** 30 minutes **MATERIALS** sheet of white paper, black marker, 3 thermometers, prism

SECTION 3

INVESTIGATE Artificial Lighting, p. 570 Students design an experiment to examine various kinds of bulbs.	**TIME** 30 minutes **MATERIALS** a variety of bulb types and sizes

SECTION 4

EXPLORE Light and Matter, p. 573 Students observe the scattering of light in a translucent material.	**TIME** 10 minutes **MATERIALS** clear plastic container with lid, 4–6 cups water, measuring spoons, 10 mL milk, flashlight
INVESTIGATE Mixing Colors, p. 578 Students discover the colors that make up black ink.	**TIME** 30 minutes **MATERIALS** 3 coffee filters, scissors, 3 black felt-tip markers (different brands), 3 cups water
CHAPTER INVESTIGATION Wavelength and Color, pp. 580–581 Students use a light box to learn that an object's color is determined by the wavelengths of light it reflects.	**TIME** 40 minutes **MATERIALS** sheets of acetate (red, blue, green), ruler, scissors, shoe box, masking tape, light source, solid-colored objects

Additional INVESTIGATION, Seeing the Invisible, A, B, & C, pp. 203–211, Teacher Instructions, pp. 284–285

Chapter 17: **Electromagnetic Waves** 549D

Previewing Chapter Resources

	INTEGRATED TECHNOLOGY	LABS AND ACTIVITIES
CHAPTER 17 **Electromagnetic Waves**	**CLASSZONE.COM** • eEdition Plus • EasyPlanner Plus • Misconception Database • Content Review • Test Practice • Visualization • Resource Centers • Internet Activity: EM Waves • Math Tutorial **SCILINKS.ORG** **CD-ROMS** • eEdition • EasyPlanner • Power Presentations • Content Review • Lab Generator • Test Generator **AUDIO CDS** • Audio Readings • Audio Readings in Spanish	**EXPLORE the Big Idea, p. 551** • What Melts the Ice Cubes? • What Is White Light Made Of? • Internet Activity: Electromagnetic Waves **UNIT RESOURCE BOOK** Unit Projects, pp. 5–10 **Lab Generator CD-ROM** Generate customized labs.
SECTION 1 **Electromagnetic waves have unique traits.** pp. 553–558 Time: 2 periods (1 block) Lesson Plan, pp. 143–144	• **VISUALIZATION,** EM Waves • **MATH TUTORIAL** **UNIT TRANSPARENCY BOOK** • Big Idea Flow Chart, p. T17 • Daily Vocabulary Scaffolding, p. T18 • Note-Taking Model, p. T19 • 3-Minute Warm-Up, p. T20	• EXPLORE Electromagnetic Waves, p. 553 • INVESTIGATE Wave Behavior, p. 556 • Math in Science, p. 558 **UNIT RESOURCE BOOK** • Datasheet, Wave Behavior, p. 152 • Math Support & Practice, pp. 192–193
SECTION 2 **Electromagnetic waves have many uses.** pp. 559–567 Time: 2 periods (1 block) Lesson Plan, pp. 154–155	**RESOURCE CENTER,** EM Spectrum **UNIT TRANSPARENCY BOOK** • Daily Vocabulary Scaffolding, p. T18 • 3-Minute Warm-Up, p. T20 • "The Electromagnetic Spectrum" Visual, p. T22	• EXPLORE Radio Waves, p. 559 • INVESTIGATE The EM Spectrum, p. 564 • Think Science, p. 567 **UNIT RESOURCE BOOK** • Datasheet, The EM Spectrum, p. 163 • Additional INVESTIGATION, Seeing the Invisible, A, B, & C, pp. 203–211
SECTION 3 **The Sun is the source of most visible light.** pp. 568–572 Time: 2 periods (1 block) Lesson Plan, pp. 165–166	**RESOURCE CENTER,** Visible Light **UNIT TRANSPARENCY BOOK** • Daily Vocabulary Scaffolding, p. T18 • 3-Minute Warm-Up, p. T21	INVESTIGATE Artificial Lighting, p. 570 **UNIT RESOURCE BOOK** Datasheet, Artificial Lighting, p. 174
SECTION 4 **Light waves interact with materials.** pp. 573–581 Time: 4 periods (2 blocks) Lesson Plan, pp. 176–177	**UNIT TRANSPARENCY BOOK** • Big Idea Flow Chart, p. T17 • Daily Vocabulary Scaffolding, p. T18 • 3-Minute Warm-Up, p. T21 • Chapter Outline, pp. T23–T24	• EXPLORE Light and Matter, p. 573 • INVESTIGATE Mixing Colors, p. 578 • CHAPTER INVESTIGATION, Wavelength and Color, pp. 580–581 **UNIT RESOURCE BOOK** • Datasheet, Mixing Colors, p. 185 • CHAPTER INVESTIGATION, A, B, & C, pp. 194–202

KEY TO ICONS CD/CD-ROM Teacher Edition — UNIT TRANSPARENCY BOOK — SPANISH ASSESSMENT BOOK
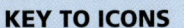 INTERNET — Pupil Edition — UNIT RESOURCE BOOK — UNIT ASSESSMENT BOOK — SCIENCE TOOLKIT

READING AND REINFORCEMENT | ASSESSMENT | STANDARDS

- Frame Game, B26–27
- Supporting Main Ideas, C42
- Daily Vocabulary Scaffolding, H1–8

 UNIT RESOURCE BOOK
- Vocabulary Practice, pp. 189–190
- Decoding Support, p. 191
- Summarizing the Chapter, pp. 212–213

 Audio Readings CD
Listen to Pupil Edition.

 Audio Readings in Spanish CD
Listen to Pupil Edition in Spanish.

- Chapter Review, pp. 583–584
- Standardized Test Practice, p. 585

 UNIT ASSESSMENT BOOK
- Diagnostic Test, pp. 40–41
- Chapter Test, A, B, & C, pp. 46–51
- Alternative Assessment, pp. 58–59

 Spanish Chapter Test, pp. 289–292

 Test Generator CD-ROM
Generate customized tests.

 Lab Generator CD-ROM
Rubrics for Labs

National Standards
A.2–8, A.9.a–f, B.3.c, B.3.f, E.2–5, F.4.c, F.5.c

See p. 550 for the standards.

 **UNIT RESOURCE BOOK**
- Reading Study Guide, A & B, pp. 145–148
- Spanish Reading Study Guide, pp. 149–150
- Challenge and Extension, p. 151
- Reinforcing Key Concepts, p. 153
- Challenge Reading, pp. 187–188

 Ongoing Assessment, pp. 554–557

 Section 17.1 Review, p. 557

 UNIT ASSESSMENT BOOK
Section 17.1 Quiz, p. 42

National Standards
A.2–8, A.9.a–f, E.2–5

 UNIT RESOURCE BOOK
- Reading Study Guide, A & B, pp. 156–159
- Spanish Reading Study Guide, pp. 160–161
- Challenge and Extension, p. 162
- Reinforcing Key Concepts, p. 164

 Ongoing Assessment, pp. 559, 561–562, 565

 Section 17.2 Review, p. 566

 UNIT ASSESSMENT BOOK
Section 17.2 Quiz, p. 43

National Standards
A.2–7, A.9.a–b, A.9.d–f, F.4.c, F.5.c

UNIT RESOURCE BOOK
- Reading Study Guide, A & B, pp. 167–170
- Spanish Reading Study Guide, pp. 171–172
- Challenge and Extension, p. 173
- Reinforcing Key Concepts, p. 175

 Ongoing Assessment, pp. 568–572

Section 17.3 Review, p. 572

 UNIT ASSESSMENT BOOK
Section 17.3 Quiz, p. 44

National Standards
A.2–7, A.9.a–b, A.9.d–f, B.3.f, E.2–5, F.5.c

 UNIT RESOURCE BOOK
- Reading Study Guide, A & B, pp. 178–181
- Spanish Reading Study Guide, pp. 182–183
- Challenge and Extension, p. 184
- Reinforcing Key Concepts, p. 186

 Ongoing Assessment, pp. 573–575, 577–579

 Section 17.4 Review, p. 579

 UNIT ASSESSMENT BOOK
Section 17.4 Quiz, p. 45

National Standards
A.2–7, A.9.a–b, A.9.e–f, B.3.c

Chapter 17: **Electromagnetic Waves**

Previewing Resources for Differentiated Instruction

CHAPTER INVESTIGATION

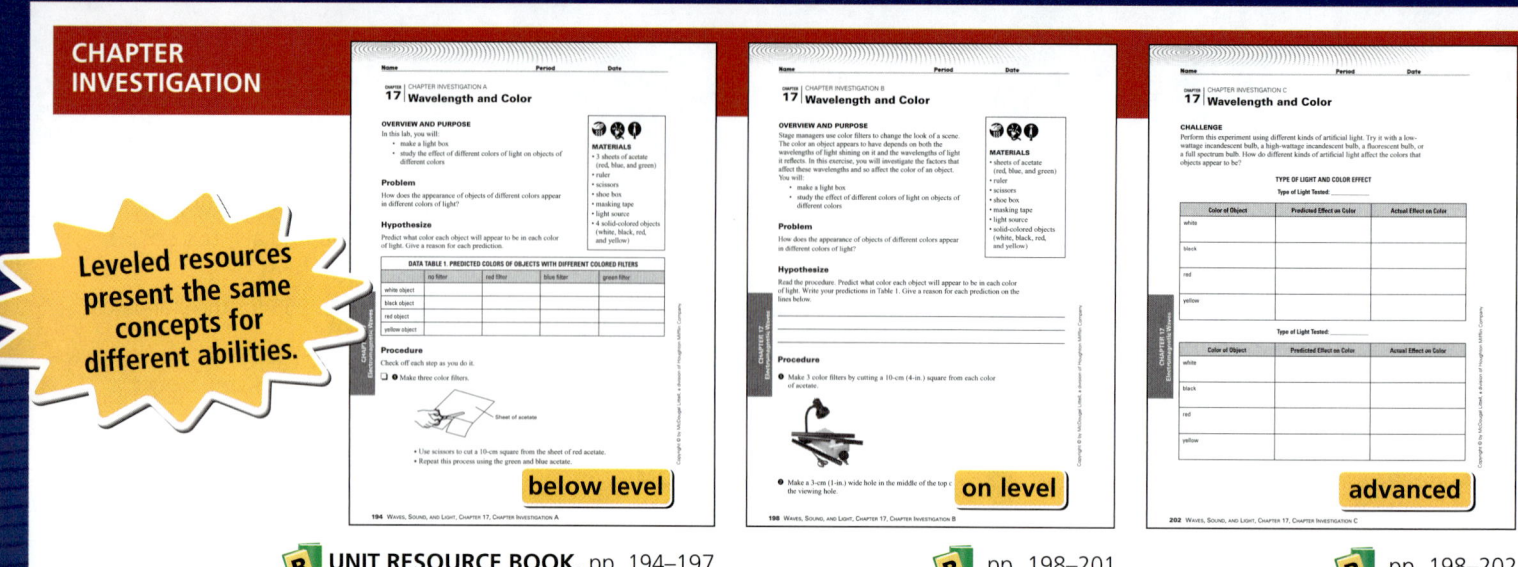

Leveled resources present the same concepts for different abilities.

UNIT RESOURCE BOOK, pp. 194–197   pp. 198–201   pp. 198–202

READING STUDY GUIDE

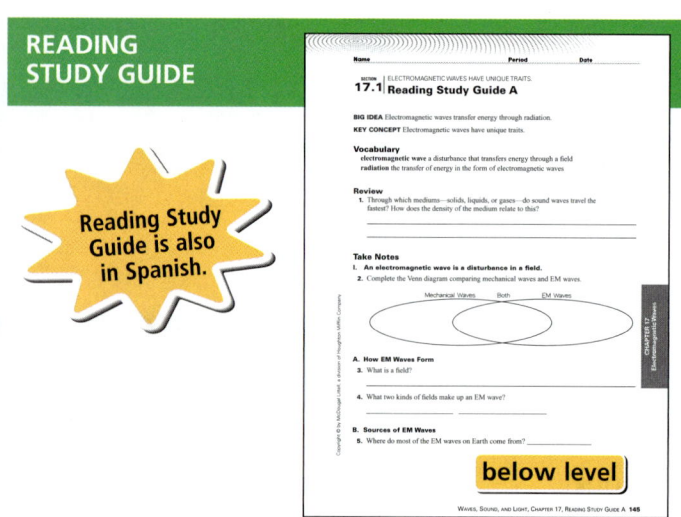
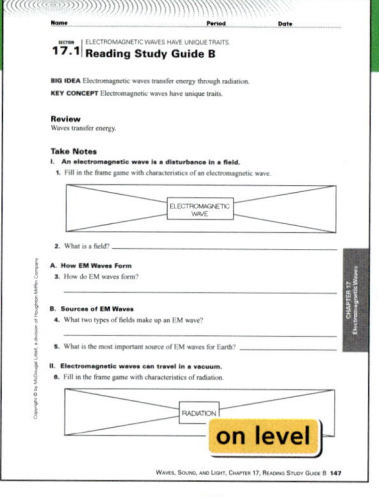
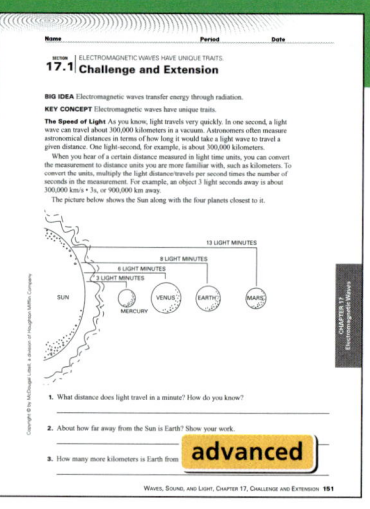

Reading Study Guide is also in Spanish.

UNIT RESOURCE BOOK, pp. 145–146   pp. 147–148   p. 151

CHAPTER TEST

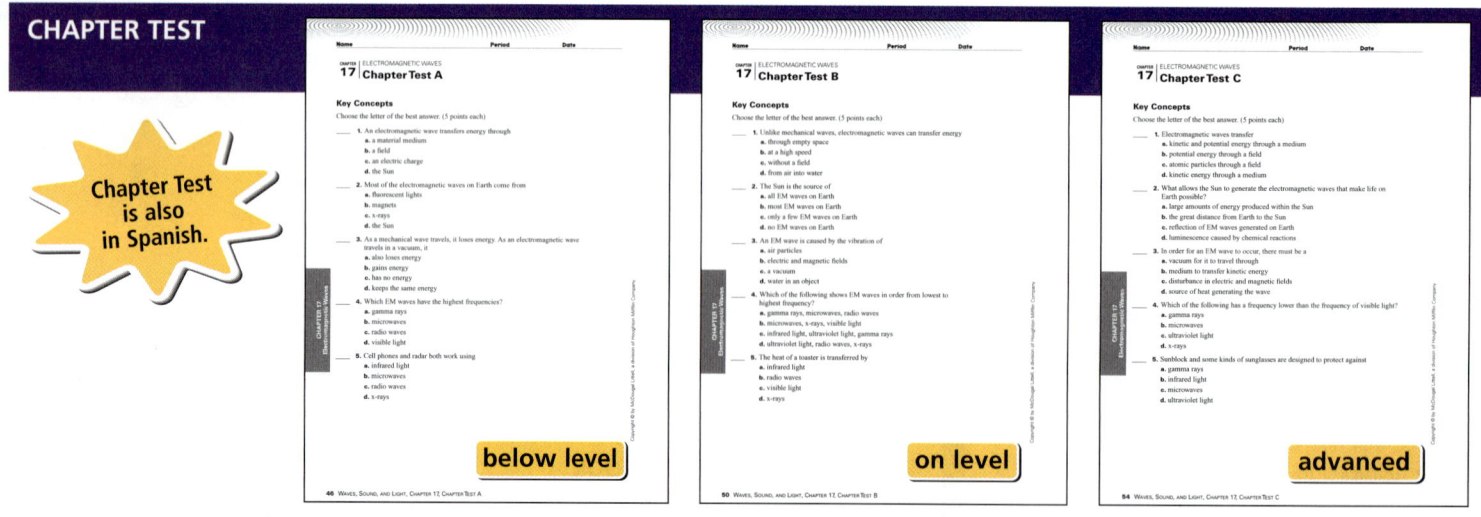

Chapter Test is also in Spanish.

UNIT ASSESSMENT BOOK, pp. 46–49   pp. 50–53   pp. 54–57

549G   Unit 4: Waves, Sound, and Light

TECHNOLOGY

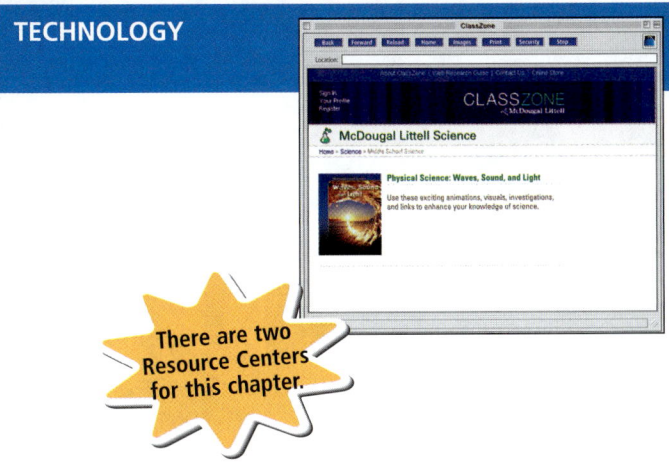
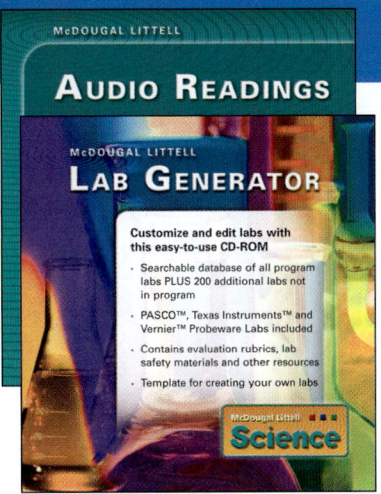
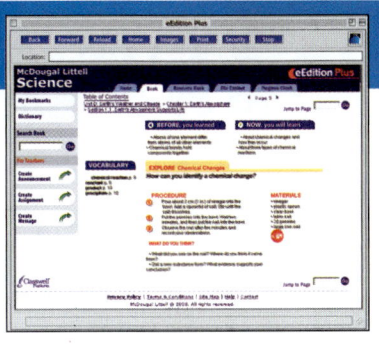

There are two Resource Centers for this chapter.

CLASSZONE.COM   **CD/CD-ROMS**   **CLASSZONE.COM**

VISUAL CONTENT

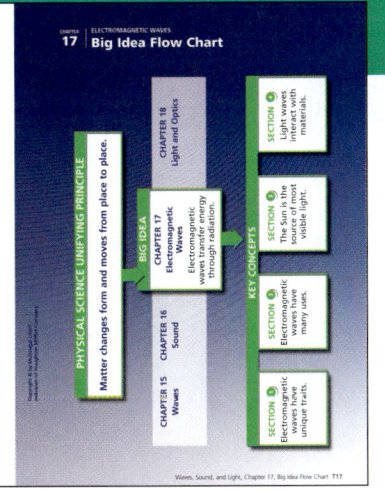
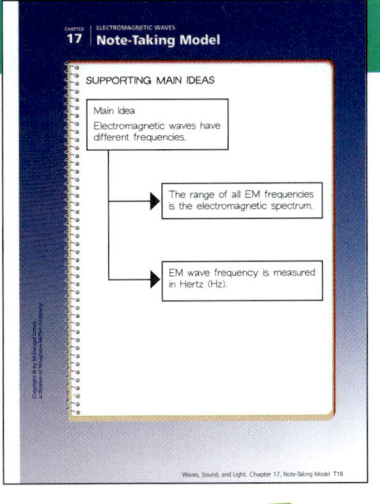
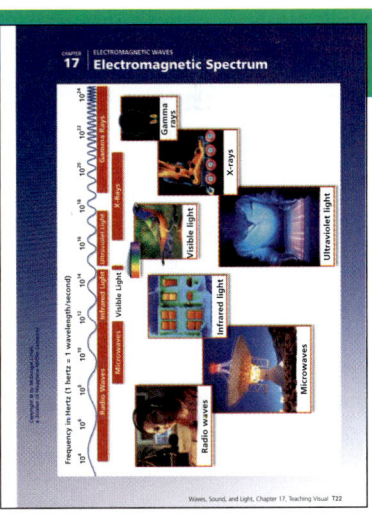

UNIT TRANSPARENCY BOOK, p. T17   p. T19   p. T22

MORE SUPPORT

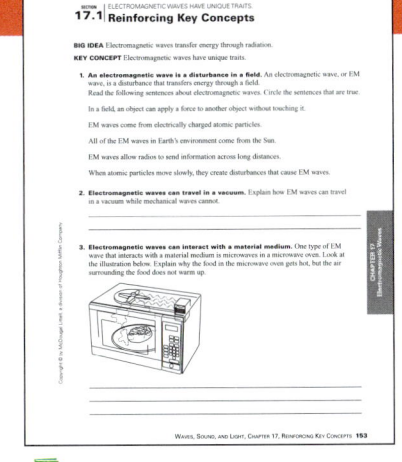
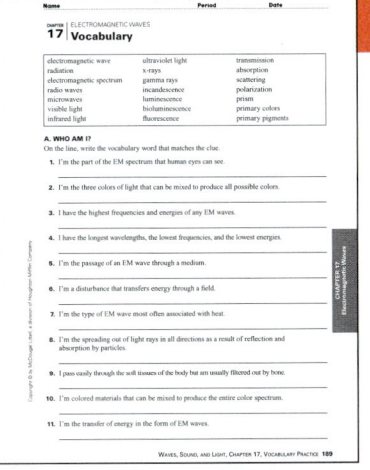
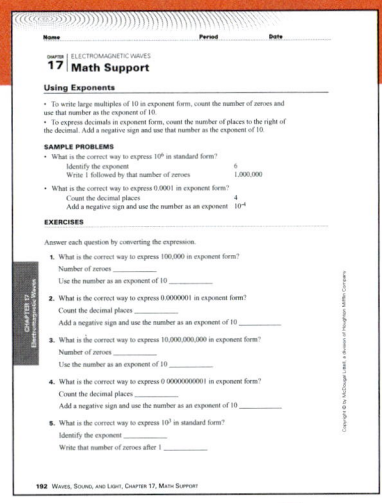

Reinforcing Key Concepts for each section

UNIT RESOURCE BOOK, p. 153   pp. 189–190   p. 192

Chapter 17: **Electromagnetic Waves 549H**

CHAPTER 17 Electromagnetic Waves

INTRODUCE

Have students look at the photograph of the cell phone user and discuss how the question in the box links to the Big Idea:

- If waves are involved in cell phone technology, what kind of waves might they be?
- How can waves travel from one cell phone to another?
- What other devices use the same kind of waves as a cell phone?

National Science Education Standards

Content

B.3.c Light interacts with matter by transmission, absorption, and scattering.

B.3.f The Sun is a major source of energy for changes on Earth's surface. Energy from the Sun is transferred to Earth in the form of visible light, infrared, and ultraviolet radiation.

Process

A.2–8 Design and conduct an investigation; use tools to gather and interpret data; use evidence to describe, predict, explain, model; think critically to make relationships between evidence and explanation; recognize different explanations and predictions; communicate scientific procedures and explanations; use mathematics.

A.9.a–f Understand scientific inquiry by using different investigations, methods, mathematics, technology, and explanations based on logic, evidence, and skepticism.

E.2–5 Design, implement, and evaluate a solution or product; communicate technological design.

F.4.c–d Risks and benefits

F.5.c Science and technology in society

550 Unit 4: **Waves, Sound, and Light**

CHAPTER 17 Electromagnetic Waves

the BIG idea

Electromagnetic waves transfer energy through radiation.

How does this phone stay connected?

Key Concepts

SECTION 1 Electromagnetic waves have unique traits.
Learn how electromagnetic waves differ from mechanical waves.

SECTION 2 Electromagnetic waves have many uses.
Learn about the behaviors and uses of different types of electromagnetic waves.

SECTION 3 The Sun is the source of most visible light.
Learn about the natural and artificial production of light.

SECTION 4 Light waves interact with materials.
Learn how light waves behave in a material medium.

Internet Preview

CLASSZONE.COM
Chapter 17 online resources: Content Review, Simulation, Visualization, two Resource Centers, Math Tutorial, Test Practice.

550 Unit 4: Waves, Sound, and Light

INTERNET PREVIEW

CLASSZONE.COM For student use with the following pages:

Review and Practice
- Content Review, pp. 552, 582
- Math Tutorial: Positive and Negative Exponents, p. 558
- Test Practice, p. 585

Activities and Resources
- Internet Activity: EM Waves, p. 551
- Visualization: EM Waves, p. 554
- Resource Centers: EM Spectrum, p. 560; Visible Light, p. 568

Light and Color
Code: MDL029

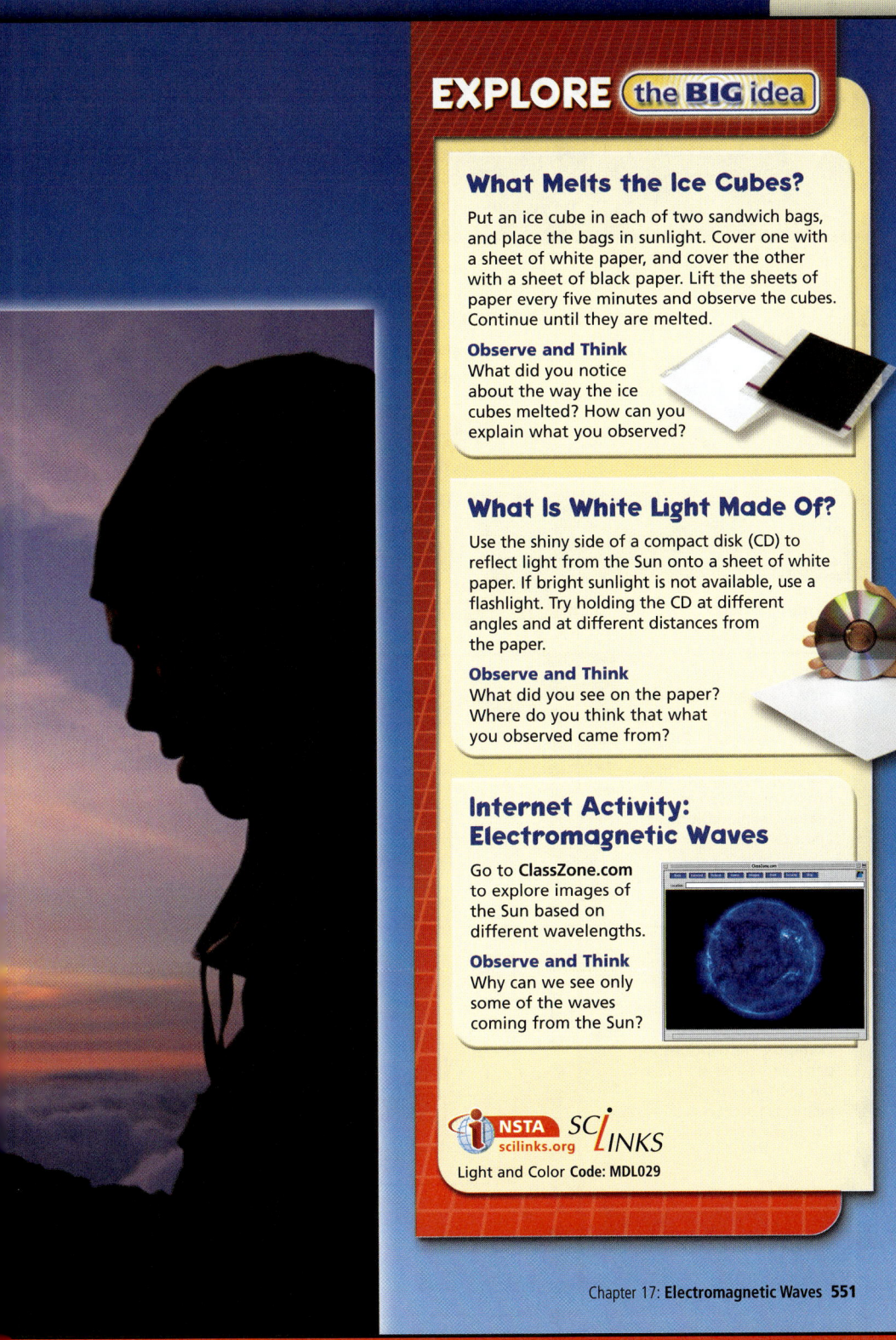

EXPLORE the BIG idea

What Melts the Ice Cubes?
Put an ice cube in each of two sandwich bags, and place the bags in sunlight. Cover one with a sheet of white paper, and cover the other with a sheet of black paper. Lift the sheets of paper every five minutes and observe the cubes. Continue until they are melted.

Observe and Think
What did you notice about the way the ice cubes melted? How can you explain what you observed?

What Is White Light Made Of?
Use the shiny side of a compact disk (CD) to reflect light from the Sun onto a sheet of white paper. If bright sunlight is not available, use a flashlight. Try holding the CD at different angles and at different distances from the paper.

Observe and Think
What did you see on the paper? Where do you think that what you observed came from?

Internet Activity: Electromagnetic Waves
Go to ClassZone.com to explore images of the Sun based on different wavelengths.

Observe and Think
Why can we see only some of the waves coming from the Sun?

NSTA scilinks.org SCLINKS
Light and Color Code: MDL029

Chapter 17: **Electromagnetic Waves** 551

EXPLORE the BIG idea

These inquiry-based activities are appropriate for use at home or as a supplement to classroom instruction.

What Melts the Ice Cubes?
PURPOSE To observe the difference between reflection and absorption of EM radiation. Students observe different amounts of light energy absorbed by black paper and white paper.

TIP *10 min.* The two ice cubes should be the same size when they are placed in the bags. Students can also try covering a bag with aluminum foil, shiny side out, and observe the rate of melting.

Answer: The cube under the black paper melts more quickly. The black paper gets hotter in the sun because it absorbs more light than the white paper.

REVISIT after p. 577.

What Is White Light Made Of?
PURPOSE To observe that white light is made up of different wavelengths and individual colors. Students use a CD as a prism to separate white light.

TIP *10 min.* Prompt students to think about why the silver CD reflects different colors and why the colors change as the CD moves.

Answer: A rainbow of colors from the light being reflected by the CD. The colors were part of the light.

REVISIT after p. 577.

Internet Activity: Electromagnetic Waves
PURPOSE To see that the Sun emits different wavelengths and that they must be detected and visualized in different ways.

TIP *20 min.* Before they use the simulation, have students predict how the different types of EM radiation coming from the Sun will look.

Answer: The human eye can detect waves only in the visible range.

REVISIT after p. 565.

TEACHING WITH TECHNOLOGY

CBL and Probeware If probeware is available, students can use temperature-sensing probes instead of thermometers for "Investigate the Electromagnetic Spectrum" on p. 564.

Digital Camera Take photographs of each step during "Investigate Mixing Colors" on p. 578 to document the activity. Use the camera to show time-elapsed images of the ink samples, taking photographs every few minutes to show how the samples have changed. Compare the final images.

PREPARE

 CONCEPT REVIEW

Activate Prior Knowledge

- Give students a list of phrases or objects that waves travel through. Be sure to include "vacuum" or "outer space."
- Ask if there is any place or object on the list that a mechanical wave cannot travel through. *yes; vacuum*
- Ask how speed of sound is affected by different mediums on the list. *Answers should recognize that sound travels faster in denser materials and not at all in a vacuum.*

TAKING NOTES

Supporting Main Ideas

Making a chart of the main ideas will help students organize the material in the chapter. Using the section's heads is a good start; students can then add information, explanations, and examples that support these ideas.

Vocabulary Strategy

By surrounding each vocabulary term with examples and descriptions, students will develop a thorough understanding of the meaning of each term. Respellings should be included if appropriate.

Vocabulary and Note-Taking Resources

- Vocabulary Practice, pp. 189–190
- Decoding Support, p. 191

- Daily Vocabulary Scaffolding, p. T18
- Note-Taking Model, p. T19

- Frame Game, B26–27
- Supporting Main Ideas, C42
- Daily Vocabulary Scaffolding, H1–8

552 Unit 4: **Waves, Sound, and Light**

CHAPTER 17
Getting Ready to Learn

CONCEPT REVIEW

- A wave is a disturbance that transfers energy.
- Mechanical waves have a medium.
- Waves can be measured.
- Waves react to a change in medium.

VOCABULARY REVIEW

mechanical wave p. 491
wavelength p. 497
frequency p. 497
reflection p. 505
field *See Glossary.*

CONTENT REVIEW
CLASSZONE.COM
Review concepts and vocabulary.

TAKING NOTES

SUPPORTING MAIN IDEAS

Make a chart to show main ideas and the information that supports them. Copy each blue heading. Below each heading, add supporting information, such as reasons, explanations, and examples.

VOCABULARY STRATEGY

Write each new vocabulary term in the center of a **frame game** diagram. Decide what information to frame it with. Use examples, descriptions, parts, sentences that use the term in context, or pictures. You can change the frame to fit each term.

See the Note-Taking Handbook on pages R45–R51.

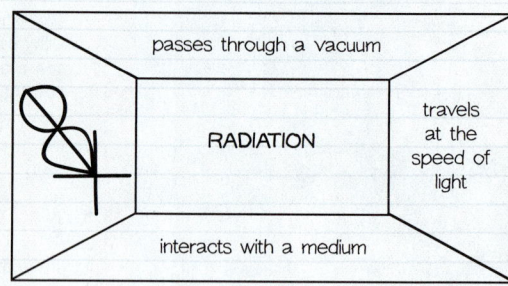

552 Unit 4: Waves, Sound, and Light

CHECK READINESS

Administer the Diagnostic Test to determine students' readiness for new science content and their mastery of requisite math skills.

 Diagnostic Test, pp. 40–41

Technology Resources

Students needing content and math skills should visit **ClassZone.com**.

- **CONTENT REVIEW**
- **MATH TUTORIAL**

 CONTENT REVIEW CD-ROM

KEY CONCEPT

Electromagnetic waves have unique traits.

◄ **BEFORE, you learned**
- Waves transfer energy
- Mechanical waves need a medium to travel

► **NOW, you will learn**
- How electromagnetic waves differ from mechanical waves
- Where electromagnetic waves come from
- How electromagnetic waves transfer energy

VOCABULARY
electromagnetic wave p. 553
radiation p. 555

EXPLORE Electromagnetic Waves

How does the signal from a remote control travel?

PROCEDURE

 Turn the TV on and off using the remote control.

 Work with a partner to try to turn on the TV by aiming the remote control at the mirror.

WHAT DO YOU THINK?
How did you have to position the remote control and the mirror in order to operate the TV? Why do you think this worked?

MATERIALS
- TV with remote control unit
- mirror with stand

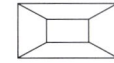

VOCABULARY
Create a frame game diagram for the term *electromagnetic wave.*

An electromagnetic wave is a disturbance in a field.

Did you know that you are surrounded by thousands of waves at this very moment? Waves fill every cubic centimeter of the space around you. They collide with or pass through your body all the time.

Most of these waves are invisible, but you can perceive many of them. Light is made up of these waves, and heat can result from them. Whenever you use your eyes to see, or feel the warmth of the Sun on your skin, you are detecting their presence. These waves also allow radios, TVs, and cell phones to send or receive information over long distances. These waves have the properties shared by all waves, yet they are different from mechanical waves in important ways. This second type of wave is called an electromagnetic wave. An **electromagnetic wave** (ih-LEHK-troh-mag-NEHT-ihk) is a disturbance that transfers energy through a field. Electromagnetic waves are also called EM (EE-EHM) waves.

Chapter 17: **Electromagnetic Waves** 553

RESOURCES FOR DIFFERENTIATED INSTRUCTION

Below Level
UNIT RESOURCE BOOK
- Reading Study Guide A, pp. 145–146
- Decoding Support, p. 191

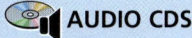 **AUDIO CDS**

Advanced
UNIT RESOURCE BOOK
- Challenge and Extension, p. 162
- Challenge Reading, pp. 187–188

English Learners
UNIT RESOURCE BOOK
Spanish Reading Study Guide, pp. 149–150

 **AUDIO CDS**
- Audio Readings in Spanish
- Audio Readings (English)

17.1 FOCUS

► **Set Learning Goals**
Students will
- Explain how EM waves differ from mechanical waves.
- Identify the sources of EM waves.
- Recognize how EM waves transfer energy.
- Observe through an experiment how EM waves interact with matter.

◄ **3-Minute Warm-Up**

Display Transparency 20 or copy this exercise on the board:

Are these statements true? If not, correct them.

1. Mechanical waves transfer energy through a vacuum. *Mechanical waves transfer energy through a medium.*
2. A wave is a disturbance that transfers energy. *true*
3. Most EM waves are invisible but detectable. *true*

 3-Minute Warm-Up, p. T20

17.1 MOTIVATE

EXPLORE Electromagnetic Waves

PURPOSE To show that EM waves can be reflected

TIP 10 min. Stick a hand-held mirror into a blob of modeling clay if you don't have a mirror with a stand.

WHAT DO YOU THINK? *The remote control has to be aimed so that its beam reflects off the mirror in the same direction that light would, showing that EM waves can be reflected.*

Chapter 17 **553**

17.1 INSTRUCT

Teach from Visuals

To help students interpret the visual of an electromagnetic wave, review the parts of a wave (such as trough and crest) and ask:

- How is the wavelength of the wave in the figure measured? *from one trough to another*
- What is the geometrical relationship between the magnetic and the electrical fields? *The fields are at right angles to each other.*
- How would a diagram of a wave with lower frequency differ from the wave in the figure? *The crests would be farther apart.*

Ongoing Assessment

Explain how EM waves differ from mechanical waves.

Ask: How do EM and mechanical waves differ in the way they form? *EM waves form when moving charged particles transfer energy through a field. Mechanical waves form when energy is transferred to particles of matter in a material medium.*

Identify the sources of EM waves.

Ask: Why do we receive so few EM waves from stars other than the Sun? *They are so far away from Earth.*

 Answer: electric and magnetic

 Answer: the Sun and human technology

---

A field is an area around an object where the object can apply a force—a push or a pull—to another object without touching it. You have seen force applied through a field if you have ever seen a magnet holding a card on the door of a refrigerator. The magnet exerts a pull on the door, even though it does not touch the door. The magnet exerts a force through the magnetic field that surrounds the magnet. When a disturbance occurs in an electric or magnetic field rather than in a medium, the wave that results is an electromagnetic wave.

How EM Waves Form

Learn more about the nature of EM waves.

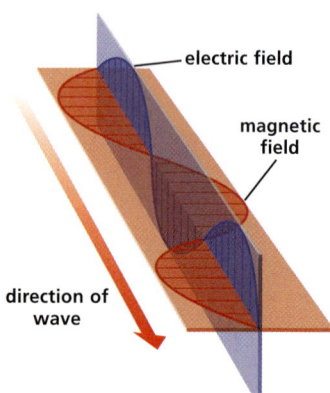

EM waves occur when electrically charged atomic particles move. Charged particles exert an electric force on each other, so they have electric fields. A moving charged particle creates a magnetic force, so a moving charge also has a magnetic field around it.

When electrically charged particles move quickly, they can start a disturbance of electric and magnetic fields. The fields vibrate at right angles to each other, as shown in the diagram above. The EM wave travels in the form of these vibrating fields. As you read in Chapter 15, waves have the properties of wavelength and frequency. In an EM wave, both the electric and the magnetic fields have these properties.

 What are the two types of fields that make up an EM wave?

Sources of EM Waves

Many of the EM waves present in Earth's environment come from the Sun. The Sun's high temperature allows it to give off countless EM waves. Other stars give off as many EM waves as the Sun, but because these bodies are so far away, fewer of their EM waves reach Earth. In addition to the Sun, technology is a source of EM waves that humans use for a wide variety of purposes.

EM waves from the Sun provide most of the energy for the environment on Earth. Some of the energy goes into Earth's surface, which then gives off EM waves of different wavelengths.

 What are two sources of EM waves on Earth?

DIFFERENTIATE INSTRUCTION

More Reading Support

A Where do EM waves come from? *electrically charged atomic particles*

B In what form does an EM wave travel? *as vibrating electric and magnetic fields*

English Learners English learners may have difficulty with nouns that are also used as adjectives. For example, "An EM wave can travel without any medium at all . . . " (p. 555). Here, the word *medium* is used as a noun. Help English learners understand that for a word to be an adjective it must describe a noun.

Advanced Have students who are interested in the speed of light read the following article:

 Challenge Reading, pp. 187–188

Electromagnetic waves can travel in a vacuum.

Energy that moves in the form of EM waves is called **radiation** (RAY-dee-AY-shuhn). Radiation is different from the transfer of energy through a medium by a mechanical wave. A mechanical wave must vibrate the medium as it moves, and this uses some of the wave's energy. Eventually, every mechanical wave will give up all of its energy to the medium and disappear. An EM wave can travel without a material medium—that is, in a vacuum or space empty of matter—and does not lose energy as it moves. In theory, an EM wave can travel forever.

READING TIP
EM waves are also called rays. The words *radiation* and *radiate* come from the Latin word *radius*, which means "ray" or "spoke of a wheel."

How EM Waves Travel in a Vacuum

Because they do not need a medium, EM waves can pass through outer space, which is a near vacuum. Also, because they do not give up energy in traveling, EM waves can cross the great distances that separate stars and galaxies. For example, rays from the Sun travel about 150 million kilometers (93 million mi) to reach Earth. Rays from the most distant galaxies travel for billions of years before reaching Earth.

Usually, EM waves spread outward in all directions from the source of the disturbance. The waves then travel until something interferes with them. The farther the waves move from their source, the more they spread out. As they spread out, there are fewer waves in a given area and less energy is transferred. Only a very small part of the energy radiated from the Sun is transferred to Earth. But that energy is still a great amount—enough to sustain life on the planet.

The Speed of EM Waves in a Vacuum

In a vacuum, EM waves travel at a constant speed, and they travel very fast—about 300,000 kilometers (186,000 mi) per second. In 1 second, an EM wave can travel a distance greater than 7 times the distance around Earth. Even at this speed, rays from the Sun take about 8 minutes to reach Earth. This constant speed is called the speed of light. The vast distances of space are often measured in units of time traveled at this speed. For example, the Sun is about 8 light-minutes away from Earth. The galaxy shown in the photograph is 60 million light-years from Earth.

The light and other EM waves from this galaxy took approximately 60 million years to reach Earth.

CHECK YOUR READING How are EM waves used to measure distances in space?

DIFFERENTIATE INSTRUCTION

More Reading Support

C Why can EM waves travel in a vacuum? *They do not need a medium.*

D What do we call the time it takes for the Sun's rays to hit Earth? *the speed of light*

Advanced Challenge students to use a calculator to answer: If light from a galaxy takes 60 million years to reach Earth, about how far away is it? *about 6×10^{20} km*

Calculations: First, find seconds in a year: $60 \cdot 60 = 3,600 \cdot 24 = 86,400 \cdot 365 = 31,536,000$ Second, find distance for 1 year: $300,000 \cdot 31,536,000 = 9.4608 \cdot 10^{12}$ Third, find distance for 60 million years: $(9.4608 \cdot 10^{12}) \cdot (6 \cdot 10^7) = 5.67648 \cdot 10^{20} = 6 \cdot 10^{20}$ km

 Challenge and Extension, p. 151

Address Misconceptions

IDENTIFY Ask: What happens to an EM wave when it travels? If students respond that the EM wave must pass through matter, they may hold the misconception that a medium is necessary for an EM wave to continue through.

CORRECT Light waves from the Sun can travel through outer space to Earth, but sound waves, which need a medium, cannot. So we can see the Sun, but not hear it. (Actually, the Sun's sound waves are at frequencies too low for humans to hear.) Point out that light waves do not need matter to travel.

REASSESS Have students list examples of waves that need a medium to travel and waves that do not need a medium.

Technology Resources

Visit **ClassZone.com** for background on common student misconceptions.

 MISCONCEPTION DATABASE

History of Science

In the nineteenth century, scientists believed that light must travel through a hypothetical substance called "ether" that filled space. It was not until 1887 that Albert Michelson and Edward Morley demonstrated that ether does not exist.

Ongoing Assessment

CHECK YOUR READING *Answer: by the time it takes an EM wave to travel at the speed of light from one place to another*

INVESTIGATE Wave Behavior

PURPOSE To design an experiment to determine what makes a radiometer's vanes move

TIPS 30 min. Allow students a few minutes to explore, then suggest the following:

- Aim a light at various parts of the radiometer.
- Remind students that the energy in light can be converted to heat.

WHAT DO YOU THINK? *The vanes turn with the white side forward and the black side on the back. Yes, light appears to push on the dark surfaces but not on the light surfaces. Answers will vary depending on student designs.*

CHALLENGE *The radiometer measures the relative brightness of the light falling on the radiometer. The brighter the light, the faster it spins.*

 Datasheet, Wave Behavior, p. 152

Technology Resources

Customize this student lab as needed or look for an alternative. Print rubrics to assess student lab reports.

 Lab Generator CD-ROM

Metacognitive Strategy

Ask students if they are convinced that EM waves interact with matter. Have them write a paragraph that explains when they realized this interaction, or what doubts they still have and another experiment they would like to try.

Ongoing Assessment

Recognize how EM waves transfer energy.

Ask: What happens when EM waves encounter a material medium? *They transfer energy to the medium.*

 Answer: *They transfer energy by moving potential energy from place to place.*

556 Unit 4: **Waves, Sound, and Light**

Electromagnetic waves can interact with a material medium.

 When EM waves encounter a material medium, they can interact with it in much the same way that mechanical waves do. They can transfer energy to the medium itself. Also, EM waves can respond to a change of medium by reflecting, refracting, or diffracting, just as mechanical waves do. When an EM wave responds in one of these ways, its direction changes. When the direction of the wave changes, the direction in which the energy is transferred also changes.

Transferring Energy

REMINDER Potential energy comes from position or form; kinetic energy comes from motion.

A mechanical wave transfers energy in two ways. As it travels, the wave moves potential energy from one place to another. It also converts potential energy into kinetic energy by moving the medium back and forth.

In a vacuum, EM waves transfer energy only by moving potential energy from one place to another. But when EM waves encounter matter, their energy can be converted into many different forms.

 In what form do EM waves transfer energy in a vacuum?

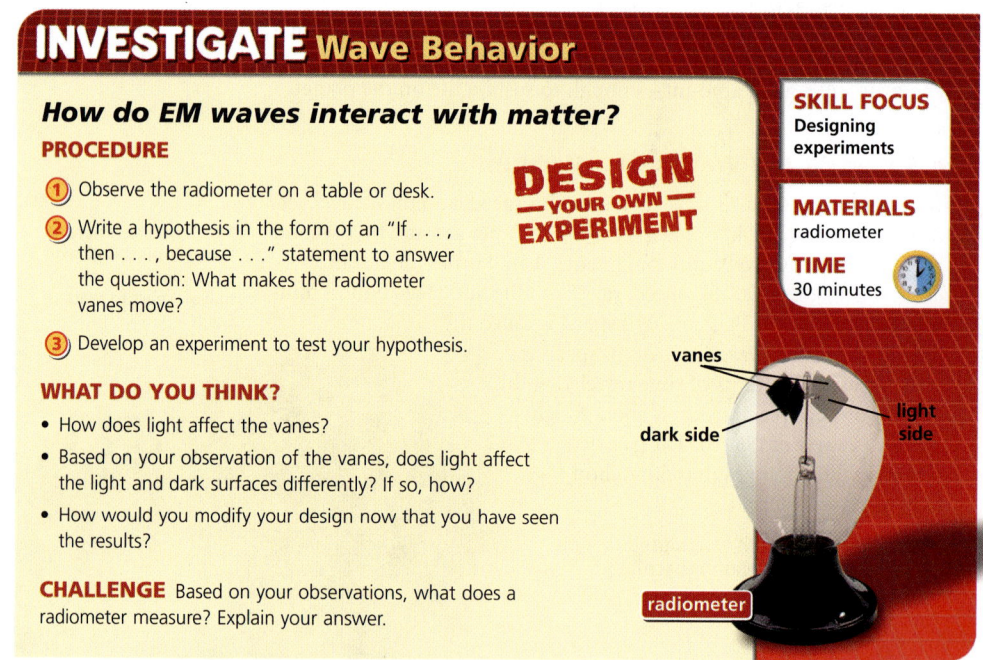

INVESTIGATE Wave Behavior

How do EM waves interact with matter?

PROCEDURE

1. Observe the radiometer on a table or desk.
2. Write a hypothesis in the form of an "If . . . , then . . . , because . . ." statement to answer the question: What makes the radiometer vanes move?
3. Develop an experiment to test your hypothesis.

WHAT DO YOU THINK?

- How does light affect the vanes?
- Based on your observation of the vanes, does light affect the light and dark surfaces differently? If so, how?
- How would you modify your design now that you have seen the results?

CHALLENGE Based on your observations, what does a radiometer measure? Explain your answer.

DESIGN YOUR OWN EXPERIMENT

SKILL FOCUS Designing experiments

MATERIALS radiometer

TIME 30 minutes

556 Unit 4: Waves, Sound, and Light

DIFFERENTIATE INSTRUCTION

More Reading Support

E What does an EM wave transfer to the medium? *energy*

Below Level Students may have a hard time visualizing how a wave responds to a change of medium. Have them draw diagrams showing how a wave changes direction when it is reflected, refracted, and diffracted by a change of medium.

Converting Energy from One Form to Another

How EM waves interact with a medium depends on the type of the wave and the nature of the material. For example, a microwave oven uses a type of EM wave called microwaves. Microwaves pass through air with very little interaction. However, they reflect off the oven's fan and sides. But when microwaves encounter water, such as that inside a potato, their energy is converted into thermal energy. As a result, the potato gets cooked, but the oven remains cool.

 A device on the oven produces microwaves and sends them toward the reflecting fan.

 Microwaves are reflected in many directions by the blades of the fan and then again by the sides of the oven.

 Microwaves move through the air without transferring energy to the air.

 Microwaves transfer energy to the water molecules inside the potato in the form of heat, cooking the potato.

EM waves usually become noticeable and useful when they transfer energy to a medium. You do not observe the microwaves in a microwave oven. All you observe is the potato cooking. In the rest of this chapter, you will learn about different types of EM waves, including microwaves, and about how people use them.

 How does microwave cooking depend on reflection?

17.1 Review

KEY CONCEPTS
1. How are EM waves different from mechanical waves?
2. What are two sources of EM waves in Earth's environment?
3. How can EM waves transfer energy differently in a material medium as compared to a vacuum?

CRITICAL THINKING
4. **Predict** What would happen to an EM wave that never came into contact with matter?
5. **Infer** What might be one cause of uneven heating in a microwave oven?

CHALLENGE
6. **Synthesize** EM waves can interact with a medium. How might this fact be used to make a device for detecting a particular type of EM radiation?

Chapter 17: **Electromagnetic Waves** 557

ANSWERS

1. EM waves can travel through a vacuum, while mechanical waves need a material medium; EM waves travel at speed of light, while speed of mechanical waves varies and is slower.

2. the Sun and human technology

3. In a vacuum, EM waves move potential energy from one place to another. In a material medium, they can both move potential energy and convert energy into other forms.

4. It would continue to travel indefinitely.

5. uneven distribution of microwaves by the fan, or uneven reflection by sides of the oven

6. Sample answer: Since infrared rays warm things, a device with a thermometer could be used to detect infrared radiation.

MATH IN SCIENCE
Math Skills Practice for Science

Set Learning Goal
To gain skill in converting decimals to exponents and vice versa

Present the Science
The use of exponents makes working with very large and very small numbers easier. EM waves can have frequencies as great as a trillion trillion wavelengths per second and have wavelengths as small as trillionths of a centimeter. Working with so many zeros or decimal places is confusing and can lead to errors.

Develop Number Sense
Students should be proficient at using exponents before they begin the next section.

Emphasize that the final decimal place is counted when converting a decimal into exponent form and that the first integer of a large number is not counted when converting a large number.

DIFFERENTIATION TIP Demonstrate several conversion problems on the board before below-level students do the problems in the text.

Close
Ask: In what branches of science are numbers in exponent form used?
Sample answer: in astronomy to represent vast distances of space; in microbiology to count large numbers of microbes

- Math Support, p. 192
- Math Practice, p. 193

Technology Resources
Students can visit **ClassZone.com** for practice using exponents.

 MATH TUTORIAL

MATH in SCIENCE

MATH TUTORIAL
CLASSZONE.COM
Click on Math Tutorial for more help with positive and negative exponents.

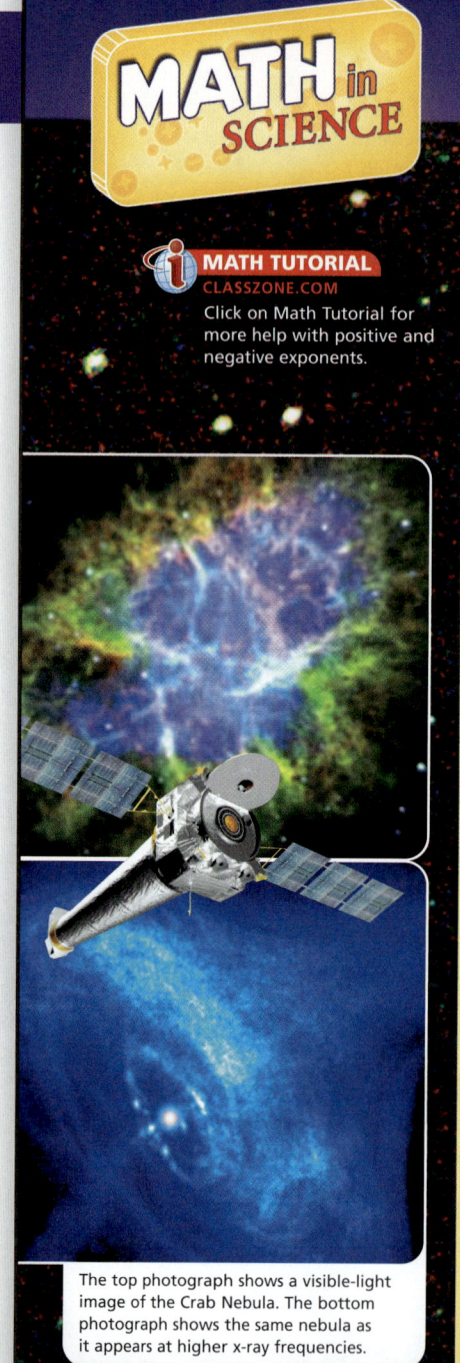

The top photograph shows a visible-light image of the Crab Nebula. The bottom photograph shows the same nebula as it appears at higher x-ray frequencies.

558 Unit 4: Waves, Sound, and Light

SKILL: USING EXPONENTS

EM Frequencies

The Chandra X-Ray Observatory in the photograph is a space telescope that detects high-frequency EM waves called x-rays. A wave's frequency is the number of peaks that pass a given point in 1 second. EM frequencies usually run from about 100 Hz to about 1 trillion trillion Hz. If written in standard form (using zeros), 1 trillion trillion would look like this:

1,000,000,000,000,000,000,000,000

Because this number is hard to read, it would be helpful to write it more simply. Using exponents, 1 trillion trillion can be written as 10^{24}.

Exponents can also be used to simplify very small numbers. For example, the wavelength of a wave with a frequency of 10^{24} Hz is about one ten-thousandth of one trillionth of a meter. That number can be written in standard form as **0.000,000,000,000,000,1 m**. Using exponents, the number can be written more simply as 10^{-16} m.

Examples

Large Numbers
To write a multiple of 10 in exponent form, just count the zeros. Then, use the total as the exponent.
(1) 10,000 has 4 zeros.
(2) 4 is the exponent.
ANSWER 10^4 is the way to write 10,000 using exponents.

Decimals
To convert a decimal into exponent form, count the number of places to the right of the decimal point. Then, use the total with a negative sign as the exponent.
(1) 0.000,001 has 6 places to the right of the decimal point.
(2) Add a negative sign to make the exponent –6.
ANSWER 10^{-6} is the way to write 0.000,001 using exponents.

Answer the following questions.

Write each number using an exponent.
1. 10,000,000
2. 0.000,01
3. 100,000
4. 0.0001
5. 10,000,000,000
6. 0.000,000,001

Write the number in standard form.
7. 10^8
8. 10^{-8}
9. 10^{11}
10. 10^{-12}
11. 10^{17}
12. 10^{-15}

CHALLENGE Using exponents, multiply 10^2 by 10^3. Explain how you got your result.

ANSWERS

1. 10^7
2. 10^{-5}
3. 10^5
4. 10^{-4}
5. 10^{10}
6. 10^{-9}
7. 100,000,000
8. 0.000,000,01
9. 100,000,000,000
10. 0.000,000,000,001
11. 100,000,000,000,000,000
12. 0.000,000,000,000,001

CHALLENGE 10^5; *multiply powers of 10 by adding exponents.*

558 Unit 4: **Waves, Sound, and Light**

17.2 KEY CONCEPT
Electromagnetic waves have many uses.

BEFORE, you learned
- EM waves transfer energy through fields
- EM waves have measurable properties
- EM waves interact with matter

NOW, you will learn
- How EM waves differ from one another
- How different types of EM waves are used

VOCABULARY

electromagnetic spectrum p. 560
radio waves p. 562
microwaves p. 563
visible light p. 564
infrared light p. 564
ultraviolet light p. 565
x-rays p. 566
gamma rays p. 566

EXPLORE Radio Waves

How can you make radio waves?

PROCEDURE

1. Tape one end of one length of wire to one end of the battery. Tape one end of the second wire to the other end of the battery.
2. Wrap the loose end of one of the wires tightly around the handle of the fork.
3. Turn on the radio to the AM band and move the selector past all stations until you reach static.
4. Hold the fork close to the radio. Gently pull the free end of wire across the fork's prongs.

MATERIALS
- two 25 cm lengths of copper wire
- C or D battery
- electrical tape
- metal fork
- portable radio

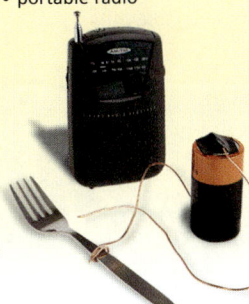

WHAT DO YOU THINK?
- What happens when you stroke the prongs with the wire?
- How does changing the position of the dial affect the results?

EM waves have different frequencies.

It might seem hard to believe that the same form of energy browns your toast, brings you broadcast television, and makes the page you are now reading visible. Yet EM waves make each of these events possible. The various types of EM waves differ from each other in their wavelengths and frequencies.

The frequency of an EM wave also determines its characteristics and uses. Higher-frequency EM waves, with more electromagnetic vibrations per second, have more energy. Lower-frequency EM waves, with longer wavelengths, have less energy.

REMINDER
Remember that frequency is the number of waves that pass a given point per second. The shorter the wavelength, the higher the frequency.

Chapter 17: Electromagnetic Waves 559

17.2 INSTRUCT

Teach from Visuals

To help students interpret the diagram of the EM spectrum, point out the various parts. Ask:

- What is the smallest portion of the spectrum? *visible light*
- What is the frequency range of microwaves? *roughly 10^8 to 10^{12} hertz*
- Where do X-rays fall on the spectrum? *at the high-frequency end*

 The visual "The Electromagnetic Spectrum" is also available as T22 in the Unit Transparency Book.

Learn more about the electromagnetic spectrum.

The Electromagnetic Spectrum

The range of all EM frequencies is known as the **electromagnetic spectrum** (SPEHK-truhm), or EM spectrum. The spectrum can be represented by a diagram like the one below. On the left are the waves with the longest wavelengths and the lowest frequencies and energies. Toward the right, the wavelengths become shorter, and the frequencies and energies become higher. The diagram also shows different parts of the spectrum: radio waves, microwaves, infrared light, visible light, ultraviolet light, x-rays, and gamma rays.

The EM spectrum is a smooth, gradual progression from the lowest frequencies to the highest. Divisions between the different parts of the spectrum are useful, but not exact. As you can see from the diagram below, some of the sections overlap.

The Electromagnetic Spectrum

Frequency in Hertz (1 hertz = 1 wavelength/second)

10^4 10^5 10^6 10^7 10^8 10^9 10^{10} 10^{11} 10^{12} 10^{13}

Radio Waves | Infrared Lig

Microwaves

This woman is speaking on the radio. **Radio waves** are used for radio and television broadcasts. They are also used for cordless phones, garage door openers, alarm systems, and baby monitors.

Not all astronomy involves visible light. Telescopes like the one above pick up **microwaves** from space. Microwaves are also used for radar, cell phones, ovens, and satellite communications.

The amount of **infrared ligh** object gives off depends on temperature. Above, differe colors indicate different am of infrared light.

560 Unit 4: Waves, Sound, and Light

DIFFERENTIATE INSTRUCTION

 More Reading Support

A Describe the EM waves at the left end of the EM spectrum. *They have the longest wavelengths and the lowest frequencies and energies.*

Inclusion Make a large copy of the EM spectrum on shelf paper and display it in the classroom.

Divide the class into seven groups. Have each group make a poster, containing information and examples about one type of EM wave shown on the spectrum. Students who are visually impaired can contribute ideas for tactile or aural representations of waves. Those with hearing impairments can create or obtain visuals of examples for each type. Display posters in their proper position on the spectrum.

Measuring EM Waves

Because all EM waves move at the same speed in a vacuum, the frequency of an EM wave can be determined from its wavelength. EM wavelengths run from about 30 kilometers for the lowest-frequency radio waves to trillionths of a centimeter for gamma rays. EM waves travel so quickly that even those with the largest wavelengths have very high frequencies. For example, a low-energy radio wave with a wavelength of 30 kilometers has a frequency of 10,000 cycles per second.

EM wave frequency is measured in hertz (Hz). One hertz equals one cycle per second. The frequency of the 30-kilometer radio wave mentioned above would be 10,000 Hz. Gamma ray frequencies reach trillions of trillions of hertz.

SUPPORTING MAIN IDEAS Write details that support the main idea that EM waves form a spectrum based on frequency.

CHECK YOUR READING Why is wavelength all you need to know to calculate EM wave frequency in a vacuum?

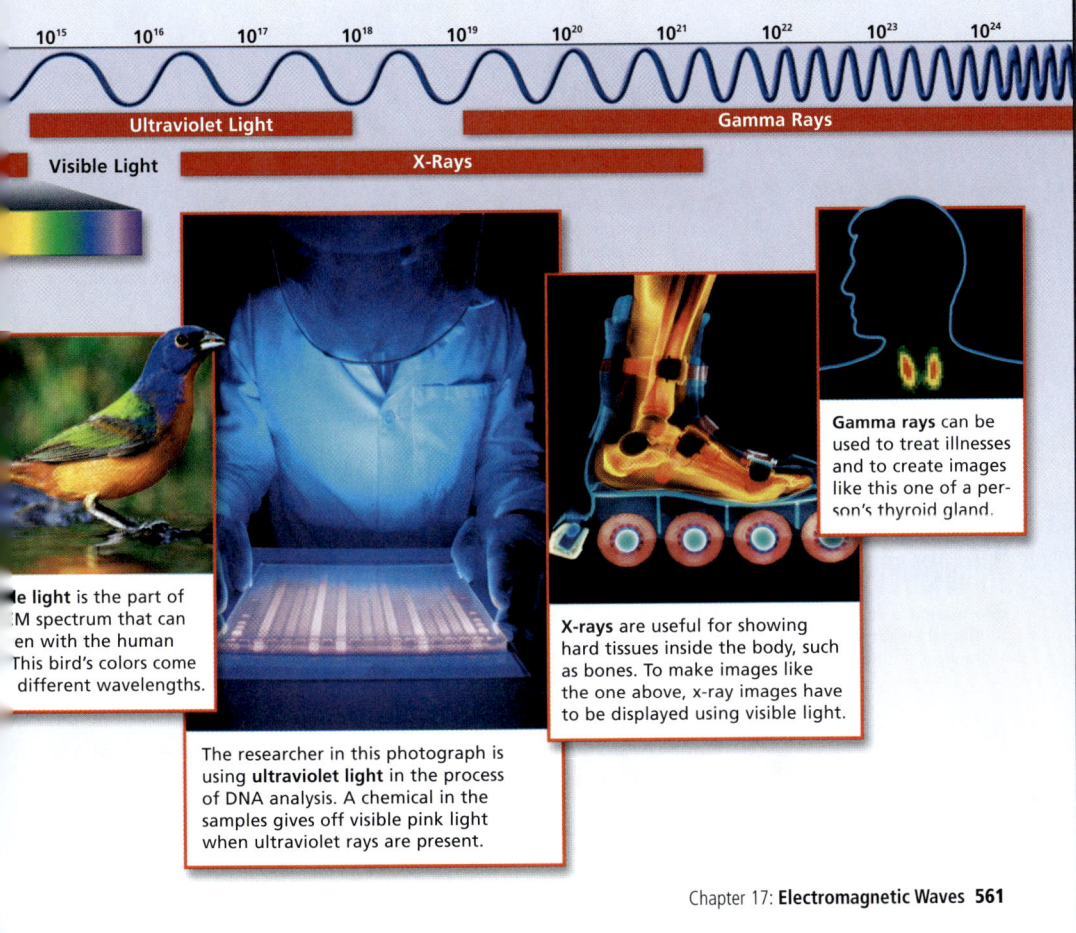

Visible light is the part of the EM spectrum that can be seen with the human eye. This bird's colors come from different wavelengths.

The researcher in this photograph is using **ultraviolet light** in the process of DNA analysis. A chemical in the samples gives off visible pink light when ultraviolet rays are present.

X-rays are useful for showing hard tissues inside the body, such as bones. To make images like the one above, x-ray images have to be displayed using visible light.

Gamma rays can be used to treat illnesses and to create images like this one of a person's thyroid gland.

Integrate the Sciences
Many objects in space emit X-rays, radio waves, infrared light, or ultraviolet light as well as visible light. Newly developed devices can detect these EM waves and provide pictures of objects in the universe. You can see on the Internet some of the photographs that have been taken with these devices.

Develop Critical Thinking
APPLY Ask students to describe the mathematical relationship between frequency and wavelength. *As the frequency of a wave increases, its wavelength decreases. This is an inverse relationship. The frequency of any EM wave times its wavelength is always a constant—the speed of the wave in a vacuum (300,000 kilometers per second).*

Ongoing Assessment
CHECK YOUR READING *Answer: The speed of an EM wave in a vacuum is a constant. If you know the wavelength, you know both wavelength and speed, which are enough to calculate frequency.*

DIFFERENTIATE INSTRUCTION

More Reading Support

B What part of the wave determines frequency? *wavelength*

C What is the unit of measurement of EM wave frequency? *hertz*

Alternative Assessment Give students copies of the EM spectrum that have the ranges marked but not labeled. Have students label each range of frequencies. The finished diagram should look like the spectrum on pp. 560 and 561.

Radio waves and microwaves have long wavelengths and low frequencies.

Radio waves are EM waves that have the longest wavelengths, the lowest frequencies, and the lowest energies. Radio waves travel easily through the atmosphere and many materials. People have developed numerous technologies to take advantage of the properties of radio waves.

VOCABULARY
Make a frame game diagram for *radio waves* and the other types of EM waves.

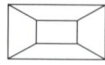

Radio Waves

Radio was the first technology to use EM waves for telecommunication, which is communication over long distances. A radio transmitter converts sound waves into radio waves and broadcasts them in different directions. Radio receivers in many locations pick up the radio waves and convert them back into sound waves.

① Sound waves enter the microphone and are converted into electrical impulses.

② The electrical impulses are converted into radio waves and broadcast by the transmitter.

③ The radio waves reach a radio receiver and are converted back into sound.

AM Signal

Information is encoded in the signal by varying the radio wave's amplitude.

FM Signal

Information is encoded in the signal by varying the radio wave's frequency.

Different radio stations broadcast radio waves at different frequencies. To pick up a particular station, you have to tune your radio to the frequency for that station. The numbers you see on the radio—such as 670 or 99.5—are frequencies.

Simply transmitting EM waves at a certain frequency is not enough to send music, words, or other meaningful sounds. To do that, the radio transmitter must attach information about the sounds to the radio signal. The transmitter attaches the information by modulating—that is, changing—the waves slightly. Two common ways of modulating radio waves are varying the amplitude of the waves and varying the frequency of the waves. Amplitude modulation is used for AM radio, and frequency modulation is used for FM radio.

You might be surprised to learn that broadcast television also uses radio waves. The picture part of a TV signal is transmitted using an AM signal. The sound part is transmitted using an FM signal.

CHECK YOUR READING — What two properties of EM waves are used to attach information to radio signals?

562 Unit 4: Waves, Sound, and Light

Microwaves

A type of EM waves called microwaves comes next on the EM spectrum. **Microwaves** are EM waves with shorter wavelengths, higher frequencies, and higher energy than other radio waves. Microwaves get their name from the fact that their wavelengths are generally shorter than those of radio waves. Two important technologies that use microwaves are radar and cell phones.

Radar The term *radar* stands for "radio detection and ranging." Radar came into wide use during World War II (1939–1945) as a way of detecting aircraft and ships from a distance and estimating their locations. Radar works by transmitting microwaves, receiving reflections of the waves from objects the waves strike, and converting these patterns into visual images on a screen. Today, radar technology is used to control air traffic at airports, analyze weather conditions, and measure the speed of a moving vehicle.

Radar led to the invention of the microwave oven. The discovery that microwaves could be used to cook food was made by accident when microwaves melted a candy bar inside a researcher's pocket.

Cell Phones A cell phone is actually a radio transmitter and receiver that uses microwaves. Cell phones depend on an overlapping network of cells, or areas of land several kilometers in diameter. Each cell has at its center a tower that sends and receives microwave signals. The tower connects cell phones inside the cell to each other or to the regular wire-based telephone system. These two connecting paths are shown below.

> **READING TIP**
> As you read about the different categories of EM waves, refer to the diagram on pages 560 and 561.

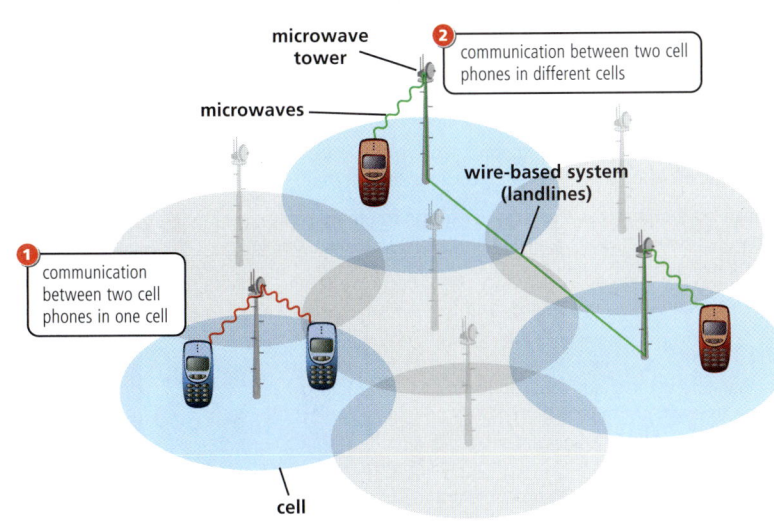

Chapter 17: **Electromagnetic Waves** 563

History of Science

Radar, an acronym for radio detection and ranging, was first used during World War II to detect incoming enemy aircraft. A radar station sends out EM waves. Electronic equipment measures the time it takes for the waves to travel to the plane, reflect, and return to the station. The plane can then be located.

Teach from Visuals

To help students interpret the visual illustrating cellular communication, ask:

- What kind of waves are used in cell phones? *microwaves*
- How large is an overlapping network of cells? *several kilometers in diameter*
- What is the function of a tower in cell phone operation? *The tower receives microwave signals from the phone and sends the signal to another cell phone or to the wire-based telephone system.*

DIFFERENTIATE INSTRUCTION

More Reading Support

F What technologies use microwaves? *radar and cell phones*

G What connects cell phones to each other? *a tower that sends and receives signals*

Advanced Have interested students research and compare Doppler radar and conventional radar. Ask students to find out how Doppler radar is used and why it is used in weather prediction.

R Challenge and Extension, p. 162

Chapter 17 **563**

INVESTIGATE The Electromagnetic Spectrum

PURPOSE To demonstrate the existence of invisible light waves

TIPS 30 min. Suggest the following:
- Position the prism so that the spectrum is large enough to allow the thermometers not to touch each other.
- Use a glass or crystal optical-quality prism, the larger the better; don't use a plastic prism. The thermometers should show tenths of a degree.
- This activity will work best outdoors in bright sunlight. Window glass absorbs infrared radiation and will reduce results.
- The paper must be in the shade; students can put the paper in an open cardboard box in the shade of one side and mount the prism in a small rectangle cut into the upper edge.

WHAT DO YOU THINK? *The temperature in the shade was lower. The thermometers in the light, including the thermometer in the invisible infrared range, show higher temperatures because they absorb energy from EM radiation.*

CHALLENGE *Put three thermometers in different parts of the area outside the color spectrum next to the red area, and measure the temperatures.*

 Datasheet, The Electromagnetic Spectrum, p. 163

Technology Resources

Customize this student lab as needed or look for an alternative. Print rubrics to assess student lab reports.

 Lab Generator CD-ROM

Teaching with Technology

This investigate can be done using CBL probeware. Place temperature probes in different parts of the spectrum to measure the temperature of various wavelengths.

564 Unit 4: Waves, Sound, and Light

Infrared, visible, and ultraviolet light have mid-range wavelengths and frequencies.

Visible light is the part of the EM spectrum that human eyes can see. It lies between 10^{14} Hz and 10^{15} Hz. We perceive the longest wavelengths of visible light as red and the shortest as violet. This narrow band is very small compared with the rest of the spectrum. In fact, visible light is only about 1/100,000 of the complete EM spectrum. The area below visible light and above microwaves is the infrared part of the EM spectrum. Above visible light is the ultraviolet part of the spectrum. You will read more about visible light in the next section.

READING TIP
Infrared means "below red." *Ultraviolet* means "beyond violet."

Infrared Light

The **infrared light** part of the spectrum consists of EM frequencies between microwaves and visible light. Infrared radiation is the type of EM wave most often associated with heat. Waves in this range are sometimes called heat rays. Although you cannot see infrared radiation, you can feel it as warmth coming from the Sun, a fire, or a radiator. Infrared lamps are used to provide warmth in bathrooms and to keep food warm after it is cooked. Infrared rays also help to cook food—for example, in a toaster or over charcoal.

INVESTIGATE The Electromagnetic Spectrum

How can you detect invisible light?

PROCEDURE

1. Find a place that has both bright sunlight and shade, such as a windowsill. Place the white paper in the shade.
2. Using the marker, color the bulbs of the thermometers black. Place one thermometer on the paper. After three minutes, record the temperature.
3. Position the prism so that it shines a bright color spectrum on the white paper. Place the thermometers so that one bulb is in the blue area, one in the red, and one just outside the red, as shown.
4. After five minutes, record the three temperatures.

WHAT DO YOU THINK?
- How did the temperature in the shade compare to the temperature in the light and just outside of it?
- How might you explain the difference?

CHALLENGE How could you modify the experiment to find the hottest location in the infrared range?

SKILL FOCUS
Drawing conclusions

MATERIALS
- white paper
- black marker
- 3 thermometers
- prism

TIME 30 minutes

564 Unit 4: Waves, Sound, and Light

DIFFERENTIATE INSTRUCTION

 **Reading Support**

H How large is the visible light part of the spectrum? *very small*

I What EM waves are sometimes called heat rays? *infrared waves*

Additional Investigation To reinforce Section 17.2 learning goals, use the following full-period investigation:

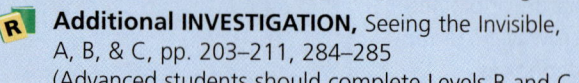 **Additional INVESTIGATION,** Seeing the Invisible, A, B, & C, pp. 203–211, 284–285 (Advanced students should complete Levels B and C.)

Alternative Assessment Have students draw a diagram showing how they would modify the experiment as described in the Challenge question. *The diagram should show three thermometers placed on a spectrum in different places to the left of the visible red waves.*

Some animals, such as pit viper snakes, can actually see infrared light. Normally, human beings cannot see infrared light. However, infrared scopes and cameras convert infrared radiation into visible wavelengths. They do this by representing different levels of infrared radiation with different colors of visible light. This technology can create useful images of objects based on the objects' temperatures.

 How do human beings perceive infrared radiation?

In this infrared image, warmer areas appear red and orange, while cooler ones appear blue, green, and purple.

Ultraviolet Light

The **ultraviolet light** part of the EM spectrum consists of frequencies above those of visible light and partially below those of x-rays. Because ultraviolet (UV) light has higher frequencies than visible light, it also carries more energy. The waves in this range can damage your skin and eyes. Sunblock and UV-protection sunglasses are designed to filter out these frequencies.

Ultraviolet light has beneficial effects as well. Because it can damage cells, UV light can be used to sterilize medical instruments and food by killing harmful bacteria. In addition, UV light causes skin cells to produce vitamin D, which is essential to good health. Ultraviolet light can also be used to treat skin problems and other medical conditions.

Like infrared light, ultraviolet light is visible to some animals. Bees and other insects can see higher frequencies than people can. They see nectar guides—marks that show where nectar is located—that people cannot see with visible light. The photographs below show how one flower might look to a person and to a bee.

This photograph shows the flower as it appears in visible light.

This photograph shows the flower as it might appear to a bee in ultraviolet light. Bees are able to see nectar guides in the UV range.

Chapter 17: Electromagnetic Waves 565

DIFFERENTIATE INSTRUCTION

More Reading Support

J Which carries more energy: visible light or ultraviolet light?
ultraviolet light

K Can any animals see UV light? *Yes; bees and other insects.*

English Learners Have English learners look up the word *radiation* in the dictionary. Explain to them that, although many people use the word to describe the energy given off during nuclear reactions, this is a very narrow interpretation of the word. Most EM waves are not involved in nuclear reactions. This explanation may also help to allay any fears that the activities in this chapter produce radioactivity.

Address Misconceptions

IDENTIFY Ask: Where does infrared light fall in the EM spectrum in relation to visible light? If students respond that infrared light falls within the visible range, they may hold the misconception that humans can see these EM waves.

CORRECT To help students see that infrared light is not visible, have them use a remote control to operate a TV or VCR in a dark room. Explain that most remote controls work using an infrared beam, but you cannot see it.

REASSESS Have students draw the EM spectrum and label visible light and infrared light.

Technology Resources
Visit **ClassZone.com** for background on common student misconceptions.

MISCONCEPTION DATABASE

Real World Example

Infrared detectors are used to find heat leaks in homes and buildings. A house is photographed on film that is sensitive to infrared waves. Places where heat is leaking out show up as bright spots on the film.

Ongoing Assessment

Draw conclusions about how to detect infrared radiation.

Ask: How can infrared radiation be detected if it cannot be seen? *when it is converted to a different form of energy*

Describe how different types of EM waves are used.

Ask: How is ultraviolet light used by animals? *Ultraviolet light helps skin cells make vitamin D. Insects that can see ultraviolet light use it to see nectar guides in flowers.*

 Answer: as warmth

Chapter 17 565

EXPLORE the BIG idea

Revisit "Internet Activity: Electromagnetic Waves" on p. 551. Have students explain their results.

Develop Critical Thinking

INFER Ask students why gamma rays cannot be used to image bones and teeth. *Gamma rays have so much energy that they pass through hard tissue such as bones and teeth as well as soft tissue. If gamma rays were used to image teeth, no image would appear on the film.* Ask what exposed photographic film would look like if gamma rays were used to image teeth. *The film would be overexposed (white).*

Reinforce the BIG idea

All students can benefit from the following worksheet:

 Reinforcing Key Concepts, p. 164

Assess

 Section 17.2 Quiz, p. 43

Reteach

Create a puzzle for your students.

- Write a quiz consisting of ten to fifteen statements such as "These waves can pop popcorn" and "These waves have the shortest frequency."
- Include statements that are definitions of wavelength, frequency, and energy.
- Create a hidden-word puzzle in which the answers to the quiz statements are embedded.

Technology Resources

Have students visit ClassZone.com for reteaching of Key Concepts.

 CONTENT REVIEW

 CONTENT REVIEW CD-ROM

566 Unit 4: **Waves, Sound, and Light**

X-rays and gamma rays have short wavelengths and high frequencies.

At the opposite end of the EM spectrum from radio waves are x-rays and gamma rays. Both have very high frequencies and energies. **X-rays** have frequencies from about 10^{16} Hz to 10^{21} Hz. **Gamma rays** have frequencies from about 10^{19} Hz to more than 10^{24} Hz. Like other EM waves, x-rays and gamma rays are produced by the Sun and by other stars. People have also developed technologies that use these EM frequencies.

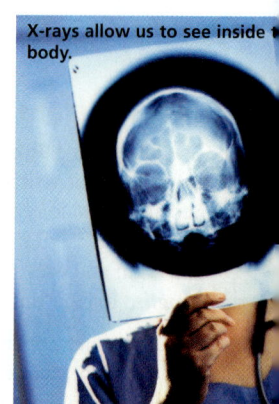

X-rays allow us to see inside the body.

X-rays pass easily through the soft tissues of the body, but many are absorbed by denser matter such as bone. If photographic film is placed behind the body and x-rays are aimed at the film, only the x-rays that pass through the body will expose the film. This makes x-ray images useful for diagnosing bone fractures and finding dense tumors. But too much exposure to x-rays can damage tissue. Even in small doses, repeated exposure to x-rays can cause cancer over time. When you have your teeth x-rayed, you usually wear a vest made out of lead for protection. Lead blocks high-frequency radiation.

Gamma rays have the highest frequencies and energies of any EM waves. Gamma rays are produced by some radioactive substances as well as by the Sun and other stars. Gamma rays can penetrate the soft and the hard tissues of the body, killing normal cells and causing cancer cells to develop. If carefully controlled, this destructive power can be beneficial. Doctors can also use gamma rays to kill cancer cells and fight tumors.

17.2 Review

KEY CONCEPTS

1. What two properties of EM waves change from one end of the EM spectrum to the other?
2. Describe two uses for microwave radiation.
3. How are EM waves used in dentistry and medicine?

CRITICAL THINKING

4. **Infer** Why do you think remote controls for TVs, VCRs, and stereos use infrared light rather than ultraviolet light?
5. **Apply** For a camera to make images of where heat is escaping from a building in winter, what type of EM wave would it need to record?

CHALLENGE

6. **Synthesize** When a person in a car is talking on a cell phone, and the car moves from one cell to another, the conversation continues without interruption. How might this be possible?

566 Unit 4: Waves, Sound, and Light

ANSWERS

1. wavelength and frequency

2. Answers might include ovens to cook and heat food; radar to measure distance, location, or speed; cell phones to communicate.

3. Sample answer: X-rays are used to make images of hard tissues such as bones and teeth.

4. Infrared waves have low energies. They do not harm human tissue.

5. infrared light

6. The connection to the cell phone is switched from the microwave tower in the first cell to the microwave tower in the second cell without any disruption of the signal.

Think Science

SKILL: DETERMINING RELEVANCE

Are Cell Phones Harmful?

In 1993, a man appearing on a popular television talk show claimed that cell phone radiation had caused his wife's brain cancer. Since that time, concerned scientists have conducted more than a dozen studies. None of them have shown clear evidence of a connection between cell phones and cancer. However, researchers have made a number of experimental observations.

▶ Experimental Observations

Here are some results from scientists' investigations.

1. Substances that cause cancer work by breaking chemical bonds in DNA.
2. Only EM radiation at ultraviolet frequencies and above can break chemical bonds.
3. Microwave radiation may make it easier for molecules called free radicals to damage DNA bonds.
4. Other factors such as psychological stress may cause breaks in DNA bonds.
5. Performing multiple tasks like driving and talking on the phone reduces the brain's ability to perform either task.
6. Exposing the brain to microwave radiation may slow reaction times.

▶ Hypotheses

Here are some hypotheses that could be used for further research.

A. Microwaves from cell phones can break DNA bonds.
B. Cell phones may contribute to cancer.
C. Holding and talking into a cell phone while driving increases a person's risk of having an accident.
D. Worrying about cell phones may be a health risk.

▶ Determining Relevance

On Your Own On a piece of paper, write down each hypothesis. Next to the hypothesis write each observation that you think is relevant. Include your reasons.

As a Group Discuss how each observation on your list is or is not relevant to a particular hypothesis.

CHALLENGE Based on the observations listed above, write a question that you think would be a good basis for a further experiment. Then explain how the answer to this question would be helpful.

Chapter 17: **Electromagnetic Waves** 567

Talking on a cell phone while driving may increase the risk of accidents.

THINK SCIENCE
Scientific Methods of Thinking

Set Learning Goal
To evaluate hypotheses in terms of experimental observations

Present the Science
Scientists currently believe that a major cause of cancer is genetic, that is, breakage of the chemical bonds in the DNA molecule. Students will read about some of the facts related to the breaking of bonds in DNA and evaluate these facts to develop hypotheses about the safety of cell phones.

Guide the Activity
- Remind students that to evaluate means to judge a statement based on criteria.
- Ask students whether all four hypotheses listed are testable. *Hypothesis D would be difficult to test.*
- Ask students whether a hypothesis must explain all of the observations or just some of them. *A hypothesis must be supported by all of the observations. If some observations contradict a hypothesis, the hypothesis must be revised or discarded.*

COOPERATIVE LEARNING STRATEGY
Divide the class into small groups. In each group, assign a facilitator, a recorder, and a reporter. Assign each group one hypothesis to evaluate. The facilitator ensures that everyone has a chance to respond. The recorder writes the group's consensus. The reporter presents each observation in class.

Close
Ask: Why is it important to form hypotheses that are relevant to experimental observations? *You can build on information already acquired, instead of starting from scratch.*

ANSWERS

For hypothesis A, relevant observations are 1, 2, 3.

For hypothesis B, relevant observations are 1, 2, 3.

For hypothesis C, relevant observations are 5 and 6.

For hypothesis D, relevant observations are 1 and 4.

CHALLENGE Questions will vary. Sample question: Can DNA damaged by free radicals cause cancer? If the answer is yes, then observation 3 supports the view that microwaves can contribute to cancer. If the answer is no, then observation 3 does not support the view that microwaves contribute to cancer.

Chapter 17 **567**

17.3 FOCUS

◉ Set Learning Goals

Students will
- Explain how visible light is produced.
- Describe how living organisms produce light.
- Describe how humans produce light artificially.
- Observe in an experiment the different types of artificial light.

◉ 3-Minute Warm-Up

Display Transparency 21 or copy this exercise on the board:

Predict what would happen if you kept a green plant in the dark for one month. Explain why. *It would probably die. Plants require light from the Sun to survive.*

 3-Minute Warm-Up, p. T21

17.3 MOTIVATE

THINK ABOUT

PURPOSE To understand why light is important to living organisms

DISCUSS Have students brainstorm the following scenario: What would happen to living things if the Sun suddenly went dark? *Everything on Earth would die. There would be no energy to produce food or, in the long run, to keep from freezing.*

Ongoing Assessment

 Answer: Green plants use light to make food. Plant material provides food, directly or indirectly, for most animals.

KEY CONCEPT

17.3 The Sun is the source of most visible light.

BEFORE, you learned
- Visible light is part of the EM spectrum
- EM waves are produced both in nature and by technology

NOW, you will learn
- How visible light is produced by materials at high temperatures
- How some living organisms produce light
- How humans produce light artificially

VOCABULARY

incandescence p. 569
luminescence p. 569
bioluminescence p. 569
fluorescence p. 571

THINK ABOUT

Why is light important?

This railroad worm has eleven pairs of green lights on its sides and a red light on its head. The animal probably uses these lights for illumination and to frighten away predators. Almost every living organism, including humans, depends on visible light. Think of as many different ways as you can that plants, animals, and people use light. Then, think of all the sources of visible light that you know of, both natural and artificial. Why is light important to living organisms?

Light comes from the Sun and other natural sources.

Learn more about visible light.

It is hard to imagine life without light. Human beings depend on vision in countless ways, and they depend on light for vision. Light is the only form of EM radiation for which human bodies have specialized sensory organs. The human eye is extremely sensitive to light and color and the many kinds of information they convey.

Most animals depend on visible light to find food and to do other things necessary for their survival. Green plants need light to make their own food. Plants, in turn, supply food directly or indirectly for nearly all other living creatures. With very few exceptions, living creatures depend on light for their existence.

 How is plants' use of light important to animals?

568 Unit 4: Waves, Sound, and Light

RESOURCES FOR DIFFERENTIATED INSTRUCTION

Below Level
UNIT RESOURCE BOOK
- Reading Study Guide A, pp. 167–168
- Decoding Support, p. 191

 **AUDIO CDS**

Advanced
UNIT RESOURCE BOOK
Challenge and Extension, p. 173

English Learners
UNIT RESOURCE BOOK
Spanish Reading Study Guide, pp. 170–171

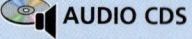 **AUDIO CDS**

- Audio Readings in Spanish
- Audio Readings (English)

Most of the visible light waves in the environment come from the Sun. The Sun's high temperature produces light of every wavelength. The production of light by materials at high temperatures is called **incandescence** (IHN-kuhn-DEHS-uhns). When a material gets hot enough, it gives off light by glowing or by bursting into flames.

Other than the Sun, few natural sources of incandescent light strongly affect life on Earth. Most other stars give off as much light as the Sun, or even more, but little light from stars reaches Earth because they are so far away. Lightning produces bright, short-lived bursts of light. Fire, which can occur naturally, is a lower-level, longer-lasting source of visible light. The ability to make and use fire was one of the first light technologies, making it possible for human beings to see on a dark night or inside a cave.

 Why does little light reach Earth from stars other than the Sun?

Some living things produce visible light.

Many organisms produce their own visible light, which they use in a variety of ways. They produce this light through luminescence. **Luminescence** is the production of light without the high temperatures needed for incandescence. The production of light by living organisms is called **bioluminescence**. Bioluminescent organisms produce light from chemical reactions rather than from intense heat. Bioluminescence enables organisms to produce light inside their tissues without being harmed.

Bioluminescent organisms include insects, worms, fish, squid, jellyfish, bacteria, and fungi. Some of these creatures have light-producing organs that are highly complex. These organs might include light-producing cells but also reflectors, lenses, and even color filters.

The firefly, a type of beetle, uses bioluminescence to attract mates. A chemical reaction in its abdomen allows the firefly to glow at specific intervals. The pattern of glowing helps fireflies of the same species identify each other at night. Most often, the male flashes a signal while flying, and the female responds with a flash. After they have identified each other, the fireflies may continue to exchange flashes until the male has located the female.

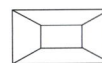 **VOCABULARY**
Don't forget to make word frames for the terms *luminescence* and *bioluminescence*.

Chapter 17: Electromagnetic Waves 569

DIFFERENTIATE INSTRUCTION

 **More Reading Support**

A Where do most of the visible light waves in the environment come from? *the Sun*

English Learners English learners may be unfamiliar with some of the non-literal phrases used in the text. For example, the direction *Write up your experiment and carry it out* (p. 570) may be confusing to an English learner when taken literally. Be watchful for confusing language such as "carry it out," and explain unfamiliar phrases and idioms in clear terms.

17.3 INSTRUCT

Address Misconceptions

IDENTIFY Ask: Where does the energy for bioluminescence come from? If students respond that the light comes from heat or electricity produced by the organism, they may hold the misconception that bioluminescence is an electrical process rather than a chemical process.

CORRECT Have students experiment with a chemical glow stick (available at a hardware store). Show students that the stick is activated when a container inside the stick is broken. Have them observe that the stick remains cool to the touch. If possible, let them see a stick after it has stopped making light. Explain that the light in the stick comes from chemical reactions rather than heat or electricity.

REASSESS Ask students the following question: How does a glowstick model bioluminescence? *It glows because of a chemical reaction, not because of electricity.*

Technology Resources
Visit **ClassZone.com** for background on common student misconceptions.

MISCONCEPTION DATABASE

Ongoing Assessment

Explain how visible light is produced.
Ask: How does the Sun produce light? *It emits radiation.*

Describe how living organisms produce light.
How do living things produce light? *chemicals in body*

CHECK YOUR READING *Answer: Except for the Sun, stars are too far away for much of their light to reach Earth.*

Chapter 17 **569**

INVESTIGATE Artificial Lighting

PURPOSE To examine properties of various types of artificial lighting

TIPS 30 min. Allow students a few minutes to explore, then suggest the following:

- Use direct sunlight to test how different colored materials appear.
- Compare the properties of artificial lighting to those of natural sunlight.

WHAT DO YOU THINK? *Light qualities vary among different bulbs and lighting types. Light from any source can be broken up into a spectrum. One source's spectrum may be very different from another's. Answers will vary depending on student experiments.*

 Datasheet, Artificial Lighting, p. 174

Technology Resources
Customize this student lab as needed or look for an alternative. Print rubrics to assess student lab reports.

 Lab Generator CD-ROM

Metacognitive Strategy
Ask students to make a diagram of the experimental steps they tried and discarded. Have them write briefly about the problems that arose.

Ongoing Assessment
Design an experiment to compare different types of artificial light.

Ask: How could you compare the amount of heat given off by a halogen bulb and a regular incandescent bulb? *Measure the temperature at the same distance from two bulbs of equal wattage.*

 Incandescence is the production of light from high temperatures, or intense heat. Bioluminescence is the production of light from chemical reactions rather than from intense heat.

570 Unit 4: Waves, Sound, and Light

A female firefly responds to a male's signal.

The process of bioluminescence is very efficient. Almost all of the energy released by the chemical reactions of bioluminescence is converted into light. Very little heat is produced. Researchers in lighting technology wanted for years to imitate this efficiency, and that became possible with the development of light-emitting diodes (LEDs). LEDs produce little heat, converting almost all of the incoming electrical energy into light.

 CHECK YOUR READING How is bioluminescence different from incandescence?

Human technologies produce visible light.

Human beings invented the first artificial lighting when they learned to make and control fire. For most of human history, people have made light with devices that use fire in some form, such as oil lamps, candles, and natural gas lamps. After the discovery of electricity, people began to make light through a means other than fire. However, the technique of using a very hot material as a light source stayed the same until the invention of fluorescent lighting. In recent years, "cool" lighting has become much more common.

INVESTIGATE Artificial Lighting

Is all artificial light the same?
Many types of artificial light sources are available. These sources differ in the amount of light they produce, the way the light beams are directed, and the characteristics of the light itself.

DESIGN YOUR OWN EXPERIMENT

PROCEDURE
1. Design a procedure to discover and record differences among several different types of artificial lighting. Your procedure should test how different colored materials appear in different types of lighting. You should compare the results with how these materials appear in direct sunlight.
2. Write up your experiment and carry it out.

WHAT DO YOU THINK?
- What differences did you discover among bulbs of different types and sizes?
- How would you improve your design if you were to repeat your experiment?

SKILL FOCUS
Designing experiments

MATERIALS
Artificial lighting with a variety of bulb types and sizes

TIME
30 minutes

570 Unit 4: Waves, Sound, and Light

DIFFERENTIATE INSTRUCTION

 More Reading Support

B What was the first artificial lighting used by humans? *fire*

Below Level Have students make a flow diagram showing how making light has changed throughout human history. *Diagrams should begin with fire, progress through oil lamps, candles, and natural gas, and end with electricity.*

Advanced

 Challenge and Extension, p. 173

Incandescent and Fluorescent Lighting

The development of the electric light bulb in the late 1800s made light available at a touch. An ordinary light bulb is a sealed glass tube with a thin tungsten wire running through it. This wire is called a filament. When electrical current passes through the filament, the tungsten gets hotter and begins to glow. Because these light bulbs use high temperatures to produce light, they are called incandescent bulbs.

Tungsten can become very hot—about 3500 degrees Celsius (6300°F)—without melting. At such high temperatures, tungsten gives off a bright light. However, the tungsten filament also produces much infrared radiation. In fact, the filament produces more infrared light than visible light. As a result, incandescent bulbs waste a lot of energy that ends up as heat. At such high temperatures, tungsten also slowly evaporates and collects on the inside of the bulb. Eventually, the filament weakens and breaks, and the bulb burns out.

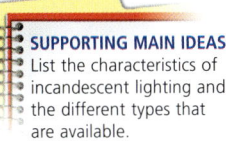

SUPPORTING MAIN IDEAS
List the characteristics of incandescent lighting and the different types that are available.

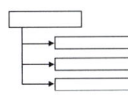

 What causes ordinary light bulbs to burn out?

Since the 1980s, halogen (HAL-uh-juhn) bulbs have come into wide use. Halogen bulbs have several advantages over ordinary incandescent bulbs. They contain a gas from the halogen group. This gas combines with evaporating tungsten atoms and deposits the tungsten back onto the filament. As a result, the filament lasts longer. The filament can also be raised to a higher temperature without damage, so it produces more light. Halogen bulbs, which are made of quartz, resist heat better than glass.

Incandescent Light Bulb
- tungsten filament
- glass bulb

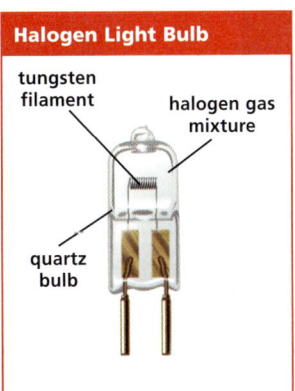

Halogen Light Bulb
- tungsten filament
- halogen gas mixture
- quartz bulb

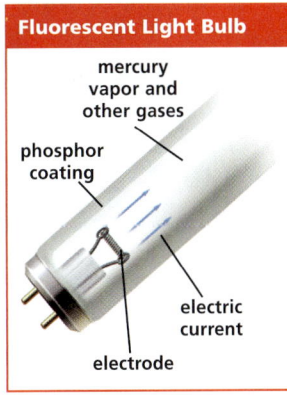

Fluorescent Light Bulb
- mercury vapor and other gases
- phosphor coating
- electric current
- electrode

Many electric lights in use today are fluorescent. **Fluorescence** (flu-REHS-uhns) occurs when a material absorbs EM radiation of one wavelength and gives off EM radiation of another. Fluorescent bulbs are filled with a mixture of mercury vapor and other gases that give off ultraviolet light when an electric current passes through them.

Chapter 17: **Electromagnetic Waves** 571

Ongoing Assessment

 Answer: Fluorescent light is cool and does not waste much energy as heat, unlike incandescent light.

Reinforce

All students can benefit from the following worksheet:

 Reinforcing Key Concepts, p. 175

17.3 ASSESS & RETEACH

Assess
 Section 17.3 Quiz, p. 44

Reteach
Show students a regular incandescent light bulb and an LED. Have them list some visible differences between the two. Ask:

- What are the working elements of an incandescent bulb? *filament, vacuum or special gas enclosed in a bulb*
- Does the LED have these elements? What does it have instead? *no; semiconductor and wires*
- Compare heat, efficiency, and longevity of these two types of artificial lighting. *An LED lasts longer and is more efficient than an incandescent bulb; the incandescent bulb produces more heat.*

Technology Resources
Have students visit ClassZone.com for reteaching of Key Concepts.

- CONTENT REVIEW
- CONTENT REVIEW CD-ROM

The insides of the bulbs are coated with a powder called phosphor that fluoresces. Phosphor absorbs ultraviolet light and gives off visible light. Because fluorescent lighting is cool and does not waste much energy as heat, it is more efficient and more economical than incandescent lighting.

 Why are fluorescent lights more efficient than incandescent lights?

Other Types of Artificial Lighting

Like fluorescent lights, many other artificial light sources use a gas in place of a filament. For example, neon lights use gas-filled tubes to produce light. However, instead of ultraviolet light, the gas gives off visible light directly. The colors of neon lights come from the particular mixtures of gases and filters used. Vapor lights, which are commonly used for street lights, work in a similar way. In a vapor light, a material such as sodium is heated until it becomes a gas, or vapor. The vapor responds to an electric current by glowing brightly.

LEDs are being used more and more in place of incandescent bulbs.

One of fastest-growing types of artificial lighting is the light emitting diode, or LED. LEDs do not involve bulbs, filaments, or gases. Instead, they produce light electronically. A diode is a type of semiconductor—a device that regulates electric current. An LED is a semiconductor that converts electric energy directly into visible light.

LEDs have many advantages over traditional forms of lighting. They produce a very bright light, do not break easily, use little energy, produce little heat, and can last for decades. Some technologists believe that LEDs will eventually replace most traditional forms of artificial lighting.

17.3 Review

KEY CONCEPTS

1. Describe natural, nonliving sources of incandescent light.
2. What advantages does bioluminescence have over incandescence as a way for living organisms to produce light?
3. What are some advantages and disadvantages of artificial incandescent lighting?

CRITICAL THINKING

4. **Classify** Make a chart summarizing the different types of artificial lighting discussed in this section.
5. **Infer** Why do you think moonlight does not warm you, even though the Moon reflects light from the hot Sun?

CHALLENGE

6. **Compare and Contrast** What does LED lighting have in common with bioluminescence? How are the two different?

572 Unit 4: Waves, Sound, and Light

ANSWERS

1. The Sun produces most of the natural light we use. Other sources are other stars, lightning, and fire.

2. Bioluminescence does not produce high temperatures, which could damage tissues.

3. advantages: give off bright light, no open flame; disadvantages: can get very hot, wastes energy

4. Charts should summarize the information from pp. 570–572.

5. The Moon reflects mostly visible light and not much infrared light. Only a small part of the radiation from the Sun strikes the Moon.

6. Both do not involve bulbs, filaments, or gases. They produce cool light. LEDs produce light electronically, bioluminescence chemically.

17.4 KEY CONCEPT
Light waves interact with materials.

BEFORE, you learned
- Mechanical waves respond to a change in medium
- Visible light is made up of EM waves
- EM waves interact with a new medium in the same ways that mechanical waves do

NOW, you will learn
- How the wave behavior of light affects what we see
- How light waves interact with materials
- Why objects have color
- How different colors are produced

VOCABULARY
transmission p. 573
absorption p. 573
scattering p. 575
polarization p. 576
prism p. 577
primary colors p. 578
primary pigments p. 579

EXPLORE Light and Matter
How can a change in medium affect light?

PROCEDURE
1. Fill the container with water.
2. Add 10 mL (2 tsp) of milk to the water. Put on the lid, and gently shake the container until the milk and water are mixed.
3. In a dark room, shine the light at one side of the container from about 5 cm (2 in.) away. Observe what happens to the beam of light.

WHAT DO YOU THINK?
- What happened to the beam of light from the flashlight?
- Why did the light behave in this way?

MATERIALS
- clear plastic container with lid
- water
- measuring spoons
- milk
- flashlight

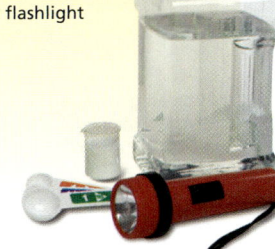

Light can be reflected, transmitted, or absorbed.

You have read that EM waves can interact with a material medium in the same ways that mechanical waves do. Three forms of interaction play an especially important role in how people see light. One form is reflection. Most things are visible because they reflect light. The two other forms of interaction are transmission and absorption.

Transmission (trans-MIHSH-uhn) is the passage of an EM wave through a medium. If the light reflected from objects did not pass through the air, windows, or most of the eye, we could not see the objects. **Absorption** (uhb-SAWRP-shun) is the disappearance of an EM wave into the medium. Absorption affects how things look, because it limits the light available to be reflected or transmitted.

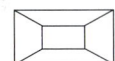
VOCABULARY
Don't forget to make word frames for *transmission* and *absorption*.

Chapter 17: Electromagnetic Waves 573

17.4 FOCUS

▶ Set Learning Goals
Students will
- Describe how the wave behavior of light affects what we see.
- Recognize how light waves interact with materials.
- Recognize why objects have color.
- Explain how colors are produced.
- Observe through an experiment what makes up the color black.

◀ 3-Minute Warm-Up
Display Transparency 21 or copy this exercise on the board:

Match each definition to the correct term.

Definitions
1. the production of light without high temperatures *a*
2. the production of light by living organisms *b*
3. the production of light with high temperatures *c*

Terms
a. luminescence
b. bioluminescence
c. incandescence

 3-Minute Warm-Up, p. T21

17.4 MOTIVATE

EXPLORE Light and Matter
PURPOSE To introduce the concept of light scattering

TIP 10 min. Tell students that milk is composed of large molecules, like fats and proteins.

WHAT DO YOU THINK? *light spreads out inside the container; the color and direction of the light beam changes when light strikes the particles of milk*

Ongoing Assessment
Describe how the wave behavior of light affects what we see.

Ask: How does absorption of light waves affect how things look? *by what light it reflects or transmits*

Chapter 17 573

RESOURCES FOR DIFFERENTIATED INSTRUCTION

Below Level
UNIT RESOURCE BOOK
- Reading Study Guide A, pp. 178–179
- Decoding Support, p. 191

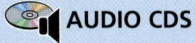 AUDIO CDS

Advanced
UNIT RESOURCE BOOK
Challenge and Extension, p. 184

English Learners
UNIT RESOURCE BOOK
Spanish Reading Study Guide, pp. 182–183

 AUDIO CDS

- Audio Readings in Spanish
- Audio Readings (English)

17.4 INSTRUCT

History of Science

Not all glass is transparent to visible light. Opaque glass, often called milk glass, is creamy white and feels silky. It was first developed by the Egyptians about 1500 B.C., when they added chemicals to glass. The Chinese made milk-glass snuff bottles around 140 B.C., and the Persians kept their spices and medicines in milk-glass jars beginning in the eighth century. Today, opaque glass is made in all colors and textures.

Ongoing Assessment

Recognize how light waves interact with materials.

Ask: Why do some materials appear opaque? *All the light waves that strike them are reflected, absorbed, or both.*

CHECK YOUR READING *Answer: Translucent materials let some light pass through, causing it to spread out in all directions. Objects can be seen indistinctly through a translucent material. Opaque materials do not allow any light to pass through because they reflect light, absorb light, or both.*

How Materials Transmit Light

Materials can be classified according to the amount and type of light they transmit.

❶ **Transparent** (trans-PAIR-uhnt) materials allow most of the light that strikes them to pass through. It is possible to see objects through a transparent material. Air, water, and clear glass are transparent. Transparent materials are used for items such as windows, light bulbs, thermometers, sandwich bags, and clock faces.

❷ **Translucent** (trans-LOO-suhnt) materials transmit some light, but they also cause it to spread out in all directions. You can see light through translucent materials, but you cannot see objects clearly through them. Some examples are lampshades, frosted light bulbs, frosted windows, sheer fabrics, and notepaper.

❸ **Opaque** (oh-PAYK) materials do not allow any light to pass through them, because they reflect light, absorb light, or both. Heavy fabrics, construction paper, and ceramic mugs are opaque. Shiny materials may be opaque mainly because they reflect light. Other materials, such as wood and rock, are opaque mainly because they absorb light.

CHECK YOUR READING What is the difference between translucent and opaque materials?

This stained-glass window contains transparent, translucent, and opaque materials.

574 Unit 4: Waves, Sound, and Light

DIFFERENTIATE INSTRUCTION

 **More Reading Support**

A What two types of material transmit light? *transparent, translucent*

B What makes a material opaque? *no light passes through it*

English Learners Be aware that English learners do not always have the same background knowledge as the rest of the class. For example, the paragraph on scattering refers to what happens when students shine a flashlight into fog. Some students may have never had such an opportunity due to the climate in their native country or their lack of access to a flashlight.

574 Unit 4: **Waves, Sound, and Light**

A light filter is a material that is transparent to some kinds of light and opaque to others. For example, clear red glass transmits red light but absorbs other wavelengths. Examples of light filters are the colored covers on taillights and traffic lights, infrared lamp bulbs, and UV-protected sunglasses. Filters that transmit only certain colors are called color filters.

Scattering

Sometimes fine particles in a material interact with light passing through the material to cause scattering. **Scattering** is the spreading out of light rays in all directions, because particles reflect and absorb the light. Fog or dust in the air, mud in water, and scratches or smudges on glass can all cause scattering. Scattering creates glare and makes it hard to see through even a transparent material. Making the light brighter causes more scattering, as you might have noticed if you have ever tried to use a flashlight to see through fog.

Fine particles, such as those in fog, scatter light and reduce visibility.

Scattering is what makes the sky blue. During the middle of the day, when the Sun is high in the sky, molecules in Earth's atmosphere scatter the blue part of visible light more than they scatter the other wavelengths. This process makes the sky light and blue. It is too bright to see the faint stars beyond Earth's atmosphere. At dawn and dusk, light from the Sun must travel farther through the atmosphere before it reaches your eyes. By the time you see it, the greens and blues are scattered away and the light appears reddish. At night, because there is so little sunlight, the sky is dark and you can see the stars.

SUPPORTING MAIN IDEAS
Be sure to add to your chart the different ways light interacts with materials.

CHECK YOUR READING How does scattering make the sky blue?

Chapter 17: **Electromagnetic Waves** 575

Teach from Visuals

To help students interpret the visual of light waves and filters, ask:

- In what direction are the light waves absorbed by the first filter? *horizontally*
- Why does no light pass through the second filter? *Only light waves vibrating vertically pass through the first filter. The second filter stops all waves except those vibrating horizontally.*

Teach Difficult Concepts

Students may have a hard time understanding polarization. It may help them visualize the process if they think of a polarizing filter as a picket fence. Only vertical objects can pass through an upright fence. If the fence were rotated to its side, only horizontal objects could pass through. To help students understand polarization, explain that light can become polarized when a nonmetallic surface reflects light. When the reflected light waves have a large concentration of horizontal vibrations, that is, in a plane parallel to the object's surface, they are called *glare*. Polarized sunglasses have microscopic vertical slits that block out the horizontally polarized light and therefore reduce glare. Have several pairs of polarized sunglasses available for students to take outdoors. Have students notice how the glare changes when they rotate the glasses.

Polarization

Polarizing filters reduce glare and make it easier to see objects. **Polarization** (POH-luhr-ih-ZAY-shuhn) is a quality of light in which all of its waves vibrate in the same direction. Remember that EM waves are made of electric and magnetic fields vibrating at right angles to each other. Polarization describes the electric fields of a light wave. When all of the electric fields of a group of light waves vibrate in the same direction, the light is polarized.

Light can be polarized by a particular type of light filter called a polarizing filter. A polarizing filter acts on a light wave's electric field like the bars of a cage. The filter allows through only waves whose electric fields vibrate in one particular direction. Light that passes through the filter is polarized. In the illustration below, these waves are shown in darker yellow.

Light reflecting off the surface of this pond causes glare.

A polarizing filter reduces glare, making it possible to see objects under the water.

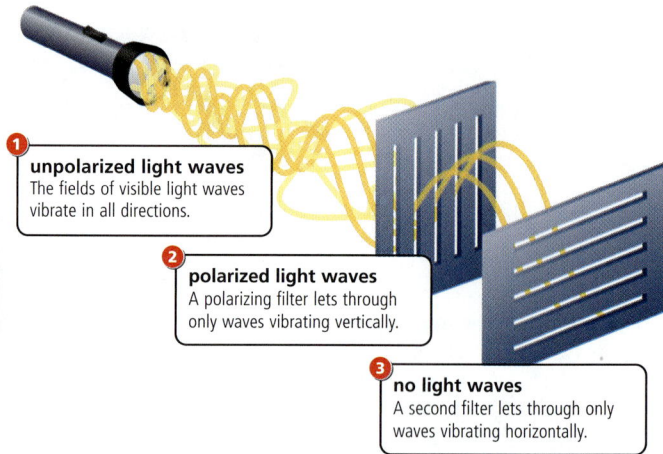

1 unpolarized light waves
The fields of visible light waves vibrate in all directions.

2 polarized light waves
A polarizing filter lets through only waves vibrating vertically.

3 no light waves
A second filter lets through only waves vibrating horizontally.

What do you think happens when polarized light passes into a second polarizing filter? If the direction of the second filter is the same as the first, then all of the light will pass through the second filter. The light will still be polarized. If the second filter is at a right angle to the first, as in the illustration above, then no light at all will pass through the second filter.

Wavelengths determine color.

The section of the EM spectrum called visible light is made up of many different wavelengths. When all of these wavelengths are present together, as in light from the Sun or a light bulb, the light appears white.

576 Unit 4: Waves, Sound, and Light

DIFFERENTIATE INSTRUCTION

 More Reading Support

D How do you make the electric fields of a wave vibrate in the same direction? *using polarization*

Advanced Unpolarized light (natural sunlight, for example) can become polarized to a certain degree when it is reflected from a flat surface such as a highway. This polarized light is termed glare and can be demonstrated by viewing the distant part of a highway on a sunny day. Have students make light diagrams showing how glare is formed. Have them investigate the conditions under which glare is formed, such as the angle at which the light approaches the surface, the time of day, and the material that is reflecting the light.

 Challenge and Extension, p. 184

Seen individually, different wavelengths appear as different colors of light. This fact can be demonstrated by using a prism. A **prism** is a tool that uses refraction to spread out the different wavelengths that make up white light. The prism bends some of the wavelengths more than others. The lightwaves, bent at slightly different angles, form a color spectrum. The color spectrum could be divided into countless individual wavelengths, each with its own color. However, the color spectrum is usually divided into seven named color bands. In order of decreasing wavelength, the bands are red, orange, yellow, green, blue, indigo, and violet. You see a color spectrum whenever you see a rainbow.

Prisms split light into colors by refracting wavelengths in different amounts.

Color Reflection and Absorption

The color of an object or material is determined by the wavelengths it absorbs and those it reflects. An object has the color of the wavelengths it reflects. A material that reflects all wavelengths of visible light appears white. A material that absorbs all wavelengths of visible light appears black. A green lime absorbs most wavelengths but reflects green, so the lime looks green, as shown below.

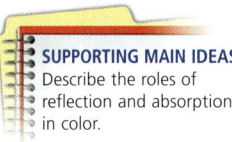

SUPPORTING MAIN IDEAS
Describe the roles of reflection and absorption in color.

① In this simplified diagram, light of all colors strikes the lime.

② The lime absorbs all wavelengths except green.

③ The lime reflects mostly green, so it appears green.

The color that an object appears to the eye depends on another factor besides the wavelengths the object absorbs and reflects. An object can reflect only wavelengths that are in the light that shines on it. In white light, a white object reflects all the wavelengths of visible light and appears white. If you shine only red light on a white piece of paper, however, the paper will appear red, not white, because only red light is available to be reflected.

In summary, two factors determine the color of an object: first, the wavelengths that the object itself reflects or absorbs, and second, the wavelengths present in the light that shines on the object.

 What color band or bands does a red apple absorb? a white flower?

Chapter 17: **Electromagnetic Waves** 577

Teach from Visuals

To help students interpret the visual of the prism, ask:

- What color would the lime seem to be if you shined a red light on it? Why? *It would appear black. The green lime absorbs red, so no light would be reflected.*

- What would have to happen for the lime to appear white? *The lime would have to reflect all the wavelengths of visible light.*

Teach Difficult Concepts

Some students may have a hard time understanding that matter can absorb light. Remind them of the ice cube melting under black and white paper. Ask:

- Where did the ice melt faster? *under the black paper*

- Why was black paper warmer than white? *It absorbs more light waves.*

- A ginger (orange) cat and a blue (dark gray) cat are sitting on a window sill. Which cat's fur will absorb more light? How could you tell? *The blue cat; it will feel warmer to the touch.*

EXPLORE the BIG idea

Revisit "What Melts the Ice Cubes?" and "What Is White Light Made Of?" on p. 551. Have students explain the reasons for their results.

Ongoing Assessment

Recognize why objects have color.

Ask: Why does an object appear black? *The object absorbs all wavelengths of light that strike it.*

 Answer: all visible wavelengths except red; no visible wavelengths

---

DIFFERENTIATE INSTRUCTION

Reading Support

E What can create a color spectrum from white light? *a prism*

F What determines the color of a material? *the wavelengths it absorbs and those that it reflects*

Chapter 17 **577**

INVESTIGATE Mixing Colors

PURPOSE To observe the colors that make up black ink

TIPS 30 min. To get the best results in this lab:

- Use cups with wide mouths so students can cut a long flap in the filter. The farther the ink moves, the more clearly the colors will separate.
- Handle the filters as little as possible. Oils from skin interfere with the movement of pigments.
- The felt-tip markers must be water soluble (washable). Try to get pens made by different manufacturers.

WHAT DO YOU THINK? *The colors in black ink separated. Each brand of black ink is made of a different combination of colors.*

CHALLENGE *If black ink is put on a filter, then it will separate into colors because black is a combination of different colors of pigments.*

 Datasheet, Mixing Colors, p. 185

Technology Resources

Customize this student lab as needed or look for an alternative. Print rubrics to assess student lab reports.

 Lab Generator CD-ROM

Teaching with Technology

You may wish to photograph this lab if you have access to a digital camera. Students can see how the ink samples change over time.

Ongoing Assessment

Observe what makes up the color black.

Ask: Why does black ink appear black? *It absorbs all wavelengths of light.*

 Answer: *produces all possible colors*

Primary colors of light combine to make the secondary colors yellow, cyan (light blue), and magenta (dark pink).

Primary Colors of Light

The human eye can detect only three color bands: red, green, and blue. Your brain perceives these three colors and various mixtures of them as all the colors. These three colors of light, which can be mixed to produce all possible colors, are called **primary colors.** When all three colors are mixed together equally, they appear white, or colorless. Whenever colored light is added to a mixture, specific wavelengths are added. Mixing colors by adding wavelengths is called additive color mixing.

An example of the practical use of primary colors is a color television or computer monitor. The screen is divided into thousands of tiny bundles of red, green, and blue dots, or pixels. A television broadcast or DVD sends signals that tell the monitor which pixels to light up and when to do so. By causing only some pixels to give off light, the monitor can mix the three colors to create an amazing variety of colorful images.

 What does an equal mix of all three primary colors produce?

INVESTIGATE Mixing Colors

What is black ink made of?

PROCEDURE

1. Trim each of the filter papers to a disk about 10 cm (4 in.) in diameter. Make two parallel cuts about 1 cm (.5 in.) apart and 5 cm (2 in.) long from the edge of each disk toward the center. Fold the paper to make a flap at a right angle.
2. Use a different marker to make a dark spot in the middle of the flap on each disk.
3. Fill each of the cups with water. Set one of the disks on top of each cup so that the water covers the end of the flap but does not reach the ink spot.
4. After 15 minutes, examine each of the flaps.

WHAT DO YOU THINK?

- What did you observe about the effects of water on the ink spots?
- How do the three different samples compare?

CHALLENGE Write a hypothesis to explain what you observed about the colors in a black marker.

SKILL FOCUS
Observing

MATERIALS
- 3 coffee filters
- scissors
- 3 brands of black felt-tip marker
- 3 cups
- water

TIME
30 minutes

578 Unit 4: Waves, Sound, and Light

DIFFERENTIATE INSTRUCTION

 **More Reading Support**

G What are the three primary colors visible to human eyes? *red, green, and blue*

Alternative Assessment Have interested students videotape "Investigate Mixing Colors," then play back the tape at a slow speed. They can write and record a script to describe and explain what is happening as the separation of ink colors proceeds. The script should also explain why black ink has to be mixed this way.

Primary Pigments

Remember that two factors affect an object's color. One is the wavelengths present in the light that shines on the object. The other is the wavelengths that the object's material reflects or absorbs. Materials can be mixed to produce colors just as light can. Materials that are used to produce colors are called pigments. The **primary pigments** are cyan, yellow, and magenta. You can mix primary pigments just as you can mix primary colors to produce all the colors.

The primary pigment colors are the same as the secondary colors of light. The secondary pigment colors are red, blue, and green—the same as the primary colors of light.

The effect of mixing pigments is different from the effect of mixing light. Remember that a colored material absorbs all wavelengths except those of the color it reflects. Yellow paint absorbs all wavelengths except yellow. Because pigments absorb wavelengths, whenever you mix pigments, you are subtracting wavelengths rather than adding them. Mixing colors by subtracting wavelengths is called subtractive color mixing. When all three primary pigments are mixed together in equal amounts, all wavelengths are subtracted. The result is black—the absence of reflected light.

The inks used to make the circles on this page are primary pigments. They combine to make the secondary pigments red, blue, and green.

 How is mixing pigments different from mixing light?

17.4 Review

KEY CONCEPTS

1. What are some ways in which materials affect how light is transmitted?
2. How does a polarizing filter reduce glare?
3. In order for an object to appear white, which wavelengths must the light contain and the object reflect?

CRITICAL THINKING

4. **Apply** Imagine that you are a firefighter searching a smoke-filled apartment. Would using a stronger light help you see better? Explain your answer.
5. **Predict** Higher-energy EM waves penetrate farthest into a dense medium. What colors are more likely to penetrate to the bottom of a lake?

CHALLENGE

6. **Synthesize** If you focus a red light, a green light, and a blue light on the same part of a black curtain, what color will the curtain appear to be? Why?

Chapter 17: **Electromagnetic Waves** 579

ANSWERS

1. Reflection can diffuse light, as in translucent material. Absorption can filter out some wavelengths, as in a color filter, or all wavelengths, as in an opaque material.

2. A polarizing filter allows waves through only if their electric fields vibrate in the same direction, eliminating the random reflection and diffusion that cause glare.

3. all wavelengths of visible light

4. No; stronger light would cause more scattering and decrease visibility.

5. green, blue, indigo, and violet

6. The curtain will appear black because the black curtain absorbs all wavelengths.

Ongoing Assessment

Explain how different colors are produced.

Ask: How are secondary pigments produced? *by mixing primary pigments*

 Answer: *Mixing colors of light produces new colors by the addition of wavelengths. Mixing pigments produces new colors by the subtraction of wavelengths.*

Reinforce the BIG idea

All students can benefit from the following worksheet:

Reinforcing Key Concepts, p. 186

17.4 ASSESS & RETEACH

Assess

 Section 17.4 Quiz, p. 45

Reteach

Have each student or groups of students make a poster to review one of the main concepts of this section: reflection, transmission, absorption, scattering, polarization, color reflection and absorption, and how colors are mixed. Students can explain the concepts on their posters in oral presentations to the class.

Technology Resources

Have students visit ClassZone.com for reteaching of Key Concepts.

CONTENT REVIEW

CONTENT REVIEW CD-ROM

CHAPTER INVESTIGATION

Focus

PURPOSE Students will learn that an object's color is determined by the wavelengths of light that shine upon it and those that it reflects.

OVERVIEW Students will make a light box and observe objects in blue, red, and green light. Students will find that

- a white object appears white in white light, red in red light, blue in blue light, and green in green light.
- a black object appears black in all colors of light.
- a red object appears red in white and red light, purple in blue light, and yellow in green light.
- a yellow object appears yellow in white light, orange in red light, green in blue light, and yellow-green in green light.

Lab Preparation

- Ask students to bring shoe boxes from home, or check with discount stores. Boxes without lids can be used upside down.
- Acetate sheets are available as report covers from school supply stores.
- Have students read the lab, write their hypotheses, and make data tables before class. Or copy and distribute datasheets and rubrics.

UNIT RESOURCE BOOK, pp. 194–202

SCIENCE TOOLKIT, F14

Lab Management

- This investigation can be set up with four viewing stations, each with a box testing one color of light. Students can circulate to each box.
- Remind students that they should examine each of the four objects in four colors of light.

INCLUSION If you have physically challenged students in your class, you might make their boxes before class. Team up color-blind students with those who can distinguish colors.

CHAPTER INVESTIGATION

Wavelength and Color

OVERVIEW AND PURPOSE Lighting directors use color filters to change the look of a scene. The color an object appears depends on both the wavelengths of light shining on it and the wavelengths of light it reflects. In this exercise, you will investigate the factors that affect these wavelengths and so affect the color of an object. You will

- make a light box
- study the effect of different colors of light on objects of different colors

 Problem

How does the appearance of objects of different colors change in different colors of light?

 Hypothesize

Read the procedure below and look at the sample notebook page. Predict what color each object will appear in each color of light. Give a reason for each prediction.

 Procedure

MATERIALS
- 3 sheets of acetate (red, blue, and green)
- ruler
- scissors
- shoe box
- masking tape
- light source
- 4 solid-colored objects (white, black, red, and yellow)

1. Draw a data table like the one in the sample **Science Notebook**.

2. Make 3 color filters by cutting a 10 cm (4 in.) square from each color of acetate.

3. Make a 3 cm (1 in.) wide hole in the middle of the top of the box. This will be the viewing hole.

4. Make an 8 cm (3 in.) hole in one end of the box. This will be the light hole.

5. You will observe each of the four colored objects four times—with no filter and with the red, blue, and green filters. Use masking tape to position the filters in the light hole, as shown.

step 5

INVESTIGATION RESOURCES

 CHAPTER INVESTIGATION, Wavelength and Color
- Level A, pp. 194–197
- Level B, pp. 198–201
- Level C, p. 202

Advanced students should complete Levels B & C.

 Writing a Lab Report, D12–13

Technology Resources

Customize this student lab as needed or look for an alternative. Print rubrics to assess student lab reports.

 Lab Generator CD-ROM

6. Place the light box on a flat surface near a strong white light source, such as sunlight or a bright lamp. Position the box with the uncovered light hole facing the light source. Place the white object inside the box, look through the eyehole, and observe the object's color. Record your observations.

7. Use the light box to test each of the combinations of object color and filter shown in the table on the sample notebook page. Record your results.

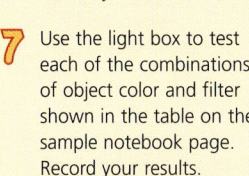
step 7

INVESTIGATE Further

CHALLENGE Perform this experiment using different kinds of artificial light. Try it with a low-wattage incandescent bulb, a high-wattage incandescent bulb, a fluorescent bulb, or a full-spectrum bulb. How do different kinds of artificial light affect the colors that objects appear to be?

Observe and Analyze [Write It Up]

1. **RECORD OBSERVATIONS** Be sure your data table is complete.
2. **COMPARE** What color did the red object appear to be when viewed with a blue filter? a red filter?

Conclude [Write It Up]

1. **INTERPRET** Answer your problem question.
2. **ANALYZE** Compare your results to your predictions. How do the results support your hypothesis?
3. **IDENTIFY VARIABLES** What different variables affected the outcome of your experiment?
4. **INFER** Why do colors of objects appear to change in different types of light?
5. **IDENTIFY LIMITS** What possible limitations or sources of error could have affected your results?
6. **APPLY** If you were going to perform on a stage that was illuminated using several different color filters, what color clothing should you wear in order to look as bright and colorful as possible?

Wavelength and Color
Problem
How does the appearance of objects of different colors change in different colors of light?
Hypothesize
Observe and Analyze
Table 1. Predicted and Observed Colors of Objects with Different Colored Filters

Predicted	no filter	red filter	blue filter	green filter
white object				
black object				
red object				
yellow object				
Observed	no filter	red filter	blue filter	green filter
white object				

Chapter 17: Electromagnetic Waves 581

Observe and Analyze [Write It Up]

SAMPLE DATA White object: white in white light, red in red light, blue in blue light, green in green light; Black object: black in all colors of light; Red object: red in white and red light, purple in blue light, and yellow in green light; Yellow object: yellow in white light, orange in red light, green in blue light, and yellow-green in green light.

1. See students' data tables.
2. purple, red

Conclude [Write It Up]

1. The color of an object depends both on the wavelengths of the light that shines on it and the wavelengths that it reflects.
2. Student answers will vary.
3. The variables are the color of the object and the color of the filter.
4. The color that an object reflects depends on the type of light shining on it.
5. Possible limitations or sources of error might include the shade of the colored acetate, the brightness of the light, leakage of white light into the box, and a person's sense of color.
6. You should wear white so your clothing will reflect any filter color.

INVESTIGATE Further

CHALLENGE Results will vary depending on the type of light bulb tested. Different kinds of light bulbs emit different wavelengths of light.

Post-Lab Discussion

- Copy the data table onto the board. Have students fill in the object colors they observed. Discuss why results might have varied. Ask if other variables were introduced in the experiment.
- Ask students why it is wise to examine a paint sample in the same kind of light that it will be used in. Discuss how the objects appeared under various kinds of artificial lighting.

Chapter 17 **581**

CHAPTER 17 • REVIEW

BACK TO

Have students compare the frequency of the following EM waves: a burning ember glowing red, a yellow candle flame, the blue-white flame of a blowtorch. *The colors represent different frequencies of light. The red glowing ember has low frequency, the yellow candle flame has a higher frequency, and the blue-white flame of the blowtorch has the highest frequency.*

KEY CONCEPTS SUMMARY

SECTION 17.1
Ask: What is the spatial relationship between the electrical field and the magnetic field of an EM wave? *They are at right angles to each other.*

SECTION 17.2
Ask: What determines the characteristics of an EM wave? *frequency*

Ask: How would the wave pictured change if its frequency were increased? *The wavelength would be smaller.*

SECTION 17.3
Ask: What is the difference between the light produced from the two pictures? *The incandescent light bulb produces light from heat. The caterpillar produces light from chemical reactions.*

SECTION 17.4
Ask: What does a prism do? *separates white light into its component wavelengths*

Review Concepts

- Big Idea Flow Chart, p. T17
- Chapter Outline, p. T23–T24

---

17 Chapter Review

the BIG idea
Electromagnetic waves transfer energy through radiation.

CONTENT REVIEW
CLASSZONE.COM

KEY CONCEPTS SUMMARY

1 Electromagnetic waves have unique traits.

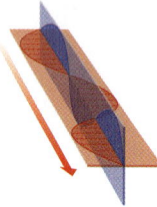

- Electromagnetic (EM) waves are made of vibrating electric and magnetic fields.
- EM waves travel at the speed of light through a vacuum.
- EM waves transfer energy and can interact with matter.

VOCABULARY
electromagnetic wave p. 553
radiation p. 555

2 Electromagnetic waves have many uses.

- EM waves are grouped by frequency on the EM spectrum.
- The EM spectrum is divided into radio waves, microwaves, infrared light, visible light, ultraviolet light, x-rays, and gamma rays.

VOCABULARY
EM spectrum p. 560
radio waves p. 562
microwaves p. 563
visible light p. 564
infrared light p. 564
ultraviolet light p. 565
x-rays p. 566
gamma rays p. 566

3 The Sun is the source of most visible light.

- Most visible light in the environment comes from the Sun.
- Many living organisms produce visible light for their own use.
- Humans produce visible light artificially.

VOCABULARY
incandescence p. 569
luminescence p. 569
bioluminescence p. 569
fluorescence p. 571

4 Light waves interact with materials.

- Reflection, transmission, and absorption affect what light we see.
- Light can be scattered and polarized.
- Visible light is made up of many wavelengths.
- The primary colors are red, blue, and green.
- The primary pigments are yellow, cyan, and magenta.

VOCABULARY
transmission p. 573
absorption p. 573
scattering p. 575
polarization p. 576
prism p. 577
primary colors p. 578
primary pigments p. 579

Technology Resources

Have students visit **ClassZone.com** or use the CD-ROM for a cumulative review of concepts.

 CONTENT REVIEW

 CONTENT REVIEW CD-ROM

Engage students in a whole-class interactive review of Key Concepts. Edit content as you wish.

 POWER PRESENTATIONS

Reviewing Vocabulary

Make a four-square diagram for each of the listed terms. Write the term in the center. Define the term in one square. Write characteristics, examples, and nonexamples in other squares. A sample is shown below.

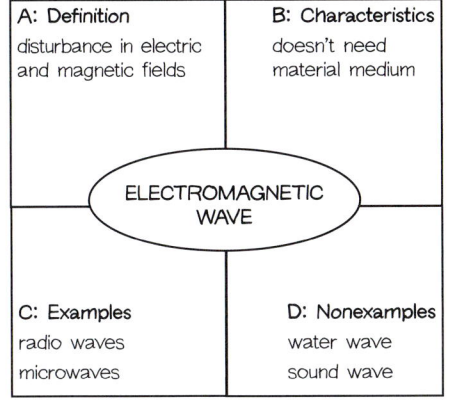

A: Definition	B: Characteristics
disturbance in electric and magnetic fields	doesn't need material medium

ELECTROMAGNETIC WAVE

C: Examples	D: Nonexamples
radio waves, microwaves	water wave, sound wave

1. gamma rays
2. infrared light
3. transmission
4. absorption
5. pigment
6. radiation
7. bioluminescence
8. EM spectrum
9. incandescence
10. polarization

Reviewing Key Concepts

Multiple Choice *Choose the letter of the best answer.*

11. An electromagnetic wave is a disturbance that transfers energy through a field. In this sense, a disturbance is the same as a
    a. confusion   c. vibration
    b. magnification d. conflict

12. Unlike mechanical waves, EM waves can travel through
    a. a vacuum   c. the ground
    b. water   d. air

13. A light year is a measure of
    a. time   c. speed
    b. distance   d. wavelength

14. The Sun and a light bulb both produce light through
    a. bioluminescence c. luminescence
    b. incandescence   d. polarization

15. Which of the following types of light bulb converts ultraviolet waves into visible light waves?
    a. incandescent c. halogen
    b. fluorescent   d. tungsten

16. An object seen through translucent material appears less clear than one seen through transparent material because the translucent material
    a. transmits none of the light coming from the object
    b. reflects all the light coming from the object
    c. transmits all the light coming from the object
    d. diffuses some light coming from the object

17. An object appears red because it
    a. reflects light waves of all colors
    b. reflects light waves of red
    c. absorbs light waves of red
    d. transmits light waves of all colors

18. Primary colors of light can combine to make
    a. black light   c. primary pigments
    b. white light   d. ultraviolet light

Short Answer *Write a short answer to each question.*

19. What vibrates in an EM wave?
20. How can EM waves be used to measure distance?
21. Describe how microwaves are used in communications.
22. What two properties of an EM wave change as you move from one part of the EM spectrum to another?
23. How does visible light differ from other EM waves? How is it similar?
24. Explain briefly how an incandescent light bulb works.

Chapter 17: Electromagnetic Waves 583

ASSESSMENT RESOURCES

UNIT ASSESSMENT BOOK
- Chapter Test A, pp. 46–49
- Chapter Test B, pp. 50–53
- Chapter Test C, pp. 54–57
- Alternative Assessment, pp. 58–59

SPANISH ASSESSMENT BOOK
Spanish Chapter Test, pp. 289–292

Technology Resources

Edit test items and answer choices.

 Test Generator CD-ROM

Visit ClassZone.com to extend test practice.

 Test Practice

Reviewing Vocabulary

1. A: EM waves with highest frequencies and energies; B: 10^{19} Hz to 10^{24} Hz; C: the Sun; D: radio waves
2. A: EM frequencies between microwaves and visible light; B: invisible; C: lamps; D: x-rays
3. A: the passage of an EM wave through a medium; B: makes it possible to see through things; C: clear glass; D: wood
4. A: disappearance of an EM wave into the medium; B: causes materials to be opaque; C: wood; D: air
5. A: material used to mix colors; B: subtracts wavelengths rather than adding them; C: paint; D: colored light
6. A: transfer of energy in the form of EM waves; B: spreads outward in straight line from source; passes through vacuum; C: light from Sun; D: ocean waves
7. A: production of light by living organisms; B: light produced from chemical reactions; C: firefly; D: fire
8. A: range of all EM frequencies; B: smooth, gradual progression; C: microwaves, D: ultrasound
9. A: production of light from high temperatures; B: dangerous for living tissue; C: sunlight; D: firefly
10. A: filtering light so that all of its waves vibrate in the same direction; B: affects only electric fields of wave; C: sunglasses; D: glare

Reviewing Key Concepts

11. c	14. b	17. b
12. a	15. b	18. b
13. b	16. d	

19. electric and magnetic fields
20. by how far they travel in a certain amount of time
21. Cell phones and radar send and receive microwave signals.
22. wavelength and frequency
23. Visible light has different frequencies and wavelengths. Visible light, like all EM waves, is a disturbance in a field.
24. Electricity passes through the filament. Resistance causes the filament to heat up and glow.

Chapter 17 583

Thinking Critically

25. absorption
26. Violet light should penetrate even deeper into the water than blue.
27. Objects near the ocean floor should appear blue.
28. when it interacts with a medium
29. The light source must contain red wavelengths and the object must reflect red light.
30. blue, all the other colors
31. Sample answer: Incandescent lighting wastes energy as heat, and lighting is more energy efficient.
32. The black numbers could be caused by polarizing filters at right angles that would screen out all light.
33. Like a sieve, a polarizing filter screens out certain kinds of light waves while letting others pass through. Unlike a sieve, a polarizing filter screens waves on the basis of orientation rather than size.
34. Fluorescent bulbs remain cooler than regular or halogen bulbs, so they waste less energy as heat.
35. blue, because only blue wavelengths pass through filter to your eye

the BIG idea

36. Sample answer: A cell phone uses microwaves. Cell phones depend on an overlapping network of cells. Each cell has a tower that sends and receives microwave signals. The tower connects cell phones to each other or the regular wired telephone system.
37. See students' summaries.
38. Infrared waves leave the radiator. They are transmitted by the air, which absorbs only a little of their energy. The kitten absorbs waves that travel toward it, and is warmed by energy transferred in the form of heat.

UNIT PROJECTS

Collect schedules, materials lists, and questions. Be sure dates and materials are obtainable, and questions are focused.

 Unit Projects, pp. 5–10

584 Unit 4: **Waves, Sound, and Light**

Thinking Critically

The diagram below shows how far different wavelengths of visible light penetrate into ocean water. Use information from this diagram to answer the next three questions.

25. **OBSERVE** An EM wave can interact with a material in different ways. Which type of interaction keeps some light waves from reaching the ocean floor?
26. **PREDICT** How would violet light behave in the same water? Think of where violet is on the color spectrum.
27. **SYNTHESIZE** How is the apparent color of objects near the ocean floor affected by the interactions shown in the diagram?

28. **ANALYZE** Under what circumstances can an EM wave begin to convert some of its electromagnetic energy into other forms of energy?
29. **ANALYZE** What two things must be true about the light source and the material of an object for you to see an object as red?
30. **PREDICT** If you shine a blue light on a white object, what color will the object appear to be? What color light would you need to add to make the white object appear white?
31. **APPLY** Why might incandescent lighting become less common in the future? Explain your reasoning.

584 Unit 4: Waves, Sound, and Light

32. **IDENTIFY CAUSE AND EFFECT** Liquid crystal displays like the ones used in some calculators work by polarizing light. Describe how two polarizing filters could cause the numbers on the display panel to appear black.
33. **COMPARE AND CONTRAST** In what way would a sieve be a good model for a polarizing light filter? In what ways would it not be?
34. **CONTRAST** In what ways is a fluorescent bulb more efficient than incandescent and halogen bulbs?
35. **PREDICT** What color will a white object appear to be if you look at it through a blue filter?

the BIG idea

36. **ANALYZE** Return to the question on page 550. Answer the question again, using what you have learned in the chapter.
37. **SUMMARIZE** Write a summary of this chapter. Use the Big Idea statement from page 550 as the title for your summary. Use the Key Concepts listed on page 550 as the topic sentences for each paragraph. Provide an example for each key concept.
38. **ANALYZE** Describe all of the EM wave behaviors and interactions that occur when a radiator warms a kitten.

UNIT PROJECTS

Check your schedule for your unit project. How are you doing? Be sure that you've placed data or notes from your research in your project folder.

MONITOR AND RETEACH

If students have trouble applying the concepts in items 25–27, have them create a three-part visual aid showing how deeply various colors of light would penetrate the water.

Part 1 should show red, orange, yellow, green, blue, indigo, and violet light; **Part 2** should show relative frequencies of the various colors of light; **Part 3** should list the relative energies of the various colors of light. Students may benefit from summarizing one or more sections of the chapter.

 Summarizing the Chapter, pp. 212–213

Standardized Test Practice

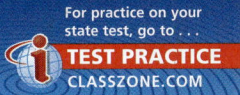

For practice on your state test, go to...
TEST PRACTICE
CLASSZONE.COM

Interpreting Diagrams

The diagram below shows part of the electromagnetic (EM) spectrum. The lower band shows frequency in hertz. The upper band shows part of the spectrum used by different technologies.

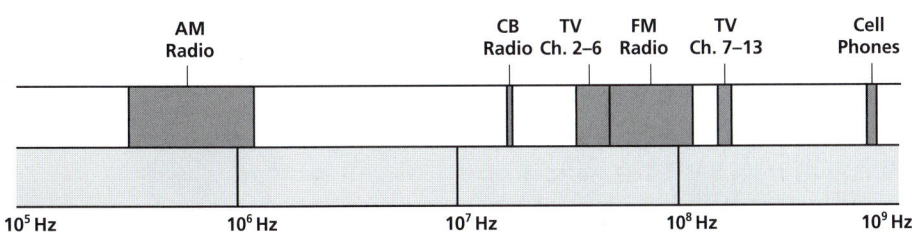

Use the diagram to answer the following questions.

1. Which of the technologies listed below uses the highest frequencies?
   a. AM radio
   b. CB radio
   c. FM radio
   d. TV channels 2–6

2. If you were receiving a signal at a frequency of nearly 10^9 Hz, what would you be using?
   a. a CB radio
   b. an AM radio
   c. an FM radio
   d. a cell phone

3. A television station broadcasts its video signal at 10^6 Hz and its audio signal at 10^8 Hz. To receive the broadcasts, your television would need to use the technologies of
   a. both AM and FM radio
   b. both CB and AM radio
   c. both CB and FM radio
   d. both CB radio and cell phone transmissions

4. Signals with similar frequencies sometimes interfere with each other. For this reason, you might expect interference in which of the following?
   a. lower television channels from cell phones
   b. upper television channels from FM radio
   c. lower television channels from FM radio
   d. upper television channels from cell phones

Extended Response

Answer the two questions below in detail. Include some of the terms from the word box. Underline each term you use in your answer.

| frequency | energy | interaction |
| field | medium | vacuum |

5. What are the similarities and differences between mechanical waves and electromagnetic waves?

6. What are some advantages and disadvantages of different types of artificial lighting?

Chapter 17: **Electromagnetic Waves** 585

Interpreting Diagrams
1. c   3. a
2. d   4. c

Extended Response

5. RUBRIC
4 points for a response that correctly answers the question and that uses the following terms accurately:
- wavelength
- medium
- amplitude
- field
- frequency

Sample: Mechanical and electromagnetic waves are disturbances that transfer energy. They have <u>wavelength</u>, <u>amplitude</u>, and <u>frequency</u>. Mechanical waves need a <u>medium</u>, while EM waves do not. EM waves are disturbances in electric and magnetic <u>fields</u>. Mechanical waves give up some energy when they travel, but EM waves can travel in a vacuum without losing energy.

3 points answers the question correctly and uses three of the listed terms accurately

2 points response is correct, but partial, and uses two terms correctly

1 point for a response that is partially correct, but contains some inaccuracies

6. RUBRIC
4 points for a response that correctly identifies advantages and disadvantages of the following types of artificial lighting:
- incandescent
- halogen
- fluorescent
- LED

Sample: <u>Incandescent</u> lighting is a good source of bright light, is relatively cheap, and is convenient to use. <u>Fluorescent</u> lights waste less energy than incandescent lights, because fluorescent bulbs produce less heat and they last longer. <u>Halogen</u> bulbs last longer than incandescent bulbs, but halogen bulbs are more of a fire and injury hazard because they get very hot. <u>LEDs</u> are very cheap, last a long time, are safe, and waste almost no energy.

3 points identifies advantages and disadvantages of three types of artificial lighting listed

2 points identifies advantages and disadvantages of two types of artificial lighting listed

1 point identifies advantages and disadvantages of one type of artificial lighting listed

METACOGNITIVE ACTIVITY

Have students answer the following questions in their **Science Notebook:**
1. What questions do you still have about electromagnetic waves?
2. What were you surprised to find out about visible light?
3. How do the concepts of this chapter relate to your Unit Project?

Chapter 17 585

TIMELINES in Science

FOCUS

▶ Set Learning Goals
Students will
- Observe how scientists historically studied light.
- Examine how observations about the properties of light led to explanations of its behavior.
- Make a camera obscura and write a news article about a discovery regarding light.

National Science Education Standards
A.9.a–g Understandings About Scientific Inquiry

E.6.a–c Understandings About Science and Technology

F.5.a–e, F.5.g Science and Technology in Society

G.1.a–b Science as a Human Endeavor

G.2.a Nature of Science

G.3.a–c History of Science

INSTRUCT

History Connection
Point out to students that the top half of the timeline shows some major events in the scientific study of light that were historically recorded. The bottom half of the timeline illustrates advances in the technology that enables study of light and practical applications of the results of this study. The two gaps in the timeline represent periods of time in which no advances in the study of light are highlighted.

Technology
REFLECTING TELESCOPES The first telescope was a refractor, built by Galileo, and many current telescopes use lenses to refract light. When light travels through lenses, it bends. The amount it is bent depends on the shape, composition, and thickness of the lens. Many telescopes are both reflecting and refracting because they use both mirrors and lenses.

586 Unit 4: **Waves, Sound, and Light**

TIMELINES in Science

THE STORY OF LIGHT

Light has fascinated people since ancient times. The earliest ideas about light were closely associated with beliefs and observations about vision. Over the centuries, philosophers and scientists developed an increasingly better understanding of light as a physical reality that obeyed the laws of physics.

With increased understanding of the nature and behavior of light has come the ability to use light as a tool. Many applications of light technology have led to improvements in human visual abilities. People can now make images of a wide range of objects that were invisible to earlier generations. The study of light has also led to technologies that do not involve sight at all.

This timeline shows just a few of the many steps on the road to understanding light. The boxes below the timeline show how these discoveries have been applied and developed into new technologies.

400 B.C.
Light Travels in a Straight Line
Observing the behavior of shadows, Chinese philosopher Mo-Ti finds that light travels in a straight line. His discovery helps explain why light passing through a small opening forms an upside-down image.

300 B.C.
Reflection Obeys Law
Greek mathematician Euclid discovers that light striking mirrors obeys the law of reflection. The angle at which light reflects off a mirror is equal to the angle at which it strikes the mirror.

EVENTS
450 B.C.   425 B.C.   400 B.C.   375 B.C.   350 B.C.   325 B.C.   300 B.C.

APPLICATIONS AND TECHNOLOGY

APPLICATION
Camera Obscura
The principle described by Mo-Ti in 400 B.C. led to the development of the camera obscura. When light from an object shines through a small hole into a dark room, an image of the object appears on the far wall. The darkened room is called, in Latin, *camera obscura*. Because light travels in a straight line, the highest points on the object appear at the lowest points on the image; thus, the image appears upside down. Room-sized versions of the camera obscura like the one shown here were a popular attraction in the late 1800s.

586 Unit 4: Waves, Sound, and Light

DIFFERENTIATE INSTRUCTION

Advanced Tell students that a line that is perpendicular to a flat surface is called the *normal*. Have students state generalizations about the following angles: the angle formed by the normal and a beam of light hitting a surface and the angle formed by the normal and the beam of light reflecting from the surface. *Sample answer: The angle formed by the normal and a beam of light hitting a surface is equal to the angle formed by the normal and the beam of light reflecting from the surface.*

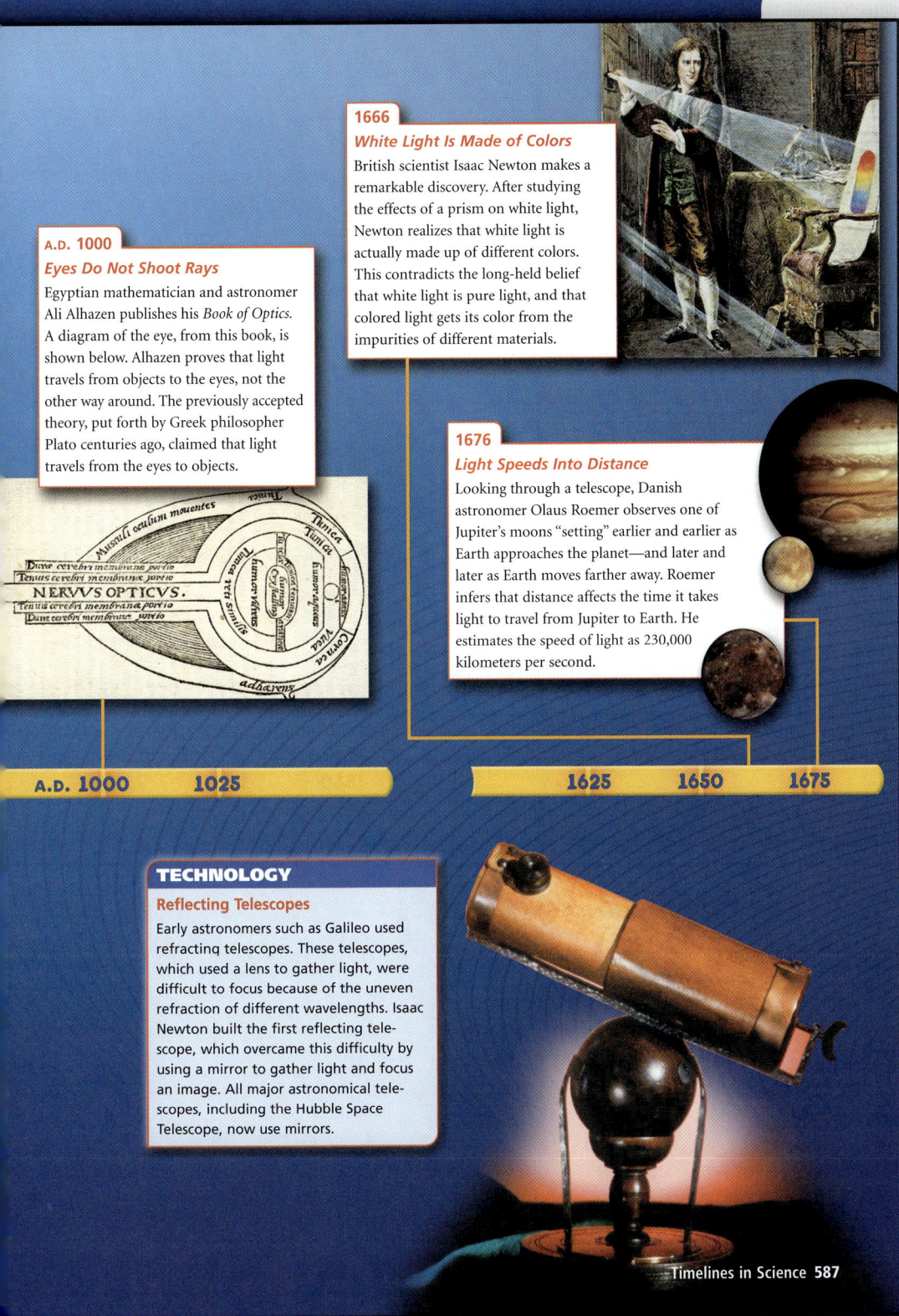

A.D. 1000
Eyes Do Not Shoot Rays
Egyptian mathematician and astronomer Ali Alhazen publishes his *Book of Optics*. A diagram of the eye, from this book, is shown below. Alhazen proves that light travels from objects to the eyes, not the other way around. The previously accepted theory, put forth by Greek philosopher Plato centuries ago, claimed that light travels from the eyes to objects.

1666
White Light Is Made of Colors
British scientist Isaac Newton makes a remarkable discovery. After studying the effects of a prism on white light, Newton realizes that white light is actually made up of different colors. This contradicts the long-held belief that white light is pure light, and that colored light gets its color from the impurities of different materials.

1676
Light Speeds Into Distance
Looking through a telescope, Danish astronomer Olaus Roemer observes one of Jupiter's moons "setting" earlier and earlier as Earth approaches the planet—and later and later as Earth moves farther away. Roemer infers that distance affects the time it takes light to travel from Jupiter to Earth. He estimates the speed of light as 230,000 kilometers per second.

TECHNOLOGY
Reflecting Telescopes
Early astronomers such as Galileo used refracting telescopes. These telescopes, which used a lens to gather light, were difficult to focus because of the uneven refraction of different wavelengths. Isaac Newton built the first reflecting telescope, which overcame this difficulty by using a mirror to gather light and focus an image. All major astronomical telescopes, including the Hubble Space Telescope, now use mirrors.

Mathematics Connection
1676 Working with the knowledge available in 1676, Roemer's estimated speed of light is relatively close to the currently accepted value of 3.00×10^8 m/s. The relationship among speed, frequency, and wavelength of light (or any other wave) can be expressed by the equation $S = f \lambda$, where S is the speed, f is the frequency, and λ is the wavelength.

Integrate the Sciences
Students are familiar with the spectrum of colors seen in a rainbow. This splitting of visible light into its various colors occurs when sunlight strikes droplets of water and light is refracted into different colors. Some of the light reflects off the back surface of the drop, and it refracts further when it leaves the water drop and reenters the air. Violet light is at one end of the visible spectrum, and it is seen coming from droplets lower in the atmosphere. Violet light emerges from the droplets at an angle of approximately 40°. Red light is at the opposite end of the visible spectrum, and it is seen coming from droplets higher in the air. Red light leaves the droplets at an angle of about 42°. The other colors of light are between these two extremes.

Language Arts Connection
All types of light make up the electromagnetic spectrum, of which visible light is only a small portion. Ask: Ultrasound is sound that is in a higher range than can be heard by humans. From this meaning of *ultra-*, what conclusion might you draw about ultraviolet light? *It has a frequency higher than that of violet light.* The prefix *infra-* has the opposite meaning of the prefix *ultra-*. Based on this information, where would infrared light be located in the electromagnetic spectrum? *It would have a frequency less than that of red light.*

DIFFERENTIATE INSTRUCTION
Advanced Have students use the mathematical relationship and the speed of light shown in the Mathematics Connection on this page to make the following calculations:
1. What is the wavelength of visible light that has a frequency of 5.0×10^{14} s? $(3.00 \times 10^8 \text{ m/s})(5.0 \times 10^{14}/\text{s}) = 6.0 \times 10^{-7}$ m
2. What is the frequency of x-rays that have a wavelength of 2.0×10^{-8} m? $(3.00 \times 10^8 \text{ m/s})(2.0 \times 10^{-8} \text{ m}) = 1.5 \times 10^{16}$ s

Scientific Process

Observations of light led to hypotheses that light is a wave. Observations also support light's being a particle. Experiments that test these hypotheses support both of them. As a result, light is considered to be both a wave and a particle made up of discrete packets of energy.

Application

HOLOGRAMS Because holograms look different from various angles, holograms are difficult to reproduce. As a result, they are used on certain credit cards and other documents to help prevent forgery.

Art Connection

Art forgery is a common problem for artists, art dealers, and art buyers. Some art forgeries are so well done that special technology is necessary to tell the real item from a forgery. What is done to tell forgeries from original art? There is a difference in modern paint and paints that were used years ago, but no one wants to chip off paint from an original painting to test it. One way to test a painting without damaging it is to use ultraviolet and infrared light and x-rays.

The human eye cannot see the varnish that is painted on the top of oil paintings, but it glows under ultraviolet light. Irregularities in the varnish and places that have had paint added show up as dark spots when this light is shined on it. Infrared light penetrates layers of oil paints, and if there is an image hidden under the surface oil paints, it shows up when infrared light is shined on the painting. X-rays show dense materials, such as metals and paints that contain metallic pigments. If metallic objects or materials that are inconsistent with when the painting was supposed to have been painted are seen, forgeries can be detected.

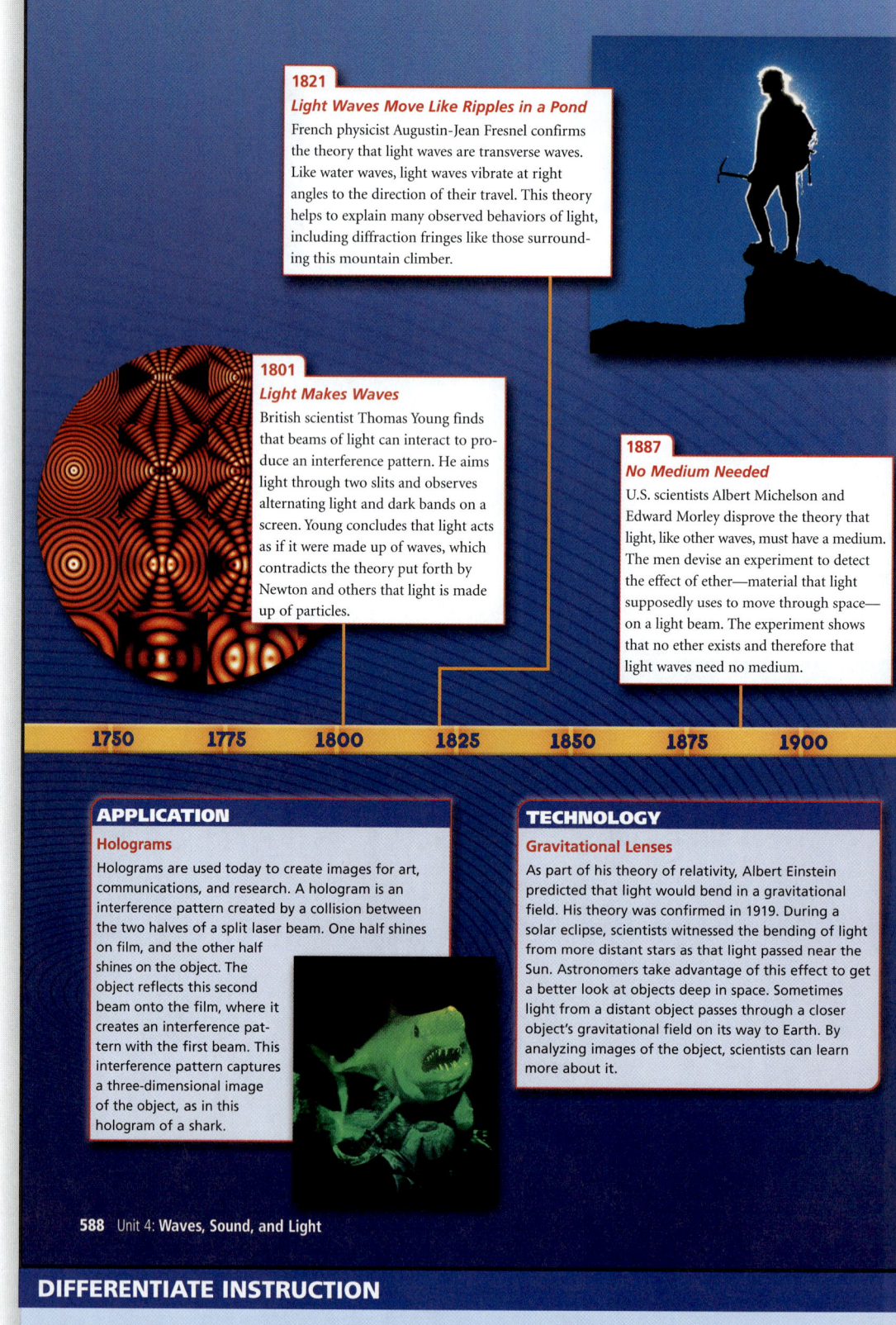

1821
Light Waves Move Like Ripples in a Pond
French physicist Augustin-Jean Fresnel confirms the theory that light waves are transverse waves. Like water waves, light waves vibrate at right angles to the direction of their travel. This theory helps to explain many observed behaviors of light, including diffraction fringes like those surrounding this mountain climber.

1801
Light Makes Waves
British scientist Thomas Young finds that beams of light can interact to produce an interference pattern. He aims light through two slits and observes alternating light and dark bands on a screen. Young concludes that light acts as if it were made up of waves, which contradicts the theory put forth by Newton and others that light is made up of particles.

1887
No Medium Needed
U.S. scientists Albert Michelson and Edward Morley disprove the theory that light, like other waves, must have a medium. The men devise an experiment to detect the effect of ether—material that light supposedly uses to move through space—on a light beam. The experiment shows that no ether exists and therefore that light waves need no medium.

APPLICATION
Holograms
Holograms are used today to create images for art, communications, and research. A hologram is an interference pattern created by a collision between the two halves of a split laser beam. One half shines on film, and the other half shines on the object. The object reflects this second beam onto the film, where it creates an interference pattern with the first beam. This interference pattern captures a three-dimensional image of the object, as in this hologram of a shark.

TECHNOLOGY
Gravitational Lenses
As part of his theory of relativity, Albert Einstein predicted that light would bend in a gravitational field. His theory was confirmed in 1919. During a solar eclipse, scientists witnessed the bending of light from more distant stars as that light passed near the Sun. Astronomers take advantage of this effect to get a better look at objects deep in space. Sometimes light from a distant object passes through a closer object's gravitational field on its way to Earth. By analyzing images of the object, scientists can learn more about it.

DIFFERENTIATE INSTRUCTION

Below Level Have students show how light is separated into different colors by shining a light on bubbles made by using liquid dishwashing detergent. The colors can be seen better if this activity is done in a darkened room.

1960
Light Beams Line Up
U.S. inventor Theodore Harold Maiman builds a working laser by stimulating emission of light in a cylinder of ruby crystal. Laser light waves all have the same wavelength, and their peaks occur together.

2001
Light Is Completely Stopped
After slowing light to the speed of a bicycle, Danish physicist Lene Vestergaard Hau brings it to a complete halt in a super-cold medium. Controlling the speed of light could revolutionize computers, communications, and other electronic technology.

 RESOURCE CENTER
CLASSZONE.COM
Learn more about current research involving light.

1925 1950 1975 2000

APPLICATION
Lasers in Eye Surgery
For centuries, people have used corrective lenses to help their eyes focus images more clearly. Today, with the help of lasers, doctors can correct the eye itself. Using an ultraviolet laser, doctors remove microscopic amounts of a patient's cornea to change the way it refracts light. As a result, the eye focuses images exactly on the retina. For many nearsighted people, the surgery results in 20/20 vision or better.

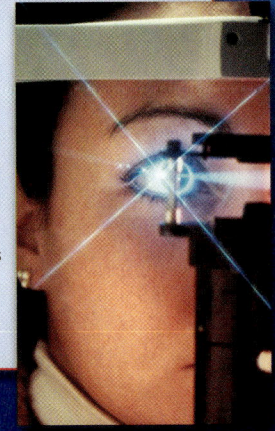

INTO THE FUTURE

Much of our current knowledge in science, from the workings of our bodies to the universe as a whole, is founded upon experiments that used light. Evidence from new light applications will continue to shape our knowledge. In the future, the nature of light, itself, may again come into question as new experiments are performed.

As new light microscopes are developed, scientists will gain more detailed information about how systems within our bodies work, such as how our brain cells interact with each other to perform a complex task. With powerful telescopes, scientists will gain a better understanding of the universe at its beginnings and how galaxies are formed.

Finally, as we continue to study the behavior of light, we may continue to modify its very definition. Sometimes considered a stream of particles, and other times considered waves, light is now understood to have qualities of both particles and waves.

ACTIVITIES

Make a Camera Obscura
Take a small box and paint the interior black. On one side, make a pinhole. On a side next to that one, make a hole about 5 cm in diameter.

On a bright, sunny day, hold the box so that sunlight enters the box through the pinhole. Fit your eye snugly against the larger hole and look inside.

Writing About Science
Lasers are currently used in entertainment, medicine, communication, supermarkets, and so on. Write a prediction about a specific use of lasers in the future. You might describe a new invention.

Timelines in Science 589

DIFFERENTIATE INSTRUCTION

Inclusion Pair any visually impaired student with another student who can explain the timeline content to them. When making the camera, outline with yarn the area on the side of the camera where the image is shown. Have the visually impaired student feel the box, the two holes, and the area where the image is shown.

INTO THE FUTURE

Have students divide into two groups. Have one group list the ways they think that the use of light can provide information about the formation of the universe. Have the other group make a similar list that refers to using light to study the cells of the human body. Then have students in each group research actual scientific investigations in the area they have been assigned. Have each group prepare a presentation of their results. Presentations might consist of bulletin boards, videos done as news segments, or oral reports with visual aids.

ACTIVITIES

Make a Camera Obscura
Be sure the box does not allow any light to enter, other than the light that enters through the holes made in the box. A full-spectrum artificial light, such as a sunlamp, can be used instead of natural sunlight. Ask students to explain why a camera obscura might be a safe way to view a solar eclipse. *The gradual darkening of the Sun could be viewed on the side of the camera. Looking directly at the Sun can damage eyes, but the intensity of the light in the camera obscura is much less than direct sunlight.*

Writing About Science
Students can use Internet sources for information, as well as reference books. While writing their predictions, students should be aware of current uses of lasers.

Technology Resources
Students can visit **ClassZone.com** for current news about new advances in technology involving light.

Timelines in Science **589**

CHAPTER 18 Light and Optics

Physical Science
UNIFYING PRINCIPLES

PRINCIPLE 1
Matter is made of particles too small to see.

PRINCIPLE 2
Matter changes form and moves from place to place.

PRINCIPLE 3
Energy changes from one form to another, but it cannot be created or destroyed.

PRINCIPLE 4
Physical forces affect the movement of all matter on Earth and throughout the universe.

Unit 4: Waves, Sound, and Light
BIG IDEAS

CHAPTER 15 Waves
Waves transfer energy and interact in predictable ways.

CHAPTER 16 Sound
Sound waves transfer energy through vibrations.

CHAPTER 17 Electromagnetic Waves
Electromagnetic waves transfer energy through radiation.

CHAPTER 18 Light and Optics
Optical tools depend on the wave behavior of light.

CHAPTER 18 KEY CONCEPTS

SECTION 1
Mirrors form images by reflecting light.
1. Optics is the science of light and vision.
2. Mirrors use regular reflection.
3. Shape determines how mirrors form images.

SECTION 2
Lenses form images by refracting light.
1. A medium can refract light.
2. Shape determines how lenses form images.

SECTION 3
The eye is a natural optical tool.
1. The eye gathers and focuses light.
2. Corrective lenses can improve vision.

SECTION 4
Optical technology makes use of light waves.
1. Mirrors and lenses can be combined to make more powerful optical tools.
2. Lasers use light in new ways.

The Big Idea Flow Chart is available on p. T25 in the UNIT TRANSPARENCY BOOK.

Previewing Content

SECTION
1 Mirrors form images by reflecting light. pp. 593–598

1. **Optics is the science of light and vision.**
   Optics is the study and application of visible light and its interaction with the eye to produce vision. Optical tools can improve vision or use light to do work.

2. **Mirrors use regular reflection.**
   A mirror forms an image by reflecting light from an object. Light reflecting off a mirror follows the **law of reflection**, which states that the angle formed by a line perpendicular to the mirror and the light hitting the mirror (the incident ray) is equal to the angle formed by the perpendicular and the light leaving the mirror (the reflected ray).

3. **Shape determines how mirrors form images.**
   Different mirror shapes produce different kinds of images.
   - A flat mirror produces a virtual image. The image seems to come from behind the mirror.
   - A **convex** mirror reflects light waves so that they spread out, never meeting at a focal point.
   - A **concave** mirror reflects light waves so that they converge at a **focal point.**

Convex Mirror

Concave Mirror, Far Away

Concave Mirror, Up Close

The images formed in mirrors depend on the curve of the mirror's surface and the distance of the object from the mirror.

SECTION
2 Lenses form images by refracting light. pp. 599–605

1. **A medium can refract light.**
   When a light wave moves into a new medium, it may change speed. If it hits the medium at an angle, one side of the wave changes speed before the other side, bending the wave. This is refraction.
   - When light waves refract, they can bend toward or away from the normal.
   - Refraction can occur when light moves from cool air in the sky to warmer air near the ground. Mirages occur in this way.

2. **Shape determines how lenses form images.**
   Lenses produce predictable images when waves of light pass through the lens and refract. The shape of the lens determines the way objects look.
   - A convex lens refracts parallel light waves so they meet at a focal point. As with a concave mirror, the type of image formed depends on the distance between the object and the lens.
   - A concave lens spreads out light waves, which do not meet at a focal point. As with a convex mirror, the image formed is upright and reduced in size.

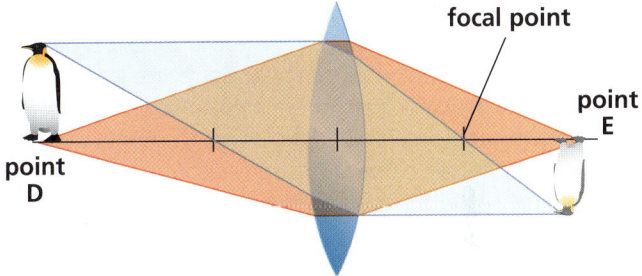

As the diagram shows, the image is inverted and reduced if the object is more than two focal lengths from the lens. Between one and two focal lengths from the lens, the image is inverted and enlarged. If the object is within one focal length from the lens, the image is virtual, upright, and enlarged.

Common Misconceptions

FULL-LENGTH REFLECTION Students might think that a flat mirror turns the image of a person's body around. Actually, in a mirror image a person's left hand still appears on the left. The image is reversed front to back, but not left to right.

 This misconception is addressed on p. 596.

MISCONCEPTION DATABASE
CLASSZONE.COM Background on student misconceptions

MAGNIFYING GLASSES Students may think that a magnifying glass always magnifies images of objects. However, a magnifying glass is simply a convex lens. It magnifies only when an object is the right distance from the lens.

 This misconception is addressed on p. 602.

Chapter 18: **Light and Optics** 589B

Previewing Content

SECTION

 The eye is a natural optical tool. pp. 606–610

1. The eye gathers and focuses light.
Light travels through the eye from the **cornea**, through the **pupil**, through the lens, and hits the **retina**.
- The cornea and the lens are convex lenses that refract light in the eye.
- Pupil size, controlled by the iris, determines how much light enters.
- Light strikes the retina, forming a reduced, inverted image. The retina has cells called rods that distinguish brightness and cells called cones that detect color.

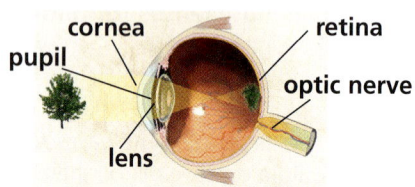

- The brain receives signals from the retina and interprets the image as an object that is right side up.

2. Corrective lenses can improve vision.
Vision is blurry if an image does not fall exactly on the retina. This occurs because the shape of the eye is imperfect or because the eye's lens does not work correctly. Corrective lenses, contact lenses, or surgery can correct these problems.
- Nearsightedness occurs when the image focuses in front of the retina. A corrective concave lens spreads out the light rays before they enter the eye and moves the image back toward the retina.
- Farsightedness occurs when the image focuses behind the retina. A corrective convex lens refracts the light rays inward before they enter the eye and moves the image forward toward the retina.
- Cornea shape can be changed by surgery so that the image will focus on the retina.
- Contact lenses correct vision by changing the way the cornea refracts light.

Common Misconceptions

REFRACTION IN THE EYE Students commonly think that refraction takes place only in the lens of the eye. Actually, most of the refraction takes place in the cornea, which is a membrane that covers the eye. The lens makes additional focusing adjustments so the image falls exactly on the retina.

 This misconception is addressed on p. 607.

SECTION

 Optical technology makes use of light waves. pp. 611–619

1. Mirrors and lenses can be combined to make more powerful optical tools.
Microscopes enlarge tiny objects by combining convex lenses. The objective lens produces an enlarged image. The eyepiece lens forms an enlarged virtual image of the first image.

A **refracting telescope** combines convex lenses. Because the object is more than two focal lengths from the objective lens, the first image is reduced. The eyepiece lens forms an enlarged virtual image of the first image.

A **reflecting telescope** has a concave mirror that focuses an image of the object. The eyepiece lens then forms a virtual enlarged image of the first image. A small flat mirror redirects the image to the telescope's side.

A **film camera** uses a convex lens to focus an image on light-sensitive film. A **digital camera** focuses the image on a sensor, which converts light waves into electrical charges and sends the information to a small computer. The computer reconstructs the image and displays it.

2. Lasers use light in new ways.
A **laser** is intense and concentrated light that carries a lot of energy. A laser beam has light waves with a single wavelength and a pure color. Lasers are made in tubes containing a stimulus that gives off light. The light is concentrated into a beam as it passes back and forth between two mirrors.

Fiber optics use total internal reflection to send signals through thin transparent fibers. Light reflects off the internal surface of a fiber. Fiber optic technology is important in communications and in medical imaging.

MISCONCEPTION DATABASE
CLASSZONE.COM Background on student misconceptions

REFRACTING TELESCOPES Some students may think that each lens of a refracting telescope enlarges the image of the object being observed and that the main function of a telescope is to produce an enlarged image. The main function of the objective lens is not to magnify the object, but to collect as much light from the faraway object as possible to clarify the object's details. The objective lens actually produces a slightly reduced image.

 This misconception is addressed on p. 613.

Previewing Labs

Lab Generator CD-ROM — Edit these Pupil Edition labs and generate alternative labs.

EXPLORE the BIG idea

How Does a Spoon Reflect Your Face? p. 591 Students observe their reflections in the concave and convex surfaces of a spoon.	**TIME** 10 minutes **MATERIALS** shiny metal spoon
Why Do Things Look Different Through Water? p. 591 Students examine objects while looking though a glass of water.	**TIME** 10 minutes **MATERIALS** glass jar filled with water
Internet Activity: Optics, p. 591 Students are introduced to the science of light and vision.	**TIME** 20 minutes **MATERIALS** computer with Internet access

SECTION 1

EXPLORE Reflection, p. 593 Students observe how different surface textures of aluminum foil affect reflection.	**TIME** 10 minutes **MATERIALS** one square sheet of new aluminum foil
INVESTIGATE The Law of Reflection, p. 595 Students make a periscope and analyze how light travels through it.	**TIME** 30 minutes **MATERIALS** quart-sized milk or juice carton, scissors, 0.5 m masking tape, 2 mirrors slightly smaller than the bottom of the carton, protractor

SECTION 2

EXPLORE Refraction, p. 599 Students explore refraction of light in water and in mineral oil.	**TIME** 10 minutes **MATERIALS** clear plastic cup, pencil, 0.25 L water, 0.25 L mineral oil
CHAPTER INVESTIGATION Looking at Lenses, pp. 604–605 Students use a convex lens to focus different types of images.	**TIME** 40 minutes **MATERIALS** index card, marker, 0.25 lbs. modeling clay, convex lens, meter stick, flashlight, 6 cm masking tape, white poster board

SECTION 3

EXPLORE Focusing Vision, p. 606 Students explore the way the eye focuses close and distant images.	**TIME** 10 minutes **MATERIALS** object to view
INVESTIGATE Vision, p. 608 Students use a magnifying glass to observe an image, as an analogy to the way an image forms in the eye.	**TIME** 10 minutes **MATERIALS** convex lens, index card, white paper plate, 0.25 kg modeling clay, lamp

SECTION 4

EXPLORE Combining Lenses, p. 611 Students determine how two convex lenses work together to focus different types of images.	**TIME** 10 minutes **MATERIALS** 2 convex lenses, 0.25 kg modeling clay, 2 index cards, object to view
INVESTIGATE Optical Tools, p. 614 Students make a model of a refracting telescope and determine how to position the lenses to produce a clear image.	**TIME** 30 minutes **MATERIALS** 2 convex lenses, 2 cardboard tubes, 0.5 m duct tape

 Additional INVESTIGATION, Bending Light, A, B, & C, pp. 273–281; Teacher Instructions, pp. 284–285

Chapter 18: **Light and Optics** 589D

Previewing Chapter Resources

	INTEGRATED TECHNOLOGY	LABS AND ACTIVITIES
CHAPTER 18 **Light and Optics**	**CLASSZONE.COM** • eEdition Plus • EasyPlanner Plus • Misconception Database • Content Review • Test Practice • Visualization • Simulation • Resource Centers • Internet Activity: Optics • Math Tutorial 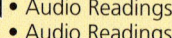 **SCILINKS.ORG** **CD-ROMS** • eEdition • EasyPlanner • Power Presentations • Content Review • Lab Generator • Test Generator **AUDIO CDS** • Audio Readings • Audio Readings in Spanish	**EXPLORE the Big Idea, p. 591** • How Does a Spoon Reflect Your Face? • Why Do Things Look Different Through Water? • Internet Activity: Optics **UNIT RESOURCE BOOK** Unit Projects, pp. 5–10 **Lab Generator CD-ROM** Generate customized labs.
SECTION 1 **Mirrors form images by reflecting light.** pp. 593–598 Time: 2 periods (1 block) Lesson Plan, pp. 214–215	• **VISUALIZATION,** Reflection • **MATH TUTORIAL** **UNIT TRANSPARENCY BOOK** • Big Idea Flow Chart, p. T25 • Daily Vocabulary Scaffolding, p. T26 • Note-Taking Model, p. T27 • 3-Minute Warm-Up, p. T28	• EXPLORE Reflection, p. 593 • INVESTIGATE The Law of Reflection, p. 595 • Math in Science, p. 598 **UNIT RESOURCE BOOK** • Datasheet, The Law of Reflection, p. 223 • Math Support & Practice, pp. 262–263
SECTION 2 **Lenses form images by refracting light.** pp. 599–605 Time: 3 periods (1.5 block) Lesson Plan, pp. 225–226	**SIMULATION,** Using Lenses to Form Images **UNIT TRANSPARENCY BOOK** • Daily Vocabulary Scaffolding, p. T26 • 3-Minute Warm-Up, p. T28 • "How a Convex Lens Forms an Image" Visual, p. T30	• EXPLORE Refraction, p. 599 • CHAPTER INVESTIGATION, Looking at Lenses, pp. 604–605 **UNIT RESOURCE BOOK** • CHAPTER INVESTIGATION, Looking at Lenses, Levels A, B, & C, pp. 264–272 • Additional INVESTIGATION, Bending Light, A, B, & C, pp. 273–281
SECTION 3 **The eye is a natural optical tool.** pp. 606–610 Time: 2 periods (1 block) Lesson Plan, pp. 235–236	**UNIT TRANSPARENCY BOOK** • Daily Vocabulary Scaffolding, p. T26 • 3-Minute Warm-Up, p. T29	• EXPLORE Focusing Vision, p. 606 • INVESTIGATE Vision, p. 608 **UNIT RESOURCE BOOK** Datasheet, Vision, p. 244
SECTION 4 **Optical technology makes use of light waves.** pp. 611–619 Time: 3 periods (1.5 block) Lesson Plan, pp. 246–247	**RESOURCE CENTERS,** Microscopes and Telescopes, Lasers **UNIT TRANSPARENCY BOOK** • Big Idea Flow Chart, p. T25 • Daily Vocabulary Scaffolding, p. T26 • 3-Minute Warm-Up, p. T29 • Chapter Outline, pp. T31–T32	• EXPLORE Combining Lenses, p. 611 • INVESTIGATE Optical Tools, p. 614 • Science on the Job, p. 619 **UNIT RESOURCE BOOK** Datasheet, Optical Tools, p. 255

KEY TO ICONS			
 INTERNET	CD/CD-ROM  Pupil Edition	Teacher Edition UNIT RESOURCE BOOK	UNIT TRANSPARENCY BOOK UNIT ASSESSMENT BOOK	SPANISH ASSESSMENT BOOK SCIENCE TOOLKIT

READING AND REINFORCEMENT

- Choose Your Own Strategy, B20–27
- Combination Notes, C36
- Daily Vocabulary Scaffolding, H1–8

 UNIT RESOURCE BOOK
- Vocabulary Practice, pp. 259–260
- Decoding Support, p. 261
- Summarizing the Chapter, pp. 282–283

Audio Readings CD
Listen to Pupil Edition

Audio Readings in Spanish CD
Listen to Pupil Edition in Spanish

 UNIT RESOURCE BOOK
- Reading Study Guide, A & B, pp. 216–219
- Spanish Reading Study Guide, pp. 220–221
- Challenge and Extension, p. 222
- Reinforcing Key Concepts, p. 224

 UNIT RESOURCE BOOK
- Reading Study Guide, A & B, pp. 227–230
- Spanish Reading Study Guide, pp. 231–232
- Challenge and Extension, p. 233
- Reinforcing Key Concepts, p. 234

 UNIT RESOURCE BOOK
- Reading Study Guide, A & B, pp. 237–240
- Spanish Reading Study Guide, pp. 241–242
- Challenge and Extension, p. 243
- Reinforcing Key Concepts, p. 245
- Challenge Reading, pp. 257–258

 UNIT RESOURCE BOOK
- Reading Study Guide, A & B, pp. 248–251
- Spanish Reading Study Guide, pp. 252–253
- Challenge and Extension, p. 254
- Reinforcing Key Concepts, p. 256

ASSESSMENT

- Chapter Review, pp. 621–622
- Standardized Test Practice, p. 623

 UNIT ASSESSMENT BOOK
- Diagnostic Test, pp. 60–61
- Chapter Test, Levels A, B, & C, pp. 66–77
- Alternative Assessment, pp. 78–79
- Unit Test, A, B, & C, pp. 80–91
- Spanish Chapter Test, pp. 241–244
- Spanish Unit Test, pp. 297–300

Test Generator CD-ROM
Generate customized tests.

Lab Generator CD-ROM
Rubrics for Labs

 Ongoing Assessment, pp. 593–597

 Section 18.1 Review, p. 597

 UNIT ASSESSMENT BOOK
Section 18.1 Quiz, p. 62

 Ongoing Assessment, pp. 600, 602–603

 Section 18.2 Review, p. 603

 UNIT ASSESSMENT BOOK
Section 18.2 Quiz, p. 63

 Ongoing Assessment, pp. 607–610

Section 18.3 Review, p. 610

 UNIT ASSESSMENT BOOK
Section 18.3 Quiz, p. 64

 Ongoing Assessment, pp. 612–617

 Section 18.4 Review, p. 618

UNIT ASSESSMENT BOOK
Section 18.4 Quiz, p. 65

STANDARDS

National Standards
A.2–8, A.9.a–f, B.3.c, E.2–5, E.6.a–f, F.5.a–c

See p. 590 for the standards.

National Standards
A.2–8, A.9.a–c, A.9.e–f, B.3.c

National Standards
A.2–7, A.9.a–b, A.9.e–f, B.3.c

National Standards
A.2–7, A.9.a–b, A.9.d–f, B.3.c

National Standards
A.2–7, A.9.a–b, A.9.d–f, B.3.c, E.2–5, E.6.a–f, F.5.a–c

Chapter 18: **Light and Optics**

Previewing Resources for Differentiated Instruction

CHAPTER INVESTIGATION

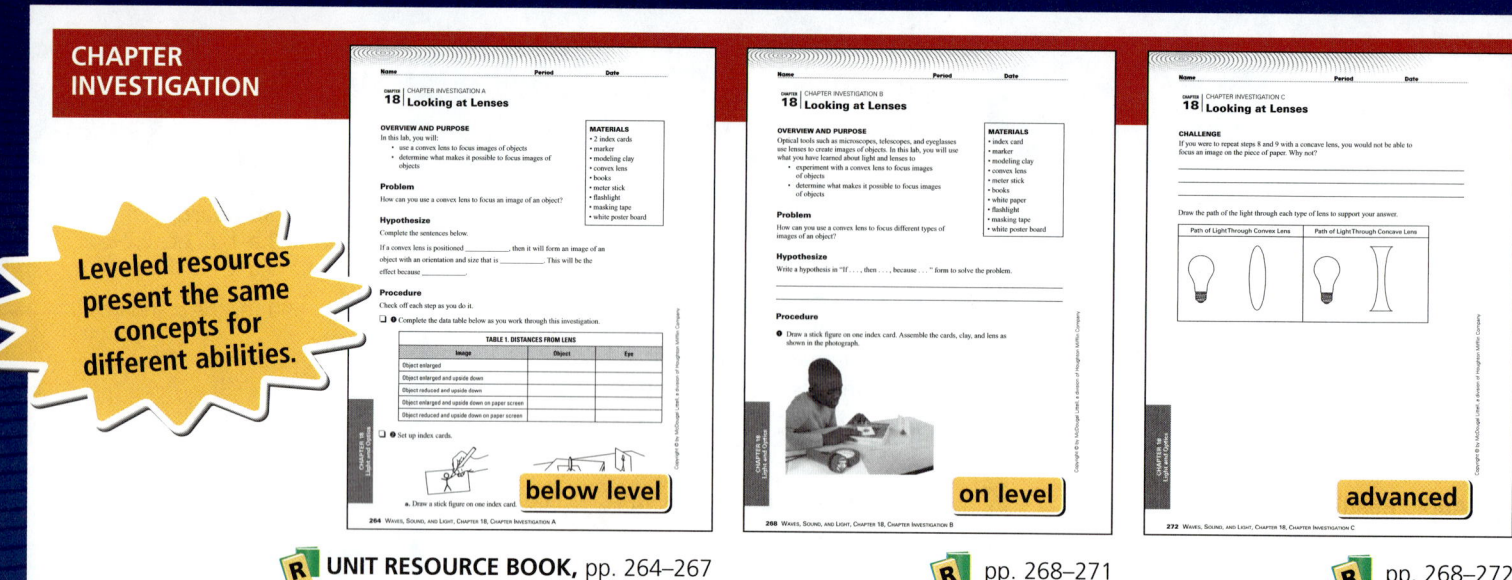

Leveled resources present the same concepts for different abilities.

UNIT RESOURCE BOOK, pp. 264–267 | pp. 268–271 | pp. 268–272

READING STUDY GUIDE

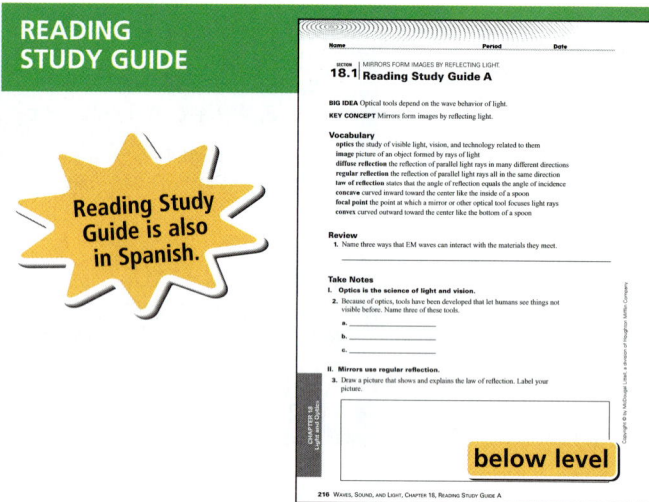
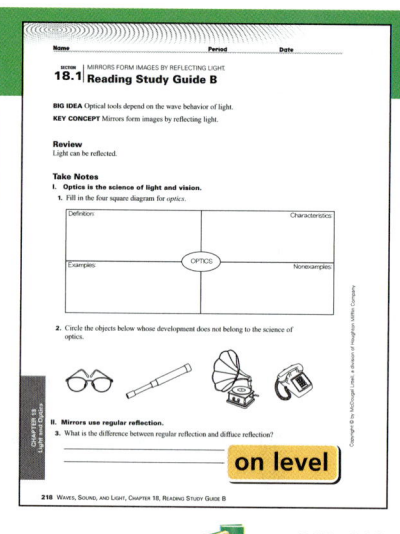
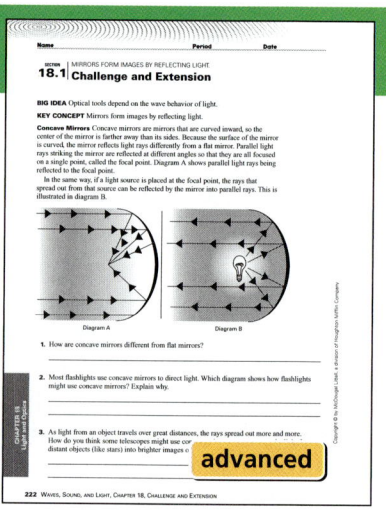

Reading Study Guide is also in Spanish.

UNIT RESOURCE BOOK, pp. 216–217 | pp. 218–219 | p. 222

CHAPTER TEST

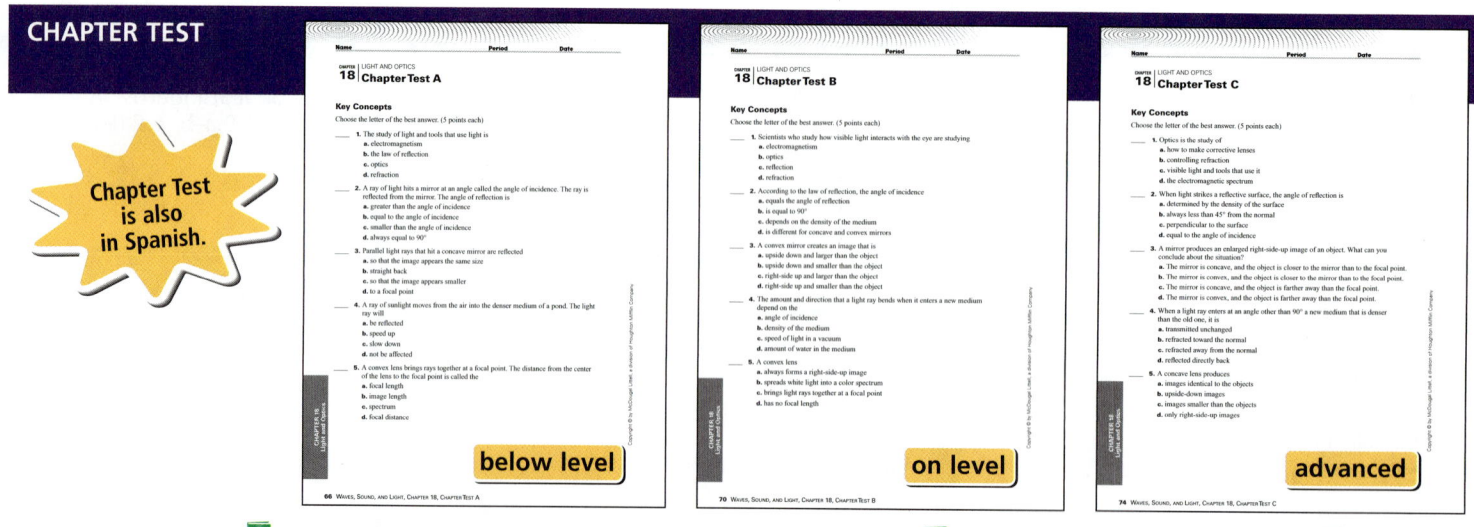

Chapter Test is also in Spanish.

UNIT ASSESSMENT BOOK, pp. 66–69 | pp. 70–73 | pp. 74–77

TECHNOLOGY

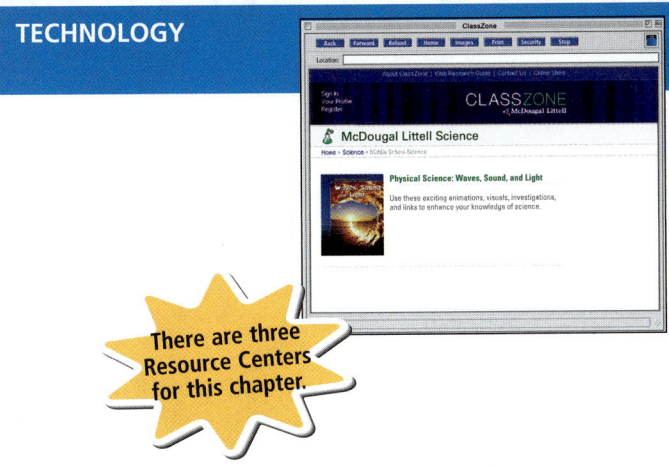
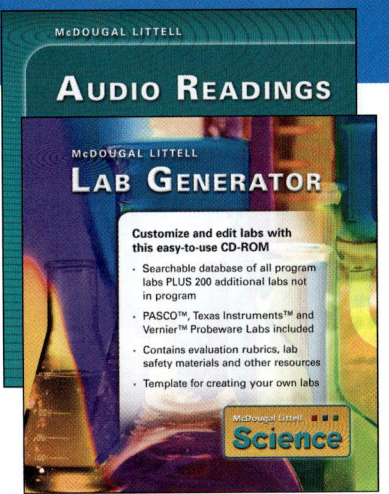
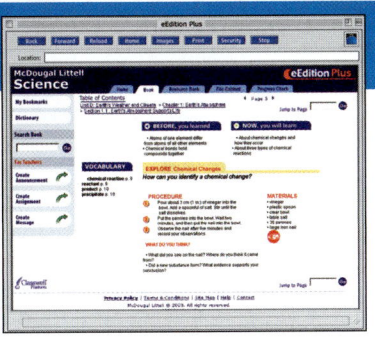

There are three Resource Centers for this chapter.

 CLASSZONE.COM
 CD/CD-Roms
 CLASSZONE.COM

VISUAL CONTENT

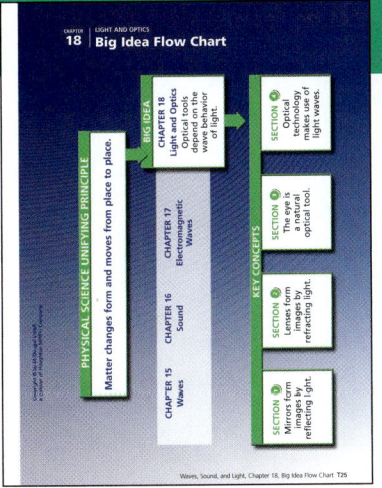
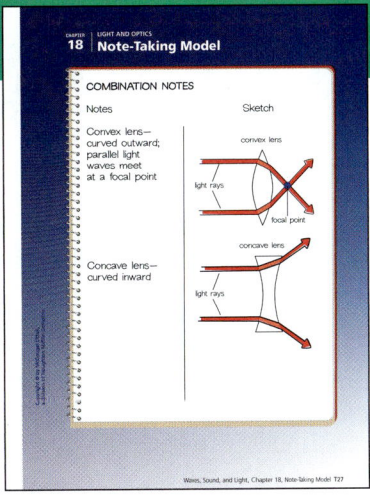
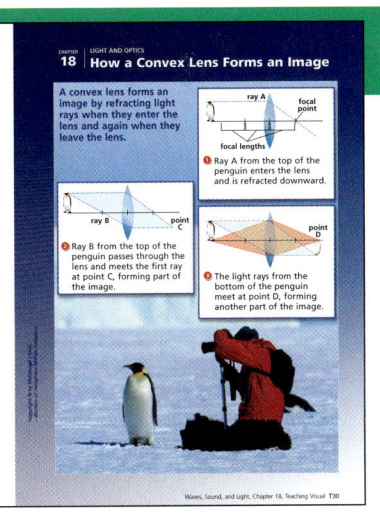

UNIT TRANSPARENCY BOOK, p. T25   p. T27   p. T30

MORE SUPPORT

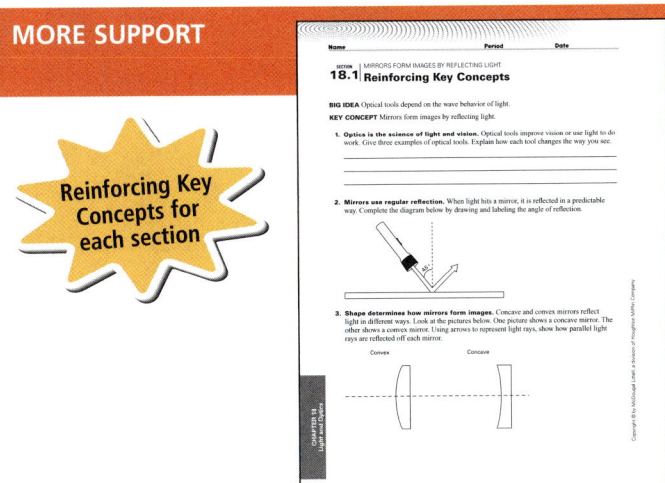
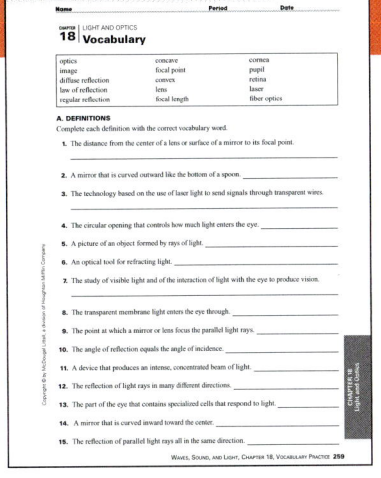
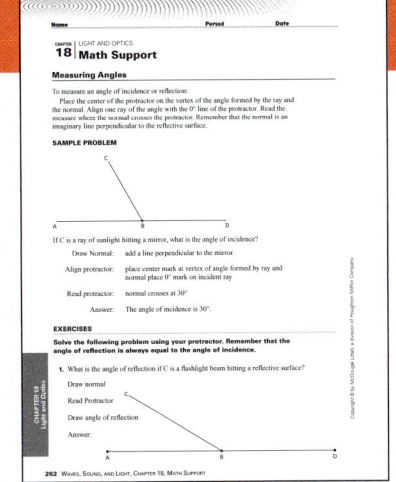

Reinforcing Key Concepts for each section

UNIT RESOURCE BOOK, p. 224   pp. 259–260   p. 262

Chapter 18: **Light and Optics** 589H

CHAPTER 18 Light and Optics

INTRODUCE

Have students look at the photograph of the optical refractor and discuss how the question in the box links to the Big Idea:

- How is the device in the photograph used?
- Why is the device called a refractor?

National Science Education Standards

Content

B.3.c Light interacts with matter by transmission (including refraction), absorption, or scattering (including reflection). To see an object, light from that object—emitted or scattered from it—must enter the eye.

Process

A.2–8 Design and conduct an investigation; use tools to gather and interpret data; use evidence to describe, predict, explain, model; think critically to make relationships between evidence and explanation; recognize different explanations and predictions; communicate scientific procedures and explanations; use mathematics.

A.9.a–f Understand scientific inquiry by using different investigations, methods, mathematics, technology, and explanations based on logic, evidence, and skepticism.

E.2–5 Design, implement, and evaluate a solution or product; communicate technological design.

E.6.a–f Understandings about science and technology

F.5.a–c Science influences society; societal challenges inspire scientific research; technology influences society through its products and processes.

590 Unit 4: **Waves, Sound, and Light**

CHAPTER 18 Light and Optics

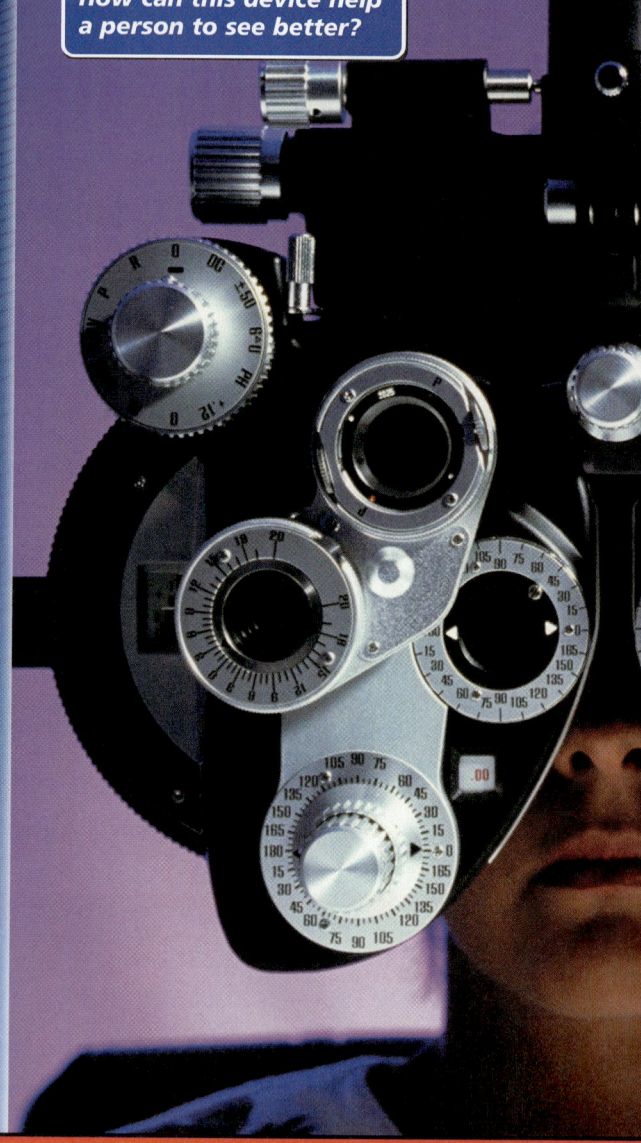

How can this device help a person to see better?

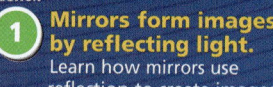

Optical tools depend on the wave behavior of light.

Key Concepts

SECTION 1 Mirrors form images by reflecting light.
Learn how mirrors use reflection to create images.

SECTION 2 Lenses form images by refracting light.
Learn how lenses use refraction to create images.

SECTION 3 The eye is a natural optical tool.
Learn about how eyes work as optical tools.

SECTION 4 Optical technology makes use of light waves.
Learn about complex optical tools.

Internet Preview

CLASSZONE.COM
Chapter 18 online resources: Content Review, Simulation, Visualization, three Resource Centers, Math Tutorial, Test Practice.

590 Unit 4: Waves, Sound, and Light

INTERNET PREVIEW

CLASSZONE.COM For student use with the following pages:

Review and Practice
- Content Review, pp. 592, 620
- Math Tutorial: Measuring Angles, p. 598
- Test Practice, p. 623

Activities and Resources
- Internet Activity: Optics, p. 591
- Visualization: Reflection, p. 595; Simulation, p. 603
- Resource Centers: Microscopes and Telescopes, p. 612; Lasers, p. 616

Lenses **Code: MDL030**

EXPLORE the BIG idea

How Does a Spoon Reflect Your Face?

Look at the reflection of your face in the bowl of a shiny metal spoon. How does your face look? Is it different from what you would expect? Now turn the spoon over and look at your face in the round side. How does your face look this time?

Observe and Think Why do the two sides of the spoon affect the appearance of your face in these ways?

Why Do Things Look Different Through Water?

Fill a clear, round jar with straight, smooth sides with water. Look through the jar at different objects in the room. Experiment with different distances between the objects and the jar and between yourself and the jar.

Observe and Think How does the jar change the way things look? What do you think causes these changes?

Internet Activity: Optics

Go to **ClassZone.com** to learn more about optics.

Observe and Think How does research in optics benefit other areas of scientific investigation?

NSTA scilinks.org SCLINKS
Lenses Code: MDL030

Chapter 18: **Light and Optics** 591

EXPLORE the BIG idea

These inquiry-based activities are appropriate for use at home or as a supplement to classroom instruction.

How Does a Spoon Reflect Your Face?

PURPOSE To demonstrate that a mirror's shape affects the image it produces. Students observe the images that concave and convex mirrors produce.

TIP *10 min.* Students should think about why the image is inverted inside the spoon but not on the back.

Answer: The inside reflects an inverted image of a face because the reflected light rays cross each other. The back of the spoon reflects a right-side-up image because the reflected rays do not meet.

REVISIT after p. 597.

Why Do Things Look Different Through Water?

PURPOSE To see how refraction of light affects images. Students look at objects through a jar of water.

TIP *10 min.* Students can also try moving the jar as they look at an object to observe how the image of the object moves in relation to the object.

Answer: The jar appears to change the position and shape of objects. The water in the jar bends the light rays that make up images of objects.

REVISIT after p. 603.

Internet Activity: Optics

PURPOSE To examine how advances in optics affect other sciences.

TIP *20 min.* Ask students how research in optics can benefit other areas of scientific research.

Answer: Better microscopes or telescopes allow microbiology or astronomy researchers to see small or faraway objects more clearly. The invention of the laser benefits many areas of science.

REVISIT after p. 618.

Chapter 18 **591**

TEACHING WITH TECHNOLOGY

CBL and Probeware If students have probeware, encourage them to use a light sensor with some of the activities in this chapter.

Telescope If you have access to a telescope, you may want to let students compare the images it shows to the images their telescope model from "Investigate Optical Tools" on p. 614 shows.

PREPARE

CONCEPT REVIEW

Activate Prior Knowledge

- Cut three equal circles out of cardboard and punch a pinhole in each.
- Cover a flashlight with one disk.
- Align the holes in the other two disks.
- Ask students why you can see the light only if the three pinholes and your eye are aligned.

TAKING NOTES

Combination Notes

Making an outline of the main ideas of a concept will help students organize new material. Students who are visual learners will benefit by making a labeled sketch of a new concept.

Choose Your Own Strategy

Students can choose the strategies that best fit their individual learning styles. By surrounding a vocabulary term with information in a four square, description wheel, or frame game, students will develop a thorough understanding of the meaning of the term. Respellings should be included if appropriate.

Vocabulary and Note-Taking Resources

- Vocabulary Practice, p. 259–260
- Decoding Support, p. 261

- Daily Vocabulary Scaffolding, p. T26
- Note-Taking Model, p. T27

- Choose Your Own Strategy, B20–27
- Combination Notes, C36
- Daily Vocabulary Scaffolding, H1–8

592 Unit 4: Waves, Sound, and Light

CHAPTER 18
Getting Ready to Learn

CONCEPT REVIEW

- Light tends to travel in a straight line.
- The speed of light is affected by a material medium.
- Reflection and refraction are two ways light interacts with materials.

VOCABULARY REVIEW

reflection p. 505
refraction p. 505
visible light p. 564

CONTENT REVIEW
CLASSZONE.COM
Review concepts and vocabulary.

TAKING NOTES

COMBINATION NOTES

To take notes about a new concept, first make an informal outline of the information. Then make a sketch of the concept and label it so you can study it later.

SCIENCE NOTEBOOK

NOTES
The angle of incidence (x) equals the angle of reflection (y).

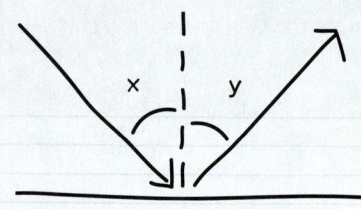

CHOOSE YOUR OWN STRATEGY

Take notes about new vocabulary terms, using one or more of the strategies from earlier chapters—**four square, description wheel,** or **frame game.** Feel free to mix and match the strategies, or to use an entirely different vocabulary strategy.

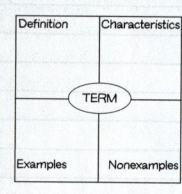
FOUR SQUARE

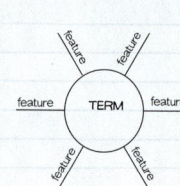
DESCRIPTION WHEEL

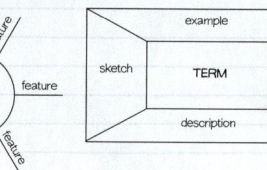
FRAME GAME

See the Note-Taking Handbook on pages R45–R51.

592 Unit 4: Waves, Sound, and Light

CHECK READINESS

Administer the Diagnostic Test to determine students' readiness for new science content and their mastery of requisite math skills.

 Diagnostic Test, pp. 60–61

Technology Resources

Students needing content and math skills should visit ClassZone.com.

- **CONTENT REVIEW**
- **MATH TUTORIAL**

 CONTENT REVIEW CD-ROM

KEY CONCEPT

Mirrors form images by reflecting light.

◀ **BEFORE,** you learned
- EM waves interact with materials
- Light can be reflected

▶ **NOW, you will learn**
- About the science of optics
- How light is reflected
- How mirrors form images

VOCABULARY

optics p. 593
law of reflection p. 594
regular reflection p. 594
diffuse reflection p. 594
image p. 595
convex p. 596
concave p. 596
focal point p. 597

EXPLORE Reflection

How does surface affect reflection?

PROCEDURE

1. Tear off a square sheet of aluminum foil. Look at your reflection in the shiny side of the foil.
2. Turn the foil over and look at your reflection in the dull side.
3. Crumple up the piece of foil, then smooth it out again, shiny side up. Again, look at your reflection in the foil.

MATERIALS
aluminum foil

WHAT DO YOU THINK?
- How did the three reflections differ from one another?
- What might explain these differences?

Optics is the science of light and vision.

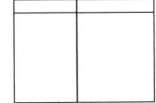

COMBINATION NOTES
Don't forget to include sketches of important concepts in your notebook.

Optics (AHP-tihks) is the study of visible light and the ways in which visible light interacts with the eye to produce vision. Optics is also the application of knowledge about visible light to develop tools—such as eyeglasses, mirrors, magnifying lenses, cameras, and lasers—that extend vision or that use light in other ways.

Mirrors, lenses, and other optical inventions are called optical tools. By combining optical tools, inventors have developed powerful instruments to extend human vision. For example, the microscope uses a combination of mirrors and lenses to make very small structures visible. Telescopes combine optical tools to extend vision far into space. As you will see, some of the latest optical technology—lasers—use visible light in ways that do not involve human vision at all.

Chapter 18: **Light and Optics** 593

18.1 FOCUS

▶ Set Learning Goals

Students will
- Summarize the science of optics.
- Describe how mirrors control reflection.
- Describe how mirrors produce images.
- Analyze through experimentation how mirrors direct the path of light through a periscope.

◯ 3-Minute Warm-Up

Display Transparency 28 or copy this exercise on the board:

Name the term described by each of the following:

1. How a light wave bends when it enters a new medium at an angle *refraction*
2. How a light wave bounces back when it hits a barrier *reflection*
3. The type of wave visible light is *electromagnetic wave*

 3-Minute Warm-Up, p. T28

18.1 MOTIVATE

EXPLORE Reflection

PURPOSE To show that surface texture affects reflection

TIP *10 min.* Use a fresh piece of foil with no wrinkles. Remind students to smooth out the foil carefully to avoid tearing.

WHAT DO YOU THINK? *Students should see a recognizable image in the shiny side, but not in the dull side. The image in the crumpled foil should be less clear than before. Differences can be explained by the surface of the foil.*

Ongoing Assessment

Summarize the science of optics.

Ask: What are two parts of the definition of optics? *Sample answer: the study of light and how it interacts with the eye, and the application of that knowledge to develop tools that use light*

Chapter 18 **593**

RESOURCES FOR DIFFERENTIATED INSTRUCTION

Below Level
UNIT RESOURCE BOOK
- Reading Study Guide, A, pp. 216–217
- Decoding Support, p. 261

 **AUDIO CDS**

Advanced
UNIT RESOURCE BOOK
Challenge and Extension, p. 222

English Learners
UNIT RESOURCE BOOK
Spanish Reading Study Guide, pp. 220–221

AUDIO CDS
- Audio Readings in Spanish
- Audio Readings (English)

18.1 INSTRUCT

Teach from Visuals

To help students interpret the mirror visual, ask:

- If the angle of incidence is 1 degree, what is the angle of reflection? *1 degree*
- How would a diagram of diffuse reflection look different from the diagram of regular reflection? *The angle of reflection of the light rays would not equal the angle of incidence. The reflected rays would go in different directions.*

Teacher Demo

To illustrate the law of reflection, set a protractor at right angles to the tabletop in a blob of clay. Place a mirror on the table in front of the protractor. Use a flashlight to make a beam of light visible to the class. Shine the flashlight at an angle to the surface of the mirror so that it strikes the mirror and is reflected onto a piece of paper or a wall. Point out the normal. Show that the angle of incidence equals the angle of reflection.

Ongoing Assessment

Describe how mirrors control reflection.

Ask: How do mirrors reflect light? *Parallel light rays reflected off the surface of mirrors remain parallel to each other.*

Mirrors use regular reflection.

You have read that when light waves strike an object, they either pass through it or they bounce off its surface. Objects are made visible by light waves, or rays, bouncing off their surfaces. In section 3 you will see how the light waves create images inside the human eye.

Light rays bounce off objects in a very predictable way. For example, look at the diagram on the left below. Light rays from a flashlight strike a mirror at an angle of 60° as measured from the normal, an imaginary line perpendicular to the surface of the mirror. This angle is called the angle of incidence. The angle at which the rays reflect off the mirror, called the angle of reflection, is also 60° as measured from the normal. The example illustrates the **law of reflection,** which states that the angle of reflection equals the angle of incidence. As you can see in the second diagram, holding the flashlight at a different angle changes both the angle of incidence and the angle of reflection. However, the two angles remain equal.

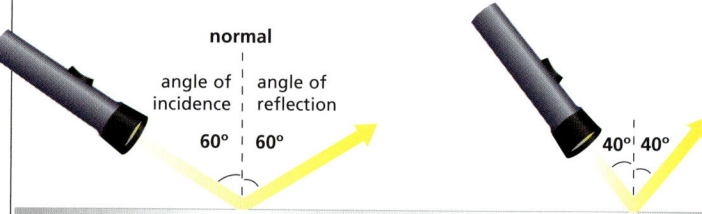

The angle of reflection equals the angle of incidence.

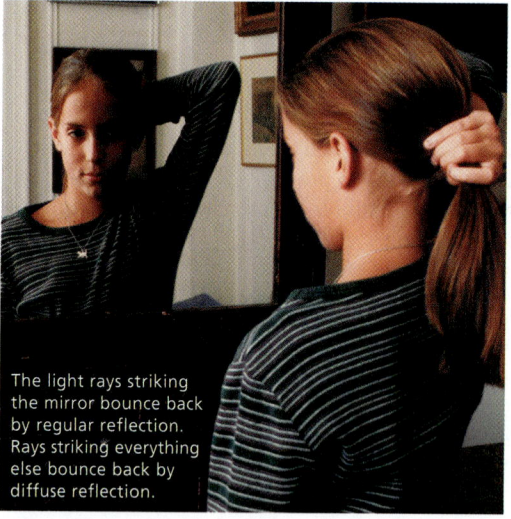

The light rays striking the mirror bounce back by regular reflection. Rays striking everything else bounce back by diffuse reflection.

If the surface of an object is very smooth, like a mirror, light rays that come from the same direction will bounce off in the same new direction. The reflection of parallel light rays all in the same direction is called **regular reflection.**

If the surface is not very smooth—even if it feels smooth to the touch, like a piece of paper—light rays striking it from the same direction bounce off in many new directions. Each light ray follows the law of reflection, but rays coming from the same direction bounce off different bumps and hollows of the irregular surface. The reflection of parallel light rays in many different directions is called **diffuse reflection.**

DIFFERENTIATE INSTRUCTION

? More Reading Support

A What is regular reflection? *the reflection of parallel light rays all in the same direction*

English Learners Help students with the two "if-then" situations on this page by setting them up as cause and effect. (Smooth surfaces cause regular reflection. Unsmooth surfaces cause diffuse reflection.) Help them use the same type of reasoning for the different shaped mirrors on pp. 595–597.

INVESTIGATE The Law of Reflection

How can you use mirrors to see around a corner?

PROCEDURE

1. To make a periscope, cut two flaps on opposite sides of the carton, one from the top and one from the bottom, as shown in the illustration.
2. Fold each flap inward until it is at a 45-degree angle to the side cuts and tape it into place.
3. Attach a mirror to the outside surface of each of the flaps.
4. Holding the periscope straight up, look through one of the openings. Observe what you can see through the other opening.

WHAT DO YOU THINK?

- Where are the objects you see when you look through the periscope?
- How does the angle of the mirrors affect the path of light through the periscope?

CHALLENGE How would it affect what you see through the periscope if you changed the angle of the mirrors from 45 degrees to 30 degrees? Try it.

SKILL FOCUS Analyzing

MATERIALS
- paper milk or juice carton
- scissors
- tape
- 2 mirrors slightly smaller than the bottom of the carton
- protractor

TIME 30 minutes

Shape determines how mirrors form images.

When you look in a mirror, you see an image of yourself. An **image** is a picture of an object formed by waves of light. The image of yourself is formed by light waves reflecting off you, onto the mirror, and back toward your eyes. Mirrors of different shapes can produce images that are distorted in certain ways.

VISUALIZATION CLASSZONE.COM
See reflection in action.

Flat Mirrors

Your image in a flat mirror looks exactly like you. It appears to be the same size as you, and it's wearing the same clothes. However, if you raise your right hand, the image of yourself in the mirror will appear to raise its left hand. That is because you see the image as a person standing facing you. In fact, your right hand is reflected on the right side of the image, and your left on the left side.

 **CHECK YOUR READING** If you wink your left eye while looking in the mirror, which eye in the image of you will wink?

DIFFERENTIATE INSTRUCTION

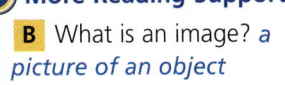 **More Reading Support**

B What is an image? *a picture of an object formed by waves of light*

C How does your reflection look in a flat mirror? *The image looks backward.*

Alternative Assessment Have students make diagrams to answer the questions in "Investigate The Law of Reflection." Diagrams should show the shifted position of the object and the path of light through the periscope.

Advanced

 Challenge and Extension, p. 222

INVESTIGATE The Law of Reflection

PURPOSE To analyze the path of light through a periscope in order to learn about reflection

TIPS 30 min. Suggest the following to students:
- Aluminum foil or squares of foil duct tape can be used in place of mirrors.
- Do not use the periscope to look at very bright light, including the Sun.

WHAT DO YOU THINK? The objects are actually in front of and somewhat above the periscope. Having the mirrors aligned at 45 degrees means that the line of sight out of the periscope is parallel to the line of sight into the periscope.

CHALLENGE If the mirrors were positioned at an angle of 30 degrees, the line of sight out of the periscope would still be parallel to the line of sight into the periscope.

 Datasheet, The Law of Reflection, p. 223

Technology Resources

Customize this student lab as needed or look for an alternative. Print rubrics to assess student lab reports.

Lab Generator CD-ROM

Metacognitive Strategy

Ask students to write a paragraph describing a scenario in which a periscope would be useful.

Ongoing Assessment

 CHECK YOUR READING Answer: The eye to the left in the mirror will blink; if you think of the image as a person facing you, it would appear that the image's right eye was blinking.

Address Misconceptions

IDENTIFY Ask: Is a person's body turned around in a mirror image? If students answer yes, they may hold the misconception that what you see when you look at yourself in a mirror is the same as what you would see if your body were turned around to face you.

CORRECT Have students experiment by standing in front of a mirror, raising a hand on one side, and observing on which side the movement is reflected. The movement will be reflected on the same side as the hand that moves. Point out that if the mirror image were the same as one's body turned around, the movement would be reflected on the opposite side.

REASSESS Students should understand that the appearance that one's body is turned around in a mirror image is an illusion. Ask: If you wear a watch on your right wrist, which side of a mirror image will the watch appear on? *the right*

Technology Resources
Visit **ClassZone.com** for background on common student misconceptions.
MISCONCEPTION DATABASE

Teach from Visuals

To help students interpret the mirror visuals on pp. 596 and 597, ask:

- Where does the image appear to be in the flat mirror? *behind the mirror*
- How do images appear in a convex mirror? *always right-side up and smaller*
- Does the image in a concave mirror always appear the same? *No, the image may be inverted, smaller, right-side up, or larger. This depends on the position of the object relative to the focal point and the mirror.*

Ongoing Assessment

Describe how mirrors produce images.
Ask: In a concave mirror, where do parallel light rays meet after reflecting off the mirror? *at the focal point*

The solid line shows the actual path of light. The broken line shows where the light appears to be coming from.

If you look closely at your image in a mirror, you will notice that it actually appears to be on the far side of the mirror, exactly as far from the mirror as you are. This is a trick of light. The solid yellow arrows in the photograph above show the path of the light rays from the boy's elbow to the mirror and back to his eyes. The light rays reflect off the mirror. The broken line shows the apparent path of the light rays. They appear to his eyes to be coming through the mirror from a spot behind it.

Concave and Convex Mirrors

VOCABULARY Try making sketches to help you remember the new terms on this page.

Unlike light rays hitting a flat mirror, parallel light rays reflecting off a curved mirror do not move in the same direction. A **convex** mirror is curved outward, like the bottom of a spoon. In a convex mirror, parallel light rays move away from each other, as you can see in the diagram below on the left. A **concave** mirror is curved inward toward the center, like the inside of a spoon. Parallel light rays reflecting off a concave mirror move toward each other, as shown on the right.

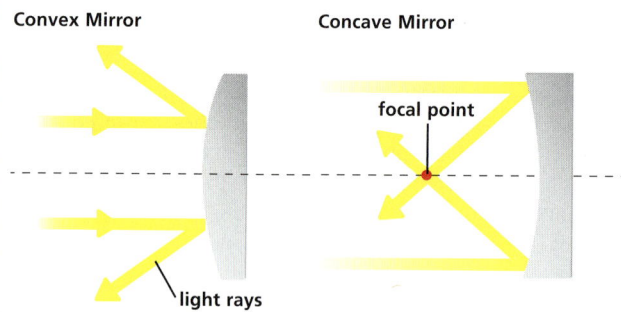

596 Unit 4: Waves, Sound, and Light

DIFFERENTIATE INSTRUCTION

More Reading Support
D How is a convex mirror curved? *A convex mirror is curved outward, like the underside of a spoon.*

Below Level If some students have trouble distinguishing concave and convex mirrors, tell them that a *concave* mirror is shaped like a *cave*.

The rays striking a concave mirror cross and then move apart again. The point at which the rays meet is called the **focal point** of the mirror. The distance between the mirror and its focal point depends on the shape of the curve.

The images formed in these mirrors depend on the curve of the mirror's surface and the distance of the object from the mirror. Your image in a curved mirror may appear larger or smaller than you are, and it may even be upside down.

Convex Mirror

Your image in a convex mirror appears smaller than you.

Concave Mirror, Far Away

If you are standing far away, your image in a concave mirror appears upside down and smaller than you.

Concave Mirror, Up Close

If you are standing inside the focal point, your image in a concave mirror appears right-side up and larger.

All rays parallel to a line through the center of the mirror are reflected off the mirror and pass through the mirror's focal point. Rays from the top of the object are reflected downward and those from the bottom are reflected upward.

 How does your distance from the mirror affect the way your image appears in a concave mirror?

18.1 Review

KEY CONCEPTS
1. Explain the term *optics* in your own words.
2. How is diffuse reflection similar to regular reflection? How is it different?
3. Describe the path that light rays take when they form an image of your smile when you look into a flat mirror.

CRITICAL THINKING
4. **Infer** Imagine seeing your reflection in a polished table top. The image is blurry and hard to recognize. What can you tell about the surface of the table from your observations?
5. **Analyze** Why do images formed by concave mirrors sometimes appear upside down?

CHALLENGE
6. **Synthesize** Draw the letter *R* below as it would appear if you held the book up to (a) a flat mirror and (b) a convex mirror.

R

Chapter 18: **Light and Optics** 597

Ongoing Assessment

 CHECK YOUR READING Answer: Distance determines whether your image is enlarged and right side up, or reduced and upside down.

Real World Example
Convex mirrors are useful to provide a wider field of vision. They collect rays from a wide area, but they produce a small image. They are used for mirrors on cars, and are sometimes mounted at difficult corners to allow drivers to see oncoming traffic. Because convex mirrors produce images that are smaller than the object, the objects appear to be farther away than they are.

EXPLORE the BIG idea
Revisit "How Does a Spoon Reflect Your Face?" on p. 591. Have students explain the reasons for their results.

Reinforce the BIG idea
Have students relate the section to the Big Idea.

 Reinforcing Key Concepts, p. 224

18.1 ASSESS & RETEACH

Assess
Section 18.1 Quiz, p. 62

Reteach
Have students review the concepts of mirrors and reflection by making ray diagrams. Ask students to write on one side of an index card a type of mirror (flat, convex, concave with object inside focal point, concave with object outside focal point). On the other side of the card, have them draw a ray diagram, illustrating how that mirror forms an image.

Technology Resources
Have students visit **ClassZone.com** for reteaching of Key Concepts.

 CONTENT REVIEW

 CONTENT REVIEW CD-ROM

Chapter 18 **597**

ANSWERS

1. Optics is the study of light and vision.
2. Diffuse reflection and regular reflection both obey the law of reflection. Diffuse reflection sends parallel light rays in many different directions; regular reflection sends parallel rays in the same direction.
3. Light rays reflected from your smile strike the mirror, bounce off, and enter your eye.
4. The surface is not perfectly smooth, and the reflection is not perfectly regular.
5. When light rays pass through a focal point, they cross to the side opposite the side from which they were reflected.
6. (a)   (b) Я

MATH IN SCIENCE
Math Skills Practice for Science

Set Learning Goal
To measure and calculate the angles of incidence and reflection in various situations

Present the Science
If you were trying to attract the attention of a search plane, you could use a mirror to reflect sunlight toward the plane and attract a pilot's attention.

Develop Measurement Skills
Students should measure the angles between the rays and the normal, not between the rays and the horizon.

Advise students to draw diagrams when answering the questions, especially the Challenge question.

DIFFERENTIATION TIP Below level: Review the definition of *normal* and the use of a protractor with students who need help.

Close
Ask: If you were lost in the desert but didn't have a mirror, what else could you use to signal a search plane? How could you tell if the object might work? *Anything shiny would reflect rays. If you can see your image in the object's surface, it might work as a mirror.*

- Math Support, p. 262
- Math Practice, p. 263

Technology Resources
Students can visit ClassZone.com for practice in measuring angles.

 MATH TUTORIAL

A mirror can be used to signal for help.

598 Unit 4: Waves, Sound, and Light

SKILL: MEASURING ANGLES

Send Help!

Survival kits often contain a small mirror that can be used to signal for help. If you were lost in the desert and saw a search plane overhead, you could use the mirror to reflect sunlight toward the plane and catch the pilot's attention. To aim your signal, you would use the law of reflection. The angle at which a ray of light bounces off a mirror—the angle of reflection—is always equal to the angle at which the ray strikes the mirror—the angle of incidence.

Example

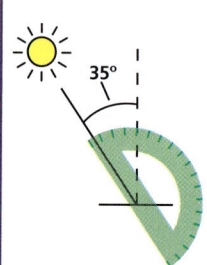

Measure the angle of incidence using a protractor as follows:

(1) Place the center mark of the protractor over the vertex of the angle formed by the incident ray and the normal.

(2) Place the left 0° mark of the protractor on the incident ray.

(3) Read the number where the normal crosses the scale (35°).

(4) The angle of incidence is 35°.

ANSWER Therefore, the angle of reflection will be 35°.

Copy each of the following angles of incidence, extend its sides, and use a protractor to measure it.

1. 2. 3. 4.

CHALLENGE Copy the drawing below. Use a protractor to find the angle of reflection necessary to signal the plane from point A.

· A

ANSWERS

1. 28°
2. 60°
3. 20°
4. 45°

CHALLENGE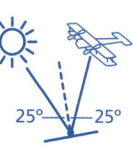

KEY CONCEPT

Lenses form images by refracting light.

BEFORE, you learned
- Waves can refract when they move from one medium to another
- Refraction changes the direction of a wave

NOW, you will learn
- How a material medium can refract light
- How lenses control refraction
- How lenses produce images

VOCABULARY
lens p. 601
focal length p. 603

EXPLORE Refraction

How does material bend light?

PROCEDURE

1. Place the pencil in the cup, as shown in the photograph. Look at the cup from the side so that you see part of the pencil through the cup.
2. Fill the cup one-third full with water and repeat your observations.
3. Gently add oil until the cup is two-thirds full. After the oil settles into a separate layer, observe.

WHAT DO YOU THINK?
- How did the appearance of the pencil change when you added the water? the oil?
- What might explain these changes?

MATERIALS
- clear plastic cup
- pencil
- water
- mineral oil

A medium can refract light.

When sunlight strikes a window, some of the light rays reflect off the surface of the glass. Other rays continue through the glass, but their direction is slightly changed. This slight change in direction is called refraction. Refraction occurs when a wave strikes a new medium—such as the window—at an angle other than 90° and keeps going forward in a slightly different direction.

Refraction occurs because one side of the wave reaches the new medium slightly before the other side does. That side changes speed, while the other continues at its previous speed, causing the wave to turn.

 How does the motion of a light wave change when it refracts?

Chapter 18: **Light and Optics** 599

RESOURCES FOR DIFFERENTIATED INSTRUCTION

Below Level
UNIT RESOURCE BOOK
- Reading Study Guide A, pp. 227–228
- Decoding Support, p. 261

 **AUDIO CDS**

R Additional INVESTIGATION, Bending Light, A, B, & C, pp. 273–281
Teacher Instructions, pp. 284–285

Advanced
UNIT RESOURCE BOOK
Challenge and Extension, p. 233

English Learners
UNIT RESOURCE BOOK
Spanish Reading Study Guide, pp. 231–232

 **AUDIO CDS**
- Audio Readings in Spanish
- Audio Readings (English)

18.2 FOCUS

▶ Set Learning Goals
Students will
- Identify how a material medium can refract light.
- Describe how lenses control refraction.
- Recognize how lenses produce images.
- Discover through experimentation how to use a convex lens to focus an image.

◯ 3-Minute Warm-Up

Display Transparency 28 or copy this exercise on the board:

Match each definition to the correct term.

Definitions
1. a picture of an object formed by light rays **e**
2. the point where parallel light rays striking a concave mirror meet **c**
3. a surface that curves out like the back of a spoon **b**

Terms
a. concave
b. convex
c. focal point
d. optics
e. image

T *3-Minute Warm-Up, p. T28*

18.2 MOTIVATE

EXPLORE Refraction

PURPOSE To show how different materials bend light rays

TIP *10 min.* Have students think about their observations in terms of the direction of light waves.

WHAT DO YOU THINK? *The pencil appears to break where the water and air meet and where the water and the oil meet. The oil bends light more than the water does.*

 Answer: Light waves change direction slightly when they refract.

Chapter 18 **599**

18.2 INSTRUCT

Teach from Visuals

To help students interpret the diagram of a light wave passing through air and glass, ask:

- Does light move faster through air or through glass? *through air*
- Is glass a thin or a dense medium? *dense*

Develop Critical Thinking

APPLY Have students do the following experiment and apply their knowledge of refraction to explain the results. Put a penny in the bottom of a teacup. Lower your head until the penny just disappears from view behind the rim of the cup. Without moving your head or the cup, have a partner fill the cup with water. The penny will appear to float into view. *When you add water, rays of light reflected from the penny refract enough to reach your eye as they pass into the air from the water.*

Ongoing Assessment

Identify how a material medium can refract light.

Ask: In what direction does light turn when it refracts? *If the new medium slows the wave, the wave will turn toward the normal. If the new medium speeds the wave up, the wave will turn away from the normal.*

COMBINATION NOTES Sketch the ways light is refracted when it moves into a denser medium and into a thinner medium.

Refraction of Light

Recall that waves travel at different speeds in different mediums. The direction in which a light wave turns depends on whether the new medium slows the wave down or allows it to travel faster. Like reflection, refraction is described in terms of an imaginary line—called the normal—that is perpendicular to the new surface. If the medium slows the wave, the wave will turn toward the normal. If the new medium lets the wave speed up, the wave will turn away from the normal. The wave in the diagram below turns toward the normal as it slows down in the new medium.

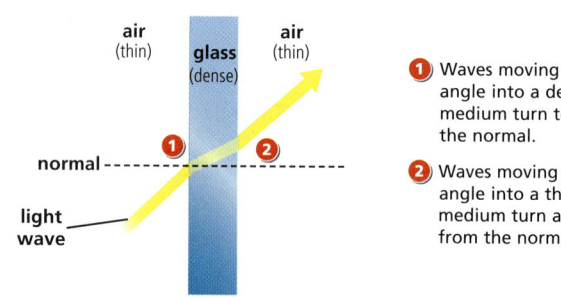

① Waves moving at an angle into a denser medium turn toward the normal.

② Waves moving at an angle into a thinner medium turn away from the normal.

READING TIP A dense medium has more mass in a given volume than a thin medium.

Light from the Sun travels toward Earth through the near vacuum of outer space. Sunlight refracts when it reaches the new medium of Earth's upper atmosphere. Earth's upper atmosphere is relatively thin and refracts light only slightly. Denser materials, such as water and glass, refract light more.

By measuring the speed of light in different materials and comparing this speed to the speed of light in a vacuum, scientists have been able to determine exactly how different materials refract light. This knowledge has led to the ability to predict and control refraction, which is the basis of much optical technology.

Light passing through a droplet of water is refracted twice, forming a color spectrum.

Refraction and Rainbows

You've seen rainbows in the sky after a rainstorm or hovering in the spray of a sprinkler. Rainbows are caused by refraction and reflection of light through spherical water drops, which act as prisms. Just as a prism separates the colors of white light, producing the color spectrum, each water drop separates the wavelengths of sunlight to produce a spectrum. Only one color reaches your eye from each drop. Red appears at the top of a rainbow because it is coming from higher drops, while violet comes from lower drops.

DIFFERENTIATE INSTRUCTION

More Reading Support

A Can Earth's atmosphere refract light? *yes*

B How do spherical water drops cause rainbows? *act as prisms to separate wavelengths of white light*

Additional Investigation To reinforce Section 18.2 learning goals, use the following full-period investigation:

R **Additional INVESTIGATION,** Bending Light, A, B, & C, pp. 273–281, 284–285 (Advanced students should complete Levels B & C.)

Shape determines how lenses form images.

When you look at yourself in a flat mirror, you see your image clearly, without distortions. Similarly, when you look through a plain glass window, you can see what is on the other side clearly. Just as curved mirrors distort images, certain transparent mediums called lenses alter what you see through them. A **lens** is a clear optical tool that refracts light. Different lenses refract light in different ways and form images useful for a variety of purposes.

READING TIP
Distort means to change the shape of something by twisting or moving the parts around.

Convex and Concave Lenses

Like mirrors, lenses can be convex or concave. A convex lens is curved outward; a concave lens is curved inward. A lens typically has two sides that are curved, as shown in the illustration below.

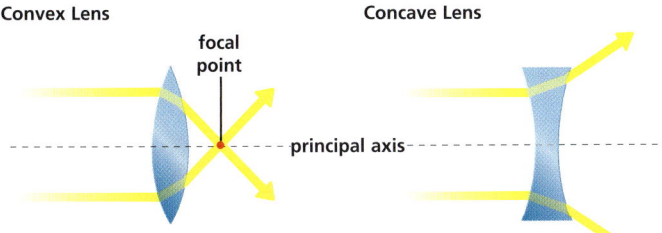

A convex lens causes parallel light rays to meet at a focal point.

A concave lens causes parallel light rays to spread out.

Convex Parallel light rays passing through a convex lens are refracted inward. They meet at a focal point on the other side of the lens. The rays are actually refracted twice—once upon entering the lens and once upon leaving it. This is because both times they are entering a new medium at an angle other than 90 degrees. Rays closest to the edges of the lens are refracted most. Rays passing through the center of the lens—along the principal axis, which connects the centers of the two curved surfaces—are not refracted at all. They pass through to the same focal point as all rays parallel to them.

REMINDER
The focal point is the point at which parallel light rays meet after being reflected or refracted.

Concave Parallel light rays that pass through a concave lens are refracted outward. As with a convex lens, the rays are refracted twice. Rays closest to the edges of the lens are refracted most; rays at the very center of the lens pass straight through without being deflected. Because they are refracted away from each other, parallel light rays passing through a concave lens do not meet.

 Compare what happens to parallel light rays striking a concave mirror with those striking a concave lens.

Chapter 18: **Light and Optics** 601

DIFFERENTIATE INSTRUCTION

More Reading Support

 How does a convex lens refract light? *It bends parallel light rays so that they meet at a focal point on the other side of the lens.*

English Learners Words that have multiple meanings may be confusing for English learners. For example, words like *vacuum* and *medium* are presented in a new context in this chapter. Have students write down each of these words and all their possible meanings. Then have them decide which meaning makes the most sense in the context of the sentence where it is found. To illustrate the concept of concave and convex lenses, put these terms on the Science Word Wall with visual reminders of how each lens refracts light.

Teach from Visuals

To help students interpret the lens diagrams, ask:

- Do the light waves passing through a convex lens move toward or away from each other? *toward each other*
- What is a focal length? *the distance from the center of a lens to its focal point*
- The images formed by a convex lens are similar to the images formed by what type of mirror? *concave*

 This visual is also available as T30 in the Unit Transparency Book.

Address Misconceptions

IDENTIFY Ask: Do magnifying glasses always enlarge images of an object, or can they form smaller images as well? If students say "enlarged images only," they may think that a magnifying glass is made with a special kind of lens that only magnifies.

CORRECT Pass out magnifying glasses and let students experiment with them. Students should discover that when the object is more than one focal length from the lens, a magnifying glass forms upside down images that can be enlarged, the same size as the object, or reduced.

REASSESS Ask students what a magnifying glass is. *A magnifying glass is simply a convex lens that is used in a particular way.*

Technology Resources

Visit ClassZone.com for background on common student misconceptions.

 MISCONCEPTION DATABASE

Ongoing Assessment

Recognize how lenses form images.

Ask: Which types of lens forms images by causing light rays to meet at a focal point? *convex*

 *Answer: at the middle of the image of the penguin*

How a Convex Lens Forms an Image

A convex lens forms an image by refracting light rays. Light rays reflected from an object are refracted when they enter the lens and again when they leave the lens. They meet to form the image.

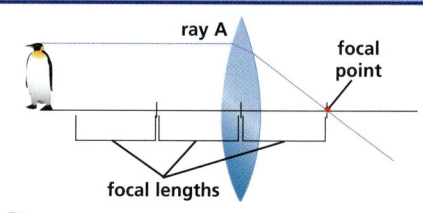

① Light rays reflect off the penguin in all directions, and many enter the lens. Here a single ray (A) from the top of the penguin enters the lens and is refracted downward.

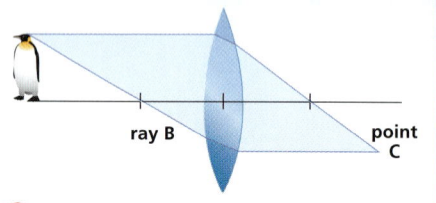

② Another light ray (B) from the top of the penguin passes through the lens at the bottom and meets the first ray at point C. All of the rays from the top of the penguin passing through the lens meet at this point.

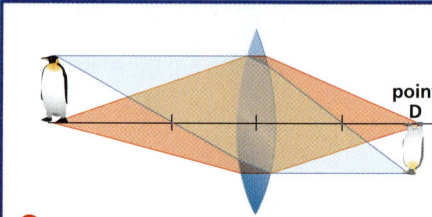

③ All of the light rays from the bottom of the penguin meet at a different point (D). Light rays from all parts of the penguin meet at corresponding points on the image.

READING VISUALS Where do light rays reflected from the middle of the penguin meet?

602 Unit 4: Waves, Sound, and Light

DIFFERENTIATE INSTRUCTION

Advanced If light is traveling in a direction that is perpendicular to the boundary between mediums, no refraction occurs even though the light's speed changes. Ask students to explain why this is so. *The light strikes the boundary at a right angle, so all sides of the wave enter the medium at the same time, all sides change speed at the same time, and no refraction occurs.*

 Challenge and Extension, p. 233

Images Formed by Lenses

When light rays from an object pass through a lens, an image of the object is formed. The type of image depends on the lens and, for convex lenses, on the distance between the lens and the object.

Notice the distance between the penguin and the lens in the illustration on page 602. The distance is measured in terms of a **focal length,** which is the distance from the center of the lens to the lens's focal point. The penguin is more than two focal lengths from the camera lens, which means the image formed is upside down and smaller.

If the penguin were between one and two focal lengths away from a convex lens, the image formed would be upside down and larger. Overhead projectors form this type of image, which is then turned right side up by a mirror and projected onto a screen for viewing.

Finally, if an object is less than one focal length from a convex lens, it will appear right side up and larger. In order to enlarge an object so that you can see details, you hold a magnifying lens close to the object. In the photograph, you see a face enlarged by a magnifying lens. The boy's face is less than one focal length from the lens.

If you look at an object through a concave lens, you'll see an image of the object that is right side up and smaller than the object normally appears. In the case of concave lenses, the distance between the object and the lens does not make a difference in the type of image that is formed. In the next section you'll see how the characteristics of the images formed by different lenses play a role in complex optical tools.

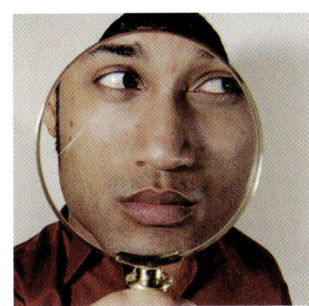

SIMULATION CLASSZONE.COM
Work with convex and concave lenses to form images.

 When will an image formed by a convex lens be upside down?

18.2 Review

KEY CONCEPTS
1. What quality of a material affects how much it refracts light?
2. How does the curve in a lens cause it to refract light differently from a flat piece of glass?
3. How does a camera lens form an image?

CRITICAL THINKING
4. **Infer** You look through a lens and see an image of a building upside down. What type of lens are you looking through?
5. **Make a Model** Draw the path of a light ray moving at an angle from air into water. Write a caption to explain the process.

CHALLENGE
6. Study the diagram on the opposite page. Describe the light rays that would pass through the labeled focal point. Where are they coming from, and how are they related to each other?

Chapter 18: Light and Optics 603

ANSWERS

1. the speed of light in the material

2. Because the angle at which light strikes a curved surface varies across the surface, the amount of refraction for different light rays varies also.

3. A camera lens refracts light waves inward toward a focal point.

4. a convex lens

5. Diagrams should show the refracted light beam turning toward the normal. Sample caption: Because water slows the light wave, the wave bends toward the normal.

6. All light rays reflected off the penguin that are parallel to the principal axis of the lens will pass through the focal point of the lens.

CHAPTER INVESTIGATION

Focus

PURPOSE Students will focus images using a convex lens and determine the conditions that produce different kinds of images

OVERVIEW Students will examine the images formed by a convex lens as they vary the distance between the lens and the object. Students will see

- an enlarged, upright, virtual image when the distance between the object and the lens is less than one focal length
- an enlarged, inverted, real image when the distance between the object and the lens is between one and two focal lengths
- a reduced, inverted, real image when the distance between the object and the lens is more than two focal lengths

Lab Preparation

- Review the concepts of focal point and focal length.
- Prior to the investigation, have students read through the investigation and prepare their data tables. Or you may wish to copy and distribute datasheets and rubrics.

 UNIT RESOURCE BOOK, pp. 264–272

 SCIENCE TOOLKIT, F15

Lab Management

- The lens can be mounted in an upright position in some modeling clay on the table surface.
- Students may need help setting up the lens and the light.
- Darken the room as much as possible. If the tape arrow does not produce clear images, have students make a light arrow by masking most of the flashlight cover instead.

SAFETY Caution students not to look directly into the flashlight.

INCLUSION Have students with visual impairments use large lenses and meter sticks with large numbers.

604 Unit 4: Waves, Sound, and Light

CHAPTER INVESTIGATION

Looking at Lenses

OVERVIEW AND PURPOSE Optical tools such as microscopes, telescopes, and eyeglasses use lenses to create images of objects. In this lab, you will use what you have learned about light and lenses to

- experiment with a convex lens to focus images of objects
- determine what makes it possible to focus images of objects

▶ Procedure

PART A

1. Make a data table like the one shown on the sample notebook page.

2. Draw a stick figure on one index card. Assemble the cards, clay, and lens as shown in the photograph.

3. Position the convex lens so that you can see an enlarged, right-side up image of the stick figure. Measure the distances between the lens and the card, and between the lens and your eye. Record the distances in your data table.

4. Position the lens so that you can see an enlarged, upside down image of the stick figure. Measure the distances between the lens and the object, and between the lens and your eye. Record the distances in your data table.

5. Position the lens so that you can see a reduced, upside down image of the stick figure. Measure the distances between the lens and the object, and between the lens and your eye. Record the distances in your data table.

MATERIALS
- index cards
- marker
- modeling clay
- convex lens
- books
- meter stick
- flashlight
- masking tape
- white poster board

604 Unit 4: **Waves, Sound, and Light**

INVESTIGATION RESOURCES

 CHAPTER INVESTIGATION, Looking at Lenses
- Level A, pp. 264–267
- Level B, pp. 268–271
- Level C, p. 272

Advanced students should complete Levels B & C.

 Writing a Lab Report, D12–13

Technology Resources

Customize this student lab as needed or look for an alternative. Print rubrics to assess student lab reports.

 Lab Generator CD-ROM

PART B

6. Put an arrow made of tape on the lens of the flashlight as shown.

7. Assemble poster board and clay to make a screen. Arrange the flashlight, lens, and screen as shown below right.

8. Shine the beam from the flashlight through the lens to form an enlarged, upside down image on the screen. Measure the distances between the lens and the flashlight and between the lens and the screen.

9. Position the light and screen to produce a reduced, upside down image. Measure the distances between the lens and the flashlight and between the lens and the screen.

10. Position the light and screen to produce an enlarged right-side up image.

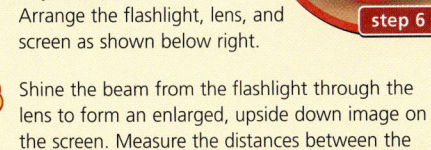
step 6

2. **IDENTIFY LIMITS** Describe possible sources of error in your procedure or any places where errors might have occurred.

3. **APPLY** What kind of lenses are magnifying glasses? When a magnifying glass produces a sharp clear image, where is the object located in relation to the lens?

step 7

Observe and Analyze

1. **RECORD OBSERVATIONS** Draw pictures of each setup in steps 3–9 to show what happened. Be sure your data table is complete.

2. **ANALYZE** What was the distance from the lens to the object in step 3? Answer this question for each of the other steps. How do the distances compare?

3. **ANALYZE** What happened when you tried to form the three types of images on the screen? How can you explain these results?

Conclude

1. **ANALYZE** What conclusions can you draw about the relationship between the distances you measured and the type of image that was produced?

INVESTIGATE Further

CHALLENGE If you were to repeat steps 8 and 9 with a concave lens, you would not be able to focus an image on the screen. Why not?

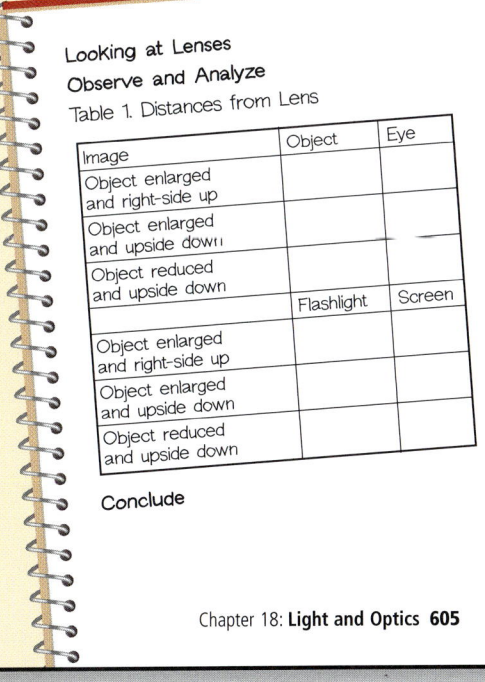

Looking at Lenses
Observe and Analyze
Table 1. Distances from Lens

Image	Object	Eye
Object enlarged and right-side up		
Object enlarged and upside down		
Object reduced and upside down		

	Flashlight	Screen
Object enlarged and right-side up		
Object enlarged and upside down		
Object reduced and upside down		

Conclude

Chapter 18: **Light and Optics** 605

Post-Lab Discussion

- Have students make ray diagrams to summarize their results. Diagrams should clearly show why images can be enlarged or reduced and inverted or upright when the object is at different distances.

- Describe this scenario: You are camping and want to start a fire, but you have no matches. You have a lens. Can you start a fire in a pile of dead leaves? What kind of lens would you need? *yes; convex* Where would the lens have to be? *exactly one focal length from the leaves. The Sun's rays would focus on the leaves, and the concentration of light could start a fire.*

Observe and Analyze

SAMPLE DATA Object enlarged, right-side up: 0–1 focal length from lens; Object enlarged, upside down: 1–2 focal lengths from lens; Object reduced, upside down: more than 2 focal lengths from lens; Lightbulb enlarged, right-side up: no image; Lightbulb image enlarged, upside down: 1–2 focal lengths from lens; Lightbulb image reduced, upside down: more than 2 focal lengths from lens.

1. See students' diagrams.

2. Step 3: less than one focal length; Steps 4 and 8: between one and two focal lengths; Steps 5 and 9: more than two focal lengths

3. Step 8: enlarged, upside down image appears on screen when distance from lens to screen is about twice the distance from light to lens. Step 9: reduced, upside down image is visible on screen when distance from lens to screen is about equal to the distance from light to lens. Step 10: enlarged, right side up image appears on screen when lens is very close to screen and the flashlight very close to the lens.

Explanation: Different images are formed when the screen is within one focal length, about one focal length, and outside one focal length from the lens.

Conclude

1. When the distance between an object and a convex lens is: 1. less than one focal length, an enlarged, upright image forms. 2. between one and two focal lengths, an enlarged, upside down image forms. 3. more than two focal lengths, a reduced, upside down image forms.

2. misidentifying the type of image, measuring incorrectly, and not having the lens in the correct position

3. convex lens; an object must be located less than one focal length in front of the lens.

INVESTIGATE Further

CHALLENGE Answer: They do not cause light rays to meet at a focal point.

Chapter 18 **605**

18.3 FOCUS

▶ Set Learning Goals

Students will
- Recognize how the eye depends on natural lenses.
- Explain how artificial lenses can be used to correct vision problems.
- Observe and describe through an experiment how the eye focuses an image.

◉ 3-Minute Warm-Up

Display Transparency 29 or copy this exercise on the board:

Imagine a woman is spearfishing at a lake. She sees a fish through the water ahead of her and aims her spear directly at the image. Will she hit the fish? Explain your answer. *No; the image and the actual location of the fish are different because the light is refracted.*

If the woman is spearfishing underwater while scuba diving and she aims directly at a fish, will she hit it? Why? *Yes; because both the woman and the fish are underwater, there is no refraction.*

 3-Minute Warm-Up, p. T29

18.3 MOTIVATE

EXPLORE Focusing Vision

PURPOSE To investigate how the human eye focuses

TIP *10 min.* Students who cannot keep one eye closed should hold one hand over the eye.

WHAT DO YOU THINK? *The nearby object looks out of focus. The eye changes its focal point.*

KEY CONCEPT

The eye is a natural optical tool.

◀ BEFORE, you learned
- Mirrors and lenses focus light to form images
- Mirrors and lenses can alter images in useful ways

▶ NOW, you will learn
- How the eye depends on natural lenses
- How artificial lenses can be used to correct vision problems

VOCABULARY
cornea p. 607
pupil p. 607
retina p. 607

EXPLORE Focusing Vision

How does the eye focus an image?

PROCEDURE
1. Position yourself so you can see an object about 6 meters (20 feet) away.
2. Close one eye, hold up your index finger, and bring it as close to your open eye as you can while keeping the finger clearly in focus.
3. Keeping your finger in place, look just to the side at the more distant object and focus your eye on it.
4. Without looking away from the more distant object, observe your finger.

WHAT DO YOU THINK?
- How does the nearby object look when you are focusing on something distant?
- What might be happening in your eye to cause this change in the nearby object?

The eye gathers and focuses light.

The eyes of human beings and many other animals are natural optical tools that process visible light. Eyes transmit light, refract light, and respond to different wavelengths of light. Eyes contain natural lenses that focus images of objects. Eyes convert the energy of light waves into signals that can be sent to the brain. The brain interprets these signals as shape, brightness, and color. Altogether, these processes make vision possible.

In this section, you will learn how the eye works. You will also learn how artificial lenses can be used to improve vision.

606 Unit 4: Waves, Sound, and Light

RESOURCES FOR DIFFERENTIATED INSTRUCTION

Below Level
UNIT RESOURCE BOOK
- Reading Study Guide A, pp. 237–238
- Decoding Support, p. 261

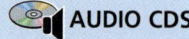 **AUDIO CDS**

Advanced
UNIT RESOURCE BOOK
- Challenge and Extension, p. 243
- Challenge Reading, pp. 257–258

English Learners
UNIT RESOURCE BOOK
Spanish Reading Study Guide, pp. 241–242

 **AUDIO CDS**
- Audio Readings in Spanish
- Audio Readings (English)

How Light Travels Through the Human Eye

A ❶ Light enters the eye through the **cornea** (KAWR-nee-uh), a transparent membrane that covers the eye. The cornea acts as a convex lens and does most of the refracting in the eye.

❷ The light then continues through the **pupil,** a circular opening that controls how much light enters the eye. The pupil is surrounded by the iris, which opens and closes to change the size of the pupil.

❸ Next the light passes through the part of the eye called the lens. The lens is convex on both sides. It refracts light to make fine adjustments for near and far objects. Unlike the cornea, the lens is attached to tiny muscles that contract and relax to control the amount of refraction that occurs and to move the focal point.

> **READING TIP**
> The word *lens* can refer both to an artificial optical tool and to a specific part of the eye.

B ❹ The light passes through the clear center of the eye and strikes the **retina** (REHT-uhn-uh). The retina contains specialized cells that respond to light. Some of these cells send signals through the optic nerve to the brain. The brain interprets these signals as images.

How the Human Eye Forms an Image

The cornea and lens together focus a reduced, inverted image on the retina.

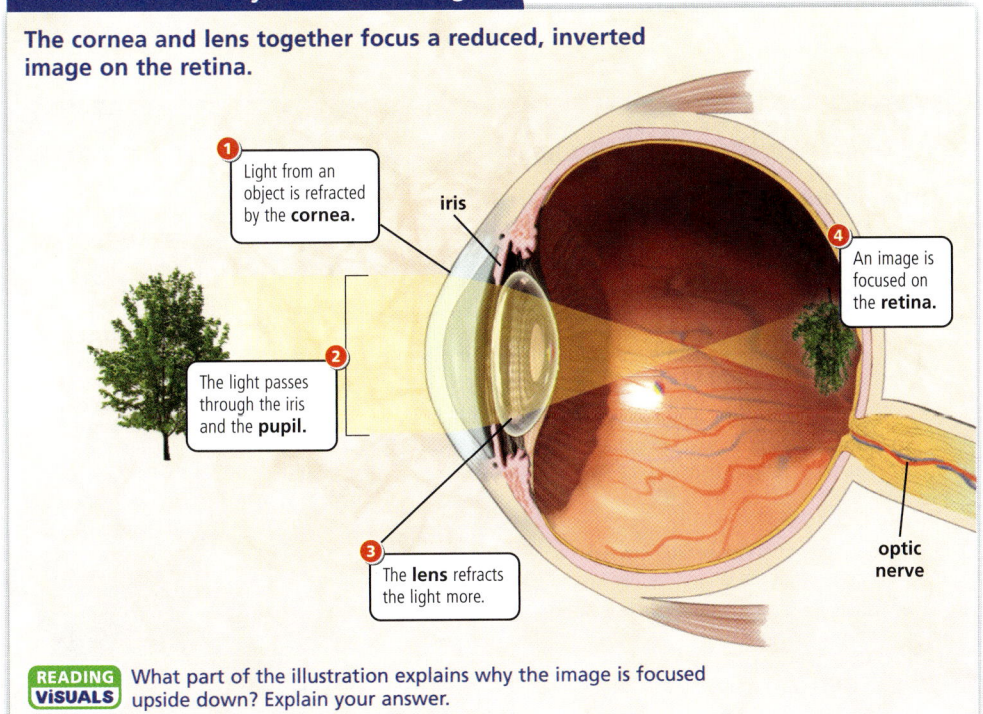

① Light from an object is refracted by the **cornea.**

② The light passes through the iris and the **pupil.**

③ The **lens** refracts the light more.

④ An image is focused on the **retina.**

iris

optic nerve

READING VISUALS What part of the illustration explains why the image is focused upside down? Explain your answer.

Chapter 18: Light and Optics 607

DIFFERENTIATE INSTRUCTION

More Reading Support

A What part of the eye does most light refraction? *the cornea*

B Where does the eye focus an image? *on the retina*

English Learners Developing a Science Word Wall in the classroom will help English learners learn new vocabulary. Offering a visual reminder with the word can reinforce meaning as well. Place the words *pupil, cornea,* and *retina* on the Science Word Wall and include a diagram of the eye showing the location of each part.

18.3 INSTRUCT

Address Misconceptions

IDENTIFY Ask: What is the main focusing part of the eye? If students say the lens, they may hold the misconception that most or all refraction occurs in the lens.

CORRECT Call students' attention to the diagram on this page. Point out that the cornea is shaped like a convex lens and does most of the refracting for the eye. Because the cornea covers the eye, most refraction actually takes place in the cornea rather than in the lens.

REASSESS Have students draw a diagram of light rays approaching an eye and being refracted by the cornea. The light should be further refracted by the lens.

Technology Resources
Visit **ClassZone.com** for background on common student misconceptions.

MISCONCEPTION DATABASE

Teach from Visuals

To help students interpret the eye visual, ask:

- What is the shape of the cornea? *convex*
- Where is the focal point? *where the lines cross*
- What does the optic nerve do? *sends signals to the brain*

Ongoing Assessment

Recognize how the eye depends on natural lenses.

Ask: What two lenses are part of the eye? *the cornea and the lens*

READING VISUALS *Answer: The part that shows light rays crossing at a focal point so that the ones on top go to the bottom of the image and vice versa.*

Chapter 18 607

INVESTIGATE Vision

PURPOSE To use a magnifying glass to observe how an image becomes focused

TIPS 10 min.
- Use a meter stick to measure all distances.
- The distance between the plate and the glass will vary, depending on the focal length of the lens used.

WHAT DO YOU THINK? *The distance gets smaller. Instead of moving the position of the retina, the eye changes the focal point of the lens.*

CHALLENGE *Use a lens with a different focal point to refocus the image.*

 Datasheet, Vision, p. 244

Technology Resources

Customize this student lab as needed or look for an alternative. Print rubrics to assess student lab reports.

 Lab Generator CD-ROM

Metacognitive Strategy

Ask students to summarize in their own words how images are focused.

Ongoing Assessment

 *Answer: cone cell*

How the Eye Forms Images

For you to see an object clearly, your eye must focus an image of the object on your retina. The light reflected from each particular spot on the object must converge on a matching point on your retina. Many such points make up an image of an entire object. Because the light rays pass through the lens's focal point, the image is upside down. The brain interprets this upside down image as an object that is right-side up.

For a complete image to be formed in the eye and communicated to the brain, more than the lens and the cornea are needed. The retina also plays an important role. The retina contains specialized cells that detect brightness and color and other qualities of light.

COMBINATION NOTES Make a chart showing how light interacts with different parts of the eye.

Rod Cells Rod cells distinguish between white and black and shades of gray. Rods respond to faint light, so they help with night vision.

Cone Cells Cone cells respond to different wavelengths of light, so they detect color. There are three types of cones, one for each of the colors red, blue, and green. Cones respond to other colors with combinations of these three, as the screen of a color monitor does. The brain interprets these combinations as the entire color spectrum.

 Which type of cell in the retina detects color?

INVESTIGATE Vision

How does distance affect vision?

PROCEDURE

1. Arrange the materials as shown so that the lamp shines through the lens onto the plate. The lens should be about $\frac{2}{3}$ a meter from the lamp.
2. Adjust the distance between the plate and the lens until you see a focused image of the bulb on the plate. Measure this distance.
3. Move the lens until it is about a meter and a half from the lamp. Adjust the plate once again to get a focused image, then measure the distance between the plate and the lens.

WHAT DO YOU THINK?
- How does the distance needed between the plate and the lens change when the lamp is farther from the lens?
- How is what happens in the eye different from what you did to refocus the image?

CHALLENGE How could you change the model to make it more like what happens in the eye?

SKILL FOCUS Observing

MATERIALS
- convex lens
- index card
- modeling clay
- white paper plate
- lamp

TIME 10 minutes

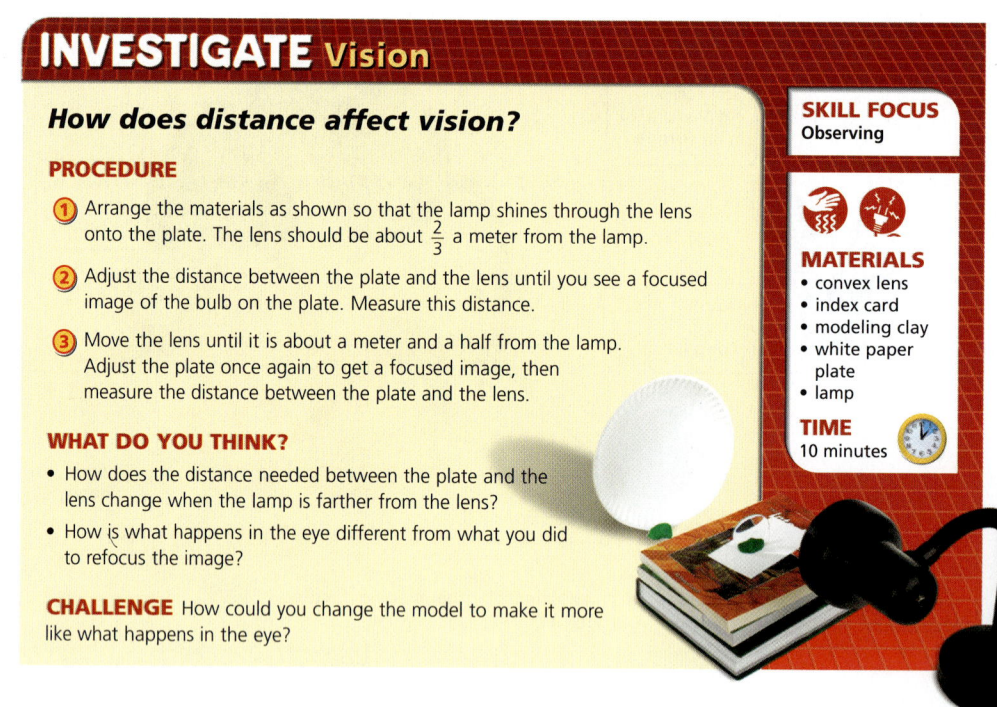

608 Unit 4: Waves, Sound, and Light

DIFFERENTIATE INSTRUCTION

 More Reading Support

C The eye forms what type of image? *upside down*

D What do rod cells do? *distinguish between black and white and shades of gray*

English Learners Some English learners may have never had a vision test or seen an optometrist. Go over the different ways a doctor can correct a person's vision. Explain how eyeglasses correct nearsightedness or farsightedness. Talk about how contact lenses are used. Encourage students to use the Internet to find out more about surgical methods of vision correction.

Advanced

 Challenge and Extension, p. 243

Corrective lenses can improve vision.

What happens when the image formed by the lens of the eye does not fall exactly on the retina? The result is that the image appears blurry. This can occur either because of the shape of the eye or because of how the lens works. Artificial lenses can be used to correct this problem.

Corrective Lenses

A person who is nearsighted cannot see objects clearly unless they are near. Nearsightedness occurs when the lens of the eye focuses the image in front of the retina. The farther away the object is, the farther in front of the retina the image forms. This problem can be corrected with glasses made with concave lenses. The concave lenses spread out the rays of light before they enter the eye. The point at which the rays meet then falls on the retina.

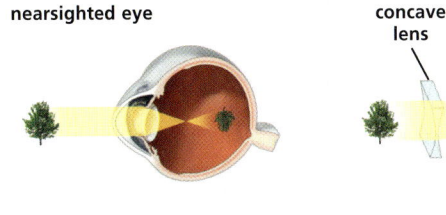

nearsighted eye **concave lens**

 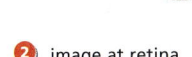

❶ image in front of retina   ❷ image at retina

Objects are clearer to a farsighted person when the objects are farther away. Farsightedness occurs when the lens of the eye focuses an object's image behind the retina. This condition can result from aging, which may make the lens less flexible. The closer the object is, the farther behind the retina the image forms. Farsightedness can be corrected with glasses made from convex lenses. The convex lenses bend the light rays inward before they enter the eye. The point at which the rays meet then falls on the retina.

READING TIP
Nearsighted people can see objects near to them best. *Farsighted* people can see objects better when the objects are farther away.

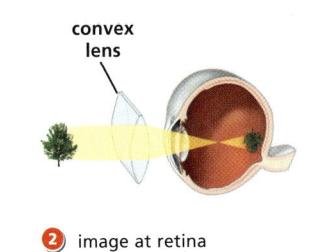

farsighted eye   **convex lens**

❶ image behind retina   ❷ image at retina

 What kind of lens is used for correcting nearsightedness?

Chapter 18: **Light and Optics** 609

DIFFERENTIATE INSTRUCTION

E What are corrective lenses? *artificial lenses that correct vision problems*

Inclusion Ray diagrams showing the path of light in the eye can be made for students with visual impairments. Use yarn or string to represent light rays. To represent the retina, use a heavier yarn. Use another three-dimensional material to represent the image.

Advanced Have students who are interested in why people have red eyes read the following article:

 Challenge Reading, pp. 257–258

Teach from Visuals
To help students understand corrective lenses, ask:
- Where does the image form in a nearsighted eye? *in front of the retina*
- Where does the image form in a farsighted eye? *behind the retina*

Integrate the Sciences
Perfect vision is measured at 20/20, which means that your eye sees at 20 feet what a normal eye can see at the same distance. The larger the second number, the blurrier the image. So 20/40 means that your eye sees at 20 feet what a normal eye can see at 40 feet. Legal blindness is 20/200 or worse in both eyes.

Ongoing Assessment
Explain how artificial lenses can be used to correct vision problems.

Ask: How does a concave lens correct nearsightedness? *By spreading out the light before it enters the eye, the lens lengthens the focal length in the eye, and the image focuses on the retina.*

 Answer: *Nearsightedness can be corrected with a concave lens.*

Chapter 18 **609**

Ongoing Assessment

 Answer: surgery and contact lenses

Reinforce

Have students relate the section to the Big Idea.

 Reinforcing Key Concepts, p. 245

18.3 ASSESS & RETEACH

Assess

 Section 18.3 Quiz, p. 64

Reteach

Ask students the following questions to extend their understanding of sight:

- Where are the images projected on the retina interpreted? *in the brain*
- What happens to the lens of the eye when light passes through? *It refracts light to make adjustments for near and far objects.*

Have students find their blind spot—the place where the retina joins the optic nerve.

- Make a diagram of an X and a black spot located about 6 cm apart.
- Close your left eye, look at the X, and gradually move the diagram away from the eye.

At a distance of about 25 cm, the spot will disappear.

Technology Resources

Have students visit **ClassZone.com** for reteaching of Key Concepts.

 CONTENT REVIEW

 CONTENT REVIEW CD-ROM

Surgery and Contact Lenses

Wearing glasses is an effective way to correct vision. It is also possible to change the shape of the cornea to make the eye refract properly. The cornea is responsible for two-thirds of the refraction that takes place inside the eye. As you know, the eye's lens changes shape to focus an image, but the shape of the cornea does not ordinarily change.

However, using advanced surgical technology, doctors can change the shape of the cornea. By doing this, they change the way light rays focus in the eye so that the image lines up with the retina. To correct for nearsightedness, surgeons remove tissue from the center of the cornea. This flattens the cornea and makes it less convex so that it will refract less. To correct for farsightedness, surgeons remove tissue from around the edges of the cornea. This increases the cornea's curvature to make it refract more. Surgery changes the shape of the cornea permanently and can eliminate the need for eyeglasses.

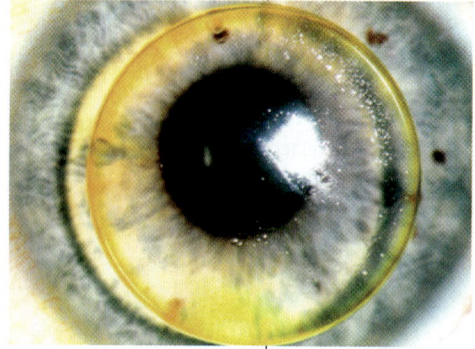

Contact lenses fit directly onto the cornea, changing the way light is refracted as it enters a person's eye.

Contact lenses also correct vision by changing the way the cornea refracts light. Contact lenses are corrective lenses that fit directly onto the cornea. The lenses actually float on a thin layer of tears. The moisture, the contact lens, and the cornea all function together. The lens of the eye then focuses the light further. Because the change is temporary, contacts, like eyeglasses, can be adapted to new changes in the eye.

 What are two ways of changing the way the cornea refracts light to correct vision?

18.3 Review

KEY CONCEPTS

1. Where are images focused in an eye with perfect vision?
2. What causes people with nearsightedness to see blurry images of objects at a distance?
3. What kind of lens is used for correcting farsightedness? Why?

CRITICAL THINKING

4. **Make a Model** Draw a diagram to answer the following question: How does a convex lens affect the way a nearsighted eye focuses an image?
5. **Analyze** What distance would an eye doctor need to measure to correct a problem with nearsightedness or farsightedness?

CHALLENGE

6. **Apply** A person alternates between wearing glasses and wearing contact lenses to correct farsightedness. Are the contact lenses more or less convex than the lenses of the glasses? Explain the reasoning behind your response.

610 Unit 4: Waves, Sound, and Light

ANSWERS

1. on the retina

2. The eye focuses the image in front of the retina.

3. Convex lens; it bends light inward, which moves the focal point of the image forward toward the retina.

4. Student diagrams should show that the focal point has moved even farther away from the retina, making the eye even more nearsighted.

5. the distance between the image and the retina

6. more convex, because they are closer to the eye and must do the same amount of refraction in less space

KEY CONCEPT

Optical technology makes use of light waves.

◀ BEFORE, you learned
- Mirrors are optical tools that use reflection
- Lenses are optical tools that use refraction
- The eye is a natural optical tool
- Lenses can correct vision

▶ NOW, you will learn
- How mirrors and lenses can be combined to make complex optical tools
- How optical tools are used to extend natural vision
- How laser light is made and used in optical technology

VOCABULARY
laser p. 615
fiber optics p. 617

EXPLORE Combining Lenses

How can lenses be combined?

PROCEDURE

① Assemble the lenses, clay, and index cards as shown in the photograph.

② Line the lenses up so that you have a straight line of sight through them.

③ Experiment with different distances between
  - the lenses
  - the far lens and an object
  - the near lens and your eye
  Find an arrangement that allows you to see a clear image of an object through both lenses.

MATERIALS
- 2 convex lenses
- modeling clay
- 2 index cards

WHAT DO YOU THINK?
- What kind of image could you see? What arrangement or arrangements work best to produce an image?
- How do you think the lenses are working together to focus the image?

COMBINATION NOTES
As you read this section, make a list of optical tools. Add sketches to help you remember important concepts.

Mirrors and lenses can be combined to make more powerful optical tools.

If you know about submarines, then you know how much they depend on their periscopes to see above the water. Periscopes are made by combining mirrors. Lenses can also be combined. In the eye, for example, the cornea and the eye's lens work together to focus an image. Mirrors and lenses can be combined with each other, as they are in an overhead projector. Many of the most powerful and complex optical tools are based on different combinations of mirrors and lenses.

Chapter 18: **Light and Optics** 611

18.4 FOCUS

◉ Set Learning Goals

Students will
- Describe how mirrors and lenses can be combined to make complex optical tools.
- Explain how optical tools are used to extend natural vision.
- Recognize how laser light is made and used in optical technology.
- Design their own experiment by making a model of a telescope and explaining how it works.

◉ 3-Minute Warm-Up

Display Transparency 29 or copy this exercise on the board:

Decide if these statements are true. If not true, correct them.

1. The lens of the human eye is concave on both sides. *The lens of the human eye is convex on both sides.*

2. Rods and cones, located in the retina, are important in night and color vision. *true*

3. The eyes convert the energy of light waves into nerve signals that travel to the brain. *true*

 3-Minute Warm-Up, p. 129

18.4 MOTIVATE

EXPLORE Combining Lenses

PURPOSE To determine how two lenses work together to focus an image

TIP *10 min.* Use a protractor to ensure that the lenses are exactly vertical.

WHAT DO YOU THINK? *An enlarged image can be seen when the lenses are the distance of their combined focal lengths apart, the object is more than one focal length from the far lens, and the viewer is about one focal length from the near lens.*

RESOURCES FOR DIFFERENTIATED INSTRUCTION

Below Level
UNIT RESOURCE BOOK
- Reading Study Guide A, pp. 248–249
- Decoding Support, p. 261

 AUDIO CDS

Advanced
UNIT RESOURCE BOOK
Challenge and Extension, p. 254

English Learners
UNIT RESOURCE BOOK
Spanish Reading Study Guide, pp. 252–253

 AUDIO CDS
- Audio Readings in Spanish
- Audio Readings (English)

Chapter 18 **611**

18.4 INSTRUCT

History of Science

In the 17th century, Robert Hooke and Anton van Leeuwenhoek both developed microscopes and discovered the world of tiny living things. Although Hooke's microscope had two lenses and was similar to modern compound microscopes, poor-quality lenses provided little detail. Van Leeuwenhoek's microscope had only one lens, but it was good enough to show many details in cells and organisms.

Ongoing Assessment

Describe how mirrors and lenses can be combined to make complex optical tools.

Ask: What type of telescope combines mirrors and lenses? *a reflecting telescope*

 Answer: The objective lens forms an enlarged real image. The eyepiece forms an enlarged virtual image of the first image.

 Answer: A reflecting telescope uses two mirrors and one lens to focus an image. A refracting telescope uses two lenses to focus an image.

Microscopes

Microscopes are used to see objects that are too small to see well with the naked eye. An ordinary microscope works by combining convex lenses. The lens closer to the object is called the objective. The object is between one and two focal lengths from this lens, so the lens focuses an enlarged image of the object inside the microscope.

The other microscope lens—the one you look through—is called the eyepiece. You use this lens to look at the image formed by the objective. Like a magnifying glass, the eyepiece lens forms an enlarged image of the first image.

Very small objects do not reflect much light. Most microscopes use a lamp or a mirror to shine more light on the object.

 Which types of images do the lenses in a microscope form?

Telescopes

Telescopes are used to see objects that are too far away to see well with the naked eye. One type of telescope, called a refracting telescope, is made by combining lenses. Another type of telescope, called a reflecting telescope, is made by combining lenses and mirrors.

Refracting telescopes combine convex lenses, just as microscopes do. However, the objects are far away from the objective lens instead of near to it. The object is more than two focal lengths from the objective lens, so the lens focuses a reduced image of the object inside the telescope. The eyepiece of a telescope then forms an enlarged image of the first image, just as a microscope does. This second image enlarges the object.

RESOURCE CENTER
CLASSZONE.COM
Find out more about microscopes and telescopes.

Reflecting telescopes work in the same way that refracting telescopes do. However, there is no objective lens where light enters the telescope. Instead, a concave mirror at the opposite end focuses an image of the object. A small flat mirror redirects the image to the side of the telescope. With this arrangement, the eyepiece does not interfere with light on its way to the concave mirror. The eyepiece then forms an enlarged image of the first image.

Both refracting and reflecting telescopes must adjust for the small amount of light received from distant objects. The amount of light gathered can be increased by increasing the diameter of the objective lens or mirror. Large mirrors are easier and less expensive to make than large lenses. So reflecting telescopes can produce brighter images more cheaply than refracting telescopes.

 How is a reflecting telescope different from a refracting telescope?

612 Unit 4: Waves, Sound, and Light

DIFFERENTIATE INSTRUCTION

More Reading Support

A What does the eyepiece of a microscope do? *forms an enlarged image of the first image*

B What type of telescope has two convex lenses? *refracting*

English Learners Label any refracting telescopes, reflecting telescopes, or microscopes in the classroom. English learners might be confused by phrasal verbs such as *made up* (p. 615). Tell students that in this context, "up" is not a literal direction, but rather a part of the verb. If students still have trouble, offer synonyms such as "composed" or "consists of."

Microscopes and Telescopes

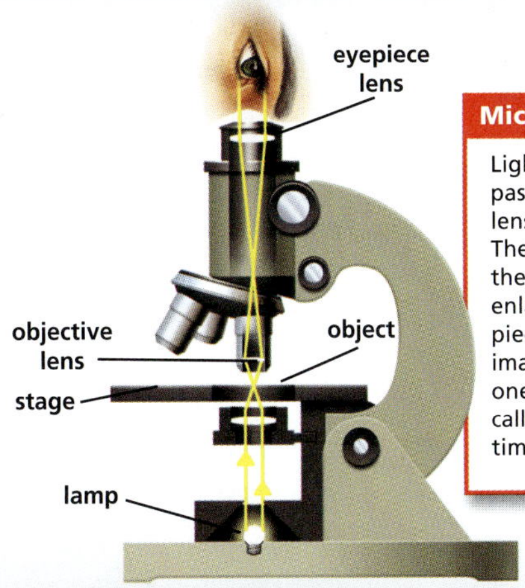

Microscope
Light from an object passes through a convex lens called an objective. The objective lens focuses the light to form an enlarged image. The eyepiece lens enlarges the image even more. The one-celled algae at right, called diatoms, appear 400 times their normal size.

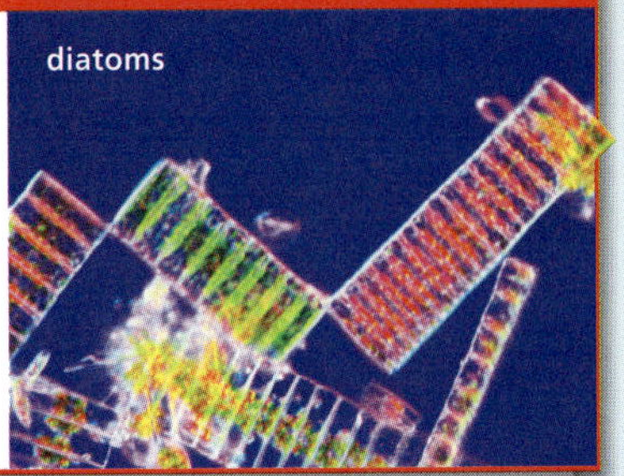

diatoms

Refracting Telescope
The objective lens gathers and focuses light from a distant object to form an image of the object. The eyepiece enlarges the image. The telescope image of the Moon at left shows fine details of the lunar surface.

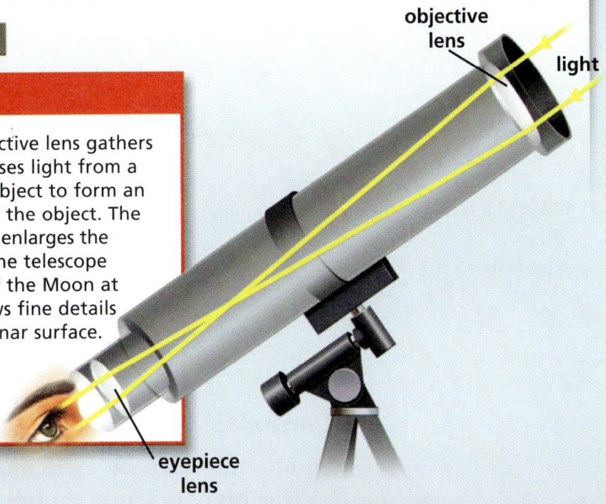

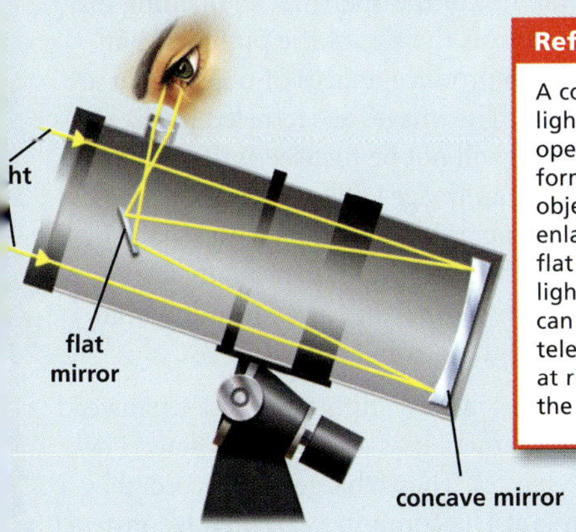

surface of the Moon

Reflecting Telescope
A concave mirror gathers light through a wide opening and focuses it to form an image of the object. The eyepiece lens enlarges the image. The flat mirror redirects the light so that the eyepiece can be out of the way. The telescope image of Saturn at right shows details of the planet's rings.

the planet Saturn

READING VISUALS Which type of telescope is similar in construction to a microscope?

Chapter 18: **Light and Optics** 613

Teach from Visuals

To help students interpret the microscope and telescope visual:

- Both microscopes and refracting telescopes contain two lenses. Ask: How are these two instruments different? *The image in a microscope is enlarged twice. The refracting telescope enlarges the image once.*

- Ask: What is the advantage to having the eyepiece out of the way in a reflecting telescope? *The advantage of having the eyepiece out of the way is that it will not block light from entering the telescope.*

Address Misconceptions

IDENTIFY Ask: What is the function of each lens in a telescope? If students respond that both lenses produce enlarged images, they may hold the misconception that the only purpose of a telescope is to enlarge an image.

CORRECT Have students reexamine the visual on page 602, which shows that the image of an object located more than two focal lengths from a convex lens is reduced and inverted. Drawing a ray diagram will help reinforce this concept.

REASSESS Ask: What is the main function of an objective lens? *to collect as much light from the distant object as possible*

Technology Resources
Visit **ClassZone.com** for background on common student misconceptions.

 MISCONCEPTION DATABASE

Ongoing Assessment

 *Answer: a refracting telescope*

DIFFERENTIATE INSTRUCTION

Advanced Have students investigate the focal lengths of the lenses in microscopes and refracting telescopes. Students should understand why lenses with long or short focal lengths are used. Students can make ray diagrams tracing the path of light through these instruments. *Microscopes use an objective lens with a very short focal length because the object being examined is very close to this lens. Telescopes use an objective lens with a very long focal length because the object being viewed is very far away.*

 Challenge and Extension, p. 254

Chapter 18 **613**

INVESTIGATE Optical Tools

PURPOSE To design and build a telescope to find out how two lenses work together

TIPS 30 min. Let students explore for a few minutes. Offer these suggestions if necessary.

- The two lenses should be at a distance equal to the sum of the focal lengths of the two lenses.
- Use a large convex lens with a long focal length for the objective and a smaller convex lens with a short focal length for the eyepiece.

WHAT DO YOU THINK? *The object should be more than two focal lengths from the objective lens. Students will see an enlarged inverted image if their telescope works.*

CHALLENGE *The image is first upside down, because the objective lens forms an inverted image. The eyepiece then forms an upright image of the inverted image.*

 Datasheet, Optical Tools, p. 255

Technology Resources

Customize this student lab as needed or look for an alternative. Print rubrics to assess student lab reports.

 Lab Generator CD-ROM

Teaching with Technology

If you have access to a telescope, let students use it to compare its images with the images created by their homemade telescope.

Ongoing Assessment

Explain how optical tools are used to extend natural vision.

Ask: How do microscopes and telescopes extend natural vision? *They enlarge objects that are either too small or too far away to be seen with the naked eye.*

614 Unit 4: Waves, Sound, and Light

INVESTIGATE Optical Tools

How can you make a simple telescope?

Use what you have learned about how a telescope works to build one. Figure out how far apart the two lenses need to be and use that information to construct a working model.

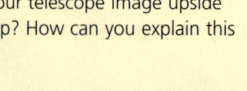

PROCEDURE

1. Decide how the lenses should be positioned in relation to an object you select to view.
2. Adjust the lenses until you get a clear image.
3. Use the other materials to fix the lenses into place and to make it possible to adjust the distance between them.

WHAT DO YOU THINK?

- How did you end up positioning the lenses in relation to the object?
- Did your telescope work? Why do you think you got this result?

CHALLENGE Is your telescope image upside down or right-side up? How can you explain this observation?

SKILL FOCUS
Making models

MATERIALS
- 2 convex lenses
- 2 cardboard tubes
- duct tape

TIME
30 minutes

Cameras

Most film cameras focus images in the same way that the eye does. The iris of a camera controls the size of the aperture, an opening for light, just as the iris of an eye controls the size of the pupil. Like an eye, a camera uses a convex lens to produce images of objects that are more than two focal lengths away. The images are reduced in size and upside down. In the eye, an image will not be focused unless it falls exactly on the retina. In a camera, an image will not be focused unless it falls exactly on the film. The camera does not change the shape of its lens as the eye does to change the focal point. Instead, the camera allows you to move the lens nearer to or farther away from the film until the object you want to photograph is in focus.

A digital camera focuses images just as a film camera does. Instead of using film, though, the digital camera uses a sensor that detects light and converts it into electrical charges. These charges are recorded by a small computer inside the camera. The computer can then reconstruct the image immediately on the camera's display screen.

READING TIP
The term *digital* is often used to describe technology involving computers. Computers process information digitally, that is, using numbers.

614 Unit 4: Waves, Sound, and Light

DIFFERENTIATE INSTRUCTION

 More Reading Support

C What kind of an image is produced in a camera? *reduced in size and upside down*

Alternative Assessment Have students make diagrams showing how the lenses in a refracting telescope have to be positioned in relation to each other. Ask them to explain why the lenses have to be positioned in this way.

How Cameras Work

A camera focuses an image in the same way as an eye.

film camera

light · lens · iris · aperture · film

READING VISUALS What part of a camera corresponds to the pupil of an eye?

Eye and Camera

lens · image · retina · pupil

film · iris · lens · aperture · image

Digital Camera

A **digital camera** records images digitally, that is, using a computer.

Lasers use light in new ways.

A **laser** (LAY-zuhr) is a device that produces an intense, concentrated beam of light that is brighter than sunlight. The word *laser* means "light amplification by stimulated emission of radiation." Laser light has many uses. It carries a lot of energy and can be controlled precisely.

Ordinary visible light is made up of many different wavelengths. Even colored light usually contains many different wavelengths. But a laser beam is made up of light waves with a single wavelength and a pure color. In addition, the waves are in phase, which means the peaks are lined up so they match exactly.

REMINDER
The peak of a wave is where it has the greatest energy.

Visible light waves of different wavelengths

Light waves of a single wavelength

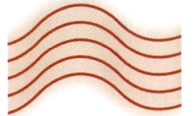
Single wavelength waves in phase

Chapter 18: **Light and Optics** 615

DIFFERENTIATE INSTRUCTION

More Reading Support

D What is a laser? *a device that produces an intense, concentrated beam of light*

Below Level Ask students who have a hard time reading to describe and compare the path of light in a camera and in the human eye. Ask them to bring in a camera to show the class the different parts.

Teach from Visuals

To help students interpret the visual of how cameras work, ask:

- What part of a camera corresponds to the retina of the eye? *the film*
- What replaces the film in a digital camera? *A small computer stores light waves from the object in the form of a digitized image.*

Teach Difficult Concepts

Some students may still be having trouble understanding where a lens focuses a real image. Remind them that the focal point of a lens is the point where parallel rays passing through the lens meet. Rays from different points on an object are not parallel and so meet a little beyond the focal point of the lens. Every point on the object has a corresponding point where light rays meet on the image.

Teacher Demo

Light a candle in a darkened room, and hold a magnifying glass between the candle and the wall. An inverted image of the candle will appear on the wall. If the light waves from a particular point on the object don't quite converge at the wall, the real image of the candle will not fall exactly on the wall, and it will be blurry. To focus the image, move the magnifying glass closer or farther away from the candle. When you focus a camera, you turn the lens to move it closer or farther away from the film surface. As you move the lens, you line up the focused real image of an object so it falls directly on the surface of the film.

Ongoing Assessment

READING VISUALS *Answer: the iris*

Chapter 18 **615**

Teach from Visuals

To help students interpret the laser visual, ask:

- What happens to the light as the mirrors reflect it back and forth? *It becomes stronger and more concentrated.*
- What do the light waves in a laser look like? *They are all one wavelength and parallel, and their troughs and crests line up.*

Real World Example

A bar code is a specific arrangement of bars and spaces. When a cashier moves a bar-coded item in front of a scanner, a laser scans the bar code. The white spaces between the bars reflect light in bursts through the scanner window, through a partial mirror, and onto a detector. The detector changes these light bursts into digital signals, which travel to a central computer. The computer processes the signals and sends information about the price of the item to the cash register.

Ongoing Assessment

Recognize how laser light is made and used in optical technology.

Ask: How is a laser beam made? *An energy source stimulates the atoms in a material to give off light waves of a single wavelength. Mirrors concentrate the light waves to produce a laser.*

Light waves in a laser beam are highly concentrated and exactly parallel. Ordinary light spreads out, growing more faint as it gets farther from its source. Laser light spreads out very little. After traveling 1 kilometer (0.6 mi), a laser beam may have a diameter of only one meter.

Making Laser Light

Learn more about lasers.

A laser is made in a special tube called an optical cavity. A material that is known to give off a certain wavelength of light, such as a ruby crystal, is placed inside the tube. Next, an energy source, such as a bright flash of light, stimulates the material, causing it to emit, or give off, light waves. Both ends of the crystal are mirrored so that they reflect light back and forth between them. One end is mirrored more than the other. As the light waves pass through the crystal, they cause the material to give off more light waves—all perfectly parallel, all with the same wavelength, and all with their crests and troughs lined up. Eventually the beam becomes concentrated and strong enough to penetrate the less-mirrored end of the crystal. What comes out of the end is a laser beam.

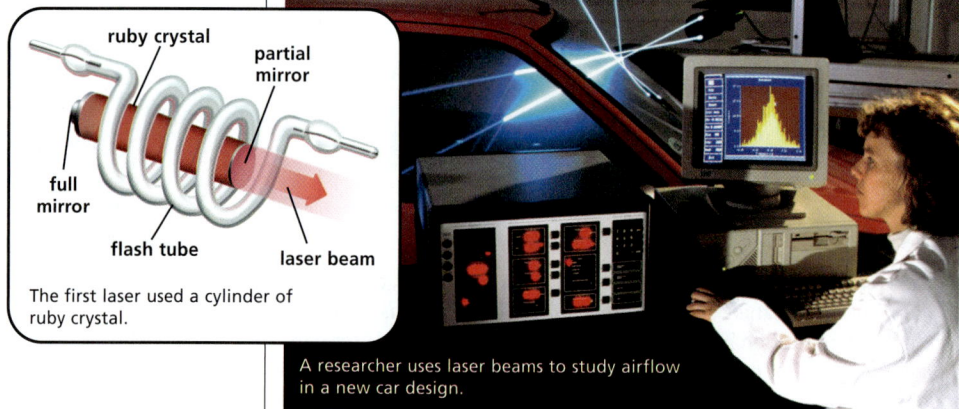

The first laser used a cylinder of ruby crystal.

A researcher uses laser beams to study airflow in a new car design.

Visual Uses of Lasers

Lasers are used today in an amazing variety of ways. One of these ways is to create devices that do the kind of work the human eye does—detecting and interpreting light waves. For example, surveyors once used telescopes to measure distances and angles. Now lasers can be used to take these measurements more precisely. Lasers are used to read bar codes, to scan images and pages of text, and to create holograms—three-dimensional images that appear to hover in the air. Holograms, which are hard to reproduce, are sometimes used in important documents so that the documents cannot be duplicated.

616 Unit 4: Waves, Sound, and Light

DIFFERENTIATE INSTRUCTION

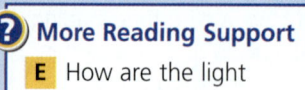
More Reading Support

E How are the light waves in a laser beam arranged? *exactly parallel*

F How are lasers used today? *to detect and interpret light waves*

English Learners English learners may not have prior knowledge of some concepts in this section. Explain holograms on p. 616 and aquariums on p. 617. Be sure students understand the difference between the film camera and the digital camera on p. 614.

Fiber Optics

Some laser applications use visible light in ways that have nothing to do with vision. One of the fastest growing technologies is fiber optics. **Fiber optics** is technology based on the use of laser light to send signals through transparent wires called optical fibers. Fiber optics makes use of a light behavior called total internal reflection. Total internal reflection occurs when all of the light inside a medium reflects off the inner surface of the medium.

When light strikes the inner surface of a transparent medium, it may pass through the surface or it may be reflected back into the medium. Which one occurs depends on the angle at which the light hits the surface. For example, if you look through the sides of an aquarium, you can see what is behind it. But if you look at the surface of the water from below, it will act like a mirror, reflecting the inside of the aquarium.

Laser light is very efficient at total internal reflection. It can travel long distances inside clear fibers of glass or other materials. Light always travels in a straight line; however, by reflecting off the sides of the fibers, laser light inside fibers can go around corners and even completely reverse direction.

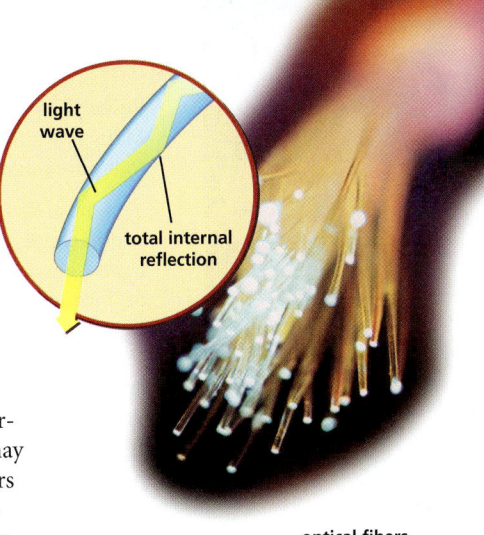

optical fibers

CHECK YOUR READING What is total internal reflection? What questions do you have about this light behavior?

Fiber optics is important in communications, because it can be used to transmit information very efficiently. Optical fibers can carry more signals than a corresponding amount of electrical cable. Optical cables can be used in place of electrical wires for telephone lines, cable television, and broadband Internet connections.

Fiber optics also has visual uses. For example, fiber optics is used in medicine to look inside the body. Using optical cable, doctors can examine organs and diagnose illnesses without surgery or x-rays. Optical fibers can also deliver laser light to specific points inside the body to help surgeons with delicate surgery.

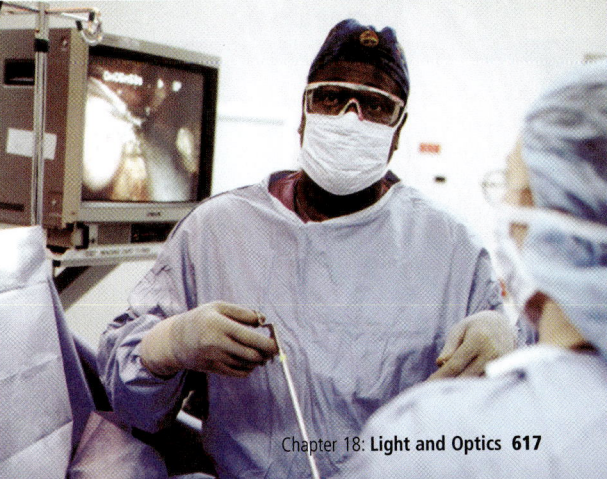

This surgeon uses fiber optics to see inside a patient's body.

Teach from Visuals

To help students interpret the fiber optics visual, ask:

What happens to light as it travels along an optical fiber? *It reflects off the inside surface of the fiber.*

Develop Critical Thinking

PROVIDE EXAMPLES Tell students that total internal reflection takes place only if the light is traveling within a more dense medium toward a less dense medium. Ask students for an example of this. *light traveling from water toward air*

Ongoing Assessment

CHECK YOUR READING Answer: *the reflection of the light from the inside surface of a transparent medium*

DIFFERENTIATE INSTRUCTION

More Reading Support

G How is fiber optics used in medicine? *to let doctors look inside the body*

Inclusion This activity can benefit students who are visually impaired as well as those who have learning disabilities. Have groups of students research the structure of an optical fiber and make a model, using any materials they wish. Several of these "optical fibers" can be bundled into a piece of PVC pipe, which can represent the outer jacket of an optical cable.

Integrate the Sciences

Because optical fibers are so flexible and can transmit and receive light, they are used in flexible digital cameras for medical imaging. An endoscope uses fiber optics and powerful lens systems to provide lighting and visualization of the interior of a body part. The endoscope uses two fiber-optic lines. One carries light into the body cavity, and the other carries the image of the body cavity back to the physician's viewing lens.

Reinforce the BIG idea

Have students relate the section to the Big Idea.

 Reinforcing Key Concepts, p. 256

Assess

 Section 18.4 Quiz, p. 65

Reteach

Have groups each make a poster of an optical tool of their choosing. They should give a short history of the development of the tool, show a ray diagram explaining the optics of the tool, and include pictures of various types of the tool. If students choose optical tools that have not been covered in the text, you may want them to give reports to the class.

Technology Resources

Have students visit **ClassZone.com** for reteaching of Key Concepts.

 CONTENT REVIEW

 CONTENT REVIEW CD-ROM

In this artist's illustration, a space elevator of the future draws power from a laser beam to climb to an orbiting space station.

Future Uses of Lasers

Research involving new uses of lasers continues at an amazing pace. Many new discoveries and developments in science and technology today are possible only because of lasers.

One area of research in which lasers have made a big impact is nanotechnology—the development of super-tiny machines and tools. Laser light can be controlled very precisely, so scientists can use it to perform extremely fine operations. For example, lasers could be used to cut out parts to make molecule-size motors. Lasers can also be used as "optical tweezers" to handle extremely small objects such as molecules. Scientists are even beginning to use lasers to change the shape of molecules. They do this by varying the laser's wavelength.

Future applications of lasers are also sure to involve new ways of transferring energy. Remember that a wave is a disturbance that transfers energy. Laser light is made up of EM waves. EM waves can move energy over great distances without losing any of it. When EM waves encounter a material medium, their energy can then be converted into other forms and put to use.

One possible future use of lasers is to supply energy to spacecraft. Scientists imagine a day when orbiting space stations will make rockets unnecessary. A cable between the ground and the station will make it possible for a "space elevator" to escape Earth's gravity by climbing up the cable. The elevator will be powered by an Earth-based laser. A device on board the elevator will convert the laser's energy into electrical power.

18.4 Review

KEY CONCEPTS
1. How do refracting and reflecting telescopes use convex lenses and mirrors?
2. What is different about the way a camera focuses images from the way an eye focuses images?
3. How is laser light different from ordinary light?

CRITICAL THINKING
4. **Predict** What would happen to laser light if it passed through a prism?
5. **Analyze** What are two ways reflection is involved in fiber optics?

◉ CHALLENGE
6. **Apply** How could the speed of light and a laser beam be used to measure the distance between two satellites?

618 Unit 4: Waves, Sound, and Light

ANSWERS

1. Refracting telescopes use one lens to focus and another to magnify the image; reflecting telescopes use a lens to magnify an image focused by a mirror.

2. The eye focuses by changing shape of the lens. A camera focuses by changing distance between the lens and the film.

3. Laser light is made up of a single wavelength and a pure color. Ordinary light is made up of many different wavelengths.

4. It would not produce a color spectrum, because all of it would be refracted the same amount.

5. to make a laser and to keep the laser light within optical fibers

6. One satellite could shine the beam at the other satellite. Measure the time it takes for the beam to reflect and return from the other satellite. Use the speed of light to calculate the distance.

SCIENCE on the JOB

PHOTOGRAPHER

Optics in Photography

Photographers use the science of optics to help them make the best photographs possible. For example, a portrait photographer chooses the right equipment and lighting to make each person look his or her best. A photographer needs to understand how light reflects, refracts, and diffuses to achieve just the right effect.

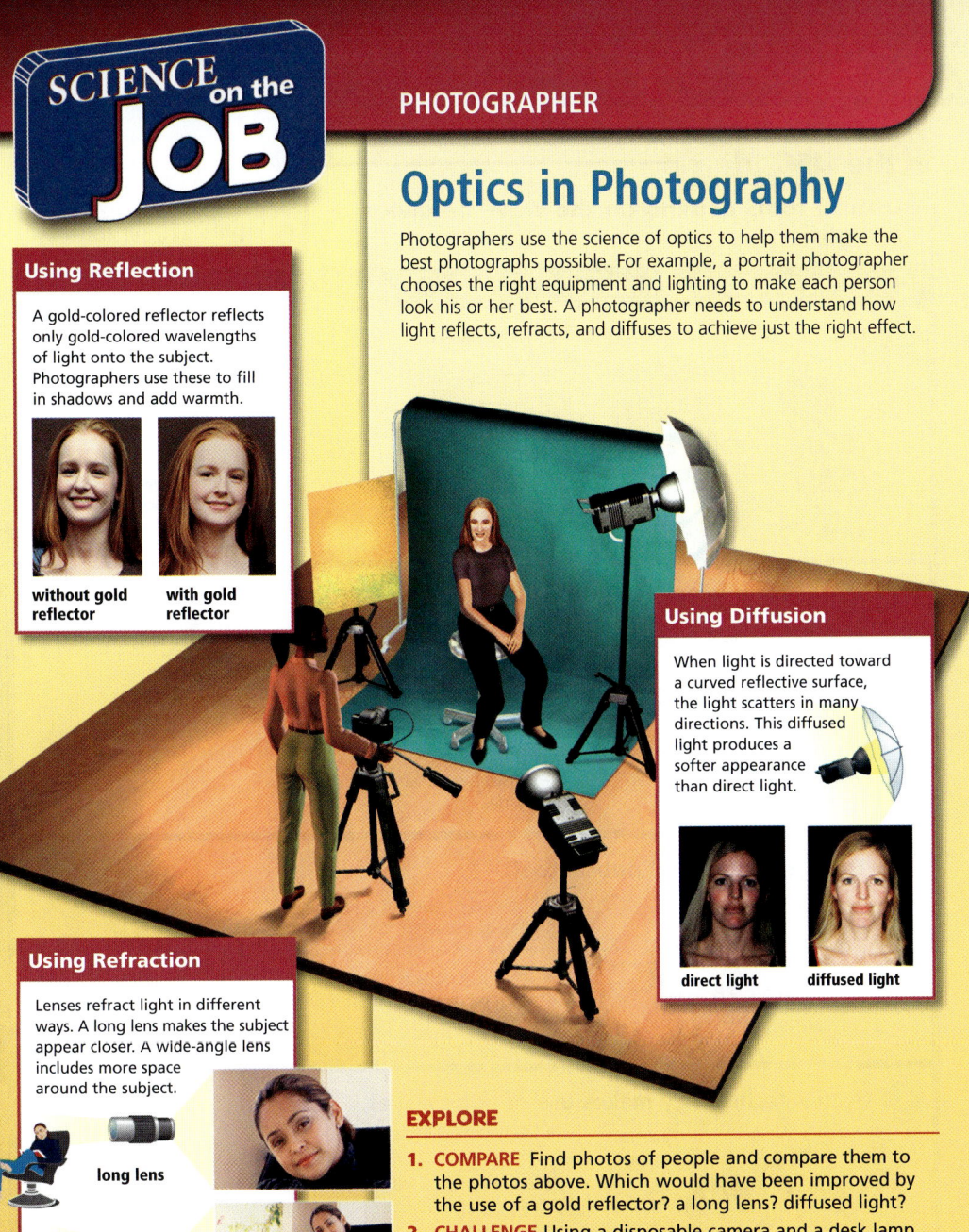

Using Reflection
A gold-colored reflector reflects only gold-colored wavelengths of light onto the subject. Photographers use these to fill in shadows and add warmth.

without gold reflector | with gold reflector

Using Diffusion
When light is directed toward a curved reflective surface, the light scatters in many directions. This diffused light produces a softer appearance than direct light.

direct light | diffused light

Using Refraction
Lenses refract light in different ways. A long lens makes the subject appear closer. A wide-angle lens includes more space around the subject.

long lens
wide-angle lens

EXPLORE

1. **COMPARE** Find photos of people and compare them to the photos above. Which would have been improved by the use of a gold reflector? a long lens? diffused light?
2. **CHALLENGE** Using a disposable camera and a desk lamp, experiment with photography yourself. Try using a piece of paper as a reflector and observe its effects on the photograph. What happens if you use more than one reflector? What happens if you use a different color of paper?

Chapter 18: Light and Optics 619

SCIENCE ON THE JOB
Relevance of Science to Non-science Jobs

Set Learning Goal
To understand why photographers need a knowledge of optics

Present the Science
Photographers can choose from a wide variety of lenses.
- A **wide-angle lens** has a very short focal length, which takes in a wide field of view. Because of its short focal length, it must be close to the film to form a sharp image. Wide-angle lenses produce a relatively small image of the subject and include much of the background.
- **Telephoto lenses,** also called **long lenses,** have a long focal length and a narrow field of view. They must be relatively far from the film. They produce an enlarged image that seems closer than it really is.
- A **zoom lens** has a variable focal length. Many photographers like using this lens so they don't have to carry several lenses.

Discussion Question
Ask: Why must photographers understand how colors form from the interaction of different wavelengths of light? *Color affects the appearance of a photograph in subtle ways. Photographers can insert color filters in front of the camera lens to soften the image, create shadows and contrast, or tone down harsh colors.*

Close
Ask: When would a photographer want to use a wide-angle lens? a long lens? *Sample Answer: A wide-angle lens could be used for panoramic photographs of scenery or crowd scenes. Long lenses are useful for close-ups of small details or for blow-ups.*

EXPLORE

1. **COMPARE** Sample Answer: A gold reflector will improve photographs by filling in shadows and adding warmth. A long lens enlarges details. Diffused light softens images.
2. **CHALLENGE** Multiple reflectors scatter the light coming from all directions and eliminate shadows. Colored reflectors absorb some wavelengths of light, changing the color of the light reflected off the subject.

Chapter 18 **619**

CHAPTER 18 • REVIEW

BACK TO

All optical technology uses reflection or refraction of light waves. Give students a list of optical tools and ask them to state which of these two phenomena are important for the operation of the tool. *refraction: microscope, camera, refracting telescope, contact lenses, corrective eyeglasses; reflection: lasers, periscope, fiber optics; both: reflecting telescope*

KEY CONCEPTS SUMMARY

SECTION 18.1
Ask: How does regular reflection help mirrors form images? *Regular reflection causes the rays reflected from the mirror to keep the same arrangement as the rays coming from the object.*

SECTION 18.2
Ask: If the penguin is more than two focal lengths from the lens, what kind of image is formed? *a reduced inverted image*

Ask: If the penguin is between one and two focal lengths from the lens, what kind of image is formed? *an inverted image that is larger than the penguin*

SECTION 18.3
Ask: Does the eye shown need a corrective lens for normal sight? Why? *No; the image is focused directly on the retina.*

SECTION 18.4
Ask: Why does the tube have mirrors at both ends? *The mirrors reflect the light back and forth. One of the mirrors allows some of the light waves through, producing a laser beam.*

Review Concepts

- Big Idea Flow Chart, p. T25
- Chapter Outline, pp. T31–T32

---

18 Chapter Review

the BIG idea
Optical tools depend on the wave behavior of light.

CONTENT REVIEW
CLASSZONE.COM

KEY CONCEPTS SUMMARY

1 Mirrors form images by reflecting light.

flat mirror

- Light rays obey the law of reflection.
- Mirrors work by regular reflection.
- Curved mirrors can form images that are distorted in useful ways.

VOCABULARY
optics p. 593
law of reflection p. 594
regular reflection p. 594
diffuse reflection p. 594
image p. 595
convex p. 596
concave p. 596
focal point p. 597

2 Lenses form images by refracting light.

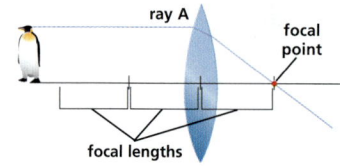
ray A
focal point
focal lengths

- Lenses have curved surfaces that refract parallel light waves in different amounts.
- Convex lenses bend light inward toward a focal point.
- Concave lenses spread light out.
- Lenses form a variety of useful images.

VOCABULARY
lens p. 601
focal length p. 603

3 The eye is a natural optical tool.

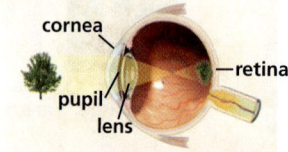
cornea
pupil
lens
retina

- The eyes of humans and many animals use lenses to focus images on the retina.
- The retina detects images and sends information about them to the brain.

VOCABULARY
cornea p. 607
pupil p. 607
retina p. 607

4 Optical technology makes use of light waves.

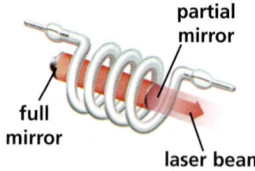
partial mirror
full mirror
laser beam

- Many optical tools are made by combining mirrors and lenses.
- Examples of optical tools include telescopes, microscopes, cameras, and lasers.
- Lasers have a wide variety of uses.

VOCABULARY
laser p. 615
fiber optics p. 617

620 Unit 4: Waves, Sound, and Light

Technology Resources

Have students visit ClassZone.com or use the CD-ROM for a cumulative review of concepts.

 CONTENT REVIEW

 CONTENT REVIEW CD-ROM

Engage students in a whole-class interactive review of Key Concepts. Edit content as you wish.

 POWER PRESENTATIONS

Reviewing Vocabulary

For each item below, fill in the blank. If the right column is blank, give a brief description or definition. If the left column is blank, give the correct term.

Term	Description
1.	shape like the inside of a bowl
2. convex	
3.	science of light, vision, and related technology
4.	picture of object formed by light rays
5. focal point	
6.	controls the amount of light entering the eye
7.	distance between mirror or lens and place where light rays meet
8. fiber optics	
9. law of reflection	
10.	concentrated, parallel light waves of a single wavelength

Reviewing Key Concepts

Multiple Choice *Choose the letter of the best answer.*

11. What shape is a mirror that reflects parallel light rays toward a focal point?
    a. convex   c. concave
    b. flat   d. regular

12. According to the law of reflection, a light ray striking a mirror
    a. continues moving through the mirror in the same direction
    b. moves into the mirror at a slightly different angle
    c. bounces off the mirror toward the direction it came from
    d. bounces off the mirror at the same angle it hits

13. Reflecting telescopes focus images using
    a. several mirrors
    b. several lenses
    c. both mirrors and lenses
    d. either a mirror or a lens, but not both

14. Ordinary light differs from laser light in that ordinary light waves
    a. all have the same wavelength
    b. tend to spread out
    c. stay parallel to one another
    d. all have their peaks lined up

15. Nearsighted vision is corrected when lenses
    a. reflect light away from the eye
    b. allow light rays to focus on the retina
    c. allow light to focus slightly past the retina
    d. help light rays reflect regularly

16. Lasers do work similar to that of human vision when they are used to
    a. perform surgery
    b. send phone signals over optical cable
    c. scan bar codes at the grocery store
    d. change the shape of molecules

Short Answer *Write a short answer to each question.*

17. Name one optical tool, describe how it works, and explain some of its uses.

18. How are the images that are produced by a convex mirror different from those produced by a concave mirror?

19. Describe what typically happens to a ray of light from the time it enters the eye until it strikes the retina.

20. How do lenses correct nearsightedness and farsightedness?

21. What does a refracting telescope have in common with a simple microscope?

22. Describe two ways the distance of an object from a lens can affect the appearance of the object's image.

Chapter 18: **Light and Optics** 621

ASSESSMENT RESOURCES

UNIT ASSESSMENT BOOK
- Chapter Test A, pp. 66–69
- Chapter Test B, pp. 70–73
- Chapter Test C, pp. 74–77
- Alternative Assessment, pp. 78–79
- Unit Test, A, B, & C, pp. 80–91

SPANISH ASSESSMENT BOOK
- Spanish Chapter Test, pp. 293–296
- Spanish Unit Test, pp. 297–300

Technology Resources

Edit test items and answer choices.

 Test Generator CD-ROM

Visit ClassZone.com to extend test practice.

 Test Practice

Reviewing Vocabulary

1. concave
2. curved outward like the bottom of a spoon
3. optics
4. image
5. the point where a concave mirror focuses light rays
6. pupil
7. focal length
8. technology based on the use of laser light
9. states that the angle of reflection equals the angle of incidence
10. laser beam

Reviewing Key Concepts

11. c
12. d
13. c
14. b
15. b
16. c
17. Answers will vary. For example, students might name a microscope and describe how it uses lenses to make images of small objects.
18. Convex mirrors produce reduced, right-side up images. Concave mirrors can produce images that are reduced, enlarged, right-side up, or upside down.
19. Light first enters the eye through the cornea, where it is refracted. It then continues through the pupil, which controls how much light enters the eye. After the pupil, the light passes through the lens of the eye, where the light is refracted to make adjustments for nearby and distant objects.
20. by spreading out the rays of light for nearsightedness and bending light rays inward for farsightedness; in both cases, they cause the image to fall on the retina
21. Both use a convex lens to focus and enlarge an image.
22. The distance can change the image's size and determine whether the image is upside down or right side up.

Chapter 18 **621**

Thinking Critically

23. C 24. D 25. A 26. B

For 27–32, sample answers are given.

27. reflect light; curved changes direction of light
28. bend light rays; convex bends rays inward, concave bends rays outward
29. involved in refraction of light by lenses; focal point is a point, focal length is a distance.
30. both are vision problems; nearsighted people can't see far objects clearly, farsighted people can't see near objects clearly
31. contain convex lenses; microscope focuses enlarged image, telescope focuses reduced image
32. involve reflection of light rays; in regular reflection parallel light rays reflect in the same direction, while in total internal reflection light inside a transparent medium reflects off the inner surface
33. distance from the lens to retina; image forms on the retina.
34. Laser light waves don't spread out; they stay parallel as they are reflected through the fiber.
35. more curved to shorten focal length
36. Lasers used in surgery have narrow beams that can be precisely controlled and carry energy to cut tissues and seal blood vessels.

the BIG idea

37. The refractor is used to test a person's eyesight. Light waves bend when they pass through the lens of a refractor. The patient benefits by having vision problems corrected with eyeglasses.
38. Sketches should show two mirrors at right angles and standing on a third mirror to form a half cube. Light rays bounce off each mirror at the same angle that they hit. Light striking the corner where mirrors meet is reflected from mirror to mirror, then reflected back parallel to original path.

UNIT PROJECTS

Have students present their projects. Use the appropriate rubrics from the URB to evaluate their work.

Unit Projects, pp. 5–10

Thinking Critically

INTERPRET In the four diagrams below, light rays are shown interacting with a material medium. For the next four questions, choose the letter of the diagram that answers the question.

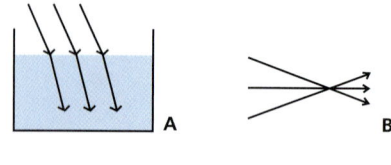
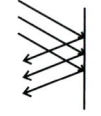
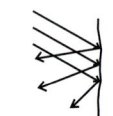

23. Which diagram shows regular reflection?
24. Which diagram shows diffuse reflection?
25. Which diagram shows refraction?
26. Which diagram shows light rays converging at a focal point?

COMPARE AND CONTRAST Copy the chart below. For each pair of terms, write down one way they are alike (compare) and one way they are different (contrast).

Terms	Compare	Contrast
27. flat mirror, curved mirror		
28. convex lens, concave lens		
29. focal point, focal length		
30. nearsighted, farsighted		
31. simple microscope, refracting telescope		
32. regular reflection, total internal reflection		

33. **INFER** What is the approximate focal length of the eye's lens? How do you know?
34. **ANALYZE** Why is laser light used in fiber optics?
35. **APPLY** In order to increase the magnification of a magnifying glass, would you need to make the convex surfaces of the lens more or less curved?
36. **APPLY** Describe a possible use for laser light not mentioned in the chapter. What characteristics of laser light does this application make use of?

the BIG idea

37. **SYNTHESIZE** Using what you have learned in this chapter, describe two possible uses of an optical tool like the one shown on pages 590–591. Explain what wave behaviors of light would be involved in these uses. Then explain how these uses could benefit the person in the photo.
38. **APPLY** Make a sketch of an optical tool that would use three mirrors to make a beam of light return to its source. Your sketch should include:
    - the path of light waves through the tool
    - labels indicating the names of parts and how they affect the light
    - several sentences describing one possible use of the tool

UNIT PROJECTS

Evaluate all the data, results, and information from your project folder. Prepare to present your project.

MONITOR AND RETEACH

If students have trouble applying the concepts in items 23–26, conduct a demonstration using a mirror, a flashlight, a prism, and a convex lens. Use the mirror to redirect a beam of light by reflection. Use the prism to redirect the beam by refraction. Use the lens to focus the beam into a concentrated spot. Then have students diagram the path of the light rays in each of the three events.

Students may benefit from summarizing sections of the chapter.

Summarizing the Chapter, pp. 282–283

Standardized Test Practice

For practice on your state test, go to...
TEST PRACTICE
CLASSZONE.COM

Interpreting Diagrams

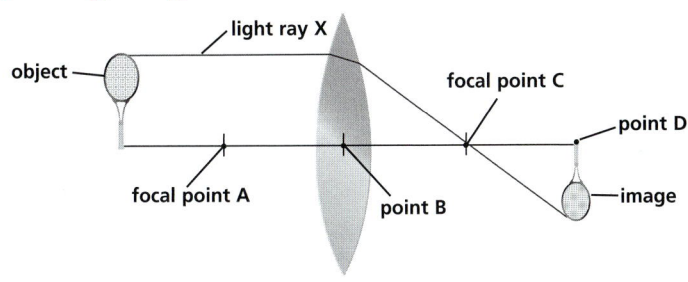

Study the diagram above and then answer the questions that follow.

1. What kind of lens is shown in the diagram?
   a. concave
   b. convex
   c. flat
   d. prism

2. What happens to parallel light rays passing through this type of lens?
   a. They become polarized.
   b. They form a rainbow.
   c. They bend inward.
   d. They bend outward.

3. All light rays parallel to light ray X will pass through what point?
   a. point A
   b. point B
   c. point C
   d. point D

4. How far is the object in the diagram from the lens?
   a. less than one focal length
   b. one focal length
   c. about two focal lengths
   d. more than three focal lengths

5. Where would you position a screen in order to see the image in focus on the screen?
   a. at point A
   b. at point B
   c. at point C
   d. at point D

Extended Response

Answer the two questions below in detail. Include some of the terms from the word box. Underline each term you use in your answer.

concave	focal point	real image
convex	refraction	virtual image
flat mirror	reflection	magnifying glass

6. What kind of mirror would you use to see what is happening over a broad area? Why?

7. Choose one of the following optical tools and explain how it uses mirrors and/or lenses to form an image: camera, telescope, periscope, microscope.

Chapter 18: **Light and Optics** 623

Interpreting Diagrams

1. b 3. c 5. d
2. c 4. c

Extended Response

6. RUBRIC
4 points for a response that thoroughly answers the question and uses the following terms accurately:
  • convex   • concave

Sample: I would use a <u>convex</u> mirror because parallel light rays move away from each other. My image in a convex mirror will appear smaller than me. You will be able to see a broad area because the images would look like they have shrunk. If I use a <u>concave</u> mirror and stand inside the focal point, my image will appear very large, and I would not be able to see a broad area.

3 points for a less thorough response that uses both terms accurately
2 points for a response that adequately answers the question and uses one term accurately
1 point for a response that adequately answers the question, but does not use the terms

7. RUBRIC
4 points for a response that correctly answers the question and uses the following terms accurately:
  • convex • focal point • real image

Sample: A film camera uses a <u>convex</u> lens to produce images of objects that are more than two focal lengths away. The images are reduced in size and upside down. The camera does not change the shape of its lens to change the <u>focal point</u>. Instead, you can move the lens nearer to or farther away from the film until the object you want to photograph is in focus. In a camera, the focal length is the distance between the lens and the <u>real image</u> of the object.

3 points for a response that correctly answers the question and uses two terms accurately
2 points for a response that uses one term accurately
1 point for a response that correctly answers the question, but does not use the terms

METACOGNITIVE ACTIVITY

Have students answer the following questions in their **Science Notebook:**
1. How does what you learned about the eye relate to your life?
2. Describe a scenario in which you might use an optical tool.
3. Summarize the key concepts and main ideas of this chapter that apply to your Unit Project.

Chapter 18 **623**

McDougal Littell Science

Electricity and Magnetism

Electricity and Magnetism
Contents Overview

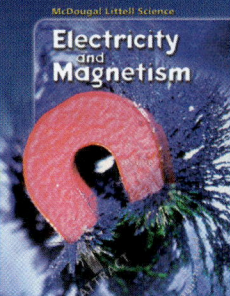

Unit Features
FRONTIERS IN SCIENCE Electronics in Music 626
TIMELINES IN SCIENCE The Story of Electronics 696

19 Electricity 630
the BIG idea
Moving electric charges transfer energy.

20 Circuits and Electronics 664
the BIG idea
Circuits control the flow of electric charge.

21 Magnetism 700
the BIG idea
Current can produce magnetism, and magnetism can produce current.

FRONTIERS in Science

VIDEO SUMMARY

SCIENTIFIC AMERICAN FRONTIERS

"Toy Symphony," a segment of the *Scientific American Frontiers* series that aired on PBS stations, documents new technologies being used in music composition and performance. At MIT's Media Lab, music professor Tod Machover has developed a "hyperviolin," which can record subtle aspects of violin playing such as bow tilt, speed, and pressure, and use these data to create new sounds. As violinist Joshua Bell plays Machover's *Toy Symphony*, a computer program picks up the sound and doubles the melody an octave lower. Another musical invention demonstrated in the video is the Beatbug, an electronic device that loops and replays simple rhythms made when the player strikes the outer shell of the instrument. In another part of the lab, students create music with the Hyperscore computer program, which uses shapes, colors, and textures instead of traditional musical notation.

National Science Education Standards

A.9.a–d Understandings About Scientific Inquiry

E.6.a–f Understandings About Science and Technology

F.5.a–e Science and Technology in Society

G.1.a–b Science as a Human Endeavor

G.2.a Nature of Science

FRONTIERS in Science

Electronics in Music

How are electronics changing the way we make and listen to music?

SCIENTIFIC AMERICAN FRONTIERS

View the video segment "Toy Symphony" to learn about some creative new ways in which music and electronics can be combined.

626 Unit 5: Electricity and Magnetism

ADDITIONAL RESOURCES

Technology Resources

 Scientific American Frontiers Video: *Toy Symphony:* 11-minute video segment that introduces the unit.

 ClassZone.com
CAREER LINK, recording engineer, audio engineer

Guide student viewing and comprehension of the video:

 Video Teaching Guide, pp. 1–2; Video Viewing Guide, p. 3; Video Wrap-Up, p. 4

Scientific American Frontiers Video Guide, pp. 55–58

Unit projects procedures and rubrics:

 Unit Projects, pp. 5–10

626 Unit 5: **Electricity and Magnetism**

The quality of amplified sound waves can be controlled using electronics. Controls on this soundboard are adjusted in preparation for an outdoor concert.

Catching a Sound Wave

Everyone knows that music and electronics go together. If you want to hear music, you turn on a radio or TV, choose a CD or DVD to play, or listen to a computer file downloaded in MP3. All of these formats use electronics to record, play, and amplify music. Some of the most recent developments in music also use electronics to produce the music in the first place. For example, the orchestral music playing in the background of the last blockbuster movie you saw may not have been played by an orchestra at all. It may have been produced electronically on a computer.

Music consists of sound, and sound is a wave. Inside your TV or stereo equipment, electronic circuits represent sound waves as analog signals or digital signals. In analog recordings a peak in the original sound wave corresponds to a peak in the current. Radio and TV broadcasts are usually analog signals. The sound wave is converted to electromagnetic waves sent out through the air. Your radio or TV set receives these waves and converts them back to a sound wave.

In digital sound recordings the system samples the incoming sound wave at frequent intervals of time, such as 44,100 times per second. The system measures the height of each wave and assigns it a number. The numbers form a digital signal. This information can then be stored and transmitted. The playback electronics, such as CD players and DVD players, convert the signal back to a sound wave for you to hear.

Technology

Focus students' attention on "Making Music" on pages 628–629. Discuss how electronic technology provides ways to change or create music. Ask:

- What device did recording engineers use in the past to record sound? What can they use now? *large electronic consoles; Musical Instrument Digital Interface (MIDI)*
- How is MIDI technology different from CD, DVD, or MP3 players? *MIDI represents the instructions for another device to play the music, while digital devices such as CD players represent the actual sound waves.*

Design Technology

Ask: In developing the technology to record and store sound, what questions might engineers have asked? *Sample answer: How much computer space is needed to store a song in a digital format?*

Digital Devices

In a compact disc (CD), the numbers representing the sound wave are coded into a series of microscopic pits in a long spiral track burned into the plastic of the CD. A laser beam scans the track and reads the pits, converting the data back into numbers. This information is then converted into sound waves by an electronic circuit in the CD player. CDs can store up to 74 minutes of music because the pits are only a few millionths of a meter in size. Digital videodiscs (DVDs) often have several layers, each with a separate data track, and use even smaller tracks and pits than CDs use. As a result, a DVD can store seven times as much information as a CD.

The amount of computer space needed to represent a song in normal digital format is too large to store very many songs on a single device. However, the development of a compression program called MP3 decreases the size of a typical song to one-tenth its original size. This enables you to buy and download a song from the Internet in minutes instead of hours and store files on your computer or MP3 player without taking up too much space.

MP3 players store digital files that are compressed in size.

Making Music

These advances in recording and playing music enables you to listen to music, whatever your taste in music happens to be. Electronic technology also allows you to change the music or even generate your own music, as shown in the video. Recording engineers used to work with large electronic consoles with hundreds of switches in order to blend different singers and background

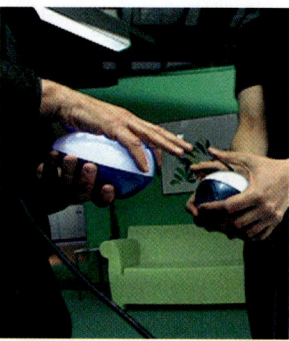

SCIENTIFIC AMERICAN FRONTIERS

View the "Toy Symphony" segment of your *Scientific American Frontiers* video to learn how electronic devices allow people to interact with music in new ways.

IN THIS SCENE FROM THE VIDEO Kids play with Beatbugs at MIT's Media Lab.

PLAYING WITH SOUNDS At the Massachusetts Institute of Technology (MIT) Media Lab, Tod Machover and his colleagues have invented several new musical instruments that are based on electronics. One such invention is the hypervoilin, demonstrated by concert violinist Joshua Bell. As Joshua plays the violin, a computer registers the movements of the bow and produces new and different sounds from the movements. Other musical electronic devices in the lab are designed to allow someone with little or no experience with an instrument to play and compose music.

With Beatbugs—small interactive devices—kids can play music and collaborate with others. They can also compose and edit their own music. Using new computer software, a ten-year-old boy was able to compose an entire symphony played by the German Symphony Orchestra.

628 Unit 5: Electricity and Magnetism

DIFFERENTIATE INSTRUCTION

More Reading Support

 About how many minutes of music can a CD store? *74 minutes*

D What does the compression program MP3 do to a song file? *decreases its size*

Below Level Group students in pairs and ask each pair to make a chart comparing the characteristics of digital devices. Have students write down the name of each digital device, such as a CD, and then organize them in order of storage capacity, least to greatest. Then have students describe each device's characteristics on the chart.

628 Unit 5: **Electricity and Magnetism**

Home recording studios are possible because of new electronic technology.

instruments or to add special effects such as echoes or distortion. Now this can all be done on a laptop computer, using the Musical Instrument Digital Interface (MIDI).

MIDI technology is an advancement in digital technology. Whereas CD, DVD, and MP3 files represent the sound waves themselves, MIDI files represent the instructions for another device—such as an electronic instrument—to play the music. With MIDI, you can connect an electronic keyboard directly to a computer and compose and edit your own music, layer in the sounds of different instruments, and dub in special effects. Once you understand how to use electronics to produce the sound waves you want, you can become your own favorite band.

UNANSWERED Questions

Every year, scientists develop new technologies affecting the way we produce and listen to music. As advances in music technology are made, new question arise.

- Are there electronic sounds that no one has heard before?
- How will the development of music technology affect who is producing music?
- What type of devices will people be using to listen to music in 50 years?

UNIT PROJECTS

As you study this unit, work alone or with a group on one of these projects.

Multimedia Presentation

Put together an informative presentation that explains how electric guitars work.

- Gather information about electric guitars. Learn how they use both electricity and magnetism.
- Give a presentation that uses mixed media, such as a computer slide show, model, poster, or tape recording.

Build a Radio

Build a working radio from simple materials.

- Using books or the Internet, find instructions for building a simple crystal radio.
- Collect the materials and assemble the radio. Modify the design of the radio to improve it.
- Demonstrate the radio to the class and explain how it works.

Design an Invention

Design an electronic invention.

- Select a purpose for your invention, such as a toy, a fan, or a burglar alarm. Write a paragraph that explains the purpose of your invention.
- Draw a sketch of your design and modify it if necessary.
- Make a pamphlet to advertise your invention. If possible, build the invention and include photographs of it in the pamphlet.

Learn more about careers in music and computer science.

UNANSWERED Questions

Have students read the questions and think of some of their own. Remind them that scientists usually end up with more questions—that inquiry is the driving force of science.

- With the class, generate on the board a list of new questions.
- Students can add to the list after they watch the *Scientific American Frontiers* Video.
- Students can use the list as a springboard for choosing their Unit Projects.

UNIT PROJECTS

Encourage students to pick the project that most appeals to them. Point out that each is long-term and will take several weeks to complete. You might group or pair students to work on projects and in some cases guide student choice. Some of the projects have student choice built into them.

Each project has two worksheet pages, including a rubric. Use the pages to guide students through criteria, process, and schedule.

 Unit Projects, pp. 5–10

REVISIT concepts introduced in this article:

Chapter 19
- Materials can become electrically charged, pp. 633–640
- Charges can move, pp. 642–649
- Electric current, pp. 652–658

Chapter 20
- Charge needs a continuous path, pp. 667–673
- Circuits, pp. 675–679
- Electronic technology, pp. 681–689

Chapter 21
- Magnetism is a force, pp. 703–710
- Current can produce magnetism, pp. 712–718
- Magnetism can produce current, pp. 719–723
- Generators supply electrical energy, pp. 726–730

DIFFERENTIATE INSTRUCTION

More Reading Support

E What does MIDI allow musicians and recording engineers to do to music?
Sample answers: compose and edit music; layer in different sounds from various instruments

Differentiate Unit Projects Projects are appropriate for varying abilities. Allow students to choose the ones that interest them most. Encourage them to vary the products they produce throughout the year.

Below Level Encourage students to try "Design an Invention."

Advanced Challenge students to complete "Build a Radio."

CHAPTER 19 Electricity

Physical Science
UNIFYING PRINCIPLES

PRINCIPLE 1
Matter is made of particles too small to see.

PRINCIPLE 2
Matter changes form and moves from place to place.

PRINCIPLE 3
Energy changes from one form to another, but it cannot be created or destroyed.

PRINCIPLE 4
Physical forces affect the movement of all matter on Earth and throughout the universe.

Unit 5: Electricity and Magnetism
BIG IDEAS

CHAPTER 19 Electricity
Moving electric charges transfer energy.

CHAPTER 20 Circuits and Electronics
Circuits control the flow of electric charge.

CHAPTER 21 Magnetism
Current can produce magnetism, and magnetism can produce current.

CHAPTER 19 KEY CONCEPTS

SECTION 1
Materials can become electrically charged.
1. Electric charge is a property of matter.
2. Static charges are caused by the movement of electrons.
3. Technology uses static electricity.

SECTION 2
Charges can move from one place to another.
1. Static charges have potential energy.
2. Materials affect charge movement.

SECTION 3
Electric current is a flow of charge.
1. Electric charge can flow continuously.
2. Electric cells supply electric current.

The Big Idea Flow Chart is available on p. T1 in the **UNIT TRANSPARENCY BOOK**.

629A Unit 5: **Electricity and Magnetism**

Previewing Content

SECTION 1 — Materials can become electrically charged. pp. 633–641

1. **Electric charge is a property of matter.**
   Objects can have a positive, negative, or neutral charge. A proton has a positive charge. An electron has a negative charge. Electric charge is measured in a unit called coulombs. Two objects with **electric charge** exert an electric force on each other. Electric force can be exerted even if the objects are separated by empty space. The amount of force is greater if the charges are greater and less if the distance between the objects is greater. Like charges, such as two positive charges, will repel each other, while unlike charges will attract each other. (Neutrally charged objects do not exert an electric force on each other.) The space around a charge where an electric force can be exerted if another charged particle is present is called an **electric field.**

2. **Static charges are caused by the movement of electrons.**
   Objects that have equal numbers of electrons and protons have a neutral, or zero, charge. An object with more protons than electrons has a positive charge, and an object with more electrons than protons has a negative charge. The greater the imbalance, the greater the charge an object has. In most cases, it is the movement of electrons that causes an object to gain a **static charge.**
   - Charging by contact occurs when electrons move because materials are touching. In this case, one material attracts electrons more strongly than the other.
   - Charging by **induction** occurs when a charged object produces a temporary movement of electrons in another object. This movement creates a temporary charge imbalance within the object.

3. **Technology uses static electricity.**
   Differences in charge attract toner to letters or images on paper in a photocopier. In electrostatic air filters, charged plates attract oppositely charged particles from the air. Static charges are used to make paint stick better to new cars.

SECTION 2 — Charges can move from one place to another. pp. 642–651

1. **Static charges have potential energy.**
   A charged object held near another charged object has potential energy. Just as a rock falls to the ground when it is let go, one charge will move toward or away from another charge if it is not fixed in place. A proton placed near a charged object will have a certain amount of potential energy due to its position. The **electric potential** of a charged object is the potential energy per unit charge that another charge would have if it were in the object's electric field. Electric potential is measured in **volts.** The difference in the electric potential at two different points is called the voltage between those two points. If there is a path for the charges to follow, they will move from higher potential energy to a lower potential energy.

2. **Materials affect charge movement.**
   Electrical **resistance** is a measure of how easily charge moves through a material. Resistance is measured in **ohms.** Resistance depends on the size, the shape, and the type of material.
   - Charge moves easily through a **conductor.**
   - Charge does not move easily through an **insulator.**
   - Superconductors have almost no resistance at extremely low temperatures.

   Grounding provides a charge with a safe path through a low-resistance material instead of one with a high resistance. In the picture below, the cable has less resistance than the building.

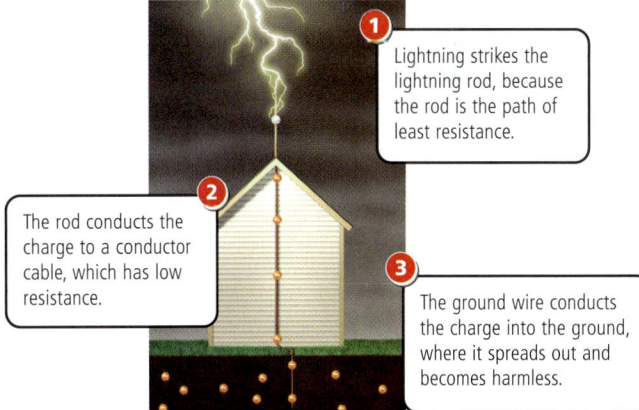

1. Lightning strikes the lightning rod, because the rod is the path of least resistance.
2. The rod conducts the charge to a conductor cable, which has low resistance.
3. The ground wire conducts the charge into the ground, where it spreads out and becomes harmless.

Common Misconceptions

CHARGING BY CONTACT Students may think that charging by contact can occur only when two objects are rubbed together. In fact, electrons can move from one object to another without rubbing, although rubbing does increase the contact, and therefore the amount of charge transferred.

This misconception is addressed on p. 635.

MISCONCEPTION DATABASE
CLASSZONE.COM Background on student misconceptions

MOVING STATIC CHARGES Students may think that static charges don't move. In reality, static charges move when a path is available and there is a difference in electric potential.

This misconception is addressed on p. 644.

Chapter 19: **Electricity** 629B

Previewing Content

SECTION 3
Electric current is a flow of charge.
pp. 652–659

1. Electric charge can flow continuously.
If a constant potential difference, or voltage, is maintained between two points and there is a path along which electrons can move between those two points, **electric current** results.

- Electric current, the continuous flow of charge between two points at different potentials, is measured in **amperes.** One ampere is equal to a flow rate of one coulomb per second.
- You can measure current using an ammeter, voltage using a voltmeter, and resistance using an ohmmeter. A multimeter can measure all three values. **Ohm's law** shows the relationships among current (*I*), voltage (*V*), and resistance (*R*).

$$I = \frac{V}{R}$$

2. Electric cells supply electric current.
An **electric cell** maintains a constant voltage between its two terminals by using the physical and chemical properties of different materials.

- An electrochemical cell contains two electrodes suspended in an electrolyte, which undergoes chemical reactions with the electrodes. Batteries contain two or more electrochemical cells.
- Primary cells are either wet cells or dry cells in which chemical reactions continue until at least one reactant is used up. Most household batteries are primary dry cells, like the one shown below.

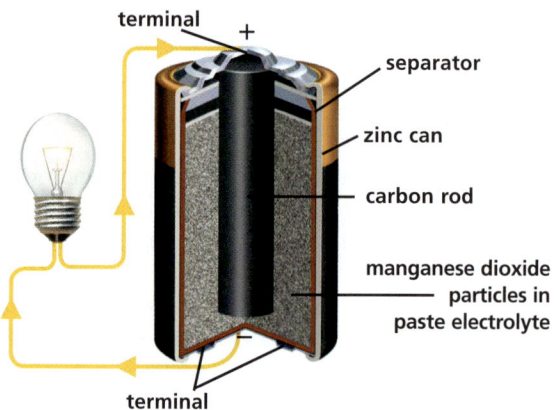

- Some batteries are storage cells in which the chemical reactions can be reversed. Such batteries are rechargeable.
- Solar cells contain materials that absorb energy from the Sun or other sources of light and then release electrons to create an electric current.

MISCONCEPTION DATABASE
CLASSZONE.COM Background on student misconceptions

Common Misconceptions

SPEED OF ELECTRON MOVEMENT IN CIRCUITS Students may think that electrons move through a circuit instantly or at the speed of light. Electrons actually move very slowly through a circuit. The energy changes in the electric field, however, do move at the speed of light.

 This misconception is addressed in Teach Difficult Concepts on p. 653.

Previewing Labs

Lab Generator CD-ROM — Edit these Pupil Edition labs and generate alternative labs.

EXPLORE the BIG idea

How Do the Pieces of Tape Interact? p. 631
Students produce static electricity in strips of tape and note its effects.
TIME 10 minutes
MATERIALS 3 strips of transparent tape

Why Does the Water React Differently? p. 631
Students observe the effect of a charged and discharged comb on a stream of water coming from a faucet.
TIME 10 minutes
MATERIALS water faucet, comb

Internet Activity: Static Electricity, p. 631
Students observe how different types of materials affect charging by contact.
TIME 20 minutes
MATERIALS computer with Internet access

SECTION 1

EXPLORE Static Electricity, p. 633
Students explore how paper and plastic interact electrically.
TIME 10 minutes
MATERIALS 2 strips of newspaper, plastic bag

INVESTIGATE Making a Static Detector, p. 638
Students construct a static detector and infer the presence of static electric charge.
TIME 20 minutes
MATERIALS metal paper clip, clear plastic cup with hole, small piece of modeling clay, ball of aluminum foil, 2 strips of aluminum foil, balloon

SECTION 2

EXPLORE Static Discharge, p. 642
Students use a fluorescent bulb to observe static discharge.
TIME 10 minutes
MATERIALS inflated balloon, wool cloth, fluorescent light bulb

INVESTIGATE Conductors and Insulators, p. 646
Students interpret data to determine what materials conduct electricity.
TIME 20 minutes
MATERIALS D cell battery, 3 pieces of low-voltage wire (20 cm each), 25 cm duct tape, flashlight bulb, bulb holder, objects made from different materials

CHAPTER INVESTIGATION
Lightning, pp. 650–651
Students model the buildup of charges that can occur during a storm and a lightning strike, and use a ground to control the path of discharge.
TIME 40 minutes
MATERIALS small piece of modeling clay, 2 aluminum pie pans, Styrofoam plate, wool cloth, metal paper clip

SECTION 3

EXPLORE Current, p. 652
Students relate resistance to flow of charge through different lengths of graphite.
TIME 20 minutes
MATERIALS pencil lead, posterboard, 25 cm electrical tape, 3 lengths of low-voltage wire (20 cm each), D cell battery, flashlight bulb, bulb holder

INVESTIGATE Electric Cells, p. 655
Students infer how electric current can be produced by a lemon and different types of metal.
TIME 20 minutes
MATERIALS metal paper clip, penny, large lemon, multimeter, additional fruits or vegetables, additional metal objects

Additional INVESTIGATION, Making a Coin Battery, A, B, & C, pp. 62–70; Teacher Instructions, pp. 206–207

Chapter 19: **Electricity** 629D

Previewing Chapter Resources

	INTEGRATED TECHNOLOGY	LABS AND ACTIVITIES
CHAPTER 19 Electricity	**CLASSZONE.COM** • eEdition Plus • EasyPlanner • Misconception Database • Content Review • Test Practice • Simulations • Resource Centers • Internet Activity: Static Electricity • Math Tutorial **SCILINKS.ORG**	 **CD-ROMS** • eEdition • EasyPlanner • Power Presentations • Content Review • Lab Generator • Test Generator **AUDIO CDS** • Audio Readings • Audio Readings in Spanish	EXPLORE the Big Idea, p. 631 • How Do the Pieces of Tape Interact? • Why Does the Water React Differently? • Internet Activity: Static Electricity **UNIT RESOURCE BOOK** • Family Letter, p. vii • Spanish Family Letter, p. viii • Unit Projects, pp. 5–10 **Lab Generator CD-ROM** Generate customized labs.
SECTION 1 Materials can become electrically charged. pp. 633–641 Time: 2 periods (1 block) Lesson Plan, pp. 11–12	**UNIT TRANSPARENCY BOOK** • Big Idea Flow Chart, p. T1 • Daily Vocabulary Scaffolding, p. T2 • Note-Taking Model, p. T3 • 3-Minute Warm-Up, p. T4		• EXPLORE Static Electricity, p. 633 • INVESTIGATE Making a Static Detector, p. 638 • Connecting Sciences, p. 641 **UNIT RESOURCE BOOK** Datasheet, Making a Static Detector, p. 20
SECTION 2 Charges can move from one place to another. pp. 642–651 Time: 3 periods (1.5 blocks) Lesson Plan, pp. 22–23	**RESOURCE CENTER,** Lightning and Lightning Safety **UNIT TRANSPARENCY BOOK** • Daily Vocabulary Scaffolding, p. T2 • 3-Minute Warm-Up, p. T4 • "How Lightning Forms" Visual, p. T6	• EXPLORE Static Discharge, p. 642 • INVESTIGATE Conductors and Insulators, p. 646 • CHAPTER INVESTIGATION, Lightning, pp. 650–651 **UNIT RESOURCE BOOK** • Datasheet, Conductors and Insulators, p. 31 • CHAPTER INVESTIGATION, Lightning, A, B, & C, pp. 53–61
SECTION 3 Electric current is a flow of charge. pp. 652–659 Time: 3 periods (1.5 blocks) Lesson Plan, pp. 33–34	• **SIMULATION,** Ohm's Law • **RESOURCE CENTER,** Electrochemical Cells • **MATH TUTORIAL** **UNIT TRANSPARENCY BOOK** • Big Idea Flow Chart, p. T1 • Daily Vocabulary Scaffolding, p. T2 • 3-Minute Warm-Up, p. T5 • Chapter Outline, pp. T7–T8	• EXPLORE Current, p. 652 • INVESTIGATE Electric Cells, p. 655 • Math in Science, p. 659 **UNIT RESOURCE BOOK** • Datasheet, Electric Cells, p. 42 • Math Support, pp. 49, 51 • Math Practice, pp. 50, 52 • Additional INVESTIGATION, Making a Coin Battery, A, B, & C, pp. 62–70

629E Unit 5: **Electricity and Magnetism**

KEY TO ICONS	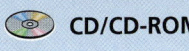 CD/CD-ROM	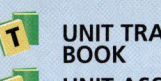 Teacher Edition	T UNIT TRANSPARENCY BOOK	SP A SPANISH ASSESSMENT BOOK
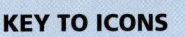 INTERNET	PE Pupil Edition	R UNIT RESOURCE BOOK	A UNIT ASSESSMENT BOOK	SCIENCE TOOLKIT

READING AND REINFORCEMENT

- Four Square, B22–23
- Combination Notes, C36
- Daily Vocabulary Scaffolding, H1–8

 UNIT RESOURCE BOOK
- Vocabulary Practice, pp. 46–47
- Decoding Support, p. 48
- Summarizing the Chapter, pp. 71–72

Audio Readings CD
Listen to Pupil Edition.

Audio Readings in Spanish CD
Listen to Pupil Edition in Spanish.

 UNIT RESOURCE BOOK
- Reading Study Guide, A & B, pp. 13–16
- Spanish Reading Study Guide, pp. 17–18
- Challenge and Extension, p. 19
- Reinforcing Key Concepts, p. 21

 UNIT RESOURCE BOOK
- Reading Study Guide, A & B, pp. 24–27
- Spanish Reading Study Guide, pp. 28–29
- Challenge and Extension, p. 30
- Reinforcing Key Concepts, p. 32
- Challenge Reading, pp. 44–45

 UNIT RESOURCE BOOK
- Reading Study Guide, A & B, pp. 35–38
- Spanish Reading Study Guide, pp. 39–40
- Challenge and Extension, p. 41
- Reinforcing Key Concepts, p. 43

ASSESSMENT

- Chapter Review, pp. 661–662
- Standardized Test Practice, p. 663

 UNIT ASSESSMENT BOOK
- Diagnostic Test, pp. 1–2
- Chapter Test, A, B, & C, pp. 6–17
- Alternative Assessment, pp. 18–19

Spanish Chapter Test, pp. 301–304

Test Generator CD-ROM
Generate customized tests.

Lab Generator CD-ROM
Rubrics for Labs

 Ongoing Assessment, pp. 634, 636, 639–640

 Section 19.1 Review, p. 640

 UNIT ASSESSMENT BOOK
Section 19.1 Quiz, p. 3

 Ongoing Assessment, pp. 642–649

 Section 19.2 Review, p. 649

UNIT ASSESSMENT BOOK
Section 19.2 Quiz, p. 4

 Ongoing Assessment, pp. 653–654, 656–658

 Section 19.3 Review, p. 658

 UNIT ASSESSMENT BOOK
Section 19.3 Quiz, p. 5

STANDARDS

National Standards
A.2–8, A.9.a–f, B.3.a, B.3.e, E.6.c–f, F.5.c

See p. 631 for the standards.

National Standards
A.2–8, A.9.a–f, B.3.a, B.3.e

National Standards
A.2–8, A.9.a–f, B.3.a, B.3.e, E.6.c–f, F.5.c

National Standards
A.2–8, A.9.a–f, B.3.a, B.3.e, E.6.c–f, F.5.c

Chapter 19: **Electricity** 629F

Previewing Resources for Differentiated Instruction

CHAPTER INVESTIGATION

Leveled resources present the same concepts for different abilities.

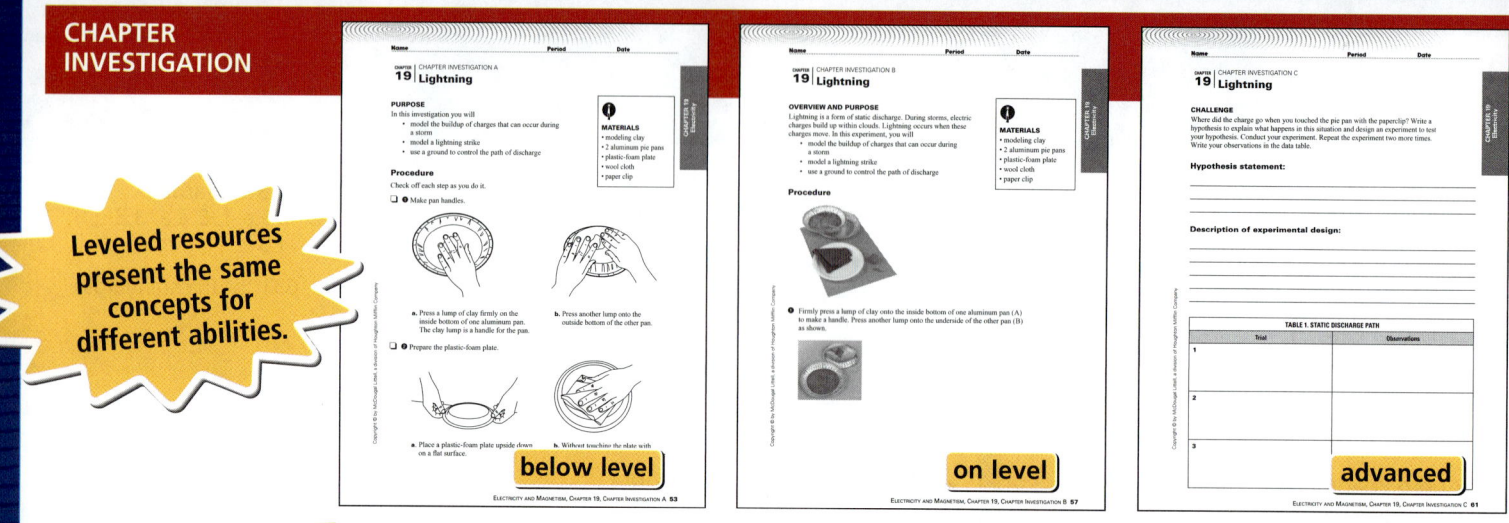

UNIT RESOURCE BOOK, pp. 53–56 (below level) | pp. 57–60 (on level) | pp. 57–61 (advanced)

READING STUDY GUIDE

Reading Study Guide is also in Spanish.

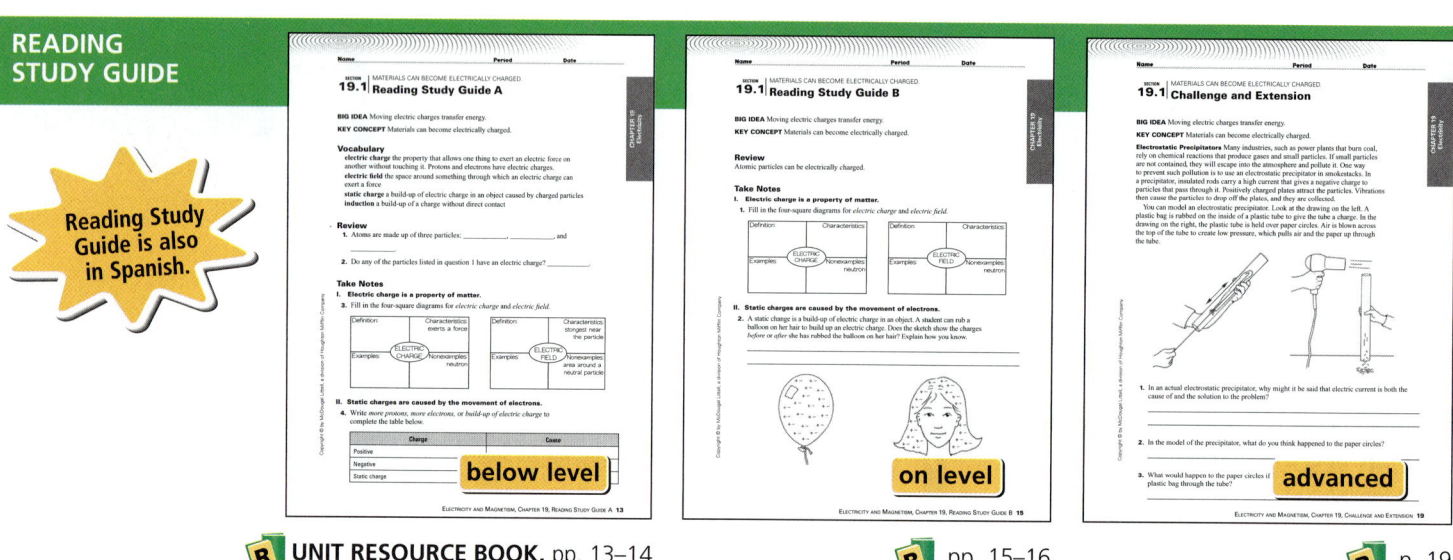

UNIT RESOURCE BOOK, pp. 13–14 (below level) | pp. 15–16 (on level) | p. 19 (advanced)

CHAPTER TEST

Chapter Test is also in Spanish.

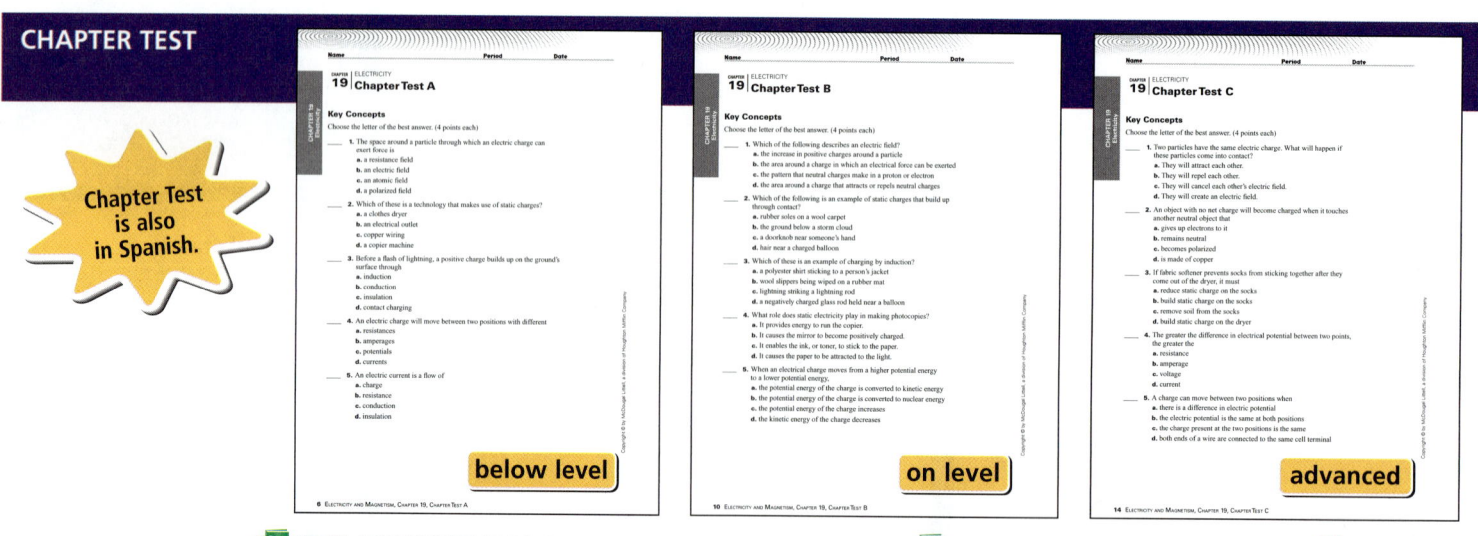

UNIT ASSESSMENT BOOK, pp. 6–9 (below level) | pp. 10–13 (on level) | pp. 14–17 (advanced)

629G Unit 5: Electricity and Magnetism

TECHNOLOGY

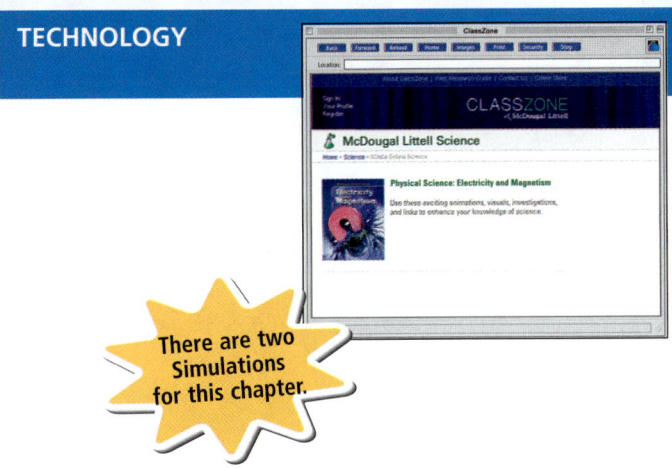
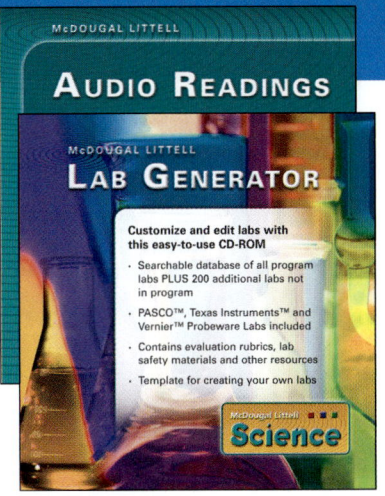
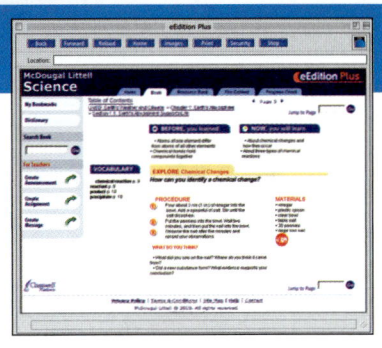

There are two Simulations for this chapter.

CLASSZONE.COM   CD/CD-ROMS   CLASSZONE.COM

VISUAL CONTENT

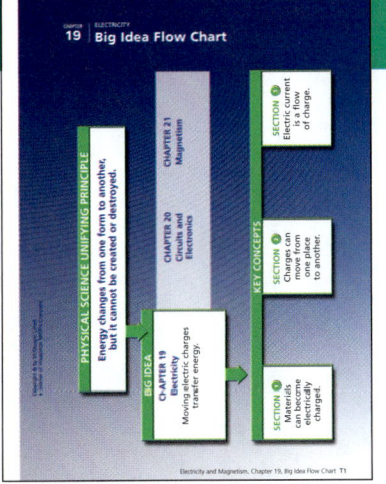
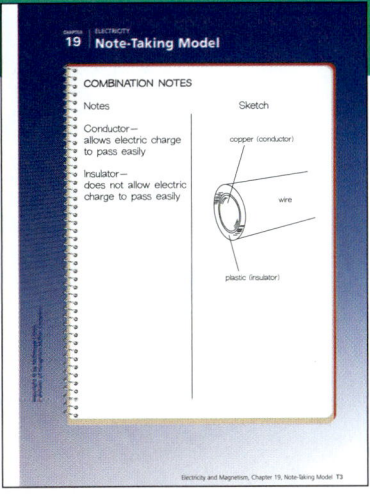

UNIT TRANSPARENCY BOOK, p. T1   p. T3   p. T6

MORE SUPPORT

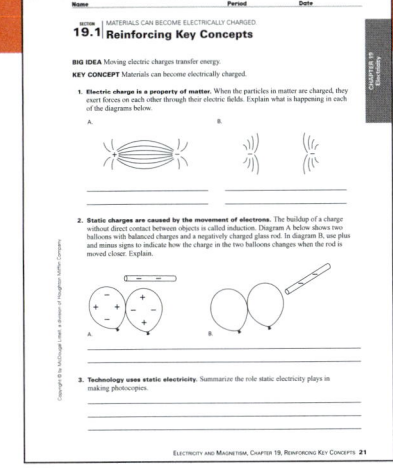
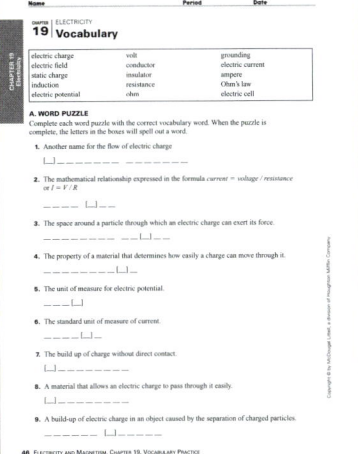
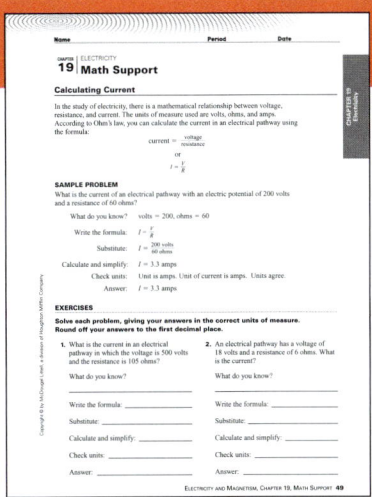

Reinforcing Key Concepts for each section

UNIT RESOURCE BOOK, p. 21   pp. 46–47   p. 49

Chapter 19: **Electricity 629H**

CHAPTER 19 Electricity

INTRODUCE the BIG idea

Have students look at the photograph of the glowing dragon. Discuss how the question in the box links to the Big Idea:

- What might stop the dragon from glowing?
- What might make the dragon glow more brightly?

National Science Education Standards

Content

B.3.a Energy is a property of many substances and is associated with heat, light, electricity, mechanical motion, sound, nuclei, and the nature of a chemical. Energy is transferred in many ways.

B.3.e In most chemical and nuclear reactions, energy is transferred into or out of a system. Heat, light, mechanical motion, or electricity might all be involved in such transfers.

Process

A.2–8 Design and conduct an investigation; use tools to gather and interpret data; use evidence to describe, predict, explain, model; think critically to make relationships between evidence and explanation; recognize different explanations and predictions; communicate scientific procedures and explanations; use mathematics.

A.9.a–f Understand scientific inquiry by using different investigations, methods, mathematics, technology, explanations based on logic, evidence, and skepticism.

E.6.c–f Understandings about science and technology

F.5.c Technology influences society through its products and processes.

CHAPTER 19 Electricity

the BIG idea

Moving electric charges transfer energy.

What keeps this dragon glowing brightly?

Key Concepts

SECTION 1 Materials can become electrically charged.
Learn how the movement of electrons builds static charges and how static charges are used in technology.

SECTION 2 Charges can move from one place to another.
Learn what factors control the movement of charges.

SECTION 3 Electric current is a flow of charge.
Learn how electric current is measured and how it can be produced.

Internet Preview

CLASSZONE.COM
Chapter 19 online resources: Content Review, two Simulations, two Resource Centers, Math Tutorial, Test Practice.

INTERNET PREVIEW

CLASSZONE.COM For student use with the following pages:

Review and Practice
- Content Review, pp. 632, 660
- Math Tutorial: Equations, p. 659
- Test Practice, p. 663

Activities and Resources
- Internet Activity: Static Electricity, p. 631
- Resource Centers: Lightning, p. 644; Electrochemical Cells, p. 656
- Simulation: Ohm's Law, p. 653

NSTA scilinks.org
Electricity Code: MDL065

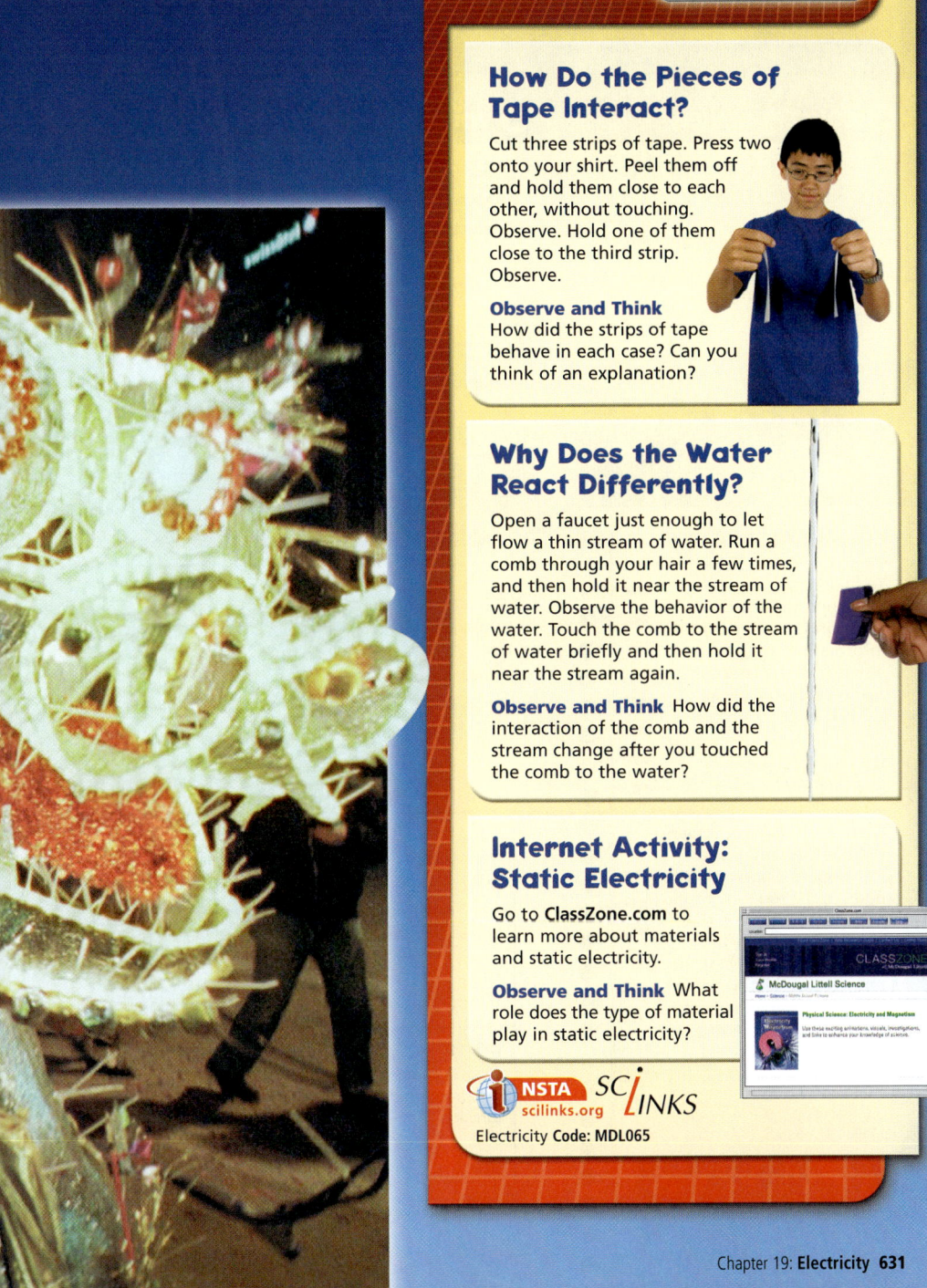

EXPLORE the BIG idea

How Do the Pieces of Tape Interact?

Cut three strips of tape. Press two onto your shirt. Peel them off and hold them close to each other, without touching. Observe. Hold one of them close to the third strip. Observe.

Observe and Think
How did the strips of tape behave in each case? Can you think of an explanation?

Why Does the Water React Differently?

Open a faucet just enough to let flow a thin stream of water. Run a comb through your hair a few times, and then hold it near the stream of water. Observe the behavior of the water. Touch the comb to the stream of water briefly and then hold it near the stream again.

Observe and Think How did the interaction of the comb and the stream change after you touched the comb to the water?

Internet Activity: Static Electricity

Go to ClassZone.com to learn more about materials and static electricity.

Observe and Think What role does the type of material play in static electricity?

NSTA scilinks.org
SCLINKS
Electricity Code: MDL065

Chapter 19: Electricity 631

TEACHING WITH TECHNOLOGY

CBL and Probeware Use probeware to measure current in "Investigate Electric Cells" on p. 655.

Multimeter Once students are familiar with multimeters, have them check voltage and resistance for the setup in "Explore Current" on p. 652.

EXPLORE the BIG idea

These inquiry-based activities are appropriate for use at home or as a supplement to classroom instruction.

How Do the Pieces of Tape Interact?

PURPOSE To introduce students to the production and effects of a static charge through contact. Students note repulsion and attraction in charged tape.

TIP *10 min.* Different types of tape might produce different results. Check effectiveness of the tape before class.

Answer: The strips from the shirt repel each other but attract the third piece. The tape becomes charged from contact with the shirt. Like charges repel; unlike charges attract.

REVISIT after p. 635.

Why Does the Water React Differently?

PURPOSE To introduce students to charge induction and grounding. Students observe the effects of a charged and discharged comb on a stream of water.

TIP *10 min.* If possible, perform this activity on a cool, dry day to maximize the amount of charge on the comb.

Answer: The comb attracts the stream of water before it touches it. After touching the water, the comb no longer attracts the water.

REVISIT after p. 637.

Internet Activity: Static Electricity

PURPOSE To have students relate types of materials to charging by contact.

TIP *20 min.* After students try a couple of examples, have them predict the results before trying additional materials.

Answer: It determines whether objects charge spontaneously on contact.

REVISIT after p. 636.

Chapter 19 **631**

PREPARE

 CONCEPT REVIEW

Activate Prior Knowledge

- Cover the sides and top of a container with black paper.
- Place a thermometer in the container. Take a temperature reading.
- Place the container and thermometer in the sun or under a sun lamp. Take a temperature reading again in five minutes.
- Ask students to describe what forms of energy moved from one place to another. *Light from the Sun moved to Earth. Solar energy absorbed by the black paper warmed the air and the thermometer in the container.*

 TAKING NOTES

Combination Notes

To clarify relationships, students can number parts of their sketches and label corresponding notes with the same numbers.

Vocabulary Strategy

Emphasize that there is more than one acceptable entry for characteristics, examples, and nonexamples. Comparing diagrams will help students add information to their own diagrams.

Vocabulary and Note-Taking Resources

- Vocabulary Practice, pp. 46–47
- Decoding Support, p. 48

- Daily Vocabulary Scaffolding, p. T2
- Note-Taking Model, p. T3

- Four Square, B22–23
- Combination Notes, C36
- Daily Vocabulary Scaffolding, H1–8

632 Unit 5: **Electricity and Magnetism**

CHAPTER 19
Getting Ready to Learn

 **CONCEPT REVIEW**

- Matter is made of particles too small to see.
- Energy and matter can move from one place to another.
- Electromagnetic energy is one form of energy.

 **VOCABULARY REVIEW**

See Glossary for definitions.

atom
electron
joule
proton

CONTENT REVIEW
CLASSZONE.COM
Review concepts and vocabulary.

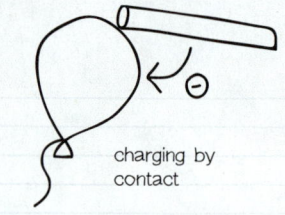

▶ **TAKING NOTES**

COMBINATION NOTES

To take notes about a new concept, first make an informal outline of the information. Then make a sketch of the concept and label it so you can study it later.

VOCABULARY STRATEGY

Write each new vocabulary term in the center of a **four square** diagram. Write notes in the squares around each term. Include a definition, some characteristics, and some examples of the term. If possible, write some things that are not examples of the term.

SCIENCE NOTEBOOK

NOTES
How static charges are built
- Contact
- Induction
- Charge polarization

charging by contact

Definition	Characteristics
imbalance of charge in material	results from movement of electrons; affected by type of material

STATIC CHARGE

Examples	Nonexample
clinging laundry, doorknob shock, lightning	electricity from an electrical outlet

See the Note-Taking Handbook on pages R45–R51.

632 Unit 5: Electricity and Magnetism

CHECK READINESS

Administer the Diagnostic Test to determine students' readiness for new science content and their mastery of requisite math skills.

 Diagnostic Test, pp. 1–2

Technology Resources

Students needing content and math skills should visit **ClassZone.com**.

- **CONTENT REVIEW**
- **MATH TUTORIAL**

 CONTENT REVIEW CD-ROM

KEY CONCEPT
19.1 Materials can become electrically charged.

BEFORE, you learned
- Atoms are made up of particles called protons, neutrons, and electrons
- Protons and electrons are electrically charged

NOW, you will learn
- How charged particles behave
- How electric charges build up in materials
- How static electricity is used in technology

VOCABULARY

electric charge p. 634
electric field p. 634
static charge p. 635
induction p. 637

EXPLORE Static Electricity

How can materials interact electrically?

PROCEDURE

1. Hold the newspaper strips firmly together at one end and let the free ends hang down. Observe the strips.
2. Put the plastic bag over your other hand, like a mitten. Slide the plastic down the entire length of the strips and then let go. Repeat several times.
3. Notice how the strips of paper are hanging. Describe what you observe.

MATERIALS
- 2 strips of newspaper
- plastic bag

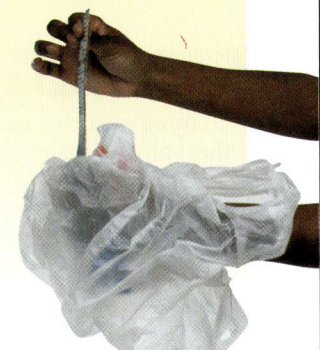

WHAT DO YOU THINK?
- How did the strips behave before step 2? How did they behave after step 2?
- How might you explain your observations?

Electric charge is a property of matter.

You are already familiar with electricity, static electricity, and magnetism. You know electricity as the source of power for many appliances, including lights, tools, and computers. Static electricity is what makes clothes stick together when they come out of a dryer and gives you a shock when you touch a metal doorknob on a dry, winter day. Magnetism can hold an invitation or report card on the door of your refrigerator.

You may not know, however, that electricity, static electricity, and magnetism are all related. All three are the result of a single property of matter—electric charge.

COMBINATION NOTES
As you read this section, write down important ideas about electric charge and static charges. Make sketches to help you remember these concepts.

Chapter 19: **Electricity** 633

19.1 FOCUS

▶ Set Learning Goals

Students will
- Describe how charged particles behave.
- Determine how electrons cause electric charges to build up in materials.
- Explain how static electricity is used in technology.
- Infer from an experiment how to detect a static electric charge.

◯ 3-Minute Warm-Up

Display Transparency 4 or copy this exercise on the board:

Decide if these statements are true. If not, correct them.

1. The basic particles of an atom are protons, neutrons, and nuclei. *protons, neutrons, and electrons*

2. Particles that make up an atom have no charge. *Some particles (protons and electrons) that make up an atom are charged.*

3. Electrons are negatively charged. *true*

 3-Minute Warm-Up, p. T4

19.1 MOTIVATE

EXPLORE Static Electricity

PURPOSE To explore how materials interact electrically

TIPS 10 min. Tell students to rub the strips firmly but to be careful not to tear the strips. A flexible plastic bag works best.

WHAT DO YOU THINK? *They hung straight down while touching each other. They repelled each other. Rubbing with the plastic bag charges the strips with like charges, which repel each other.*

RESOURCES FOR DIFFERENTIATED INSTRUCTION

Below Level
UNIT RESOURCE BOOK
- Reading Study Guide A, pp. 13–14
- Decoding Support, p. 48

 **AUDIO CDS**

Advanced
UNIT RESOURCE BOOK
Challenge and Extension, p. 19

English Learners
UNIT RESOURCE BOOK
Spanish Reading Study Guide, pp. 17–18

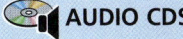 **AUDIO CDS**
- Audio Readings in Spanish
- Audio Readings (English)

Chapter 19 **633**

19.1 INSTRUCT

History of Science

The first recorded observation of static charge is from ancient Greece. The Greeks noticed that fossilized tree sap—the material known as amber—attracted objects such as feathers after it was rubbed with fur or certain other materials. Many words with the root *electr-*, such as *electron*, *electricity*, and *electronic*, come from the Greek word *elecktron*, which means "amber."

Teach from Visuals

Point out that the charges in the diagram of electric charge are equal in size but opposite in sign. Ask:

- Which has more mass, an electron or a proton? **proton**
- Is the charge on the proton equal to, larger than, or smaller than the charge on the electron? **equal to**

Ongoing Assessment

Describe how charged particles behave.

Ask: If a balloon has a negative charge and a rod has a positive charge, will the balloon and the rod repel or attract each other? **attract**

READING VISUALS *Answer: Each particle's force lines bend toward the other particle.*

VOCABULARY
Make a four square diagram for the term *electric charge* and the other vocabulary terms in this section.

The smallest unit of a material that still has the characteristics of that material is an atom or a molecule. A molecule is two or more atoms bonded together. Most of an atom's mass is concentrated in the nucleus at the center of the atom. The nucleus contains particles called protons and neutrons. Much smaller particles called electrons move at high speeds outside the nucleus.

Protons and electrons have electric charges. **Electric charge** is a property that allows an object to exert an electric force on another object without touching it. Recall that a force is a push or a pull. The space around a particle through which an electric charge can exert this force is called an **electric field.** The strength of the field is greater near the particle and weaker farther away.

All protons have a positive charge (+), and all electrons have a negative charge (−). Normally, an atom has an equal number of protons and electrons, so their charges balance each other, and the overall charge on the atom is neutral.

Particles with the same type of charge—positive or negative—are said to have like charges, and particles with different charges have unlike charges. Particles with like charges repel each other, that is, they push each other away. Particles with unlike charges attract each other, or pull on each other.

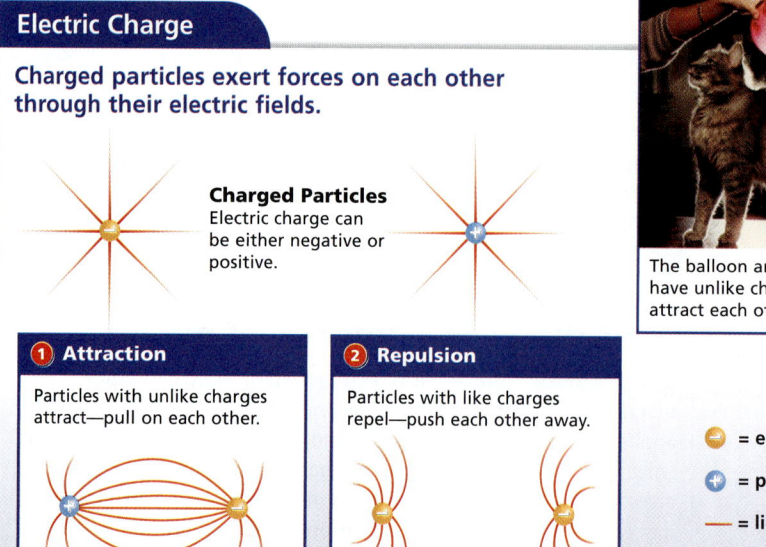

Electric Charge

Charged particles exert forces on each other through their electric fields.

Charged Particles Electric charge can be either negative or positive.

1 Attraction Particles with unlike charges attract—pull on each other.

2 Repulsion Particles with like charges repel—push each other away.

The balloon and the cat's fur have unlike charges, so they attract each other.

- = electron
- = proton
- = lines of force

READING VISUALS How do the force lines change when particles attract?

634 Unit 5: Electricity and Magnetism

DIFFERENTIATE INSTRUCTION

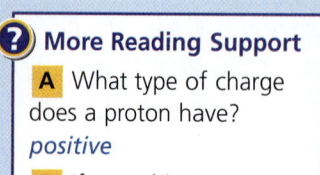

More Reading Support

A What type of charge does a proton have? **positive**

B If two objects are both positive, will they attract or repel? **repel**

English Learners The similar words, *buildup* and *build up*, may confuse English learners. Explain that *buildup* is a noun, while *build up* is a verb. *Buildup* is an informal way of describing something that has gathered over time. *Build up* is a phrasal verb that refers to the action of accumulating something over time.

634 Unit 5: Electricity and Magnetism

Static charges are caused by the movement of electrons.

You have read that protons and electrons have electric charges. Objects and materials can also have charges. A **static charge** is a buildup of electric charge in an object caused by the presence of many particles with the same charge. Ordinarily, the atoms that make up a material have a balance of protons and electrons. A material develops a static charge—or becomes charged—when it contains more of one type of charged particle than another.

▼ **READING TIP**
The word *static* comes from the Greek word *statos*, which means "standing."

If there are more protons than electrons in a material, the material has a positive charge. If there are more electrons than protons in a material, it has a negative charge. The amount of the charge depends on how many more electrons or protons there are. The total number of unbalanced positive or negative charges in an object is the net charge of the object. Net charge is measured in coulombs (KOO-LAHMZ). One coulomb is equivalent to more than 10^{19} electrons or protons.

▼ **REMINDER**
10^{19} is the same as 1 followed by 19 zeros.

Electrons can move easily from one atom to another. Protons cannot. For this reason, charges in materials usually result from the movement of electrons. The movement of electrons through a material is called conduction. If electrons move from one atom to another, the atom they move to develops a negative charge. The atom they move away from develops a positive charge. Atoms with either a positive or a negative charge are called ions.

A static charge can build up in an uncharged material when it touches or comes near a charged material. Static charges also build up when some types of uncharged materials come into contact with each other.

Charging by Contact

When two uncharged objects made of certain materials—such as rubber and glass—touch each other, electrons move from one material to the other. This process is called charging by contact. It can be demonstrated by a balloon and a glass rod, as shown below.

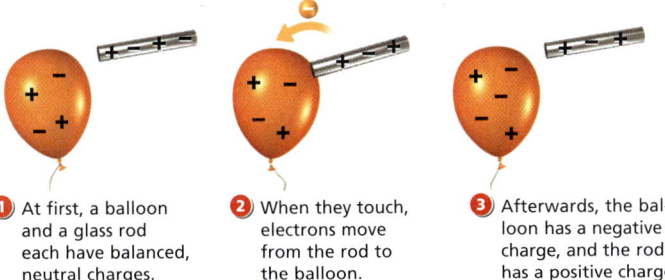

① At first, a balloon and a glass rod each have balanced, neutral charges.

② When they touch, electrons move from the rod to the balloon.

③ Afterwards, the balloon has a negative charge, and the rod has a positive charge.

Chapter 19: **Electricity** 635

Teach from Visuals

Have students examine the list of materials in the charging-by-contact chart. To help them better interpret the visual of the diagrams of wool and rubber contacts, ask:

- What type of charge would you have if you walked barefoot across a wool carpet? *positive*
- Across a rubber mat? *positive*

Develop Critical Thinking

SYNTHESIZE Tell students that a silk cloth acquires a negative charge when it rubs a neutral glass rod. If the same neutral glass rod rubs against a rubber rod, the rubber rod becomes negatively charged. If a rubber rod is rubbed with silk, the rubber rod becomes negatively charged.

- Ask: Which of the three materials—glass rod, rubber rod, or silk—has the greatest attraction for electrons? *rubber rod*
- Ask: Which has the least attraction? *glass*

Have students check their answers against the "Charging by Contact" chart on this page.

EXPLORE the BIG idea

Revisit "Internet Activity: Static Electricity" on p. 631. Have students explain their results.

Ongoing Assessment

Determine how electrons cause electric charges to build up in materials.

Ask: Electrons and protons are both charged. Why is charge buildup typically caused by the movement of electrons rather than protons? *Electrons can move from atom to atom but protons cannot.*

CHECK YOUR READING *Answer: The hair acquires a negative charge from the generator. Because the hairs contain like charges, they repel each other.*

636 Unit 5: **Electricity and Magnetism**

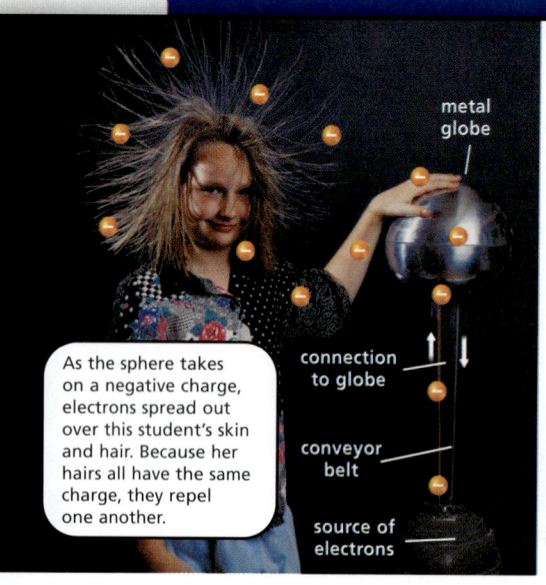

As the sphere takes on a negative charge, electrons spread out over this student's skin and hair. Because her hairs all have the same charge, they repel one another.

metal globe
connection to globe
conveyor belt
source of electrons

A Van de Graaff generator is a device that builds up a strong static charge through contact. This device is shown at left. At the bottom of the device, a rubber conveyer belt rubs against a metal brush and picks up electrons. At the top, the belt rubs against metal connected to the sphere, transferring electrons to the sphere. As more and more electrons accumulate on the sphere, the sphere takes on a strong negative charge. In the photograph, the student touches the sphere as it is being charged. Some of the electrons spread across her arm to her head. The strands of her hair, which then all have a negative charge, repel one another.

CHECK YOUR READING How can a Van de Graaff generator make a person's hair stand on end?

How Materials Affect Static Charging

Charging by contact occurs when one material's electrons are attracted to another material more than they are attracted to their own. Scientists have determined from experience which materials are likely to give up or to accept electrons. For example, glass gives up electrons to wool. Wool accepts electrons from glass, but gives up electrons to rubber. The list at left indicates how some materials interact. Each material tends to give up electrons to anything below it on the list and to accept electrons from anything above it. The farther away two materials are from each other on the list, the stronger the interaction.

When you walk across a carpet, your body can become either positively or negatively charged. The type of charge depends on what materials the carpet and your shoes are made of. If you walk in shoes with rubber soles across a wool carpet, you will probably become negatively charged, because wool gives up electrons to rubber. But if you walk in wool slippers across a rubber mat, you will probably become positively charged.

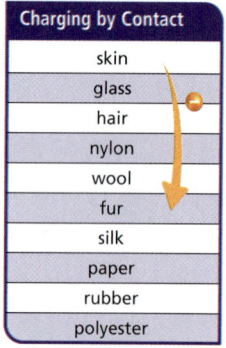

Materials higher on the list tend to give up electrons to materials lower on the list.

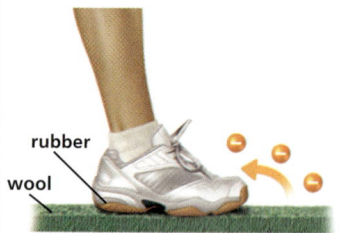

Rubber soles on a wool carpet give a person a negative charge.

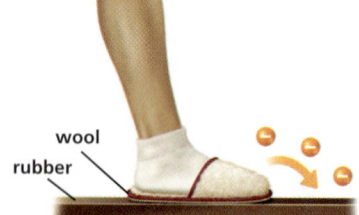

Wool slippers on a rubber mat give a person a positive charge.

636 Unit 5: Electricity and Magnetism

DIFFERENTIATE INSTRUCTION

More Reading Support

E Fur becomes negatively charged when it touches skin. Which of these materials—fur or skin—has a stronger attraction for electrons? *fur*

Advanced Have interested students investigate the branch of science known as triboelectricity and report on it to the class. Encourage students to find lists known as triboelectric series on the Internet. These series rank different materials as to how easily they gain or lose electrons when they touch other materials. Have them plan and present a demonstration of the effects when different materials on the lists are placed in contact with each other.

 Challenge and Extension, p. 19

Charging by Induction

Charging can occur even when materials are not touching if one of the materials already has a charge. Remember that charged particles push and pull each other through their electric fields without touching. The pushing and pulling can cause a charge to build in another material. The first charge is said to induce the second charge. The buildup of a charge without direct contact is called **induction.**

> **READING TIP**
> *Induce* and *induction* both contain the Latin root *ducere,* which means "to lead."

Induction can produce a temporary static charge. Consider what happens when a glass rod with a negative charge is brought near a balloon, as shown below. The unbalanced electrons in the rod repel the electrons in the material of the balloon. Many electrons move to the side of the balloon that is farthest away from the rod. The side of the balloon that has more electrons becomes negatively charged. The side of the balloon with fewer electrons becomes positively charged. When the rod moves away, the electrons spread out evenly once again.

① At first, the rod has a negative charge and the balloon has a balanced charge.
② When the rod comes close to the balloon, electrons in the balloon move away from the rod.
③ When the rod moves away, electrons in the balloon spread out evenly as before.

If the electrons cannot return to their original distribution, however, induction can leave an object with a stable static charge. For example, if a negatively charged rod approaches two balloons that are touching each other, electrons will move to the balloon farther from the rod. If the balloons are then separated, preventing the electrons from moving again, the balloon with more electrons will have a negative charge and the one with fewer electrons will have a positive charge. When the rod is taken away, the balloons keep their new charges.

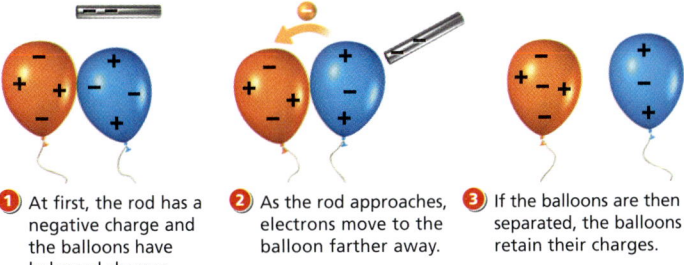

① At first, the rod has a negative charge and the balloons have balanced charges.
② As the rod approaches, electrons move to the balloon farther away.
③ If the balloons are then separated, the balloons retain their charges.

Chapter 19: Electricity 637

Integrate the Sciences

Television sets and computers can make allergies worse. The static charge on the screens of televisions and computer monitors attracts dust from the air. Accompanying the dust are dust mites and their feces, which are common allergens and can bring on asthma attacks and other bronchial problems.

Real World Example

When clothes rub together in a clothes dryer, they may become charged and stick together when they come out of the dryer. Fabric softeners solve this problem. Fabric softeners contain active ingredients made from long-chain molecules that have a positive charge. These positively charged molecules are attracted to negatively charged areas of fabric, with the result that smaller charge imbalances develop than there would be without the softener. Once the fabrics are out of the dryer, the softener attracts water molecules from the air, which further reduces the accumulation of charge.

Teach Difficult Concepts

Students may have difficulty distinguishing between the concepts represented by the sets of diagrams on the page in the textbook. Take the students step-by-step through the diagrams by using actual materials. You can give a rubber rod a negative charge by rubbing it with wool, nylon, or silk.

EXPLORE the BIG idea

Revisit "Why Does the Water React Differently?" on p. 631. Have students explain their results.

DIFFERENTIATE INSTRUCTION

More Reading Support

F What is the buildup of charge without direct contact? *induction*

G Are induced charges temporary or stable? *They can be either.*

Inclusion Cut out paper models of balloons from construction paper. Use pennies to represent negative charges and buttons of the same size to represent positive charges. Model the diagrams on the page.

Chapter 19 637

INVESTIGATE Making a Static Detector

PURPOSE To infer the presence of a static electric charge

TIPS 20 min.

- Have students use a flow chart or sequence-diagram map to describe the procedure.
- Nothing at all should touch the ball of foil once the apparatus is assembled.

WHAT DO YOU THINK? *The strips moved apart. The balloon induced a charge on the ball. This charge passed through the paper clip into the strips. The strips then had a like charge, so they repelled each other.*

CHALLENGE *The strips would still repel because they would still have like charges.*

 Datasheet, Making a Static Detector, p. 20

Technology Resources

Customize this student lab as needed or look for an alternative. Print rubrics to assess student lab reports.

 Lab Generator CD-ROM

Metacognitive Strategy

Ask: What generalizations about static charging do your lab results reinforce? Have students support their answers by citing the text. *Sample answers: Like charges repel each other—last paragraph, p. 634. Hair tends to give up electrons to rubber (the balloon)—"Charging by Contact" table, p. 636. Charged particles push and pull each other through their electric fields without touching, and the pushing and pulling can cause a charge to build in another material (the aluminum foil)—first paragraph, p. 637.*

Charge Polarization

Induction can build a charge by changing the position of electrons, even when electrons do not move between atoms. Have you ever charged a balloon by rubbing it on your head, and then stuck the balloon to a wall? When you bring the balloon close to the wall, the balloon's negative charge pushes against the electrons in the wall. If the electrons cannot easily move away from their atoms, the negative charges within the atoms may shift to the side away from the balloon. When this happens, the atoms are said to be polarized. The surface of the wall becomes positively charged, and the negatively charged balloon sticks to it.

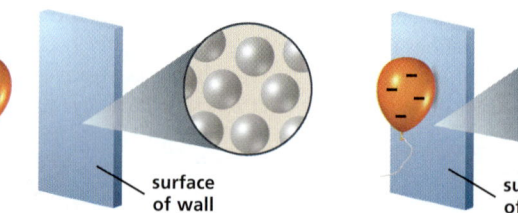

1 Before the charged balloon comes near the wall, the atoms in the surface of the wall are not polarized.

2 As the balloon nears the wall, atoms in the surface of the wall become polarized and attract the balloon.

INVESTIGATE Making a Static Detector

How can you detect a static electric charge?

PROCEDURE

1 Straighten one end of the paper clip and insert it through the hole in the cup. Use clay to hold the paper clip in place. Stick the ball of foil onto the straight end. Hang both foil strips from the hook end.

2 Give the balloon a static charge by rubbing it over your hair. Slowly bring the balloon near the ball of foil without letting them touch. Observe what happens to the foil strips inside the cup.

WHAT DO YOU THINK?

- What happened to the strips hanging inside the cup when the charged balloon came near the ball of foil?
- How can you explain what you observed?

CHALLENGE Suppose the balloon had the opposite charge of the one you gave it. What would happen to the strips if you brought the balloon near the ball of foil? Explain your answer.

SKILL FOCUS
Inferring

MATERIALS
- metal paper clip
- clear plastic cup with hole
- modeling clay
- ball of foil
- 2 strips of foil
- inflated balloon

TIME
20 minutes

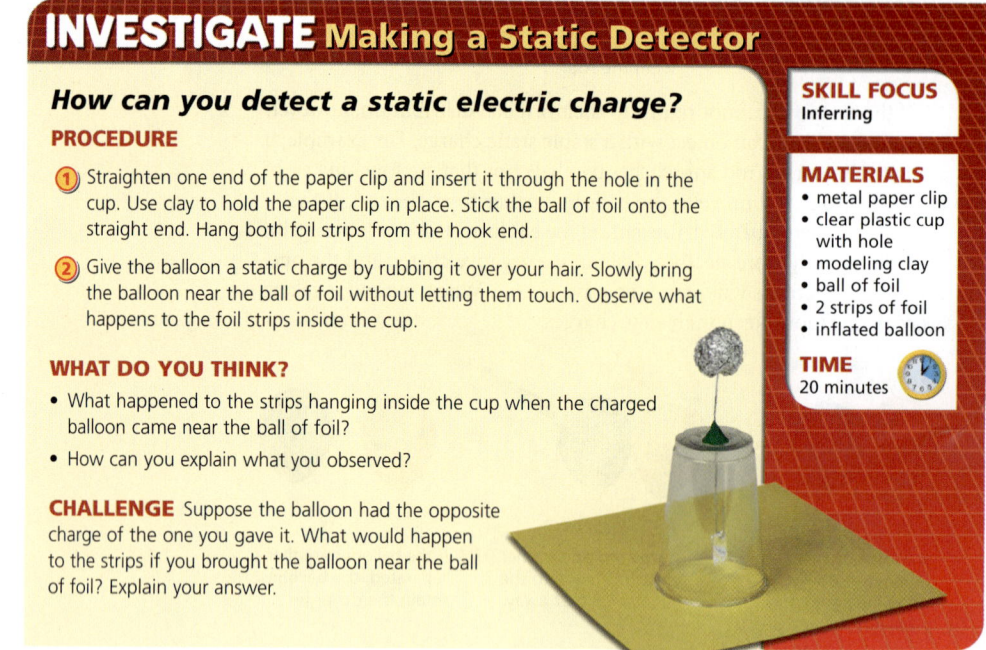

638 Unit 5: Electricity and Magnetism

DIFFERENTIATE INSTRUCTION

 More Reading Support

H What happens when an atom is polarized? *Electrons shift to the side away from a negatively charged object*

Alternative Assessment Have students design an experiment that uses different materials in place of the foil ball (e.g., cork, clay, paper clip, copper wire) and report on which materials yield the same results. Have them organize their results in a chart or a table.

Technology uses static electricity.

Static charges can be useful in technology. An example is the photocopy machine. Photocopiers run on electricity that comes to them through wires from the power plant. But static charges play an important role in how they work.

How a Photocopier Works

A photocopier uses static charges to make copies.

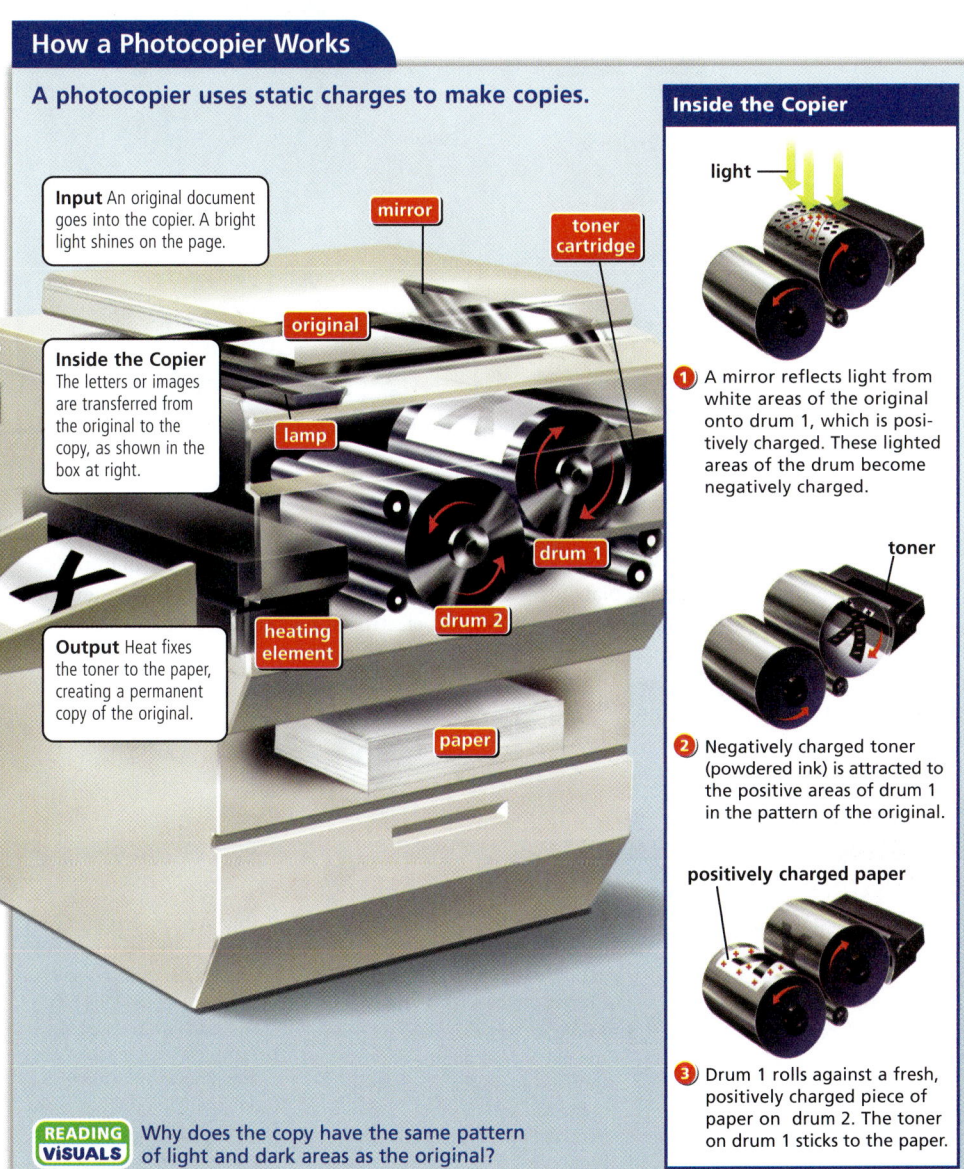

Input An original document goes into the copier. A bright light shines on the page.

Inside the Copier The letters or images are transferred from the original to the copy, as shown in the box at right.

Output Heat fixes the toner to the paper, creating a permanent copy of the original.

Inside the Copier

1. A mirror reflects light from white areas of the original onto drum 1, which is positively charged. These lighted areas of the drum become negatively charged.

2. Negatively charged toner (powdered ink) is attracted to the positive areas of drum 1 in the pattern of the original.

3. Drum 1 rolls against a fresh, positively charged piece of paper on drum 2. The toner on drum 1 sticks to the paper.

READING VISUALS Why does the copy have the same pattern of light and dark areas as the original?

Teach from Visuals

To help students to better interpret the visual of how a photocopier works, ask:

- What is the purpose of the bright light in a copier? *The bright light provides the light that is reflected or absorbed by the original.*

- Why does a copier contain mirrors? *Mirrors reflect the light from the white areas of the original onto a metal drum.*

Ongoing Assessment

Explain how static electricity is used in technology.

Ask: How can static electricity that occurs naturally interfere with photocopying? *Static electricity might cause toner to be attracted to areas of the drum that are not in the pattern of what is being copied.*

READING VISUALS *Answer: The pattern on the original is reproduced on the drum with a positive static charge. This positive charge attracts the negatively charged toner.*

DIFFERENTIATE INSTRUCTION

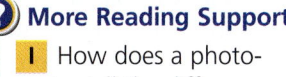 **More Reading Support**

I How does a photocopier tell the difference between the light and dark areas of the original? *by the difference in the type of charge*

Advanced Have students design a model of the way that a photocopier roll picks up toner that it then transfers to a piece of paper. They could use pepper as toner, cardboard tubes as the rollers, and other materials of their choosing. Have students present their model as a demonstration to the class.

Ongoing Assessment

 CHECK YOUR READING Answer: *Particles in the air become charged and are attracted to an oppositely charged plate in an electrostatic filter.*

Reinforce

Have students relate the section to the Big Idea.

  Reinforcing Key Concepts, p. 21

19.1 ASSESS & RETEACH

Assess

 Section 19.1 Quiz, p. 3

Reteach

Have small groups of students outline the section by using heads as main topics. Tell students that vocabulary terms, visual titles and captions, and topic sentences can serve as clues to subtopics. When the groups complete their outlines, lead a discussion and bring the class to a consensus about which subtopics should be included in the outline. From their conclusions, create a master outline on the board.

Technology Resources

Have students visit ClassZone.com for reteaching of Key Concepts.

 CONTENT REVIEW

 CONTENT REVIEW CD-ROM

Static electricity is also used in making cars. When new cars are painted, the paint is given an electric charge and then sprayed onto the car in a fine mist. The tiny droplets of paint stick to the car more firmly than they would without the charge. This process results in a coat of paint that is very even and smooth.

Another example of the use of static electricity in technology is a device called an electrostatic air filter. This device cleans air inside buildings with the help of static charges. The filter gives a static charge to pollen, dust, germs, and other particles in the air. Then an oppositely charged plate inside the filter attracts these particles, pulling them out of the air. Larger versions of electrostatic filters are used to remove pollutants from industrial smokestacks.

 **CHECK YOUR READING** How can static charges help clean air?

19.1 Review

KEY CONCEPTS

1. How do a positive and a negative particle interact?
2. Describe how the movement of electrons between two objects with balanced charges could cause the buildup of electric charge in both objects.
3. Describe one technological use of static electricity.

CRITICAL THINKING

4. **Infer** A sock and a shirt from the dryer stick together. What does this tell you about the charges on the sock and shirt?
5. **Analyze** You walk over a rug and get a shock from a doorknob. What do the materials of the rug and the shoes have to do with the type of charge your body had?

CHALLENGE

6. **Apply** Assume you start with a negatively charged rod and two balloons. Describe a series of steps you could take to create a positively charged balloon, pick up negatively charged powder with the balloon, and drop the powder from the balloon.

640 Unit 5: Electricity and Magnetism

ANSWERS

1. They attract each other.
2. The object that the electrons move to acquires a net negative charge and the object they move from acquires a positive charge.
3. photocopying, air filtering, or painting cars

4. They are oppositely charged.
5. If the shoe material had a greater attraction for electrons, your body acquired a negative charge. If the carpet material had a greater attraction for electrons, your body acquired a positive charge.

6. Place the two balloons side by side, touching. Touch one of the balloons with the rod, and then withdraw the rod. Separate the balloons. Use the balloon you touched with the rod to attract the powder. Touch the rod to the balloon again to release the powder.

CONNECTING SCIENCES

PHYSICAL SCIENCE AND LIFE SCIENCE

Electric Eels

An electric eel is a slow-moving fish with no teeth and poor eyesight. It lives in the murky waters of muddy rivers in South America. Instead of the senses that most animals use—vision, hearing, smell, and touch—an electric eel uses electricity to find its next meal. Since the fish that it eats often can swim much faster than the eel, it also uses electricity to catch its prey.

Electric Sense

An electric eel actually has three pairs of electric organs in its body. Two of them build electric charge for stunning prey and for self-defense. The third electric organ builds a smaller charge that helps in finding prey. The charge produces an electric field around the eel. Special sense organs on its body detect small changes in the electric field caused by nearby fish and other animals.

Shocking Organs

The electric eel builds an electric charge with a series of thousands of cells called electrocytes. Every cell in the series has a positive end and a negative end. Each electrocyte builds only a small charge. However, when all of the cells combine their charge, they can produce about five times as much electricity as a standard electrical outlet in a house. The charge is strong enough to paralyze or kill a human. Typically, though, the charge is used to stun or kill small fish, which the eel then swallows whole. Electric charge can also be used to scare away predators.

An electric eel (Electrophorus electricus) can deliver a jolt five times as powerful as an electrical outlet.

EXPLORE

1. **INFER** Electric eels live for 10 to 20 years, developing a stronger shock as they grow older. What could account for this increase in electric charge?
2. **CHALLENGE** Sharks and other animals use electricity also. Use the library or Internet to find out how.

CONNECTING SCIENCES
Integration of Sciences

Set Learning Goal
To show how electricity is produced and used by some living organisms

Present the Science
The organ in an electric eel that produces low-voltage pulses is the Sach's organ and is near the back of the eel. The Main and Hunters' organs are in back of the head. They can produce over 500 volts. The eel's head is the positive terminal, and its tail is the negative terminal. This structure allows for voltage flow. Each electrocyte generates 0.15 volt. Thus, the more electrocytes the eel has, the greater the voltage produced.

Discussion Question
Ask: An electric eel has no teeth and poor eyesight and moves slowly. Why is it important that the eel produce both weak and strong voltage? *Because the eel has poor eyesight, it needs weak voltage to find food. Because it cannot move quickly or grab other fish without teeth, it must have another way to stun or kill its prey.*

DIFFERENTIATION TIP Have students sketch a cutaway drawing of an eel that shows its voltage-producing organs and uses arrows showing that electricity flows from the tail to the head.

Close
Ask: Why is it important for scientists to study fish that produce and use electricity? *They can learn how to use weak electric fields for locating objects and communicating.*

EXPLORE

1. **INFER** Bigger eels have more electrocytes and therefore can produce a larger charge.
2. **CHALLENGE** Many of these animals produce weak electric fields and use these fields to find food and to communicate.

19.2 FOCUS

► Set Learning Goals
Students will
- Describe how charges move.
- Explain how charges store energy.
- Observe how differences in materials affect the movement of charges.
- Determine which materials conduct electricity in an experiment.

◁ 3-Minute Warm-Up
Display Transparency 4 or copy this exercise on the board:

Suppose you've blown up about 50 balloons for party decorations and want to put them on the walls. You've run out of tape. Explain how you could place the balloons without tape, and why your idea will work. *Rub a balloon on your hair or shirt, then put it on a wall. The balloon will have negative charge from the hair, will induce a positive charge in the wall, and will be attracted to the positive charge. This attraction will be strong enough to hold the balloon there against gravity for a short time.*

 3-Minute Warm-Up, p. T4

19.2 MOTIVATE

EXPLORE Static Discharge
PURPOSE To observe electrical energy

TIP *10 min.* Lighting the bulb can be best observed in a darkened room or against a dark background.

WHAT DO YOU THINK? *The bulb lit up briefly. A static charge moved from the balloon to the bulb and lit the bulb.*

Ongoing Assessment
 Answer: the force of attraction or repulsion between charged particles

---

KEY CONCEPT

19.2 Charges can move from one place to another.

◁ BEFORE, you learned
- Static charges are built up by the separation of electrons from protons
- Materials affect how static charges are built up
- Energy is the ability to cause change

▷ NOW, you will learn
- How charges move
- How charges store energy
- How differences in materials affect the movement of charges

VOCABULARY
electric potential p. 643
volt p. 643
conductor p. 646
insulator p. 646
resistance p. 647
ohm p. 647
grounding p. 649

EXPLORE Static Discharge
How can you observe electrical energy?

PROCEDURE
1. Rub the balloon against the wool cloth several times to give the balloon a static charge.
2. Slowly bring the balloon toward the middle part of the fluorescent bulb until a spark jumps between them.

WHAT DO YOU THINK?
- What happened in the fluorescent bulb when the spark jumped?
- How might you explain this observation?

MATERIALS
- inflated balloon
- wool cloth
- fluorescent light bulb

▼ **REMINDER**
Energy can be either kinetic (energy of motion) or potential (stored energy). Energy is measured in joules.

Static charges have potential energy.

You have read how a static charge is built up in an object such as a balloon. Once it is built up, the charge can stay where it is indefinitely. However, the charge can also move to a new location. The movement of a static charge out of an object is known as static discharge. When a charge moves, it transfers energy that can be used to do work.

What causes a charge to move is the same thing that builds up a charge in the first place—that is, the force of attraction or repulsion between charged particles. For example, suppose an object with a negative charge touches an object with a positive charge. The attraction of the unbalanced electrons in the first object to the unbalanced protons in the second object can cause the electrons to move to the second object.

 What can cause a charge to move?

642 Unit 5: **Electricity and Magnetism**

RESOURCES FOR DIFFERENTIATED INSTRUCTION

Below Level
UNIT RESOURCE BOOK
- Reading Study Guide A, pp. 24–25
- Decoding Support, p. 48

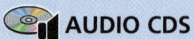 AUDIO CDS

Advanced
UNIT RESOURCE BOOK
- Challenge and Extension, p. 30
- Challenge Reading, pp. 44–45

English Learners
UNIT RESOURCE BOOK
Spanish Reading Study Guide, pp. 28–29

AUDIO CDS
- Audio Readings in Spanish
- Audio Readings (English)

Electric Potential Energy

Potential energy is stored energy an object may have because of its position. Water in a tower has gravitational potential energy because it is high above the ground. The kinetic energy—energy of motion—used to lift the water to the top of the tower is stored as potential energy. If you open a pipe below the tower, the water moves downward and its potential energy is converted back into kinetic energy.

Similarly, electric potential energy is the energy a charged particle has due to its position in an electric field. Because like charges repel, for example, it takes energy to push a charged particle closer to another particle with a like charge. That energy is stored as the electric potential energy of the first particle. When the particle is free to move again, it quickly moves away, and its electric potential energy is converted back into kinetic energy.

When water moves downward out of a tower and some of its potential energy is converted into kinetic energy, its potential energy decreases. Similarly, when a charged particle moves away from a particle with a like charge, its electric potential energy decreases. The water and the particle both move from a state of higher potential energy to one of lower potential energy.

Electric Potential

To push a charged particle closer to another particle with the same charge takes a certain amount of energy. To push two particles into the same position near that particle takes twice as much energy, and the two particles together have twice as much electric potential energy as the single particle. Although the amount of potential energy is higher, the amount of energy per unit charge at that position stays the same. **Electric potential** is the amount of electric potential energy per unit charge at a certain position in an electric field.

Electric potential is measured in units called volts, and voltage is another term for electric potential. A potential of one **volt** is equal to one joule of energy per coulomb of charge.

Just as water will not flow between two towers of the same height, a charge will not move between two positions with the same electric potential. For a charge to move, there must be a difference in potential between the two positions.

Like water in a tower, a static charge has potential energy. Just as gravity moves water down the supply pipe attached under the tank, the electric potential energy of a charge moves the charge along an electrical pathway.

Chapter 19: Electricity 643

DIFFERENTIATE INSTRUCTION

More Reading Support

A What is the amount of electric potential energy per unit charge? *electric potential*

B What is another term for electric potential? *voltage*

English Learners This page has many introductory clauses and phrases. Copy the page for students and ask them to underline sentences that use them. Here are some of the introductory clauses and phrases used:

"If you open a pipe below the tower," "Because like charges repel," "When the article is free to move again," "When water moves downward. . .," "Although the amount of energy is higher," and "For a charge to move."

19.2 INSTRUCT

Teacher Demo
Demonstrate the concept of potential energy and the reason that a difference in potential is needed to convert potential energy to kinetic energy.

- Fill a shallow pan with just enough water to cover the bottom. Place it flat on a table.
- Ask: Is the water evenly distributed, or is there more water at one end than another? *evenly distributed*
- Ask what will happen if you lift one end of the pan. *The water will collect at the lower end of the pie pan.* Demonstrate.
- Ask what would happen if you picked the pan straight up and held it there so it was flat. Would the water move? *no* How could you get the water to move? *tilt the pan as before* Relate this to the idea of a potential difference. *Although the pan and water have more potential energy than before, all the water would have the same potential energy, so it wouldn't move. Tilting the pan creates a difference in potential.*

Ongoing Assessment

Explain how charges store energy.

Ask: Why does the electric potential energy of an object depend on its position within an electric field? *Electric potential energy represents the potential to move, which depends on the strength of the field in which the object is located.*

Address Misconceptions

IDENTIFY Ask: Do static charges move from one object to another, or stay in one place? If students answer that static charges stay in one place, they may hold the misconception that static charges cannot move.

CORRECT Have groups of students list examples of moving static charges. Compile a class list of the examples. Examples might include the static cling they sometimes feel from clothes.

REASSESS Ask: What has happened when you feel a shock on a doorknob after walking across a carpet? *A static charge has passed from your hand to the doorknob.*

Technology Resources
Visit **ClassZone.com** for background on common student misconceptions.
MISCONCEPTION DATABASE

Integrate the Sciences

Sprites are phenomena that are associated with lightning storms and have been the subject of great interest in the scientific community over the past few years. Sprites are electrical discharges that occur between the clouds of thunderstorms and the lower ionosphere. Sprites differ from lightning in that they are dimmer and they seem to generate upward rather than downward. These high-altitude phenomena typically last just a few milliseconds.

Ongoing Assessment

Describe how charges move.

Ask: How does electric potential determine how charges move? *For a charge to move, there must be a difference in potential.*

 Answer: The charge must have a path to follow, and there must be a large enough difference in electric potential to move the charge through the path.

Charge Movement

When water moves from a higher to a lower position, some of its potential energy is used to move it. Along the way, some of its potential energy can be used to do other work, such as turning a water wheel. Similarly, when a charge moves, some of its electric potential energy is used in moving the charge and some of it can be used to do other work. For example, moving an electric charge through a material can cause the material to heat up, as in a burner on an electric stove.

You can see how a moving charge transfers energy when you get a shock from static electricity. As you walk across a rug, a charge builds up on your body. Once the charge is built up, it cannot move until you come in contact with something else. When you reach out to touch a doorknob, the charge has a path to follow. The electric potential energy of the charge moves the charge from you to the doorknob.

Why do you get a shock? Recall that the force of attraction or repulsion between charged particles is stronger when they are close together. As your hand gets closer to the doorknob, the electric potential of the static charge increases. At a certain point, the difference in electric potential between you and the doorknob is great enough to move the charge through the air to the doorknob. As the charge moves, some of its potential energy is changed into the heat, light, and sound of a spark.

 What two factors determine whether a static charge will move?

Lightning

Find out more about lightning and lightning safety.

The shock you get from a doorknob is a small-scale version of lightning. Lightning is a high-energy static discharge. This static electricity is caused by storm clouds. Lightning comes from the electric potential of millions of volts, which releases large amounts of energy in the form of light, heat, and sound. As you read about how lightning forms, follow the steps in the illustration on page 645.

① Charge Separation Particles of moisture inside a cloud collide with the air and with each other, causing the particles to become electrically charged. Wind and gravity separate charges, carrying the heavier, negatively charged particles to the bottom of the cloud and the lighter, positively charged particles to the top of the cloud.

② Charge Buildup Through induction, the negatively charged particles at the bottom of the cloud repel electrons in the ground, causing the surface of the ground to build up a positive charge.

③ Static Discharge When the electric potential, or voltage, created by the difference in charges is large enough, the negative charge moves from the cloud to the ground. The energy released by the discharge produces the flash of lightning and the sound of thunder.

DIFFERENTIATE INSTRUCTION

 **More Reading Support**

C Does potential energy increase or decrease when a charge moves? *It decreases.*

D What is lightning? *high-energy static discharge*

Advanced Have students investigate why a television screen acquires a static charge when the television is turned on. *The picture on the screen is created by a beam of electrons. Excess electrons cause a negative static charge on the screen.*

 Challenge and Extension, p. 30

How Lightning Forms

Lightning is a type of static discharge. Storm clouds may develop very large charges, each with an electric potential of millions of volts.

① Charge Separation

Collisions between particles in storm clouds separate charges. Negatively charged particles collect at the bottom of the cloud.

② Charge Buildup

The negatively charged bottom part of the cloud induces a positive charge in the surface of the ground.

③ Static Discharge

The charge jumps through the air to the ground. Energy released by the discharge causes thunder and lightning.

READING VISUALS How is lightning like the shock you can get from a doorknob? How is it different?

Chapter 19: **Electricity** 645

DIFFERENTIATE INSTRUCTION

More Reading Support

E What causes particles in a cloud to become charged? *collisions between particles*

F What type of charge is at the bottom of clouds? *negative*

Advanced Ask students to explain why you can tell how far away a lightning strike is by comparing the time when you see the lightning and the time when you hear the thunder. *The speed of light is much greater than the speed of sound, so the farther away the lightning strike is, the more time between the lightning and the thunder.*

Have students who are interested in lightning read the following article:

 Challenge Reading, pp. 44–45

Teach from Visuals

To help students interpret the visual of how lightning is formed, have students think about what happens in the visual illustrating static discharge. Ask:

- Do positively charged particles or negatively charged particles move when lightning strikes? *negative particles*
- What happens to some of the potential energy in the cloud? *It becomes light energy and sound.*

T This visual is also available as T6 in the Unit Transparency Book.

Integrate the Sciences

Nitrogen is essential to all organisms because it is part of proteins, DNA, and RNA. However, almost all nitrogen on Earth is in the form of atmospheric nitrogen, which is not usable by most organisms. Lightning helps to enrich soil by providing the energy needed to cause a chemical reaction between nitrogen and other chemicals in the air, to make compounds that organisms can use.

Develop Critical Thinking

EVALUATE The following safety precautions should be taken during a thunderstorm. Have students explain why each guideline should be observed, using what they know about electricity.

- Do not take shelter under an isolated tree. *The tree is positively charged and will attract lightning because of its height.*
- Move away from bodies of water. *Water conducts electricity.*
- Unplug appliances and use phones only in an emergency. *Electrical and phone wires conduct electricity.*

Ongoing Assessment

READING VISUALS Answer: Both are discharges of static electricity. Lightning has much more charge and a much higher voltage.

Chapter 19 **645**

INVESTIGATE Conductors and Insulators

PURPOSE To determine what materials conduct electricity

TIPS 20 min.
- You could assemble the battery, bulb, and wires ahead of time.
- Electrical tape can be used instead of duct tape.

WHAT DO YOU THINK? *Objects that allowed the bulb to light up are made from materials that are conductors. Those that did not allow the bulb to light up are insulators.*

CHALLENGE *The brightness of the bulb can be used to indicate how well different materials conduct a charge.*

R Datasheet, Conductors and Insulators, p. 31

Technology Resources
Customize this student lab as needed or look for an alternative. Print rubrics to assess student lab reports.

Lab Generator CD-ROM

Metacognitive Strategy
Ask students to list questions that arose during the investigation. Have them write answers to questions that were answered during the investigation.

Ongoing Assessment
 Answer: A conductor allows an electric charge to pass through it easily, but an insulator does not.

COMBINATION NOTES Make notes on the different ways materials can affect charge movement. Use sketches to help explain the concepts.

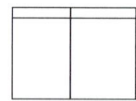

Materials affect charge movement.

After you walk across a carpet, a charge on your skin has no place to go until you touch or come very close to something. That is because an electric charge cannot move easily through air. However, a charge can move easily through the metal of a doorknob.

Conductors and Insulators

 A material that allows an electric charge to pass through it easily is called a **conductor.** Metals such as iron, steel, copper, and aluminum are good conductors. Most wire used to carry a charge is made of copper, which conducts very well.

 A material that does not easily allow a charge to pass through it is called an **insulator.** Plastic and rubber are good insulators. Many types of electric wire are covered with plastic, which insulates well. The plastic allows a charge to be conducted from one end of the wire to the other, but not through the sides of the wire. Insulators are also important in electrical safety, because they keep charges away from the body.

 What is the difference between a conductor and an insulator?

INVESTIGATE Conductors and Insulators

What materials conduct electricity?

PROCEDURE

1. Use tape to connect the battery, wires, and bulb holder as shown in the photograph. Make sure that the wires connected to the battery stay in full contact with the metal parts on either end. Test the bulb and the battery by touching the free ends of wire together. The bulb should light up.

2. Test each object in turn by touching it simultaneously with both free ends of wire. Make sure the ends of wire do not touch each other.

WHAT DO YOU THINK?
- Which objects allowed the light bulb to light up when the wires touched them? Which did not?
- How can you explain the difference between the two groups of objects?

CHALLENGE Do any of the materials you tested seem to conduct a charge better than other conductors? How could you use the setup you have to compare the degree of conducting ability of materials?

SKILL FOCUS Interpreting data

MATERIALS
- D cell (battery)
- 3 pieces of low-voltage wire
- duct tape
- flashlight bulb
- bulb holder
- objects of different materials

TIME 20 minutes

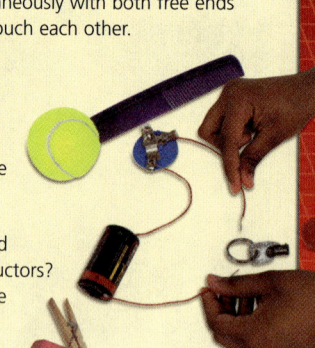

646 Unit 5: Electricity and Magnetism

DIFFERENTIATE INSTRUCTION

 More Reading Support

G Is a copper penny an insulator or a conductor? *a conductor*

H Is plastic a conductor or an insulator? *an insulator*

Alternative Assessment Have students create a two-column chart that lists insulators and conductors. As they read this section and test the different materials in "Investigate Conductors and Insulators," have them fill in their charts.

Electrons can move freely in a material with low resistance, such as the copper wire in these power lines. Electrons cannot move freely in a material with high resistance, such as the ceramic insulator this worker is putting in place or his safety gloves.

Resistance

Think about the difference between walking through air and walking through waist-deep water. The water resists your movement more than the air, so you have to work harder to walk. If you walked waist-deep in mud, you would have to work even harder.

Materials resist the movement of a charge in different amounts. Electrical **resistance** is the property of a material that determines how easily a charge can move through it. Electrical resistance is measured in units called **ohms**. The symbol for ohms is the Greek letter *omega* (Ω).

Most materials have some resistance. A good conductor such as copper, though, has low resistance. A good insulator, such as plastic or wood, has high resistance.

Resistance depends on the amount and shape of the material as well as on the type of material itself. A wire that is thin has more resistance than a wire that is thick. Think of how you have to work harder to drink through a narrow straw than a wide one. A wire that is long has more resistance than a wire that is short. Again, think of how much harder it is to drink through a long straw than a short one.

Like a thick drink in a straw, an electric charge moves more easily through a short, wide pathway than a long, narrow one.

 What three factors affect how much resistance an object has?

History of Science

One of the pioneers in the study of electricity was Benjamin Franklin. His most famous experiment with charges occurred in the early 1750s, when he attached a key to a kite string to show the relationship between lightning and electricity. After his kite experiment, Franklin developed a lightning rod connected to bells that would ring when lightning was in the vicinity. The lightning rod quickly became a standard way to protect buildings from lightning strikes.

Teacher Demo

Show students the difference between a conductor and an insulator. Charge an electroscope with a rubber rod that has been rubbed with fur. Touch the electroscope with an insulator, such as a glass rod or a wooden dowel rod. The electroscope will not discharge. Touch the electroscope with a metal rod. The electroscope will discharge because the metal rod is a conductor.

Ongoing Assessment

Observe how differences in materials affect the movement of charges.

Ask: Would a penny or a dollar bill have greater resistance? *a dollar bill, because it is paper, which is made from wood*

Answer: the amount, shape, and type of material

Chapter 19: Electricity 647

DIFFERENTIATE INSTRUCTION

More Reading Support

I What is the unit of measure for resistance? *ohm*

J Which has more resistance, a thick or a thin wire? *thin*

Below Level Ask students to explain in their own words why resistance depends in part on the amount of a material. *Answers will vary but should reflect that more material means there is more surface area for an electric charge to move through.* To reinforce this notion with a visual example, draw a cross section of a large wire and a cross section of a smaller wire on the board. Ask: Which of these wires has less resistance? *the larger one*

Chapter 19 **647**

Real World Example

One way of determining which type of wire to use is to consider its gauge. Gauge is a number that reflects the diameter of a single wire or the area of a cross section of a strand of wires. As gauge increases, the diameter of the wire decreases. If wires are made of the same material, resistance increases as gauge increases.

Teacher Demo

Bring to class a three-way lamp that contains a three-way light bulb. Turn on each level of brightness so that students can compare them. For each brightness, have students explain the relative resistance of the filaments.

Ongoing Assessment

CHECK YOUR READING *Answer: practically none at extremely low temperatures*

By taking advantage of resistance, we can use an electric charge to do work. When a moving charge overcomes resistance, some of the charge's electrical energy changes into other forms of energy, such as light and heat. For example, the filament of a light bulb is often made of tungsten, a material with high resistance. When electricity moves through the tungsten, the filament gives off light, which is useful. However, the bulb also gives off heat. Because light bulbs are not usually used to produce heat, we think of the heat they produce as wasted energy.

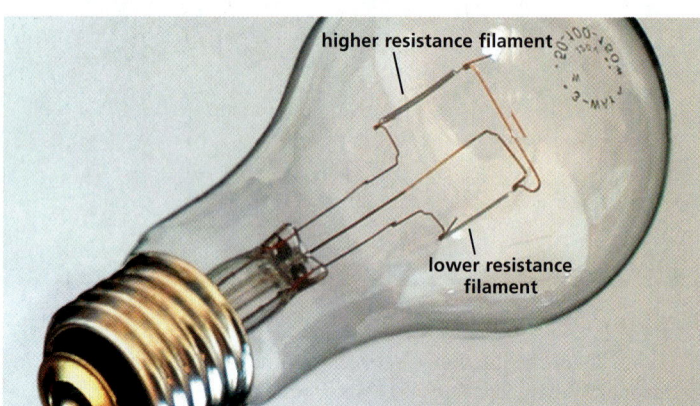

A three-way light bulb has two filaments, each with a different level of resistance. The one with higher resistance produces brighter light. Both together give the brightest setting.

A material with low resistance is one that a charge can flow through with little loss of energy. Materials move electricity more efficiently when they have low resistances. Such materials waste less energy, so more is available to do work at the other end. That is why copper is used for electrical wiring. Even copper has some resistance, however, and using it wastes some energy.

Superconductors

Scientists have known for many years that some materials have practically no resistance at extremely low temperatures. Such materials are called superconductors, because they conduct even better than good conductors like copper. Superconductors have many uses. They can be used in power lines to increase efficiency and conserve energy, and in high-speed trains to reduce friction. Engineers are also testing superconducting materials for use in computers and other electronic devices. Superconductors would make computers work faster and might also be used to make better motors and generators.

Because superconductors must be kept extremely cold, they have not always been practical. Scientists are solving this problem by developing superconductors that will work at higher temperatures.

 How much resistance does a superconducting material have?

648 Unit 5: Electricity and Magnetism

DIFFERENTIATE INSTRUCTION

 More Reading Support

K Why might superconductors not be practical? *They must be kept extremely cold.*

Below Level Ask: Why is it impractical to keep superconductors? *Even though the use of a superconductor decreases resistance and saves energy, the energy saved is much less than the energy used to keep the superconductor cold.*

Grounding

If a charge can pass through two different materials, it will pass through the one with the lower resistance. This is the principle behind an important electrical safety procedure—grounding. **Grounding** means providing a harmless, low-resistance path—a ground—for electricity to follow. In many cases, this path actually leads into the ground, that is, into the Earth.

Grounding is used to protect buildings from damage by lightning. Most buildings have some type of lightning rod, which is made from a material that is a good conductor. The rod is placed high up, so that it is closer to the lightning charge. The rod is connected to a conductor cable, and the cable is attached to a copper pole, which is driven into the ground.

Because of the rod's low resistance, lightning will strike the rod before it will strike the roof, where it might have caused a fire. Lightning hits the rod and passes harmlessly through the cable into the ground.

Grounding provides a path for electric current to travel into the ground, which can absorb the charge and make it harmless. The charge soon spreads out so that its voltage in any particular spot is low.

 What is a ground cable?

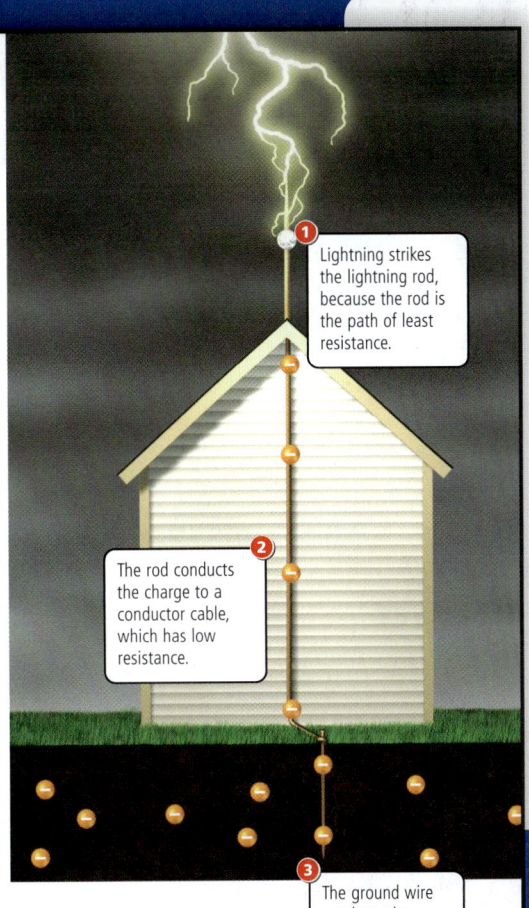

1. Lightning strikes the lightning rod, because the rod is the path of least resistance.
2. The rod conducts the charge to a conductor cable, which has low resistance.
3. The ground wire conducts the charge into the ground, where it spreads out and becomes harmless.

19.2 Review

KEY CONCEPTS
1. Explain what happens when you get a static electric shock as you touch a doorknob.
2. What is electric potential?
3. What three factors affect how much electrical resistance an object has?
4. How can a lightning rod protect a building from fire?

CRITICAL THINKING
5. **Infer** Object A has a positive charge. After Object A touches Object B, A still has a positive charge and the same amount of charge. What can you infer about the charge of B?
6. **Analyze** Why do lightning rods work better if they are placed high up, closer to the lightning charge?

CHALLENGE
7. **Apply** Could the same material be used as both a conductor and an insulator? Explain your answer.

Chapter 19: **Electricity** 649

Ongoing Assessment

 Answer: a low-resistance conductor that supplies a safe path for electricity

Develop Critical Thinking
EVALUATE Ask: Why is it essential that ladders be kept away from power lines? *Ladders rest on the ground and thus are grounded. If they are made of the right materials, they could conduct charge and injure someone on the ladder.*

Reinforce the BIG idea
Have students relate the section to the Big Idea.

 Reinforcing Key Concepts, p. 32

19.2 ASSESS & RETEACH

Assess
 Section 19.2 Quiz, p. 4

Reteach
Write "Charges can move from one place to another" on the board. Then write "when," "by," "as," and "through," on separate lines underneath, and encourage students to complete the thoughts using information from the section. *Sample answers:* when *there is attraction or repulsion between charged particles (p. 642),* when *there is a difference in electric potential energy (p. 643),* as *lightning and other static discharge (p. 644),* through *conductors (p. 646).*

Technology Resources
Have students visit **ClassZone.com** for reteaching of Key Concepts.

 CONTENT REVIEW

CONTENT REVIEW CD-ROM

ANSWERS

1. Your body builds up a charge. As your hand nears the doorknob, an opposite charge is induced in the doorknob. The charge moves and shocks your hand.
2. the amount of electric potential energy per unit of charge at a particular point in an electric field
3. the amount, the shape, and the type of material
4. It provides a path of lower resistance and thus allows the lightning to pass harmlessly from the sky through the ground wire into the ground without going through the house.
5. It was the same as object A.
6. The lightning is more likely to initially hit the lightning rod than the building.
7. Yes; a material with relatively low resistance would resist the passage of a weak charge but allow the passage of a strong charge.

Chapter 19 **649**

CHAPTER INVESTIGATION

Focus

PURPOSE To model a lightning strike and the use of a lightning rod to control the path of lightning

OVERVIEW Students will model the buildup and discharge of a static charge. They will use wool to create a charge on a foam plate. They will transfer this charge to an aluminum pan. Then they will observe a static discharge as they bring other metal objects close to the pan. Students will find the following:

- Static discharge occurs when electric potential, which increases as distance decreases, is high enough.
- A low-resistance conductor can be used to control the path of the discharge.

Lab Preparation

- Ask students to bring in wool cloth and aluminum pie pans from home.
- Cut the wool cloth into conveniently sized pieces.
- Prior to the investigation have students read through the investigation and prepare their data tables. Or you may wish to copy and distribute datasheets and rubrics.

 UNIT RESOURCE BOOK, pp. 53–61

SCIENCE TOOLKIT, F15

Lab Management

- Students should understand that the clay acts as an insulator, so that the charge does not pass to a student's hand.
- The surface on which the plate is placed must be nonconducting.

COOPERATIVE LEARNING Students should take turns doing each task, so that each student at some time charges the plate and observes the discharge.

650 Unit 5: **Electricity and Magnetism**

CHAPTER INVESTIGATION

Lightning

OVERVIEW AND PURPOSE Lightning is a form of static discharge. During storms, electric charges build up within clouds. Lightning occurs when these charges move. In this experiment, you will
- model the buildup of charges that can occur during a storm
- model a lightning strike
- use a ground to control the path of discharge

Procedure

1. Draw a data table like the one on the sample notebook page.

2. Firmly press a lump of clay onto the inside bottom of one aluminum pan (A) to make a handle. Press another lump onto the underside of the other pan (B) as shown.

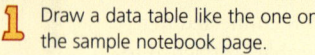

3. Place the foam plate upside down on a flat surface. Without touching the plate with your bare skin, rub the bottom of the plate vigorously with the wool cloth for 1–2 minutes.

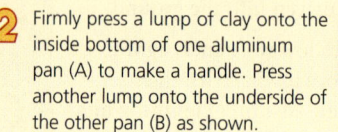

4. Pick up aluminum pan A by the handle and hold it about 5 cm above the foam plate. Drop the pan so that it rests centered on top of the foam plate as shown. Be careful not to touch the pan or the plate.

5. Make the room as dark as possible. Slowly lower aluminum pan B over the rim of the first pan until they touch. Describe what occurs and where, in your notebook.

MATERIALS
- modeling clay
- 2 aluminum pie pans
- foam plate
- wool cloth
- paper clip

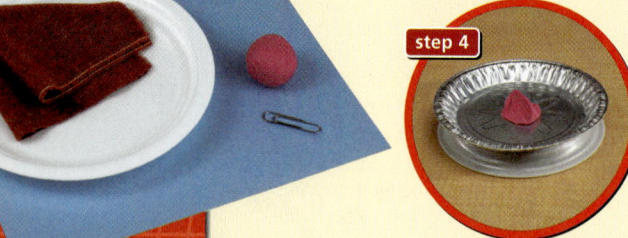

INVESTIGATION RESOURCES

 CHAPTER INVESTIGATION, Lightning
- Level A, pp. 53–56
- Level B, pp. 57–60
- Level C, p. 61

Advanced students should complete Levels B & C.

 Writing a Lab Report, D12–13

Technology Resources

Customize this student lab as needed or look for an alternative. Print rubrics to assess student lab reports.

 Lab Generator CD-ROM

6. Repeat steps 3–5 two more times, recording your observations in your notebook.

7. Open the paper clip partway, as shown. Repeat steps 3–4. Then, instead of using the second aluminum pan, slowly bring the pointed end of the paper clip toward the rim of the first pan until they touch. Record your observations.

8. Repeat step 7 two more times, touching the paper clip to the aluminum pan in different places.

Observe and Analyze

1. **RECORD OBSERVATIONS** Be sure your data table is complete. Draw pictures to show how the procedure varied between steps 5–6 and steps 7–8.

2. **ANALYZE** What did you observe in step 5 when the two aluminum pans touched? What do you think caused this to occur?

3. **COMPARE** How were your observations when you touched the aluminum pan with the paper clip different from those you made when you touched it with the other pan? How can you explain the difference?

Conclude

1. **ANALYZE** Use the observations recorded in your data table to answer the following question: When you used the paper clip, why were you able to control the point at which the static discharge occurred?

2. **INFER** What charges did the foam plate and aluminum pan have before you began the experiment? after you dropped the pan on the plate? after you touched the pan with the paper clip?

3. **IDENTIFY VARIABLES** What variables and controls affected the outcome of your experiment?

4. **IDENTIFY LIMITS** What limitations or sources of error could have affected your results?

5. **APPLY** In your experiment, what corresponds to storm clouds and lightning? How did the paper clip work like a lightning rod?

INVESTIGATE Further

CHALLENGE Where did the charge go when you touched the pie pan with the paper clip? Write a hypothesis to explain what happens in this situation and design an experiment to test your hypothesis.

Lightning
Observe and Analyze
Table 1. Observations of Static Discharge

Trial	Observations
With second aluminum pan	
1	
2	
3	
With paper clip	
4	
5	
6	

Conclude

Observe and Analyze

1. Sketches should show that in step 5 the aluminum pan was discharged with a second aluminum pan. In step 7, a paper clip discharged the pan.

2. A spark jumped from a random point on the outer edge of one pan to the other pan. A charge built up in the first pan and discharged to the second pan.

3. The spark jumped wherever the paper clip touched the pan instead of at some random point. The paper clip provided a path for the discharge.

Conclude

1. The paper clip gave the charge a path of least resistance to follow at a specific point on the pan.

2. The plate and pan initially had no charge. After the pan was dropped, they both had the same type of charge. The pan again had no net charge after being touched by the paper clip.

3. Variables: the size and shape of the metal object used to discharge the pan. Controls: the materials used to build up a charge, method of creating the charge, procedure used to discharge the charge.

4. accidentally touching the plate or the pans, the way that the wool was rubbed on the plate

5. The first aluminum pan is like the storm cloud because it is charged. The spark is like lightning. The paper clip grounded the discharge.

INVESTIGATE Further

CHALLENGE The charge passed onto the person holding the paper clip. Sample hypothesis: If the charge moved away from the paper clip, then the paper clip should not be attracted to a charged object, because it has no charge itself.

Post-Lab Discussion

- Ask: What could have been used to form a handle instead of the clay? *any item made of material that is a nonconductor*
- If students did not observe the expected results, have them reread the procedure. Ask: Where might you have made a mistake that affected your experiment? *Sample answer: Step 3 (could not generate a strong charge) or step 4 (accidentally touched the plate)*

19.3 FOCUS

◉ Set Learning Goals

Students will
- Describe electric current.
- Explain how current is related to voltage and resistance.
- Distinguish among different types of electric power cells.
- Perform an experiment to infer how electric current can be produced.

◉ 3-Minute Warm-Up

Display Transparency 5 or copy this exercise on the board:

Draw a diagram using the width of a horizontal arrow to show the amount of a charge. Adjust the width of the arrow to show what happens when the charge

- enters a material with low resistance.
  The width of the arrow decreases slightly.
- enters a material with high resistance.
  The width of the arrow decreases a lot.

 3-Minute Warm-Up, p. T5

19.3 MOTIVATE

EXPLORE Current

PURPOSE To observe how resistance affects the flow of charge

TIP 20 min. Check the setup ahead of class. If the bulb doesn't light, use a stronger battery or a thinner piece of graphite.

WHAT DO YOU THINK? *The bulb glows more dimly. As the wires are moved apart, the bulb receives less current.*

Teaching with Technology

Students can use a multimeter to check voltage and resistance for the setup in this exploration. (Directions for using a multimeter are discussed on p. 654.)

652 Unit 5: Electricity and Magnetism

KEY CONCEPT
19.3 Electric current is a flow of charge.

BEFORE, you learned
- Charges move from higher to lower potential
- Materials can act as conductors or insulators
- Materials have different levels of resistance

NOW, you will learn
- About electric current
- How current is related to voltage and resistance
- About different types of electric power cells

VOCABULARY
electric current p. 652
ampere p. 653
Ohm's law p. 653
electric cell p. 655

EXPLORE Current
How does resistance affect the flow of charge?

PROCEDURE

1. Tape the pencil lead flat on the posterboard.
2. Connect the wires, cell, bulb, and bulb holder as shown in the photograph.
3. Hold the wire ends against the pencil lead about a centimeter apart from each other. Observe the bulb.
4. Keeping the wire ends in contact with the lead, slowly move them apart. As you move the wire ends apart, observe the bulb.

WHAT DO YOU THINK?
- What happened to the bulb as you moved the wire ends apart?
- How might you explain your observation?

MATERIALS
- pencil lead
- posterboard
- electrical tape
- 3 lengths of wire
- D cell battery
- flashlight bulb
- bulb holder

Electric charge can flow continuously.

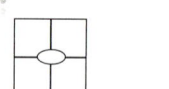

VOCABULARY Don't forget to make a four square diagram for the term *electric current*.

Static charges cannot make your television play. For that you need a different type of electricity. You have learned that a static charge contains a specific, limited amount of charge. You have also learned that a static charge can move and always moves from higher to lower potential. However, suppose that, instead of one charge, an electrical pathway received a continuous supply of charge and the difference in potential between the two ends of the pathway stayed the same. Then, you would have a continuous flow of charge. Another name for a flow of charge is **electric current**. Electric current is the form of electricity used to supply energy in homes, schools, and other buildings.

652 Unit 5: Electricity and Magnetism

RESOURCES FOR DIFFERENTIATED INSTRUCTION

Below Level
UNIT RESOURCE BOOK
- Reading Study Guide A, pp. 35–36
- Decoding Support, p. 48

 **AUDIO CDS**

R Additional INVESTIGATION,
Making a Coin Battery, A, B, & C, pp. 62–70;
Teacher Instructions, pp. 206–207

Advanced
UNIT RESOURCE BOOK
Challenge and Extension, p. 41

English Learners
UNIT RESOURCE BOOK
Spanish Reading Study Guide, pp. 39–40

 **AUDIO CDS**
- Audio Readings in Spanish
- Audio Readings (English)

Current, Voltage, and Resistance

Electric current obeys the same rules as moving static charges. Charge can flow only if it has a path to follow, that is, a material to conduct it. Also, charge can flow only from a point of higher potential to one of lower potential. However, one concept that does not apply to a moving static charge applies to current. Charge that flows steadily has a certain rate of flow. This rate can be measured. The standard unit of measure for current is the **ampere,** or amp. An amp is the amount of charge that flows past a given point per unit of time. One amp equals one coulomb per second. The number of amps—or amperage—of a flowing charge is determined by both voltage and resistance.

Electric current, or amperage, can be compared to the flow of water through a pipe. Electric potential, or voltage, is like pressure pushing the water through the pipe. Resistance, or ohms, is like the diameter of the pipe, which controls how much water can flow through. Water pressure and pipe size together determine the rate of water flow. Similarly, voltage and resistance together determine the rate of flow of electric charge.

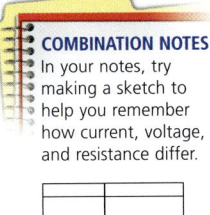

COMBINATION NOTES In your notes, try making a sketch to help you remember how current, voltage, and resistance differ.

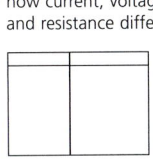

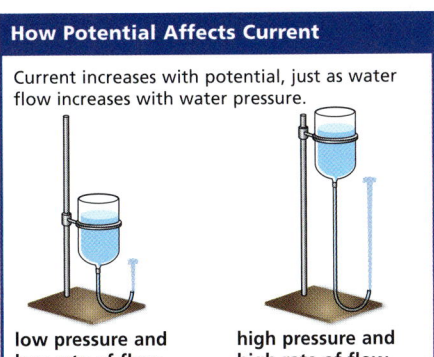

How Potential Affects Current
Current increases with potential, just as water flow increases with water pressure.

low pressure and low rate of flow

high pressure and high rate of flow

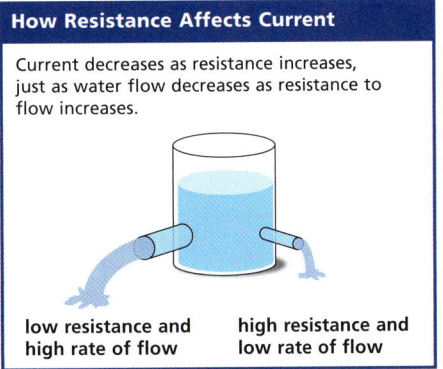

How Resistance Affects Current
Current decreases as resistance increases, just as water flow decreases as resistance to flow increases.

low resistance and high rate of flow

high resistance and low rate of flow

Ohm's Law

You now have three important measurements for the study of electricity: volts, ohms, and amps. The scientist for whom the ohm is named discovered a mathematical relationship among these three measurements. The relationship, called **Ohm's law,** is expressed in the formula below.

SIMULATION
CLASSZONE.COM
See Ohm's law in action.

$$\text{Current} = \frac{\text{Voltage}}{\text{Resistance}} \qquad I = \frac{V}{R}$$

I is current measured in amps (A), V is voltage measured in volts (V), and R is resistance measured in ohms (Ω).

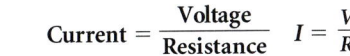 What two values do you need to know to calculate the amperage of electric current?

Chapter 19: **Electricity** 653

Integrate the Sciences

Current can cause discomfort or even damage to the human body.

- At .001 amperes a person will feel a faint tingle.
- A person will feel a painful shock at .006 amperes.
- A person holding a charge source that is producing current ranging from 0.05 to .15 amperes cannot let go of the source.
- A person experiences difficulty breathing at exposure to current ranging from 0.05 to 0.15 amperes.
- A current ranging from 1.0 to 4.3 amperes can stop the rhythmic pumping of the heart.
- Cardiac arrest occurs at 10 amperes.

Mathematics Connection

Tell students to assume that the resistance of skin may be as low as 1000 ohms on a day with high humidity but 100 times as much on a dry day. Ask: If you touch the poles of a 1.5-volt battery on a dry day, how much current might move through your hand? *1.5×10^{-5} amps* How much current might be there on a day with high humidity? *1.5×10^{-3} amps*

Although the practice problems involve determining current if voltage and resistance are known, students should realize that the formula for Ohm's law can be rearranged to solve for a different variable in the equation when that variable is the unknown.

Developing Algebra Skills

- Math Support, p. 49
- Math Practice, p. 50

Practice the Math Answers:

1. $I = \dfrac{V}{R} = \dfrac{220 \text{ volts}}{55 \text{ ohms}} = 4 \text{ amps}$

2. $I = \dfrac{V}{R} = \dfrac{12 \text{ volts}}{24 \text{ ohms}} = 0.5 \text{ amp}$

Ongoing Assessment

 *Answer: resistance*

654 Unit 5: **Electricity and Magnetism**

You have read that current is affected by both voltage and resistance. Using Ohm's law, you can calculate exactly how much it is affected and determine the exact amount of current in amps. Use the formula for current to solve the sample problem below.

Calculating Current

Sample Problem

What is the current in an electrical pathway with an electric potential of 120 volts and a resistance of 60 ohms?

What do you know?	voltage = 120 V, resistance = 60 Ω
What do you want to find out?	current
Write the formula:	$I = \dfrac{V}{R}$
Substitute into the formula:	$I = \dfrac{120 \text{ V}}{60 \text{ Ω}}$
Calculate and simplify:	$I = 2$ A
Check that your units agree:	Unit is amps. Unit of current is amps. Units agree.
Answer:	2 A

Practice the Math

1. What is the current in an electrical pathway in which the voltage is 220 V and the resistance is 55 Ω?
2. An electrical pathway has a voltage of 12 volts and a resistance of 24 ohms. What is the current?

READING TIP
The terms *voltmeter*, *ohmmeter*, *ammeter*, and *multimeter* are all made by adding a prefix to the word *meter*.

Measuring Electricity

Volts, ohms, and amps can all be measured using specific electrical instruments. Volts can be measured with a voltmeter. Ohms can be measured with an ohmmeter. Amps can be measured with an ammeter. These three instruments are often combined in a single electrical instrument called a multimeter.

To use a multimeter, set the dial on the type of unit you wish to measure. For example, the multimeter in the photograph is being used to test the voltage of a 9-volt battery. The dial is set on volts in the 0–20 range. The meter shows that the battery's charge has an electric potential of more than 9 volts, which means that the battery is good. A dead battery would have a lower voltage.

 What does an ohmmeter measure?

DIFFERENTIATE INSTRUCTION

More Reading Support

C What type of meter measures current?
ammeter

D What does a multimeter measure?
volts, ohms, and amps

Inclusion To enable students with learning disabilities to visualize the effect of electrical energy in their lives, have them locate on the Internet satellite photographs of the United States taken at night during the massive blackout on August 14, 2003. For comparison, have students also find photographs showing the same area before the blackout. Advise students to enter the date and the term *satellite* in a search engine. Be sure to find sites with the actual photographs of the blackout rather than ones that have been touched up.

INVESTIGATE Electric Cells

How can you produce electric current?

PROCEDURE

1. Insert the paper clip and the penny into the lemon, as shown in the photograph. The penny and paper clip should go about 3 cm into the lemon. They should be close, but not touching.
2. On the multimeter, go to the DC volts (V⎓) section of the dial and select the 0–2000 millivolt range (2000 m).
3. Touch one of the leads of the multimeter to the paper clip. Touch the other lead to the penny. Observe what is shown on the display of the multimeter.

WHAT DO YOU THINK?
- What did you observe on the display of the multimeter?
- How can you explain the reading on the multimeter?

CHALLENGE Repeat this experiment using different combinations of fruits or vegetables and metal objects. Which combinations work best?

SKILL FOCUS Inferring

MATERIALS
- paper clip
- penny
- large lemon
- multimeter

For Challenge
- additional fruits or vegetables
- metal objects

TIME 20 minutes

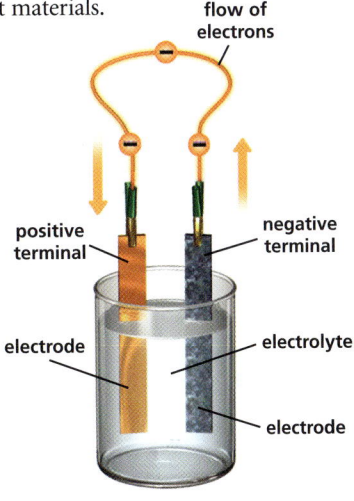

Electric cells supply electric current.

Electric current can be used in many ways. Two basic types of device have been developed for producing current. One type produces electric current using magnets. You will learn more about this technology in Chapter 21. The other type is the **electric cell,** which produces electric current using the chemical or physical properties of different materials.

Electrochemical Cells

An electrochemical cell is an electric cell that produces current by means of chemical reactions. As you can see in the diagram, an electrochemical cell contains two strips made of different materials. The strips are called electrodes. The electrodes are suspended in a third material called the electrolyte, which interacts chemically with the electrodes to separate charges and produce a flow of electrons from the negative terminal to the positive terminal.

Batteries are made using electrochemical cells. Technically, a battery is two or more cells connected to each other. However, single cells, such as C cells and D cells, are often referred to as batteries.

Chapter 19: **Electricity** 655

INVESTIGATE Electric Cells

PURPOSE To infer how electric current can be produced

TIPS 20 min.
- Demonstrate how to use the multimeter.
- Have sandpaper available. If pennies are corroded, results will be better if students sand the corrosion off the coin.

WHAT DO YOU THINK? *The meter shows a steady voltage in the circuit, usually between 0.03 V and 0.05 V. The lemon, the penny, and the paper clip interact to produce current.*

CHALLENGE *The most current will come from acidic fruits and relatively active metals.*

 Datasheet, Electric Cells, p. 42

Technology Resources

Customize this student lab as needed or look for an alternative. Print rubrics to assess student lab reports.

 Lab Generator CD-ROM

Teaching with Technology

If you have probeware, you may wish to adapt this activity so a current and voltage probe system can be used instead of a multimeter.

DIFFERENTIATE INSTRUCTION

 More Reading Support

E How do electrochemical cells produce current? *by chemical reactions*

F What do the electrodes react with in an electrochemical cell? *the electrolyte*

Additional Investigation To reinforce Section 19.3 learning goals, use the following full-period investigation:

 Additional INVESTIGATION, Making a Coin Battery, A, B, & C, pp. 62–70, 206–207

Advanced Have students research the details of electrochemical cells. Have them investigate how different metals and electrolytes interact and use the information to design an electrochemical cell that could produce a relatively high voltage.

 Challenge and Extension, p. 41

Chapter 19 **655**

Real World Example

Alkaline cells are commonly used dry cells. These cells differ from carbon-zinc cells in that they use potassium hydroxide instead of ammonium chloride in the electrolyte. Potassium hydroxide is a base (alkaline) material, so these cells are referred to as alkaline batteries. These cells have a much longer shelf life than zinc-carbon cells, and they perform better while being used and in cold weather. They do not use ammonium ions, which corrode zinc and cause the cells to be more likely to leak. Alkaline cells also do not produce any gaseous products.

Integrate the Sciences

The heart beats in a regular pattern because it receives a consistent pattern of electrical signals. If the pattern becomes irregular or is interrupted, a pacemaker can be surgically implanted to provide regular signals. Because surgery is required to change the battery in a pacemaker, the batteries must last a long time. Pacemaker batteries normally last from 4 to 8 years.

Ongoing Assessment

Distinguish among different types of electric power cells.

Ask: Are rechargeable batteries primary cells or storage cells? *storage cells*

 *Answer: They contain a solid paste electrolyte.*

 *Answer: storage cell*

 Learn more about electrochemical cells.

Primary Cells The electrochemical cell shown on page 655 is called a wet cell, because the electrolyte is a liquid. Most household batteries in use today have a solid paste electrolyte and so are called dry cells. Both wet cells and dry cells are primary cells. Primary cells produce electric current through chemical reactions that continue until one or more of the chemicals is used up.

The primary cell on page 657 is a typical zinc-carbon dry cell. It has a negative electrode made of zinc. The zinc electrode is made in the shape of a can and has a terminal—in this case, a wide disk of exposed metal—on the bottom of the cell. The positive electrode consists of a carbon rod and particles of carbon and manganese dioxide. The particles are suspended in an electrolyte paste. The positive electrode has a terminal—a smaller disk of exposed metal—at the top of the rod. A paper separator prevents the two electrodes from coming into contact inside the cell.

When the two terminals of the cell are connected—for example, when you turn on a flashlight—a chemical reaction between the zinc and the electrolyte produces electrons and positive zinc ions. The electrons flow through the wires connecting the cell to the flashlight bulb, causing the bulb to light up. The electrons then travel through the carbon rod and combine with the manganese dioxide. When the zinc and manganese dioxide stop reacting, the cell dies.

 Why are most household batteries called dry cells?

Storage Cells Some batteries produce current through chemical reactions that can be reversed inside the battery. These batteries are called storage cells, secondary cells, or rechargeable batteries. A car battery like the lead-acid battery shown on page 657 is rechargeable. The battery has a negative electrode of lead and a positive electrode of lead peroxide. As the battery produces current, both electrodes change chemically into lead sulfate, and the electrolyte changes into water.

When storage cells are producing current, they are said to be discharging. Whenever a car engine is started, the battery discharges to operate the ignition motor. A car's battery can also be used when the car is not running to operate the lights or other appliances. If the battery is used too long in discharge mode, it will run down completely.

While a car is running, however, the battery is continually being charged. A device called an alternator, which is run by the car's engine, produces current. When electrons flow into the battery in the reverse direction from discharging, the chemical reactions that produce current are reversed. The ability of the battery to produce current is renewed.

 What kind of battery can be charged by reversing chemical reactions?

656 Unit 5: Electricity and Magnetism

DIFFERENTIATE INSTRUCTION

 **More Reading Support**

G What type of primary cell contains a liquid electrolyte? *a wet cell*

H Which type of cell is in a car battery? *storage cell*

Alternative Assessment Batteries contain active electrolytes. Divide the class into three groups and have each group prepare a presentation about what safety precautions should be observed for common dry cells, alkaline batteries, and lead–acid storage batteries in cars.

656 Unit 5: **Electricity and Magnetism**

Batteries

Both primary cells and storage cells produce electricity through chemical reactions.

Flashlights use **primary cells**.

Car batteries and cell phones use **storage cells**.

Primary Cell

Primary cells produce electric current through chemical reactions. The reactions continue until the chemicals are used up.

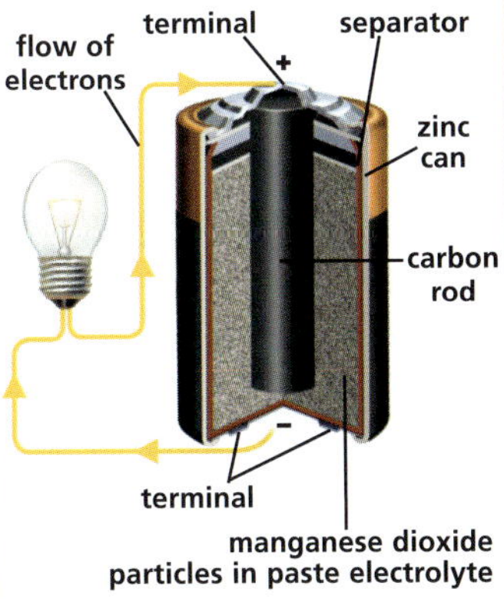

flow of electrons, terminal, +, separator, zinc can, carbon rod, terminal, manganese dioxide particles in paste electrolyte

Storage Cell

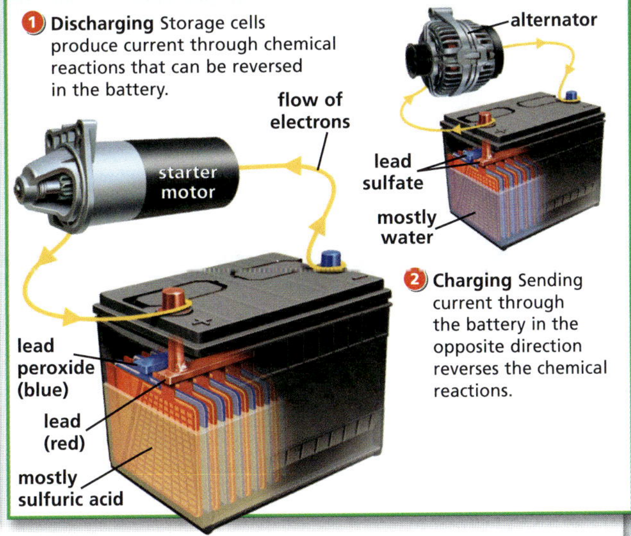

① **Discharging** Storage cells produce current through chemical reactions that can be reversed in the battery.

starter motor, flow of electrons, alternator, lead sulfate, mostly water

② **Charging** Sending current through the battery in the opposite direction reverses the chemical reactions.

lead peroxide (blue), lead (red), mostly sulfuric acid

READING VISUALS In which direction do electrons flow when a storage cell is being charged?

Chapter 19: Electricity 657

Teach from Visuals

To help students interpret the diagrams of a primary cell and a storage cell, ask:

- Why is a paper separator needed for the primary cell that is shown? *The electrolyte is active and might react with the zinc can if the paper separator were not present.*

- What is likely to happen when an alternator is not working correctly? *The battery will not recharge, and it will stop producing current.*

Ongoing Assessment

READING VISUALS *Answer: from the positive terminal to the negative terminal*

DIFFERENTIATE INSTRUCTION

Advanced Have interested students research why dry cells containing mercury were popular and why they have been outlawed in the United States. *The voltage remains consistent throughout the battery life. The mercury causes a disposal problem because it pollutes the environment.* Tell students that one use of mercury batteries was to power small pieces of equipment in the space program. Ask: What can you infer about a mercury battery that would make it suitable for this use? *A small mercury battery produces adequate and consistent current. It can produce current for a long period of time.*

Chapter 19 **657**

Ongoing Assessment

Answer: from the Sun

Reinforce the BIG idea

Have students relate the section to the Big Idea.

 Reinforcing Key Concepts, p. 43

19.3 ASSESS & RETEACH

Assess

 Section 19.3 Quiz, p. 5

Reteach

Have students draw a concept map that shows that both primary cells and storage cells are types of electrochemical cells. Have them list the following terms under the appropriate type of cell: *can be reversed, cannot be reversed, liquid electrolyte, paste electrolyte.*

Technology Resources

Have students visit ClassZone.com for reteaching of Key Concepts.

- CONTENT REVIEW
- CONTENT REVIEW CD-ROM

READING TIP
The word *solar* comes from the Latin word *sol*, which means the Sun.

Solar Cells

Some materials, such as silicon, can absorb energy from the Sun or other sources of light and then give off electrons, producing electric current. Electric cells made from such materials are called solar cells.

Solar cells are often used to make streetlights come on automatically at night. Current from the cell operates a switch that keeps the lights turned off. When it gets dark, the current stops, the switch closes, and the streetlights come on.

This NASA research aircraft is powered only by the solar cells on its upper surface.

Many houses and other buildings now get at least some of their power from solar cells. Sunlight provides an unlimited source of free, environmentally safe energy. However, it is not always easy or cheap to use that energy. It must be collected and stored because solar cells do not work at night or when sunlight is blocked by clouds or buildings.

 Where do solar cells get their energy?

19.3 Review

KEY CONCEPTS

1. How is electric current different from a static charge that moves?
2. How can Ohm's law be used to calculate the electrical resistance of a piece of wire?
3. How do rechargeable batteries work differently from nonrechargeable ones?

CRITICAL THINKING

4. **Infer** Electrical outlets in a house maintain a steady voltage, even when the amount of resistance on them changes. How is this possible?
5. **Analyze** Why don't solar cells eventually run down as electrochemical cells do?

CHALLENGE

6. **Apply** Several kinds of electric cells are discussed in this section. Which do you think would be the most practical source of electrical energy on a long trek through the desert? Explain your reasoning.

658 Unit 5: **Electricity and Magnetism**

ANSWERS

1. Electric current is a continuous flow of charge; static charge changes position but does not flow continuously.

2. Run current through the wire; measure voltage and amperage. Divide voltage by amperage to get resistance.

3. Rechargeable batteries use chemical reactions that can be reversed by sending current through the battery.

4. The amperage also changes.

5. Solar cells obtain their energy from the Sun rather than from chemical reactions, so there are no reactants to be used up.

6. solar cells; because sunlight is abundant in the desert, solar cells would not stop producing power over time and do not require a current to recharge

A volume control works by changing the amount of resistance to the flow of current.

MATH in SCIENCE

MATH TUTORIAL
CLASSZONE.COM
Click on Math Tutorial for more help with equations.

SKILL: USING VARIABLES

Which Formula Is Best?

A rock band needs an amplifier, and an amplifier needs a volume control. A volume control works by controlling the amount of resistance in an electrical pathway. When resistance goes down, the current—and the volume—go up. Ohm's law expresses the relationship among voltage (V), resistance (R), and amperage (I). If you know the values of two variables, you can use Ohm's law to find the third. The law can be written in three ways, depending on which variable you wish to find.

$$I = \frac{V}{R} \qquad R = \frac{V}{I} \qquad V = IR$$

A simple way to remember these three versions of the formula is to use the pyramid diagram below. Cover up the variable you are looking for. The visible part of the diagram will give you the correct formula to use.

```
    V
  I | R
```

Example

What is the voltage of a battery that produces a current of 1 amp through a wire with a resistance of 9 ohms?

(1) You want to find voltage, so cover up the V in the pyramid diagram. To find V, the correct formula to use is V = IR.
(2) Insert the known values into the formula. $V = 1 A \cdot 9 \Omega$
(3) Solve the equation to find the missing variable. $1 \cdot 9 = 9$

ANSWER 9 volts

Answer the following questions.

1. What is the voltage of a battery that sends 3 amps of current through a wire with a resistance of 4 ohms?

2. What is the resistance of a wire in which the current is 2 amps if the battery producing the current has a voltage of 220 volts?

3. What is the amperage of a current at 120 volts through a wire with a resistance of 5 ohms?

CHALLENGE Dimmer switches also work by varying resistance. A club owner likes the way the lights look at 1/3 normal current. The normal current is 15 amps. The voltage is constant at 110 V. How much resistance will he need?

Chapter 19: **Electricity** 659

ANSWERS

1. $V = IR = 3 \text{ amps} \cdot 4 \text{ ohms} = 12 \text{ V}$

2. $R = \frac{V}{I} = \frac{220 \text{ V}}{2 \text{ amps}} = 110 \text{ ohms}$

3. $I = \frac{V}{R} = \frac{120 \text{ V}}{5 \text{ ohms}} = 24 \text{ amps}$

CHALLENGE $R = \frac{V}{I} = \frac{110 \text{ V}}{5 \text{ amps}} = 22 \text{ ohms}$

MATH IN SCIENCE
Math Skills Practice for Science

Set Learning Goal
To use inverse operations to manipulate variables in an equation

Present the Science
The voltage between the two terminals in a house outlet is kept at a constant average of 120 volts. According to Ohm's law, plugging in items with different resistances will produce different currents through those items.

Develop Algebra Skills
Point out that if one form of the Ohm's law equation is known, other forms can be derived by using inverse operations. One form of Ohm's law, $I = \frac{V}{R}$ is introduced on p. 653. To solve for V, multiply both sides of the equation by R. Ask: How would you solve for R? *Multiply both sides by R, then divide both by I.*

DIFFERENTIATION TIP For students with learning disabilities, provide a pyramid on pieces of tagboard. Have them cut out the pyramid, then cut the pieces of the pyramid apart. Students can move the variable they are solving for to the left of the pyramid so they can see the rest of the equation to the right.

Close
Ask: Current used to operate stoves, dryers, and certain other appliances is 220 volts. If the resistance in the wires is 10 ohms, what is the amperage?

$$I = \frac{V}{R} = \frac{220V}{10 \text{ ohms}} = 22 \text{ amps}$$

 • Math Support, p. 51
• Math Practice, p. 52

Technology Resources
Students can visit **ClassZone.com** for practice in using variables.

 MATH TUTORIAL

Chapter 19 **659**

CHAPTER 19 • REVIEW

BACK TO

Have students look at the photograph on pp. 630–631. Ask them to use the photograph to summarize what they have learned about the difference between static electricity and electric current. *Sample answer: The dragon must be powered by electric current because it stays lit. A current can be supplied by batteries.*

KEY CONCEPTS SUMMARY

SECTION 19.1

Ask: What particle is shown on the left? *an electron*

Ask: How does the type of charge affect the way that two charged particles interact? *Two charged particles attract if the charges differ. They repel if the charges are alike.*

SECTION 19.2

Ask: What are two factors that affect charge movement? *electric potential and resistance*

Ask: Should a grounding wire be made of high-resistance or low-resistance material? *low resistance*

SECTION 19.3

Ask: What type of apparatus for producing electric current is shown? *an electrochemical cell*

Ask: Identify the electrodes and the electrolyte in the diagram. *The metal strips suspended in the liquid are the electrodes, and the liquid is the electrolyte.*

Review Concepts

- Big Idea Flow Chart, p. T1
- Chapter Outline, pp. T7–T8

---

19 Chapter Review

the BIG idea
Moving electric charges transfer energy.

CONTENT REVIEW
CLASSZONE.COM

KEY CONCEPTS SUMMARY

1 Materials can become electrically charged.

Electric charge is a property of matter.

Electrons have a negative charge. | Protons have a positive charge. | Unlike charges attract. | Like charges repel.

Static charges are caused by the movement of electrons, resulting in an imbalance of positive and negative charges.

VOCABULARY
electric charge p. 634
electric field p. 634
static charge p. 635
induction p. 637

2 Charges can move from one place to another.

Charge movement is affected by
- electric potential, measured in volts
- resistance, measured in ohms

A conductor has low resistance.
An insulator has high resistance.
A ground is the path of least resistance.

VOCABULARY
electric potential p. 643
volt p. 643
conductor p. 646
insulator p. 646
resistance p. 647
ohm p. 647
grounding p. 649

3 Electric current is a flow of charge.

Electric current is measured in amperes, or amps.
Ohm's law states that current equals voltage divided by resistance.
Electrochemical cells produce electric current through chemical reactions.

VOCABULARY
electric current p. 652
ampere p. 653
Ohm's law p. 653
electric cell p. 655

660 Unit 5: Electricity and Magnetism

Technology Resources

Have students visit **ClassZone.com** or use the CD-ROM for a cumulative review of concepts.

 CONTENT REVIEW

 CONTENT REVIEW CD-ROM

Engage students in a whole-class interactive review of Key Concepts. Edit content as you wish.

 POWER PRESENTATIONS

Reviewing Vocabulary

Copy the chart below, and write each term's definition. Use the meanings of the underlined roots to help you.

Word	Root	Definition
EXAMPLE current	to run	continuous flow of charge
1. static charge	standing	
2. induction	into + to lead	
3. electric cell	chamber	
4. conductor	with + to lead	
5. insulator	island	
6. resistance	to stop	
7. electric potential	power	
8. grounding	surface of Earth	

Write a vocabulary term to match each clue.

9. In honor of scientist Alessandro Volta (1745–1827)
10. In honor of the scientist who discovered the relationship among voltage, resistance, and current
11. The amount of charge that flows past a given point in a unit of time.

Reviewing Key Concepts

Multiple Choice *Choose the letter of the best answer.*

12. An electric charge is a
    a. kind of liquid
    b. reversible chemical reaction
    c. type of matter
    d. force acting at a distance

13. A static charge is different from electric current in that a static charge
    a. never moves
    b. can either move or not move
    c. moves only when resistance is low enough
    d. moves only when voltage is high enough

14. Charging by induction means charging
    a. with battery power
    b. by direct contact
    c. at a distance
    d. using solar power

15. Electric potential describes
    a. the electric potential energy per unit charge
    b. the electric kinetic energy per unit charge
    c. whether an electric charge is positive or negative
    d. how an electric charge is affected by gravity

16. A superconductor is a material that, when very cold, has no
    a. amperage
    b. resistance
    c. electric charge
    d. electric potential

17. Ohm's law says that when resistance goes up, current
    a. increases
    b. decreases
    c. stays the same
    d. matches voltage

18. Electrochemical cells include
    a. all materials that build up a charge
    b. primary cells and storage cells
    c. batteries and solar cells
    d. storage cells and lightning rods

Short Answer *Write a short answer to each question.*

19. What determines whether a charge you get when walking across a rug is positive or negative?
20. What is the difference between resistance and insulation?
21. What is one disadvantage of solar cells?

Chapter 19: **Electricity** 661

ASSESSMENT RESOURCES

UNIT ASSESSMENT BOOK
- Chapter Test A, pp. 6–9
- Chapter Test B, pp. 10–13
- Chapter Test C, pp. 14–17
- Alternative Assessment, pp. 18–19

SPANISH ASSESSMENT BOOK
Spanish Chapter Test, pp. 301–304

Technology Resources

Edit test items and answer choices.

 Test Generator CD-ROM

Visit **ClassZone.com** to extend test practice.

 Test Practice

Reviewing Vocabulary

1. buildup of electric charge in an object caused by many particles with the same charge
2. buildup of a charge without direct contact
3. a device that produces electric current using chemical or physical properties of different materials
4. a material that allows an electric charge to pass through it
5. a material that resists passage of an electric charge through it
6. the property that determines how much a material resists the flow of electric charge
7. the amount of electric potential energy per unit charge at a point in an electric field
8. providing a harmless low-resistance path for an electric charge to flow into the ground
9. volt
10. ohm and Ohm's law
11. ampere

Reviewing Key Concepts

12. d
13. c
14. c
15. a
16. b
17. b
18. b
19. the materials that make up the carpet and your shoes
20. Resistance is the degree to which an object resists the passage of an electric charge through it. If the resistance of a particular object is high enough to prevent a charge from flowing through it, the object is an insulator.
21. They don't provide current at night or when an obstruction keeps sunlight from hitting them.

Chapter 19 **661**

Thinking Critically

22. from the negative terminal to the positive terminal
23. The chemicals involved in the reaction will be used up, and the flow of charge will decrease.
24. whether the chemical reaction can be reversed by reversing the flow of current
25. PVC plastics
26. copper
27. germanium

Using Math in Science

28. $\dfrac{240}{10} = 24$ ohms

29. $\dfrac{240}{8} = 30$ amps

30. $1.2 \cdot 40 = 48$ volts

31. $\dfrac{400}{2000} = 0.2$ amp

the BIG idea

32. Moving electric charges in the form of electric current transfer energy to the light bulbs. The resistance of the filaments causes electrical energy to be converted into light.

33. The diagrams and paragraph should demonstrate an understanding of the difference between static charges and electric current. Sample answer: Static charges contain specific, limited amount of charge; they build up and discharge at once. Circuits provide a steady continuous current, with a potential difference that is maintained.

UNIT PROJECTS

Give students the appropriate Unit Project worksheets from the URB for their projects. Both directions and rubrics can be used as a guide.

Unit Projects, pp. 5–10

Thinking Critically

Use the diagram of an electrochemical cell below to answer the next three questions.

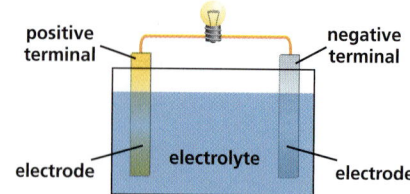

22. **ANALYZE** In which direction do electrons flow between the two terminals?

23. **PREDICT** What changes will occur in the cell as it discharges?

24. **ANALYZE** What determines whether the cell is rechargeable or not?

Use the graph below to answer the next three questions.

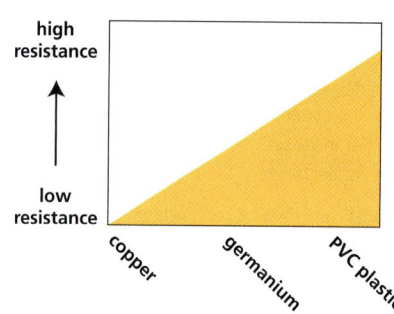

25. **INFER** Which material could you probably use as an insulator?

26. **INFER** Which material could be used in a lightning rod?

27. **APPLY** Materials that conduct electrons under some—but not all—conditions are known as semiconductors. Which material is probably a semiconductor?

Using Math in Science

Use the formula for Ohm's law to answer the next four questions.

$$I = \dfrac{V}{R}$$

28. An electrical pathway has a voltage of 240 volts and a current of 10 amperes. What is the resistance?

29. A 240-volt air conditioner has a resistance of 8 ohms. What is the current?

30. An electrical pathway has a current of 1.2 amperes and resistance of 40 ohms. What is the voltage?

31. An electrical pathway has a voltage of 400 volts and resistance of 2000 ohms. What is the current?

the BIG idea

32. **INFER** Look back at the photograph on pages 630 and 631. Based on what you have learned in this chapter, describe what you think is happening to keep the dragon lit.

33. **COMPARE AND CONTRAST** Draw two simple diagrams to compare and contrast static charges and electric current. Add labels and captions to make your comparison clear. Then write a paragraph summarizing the comparison.

UNIT PROJECTS

If you are doing a unit project, make a folder for your project. Include in your folder a list of the resources you will need, the date on which the project is due, and a schedule to keep track of your progress. Begin gathering data.

MONITOR AND RETEACH

If students have trouble applying the concepts in items 22–24, have them refer to the diagrams on pp. 655 and 657. Ask: How do the diagrams on pp. 655 and 657 correspond to the diagram for the Thinking Critically problems? *both are diagrams of an electrochemical cell* Have students discuss the flow of electrons and the chemical reaction that occur in the cell.

Students may benefit from summarizing one or more sections of the chapter.

Summarizing the Chapter, pp. 71–72

Standardized Test Practice

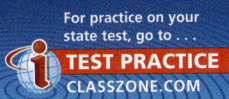

For practice on your state test, go to...
TEST PRACTICE
CLASSZONE.COM

Interpreting Diagrams

Use the illustration below to answer the following questions. Assume that the balloons start off with no net charge.

1. What will happen if a negatively charged rod is brought near one of the balloons without touching it?
   a. The balloons will move toward each other.
   b. The balloons will move away from each other.
   c. Electrons on the balloons will move toward the rod.
   d. Electrons on the balloons will move away from the rod.

2. What will happen if a positively charged rod is brought near one of the balloons without touching it?
   a. The balloons will move toward each other.
   b. The balloons will move away from each other.
   c. Electrons on the balloons will move toward the rod.
   d. Electrons on the balloons will move away from the rod.

3. In the previous question, the effect of the rod on the balloons is an example of
   a. charging by contact
   b. charge polarization
   c. induction
   d. conduction

4. What will happen if a negatively charged rod is brought near one of the balloons and the balloons are then separated?
   a. The balloon farthest from the rod will become positively charged.
   b. The balloon farthest from the rod will become negatively charged.
   c. Both balloons will become positively charged.
   d. Both balloons will have no net charge.

5. If you rub one balloon in your hair to charge it and then move it close to the other balloon, the balloons will
   a. not move
   b. move away from each other
   c. move toward the ground
   d. move toward each other

6. What will happen if a negatively charged rod is brought near one of the balloons, then taken away, and the balloons are then separated?
   a. The balloon farthest from the rod will become positively charged.
   b. The balloon farthest from the rod will become negatively charged.
   c. Both balloons will become positively charged.
   d. Both balloons will have no net charge.

Extended Response

Answer the two questions below in detail. Include some of the terms from the word box. Underline each term that you use in your answers.

| charge separation | recharging | resistance |
| source of current | static charge | induce |

7. Describe the events leading up to and including a bolt of lightning striking Earth from a storm cloud.

8. Explain the advantages and disadvantages of storage cells over other types of electric cells.

Interpreting Diagrams

1. d 3. c 5. d
2. c 4. b 6. d

Extended Response

7. RUBRIC
4 points for a response that correctly answers the question and uses the following terms accurately:
- charge separation
- induce
- static charge
- resistance

Sample: Collisions between particles in a storm cloud cause <u>charge separation</u>. Positively charged particles move to the top of the cloud; negatively charged particles move to the bottom. The bottom of the cloud <u>induces</u> a positive charge in the ground. When the difference in electric potential becomes great enough, the <u>static charge</u> overcomes the <u>resistance</u> of the air, and the charge moves from the cloud to the ground.

3 points correctly answers the question and uses three terms accurately
2 points correctly answers the question and uses two terms accurately
1 point correctly answers the question or uses one term accurately

8. RUBRIC
3 points for a response that compares and contrasts and uses the following terms accurately:
- source of current
- recharging

Sample: Storage cells can be recharged repeatedly and so can last a lot longer than primary cells. Storage cells work at night or other times when sunlight is not available, which is not true of solar cells. However, storage cells do run down. They also need a <u>source of current</u> and can't be used while they are <u>recharging</u>.

2 points compares and contrasts and uses one term accurately
1 point compares or contrasts without using either of the terms

METACOGNITIVE ACTIVITY

Have students answer the following questions in their **Science Notebook:**
1. What did you find the most challenging to understand about electricity?
2. What questions do you still have about electricity?
3. How did you determine which resources to include for your Unit Project?

CHAPTER 20: Circuits and Electronics

Physical Science
UNIFYING PRINCIPLES

PRINCIPLE 1
Matter is made of particles too small to see.

PRINCIPLE 2
Matter changes form and moves from place to place.

PRINCIPLE 3
Energy changes from one form to another, but it cannot be created or destroyed.

PRINCIPLE 4
Physical forces affect the movement of all matter on Earth and throughout the universe.

Unit 5: Electricity and Magnetism
BIG IDEAS

CHAPTER 19
Electricity
Charged particles transfer electric energy.

CHAPTER 20
Circuits and Electronics
Circuits control the flow of electric charge.

CHAPTER 21
Magnetism
Current can produce magnetism, and magnetism can produce current.

CHAPTER 20 KEY CONCEPTS

SECTION 1

Charge needs a continuous path to flow.
1. Electric charge flows in a loop.
2. Current follows the path of least resistance.
3. Safety devices control current.

SECTION 2

Circuits make electric current useful.
1. Circuits are constructed for specific purposes.
2. Circuits can have multiple paths.
3. Circuits convert electrical energy into other forms of energy.

SECTION 3

Electronic technology is based on circuits.
1. Electronics use coded information.
2. Computer circuits process digital information.
3. Computers can be linked with other computers.

 The Big Idea Flow Chart is available on p. T9 in the **UNIT TRANSPARENCY BOOK**.

Previewing Content

SECTION 1 Charge needs a continuous path to flow. pp. 667–674

1. **Electric charge flows in a loop.**
   A **circuit** is a closed path through which a charge can flow. It has at least four basic parts.

Parts of a Circuit	
Voltage source	Provides electric potential Example: battery
Conductor	Provides connecting path Example: copper wire
Switch	Closes or opens the path Example: light switch
Electrical device	Changes electrical energy into other energy forms Example: resistor

2. **Current follows the path of least resistance.**
   Conductors, such as many metals, have a lower resistance than the materials around them, and provide a path through which charge will flow. Insulators have high resistance.
   - A **short circuit** is a path that allows current to go where it is not intended, and may be dangerous.
   - In a grounded circuit a third wire leads stray current safely into the ground.

3. **Safety devices control current.**
   Fuses and circuit breakers open a circuit when the level of current becomes dangerously high, thereby stopping the flow of charge.
   - Fuses have to be replaced when they blow.
   - Circuit breakers can be used over and over again.
   - A ground-fault circuit interrupter (GFCI) outlet can be reset repeatedly. It breaks a circuit when it detects a change in current.

SECTION 2 Circuits make electric current useful. pp. 675–680

1. **Circuits are constructed for specific purposes.**
   Circuits are designed to be used for specific purposes, such as lighting bulbs, moving motors, and performing calculations.

2. **Circuits can have multiple paths.**
   In a **series circuit,** current follows a single path.
   - Every element in a series circuit must be functional, or the whole circuit stops working.
   - Every resistor added to a series circuit decreases the current available to each resistor.
   - The voltages of batteries in series add together.

   In a **parallel circuit,** current follows multiple paths.
   - If an element in a parallel circuit is not functional, the other elements still work.
   - Every device on a parallel circuit gets full current.
   - The voltages of batteries in parallel do not add together.

Series Circuit	Parallel Circuit
Each device in a series circuit is wired on a single path.	Each device in a parallel circuit has its own connection to the voltage source.
	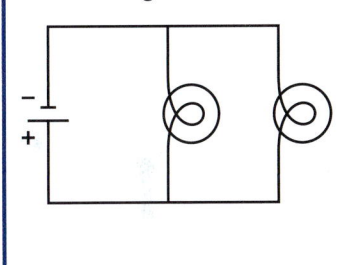

3. **Circuits convert electrical energy into other forms of energy.**
   Circuit elements can convert electrical energy into other forms of energy. They make electrical energy useful.

Common Misconceptions

HOW TO MAKE A COMPLETE CIRCUIT Students may hold the misconception that a circuit is complete if there is a wire connecting a battery to a bulb. There must be a complete conductive path from the battery to the bulb and back.

 This misconception is addressed on p. 668.

MISCONCEPTION DATABASE
CLASSZONE.COM Background on student misconceptions

HOW CURRENT IS DISTRIBUTED Students may hold the misconception that lights added to a series circuit dim progressively from one to the next instead of universally across the circuit. Adding light bulbs in a series circuit causes all the lights to dim due to diminishing current available to any one bulb.

 This misconception is addressed on p. 676.

Previewing Content

SECTION

 Electronic technology is based on circuits. pp. 681–691

1. **Electronics use coded information.**
   An **electronic** device uses electric current to represent coded information. Many electronic devices use a **binary code**.
   • **Digital** electronic devices, such as computers, use a binary code consisting of 1s and 0s.
   • **Analog** signals, such as sound waves, can be converted to digital information that computers recognize.

2. **Computer circuits process digital information.**
   Integrated circuits are highly complex, tiny circuits. They are usually built on chips made of silicon. They provide processing in computers, cars, calculators, and other devices. **Computer** hardware is the physical equipment required to do computer work. Computer software is the set of instructions and languages required to run the equipment. Personal computers have parts that perform four basic functions: input, storage, processing, and output.

3. **Computers can be linked with other computers.**
   Computers can be linked together in networks. The largest computer network is the Internet, a decentralized network devised to keep going even if many links are not functioning.

The World Wide Web is an international Internet-based environment in which Web sites can be posted and viewed.

Previewing Labs

EXPLORE the BIG idea

Will the Flashlight Still Work? p. 665
Students rearrange batteries in a flashlight to observe that a circuit must be complete and its parts arranged properly for it to work.

TIME 10 minutes
MATERIALS flashlight with batteries, piece of paper

What's Inside a Calculator? p. 665
Students explore the circuit board in a calculator to think about the function of different parts.

TIME 10 minutes
MATERIALS hand-held calculator, small screwdriver

Internet Activity: Circuits, p. 665
Students use the Internet to build a virtual circuit, including a switch.

TIME 20 minutes
MATERIALS computer with Internet access

 SECTION 1

EXPLORE Circuits, p. 667
Students use a battery, light bulb, and aluminum foil to complete a simple circuit.

TIME 10 minutes
MATERIALS strips of aluminum foil, electrical tape, D battery, light bulb

INVESTIGATE Fuses, p. 672
Students model a fuse using steel wool and a battery in a simple circuit

TIME 15 minutes
MATERIALS 2 pieces of insulated wire (30 cm in length) with alligator clips, single strand of steel wool, glass jar, 15 cm tape, 6-volt battery

 SECTION 2

INVESTIGATE Circuits, p. 678
Students experiment with series and parallel arrangements of batteries to determine which causes bulbs to burn brighter.

TIME 15 minutes
MATERIALS 4 insulated wires (30 cm in length) with alligator clips, small light bulb in a holder, 2 batteries in holders

 SECTION 3

EXPLORE Codes, p. 681
Students write the name of their street using numbers instead of letters to model information coding.

TIME 10 minutes
MATERIALS notebook, small piece of paper

INVESTIGATE Digital Information, p. 683
Students exchange codes to recreate a simple model of a digital image.

TIME 30 minutes
MATERIALS graph paper, plain paper

CHAPTER INVESTIGATION
Design an Electronic Communication Device, pp. 690–691
Students design, build, and test a battery-powered Morse code communicator to be marketed as a toy.

 Morse Code Chart, p. 113

TIME 40 minutes
MATERIALS 2 batteries, light bulb in holder, 50 cm copper wire (22 gauge), 2 insulated wire leads (30 cm in length) with alligator clips, 2 craft sticks, toothpick, paper clip, 20 cm × 20 cm piece of cardboard, clothespin, 10 cm × 10 cm piece of aluminum foil, rubber band, scissors, 10 cm electrical tape, wire cutters, Morse Code Chart

Additional INVESTIGATION, Wire a Room, A, B, & C, pp. 123–131; Teacher Instructions, pp. 206–207

Previewing Chapter Resources

	INTEGRATED TECHNOLOGY		LABS AND ACTIVITIES

CHAPTER 20
Circuits and Electronics

 CLASSZONE.COM
- eEdition Plus
- EasyPlanner Plus
- Misconception Database
- Content Review
- Test Practice
- Visualization
- Resource Center
- Internet Activity: Circuits
- Math Tutorial

 SCILINKS.ORG

CD-ROMS
- eEdition
- EasyPlanner
- Power Presentations
- Content Review
- Lab Generator
- Test Generator

 AUDIO CDS
- Audio Readings
- Audio Readings in Spanish

 EXPLORE the Big Idea, p. 665
- Will the Flashlight Still Work?
- What's Inside a Calculator?
- Internet Activity: Circuits

UNIT RESOURCE BOOK
Unit Projects, pp. 5–10

 Lab Generator CD-ROM
Generate customized labs.

SECTION 1
Charge needs a continuous path to flow.
pp. 667–674

Time: 2 periods (1 block)

 Lesson Plan, pp. 73–74

 RESOURCE CENTER, Electrical Safety

UNIT TRANSPARENCY BOOK
- Big Idea Flow Chart, p. T9
- Daily Vocabulary Scaffolding, p. T10
- Note-Taking Model, p. T11
- 3-Minute Warm-Up, p. T12

 • EXPLORE Circuits, p. 667
- INVESTIGATE Fuses, p. 672
- Science on the Job, p. 674

 UNIT RESOURCE BOOK
- Datasheet, Fuses, p. 82
- Additional INVESTIGATION, Wire a Room, A, B, & C, pp. 123–131

SECTION 2
Circuits make electric current useful.
pp. 675–680

Time: 2 periods (1 block)

 Lesson Plan, pp. 84–85

 MATH TUTORIAL

 UNIT TRANSPARENCY BOOK
- Daily Vocabulary Scaffolding, p. T10
- 3-Minute Warm-Up, p. T12

 • INVESTIGATE Circuits, p. 678
- Math in Science, p. 680

 UNIT RESOURCE BOOK
- Datasheet, Circuits, p. 93
- Math Support, p. 111
- Math Practice, p. 112

SECTION 3
Electronic technology is based on circuits.
pp. 681–691

Time: 4 periods (2 blocks)

 Lesson Plan, pp. 95–96

 • **RESOURCE CENTER,** Electronics
- **VISUALIZATION,** Hard Drive

 UNIT TRANSPARENCY BOOK
- Big Idea Flow Chart, p. T9
- Daily Vocabulary Scaffolding, p. T10
- 3-Minute Warm-Up, p. T13
- "Analog and Digital Signals" Visual, p. T14
- Chapter Outline, pp. T15–T16

 • EXPLORE Codes, p. 681
- INVESTIGATE Digital Information, p. 683
- CHAPTER INVESTIGATION, Design an Electronic Communication Device, pp. 690–691

 UNIT RESOURCE BOOK
- Datasheet, Digital Information, p. 104
- Morse Code Chart, p. 113
- CHAPTER INVESTIGATION, Design an Electronic Communication Device, A, B, & C, pp. 114–122

KEY TO ICONS	CD/CD-ROM	Teacher Edition	UNIT TRANSPARENCY BOOK	SPANISH ASSESSMENT BOOK
INTERNET	Pupil Edition	UNIT RESOURCE BOOK	UNIT ASSESSMENT BOOK	SCIENCE TOOLKIT

READING AND REINFORCEMENT

- Frame Game, B26–27
- Outline, C43
- Daily Vocabulary Scaffolding, H1–8

UNIT RESOURCE BOOK
- Vocabulary Practice, pp. 108–109
- Decoding Support, p. 110
- Summarizing the Chapter, pp. 132–133

Audio Readings CD
Listen to Pupil Edition.

Audio Readings in Spanish CD
Listen to Pupil Edition in Spanish.

UNIT RESOURCE BOOK
- Reading Study Guide, A & B, pp. 75–78
- Spanish Reading Study Guide, pp. 79–80
- Challenge and Extension, p. 81
- Reinforcing Key Concepts, p. 83

UNIT RESOURCE BOOK
- Reading Study Guide, A & B, pp. 86–89
- Spanish Reading Study Guide, pp. 90–91
- Challenge and Extension, p. 92
- Reinforcing Key Concepts, p. 94

UNIT RESOURCE BOOK
- Reading Study Guide, A & B, pp. 97–100
- Spanish Reading Study Guide, pp. 101–102
- Challenge and Extension, p. 103
- Reinforcing Key Concepts, p. 105
- Challenge Reading, pp. 106–107

ASSESSMENT

- Chapter Review, pp. 693–694
- Standardized Test Practice, p. 695

UNIT ASSESSMENT BOOK
- Diagnostic Test, pp. 20–21
- Chapter Test, A, B, & C, pp. 25–36
- Alternative Assessment, pp. 37–38

Spanish Chapter Test, pp. 305–308

Test Generator CD-ROM
Generate customized tests.

Lab Generator CD-ROM
Rubrics for Labs

Ongoing Assessment, pp. 667–673

Section 20.1 Review, p. 673

UNIT ASSESSMENT BOOK
Section 20.1 Quiz, p. 22

Ongoing Assessment, pp. 675–679

Section 20.2 Review, p. 679

UNIT ASSESSMENT BOOK
Section 20.2 Quiz, p. 23

Ongoing Assessment, pp. 681–688

Section 20.3 Review, p. 689

UNIT ASSESSMENT BOOK
Section 20.3 Quiz, p. 24

STANDARDS

National Standards
A.1–8, A.9.a–g, B.3.a, B.3.d, E.1–5

See p. 664 for the standards.

National Standards
A.2–7, A.9.a–b, A.9.e–f, B.3.a

National Standards
A.2–8, A.9.a–f, B.3.a, B.3.d

National Standards
A.1–8, A.9.a–g, E.1–5

Previewing Resources for Differentiated Instruction

CHAPTER INVESTIGATION

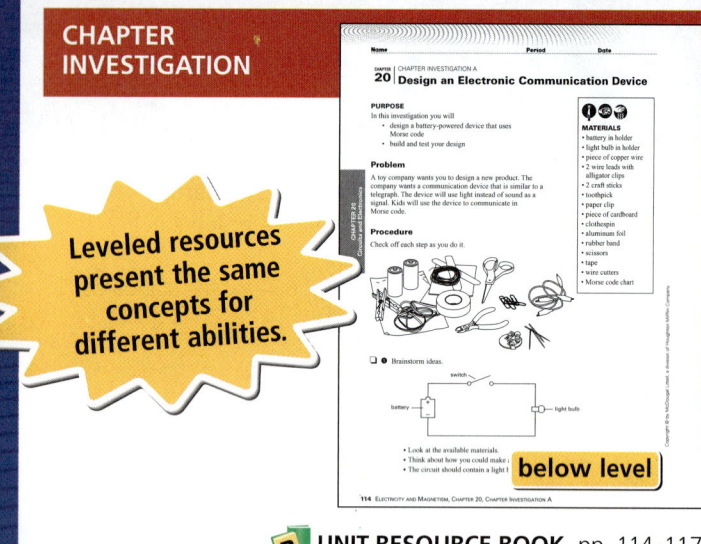
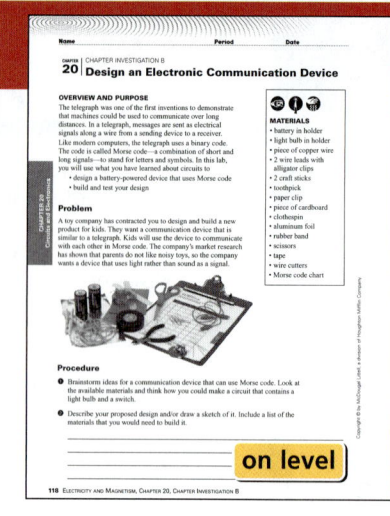
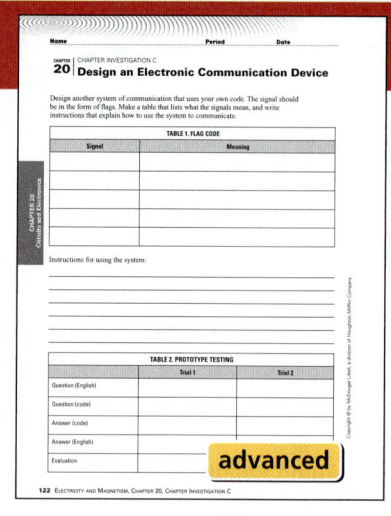

Leveled resources present the same concepts for different abilities.

R UNIT RESOURCE BOOK, pp. 114–117   **R** pp. 118–121   **R** pp. 118–122

READING STUDY GUIDE

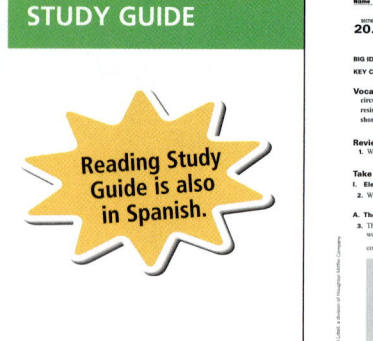
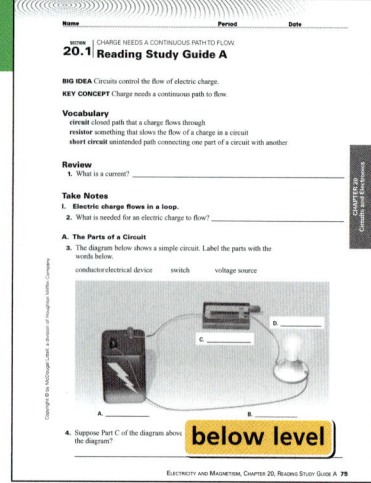
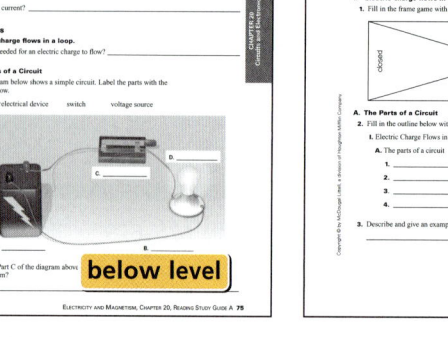
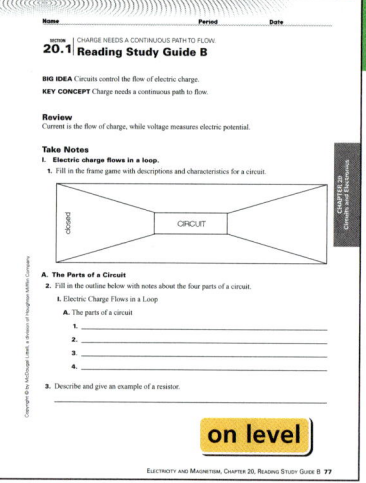
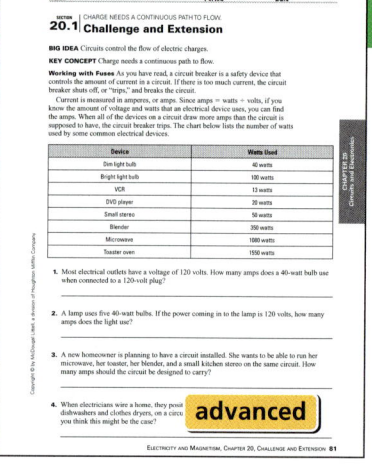

Reading Study Guide is also in Spanish.

R UNIT RESOURCE BOOK, pp. 75–76   **R** pp. 77–78   **R** p. 81

CHAPTER TEST

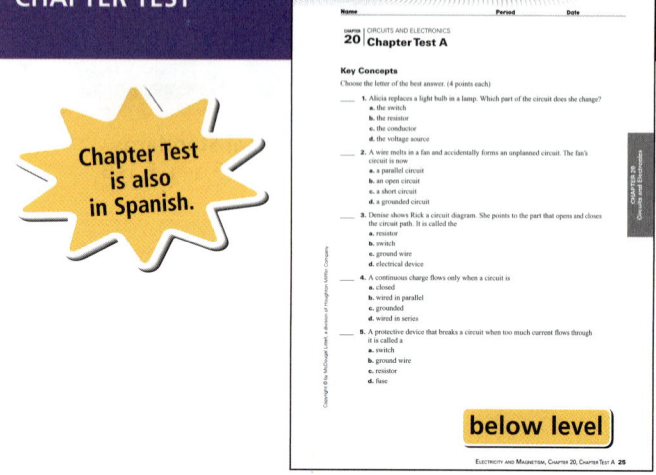
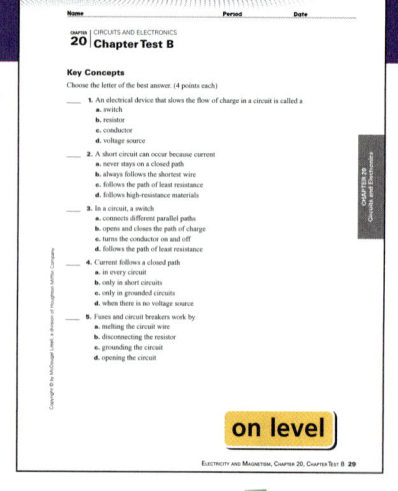
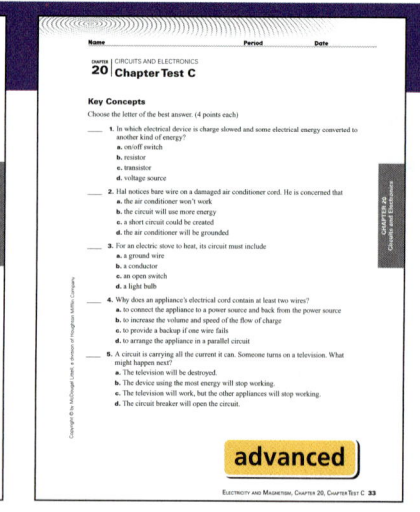

Chapter Test is also in Spanish.

A UNIT ASSESSMENT BOOK, pp. 25–28   **A** pp. 29–32   **A** pp. 33–36

663G Unit 5: Electricity and Magnetism

CHAPTER 2

TECHNOLOGY

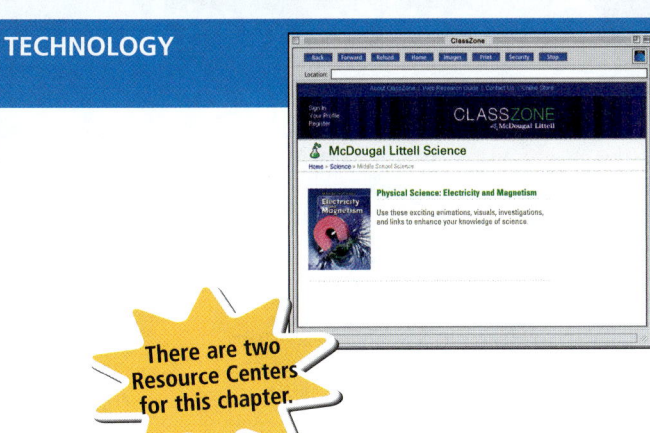
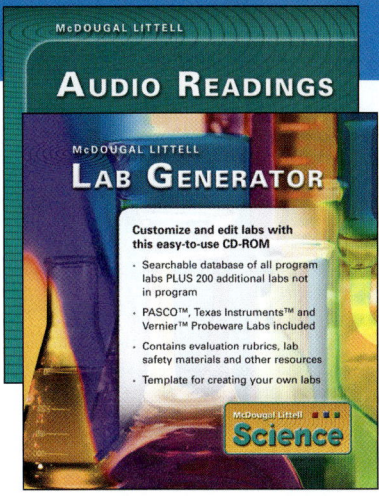
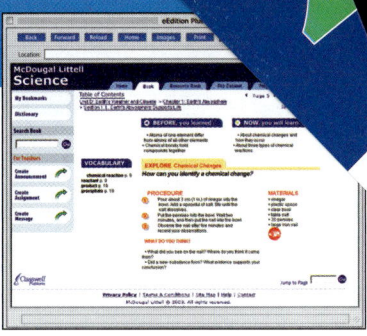

There are two Resource Centers for this chapter.

 CLASSZONE.COM    CD/CD-ROMS    CLASSZONE.COM

VISUAL CONTENT

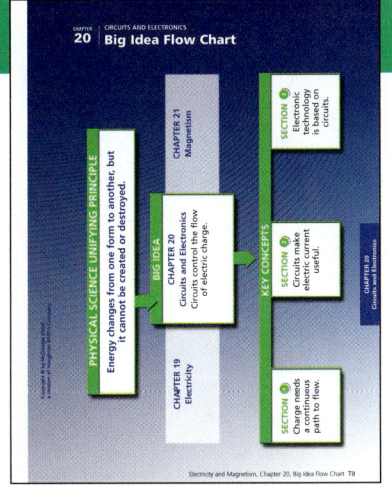
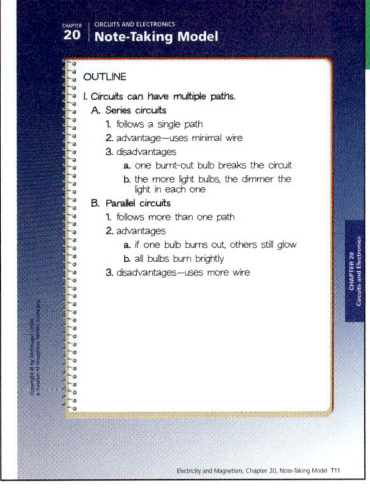
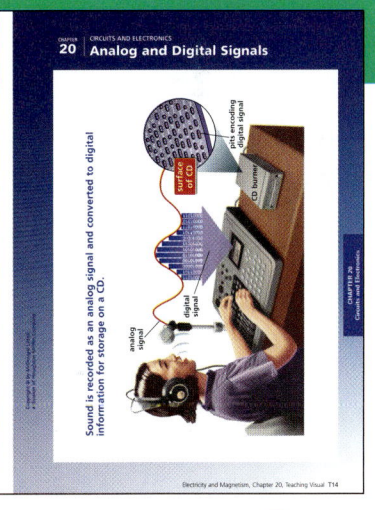

T UNIT TRANSPARENCY BOOK, p. T9    p. T11   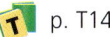 p. T14

MORE SUPPORT

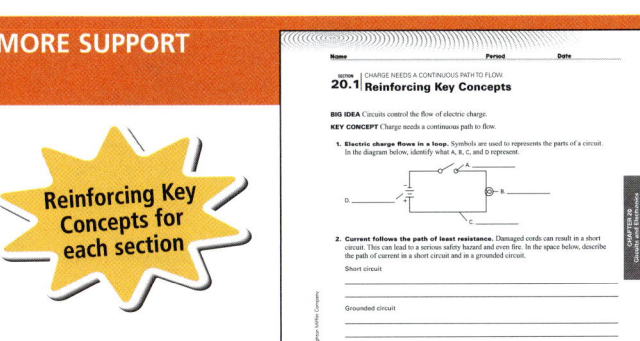
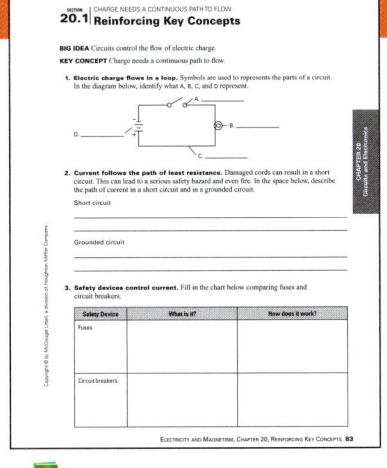
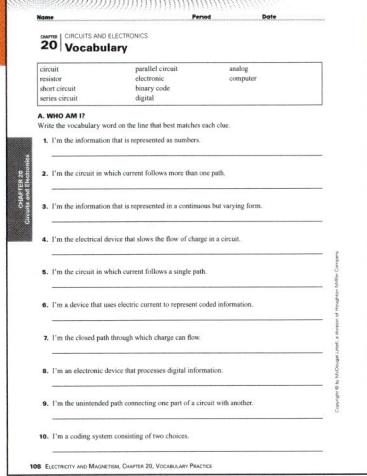
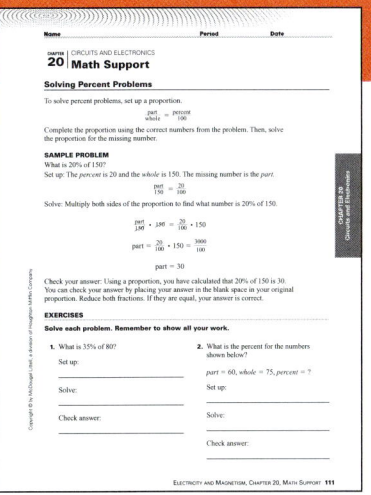

Reinforcing Key Concepts for each section

R UNIT RESOURCE BOOK, p. 83   pp. 108–109   p. 111

Chapter 20: **Circuits and Electronics** 663H

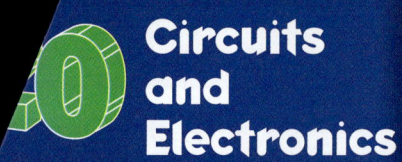

Circuits and Electronics

INTRODUCE

the BIG idea

Have students look at the photograph of the student handling electronic equipment and discuss how the question in the box links to the Big Idea:

- How would you describe the equipment that the student is holding?
- Look closely at the equipment. Can you see patterns on the circuit boards? What might these patterns have to do with charges that move from place to place?

National Science Education Standards

Content

B.3.a Energy is a property of many substances that is often associated with electricity. Energy is transferred in many ways.

B.3.d Circuits transfer electrical energy. Heat, light, sound, and chemical changes are produced.

Process

A.1–8 Identify questions that can be answered through scientific investigations; design and conduct an investigation; use tools; use evidence; think critically between evidence and explanation; recognize different explanations and predictions; communicate procedures and explanations; use mathematics.

A.9.a–g Understand scientific inquiry by using different investigations, methods, mathematics, technology, and explanations based on logic and evidence. Data often results in new investigations.

E.1–5 Identify a problem; design, implement, and evaluate a solution or product; communicate technological design.

CHAPTER 20
Circuits and Electronics

the BIG idea

Circuits control the flow of electric charge.

Key Concepts

SECTION 1 **Charge needs a continuous path to flow.** Learn how circuits are used to control the flow of charge.

SECTION 2 **Circuits make electric current useful.** Learn about series circuits and parallel circuits.

SECTION 3 **Electronic technology is based on circuits.** Learn about computers and other electronic devices.

How can circuits control the flow of charge?

Internet Preview

CLASSZONE.COM

Chapter 20 online resources: Content Review, Simulation, Visualization, two Resource Centers, Math Tutorial, Test Practice

664 Unit 5: Electricity and Magnetism

INTERNET PREVIEW

CLASSZONE.COM For student use with the following pages:

Review and Practice
- Content Review, pp. 666, 692
- Math Tutorial: Percents and Proportions, p. 680
- Test Practice, p. 695

Activities and Resources
- Internet Activity: Circuits, p. 665
- Resource Centers: Electrical Safety, p. 670; Electronics, p. 681
- Visualization: Hard Drive, p. 687

Electronic Circuits
Code: MDL066

EXPLORE the BIG idea

Will the Flashlight Still Work?
Experiment with a flashlight to find out if it will work in any of the following arrangements: with one of the batteries facing the wrong way, with a piece of paper between the batteries, or with one battery removed. In each case, switch on the flashlight and observe.

Observe and Think
When did the flashlight work? Why do you think it worked or did not work in each case?

What's Inside a Calculator?
Use a small screwdriver to open a simple calculator. Look at the circuit board inside.

Observe and Think How do you think the metal lines relate to the buttons on the front of the calculator? to the display? What is the source of electrical energy? How is it connected to the rest of the circuit?

Internet Activity: Circuits
Go to **ClassZone.com** to build a virtual circuit. See if you can complete the circuit and light the bulb.

Observe and Think
What parts are necessary to light the bulb? What happened when you opened the switch? closed the switch?

NSTA **SC**/*INKS*
scilinks.org
Electronic Circuits Code: MDL066

Chapter 20: **Circuits and Electronics** 665

TEACHING WITH TECHNOLOGY

Graphics Software Have students use graphics software to draw schematic diagrams of the circuits they design in "Investigate Circuits" on p. 678.

Digital Camera You might want to take photographs of some students' circuits during the Chapter Investigation on pp. 690–691.

EXPLORE the BIG idea

These inquiry-based activities are appropriate for use at home or as a supplement to classroom instruction.

Will the Flashlight Still Work?

PURPOSE To observe an incomplete circuit. Students rearrange batteries in a flashlight to test different arrangements.

TIP *10 min.* Make sure students put the batteries in the correct position and remove the paper at the end of the activity.

Answer: The flashlight did not work in any of the arrangements. None was a complete circuit.

REVISIT after p. 668.

What's Inside a Calculator?

PURPOSE To infer the function of a circuit board and hypothesize what the parts do.

TIP *10 min.* Ask students not to touch the inside of the calculator. Tell students to keep track of the small screws so that the calculator can be reassembled.

Answer: Metal lines connect the circuit to the buttons and the display. The source of electrical energy is the battery. It is connected to the rest of the circuit with a metal strip.

REVISIT after p. 681.

Internet Activity: Circuits

PURPOSE To build a virtual circuit.

TIP *20 min.* Before they begin building a virtual circuit, students can try different parts of the simulation to get a feel for what the individual parts do.

Answer: The battery and the wire are necessary to light the bulb. The light bulb turned off when the switch was opened and on when the switch was closed.

REVISIT after p. 669.

PREPARE

◐ CONCEPT REVIEW

Activate Prior Knowledge

- Remind students that electric charge can build up in an object, then move suddenly out of that object to a region of lesser charge. Ask students to think of a situation in nature like this.
  lightning
- Have students think about what unseen activity happens when they plug a device or an appliance into an electrical wall socket and turn it on. Prompt students to compare this with lightning.
- Have students list materials that make good conductors of electricity and those that make good insulators.

◐ TAKING NOTES

Outline

Students may need to be reminded that successive lines should be indented. Indenting is part of the visual enhancement that helps the reader quickly organize details and sub-topics with a main idea or concept.

Vocabulary Strategy

Suggest that students, when using the frame game diagram, write the vocabulary term with larger lettering in the center, or with a contrasting color, or any other way that makes it stand out.

Vocabulary and Note-Taking Resources

- Vocabulary Practice, pp. 108–109
- Decoding Support, p. 110

- Note-Taking Model, p. T11
- Daily Vocabulary Scaffolding, p. T10

- Frame Game, B26–27
- Outline, C43
- Daily Vocabulary Scaffolding, H1–8

666 Unit 5: **Electricity and Magnetism**

CHAPTER 20
Getting Ready to Learn

◐ CONCEPT REVIEW
- Energy can change from one form to another.
- Energy can move from one place to another.
- Current is the flow of charge through a conductor.

◐ VOCABULARY REVIEW
electric potential p. 643
conductor p. 646
resistance p. 647
electric current p. 652
ampere p. 653

CONTENT REVIEW
CLASSZONE.COM
Review concepts and vocabulary.

▶ TAKING NOTES

OUTLINE
As you read, copy the headings on your paper in the form of an outline. Then add notes in your own words that summarize what you read.

VOCABULARY STRATEGY
Write each new vocabulary term in the center of a **frame game** diagram. Decide what information to frame it with. Use examples, descriptions, parts, sentences that use the term in context, or pictures. You can change the frame to fit each term.

SCIENCE NOTEBOOK

I. ELECTRIC CHARGE FLOWS IN A LOOP.
   A. THE PARTS OF A CIRCUIT
      1. voltage source
      2. connection
      3. electrical device
      4. switch

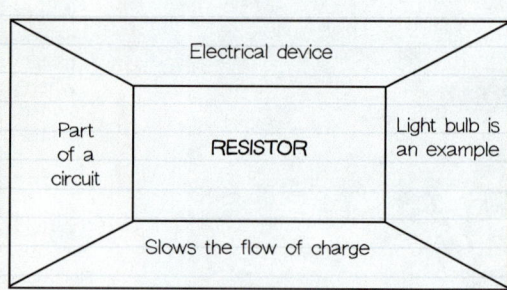

See the Note-Taking Handbook on pages R45–R51.

666 Unit 5: Electricity and Magnetism

CHECK READINESS

Administer the Diagnostic Test to determine students' readiness for new science content and their mastery of requisite math skills.

 Diagnostic Test, pp. 20–21

Technology Resources

Students needing content and math skills should visit ClassZone.com.

- CONTENT REVIEW
- MATH TUTORIAL

 CONTENT REVIEW CD-ROM

KEY CONCEPT

Charge needs a continuous path to flow.

▶ **BEFORE, you learned**
- Current is the flow of charge
- Voltage is a measure of electric potential
- Materials affect the movement of charge

▶ **NOW, you will learn**
- About the parts of a circuit
- How a circuit functions
- How safety devices stop current

VOCABULARY
circuit p. 667
resistor p. 668
short circuit p. 670

EXPLORE Circuits

How can you light the bulb?

PROCEDURE

1. Tape one end of a strip of foil to the negative terminal, or the flat end, of the battery. Tape the other end of the foil to the tip at the base of the light bulb, as shown.
2. Tape the second strip of foil to the positive terminal, or the raised end, of the battery.
3. Find a way to make the bulb light.

WHAT DO YOU THINK?
- How did you make the bulb light?
- Can you find other arrangements that make the bulb light?

MATERIALS
- 2 strips of aluminum foil
- electrical tape
- D cell (battery)
- light bulb

VOCABULARY
Use a frame game diagram to record the term *circuit* in your notebook.

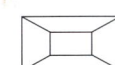

Electric charge flows in a loop.

In the last chapter, you read that current is electric charge that flows from one place to another. Charge does not flow continuously through a material unless the material forms a closed path, or loop. A **circuit** is a closed path through which a continuous charge can flow. The path is provided by a low-resistance material, or conductor, usually wire. Circuits are designed to do specific jobs, such as light a bulb.

Circuits can be found all around you and serve many different purposes. In this chapter, you will read about simple circuits, such as the ones in flashlights, and more complex circuits, such as the ones that run toys, cameras, computers, and more.

 How are circuits related to current?

Chapter 20: **Circuits and Electronics** 667

RESOURCES FOR DIFFERENTIATED INSTRUCTION

Below Level
UNIT RESOURCE BOOK
- Reading Study Guide A, pp. 75–76
- Decoding Support, p. 110

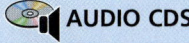 **AUDIO CDS**

 Additional INVESTIGATION,
Wire a Room, A, B, & C, pp. 123–131;
Teacher Instruction, pp. 206–207

Advanced
UNIT RESOURCE BOOK
Challenge and Extension, p. 81

English Learners
UNIT RESOURCE BOOK
Spanish Reading Study Guide, pp. 79–80

 **AUDIO CDS**
- Audio Readings in Spanish
- Audio Readings (English)

20.1 FOCUS

▶ Set Learning Goals
Students will
- Describe the parts of a circuit.
- Explain how a circuit functions.
- Explain how electrical safety devices stop current.
- Model a fuse in an experiment using a simple circuit.

▶ 3-Minute Warm-Up
Display Transparency 12 or copy this exercise on the board:

Match the definitions to the terms.

Definitions
1. the flow of charge e
2. a measure of electric potential c
3. a path for current a

Terms
a. conductor   d. charge
b. insulator   e. current
c. voltage

 3-Minute Warm-Up, p. T12

20.1 MOTIVATE

EXPLORE Circuits

PURPOSE To introduce the idea that completing (closing) a circuit allows charge to flow

TIP *10 min.* Students may want to fold the foil into a narrower strip. Make sure the aluminum foil is in direct contact with the battery terminals. Alert students that the foil will get warm if it is left connected.

WHAT DO YOU THINK? *By touching the aluminum foil to the metal part of the light bulb. As long as metal is touching metal and the circuit is complete, the bulb will light.*

Ongoing Assessment

 *Answer: Circuits provide a closed path for current.*

Chapter 20 **667**

20.1 INSTRUCT

Address Misconceptions

IDENTIFY Ask: How do you complete a circuit? If students answer by connecting a wire from a battery to a bulb, then they may not realize that there must be a complete conductive path from the battery to the bulb and back.

CORRECT Have students examine a standard home battery and describe the two ends. Point out the plus or minus sign at each end, explaining that it indicates charge. Remind students that current flows around a circuit *from* one charge *to* the opposite charge.

REASSESS Ask students to imagine they have an incomplete light-bulb circuit from which the battery is missing. Ask: How would you connect a battery to complete the circuit? *Connect one end of the circuit wire to the battery's negative terminal and the other end to the positive terminal.*

Technology Resources
Visit **ClassZone.com** for background on common student misconceptions.
MISCONCEPTION DATABASE

Teach Difficult Concepts
Help students review voltage and current. Use the analogy of a person squeezing a tube of toothpaste to force it out of the tube. Compare voltage to the squeezing force applied by the person's hand to the tube and current to the surge of toothpaste.

EXPLORE the BIG idea
Revisit "Will the Flashlight Still Work?" on p. 665. Have students explain their results.

Ongoing Assessment
Describe the parts of a circuit.

Ask: Suppose an incomplete circuit has three elements: a conductor, a resistor, and a switch. What does the circuit lack? *a voltage source*

 Answer: Yes; the circuit would still be complete.

668 Unit 5: Electricity and Magnetism

The Parts of a Circuit

The illustration below shows a simple circuit. Circuits typically contain the following parts. Some circuits contain many of each part.

> **REMINDER** Remember, a battery consists of two or more cells.

① Voltage Source The voltage source in a circuit provides the electric potential for charge to flow through the circuit. Batteries are often the voltage sources in a circuit. A power plant may also be a voltage source. When you plug an appliance into an outlet, a circuit is formed that goes all the way to a power plant and back.

② Conductor A circuit must be a closed path in order for charge to flow. That means that there must be a conductor, such as wire, that forms a connection from the voltage source to the electrical device and back.

③ Switch A switch is a part of a circuit designed to break the closed path of charge. When a switch is open, it produces a gap in the circuit so that the charge cannot flow.

 A

 B

④ Electrical Device An electrical device is any part of the circuit that changes electrical energy into another form of energy. A **resistor** is an electrical device that slows the flow of charge in a circuit. When the charge is slowed, some energy is converted to light or heat. A light bulb is an example of a resistor.

Circuit Parts

The parts of a basic circuit include a voltage source, conductor, switch, and one or more electrical devices.

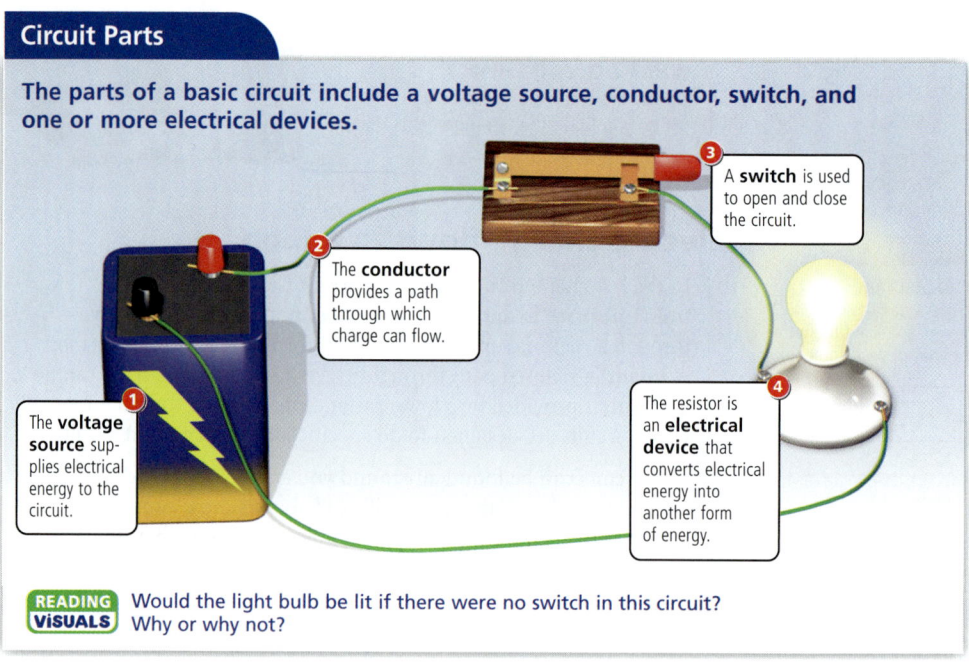

The **voltage source** supplies electrical energy to the circuit.

The **conductor** provides a path through which charge can flow.

A **switch** is used to open and close the circuit.

The resistor is an **electrical device** that converts electrical energy into another form of energy.

READING VISUALS Would the light bulb be lit if there were no switch in this circuit? Why or why not?

668 Unit 5: Electricity and Magnetism

DIFFERENTIATE INSTRUCTION

 **More Reading Support**

A How does an open switch affect a circuit? *It stops the flow of charge.*

B How does a resistor affect the flow of charge? *It slows the flow.*

English Learners This section uses the word "or" several times to signal a definition. For example, "Tape the second strip of foil to the positive terminal, or the raised end, of the battery." English learners may mistakenly read such sentences in terms of "either/or." Help students understand that in these cases "or" indicates a definition or an alternate term.

Below Level Copy the four parts of a circuit on the board, or have students list them on an index card for reference.

Open and Closed Circuits

Current in a circuit is similar to water running through a hose. The flow of charge differs from the flow of water in an important way, however. The water does not require a closed path to flow. If you cut the hose, the water continues to flow. If you cut a wire, the charge stops flowing.

Batteries have connections at both ends so that charge can follow a closed path to and from the battery. The cords that you see on appliances might look like single cords but actually contain at least two wires. The wires connect the device to a power plant and back to make a closed path.

Switches work by opening and closing the circuit. A switch that is on closes the circuit and allows charge to flow through the electrical devices. A switch that is off opens the circuit and stops the current.

> **REMINDER**
> Current requires a closed loop.

CHECK YOUR READING How are switches used to control the flow of charge through a circuit?

Standard symbols are used to represent the parts of a circuit. Some common symbols are shown in the circuit diagrams below. The diagrams represent the circuit shown on page 668 with the switch in both open and closed positions. Electricians and architects use diagrams such as these to plan the wiring of a building.

Circuit Diagrams

Symbols are used to represent the parts of a circuit. The circuit diagrams below show the circuit from page 668 in both an open and closed position.

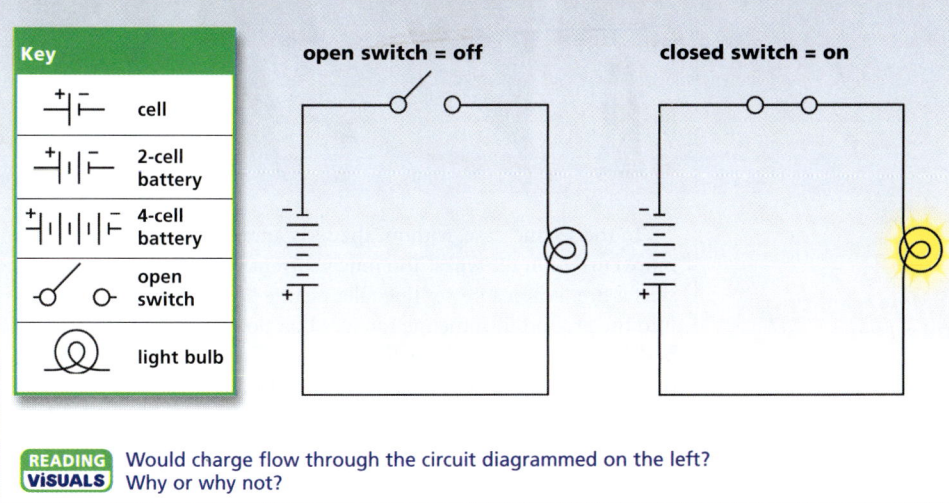

READING VISUALS Would charge flow through the circuit diagrammed on the left? Why or why not?

Chapter 20: **Circuits and Electronics** 669

DIFFERENTIATE INSTRUCTION

More Reading Support

C What happens to the flow of charge in a circuit if you cut a wire? *It stops.*

D What happens when you close a switch? *You turn on the circuit.*

Inclusion Students with visual impairments might find this activity helpful. Set up a simple circuit with a battery, switch, and light bulb. Make a photocopy of the diagrams on this page. Trace the diagrams (but not the key) with a pointed pen, pressing heavily into a soft backing, to create a raised pattern on the back of the sheet. Have students explore the physical setup and then use their fingers to feel the raised circuit that was traced on the back of the paper.

Teach from Visuals

Have students study the "Circuit Parts" and the "Circuit Diagrams" visuals on pp. 668–669.

- Ask: What is different about these two ways of drawing a circuit? *The diagrams on p. 669 uses special symbols instead of a realistic drawing.*
- Ask: If the circuit diagram was flipped so that the bulb was on the left and the battery was on the right, would it still represent the circuit in the drawing? *Yes*

Teacher Demo

Use this demonstration to help students understand the distinction between a closed switch and an open one. Turn off the room's light. Ask:

- Is the switch open or closed? *open*
- Is there current in the circuit that goes to the lights? *no*

Now turn on the light. Ask:

- Is the switch open or closed? *closed*
- Is there current in the circuit that goes to the lights? *yes*

EXPLORE the BIG idea

Revisit "Internet Activity: Circuits" on p. 665. Have students describe the circuit they built.

Ongoing Assessment

Explain how a circuit functions.

Ask: How does the design of a battery allow it to fit into a circuit and complete the path? *The battery has connections at both ends so that charge can follow a closed path to and from the battery.*

CHECK YOUR READING Answer: They open and close the circuit.

READING VISUALS Answer: No; the circuit is not complete.

Chapter 20 **669**

Integrate the Sciences

Multiple sclerosis (MS) is caused by the "short circuiting" of electrical impulses along nerve pathways. Messages between the human brain and other body parts travel along nerve paths that are similar to wires in circuits. These nerve paths are covered and protected with myelin, which acts as insulation. In MS, the myelin begins to break down, electrical impulses leak out of the nerve path, and a "short circuit" results. People with MS may have difficulty with movement, balance, sight, and other bodily functions.

Teach from Visuals

To help students interpret the two illustrations of wiring in a lamp, ask:

- In which lamp is the wiring damaged? *lamp 2*
- How can you tell? *Frayed ends are unintentionally connecting the input and output wires to create a short circuit.*

Ongoing Assessment

CHECK YOUR READING *Answer: Charge flows where it is not meant to, and it could flow through a person if the person touches it or start a fire if the wires become overheated.*

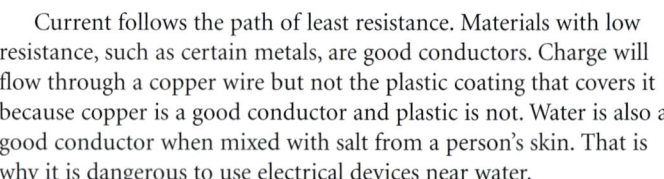

OUTLINE
Add this heading to your outline, along with supporting ideas.

I. Main idea
　A. Supporting idea
　　1. Detail
　　2. Detail
　B. Supporting idea

Current follows the path of least resistance.

Since current can follow only a closed path, why are damaged cords so dangerous? And why are people warned to stay away from fallen power lines? Although current follows a closed path, the path does not have to be made of wire. A person can become a part of the circuit, too. Charge flowing through a person is dangerous and sometimes deadly.

Current follows the path of least resistance. Materials with low resistance, such as certain metals, are good conductors. Charge will flow through a copper wire but not the plastic coating that covers it because copper is a good conductor and plastic is not. Water is also a good conductor when mixed with salt from a person's skin. That is why it is dangerous to use electrical devices near water.

Short Circuits

A **short circuit** is an unintended path connecting one part of a circuit with another. The current in a short circuit follows a closed path, but the path is not the one it was intended to follow. The illustration below shows a functioning circuit and a short circuit.

① Functioning Circuit The charge flows through one wire, through the light bulb, and then back through the second wire to the outlet.

② Short Circuit The cord has been damaged and the two wires inside have formed a connection. Now the path of least resistance is through one wire and back through the second wire.

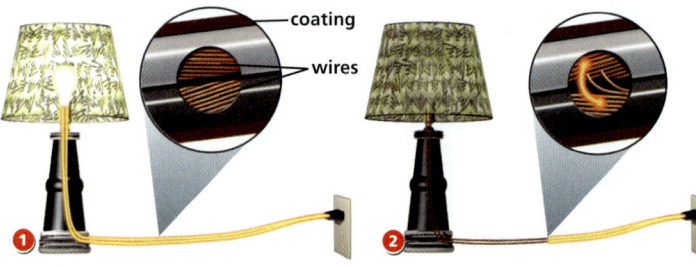

In the second case, without the resistance from the lamp, there is more current in the wires. Too much current can overheat the wires and start a fire. When a power line falls, charge flows along the wire and into the ground. If someone touches that power line, the person's body becomes part of the path of charge. That much charge flowing through a human body is almost always deadly.

CHECK YOUR READING Why are short circuits dangerous?

RESOURCE CENTER CLASSZONE.COM
Explore resources on electrical safety.

670 Unit 5: Electricity and Magnetism

DIFFERENTIATE INSTRUCTION

More Reading Support

E In an electrical circuit, what follows the path of least resistance? *current*

F What do you call an unintended path connecting one part of a circuit with another? *short circuit*

Below Level Review the concepts of conductors and insulators. Relate these concepts to a short circuit. Help students understand the critical role of proper insulation in preventing short circuits. Ask: What might happen if you drove a nail into an electric cord? Why would this be very dangerous? *The nail could create a short circuit, because it is made of metal and is a good conductor. A short circuit would be dangerous because the nail could conduct a high current to another low-resistance material outside of the cord.*

Grounding a Circuit

Recall that when lightning strikes a lightning rod, charge flows into the ground through a highly conductive metal rod rather than through a person or a building. In other words, the current follows the path of least resistance. The third prong on some electrical plugs performs a similar function. A circuit that connects stray current safely to the ground is known as a grounded circuit. Because the third prong grounds the circuit, it is sometimes called the ground.

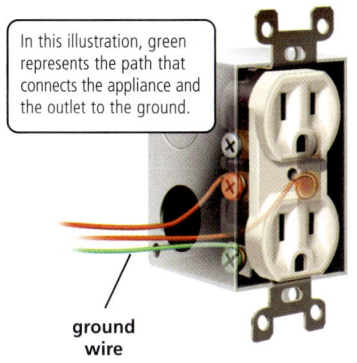

In this illustration, green represents the path that connects the appliance and the outlet to the ground.

Orange is used in this illustration to represent the path that connects the appliance's circuit to a power source and back.

ground wire   connects to ground wire

⚠ **SAFETY TIPS**

- Never go near a fallen power line.
- Never touch an electrical appliance when you are in the shower or bathtub.
- Always dry your hands thoroughly before using an electrical appliance.
- Never use an electrical cord that is damaged in any way.
- Never bend or cut a ground prong in order to make a grounded plug fit into an ungrounded outlet.

Normally, charge flows through one prong, along a wire to an appliance, then back along a second wire to the second prong. If there is a short circuit, the charge might flow dangerously to the outside of the shell of the appliance. If there is a ground wire, the current will flow along the third wire and safely into the ground, along either a buried rod or a cold water pipe.

 What is the purpose of a ground wire?

Safety devices control current.

Suppose your living room wiring consists of a circuit that supplies current to a television and several lights. One hot evening, you turn on an air conditioner in the living room window. The wires that supply current to the room are suddenly carrying more current than before. The lights in the room become dim. Too much current in a circuit is dangerous. How do you know if there is too much current in a wire?

Fortunately, people have been using electric current for over a hundred years. An understanding of how charge flows has led to the development of safety devices. These safety devices are built into circuits to prevent dangerous situations from occurring.

Chapter 20: Circuits and Electronics 671

DIFFERENTIATE INSTRUCTION

More Reading Support

G What is a grounded circuit? *an electric circuit that conduct stray current safely to the ground*

H What happens if there is to much current in a wire? *it is dangerous*

Additional Investigation To reinforce Section 20.1 learning goals, use the following full-period investigation:

Additional INVESTIGATION, Wire a Room, A, B, & C, pp. 123–131, 206–207
(Advanced students should complete Levels B and C.)

Teach from Visuals

Ask: How do the pictures of a new fuse and a blown fuse differ? *The new fuse shows the metal strip from end-to-end of the tube; the metal strip of the blown fuse does not reach the other end.*

INVESTIGATE Fuses

PURPOSE To model a fuse by using steel wool to open a simple circuit

TIP 15 min.

SAFETY Students should not complete the circuit with the clips until the steel wool strand is inside the jar. Resistance can produce enough heat in the steel wool to cause burns.

INCLUSION Carefully monitor the proceedings of any ADD or ADHD students during this investigation or pair them with students who follow directions very carefully. Make sure they do not complete the circuit while the steel wool strand is touching skin or flammable materials. (It should be inside the jar.)

WHAT DO YOU THINK? *The circuit was opened because the current melted the steel wool strand. Opening the circuit stopped the current.*

CHALLENGE *Both a fuse and the steel wool melt and open a circuit when there is too much current in them. In a home circuit, there would be other devices in a circuit that would stop working when a fuse was blown.*

 Datasheet, Fuses, p. 82

Technology Resources

Customize this student lab as needed or look for an alternative. Print rubrics to assess student lab reports.

 Lab Generator CD-ROM

Ongoing Assessment

Identify electrical safety devices and explain how they stop current.

Ask: Why does a normal level of current leave a fuse intact? *A fuse is designed with metal that is solid at normal current. It melts only if there is enough current to heat it up.*

How Fuses Work

If you turn on an air conditioner in a room full of other electrical appliances that are already on, the circuit could overheat. But if the circuit contains a fuse, the fuse will automatically shut off the current. A fuse is a safety device that opens a circuit when there is too much current in it. Fuses are typically found in older homes and buildings. They are also found in cars and electrical appliances like air conditioners.

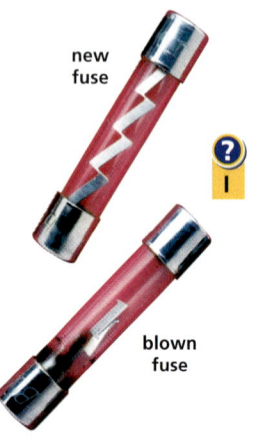

new fuse

blown fuse

A fuse consists of a thin strip of metal that is inserted into the circuit. The charge in the closed circuit flows through the fuse. If too much charge flows through the fuse, the metal strip melts. When the strip has melted and the circuit is open, the fuse is blown. The photographs on the left show a new fuse and a blown fuse. As you can see, charge cannot flow across the melted strip. It has broken the circuit and stopped the current.

How much current is too much? That varies. The electrician who installs a circuit knows how much current the wiring can handle. He or she uses that knowledge to choose the right kind of fuse. Fuses are measured in amperes, or amps. Remember that amperage is a measure of current. If a fuse has blown, it must be replaced with a fuse of the same amperage. But a fuse should be replaced only after the problem that caused it to blow has been fixed.

INVESTIGATE Fuses

How can you stop a current?
PROCEDURE

1. Use the alligator clips to clip one end of each wire to the steel wool strand.
2. Place the steel wool strand in the jar. Tape the wires to the sides of the jar.
3. Clip the free end of one wire to the negative terminal of the battery.
4. What do you predict will happen when you complete the circuit? Clip the free end of the remaining wire to the positive terminal of the battery and observe the steel wool strand.

WHAT DO YOU THINK?
- What did you observe when you completed the circuit? Why did that happen?
- How can you stop the current?

CHALLENGE How is the setup in this activity similar to a fuse that would be found in a home circuit? How does it differ?

SKILL FOCUS
Making Models

MATERIALS
- 2 pieces of insulated wire with alligator clips
- single strand of steel wool
- glass jar
- tape
- 6 V battery

TIME
15 minutes

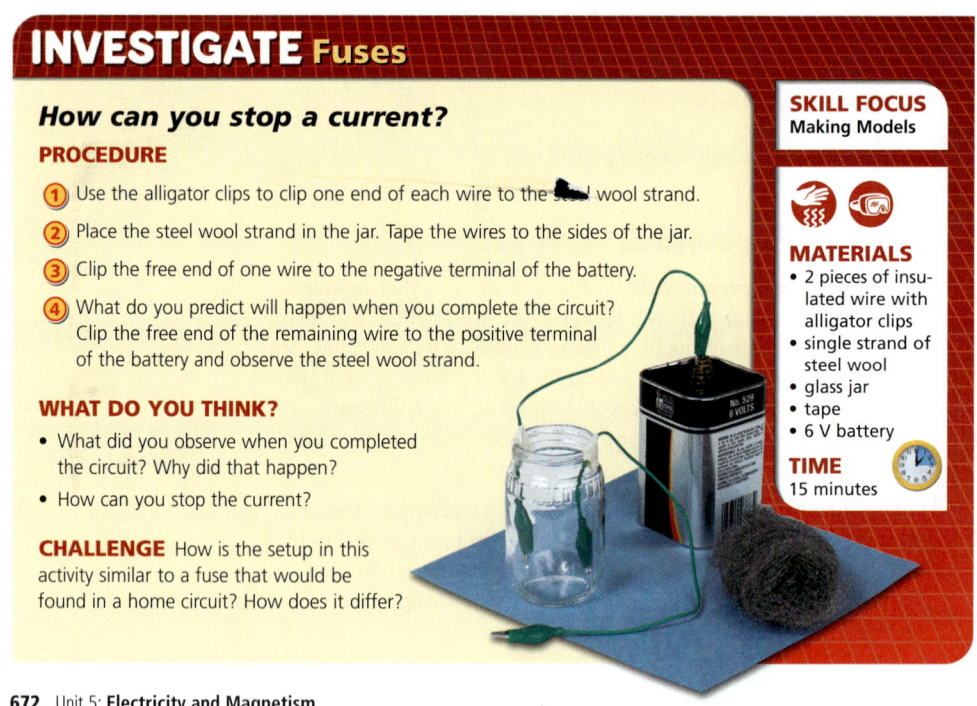

672 Unit 5: Electricity and Magnetism

DIFFERENTIATE INSTRUCTION

 More Reading Support

I What happens to a fuse when too much current flows in a circuit? *Metal in the fuse melts and breaks the circuit so that current can no longer flow in it.*

Advanced Have students borrow the instruction manual for a car. Prompt them to find information about fuses used in the car. Students might find where fuses are used, what the fuse ratings are (in amps), and how often particular fuses should be replaced during regular maintenance. Encourage participants to connect their findings with the concepts presented in this chapter, and share their ideas with the class.

 Challenge and Extension, p. 81

672 Unit 5: **Electricity and Magnetism**

Other Safety Devices

Most modern homes do not use fuses. Instead, they use safety devices called circuit breakers. Circuit breakers, unlike fuses, do not have to be replaced every time they open the circuit. Like fuses, circuit breakers automatically open the circuit when too much charge flows through it. If the circuit becomes overloaded or there is a short circuit, the wire and the breaker grow hot. That makes a piece of metal inside the breaker expand. As it expands, it presses against a switch. The switch is then flipped to the off position and the current is stopped. Once the problem is solved, power can be restored manually by simply flipping the switch back. The illustration on the right shows a circuit breaker.

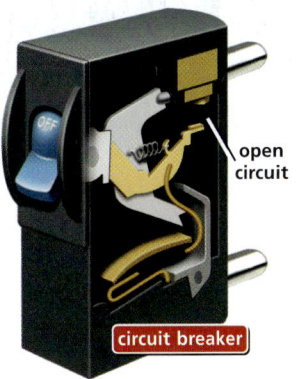
open circuit
circuit breaker

 How are circuit breakers similar to fuses?

The photograph at the bottom right shows another safety device—a ground-fault circuit interrupter (GFCI) outlet. Sometimes a little current leaks out of an outlet or an appliance. Often it is so small you do not notice it. But if you happen to have wet hands, touching even a small current can be very dangerous.

GFCI outlets are required in places where exposure to water is common, such as in kitchens and bathrooms. A tiny circuit inside the GFCI outlet monitors the current going out and coming in. If some of the current starts to flow through an unintended path, there will be less current coming in to the GFCI. If that happens, a circuit breaker inside the GFCI outlet opens the circuit and stops the current. To close the circuit again, you push "Reset."

ground-fault circuit interrupter

20.1 Review

KEY CONCEPTS
1. Describe three parts of a circuit and explain what each part does.
2. Explain the function of a ground wire.
3. What do fuses and circuit breakers have in common?

CRITICAL THINKING
4. **Apply** Suppose you have built a circuit for a class project. You are using a flat piece of wood for its base. How could you make a switch out of a paperclip and two nails?
5. **Communicate** Draw a diagram of a short circuit. Use the symbols for the parts of a circuit.

CHALLENGE
6. **Evaluate** A fuse in a home has blown and the owner wants to replace it with a fuse that can carry more current. Why might the owner's decision lead to a dangerous situation?

ANSWERS

1. Sample answer: The voltage source provides the electric potential for charge to flow in a circuit. The conductor provides a path on which charge can flow. A switch turns the circuit on and off.
2. It prevents current from flowing where it could be dangerous and instead sends it into the ground.
3. Both are safety devices; both stop the current.
4. You could attach the paper clip to one nail. To close the switch, bend it down so that it connects with the other nail.
5. Diagrams should include a voltage source and connection.
6. It might allow too much current in the circuit, which could heat wires and start a fire.

SCIENCE ON THE JOB
Relevance of Science to Non-science Jobs

Set Learning Goal
To understand how electricians use their knowledge about electricity

Present the Science
Electricians have special meters that enable them to safely test current, voltage, and resistance in circuits. A multimeter is one such device. You can use a multimeter to test for continuity (whether a circuit is open or closed) and to measure the resistance of parts of a circuit.

Discussion Questions
Tell students to think of themselves in the role of an electrician modernizing an electrical system in an old building. Ask:

- How would you evaluate the old system? *test the function with meters, lamps, etc.*
- Which safety devices would you upgrade or add? *add new wire to carry more current, install circuit breakers instead of fuses, replace wires that had worn insulation*
- How would you test the new system? *load up with some appliances, see if breakers work and wires stay cool; use meters to make sure ground wires work*

Close
Ask: Why is it important that a person studying to be an electrician learn his or her coursework thoroughly? *The coursework would include safety information that an electrician must know. If students studying to be electricians failed to learn critical safety information, they could seriously injure themselves or others.*

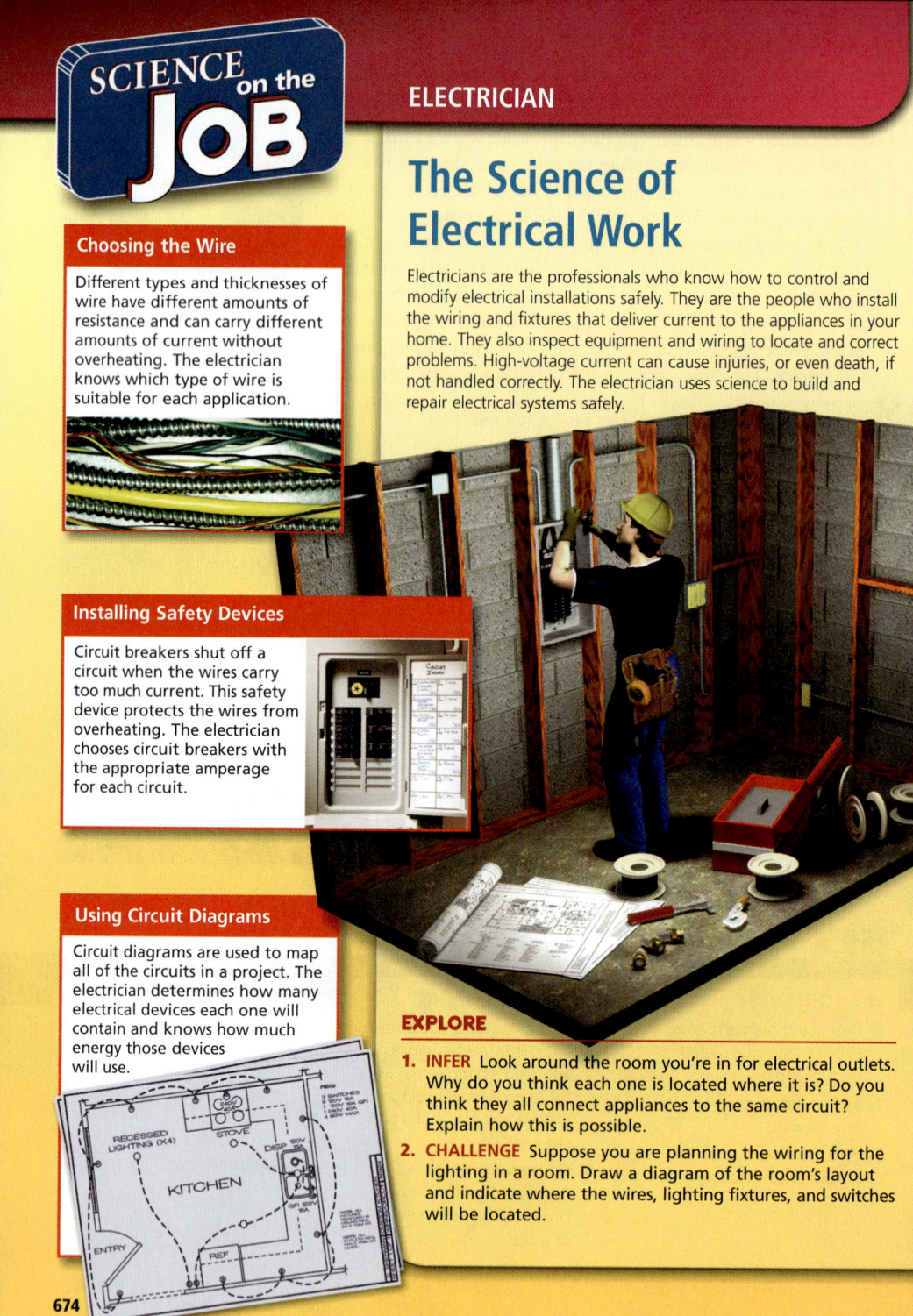

SCIENCE on the JOB

ELECTRICIAN

The Science of Electrical Work

Electricians are the professionals who know how to control and modify electrical installations safely. They are the people who install the wiring and fixtures that deliver current to the appliances in your home. They also inspect equipment and wiring to locate and correct problems. High-voltage current can cause injuries, or even death, if not handled correctly. The electrician uses science to build and repair electrical systems safely.

Choosing the Wire
Different types and thicknesses of wire have different amounts of resistance and can carry different amounts of current without overheating. The electrician knows which type of wire is suitable for each application.

Installing Safety Devices
Circuit breakers shut off a circuit when the wires carry too much current. This safety device protects the wires from overheating. The electrician chooses circuit breakers with the appropriate amperage for each circuit.

Using Circuit Diagrams
Circuit diagrams are used to map all of the circuits in a project. The electrician determines how many electrical devices each one will contain and knows how much energy those devices will use.

EXPLORE
1. **INFER** Look around the room you're in for electrical outlets. Why do you think each one is located where it is? Do you think they all connect appliances to the same circuit? Explain how this is possible.
2. **CHALLENGE** Suppose you are planning the wiring for the lighting in a room. Draw a diagram of the room's layout and indicate where the wires, lighting fixtures, and switches will be located.

EXPLORE
1. **INFER** Sample answer: The outlets are placed low so that cords can reach them, and there are more of them in the front of the room where the computer and overhead projector are. They could all be on one circuit if they each form their own complete connection to and from the power source.
2. **CHALLENGE** Students' diagrams should include wires, fixtures, and switches drawn in reasonable places.

KEY CONCEPT

20.2 Circuits make electric current useful.

BEFORE, you learned
- Charge flows in a closed circuit
- Circuits have a voltage source, conductor, and one or more electrical devices
- Current follows the path of least resistance

NOW, you will learn
- How circuits are designed for specific purposes
- How a series circuit differs from a parallel circuit
- How electrical appliances use circuits

VOCABULARY
series circuit p. 676
parallel circuit p. 677

THINK ABOUT

How does it work?

You know what a telephone does. But did you ever stop to think about how the circuits and other electrical parts inside of it work together to make it happen?

This photo shows an old telephone that has been taken apart to reveal its circuits. As you can see, there are a lot of different parts. Each one has a function. Pick two or three of the parts. What do you think each part does? How do you think it works? How might it relate to the other parts inside the telephone?

OUTLINE
Remember to include this heading in your outline.
  I. Main idea
    A. Supporting idea
      1. Detail
      2. Detail
    B. Supporting idea

Circuits are constructed for specific purposes.

How many things around you right now use electric current? Current is used to transfer energy to so many things because it is easy to store, distribute, and turn off and on. Each device that uses current is a part of at least one circuit—the circuit that supplies its voltage.

Most electrical appliances have many circuits inside of them that are designed to carry out specific functions. Those circuits may be designed to light bulbs, move motor parts, or calculate. Each of those circuits may have thousands—or even millions—of parts. The functions that a circuit can perform depend on how those parts are set up within the circuit.

 Why is the design of a circuit important?

Chapter 20: **Circuits and Electronics** 675

RESOURCES FOR DIFFERENTIATED INSTRUCTION

Below Level
UNIT RESOURCE BOOK
- Reading Study Guide A, pp. 86–87
- Decoding Support, p. 110

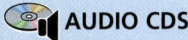 **AUDIO CDS**

Advanced
UNIT RESOURCE BOOK
Challenge and Extension, p. 92

English Learners
UNIT RESOURCE BOOK
Spanish Reading Study Guide, pp. 90–91

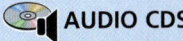 **AUDIO CDS**
- Audio Readings in Spanish
- Audio Readings (English)

20.2 FOCUS

◗ Set Learning Goals
Students will
- Identify how circuits are designed for specific purposes.
- Contrast series and parallel circuits.
- Explain how electrical appliances use circuits.
- Experiment with parallel and series circuits.

◗ 3-Minute Warm-Up
Display Transparency 12 or copy this exercise on the board:

Decide if these statements are true. If not, correct them.
1. When a light is switched off, the circuit is closed. *open*
2. A fuse is a safely device that prevents electrical fires. *true*
3. Electric current flows in the most resistant path. *least resistant*

 3-Minute Warm-Up, p. T12

20.2 MOTIVATE

THINK ABOUT
PURPOSE To show that electrical devices include many circuits

DISCUSS Have volunteers explain what they see in the telephone circuitry and offer their ideas about the functions of the circuits. If possible, bring in the parts of an old telephone to pass around. Speculate about how different functional circuits might be linked together inside the telephone.

Ongoing Assessment
Identify how circuits are designed for specific purposes.
Ask: What makes an electrical appliance appropriate for its job? *the combination of many circuits*

 Answer: The design determines the circuit's function.

Chapter 20 **675**

20.2 INSTRUCT

Teach from Visuals

To help students understand the relationship between the realistic rendering of the series circuit and the schematic diagram, ask:

- How are the two pictures of the series circuit similar? *Both pictures show the same circuit.*
- How are they different? *One is a real photograph while the other is a diagram with symbols.*

Address Misconceptions

IDENTIFY Ask: Suppose you have a series circuit with three identical light bulbs. You know that each bulb converts some of the electrical energy into light and heat. How do you think the brightness of the third bulb will compare to the brightness of the first bulb? If students answer that it will be dimmer, they may hold the misconception that diminution—or reduction—of current in a series circuit is progressive per resistor, rather than universal across the circuit.

CORRECT Remind students that a circuit is a closed loop. Any change in resistance anywhere in the circuit affects current everywhere in the closed loop. The effect of a change in resistance is not limited to just part of the circuit.

REASSESS Again have students imagine a closed circuit with three light bulbs that are lit. Ask: What will happen to the brightness of the three bulbs when I add a fourth bulb? *All the light bulbs will dim.*

Technology Resources

Visit **ClassZone.com** for background on common student misconceptions.

MISCONCEPTION DATABASE

Ongoing Assessment

 Answer: If one light bulb burns out, the rest of the bulbs turn off. The bulbs in a series circuit dim with each added bulb.

676 Unit 5: Electricity and Magnetism

Circuits can have multiple paths.

Even a simple circuit can contain several parts. When you flip the light switch in your classroom, how many different lights go on? If you count each light bulb or each fluorescent tube, there might be as many as ten or twelve light bulbs. There is more than one way those light bulbs could be connected in one circuit. Next, you will read about two simple ways that circuits can be constructed.

Series Circuits

READING TIP The word *series* means a number of things arranged one after another.

 A **series circuit** is a circuit in which current follows a single path. That means that all of the parts in a series circuit are part of the same path. The photograph and diagram below show a series circuit. The charge coming from the D cell flows first through one light bulb, and then through the next one.

Series Circuit

Each device in a series circuit is wired on a single path.

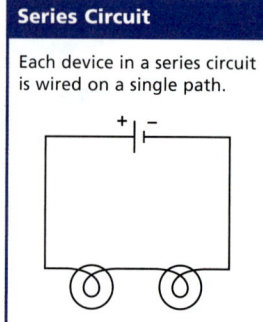

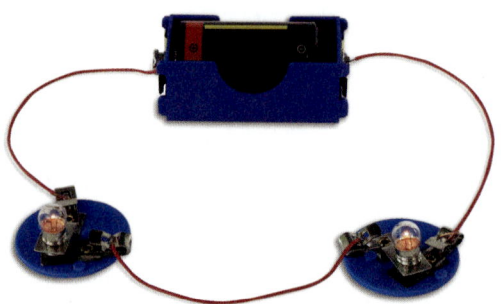

A series circuit uses a minimal amount of wire. However, a disadvantage of a series circuit is that all of the elements must be in working order for the circuit to function. If one of the light bulbs burns out, the circuit will be broken and the other bulb will be dark, too. Series circuits have another disadvantage. Light bulbs and other resistors convert some energy into heat and light. The more light bulbs that are added to a series circuit, the less current there is available, and the dimmer all of the bulbs become.

CHECK YOUR READING Give two disadvantages of a series circuit.

If voltage sources are arranged in series, the voltages will add together. Sometimes batteries are arranged in series to add voltage to a circuit. For example, the circuits in flashlights are usually series circuits. The charge flows through one battery, through the next, through the bulb, and back to the first battery. The flashlight is brighter than it would be if its circuit contained only a single battery.

676 Unit 5: Electricity and Magnetism

DIFFERENTIATE INSTRUCTION

More Reading Support

A In which type of circuit does current follow a single path? *series circuit*

B What happens when one bulb out of several goes out in a series circuit? *They all go out.*

English Learners
Help students recognize sentences that indicate a cause-effect relationship. Have them make a two-column chart like the one below. Give them several cause-effect sentences and have them put each sentence part under the correct heading. (The examples are from this page.)

Cause	Effect
If one of the light bulbs burns out,	the circuit will be broken and the other bulb will be dark, too.
The more light bulbs that are added to a series circuit,	the less current there is available, and the dimmer all of the bulbs become.

Parallel Circuits

A **parallel circuit** is a circuit in which current follows more than one path. Each path is called a branch. The current divides among all possible branches, so that the voltage is the same across each branch. The photograph and diagram below show a simple parallel circuit.

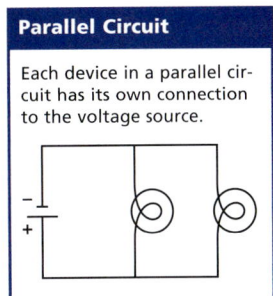

Parallel Circuit

Each device in a parallel circuit has its own connection to the voltage source.

Parallel circuits require more wire than do series circuits. On the other hand, there is more than one path on which the charge may flow. If one bulb burns out, the other bulb will continue to glow. As you add more and more light bulbs to a series circuit, each bulb in the circuit grows dimmer and dimmer. Because each bulb you add in a parallel circuit has its own branch to the power source, the bulbs burn at their brightest.

A flashlight contains batteries wired in a series circuit. Batteries can be wired in parallel, too. If the two positive terminals are connected to each other and the two negative terminals are connected to each other, charge will flow from both batteries. Adding batteries in parallel will not increase the voltage supplied to the circuit, but the batteries will last longer.

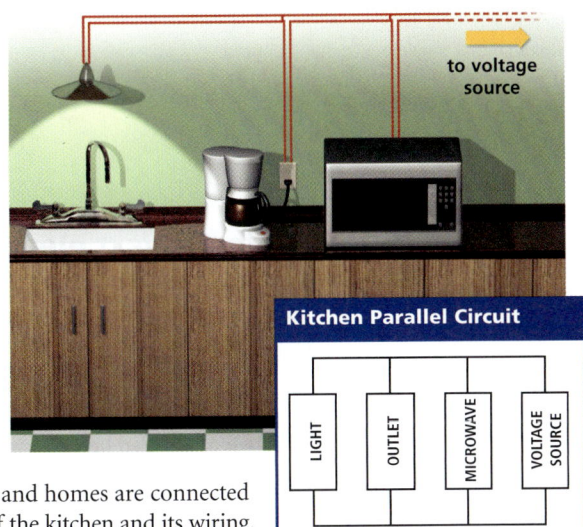

The circuits in most businesses and homes are connected in parallel. Look at the illustration of the kitchen and its wiring. This is a parallel circuit, so even if one electrical device is switched off, the others can still be used. The circuits within many electrical devices are combinations of series circuits and parallel circuits. For example, a parallel circuit may have branches that contain several elements arranged in series.

 Why are the circuits in buildings and homes arranged in parallel?

Chapter 20: **Circuits and Electronics** 677

DIFFERENTIATE INSTRUCTION

 More Reading Support

C In which type of circuit does the current follow more than one path? *a parallel circuit*

Below Level Some students may take the diagrams of series and parallel circuits too literally. Draw diagrams representing both types of circuits that show the symbols for the bulbs and wire in different configurations. For example, the diagram does not have to be rectangular in shape. Have students find similarities among the diagrams.

INVESTIGATE Circuits

PURPOSE To experiment with series and parallel circuits in order to determine which arrangement makes light bulbs burn brighter

TIPS 15 min.

- The clips may get warm from carrying current. Have students disconnect the wires when they are finished.
- Students with motor disabilities can be paired with students who can perform tasks requiring manual dexterity, such as clipping wires to battery terminals.

WHAT DO YOU THINK? *The first circuit; series; the voltages added together.*

CHALLENGE *The diagram or sketch should show four light bulbs connected in a parallel circuit.*

 Datasheet, Circuits, p. 93

Technology Resources

Customize this student lab as needed or look for an alternative. Print rubrics to assess student lab reports.

 Lab Generator CD-ROM

Teaching with Technology

Have students use graphics software to draw a schematic diagram of the circuits they create in the investigation. Have them include a key like that on p. 669.

Integrate the Sciences

Like electrical appliances that convert electrical energy into other forms of energy, the human body converts chemical energy into other forms of energy. For example, muscle cells break down glucose (blood sugar) molecules, releasing chemical energy. The muscle tissue converts this energy into energy of motion so the person can push, pull, lift, walk, and so on.

Ongoing Assessment

 *Answer: heat, motion, sound*

678 Unit 5: Electricity and Magnetism

INVESTIGATE Circuits

How can you produce brighter light?

PROCEDURE

1. Clip one end of a wire to the light bulb and the other end to the negative terminal of one battery to form a connection.
2. Use another wire to connect the positive terminal of the battery with the negative terminal of a second battery, as shown in the photograph.
3. Use a third wire to connect the positive terminal of the second battery to the light bulb. Observe the light bulb.
4. Remove the wires. Find a way to reconnect the wires to produce the other type of circuit.

WHAT DO YOU THINK?

- Which circuit produced brighter light? What type of circuit was it?
- Why did the light bulb glow brighter in that circuit?

CHALLENGE Suppose you wanted to construct a new circuit consisting of four light bulbs and only one battery. How would you arrange the light bulbs so that they glow at their brightest? Your answer should be in the form of either a diagram or a sketch of the circuit.

SKILL FOCUS
Inferring

MATERIALS
- 4 insulated wires with alligator clips
- small light bulb in a holder
- 2 batteries in holders

TIME
15 minutes

Circuits convert electrical energy into other forms of energy.

We use electrical energy to do many things besides lighting a string of light bulbs. For example, a circuit in a space heater converts electrical energy into heat. A circuit in a fan converts electrical energy into motion. A circuit in a bell converts electrical energy into sound. That bell might also be on a circuit that makes it ring at certain times, letting you know when class is over.

Branches, switches, and other elements in circuits allow for such control of current that our calculators and computers can use circuits to calculate and process information for us. All of these things are possible because voltage is electric potential that can be converted into energy in a circuit.

 Name three types of energy that electrical energy can be converted into.

678 Unit 5: Electricity and Magnetism

DIFFERENTIATE INSTRUCTION

 More Reading Support

D What kind of energy do circuits carry? *electrical energy*

Advanced Challenge students to find out what type of energy a microwave oven converts electrical energy into and how that type of energy cooks food. For example, one way is by dispersing the energy so that it reaches all surfaces of the food. Students could contrast the way a microwave oven cooks food with the way a conventional electrical oven does.

 Challenge and Extension, p. 92

A toaster is an example of an electrical appliance containing a circuit that converts energy from one form to another. In a toaster, electrical energy is converted into heat. Voltage is supplied to the toaster by plugging it into a wall outlet, which completes the circuit from a power plant. The outlet is wired in parallel with other outlets, so the appliance will always be connected to the same amount of voltage.

① When you push the handle down, a piece of metal connects to contact points on a circuit board that act as a switch and run current through the circuit.

② Charge flows through a resistor in the circuit called a heating element. The heating element is made up of a type of wire that has a very high resistance. As charge flows through the heating element, electrical energy is converted into heat.

③ The holder in the toaster is loaded onto a timed spring. After a certain amount of time passes, the spring is released, the toast pops up, and the circuit is opened. The toaster shuts off automatically, and your toast is done.

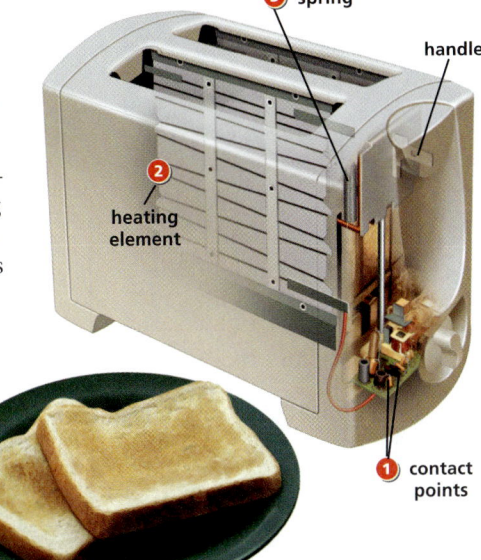

 Summarize the way a circuit in a toaster works. (Remember that a summary includes only the most important information.)

20.2 Review

KEY CONCEPTS
1. Explain how a circuit can perform a specific function.
2. How are series circuits and parallel circuits similar? How do they differ?
3. Describe three electrical appliances that use circuits to convert electrical energy into other forms of energy.

CRITICAL THINKING
4. **Analyze** Why are the batteries of flashlights often arranged in series and not in parallel?
5. **Infer** You walk past a string of small lights around a window frame. Only two of the bulbs are burned out. What can you tell about the string of lights?

⚠ CHALLENGE
6. **Apply** Explain how the circuit in a space heater converts electrical energy into heat. Draw a diagram of the circuit, using the standard symbols for circuit diagrams.

ANSWERS
1. Sample answer: A circuit that contains light bulbs can light a room.
2. Both provide a path for current. Series circuits have all the devices arranged so that current follows in one path; parallel circuits have each device on its own path to the voltage source.
3. Sample answer: A fan converts electrical energy into motion; a doorbell converts electrical energy into motion, which then creates sound; a toaster converts electrical energy into heat.
4. to make the light bulb in the flashlight shine brighter
5. They are wired in parallel.
6. The circuit contains a heating element with high resistance that converts electrical energy into heat.

MATH IN SCIENCE
Math Skills Practice for Science

Set Learning Goal
To calculate voltage drop in a circuit by using percentages

Present the Science
Voltage drop is directly proportional to the resistance of a device: the higher a device's resistance, the greater the voltage drop when current passes through it. In a series circuit, the voltage drop of all the devices add up to the voltage supplied by the voltage source.

Develop Number Sense
Make sure students understand the difference between proportions and equations. A proportion is an equation in which the items are ratios. What this means is that when two ratios are equal to each other, a proportion is formed. For example, a/b = c/d. A good way to remember the difference is that proportions include ratios.

DIFFERENTIATION TIP For students with perceptual difficulties, work out the proportion on graph paper, magnifying the dimensions. Place parts of the proportion so that numerator and denominator positions—and the line separating each pair—are very clear.

Close
Direct students' attention to the lights in the picture and have them read the caption. Ask: How could an electrician decide whether the voltage drop in this light display is safe or not? *The electrician could determine the rated voltage for the wires and then figure out what 5 percent of those values would be. He or she could test the wires with special equipment and compare the test values with the calculated percentage.*

- Math Support, p. 111
- Math Practice, p. 112

Technology Resources
Students can visit ClassZone.com for practice with percents and proportions.

 MATH TUTORIAL

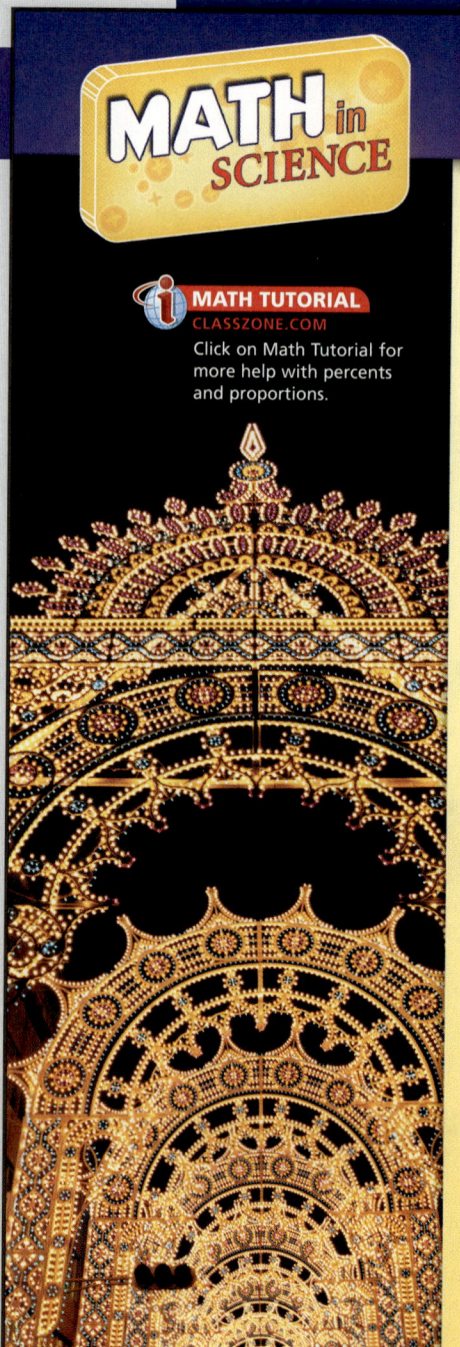

MATH in SCIENCE

MATH TUTORIAL
CLASSZONE.COM
Click on Math Tutorial for more help with percents and proportions.

SKILL: SOLVING PERCENT PROBLEMS

Voltage Drop

A voltage drop occurs when current passes through a wire or an electrical device. The higher the resistance of a wire, the greater the voltage drop. Too much voltage drop can cause the device to overheat.

The National Electric Code—a document of guidelines for electricians—states that the voltage drop across a wire should be no more than 5 percent of the voltage from the voltage source. To find 5 percent of a number, you can set up the calculation as a proportion.

Example
The lighting in a hotel includes many fixtures that will be arranged on long wires. The electrician needs to know the maximum voltage drop allowed in order to choose the proper wire. The circuit will use a voltage source of 120 V. What is 5% of 120?

(1) Write the problem as a proportion.

$$\frac{\text{voltage drop}}{\text{voltage}} = \frac{\text{percent}}{100}$$

(2) Substitute.

$$\frac{\text{voltage drop}}{120} = \frac{5}{100}$$

(3) Calculate and simplify.

$$\frac{\text{voltage drop}}{120} \cdot 120 = \frac{5}{100} \cdot 120$$

$$\text{voltage drop} = 6$$

ANSWER The maximum voltage drop in the wire is 6 V.

Use the proportion to answer the following questions.

1. If the voltage source is increased to 277 V, what is the maximum voltage drop in the wire?

2. To be on the safe side, the electrician decided to find a wire with a voltage drop that is 3 percent of the voltage from the voltage source. What is the voltage drop in the wire?

CHALLENGE A student wants to hang a string of lights outside and connect it to an extension cord. The voltage drop across the extension cord is 3.1 V. The outlet supplies 240 V. Does the voltage drop in the extension cord meet the code guidelines?

The many lights in this spectacular display in Kobe, Japan, produce a large voltage drop. The appropriate type of wire must be used to supply its current.

ANSWERS

1. voltage drop/voltage = percent/100; voltage drop/277 = 5/100; voltage drop = 5/100 · 277; voltage drop = 13.85 V
2. voltage drop/voltage = percent/100; voltage drop/120 = 3/100; voltage drop = (3/100) · 120; voltage drop = 3.6 V

CHALLENGE 3.1/240 = percent/100; percent = (3.1/240) · 100; percent = 1.3
Yes; 1.3 percent is less than 5 percent.

KEY CONCEPT
20.3 Electronic technology is based on circuits.

◀ **BEFORE, you learned**
- Charge flows in a closed loop
- Circuits are designed for specific purposes
- Electrical appliances use circuits

▶ **NOW, you will learn**
- How information can be coded
- How computer circuits use digital information
- How computers work

VOCABULARY
electronic p. 681
binary code p. 682
digital p. 682
analog p. 684
computer p. 685

EXPLORE Codes

How can information be coded?

PROCEDURE

1. Write the numbers 1 to 26 in your notebook. Below each number, write a letter of the alphabet. This will serve as your key.
2. On a separate piece of paper, write the name of the street you live on using numbers instead of words. For each letter of the word, use the number that is directly above it on your key.
3. Exchange messages with a partner and use your key to decode your partner's information.

MATERIALS
- notebook
- small piece of paper

WHAT DO YOU THINK?
- How can information be coded?
- Under what types of circumstances would information need to be coded?

Electronics use coded information.

A code is a system of symbols used to send a message. Language is a code, for example. The symbols used in written language are lines and shapes. The words on this page represent meanings coded into the form of letters. As you read, your brain decodes the lines and shapes that make up each word, and you understand the message that is encoded.

An **electronic** device is a device that uses electric current to represent coded information. In electronics, the signals are variations in the current. Examples of electronic devices include computers, calculators, CD players, game systems, and more.

 Describe the signals used in electronic devices.

RESOURCE CENTER CLASSZONE.COM
Find out more about electronics.

Chapter 20: Circuits and Electronics 681

RESOURCES FOR DIFFERENTIATED INSTRUCTION

Below Level
UNIT RESOURCE BOOK
- Reading Study Guide A, pp. 97–98
- Decoding Support, p. 110

 **AUDIO CDS**

Advanced
UNIT RESOURCE BOOK
- Challenge and Extension, p. 103
- Challenge Reading, pp. 106–107

English Learners
UNIT RESOURCE BOOK
Spanish Reading Study Guide, pp. 101–102

 **AUDIO CDS**
- Audio Readings in Spanish
- Audio Readings (English)

20.3 FOCUS

● Set Learning Goals
Students will
- Learn how electronics use coded information.
- Explain what digital information is.
- Understand how the parts of a computer work together.
- Make a model of a digital image in an experiment.

● 3-Minute Warm-Up
Display Transparency 13 or copy this exercise on the board:
Draw simple circuit diagrams for
- a series circuit
- a parallel circuit
Use standard symbols or label the parts.

T 3-Minute Warm-Up, p. T13

20.3 MOTIVATE

EXPLORE Codes
PURPOSE To encode information according to a specific set of rules

TIPS 10 min. Leave a space between each number. Graph paper may be useful to students with visual impairments or messy handwriting.

WHAT DO YOU THINK? by using symbols to represent letters; when sending confidential information

EXPLORE (the BIG idea)
Revisit "What's Inside a Calculator?" on p. 665. Have students explain their inferences.

Ongoing Assessment
 Answer: They are variations in an electric current.

Chapter 20 681

20.3 INSTRUCT

Teach from Visuals

To help students understand the binary decision tree, ask:

- Where in the diagram are the questions asked? *in the word bubbles to the left*
- Where are the questions answered? *above or beside the arrows*
- Where are directions given? *in the word bubbles to the right, or for the last question, in the word bubble at the bottom*

Develop Critical Thinking

INFER Have students infer a plausible explanation for the development of computer technology based on binary code, rather than some other type. Ask: Why do you suppose computer scientists developed computer technology based on binary code, rather than on some other type of number code? *Binary code is the simplest possible code to use in circuits because they require only off and on states.*

Ongoing Assessment

Learn how electronics use coded information.

Ask: What kind of information does a computer understand? *information that is binary, or digital information*

 *Answer: Make it a series of binary questions.*

Binary Code

The English alphabet contains only 26 letters, yet there is no limit to the number of messages that can be expressed with it. That is because the message is conveyed not only by the letters that are chosen but also by the order in which they are placed.

Many electronic devices use a coding system with only two choices, as compared with the 26 in the alphabet. A coding system consisting of two choices is a **binary code.** As with a language, complex messages can be sent using binary code. In electronics, the two choices are whether an electric current is on or off. Switches in electronic circuits turn the current on and off. The result is a message represented in pulses of current.

It may be hard to imagine how something as complex as a computer game can be expressed with pulses of current. But it is a matter of breaking down information into smaller and smaller steps. You may have played the game 20 questions. In that game, you receive a message by asking someone only yes-or-no questions. The player answering the questions conveys the message only in *yes*'s and *no*'s, a binary code.

The diagram on the left shows how a decision-making process can be written in simple steps. The diagram is similar to a computer program, which tells a computer what to do. Each step of the process has been broken down into a binary question. If you determine exactly what you mean by *cold* and *hot*, then anyone using this program—or even a computer—would arrive at the same conclusion for a given set of conditions.

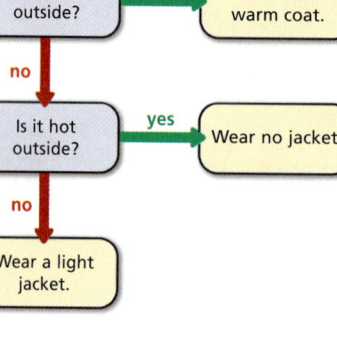

CHECK YOUR READING How can a process be broken down into simple steps?

Digital Information

You can think of the yes-or-no choices in a binary system as being represented by the numbers 0 and 1. Information that is represented as numbers, or digits, is called **digital** information. In electronics, a circuit that is off is represented by 0, and a circuit that is on is represented by 1.

Digital information is represented in long streams of digits. Each 0 or 1 is also known as a bit, which is short for *binary digit*. A group of 8 bits is known as a byte. You might have heard the term *gigabyte* in reference to the amount of information that can be stored on a computer. One gigabyte is equal to about 1 billion bytes. That's 8 billion 0s and 1s!

682 Unit 5: Electricity and Magnetism

DIFFERENTIATE INSTRUCTION

More Reading Support

A How many choices does a binary code allow? *two*

B What word describes information represented by digits? *digital*

English Learners Have students write the definitions of *electronic, binary code, digital, analog,* and *computer* in their Science Word Dictionaries. Help students recognize when prepositional phrases begin a sentence. For example, "Below each number, write a letter of the alphabet" and "On a separate piece of paper, write the name of the street you live on" ("Explore Codes," p. 681). List common prepositions on a poster or on the board for students to reference.

682 Unit 5: **Electricity and Magnetism**

Computers, digital cameras, CD players, DVD players, and other devices use digital information. Digital information is used in electronic devices more and more. There are at least two reasons for this:

- Digital information can be copied many times without losing its quality. The 1s are always copied as 1s, and the 0s are always copied as 0s.
- Digital information can be processed, or worked with, on computers.

For example, a photograph taken on a digital camera can be input to a computer in the form of digital information. Once the photograph is on a computer, the user can modify it, copy it, store it, and send it.

Many portable devices such as game systems and MP3 players can also be used with computers. Because computers and the devices use the same type of information, computers can be used to add games, music, and other programs to the devices. The photograph at right of a watch shows an example of a portable device that uses digital information.

This watch also functions as an MP3 player—it can store songs as digital files.

CHECK YOUR READING Why is digital information often used in electronic devices?

INVESTIGATE Digital Information

How can you save a drawing in 1s and 0s?

PROCEDURE

1. Draw a 10-square by 10-square grid on a piece of graph paper.
2. Fill in some of the squares of the grid to draw a picture or pattern. Look at the example shown, but draw your own picture.
3. Starting in the upper left-hand corner of your grid, write 0 for every blank square and 1 for every filled-in square. Write a continuous series of 1s and 0s for all rows.
4. Exchange coded information with a partner who has not seen your picture. Draw a new grid in your notebook and fill it in using your partner's information.

WHAT DO YOU THINK?
- How were you able to reproduce your partner's picture?
- How is this activity similar to saving an image on a computer?

CHALLENGE Suppose you used three colored markers in your drawing—red, yellow, and green. How could you represent your color drawing using only 1s and 0s?

SKILL Making models

MATERIALS
- graph paper
- plain paper

TIME 30 minutes

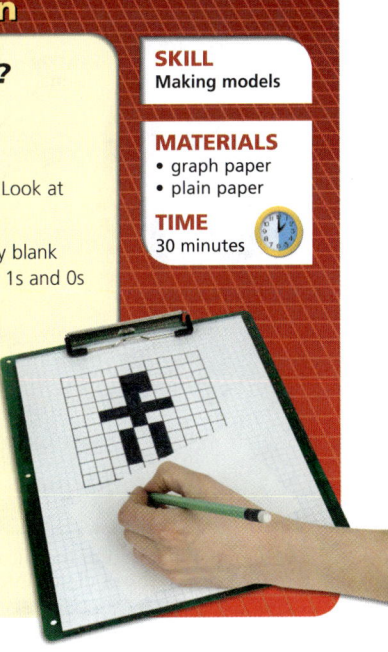

Chapter 20: **Circuits and Electronics** 683

INVESTIGATE Digital Information

PURPOSE To make a simple model of a computer graphic to demonstrate how information can be stored digitally.

TIPS *30 min.*
- Use graph paper with a large cell size.
- Some possibilities for the image include smiley faces, simple flowers, sunbursts, numbers, capital letters, and familiar symbols such as dollar and cent signs.

WHAT DO YOU THINK? *By translating the filled squares as 1s and the blank squares as 0s; the computer translates an image into a stream of 1s and 0s, or digital information.*

CHALLENGE *Use more than one digit to represent each color.*

Datasheet, Digital Information, p. 104

Technology Resources

Customize this student lab as needed or look for an alternative. Print rubrics to assess student lab reports.

Lab Generator CD-ROM

Ongoing Assessment

Explain what digital information is.

Ask: How are the two states of current in a digital circuit represented? *with 1s and 0s*

CHECK YOUR READING *Answer: because it can be used with computers and it can be copied many times without losing its quality*

DIFFERENTIATE INSTRUCTION

More Reading Support

C Name three devices that use digital information. *computers, digital cameras, DVD players*

Advanced Have students write the number 18 in digital code. To do so, have students write the numbers 16, 8, 4, 2, and 1 on separate note cards and lay them out in that order from left to right. Have them identify the two numbers that add up to 18 (16 and 2), and turn over the other cards (8, 4, and 1). On a piece of paper, have them write 1 for each face-up card, and 0 for each face-down. They should end up with 1-0-0-1-0, which is the way the number 18 is written in digital code.

Challenge and Extension, p. 103

Chapter 20 **683**

Teach Difficult Concepts

Have students graph clock motion to illustrate the difference between analog and digital values. The hands of a clock move in a continuous circle over and over again. You can represent this movement on a line graph by showing a continuing wave with repeating high and low values. The line graph is an analog representation that connects each moment in time with the next.

Alternatively, you can represent a digital clock on a bar graph by plotting hours (one o'clock, two o'clock, etc.) or smaller time intervals as bars in repeating patterns. This bar graph would not connect one moment of time with the next. It is either one o'clock or two o'clock, for example. To help students with this concept, try the demo.

Teacher Demo

Compare a digital clock with one that has a second hand, both showing the correct time. The digital clock shows when each minute has passed, but nothing in between, even though time is passing. However, the analog clock shows a continuous movement to represent the passage of time.

Teach from Visuals

To help students understand microscopic pits in the illustration of analog and digital signals, ask: What do the pits represent? *a stream of 1s*

 This visual is also available as T14 in the Unit Transparency Book.

Real World Connection

Telephone exchanges convert analog speech into digital code before sending the signals. At the receiving end, the binary code is translated back into analog sound and delivered to the listener. Digital code allows more information to be sent along existing telephone lines.

Ongoing Assessment

 *Answer: the curved line; the numbers*

684 Unit 5: **Electricity and Magnetism**

Analog to Digital

Some electronic devices use a system of coding electric current that differs from the digital code. Those electronics use analog information. **Analog** information is information that is represented in a continuous but varying form.

For example, a microphone records sound waves as analog information. The analog signal that is produced varies in strength as the sound wave varies in strength, as shown below. In order for the signal to be burned onto a CD, it is converted into digital information.

❶ The sound waves are recorded in the microphone as an analog electrical signal.

❷ The signal is sent through a computer circuit that measures, or samples, each part of the wave. The signal is sampled many thousands of times every second.

❸ Each measurement of the wave is converted into a stream of digits. Microscopic pits representing the stream of digits are burned onto the CD. A stereo converts the signal from digital back to analog form, making it possible for people to hear what was recorded.

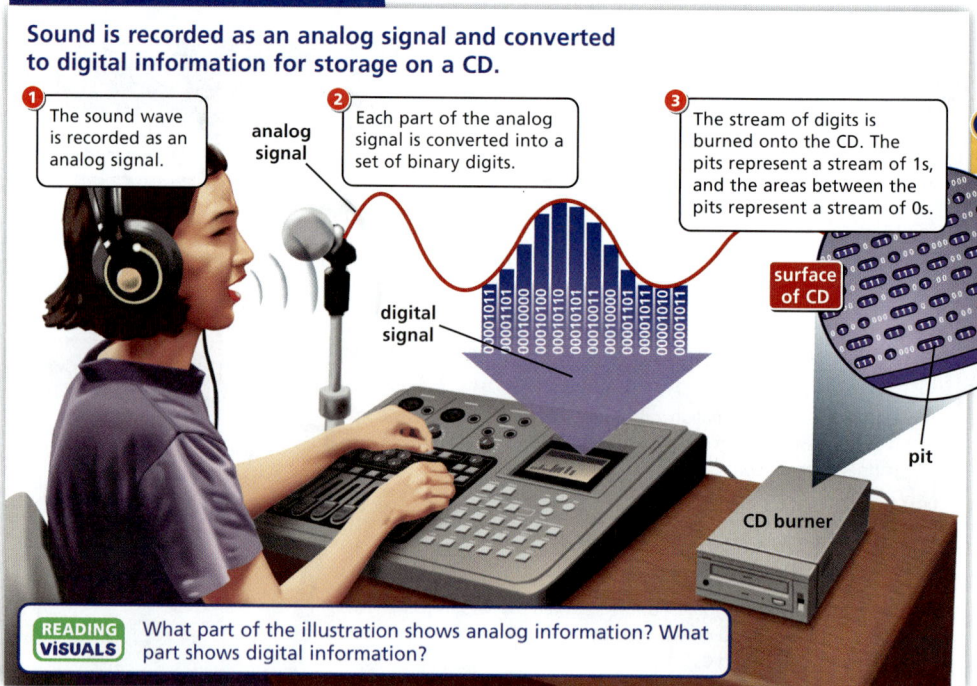

Analog and Digital Signals

Sound is recorded as an analog signal and converted to digital information for storage on a CD.

❶ The sound wave is recorded as an analog signal.
❷ Each part of the analog signal is converted into a set of binary digits.
❸ The stream of digits is burned onto the CD. The pits represent a stream of 1s, and the areas between the pits represent a stream of 0s.

READING VISUALS: What part of the illustration shows analog information? What part shows digital information?

684 Unit 5: Electricity and Magnetism

DIFFERENTIATE INSTRUCTION

 More Reading Support

D Which type of information is represented in a continuous but varying form? *analog*

E Which type of information consists of a stream of digits? *digital*

Alternative Assessment Encourage students to devise their own demonstrations to illustrate the concept of analog versus digital. Have participants write a short paragraph interpreting the demonstration.

Advanced Have students who are interested in thought-communication devices read the following article:

 Challenge Reading, pp. 106–107

Computer circuits process digital information.

A **computer** is an electronic device that processes digital information. Computers have been important in science and industry for a long time. Scientists use computers to gather, store, process, and share scientific data. As computers continue to get faster, smaller, and less expensive, they are turning up in many places.

Suppose you get a ride to the store. If the car you're riding in is a newer car, it probably has a computer inside it. At the store, you buy a battery, and the clerk records the sale on a register that is connected to a computer. You put the battery in your camera and take a picture, and the camera has a computer inside it.

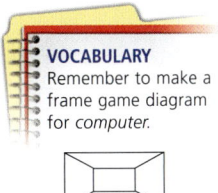

VOCABULARY
Remember to make a frame game diagram for *computer*.

Integrated Circuits

The first digital computer weighed 30 tons and took up a whole room. After 60 years of development, computers the size of a postage stamp are able to complete the same tasks in less time. New technology in computer circuits has led to very small and powerful computers.

Computers process information on circuits that contain many switches, branches, and other elements that allow for a very fine control of current. An integrated circuit is a miniature electronic circuit. Tiny switches, called transistors, in these circuits turn off and on rapidly, signaling the stream of digits that represent information. Over a million of these switches may be on one small integrated circuit!

CHECK YOUR READING How do integrated circuits signal digital information?

Most integrated circuits are made from silicon, an element that is very abundant in Earth's crust. When silicon is treated with certain chemicals, it becomes a good semiconductor. A semiconductor is a material that is more conductive than an insulator but less conductive than a conductor. Silicon is a useful material in computers because the flow of current in it can be finely controlled.

Microscopic circuits are etched onto treated silicon with chemicals or lasers. Transistors and other circuit parts are constructed layer by layer on the silicon. A small, complex circuit on a single piece of silicon is known as a silicon chip, or microchip.

This integrated circuit is smaller than the common ant, *Camponotus pennsylvanicus*, which ranges in length from 6 to 17 mm.

Chapter 20: **Circuits and Electronics** 685

History of Science

The proliferation of computers has depended on their shrinking over the years. Circuit parts have shrunk from tubes and wires to transistors on integrated circuits. Computer size has followed suit—from main frames, to minicomputers, to personal computers, to handheld computers. Miniaturization has made it possible to computerize cars, pacemakers, and ovens, for example.

Integrate the Sciences

Fortunately for consumers of computers, silicon is the second most abundant element in Earth's crust. Almost 28 percent of the crust is silicon. Only oxygen is more abundant. While silicon never occurs in nature in its pure form, it is very common in chemical compounds in rock, sand, clay, soil, and sea water, and even in body tissues of many plants and animals.

Ongoing Assessment

CHECK YOUR READING Answer: Tiny switches (transistors) turn on and off.

DIFFERENTIATE INSTRUCTION

 More Reading Support

F What are the tiny switches that carry the digital signal called? *transistors*

English Learners Ask students to think of other contexts for the word *chip*. From their examples, have students discuss a reasonable definition for *chip*, such as "a thin, rigid piece of material." Have students connect their definition to integrated circuits.

Teach from Visuals

Make sure students understand that the illustration is spread across two pages. Ask: What do the numbers in the big illustration at the bottom of pp. 686 and 687 correspond to on the pages? *the numbered paragraphs on p. 687*

Metacognitive Strategy

Have students write and illustrate an analogy to computer hardware and software. For example, computer hardware is like the cover and pages of a book while the software is the actual story.

Develop Critical Thinking

PROVIDE EXAMPLES Have students investigate the types of software that are on computers at home, in the library, or at school. Ask students to think of games they have played on the computer. Discuss with students what some of the more common software programs are. *Sample answers might include spreadsheet software, graphic design software, and word processing software.*

Ongoing Assessment

Answer: The physical parts of the computer are the hardware; the computer programs and instructions and languages are the software.

OUTLINE
Use an outline to take notes about personal computers.

  I. Main idea
     A. Supporting idea
        1. Detail
        2. Detail
     B. Supporting idea

Personal Computers

When you think of a computer, you probably think of a monitor, mouse, and keyboard—a personal computer (PC). All of the physical parts of a computer and its accessories are together known as hardware. Software refers to the instructions, or programs, and languages that control the hardware. The hardware, software, and user of a computer all work together to complete tasks.

 What is the difference between hardware and software?

Computers have two kinds of memory. As the user is working, information is saved on the computer's random-access memory, or RAM. RAM is a computer's short-term memory. Most computers have enough RAM to store billions of bits. Another type of memory is called read-only memory, or ROM. ROM is a computer's long-term memory, containing the programs to start and run the computer. ROM can save information even after a computer is turned off.

The illustration below shows how a photograph is scanned, modified, and printed using a personal computer. The steps fall into four main functions—input, storage, processing, and output.

How a PC Works

Digital information can move through input, processing, storage, and output devices.

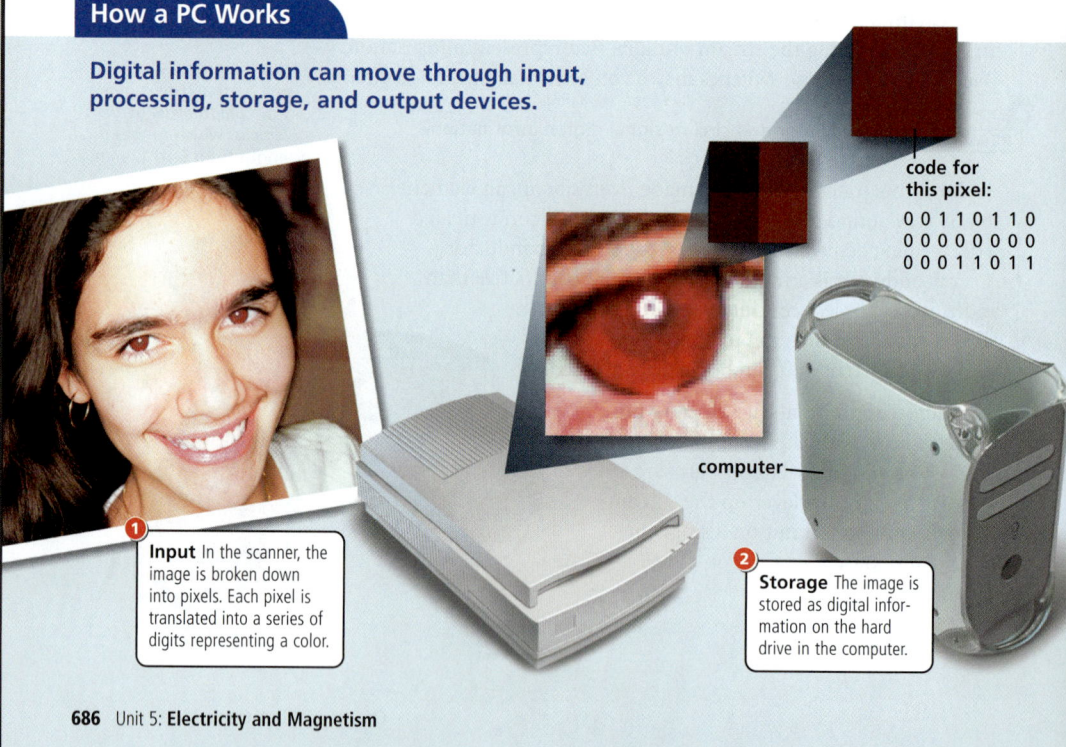

① **Input** In the scanner, the image is broken down into pixels. Each pixel is translated into a series of digits representing a color.

② **Storage** The image is stored as digital information on the hard drive in the computer.

code for this pixel:
0 0 1 1 0 1 1 0
0 0 0 0 0 0 0 0
0 0 0 1 1 0 1 1

computer

686 Unit 5: Electricity and Magnetism

DIFFERENTIATE INSTRUCTION

 **More Reading Support**

G What are the four main functions of a computer? *input, storage, processing, output*

Below Level Write the terms from the chart below in random order on the board. Have students copy the terms and write *H* for hardware or *S* for software after each. Discuss why they made the choices they did.

Hardware	Software
• mouse	• the computer's instructions for displaying colors
• key on keyboard	• word-processing program
• integrated circuit	• spreadsheet program
• computer screen	• a search engine

1 Input The user scans the photograph on a scanner. Each small area, or pixel, of the photograph is converted into a stream of digits. The digital information representing the photograph is sent to the main computer circuit, which is called the central processing unit, or CPU.

2 Storage The user saves the photograph on a magnetic storage device called the hard drive. Small areas of the hard drive are magnetized in one of two directions. The magnetized areas oriented in one direction represent 1s, and the areas oriented in the opposite direction represent 0s, as a way to store the digital information.

3 Processing The photograph is converted back into pixels on the monitor, or screen, for the user to see. The computer below has a software program installed for altering photographs. The user adds more input to the computer with the mouse and the keyboard to improve the photograph.

4 Output The user sends the improved photograph to a printer. The printer converts the digital information back to pixels, and the photograph is printed.

VISUALIZATION CLASSZONE.COM
See how hard drives store information.

CHECK YOUR READING During which one of the four main computer functions is information converted into digital information?

monitor

printer

Output Digital information is translated back into pixels and the photograph is printed.

Processing The image is altered using software on the computer.

READING VISUALS How has the photograph of the girl been altered on the computer?

Chapter 20: Circuits and Electronics 687

Art Connection

Ultrahigh-speed imaging allows scientists to capture processes that happen in microseconds, such as shock waves and electrical "streamers." Regular cameras are at least 100 times slower than electronic cameras, which can capture up to 600 million images per second. Because the rate for conventional cameras is limited and because they are prone to mechanical failures, they are not reliable for photographing high-speed images. Electronic cameras have no moving parts and have high sensitivity, which makes them ideal for recording subtle ultrafast processes. The digital images can also be analyzed in greater detail than conventional photographs.

Ongoing Assessment

Understand how the parts of a computer work together.

Ask: What does a computer need in order to tell the electronic circuitry exactly what to do? *software*

 *Answer: input*

 *Answer: The color of the eyes has been changed.*

DIFFERENTIATE INSTRUCTION

? More Reading Support

H Which piece of hardware provides storage? *hard drive*

I Which piece of hardware provides output? *printer*

Alternative Assessment Have interested students make an extensive list of output devices available for use with personal computers. They should provide clear descriptions of the devices and how they work. If students need help getting started, tell them to see what products are available at computer and electronics stores, or search online catalogs for accessories.

Chapter 20 687

Teach from Visuals

To verify that students interpret the Internet network map correctly, ask: Where is the center of the Web? *The Web is a network does not have a center.*

History of Science

Though the Internet was in existence long before the early 1990s, there was no universal language for posting and browsing Web sites. A British computer engineer, Tim Berners-Lee, conceived of the World Wide Web (WWW) in 1989. In 1990, he wrote the computer language HTML, which is used to structure text on Web sites, and the first Web browser and Web server, special programs that allow users to post and access Web sites.

Ongoing Assessment

CHECK YOUR READING *Answer: Earlier networks behaved like a series circuit, so if a link to one computer was broken, the entire network of links went down. If some links go down on the Internet, however, the others still work.*

Computers can be linked with other computers.

You may have been at a computer lab or a library and had to wait for a printer to print something for you. Offices, libraries, and schools often have several computers that are all connected to the same printer. A group of computers that are linked together is known as a network. Computers can also be linked with other computers to share information. The largest network of computers is the Internet.

The Origin of the Internet

People have been using computer networks to share information on university campuses and military bases for decades. The computers within those networks were connected over telephone systems from one location to another. But those networks behaved like a series circuit. If the link to one computer was broken, the whole network of links went down.

The network that we now call the Internet is different. The United States Department of Defense formed the Internet by linking computers on college campuses across the country. Many extra links were formed, producing a huge web of connected computers. That way, if some links are broken, others still work.

 How does the Internet differ from earlier networks?

The Internet Today

The Internet now spans the world. E-mail uses the Internet. E-mail has added to the ways in which people can "meet," communicate, conduct business, and share stories. The Internet can also be used to work on tasks that require massive computing power. For example, millions of computers linked together, along with their combined information, might one day be used to develop a cure for cancer or model the workings of a human mind.

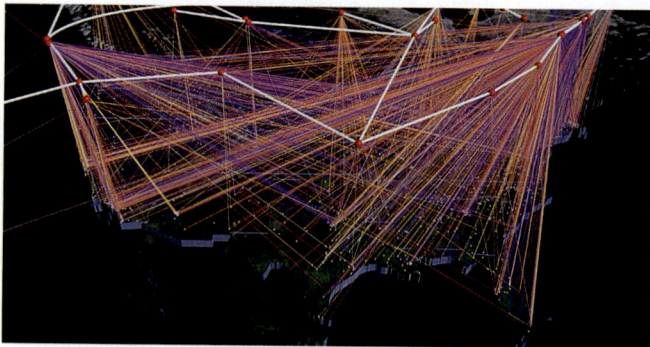

This map shows a representation of Internet traffic in the early 1990s. A map of Internet traffic now would be even more full of lines.

688 Unit 5: Electricity and Magnetism

DIFFERENTIATE INSTRUCTION

More Reading Support

J What is a computer network? *a group of computers that are linked together*

K What is the largest network of computers? *the Internet*

Inclusion There are various hardware and software programs available for students with disabilities. Some examples include screen magnification and enhancement software that provides higher levels of magnification, contrast, and color enhancement; screen reading software that takes information shown on a computer screen and translates it into spoken words using a speech synthesizer; and voice input, which is a keyboard and mouse alternative for typing words and sentences into a word processor, and operating program controls such as menus and buttons.

688 Unit 5: **Electricity and Magnetism**

When you think of the Internet, you might think of the World Wide Web, or the Web. The Web consists of all of the information that can be accessed on the Internet. This information is stored on millions of host computers all over the world. The files that you locate are called Web pages. Each Web page has an address that begins with *www*, which stands for World Wide Web. The system allows you to search or surf through all of the information that is available on it. You might use the Web to research a project. Millions of people use the Web every day to find information, to shop, or for entertainment.

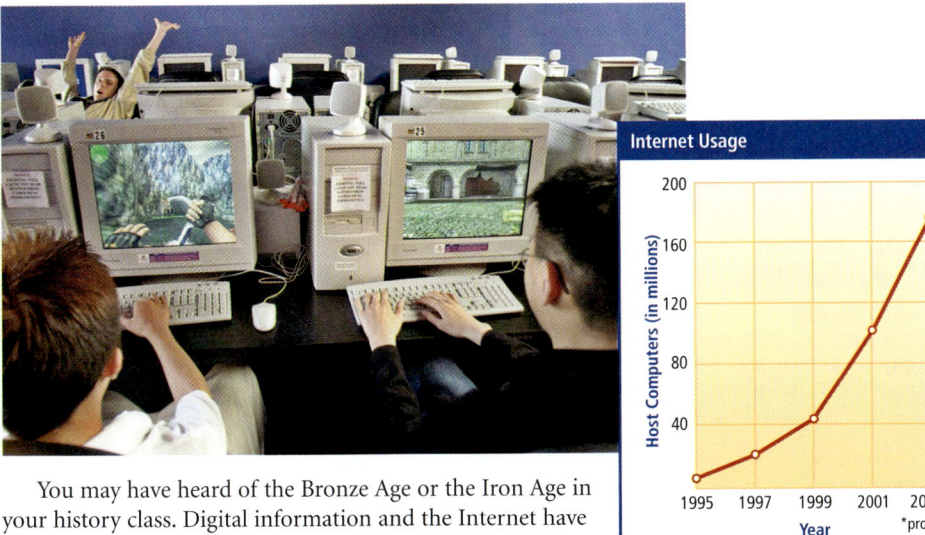

SOURCE: *Internet Software Consortium* (http://www.isc.org)

You may have heard of the Bronze Age or the Iron Age in your history class. Digital information and the Internet have had such a strong impact on the way we do things that some people refer to the era we live in as the Information Age.

20.3 Review

KEY CONCEPTS

1. Describe an example of coded information.
2. What is digital information? Give three examples of devices that use digital information.
3. Give an example of each of the following in terms of computers: input, storage, processing, and output.

CRITICAL THINKING

4. **Compare** Morse code uses a signal of dots and dashes to convey messages. How is Morse code similar to digital code?
5. **Infer** The word *integrated* means "brought together to form a whole." How does that definition apply to an integrated circuit?

CHALLENGE

6. **Predict** Computers as we know them did not exist 50 years ago, and now they are used for many purposes. How do you think people will use computers 50 years from now? Write a paragraph describing what you think the computers of the future will be like and how they will be used.

Chapter 20: **Circuits and Electronics** 689

Teach from Visuals

To help students interpret the graph, ask: What does the increasing steepness of the curve mean? *Every year, more and more host computers contribute to the Internet.*

Reinforce the BIG idea

Have students relate the section to the Big Idea.

R Reinforcing Key Concepts, p. 105

20.3 ASSESS & RETEACH

Assess

A Section 20.3 Quiz, p. 24

Reteach

Have students make a drawing or diagram that represents all of the following concepts:

- computer
- binary code
- digital

Instruct them to include appropriate captions and labels. Then have students share and discuss their work.

Technology Resources

Have students visit **ClassZone.com** for reteaching of Key Concepts.

 CONTENT REVIEW

 CONTENT REVIEW CD-ROM

ANSWERS

1. Sample answer: Each part of a photograph is represented as a 1 or a 0.

2. information that is represented as numbers; examples may include computers, digital cameras, CD or DVD players, MP3 players.

3. Answers might include keystrokes, CD, calculations, communication.

4. Both use binary code to send a message.

5. Many circuit parts have been brought together to form an integrated circuit.

6. Answers should include a description of computers and some applications.

Chapter 20 **689**

CHAPTER INVESTIGATION

Focus

PURPOSE To design a battery-powered communicator to be marketed as a toy

OVERVIEW Students will design a simple device capable of visual signaling in Morse code. They will

- build a prototype,
- test it,
- and write up an evaluation.

Lab Preparation

- Copy and distribute the Morse Code Chart to students.
- Prior to the investigation have students read through the investigation and prepare their data tables. Or you may wish to copy and distribute datasheets and rubrics.

 UNIT RESOURCE BOOK, pp. 113–122

 SCIENCE TOOLKIT, F13

Lab Management

- Assign students to teams of three to five people.
- Have students make careful notes of all prototype trials. If time is short, have them write up their prototype evaluations as homework.

INCLUSION If any participants have hearing-impairments, have their team summarize the brainstorming ideas on paper or on the board. Invite students with hearing impairments to be physically involved in the experiment by letting them make the long and short signals of light.

Teaching with Technology

Use a digital camera to photograph the circuits that students produce. Post the pictures on a bulletin board, or make color photocopies to distribute to the class.

690 Unit 5: **Electricity and Magnetism**

CHAPTER INVESTIGATION

Design an Electronic Communication Device

OVERVIEW AND PURPOSE
DESIGN YOUR OWN

The telegraph was one of the first inventions to demonstrate that machines could be used to communicate over long distances. In a telegraph, messages are sent as electrical signals along a wire from a sending device to a receiver.

Like modern computers, the telegraph uses a binary code. The code is called Morse code—a combination of short and long signals—to stand for letters and symbols. In this lab, you will use what you have learned about circuits to
- design a battery-powered device that uses Morse code
- build and test your design

MATERIALS
- 2 batteries
- light bulb in holder
- piece of copper wire
- 2 wire leads with alligator clips
- 2 craft sticks
- toothpick
- paper clip
- piece of cardboard
- clothespin
- aluminum foil
- rubber band
- scissors
- tape
- wire cutters
- Morse Code Chart

Problem

A toy company has contracted you to design and build a new product for kids. They want a communication device that is similar to a telegraph. Kids will use the device to communicate with each other in Morse code. The company's market research has shown that parents do not like noisy toys, so the company wants a device that uses light rather than sound as a signal.

Procedure

1. Brainstorm ideas for a communication device that can use Morse code. Look at the available materials and think how you could make a circuit that contains a light bulb and a switch.

2. Describe your proposed design and/or draw a sketch of it in your **Science Notebook**. Include a list of the materials that you would need to build it.

690 Unit 5: **Electricity and Magnetism**

INVESTIGATION RESOURCES

 CHAPTER INVESTIGATION, Design an Electronic Communication Device
- Morse Code Chart, p. 113
- Level A, pp. 114–117
- Level B, pp. 118–121
- Level C, p. 122
Advanced students should complete Levels B & C.

 Writing a Lab Report, D12–13

Technology Resources

Customize this student lab as needed or look for an alternative. Print rubrics to assess student lab reports.

 Lab Generator CD-ROM

3. Show your design to a team member. Consider the constraints of each of your designs, such as what materials are available, the complexity of the design, and the time available.

4. Choose one idea or combine two ideas into a final design to test with your group. Build a sample version of your device, called a prototype.

5. Test your device by writing a short question. Translate the question into Morse code. Make long and short flashes of light on your device to send your message. Another person on your team should write down the message received in Morse code, translate the message, and send an answer.

6. Complete at least two trials. Each time, record the question in English, the question in code, the answer in code, and the answer in English.

7. Write a brief evaluation of how well the signal worked. Use the following criteria for your evaluation for each trial.
   - What errors, if any, occurred while you were sending the signal?
   - What errors, if any, occurred while you were receiving the signal?
   - Did the translated answer make sense? Why or why not?

Observe and Analyze

1. **MODEL** Draw a sketch of your final design. Label the parts. Next to your sketch, draw a circuit diagram of your device.
2. **INFER** How do the parts of your circuit allow you to control the flow of current?
3. **COMPARE** How is the signal that is used in your system similar to the digital information used by computers to process information? How does the signal differ?
4. **APPLY** A small sheet of instructions will be packaged with the device. Write a paragraph for the user that explains how to use it. Keep in mind that the user will probably be a child.

Conclude

1. **EVALUATE** What problems, if any, did you encounter when testing your device? How might you improve upon the design?
2. **IDENTIFY LIMITS** What are the limitations of your design? You might consider its estimated costs, where and how kids will be able to use it, and the chances of the device breaking.
3. **APPLY** How might you modify your design so that it could be used by someone with limited vision?
4. **SYNTHESIZE** Write down the steps that you have used to develop this new product. Your first step was to brainstorm an idea.

INVESTIGATE Further

CHALLENGE Design another system of communication that uses your own code. The signal should be in the form of flags. Make a table that lists what the signals mean and write instructions that explain how to use the system to communicate.

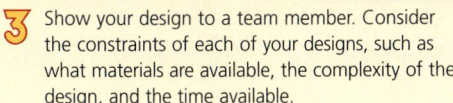

Design an Electronic Communication Device
Observe and Analyze
Table 1. Prototype Testing

	Trial 1	Trial 2
Question (English)		
Question (code)		
Answer (code)		
Answer (English)		
Evaluation		

Conclude

Observe and Analyze

1. Drawings should be labeled and include circuit diagrams.
2. The switch allows you to start and stop the flow of current.
3. Both are binary codes. The signal is different from digital information in that it is conveyed in long and short flashes of light instead of 0s and 1s.
4. The instructions should be simple and in logical order. If students need help, refer them back to the procedure and their datasheets.

Conclude

1. Improvements should reflect problems encountered.
2. Answers should indicate an understanding of the intended audience (children) and technological constraints. Sample answer: using light signals to communicate with Morse code takes some time; if you make a mistake, you have to go back.
3. Sample answer: A buzzer or bell could be wired into the circuit instead of a light bulb.
4. Brainstorm an idea, describe or sketch a design, compare design limitations, choose a design, build a prototype, test the device, improve on the design.

INVESTIGATE Further

CHALLENGE Answer: Accept any signaling system that is logical, well thought out, and presented neatly and legibly.

Post-Lab Discussion

- Ask: What do you think was the hardest part of the process for designing the toy? Why? *Sample answers: getting started; realizing from instructions that purpose was to build a circuit with light bulbs; recognizing that light flashes were coded information.*
- Invite students to think of a different signal that could be used to communicate Morse code to people with visual impairments. Have them design a follow-up experiment that tests a device that uses sound signals.

CHAPTER 20 • REVIEW

BACK TO

Have students look at the photograph on pp. 664–665. Ask how they know that the student is handling circuit boards and how those circuits might be used. *Circuit boards are parts of computers and other digital devices.*

◗ KEY CONCEPTS SUMMARY

SECTION 20.1

Ask: Which device interrupts the path of an electric charge? *the switch*

Ask: Is the circuit open or closed? *closed*

SECTION 20.2

Ask: What does a parallel circuit have that a similar series circuit does not have? *separate branches from the devices to the voltage source in the circuit*

SECTION 20.3

Ask: What type of information do computer circuits use? *digital*

Review Concepts

- Big Idea Flow Chart, p. T9
- Chapter Outline, pp. T15–T16

---

20 Chapter Review

the BIG idea

Circuits control the flow of electric charge.

CONTENT REVIEW
CLASSZONE.COM

◗ KEY CONCEPTS SUMMARY

① Charge needs a continuous path to flow.

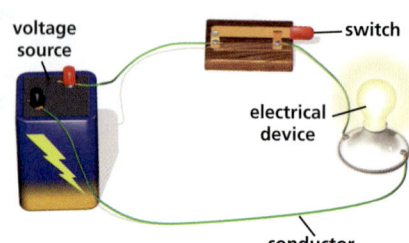

Charge flows in a closed path. Circuits provide a closed path for current. Circuit parts include voltage sources, switches, conductors, and electrical devices such as resistors.

VOCABULARY
circuit p. 667
resistor p. 668
short circuit p. 670

② Circuits make electric current useful.

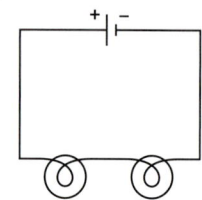 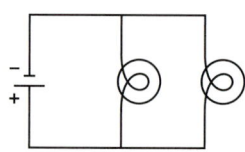

Each device in a **series circuit** is wired on a single path.

Each device in a **parallel circuit** has its own connection to the voltage source.

VOCABULARY
series circuit p. 676
parallel circuit p. 677

③ Electronic technology is based on circuits.

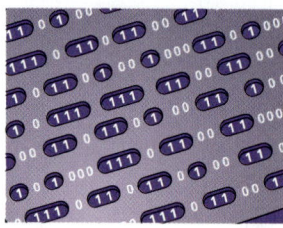

Electronic devices use electrical signals to represent coded information. Computers process information in digital code which uses 1s and 0s to represent the information.

VOCABULARY
electronic p. 681
binary code p. 682
digital p. 682
analog p. 684
computer p. 685

692 Unit 5: Electricity and Magnetism

Technology Resources

Have students visit **ClassZone.com** or use the CD-ROM for a cumulative review of concepts.

 CONTENT REVIEW

 CONTENT REVIEW CD-ROM

Engage students in a whole-class interactive review of Key Concepts. Edit content as you wish.

 POWER PRESENTATIONS

Reviewing Vocabulary

Draw a Venn diagram for each of the term pairs below. Write the terms above the circles. In the center, write characteristics that the terms have in common. In the outer circles write the ways in which they differ. A sample diagram has been completed for you.

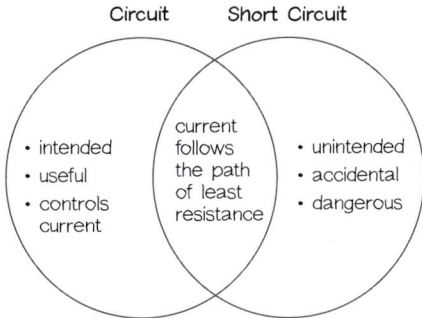

1. resistor; switch
2. series circuit; parallel circuit
3. digital; analog
4. digital; binary code
5. electronic; computer

Reviewing Key Concepts

Multiple Choice *Choose the letter of the best answer.*

6. Current always follows
   a. a path made of wire
   b. a path containing an electrical device
   c. a closed path
   d. an open circuit

7. When you open a switch in a circuit, you
   a. form a closed path for current
   b. reverse the current
   c. turn off its electrical devices
   d. turn on its electrical devices

8. Which one of the following parts of a circuit changes electrical energy into another form of energy?
   a. resistor
   b. conductor
   c. base
   d. voltage source

9. A circuit breaker is a safety device that
   a. must be replaced after each use
   b. has a wire that melts
   c. supplies voltage to a circuit
   d. stops the current

10. What happens when more than one voltage source is added to a circuit in series?
    a. The voltages are added together.
    b. The voltages cancel each other out.
    c. The voltages are multiplied together.
    d. The voltage of each source decreases.

11. Which of the following is an electronic device?
    a. flashlight
    b. calculator
    c. lamp
    d. electric fan

12. Which word describes the code used in digital technology?
    a. binary
    b. analog
    c. alphabetical
    d. Morse

13. Computers process information that has been
    a. broken down into simple steps
    b. converted into heat
    c. represented as a wave
    d. coded as an analog signal

Short Answer *Write a short answer to each question.*

14. How can hardware, software, and the user of a computer work together to complete a task?

15. Describe three parts of a personal computer and explain the main function of each.

Chapter 20: **Circuits and Electronics** 693

ASSESSMENT RESOURCES

UNIT ASSESSMENT BOOK
- Chapter Test A, pp. 25–28
- Chapter Test B, pp. 29–32
- Chapter Test C, pp. 33–36
- Alternative Assessment, pp. 37–38

SPANISH ASSESSMENT BOOK
Spanish Chapter Test, pp. 305–308

Technology Resources

Edit test items and answer choices.

 Test Generator CD-ROM

Visit **ClassZone.com** to extend test practice.

 Test Practice

Reviewing Vocabulary

1. Resistor: slows current, produces heat and light, light bulb is an example. Switch: opens and closes a circuit, turns electrical devices on and off. Shared: are circuit parts, control the flow of current

2. Series circuit: each part wired in same path, uses minimum amount of wire; all elements must be in working order for circuit to function; resistors in it convert some energy into light and heat. Parallel circuit: each part has its own path to voltage source, it requires more wire, light bulbs burn brighter then they do in a series circuit. Shared: they are ways to wire a circuit.

3. Digital: a series of 1s and 0s, binary. Analog: continuous signal. Shared: types of electrical signal.

4. Digital: uses numbers. Binary code: uses two choices. Shared: type of code.

5. Electronic: uses electrical signals. Computer: carries out programs. Shared: use coded information.

Reviewing Key Concepts

6. c
7. c
8. a
9. d
10. a
11. b
12. a
13. a
14. A user adds input to a computer by using hardware, such as a keyboard or mouse. Software allows a user to operate programs on a computer.
15. Sample answer: A computer contains a hard drive, which is the main storage device. The monitor allows a user to see a document. The printer allows a user to print a document.

Chapter 20 **693**

Thinking Critically

16. A–C will glow. D and E will not glow because they do not form a closed path from one battery terminal to the other.

17. A, B, or C; wire, light bulb

18. series

19. The other bulbs would go out.

20. All of the bulbs would become dimmer.

21. Diagrams should show a battery and three bulbs in a parallel circuit using more wire. (Accept any number between 2 and 4.)

22. The switch should be placed near the battery, not on a branch to a single bulb.

23. 1011; by finding a pattern

24. Accept any three—heat, light, sound, and motion.

25. The CD uses digital information.

26. integrated circuit, or microprocessor

27. Even if one link goes down, the others can function.

the BIG idea

28. Answers should reflect information learned in the chapter.

29. Answers should discuss movement of current and devices that convert electrical energy into other forms of energy.

30. Sample answer: Charge needs a continuous path to flow. Charge flows in a loop, or circuit. The parts of a circuit are a voltage source, conductor, switch, and electrical device. Charge flows through closed circuits. Switches turn a circuit's electrical devices off and on by opening and closing the circuit.

UNIT PROJECTS

Check to make sure students are working on their projects. Check schedules and work in progress.

 Unit Projects, pp. 5–10

Thinking Critically

Use the illustrations below to answer the next two questions.

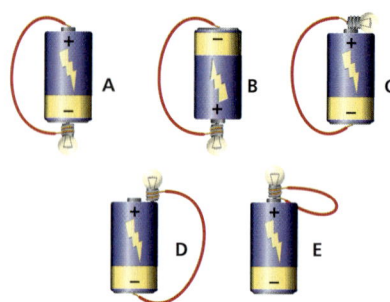

16. **PREDICT** In which arrangement(s) above will the light bulb glow? For each arrangement in which you think the bulb will not glow, explain your reasoning.

17. **APPLY** Which arrangement could be used as a battery tester? List the materials that you would use to make a battery tester.

Use the diagram below to answer the next five questions.

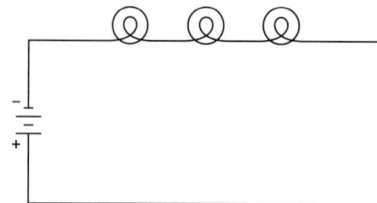

18. Is this a series circuit or a parallel circuit?

19. Explain what would happen if you unscrewed one of the bulbs in the circuit.

20. Explain what would happen if you wired three more bulbs into the circuit.

21. Draw and label a diagram of the same elements wired in the other type of circuit. Does your sketch involve more or fewer pieces of wire? How many?

22. Imagine you want to install a switch into your circuit. Where would you add the switch? Explain your answer.

694 Unit 5: Electricity and Magnetism

23. **ANALYZE** Look for a pattern in the digital codes below, representing the numbers 1–10. What is the code for the number 11? How do you know?

0001; 0010; 0011; 0100; 0101; 0110; 0111; 1000; 1001; 1010

24. **APPLY** A computer circuit contains millions of switches that use temperature-dependent materials to operate lights, sounds, and a fan. How many different types of energy is current converted to in the computer circuit? Explain.

25. **ANALYZE** A music recording studio makes a copy of a CD that is itself a copy of another CD. Explain why the quality of the copied CDs is the same as the original CD.

26. **INFER** A new watch can be programmed to perform specific tasks. Describe what type of circuit the watch might contain.

27. **SYNTHESIZE** Explain how the Internet is like a worldwide parallel circuit.

the BIG idea

28. **ANALYZE** Look back at the photograph on pages 664–665. Think about the answer you gave to the question. How has your understanding of circuits changed?

29. **SYNTHESIZE** Explain how the following statement relates to electric circuits: "Energy can change from one form to another and can move from one place to another."

30. **SUMMARIZE** Write a paragraph summarizing how circuits control current. Using the heading at the top of page 667 as your topic sentence. Then give an example from each red and blue heading on pages 667–669.

UNIT PROJECTS

If you need to do an experiment for your unit project, gather the materials. Be sure to allow enough time to observe results before the project is due.

MONITOR AND RETEACH

If students have trouble applying the concepts in items 18–22, review the differences between series and parallel circuits. Have students make their own schematic sketches of the two types of circuits.

Students may benefit from summarizing one or more sections of the chapter.

 Summarizing the Chapter, pp. 132–133

Standardized Test Practice

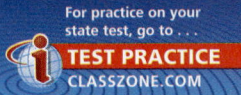

For practice on your state test, go to...
TEST PRACTICE
CLASSZONE.COM

Interpreting Diagrams

The four circuit diagrams below use the standard symbols for the parts of a circuit.

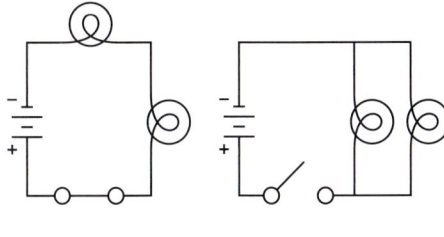
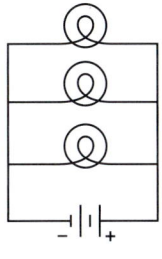
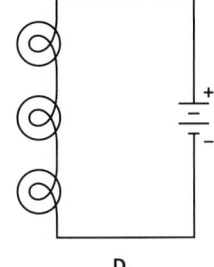

A.   B.   C.   D.

Study the diagrams and answer the questions that follow.

1. Which diagram shows a series circuit, with one voltage source and two light bulbs?
   a. A   **c.** C
   b. B   **d.** D

2. Which diagram shows a parallel circuit powered by a battery, with three light bulbs?
   a. A   **c.** C
   b. B   **d.** D

3. The light bulbs in these diagrams limit the flow of charge and give off heat and light. Under which category of circuit parts do light bulbs belong?
   a. switches   **c.** resistors
   b. conductors   **d.** voltage sources

4. In which diagram would the light bulbs be dark?
   a. A   **c.** C
   b. B   **d.** D

5. If all light bulbs and voltage sources were equal, how would the light from each of the bulbs in diagram C compare to the light from each of the bulbs in diagram A?
   a. The bulbs in diagram C would give less light than the bulbs in diagram A.
   b. The bulbs in diagram C would give more light than the bulbs in diagram A.
   c. The bulbs in diagram C would give the same amount of light as the bulbs in diagram A.
   d. It cannot be determined which bulbs would give more light.

Extended Response

Answer the two questions below in detail. Include some of the terms from the word box. Underline each term you use in your answer.

| flow of charge | electric current | binary code |
| open circuit | digital | signal |

6. What are two types of safety devices designed to control electric current and prevent dangerous accidents? How does each work?

7. Explain how an electronic circuit differs from an electric circuit. What role do electronic circuits play in computer operations?

Chapter 20: Circuits and Electronics 695

METACOGNITIVE ACTIVITY

Have students answer the following questions in their **Science Notebook:**

1. What did you find most surprising about the uses of circuits and control of electric charge?
2. Which topics in this chapter would you like to learn more about?
3. How have you solved a problem while working on your Unit Project?

Interpreting Diagrams

1. a   3. c   5. b
2. c   4. b

Extended Response

6. RUBRIC
4 points for a response including two of the following safety features and an explanation of how each works:
• fuse   • GFCI outlet
• circuit breaker

Sample: Fuses and circuit breakers are common safety devices in homes. Both stop the <u>flow of charge</u> when wires become dangerously hot. A fuse has a strip of metal that melts if it gets hot enough; that <u>opens</u> the <u>circuit</u>. A circuit breaker flips to the off position when a metal switch heats up, expands, and pushes the breaker switch off.

3 points for a response that includes two safety features and an explanation for how one of them works
2 points for a response that contains one safety feature and an explanation of how it works
1 point for a response that names one or two safety features but gives no explanation of how they work

7. RUBRIC
4 points for a response that correctly answers the question and uses the following terms accurately:
• binary code   • signal
• digital   • electric current

Sample: Electronic circuits carry a <u>signal</u> coded in <u>electric current</u>, but electric circuits do not necessarily carry such a signal. The electric impulses in an electronic circuit are interpreted as <u>binary code</u> in <u>digital</u> processing. Computers and other digital devices process data for a variety of functions, including graphics, mathematical analysis, word processing, and controlling machines such as car engines or factory robots.

3 points for a response that correctly answers the question and uses two of the terms accurately
2 points for a response that correctly answers the question and uses one of the terms accurately
1 point for a response that correctly answers the question but does not use the terms accurately

Chapter 20   695

TIMELINES in Science

FOCUS

▶ Set Learning Goals
Students will
- Observe how scientists have developed electrical versions of existing devices as well as new electronic technologies
- Examine the various ways electricity is used
- Make a simple capacitor and test its ability to store charge

National Science Education Standards
A.9.a–g Understandings About Scientific Inquiry

E.6.a–c Understandings About Science and Technology

F.5.a–e, F.5.g Science and Technology in Society

G.1.a–b Science as a Human Endeavor

G.2.a Nature of Science

G.3.a–c History of Science

INSTRUCT

The top half of the timeline presents some of the major events in the scientific study of electronics that were historically recorded. The bottom half of the timeline shows advances in technology and the practical applications of electronics. The gap between 600 B.C. and A.D. 1740 represents a period of time that has been omitted on this timeline.

Application
LEYDEN JAR The first actual capacitor—a device for storing electric charge—was the Leyden jar. The basic capacitor design created in 1745 has not changed much even today. A capacitor consists of two parallel conducting plates separated by an insulating layer. While capacitors may vary in size and shape, they work in about the same way, storing and releasing charges. Capacitors are used in various electronic devices from portable radios to the electronic flash on a camera to home computers.

TIMELINES in Science

THE STORY OF ELECTRONICS

Inventions such as the battery, the dynamo, and the motor created a revolution in the production and use of electrical energy. Think of how many tools and appliances that people depend on every day run on electric current. Try to imagine not using electricity in any form for an entire day.

The use of electricity as an energy source only begins the story of how electricity has changed our lives. Parts of the story are shown on this timeline. Research in electronics has given us not only electrical versions of machines that already existed but also entirely new technologies.

These technologies include computers. Electricity is used as a signal inside computers to code and transmit information. Electricity can even mimic some of the processes of logical reasoning and decision making, giving computers the power to solve problems.

600 B.C.
Thales Studies Static Electricity
Greek philosopher-scientist Thales of Miletus discovers that when he rubs amber with wool or fur, the amber attracts feathers and straw. The Greek word for amber, *elektron*, is the origin of the word *electricity*.

EVENTS

640 B.C.   620 B.C.   600 B.C.   A.D. 1740

APPLICATIONS AND TECHNOLOGY

APPLICATION

Leyden Jar
In 1745 German inventor Ewald Georg von Kleist invented a device that would store a static charge. The device, called a Leyden jar, was a glass container filled with water. A wire ran from the outside of the jar through the cork into the water. The Leyden jar was the first capacitor, an electronic component that stores and releases charges. Capacitors have been key to the development of computers.

696 Unit 5: Electricity and Magnetism

DIFFERENTIATE INSTRUCTION

Below Level To help students better understand the concept of a static electric charge, have students rub a piece of wool on a blown-up balloon. Then have them touch the balloon with their finger. Discuss with students what happens between the balloon and their finger.

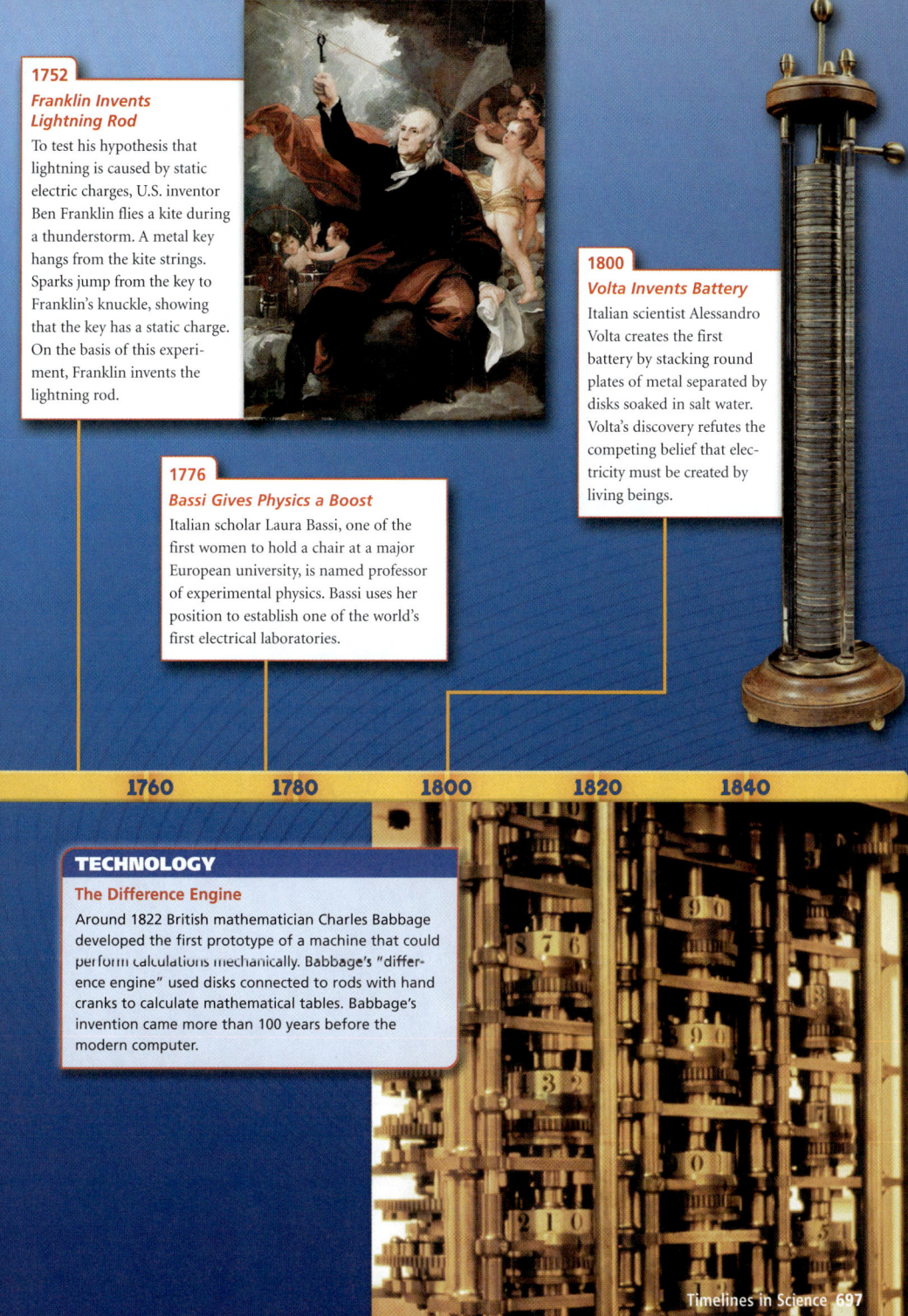

1752
Franklin Invents Lightning Rod
To test his hypothesis that lightning is caused by static electric charges, U.S. inventor Ben Franklin flies a kite during a thunderstorm. A metal key hangs from the kite strings. Sparks jump from the key to Franklin's knuckle, showing that the key has a static charge. On the basis of this experiment, Franklin invents the lightning rod.

1776
Bassi Gives Physics a Boost
Italian scholar Laura Bassi, one of the first women to hold a chair at a major European university, is named professor of experimental physics. Bassi uses her position to establish one of the world's first electrical laboratories.

1800
Volta Invents Battery
Italian scientist Alessandro Volta creates the first battery by stacking round plates of metal separated by disks soaked in salt water. Volta's discovery refutes the competing belief that electricity must be created by living beings.

TECHNOLOGY
The Difference Engine
Around 1822 British mathematician Charles Babbage developed the first prototype of a machine that could perform calculations mechanically. Babbage's "difference engine" used disks connected to rods with hand cranks to calculate mathematical tables. Babbage's invention came more than 100 years before the modern computer.

Timelines in Science 697

Scientific Process
When scientists experiment with new technologies, they may find that old theories no longer hold true. In 1799 Alessandro Volta invented the first battery, proving that metallic objects were a source of current electricity. Ask: What old theory did Volta's battery refute? *Electricity must be created by living things.*

Social Studies Connection
1752 Benjamin Franklin is one of the most widely known and recognized Americans in history. He is best known for his invention of the lightning rod but he also invented bifocals, the rocking chair, and the street lamp. Franklin's skills did not stop at just experimentation and invention. He was also a writer and a politician. He founded the first public library, wrote and published *Poor Richard's Almanak*, was elected to Congress, and signed the Declaration of Independence.

Technology
THE DIFFERENCE ENGINE The calculating engines of Charles Babbage had a significant impact on modern computers. His Difference Engine No.1 was the first successful automatic calculator. Discuss with students ways in which computers are used today.

DIFFERENTIATE INSTRUCTION
Advanced Explain to students that batteries produce a continuous flow of charge, or current. Have them compare the simple battery, above, to the Leyden jar capacitor on p. 696. How are they similar? How do they differ? Encourage students to demonstrate their findings through either diagrams or a chart.

Social Studies Connection

1879 It's difficult to go through an ordinary day without using one of Thomas Edison's important discoveries. Edison invented the phonograph, the kinetoscope (a motion-picture device), and the light bulb. He also made improvements to existing technologies, including the electric generator, the telegraph, the typewriter, and the telephone. Having received over 1000 patents, Edison is considered one of the greatest inventors in history.

Scientific Process

1904 While the vacuum tube is an important invention, it produces excess heat and can burn out. By examining the problems of one technology, another technology can be created. Scientists at Bell Labs developed the transistor to replace the vacuum tube in electronic circuitry. Refer students to "Scientists Shrink Circuits to Atomic Level" on page 699, and ask: What is one of the key steps of the scientific process that the IBM researchers might have used to improve on the transistor? *Sample answer: collecting data*

Application

DIGITAL COMPUTER ENIAC was considered to be the world's first digital computer. It weighed 30 tons, used miles of wiring, had thousands of vacuum tubes and manual switches, and was 100 feet long and 10 feet high. Computer technology has come a long way since ENIAC. Have students compare and contrast ENIAC with today's computers. Discuss with students why they think the first digital computer filled a large room while today's computers are small enough to be held in one hand.

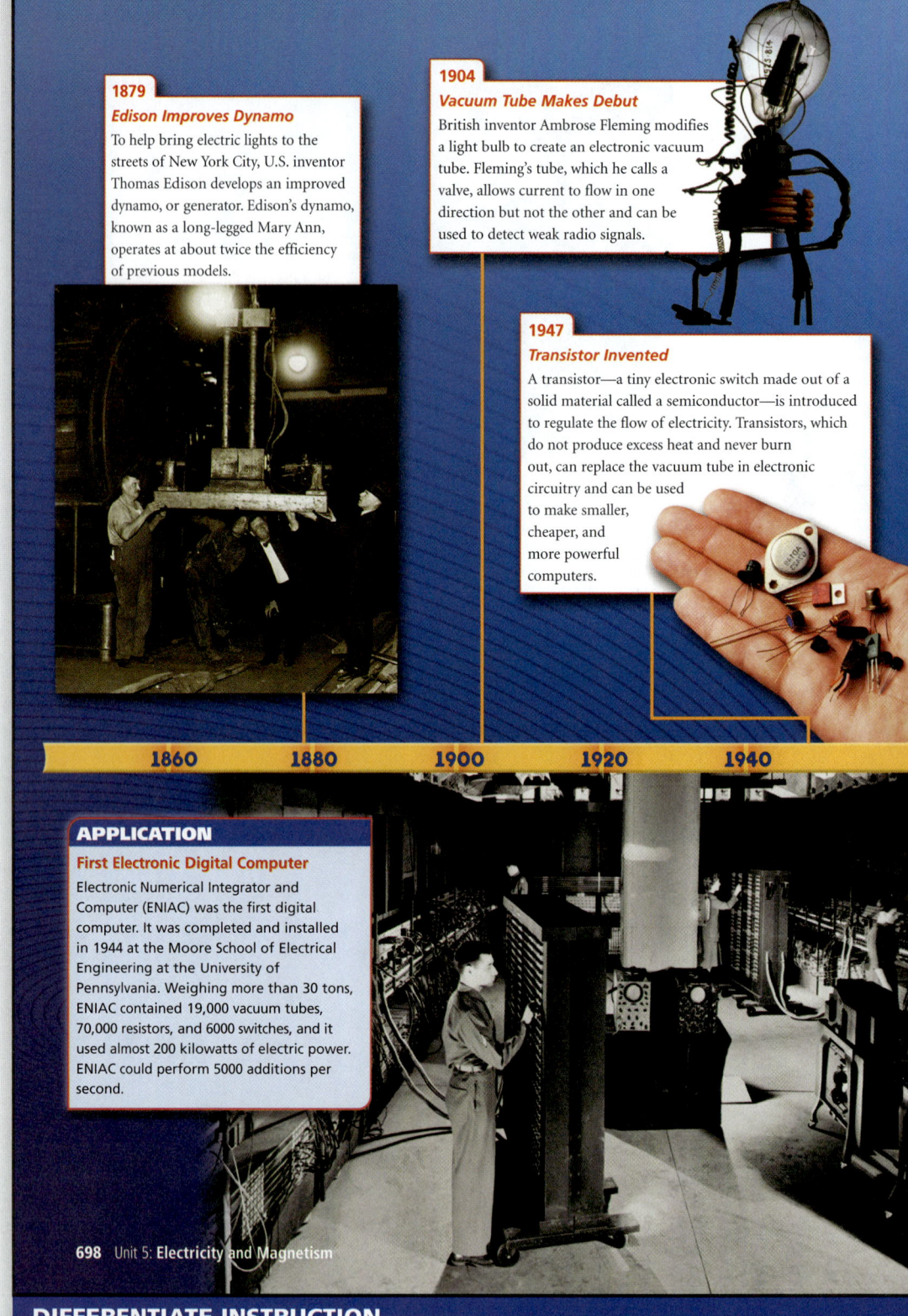

1879 Edison Improves Dynamo
To help bring electric lights to the streets of New York City, U.S. inventor Thomas Edison develops an improved dynamo, or generator. Edison's dynamo, known as a long-legged Mary Ann, operates at about twice the efficiency of previous models.

1904 Vacuum Tube Makes Debut
British inventor Ambrose Fleming modifies a light bulb to create an electronic vacuum tube. Fleming's tube, which he calls a valve, allows current to flow in one direction but not the other and can be used to detect weak radio signals.

1947 Transistor Invented
A transistor—a tiny electronic switch made out of a solid material called a semiconductor—is introduced to regulate the flow of electricity. Transistors, which do not produce excess heat and never burn out, can replace the vacuum tube in electronic circuitry and can be used to make smaller, cheaper, and more powerful computers.

APPLICATION
First Electronic Digital Computer
Electronic Numerical Integrator and Computer (ENIAC) was the first digital computer. It was completed and installed in 1944 at the Moore School of Electrical Engineering at the University of Pennsylvania. Weighing more than 30 tons, ENIAC contained 19,000 vacuum tubes, 70,000 resistors, and 6000 switches, and it used almost 200 kilowatts of electric power. ENIAC could perform 5000 additions per second.

DIFFERENTIATE INSTRUCTION

English Learners English learners may be confused by the use of present tense above the timeline. They have learned to use past tense when writing about events in the past. Explain that the use of present tense in the timeline imitates a newspaper of the times, as if the inventions or discoveries were just made. It allows the reader to feel connected to that time period.

1958
Chip Inventors Think Small
Jack Kilby, a U.S. electrical engineer, conceives the idea of making an entire circuit out of a single piece of germanium. The integrated circuit, or "computer chip," is born. This invention enables computers and other electronic devices to be made much smaller than before.

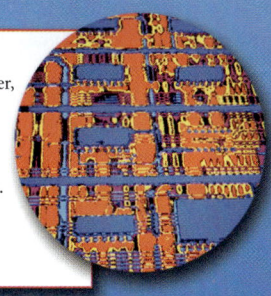

2001
Scientists Shrink Circuits to Atomic Level
Researchers succeed in building a logic circuit, a kind of transistor the size of a single molecule. The molecule, a tube of carbon atoms called a carbon nanotube, can be as small as 10 atoms across—500 times smaller than previous transistors. Computer chips, which currently contain over 40 million transistors, could hold hundreds of millions or even billions of nanotube transistors.

 RESOURCE CENTER
CLASSZONE.COM
Explore current research in electronics and computers.

1960   1980   2000

TECHNOLOGY
Miniaturization
Miniaturization has led to an explosion of computer technology. As circuits have shrunk, allowing more components in less space, computers have become smaller and more powerful. They have also become easier to integrate with other technologies, such as telecommunications. When not being used for a phone call, this cell phone can be used to connect to the Internet, to access e-mail, and even to play computer games.

INTO THE FUTURE

Electronic computer components have become steadily smaller and more efficient over the years. However, the basic mechanism of a computer—a switch that can be either on or off depending on whether an electric charge is present—has remained the same. These switches represent the 1s and 0s, or the "bits," of binary code.

Quantum computing is based on an entirely new way of representing information. In quantum physics, individual subatomic particles can be described in terms of three states rather than just two. Quantum bits, or "qubits," can carry much more information than the binary bits of ordinary computers. Using qubits, quantum computers could be both smaller and faster than binary computers and perform operations not possible with current technology.

Quantum computing is possible in theory, but the development of hardware that can process qubits is just beginning. Scientists are currently looking for ways to put the theory into practice and to build computers that will make current models look as bulky and as slow as ENIAC.

ACTIVITIES

Reliving History
Make a Leyden jar capacitor. Line the inside of a jar with aluminum foil. Stop the jar with clay. Insert a copper wire through the plug so that one end touches the foil and the other sticks out of the jar about 2 centimeters.

To test for a voltage difference between the wire and the glass, touch one end of a multimeter to the exposed wire and the other end to the glass. Run a comb through your hair several times and touch it to the wire. Test the voltage difference again.

Writing About Science
Learn more about the current state of electronic circuit miniaturization. Write up the results of your research in the form of a magazine article.

INTO THE FUTURE

To show how a particular technology changes and improves, make two columns on the board and label them *Existing Technology* and *Improved Technology*. With the class, list existing technologies that have recently been replaced or improved upon. For example, videotape might be listed under the first column and DVDs under the second column. Discuss with students what advantages the improved technology provides over the existing technology.

ACTIVITIES

Reliving History
Before students get started, remind them of the following tips:
- Use a pencil to help you press the aluminum foil against the inside of the glass jar.
- Students should watch the multimeter while they are testing voltage because the number will appear only briefly.

Writing About Science
Suggest that student's imitate the style of the timeline—writing as journalists in the present tense, reporting who, what, where, and why, and using a punchy headline for their magazine article.

Technology Resources
Students can visit **ClassZone.com** for news about advances in technology involving electronics.

DIFFERENTIATE INSTRUCTION

Advanced Ask students why they think the voltage difference shown on the multimeter display drops to zero shortly after the multimeter is touched to the wire. *The Leyden jar stores charge. Because the multimeter contains conductive metal wire, the charge is released into the multimeter when the multimeter and the Leyden jar touch.*

CHAPTER 21: Magnetism

Physical Science
UNIFYING PRINCIPLES

PRINCIPLE 1
Matter is made of particles too small to see.

PRINCIPLE 2
Matter changes form and moves from place to place.

PRINCIPLE 3
Energy changes from one form to another, but it cannot be created or destroyed.

PRINCIPLE 4
Physical forces affect the movement of all matter on Earth and throughout the universe.

Unit 5: Electricity and Magnetism
BIG IDEAS

CHAPTER 19
Electricity
Charged particles transfer electrical energy.

CHAPTER 20
Circuits and Electronics
Circuits control the flow of electrical charge.

CHAPTER 21
Magnetism
Current can produce magnetism, and magnetism can produce current.

CHAPTER 21
KEY CONCEPTS

SECTION 1	SECTION 2	SECTION 3	SECTION 4
Magnetism is a force that acts at a distance. 1. Magnets attract and repel other magnets. 2. Some materials are magnetic. 3. Earth is a magnet.	**Current can produce magnetism.** 1. An electric current produces a magnetic field. 2. Motors use electromagnets.	**Magnetism can produce current.** 1. Magnets are used to generate an electric current. 2. Magnets are used to control voltage.	**Generators supply electrical energy.** 1. Generators provide most of the world's electrical energy. 2. Electric power can be measured.

 The Big Idea Flow Chart is available on p. T17 in the **UNIT TRANSPARENCY BOOK**.

Previewing Content

SECTION

 Magnetism is a force that acts at a distance. pp. 703–711

1. Magnets attract and repel other magnets.
The attraction between the north pole of a **magnet** and the south pole of another magnet is based on the **magnetic field** lines that go from the north to the south pole of a magnet.
- If two like poles are placed near each other, the magnetic fields oppose, and the poles repel each other.
- If opposite poles are brought near each other, the magnetic field goes from one magnet to another, and the poles attract.

Attraction and Repulsion of Magnetic Poles

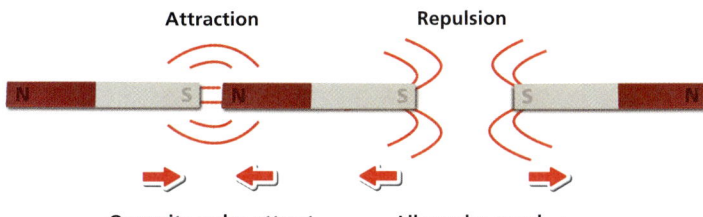

2. Some materials are magnetic.
Of all the common elements on the periodic table, only iron, nickel, cobalt and a few other metals are magnetic. Other materials, such as steel, are magnetic because they contain one or more of these elements. Iron, nickel, and cobalt are next to each other in the periodic table. This location indicates that the properties of these elements are similar because their electron configurations are similar.
Each of these elements contains unpaired electrons that produce a very small but strong magnetic field. Atoms in a magnetic material align so that these small magnetic fields form a **magnetic domain**. When placed within a larger magnetic field, the magnetic domains align, and the material becomes a magnet.

3. Earth is a magnet.
Because the north pole of a suspended magnet always points in a northerly direction on Earth, it can be inferred that Earth itself is a magnet. We commonly call the direction that the north pole of the magnet points to magnetic north. Because it attracts the north pole of a magnet, however, the magnetic north pole of Earth is actually the south pole of the magnet formed by Earth.

Common Misconceptions

MAGNETIC METALS Students may think that all metals are attracted to magnets. Of the common metals, only three—iron, nickel, and cobalt—can become magnetic or be attracted to magnets to a noticeable extent.

 This misconception is addressed on p. 706.

SECTION

 Current can produce magnetism. pp. 712–718

1. An electric current produces a magnetic field.
Both permanent and temporary magnets result from the magnetic field formed from a moving electric charge.
- Permanent magnets result from the spinning of unpaired electrons, which are electrically charged particles.
- Temporary magnets can also be formed in this manner, but the magnetic domains don't remain aligned. Temporary magnets known as **electromagnets** are produced by electric current, which consists of moving charge.

In the electromagnet below, coils of wire around an iron core create a magnet as long as electric charge flows. When current stops, the magnetism stops.

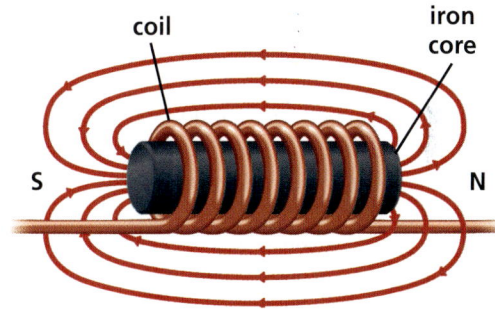

2. Motors use electromagnets.
The basic parts of an electric motor are a voltage source, a shaft, a commutator, an electro-magnet, and at least one additional magnet.
- Forces of repulsion between the two magnets turn the shaft.
- The commutator reverses the poles of the electromagnet when it starts to align poles with the permanent magnet.
- This reversal renews the repulsion force and keeps the shaft moving.

 MISCONCEPTION DATABASE
CLASSZONE.COM Background on student misconceptions

Previewing Content

SECTION
Magnetism can produce current.
pp. 719–725

1. **Magnets are used to generate an electric current.**
   Essentially, a **generator** is the opposite of an electric motor. The motor uses a moving charge to produce a magnetic field, and a generator uses a moving magnet to produce an electric charge.
   • The magnet and the wire through which the current passes must be moving relative to each other. It doesn't matter which one moves, as long as one of them does.
   • The current produced can be either **direct current,** which flows in one direction only, or **alternating current,** which changes direction at regular intervals.

2. **Magnets are used to control voltage.**
   A **transformer** either increases or decreases voltage. In a transformer, two coils of wire are wrapped around an iron ring. Current through the first coil causes the ring to become an electromagnet. This electromagnet induces a current in the second coil.
   • If the first coil has more loops, the voltage decreases, and the system is a step-down transformer.
   • If the first coil has fewer loops than the second coil, the transformer is a step-up transformer, and voltage increases.

Step-Down Transformer

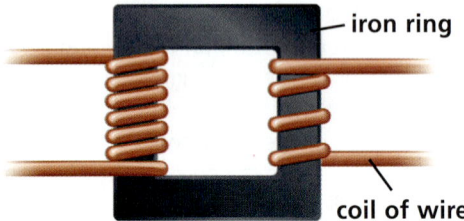

iron ring

coil of wire

SECTION
Generators supply electrical energy.
pp. 726–731

1. **Generators provide most of the world's electrical energy.**
   Electric power is not the electrical energy produced, but a measure of the rate at which some other form of energy is converted to electrical energy. It is also the rate at which an appliance converts electrical energy into another form of energy, such as light or heat. For example,
   • most electrical energy is produced by generators
   • the rate at which the chemical energy in fossil fuels or the kinetic energy of falling water is converted to electrical energy is electric power

   The current distributed from electrical generating plants is too great to be useful in homes and businesses. The current must pass through step-down transformers before it is useful.

2. **Electric power can be measured.**
   The unit used to measure power is the **watt.** Because the watt is a small unit, **kilowatts** are often used to measure power in a building.

   The amount of energy used is the product of the rate at which the energy is used (power) and the time over which it is used. Its unit of measurement is the **kilowatt-hour** (kWh).

Common Misconceptions

ENERGY AND POWER Students might think that electrical energy and power are the same thing because the two terms are often used synonymously. In reality, current supplies electrical energy for use. The rate at which this energy is transformed from or to other forms of energy is electric power.

 This misconception is addressed on p. 728.

 MISCONCEPTION DATABASE
CLASSZONE.COM Background on student misconceptions

Previewing Labs

EXPLORE the BIG idea

Is It Magnetic? p. 701 Students are introduced to magnetism as they test the attraction of various materials to a magnet.	**TIME** 10 minutes **MATERIALS** magnet; various metallic materials with various amounts of iron, such as coins, foil, washers, paper clips, and wire
How Can You Make a Chain? p. 701 Students use paperclips to learn about magnetic fields.	**TIME** 10 minutes **MATERIALS** magnet, several metal paper clips
Internet Activity: Electromagnets, p. 701 Students use the Internet to work with a virtual electromagnet.	**TIME** 20 minutes **MATERIALS** computer with Internet access

 SECTION 1

EXPLORE Magnetism, p. 703 Students manipulate magnets on a dowel rod to explore attraction and repulsion.	**TIME** 5 minutes **MATERIALS** wooden dowel, spring clothespin, 3 disk magnets, ruler
INVESTIGATE Earth's Magnetic Field, p. 709 Students use a magnet, a needle, and aluminum foil to infer the effects of Earth's magnetic field on a compass.	**TIME** 15 minutes **MATERIALS** small square of aluminum foil, bowl, water, strong magnet, sewing needle

 SECTION 2

EXPLORE Magnetism from Electric Current, p. 712 Students set up a compass and a circuit to observe how an electric current produces a magnetic field.	**TIME** 10 minutes **MATERIALS** electrical tape, 15 cm copper wire, AA battery, compass
INVESTIGATE Electromagnets, p. 714 Students make an electromagnet and observe how it uses current to produce magnetism.	**TIME** 20 minutes **MATERIALS** 40 cm insulated wire, large iron nail, 2 D batteries, electrical tape, metal paper clip

 SECTION 3

EXPLORE Energy Conversion, p. 719 Students use a small motor to produce current.	**TIME** 10 minutes **MATERIALS** small motor with wires, AA battery, light bulb in holder
INVESTIGATE Electric Current, p. 722 Students build a current detector using wire and a compass to infer the properties of alternating current.	**TIME** 15 minutes **MATERIALS** 2 m of 22-gauge magnet wire, compass, ruler, 14 in electrical tape, sandpaper, D battery
CHAPTER INVESTIGATION **Build a Speaker,** pp. 724–725 Students construct a speaker to explore the relationship between the strengths of three magnets and the volume of the speaker.	**TIME** 40 minutes **MATERIALS** 3 magnets of different strengths, metal paper clip, ruler, wire (2 m of 22-gauge), marker, foam cup, masking tape, 2 wire leads with alligator clips, stereo system

 SECTION 4

INVESTIGATE Power, p. 729 Students model using electrical energy to power appliances. Power Ratings Chart, p. 176	**TIME** 30 minutes **MATERIALS** graph paper, colored pencils, Power Ratings Chart

 Additional INVESTIGATION, It's a Plot! A, B, & C, pp. 195–203; Teacher Instructions, pp. 206–207

Chapter 21: **Magnetism** 699D

Previewing Chapter Resources

	INTEGRATED TECHNOLOGY	LABS AND ACTIVITIES
CHAPTER 21 **Magnetism**	**CLASSZONE.COM** • eEdition Plus • EasyPlanner Plus • Misconception Database • Content Review • Test Practice • Simulation • Visualization • Resource Centers • Internet Activity: Electromagnets • Math Tutorial **SCILINKS.ORG** **CD-ROMS** • eEdition • EasyPlanner • Power Presentations • Content Review • Lab Generator • Test Generator **AUDIO CDS** • Audio Readings • Audio Readings in Spanish	EXPLORE the Big Idea, p. 701 • Is It Magnetic? • How Can You Make a Chain? • Internet Activity: Electromagnets **UNIT RESOURCE BOOK** Unit Projects, pp. 5–10 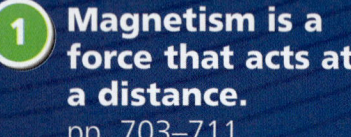 **Lab Generator CD-ROM** Generate customized labs.
SECTION 1 **Magnetism is a force that acts at a distance.** pp. 703–711 Time: 2 periods (1 block) Lesson Plan, pp. 134–135	**RESOURCE CENTER,** Magnetism 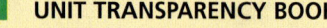 **UNIT TRANSPARENCY BOOK** • Big Idea Flow Chart, p. T17 • Daily Vocabulary Scaffolding, p. T18 • Note-Taking Model, p. T19 • 3-Minute Warm-Up, p. T20 • "How Magnets Differ from Other Materials" Visual, p. T22	• EXPLORE Magnetism, p. 703 • INVESTIGATE Earth's Magnetic Field, p. 709 • Think Science, p. 711 **UNIT RESOURCE BOOK** • Datasheet, Earth's Magnetic Field, p. 143 • Additional INVESTIGATION, It's a Plot! A, B, & C, pp. 195–203
SECTION 2 **Current can produce magnetism.** pp. 712–718 Time: 2 periods (1 block) Lesson Plan, pp. 145–146	**VISUALIZATION,** Motor **UNIT TRANSPARENCY BOOK** • Daily Vocabulary Scaffolding, p. T18 • 3-Minute Warm-Up, p. T20	• EXPLORE Magnetism from Electric Current, p. 712 • INVESTIGATE Electromagnets, p. 714 **UNIT RESOURCE BOOK** Datasheet, Electromagnets, p. 154
SECTION 3 **Magnetism can produce current.** pp. 719–725 Time: 3 periods (1.5 blocks)  Lesson Plan, pp. 156–157	**UNIT TRANSPARENCY BOOK** • Daily Vocabulary Scaffolding, p. T18 • 3-Minute Warm-Up, p. T21	• EXPLORE Energy Conversion, p. 719 • INVESTIGATE Electric Current, p. 722 • CHAPTER INVESTIGATION, Build a Speaker, pp. 724–725 **UNIT RESOURCE BOOK** • Datasheet, Electric Current, p. 165 • CHAPTER INVESTIGATION, Build a Speaker, A, B, & C, pp. 186–194
SECTION 4 **Generators supply electrical energy.** pp. 726–731 Time: 3 periods (1.5 blocks)  Lesson Plan, pp. 167–168	• **RESOURCE CENTERS,** Dams, Energy Use • **MATH TUTORIAL** **UNIT TRANSPARENCY BOOK** • Big Idea Flow Chart, p. T17 • Daily Vocabulary Scaffolding, p. T18 • 3-Minute Warm-Up, p. T21 • Chapter Outline, pp. T23–T24	• INVESTIGATE Power, p. 729 • Math in Science, p. 731 **UNIT RESOURCE BOOK** • Power Ratings Chart, p. 176 • Datasheet, Power, p. 177 • Math Support, p. 184 • Math Practice, p. 185

KEY TO ICONS 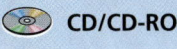 CD/CD-ROM   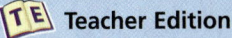 Teacher Edition   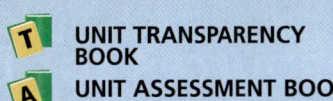 UNIT TRANSPARENCY BOOK   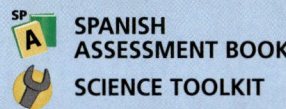 SPANISH ASSESSMENT BOOK
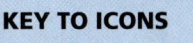 INTERNET   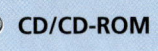 Pupil Edition   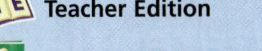 UNIT RESOURCE BOOK   UNIT ASSESSMENT BOOK   SCIENCE TOOLKIT

READING AND REINFORCEMENT

- Description Wheel, B20–21
- Main Idea Web, C38–39
- Daily Vocabulary Scaffolding, H1–8

 UNIT RESOURCE BOOK
- Vocabulary Practice, pp. 181–182
- Decoding Support, p. 183
- Summarizing the Chapter, pp. 204–205

Audio Readings CD
Listen to Pupil Edition.

Audio Readings in Spanish CD
Listen to Pupil Edition in Spanish.

 UNIT RESOURCE BOOK
- Reading Study Guide, A & B, pp. 136–139
- Spanish Reading Study Guide, pp. 140–141
- Challenge and Extension, p. 142
- Reinforcing Key Concepts, p. 144

 UNIT RESOURCE BOOK
- Reading Study Guide, A & B, pp. 147–150
- Spanish Reading Study Guide, pp. 151–152
- Challenge and Extension, p. 153
- Reinforcing Key Concepts, p. 155

 UNIT RESOURCE BOOK
- Reading Study Guide, A & B, pp. 158–161
- Spanish Reading Study Guide, pp. 162–163
- Challenge and Extension, p. 164
- Reinforcing Key Concepts, p. 166
- Challenge Reading, pp. 179–180

 UNIT RESOURCE BOOK
- Reading Study Guide, A & B, pp. 169–172
- Spanish Reading Study Guide, pp. 173–174
- Challenge and Extension, p. 175
- Reinforcing Key Concepts, p. 178

ASSESSMENT

- Chapter Review, pp. 733–734
- Standardized Test Practice, p. 735

 UNIT ASSESSMENT BOOK
- Diagnostic Test, pp. 39–40
- Chapter Test, A, B, & C, pp. 45–56
- Alternative Assessment, pp. 57–58
- Unit Test A, B, C, pp. 59–70
- Spanish Chapter Test, pp. 309–312
- Spanish Unit Test, pp. 313–316

Test Generator CD-ROM
Generate customized tests.

Lab Generator CD-ROM
Rubrics for Labs

 Ongoing Assessment, pp. 704–708, 710

 Section 21.1 Review, p. 710

 UNIT ASSESSMENT BOOK
Section 21.1 Quiz, p. 41

 Ongoing Assessment, pp. 713–718

 Section 21.2 Review, p. 718

UNIT ASSESSMENT BOOK
Section 21.2 Quiz, p. 42

 Ongoing Assessment, pp. 719–722

 Section 21.3 Review, p. 723

UNIT ASSESSMENT BOOK
Section 21.3 Quiz, p. 43

 Ongoing Assessment, pp. 726–728, 730

 Section 21.4 Review, p. 730

 UNIT ASSESSMENT BOOK
Section 21.4 Quiz, p. 44

STANDARDS

National Standards
A.2–8, A.9.a–f, G.1.a–b, G.2.b
See p. 700 for the standards.

National Standards
A.2–7, A.9.a–b, A.9.e–f

National Standards
A.2–7, A.9.a–b, A.9.e–f

National Standards
A.2–7, A.9.a–b, A.9.e–f

National Standards
A.2–8, A.9.a–c, A.9.e–f

Chapter 21: **Magnetism** 699F

Previewing Resources for Differentiated Instruction

CHAPTER INVESTIGATION

Leveled resources present the same concepts for different abilities.

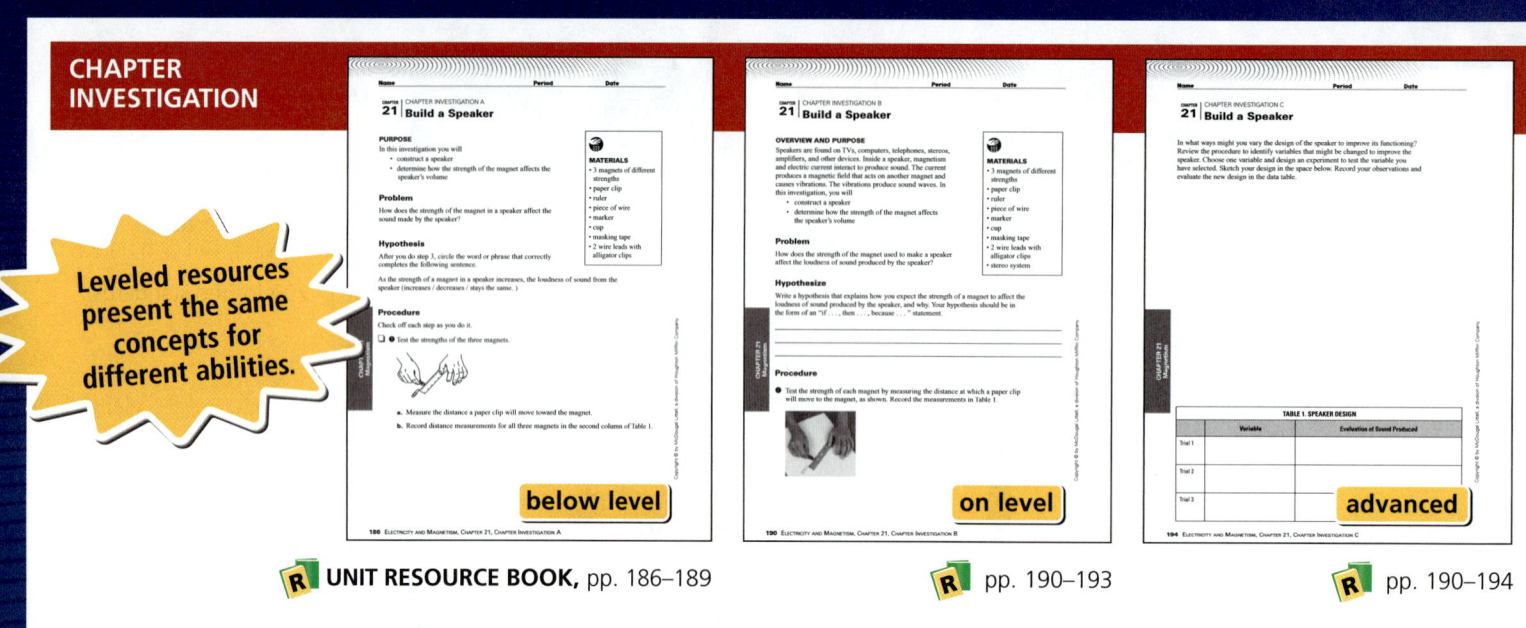

UNIT RESOURCE BOOK, pp. 186–189 | pp. 190–193 | pp. 190–194

READING STUDY GUIDE

Reading Study Guide is also in Spanish.

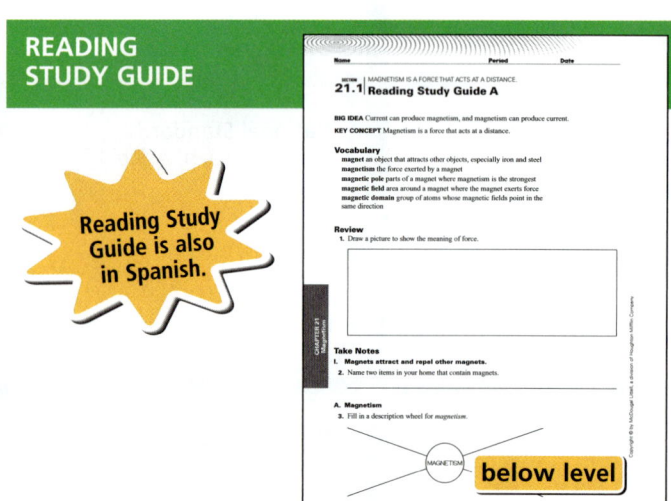 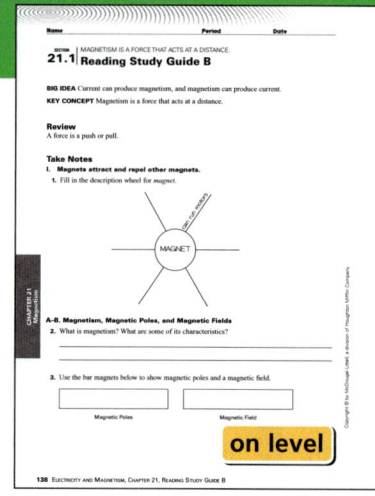 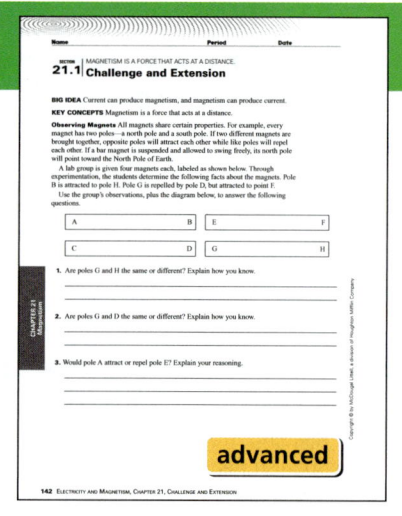

UNIT RESOURCE BOOK, pp. 136–137 | pp. 138–139 | p. 142

CHAPTER TEST

Chapter Test is also in Spanish.

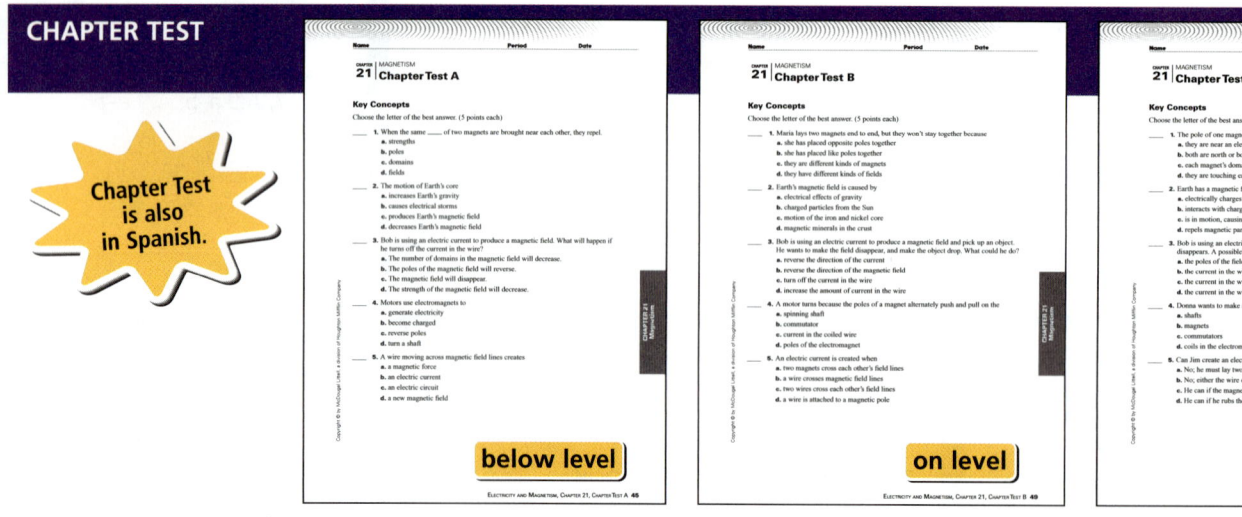

UNIT ASSESSMENT BOOK, pp. 45–48 | pp. 49–52 | pp. 53–56

Unit 5: Electricity and Magnetism

TECHNOLOGY

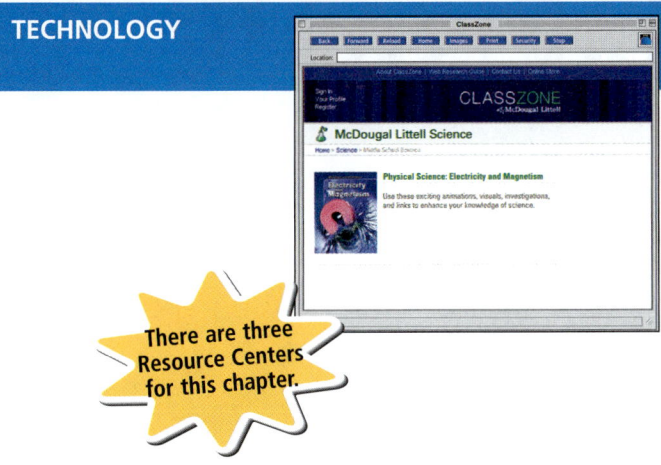
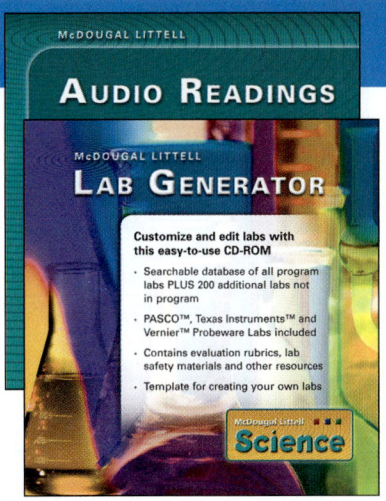

There are three Resource Centers for this chapter.

CLASSZONE.COM — **CD/CD-ROMS** — **CLASSZONE.COM**

VISUAL CONTENT

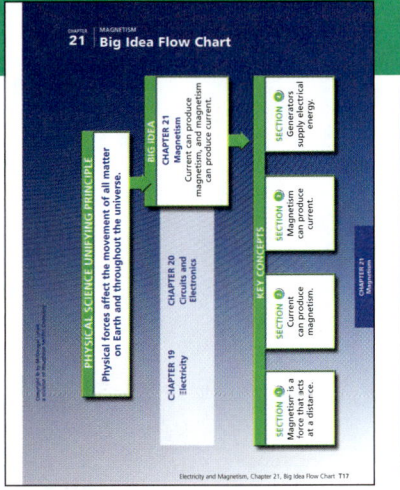
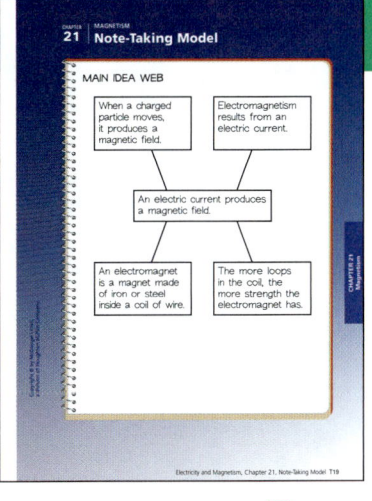
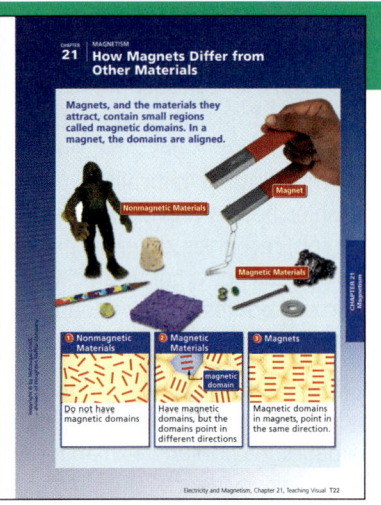

UNIT TRANSPARENCY BOOK, p. T17 — p. T19 — p. T22

MORE SUPPORT

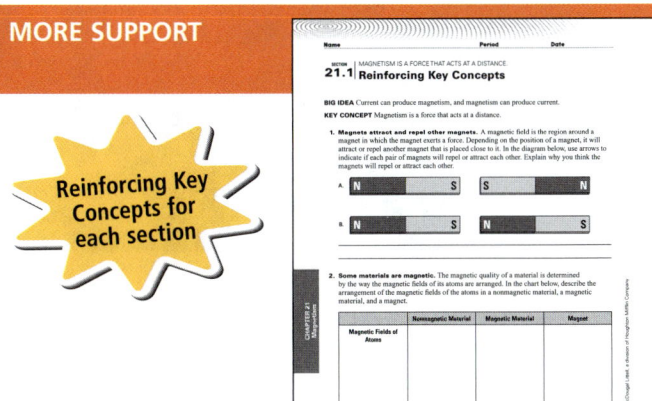
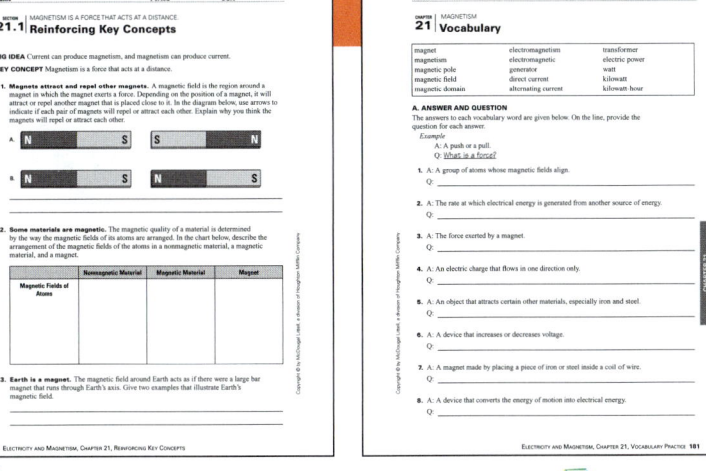
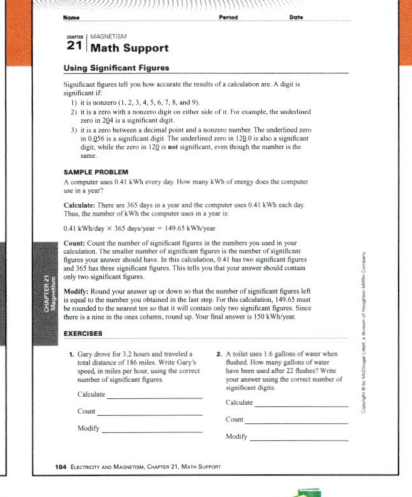

Reinforcing Key Concepts for each section

UNIT RESOURCE BOOK, p. 144 — pp. 181–182 — p. 184

Chapter 21: **Magnetism** 699H

CHAPTER 21 Magnetism

INTRODUCE
the BIG idea

Have students look at the photograph of a hiker using a compass. Discuss how the question in the box links to the Big Idea:
- What makes a compass needle point toward the North Pole?
- What do you think compass needles are made of?

National Science Education Standards

Process

A.2–8 Design and conduct an investigation; use tools to gather and interpret data; use evidence to describe, predict, explain, model; think critically to make relationships between evidence and explanation; recognize different explanations and predictions; communicate scientific procedures and explanations; use mathematics.

A.9.a–f Understand scientific inquiry by using different investigations, methods, mathematics, technology, explanations based on logic, evidence, and skepticism.

G.1.a–b Science as a human endeavor

G.2.b Nature of Science

CHAPTER 21 Magnetism

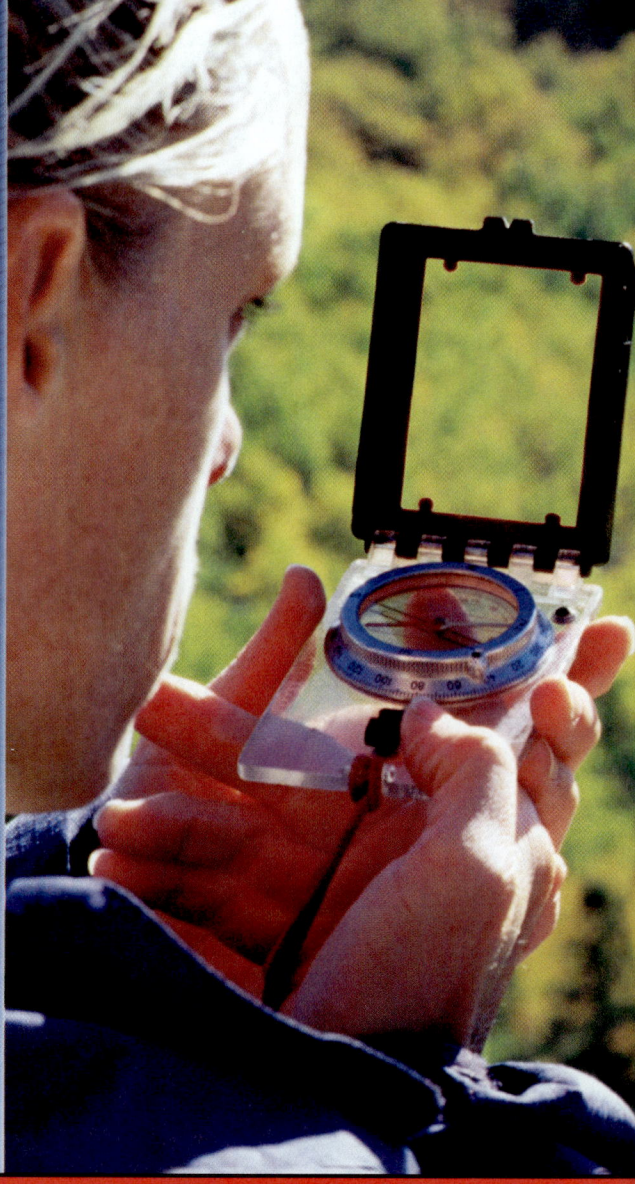

the BIG idea

Current can produce magnetism, and magnetism can produce current.

Key Concepts

SECTION 1 Magnetism is a force that acts at a distance.
Learn how magnets exert forces.

SECTION 2 Current can produce magnetism.
Learn about electromagnets and their uses.

SECTION 3 Magnetism can produce current.
Learn how magnetism can produce an electric current.

SECTION 4 Generators supply electrical energy.
Learn how generators are used in the production of electrical energy.

Internet Preview

CLASSZONE.COM
Chapter 21 online resources: Content Review, Simulation, Visualization, three Resource Centers, Math Tutorial, Test Practice

700 Unit 5: **Electricity and Magnetism**

INTERNET PREVIEW

CLASSZONE.COM For student use with the following pages:

Review and Practice
- Content Review, pp. 702, 732
- Math Tutorial: Rounding Decimals, p. 731
- Test Practice, p. 735

Activities and Resources
- Internet Activity: p. 701
- Resource Centers: Magnetism, p. 704; Dams and Electricity, p. 727; Energy Use and Conservation, p. 728
- Visualization: Motor, p. 716

Electromagnetism
Code: MDL067

EXPLORE the BIG idea

Is It Magnetic?
Experiment with a magnet and several objects made of different materials.

Observe and Think Which objects are attracted to the magnet? Why do you think the magnet attracts some objects and not others?

How Can You Make a Chain?
Hang a paper clip on the end of a magnet. Then hang a second paper clip by touching it to the end of the first paper clip. Add more paper clips to make a chain.

Observe and Think How many paper clips did you add? What held the chain together?

Internet Activity: Electromagnets
Go to ClassZone.com to work with a virtual electromagnet. Explore how current and magnetism are related.

Observe and Think What happens when you increase the voltage?

NSTA SCLINKS
scilinks.org
Electromagnetism Code: MDL067

What force is acting on this compass needle?

EXPLORE the BIG idea

These inquiry-based activities are appropriate for use at home or as a supplement to classroom instruction.

Is It Magnetic?
PURPOSE To discover that not all metals are magnetic. Students test different materials with a magnet.

TIP *10 min.* Encourage students to predict whether each item is magnetic before testing it.

Answer: Items that contain iron are attracted to the magnet. Some metals are affected by magnetism, and some are not.

REVISIT after p. 707.

How Can You Make a Chain?
PURPOSE To demonstrate the magnetic field that surrounds a magnet. Students observe induced magnetism as evidence of magnetic fields.

TIP *10 min.* Make sure students do not link the paper clips together.

Answer: usually three or four paper clips; the magnetic field

REVISIT after p. 708.

Internet Activity: Electromagnets
PURPOSE To use a simulated electromagnet to explore the relationship between electricity and magnetism.

TIP *20 min.* Have students experiment with the level of voltage supplied to the virtual electromagnet.

Answer: The magnetic field increases.

REVISIT after p. 714.

TEACHING WITH TECHNOLOGY

CBL and Probeware Many activities in this chapter can be made more interesting with a magnetic field sensor. Try using this probeware with activities on pp. 701, 709, 712, and 714.

Ammeter Students could use an AC ammeter instead of a compass in "Investigate Electric Current" on p. 722.

PREPARE

◯ CONCEPT REVIEW

Activate Prior Knowledge

- Turn a flashlight on and ask students how energy is changing. *Electrical energy from the battery is changing to light and heat.*
- Crumple a piece of paper and drop it on the floor.
- Ask students to explain why the paper was pulled to the floor.
- Students should answer that the force of gravity acting on the paper pulled it to the floor.

◯ TAKING NOTES

Main Idea Web

Upon completion of individual main idea webs, have students work in small groups to compare them. Have students discuss any differences. Emphasize that many items are acceptable in the web, but each one must relate to the main idea.

Vocabulary Strategy

Description wheels can contain as much information as students want to add. They can be used as a study guide at the end of the chapter.

Vocabulary and Note-Taking Resources

- Vocabulary Practice, pp. 181–182
- Decoding Support, p. 183

- Daily Vocabulary Scaffolding, p. T18
- Note-Taking Model, p. T19

- Description Wheel, B20–21
- Main Idea Web, C38–39
- Daily Vocabulary Scaffolding, H1–8

702 Unit 5: **Electricity and Magnetism**

CHAPTER 21
Getting Ready to Learn

◯ CONCEPT REVIEW
- Energy can change from one form to another.
- A force is a push or a pull.
- Power is the rate of energy transfer.

◯ VOCABULARY REVIEW
electric current p. 652
circuit p. 667
kinetic energy *See Glossary.*

CONTENT REVIEW
CLASSZONE.COM
Review concepts and vocabulary.

▶ TAKING NOTES

MAIN IDEA WEB

Write each new blue heading in a box. Then write notes in boxes around the center box that give important terms and details about that blue heading.

VOCABULARY STRATEGY

Place each vocabulary term at the center of a **description wheel** diagram. As you read about the term, write some words describing it on the spokes.

See the Note-Taking Handbook on pages R45–R51.

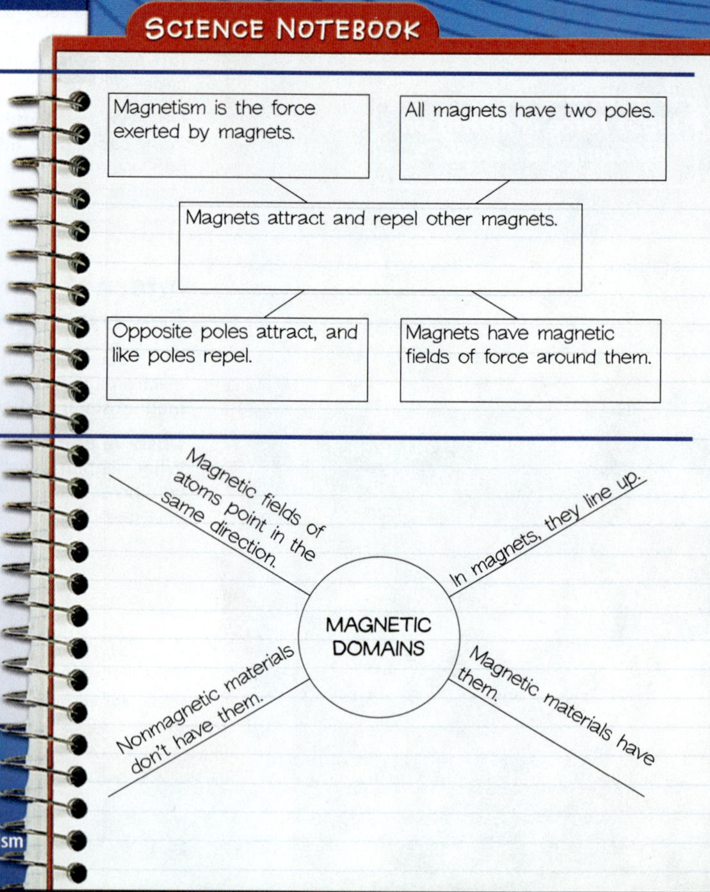

702 Unit 5: Electricity and Magnetism

CHECK READINESS

Administer the Diagnostic Test to determine students' readiness for new science content and their mastery of requisite math skills.

 Diagnostic Test, pp. 39–40

Technology Resources

Students needing content and math skills should visit **ClassZone.com**.

- **CONTENT REVIEW**
- **MATH TUTORIAL**

 CONTENT REVIEW CD-ROM

KEY CONCEPT
Magnetism is a force that acts at a distance.

◀ **BEFORE, you learned**
- A force is a push or pull
- Some forces act at a distance
- Atoms contain charged particles

▶ **NOW, you will learn**
- How magnets attract and repel other magnets
- What makes some materials magnetic
- Why a magnetic field surrounds Earth

VOCABULARY

magnet p. 703
magnetism p. 704
magnetic pole p. 704
magnetic field p. 705
magnetic domain p. 706

EXPLORE Magnetism

How do magnets behave?

PROCEDURE

① Clamp the clothespin on the dowel so that it makes a stand for the magnets, as shown.

② Place the three magnets on the dowel. If there is a space between pairs of magnets, measure and record the distance between them.

③ Remove the top magnet, turn it over, and replace it on the dowel. Record your observations. Experiment with different arrangements of the magnets and record your observations.

MATERIALS
- clothespin
- wooden dowel
- 3 disk magnets
- ruler

WHAT DO YOU THINK?
- How did the arrangement of the magnets affect their behavior?
- What evidence indicates that magnets exert a force?

Magnets attract and repel other magnets.

Suppose you get home from school and open the refrigerator to get some milk. As you close the door, it swings freely until it suddenly seems to close by itself. There is a magnet inside the refrigerator door that pulls it shut. A **magnet** is an object that attracts certain other materials, particularly iron and steel.

There may be quite a few magnets in your kitchen. Some are obvious, like the seal of the refrigerator and the magnets that hold notes to its door. Other magnets run the motor in a blender, provide energy in a microwave oven, operate the speakers in a radio on the counter, and make a doorbell ring.

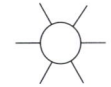
VOCABULARY
Make a description wheel for the term *magnet*.

Chapter 21: **Magnetism** 703

RESOURCES FOR DIFFERENTIATED INSTRUCTION

Below Level
UNIT RESOURCE BOOK
- Reading Study Guide A, pp. 136–137
- Decoding Support, p. 183

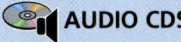 **AUDIO CDS**

R **ADDITIONAL INVESTIGATION,**
It's a Plot! A, B, & C, pp. 195–203;
Teacher Instructions, pp. 206–207

Advanced
UNIT RESOURCE BOOK
Challenge and Extension, p. 142

English Learners
UNIT RESOURCE BOOK
Spanish Reading Study Guide, pp. 140–141

 **AUDIO CDS**
- Audio Readings in Spanish
- Audio Readings (English)

21.1 FOCUS

▶ **Set Learning Goals**

Students will
- Observe that magnets attract and repel other magnets.
- Discover what makes some materials magnetic.
- Learn why a magnetic field surrounds Earth.
- Infer from an experiment that Earth's magnetic field moves a compass needle.

◯ **3-Minute Warm-Up**

Display Transparency 20 or copy this exercise on the board:

Decide if these statements are true. If not, correct them.

- A force is a push or a pull. *true*
- All forces act at a distance. *Some forces, such as gravity, act at a distance but others act as a constant force.*
- Atoms contain charged particles. *true*

 3-Minute Warm-Up, p. T20

21.1 MOTIVATE

EXPLORE Magnetism

PURPOSE To observe the attraction and repulsion of magnets

TIP 5 min. If the stand falls over, tape the clothespin to the table.

WHAT DO YOU THINK? *When the magnets are arranged one way, they attract each other; when one magnet is turned over, they push each other apart. Magnets either attract or repel other magnets.*

Chapter 21 703

21.1 INSTRUCT

Real World Example

Transportation by maglev was first proposed more than a century ago. The first commercial maglev train started operation in China in 2002, using a train developed in Germany. Similar trains are being tested in Germany and Japan. Developers in the United States have considered similar prototypes, but the cost is prohibitive. It is estimated that it would cost over $25 million a mile to build such a train. The main benefit of maglev trains is that they are faster and smoother than many conventional trains because friction is dramatically reduced.

Ongoing Assessment

CHECK YOUR READING Answer: Like poles of magnets repel each other, raising the train off the track. Other magnets pull the train forward.

The train is pushed up by magnets beneath it and pulled forward by magnets ahead of it.

RESOURCE CENTER CLASSZONE.COM
Find out more about magnetism.

Magnetism

The force exerted by a magnet is called **magnetism**. The push or pull of magnetism can act at a distance, which means that the magnet does not have to touch an object to exert a force on it. When you close the refrigerator, you feel the pull before the magnet actually touches the metal frame. There are other forces that act at a distance, including gravity and static electricity. Later you will read how the force of magnetism is related to electricity. In fact, magnetism is the result of a moving electric charge.

You may be familiar with magnets attracting, or pulling, metal objects toward them. Magnets can also repel, or push away, objects. The train in the photograph at the left is called a maglev train. The word *maglev* is short for *mag*netic *lev*itation, or lifting up. As you can see in the diagram, the train does not touch the track. Magnetism pushes the entire train up and pulls it forward. Maglev trains can move as fast as 480 kilometers per hour (300 mi/h).

CHECK YOUR READING How can a train operate without touching the track?

Magnetic Poles

The force of magnetism is not evenly distributed throughout a magnet. **Magnetic poles** are the parts of a magnet where the magnetism is the strongest. Every magnet has two magnetic poles. If a bar magnet is suspended so that it can swing freely, one pole of the magnet always points toward the north. That end of the magnet is known as the north-seeking pole, or north pole. The other end of the magnet is called the south pole. Many magnets are marked with an *N* and an *S* to indicate the poles.

As with electric charges, opposite poles of a magnet attract and like poles—or poles that are the same—repel, or push each other away. Every magnet has both a north pole and a south pole. A horseshoe magnet is like a bar magnet that has been bent into the shape of a *U*. It has a pole at each of its ends. If you break a bar magnet between the two poles, the result is two smaller magnets, each of which has a north pole and a south pole. No matter how many times you break a magnet, the result is smaller magnets.

704 Unit 5: Electricity and Magnetism

DIFFERENTIATE INSTRUCTION

More Reading Support

A What is the name of the force exerted by a magnet? *magnetism*

B What does every magnet have? *a north and south pole*

English Learners The use of dashes in writing may be confusing to English learners. The dash is often used to interject an idea into a sentence. For example, "As with electric charges, opposite poles of a magnet attract and like poles—or poles that are the same—repel, or push each other away." Show students that the sentence would still be complete if the words inside the dashes were not there.

704 Unit 5: **Electricity and Magnetism**

Magnetic Fields

You have read that magnetism is a force that can act at a distance. However magnets cannot exert a force on an object that is too far away. A **magnetic field** is the region around a magnet in which the magnet exerts force. If a piece of iron is within the magnetic field of a magnet, it will be pulled toward the magnet. Many small pieces of iron, called iron filings, are used to show the magnetic field around a magnet. The iron filings form a pattern of lines called magnetic field lines.

READING TIP
Thin red lines in the illustrations below indicate the magnetic field.

The Magnetic Field Around a Magnet

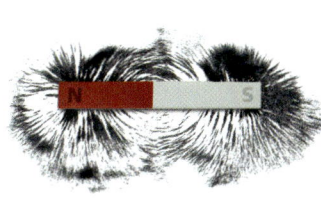
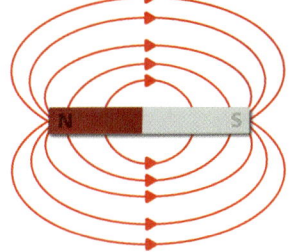
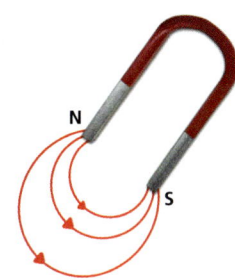

The arrangement of the magnetic field lines depends on the shape of the magnet, but the lines always extend from one pole to the other pole. The magnetic field lines are always shown as starting from the north pole and ending at the south pole. In the illustrations above, you can see that the lines are closest together near the magnets' poles. That is where the force is strongest. The force is weaker farther away from the magnet.

CHECK YOUR READING Where is the magnetic field of a magnet the strongest?

What happens to the magnetic fields of two magnets when the magnets are brought together? As you can see below, each magnet has an effect on the field of the other magnet. If the magnets are held so that the north pole of one magnet is close to the south pole of the other, the magnetic field lines extend from one magnet to the other. The magnets pull together. On the other hand, if both north poles or both south poles of two magnets are brought near one another, the magnets repel. It is very difficult to push like poles of strong magnets together because magnetic repulsion pushes them apart.

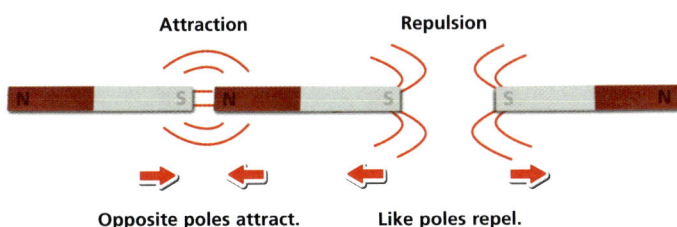

Opposite poles attract.   Like poles repel.

Chapter 21: Magnetism 705

Integrate the Sciences

Magnetic resonance imaging (MRI) uses magnetic fields to create detailed images of the inside of the human body, showing irregularities such as tumors. The patient lies in a stable magnetic field produced by a strong, tubular magnet. As the patient moves through the machine, three other magnets produce varying magnetic fields. Because of these magnetic fields and additional radio waves, hydrogen atoms in the body absorb and release energy. The released energy is detected and used to create images.

History of Science

In the late 1500s, William Gilbert, an English physician, discovered that materials that contained iron could be magnetized by stroking them with lodestone. His other contributions include showing that magnetism gets weaker as a magnet gets hotter, and discovering Earth's magnetic field.

Ongoing Assessment

Observe that magnets attract and repel other magnets.

Ask: What happens when two unlike poles of magnets are brought near each other? *They attract each other.*

CHECK YOUR READING   Answer: at the poles

DIFFERENTIATE INSTRUCTION

More Reading Support

C What is a magnetic field? *the region where a magnet exerts force*

D What happens when you bring the north poles of two magnets together? *They repel.*

Below Level Keep a supply of magnets, magnetic materials, and wire available for students to model chapter concepts.

Inclusion Encourage students with visual impairments to hold two large magnets, one in each hand. What happens if students feel resistance when they bring their hands together? *like poles are facing each other and repelling* What if they feel an attraction pulling their hands together? *opposite poles are attracting*

History of Science

People have used lodestone as a magnet for over 2000 years. When the first European explorers went to China, the Chinese people were using lodestone bowls as compass needles for navigation. A lodestone bowl about the size of the curved part of a spoon was placed on a flat surface. The handle of the bowl always pointed in the same direction and could be used for navigation.

Address Misconceptions

IDENTIFY Ask: Will a magnet pick up an aluminum can, or will there be no magnetic attraction between the two objects? If students answer that the magnet will pick up the can, they may hold the misconception that all metals are attracted to magnets.

CORRECT Provide students with various metals that might be collected for recycling, such as aluminum and steel cans, wire, and copper pipe. Have students use a magnet to determine which objects could be magnetically separated from other items to be recycled. Point out that what is commonly referred to as a tin can is actually steel, which contains iron, covered by a protective layer of another metal.

REASSESS Ask: In general, what metals could be separated from other metals because they are attracted to magnets? *metals that contain iron*

Technology Resources

Visit **ClassZone.com** for background on common student misconceptions.

MISCONCEPTION DATABASE

Ongoing Assessment

 Answer: In magnets, the magnetic fields of atoms align; in nonmagnetic materials, magnetic fields do not align.

Some materials are magnetic.

Some magnets occur naturally. Lodestone is a type of mineral that is a natural magnet and formed the earliest magnets that people used. The term *magnet* comes from the name *Magnesia*, a region of Greece where lodestone was discovered. Magnets can also be made from materials that contain certain metallic elements, such as iron.

If you have ever tried picking up different types of objects with a magnet, you have seen that some materials are affected by the magnet and other materials are not. Iron, nickel, cobalt, and a few other metals have properties that make them magnetic. Other materials, such as wood, cannot be made into magnets and are not affected by magnets. Whether a material is magnetic or not depends on its atoms—the particles that make up all matter.

You read in Chapter 19 that the protons and electrons of an atom have electric fields. Every atom also has a weak magnetic field, produced by the electron's motion around a nucleus. In addition, each electron spins around its axis, an imaginary line through its center. The spinning motion of the electrons in magnetic materials increases the strength of the magnetic field around each atom. The magnetic effect of one electron is usually cancelled by another electron that spins in the opposite direction.

 **READING TIP**
The red arrows in the illustration on page 707 are tiny magnetic fields.

Inside Magnetic Materials

The illustration on page 707 shows how magnets and the materials they affect differ from other materials.

❶ In a material that is not magnetic, such as wood, the magnetic fields of the atoms are weak and point in different directions. The magnetic fields cancel each other out. As a result, the overall material is not magnetic and could not be made into a magnet.

❷ In a material that is magnetic, such as iron, the magnetic fields of a group of atoms align, or point in the same direction. A **magnetic domain** is a group of atoms whose magnetic fields are aligned. The domains of a magnetic material are not themselves aligned, so their fields cancel one another out. Magnetic materials are pulled by magnets and can be made into magnets.

❸ A magnet is a material in which the magnetic domains are all aligned. The material is said to be magnetized.

 How do magnets differ from materials that are not magnetic?

706 Unit 5: Electricity and Magnetism

DIFFERENTIATE INSTRUCTION

More Reading Support

E What are some magnetic elements? *iron, cobalt, nickel*

F What are a group of atoms whose magnetic fields are aligned? *a magnetic domain*

Alternative Assessment Have groups of students create diagrams that show how magnetic tags are used as antitheft devices in stores. To help them, tell them that some of the detectors people walk through as they leave the store exert a magnetic field. The activated tags on merchandise contain demagnetized magnetic materials. As they pass through the field, the domains align, a signal is sent, and the alarm goes off.

How Magnets Differ from Other Materials

Magnets, and the materials they attract, contain small regions called magnetic domains. In a magnet, the domains are aligned.

Nonmagnetic Materials

Magnet

Magnetic Materials

① Nonmagnetic Materials
Some materials, like wood, are not magnetic. The tiny magnetic fields of their spinning electrons point in different directions and cancel each other out.

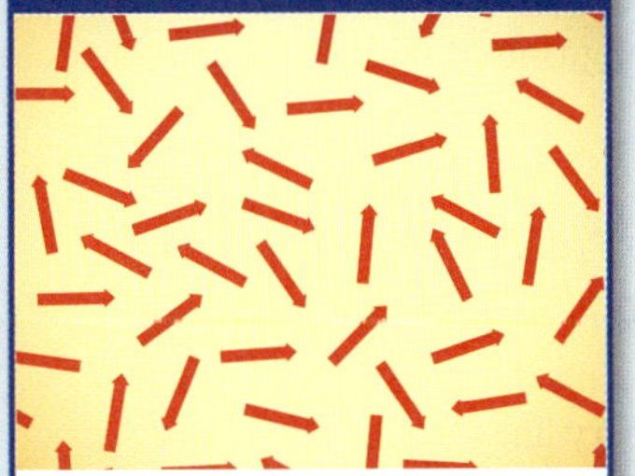

② Magnetic Materials
Other materials, like iron, are magnetic. Magnetic materials have magnetic domains, but the fields of the domains point in different directions.

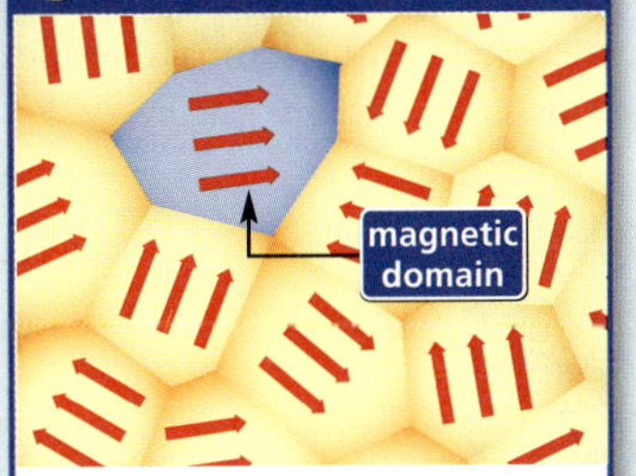

magnetic domain

③ Magnets
When a material is magnetized, the magnetic fields of all the domains point in the same direction.

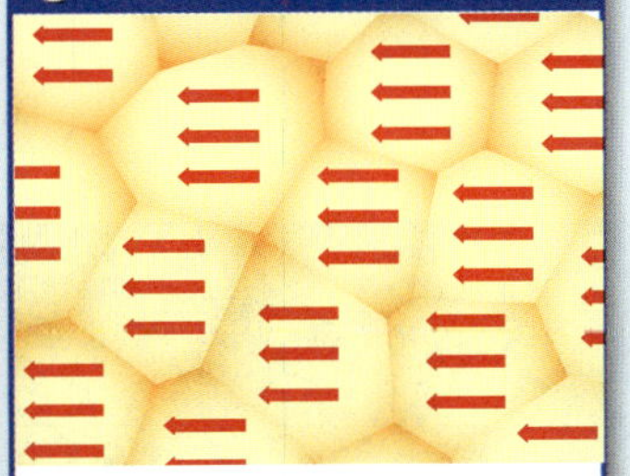

READING VISUALS Do the paper clips in this photograph contain magnetic domains? Why or why not?

Chapter 21: **Magnetism** 707

Teach from Visuals

Have students examine the visual of magnets. Ask:

- Which box describes electrons in a pencil? *Box 1*
- Do you think that all parts of a pencil are nonmagnetic? If not, what part might be magnetic? *No; the metal below the eraser might be magnetic.*
- How could you test this hypothesis? *Check to see whether the metal is attracted to a magnet.*
- If the metal below the eraser is magnetic, how would these atoms compare to the atoms in the rest of the pencil? *The metal atoms would form magnetic domains, unlike the atoms in the rest of the pencil.*

T This visual is also available as T22 in the Unit Transparency Book.

Develop Critical Thinking

SYNTHESIZE Have students use what they know regarding the arrangement of aligned atoms in a magnet and what happens to particles when they are heated. Ask: Why does heating a magnet tend to weaken it? *The kinetic energy of the aligned atoms increases, causing them to move out of alignment.*

EXPLORE the BIG idea

Revisit "Is It Magnetic?" on p. 701. Have students explain their results.

Ongoing Assessment

Discover what makes some materials magnetic.

Ask: Why can a magnet pick up an iron nail but not copper wire? *Copper's magnetic fields point in many directions and cancel each other out, so it doesn't have a strong magnetic field like that of iron.*

READING VISUALS *Answer: Yes; they are attracted by a magnet, so they are magnetic.*

DIFFERENTIATE INSTRUCTION

Below Level Have students classify each item in the visual according to the boxes at the bottom of the page. Have them work in small groups to compare and discuss their results.

Inclusion Gather a toy, a pencil, a paper clip, a marble, a sponge, a cork, a nail, a washer and if possible a magnetic rock. Pass them around to tactile learners and students with visual impairments. Make sure students know what they have. Then make a chart of magnetic and nonmagnetic materials on the board, and ask students to categorize the items.

Chapter 21 707

Integrate the Sciences

A few strains of bacteria, such as *Magnetospirillum magnetotacticum*, have been observed orienting themselves along the lines of Earth's magnetic field. The bacteria contain small amounts of magnetite, Fe_3O_4, which contains iron and so responds to a magnetic field. The bacteria sense the magnetic force and move in response to it.

EXPLORE the BIG idea

Revisit "How Can You Make a Chain?" on p. 701. Have students suggest ways to make their chains longer.

Develop Critical Thinking

SYNTHESIZE Have students research the magnetic fields of other planets in the solar system. Ask: How does the strength of the magnetic field provide information about the structure of the planet? *Planets with strong magnetic fields probably have a core consisting of materials that can be magnetized. Those with little or no magnetic field probably do not have such a core.*

Ongoing Assessment

Learn that a magnetic field surrounds Earth.

Ask: What relationship exists between charged particles and Earth's magnetic field? *Charged particles flow within Earth's core, causing a magnetic field.*

 Answer: Place a magnetic material in very strong magnetic fields.

 Answer: the movement of its core, which is mostly iron and nickel

708 Unit 5: Electricity and Magnetism

Temporary and Permanent Magnets

If you bring a magnet near a paper clip that contains iron, the paper clip is pulled toward the magnet. As the magnet nears the paper clip, the domains within the paper clip are attracted to the magnet's nearest pole. As a result, the domains within the paper clip become aligned. The paper clip develops its own magnetic field.

You can make a chain of paper clips that connect to one another through these magnetic fields. However, if you remove the magnet, the chain falls apart. The paper clips are temporary magnets, and their domains return to a random arrangement when the stronger magnetic field is removed.

Placing magnetic materials in very strong magnetic fields makes permanent magnets, such as the ones you use in the experiments in this chapter. You can make a permanent magnet by repeatedly stroking a piece of magnetic material in the same direction with a strong magnet. This action aligns the domains. However, if you drop a permanent magnet, or expose it to high temperatures, some of the domains can be shaken out of alignment, weakening its magnetism.

CHECK YOUR READING How can you make a permanent magnet?

Earth is a magnet.

People discovered long ago that when a piece of lodestone was allowed to turn freely, one end always pointed toward the north. Hundreds of years ago, sailors used lodestone in the first compasses for navigation. A compass works because Earth itself is a large magnet. A compass is simply a magnet that is suspended so that it can turn freely. The magnetic field of the compass needle aligns itself with the much larger magnetic field of Earth.

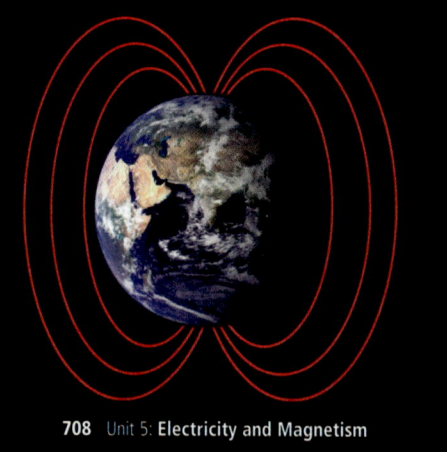

708 Unit 5: Electricity and Magnetism

Earth's Magnetic Field

The magnetic field around Earth acts as if there were a large bar magnet that runs through Earth's axis. Earth's axis is the imaginary line through the center of Earth around which it rotates. The source of the magnetic field that surrounds Earth is the motion of its core, which is composed mostly of iron and nickel. Charged particles flow within the core. Scientists have proposed several explanations of how that motion produces the magnetic field, but the process is not yet completely understood.

CHECK YOUR READING What is the source of Earth's magnetic field?

DIFFERENTIATE INSTRUCTION

 **More Reading Support**

G What happens when you remove a temporary magnet from a stronger magnetic field? *It stops being a magnet.*

Advanced Ask students to explain why a permanent magnet decreases slightly in strength over time. Refer them back to the visual "How Magnets Differ from Other Materials" on p. 707 if they need help, and point out the alignment of magnetic domains in magnets. *The magnetic domains in a permanent magnet are highly aligned. Over time, disturbances cause some disorder of the domains.*

 Challenge and Extension, p. 142

INVESTIGATE Earth's Magnetic Field

What moves a compass needle?

PROCEDURE

1. Gently place the aluminum foil on the water so that it floats.
2. Rub one pole of the magnet along the needle, from one end of the needle to the other. Lift up the magnet and repeat. Do this about 25 times, rubbing in the same direction each time. Place the magnet far away from your set-up.
3. Gently place the needle on the floating foil to act as a compass.
4. Turn the foil so that the needle points in a different direction. Observe what happens when you release the foil.

WHAT DO YOU THINK?
- What direction did the needle move when you placed it in the bowl?
- What moved the compass's needle?

CHALLENGE How could you use your compass to answer a question of your own about magnetism?

SKILL FOCUS Inferring

MATERIALS
- small square of aluminum foil
- bowl of water
- strong magnet
- sewing needle

TIME 15 minutes

Earth's magnetic field affects all the magnetic materials around you. Even the cans of food in your cupboard are slightly magnetized by this field. Hold a compass close to the bottom of a can and observe what happens. The magnetic domains in the metal can have aligned and produced a weak magnetic field. If you twist the can and check it again several days later, you can observe the effect of the domains changing their alignment.

Sailors learned many centuries ago that the compass does not point exactly toward the North Pole of Earth's axis. Rather, the compass magnet is currently attracted to an area 966 kilometers (600 mi) from the end of the axis of rotation. This area is known as the magnetic north pole. Interestingly, the magnetic poles of Earth can reverse, so that the magnetic north pole becomes the magnetic south pole. This has happened at least 400 times over the last 330 million years. The most recent reversal was about 780,000 years ago.

The evidence that the magnetic north and south poles reverse is found in rocks in which the minerals contain iron. The iron in the minerals lines up with Earth's magnetic field as the rock forms. Once the rock is formed, the domains remain in place. The evidence for the reversing magnetic field is shown in layers of rocks on the ocean floor, where the domains are arranged in opposite directions.

Chapter 21: **Magnetism** 709

DIFFERENTIATE INSTRUCTION

More Reading Support

H What evidence shows that Earth's magnetic poles have reversed over the years? *rocks on the ocean floor*

Additional Investigation To reinforce Section 21.1 learning goals, use the following full-period investigation:

Additional INVESTIGATION, It's a Plot! A, B, & C, pp. 195–203, 206–207 (Advanced students should complete Levels B and C.)

Advanced Have students investigate and report on the geo-magnetic reversal of Earth's magnetic field. They should use the terms *epoch* (long-term changes) and *event* (short-term changes) in their reports.

INVESTIGATE Earth's Magnetic Field

PURPOSE To infer that Earth's magnetic field moves a compass needle

TIPS *15 min.*

- Students should use a piece of foil just large enough to float the needle. Make sure the foil floats freely in the bowl.
- Ask students why the compass needle should be kept away from classroom magnets. *The needle will be attracted to the magnet instead of Earth's magnetic field.*

WHAT DO YOU THINK? *The needle pointed north-south. The needle was attracted to Earth's magnetic field.*

CHALLENGE *Sample answer: You could use the compass to determine whether there is a magnetic field around an object.*

Datasheet, Earth's Magnetic Field, p. 143

Technology Resources

Customize this student lab as needed or look for an alternative. Print rubrics to assess student lab reports.

Lab Generator CD-ROM

Teaching with Technology

If probeware is available, use a magnetic field sensor with "Investigate Earth's Magnetic Field."

Integrate the Sciences

Many organisms that have migratory patterns rely on Earth's magnetic field. Some scientists believe that migratory birds, such as geese and ducks, use it to guide them on seasonal flights that may be hundreds of miles long. Other organisms, such as whales and sea turtles, may use similar methods of navigation. Why would Earth's magnetic field affect these animals and not others? Some scientists hypothesize that the animals might have iron-containing materials in or near their brains that react to Earth's magnetic field, just as a compass does.

Chapter 21 709

Ongoing Assessment

 Answer: These locations are where Earth's magnetic field is strongest.

Reinforce the BIG idea

Have students relate the section to the Big Idea.

 Reinforcing Key Concepts, p. 144

21.1 ASSESS & RETEACH

Assess

 Section 21.1 Quiz, p. 41

Reteach

Have students perform this activity.

- Place a disk magnet on a piece of paper.
- Place a steel ball touching the magnet.
- Place another steel ball on the paper where it touches both the magnet and the other ball.
- Explain what happens. *The magnet makes each ball a temporary magnet, and their like poles repel each other.*

Technology Resources

Have students visit ClassZone.com for reteaching of Key Concepts.

- CONTENT REVIEW
- CONTENT REVIEW CD-ROM

Magnetism and the Atmosphere

A constant stream of charged particles is released by reactions inside the Sun. These particles could be damaging to living cells if they reached the surface of Earth. One important effect of Earth's magnetic field is that it turns aside, or deflects, the flow of the charged particles.

Observers view a beautiful display of Northern Lights in Alaska.

Many of the particles are deflected toward the magnetic poles, where Earth's magnetic field lines are closest together. As the particles approach Earth, they react with oxygen and nitrogen in Earth's atmosphere. These interactions can be seen at night as vast, moving sheets of color—red, blue, green or violet—that can fill the whole sky. These displays are known as the Northern Lights or the Southern Lights.

 Why do the Northern Lights and the Southern Lights occur near Earth's magnetic poles?

21.1 Review

KEY CONCEPTS

1. What force causes magnets to attract or repel one another?
2. Why are some materials magnetic and not others?
3. Describe three similarities between Earth and a bar magnet.

CRITICAL THINKING

4. **Apply** A needle is picked up by a magnet. What can you say about the needle's atoms?
5. **Infer** The Northern Lights can form into lines in the sky. What do you think causes this effect?

CHALLENGE

6. **Infer** Hundreds of years ago sailors observed that as they traveled farther north, their compass needle tended to point toward the ground as well as toward the north. What can you conclude about the magnet inside Earth from this observation?

710 Unit 5: Electricity and Magnetism

ANSWERS

1. magnetism

2. The magnetic fields of the atoms in magnetic materials form magnetic domains. Nonmagnetic materials do not have magnetic domains.

3. They both have magnetic poles, magnetic fields, and can magnetize other objects.

4. The magnetic fields of the atoms are aligned.

5. Charged particles align with the magnetic field lines around Earth.

6. The magnetic poles are within Earth, not on the surface.

Think SCIENCE

SKILL: EVALUATING CONCLUSIONS

Can Magnets Heal People?

Many people believe that a magnetic field can relieve pain and cure injuries or illnesses. They point out that human blood cells contain iron and that magnets attract iron.

◯ Claims

Here are some claims from advertisements and published scientific experiments.

> a. In an advertisement, a person reported back pain that went away overnight when a magnetic pad was taped to his back.
>
> b. In an advertisement, a person used magnets to treat a painful bruise. The pain reportedly stopped soon after the magnet was applied.
>
> c. In a research project, people who had recovered from polio, but still had severe pain, rated the amount of pain they experienced. People who used magnets reported slightly more pain relief than those who used fake magnets that looked like the real magnets.
>
> d. A research project studied people with severe muscle pain. Patients who slept on magnetic pads for six months reported slightly less pain than those who slept on nonmagnetic pads or no pads.
>
> e. A research project studied people with pain in their heels, placing magnets in their shoes. About sixty percent of people with real magnets reported improvements. About sixty percent of people with fake magnets also reported improvements.

◯ Controls

Scientists use control groups to determine whether a change was a result of the experimental variable or some other cause. A control group is the same as an experimental group in every way except for the variable that is tested. For each of the above cases, was a control used? If not, can you think of some other explanation for the result?

◯ Evaluating Conclusions

On Your Own Evaluate each claim or report separately. Based on all the evidence, can you conclude that magnets are useful for relieving pain? What further evidence would help you decide?

As a Group Find advertisements for companies that sell magnets for medical use. Do they provide information about how their tests were conducted and how you can contact the doctors or scientists involved?

CHALLENGE Design an experiment, with controls, that would show whether or not magnets are useful for relieving pain.

Chapter 21: **Magnetism 711**

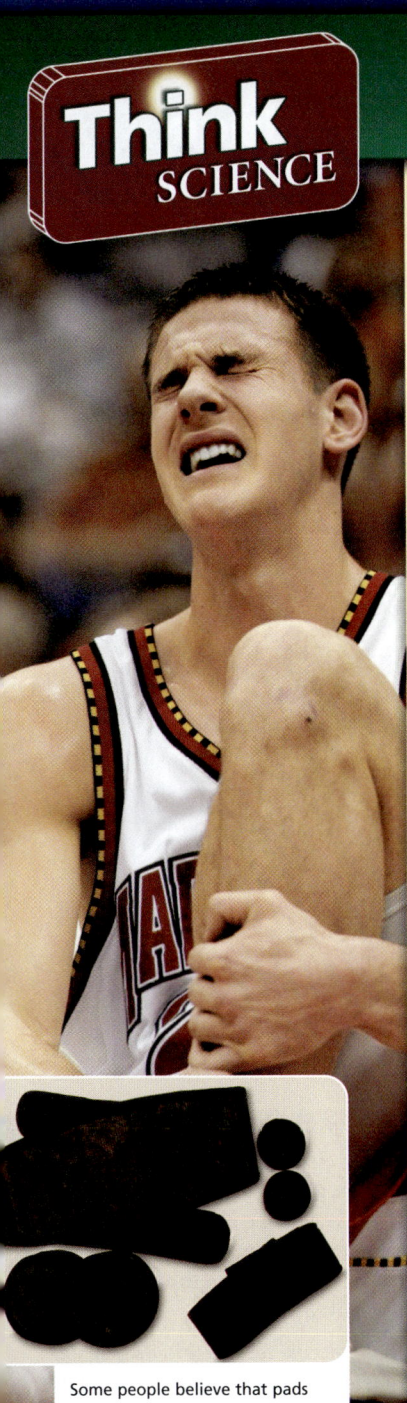

Some people believe that pads containing magnets, such as these, can relieve pain.

THINK SCIENCE
Scientific Methods of Thinking

Set Learning Goal
To evaluate claims about whether magnets are of value in healing and pain relief

Present the Science
Magnetic therapy is based on the magnetic fields that result from moving charges in the human body. Unpaired, spinning electrons in atoms and ions create magnetic fields because they are moving electrical charges. Some therapists believe that the human body functions better when these magnetic fields are aligned, and that magnets will cause this alignment.

Guide the Activity
- Remind students that conclusions are human interpretations and thus are not always objective. Tell them that conclusions can be faulty either from inaccurate or unsupported data or from incorrect interpretations of data.
- Help students find information for "As a Group." Because magnet therapy is considered to be alternative medicine, information is more likely to be in health magazines or on the Internet than in medical journals.

COOPERATIVE LEARNING STRATEGY
Have the class decide on a "Challenge" experiment to perform. Divide the class into a control group and a group that uses magnets, perform the experiment, and draw and evaluate conclusions.

Close
In claim e, can you think of an explanation for the results? *The pain might have improved in time, regardless of the magnets.*

ANSWERS

Claims a and b do not show that controls were used, so there is no way to compare results. Only one person is in the "sample." **Claims c and d** show use of controls. The slight differences in pain relief may not be significant. **Claim e** shows no difference between controls and subjects.

ON YOUR OWN Sample answer: There is not enough evidence to decide. Further studies using large sample sizes and controls would provide more evidence.

AS A GROUP Answers will vary; check students' advertisements.

CHALLENGE Experiments might include studies of athletes with similar injuries, half of whom used actual magnets and half of whom used fake magnets.

21.2 FOCUS

▶ Set Learning Goals

Students will
- Describe how an electric current can produce a magnetic field.
- Describe some uses of electromagnets.
- Examine how motors use magnets.
- Observe in an experiment how to make an electromagnet.

◀ 3-Minute Warm-Up

Display Transparency 20 or copy this exercise on the board:

Draw a diagram that shows the magnetic fields that result when like poles of two magnets are close to each other and when unlike poles are close. Use lines to show the magnetic fields that result from these situations. *Diagrams should show the repulsion of like poles and the attraction of unlike poles.*

 3-Minute Warm-Up, p. T20

21.2 MOTIVATE

EXPLORE Magnetism from Electric Current

PURPOSE To observe that an electric current produces a magnetic field

TIP 10 min. The wire and the compass must be close to each other.

WHAT DO YOU THINK? *The compass needle moved when the circuit was completed. When the battery is reversed, the compass needle also reverses.*

Teaching with Technology

If probeware is available, use a magnetic field sensor while performing "Magnetism from Electric Current."

KEY CONCEPT
21.2 Current can produce magnetism.

◀ BEFORE, you learned
- Electric current is the flow of charge
- Magnetism is a force exerted by magnets
- Magnets attract or repel other magnets

▶ NOW, you will learn
- How an electric current can produce a magnetic field
- How electromagnets are used
- How motors use electromagnets

VOCABULARY
electromagnetism p. 713
electromagnet p. 714

EXPLORE Magnetism from Electric Current

What is the source of magnetism?

PROCEDURE

1. Tape one end of the wire to the battery.
2. Place the compass on the table. Place the wire so that it is lying beside the compass, parallel to the needle of the compass. Record your observations.
3. Briefly touch the free end of the wire to the other end of the battery. Record your observations.
4. Turn the battery around and tape the other end to the wire. Repeat steps 2 and 3.

MATERIALS
- electrical tape
- copper wire
- AA cell (battery)
- compass

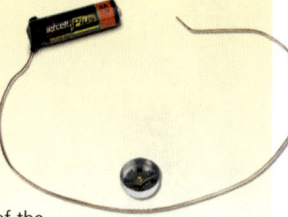

WHAT DO YOU THINK?
- What did you observe?
- What is the relationship between the direction of the battery and the direction of the compass needle?

▼ **REMINDER**
Current is the flow of electrons through a conductor.

An electric current produces a magnetic field.

Like many discoveries, the discovery that electric current is related to magnetism was unexpected. In the 1800s, a Danish physicist named Hans Christian Oersted (UR-stehd) was teaching a physics class. Oersted used a battery and wire to demonstrate some properties of electricity. He noticed that as an electric charge passed through the wire, the needle of a nearby compass moved.

When he turned the current off, the needle returned to its original direction. After more experiments, Oersted confirmed that there is a relationship between magnetism and electricity. He discovered that an electric current produces a magnetic field.

712 Unit 5: **Electricity and Magnetism**

RESOURCES FOR DIFFERENTIATED INSTRUCTION

Below Level
UNIT RESOURCE BOOK
- Reading Study Guide A, pp. 147–148
- Decoding Support, p. 183

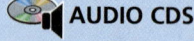 AUDIO CDS

Advanced
UNIT RESOURCE BOOK
Challenge and Extension, p. 153

English Learners
UNIT RESOURCE BOOK
Spanish Reading Study Guide, pp. 151–152

🔊 AUDIO CDS
- Audio Readings in Spanish
- Audio Readings (English)

Electromagnetism

The relationship between electric current and magnetism plays an important role in many modern technologies. **Electromagnetism** is magnetism that results from an electric current. When a charged particle such as an electron moves, it produces a magnetic field. Because an electric current generally consists of moving electrons, a current in a wire produces a magnetic field. In fact, the wire acts as a magnet. Increasing the amount of current in the wire increases the strength of the magnetic field.

> **VOCABULARY**
> Remember to record *electromagnetism* in your notebook.

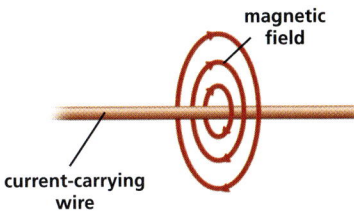

You have seen how magnetic field lines can be drawn around a magnet. The magnetic field lines around a wire are usually illustrated as a series of circles. The magnetic field of a wire actually forms the shape of a tube around the wire. The direction of the current determines the direction of the magnetic field. If the direction of the electric current is reversed, the magnetic field still exists in circles around the wire, but is reversed.

If the wire is shaped into a loop, the magnetism becomes concentrated inside the loop. The field is much stronger in the middle of the loop than it is around a straight wire. If you wind the wire into a coil, the magnetic force becomes stronger with each additional turn of wire as the magnetic field becomes more concentrated.

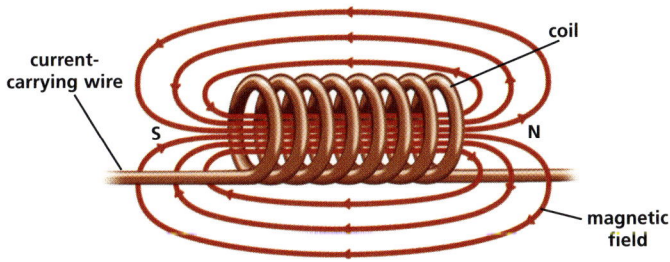

A coil of wire with charge flowing through it has a magnetic field that is similar to the magnetic field of a bar magnet. Inside the coil, the field flows in one direction, forming a north pole at one end. The flow outside the coil returns to the south pole. The direction of the electric current in the wire determines which end of the coil becomes the north pole.

 **CHECK YOUR READING** How is a coil of wire that carries a current similar to a bar magnet?

DIFFERENTIATE INSTRUCTION

 **More Reading Support**

A What is electromagnetism? *magnetism that results from an electric current*

Inclusion Use pipe cleaners for the coil and thin wire for the loops of the magnetic field to model the lower figure on p. 713 for students who have visual impairments.

Teacher Demo

To show a magnetic field, stand up three strong horseshoe magnets in a row about 10 centimeters apart. Place the first and third magnets so that their poles are the same. Reverse the second magnet so that its poles are opposite. Run a strip of extremely thin aluminum foil through the tunnel formed by the poles of the magnets. Use wire to attach the ends of the foil to the terminals of a low-voltage DC power supply that can be varied. Start the current low and increase it. The foil will arch in two places, showing that a force is acting on it.

Teach Difficult Concepts

To help students figure out the direction of the magnetic field for a current-carrying wire, have them use what is known as the right-hand rule.

- Use a pencil to represent the wire, with current flowing from the eraser to the point.
- Have students grasp the pencil with their right hand so that their fingers curl around the pencil and their thumb points to the eraser end of the pencil. In this model, the thumb is pointing in the direction of the flow of the current. The fingers curl around the pencil in the same perpendicular direction as the magnetic field.

Ongoing Assessment

Describe how an electric current can produce a magnetic field.

Ask: Why does an electric current produce a magnetic field? *The current consists of moving charged particles.*

CHECK YOUR READING Answer: *Both have magnetic fields and magnetic poles.*

INVESTIGATE Electromagnets

PURPOSE To make and observe an electromagnet, which uses current to produce magnetism

TIPS 20 min.

- Remind students that the batteries must point in the same direction.
- The batteries should make good contact when they are taped together. Make sure tape does not come between the battery terminals.
- Do not leave the batteries connected for more than a few minutes, or the wire and nail will get hot.

WHAT DO YOU THINK? *The nail became magnetized and picked up the paper clip. Yes; the nail was not a magnet before there was current in the wire.*

CHALLENGE *Yes; an aluminum nail would not form a magnet, because aluminum is not a magnetic material.*

 Datasheet, Electromagnets, p. 154

Technology Resources

Customize this student lab as needed or look for an alternative. Print rubrics to assess student lab reports.

 Lab Generator CD-ROM

Teaching with Technology

Use a magnetic field sensor to detect the magnetic field around the nail (after it is connected to the battery).

EXPLORE the BIG idea

Revisit "Internet Activity: Electromagnets" on p. 701. Have students explain their results.

Ongoing Assessment

 *Answer: Increase the number of coils or the current.*

714 Unit 5: **Electricity and Magnetism**

Making an Electromagnet

 B

 C

Recall that a piece of iron in a strong magnetic field becomes a magnet itself. An **electromagnet** is a magnet made by placing a piece of iron or steel inside a coil of wire. As long as the coil carries a current, the metal acts as a magnet and increases the magnetic field of the coil. But when the current is turned off, the magnetic domains in the metal become random again and the magnetic field disappears.

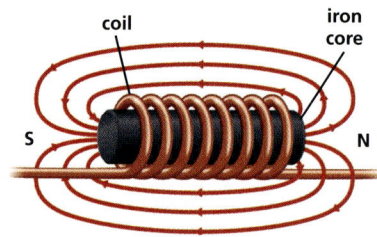

By increasing the number of loops in the coil, you can increase the strength of the electromagnet. Electromagnets exert a much more powerful magnetic field than a coil of wire without a metal core. They can also be much stronger than the strongest permanent magnets made of metal alone. You can increase the field strength of an electromagnet by adding more coils or a stronger current. Some of the most powerful magnets in the world are huge electromagnets that are used in scientific instruments.

 How can you increase the strength of an electromagnet?

INVESTIGATE Electromagnets

How can you make an electromagnet?

PROCEDURE

1. Starting about 25 cm from one end of the wire, wrap the wire in tight coils around the nail. The coils should cover the nail from the head almost to the point.
2. Tape the two batteries together as shown. Tape one end of the wire to a free battery terminal.
3. Touch the point of the nail to a paper clip and record your observations.
4. Connect the other end of the wire to the other battery terminal. Again touch the point of the nail to a paper clip. Disconnect the wire from the battery. Record your observations.

WHAT DO YOU THINK?
- What did you observe?
- Did you make an electromagnet? How do you know?

CHALLENGE Do you think the result would be different if you used an aluminum nail instead of an iron nail? Why?

SKILL FOCUS Observing

MATERIALS
- insulated wire
- large iron nail
- 2 D cells
- electrical tape
- paper clip

TIME 20 minutes

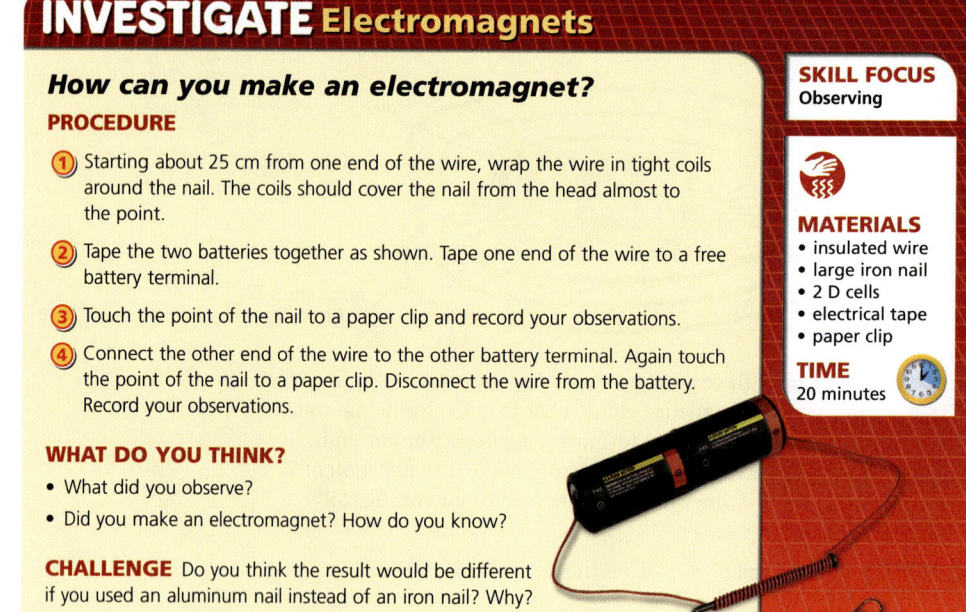

714 Unit 5: Electricity and Magnetism

DIFFERENTIATE INSTRUCTION

 **More Reading Support**

B What is a piece of iron inside a wire coil? *an electromagnet*

C What happens when you turn off the current? *The magnetic field disappears.*

Below Level Have students relate the parts of the electromagnet that they made during "Investigate Electromagnets" with the diagram of a coil and iron core at the top of the page. *The iron core is the nail, the coil is the wire that they wrapped around the nail, and the magnetic field lines are invisible but caused the nail to attract the paper clip.*

Uses of Electromagnets

Because electromagnets can be turned on and off, they have more uses than permanent magnets. The photograph below shows a powerful electromagnet on a crane. While the electric charge flows through the coils of the magnet, it lifts hundreds of cans at a recycling plant. When the crane operator turns off the current, the magnetic field disappears and the cans drop from the crane.

A permanent magnet would not be nearly as useful for this purpose. Although you could use a large permanent magnet to lift the cans, it would be hard to remove them from the magnet.

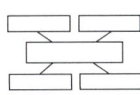

MAIN IDEA WEB
Make a main idea web for the uses of electromagnets.

This powerful electromagnet can be turned on and off to collect and move cans at a recycling plant.

electromagnet

wire supplying electric current

You use an electromagnet every time you store information on a computer. The computer hard drive contains disks that have billions of tiny magnetic domains in them. When you save a file, a tiny electromagnet in the computer is activated. The magnetic field of the electromagnet changes the orientation of the small magnetic domains. The small magnets store your file in a form that can be read later by the computer. A similar system is used to store information on magnetic tape of an audiocassette or videocassette. Sound and pictures are stored on the tape by the arrangement of magnets embedded in the plastic film.

Magnetic information is often stored on credit cards and cash cards. A black strip on the back of the card contains information about the account number and passwords. The cards can be damaged if they are frequently exposed to magnetic fields. For example, cards should not be stored with their strips facing each other, or near a magnetic clasp on a purse or wallet. These magnetic fields can change the arrangement of the tiny magnetic domains on the card and erase the stored information.

DIFFERENTIATE INSTRUCTION

 **More Reading Support**

 D Why is an electromagnet more useful than a permanent magnet to separate a mixture of metals? *Turning off the magnet is an easy way to release the objects.*

Advanced Have students work in pairs to investigate and explain the operation of a metal detector.

R Challenge and Extension, p. 153

Teach from Visuals

Have students examine the photograph of the credit card being used. Ask:

- If the stored information on the credit card can be damaged by a magnetic field, what can you infer about the material that makes up the strip? *It is magnetic.*

- What can you infer about the domains in the material that make up the strip? *They are not aligned in one direction but will align in one direction in a magnetic field.*

Ongoing Assessment

Describe some uses of electromagnets.

Ask: Which would probably have more wire coils, an electromagnet used to separate types of cans or one used to lift cars? *one used to lift cars*

History of Science

In 1821, Michael Faraday wrote *Historical Sketch of Electromagnetism,* a paper that summarizes the work of other scientists on electromagnetism. That same year, he made the first simple electrical motor. Many scientists think that one of Faraday's most important contributions to scientific knowledge was his study of electromagnetic induction. He was the first scientist to report that a current is induced by a change in magnetism, not by steady magnetism.

Real World Example

The first operating micromotor was developed in 1988 by a team of electrical engineers headed by Richard Muller at the University of California, Berkeley. Their motor has approximately the same diameter as a human hair. Currently, there are no industrial applications for a motor this small, but similar micromachines are used in airbag deployment systems and heart pacemakers. Even smaller motors have been built, using nanotechnology.

Ongoing Assessment

 *Answer: the push and pull of the other magnet in the motor*

Motors use electromagnets.

Because magnetism is a force, magnets can be used to move things. Electric motors convert the energy of an electric current into motion by taking advantage of the interaction between current and magnetism.

There are hundreds of devices that contain electric motors. Examples include power tools, electrical kitchen appliances, and the small fans in a computer. Almost anything with moving parts that uses current has an electric motor.

Motors

See a motor in motion.

Page 717 shows how a simple motor works. The photograph at the top of the page shows a motor that turns the blades of a fan. The illustration in the middle of the page shows the main parts of a simple motor. Although they may look different from each other, all motors have similar parts and work in a similar way. The main parts of an electrical motor include a voltage source, a shaft, an electromagnet, and at least one additional magnet. The shaft of the motor turns other parts of the device.

Recall that an electromagnet consists of a coil of wire with current flowing through it. Find the electromagnet in the illustration on page 717. The electromagnet is placed between the poles of another magnet.

When current from the voltage source flows through the coil, a magnetic field is produced around the electromagnet. The poles of the magnet interact with the poles of the electromagnet, causing the motor to turn.

1 The poles of the magnet push on the like poles of the electromagnet, causing the electromagnet to turn.

2 As the motor turns, the opposite poles pull on each other.

3 When the poles of the electromagnet line up with the opposite poles of the magnet, a part of the motor called the commutator reverses the polarity of the electromagnet. Now, the poles push on each other again and the motor continues to turn.

The illustration of the motor on page 717 is simplified so that you can see all of the parts. If you saw the inside of an actual motor, it might look like the illustration on the left. Notice that the wire is coiled many times. The electromagnet in a strong motor may coil hundreds of times. The more coils, the stronger the motor.

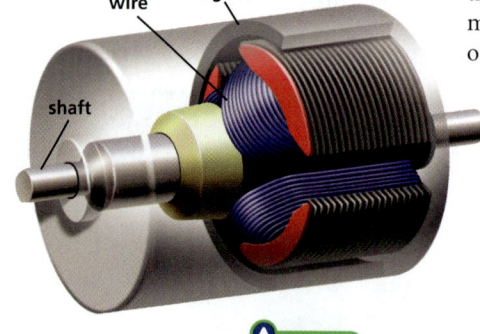

What causes the electromagnet in a motor to turn?

DIFFERENTIATE INSTRUCTION

More Reading Support

E Motors convert electrical energy into what form of energy? *motion*

F How could you make a motor stronger? *Increase the number of coils.*

Alternative Assessment Have students sketch a concept map showing the operation of a motor. Graphics should include all steps from electrical energy entering the motor to the shaft's turning.

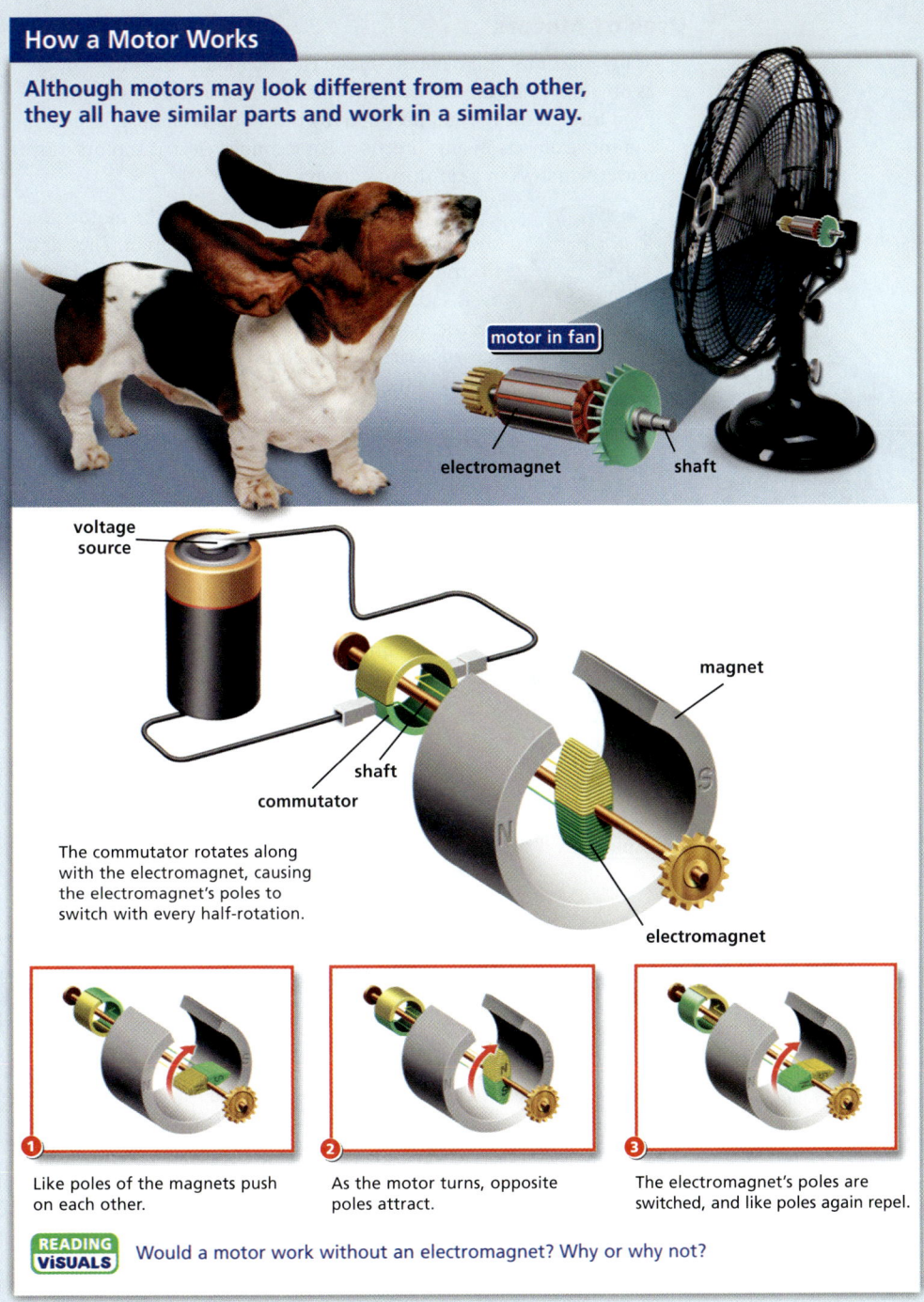

How a Motor Works

Although motors may look different from each other, they all have similar parts and work in a similar way.

motor in fan

electromagnet — shaft

voltage source

magnet

shaft
commutator

The commutator rotates along with the electromagnet, causing the electromagnet's poles to switch with every half-rotation.

electromagnet

1 Like poles of the magnets push on each other.

2 As the motor turns, opposite poles attract.

3 The electromagnet's poles are switched, and like poles again repel.

READING VISUALS Would a motor work without an electromagnet? Why or why not?

Chapter 21: **Magnetism** 717

DIFFERENTIATE INSTRUCTION

English Learners Within this section are a variety of introductory clauses and phrases. Give students these examples and have them identify the subject of the sentence.

"While the electric charge flows through the coils of the magnet, it lifts hundreds of cans at a recycling plant." (p. 715)

"When you save a file, a tiny electromagnet in the computer is activated." (p. 715)

Encourage students to use introductory clauses and phrases in their own writing.

Language Arts Connection

Explain that when people go from home to work or school and back, they are said to *commute*. One definition of commute is to travel but it also has other meanings. The word *commute* comes from the Middle English *commuten*, meaning "to transform" and from the Latin *commutare*, meaning "to change." The *commutative* math property says that in addition or multiplication, you can move the numbers around without changing the problem. Ask students to relate these meanings to the way "commutator" is used in the text.

Integrate the Sciences

Many motors occur in nature on the molecular scale. These motors convert chemical energy into kinetic energy. Molecular motors perform functions such as intercellular transport, cellular organization, and cell movement and growth. Sets of these motors move the flagella of sperm and bacteria. They also contract muscles.

Ongoing Assessment

Examine how motors use electromagnets.

Ask: Which magnet has its polarity reversed by the commutator in a motor? *the electromagnet*

READING VISUALS *Answer: No; repulsion of the poles of the magnets is the force that moves the parts of the motor.*

Chapter 21 **717**

Ongoing Assessment

 One motor spins the CD while another motor moves a laser across the CD to read it.

Reinforce

Have students relate the section to the Big Idea.

 Reinforcing Key Concepts, p. 155

21.2 ASSESS & RETEACH

Assess

 Section 21.2 Quiz, p. 42

Reteach

Have students name as many machines and devices as they can that may contain one or more motors. Remind students that motors can produce different types of movements, not just a rotating movement. Ask students to consider how the motor(s) in each machine create movement. Example: a car's motor converts energy to turn the wheels. Have pairs of students compare their descriptions and discuss any differences.

Technology Resources

Have students visit ClassZone.com for reteaching of Key Concepts.

- CONTENT REVIEW
- CONTENT REVIEW CD-ROM

718 Unit 5: **Electricity and Magnetism**

Uses of Motors

Many machines and devices contain electric motors that may not be as obvious as the motor that turns the blades of a fan, for example. Even though the motion produced by the motor is circular, motors can move objects in any direction. For example, electric motors move power windows in a car up and down.

Motors can be very large, such as the motors that power an object as large as a subway train. They draw electric current from a third rail on the track or wires overhead that carry electric current. A car uses an electric current to start the engine. When the key is turned, a circuit is closed, producing a current from the battery to the motor. Other motors are very small, like the battery-operated motors that move the hands of a wristwatch.

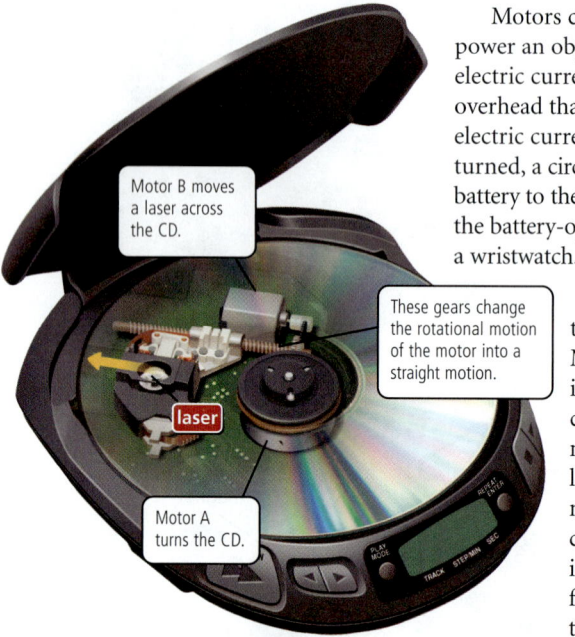

Motor B moves a laser across the CD.

These gears change the rotational motion of the motor into a straight motion.

Motor A turns the CD.

The illustration on the left shows the two small motors in a portable CD player. Motor A causes the CD to spin. Motor B is connected to a set of gears. The gears convert the rotational motion of the motor into a straight-line motion, or linear motion. As the CD spins, a laser moves straight across the CD from the center outward. The laser reads the information on the CD. The motion from Motor B moves the laser across the CD.

 Explain the function served by each motor in a CD player.

21.2 Review

KEY CONCEPTS

1. Explain how electric current and magnetism are related.
2. Describe three uses of electromagnets.
3. Explain how electrical energy is converted to motion in a motor.

CRITICAL THINKING

4. **Contrast** How does an electromagnet differ from a permanent magnet?
5. **Apply** Provide examples of two things in your home that use electric motors, and explain why they are easier to use because of the motors.

CHALLENGE

6. **Infer** Why is it necessary to change the direction of the current in the coil of an electric motor as it turns?

718 Unit 5: **Electricity and Magnetism**

ANSWERS

1. Electric current flowing through a wire produces a magnetic field around the wire.
2. to lift iron objects, to store information on a computer, to turn a motor
3. The electric current flowing through the electromagnet produces a magnetic field around the wire. A second magnet causes the electromagnet to turn.
4. The strength of an electromagnet can be altered, and electromagnets can be turned on and off.
5. Sample answer: A blender or mixer makes stirring easier because of its motor. An electrical fan keeps air moving even if the wind dies.
6. After the electromagnet turns half a turn, the poles of the permanent magnet start to repel the electromagnet. Reversing the direction of the current reverses the poles and keeps the motor running.

KEY CONCEPT

Magnetism can produce current.

◀ BEFORE, you learned
- Magnetism is a force exerted by magnets
- Electric current can produce a magnetic field
- Electromagnets can make objects move

▶ NOW, you will learn
- How a magnetic field can produce an electric current
- How a generator converts energy
- How direct current and alternating current differ

VOCABULARY

generator p. 720
direct current p. 721
alternating current p. 721
transformer p. 723

EXPLORE Energy Conversion

How can a motor produce current?

PROCEDURE

① Touch the wires on the motor to the battery terminals to see how the motor operates.

② Connect the wires to the light bulb.

③ Roll the shaft, or the movable part of the motor, between your fingers. Observe the light bulb.

④ Now spin the shaft rapidly. Record your observations.

MATERIALS
- small motor
- AA cell (battery)
- light bulb in holder

WHAT DO YOU THINK?
- How did you produce current?
- What effect did your motion have on the amount of light produced?

Magnets are used to generate an electric current.

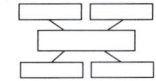

MAIN IDEA WEB Make a main idea web in your notebook for this heading.

In the 1830s, about ten years after Oersted discovered that an electric current produces magnetism, physicists observed the reverse effect—a moving magnetic field induces an electric current. When a magnet moves inside a coiled wire that is in a circuit, an electric current is generated in the wire.

It is often easier to generate an electric current by moving a wire inside a magnetic field. Whether it is the magnet or the wire that moves, the effect is the same. Current is generated as long as the wire crosses the magnetic field lines.

 What must happen for a magnetic field to produce an electric current?

Chapter 21: **Magnetism** 719

21.3 FOCUS

◑ Set Learning Goals
Students will
- Describe how a magnetic field can produce an electric current.
- Examine how a generator converts energy.
- Explain how direct current and alternating current differ.
- Infer from an experiment how to identify alternating current.

◑ 3-Minute Warm-Up

Display Transparency 21 or copy this exercise on the board:

Decide if these statements are true. If not, correct them.

1. Like charges attract one another. *repel*

2. Electric current can produce a magnetic field. *true*

3. Motors contain magnets. *true*

 3-Minute Warm-Up, p. T21

21.3 MOTIVATE

EXPLORE Energy Conversion

PURPOSE To observe how a motor uses kinetic energy to produce current

TIP *10 min.* Use small, sensitive motors, such as those used with solar cells.

WHAT DO YOU THINK? *Moving the shaft manually produced current. The faster the spin, the brighter the light.*

Ongoing Assessment

Describe how a magnetic field can produce an electric current.

Ask: To produce a current, which needs to move, the wire or the magnetic field? *either one*

 *Answer: The wire must cross magnetic field lines.*

RESOURCES FOR DIFFERENTIATED INSTRUCTION

Below Level
UNIT RESOURCE BOOK
- Reading Study Guide A, pp. 158–159
- Decoding Support, p. 183

 **AUDIO CDS**

Advanced
UNIT RESOURCE BOOK
- Challenge and Extension, p. 164
- Challenge Reading, pp. 179–180

English Learners
UNIT RESOURCE BOOK
Spanish Reading Study Guide, pp. 162–163

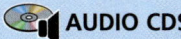 **AUDIO CDS**

- Audio Readings in Spanish
- Audio Readings (English)

Chapter 21 **719**

21.3 INSTRUCT

Teacher Demo
Show the effect of a moving magnetic field on stationary metal. Acquire 1 meter of copper tubing and two neodymium magnets small enough to easily pass through the tubing. Try to pick up the copper with the magnets to show that the copper is not magnetic. Hold the tubing vertically. Drop a small steel ball through the tubing, noticing how long it takes for it to pass through. Then drop the pair of magnets through the tube, again noticing how long it takes. Ask students to explain this difference in time. *The ball dropped as fast as gravity could pull it. The magnets induced a current in the tubing. The current produced a magnetic field that repelled the magnets, making them fall more slowly.*

Teach Difficult Concepts
Compare the relationship between a motor and a generator to other opposite processes. Ask students to explain how the motor-generator relationship is like the relationship between a speaker and a microphone. *In a motor, electrical energy produces a magnetic field, and in a generator, a magnetic field produces electrical energy. In a speaker, electrical signals produce sound, while a microphone transforms sound into electrical signals.*

Ongoing Assessment
Examine how a generator converts energy.

Ask: What energy conversion takes place in a generator? *Kinetic energy is converted to electrical energy.*

 Answer: the person turning the handle

 Answer: It produces a magnetic field that generates current in the wire.

720 Unit 5: **Electricity and Magnetism**

Generating an Electric Current

A **generator** is a device that converts the energy of motion, or kinetic energy, into electrical energy. A generator is similar to a motor in reverse. If you manually turn the shaft of a motor that contains a magnet, you can produce electric current.

The illustration below shows a portable generator that provides electrical energy to charge a cell phone in an emergency. The generator produces current as you turn the handle. Because it does not need to be plugged in, the generator can be used wherever and whenever it is needed to recharge a phone. The energy is supplied by the person turning the handle.

① As the handle is turned, it rotates a series of gears. The gears turn the shaft of the generator.

② The rotation of the shaft causes coils of wire to rotate within a magnetic field.

③ As the coils of the wire cross the magnetic field line, electric current is generated. The current recharges the battery of the cell phone.

 What is the source of energy for a cell phone generator?

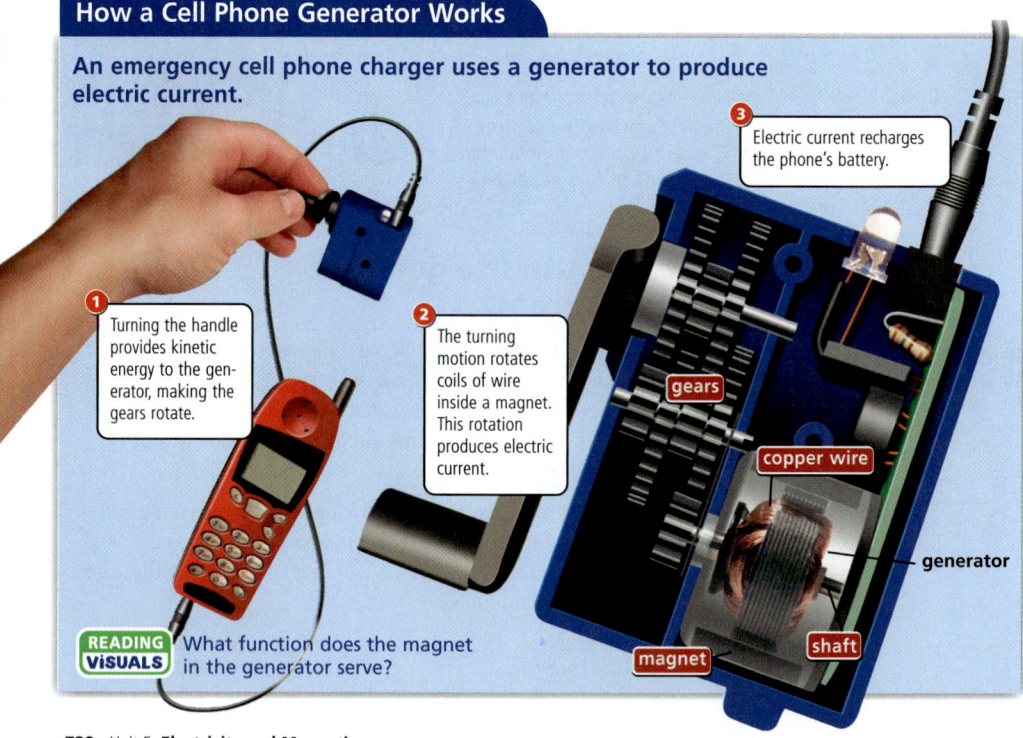

How a Cell Phone Generator Works
An emergency cell phone charger uses a generator to produce electric current.

① Turning the handle provides kinetic energy to the generator, making the gears rotate.

② The turning motion rotates coils of wire inside a magnet. This rotation produces electric current.

③ Electric current recharges the phone's battery.

READING VISUALS What function does the magnet in the generator serve?

720 Unit 5: Electricity and Magnetism

DIFFERENTIATE INSTRUCTION

 More Reading Support

A What is a generator? *a device that converts kinetic energy into electrical energy*

B How are a motor and a generator related? *They are opposites.*

English Learners English learners may be confused by subordinate (dependent) clauses when they appear at the beginning of a sentence. When this happens, tell students to rearrange the clauses into a more familiar pattern. The cause-and-effect relationship in the following sentence, for instance, is the same whether the subordinate clause beginning with "because" starts or completes the sentence. "Because it does not need to be plugged in, the generator can be used wherever and whenever it is needed to recharge a phone."

Direct and Alternating Currents

Think about how current flows in all of the circuits that you have studied so far. Electrons flow from one end of a battery or generator, through the circuit, and eventually back to the battery or generator. Electrons that flow in one direction produce one of two types of current.

- A **direct current** (DC) is electric charge that flows in one direction only. Direct current is produced by batteries and by DC generators such as the cell phone generator.
- An **alternating current** (AC) is a flow of electric charge that reverses direction at regular intervals. The current that enters your home and school is an alternating current.

CHECK YOUR READING What is the difference between direct current and alternating current?

Direct currents and alternating currents are produced by different generators. In an AC generator, the direction in which charge flows depends upon the direction in which the magnet moves in relation to the coil. Because generators use a rotating electromagnet, the poles of the electromagnet alternate between moving toward and moving away from the magnet. The result is a current that reverses with each half-rotation of the coil.

The illustration on the right shows a simple DC generator. DC generators are very similar to AC generators. The main difference is that DC generators have a commutator that causes the current to flow in only one direction.

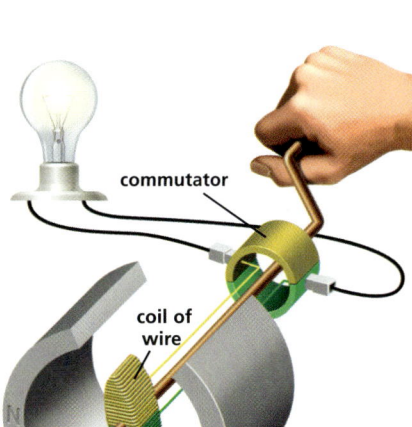

Many things in your home can work with either direct or alternating currents. In light bulbs, for instance, the resistance to motion of the electrons in the filament makes the filament glow. It doesn't matter in which direction the current is moving.

Some appliances can use only direct current. The black box that is on the plug of some devices is an AC–DC converter. AC–DC converters change the alternating current to direct current. For example, laptop computers use converters like the one shown in the photograph on the right. In a desktop computer, the converter is part of the power supply unit.

Chapter 21: **Magnetism** 721

DIFFERENTIATE INSTRUCTION

More Reading Support

C What type of current is produced by a battery?
direct current

D What type of generator contains a commutator?
direct current

Below Level To emphasize how quickly alternating current changes direction, ask groups of students to model it. They might turn their hands from one side to the other as quickly as possible or draw arrows on both sides of a card and flip it back and forth as fast as they can. Have students use a clock with a second hand to reverse direction at regular intervals. Explain that this model is a slower representation of alternating current.

Real World Example

In the United States, the frequency of AC is 60 Hz, which means that it changes direction 60 times a second. It is 50 Hz in most of Europe. Frequencies lower than this cause detectable flickering of lights. European travelers visiting the United States and U.S. travelers visiting Europe have to take adaptors for their appliances, because of the difference in frequencies.

Real World Example

When you turn on an electric car, a controller receives current from a battery. This controller changes the direct current from the battery into alternating current that can be used by the motor. Electric cars are not entirely free of fossil fuel use. Their batteries are recharged by plugging them into a current source. This current source often comes from an electric power plant that burns fossil fuels.

Ongoing Assessment

Explain how direct current and alternating current differ.

Ask: What is the difference between AC and DC generators? *AC generators rapidly alternate direction; DC generators produce current flowing in only one direction.*

CHECK YOUR READING Answer: In DC, electric charge flows in one direction only. In AC, electric charge reverses direction at regular intervals.

INVESTIGATE Electric Current

PURPOSE To observe characteristics of AC and use inference to identify it

TIPS *15 min.* For best results, use 2 meters of 22-gauge magnet wire and 14 inches of electrical tape. Students must wrap the wire across the face of the compass, not around the circumference. However, they must still be able to see the needle well enough to know in what direction it is pointing.

WHAT DO YOU THINK? *The compass needle moved back-and-forth with AC but not with DC. DC was observed in step 3, and AC in step 4. The type of current could be identified by whether the compass needle moved back-and-forth or not.*

CHALLENGE *Both use magnetism to generate an electrical current that changes direction.*

 Datasheet, Electric Current, p. 165

Technology Resources

Customize this student lab as needed or look for an alternative. Print rubrics to assess student lab reports.

 Lab Generator CD-ROM

Teaching with Technology

Students might want to design and conduct a similar investigation using an AC ammeter instead of a compass.

Metacognitive Strategy

Ask students to write a paragraph about any problems they encountered during the investigation and what they did to solve these problems and complete the activity.

Ongoing Assessment

 *Answer: It provides current to the car's electrical devices.*

722 Unit 5: Electricity and Magnetism

INVESTIGATE Electric Current

How can you identify the current?

PROCEDURE

① Wrap the wire tightly around the middle of the compass 10–15 times. Leave about 30 cm of wire free at each end. Tape the wire to the back of the compass to keep it in place.

② Sand the ends of the wire with sandpaper to expose about 2 cm of copper on each end. Arrange the compass on your desk so that the needle is parallel to, or lined up with, the coil. This will serve as your current detector.

③ Tape one end of the wire to one terminal of the battery. Touch the other end of the wire to the other battery terminal. Record your observations.

④ Observe the current detector as you tap the end of the wire to the battery terminal at a steady pace. Speed up or slow down your tapping until the needle of the compass alternates back and forth. Record your observations.

WHAT DO YOU THINK?
- What did you observe?
- What type of current did you detect in step 3? in step 4? How did you identify the type of current?

CHALLENGE How is this setup similar to an AC generator?

 **SKILL FOCUS**
Inferring

 MATERIALS
- piece of wire
- compass
- ruler
- tape
- sandpaper
- D cell (battery)

TIME
15 minutes

The energy that powers a car comes from burning gasoline, but the car also contains many devices that use electrical energy. Some of them are familiar—the headlights, turn signals, radio, power windows, and door locks. Others may be less familiar, such as the spark plugs that ignite the gasoline, the fuel and oil pumps that move fluids in the engine, and the air conditioner.

A car's engine includes a generator to provide current to its electrical devices. As the engine runs, it converts gasoline to kinetic energy. Some of that energy is transferred to the generator by a belt attached to its shaft. Inside the generator, a complex coil of copper wires turns in a magnetic field, generating a current that operates the electrical devices of the car.

The generator also recharges the battery, so that power is available when the engine is not running. Because the generator in most cars supplies alternating current, a car generator is usually called an alternator.

 E

 **CHECK YOUR READING** What function does a generator in a car serve?

722 Unit 5: Electricity and Magnetism

DIFFERENTIATE INSTRUCTION

 More Reading Support

E If the battery in a car supplies current when the motor is not running, why doesn't it quickly lose current? *The generator recharges the battery.*

Advanced Have students who are interested in how cars operate investigate the way the generator in a car runs the electrical components and what those electrical components are.

 Challenge and Extension, p. 164

Have students who are interested in electricity and circuits read the following article:

 Challenge Reading, pp. 179–180

Magnets are used to control voltage.

A **transformer** is a device that increases or decreases voltage. Transformers use magnetism to control the amount of voltage. A transformer consists of two coils of wire that are wrapped around an iron ring.

An alternating current from the voltage source in the first coil produces a magnetic field. The iron ring becomes an electromagnet. Because the current alternates, the magnetic field is constantly changing. The second coil is therefore within a changing magnetic field. Current is generated in the second coil. If the two coils have the same number of loops, the voltage in the second coil will be the same as the voltage in the first coil.

A change in the voltage is caused when the two coils have different numbers of loops. If the second coil has fewer loops than the first, as in the illustration, the voltage is decreased. This is called a step-down transformer. On the other hand, if the second coil has more loops than the first, the voltage in the second circuit will be higher than the original voltage. This transformer is called a step-up transformer.

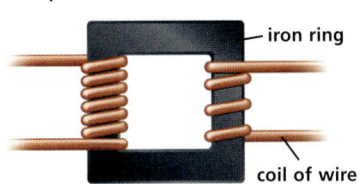
Step-Down Transformer
— iron ring
— coil of wire

Transformers are used in the distribution of current. Current is sent over power lines from power plants at a very high voltage. Step-down transformers on utility poles, such as the one pictured on the right, reduce the voltage available for use in homes. Sending current at high voltages minimizes the amount of energy lost to resistance along the way.

21.3 Review

KEY CONCEPTS
1. What is necessary for a magnetic field to produce an electric current?
2. Explain how electric generators convert kinetic energy into electrical energy.
3. Compare and contrast the ways in which direct current and alternating current are generated.

CRITICAL THINKING
4. **Apply** Many radios can be operated either by plugging them into the wall or by using batteries. How can a radio use either source of current?
5. **Draw Conclusions** Suppose that all of the electrical devices in a car stop working. Explain what the problem might be.

CHALLENGE
6. **Apply** European power companies deliver current at 220 V. Draw the design for a step-down transformer that would let you operate a CD player made to work at 110 V in France.

Reinforce the BIG idea
Have students relate the section to the Big Idea.

 Reinforcing Key Concepts, p. 166

21.3 ASSESS & RETEACH

Assess
 Section 21.3 Quiz, p. 43

Reteach
Have students create a graphic organizer that shows how an electrical motor and a generator are related. Tell students to include the terms current and magnetic field in their graphic organizer. *An organizer might have four boxes arranged in a circle, labeled generator, current, motor, and magnetic field. Arrows would then show that electrical current leaves a generator and enters a motor and that a magnetic field is produced by a motor and used by a generator.*

Technology Resources
Have students visit **ClassZone.com** for reteaching of Key Concepts.

 CONTENT REVIEW

 CONTENT REVIEW CD-ROM

ANSWERS

1. Magnetic field lines and a wire must cross each other.

2. The kinetic energy turns a magnet, producing an electrical current in a wire.

3. DC is generated without changing the polarity of the magnet that produces it. AC is produced by a magnet that frequently changes polarity.

4. For the radio to use AC, it must contain a converter that changes AC to DC.

5. The most likely cause would be a faulty generator.

6. The transformer should have twice as many coils on the input side as it does on the output side.

CHAPTER INVESTIGATION

Focus

PURPOSE To construct a speaker and determine how the strength of a magnet affects the volume of the speaker

OVERVIEW Students will use various materials to construct a speaker. They will use three magnets of different strengths to determine which one produces the loudest sound, and find that the strongest magnet produces the loudest sound on the speaker.

Lab Preparation

- For best results, use 2 meters of 22-gauge magnet wire. Strip the ends of the wire by scraping them with sandpaper, or use pre-stripped wire.
- Use an old stereo system or radio as it may become damaged by this activity if the volume level is too high. One stereo can be used by the whole class.
- To make the connections to the stereo, cut the wire to the headphone jack, and then separate and strip the two wires within. Students will clip the leads from their speakers to these two wires.
- Prior to the investigation have students read through the investigation and prepare their data tables. Or, copy and distribute datasheets and rubrics.

 UNIT RESOURCE BOOK, pp. 186–194

 SCIENCE TOOLKIT, F14

Lab Management

- Divide students into groups of three or four.
- Each student should do a different task when the group checks a magnet.

SAFETY Warn students not to turn up the sound enough to damage their ears. The volume should be turned down when the investigation is completed.

INCLUSION Ask students with hearing impairments to touch the cup so that they can feel the varying degrees of vibration as a measure of sound intensity. If students have difficulty, have a partner describe the results.

724 Unit 5: **Electricity and Magnetism**

CHAPTER INVESTIGATION

Build a Speaker

OVERVIEW AND PURPOSE Speakers are found on TVs, computers, telephones, stereos, amplifiers, and other devices. Inside a speaker, magnetism and electric current interact to produce sound. The current produces a magnetic field that acts on another magnet and causes vibrations. The vibrations produce sound waves. In this lab, you will
- construct a speaker
- determine how the strength of the magnet affects the speaker's volume

▶ Problem

How does the strength of the magnet used to make a speaker affect the loudness of sound produced by the speaker?

▶ Hypothesize

Write a hypothesis that explains how you expect the strength of a magnet to affect the loudness of sound produced by the speaker, and why. Your hypothesis should be in the form of an "if . . . , then . . . , because . . . " statement.

▶ Procedure

1. Make a data table similar to the one shown on the sample notebook page.

2. Test the strength of each magnet by measuring the distance at which a paper clip will move to the magnet, as shown. Record the measurements in your **Science Notebook**.

step 2

3. Starting about 6 cm from the end of the wire, wrap the wire around the marker 50 times to make a coil.

MATERIALS
- 3 magnets of different strengths
- paper clip
- ruler
- piece of wire
- marker
- cup
- masking tape
- 2 wire leads with alligator clips
- stereo system

724 Unit 5: **Electricity and Magnetism**

INVESTIGATION RESOURCES

 CHAPTER INVESTIGATION, Build a Speaker
- Level A, pp. 186–189
- Level B, pp. 190–193
- Level C, p. 194
Advanced students should complete Levels B & C.

 Writing a Lab Report, D12–13

Technology Resources

Customize this student lab as needed or look for an alternative. Print rubrics to assess student lab reports.

 Lab Generator CD-ROM

4. Carefully slide the coil off the marker. Wrap the ends of the wire around the coil to keep it in the shape of a circle, as shown.

5. Place the cup upside-down on your table. Tape the coil to the bottom of the cup. Clip the leads to the ends of the wire. Tape the alligator clips to the sides of the cup, as shown.

6. Take turns attaching the alligator clips to the stereo as instructed by your teacher. Place each magnet on the table near the stereo. Test the speaker by holding the cup directly over each magnet and listening. Record your observations.

Conclude

1. **INTERPRET** Which magnet produced the loudest noise when used with your speaker? Answer the question posed in the problem.

2. **ANALYZE** Compare your results with your hypothesis. Did your results support your hypothesis?

3. **IDENTIFY LIMITS** Describe possible limitations or sources of error in the procedure or any places where errors might have occurred.

4. **APPLY** You have built a simple version of a real speaker. Apply what you have learned in this lab to explain how a real speaker might work.

INVESTIGATE Further

CHALLENGE In what ways might you vary the design of the speaker to improve its functioning? Review the procedure to identify variables that might be changed to improve the speaker. Choose one variable and design an experiment to test that variable.

Observe and Analyze

1. **RECORD OBSERVATIONS** Be sure to record your observations in the data table.

2. **INFER** Why is the coil of wire held near the magnet?

3. **APPLY** The diaphragm on a speaker vibrates to produce sound. What part of your stereo is the diaphragm?

4. **IDENTIFY** What was the independent variable in this experiment? What was the dependent variable?

Build a Speaker
Problem How does the strength of the magnet used to make a speaker affect the loudness of sound produced by the speaker?
Hypothesize
Observe and Analyze
Table 1. Strength of Magnet and Loudness of Sound

Magnet	Strength (paper clip distance)	Observations
1		
2		
3		

Conclude

Chapter 21: **Magnetism** 725

Observe and Analyze

1. Data tables should be complete. Sample data: Magnet 1: 1.5 cm, could not hear any sound; Magnet 2: 2 cm, could hear a faint sound; Magnet 3: 4 cm, could hear the sound clearly

2. The magnetic field produced by the coil of wire should be close enough to affect the magnet on the table.

3. the cup

4. strength of the magnet; loudness of the sound

Conclude

1. The strongest magnet produced the loudest sound. The stronger the magnet used to make a speaker, the louder the sound produced.

2. Answers will vary depending on students' results and original hypotheses.

3. Sample answer: The wires might not be adequately connected, the magnets might not be strong enough, and sounds in the room may have interfered with the observations.

4. Current travels through a coil of wire to produce a magnetic field. The magnetic field of the coil interacts with the magnetic field of the permanent magnet, causing sound vibrations.

INVESTIGATE Further

CHALLENGE Variables might include the number of coils used, the number of permanent magnets used, and the length of the wires attached to the alligator clips.

Post-Lab Discussion

• Ask: Would the experiment have been different if some other object, such as a metal can or a glass jar, had been used instead of the paper cup? Explain. *The ability of the material to vibrate would affect the sound produced. The more the material vibrated, the louder the sound would be.*

• Ask: What questions do you still have upon completing the "Build a Speaker" activity?

Chapter 21 **725**

21.4 FOCUS

◯ Set Learning Goals

Students will
- Discover how power plants generate electrical energy.
- Describe how electric power is measured.
- Calculate energy usage.
- Model in an experiment how electrical energy is used.

◯ 3-Minute Warm-Up

Display Transparency 21 or copy this exercise on the board:

Match the definitions to the terms.

Definitions
1. the force exerted by magnets *b*
2. a device that uses magnetism to produce current *d*
3. a device that uses current to produce magnetism *e*

Terms

a. electricity   d. generator
b. magnetism   e. electromagnet
c. compass

 3-Minute Warm-Up, p. T21

21.4 MOTIVATE

THINK ABOUT

PURPOSE To think about how the kinetic energy of falling water can be used to generate electricity

DISCUSS Ask students how many of them have been in the ocean or a river and felt the energy of the moving water. Ask them to use this information to answer the question. *The force of the water can be used to turn the moving parts of a generator.*

Ongoing Assessment

 *Answer: Kinetic energy turns the moving parts of a generator to produce electricity.*

726 Unit 5: **Electricity and Magnetism**

KEY CONCEPT
21.4 Generators supply electrical energy.

◀ BEFORE, you learned
- Magnetism is a force exerted by magnets
- A moving magnetic field can generate an electric current in a conductor
- Generators use magnetism to produce current

▶ NOW, you will learn
- How power plants generate electrical energy
- How electric power is measured
- How energy usage is calculated

VOCABULARY

electric power p. 726
watt p. 728
kilowatt p. 728
kilowatt-hour p. 729

THINK ABOUT

How can falling water generate electrical energy?

This photograph shows the Hoover Dam on the Nevada/Arizona border, which holds back a large lake, almost 600 feet deep, on the Colorado River. It took thousands of workers nearly five years to build the dam, and it cost millions of dollars. One of the main purposes of the Hoover Dam is the generation of current. Think about what you have read about generators. How could the energy of falling water be used to generate current?

Generators provide most of the world's electrical energy.

The tremendous energy produced by falling water provides the turning motion for large generators at a power plant. The power plant at the Hoover Dam supplies energy to more than a million people.

Other sources of energy at power plants include steam from burning fossil fuels, nuclear reactions, wind, solar heating, and ocean tides. Each source provides the energy of motion to the generators, producing electrical energy. **Electric power** is the rate at which electrical energy is generated from another source of energy.

 **VOCABULARY** Use a description wheel to take notes about *electrical power*.

 What do power plants that use water, steam, and wind all have in common?

726 Unit 5: Electricity and Magnetism

RESOURCES FOR DIFFERENTIATED INSTRUCTION

Below Level
UNIT RESOURCE BOOK
- Reading Study Guide A, pp. 169–170
- Decoding Support, p. 183

🎧 AUDIO CDS

Advanced
UNIT RESOURCE BOOK
Challenge and Extension, p. 175

English Learners
UNIT RESOURCE BOOK
Spanish Reading Study Guide, pp. 173–174

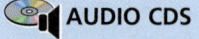 AUDIO CDS
- Audio Readings in Spanish
- Audio Readings (English)

How does the power plant convert the energy of motion into electrical energy? Very large generators in the plant hold powerful electromagnets surrounded by massive coils of copper wire. The illustration below shows how the energy from water falling from the reservoir to the river far below a dam is converted to electrical energy.

Find out more about dams that generate current.

① As the water falls from the reservoir, its kinetic energy increases and it flows very fast. The falling stream of water turns a fan-like device, called a turbine, which is connected to the generator's shaft.

② The rotation of the shaft turns powerful electromagnets that are surrounded by the coil of copper wires. The coil is connected to a step-up transformer that sends high-voltage current to power lines.

③ Far from the plant, step-down transformers reduce the voltage so that current can be sent through smaller lines to neighborhoods. Another transformer reduces the voltage to the level needed to operate lights and appliances.

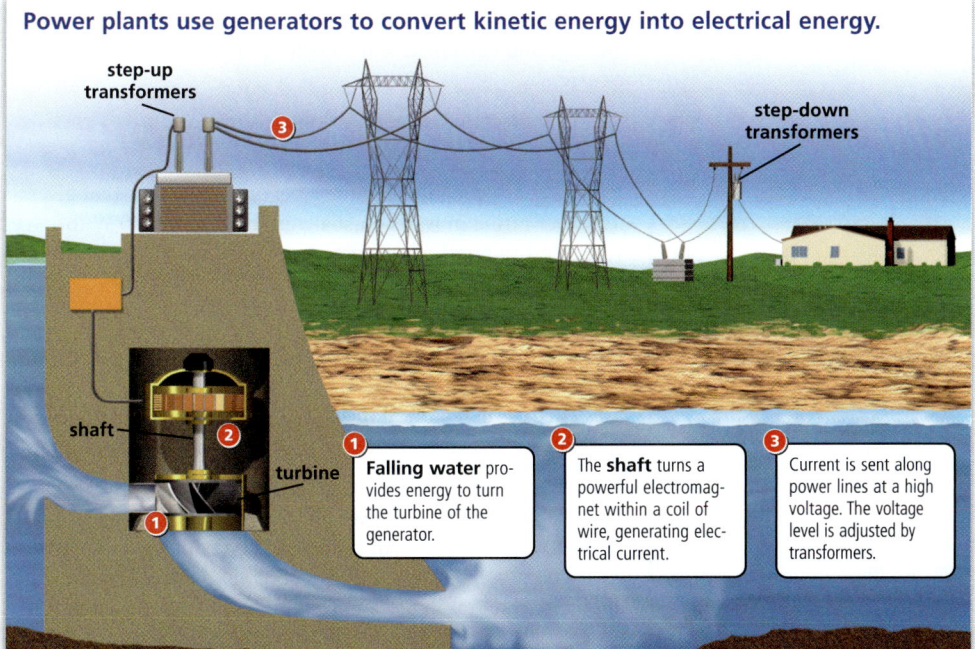

How Electrical Power Is Generated
Power plants use generators to convert kinetic energy into electrical energy.

① **Falling water** provides energy to turn the turbine of the generator.

② The **shaft** turns a powerful electromagnet within a coil of wire, generating electrical current.

③ Current is sent along power lines at a high voltage. The voltage level is adjusted by transformers.

 How is kinetic energy turned into electrical energy in a power plant?

Chapter 21: **Magnetism** 727

21.4 INSTRUCT

Teach from Visuals
Have students study the generator schematic. Ask:

- Which has a higher voltage, the current flowing from tower to tower or the current entering the house? *the current flowing from tower to tower*
- Explain your answer. *The current from the tower passes through a step-down transformer before it enters the house.*
- What role does kinetic energy play in the production of electricity? *Kinetic energy turns the turbine in a generator.*

Ongoing Assessment
Discover how power plants generate electrical energy.

Ask: The step-up transformer in a generator sends what type of current to power lines? *high-voltage*

READING VISUALS *Answer: Kinetic energy turns a turbine, which turns a magnetic field inside a coil, producing current.*

DIFFERENTIATE INSTRUCTION

More Reading Support

A What do you call the fan-like device in a generator? *a turbine*

B Which type of transformer does current pass through before it goes into neighborhoods? *step-down*

English Learners The paragraphs above describe in detail how electrical power is generated. Students from homogenous groups may need to practice describing processes or giving directions so an "outsider" can understand. Ask students to pick a place in their school and write out directions from their classroom to that place. Students should write as if the person reading has never been inside their school before—thus, they would not know landmarks such as "Mrs. Lopez's room" or "the broken water fountain."

Chapter 21 **727**

Address Misconceptions

IDENTIFY Ask: What is the difference between electrical energy and electric power? If students answer "Nothing," they hold the misconception that electric energy and electrical power are the same thing.

CORRECT Point out that power is the rate at which energy is used. Provide students with an example of another type of power. Chemical energy in your body can be used to produce kinetic energy when you move. A person who is running is using energy at a higher rate—and therefore has a higher power— than a person who is walking. Solicit other examples from students of energy being used at different rates.

REASSESS Which measures a rate, electrical energy or power? *power*

Technology Resources
Visit **ClassZone.com** for background on common student misconceptions.
 MISCONCEPTION DATABASE

Teach from Visuals

Have students refer to the power rating table on this page. Ask: If you have a room that is wired for 2000 watts, which of the following groups of appliances could you use in the room? *a, c*

a. refrigerator, stereo system, microwave oven
b. computer, clothes dryer
c. video game system, hair dryer, window fan, television
d. microwave oven, hair dryer

Ongoing Assessment

Describe how electric power is measured.
Ask: What equation shows the relationship among electric power, voltage, and current? $P = VI$

 Answer: Kilowatts measure a large amount of electric power, such as that used in a building.

728 Unit 5: **Electricity and Magnetism**

Electric power can be measured.

You have read that electric power is the rate at which electrical energy is generated from another source of energy. Power also refers to the rate at which an appliance converts electrical energy back into another form of energy, such as light, heat, or sound.

In order to provide electrical energy to homes and factories, power companies need to know the rate at which energy is needed. Power can be measured so that companies can determine how much energy is used and where it is used. This information is used to figure out how much to charge customers, and it is used to determine whether more electrical energy needs to be generated. To provide energy to an average home, a power plant needs to burn about four tons of coal each year.

RESOURCE CENTER
CLASSZONE.COM
Learn more about energy use and conservation.

Watts and Kilowatts

The unit of measurement for power is the **watt** (W). Watts measure the rate at which energy is used by an electrical appliance. For instance, a light bulb converts energy to light and heat. The power rating of the bulb, or of any device that consumes electrical energy, depends on both the voltage and the current. The formula for finding power, in watts, from voltage and current, is shown below. The letter *I* stands for current.

$$\text{Electric Power} = \text{Voltage} \cdot \text{Current}$$
$$P = VI$$

You have probably seen the label on a light bulb that gives its power rating in watts—usually in the range of 40 W to 100 W. A brighter bulb converts energy at a higher rate than one with a lower power rating.

The chart at the left shows typical power ratings, in watts, for some appliances that you might have in your home. The exact power rating depends on how each brand of appliance uses energy. You can find the actual power rating for an appliance on its label.

The combined power rating in a building is likely to be a fairly large number. A **kilowatt** (kW) is a unit of power equal to one thousand watts. All of the appliances in a room may have a combined power rating of several kilowatts, but all appliances are not in use all of the time. That is why energy is usually calculated based on how long the appliances are in use.

 Explain what kilowatts are used to measure.

Typical Power Ratings

Appliance	Watts
DVD player	20
Radio	20
Video game system	25
Electric blanket	60
Light bulb	75
Stereo system	100
Window fan	100
Television	110
Computer	120
Computer monitor	150
Refrigerator	700
Air conditioner	1000
Microwave oven	1000
Hair dryer	1200
Clothes dryer	3000

728 Unit 5: **Electricity and Magnetism**

DIFFERENTIATE INSTRUCTION

More Reading Support

C What unit measures electric power? *the watt (W)*

D What unit is used for large amounts of electric power? *the kilowatt (kW)*

Below Level Have students look around the room and identify all of the appliances in use that are listed on the table on this page, and the wattage of each appliance. Students should then use the table to estimate the total power rating of the room.

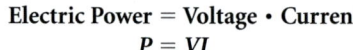

INVESTIGATE Power

How would you use your electrical energy?

PROCEDURE

1. On a sheet of graph paper, outline a box that is 10 squares long by 18 squares wide. The box represents a room that is wired to power a total of 1800 W. Each square represents 10 W of power.
2. From the chart on page 728, choose appliances that you want in your room. Using colored pencils, fill in the appropriate number of boxes for each appliance.
3. All of the items that you choose must fit within the total power available, represented by the 180 squares.

WHAT DO YOU THINK?
- How did you decide to use your electrical energy?
- Could you provide enough energy to operate everything you wanted at one time?

CHALLENGE During the summer, power companies sometimes cannot produce enough energy for the demand. Why do you think that happens?

SKILL FOCUS
Making models

MATERIALS
- graph paper
- colored pencils

TIME
30 minutes

Calculating Energy Use

The electric bill for your energy usage is calculated based on the rate at which energy is used, or the power, and the amount of time it is used at that rate. Total energy used by an appliance is determined by multiplying its power consumption by the amount of time that it is used.

$$\text{Energy used} = \text{Power} \cdot \text{time}$$
$$E = Pt$$

The kilowatt-hour is the unit of measurement for energy usage. A **kilowatt-hour** (kWh) is equal to one kilowatt of power for a one-hour period. Buildings usually have meters that measure how many kilowatt-hours of energy have been used. The meters display four or five small dials in a row, as shown in the photograph on the right. Each dial represents a different place value—ones, tens, hundreds, or thousands. For example, the meter in the photograph shows that the customer has used close to 9000 kWh of energy—8933 kWh, to be exact. To find how much energy was used in one month, the last month's reading is subtracted from this total.

Chapter 21: **Magnetism** 729

DIFFERENTIATE INSTRUCTION

More Reading Support

E What unit represents energy use? *the kilowatt-hour (kWh)*

Advanced Have students sketch the dials on an electric meter if the reading is 6534 kWh. Make sure their sketches show that the first and third dials read counterclockwise, and the second and fourth dials read clockwise.

 Challenge and Extension, p. 175

INVESTIGATE Power

PURPOSE To make models of energy use

TIPS 30 min.

- Use preprinted graph paper rather than having students draw their own grid, so that they see that each square represents the identical amount of energy.
- Review how to determine how much of a square to shade for a fraction of 10 watts.

WHAT DO YOU THINK? *Answers will vary, depending on what appliances students choose. The amount of power must total no more than 1800 W.*

CHALLENGE *Appliances used to cool buildings, such as air conditioners and fans, use more electricity than most methods for heating buildings.*

- Power Ratings Chart, p. 176
- Datasheet, Power, p. 177

Technology Resources

Customize this student lab as needed or look for an alternative. Print rubrics to assess student lab reports.

 Lab Generator CD-ROM

Real World Example

How much electricity a home appliance uses depends on how much time the appliance is actually used and what setting of power is used. If you used a personal computer and monitor for four hours a day, 365 days a year, that would be equal to 394 kWh. At 8.5 cents per kWh that would be $33.51 of electricity costs per year. The wattage of most appliances is stamped on the bottom or back of an appliance. The wattage is usually listed as the maximum power of the appliance. For example, a clock radio uses 10 watts while a dishwasher uses 1200 to 2400 watts.

Ongoing Assessment

Calculate energy usage.

Ask: If you use your computer and monitor for 4 hours a day, how much energy do you use? Use the table on p. 728.

120 + 150 = 270 watts = 0.27kW

E = 0.27kW · 4h = 1.08 kWh

▶ Practice the Math

Answers:

1. E = 3.3 kW · 6 h
   E = 19.8 kWh

2. E = 1.2 kW · 0.2 h
   E = 0.24 kWh

Reinforce

Have students relate the section to the Big Idea.

R Reinforcing Key Concepts, p. 178

21.4 ASSESS & RETEACH

Assess

 Section 21.4 Quiz, p. 44

Reteach

Have students use concepts from this section to explain how wind can be used to generate electricity. Have them accompany their explanations with diagrams.

Technology Resources

Have students visit ClassZone.com for reteaching of Key Concepts.

 CONTENT REVIEW

 CONTENT REVIEW CD-ROM

To determine the number of kilowatt-hours of energy used by an appliance, find its wattage on the chart on page 728 or from the label. Then, substitute it into the formula along with the number of hours it was in use. Solve the sample problems below.

Finding Energy Used

▶ **Sample Problem**

How much energy is used to dry clothes in a 3 kW dryer for 30 minutes?

What do you know?	Power = 3.0 kW, time = 0.5 hr
What do you want to find out?	Energy used
Write the formula:	E = Pt
Substitute into the formula:	E = 3.0 kW · 0.5 hr
Calculate and simplify:	E = 1.5 kWh
Check that your units agree:	Unit is kWh. Unit for energy used is kWh. Units agree.
Answer:	1.5 kWh

▶ **Practice the Math**

1. All of the appliances in a computer lab are in use for 6 hours every day and together use 3.3 kW. How much energy has been used in 1 day?
2. How much energy is used when a 1.2 kW hair dyer is in use for 0.2 hr?

Energy prices vary, but you can estimate the cost of using an electrical appliance by using a value of about 8 cents/kWh. You can calculate how much energy you can save by turning off the lights or television when you are not using them. Although the number may seem small, try multiplying your savings over the course of a month or year.

21.4 Review

KEY CONCEPTS

1. How do power plants generate electrical energy from kinetic energy?
2. Explain what watts measure.
3. How is energy use determined?

CRITICAL THINKING

4. **Apply** Think about reducing energy usage in your home. What changes would make the largest difference in the amount of energy used?
5. **Calculate** How much energy is used if a 3000 W clothes dryer is used for 4 hours?

● CHALLENGE

6. **Calculate** An electric bill for an apartment shows 396 kWh of energy used over one month. The appliances in the apartment have a total power rating of 2.2 kW. How many hours were the appliances in use?

ANSWERS

1. Kinetic energy turns a turbine in a generator, which produces electric current.
2. Watts measure electric power, or the rate of energy conversion.
3. Multiply the power by the number of hours of use.
4. Reduce usage of high-wattage appliances, such as air conditioners and hair dryers.
5. E = 3 kW × 4 h = 12 kWh
6. t = 396 kWh/2.2 kW
   t = 180 h

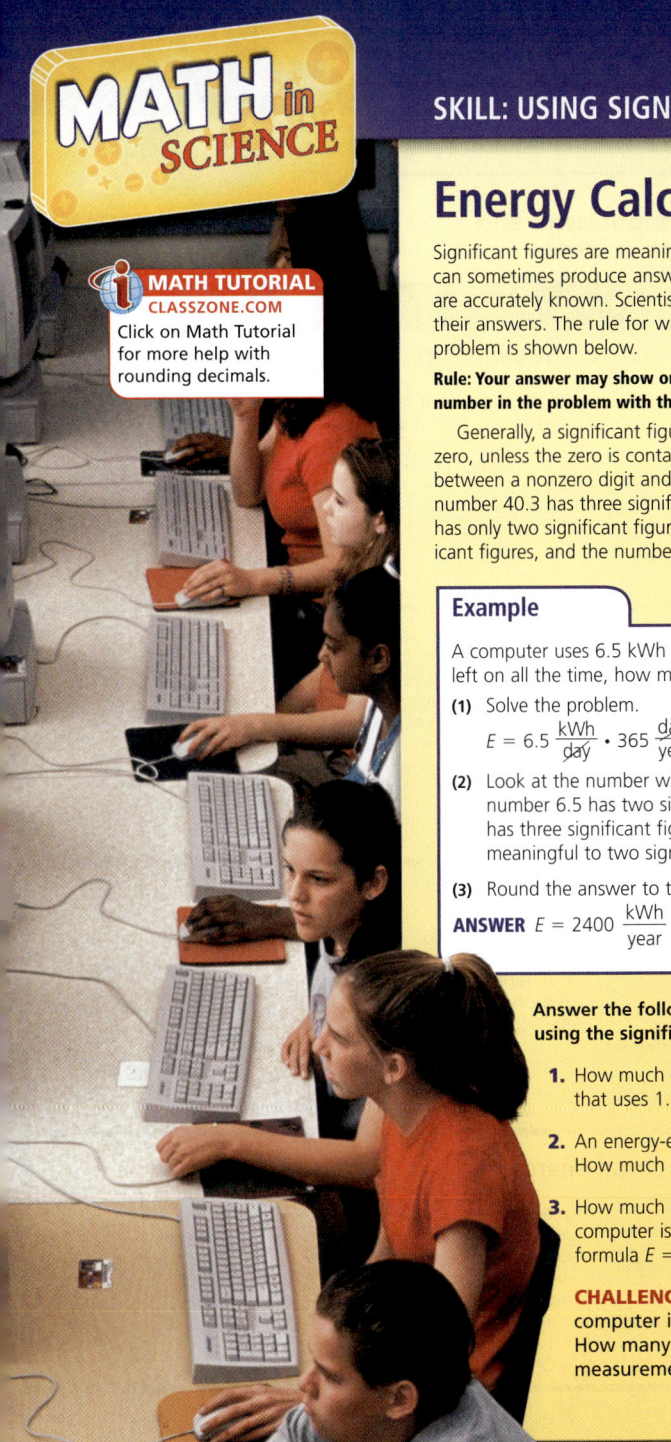

MATH in SCIENCE

SKILL: USING SIGNIFICANT FIGURES

Energy Calculations

Significant figures are meaningful digits in a number. Calculations can sometimes produce answers with more significant figures than are accurately known. Scientists use rules to determine how to round their answers. The rule for writing an answer to a multiplication problem is shown below.

Rule: Your answer may show only as many significant figures as the number in the problem with the fewest significant figures.

Generally, a significant figure is any digit shown except for a zero, unless the zero is contained between two nonzero digits or between a nonzero digit and a decimal point. For example, the number 40.3 has three significant figures, but the number 5.90 has only two significant figures. The number 0.034 has three significant figures, and the number 0.8 has only one significant figure.

Example

A computer uses 6.5 kWh of energy per day. If the computer is left on all the time, how much energy does it use in a year?

(1) Solve the problem.

$$E = 6.5 \frac{\text{kWh}}{\text{day}} \cdot 365 \frac{\text{days}}{\text{year}} = 2372.5 \frac{\text{kWh}}{\text{year}}$$

(2) Look at the number with the fewest significant figures. The number 6.5 has two significant figures, and the number 365 has three significant figures. Therefore, the answer is only meaningful to two significant figures.

(3) Round the answer to two significant figures.

ANSWER $E = 2400 \frac{\text{kWh}}{\text{year}}$

Answer the following questions. Write your answers using the significant figure rule for multiplication.

1. How much energy is used in a year by a computer that uses 1.7 kWh/day?

2. An energy-efficient computer uses 0.72 kWh/day. How much energy does it use in a week?

3. How much energy is used in one year if a 0.27 kW computer is on for 3 hours/day? (**Hint:** Use the formula $E = Pt$.)

CHALLENGE The energy usage of a computer is measured to be 0.058030 kWh. How many significant figures does this measurement have?

Chapter 21: **Magnetism** 731

MATH TUTORIAL
CLASSZONE.COM
Click on Math Tutorial for more help with rounding decimals.

MATH IN SCIENCE
Math Skills Practice for Science

Set Learning Goal
To determine the number of significant figures in a number

Present the Science
The number 2400 has two significant figures, not four, because the implied decimal point at the end of the number does not count. If the number were written 2400.0, it would have four significant figures.

Develop Number Sense
- The rules for division and significant figures are the same as those for multiplication. Thus, the quotient of 3.4 kWh divided by 2.67 h has two significant figures.
- The rules for addition and subtraction and significant figures differ from those of multiplication and division. When adding or subtracting, align the decimals, then add or subtract. The answer has the same place value as the least precise number in the problem. For example, the sum of 2.3 m, 4.85 m, 0.024 m, and 899 m will be rounded off to the unit's place, because 899 m is the least precise measurement.

Close
Ask: How many significant figures are in the product of 2.3 kW and 3.94 h? *two*

- Math Support, p. 184
- Math Practice, p. 185

Technology Resources
Students can visit **ClassZone.com** for practice with significant figures.

 MATH TUTORIAL

ANSWERS

1. $E = 1.7$ kWh/day $\cdot$ 365 days/yr $= 620$ kWh/yr
2. $E = 0.72$ kWh/day $\cdot$ 7 days/week $= 5$ kWh/week
3. $E = 0.27$ kW $\cdot$ 3 h/day $\cdot$ 365 days/yr $= 300$ kWh/yr

CHALLENGE *five*

CHAPTER 21 • REVIEW

BACK TO

Have students look at the illustrations on pp. 717 and 721. Ask them to use the diagrams to summarize what they have learned about producing a magnetic field from electric current and producing an electric current from a magnetic field. *A generator produces an electric current from a magnetic field. A motor produces a magnetic field from an electric current.*

◯ KEY CONCEPTS SUMMARY

SECTION 21.1
Ask: How would the magnetic field lines change if the magnet on the left were reversed? *They would show repulsion, not attraction.*

SECTION 21.2
Ask: In the diagram, what pushes on the electromagnet? *the poles of a magnet*
Ask: Which of the magnets is free to move in a motor? *the electromagnet*

SECTION 21.3
Ask: How does a generator differ from a motor? *It works the opposite way.*

SECTION 21.4
Ask: What is the purpose of the turbine in a generator? *It moves a magnet to generate a current.*

Review Concepts

- Big Idea Flow Chart, p. T17
- Chapter Outline, pp. T23–T24

---

21 Chapter Review

the BIG idea
Current can produce magnetism, and magnetism can produce current.

CONTENT REVIEW
CLASSZONE.COM

◯ KEY CONCEPTS SUMMARY

1 Magnetism is a force that acts at a distance.

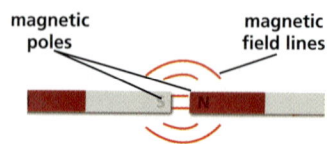

Opposite poles attract.

All magnets have a north and south pole. The like poles of two magnets repel each other and the opposite poles attract.

VOCABULARY
magnet p. 703
magnetism p. 704
magnetic pole p. 704
magnetic field p. 705
magnetic domain p. 706

2 Current can produce magnetism.

A magnet that is produced by electric current is called an electromagnet. Motors use electromagnets to convert electrical energy into the energy of motion.

VOCABULARY
electromagnetism p. 713
electromagnet p. 714

3 Magnetism can produce current.

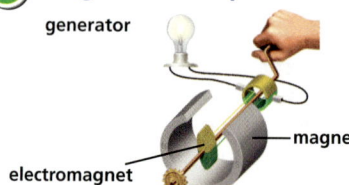

Magnetism can be used to produce electric current. In a generator the energy of motion is converted into electrical energy.

VOCABULARY
generator p. 720
direct current p. 721
alternating current p. 721
transformer p. 723

4 Generators supply electrical energy.

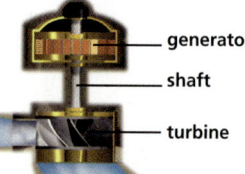

Generators at power plants use large magnets to produce electric current, supplying electrical energy to homes and businesses.

VOCABULARY
electric power p. 726
watt p. 728
kilowatt p. 728
kilowatt-hour p. 729

732 Unit 5: Electricity and Magnetism

Technology Resources

Have students visit **ClassZone.com** or use the CD-ROM for a cumulative review of concepts.

 CONTENT REVIEW

 CONTENT REVIEW CD-ROM

Engage students in a whole-class interactive review of Key Concepts. Edit content as you wish.

 POWER PRESENTATIONS

Reviewing Vocabulary

Draw a cluster diagram for each of the terms below. Write the vocabulary term in the center circle. In another circle, write the definition of the term in your own words. Add other circles that give examples or characteristics of the term. A sample diagram is completed for you.

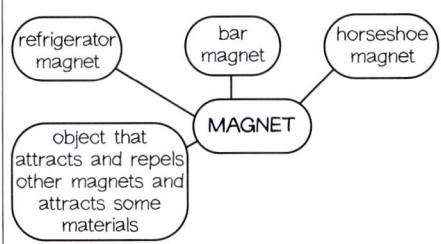

1. magnetism
2. magnetic pole
3. magnetic field
4. magnetic domain
5. electromagnet
6. generator
7. direct current
8. alternating current
9. transformer
10. electric power
11. watt
12. kilowatt-hour

Reviewing Key Concepts

Multiple Choice *Choose the letter of the best answer.*

13. Magnetic field lines flow from a magnet's
    a. north pole to south pole
    b. south pole to north pole
    c. center to the outside
    d. outside to the center

14. Which of the following is characteristic of magnetic materials?
    a. Their atoms are all aligned.
    b. Their atoms are arranged in magnetic domains.
    c. They are all nonmetals.
    d. They are all made of lodestone.

15. The Earth's magnetic field helps to protect living things from
    a. ultraviolet light
    b. meteors
    c. the Northern Lights
    d. charged particles

16. To produce a magnetic field around a copper wire, you have to
    a. place it in Earth's magnetic field
    b. run a current through it
    c. supply kinetic energy to it
    d. place it near a strong magnet

17. An electric current is produced when a wire is
    a. stationary in a magnetic field
    b. moving in a magnetic field
    c. placed between the poles of a magnet
    d. coiled around a magnet

18. In a generator, kinetic energy is converted into
    a. light energy
    b. chemical energy
    c. electrical energy
    d. nuclear energy

19. In an AC circuit, the current moves
    a. back and forth
    b. from one end of a generator to the other
    c. from one end of a battery to the other
    d. in one direction

20. What is the function of the turbine in a power plant?
    a. to increase the voltage
    b. to convert DC to AC
    c. to cool the steam
    d. to turn the coil or magnet

21. The two factors needed to measure usage of electrical energy in a building are
    a. power and time
    b. power and voltage
    c. voltage and time
    d. current and voltage

Chapter 21: **Magnetism** 733

ASSESSMENT RESOURCES

UNIT ASSESSMENT BOOK
- Chapter Test A, pp. 45–48
- Chapter Test B, pp. 49–52
- Chapter Test C, pp. 53–56
- Alternative Assessment, pp. 57–58
- Unit Test, A, B, C, pp. 59–70

SPANISH ASSESSMENT BOOK
Spanish Chapter Test, pp. 309–312
Spanish Unit Test, pp. 313–316

Technology Resources

Edit test items and answer choices.

 Test Generator CD-ROM

Visit **ClassZone.com** to extend test practice.

 Test Practice

Reviewing Vocabulary

1. **magnetism**: force exerted by magnets; acts at a distance; affects some metals; push or pull

2. **magnetic pole**: the part of a magnet where magnetic force is strongest; all magnets have two; north and south; opposite poles attract; like poles repel

3. **magnetic field**: area of magnetic force around a magnet; force acting at a distance; Earth has a magnetic field

4. **magnetic domain**: region within magnetic material with a magnetic field; in magnets they are aligned; in magnetic materials they are not aligned

5. **electromagnet**: a magnet made with electric current; a piece of iron inside a coil of wire; can be turned on and off; can be very strong

6. **generator**: a device that produces electric current from magnetism; AC; DC; opposite of a motor

7. **direct current**: current that flows in one direction; DC; used by battery-operated devices

8. **alternating current**: current that regularly reverses direction; AC; supplied by power plants; can be converted into DC

9. **transformer**: uses magnetism to adjust voltage level; step-up, more coils on output; step-down, fewer coils on output; used in distribution of electricity

10. **electric power**: the rate at which energy is generated or used; units of W and kW; appliances have power ratings

11. **watt**: measure of power of an appliance; light bulbs labeled; small unit

12. **kilowatt-hour**: measure of energy usage; power times hours of usage; read from electric meters

Reviewing Key Concepts

13. a   18. c
14. b   19. a
15. d   20. d
16. b   21. a
17. b

Thinking Critically

22. Current will cause a magnetic field to form around the coil, and the iron strip will bend toward it.
23. It will switch the poles of the electromagnet.
24. The magnet would be attracted to the coil when the current flows one direction and repelled when the current is reversed.
25. The motion turns a magnetic field inside a coil, producing current.
26. Sample answer: car, computer, hair dryer
27. It contains a generator. It contains a battery or some other device that stores energy for later use.
28. The moon does not contain a core with the same composition as Earth's core.

Using Math in Science

29. approximately 500 kWh
30. $P = E/t$, 400 kWh/2 kW = 200 h
31. Assuming usage of 350 kWh, 350 kWh · $0.08 = $28.00
32. July, August, September

the BIG idea

33. Answers should reflect knowledge of the effect of Earth's magnetic field on the compass.
34. Magnetism is a force that acts at a distance. Magnets attract and repel other magnets. For example, maglev trains are pushed forward and upward by magnetism. Every magnet has a north and south magnetic pole. A magnetic field is the region around a magnet in which the magnet exerts a force.

UNIT PROJECTS

Have students present their projects. Use the appropriate rubrics from the URB to evaluate their work.

 Unit Projects, pp. 5–10

734   Unit 5: **Electricity and Magnetism**

Thinking Critically

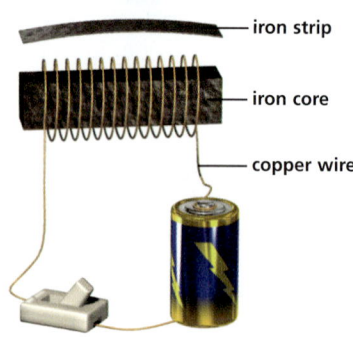

Refer to the device in the illustration above to answer the next three questions.

22. **APPLY** What will happen when the switch is closed?
23. **PREDICT** What effect will switching the direction of the current have on the operation of the device?
24. **CONTRAST** If the iron strip is replaced with a thin magnet, how would that affect the answers to the previous two questions?
25. **APPLY** Coal is burned at a power plant to produce steam. The rising steam turns a turbine. Describe how the motion of the turbine produces current at the plant.
26. **CONNECT** List three things that you use in your everyday life that would not exist without the discovery of electromagnetism.
27. **APPLY** A radio for use during power outages works when you crank a handle. How is the radio powered? How can it keep operating even after you stop turning the crank?
28. **HYPOTHESIZE** Use your understanding of magnetic materials and the source of Earth's magnetic field to form a hypothesis about the difference between Earth and the Moon that accounts for the fact that the Moon does not have a magnetic field.

Using Math in Science

Some electric bills include a bar graph of energy usage similar to the one shown below. Use the information provided in the graph to answer the next four questions.

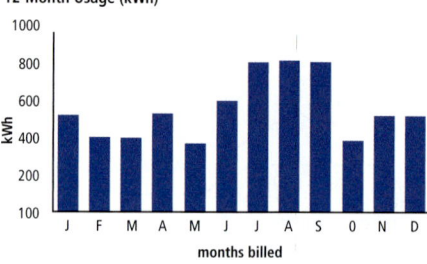

29. The first bar in the graph shows energy usage for the month of January. About how much energy, in kWh, was used in January?
30. If the appliances in the building have a combined power rating of 2 kW, how many hours were they in use during the month of March? (Hint: Use the formula $E = Pt$.)
31. The cost of energy was 8 cents per kWh. How much was charged for energy usage in May?
32. The most energy is used when the air conditioner is on. During which three months was the air conditioner on?

the BIG idea

33. **ANALYZE** Look back at pages 700–701. Think about the answer you gave to the question about the large photograph. How has your understanding of magnetism changed? Give examples.
34. **SUMMARIZE** Write a paragraph summarizing the first three pages of this chapter. Use the heading at the top of page 703 as your topic sentence. Explain each red and blue heading.

UNIT PROJECTS

Evaluate all the data, results, and information from your project folder. Prepare to present your project.

MONITOR AND RETEACH

If students have trouble applying the concepts in items 29–32, have them create a table that includes the names of the months written out fully and the approximate number of kWh used each month. Have students round the kWh numbers to the nearest 50. Students may benefit from holding a note card or ruler even with the tops of the bars to help them read the graph.

Students may benefit from summarizing one or more sections of the chapter.

 Summarizing the Chapter, pp. 204–205

Standardized Test Practice

For practice on your state test, go to...
TEST PRACTICE
CLASSZONE.COM

Analyzing Tables

The table below lists some major advances in the understanding of electromagnetism.

Scientist	Year	Advance
William Gilbert	1600	proposes distinction between magnetism and static electricity
Pieter van Musschenbroek	1745	develops Leyden jar, which stores electric charge
Benjamin Franklin	1752	shows that lightning is a form of electricity
Charles Augustin de Coulomb	1785	proves mathematically that, for electricity and magnetism, force changes with distance
Alessandro Volta	1800	invents battery, first device to generate a continuous current
Hans Christian Oersted	1820	announces he had used electric current to produce magnetic effects
André Marie Ampère	1820	shows that wires carrying current attract and repel each other, just like magnets
Georg Simon Ohm	1827	studies how well different wires conduct electric current
Michael Faraday	1831	produces electricity with a magnet; invents first electric generator

Use the table above to answer the next four questions.

1. Which scientist first produced a device that allowed experimenters to hold an electric charge for later use?
   a. Coulomb
   b. Franklin
   c. Ohm
   d. van Musschenbroek

2. Which scientist developed the first device that could be used to provide a steady source of current to other devices?
   a. Ampère
   b. Faraday
   c. Volta
   d. Gilbert

3. Which scientist had the first experimental evidence that current could produce magnetism?
   a. Gilbert
   b. Faraday
   c. van Musschenbroek
   d. Oersted

4. Why was Coulomb's work important?
   a. He showed that electricity and magnetism could be stored.
   b. He showed that electricity and magnetism behave similarly.
   c. He proved that electricity and magnetism were different.
   d. He proved that electricity and magnetism were the same.

Extended Response

Answer the two questions below in detail. Include some of the terms from the word box. Underline each term you use in your answer.

| appliance | current | generator |
| motor | coil | kilowatt-hour |

5. How are electromagnets produced? How can the strength of these devices be increased? How can electromagnets be used in ways that permanent magnets cannot?

6. Alix chats online for an average of about an hour a day 6 days a week. Her computer has a power rating of 270 watts. She has a hair dryer with a power rating of 1200 watts. She uses it twice a week for about 15 minutes at a time. Which device is likely to use more power over the course of a year? Why?

Chapter 21: **Magnetism** 735

METACOGNITIVE ACTIVITY

Have students answer the following questions in their **Science Notebook:**

1. What did you find most challenging to understand about magnets?
2. What questions do you still have about magnetism?
3. Now that you have finished the unit "Electricity and Magnetism," what might you change about your Unit Project?

Analyzing Tables

1. d   2. c   3. d   4. b

Extended Response

5. RUBRIC

4 points for a response that correctly answers all questions and uses the following terms accurately:
- appliance
- motor
- current
- coil
- generator

Sample: Electromagnets are made by placing a piece of iron or steel inside a <u>coil</u> of wire and running electric <u>current</u> through the wire. Increasing the number of coils or the amount of current increases the strength of the electromagnet. Electromagnets are used in <u>motors</u> of <u>appliances</u> and in <u>generators</u>, because they can be turned off and on.

3 points for a response that correctly answers three questions and uses three terms accurately

2 points for a response that correctly answers two questions and uses two terms accurately

1 point for a response that correctly answers one question or uses one term accurately

6. RUBRIC

4 points for a response that answers both questions and uses the following term accurately: kilowatt-hour

Sample: The computer uses more power over a year because it uses more <u>kilowatt-hours</u>. Computer: 6 days/week · 1 h/day · 52 weeks/yr · 0.270 kW = 84 kWh. Hair dryer: 2 days/week · 0.25 h/day · 52 weeks/yr · 1.2 kW = 31 kWh.

3 points for a response that correctly answers the question and calculates accurately

2 points for a response that uses the formulas correctly but contains errors in the calculations

1 point for a response that attempts to answer the questions but uses the formulas incorrectly

Student Resource Handbooks

Scientific Thinking Handbook — R2

- Making Observations — R2
- Predicting and Hypothesizing — R3
- Inferring — R4
- Identifying Cause and Effect — R5
- Recognizing Bias — R6
- Identifying Faulty Reasoning — R7
- Analyzing Statements — R8

Lab Handbook — R10

- Safety Rules — R10
- Using Lab Equipment — R12
- The Metric System and SI Units — R20
- Precision and Accuracy — R22
- Making Data Tables and Graphs — R23
- Designing an Experiment — R28

Math Handbook — R36

- Describing a Set of Data — R36
- Using Ratios, Rates, and Proportions — R38
- Using Decimals, Fractions, and Percents — R39
- Using Formulas — R42
- Finding Areas — R43
- Finding Volumes — R43
- Using Significant Figures — R44
- Using Scientific Notation — R44

Note-Taking Handbook — R45

- Note-Taking Strategies — R45
- Vocabulary Strategies — R50

Scientific Thinking Handbook

Making Observations

An **observation** is an act of noting and recording an event, characteristic, behavior, or anything else detected with an instrument or with the senses.

Observations allow you to make informed hypotheses and to gather data for experiments. Careful observations often lead to ideas for new experiments. There are two categories of observations:

- **Quantitative observations** can be expressed in numbers and include records of time, temperature, mass, distance, and volume.
- **Qualitative observations** include descriptions of sights, sounds, smells, and textures.

EXAMPLE

A student dissolved 30 grams of Epsom salts in water, poured the solution into a dish, and let the dish sit out uncovered overnight. The next day, she made the following observations of the Epsom salt crystals that grew in the dish.

Table 1. Observations of Epsom Salt Crystals

Quantitative Observations	Qualitative Observations
• mass = 30 g • mean crystal length = 0.5 cm • longest crystal length = 2 cm	• Crystals are clear. • Crystals are long, thin, and rectangular. • White crust has formed around edge of dish.

To determine the mass, the student found the mass of the dish before and after growing the crystals and then used subtraction to find the difference.

The student measured several crystals and calculated the mean length. (To learn how to calculate the mean of a data set, see page R36.)

Photographs or sketches are useful for recording qualitative observations. — Epsom salt crystals

MORE ABOUT OBSERVING

- Make quantitative observations whenever possible. That way, others will know exactly what you observed and be able to compare their results with yours.
- It is always a good idea to make qualitative observations too. You never know when you might observe something unexpected.

Predicting and Hypothesizing

A **prediction** is an expectation of what will be observed or what will happen. A **hypothesis** is a tentative explanation for an observation or scientific problem that can be tested by further investigation.

EXAMPLE

Suppose you have made two paper airplanes and you wonder why one of them tends to glide farther than the other one.

1. Start by asking a question.
2. Make an educated guess. After examination, you notice that the wings of the airplane that flies farther are slightly larger than the wings of the other airplane.
3. Write a prediction based upon your educated guess, in the form of an "If . . . , then . . ." statement. Write the independent variable after the word *if*, and the dependent variable after the word *then*.
4. To make a hypothesis, explain why you think what you predicted will occur. Write the explanation after the word *because*.

---

1. Why does one of the paper airplanes glide farther than the other?

2. The size of an airplane's wings may affect how far the airplane will glide.

3. Prediction: If I make a paper airplane with larger wings, then the airplane will glide farther.

   To read about independent and dependent variables, see page R30.

4. Hypothesis: If I make a paper airplane with larger wings, then the airplane will glide farther, because the additional surface area of the wing will produce more lift.

   Notice that the part of the hypothesis after because adds an explanation of why the airplane will glide farther.

MORE ABOUT HYPOTHESES

- The results of an experiment cannot prove that a hypothesis is correct. Rather, the results either support or do not support the hypothesis.
- Valuable information is gained even when your hypothesis is not supported by your results. For example, it would be an important discovery to find that wing size is not related to how far an airplane glides.
- In science, a hypothesis is supported only after many scientists have conducted many experiments and produced consistent results.

Scientific Thinking Handbook R3

Inferring

An **inference** is a logical conclusion drawn from the available evidence and prior knowledge. Inferences are often made from observations.

EXAMPLE

A student observing a set of acorns noticed something unexpected about one of them. He noticed a white, soft-bodied insect eating its way out of the acorn.

> The student recorded these observations.

Observations
- There is a hole in the acorn, about 0.5 cm in diameter, where the insect crawled out.
- There is a second hole, which is about the size of a pinhole, on the other side of the acorn.
- The inside of the acorn is hollow.

> Here are some inferences that can be made on the basis of the observations.

Inferences
- The insect formed from the material inside the acorn, grew to its present size, and ate its way out of the acorn.
- The insect crawled through the smaller hole, ate the inside of the acorn, grew to its present size, and ate its way out of the acorn.
- An egg was laid in the acorn through the smaller hole. The egg hatched into a larva that ate the inside of the acorn, grew to its present size, and ate its way out of the acorn.

> When you make inferences, be sure to look at all of the evidence available and combine it with what you already know.

MORE ABOUT INFERENCES

Inferences depend both on observations and on the knowledge of the people making the inferences. Ancient people who did not know that organisms are produced only by similar organisms might have made an inference like the first one. A student today might look at the same observations and make the second inference. A third student might have knowledge about this particular insect and know that it is never small enough to fit through the smaller hole, leading her to the third inference.

Identifying Cause and Effect

In a **cause-and-effect relationship,** one event or characteristic is the result of another. Usually an effect follows its cause in time.

There are many examples of cause-and-effect relationships in everyday life.

Cause	Effect
Turn off a light.	Room gets dark.
Drop a glass.	Glass breaks.
Blow a whistle.	Sound is heard.

Scientists must be careful not to infer a cause-and-effect relationship just because one event happens after another event. When one event occurs after another, you cannot infer a cause-and-effect relationship on the basis of that information alone. You also cannot conclude that one event caused another if there are alternative ways to explain the second event. A scientist must demonstrate through experimentation or continued observation that an event was truly caused by another event.

EXAMPLE

Make an Observation

Suppose you have a few plants growing outside. When the weather starts getting colder, you bring one of the plants indoors. You notice that the plant you brought indoors is growing faster than the others are growing. You cannot conclude from your observation that the change in temperature was the cause of the increased plant growth, because there are alternative explanations for the observation. Some possible explanations are given below.

- The humidity indoors caused the plant to grow faster.
- The level of sunlight indoors caused the plant to grow faster.
- The indoor plant's being noticed more often and watered more often than the outdoor plants caused it to grow faster.
- The plant that was brought indoors was healthier than the other plants to begin with.

To determine which of these factors, if any, caused the indoor plant to grow faster than the outdoor plants, you would need to design and conduct an experiment.

See pages R28–R35 for information about designing experiments.

Recognizing Bias

Television, newspapers, and the Internet are full of experts claiming to have scientific evidence to back up their claims. How do you know whether the claims are really backed up by good science?

Bias is a slanted point of view, or personal prejudice. The goal of scientists is to be as objective as possible and to base their findings on facts instead of opinions. However, bias often affects the conclusions of researchers, and it is important to learn to recognize bias.

When scientific results are reported, you should consider the source of the information as well as the information itself. It is important to critically analyze the information that you see and read.

SOURCES OF BIAS

There are several ways in which a report of scientific information may be biased. Here are some questions that you can ask yourself:

1. **Who is sponsoring the research?**

   Sometimes, the results of an investigation are biased because an organization paying for the research is looking for a specific answer. This type of bias can affect how data are gathered and interpreted.

2. **Is the research sample large enough?**

   Sometimes research does not include enough data. The larger the sample size, the more likely that the results are accurate, assuming a truly random sample.

3. **In a survey, who is answering the questions?**

   The results of a survey or poll can be biased. The people taking part in the survey may have been specifically chosen because of how they would answer. They may have the same ideas or lifestyles. A survey or poll should make use of a random sample of people.

4. **Are the people who take part in a survey biased?**

   People who take part in surveys sometimes try to answer the questions the way they think the researcher wants them to answer. Also, in surveys or polls that ask for personal information, people may be unwilling to answer questions truthfully.

SCIENTIFIC BIAS

It is also important to realize that scientists have their own biases because of the types of research they do and because of their scientific viewpoints. Two scientists may look at the same set of data and come to completely different conclusions because of these biases. However, such disagreements are not necessarily bad. In fact, a critical analysis of disagreements is often responsible for moving science forward.

Identifying Faulty Reasoning

Faulty reasoning is wrong or incorrect thinking. It leads to mistakes and to wrong conclusions. Scientists are careful not to draw unreasonable conclusions from experimental data. Without such caution, the results of scientific investigations may be misleading.

EXAMPLE

Scientists try to make generalizations based on their data to explain as much about nature as possible. If only a small sample of data is looked at, however, a conclusion may be faulty. Suppose a scientist has studied the effects of the El Niño and La Niña weather patterns on flood damage in California from 1989 to 1995. The scientist organized the data in the bar graph below.

The scientist drew the following conclusions:

1. The La Niña weather pattern has no effect on flooding in California.
2. When neither weather pattern occurs, there is almost no flood damage.
3. A weak or moderate El Niño produces a small or moderate amount of flooding.
4. A strong El Niño produces a lot of flooding.

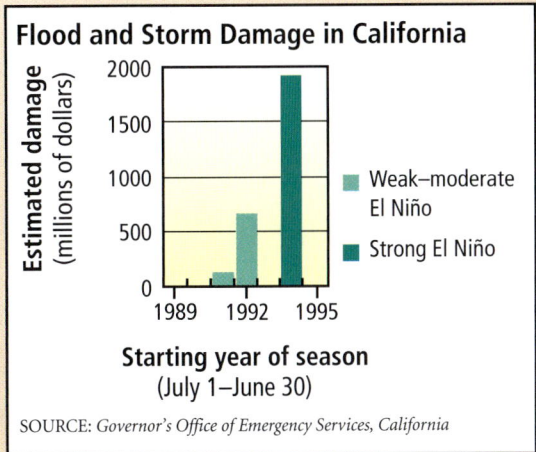

For the six-year period of the scientist's investigation, these conclusions may seem to be reasonable. However, a six-year study of weather patterns may be too small of a sample for the conclusions to be supported. Consider the following graph, which shows information that was gathered from 1949 to 1997.

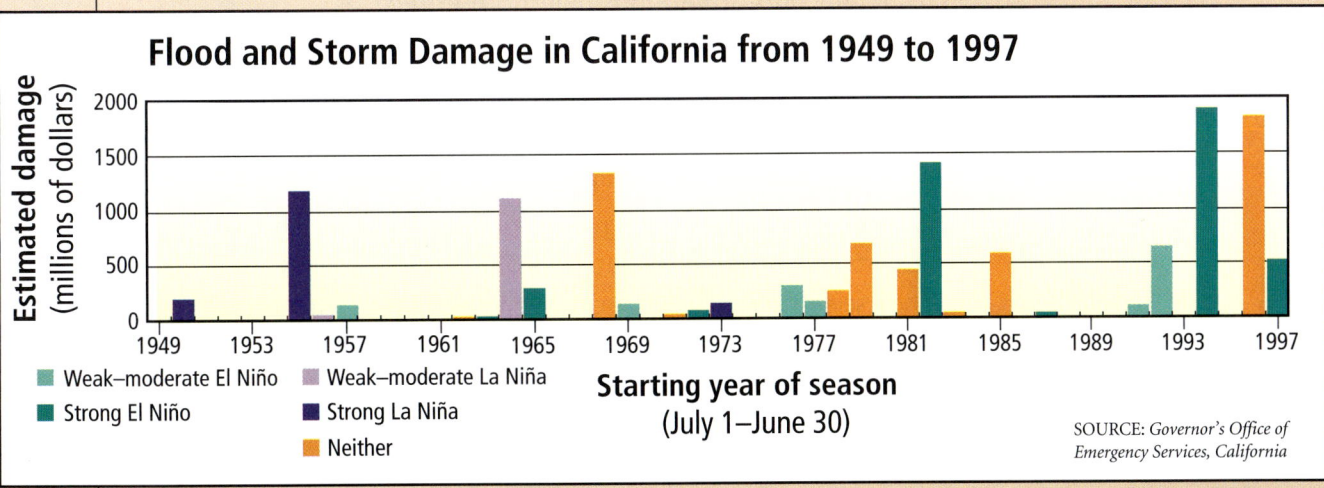

The only one of the conclusions that all of this information supports is number 3: a weak or moderate El Niño produces a small or moderate amount of flooding. By collecting more data, scientists can be more certain of their conclusions and can avoid faulty reasoning.

Scientific Thinking Handbook **R7**

Analyzing Statements

To **analyze** a statement is to examine its parts carefully. Scientific findings are often reported through media such as television or the Internet. A report that is made public often focuses on only a small part of research. As a result, it is important to question the sources of information.

Evaluate Media Claims

To **evaluate** a statement is to judge it on the basis of criteria you've established. Sometimes evaluating means deciding whether a statement is true.

Reports of scientific research and findings in the media may be misleading or incomplete. When you are exposed to this information, you should ask yourself some questions so that you can make informed judgments about the information.

1. **Does the information come from a credible source?**

   Suppose you learn about a new product and it is stated that scientific evidence proves that the product works. A report from a respected news source may be more believable than an advertisement paid for by the product's manufacturer.

2. **How much evidence supports the claim?**

   Often, it may seem that there is new evidence every day of something in the world that either causes or cures an illness. However, information that is the result of several years of work by several different scientists is more credible than an advertisement that does not even cite the subjects of the experiment.

3. **How much information is being presented?**

   Science cannot solve all questions, and scientific experiments often have flaws. A report that discusses problems in a scientific study may be more believable than a report that addresses only positive experimental findings.

4. **Is scientific evidence being presented by a specific source?**

   Sometimes scientific findings are reported by people who are called experts or leaders in a scientific field. But if their names are not given or their scientific credentials are not reported, their statements may be less credible than those of recognized experts.

Differentiate Between Fact and Opinion

Sometimes information is presented as a fact when it may be an opinion. When scientific conclusions are reported, it is important to recognize whether they are based on solid evidence. Again, you may find it helpful to ask yourself some questions.

1. **What is the difference between a fact and an opinion?**

    A **fact** is a piece of information that can be strictly defined and proved true. An **opinion** is a statement that expresses a belief, value, or feeling. An opinion cannot be proved true or false. For example, a person's age is a fact, but if someone is asked how old they feel, it is impossible to prove the person's answer to be true or false.

2. **Can opinions be measured?**

    Yes, opinions can be measured. In fact, surveys often ask for people's opinions on a topic. But there is no way to know whether or not an opinion is the truth.

HOW TO DIFFERENTIATE FACT FROM OPINION

Human Activities and the Environment

Unfortunately, human use of fossil fuels is one of the most significant developments of the past few centuries. Humans rely on fossil fuels, a non-renewable energy resource, for more than 90 percent of their energy needs.

This careless misuse of our planet's resources has resulted in pollution, global warming, and the destruction of fragile ecosystems. For example, oil pipelines carry more than one million barrels of oil each day across tundra regions. Transporting oil across such areas can only result in oil spills that poison the land for decades.

Opinions
Notice words or phrases that express beliefs or feelings. The words *unfortunately* and *careless* show that opinions are being expressed.

Opinion
Look for statements that speculate about events. These statements are opinions, because they cannot be proved.

Facts
Statements that contain statistics tend to be facts. Writers often use facts to support their opinions.

SCIENTIFIC THINKING HANDBOOK

Scientific Thinking Handbook R9

Lab Handbook

Safety Rules

Before you work in the laboratory, read these safety rules twice. Ask your teacher to explain any rules that you do not completely understand. Refer to these rules later on if you have questions about safety in the science classroom.

Directions

- Read all directions and make sure that you understand them before starting an investigation or lab activity. If you do not understand how to do a procedure or how to use a piece of equipment, ask your teacher.
- Do not begin any investigation or touch any equipment until your teacher has told you to start.
- Never experiment on your own. If you want to try a procedure that the directions do not call for, ask your teacher for permission first.
- If you are hurt or injured in any way, tell your teacher immediately.

Dress Code

goggles

apron

gloves

- Wear goggles when
  — using glassware, sharp objects, or chemicals
  — heating an object
  — working with anything that can easily fly up into the air and hurt someone's eye
- Tie back long hair or hair that hangs in front of your eyes.
- Remove any article of clothing—such as a loose sweater or a scarf—that hangs down and may touch a flame, chemical, or piece of equipment.
- Observe all safety icons calling for the wearing of eye protection, gloves, and aprons.

Heating and Fire Safety

fire safety

heating safety

- Keep your work area neat, clean, and free of extra materials.
- Never reach over a flame or heat source.
- Point objects being heated away from you and others.
- Never heat a substance or an object in a closed container.
- Never touch an object that has been heated. If you are unsure whether something is hot, treat it as though it is. Use oven mitts, clamps, tongs, or a test-tube holder.
- Know where the fire extinguisher and fire blanket are kept in your classroom.
- Do not throw hot substances into the trash. Wait for them to cool or use the container your teacher puts out for disposal.

Electrical Safety

electrical safety

- Never use lamps or other electrical equipment with frayed cords.
- Make sure no cord is lying on the floor where someone can trip over it.
- Do not let a cord hang over the side of a counter or table so that the equipment can easily be pulled or knocked to the floor.
- Never let cords hang into sinks or other places where water can be found.
- Never try to fix electrical problems. Inform your teacher of any problems immediately.
- Unplug an electrical cord by pulling on the plug, not the cord.

Chemical Safety

chemical safety

poison

fumes

- If you spill a chemical or get one on your skin or in your eyes, tell your teacher right away.
- Never touch, taste, or sniff any chemicals in the lab. If you need to determine odor, waft. Wafting consists of holding the chemical in its container 15 centimeters (6 in.) away from your nose, and using your fingers to bring fumes from the container to your nose.
- Keep lids on all chemicals you are not using.
- Never put unused chemicals back into the original containers. Throw away extra chemicals where your teacher tells you to.
- Pour chemicals over a sink or your work area, not over the floor.
- If you get a chemical in your eye, use the eyewash right away.
- Always wash your hands after handling chemicals, plants, or soil.

Wafting

Glassware and Sharp-Object Safety

sharp objects

- If you break glassware, tell your teacher right away.
- Do not use broken or chipped glassware. Give these to your teacher.
- Use knives and other cutting instruments carefully. Always wear eye protection and cut away from you.

Animal Safety

- Never hurt an animal.
- Touch animals only when necessary. Follow your teacher's instructions for handling animals.
- Always wash your hands after working with animals.

Cleanup

disposal

- Follow your teacher's instructions for throwing away or putting away supplies.
- Clean your work area and pick up anything that has dropped to the floor.
- Wash your hands.

Using Lab Equipment

Different experiments require different types of equipment. But even though experiments differ, the ways in which the equipment is used are the same.

Beakers

- Use beakers for holding and pouring liquids.
- Do not use a beaker to measure the volume of a liquid. Use a graduated cylinder instead. (See page R16.)
- Use a beaker that holds about twice as much liquid as you need. For example, if you need 100 milliliters of water, you should use a 200- or 250-milliliter beaker.

Test Tubes

- Use test tubes to hold small amounts of substances.
- Do not use a test tube to measure the volume of a liquid.
- Use a test tube when heating a substance over a flame. Aim the mouth of the tube away from yourself and other people.
- Liquids easily spill or splash from test tubes, so it is important to use only small amounts of liquids.

Test-Tube Holder

- Use a test-tube holder when heating a substance in a test tube.
- Use a test-tube holder if the substance in a test tube is dangerous to touch.
- Make sure the test-tube holder tightly grips the test tube so that the test tube will not slide out of the holder.
- Make sure that the test-tube holder is above the surface of the substance in the test tube so that you can observe the substance.

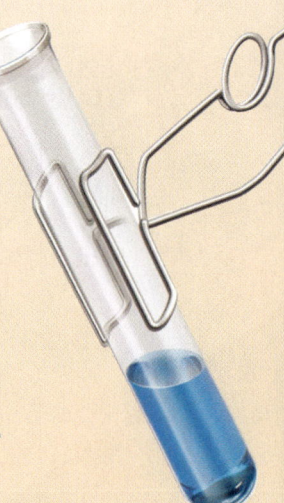

Test-Tube Rack

- Use a test-tube rack to organize test tubes before, during, and after an experiment.
- Use a test-tube rack to keep test tubes upright so that they do not fall over and spill their contents.
- Use a test-tube rack that is the correct size for the test tubes that you are using. If the rack is too small, a test tube may become stuck. If the rack is too large, a test tube may lean over, and some of its contents may spill or splash.

Forceps

- Use forceps when you need to pick up or hold a very small object that should not be touched with your hands.
- Do not use forceps to hold anything over a flame, because forceps are not long enough to keep your hand safely away from the flame. Plastic forceps will melt, and metal forceps will conduct heat and burn your hand.

Hot Plate

- Use a hot plate when a substance needs to be kept warmer than room temperature for a long period of time.
- Use a hot plate instead of a Bunsen burner or a candle when you need to carefully control temperature.
- Do not use a hot plate when a substance needs to be burned in an experiment.
- Always use "hot hands" safety mitts or oven mitts when handling anything that has been heated on a hot plate.

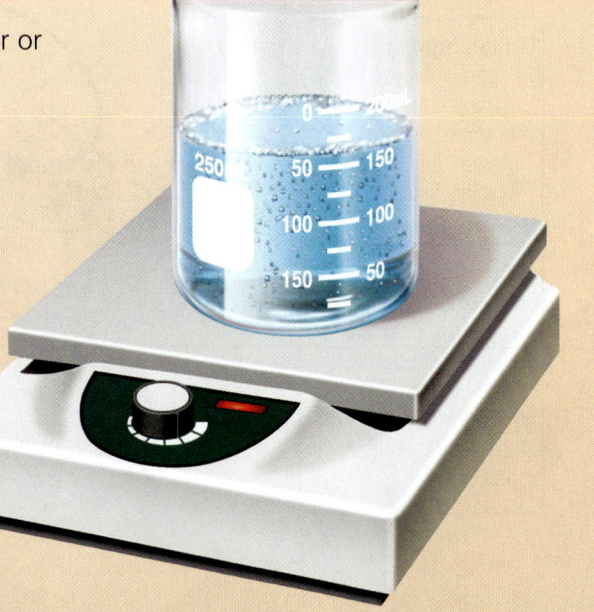

Lab Handbook R13

Microscope

Scientists use microscopes to see very small objects that cannot easily be seen with the eye alone. A microscope magnifies the image of an object so that small details may be observed. A microscope that you may use can magnify an object 400 times—the object will appear 400 times larger than its actual size.

Eyepiece Objects are viewed through the eyepiece. The eyepiece contains a lens that commonly magnifies an image 10 times.

Body The body separates the lens in the eyepiece from the objective lenses below.

Coarse Adjustment This knob is used to focus the image of an object when it is viewed through the low-power lens.

Nosepiece The nosepiece holds the objective lenses above the stage and rotates so that all lenses may be used.

Fine Adjustment This knob is used to focus the image of an object when it is viewed through the high-power lens.

High-Power Objective Lens This is the largest lens on the nosepiece. It magnifies an image approximately 40 times.

Low-Power Objective Lens This is the smallest lens on the nosepiece. It magnifies an image approximately 10 times.

Stage The stage supports the object being viewed.

Arm The arm supports the body above the stage. Always carry a microscope by the arm and base.

Diaphragm The diaphragm is used to adjust the amount of light passing through the slide and into an objective lens.

Stage Clip The stage clip holds a slide in place on the stage.

Mirror or Light Source Some microscopes use light that is reflected through the stage by a mirror. Other microscopes have their own light sources.

Base The base supports the microscope.

VIEWING AN OBJECT

1. Use the coarse adjustment knob to raise the body tube.
2. Adjust the diaphragm so that you can see a bright circle of light through the eyepiece.
3. Place the object or slide on the stage. Be sure that it is centered over the hole in the stage.
4. Turn the nosepiece to click the low-power lens into place.
5. Using the coarse adjustment knob, slowly lower the lens and focus on the specimen being viewed. Be sure not to touch the slide or object with the lens.
6. When switching from the low-power lens to the high-power lens, first raise the body tube with the coarse adjustment knob so that the high-power lens will not hit the slide.
7. Turn the nosepiece to click the high-power lens into place.
8. Use the fine adjustment knob to focus on the specimen being viewed. Again, be sure not to touch the slide or object with the lens.

MAKING A SLIDE, OR WET MOUNT

1 Place the specimen in the center of a clean slide.

2 Place a drop of water on the specimen.

3 Place a cover slip on the slide. Put one edge of the cover slip into the drop of water and slowly lower it over the specimen.

4 Remove any air bubbles from under the cover slip by gently tapping the cover slip.

5 Dry any excess water before placing the slide on the microscope stage for viewing.

Lab Handbook R15

Spring Scale (Force Meter)

- Use a spring scale to measure a force pulling on the scale.
- Use a spring scale to measure the force of gravity exerted on an object by Earth.
- To measure a force accurately, a spring scale must be zeroed before it is used. The scale is zeroed when no weight is attached and the indicator is positioned at zero.
- Do not attach a weight that is either too heavy or too light to a spring scale. A weight that is too heavy could break the scale or exert too great a force for the scale to measure. A weight that is too light may not exert enough force to be measured accurately.

Graduated Cylinder

- Use a graduated cylinder to measure the volume of a liquid.
- Be sure that the graduated cylinder is on a flat surface so that your measurement will be accurate.
- When reading the scale on a graduated cylinder, be sure to have your eyes at the level of the surface of the liquid.
- The surface of the liquid will be curved in the graduated cylinder. Read the volume of the liquid at the bottom of the curve, or meniscus (muh-NIHS-kuhs).
- You can use a graduated cylinder to find the volume of a solid object by measuring the increase in a liquid's level after you add the object to the cylinder.

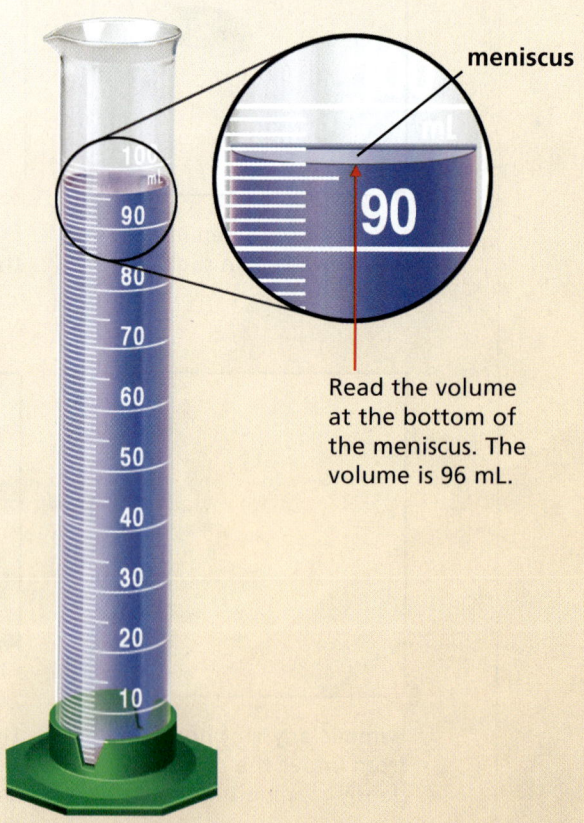

meniscus

Read the volume at the bottom of the meniscus. The volume is 96 mL.

Metric Rulers

- Use metric rulers or meter sticks to measure objects' lengths.
- Do not measure an object from the end of a metric ruler or meter stick, because the end is often imperfect. Instead, measure from the 1-centimeter mark, but remember to subtract a centimeter from the apparent measurement.
- Estimate any lengths that extend between marked units. For example, if a meter stick shows centimeters but not millimeters, you can estimate the length that an object extends between centimeter marks to measure it to the nearest millimeter.
- **Controlling Variables** If you are taking repeated measurements, always measure from the same point each time. For example, if you're measuring how high two different balls bounce when dropped from the same height, measure both bounces at the same point on the balls—either the top or the bottom. Do not measure at the top of one ball and the bottom of the other.

EXAMPLE

How to Measure a Leaf

1. Lay a ruler flat on top of the leaf so that the 1-centimeter mark lines up with one end. Make sure the ruler and the leaf do not move between the time you line them up and the time you take the measurement.

2. Look straight down on the ruler so that you can see exactly how the marks line up with the other end of the leaf.

3. Estimate the length by which the leaf extends beyond a marking. For example, the leaf below extends about halfway between the 4.2-centimeter and 4.3-centimeter marks, so the apparent measurement is about 4.25 centimeters.

4. Remember to subtract 1 centimeter from your apparent measurement, since you started at the 1-centimeter mark on the ruler and not at the end. The leaf is about 3.25 centimeters long (4.25 cm − 1 cm = 3.25 cm).

Lab Handbook R17

Triple-Beam Balance

This balance has a pan and three beams with sliding masses, called riders. At one end of the beams is a pointer that indicates whether the mass on the pan is equal to the masses shown on the beams.

1. Make sure the balance is zeroed before measuring the mass of an object. The balance is zeroed if the pointer is at zero when nothing is on the pan and the riders are at their zero points. Use the adjustment knob at the base of the balance to zero it.

2. Place the object to be measured on the pan.

3. Move the riders one notch at a time away from the pan. Begin with the largest rider. If moving the largest rider one notch brings the pointer below zero, begin measuring the mass of the object with the next smaller rider.

4. Change the positions of the riders until they balance the mass on the pan and the pointer is at zero. Then add the readings from the three beams to determine the mass of the object.

```
  300 g   position of largest rider
   90 g   position of middle rider
+   3 g   position of smallest rider
─────
  393 g   mass of beaker
```

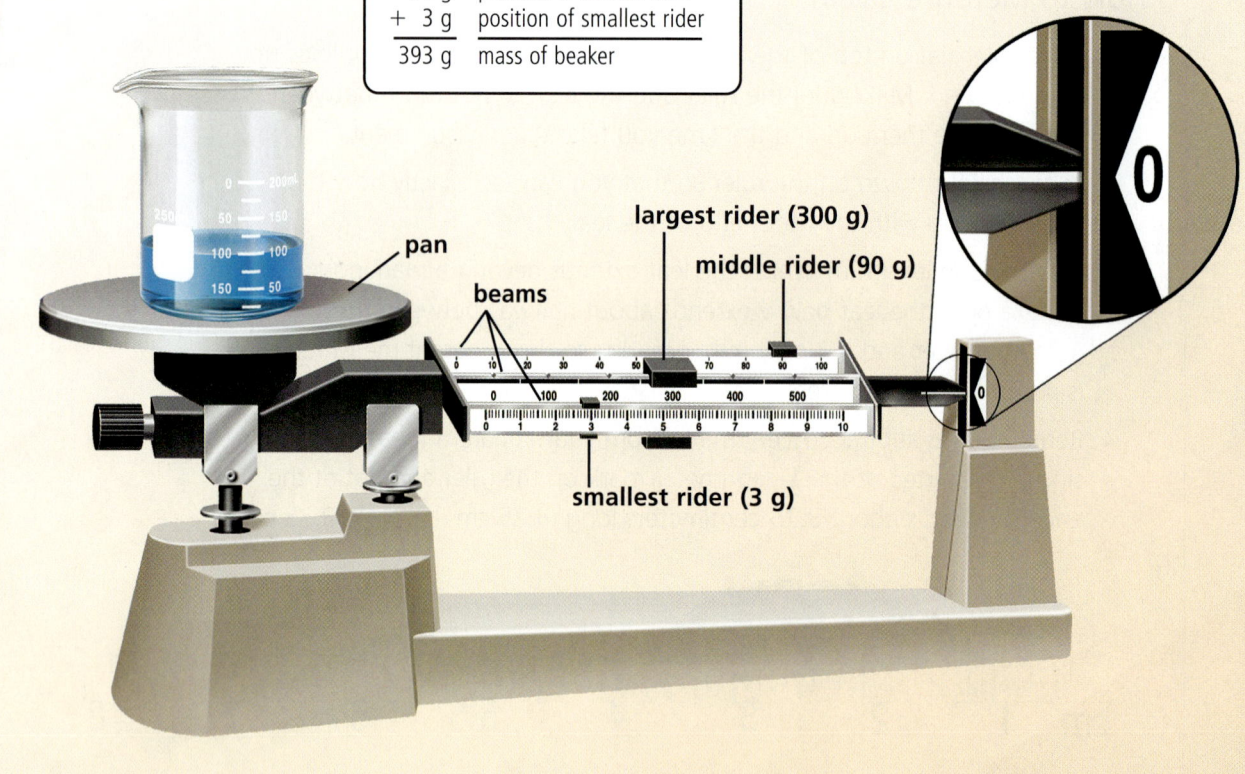

Double-Pan Balance

This type of balance has two pans. Between the pans is a pointer that indicates whether the masses on the pans are equal.

1. Make sure the balance is zeroed before measuring the mass of an object. The balance is zeroed if the pointer is at zero when there is nothing on either of the pans. Many double-pan balances have sliding knobs that can be used to zero them.

2. Place the object to be measured on one of the pans.

3. Begin adding standard masses to the other pan. Begin with the largest standard mass. If this adds too much mass to the balance, begin measuring the mass of the object with the next smaller standard mass.

4. Add standard masses until the masses on both pans are balanced and the pointer is at zero. Then add the standard masses together to determine the mass of the object being measured.

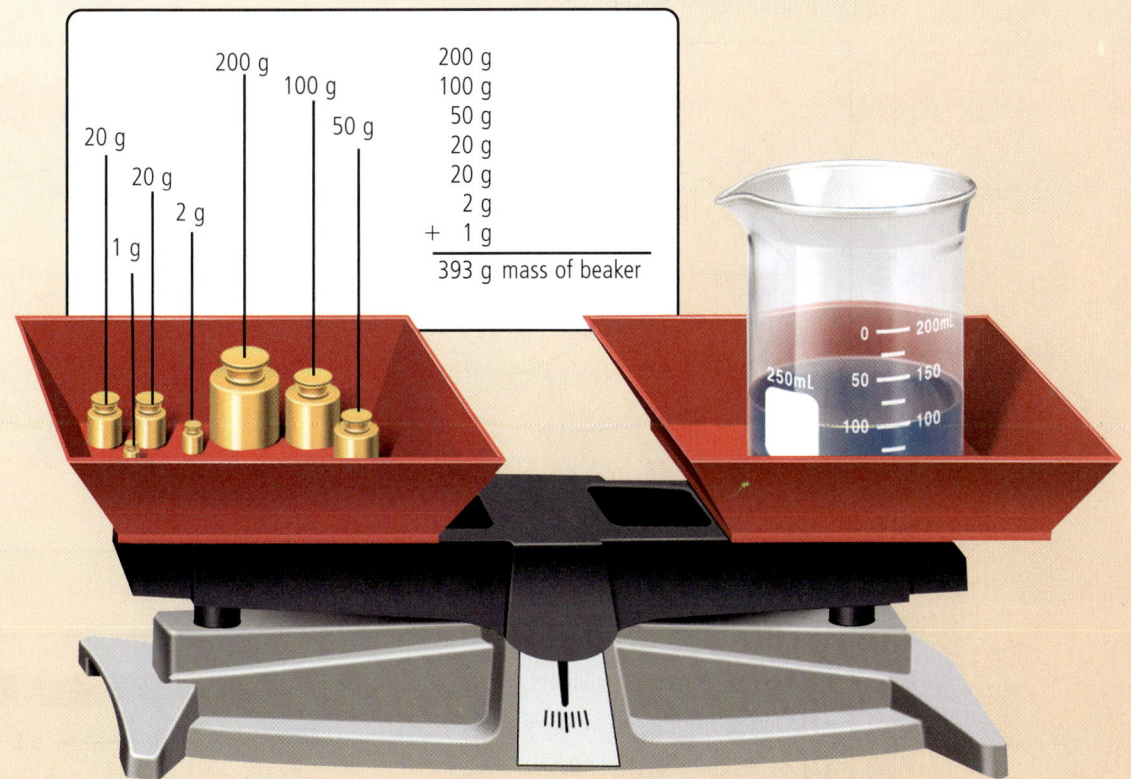

Never place chemicals or liquids directly on a pan. Instead, use the following procedure:

① Determine the mass of an empty container, such as a beaker.

② Pour the substance into the container, and measure the total mass of the substance and the container.

③ Subtract the mass of the empty container from the total mass to find the mass of the substance.

Lab Handbook R19

The Metric System and SI Units

Scientists use International System (SI) units for measurements of distance, volume, mass, and temperature. The International System is based on multiples of ten and the metric system of measurement.

Basic SI Units		
Property	Name	Symbol
length	meter	m
volume	liter	L
mass	kilogram	kg
temperature	kelvin	K

SI Prefixes		
Prefix	Symbol	Multiple of 10
kilo-	k	1000
hecto-	h	100
deca-	da	10
deci-	d	0.1 $\left(\frac{1}{10}\right)$
centi-	c	0.01 $\left(\frac{1}{100}\right)$
milli-	m	0.001 $\left(\frac{1}{1000}\right)$

Changing Metric Units

You can change from one unit to another in the metric system by multiplying or dividing by a power of 10.

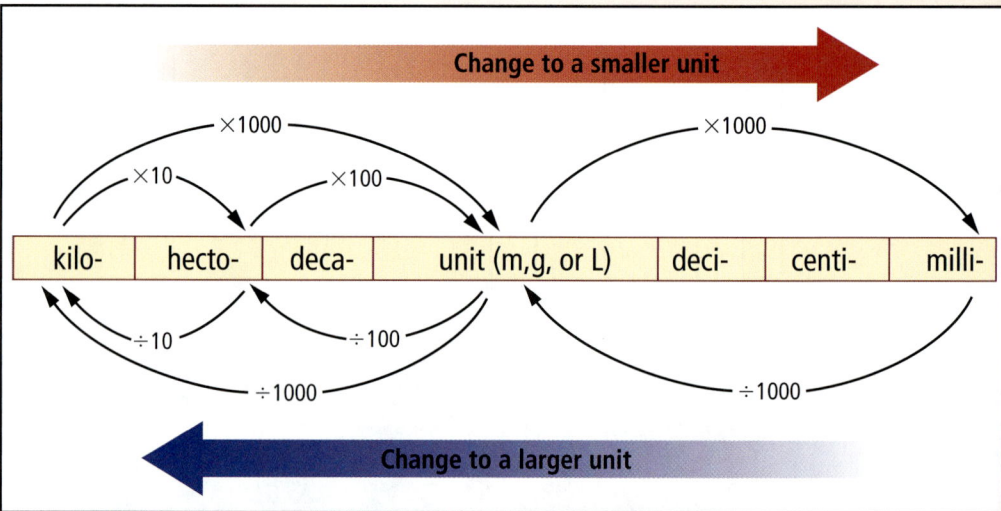

Example

Change 0.64 liters to milliliters.

(1) Decide whether to multiply or divide.
(2) Select the power of 10.

ANSWER 0.64 L = 640 mL

Change to a smaller unit by multiplying.

L ⎯⎯ ×1000 ⎯⎯→ mL

0.64 × 1000 = 640.

Example

Change 23.6 grams to kilograms.

(1) Decide whether to multiply or divide.
(2) Select the power of 10.

ANSWER 23.6 g = 0.0236 kg

Change to a larger unit by dividing.

kg ←⎯⎯ ÷ 1000 ⎯⎯ g

23.6 ÷ 1000 = 0.0236

Temperature Conversions

Even though the kelvin is the SI base unit of temperature, the degree Celsius will be the unit you use most often in your science studies. The formulas below show the relationships between temperatures in degrees Fahrenheit (°F), degrees Celsius (°C), and kelvins (K).

$$°C = \frac{5}{9}(°F - 32)$$

$$°F = \frac{9}{5}°C + 32$$

$$K = °C + 273$$

See page R42 for help with using formulas.

Examples of Temperature Conversions		
Condition	Degrees Celsius	Degrees Fahrenheit
Freezing point of water	0	32
Cool day	10	50
Mild day	20	68
Warm day	30	86
Normal body temperature	37	98.6
Very hot day	40	104
Boiling point of water	100	212

Converting Between SI and U.S. Customary Units

Use the chart below when you need to convert between SI units and U.S. customary units.

SI Unit	From SI to U.S. Customary			From U.S. Customary to SI		
Length	When you know	multiply by	to find	When you know	multiply by	to find
kilometer (km) = 1000 m	kilometers	0.62	miles	miles	1.61	kilometers
meter (m) = 100 cm	meters	3.28	feet	feet	0.3048	meters
centimeter (cm) = 10 mm	centimeters	0.39	inches	inches	2.54	centimeters
millimeter (mm) = 0.1 cm	millimeters	0.04	inches	inches	25.4	millimeters
Area	When you know	multiply by	to find	When you know	multiply by	to find
square kilometer (km^2)	square kilometers	0.39	square miles	square miles	2.59	square kilometers
square meter (m^2)	square meters	1.2	square yards	square yards	0.84	square meters
square centimeter (cm^2)	square centimeters	0.155	square inches	square inches	6.45	square centimeters
Volume	When you know	multiply by	to find	When you know	multiply by	to find
liter (L) = 1000 mL	liters	1.06	quarts	quarts	0.95	liters
	liters	0.26	gallons	gallons	3.79	liters
	liters	4.23	cups	cups	0.24	liters
	liters	2.12	pints	pints	0.47	liters
milliliter (mL) = 0.001 L	milliliters	0.20	teaspoons	teaspoons	4.93	milliliters
	milliliters	0.07	tablespoons	tablespoons	14.79	milliliters
	milliliters	0.03	fluid ounces	fluid ounces	29.57	milliliters
Mass	When you know	multiply by	to find	When you know	multiply by	to find
kilogram (kg) = 1000 g	kilograms	2.2	pounds	pounds	0.45	kilograms
gram (g) = 1000 mg	grams	0.035	ounces	ounces	28.35	grams

Precision and Accuracy

When you do an experiment, it is important that your methods, observations, and data be both precise and accurate.

low precision

precision, but not accuracy

precision and accuracy

Precision

In science, **precision** is the exactness and consistency of measurements. For example, measurements made with a ruler that has both centimeter and millimeter markings would be more precise than measurements made with a ruler that has only centimeter markings. Another indicator of precision is the care taken to make sure that methods and observations are as exact and consistent as possible. Every time a particular experiment is done, the same procedure should be used. Precision is necessary because experiments are repeated several times and if the procedure changes, the results will change.

EXAMPLE

Suppose you are measuring temperatures over a two-week period. Your precision will be greater if you measure each temperature at the same place, at the same time of day, and with the same thermometer than if you change any of these factors from one day to the next.

Accuracy

In science, it is possible to be precise but not accurate. **Accuracy** depends on the difference between a measurement and an actual value. The smaller the difference, the more accurate the measurement.

EXAMPLE

Suppose you look at a stream and estimate that it is about 1 meter wide at a particular place. You decide to check your estimate by measuring the stream with a meter stick, and you determine that the stream is 1.32 meters wide. However, because it is hard to measure the width of a stream with a meter stick, it turns out that you didn't do a very good job. The stream is actually 1.14 meters wide. Therefore, even though your estimate was less precise than your measurement, your estimate was actually more accurate.

Making Data Tables and Graphs

Data tables and graphs are useful tools for both recording and communicating scientific data.

Making Data Tables

You can use a **data table** to organize and record the measurements that you make. Some examples of information that might be recorded in data tables are frequencies, times, and amounts.

EXAMPLE

Suppose you are investigating photosynthesis in two elodea plants. One sits in direct sunlight, and the other sits in a dimly lit room. You measure the rate of photosynthesis by counting the number of bubbles in the jar every ten minutes.

1. Title and number your data table.
2. Decide how you will organize the table into columns and rows.
3. Any units, such as seconds or degrees, should be included in column headings, not in the individual cells.

Table 1. Number of Bubbles from Elodea

Time (min)	Sunlight	Dim Light
0	0	0
10	15	5
20	25	8
30	32	7
40	41	10
50	47	9
60	42	9

Always number and title data tables.

The data in the table above could also be organized in a different way.

Table 1. Number of Bubbles from Elodea

Light Condition	Time (min)						
	0	10	20	30	40	50	60
Sunlight	0	15	25	32	41	47	42
Dim light	0	5	8	7	10	9	9

Put units in column heading.

Lab Handbook R23

Making Line Graphs

You can use a **line graph** to show a relationship between variables. Line graphs are particularly useful for showing changes in variables over time.

EXAMPLE

Suppose you are interested in graphing temperature data that you collected over the course of a day.

Table 1. Outside Temperature During the Day on March 7

	Time of Day						
	7:00 A.M.	9:00 A.M.	11:00 A.M.	1:00 P.M.	3:00 P.M.	5:00 P.M.	7:00 P.M.
Temp (°C)	8	9	11	14	12	10	6

1. Use the vertical axis of your line graph for the variable that you are measuring—temperature.
2. Choose scales for both the horizontal axis and the vertical axis of the graph. You should have two points more than you need on the vertical axis, and the horizontal axis should be long enough for all of the data points to fit.
3. Draw and label each axis.
4. Graph each value. First find the appropriate point on the scale of the horizontal axis. Imagine a line that rises vertically from that place on the scale. Then find the corresponding value on the vertical axis, and imagine a line that moves horizontally from that value. The point where these two imaginary lines intersect is where the value should be plotted.
5. Connect the points with straight lines.

Be sure to add a number and a title to your graph.

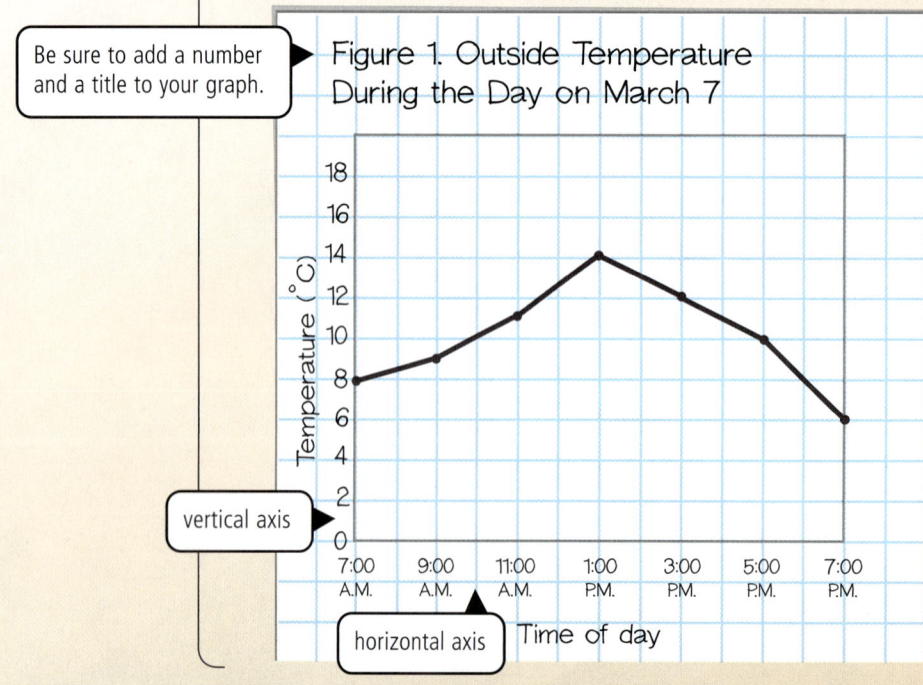

Figure 1. Outside Temperature During the Day on March 7

Making Circle Graphs

You can use a **circle graph,** sometimes called a pie chart, to represent data as parts of a circle. Circle graphs are used only when the data can be expressed as percentages of a whole. The entire circle shown in a circle graph is equal to 100 percent of the data.

EXAMPLE

Suppose you identified the species of each mature tree growing in a small wooded area. You organized your data in a table, but you also want to show the data in a circle graph.

1. To begin, find the total number of mature trees.

   $56 + 34 + 22 + 10 + 28 =$ 150

2. To find the degree measure for each sector of the circle, write a fraction comparing the number of each tree species with the total number of trees. Then multiply the fraction by 360°.

   Oak: $\frac{56}{150} \times 360° = 134.4°$

3. Draw a circle. Use a protractor to draw the angle for each sector of the graph.

4. Color and label each sector of the graph.

5. Give the graph a number and title.

Table 1. Tree Species in Wooded Area

Species	Number of Specimens
Oak	56
Maple	34
Birch	22
Willow	10
Pine	28

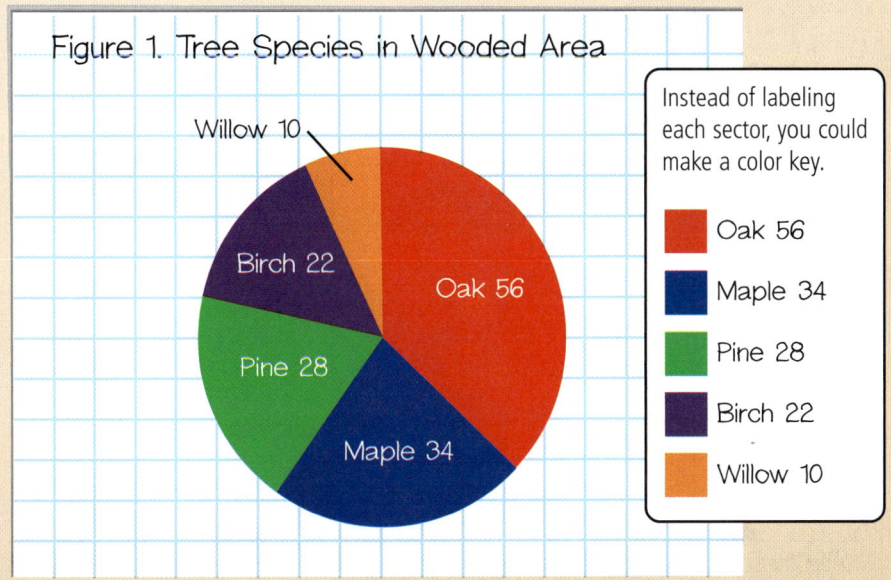

Figure 1. Tree Species in Wooded Area

Instead of labeling each sector, you could make a color key.

- Oak 56
- Maple 34
- Pine 28
- Birch 22
- Willow 10

Lab Handbook R25

Bar Graph

A **bar graph** is a type of graph in which the lengths of the bars are used to represent and compare data. A numerical scale is used to determine the lengths of the bars.

EXAMPLE

To determine the effect of water on seed sprouting, three cups were filled with sand, and ten seeds were planted in each. Different amounts of water were added to each cup over a three-day period.

Table 1. Effect of Water on Seed Sprouting

Daily Amount of Water (mL)	Number of Seeds That Sprouted After 3 Days in Sand
0	1
10	4
20	8

1. Choose a numerical scale. The greatest value is 8, so the end of the scale should have a value greater than 8, such as 10. Use equal increments along the scale, such as increments of 2.

2. Draw and label the axes. Mark intervals on the vertical axis according to the scale you chose.

3. Draw a bar for each data value. Use the scale to decide how long to make each bar.

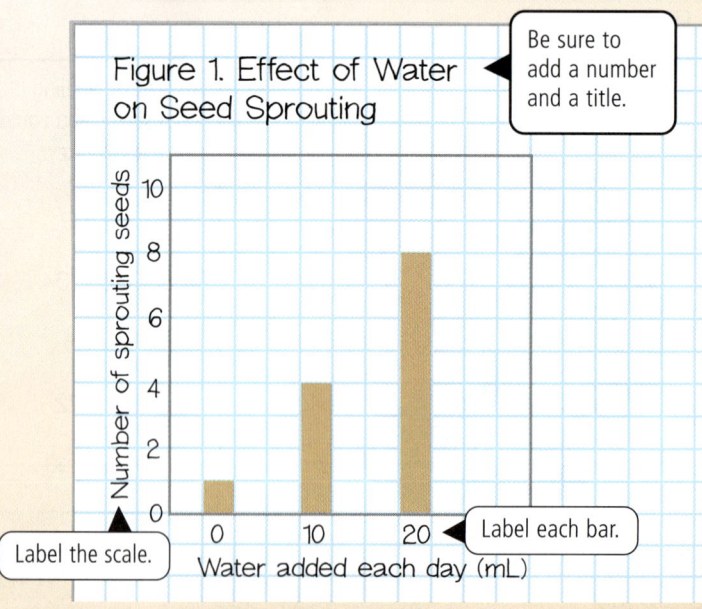

Figure 1. Effect of Water on Seed Sprouting

Double Bar Graph

A **double bar graph** is a bar graph that shows two sets of data. The two bars for each measurement are drawn next to each other.

EXAMPLE

The seed-sprouting experiment was done using both sand and potting soil. The data for sand and potting soil can be plotted on one graph.

1. Draw one set of bars, using the data for sand, as shown below.
2. Draw bars for the potting-soil data next to the bars for the sand data. Shade them a different color. Add a key.

Table 2. Effect of Water and Soil on Seed Sprouting

Daily Amount of Water (mL)	Number of Seeds That Sprouted After 3 Days in Sand	Number of Seeds That Sprouted After 3 Days in Potting Soil
0	1	2
10	4	5
20	8	9

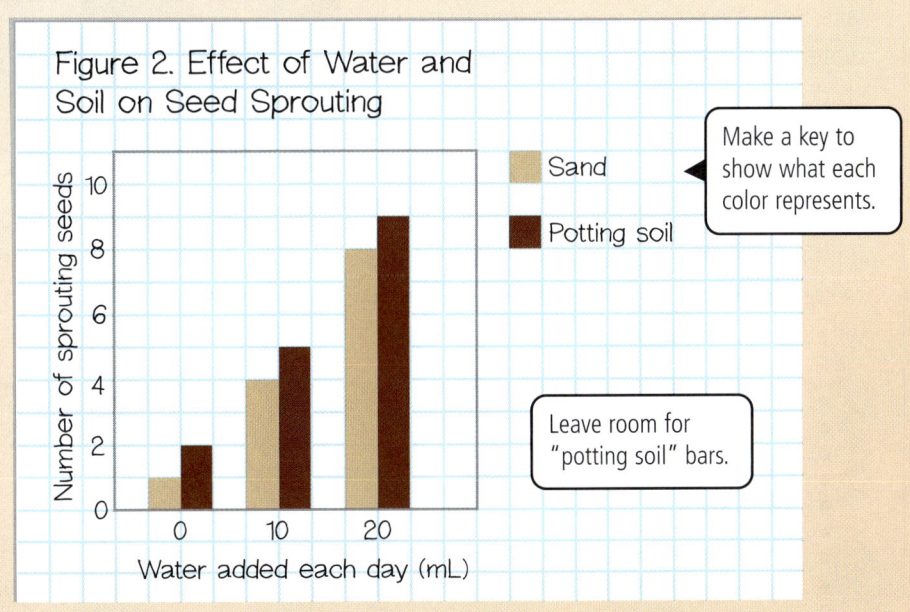

Figure 2. Effect of Water and Soil on Seed Sprouting

Make a key to show what each color represents.

Leave room for "potting soil" bars.

Lab Handbook R27

Designing an Experiment

Use this section when designing or conducting an experiment.

Determining a Purpose

You can find a purpose for an experiment by doing research, by examining the results of a previous experiment, or by observing the world around you. An **experiment** is an organized procedure to study something under controlled conditions.

> Don't forget to learn as much as possible about your topic before you begin.

1. Write the purpose of your experiment as a question or problem that you want to investigate.
2. Write down research questions and begin searching for information that will help you design an experiment. Consult the library, the Internet, and other people as you conduct your research.

EXAMPLE

Middle school students observed an odor near the lake by their school. They also noticed that the water on the side of the lake near the school was greener than the water on the other side of the lake. The students did some research to learn more about their observations. They discovered that the odor and green color in the lake came from algae. They also discovered that a new fertilizer was being used on a field nearby. The students inferred that the use of the fertilizer might be related to the presence of the algae and designed a controlled experiment to find out whether they were right.

Problem
How does fertilizer affect the presence of algae in a lake?

Research Questions
- Have other experiments been done on this problem? If so, what did those experiments show?
- What kind of fertilizer is used on the field? How much?
- How do algae grow?
- How do people measure algae?
- Can fertilizer and algae be used safely in a lab? How?

> **Research**
> As you research, you may find a topic that is more interesting to you than your original topic, or learn that a procedure you wanted to use is not practical or safe. It is OK to change your purpose as you research.

Writing a Hypothesis

A **hypothesis** is a tentative explanation for an observation or scientific problem that can be tested by further investigation. You can write your hypothesis in the form of an "If . . . , then . . . , because . . ." statement.

> **Hypothesis**
> If the amount of fertilizer in lake water is increased, then the amount of algae will also increase, because fertilizers provide nutrients that algae need to grow.

Hypotheses
For help with hypotheses, refer to page R3.

Determining Materials

Make a list of all the materials you will need to do your experiment. Be specific, especially if someone else is helping you obtain the materials. Try to think of everything you will need.

> **Materials**
> - 1 large jar or container
> - 4 identical smaller containers
> - rubber gloves that also cover the arms
> - sample of fertilizer-and-water solution
> - eyedropper
> - clear plastic wrap
> - scissors
> - masking tape
> - marker
> - ruler

Lab Handbook R29

Determining Variables and Constants

EXPERIMENTAL GROUP AND CONTROL GROUP

An experiment to determine how two factors are related always has two groups—a control group and an experimental group.

1. Design an experimental group. Include as many trials as possible in the experimental group in order to obtain reliable results.
2. Design a control group that is the same as the experimental group in every way possible, except for the factor you wish to test.

> **Experimental Group:** two containers of lake water with one drop of fertilizer solution added to each
> **Control Group:** two containers of lake water with no fertilizer solution added

Go back to your materials list and make sure you have enough items listed to cover both your experimental group and your control group.

VARIABLES AND CONSTANTS

Identify the variables and constants in your experiment. In a controlled experiment, a **variable** is any factor that can change. **Constants** are all of the factors that are the same in both the experimental group and the control group.

Hypothesis
If the amount of fertilizer in lake water is increased, then the amount of algae will also increase, because fertilizers provide nutrients that algae need to grow.

1. Read your hypothesis. The **independent variable** is the factor that you wish to test and that is manipulated or changed so that it can be tested. The independent variable is expressed in your hypothesis after the word *if*. Identify the independent variable in your laboratory report.
2. The **dependent variable** is the factor that you measure to gather results. It is expressed in your hypothesis after the word *then*. Identify the dependent variable in your laboratory report.

Table 1. Variables and Constants in Algae Experiment

Independent Variable	Dependent Variable	Constants
Amount of fertilizer in lake water	Amount of algae that grow	• Where the lake water is obtained • Type of container used • Light and temperature conditions where water will be stored

Set up your experiment so that you will test only one variable.

MEASURING THE DEPENDENT VARIABLE

Before starting your experiment, you need to define how you will measure the dependent variable. An **operational definition** is a description of the one particular way in which you will measure the dependent variable.

Your operational definition is important for several reasons. First, in any experiment there are several ways in which a dependent variable can be measured. Second, the procedure of the experiment depends on how you decide to measure the dependent variable. Third, your operational definition makes it possible for other people to evaluate and build on your experiment.

EXAMPLE 1

An operational definition of a dependent variable can be qualitative. That is, your measurement of the dependent variable can simply be an observation of whether a change occurs as a result of a change in the independent variable. This type of operational definition can be thought of as a "yes or no" measurement.

Table 2. Qualitative Operational Definition of Algae Growth

Independent Variable	Dependent Variable	Operational Definition
Amount of fertilizer in lake water	Amount of algae that grow	Algae grow in lake water

A qualitative measurement of a dependent variable is often easy to make and record. However, this type of information does not provide a great deal of detail in your experimental results.

EXAMPLE 2

An operational definition of a dependent variable can be quantitative. That is, your measurement of the dependent variable can be a number that shows how much change occurs as a result of a change in the independent variable.

Table 3. Quantitative Operational Definition of Algae Growth

Independent Variable	Dependent Variable	Operational Definition
Amount of fertilizer in lake water	Amount of algae that grow	Diameter of largest algal growth (in mm)

A quantitative measurement of a dependent variable can be more difficult to make and analyze than a qualitative measurement. However, this type of data provides much more information about your experiment and is often more useful.

Writing a Procedure

Write each step of your procedure. Start each step with a verb, or action word, and keep the steps short. Your procedure should be clear enough for someone else to use as instructions for repeating your experiment.

> **If necessary, go back to your materials list and add any materials that you left out.**

Procedure

1. Put on your gloves. Use the large container to obtain a sample of lake water.

2. Divide the sample of lake water equally among the four smaller containers.

3. Use the eyedropper to add one drop of fertilizer solution to two of the containers.

> **Controlling Variables**
> The same amount of fertilizer solution must be added to two of the four containers.

4. Use the masking tape and the marker to label the containers with your initials, the date, and the identifiers "Jar 1 with Fertilizer," "Jar 2 with Fertilizer," "Jar 1 without Fertilizer," and "Jar 2 without Fertilizer."

5. Cover the containers with clear plastic wrap. Use the scissors to punch ten holes in each of the covers.

> **Controlling Variables**
> All four containers must receive the same amount of light.

6. Place all four containers on a window ledge. Make sure that they all receive the same amount of light.

7. Observe the containers every day for one week.

8. Use the ruler to measure the diameter of the largest clump of algae in each container, and record your measurements daily.

Recording Observations

Once you have obtained all of your materials and your procedure has been approved, you can begin making experimental observations. Gather both quantitative and qualitative data. If something goes wrong during your procedure, make sure you record that too.

> **Observations**
> For help with making qualitative and quantitative observations, refer to page R2.

> For more examples of data tables, see page R23.

Table 4. Fertilizer and Algae Growth

Date and Time	Experimental Group		Control Group		Observations
	Jar 1 with Fertilizer (diameter of algae in mm)	Jar 2 with Fertilizer (diameter of algae in mm)	Jar 1 without Fertilizer (diameter of algae in mm)	Jar 2 without Fertilizer (diameter of algae in mm)	
5/3 4:00 P.M.	0	0	0	0	condensation in all containers
5/4 4:00 P.M.	0	3	0	0	tiny green blobs in jar 2 with fertilizer
5/5 4:15 P.M.	4	5	0	3	green blobs in jars 1 and 2 with fertilizer and jar 2 without fertilizer
5/6 4:00 P.M.	5	6	0	4	water light green in jar 2 with fertilizer
5/7 4:00 P.M.	8	10	0	6	water light green in jars 1 and 2 with fertilizer and in jar 2 without fertilizer
5/8 3:30 P.M.	10	18	0	6	cover off jar 2 with fertilizer
5/9 3:30 P.M.	14	23	0	8	drew sketches of each container

> Notice that on the sixth day, the observer found that the cover was off one of the containers. It is important to record observations of unintended factors because they might affect the results of the experiment.

Drawings of Samples Viewed Under Microscope on 5/9 at 100x

> Use technology, such as a microscope, to help you make observations when possible.

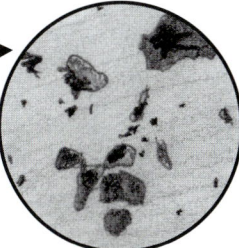 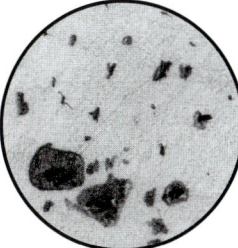  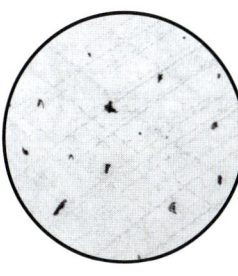

Jar 1 with Fertilizer | Jar 2 with Fertilizer | Jar 1 without Fertilizer | Jar 2 without Fertilizer

Lab Handbook R33

Summarizing Results

To summarize your data, look at all of your observations together. Look for meaningful ways to present your observations. For example, you might average your data or make a graph to look for patterns. When possible, use spreadsheet software to help you analyze and present your data. The two graphs below show the same data.

EXAMPLE 1

Always include a number and a title with a graph.

Line graphs are useful for showing changes over time. For help with line graphs, refer to page R24.

EXAMPLE 2

Bar graphs are useful for comparing different data sets. This bar graph has four bars for each day. Another way to present the data would be to calculate averages for the tests and the controls, and to show one test bar and one control bar for each day.

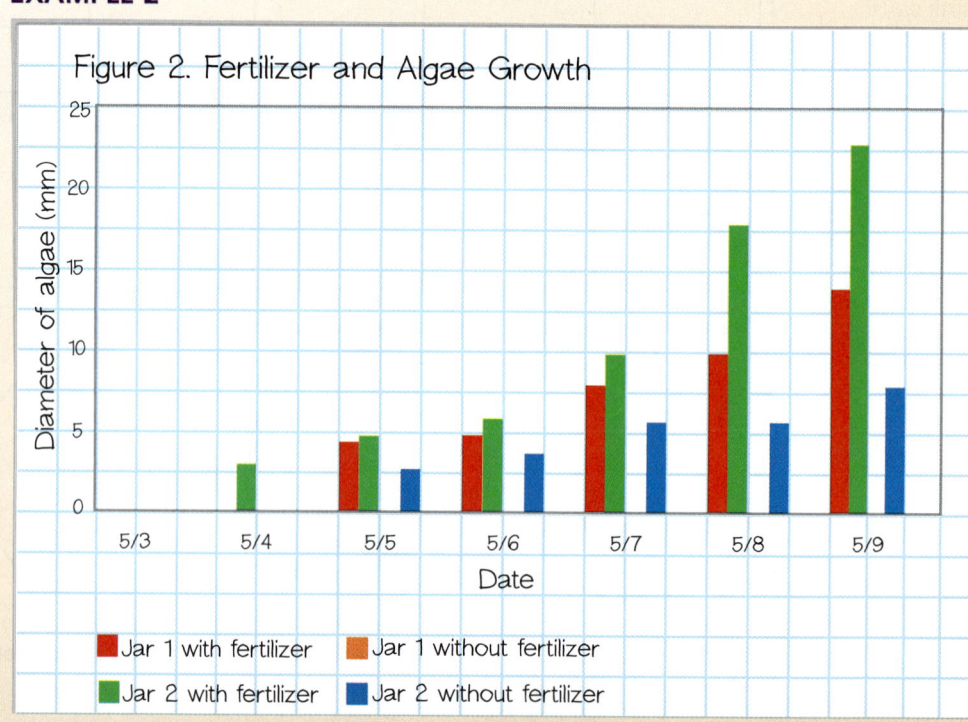

Drawing Conclusions

RESULTS AND INFERENCES

To draw conclusions from your experiment, first write your results. Then compare your results with your hypothesis. Do your results support your hypothesis? Be careful not to make inferences about factors that you did not test.

For help with making inferences, see page R4.

Results and Inferences

The results of my experiment show that more algae grew in lake water to which fertilizer had been added than in lake water to which no fertilizer had been added. My hypothesis was supported. I infer that it is possible that the growth of algae in the lake was caused by the fertilizer used on the field.

Notice that you cannot conclude from this experiment that the presence of algae in the lake was due only to the fertilizer.

QUESTIONS FOR FURTHER RESEARCH

Write a list of questions for further research and investigation. Your ideas may lead you to new experiments and discoveries.

Questions for Further Research

- What is the connection between the amount of fertilizer and algae growth?
- How do different brands of fertilizer affect algae growth?
- How would algae growth in the lake be affected if no fertilizer were used on the field?
- How do algae affect the lake and the other life in and around it?
- How does fertilizer affect the lake and the life in and around it?
- If fertilizer is getting into the lake, how is it getting there?

Math Handbook

Describing a Set of Data

Means, medians, modes, and ranges are important math tools for describing data sets such as the following widths of fossilized clamshells.

13 mm   25 mm   14 mm   21 mm   16 mm   23 mm   14 mm

Mean

The **mean** of a data set is the sum of the values divided by the number of values.

Example

To find the mean of the clamshell data, add the values and then divide the sum by the number of values.

$$\frac{13 \text{ mm} + 25 \text{ mm} + 14 \text{ mm} + 21 \text{ mm} + 16 \text{ mm} + 23 \text{ mm} + 14 \text{ mm}}{7} = \frac{126 \text{ mm}}{7} = 18 \text{ mm}$$

ANSWER The mean is 18 mm.

Median

The **median** of a data set is the middle value when the values are written in numerical order. If a data set has an even number of values, the median is the mean of the two middle values.

Example

To find the median of the clamshell data, arrange the values in order from least to greatest. The median is the middle value.

13 mm   14 mm   14 mm   **16 mm**   21 mm   23 mm   25 mm

ANSWER The median is 16 mm.

Mode

The **mode** of a data set is the value that occurs most often.

> **Example**
>
> To find the mode of the clamshell data, arrange the values in order from least to greatest and determine the value that occurs most often.
>
> 13 mm   14 mm   14 mm   16 mm   21 mm   23 mm   25 mm
>
> **ANSWER** The mode is 14 mm.

A data set can have more than one mode or no mode. For example, the following data set has modes of 2 mm and 4 mm:

2 mm   2 mm   3 mm   4 mm   4 mm

The data set below has no mode, because no value occurs more often than any other.

2 mm   3 mm   4 mm   5 mm

Range

The **range** of a data set is the difference between the greatest value and the least value.

> **Example**
>
> To find the range of the clamshell data, arrange the values in order from least to greatest.
>
> 13 mm   14 mm   14 mm   16 mm   21 mm   23 mm   25 mm
>
> Subtract the least value from the greatest value.
>
> 13 mm is the least value.
> 25 mm is the greatest value.
>
> 25 mm − 13 mm = 12 mm
>
> **ANSWER** The range is 12 mm.

Using Ratios, Rates, and Proportions

You can use ratios and rates to compare values in data sets. You can use proportions to find unknown values.

Ratios

A **ratio** uses division to compare two values. The ratio of a value a to a nonzero value b can be written as $\frac{a}{b}$.

Example

The height of one plant is 8 centimeters. The height of another plant is 6 centimeters. To find the ratio of the height of the first plant to the height of the second plant, write a fraction and simplify it.

$$\frac{8 \text{ cm}}{6 \text{ cm}} = \frac{4 \times \cancel{2}}{3 \times \cancel{2}} = \frac{4}{3}$$

ANSWER The ratio of the plant heights is $\frac{4}{3}$.

You can also write the ratio $\frac{a}{b}$ as "a to b" or as $a:b$. For example, you can write the ratio of the plant heights as "4 to 3" or as $4:3$.

Rates

A **rate** is a ratio of two values expressed in different units. A unit rate is a rate with a denominator of 1 unit.

Example

A plant grew 6 centimeters in 2 days. The plant's rate of growth was $\frac{6 \text{ cm}}{2 \text{ days}}$. To describe the plant's growth in centimeters per day, write a unit rate.

Divide numerator and denominator by 2: $\quad \frac{6 \text{ cm}}{2 \text{ days}} = \frac{6 \text{ cm} \div 2}{2 \text{ days} \div 2}$

Simplify: $\quad = \frac{3 \text{ cm}}{1 \text{ day}}$

You divide 2 days by 2 to get 1 day, so divide 6 cm by 2 also.

ANSWER The plant's rate of growth is 3 centimeters per day.

Proportions

A **proportion** is an equation stating that two ratios are equivalent. To solve for an unknown value in a proportion, you can use cross products.

Example

If a plant grew 6 centimeters in 2 days, how many centimeters would it grow in 3 days (if its rate of growth is constant)?

Write a proportion: $\dfrac{6 \text{ cm}}{2 \text{ days}} = \dfrac{x}{3 \text{ days}}$

Set cross products: $6 \text{ cm} \cdot 3 = 2x$

Multiply 6 and 3: $18 \text{ cm} = 2x$

Divide each side by 2: $\dfrac{18 \text{ cm}}{2} = \dfrac{2x}{2}$

Simplify: $9 \text{ cm} = x$

ANSWER The plant would grow 9 centimeters in 3 days.

Using Decimals, Fractions, and Percents

Decimals, fractions, and percentages are all ways of recording and representing data.

Decimals

A **decimal** is a number that is written in the base-ten place value system, in which a decimal point separates the ones and tenths digits. The values of each place is ten times that of the place to its right.

Example

A caterpillar traveled from point A to point C along the path shown.

A — 36.9 cm — B — 52.4 cm — C

ADDING DECIMALS To find the total distance traveled by the caterpillar, add the distance from A to B and the distance from B to C. Begin by lining up the decimal points. Then add the figures as you would whole numbers and bring down the decimal point.

```
  36.9 cm
+ 52.4 cm
---------
  89.3 cm
```

ANSWER The caterpillar traveled a total distance of 89.3 centimeters.

Example continued

SUBTRACTING DECIMALS To find how much farther the caterpillar traveled on the second leg of the journey, subtract the distance from A to B from the distance from B to C.

```
   52.4 cm
 - 36.9 cm
  ───────
   15.5 cm
```

ANSWER The caterpillar traveled 15.5 centimeters farther on the second leg of the journey.

Example

A caterpillar is traveling from point D to point F along the path shown. The caterpillar travels at a speed of 9.6 centimeters per minute.

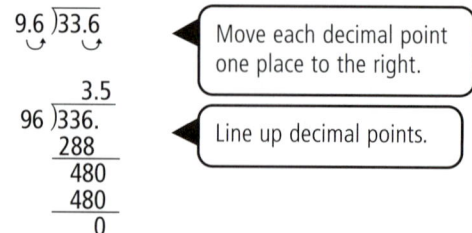

MULTIPLYING DECIMALS You can multiply decimals as you would whole numbers. The number of decimal places in the product is equal to the sum of the number of decimal places in the factors.

For instance, suppose it takes the caterpillar 1.5 minutes to go from D to E. To find the distance from D to E, multiply the caterpillar's speed by the time it took.

```
    9.6        1   decimal place
  × 1.5      + 1   decimal place
  ─────      ───
    480
    96
  ─────
  14.40        2   decimal places
```

Align as shown.

ANSWER The distance from D to E is 14.4 centimeters.

DIVIDING DECIMALS When you divide by a decimal, move the decimal points the same number of places in the divisor and the dividend to make the divisor a whole number.

For instance, to find the time it will take the caterpillar to travel from E to F, divide the distance from E to F by the caterpillar's speed.

```
9.6 )33.6
```
Move each decimal point one place to the right.

```
        3.5
   96 )336.
       288
       ───
        480
        480
        ───
          0
```
Line up decimal points.

ANSWER The caterpillar will travel from E to F in 3.5 minutes.

Fractions

A **fraction** is a number in the form $\frac{a}{b}$, where b is not equal to 0. A fraction is in **simplest form** if its numerator and denominator have a greatest common factor (GCF) of 1. To simplify a fraction, divide its numerator and denominator by their GCF.

Example

A caterpillar is 40 millimeters long. The head of the caterpillar is 6 millimeters long. To compare the length of the caterpillar's head with the caterpillar's total length, you can write and simplify a fraction that expresses the ratio of the two lengths.

$$\text{Write the ratio of the two lengths:} \quad \frac{\text{Length of head}}{\text{Total length}} = \frac{6 \text{ mm}}{40 \text{ mm}}$$

$$\text{Write numerator and denominator as products of numbers and the GCF:} \quad = \frac{3 \times 2}{20 \times 2}$$

$$\text{Divide numerator and denominator by the GCF:} \quad = \frac{3 \times \cancel{2}^{1}}{20 \times \cancel{2}_{1}}$$

$$\text{Simplify:} \quad = \frac{3}{20}$$

ANSWER In simplest form, the ratio of the lengths is $\frac{3}{20}$.

Percents

A **percent** is a ratio that compares a number to 100. The word *percent* means "per hundred" or "out of 100." The symbol for *percent* is %.

For instance, suppose 43 out of 100 caterpillars are female. You can represent this ratio as a percent, a decimal, or a fraction.

Percent	Decimal	Fraction
43%	0.43	$\frac{43}{100}$

Example

In the preceding example, the ratio of the length of the caterpillar's head to the caterpillar's total length is $\frac{3}{20}$. To write this ratio as a percent, write an equivalent fraction that has a denominator of 100.

$$\text{Multiply numerator and denominator by 5:} \quad \frac{3}{20} = \frac{3 \times 5}{20 \times 5}$$

$$= \frac{15}{100}$$

$$\text{Write as a percent:} \quad = 15\%$$

ANSWER The caterpillar's head represents 15 percent of its total length.

Using Formulas

A **formula** is an equation that shows the general relationship between two or more quantities.

In science, a formula often has a word form and a symbolic form. The formula below expresses Ohm's law.

Word Form

$$\text{Current} = \frac{\text{voltage}}{\text{resistance}}$$

Symbolic Form

$$I = \frac{V}{R}$$

> The term *variable* is also used in science to refer to a factor that can change during an experiment.

In this formula, *I*, *V*, and *R* are variables. A mathematical **variable** is a symbol or letter that is used to represent one or more numbers.

Example

Suppose that you measure a voltage of 1.5 volts and a resistance of 15 ohms. You can use the formula for Ohm's law to find the current in amperes.

Write the formula for Ohm's law: $I = \frac{V}{R}$

Substitute 1.5 volts for V and 15 ohms for R: $I = \frac{1.5 \text{ volts}}{15 \text{ ohms}}$

Simplify: $I = 0.1$ amp

ANSWER The current is 0.1 ampere.

If you know the values of all variables but one in a formula, you can solve for the value of the unknown variable. For instance, Ohm's law can be used to find a voltage if you know the current and the resistance.

Example

Suppose that you know that a current is 0.2 amperes and the resistance is 18 ohms. Use the formula for Ohm's law to find the voltage in volts.

Write the formula for Ohm's law: $I = \frac{V}{R}$

Substitute 0.2 amp for I and 18 ohms for R: $0.2 \text{ amp} = \frac{V}{18 \text{ ohms}}$

Multiply both sides by 18 ohms: $0.2 \text{ amp} \cdot 18 \text{ ohms} = V$

Simplify: $3.6 \text{ volts} = V$

ANSWER The voltage is 3.6 volts.

Finding Areas

The area of a figure is the amount of surface the figure covers.

Area is measured in square units, such as square meters (m^2) or square centimeters (cm^2). Formulas for the areas of three common geometric figures are shown below.

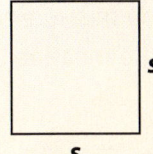

Area = (side length)²
$A = s^2$

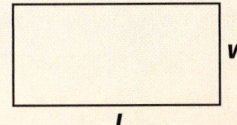

Area = length × width
$A = lw$

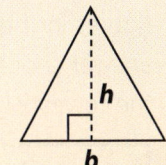

Area = $\frac{1}{2}$ × base × height
$A = \frac{1}{2}bh$

Example

Each face of a halite crystal is a square like the one shown. You can find the area of the square by using the steps below.

Write the formula for the area of a square: $A = s^2$

Substitute 3 mm for s: $= (3 \text{ mm})^2$

Simplify: $= 9 \text{ mm}^2$

ANSWER The area of the square is 9 square millimeters.

Finding Volumes

The volume of a solid is the amount of space contained by the solid.

Volume is measured in cubic units, such as cubic meters (m^3) or cubic centimeters (cm^3). The volume of a rectangular prism is given by the formula shown below.

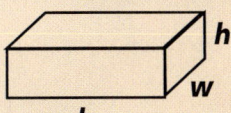

Volume = length × width × height
$V = lwh$

Example

A topaz crystal is a rectangular prism like the one shown. You can find the volume of the prism by using the steps below.

Write the formula for the volume of a rectangular prism: $V = lwh$

Substitute dimensions: $= 20 \text{ mm} \times 12 \text{ mm} \times 10 \text{ mm}$

Simplify: $= 2400 \text{ mm}^3$

ANSWER The volume of the rectangular prism is 2400 cubic millimeters.

Using Significant Figures

The **significant figures** in a decimal are the digits that are warranted by the accuracy of a measuring device.

When you perform a calculation with measurements, the number of significant figures to include in the result depends in part on the number of significant figures in the measurements. When you multiply or divide measurements, your answer should have only as many significant figures as the measurement with the fewest significant figures.

Example

Using a balance and a graduated cylinder filled with water, you determined that a marble has a mass of 8.0 grams and a volume of 3.5 cubic centimeters. To calculate the density of the marble, divide the mass by the volume.

Write the formula for density: $\text{Density} = \dfrac{\text{mass}}{\text{Volume}}$

Substitute measurements: $= \dfrac{8.0 \text{ g}}{3.5 \text{ cm}^3}$

Use a calculator to divide: $\approx 2.285714286 \text{ g/cm}^3$

ANSWER Because the mass and the volume have two significant figures each, give the density to two significant figures. The marble has a density of 2.3 grams per cubic centimeter.

Using Scientific Notation

Scientific notation is a shorthand way to write very large or very small numbers. For example, 73,500,000,000,000,000,000,000 kg is the mass of the Moon. In scientific notation, it is 7.35×10^{22} kg.

Example

You can convert from standard form to scientific notation.

Standard Form	Scientific Notation
720,000	7.2×10^5
5 decimal places left	Exponent is 5.
0.000291	2.91×10^{-4}
4 decimal places right	Exponent is −4.

You can convert from scientific notation to standard form.

Scientific Notation	Standard Form
4.63×10^7	46,300,000
Exponent is 7.	7 decimal places right
1.08×10^{-6}	0.00000108
Exponent is −6.	6 decimal places left

Note-Taking Handbook

Note-Taking Strategies

Taking notes as you read helps you understand the information. The notes you take can also be used as a study guide for later review. This handbook presents several ways to organize your notes.

Content Frame

1. Make a chart in which each column represents a category.
2. Give each column a heading.
3. Write details under the headings.

NAME	GROUP	CHARACTERISTICS	DRAWING
snail	mollusks	mantle, shell	
ant	arthropods	six legs, exoskeleton	
earthworm	segmented worms	segmented body, circulatory and digestive systems	
heartworm	roundworms	digestive system	
sea star	echinoderms	spiny skin, tube feet	
jellyfish	cnidarians	stinging cells	

Top row labeled **categories**; rows below labeled **details**.

Combination Notes

1. For each new idea or concept, write an informal outline of the information.
2. Make a sketch to illustrate the concept, and label it.

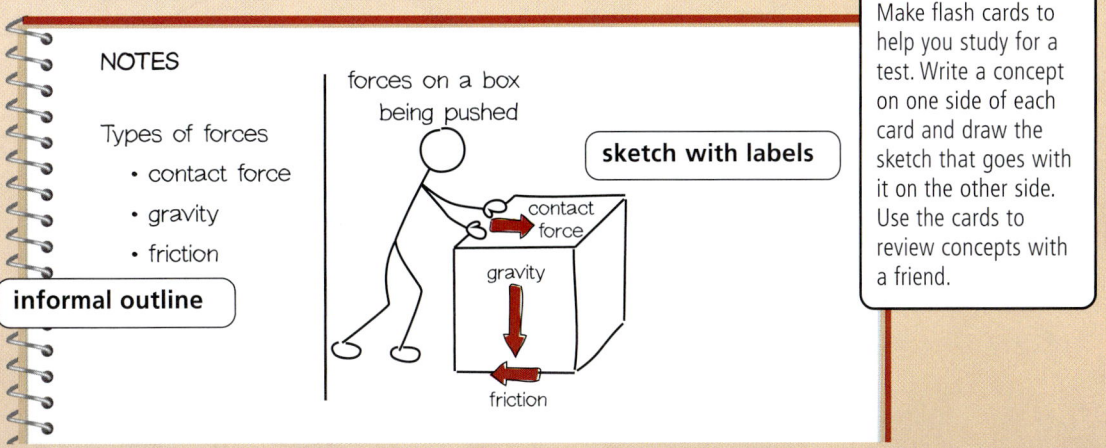

NOTES

Types of forces
- contact force
- gravity
- friction

informal outline

forces on a box being pushed — *sketch with labels*

Make flash cards to help you study for a test. Write a concept on one side of each card and draw the sketch that goes with it on the other side. Use the cards to review concepts with a friend.

Main Idea and Detail Notes

1. In the left-hand column of a two-column chart, list main ideas. The blue headings express main ideas throughout this textbook.
2. In the right-hand column, write details that expand on each main idea.

You can shorten the headings in your chart. Be sure to use the most important words.

> When studying for tests, cover up the detail notes column with a sheet of paper. Then use each main idea to form a question—such as "How does latitude affect climate?" Answer the question, and then uncover the detail notes column to check your answer.

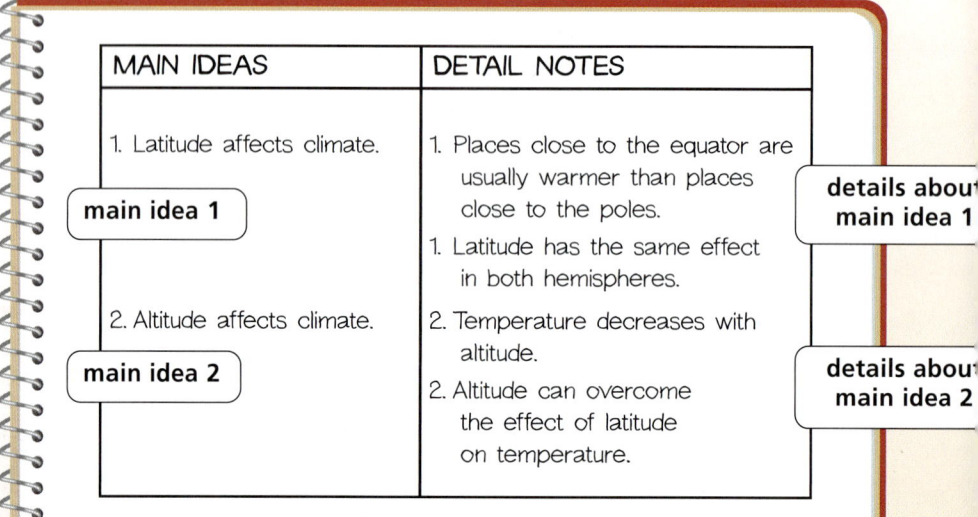

MAIN IDEAS	DETAIL NOTES
1. Latitude affects climate. *(main idea 1)*	1. Places close to the equator are usually warmer than places close to the poles. *(details about main idea 1)*
	1. Latitude has the same effect in both hemispheres.
2. Altitude affects climate. *(main idea 2)*	2. Temperature decreases with altitude. *(details about main idea 2)*
	2. Altitude can overcome the effect of latitude on temperature.

Main Idea Web

1. Write a main idea in a box.
2. Add boxes around it with related vocabulary terms and important details.

> You can find definitions near highlighted terms.

definition of *work*: Work is the use of force to move an object.

formula: Work = force · distance

main idea: Force is necessary to do work.

definition of *joule*: The joule is the unit used to measure work.

important detail: Work depends on the size of a force.

NOTE-TAKING HANDBOOK

R46 Student Resources

Mind Map

1. Write a main idea in the center.
2. Add details that relate to one another and to the main idea.

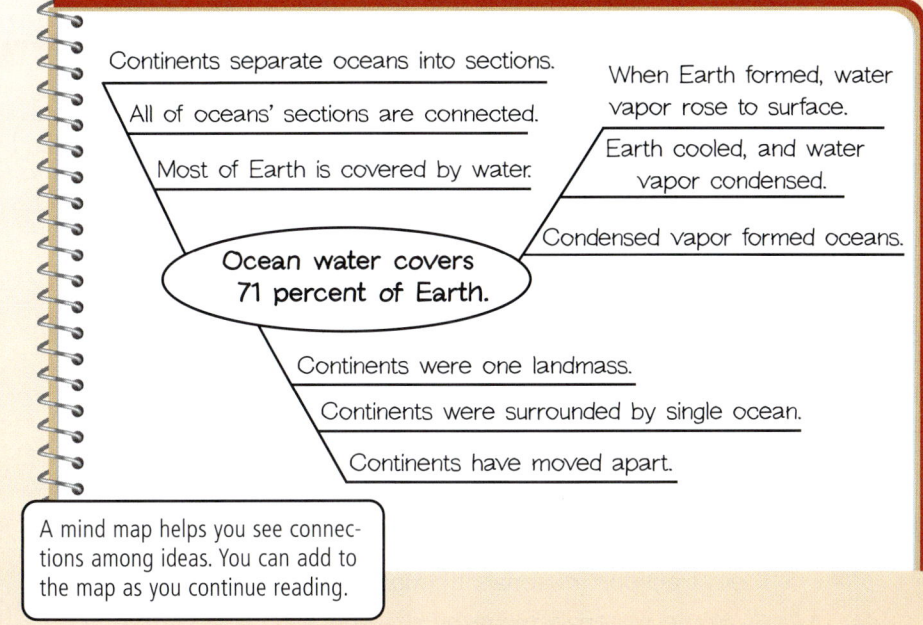

A mind map helps you see connections among ideas. You can add to the map as you continue reading.

Supporting Main Ideas

1. Write a main idea in a box.
2. Add boxes underneath with information—such as reasons, explanations, and examples—that supports the main idea.

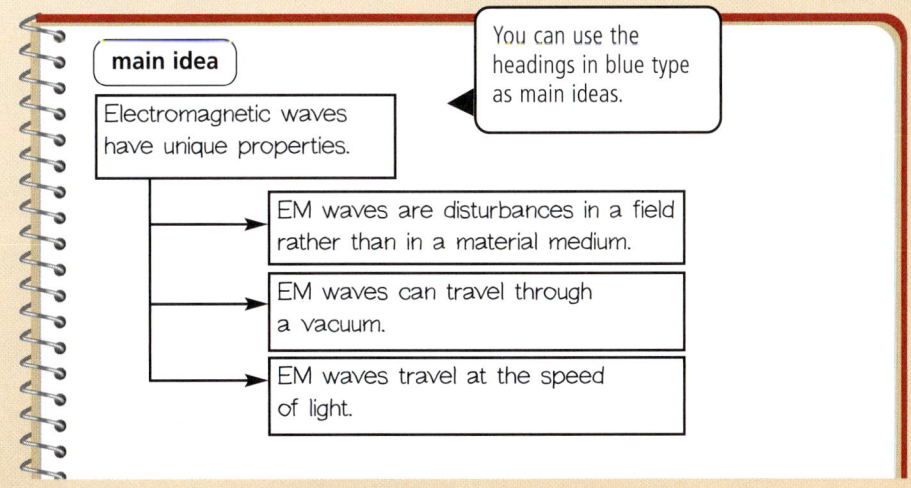

You can use the headings in blue type as main ideas.

Note-Taking Handbook R47

Outline

1. Copy the chapter title and headings from the book in the form of an outline.
2. Add notes that summarize in your own words what you read.

Cell Processes
I. Cells capture and release energy. — *1st key idea*
   A. All cells need energy. — *1st subpoint of I*
   B. Some cells capture light energy. — *2nd subpoint of I*
     1. Process of photosynthesis — *1st detail about B*
     2. Chloroplasts (site of photosynthesis) — *2nd detail about B*
     3. Carbon dioxide and water as raw materials
     4. Glucose and oxygen as products
   C. All cells release energy.
     1. Process of cellular respiration
     2. Fermentation of sugar to carbon dioxide
     3. Bacteria that carry out fermentation
II. Cells transport materials through membranes.
   A. Some materials move by diffusion.
     1. Particle movement from higher to lower concentrations
     2. Movement of water through membrane (osmosis)
   B. Some transport requires energy.
     1. Active transport
     2. Examples of active transport

Correct Outline Form
Include a title.

Arrange key ideas, subpoints, and details as shown.

Indent the divisions of the outline as shown.

Use the same grammatical form for items of the same rank. For example, if A is a sentence, B must also be a sentence.

You must have at least two main ideas or subpoints. That is, every A must be followed by a B, and every 1 must be followed by a 2.

NOTE-TAKING HANDBOOK

Concept Map

1. Write an important concept in a large oval.
2. Add details related to the concept in smaller ovals.
3. Write linking words on arrows that connect the ovals.

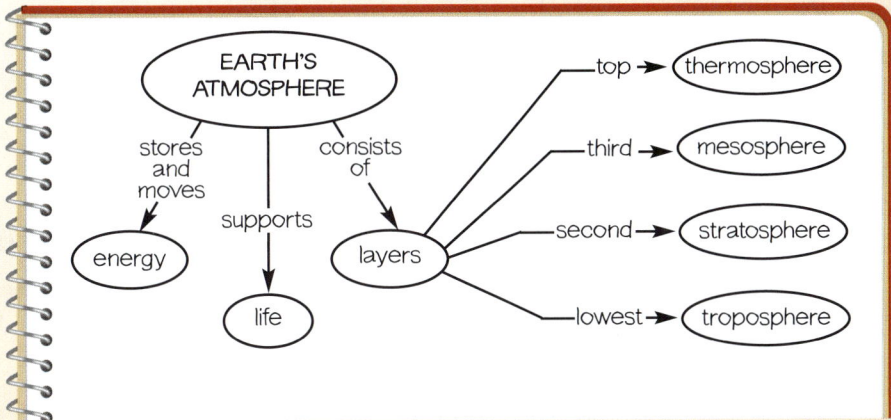

The main ideas or concepts can often be found in the blue headings. An example is "The atmosphere stores and moves energy." Use nouns from these concepts in the ovals, and use the verb or verbs on the lines.

Venn Diagram

1. Draw two overlapping circles, one for each item that you are comparing.
2. In the overlapping section, list the characteristics that are shared by both items.
3. In the outer sections, list the characteristics that are peculiar to each item.
4. Write a summary that describes the information in the Venn diagram.

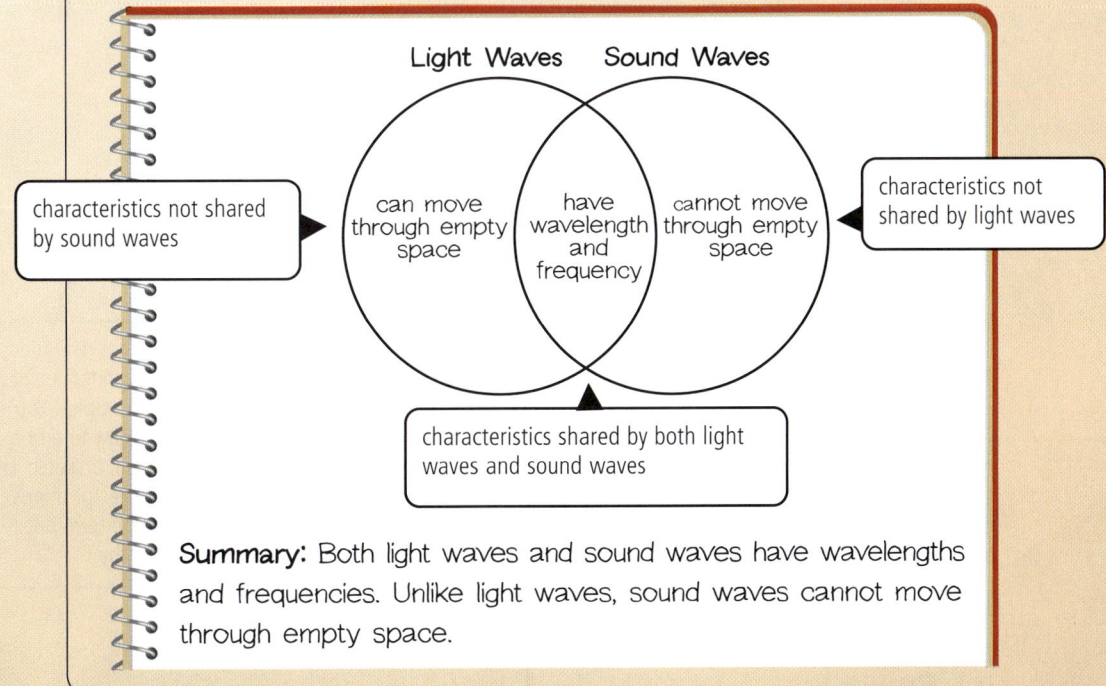

Summary: Both light waves and sound waves have wavelengths and frequencies. Unlike light waves, sound waves cannot move through empty space.

Note-Taking Handbook R49

Vocabulary Strategies

Important terms are highlighted in this book. A definition of each term can be found in the sentence or paragraph where the term appears. You can also find definitions in the Glossary. Taking notes about vocabulary terms helps you understand and remember what you read.

Description Wheel

1. Write a term inside a circle.
2. Write words that describe the term on "spokes" attached to the circle.

When studying for a test with a friend, read the phrases on the spokes one at a time until your friend identifies the correct term.

Spokes around EROSION: leads to deposition; carries particles long distances; moving water a main agent; wind and ice other agents; first stage: weathering; carries sediment

Four Square

1. Write a term in the center.
2. Write details in the four areas around the term.

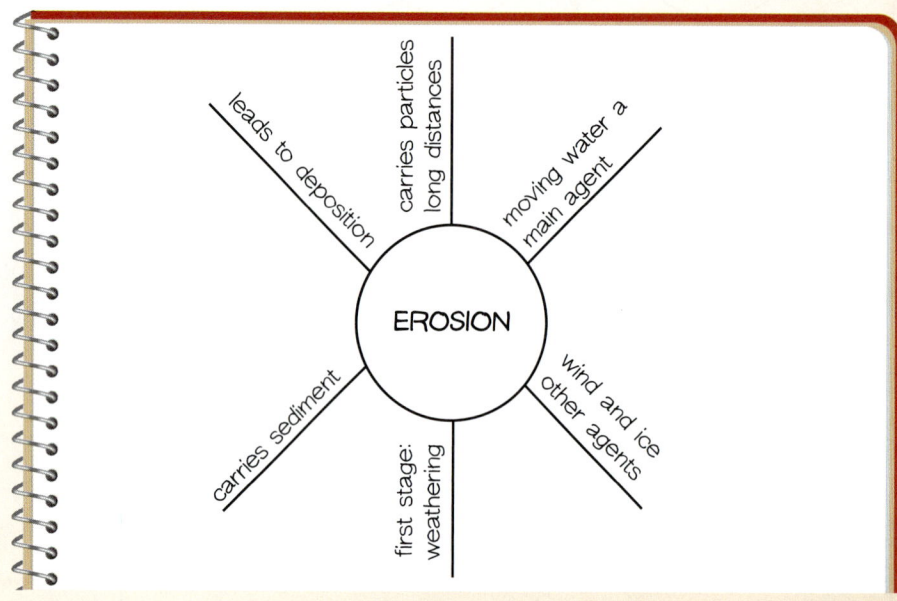

Definition	Characteristics
any living thing	needs food, water, air; needs energy; grows, develops, reproduces
Examples	Nonexamples
dogs, cats, birds, insects, flowers, trees	rocks, water, dirt

Center: ORGANISM

Include a definition, some characteristics, and examples. You may want to add a formula, a sketch, or examples of things that the term does *not* name.

Frame Game

1. Write a term in the center.
2. Frame the term with details.

Include examples, descriptions, sketches, or sentences that use the term in context. Change the frame to fit each new term.

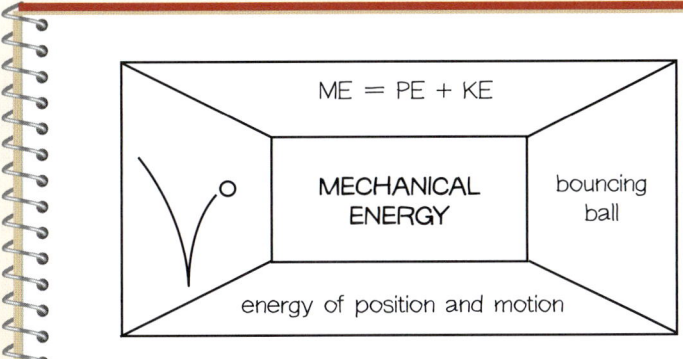

Magnet Word

1. Write a term on the magnet.
2. On the lines, add details related to the term.

You can also use phrases or sentences on the lines.

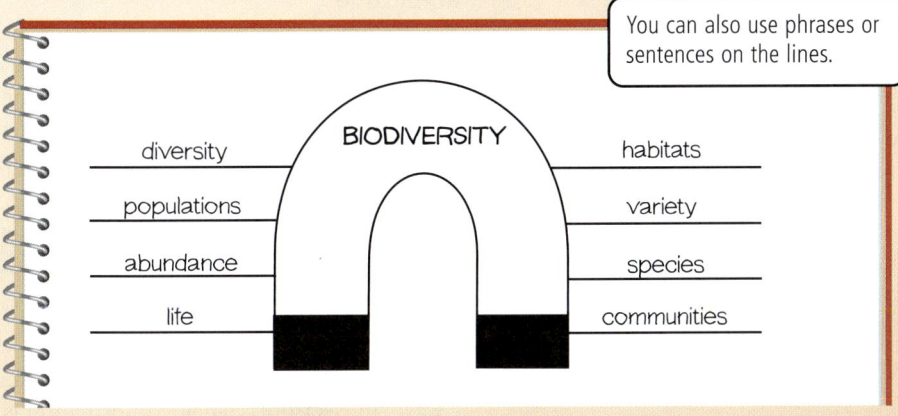

Word Triangle

1. Write a term and its definition in the bottom section.
2. In the middle section, write a sentence in which the term is used correctly.
3. In the top section, draw a small picture to illustrate the term.

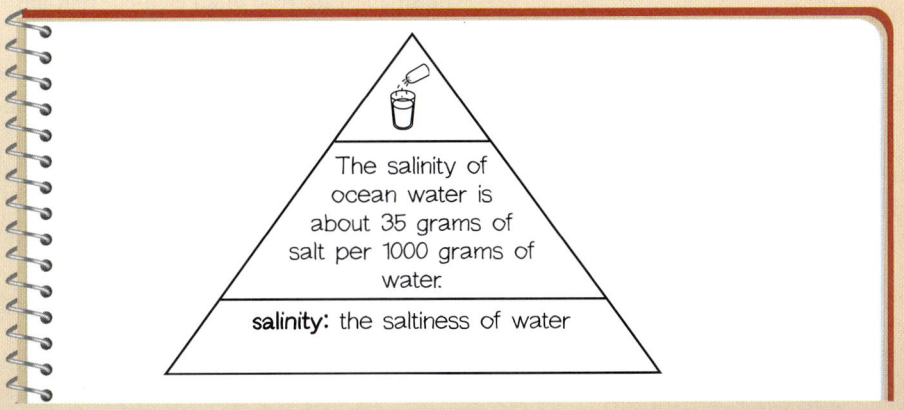

Note-Taking Handbook R51

Glossary

A

absorption (uhb-SAWRP-shuhn)
The disappearance of a wave into a medium. When a wave is absorbed, the energy transferred by the wave is converted into another form of energy, usually thermal energy. (p. 573)

absorción La desaparición de una onda dentro de un medio. Cuando se absorbe una onda, la energía transferida por la onda se convierte a otra forma de energía, normalmente a energía térmica.

acceleration
The rate at which velocity changes over time. (p. 329)

aceleración La razón a la cual la velocidad cambia con respecto al tiempo.

acid
A substance that can donate a proton to another substance and has a pH below 7. (p. 254)

ácido Una sustancia que puede donar un protón a otra sustancia y que tiene un pH menor a 7.

acoustics (uh-KOO-stihks)
The scientific study of sound; the behavior of sound waves inside a space. (p. 535)

acústica El estudio científico del sonido; el comportamiento de las ondas sonoras dentro de un espacio.

air resistance
The fluid friction due to air. (p. 393)

resistencia del aire La fricción fluida debida al aire.

alloy
A solid mixture composed of a metal and one or more other substances. (p. 262)

aleación Una mezcla sólida compuesta de un metal y una o más sustancias adicionales.

alternating current AC
Electric current that reverses direction at regular intervals. (p. 721)

corriente alterna Corriente eléctrica que invierte su dirección a intervalos regulares.

ampere amp
The unit of measurement of electric current, which is equal to one coulomb per second. The number of amps flowing through a circuit equals the circuit's amperage. (p. 653)

amperio La unidad de medición de la corriente eléctrica, la cual es igual a un culombio por segundo. El número de amperios fluyendo por un circuito es igual al amperaje del circuito.

amplification
The strengthening of an electrical signal, often used to increase the intensity of a sound wave. (p. 535)

amplificación El fortalecimiento de una señal eléctrica, a menudo se usa para aumentar la intensidad de una onda sonora.

amplitude
The maximum distance that a disturbance causes a medium to move from its rest position; the distance between a crest or trough of a wave and line through the center of a wave. (p. 497)

amplitud La distancia máxima que se mueve un medio desde su posición de reposo debido a una perturbación; la distancia entre una cresta o valle de una onda y una línea que pasa por el centro de la onda.

analog
Represented by a continuous but varying quantity, such as a wave. In electronics, analog information is represented by a continuous but varying electrical signal. (p. 684)

análogo Que es representado por una cantidad variante pero continua, como una onda. En la electrónica, la información análoga se representa mediante una señal eléctrica continua pero variante.

atom
The smallest particle of an element that has the chemical properties of that element. (p. 16)

átomo La partícula más pequeña de un elemento que tiene las propiedades químicas de ese elemento.

atomic mass
The average mass of the atoms of an element. (p. 145)

masa atómica La masa promedio de los átomos de un elemento.

atomic mass number
The total number of protons and neutrons in an atom's nucleus.

número de masa atómica El número total de protones y neutrones que hay en el núcleo de un átomo.

atomic number
The number of protons in the nucleus of an atom. (p. 140)

número atómico El número de protones en el núcleo de un átomo.

B

base
A substance that can accept a proton from another substance and has a pH above 7. (p. 254)

base Una sustancia que puede aceptar un protón de otra sustancia y que tiene un pH superior a 7.

Bernoulli's principle
A statement that describes the effects of movement on fluid pressure. According to this principle, an increase in the speed of the motion of a fluid decreases the pressure within the fluid. (p. 404)

principio de Bernoulli Un enunciado que describe los efectos del movimiento sobre la presión de un líquido. De acuerdo a este principio, un aumento en la velocidad del movimiento de un fluido disminuye la presión dentro del líquido

binary code
A coding system in which information is represented by two figures, such as 1 and 0. (p. 682)

código binario Un sistema de codificación en el cual la información se representa con dos números, como el 1 y el 0.

bioluminescence
The production of light by living organisms. (p. 569)

bioluminiscencia La producción de luz por parte de organismos vivos.

boiling
A process by which a substance changes from its liquid state to its gas state. The liquid is heated to a specific temperature at which bubbles of vapor form within the liquid. (p. 54)

ebullición Un proceso mediante el cual una sustancia cambia de su estado líquido a su estado gaseoso se calienta el líquido a una determinada temperatura a la cual se forman burbujas de vapor dentro del líquido.

boiling point
The temperature at which a substance changes from its liquid state to its gas state through boiling. (p. 54)

punto de ebullición La temperatura a la cual una sustancia cambia de su estado líquido a su estado gaseoso mediante ebullición.

bond energy
The amount of energy in a chemical bond between atoms.

energía de enlace La cantidad de energía que hay en un enlace químico entre átomos.

buoyant force
The upward force on objects in a fluid; often called buoyancy. (p. 402)

fuerza flotante La fuerza hacia arriba que ejerce un fluido sobre un objeto inmerso en él, a menudo llamada flotación.

C

calorie
The amount of energy needed to increase the temperature of one gram of water by one degree Celsius. (p. 112)

caloría La cantidad de energía que se necesita para aumentar la temperatura de un gramo de agua un grado centígrado.

carbohydrate
A type of carbon-based molecule in living things. Carbohydrates include sugars and starches used for energy or as structural materials. Carbohydrate molecules contain carbon, hydrogen, and oxygen atoms.

carbohidrato Un tipo de molécula de los organismos vivos basada en el carbono. Los carbohidratos incluyen los azúcares y los almidones usados como fuente de energía o como materiales estructurales. Las moléculas de los carbohidrato contienen átomos de carbono, hidrógeno y oxígeno.

catalyst
A substance that increases the rate of a chemical reaction but is not consumed in the reaction. (p. 204)

catalizador Una sustancia que aumenta lel a ritmo velocidad de una reacción química pero que no es consumida en la reacción.

centripetal force (sehn-TRIHP-ih-tuhl)
Any force that keeps an object moving in a circle. (p. 358)

fuerza centrípeta Cualquier fuerza que mantiene a un objeto moviéndose en forma circular.

chemical change
A change of one substance into another substance. (p. 46)

cambio químico La transformación de una sustancia a otra sustancia.

chemical formula
An expression that shows the number and types of atoms joined in a compound. (p. 171)

fórmula química Una expresión que muestra el número y los tipos de átomos unidos en un compuesto.

chemical property
A characteristic of a substance that describes how it can form a new substance. (p. 46)

propiedad química Una característica de una sustancia que describe como puede formar una nueva sustancia.

chemical reaction
The process by which chemical changes occur. In a chemical reaction, atoms are rearranged, and chemical bonds are broken and formed. (p. 197)

reacción química El proceso mediante el cual ocurren cambios químicos. En una reacción química, los átomos se reorganizan y los enlaces químicos se rompen y se vuelven a formar.

circuit
A closed path through which charge can flow. (p. 667)

circuito Una trayectoria cerrada por la cual puede fluir una carga.

coefficient
The number before a chemical formula that indicates how many molecules are involved in a chemical reaction.

coeficiente El número anterior a una fórmula química que indica cuántas moléculas están involucradas en una reaccíon química.

collision
A situation in which two objects in close contact exchange energy and momentum. (p. 370)

colisión Situación en la cual dos objetos en contacto cercano intercambian energía y momento.

compound
A substance made up of two or more different types of atoms bonded together. (p. 23)

compuesto Una sustancia formada por dos o más diferentes tipos de átomos enlazados.

compound machine
A machine that is made up of two or more simple machines. (p. 468)

máquina compuesta Una máquina que está hecha de dos o más máquinas simples.

computer
An electronic device that processes digital information. (p. 685)

computadora Un aparato electrónico que procesa información digital.

concave
Curved inward toward the center, like the inside of a spoon. (p. 596)

cóncavo Dicho de una superficie con curvatura hacia dentro, como la parte interna de una cuchara.

concentration
The amount of solute dissolved in a solvent at a given temperature.

concentración La cantidad de soluto disuelta en un solvente a una temperatura determinada.

condensation
The process by which a gas becomes a liquid. (p. 55)

condensación El proceso mediante el cual un gas se convierte en un líquido.

conduction
The process by which energy is transferred from a warmer object to a cooler object by means of physical contact. (p. 117)

conducción El proceso mediante el cual se transfiere energía de un objeto más caliente a un objeto más frío por medio de contacto físico.

conductor
1. A material that transfers energy easily. (p. 117)
2. A material that transfers electric charge easily. (p. 646)

conductor 1. Un material que transfiere energía fácilmente. 2. Un material que transfiere cargas eléctricas fácilmente.

convection
A process by which energy is transferred in gases and liquids, occurring when a warmer, less dense area of gas or liquid is pushed up by a cooler, more dense area of the gas or liquid. (p. 118)

convección Un proceso mediante el cual se transfiere energía en los gases y los líquidos; ocurre cuando un área más fría y más densa del gas o del líquido empuja hacia arriba un área más caliente y menos densa de gas o de líquido.

convex
Curved outward, like the underside of a spoon. (p. 596)

convexo Dicho de una superficie con curvatura hacia afuera, como la parte externa de una cuchara.

cornea (KAWR-nee-uh)
A transparent membrane that covers the eye. (p. 607)

córnea Una membrana transparente que cubre el ojo.

covalent bond
A pair of electrons shared by two atoms. (p. 178)

enlace covalente Un par de electrones compartidos por dos átomos.

crest
The highest point, or peak, of a wave. (p. 497)

cresta El punto más alto, o el pico, de una onda.

cycle
n. A series of events or actions that repeat themselves regularly; a physical and/or chemical process in which one material continually changes locations and/or forms. Examples include the water cycle, the carbon cycle, and the rock cycle.

v. To move through a repeating series of events or actions.

ciclo *s.* Una serie de eventos o acciones que se repiten regularmente; un proceso físico y/o químico en el cual un material cambia continuamente de lugar y/o forma. Ejemplos: el ciclo del agua, el ciclo del carbono y el ciclo de las rocas.

D

data
Information gathered by observation or experimentation that can be used in calculating or reasoning. *Data* is a plural word; the singular is *datum*.

datos Información reunida mediante observación o experimentación y que se puede usar para calcular o para razonar.

decibel dB
The unit used to measure the intensity of a sound wave. (p. 532)

decibel La unidad que se usa para medir la intensidad de una onda sonora.

degree
Evenly divided units of a temperature scale. (p. 106)

grado Unidades de una escala de temperatura distribuidas uniformemente.

density
A property of matter representing the mass per unit volume. (pp. 43, 403)

densidad Una propiedad de la materia que representa la masa por unidad de volumen.

diffraction
The spreading out of waves as they pass through an opening or around the edges of an obstacle. (p. 506)

difracción La dispersión de las ondas al pasar por una apertura o alrededor de los bordes de un obstáculo.

diffuse reflection
The reflection of parallel light rays in many different directions. (p. 594)

reflexión difusa La reflexión de rayos de luz paralelos en muchas direcciones diferentes.

digital
Represented by numbers. In electronics, digital information is represented by the numbers 1 and 0, signaled by a circuit that is either on or off. (p. 682)

digital Que es representado por números. En la electrónica, la información digital es representada por los números 1 y 0, señalados por un circuito que está encendido o apagado.

dilute
adj. Having a low concentration of solute. (p. 246)

v. To add solvent in order to decrease the concentration of a solution.

diluido *adj.* Que tiene una baja concentración de soluto.

diluir *v.* Agregar solvente para disminuir la concentración de una solución.

direct current DC
Electric current that flows in one direction only. (p. 721)

corriente directa Corriente eléctrica que fluye en una sola dirección.

Doppler effect
The change in perceived pitch that occurs when the source or the one who hears the sound is moving. (p. 530)

efecto Doppler El cambio en el tono percibido que ocurre cuando la fuente o el receptor de un sonido está en movimiento.

E

echolocation
The sending out of high-pitched sound waves and the interpretation of the returning echoes. (p. 539)

ecolocación El envío de ondas sonoras de tono alto y la interpretación de los ecos que regresan.

efficiency
The percentage of the input work done on a machine that the machine can return in output work. A machine's output work divided by its input work and multiplied by 100. (p. 454)

eficiencia El porcentaje del trabajo de entrada suministrado a una máquina que la máquina puede devolver como trabajo de salida. El trabajo de salida de una máquina dividido por su trabajo de entrada y multiplicado por cien.

electric cell
A device that produces electric current using the chemical or physical properties of different materials. A battery consists of two or more cells linked together. (p. 655)

celda eléctrica Un aparato que produce corriente eléctrica usando las propiedades químicas o físicas de diferentes materiales. Una pila consiste de dos o más celdas conectadas.

electric charge
A property that allows one object to exert an electric force on another object without touching it. Electric charge can be positive or negative: positive charge is a property of the proton, while negative charge is a property of the electron. (p. 634)

carga eléctrica Una propiedad que permite a un objeto ejercer una fuerza eléctrica sobre otro objeto sin tocarlo. La carga eléctrica puede ser positiva o negativa: la carga positiva es una propiedad del protón mientras que la carga negativa es una propiedad del electrón.

electric current
A continuous flow of electric charge, which is measured in amperes. (p. 652)

corriente eléctrica Un flujo continuo de una carga eléctrica, el cual se mide en amperios.

electric field
An area surrounding a charged object, within which the object can exert an electric force on another object without touching it. (p. 634)

campo eléctrico Un área que rodea un objeto con carga, dentro del cual el objeto puede ejercer una fuerza eléctrica sobre otro objeto sin tocarlo.

electric potential
The amount of potential energy per unit charge that a static charge or electric current has. Electric potential is measured in volts and is often called voltage. (p. 643)

potencial eléctrico La cantidad de energía potencial por unidad de carga que tiene una carga estática o una corriente eléctrica. El potencial eléctrico se mide en voltios y a menudo se llama voltaje.

electric power
The rate at which electrical energy is generated from, or converted into, another source of energy, such as kinetic energy. (p. 726)

potencia eléctrica El ritmo al cual se genera energía eléctrica a partir de, o se convierte en, otra fuente de energía, como energía cinética.

electromagnet
A magnet that consists of a piece of iron or steel inside a coil of current-carrying wire. (p. 714)

electroimán Un imán que consiste de un pedazo de hierro o de acero dentro de una bobina de alambre por la cual fluye una corriente eléctrica.

electromagnetic spectrum EM spectrum
The range of all electromagnetic frequencies, including the following types (from lowest to highest frequency): radio waves, microwaves, infrared light, visible light, ultraviolet light, x-rays, and gamma rays. (p. 560)

espectro electromagnético La escala de todas las frecuencias electromagnéticas, incluyendo los siguientes tipos (de la frecuencia más baja a la más alta): ondas de radio, microondas, luz infrarroja, luz visible, luz ultravioleta, rayos X y rayos gamma.

electromagnetic wave EM wave
A type of wave, such as a light wave or radio wave, that does not require a medium to travel; a disturbance that transfers energy through a field. (p. 553)

onda electromagnética Un tipo de onda, como una onda luminosa o de radio, que no requiere un medio para propagarse; una perturbación que transfiere energía a través de un campo.

electromagnetism
Magnetism that results from the flow of electric charge. (p. 713)

electromagnetismo Magnetismo que resulta del flujo de una carga eléctrica.

electron
A negatively charged particle located outside an atom's nucleus. An electron is about 2000 times smaller than either a proton or neutron. (p. 139)

electrón Una partícula con carga negativa localizada fuera del núcleo de un átomo. Un electrón es como aproximadamente 2000 veces más pequeño que un protón o un neutrón.

electronic
adj. Operating by means of an electrical signal. An electronic device is a device that uses electric current to represent coded information. (p. 681)
n. An electronic device or system, such as a computer, calculator, CD player, or game system.

electrónico *adj.* Que opera por medio de una señal eléctrica. Un aparato electrónico es un aparato que usa corriente eléctrica para representar información codificada.

element
A substance that cannot be broken down into a simpler substance by ordinary chemical changes. An element consists of atoms of only one type. (p. 22)

elemento Una sustancia que no puede descomponerse en otra sustancia más simple por medio de cambios químicos normales. Un elemento consta de átomos de un solo tipo.

endothermic reaction
A chemical reaction that absorbs energy. (p. 215)

reacción endotérmica Una reacción química que absorbe energía.

energy
The ability to do work or to cause a change. For example, the energy of a moving bowling ball knocks over pins; energy from food allows animals to move and to grow; and energy from the Sun heats Earth's surface and atmosphere, which causes air to move. (p. 72)

energía La capacidad para trabajar o causar un cambio. Por ejemplo, la energía de una bola de boliche en movimiento tumba los pinos; la energía proveniente de su alimento permite a los animales moverse y crecer; la energía del Sol calienta la superficie y la atmósfera de la Tierra, lo que ocasiona que el aire se mueva.

energy efficiency
A measurement of usable energy after an energy conversion; the ratio of usable energy to the total energy after an energy conversion. (p. 83)

eficiencia energética Una medida de la energía utilizable después de una conversión energética; la razón entre la energía utilizable y el total de energía después de una conversión energética.

enzyme
A type of protein that is a catalyst for chemical reactions in living things. (p. 287)

enzima Un tipo de proteína que es un catalizador de reacciones químicas en organismos vivos.

evaporation
A process by which a substance changes from its liquid state to its gas state by random particle movement. Evaporation usually occurs at the surface of a liquid over a wide range of temperatures. (p. 53)

evaporación Un proceso mediante el cual una sustancia cambia de su estado líquido a su estado gaseoso por medio del movimiento aleatorio de las partículas. La evaporación normalmente ocurre en la superficie de un líquido en una amplia gama de temperaturas.

exothermic reaction
A chemical reaction that releases energy. (p. 215)

reacción exotérmica Una reacción química que libera energía.

experiment
An organized procedure to study something under controlled conditions. (p. xl)

experimento Un procedimiento organizado para estudiar algo bajo condiciones controladas.

F

fiber optics
Technology based on the use of laser light to send signals through transparent wires called optical fibers. This technology is often used in communications. (p. 617)

fibra óptica Tecnología basada en el uso de luz de láser para mandar señales por alambres transparentes llamados fibras ópticas. Esta tecnología se usa a menudo en comunicaciones.

field
An area around an object where the object can apply a force—such as gravitational force, magnetic force, or electrical force—on another object without touching it.

campo Un área alrededor de un objeto donde el objeto puede aplicar una fuerza, como fuerza gravitacional, fuerza magnética o fuerza eléctrica, sobre otro objeto sin tocarlo.

fluid
A substance that can flow easily, such as a gas or a liquid. (p. 392)

fluido Una sustancia que fluye fácilmente, como por ejemplo un gas o un líquido.

fluorescence (flu-REHS-uhns)
A phenomenon in which a material absorbs electromagnetic radiation of one wavelength and gives off electromagnetic radiation of a different wavelength. (p. 571)

fluorescencia Un fenómeno en el cual un material absorbe radiación electromagnética de una longitud de onda y emite radiación electromagnética de longitud de onda diferente.

focal length
The distance from the center of a convex lens to its focal point. (p. 603)

distancia focal La distancia del centro de un lente convexo a su punto focal.

focal point
The point at which parallel light rays reflected from a concave mirror come together; the point at which parallel light rays refracted by a convex lens come together. (p. 597)

punto focal El punto en el cual se unen los rayos paralelos de luz reflejados por un espejo cóncavo; el punto en el cual se unen los rayos paralelos de luz refractados por un lente convexo.

force
A push or a pull; something that changes the motion of an object. (p. 345)

fuerza Un empuje o un jalón; algo que cambia el movimiento de un objeto.

freezing
The process by which a substance changes from its liquid state into its solid state. (p. 52)

congelación El proceso mediante el cual una sustancia cambia de su estado líquido a su estado sólido.

freezing point
The temperature at which a substance changes from its liquid state to its solid state through freezing. (p. 52)

punto de congelación La temperatura a la cual una sustancia cambia de su estado líquido a su estado sólido mediante congelación.

frequency
The number of waves that pass a fixed point in a given amount of time, usually one second; the number of cycles per unit time. (p. 497)

frecuencia El número de ondas que pasan un punto fijo en un período de tiempo determinado, normalmente un segundo; el número de ciclos por unidad de tiempo.

friction
A force that resists the motion between two surfaces in contact. (p. 389)

fricción Una fuerza que resiste el movimiento entre dos superficies en contacto.

fulcrum
A fixed point around which a lever rotates. (p. 459)

fulcro Un punto fijo alrededor del cual gira una palanca.

G

gamma rays
Part of the electromagnetic spectrum that consists of waves with the highest frequencies; electromagnetic waves with frequencies ranging from more than 10^{19} hertz to more than 10^{24} hertz. (p. 566)

rayos gamma Parte del espectro electromagnético que consiste de ondas con las frecuencias más altas; las ondas electromagnéticas con frecuencias de más de 10^{19} hertzios hasta más de 10^{24} hertzios.

gas
Matter with no definite volume and no definite shape. The molecules in a gas are very far apart, and the amount of space between them can change easily. (p. 28)

gas Materia sin volumen definido ni forma definida. Las moléculas en un gas están muy separadas unas de otras, y la cantidad de espacio entre ellas puede cambiar fácilmente.

generator
A device that converts kinetic energy, or the energy of motion, into electrical energy. Generators produce electric current by rotating a magnet within a coil of wire or rotating a coil of wire within a magnetic field. (p. 720)

generador Un aparato que convierte energía cinética, o la energía del movimiento, a energía eléctrica. Los generadores producen corriente eléctrica al girar un imán dentro de una bobina de alambre o haciendo rotar una bobina de alambre dentro de un campo magnético.

gravity
The force that objects exert on each other because of their mass. (p. 381)

gravedad La fuerza que los objetos ejercen entre sí debido a su masa.

grounding
The creation of a harmless, low-resistance path—a ground—for electricity to follow. Grounding is an important electrical safety procedure. (p. 649)

conexión a tierra La creación de una trayectoria inofensiva, de baja resistencia—una tierra—para que la siga la electricidad. La conexión a tierra es un importante procedimiento de seguridad eléctrica.

group
A vertical column in the periodic table of the elements. Elements in a group have similar properties. (p. 150)

grupo Una columna vertical en la tabla periódica de los elementos. Los elementos en un grupo tienen propiedades similares.

H

half-life
The amount of time it takes for half of the nuclei of a radioactive isotope to decay into atoms of another element. (p. 160)

vida media La cantidad de tiempo que se necesita para que le toma a la mitad del núcleo de un isótopo radioactivo se en descomponganerse en átomos de otro elemento.

heat
1. The flow of energy from an object at a higher temperature to an object at a lower temperature. (p. 110) 2. Energy that is transferred from a warmer object to a cooler object.

calor 1. El flujo de energía de un objeto a mayor temperatura a un objeto a menor temperatura. 2. Energía que se transfiere de un objeto más caliente a un objeto más frío.

hertz Hz
The unit used to measure frequency. One hertz is equal to one complete cycle per second. (p. 526)

hercio La unidad usada para medir frecuencia. Un hercio es igual a un ciclo completo por segundo.

horizontal
Parallel to the horizon; level.

horizontal Paralelo al horizonte; nivelado.

horsepower hp
The unit of measurement of power for engines and motors. One horsepower equals 745 watts. (p. 436)

caballos de fuerza La unidad de medición de potencia para máquinas y motores. Un caballo de fuerza es igual a 745 vatios.

hydrocarbon
A compound that contains only carbon and hydrogen. (p. 291)

hidrocarburo Un compuesto que contiene solamente carbono e hidrógeno.

hypothesis
A tentative explanation for an observation or phenomenon. A hypothesis is used to make testable predictions. (p. xl)

hipótesi Una explicación provisional de una observación o de un fenómeno. Una hipótesis se usa para hacer predicciones que se pueden probar.

I

image
A picture of an object formed by rays of light. (p. 595)

imagen Reproducción de la figura de un objeto formada por rayos de luz.

incandescence (IHN-kuhn-DEHS-uhns)
1. The production of light by materials having high temperatures. (p. 569) 2. Light produced by an incandescent object.

incandescencia 1. La producción de luz por parte de materiales a altas temperaturas. 2. La luz producida por un objeto incandescente.

inclined plane
A simple machine that is a sloping surface, such as a ramp. (p. 462)

plano inclinado Una máquina simple que es una superficie en pendiente, como por ejemplo una rampa.

induction
The build-up of a static charge in an object when the object is close to, but not touching, a charged object. (p. 637)

inducción La acumulación de carga estática en un objeto cuando el objeto está cercano a, pero no en contacto con, un objeto con carga.

inertia (ih-NUR-shuh)
The resistance of an object to a change in the speed or the direction of its motion. (p. 350)

inercia La resistencia de un objeto al cambio de la velocidad o de la dirección de su movimiento.

infrared light
Part of the electromagnetic spectrum that consists of waves with frequencies between those of microwaves and visible light. (p. 564)

luz infrarroja Parte del espectro electromagnético que consiste de ondas con frecuencias entre las de las microondas y las de la luz visible.

inorganic compound
A compound that is not considered organic. All compounds that do not contain carbon are inorganic, as are some types of carbon-containing compounds. (p. 276)

compuesto inorgánico Un compuesto que no se considera orgánico. Todos los compuestos que no contienen carbono son inorgánicos, al igual que algunos tipos de compuestos que contienen carbono.

insulator
1. A material that does not transfer energy easily. (p. 117) 2. A material that does not transfer electric charge easily. (p. 646)

aislante 1. Un material que no transfiere energía fácilmente. 2. Un material que no transfiere cargas eléctricas fácilmente.

intensity
The amount of energy of a wave, per wavelength. Intensity is associated with the amplitude of a sound wave and with the quality of loudness produced by the sound wave. (p. 532)

intensidad La cantidad de energía de una onda sonora, por longitud de onda. La intensidad está asociada con la amplitud de una onda sonora y con la calidad del volumen producido por la onda sonora.

interference
The meeting and combining of waves; the adding or subtracting of wave amplitudes that occurs as waves overlap. (p. 507)

interferencia El encuentro y la combinación de ondas; la suma o la resta de amplitudes de onda que ocurre cuando las ondas se traslapan.

ion
An atom or group of atoms that has a positive or negative electric charge. (p. 142)

ión Un átomo o un grupo de átomos que tiene una carga eléctrica positiva o negativa.

ionic bond
The electrical attraction between a negative ion and a positive ion. (p. 176)

enlace iónico La atracción eléctrica entre un ión negativo y un ión positivo.

isomer
Any of two or more compounds that contain the same atoms but that have different structures. (p. 280)

isómero Cualquiera de dos o más compuestos que contienen los mismos átomos pero que tienen estructuras diferentes.

isotope
An atom of one element that has a different number of neutrons than another atom of the same element. (p. 140)

isótopo Un átomo de un elemento que tiene un número diferente de neutrones que otro átomo del mismo elemento.

J

joule (jool) J
A unit used to measure energy and work. One calorie is equal to 4.18 joules of energy; one joule of work is done when a force of one newton moves an object one meter. (pp. 112, 421)

julio Una unidad que se usa para medir la energía y el trabajo. Una caloría es igual a 4.18 julios de energía; se hace un joule de trabajo cuando una fuerza de un newton mueve un objeto un metro.

K

kilowatt kW
A unit of measurement for power equal to 1000 watts. (p. 728)

kilovatio Una unidad de medición para la potencia equivalente a 1000 vatios.

kilowatt-hour kWh
The unit of measurement for electrical energy equal to one kilowatt of power over a one-hour period. (p. 729)

kilovatio-hora La unidad de medición de energía eléctrica igual a un kilovatio de potencia en un período de una hora.

kinetic energy (kuh-NEHT-ihk)
The energy of motion. A moving object has the most kinetic energy at the point where it moves the fastest. (pp. 74, 426)

energía cinética La energía de movimiento. Un objeto en movimiento tiene la mayor energía cinética en el punto en donde se mueve más rápidamente.

kinetic theory of matter (kuh-NEHT-ihk)
A theory stating that all matter is made of particles in motion. (p. 104)

teoría cinética de la materia Una teoría que establece que toda materia está compuesta de partículas en movimiento.

L

laser (LAY-zuhr)
A device that produces an intense, concentrated beam of light that can be brighter than sunlight. Lasers are often used in medicine and communications. (p. 615)

láser Un aparato que produce un intenso rayo de luz concentrado que es más brillante que la luz del Sol. Los láseres se usan a menudo en la medicina y las comunicaciones.

law
In science, a rule or principle describing a physical relationship that always works in the same way under the same conditions. The law of conservation of energy is an example.

ley En las ciencias, una regla o un principio que describe una relación física que siempre funciona de la misma manera bajo las mismas condiciones. La ley de la conservación de la energía es un ejemplo.

law of conservation of energy
A law stating that no matter how energy is transferred or transformed, it continues to exist in one form or another. (pp. 82, 430)

ley de la conservación de la energía Una ley que establece que no importa cómo se transfiere o transforma la energía, toda la energía sigue presente en alguna forma u otra.

law of conservation of mass
A law stating that atoms are not created or destroyed in a chemical reaction. (p. 207)

ley de la conservación de la masa Una ley que establece que los átomos ni se crean ni se destruyen en una reacción química.

law of conservation of momentum
A law stating that the amount of momentum a system of objects has does not change as long as there are no outside forces acting on that system. (p. 371)

ley de la conservación del momento Una ley que establece que la cantidad de momento que tiene un sistema de objetos no cambia mientras no haya fuerzas externas actuando sobre el sistema.

law of reflection
A law of physics stating that the angle at which light strikes a surface (the angle of incidence) equals the angle at which it reflects off the surface (the angle of reflection). (p. 594)

ley de la reflexión Una ley de la física que establece que el ángulo al cual la luz incide sobre una superficie (el ángulo de incidencia) es igual al ángulo al cual se refleja (ángulo de reflexión) de la superficie.

lens
A transparent optical tool that refracts light. (p. 601)

lente Una herramienta óptica transparente que refracta la luz.

lever
A solid bar that rotates, or turns, around a fixed point (fulcrum); one of the six simple machines. (p. 459)

palanca Una barra sólida que da vueltas o gira alrededor de un punto fijo (el fulcro); una de las seis máquinas simples.

lipid
A type of carbon-based molecule in living things. Lipids include fats and oils used for energy or as structural materials. (p. 284)

lípido Un tipo de molecula de los organismos vivos basada en el carbono. Los lípidos incluyen las grasas y los aceites usados como fuente de energía o como materiales estructurales.

liquid
Matter that has a definite volume but does not have a definite shape. The molecules in a liquid are close together but not bound to one another. (p. 28)

líquido Materia que tiene un volumen definido pero no tiene una forma definida. Las moléculas en un líquido están cerca unas de otras pero no están ligadas.

longitudinal wave (LAHN-jih-TOOD-uhn-uhl)
A type of wave in which the disturbance moves in the same direction that the wave travels. (p. 494)

onda longitudinal Un tipo de onda en la cual la perturbación se mueve en la misma dirección en la que viaja la onda.

luminescence
The production of light without the high temperatures needed for incandescence. (p. 569)

luminiscencia La producción de luz sin las altas temperaturas necesarias para la incandescencia.

M

machine
Any device that makes doing work easier. (p. 449)

máquina Cualquier aparato que facilita el trabajo.

magnet
An object that attracts certain other materials, particularly iron and steel. (p. 703)

imán Un objeto que atrae a ciertos otros materiales, especialmente al hierro y al acero.

magnetic domain
A group of atoms whose magnetic fields align, or point in the same direction. Magnetic materials have magnetic domains, whereas nonmagnetic materials do not. (p. 707)

dominio magnético Un grupo de átomos cuyos campos magnéticos se alinean, o apuntan en la misma dirección. Los materiales magnéticos tienen dominios magnéticos mientras que los materiales no magnéticos no tienen.

magnetic field
An area surrounding a magnet within which the magnet can exert a force. Magnetic fields are concentrated into a pattern of lines that extend from the magnet's north pole to its south pole. (p. 705)

campo magnético Un área alrededor de un imán dentro del cual el imán puede ejercer una fuerza. Los campos magnéticos se concentran en un patrón de líneas que se extienden del polo norte del imán a su polo sur.

magnetic pole
One of two ends of a magnet where the magnetic force is the strongest. Every magnet has two poles.

polo magnético Uno de dos extremos de un imán donde la fuerza magnética es lo más fuerte. Todos los imanes tienen dos polos.

magnetism
The force exerted by a magnet. Opposite poles of two magnets attract, or pull together, whereas like poles of two magnets repel, or push apart. (p. 704)

magnetismo La fuerza que ejerce un imán. Los polos opuestos de dos imanes se atraen, o jalan hacia si, mientras que los polos iguales de dos imanes se repelen, o se empujan para alejarse uno del otro.

mass
A measure of how much matter an object is made of. (p. 10)

masa Una medida de la cantidad de materia de la que está compuesto un objeto.

matter
Anything that has mass and volume. Matter exists ordinarily as a solid, a liquid, or a gas. (p. 9)

materia Todo lo que tiene masa y volumen. Generalmente la materia existe como sólido, líquido o gas.

mechanical advantage
The number of times a machine multiplies the input force; output force divided by input force (p. 451)

ventaja mecánica El número de veces que una máquina multiplica la fuerza de entrada; la fuerza de salida dividida por la fuerza de entrada.

mechanical energy
A combination of the kinetic energy and potential energy an object has. (p. 429)

energía mecánica La combinación de la energía cinética y la energía potencial que tiene un objeto.

mechanical wave
A wave, such as a sound wave or a seismic wave, that transfers kinetic energy through matter. (p. 491)

onda mecánica Una onda, como una onda sonora o una onda sísmica, que transfiere energía cinética a través de la materia.

medium
A substance through which a wave moves. (p. 491)

medio Una sustancia a través de la cual se mueve una onda.

melting
The process by which a substance changes from its solid state to its liquid state. (p. 51)

fusión El proceso mediante el cual una sustancia cambia de su estado sólido a su estado líquido.

melting point
The temperature at which a substance changes from its solid state to its liquid state through melting. (p. 51)

punto de fusión La temperatura a la cual una sustancia cambia de su estado sólido a su estado líquido mediante fusión.

metal
An element that tends to be shiny, easily shaped, and a good conductor of electricity and heat. (p. 155)

metal Un elemento que tiende a ser brilloso, fácilmente deformable moldeado y buen conductor de electricidad y calor.

metallic bond
A certain type of bond in which nuclei float in a sea of electrons. (p. 184)

enlace metálico Cierto tipo de enlace en el cual los núcleos flotan en un mar de electrones.

metalloid
An element that has properties of both metals and nonmetals. (p. 158)

metaloide Un elemento que tiene propiedades de los metales así como de los no metales.

meter m
The international standard unit of length, about 39.37 inches.

metro La unidad estándar internacional de longitud, aproximadamente 39.37 pulgadas.

microwaves
Part of the electromagnetic spectrum that consists of waves with higher frequencies than radio waves, but lower frequencies than infrared waves. (p. 563)

microondas Parte del espectro electromagnético que consiste de ondas con frecuencias mayores a las ondas de radio, pero menores a las de las ondas infrarrojas.

mixture
A combination of two or more substances that do not combine chemically but remain the same individual substances. Mixtures can be separated by physical means. (p. 23)

mezcla Una combinación de dos o más sustancias que no se combinan químicamente sino que permanecen como sustancias individuales. Las mezclas se pueden separar por medios físicos.

molecule
A group of atoms that are held together by covalent bonds so that they move as a single unit. (pp. 18, 179)

molécula Un grupo de átomos que están unidos mediante enlaces covalentes de tal manera que se mueven como una sola unidad.

momentum (moh-MEHN-tuhm)
A measure of mass in motion. The momentum of an object is the product of its mass and velocity. (p. 368)

momento Una medida de la masa en movimiento. El momento de un objeto es el producto de su masa y su velocidad.

monomer
One of many small, repeating units linked together to form a polymer. (p. 294)

monómero Una de muchas unidades pequeñas que se repiten y están enlazadas unas con otras para formar un polímero.

motion
A change of position over time. (p. 315)

movimiento Un cambio de posición a través del tiempo.

nanotechnology
The science and technology of building electronic circuits and devices from single atoms and molecules. (p. 471)

nanotecnología La ciencia y tecnología de fabricar circuitos y aparatos electrónicos a partir de átomos y moléculas individuales.

net force
The overall force acting on an object when all of the forces acting on it are combined. (p. 347)

fuerza neta La fuerza resultante que actúa sobre un objeto cuando todas las fuerzas que actúan sobre él son combinadas.

neutral
Describing a solution that is neither an acid nor a base. A neutral solution has a pH of 7. (p. 257)

neutro Que describe una solución que no es un ácido ni una base. Una solución neutra tiene un pH de 7.

neutron
A particle that has no electric charge and is located in an atom's nucleus. (p. 139)

neutrón Una partícula que no tiene carga eléctrica y que se encuentra en el núcleo de un átomo.

Newton's first law
A scientific law stating that objects at rest remain at rest, and objects in motion remain in motion with the same velocity, unless acted on by an unbalanced force. (p. 349)

primera ley de Newton Una ley científica que establece que los objetos en reposo permanecen en reposo, y que los objetos en movimiento permanecen en movimiento con la misma velocidad, a menos que actúe sobre ellos una fuerza no balanceada.

Newton's second law
A scientific law stating that the acceleration of an object increases with increased force and decreases with increased mass. (p. 354)

segunda ley de Newton Una ley científica que establece que la aceleración de un objeto aumenta al incrementar la fuerza que actúa sobre él y disminuye al incrementar su masa.

Newton's third law
A scientific law stating that every time one object exerts a force on another object, the second object exerts a force that is equal in size and opposite in direction back on the first object. (p. 361)

tercera ley de Newton Una ley científica que establece que cada vez que un objeto ejerce una fuerza sobre otro objeto, el segundo objeto ejerce una fuerza de la misma magnitud y en dirección opuesta sobre el primer objeto.

nonmetal
An element that is not a metal and has properties generally opposite to those of a metal. (p. 157)

no metal Un elemento que no es un metal y que tiene propiedades generalmente opuestas a las de los metales.

Glossary R63

nucleic acid
One of several carbon-based molecules that carry an organism's genetic code. One of the nucleic acids—DNA—contains the information needed to construct proteins. (p. 289)

ácido nucleico Una de varias moléculas basadas en el carbono que llevan el código genético de un organismo. Uno de los ácidos nucleicos, el ADN, contiene la información necesaria para construir proteínas.

nucleus
The central region of an atom where most of the atom's mass is found in protons and neutrons. (p. 139)

núcleo La región central de un átomo donde se encuentra la mayor parte de la masa del átomo en la forma de protones y neutrones.

O

ohm Ω
The unit of measurement for electrical resistance. (p. 647)

ohmio La unidad de medición para la resistencia eléctrica.

Ohm's law
The mathematical relationship among current, voltage, and resistance, expressed in the formula $I = V/R$ (current = voltage/resistance). (p. 653)

ley de Ohm La relación matemática entre la corriente, el voltaje y la resistencia, expresada en la fórmula $I = V/R$ (corriente = voltaje/resistencia).

optics (AHP-tihks)
The study of light, vision, and related technology. (p. 593)

óptica El estudio de la luz, la visión y la tecnología relacionada a ellas.

orbit
The elliptical path one celestial body follows around another celestial body. An object in orbit has a centripetal force acting on it that keeps the object moving in a circle or other ellipse. (p. 384)

órbita El camino elíptico que un cuerpo celeste sigue alrededor de otro cuerpo celeste. La fuerza centrípeta actúa sobre un objeto en órbita y lo mantiene en un movimiento circular o elíptico.

organic compound
A compound that is based on carbon. (p. 275)

compuesto orgánico Un compuesto basado en el carbono.

P, Q

parallel circuit
A circuit in which current follows more than one path. Each device that is wired in a parallel circuit has its own path to and from the voltage source. (p. 677)

circuito paralelo Un circuito en el cual la corriente sigue más de una trayectoria. Cada aparato que está conectado a un circuito paralelo tiene su propia trayectoria desde y hacia la fuente de voltaje.

particle
A very small piece of matter, such as an atom, molecule, or ion.

partícula Una cantidad muy pequeña de materia, como un átomo, una molécula o un ión.

pascal Pa
The unit used to measure pressure. One pascal is the pressure exerted by one newton of force on an area of one square meter, or one N/m^2. (p. 396)

pascal La unidad utilizada para medir presión. Un pascal es la presión ejercida por un newton de fuerza sobre un área de un metro cuadrado, o un N/m^2.

Pascal's principle
A statement that says when an outside pressure is applied at any point to a fluid in a container, that pressure is transmitted throughout the fluid with equal strength. (p. 406)

principio de Pascal Un enunciado que dice que cuando una presión externa es aplicada a cualquier punto de un líquido en un contenedor, esta presión es transmitida a través del fluido con igual fuerza.

period
A horizontal row in the periodic table of the elements. Elements in a period have varying properties. (p. 150)

período Un renglón horizontal en la tabla periódica de los elementos. Los elementos en un período tienen distintas propiedades.

periodic table
A table of the elements, arranged by atomic number, that shows the patterns in their properties. (p. 146)

tabla periódica Una tabla de los elementos, organizada en base a número atómico, que muestra los patrones en sus propiedades.

pH
The concentration of hydrogen ions in a solution; a measurement of acidity. (p. 257)

pH La concentración de iones de hidrógeno en una solución;, una medida de acidez.

photosynthesis
In green plants, the endothermic process in which light is absorbed and used to change carbon dioxide and water into glucose and oxygen. (p. 218)

fotosíntesis En plantas verdes, el proceso endotérmico en el cual se absorbe luz y se usa para cambiar dióxido de carbono y agua a glucosa y oxígeno.

physical change
A change in a substance that does not change the substance into a different one. (p. 44)

cambio físico Un cambio en una sustancia que no transforma la sustancia a otra sustancia.

physical property
A characteristic of a substance that can be observed without changing the identity of the substance. (p. 41)

propiedad física Una característica de una sustancia que se puede observar sin cambiar la identidad de la sustancia.

pitch
The quality of highness or lowness of a sound. Pitch is associated with the frequency of a sound wave—the higher the frequency, the higher the pitch. (p. 525)

tono La cualidad de un sonido de ser alto o bajo. El tono está asociado con la frecuencia de una onda sonora: entre más alta sea la frecuencia, más alto es el tono.

plastic
A polymer that can be molded or shaped. (p. 295)

plástico Un polímero que puede ser modelado o deformadomoldeado.

polar covalent bond
The unequal sharing of electrons between two atoms that gives rise to negative and positive regions of electric charge. (p. 179)

enlace polar covalente El compartir electrones desigualmente entre dos átomos y que lleva a la formación de regiones de carga eléctrica positiva y regiones de carga eléctrica negativa.

polarization (POH-luhr-ih-ZAY-shuhn)
A way of filtering light so that all of the waves vibrate in the same direction. (p. 576)

polarización Una manera de filtrar la luz para que todas las ondas vibren en la misma dirección.

polymer
A very large carbon-based molecule made of smaller, repeating units. (p. 294)

polímero Una molécula muy grande basada en el carbono compuesta de unidades más pequeñas que se repiten.

position
An object's location. (p. 313)

posición La ubicación de un objeto.

potential energy
Stored energy; the energy an object has due to its position, molecular arrangement, or chemical composition. (pp. 75, 426)

energía potencial Energía almacenada; o la energía que tiene un objeto debido a su posición, arreglo molecular o composición química.

power
The rate at which work is done. (p. 434)

potencia La razón a la cual se hace el trabajo.

precipitate
n. A solid substance that forms as a result of a reaction between chemicals in two liquids. (p. 200)
v. To come out of solution.

precipitado s. Una sustancia sólida que se forma como resultado de la reacción entre sustancias químicas en dos líquidos.

precipitar v. Salir de solución.

pressure
A measure of how much force is acting on a certain area; how concentrated a force is. Pressure is equal to the force divided by area. (p. 395)

presión Una medida de cuánta fuerza actúa sobre cierta área; el nivel de concentración de la fuerza. La presión es igual a la fuerza dividida entre el área.

primary colors
Three colors of light—red, green, and blue—that can be mixed to produce all possible colors. (p. 578)

colores primarios Tres colores de luz, rojo, verde y azul, que se pueden mezclar para producir todos los colores posibles.

primary pigments
Three colors of substances—cyan, yellow, and magenta—that can be mixed to produce all possible colors. (p. 579)

pigmentos primarios Tres colores de sustancias, cian, amarillo y magenta, que se pueden mezclar para producir todos los colores posibles.

prism
An optical tool that uses refraction to separate the different wavelengths that make up white light. (p. 577)

prisma Una herramienta óptica que usa la refracción para separar las diferentes longitudes de onda que componen la luz blanca.

product
A substance formed by a chemical reaction. A product is made by the rearrangement of atoms and bonds in reactants. (p. 199)

producto Una sustancia formada por una reacción química. Un producto se hace mediante la reorganización de los átomos y los enlaces en los reactivos.

protein
A macromolecule in living things that is made of smaller molecules called amino acids. (p. 286)

proteína Una macromolécula en organismos vivos compuesta de moléculas más pequeñas llamadas aminoácidos.

proton
A positively charged particle located in an atom's nucleus. (p. 139)

protón Una partícula con cargada positivamente localizada en el núcleo de un átomo.

pulley
A wheel with a grooved rim that turns on an axle; one of the six simple machines. (p. 460)

polea Una rueda con un canto acanalado que gira sobre un eje; una de las seis máquinas simples.

pupil
The circular opening in the iris of the eye that controls how much light enters the eye. (p. 607)

pupila La apertura circular en el iris del ojo que controla cuánta luz entra al ojo.

R

radiation (RAY-dee-AY-shuhn)
Energy that travels across distances in the form of electromagnetic waves. (pp. 119, 555)

radiación Energía que viaja a través de la distancia en forma de ondas electromagnéticas.

radioactivity
The process by which the nucleus of an atom of an element releases energy and particles. (p. 158)

radioactividad El proceso mediante el cual el núcleo de un átomo de un elemento libera energía y partículas.

radio waves
The part of the electromagnetic spectrum that consists of waves with the lowest frequencies. (p. 562)

ondas de radio La parte del espectro electromagnético que consiste de las ondas con las frecuencias más bajas.

reactant
A substance that is present at the beginning of a chemical reaction and is changed into a new substance. (p. 199)

reactivo Una sustancia que está presente en el comienzo de una reacción química y que se convierte en una nueva sustancia.

reactive
Likely to undergo a chemical change. (p. 154)

reactivo Que es probable que sufra un cambio químico.

reference point
A location to which another location is compared. (p. 314)

punto de referencia Una ubicación con la cual se compara otra ubicación.

reflection
The bouncing back of a wave after it strikes a barrier. (p. 505)

reflexión El rebote de una onda después de que incide sobre una barrera.

refraction
The bending of a wave as it crosses the boundary between two mediums at an angle other than 90 degrees. (p. 505)

refracción El doblamiento de una onda a medida que cruza el límite entre dos medios a un ángulo distinto a 90 grados.

regular reflection
The reflection of parallel light rays in the same direction. (p. 594)

reflexión especular La reflexión de rayos de luz paralelos en la misma dirección.

resistance
The property of a material that determines how easily a charge can move through it. Resistance is measured in ohms. (p. 653)

resistencia La propiedad de un material que determina qué tan fácilmente puede moverse una carga a través de él. La resistencia se mide en ohmios.

resistor
An electrical device that slows the flow of charge in a circuit. (p. 668)

resistencia Un aparato eléctrico que hace más lento el flujo de carga en un circuito.

resonance
The strengthening of a sound wave when it combines with an object's natural vibration. (p. 528)

resonancia El fortalecimiento de una onda sonora cuando se combina con la vibración natural de un objeto.

respiration
The exothermic process by which living things release energy from glucose and oxygen and produce carbon dioxide and water. (p. 222)

respiración El proceso exotérmico mediante el cual los organismos vivos liberan energía de la glucosa y del oxígeno y producen dióxido de carbono y agua.

retina (REHT-uhn-uh)
A light-sensitive membrane at the back of the inside of the eye. (p. 607)

retina Una membrana sensible a la luz en la parte trasera del interior del ojo.

robot
A machine that works automatically or by remote control. (p. 473)

robot Una máquina que funciona automáticamente o por control remoto.

saturated
Containing the maximum amount of a solute that can be dissolved in a particular solvent at a given temperature and pressure. (p. 246)

saturado Que contiene la máxima cantidad de soluto que se puede disolver en un solvente en particular a determinada temperatura y presión.

scattering
The spreading out of light rays in all directions as particles reflect and absorb the light. (p. 575)

dispersión La disipación de los rayos de luz en todas las direcciones a medida que las partículas reflejan y absorben la luz.

screw
A simple machine that is an inclined plane wrapped around a cylinder. A screw can be used to raise and lower weights as well as to fasten objects. (p. 463)

tornillo Una máquina simple que es un plano inclinado enrollado alrededor de un cilindro. Un tornillo se puede usar para levantar o bajar pesos y también para sujetar objetos.

second s
A unit of time equal to one-sixtieth of a minute.

segundo Una unidad de tiempo igual a una sesentava parte de un minuto.

series circuit
A circuit in which current follows a single path. Each device that is wired in a series circuit shares a path to and from the voltage source. (p. 676)

circuito en serie Un circuito en el cual la corriente sigue una sola trayectoria. Cada aparato conectado a un circuito en serie comparte una trayectoria desde y hacia la fuente de voltaje.

short circuit
An unintended and undesired path connecting one part of a circuit with another. (p. 670)

corto circuito Una trayectoria no intencionada y no deseada que conecta una parte de un circuito con otra.

simple machine
One of the basic machines on which all other mechanical machines are based. The six simple machines are the lever, inclined plane, wheel and axle, pulley, wedge, and screw. (p. 458)

máquina simple Una de las máquinas básicas sobre las cuales están basadas todas las demás máquinas mecánicas. Las seis máquinas simples son la palanca, el plano inclinado, la rueda y eje, la polea, la cuña y el tornillo.

solar cell
A type of technology in which light-sensitive materials convert sunlight into electrical energy. (p. 88)

celda solar Un tipo de tecnología en el cual materiales sensibles a la luz convierten luz solar a energía eléctrica.

solid
Matter that has a definite shape and a definite volume. The molecules in a solid are in fixed positions and are close together. (p. 28)

sólido La materia que tiene una forma definida y un volumen definido. Las moléculas en un sólido están en posiciones fijas y cercanas unas a otras.

solubility
The amount of solute that dissolves in a certain amount of a solvent at a given temperature and pressure to produce a saturated solution. (p. 247)

solubilidad La cantidad de soluto que se disuelve en cierta cantidad de solvente a determinada temperatura y presión para producir una solución saturada.

Glossary R67

solute
In a solution, a substance that is dissolved in a solvent. (p. 240)

soluto En una solución, una sustancia que se disuelve en un solvente.

solution
A mixture of two or more substances that is identical throughout; a homogeneous mixture. (p. 239)

solución Una mezcla de dos o más sustancias que es idéntica en su totalidad;, una mezcla homogénea.

solvent
In a solution, the substance that dissolves a solute and makes up the largest percentage of a solution. (p. 240)

solvente En una solución, la sustancia que disuelve un soluto y que compone el porcentaje mayor de la una solución.

sonar
Instruments that use echolocation to locate objects underwater; acronym for "sound navigation and ranging." (p. 539)

sonar Instrumentos que usan la ecolocación para localizar objetos bajo agua; acrónimo en inglés para "navegación y determinación de distancias por sonido".

sound
A type of wave that is produced by a vibrating object and that travels through matter. (p. 517)

sonido Un tipo de onda que es producida por un objeto que vibra y que viaja a través de la materia.

specific heat
The amount of energy required to raise the temperature of one gram of a substance by one degree Celsius. (p. 113)

calor específico La cantidad de energía que se necesita para aumentar la temperatura de un gramo de una sustancia un grado centígrado.

speed
A measure of how fast something moves through a particular distance over a definite time period. Speed is distance divided by time. (p. 320)

rapidez Una medida del desplazamiento de un objeto a lo largo de una distancia específica en un período de tiempo definido. La rapidez es la distancia dividida entre el tiempo.

states of matter
The different forms in which matter can exist. Three familiar states are solid, liquid, and gas. (p. 27)

estados de la materia Las diferentes formas en las cuales puede existir la materia. Los tres estados conocidos son sólido, líquido y gas.

static charge
The buildup of electric charge in an object caused by the uneven distribution of charged particles. (p. 635)

carga estática La acumulación de carga eléctrica en un objeto ocasionada por la desigual distribución de partículas con carga.

sublimation
The process by which a substance changes directly from its solid state to its gas state without becoming a liquid first. (p. 53)

sublimación El proceso mediante el cual una sustancia cambia directamente de su estado sólido a su estado gaseoso sin convertirse primero en líquido.

subscript
A number written slightly below and to the right of a chemical symbol that shows how many atoms of an element are in a compound. (p. 171)

subíndice Un número que se escribe en la parte inferior a la derecha de un símbolo químico y que muestra cuantos átomos de un elemento están en un compuesto.

substance
Matter of a particular type. Elements, compounds, and mixtures are all substances.

sustancia La materia de cierto tipo. Los elementos, los compuestos y las mezclas son sustancias.

suspension
A mixture in which the different parts are identifiable as separate substances; a heterogeneous mixture. (p. 241)

suspensión Una mezcla en la cual las diferentes partes son identificables como sustancias distintas; una mezcla heterogénea.

system
A group of objects or phenomena that interact. A system can be as simple as a rope, a pulley, and a mass. It also can be as complex as the interaction of energy and matter in the four parts of the Earth system.

sistema Un grupo de objetos o fenómenos que interactúan. Un sistema puede ser algo tan sencillo como una cuerda, una polea y una masa. También puede ser algo tan complejo como la interacción de la energía y la materia en las cuatro partes del sistema de la Tierra.

T

technology
The use of scientific knowledge to solve problems or engineer new products, tools, or processes.
tecnología El uso de conocimientos científicos para resolver problemas o para diseñar nuevos productos, herramientas o procesos.

temperature
A measure of the average amount of kinetic energy of the particles in an object. (p. 105)
temperatura Una medida de la cantidad promedio de energía cinética de las partículas en un objeto.

terminal velocity
The final, maximum velocity of a falling object. (p. 393)
velocidad terminal La velocidad máxima final de un objeto en caída libre.

theory
In science, a set of widely accepted explanations of observations and phenomena. A theory is a well-tested explanation that is consistent with all available evidence.
teoría En las ciencias, un conjunto de explicaciones de observaciones y fenómenos que es ampliamente aceptado. Una teoría es una explicación bien probada que es consecuente con la evidencia disponible.

thermal energy
The energy an object has due to the motion of its particles; the total amount of kinetic energy of particles in an object. (p. 111)
energía térmica La energía que tiene un objeto debido al movimiento de sus partículas; la cantidad total de energía cinética de las partículas en un objeto.

thermometer
A device for measuring temperature. (p. 107)
termómetro Un aparato para medir la temperatura.

transformer
A device that uses electromagnetism to increase or decrease voltage. A transformer is often used in the distribution of current from power plants. (p. 723)
transformador Un aparato que usa electromagnetismo para aumentar o disminuir el voltaje. A menudo se usa un transformador en la distribución de corriente desde las centrales eléctricas.

transmission (trans-MIHSH-uhn)
The passage of a wave through a medium. (p. 573)
transmisión El paso de una onda a través de un medio.

transverse wave
A type of wave in which the disturbance moves at right angles, or perpendicular, to the direction in which the wave travels. (p. 493)
onda transversal Un tipo de onda en el cual la perturbación se mueve en ángulo recto, o perpendicularmente, a la dirección en la cual viaja la onda.

trough (trawf)
The lowest point, or valley, of a wave (p. 497)
valle El punto más bajo de una onda.

U

ultrasound
Sound waves with frequencies above 20,000 hertz, the upper limit of typical hearing levels in humans, used for medical purposes, among other things. (p. 526)
ultrasonido Ondas sonoras con frecuencias superiores a 20,000 hertzios, el límite superior de los niveles auditivos típicos de los humanos. Estas ondas tienen usos médicos, entre otros.

ultraviolet light
The part of the electromagnetic spectrum that consists of waves with frequencies higher than those of visible light and lower than those of x-rays. (p. 565)
luz ultravioleta La parte del espectro electromagnético que consiste de ondas con frecuencias superiores a las de luz visible y menores a las de los rayos X.

V

vacuum
A space containing few or no particles of matter. (p. 521)
vacío Un espacio que no contiene partículas de materia o bien contiene muy pocas.

variable
Any factor that can change in a controlled experiment, observation, or model. (p. R30)
variable Cualquier factor que puede cambiar en un experimento controlado, en una observación o en un modelo.

vector
A quantity that has both size and direction. (p. 326)
vector Una cantidad que tiene magnitud y dirección.

velocity
A speed in a specific direction. (p. 326)
velocidad Una rapidez en una dirección específica.

vertical
Going straight up or down from a level surface.

vertical Que está dispuesto hacia arriba o hacia abajo de una superficie nivelada.

vibration
A rapid, back-and-forth motion. (p. 517)

vibración Un movimiento rápido hacia delante y hacia atrás.

visible light
The part of the electromagnetic spectrum that consists of waves detectable by the human eye. (p. 564)

luz visible La parte del espectro electromagnético que consiste de ondas detectables por el ojo humano.

volt V
The unit of measurement for electric potential, which is equal to one joule per coulomb. The number of volts of an electric charge equals the charge's voltage. (p. 643)

voltio La unidad de medición para el potencial eléctrico, el cual es igual a un julio por segundo por culombio. El número de voltios de una carga eléctrica es igual al voltaje de la carga.

volume
An amount of three-dimensional space, often used to describe the space that an object takes up. (p. 11)

volumen Una cantidad de espacio tridimensional; a menudo se usa este término para describir el espacio que ocupa un objeto.

W

watt W
The unit of measurement for power, which is equal to one joule of work done or energy transferred in one second. For example, a 75 W light bulb converts electrical energy into heat and light at a rate of 75 joules per second. (pp. 435, 728)

vatio La unidad de medición de la potencia, el cual es igual a un julio de trabajo realizado o energía transferida en un segundo. Por ejemplo, una bombilla de 75 W convierte energía eléctrica a calor y luz a un ritmo de 75 julios por segundo.

wave
A disturbance that transfers energy from one place to another without requiring matter to move the entire distance. (p. 489)

onda Una perturbación que transfiere energía de un lugar a otro sin que sea necesario que la materia se mueva toda la distancia.

wavelength
The distance from one wave crest to the next crest; the distance from any part of one wave to the identical part of the next wave. (p. 497)

longitud de onda La distancia de una cresta de onda a la siguiente cresta; la distancia de cualquier parte de una onda a la parte idéntica de la siguiente onda.

wedge
A simple machine that has a thick end and a thin end. A wedge is used to cut, split, or pierce objects, or to hold objects together. (p. 462)

cuña Una máquina simple que tiene un extremo grueso y otro extremo delgado. Una cuña se usa para cortar, partir o penetrar objetos, o para mantener objetos juntos.

weight
The force of gravity on an object. (pp. 11, 383)

peso La fuerza de la gravedad sobre un objeto.

wheel and axle
A simple machine that is a wheel attached to a shaft, or axle. (p. 460)

rueda y eje Una máquina simple que es una rueda unida a una flecha, o a un eje.

work
The use of force to move an object over a distance. (p. 419)

trabajo El uso de fuerza para mover un objeto una distancia.

X, Y, Z

x-rays
The part of the electromagnetic spectrum that consists of waves with high frequencies and high energies; electromagnetic waves with frequencies ranging from more than 10^{16} hertz to more than 10^{21} hertz. (p. 566)

rayos X La parte del espectro electromagnético que consiste de las ondas con altas frecuencias y altas energías; las ondas electromagnéticas con frecuencias de más de 10^{16} hertzios hasta más de 10^{21} hertzios.

Index

Page numbers for definitions are printed in **boldface** type.
Page numbers for illustrations, maps, and charts are printed in *italics*.

A

absolute zero, 98
absorption, **573**, 577
acceleration, **329**, 329–335, *330*, *338*, 353–359, *357*, *364*
   average, 332
   force, mass, and, 354–357, *354*, *355*, *356*, *357*, 360, *360*, *371*, *374*, *390*
   gravitational, 382–383, *383*, *384*, *385*, 427, 452, *453*
   negative, *330*, *333*, *334*, 335
   velocity, time, and, 329, *330*, 331–335, *332*, *334*, *338*
accuracy, **R22**
AC-DC converter, 721, *721*
acetic acid, 256, *256*, 257
acidity, measuring, 257
acid rain, 252, 259
acids, 252, 253–259, **254**, 268
   acetic, 256, *256*, 257
   acid-base neutralization, 252, 259
   Chapter Investigation, 260–261
   properties, 253, 255
   strength, 256–257
   testing for, 255
acoustics, *535*, **535**
actinides, 149
action and reaction, 361–364, *363*, *364*, 370, *374*, 389, 462
aeolipile, 413, *413*, 415
aerogel, *59*
air, 180, *180*
   density of, 398
   weight of, *398*
air bags, 212, *212*, 351
air conditioners, 91
air filter, 640
air pressure, 398, 404–405
air resistance, **393**, *393*, 456
alchemy, 97, 99
alkali metals, 155
alkaline earth metals, 155
alloys, 156, **262**, 262–266, 268
   aluminum, 264, 266
   cobalt, 265
   gold, 262
   Internet activity, 237
   iron, 263–266
   liquid, 266

   in medicine, 265, *265*
   memory, 263, 265
   in space flight, 266, *266*
   titanium, 265, *265*, 266
   in transportation, 264
   uses, *263*, 264–266
alternating current (AC), **721**
alternator, 722
altitude, air pressure and, 398
aluminum, 155, *155*
amino acids, 286–287
   DNA and, 288–289
ammeter, 654
ammonia, 171, *172*, 247, 256, *257*
   molecular structure, 182, *182*, *257*
ampere (amp), **653**, 660
amplification, *535*, **535**
amplitude, 496, *497*, **497**, *498*, *499*, 509, 535
AM waves, 562, *562*
analog (information), **684**
   conversion to digital, 684, *684*
analysis, critical, R8
angle of incidence, 594, *594*, 598
angle of reflection, 594, *594*, 598
angles, measuring, 598
antacids, 253, 259
antifreeze, 244
anvil (ear), 519, *519*
aperture, 614, *615*
Archimedes, 413, *413*
area, **R43**
   force, pressure, and, 395–399, *396*, *397*, 408
Aristotle, 96, 412, *412*
aromatic compounds, 278
artificial lenses, 609–610
artificial light, 570–572
astatine, 150
astronomy, 388
atmosphere (unit of pressure), 398
atomic mass, **145**, 152–153
atomic mass number, **140**
atomic model, *139*
atomic number, **140**
atomic particles, *139*, 139–140
atomic size, 151, *151*
atomic theory of matter, 16

atoms, xxxi, **xxxi**, xxxiii, **16**, 16–17, 34, 137–143, 162, *162*, 232–235
   atomic number, **140**
   carbon, 275, 280, 285
   change in identity, 158, 160
   in chemical reactions, 197, 199, 201, 207–209, 211
   compounds and, 169–170, 172, *172*, 190
   electrons, *139*, **139**, 139–140, 234
   images of, 20, *20*
   ion formation, 142–143, 176, 185
   mass, 17, **145**, 152–153
   mass number, 140
   model, *139*
   motion of, 19
   nanotechnology and, 471
   neutral, 140
   neutrons, *139*, **139**, 140–141, *141*, 158, 162, *162*
   nucleus, *139*, **139**, 162, *162*, 234
   particles, *139*, 139–140
   polarized, 638, *638*
   protons, **139**, *139*, 162, *162*, 254
   radioactive, 158–160
   ratios of, in compounds, 170, 172, *172*
   size, 140, 151, *151*
   structure, 139–140
   types, in Earth's crust, 138, *138*
   types, in humans, 138, *138*
audion, 234
audio tape, 543
automobile. *See* car.
averages, calculating, 424, **R36**
axle. *See* wheel and axle.

B

Babbage, Charles, 697
Bacon, Francis, 97
Bakelite, 295
balanced forces, **347**, 347–351, **349**, 363, **390**
bases, 253–259, **254**, 268
   acid-base neutralization, 259
   Chapter Investigation, 260–261
   properties, 253, 255
   strength, 256–257
   testing for, 255
Bassi, Laura, 697
batteries, 233, 655, 697
   car, 656, *657*
   in parallel circuits, 677
   rechargeable, 656, *657*
   in series circuits, 676
beetle, bombardier, 217, *217*
benzene, 278
Bernoulli, Daniel, 404
Bernoulli's principle, **404**, 404–405, 408
   in nature, *405*

Bessemer process, 264
bias, **R6**
   scientific, R6
   sources of, R6
bicycles
   efficiency of, *456*
   forces acting on, *348*
binary code, **682**
bioluminescence, *568*, **569**, 569–570
bit, 682
Black, Joseph, 97
block-and-tackle system. *See* pulley.
Bohr, Niels, 234
boiling, *54*, **54**, 64
boiling point, **54**, 244
   of compounds, 185–186
   of hydrocarbons, 292
bond energy, 214–216
   in endothermic reactions, 215, 217, *217*, 228
   in exothermic reactions, 215, *216*, 228
bonds. *See* chemical bonds.
Boyle, Robert, 232
brass, *263*
British thermal units (BTUs), 91
bromine, 150
bronze, 262–263, *263*
buoyancy, **402**, 402–403, 408, 413
   density and, *403*
butane, 280
byte, 682

C

calcium, 144, 155, 170, *170*
calcium chloride, 170, *170*, 190
calorie, **112**, 113
Calorie (food), 112
calorimeter, 112
calorimetry, 97
cameras, 614, *615*, 619
   digital, 614, *615*
car
   battery, 656, *657*
   catalytic converter, 224, *225*
   design of, xlii–xliii
   efficient, 87, *87*
   fuel-cell powered, xliii, *xliii*
   gas consumption, xliii
   gasoline vs. electric, 77
   generator, 722
   hybrid, 87, *87*
   hydrogen powered, 99
   pollution and, xliii, 224, 225
   solar-cell powered, 4, 5, 88, *88*
   static electricity and, 640, *640*
carbohydrates, **283**, 283–284, 300

carbon, 144, 272–300
  atomic model, *xli*
  bonding, 276–277
  carbohydrates, **283**, 283–284, 300
  chains, 278, *279*, 280, 284, 292
  cycle, 292, *292*
  forms of, 186–187, *187*
  hydrocarbon, 224, *225*, **291**, 291–292, *293*
  lipids, **284**, *284*, 284–285, 300
  in living things, 138, 144, 282–289, 292
  in materials, 291–297
  monomers, **294**, 294–297, 300
  nanotubes, 281, *281*
  nucleic acids, *288*, **289**, 300
  polymers, **294**, 294–297, 300
  products, *293*
  proteins, **286**, 286–287, *287*, 300
  rings, 278, *279*
  structures, 275–280
carbon chains, 278, *279*, 284, 292
    branched, 278, 280, *280*
    straight, 278, 280, *280*
carbon cycle, 292, *292*
carbon dioxide, *22*, 48, 53, 171, 179, *179*, 218, 222–225, *225*, 247, 250, 276
  formation, 208
carbon monoxide molecule, 18
carbon rings, 278, *279*, 283, 284, 288, 297
carbon steel, *263*
Carnot, Nicolas Sadi, 98
catalyst, *204*, **204**, 224
catalytic converter, 224, *225*
catapult, 412, *412*
cause-and-effect relationship, **R5**
CD (compact disc), 543, *543*
CD (compact disc) player, 628, 718, *718*
cell phone, 563, *563*, 567
  generator, 628, 718, *718*
cells
  cone, **608**
  hair (ear), 519, *519*, 536, *536*
  rod, **608**
celluloid, 295
cellulose, 284, *284*, 295
Celsius, Anders, 97
Celsius scale, 97, 106, *106*
  converting to Fahrenheit, 109
Chapter Investigations
  acids and bases, 260–261
  atomic masses, 152–153
  build a speaker, 724–725
  chemical bonds, 188–189
  chemical reactions, 220–221
  electronic devices, 690–691
  energy conversions, 84–85
  freezing point, 56–57
  insulators, 122–23

  lenses, 604–605
  lightning, 650–651
  mass and volume, 14–15
  polymers, 298–299
  stringed instrument, 544–545
  wavelength, 502–503
  wavelength and color, 580–581
charge buildup, 635–637, 642
  in lightning, 644, *645*
charge polarization, 638, *638*
charging by contact, *635*, 635–636
chemical bonds, 169, 175–190
  of carbon atoms, 276–279
  Chapter Investigation, 188–189
  in chemical reactions, 214–217, *216*, *217*
  comparison of, 180, *180*
  covalent, **178**, *178*, 178–180, *179*, *180*, 186–187, 190
  double, 276–277, *276*, *277*, 295, 300
  electrons and, 175–176, 190, 276
  Internet activity, 167
  ionic, *176*, 176–177, *180*, 185–186, 190
  metallic, **184**, 184–185, *185*, 190, 276
  models, *178*
  polar covalent, **178**, *179*, *180*, 250–251, *251*
  properties of substances and, 184–187
  single, *276*, 276–277, *277*, 295, 300
  structure of materials and, 181–182
  triple, *276*, 276–277, *277*, 300
chemical change, **46**, 46–48, 64
  Internet activity, 39
  signs of, 47, 48
chemical compounds, 166–190
  aromatic, 278
  atoms and, 169–170, 172, *172*, 190
  covalent, 182, *182*, 186, 242, *242*
  formulas, 171–172, *172*
  inorganic, *276*, **276**
  ionic, 177, *180*, 181, 185–186, 242, *242*
  isomers, **280**, *280*, 297
  names of ionic compounds, 177
  new, 201
  organic, **275**, 275–276, *276*
  properties, 169–170, 184–187, 190
  with same elements, 172–173, *173*
  structure, 181–182, *182*
  substances and, 169
  synthesis, 201
chemical energy, xxxiv, **73**, 76, 432
  of fossil fuels, 80
chemical equations, 208–212
  balancing, 209–212
  coefficients, 210–211
  conservation of mass, 208, 209, 212, 228
chemical formulas, **171**, 171–172, *172*
  how to write, 171
chemical properties, **46**, 64

chemical reactions, 194–228, **197**, 228
　　See also chemical change.
　　atoms and, 197, 199, 201, 207–209, 211
　　catalyst in, *204*, **204**, 224
　　in catalytic converters, 224, *225*
　　Chapter Investigation, 220–221
　　chemical changes, 199, *199*
　　classification of, 201
　　conservation of mass, 206–207, **207**, 208, 209, 212, 228
　　electronics and, 226–227, *227*
　　endothermic, **215**, *217*, 217–218, 228
　　energy changes in, 214–219, 228
　　equations of, 208–212
　　evidence of, 200, *200*, 228
　　exothermic, *215*, **215**, 215–217, *216*, 228
　　in firefighting, 213
　　in industry, 224–227, 228
　　Internet activity, 195
　　iodine clock, 205
　　in living things, 216–217, 218, 219, 222–223, 228
　　neutralization, 259
　　photosynthesis, **218**, 218–219, 222, 223
　　products, **199**
　　rates and factors, 202–204, *203*, 205
　　reactants, **199**
　　respiration, **222**, 222–223
　　thermite reaction, 215, *215*
chips, 226–227, *227*
chloride ion, 143, *143*, 176, 242, 254, *254*, 256, *256*
chlorine, 144, 150, 170, *170*
　　atom, 140, 141, *141*, 143, *143*
cholesterol, 285
circle graphs, 26
circuit diagram, 669, *669*, 674
　　of parallel circuit, *677*
　　of series circuit, *676*
circuits, **667**, 667–673
　　in appliances, 678–679
　　closed, 669, *669*
　　diagrams of, 669, 674, 676, 677
　　electronic technology and, 681–689
　　energy conversion, 678–679
　　functioning, 670, *670*
　　fuses, 672, *672*
　　grounding, 671, *671*
　　integrated, 685, *685*
　　Internet activity, 665
　　open, 669, *669*
　　parallel, **677**, *677*
　　parts of, 668, *668*
　　paths of, 676–677
　　safety devices and, 671–673, 674
　　series, **676**, *676*
　　short, 670, *670*
　　uses for, 675–679

closed circuit, 669, *669*
cobalt alloys, 265
cochlea, 519, *519*
code, 681
　　binary, 682
coefficients, 210–211
collisions, **370**, *371*, *372*, *374*. See also momentum.
　　of molecules and pressure, 397
colors, 576–579
　　mixing, 578, 579, *579*
　　primary, *578*, **578**
　　reflection and absorption, 577, *577*
　　wavelength and, 576–579, 580–581
color spectrum, 577
combustion, *201*, **201**
　　gasoline, 224
　　methane, 209, *209*, 210, *210*, 216, *216*
　　respiration, **222**, 222–223
combustion reaction, 201
commutator, *717*, 721, *721*
compact disc (CD), 543, *543*
compass, 708, 709
compounds, **23**, 24, 34. See also chemical compounds.
　　comparing mixtures with, 24
compressional waves, 494
compressions, 520, *520*
computer chips, 699
computers, **685**, 685–689, 692
　　electromagnets and, 715
　　first, 698
　　functions of, *686*, 687
　　Internet and, 688–689
　　miniaturization in, 699
　　modeling forces, 415
　　network, 688
　　personal, *686*, 686–687
　　scientific use of, *xli*
concave lens, *601*, **601**
　　images formed by, 603
　　nearsightedness and, 609, *609*
concave mirror, *596*, **596**, *597*
　　in telescopes, 612, *613*
concentration, 202, *203*, **245**, 245–246
condensation, *55*, **55**, 64
conduction, *117*, **117**, 124, 635
conductors, **117**, **646**, 660, 668, *668*, 692
cone cells, **608**
conservation of energy, xxxv, **82**, 92, **430**, *431*, *432*, **432**
conservation of mass, 206–207, **207**, 228
conservation of matter, xxxiii
constants, **R30**
constructive interference, 507, *507*
contact force, xxxvii, **xxxvii**, *346*
contact lens, 610, *610*
control group, 433, R30

convection, *118*, **118**, 124
convex lens, *601*, **601**, *602*, *603*, 604–605
    in cameras, 614, *615*
    farsightedness and, 609, *609*
    images formed by, 603, *603*
    in microscopes (objective lens), 612, *613*
    in telescopes (objective lens), 612, *613*
convex mirror, *596*, **596**, *597*
cooking, with heat, 115
copper, 155, *155*, 190
    properties of bonds in, 185, *185*
cornea, *607*, **607**, 608, 610
    surgery on, 610
coulombs, 635, 643
covalent bond, **178**, *178*, 178–180, *179*, *180*, 186–187, 190
covalent compounds
    properties of, 186
    in solutions, 242, *242*
    structure of, 182, *182*
crest, **497**, 510
critical analysis, R8
    of statements, R8–R9
crystals, 181
    of ionic compounds, 177, *177*
Curie, Marie, 158, 234
Curie, Pierre, 234
current (electrical), 439
    alternating, **721**
    direct, **721**
cycle, 526

D

Dalton, John, 139
dams, 80, *80*
data,
    analyzing, xxxvi
    describing, R36–R37
data tables, making, R23
da Vinci, Leonardo, 414
Davy, Humphrey, 233
decibel, **532**, 534, *534*
decimals, **R39**, R40
    adding, R39
    dividing, R40
    multiplying, R40
    in scientific notation, 161
    subtracting, R40
decomposition, *201*, **201**
    of sodium azide, 212
    of water, 199, *199*, 217, *217*
Deep Space 1 (spacecraft), 333
DeForest, Lee, 234
degrees, **106**

density, **43**, 403
    of air, *398*
    buoyancy and, 403
    calculating, 43, 49
    identifying substances using, 59, 64
    mass, volume, and, 403
    of minerals, 63
    of water, *399*
design, technological, xlii–xliii
destructive interference, 508, *508*
dew, 50
Dewar, James, 98
diamond, 186, *187*, 190
diesel fuel, 279, 293
diffraction, **506**, *506*, 506–507, *507*, 510
diffuse reflection, **594**
diffusion, 619, *619*
digital cameras, 614, *615*
digital (information), **682**, 682–683
digital sound, 627–628
dilute, *246*, **246**, 268
direct current (DC), **721**
direction of force, 346, 347, 451, *453*
    See also vectors.
discharge. *See* static discharge.
displacement, 13, *13*, 403, 408
distance
    distance-time graph, 324, *325*, *334*, 335, *338*
    force, work, and, 419–423
    gravity and, 382, 408
    measuring, 315, 328
    speed and, 320–323, 327, 328, 338
DNA, *288*, 289
Doppler effect, **530**, *531*
Doppler ultrasound, 540
drag, 393. *See also* air resistance.
dry ice, 22, 53
DVDs, 628
dynamo, 698

E

ear, 519, *519*
ear canal, 519
eardrum, 519, *519*
Earth
    curvature of, 384, *385*
    gravity of, 382, 383
    magnetic field of, *708*, 708–709
    mass and weight on, *384*
    orbit around Sun, 384
earthquakes, 490, *490*, 491, *491*
echolocation, *539*, **539**
Edison, Thomas, 542, 543, 698

efficiency, **83**, 86, 87, 91, 92 **454**, *454*, 454–456, *457*
   calculating, 454, *457*
   friction and, *454*, 455, 460
   ideal mechanical advantage and, 464
Einstein, Albert, 138, 388, 415
einsteinium, 138
electrical devices, **668**, *668*
electrical energy, xxxiv, 432, 439, 450, 455, 732
   in cars, 87
   conversion of, *81*
   conversion through circuits, 678–679
   generating through a power plant, 727, *727*
   from solar cells, 88–89
electric car, 77
electric cell, 655. See also electrochemical cells.
electric charge, 633–634, **634**, *634*, 660
electric current, 233, **652**, 652–658
   calculating, 653–654
   comparison of static charge and, 653
   distribution of, 723
   generating, 720
   paths of, 667–673
   production of, by magnetism, 719, 732
   production of magnetism, 712
electric eels, 641, *641*
electric fan, 83, *83*
electric field, 553–554, *554*, **634**, *634*
electrician, 674
electricity, 432, 439, 450, 455, 630–660. See also electric charge; electric current; static charge.
   electric eel, 641
   electrician, 674
   electromagnetism, *713*, **713**. See also electromagnetic (EM) waves.
   induction, *637*, **637**, 637–638
   lightning, 644, *645*, 650–651
   magnetism and, 712, 719
   measuring, 654
   movement of, 642–649, 660
   polarization, 638, *638*
   safety devices, 671–673, 674
   safety tips, 671
   technology and, 639–640
electric potential, **643**. See also voltage.
   effect on current, 653, *653*
electric power, **726**
   generating, 727, *727*
   measuring, 728
   ratings of appliances, 728, *728*
electric properties, 60, 64
electrochemical cells, *655*, 660
   primary cells, 656, *657*
   solar cells, 658, *658*
   storage cells, 656, *657*
electrolysis, 199, *199*

electromagnetic energy, 73, **73**, 432
   of Sun, 80, 119
electromagnetic (EM) waves, 550–581, **553**. See also laser; light.
   artificial light, 570–572
   as a disturbance, 553–554
   formation of, 554, *554*
   frequencies, 558, 559, 561
   gamma rays, 561, *561*, **566**
   infrared light, 560, *560*, **564**, 564–565, *565*
   Internet activity, 551
   laser light and, 618
   light waves and materials, 573–579, 582
   measuring, 561
   microwaves, 557, *557*, 560, *560*, 563, **563**
   radio waves, 559, 560, *560*, *562*, **562**
   sources of, 554
   spectrum, 560–561
   sunlight, 568–569, 582
   traits, 553–557, 582
   travel of, 555
   ultraviolet light, 561, *561*, *565*, **565**
   uses of, 559–566, 582
   visible light, 561, *561*, **564**
   x-rays, 561, *561*, *566*, **566**
electromagnetic spectrum, *560–561*, **560–561**
electromagnetism, **713**
electromagnets, **714**, *714*, *717*, 732
   making an, 714
   in a power plant, 727
   Internet activity, 701
   uses of, 715–718
electron cloud, *139*, 140, 162, *162*
electronic devices, **681**, 692, 696–699
   analog information and, 684
   Chapter Investigation, 690–691
   coded information and, 681–683
   computer. See computers.
   digital information and, 682–683
   music and, 626–629
Electronic Numerical Integrator and Computer (ENIAC), 698
electrons, **139**, *139*, 139–140, 234
   chemical bonds and, 175–176, 190
   discovery of, 233
   ion formation and, *142*, 142–143, *143*
   static charge and, 635, *635*, 660
elements, xxxi, **22**, 137–141
   atoms and, 139
   carbon. See carbon.
   compounds and, 169–173, 190
   density, trends of, 151
   in Earth's crust, 138, *138*
   half-lives, 160, *160*
   halogens, 150, *150*, 157, *157*
   in human body, 138, *138*, 144
   ion formation and periodic table, 176

metalloids, 158, *158*, 162
metals, **155**, 155–156
names and symbols, 138
noble gases, 157, *157*
nonmetals, **157**, *157*, 162
organization of, 145, 162, *162*
periodic table of, 145–151, **146**, *148–149*, 154–160
properties of, and compound properties, 169–170
rare earth (lanthanides), 149, 156, *156*
reactive, **154**, 155, *155*

ellipse, *384*
Empedocles, 96
endothermic reaction, **215**, *217*, 217–218, 228
    Chapter Investigation, 220–221
    photosynthesis, **218**, 218–219, 222, 223
energy, xxxiv, **xxxv**, 68–92, *72*, 425–432, 442.
    See also heat.
    bond energy, 215, *216*, *217*, 228
    changes in form. *See* energy conversion.
    chemical, xxxiv, **73**, 76, 80, 432
    and chemical reactions, 214–219
    conservation of, xxxv, **xxxv**, **82**, 92, **430**, *430*, *431*, 432, *442*
    efficiency, **83**, 86, 87, 91, 92, 455, 456
    elastic potential, 426
    electrical, xxxiv, *81*, 87, 88–89, 432, 439, 450, 455, 732
    electromagnetic, *73*, **73**, 80, 119, 432
    in endothermic reactions, *217*, 217–218, 218–219, 228
    in exothermic reactions, 215–216, *216*, 218–219, 228
    forms of, xxxiv, 71–76, *81*, 92, 432
    Internet activity, 69
    kinetic, 74, **74**, **426**, *426*, 428, 429–432, *431*, *442*, 491, *727*, *727*
    law of conservation of, **xxxv**, **82**, 92
    mechanical, **73**, *81*, **429**, 429–432, *431*, 450, 455
    nuclear, *73*, **73**, 432
    potential, 74, *75*, **75**, 75–76, *76*, 92, **426**, *426*, *427*, 429–432, *431*, *442*, 452, *453*, 643
    power, time, and, 437–440
    radiant, 432
    radiation, *119*, **119**, 124, **555**
    solar, 4, 88–89, 658, *658*
    sound, **73**
    sources of, xxxv, 80, *81*, 88–90
    storage and release, 218–219
    thermal, *73*, **73**, 98, 99, *111*, **111**, 114, 124, 432, 455
    transfer of, 111, 112, 116–121, 124, 425–432, *426*, 437–439, *438*, *439*, *453*, 489–492
    transformation of, 425, 426, 429–432, *431*
    wasted, 83, *83*, 86
    wind, 88, 90
energy conversion, 78–83, *79*, *81*, 92
    Chapter Investigation, 84–85
    between kinetic and potential energy, 79, 79–80, 81
    technology and, 86–91, 92
    uses for, 80, *81*
    wasted energy and, 83, *83*, 86
energy efficiency, **83**, 87, 91, 92, 455, 456
energy transfer, 111, 112, 116–121, 124, 425–432, *426*, 437–439, *438*, *439*, *453*, 489–492
    EM waves, 556, 557
    laser, 618
    sound, 517, 521
energy usage
    appliances, 728, *728*
    calculating, 729–730, 731
engine. *See also* motor.
    efficiency of car, 455, 456
    power of different types, 436
    steam, 413–414, *413*, *414*, 436
enzymes, 204, *204*, **287**
equations, chemical, 208–212
equator, *314*
Europium, 156
evaluating, **R8**
    media claims, R8
evaporation, *53*, **53**, 64
evidence, collection of, xl
exothermic reaction, *215*, **215**, 215–217, *216*, 228
    Chapter Investigation, 220–221
    in living things, 216–217, *217*, 223
expansion joints, 108
experiment, **xl**. *See also* lab.
    conclusions, drawing, R35
    constants, determining, R30
    controlled, **R28**, R30
    designing, R28–R35
    hypothesis, writing, R29
    materials, determining, R29
    observations, recording, R33
    procedure, writing, R32
    purpose, determining, R28
    results, summarizing, R34
    variables, R30–R31, R32
experimental group, R30
exponents, 161, 558, **R44**
eye, 606–608, *607*, 620
    compared with camera, 614, *615*
    formation of image, *607*, 608
eyepiece lens, 612, *613*
eyesight. *See* vision.

F

fact, **R9**
   different from opinion, R9
Fahrenheit, Gabriel, 97
Fahrenheit scale, 97, 106, *106*
   converting to Celsius, 109
farsightedness, 609, *609*, 610
fatty acids, 255, *284*, 284–285
faulty reasoning, **R7**
Fermi, Enrico, 138
fermium, 138
fiber optics, **617**, *617*
field, 553–554
filament, 571, *571*
fires and chemical reactions, 213
first law of motion. *See* Newton's laws of motion.
Fleming, Ambrose, 698
floating. *See* buoyancy.
fluids, **392**, 392–393, *397*, 397–399, 402–407. *See also* liquid; hydraulics; water.
   friction in, 392–393, *393*
   pressure in, *397*, 397–399
   transmission of force through, 406–407, 408
fluorescence, **571**
fluorescent light bulbs, *571*, 571–572
fluorine, 150
FM waves, 562, *562*
focal length, *602*, **603**
focal point, **596**, *597*, 601, *602*
force, xxxvii, **xxxvii**, 342–374, **345**, *346*
   acceleration, mass, and, *354*, *355*, *356*, *357*, *360*, *371*, *374*, 390
   action and reaction, 361–364, *363*, *364*, *370*, *374*, 389, 462
   applied, *420*
   area and, 395–399, 408
   balanced, **347**, 347–351, *349*, 363, 390
   buoyancy, **402**
   centripetal, **358**, *359*, 384, *385*
   changing direction of, 346, 347, 451, *453*
   contact, xxxvii, **xxxvii**, *346*
   direction of motion changed by, 357–359
   distance, work, and, 419–423, *420*, *422*, 442
   electrical, xxxvii
   friction, xxxvii, **xxxvii**, **389**, 389–393
   gravitational, **xxxvii**, xl, 11, 75, 346, *346*, 381–388
   input, 450–451, *450*, 453–457, *459*, 464–466
   Internet activity, 343
   machines, work, and, 449–456, *450*, *451*, 459–466, *459*, *476*
   magnetic, xxxvii. *See also* magnetism.
   mass, distance, and, 381–389, *382*, 408
   multiplication of, 450, 451
   needed to overcome friction, *390*, *391*, 408
   net, **347**, 348, *397*, 402, *403*, 453
   output, 450–451, *450*, 454–457, *459*, 464–466
   physical, xxxvi–xxxvii
   strong, 415
   transmission through fluids, 406–407
   types of, 346
   unbalanced, *347*, 347–351, *349*, *351*, 374
   waves and, 490
formulas, 91, **R42**. *See also* chemical formulas.
   density, 43, 49
   electrical power, 728
   energy use, 729–730
   Ohm's law, **653**, 653–654, 659
   volume, 12
   wave speed, 500–501
fossil fuels
   vs. alternative energy sources, 4–5, 88
   energy of, 80
fractions, **R41**
frame of reference, *317*. *See also* motion, observing.
Franklin, Benjamin, 697
free fall, 387, 394
freezing, **52**, *52*, 64
freezing point, **52**, 243
   Chapter Investigation, 56–57
frequency, 496, *497*, **497**, 498, 510, 546
   Doppler effect and, 531
   electromagnetic, 558, 559
   natural, 528
   of sound waves, 525–531, *526*
   wavelength and, 498, *498*, 526
   fundamental tone, 529
friction, xxxvii, **xxxvii**, 98, *346*, 348, **389**, 389–393, *390*, *391*, 414
   air resistance, **393**, *393*, 456
   compound machines and, 469
   efficiency and, *454*, 455, 456, 460
   fluids and, 392–393, *393*
   force needed to overcome, *390*, *391*, 408
   heat and, *391*
   reducing, 456
   surfaces and, 390–392
   weight and, *391*
fuel, future sources, 2–5
fuel cell, hydrogen, xliii, *xliii*
fuel injectors, 87
fulcrum, 413, **459**, *459*, 466, 467, *476*
fullerene, 187, *187*
fuses, 672, *672*

G

Galilei, Galileo, 348, 414
    theory of motion, 348–349
gallium, 147
gamma rays, 560, *561*, **566**
gas, **28**, *29*, 32–33
    behavior of, 33, *33*
    boiling, *54*, **54**, 64
    condensation, *55*, **55**, 64
    convection cycle, 118, 124
    evaporation, *53*, **53**, 64
    inert, 157, *157*
    kinetic theory and, 104, *104*
    studying, 232
    sublimation, **53**
    volume and, 32, *32*
gasoline, car consumption of, xliii
Gateway Arch (St. Louis), 108
gears, *469*
    mechanical advantage of, 469
    used in nanotechnology, *471*
Geiger counter, 158
generator, **720**, 721–722, 726–727, 732
    car, 722
    cell phone, 720, *720*
    DC, 721, *721*
    Van de Graaff, 636, *636*
germanium, 699
gigabyte, 682
glow sticks, 216, 222
glucose, 283–284. *See also* sugar.
    formula, 174
    model, *283*
    in respiration, 222–223
glue, 183
Goddard, Robert H., 415
gold, 22, *22*, 138, 140, *140*, 262
graduated cylinder, *13*, R16, *R16*
graphite, 187, *187*, 190
graphs,
    bar, 290, R26, R31
    circle, 26, R25
    distance-time, 324, *325*, *334*, 335, *338*
    double bar, R27
    line, 205, *394*, R24, R34
    using, 537
    velocity-time, *334*, 335, *394*
    wave properties, 498, *499*
gravity, xxxvii, xl, 11, 75, 346, *346*, 364, **381**, 381–388, *382*, *383*, 408
    acceleration, mass, and, 382–383, *383*, 452, *453*
    distance, mass, and, 381–389, *382*, 408
    Earth's, 382–385, *384*, *385*, 427
    effect on light, *388*, 415
    energy and, 427, 430, *431*
    internet activity, 379
    orbit and, 384–387, *385*
    weight and, 383–384, *384*
    work and, 422–423, *423*, 462
Greek philosophy, theory of motion in, 348, 412
ground-fault circuit interrupter (GFCI), 673, *673*
grounding, **649**, *649*, 660
group, in periodic table, *148*, *150*, **150**, 154–158, 162, *162*

H

hair, 287, *287*
hair cells, ear, 519, *519*, 536, *536*
hair dryer, energy use of, *439*
Hales, Stephen, 232
half-life, **160**
halogen light bulbs, 571, *571*
halogens, 150, *150*, 157, *157*
hammer, 519, *519*
hardware, 686
hearing loss, 536, 537
heat, 96–99, **110**. *See also* temperature; energy.
    conduction, *117*, **117**
    convection, *118*, **118**
    cooking with, 115
    friction and, 98, *391*, 455
    measuring, 112
    as motion, 97
    radiation, *119*, **119**
    vs. temperature, 110
    thermal energy and, 111, *111*
    transfer of energy, 98, 111, 112, 116–121, 124
heating properties, 60, *60*, 64
heat pack, chemical, 247
heat rays (infrared light), **564**, 564–565, *565*
hemoglobin, 144, 287, *287*
hertz, **526**, 527, 561
hexane, 300
holograms, 616
hormones, 285
horsepower, 436. *See also* power; Watt.
human body, elements in, 138, *138*, 144
hybrid car, 87, *87*
hydraulics, *407*, 470
hydrocarbon, 224, 225, **291**, 291–292, *293*
hydrochloric acid, 172, 254, 256, *256*, 257
    pH of, 257, *258*
hydrogen, 138, 144
    compounds of, 172–173
    fuel cells and, xliii
    ions, 254, 256–259, *256*
hypothesis, **xl**, xli, R3, **R3**, R29

I

ice, xxxiii, 28, 30, *30*
ice cream, 243
ideal mechanical advantage, 464–466
image, **595**, 595–596, *596*, 596–597, *597*, 603, 613
incandescence, **569**, 570–572
incandescent light bulb, 571, *571*
incidence, angle of, 594, *594*, 598
inclined plane, *451*, 452, 453, 458, **462**, *462*, 463, 464. See also wedge.
　ideal mechanical advantage of, *464*, 464–465
induction, **637**, *637*, 637–638
　in lightning, 644, *645*
inert gases, 157, *157*
inertia, **350**, *351*. See also momentum.
inference, **R4**, R35
infrared light, 560, *560*, **564**, 564–565, *565*
infrared spectroscopy 132
infrared waves, 432
infrasound, 526
inner ear, *519*
inorganic compounds, **276**, *276*
input, **686**, 687
insulators, **117**, *120*, 120–121, **646**, 660
　Chapter Investigation, 122–123
integrated circuits, **685**, *685*
intensity, sound, **532**, 532–536, *534*, 546
interference, **507**, *507*, 507–508, *508*
International Space Station, 266, *266*
International System of Units, R20–R21
Internet, 688–689
　usage, *689*
Internet activity
　alloys, 237
　chemical bonding, 167
　chemical reactions, 195
　energy, 69
　kinetic theory, 101
　periodic table, 135
　physical and chemical changes, 39
　polymers, 273
　scale, 7
Investigations. See Chapter Investigations.
iodine, 150, 178, *178*
　molecular structure, 182, *182*
iodine clock reaction, 205
ion engines, 3
ionic bond, **176**, *176*, 176–177, *180*, 190
ionic compounds
　names of, 177
　properties of, 185–186
　in solutions, 242, *242*, 251, *251*
　structures of, 181

ions, **142**
　acids and bases, 254, 256–259, *256*, *257*
　formation, *142*, 142–143, *143*, 176
　negative, 143, *143*, *176*, 176–177
　periodic table and, 150–151, 176, *176*
　positive, 142, *142*, *176*, 176–177
iris, 607, *607*
　camera, 614, *615*
isobutane, 280
isomers, **280**, *280*, 297
isotopes, **140**, 140–141, *141*
　atomic mass number and, 145
　half-life, 160, *160*
　radioactive, 158, 159–160

J

jellyfish, movement of, *361*, 362
joule, **112**, **421**, *427*, **428**, 435
Joule, James, 98

K

kangaroos, movement of, *364*
Kelvin, Lord, 98
keratin, 287, *287*
Kevlar, 297, *297*
Kilby, Jack, 699
kilowatt, 435, **728**
kilowatt-hour, **729**
kinetic energy, *74*, **74**, **426**, *426*, **428**, 429–432, *431*, *442*, 491, 727, *727*
　in cars, 87
　conversion to electrical energy, 727, *727*
　conversion to potential energy, *79*, 79–80, *81*, 92
　mass and speed, 105
　of objects, 103
　of sound waves, 520
　temperature and, 105, *105*, 124
　in wind, 90
kinetic theory of matter, **104**, *104*, 124
　Internet activity, 101
Kleist, Ewald Georg von, 696

L

lab, R10–R35. See also experiment.
　equipment, R12–R19
　safety, R10–R11
laboratory equipment
　beaker, R12, *R12*
　beam balance, 10, *14*
　double-pan balance, 10, *10*, R19, *R19*
　force meter, R16, *R16*
　forceps, R13, *R13*

graduated cylinder, 13, *14–15*, R16, *R16*
hot plate, R13, *R13*
meniscus, 15, R16, **R16**, *R16*
microscope, xl, 20, *20*, 612, *613*, *R14*, R14–R15
ruler, metric, R17, *R17*
spring scale, 11, *11*, R16, *R16*
test-tube holder, R12, *R12*
test-tube rack, R13, *R13*
test tube, R12, *R12*
triple-beam balance, *14*, R18, *R18*
Langmuir, Irving, 234
lanthanides (rare earth elements), 149, 156, *156*
laser, *615*, **615**, 615–618, *616*
    chemical reaction and, *xl*
    fiber optics, *617*, **617**
    future uses, 618, *618*
    making, 616
    visual uses, 616, 617
laser beams, 616, *616*
latitude, 314, *314*
Lavoisier, Antoine, 206–207, *207*
law of conservation of energy, xxxv, **82**, 92
law of conservation of mass, 206–207, **207**, 228
    in chemical equations, 208, 209, 212
law of reflection, **594**, 595, 596, 598
laws of motion. *See* Newton's laws of motion.
LEDs (light emitting diodes), 572, *572*
lemon, pH, 258
lenses, *601*, **601**, 601–605, 620
    camera, 614, *615*, 619, *619*
    concave, *601*, **601**, 603, 609, *609*
    contact, 610, *610*
    convex, *601*, **601**, *602*, 603, 604–605
    corrective, 609–610
    eyepiece, 612, *613*
    gravitational, *388*
    human eye, 607, *607*
    long, 619, *619*
    microscope, 612, *613*
    mirrors and, 611
    objective, 612, *613*
    telescope, 612, *613*
    wide-angle, 619, *619*
Leonardo da Vinci, 414
lever, 413, *450*, *457*, 458, **459**, *466*, *476*
    compound machines using, 468, 469, *470*, *476*
    first-class, *459*
    force and, *459*
    ideal mechanical advantage of, *466*
    in human body, 467
    real-world examples, *467*, 468
    second-class, *459*
    third-class, *459*
Lewis, G.N., 234
Leyden jar, 696
lift, 405

light. *See also* optics.
    artificial, 570–572
    bending by gravity, *388*, 415
    color, 576–581
    diffused, 619, *619*
    infrared, **564**, 564–565, *565*
    materials and, 573–579, 582
    neon, 572
    refraction and, *505*, **505**, 510, 599–600, *600*, *602*
    speed of, 555
    sunlight, 568–569, 582
    ultraviolet, *565*, **565**
    visible, 432, 561, *561*, **564**, 615
    white, 576
light bulb, 86, 571, *571*, 648, *648*
light-emitting diode (LED), 87, *87*, 572, *572*
light filters, 575, 576
lightning, 500, 524, 644, *645*
    Chapter Investigation, 650–651
lightning rod, 627
lights, efficient, 87
lipids, **284**, *284*, 284–285, 300
liquid, **28**, 29, 32–33, 51–55. *See also* fluids; hydraulics; water.
    boiling, *54*, **54**, 64
    condensation, *55*, **55**, 64
    convection, 118, 124
    evaporation, *53*, **53**, 64
    freezing, *52*, **52**, 64
    kinetic energy and, 105, *105*, 124
    kinetic theory and, 104, *104*
lithium, 138
litmus paper, 255, 257
location, ways of describing, 313, *314*
lodestone, 706, 708
logic circuit, 699
longitude, 314, *314*
longitudinal waves, **494**, 498, *498*, 510
long lens, 619, *619*
loudness, 532–536, *534*, 546
luminescence, **569**

M

machines, 412–414, **449**, 449–473, *450*, *476*
    compound, **468**, 468–473, *476*
    efficiency of, **454**, *454*, 454–456, **457**
    electronic, 450
    force, work, and, 449–456, *150*, 451, 459–466, *459*, *476*
    Internet activity, 447
    mechanical advantage of, **451**, 464–466
    perpetual motion, 413, 414
    robotic, 306–309, *306*, *308*, 472, **473**
    simple, 450, **458**, 458–466, 467, *476*. *See also* inclined plane; lever; pulley; screw; wedge;

wheel and axle.
maglev train, 704, *704*
magnesium, 138, 155
magnetic domain, **706**, 707
magnetic field, 554, *554*, **705**, *705*, 713, *713*, 732
　of Earth, *708*, 708–709
magnetic force, *xxxvii*. See also magnetism.
magnetic poles, **704**, *704*, 709, 732
magnetic properties, 60, *60*, 64
　used in separating minerals, 63
magnetism, *xxxvii*, **704**, 732
　atmosphere and, 710
　control of voltage, 723
　electricity and, 712
　electromagnetism, *713*, **713**
　magnetic materials, 706, *706*, 707
　production of electric current, 719, 732
magnets, *xxxix*, **703**, 706, 732
　Earth, *708*, 708–709
　healing properties of, 711
　permanent, 708
　temporary, 708
　vs. other materials, *707*
manufacturing
　methods, 471
　robots used in, 473
Mars, exploration of, 306–309
Mars Exploration Rover (robot), 307–309, *307*
mass, *xxxi*, **xxxi**, 10, 34, 41, 350, 353–357
　acceleration, gravitation, and, 382–383, *383*, 452, 453
　Chapter Investigation, 14–15
　force, acceleration, and, 354, 355, 356, 357, 360, 371, 374, 390
　gravitation, distance, and, 381–389, *382*, *408*
　inertia and, 350
　measuring, 10
　momentum, velocity, and, 368–369, *369*, 374
　as physical property, 41, 42
　specific heat and, 114
　thermal energy and, 114
　volume, density, and, 403
　weight and, compared, 11, 383–384, *384*
math skills. *See also* units of measurement.
　angles, measuring, 598
　area, **R43**
　averages, 424, **R36**, **R37**
　bar graphs, 290
　circle graphs, 26, R25
　decimal, **R39**, R40
　describing a set of data, R36–R37
　eliminating outlying values, 424
　examples, 659, 680, 731
　exponents, 558, **R44**
　formulas, 91, 322, 327, 355, 356, 357, 369, 396, 421, 427, 428, 429, 435, 437, 653, 728, 729, 731, **R42**

　fractions, **R41**
　graphs, using, 537
　line graphs, 205, 394
　mean, 424, 495, **R36**
　median, 495, **R36**
　metric conversions, 109
　mode, 495, **R37**
　percents, 267, 457, 680, **R41**
　proportions, **R39**
　range, **R37**
　rates, **R38**
　ratios, 174, 457, **R38**
　scientific notation, 161, 558, **R44**
　significant figures, 360, 731, **R44**
　units, 328
　variables, 659
　volume, **R43**
matter, xxx–xxxiii, **xxxi**, 9
　Aristotle's theory of, 96
　atoms and, 16–19, 34
　chemical properties and changes, 46–48, 64
　combinations of, 21–25, 34
　compound, **23**, 24, 34
　conservation of, xvii
　density, **43**, 49, 59, 63, 64
　electrical charge property, 633, 660
　element, **22**
　forms of, xxx–xxxi
　gas, **28**, *29*, 32–33, 34, 104, *104*, 157, 232
　kinetic theory and, 104, *104*, 124
　liquid, **28**, *29*, 31, 34, 51–55, 104, *104*
　mass and volume, 9–13, 34
　mixture, **23**, 23–25, 34, 61–63, 64
　movement of, xxxiii
　particles and, xxx–xxxi, 27–28, 103
　physical change, **44**, *45*, 50–55, 64
　physical forces and, xxxvi
　physical properties, **41**, 41–43, *42*, 59–60, 64
　pure, 21–22, *22*, 34
　solid, **28**, *29*, 30, 34, 48, 51, 51–52, 53, 64, 104, *104*
　states of, **27**, 27–33, *29*, 34, 50–55, 104, *104*, 124
mean, 424, 495, **R36**
measurement
　acceleration, 332, 355
　amplitude, **497**
　area, 396, R43, **R43**
　density, 403
　distance, 315, 328
　Earth's gravity, 382
　energy, 425
　force, 355, 384
　frequency, **497**, 510
　International System of Units (SI), R20–R21
　mass, **xxxi**, *xxxi*, **10**, 17, 355
　power, 435, 436

pressure, 396, 398
speed, 322
temperature, R21
volume, **xxxi**, 12–13, 14–15, **R43**
wavelength, **497**, 510
weight, **11**, 384
work, 421
mechanical advantage, **451**, 461, 464. *See also* efficiency; machines.
   calculating, 451
   compound machines, 469
   ideal, 464–466
mechanical energy, **73**, **429**, 429–432, *431*, *442*
   conversion of, 81
mechanical waves, **491**, 517, 521
median, 495, **R36**
medicine
   alloys and, 265, *265*
   from nature, 130–133
   radioactivity in, 159
medium, **491**, 492, 521, 522–523, 555, 556, 599, 600, *600*
   EM waves, 555, 556
   light, 573–579, 582
   refraction in, 599, 600, *600*
   sound, 521, 522–523
   total internal reflection and, 617, *617*
melting, **51**, 64
melting point, **51**, 51–52
   used in separating minerals, 63
Mendeleev, Dmitri, 146, *146*, 147
mercury, 155
metallic bond, **184**, 184–185, *185*, 190
metalloids, 158, *158*, 162
metals, 150, **155**, 155–156
   alkali, 155
   alkaline earth, 155
   alloys, 156, 237, **262**, 262–266, 268
   properties and bonds, 184–185
   reactive, 155, *155*
   transition, *155*, 155–156
methane, *172*
   bonding of, *178*, 178–179
   combustion, 209, *209*, 210, *210*, 216, *216*
   molecular structure, 182, *182*
metric system, R20–R21
   changing metric units, R20, *R20*
   converting between U.S. customary units, R21, *R21*
   temperature conversion, 109, R21, *R21*
microchips, 226–227, *227*, 685
microgears, *471*
microgravity, *387*
microscope, 612, *613*, **R14**, R14–R15. *See also* laboratory equipment.
   making a slide or wet mount, R15, *R15*
   scanning tunneling (STM), *xl*, 20, *20*
   viewing an object, R15

microtechnology, 470–471
microwave oven, 557, *557*
microwaves, 73, 557, *557*, 560, *560*, *563*, **563**
middle ear, 519, *519*
MIDI, 629
milk, pH, *258*
minerals, separating, 63
mirrors, 593–597, 620
   concave, *596*, **596**, *597*
   convex, *596*, **596**, *597*
   flat, 595–596, *596*
   lenses and, 611
mixtures, **23**, 23–25, 34, 239. *See also* solutions.
   comparing compounds with, 24
   heterogeneous, 25
   homogeneous, 25
   separating, 61–63, 64
mode, 495, **R37**
molecular structure, 182, *182*
   studying, 132
molecule, xxxi, **xxxi**, **18**, 34, **179**
   air, 398
   collision of, 397–399
   fluid, *397*, 397–399
   motion of, 19, *19*
   nanotechnology and, 470–471
   water, *397*, 398, *399*
momentum, **368**, 368–373, *369*, *371*, *374*. *See also* inertia.
   conservation of, **371**, *372*, *373*
   transfer of, 370, *371*
   velocity, mass, and, 368–369, *369*, *374*
monomers, **294**, 300
Moon
   exploration of, 415, *415*
   mass and weight on, *384*
   orbit around Earth, 384
mosaic, *xl*
motion, 310–338, **315**, *338*. *See also* inertia; Newton's laws of motion.
   Aristotle and, 412
   Bhaskara and, 413
   circular, 358, *359*
   direction of, force, and, 357–359, *359*, *420*
   direction of, work, and, *420*
   fluids, and, 392–393, *393*, 404–405, 408
   force, work, and, 419–423, *420*, *422*, 442, 452–453, *453*
   friction and, 346, *346*, 348, 389, 390–391, *390*, *391*
   Galileo and, 414
   Internet activity, 311
   Leonardo da Vinci and, 414
   observing, 317–318, 338
   perpetual, 413, 414, 430
   relative, 317–318, *318*, 338
motors, 455, **716**, 716–718, *717*, 732. *See also* engine.
   electromagnets and, 716

Index **R83**

how they work, 716, *717*
uses of, 718
multimeter, 654, *654*
music, 540–541
    electronics and, 626–629
musical instruments, 541, *541*, 544

N

nanotechnology, 470–471, **471**, *471*, 618
nanotubes, carbon, 281, *281*
natural frequencies, 528
natural medicines, 130–133
nearsightedness, 609, *609*, 610
negative ions, 143, *143*, 176, 176–177
neon lights, 572
Neptune, xl
Neptunium, 138
Nernst, Walther, 98
net charge, 635
network, computer, 688
neutral, **257**, *258*, 259, 268
neutral atoms, 140
neutralization reaction, 259
neutron, **139**, *139*, 162, *162*
    number of, 140–141, *141*
newton, 11
Newton, Sir Isaac, 348, 349, 384, 413, 414
Newton's laws of motion, 348, 349, *364*, 365, *374*, 413, 414, 415
    first, 348–351, **349**, *349*, *364*
    second, 353–359, **354**, *354*, *359*, *364*, 382
    third, **361**, 361–363, *363*, *364*, 371, 372–373
newton (unit of force), 355, *396*, *421*, *427*
Nitinol, 263
nitrogen, 144, 179, *179*
    compounds, 172
noble gases, **157**, *157*
Nomex, 297, *297*
nonmetals, **157**, *157*, 162
nonpolar substances, 250–251, *251*
normal line, 600, *600*
Northern Lights, 710, *710*
north pole, 705, 709
note-taking strategies, **R45–R49**
    choose your own strategy, 102, *102*
    combination notes, 196, *196*, 344, 448, 488, *488*, 592, *592*, 632, *632*, R45, *R45*
    concept map, R49, *R49*
    content frame, R45, *R45*
    main idea and detail notes, 8, *8*, 102, *102*, 168, *168*, R46, *R46*
    main idea web, 40, *40*, 102, *102*, 136, *136*, 418, 448, 702, *702*, R46, *R46*
    mind map, 70, *70*, 102, *102*, 238, *238*, R47, *R47*

outline, 312, 448, 516, *516*, 666, *666*, R48, *R48*
supporting main ideas, 274, *274*, 380, 448, 552, *552*, R47, *R47*
Venn diagram, R49, *R49*
nuclear energy, 73, *73*, 432
nuclear magnetic resonance spectoscopy, 132
nucleic acids, **288**, *289*, 300
nucleus, **139**, *139*, 162, *162*, 234
numbers. *See also* math skills.
    meaningful, 360
    outlying, 424

O

objective lens, 612, *613*
observations, xl, **R2**, R5, R33
    qualitative, R2
    quantitative, R2
ocean waves. *See* waves, ocean.
ohmmeter, 654
ohms, **647**, 653
Ohm's law, **653**, 653–654, 659, 660
oil, 24
opaque materials, 574, *574*
open circuit, 669, *669*
operational definition, **R31**
opinion, **R9**
    different from fact, R9
optical fibers, 617, *617*
optical tools, 611–619
optic nerve, 607, *607*
optics, 590–619, **593**. *See also* eye, visible light.
    fiber, *617*, **617**
    Internet activity, 591
    lenses and refraction, 599–605
    mirrors and reflection, 593–598
    photography, 619
    technology, 611–618, 620
orbit, **384**, 384–387, *385*. *See also* force, centripetal.
    humans in, 387
    velocity needed to achieve, 386
organic compounds, **275**, 275–276, *276*
oscilloscope, 529, *529*
osmium, 151
outer ear, 519, *519*
outliers, 424
output, 687, *687*
overtone, 529
oxygen
    in combustion, 201, *201*, 209, *209*
    compounds, 172–173
    fuel cells and, xliii
    molecule, 18, *18*
    in photosynthesis, 218, 223
    in respiration, 222–223
ozone molecule, 18, *18*

P

pan balance, 10, *10*, R19, *R19*
parallel circuit, **677**, *677*, 692
particle accelerators, 235
particles, xxx–xxxi
    atomic, *139*, 139–140
    electric charge and, 634, *634*
    kinetic theory, *104*, **104**, 124
    moving, 103
    speed of, 104, 105
    thermal expansion and, 108
Pascal, Blaise, 406
Pascal's principle, **406**, 406–407, *406*, 408
pascal (unit of pressure), **396**, 398
pendulum, *430*
percents, 267, 457, 680, **R41**
period, *148*, *150*, **150**, 162, *162*
periodic table, 145–158, **146**, *148–149*, 162, *162*
    atomic size and, 151, *151*
    density of elements and, 151
    group, *148*, *150*, **150**, 162, *162*
    halogens, 150, *150*, 157, *157*
    how to read, 147, *147*
    Internet activity, 135
    Mendeleev's, 146, *146*
    metalloids, 158, *158*, 162
    metals, 155–156
    modern table, 147, *148–149*
    noble gases, 157, *157*
    nonmetals, **157**, *157*, 162
    organization of, 147, 150–151
    period, *148*, *150*, **150**, 162, *162*
    regions, 154, *154*
    trends and patterns, 150–151
petroleum, 292, *292*
pewter, *263*
pH, **257**, *258*, 268
phonograph, 543
phospholipids, 285, *285*
phosphorus, 144
photocopier, 639, *639*
photography, 619
photoresist, 226–227
photosynthesis, **218**, 218–219, 222
    equation, 223
physical change, **44**, *45*, 64
    Internet activity, 39
    states of matter and, 50–55
physical properties, **41**, 41–43, *42*, 64. *See also* mass; volume.
    color, 41, *42*, 48
    density, 43, **43**, 49, 59, 63, 64
    electric, 60, 64
    heating, 60, *60*, 64
    magnetic, 60, *60*, 63, 64

    shape, 41, *42*
    size, 41
    solubility, 60, 64
    texture, 41, *42*
    used to identify substances, 59–60, 64
    used to separate mixtures, 61–63, 64
physical science, xxix. *See also* science.
    unifying principles of, xxx–xxxvii
pitch, **525**, *526*, 527, 529, *529*
    Doppler effect and, 530–531
plane, inclined, *451*, 452, *453*, 458, **462**, *462*, 463, *464*
plastic, **295**, 295–296
    recycling, 296, *296*
pneumatic trough, 232
point of view. *See* frame of reference.
polar bears, *120*, 121
polar covalent bond, **179**, *179*, 180
polarization, **576**, *576*
poles, magnetic, **704**, *704*, 705, 709, 732
pollution, xliii, 471
polymers, **294**, 300
    Chapter Investigation, 298–299
    formation, 294–295, *295*
    Internet activity, 273
    monomers and, **294**, 295–297, *295*, *296*, 300
    new materials, 296–297
    plastics, 295–296
polypropylene, 294, *295*
polystyrene, 279
positive ions, 142, *142*, **176**, 176–177
position, **313**, 313–318, *338*. *See also* reference point; motion.
    energy transfer, speed, and, 425
    potential energy and, 426
    ways of describing, *314*
potassium, 144, 155
potential energy, 74, *75*, **75**, 75–76, *76*, 92, **426**, *426*, 427, 429–432, *431*, 442, 452, *453*, 643
    chemical, xxxiv, 73, 76, 80
    conversion between kinetic energy and, *79*, 79–80, *81*, 92
pound, 11
power, **434**, 434–439, *436*, 442
    energy, time, and, 437–439, *438*, *439*, 442
    everyday usage, *439*
    work, time, and, 434–436, *436*, 442
power plants, 726, *727*
praseodymium, 156
precipitate, 48, *200*, **200**, 246–247, *247*
precision, **R22**
prediction, xl, **xl**, R3, **R3**
pressure, **395**, 395–400
    air, *398*
    area, force, and, 395–399, *396*, *397*, 408
    atmospheric, *398*

in fluids, *397*, 397–399, 404–407, *405*, *406*, *408*
solubility and, 250, *250*
water, 397, *399*
primary cells, 656, *657*
primary colors, *578*, **578**, 582
primary pigments, *579*, **579**, 582
prime meridian, *314*
principal axis, 601, *601*
prism, *577*, **577**, 600, *600*
processing, 687, *687*
products, **199**
propane, *172*
properties. *See* physical properties; chemical properties.
proportions, 49, **R39**
propylene, 294, *295*
proteins, **286**, 286–287, *287*, 300
DNA and, *288*, 289
enzymes, 204, *204*, **287**
structural, 287, *287*
transport, 287, *287*
protons, *139*, **139**, 162, *162*
in acids and bases, 254
relation to element, and, 140
static charge and, 635, 660
pulley, *451*, 458, **460**, *460*, *461*, 476
block-and-tackle system, using, 461
fixed, *460*, 461
mechanical advantage of, 461
movable, *461*
pupil, *607*, **607**
pure matter, 21–22, *22*, 34

Q

quarks, 235
quartz, 226, *226*

R

radar, 563
radiation, *119*, **119**, 124, **555**
radioactivity, **158**, 234
detection, 158
medical uses, 159, *159*
radio waves, 559, *560*, *562*, **562**
radius, 465
rainbows, 600, *600*
ramp. *See* inclined plane.
random-access memory (RAM), 686
range, **R37**
rare earth elements (lanthanides), 149, 156, *156*
rates, 321, **R38**
ratios, 174, 457, **R38**
reactants, **199**
changes in, 202–203, *203*

reaction, 361–364, *363*, *364*, 370, 381, 389, 462. *See also* chemical reactions; endothermic reaction; exothermic reaction.
combustion, 201
reactive, **154**
reactive metals, 155, *155*
read-only memory (ROM), 686
reasoning, faulty, **R7**
reference point, **314**, *314*, 338
reflecting telescope, 612, *613*
reflection, *505*, **505**, 510, 577, 593, 594, 619
angle of, 594, *594*, 598
diffuse, **594**
law of, **594**, 595, *596*, 598
in photography, 619, *619*
regular, *594*, **594**
total internal, 617, *617*
refracting telescope, 612, *613*
refraction, *505*, **505**, 510, 619
of light, 599–600, *600*, *602*
in photography, 619, *619*
rainbows and, 600, *600*
regular reflection, *594*, **594**
repulsion, *634*, 705, *705*
resistance, *647*, **647**, 647–648, *648*, 653, *653*, 660
effects on current, 653, *653*
resistor, **668**, *668*
resonance, **528**
respiration, **222**, 222–223
equation, 223
retina, *607*, **607**, 608, 609–610
retinal, 280
RNA, 289
robots, 306–309, *306*, *308*, 472, **473**, *473*
Mars exploration and, 306–309
rocket, 415
rod cells, **608**
rounding numbers, 360
ruby crystal, 616, *616*
rust, 46

S

safety, R10–R11
animal, R11
chemical, R11
clean up, R11
directions, R10
dress code, R10
electrical, R11
fire, R10
glassware, R11
heating, R10
icons, R10–R11
lab, R10–R11
sharp object, R11

salt, 259. *See also* sodium chloride.
    table, 23, 30
saturated, **246**, 246–247
saturated fat, 285
scale (size), Internet activity, 7
scanning tunneling microscope, xl, 20, *20*, 235
scattering, *575*, **575**
science, nature of, xxxviii–xli
Scientific American Frontiers, 306, 308
scientific notation, 161, 558, **R44**
scientific process, xxxix–xli
    asking questions, xxxix
    determining what is known, xxxix
    interpreting results, xli
    investigating, xl
    sharing results, xli
screw, 458, *462*, **463**, *463*
seat belts, *351*
secondary cells. *See* storage cells.
second law of motion. *See* Newton's laws of motion.
semiconductors, 158, 161, *161*, 226, 685
separation
    of minerals, 63
    of mixtures, 61–62, 64
series circuits, *676*, **676**
short circuits, *670*, **670**
SI units. *See* International System of Units.
significant figures, 360, 731, **R44**
silicon, 226–227, *227*, 685
    atoms of in Earth's crust, 138
sinking. *See* buoyancy.
SI units. *See* International System of Units.
skydiving, *393*
slides, making, R15, *R15*
slope (steepness), 452, *453*, 464
snowflakes, 30, *30*
soap, 255, *255*
    pH, *258*
sodium, 144, 155, *155*
    ion, 142, *142*
sodium azide, 212
sodium chloride, 177, *177*, *180*, 268
    freezing point and, 243
    in solution, 242, 251, *251*
sodium hydroxide, 254, 256, *257*
    pH, *258*
software, 686
soil, 25, *25*
solar cells, *88*, **88**, 88–89, 92, 658, *658*
solar energy, 4, 5, 88–89, 99
solid, **28**, *29*, 30, 34
    formation of, 48
    kinetic theory and, 104, *104*
    melting of, *51*, 51–52, 64
    sublimation, **53**
solubility, 60, 64, **247**, 247–251, 268
    changes in, 248–251

    molecular structure and, 250–251, *251*
    pressure and, 250, *250*
    temperature and, 248–249, *249*
solute, **240**. *See also* solutions.
    change in solubility, 248–251
    concentration and, 245–246, *246*, 268
    how they dissolve, 242, *242*
solutions, 236–268, **239**, *241*, 268.
    See also solute; solvent.
    acidity, 257, *258*
    acids, 253–259, **254**, 268
    alloys, **262**, 262–266, 268
    bases, 253–259, **254**, 268
    concentrated, 246, *246*, 268
    concentration, **245**, 245–246
    dilute, *246*, **246**, 268
    gases, 240
    liquids, 240
    neutral, **257**, 268
    saturated, 246
    solid, 240, 262–266
    solubility, **247**, 247–251
    solvent-solute interactions, 242, *242*
    supersaturated, 246–247, *247*, 249
    types, 240
solvent, **240**. *See also* solutions.
    boiling point, 244
    changing properties, 243–244
    freezing point, 243
    interaction with solutes, 242, *242*
sonar, *539*, **539**
sonic booms, 524, *524*
sound, 494, 514–545, **517**, 546
    acoustics, *535*, **535**
    in air, 520, *520*, 521, 522–523
    amplification, *535*, **535**
    changes in, 525
    Doppler effect, **530**, 531
    different materials and, 522
    frequency and pitch, 525–531, *526*, 546
    intensity, **532**, 532–536, *534*, 546
    Internet activity, 515
    loudness, 532–536, *534*, 546
    mediums, 521, 522–523
    music, 540–541
    pitch, **525**, *526*, 527, 529, *529*, 530–531, 546
    quality, 529
    recorded, 542, 543, *543*
    sonic booms, 524, *524*
    speed of, 522–524
    temperature and, 523
    ultrasound, 482–485, **526**, 527, 538–540
    uses of, 482–485, 538–543, 546
    vibration, **517**, 518, 520
    as a wave, 517–524, *520*, 546
sound energy, **73**

sound frequencies, 525–531, *526*
   heard by animals, 527
   high and low, 526
   natural, 528
   sound quality, 529
sound waves, 494, 518, 627
   detection of, 519, *519*
   mechanical wave, 517
   production of, 518, *518*
   vibration of particles, *520*, 520–521
Southern Lights, 710
south pole, 705, 709
spacecraft, *333*, *357*, 385–387, *387*, *473*
   fuel for, 2–4
   velocity needed to achieve orbit, 386
space elevator, 618, *618*
Space Station, International, 266, *266*
speakers, Chapter Investigation, 724–725
specific heat, **113**
   in cooking, 115
   mass and, 114
spectroscopy, 132
speed, 316, **320**, 320–327, *321*, *322*, *327*, *338*. See also velocity.
   average, 323, 327
   instantaneous, 323
   of light, 522, 555
   relation to velocity, 326–327
   time, distance, and, 320–327, *321*, *322*, *324*, *325*, *328*, *338*
   using distance-time graph to show, 324, *325*
stainless steel, *263*, 264, 265
Standardized Test Practice
   analyzing data, 377
   analyzing descriptions, 231
   analyzing experiments, 67, 549
   analyzing graphics, 479
   analyzing tables, 735
   interpreting diagrams, 127, 411, 513, 585, 623, 663, 695
   interpreting graphs, 37, 95, 271, 341
   interpreting tables, 165, 193, 303
   understanding experiments, 445
starch, 283, *283*, 284
states of matter, **27**, 27–33, *29*, *34*
   changes of, 50–55
   kinetic theory and, 104, *104*, 124
static charge, **635**, 635–636, *636*, 660
   comparison of electric current and, 653
   materials affecting, 636, *636*
   movement of, 642–649, 660
   potential energy and, 642–643
   technology and, 639–640
static discharge, 642
   lightning, 644, *645*, 650–651
static electricity. See also static charge
   Internet activity, 631

steam engine, 413–414, *413*, *414*, 436
steel, 264
   carbon, *263*
   stainless, *263*, 264, 265
steering wheel, example of wheel and axle, 460
step-down transformer, 723, *723*, 727, *727*
step-up transformer, 723, 727, *727*
stirrup, 519, *519*
storage, *686*, 687
storage cells, 656, *657*
Styrofoam, 117
sublimation, **53**
subscripts, **171**
   in chemical equations, 211
   in chemical formulas, 171–172
substances
   identifying, 59–60, 64
   Greek classification of, 96
   properties used to identify, 58
   specific heat of, 113
sugar, 275, *276*. See also glucose.
   solubility of, 249
   in solution, 242
Sun
   electromagnetic energy, 80
   radiation, 119, *119*
   solar energy, 4, 5, 88–89, 92, 99
sunlight, 568–569, 582
superconductors, 648
supersonic speed, 524
surface area. See also pressure.
   air resistance and, 393
in chemical reactions, 202–203, *203*
suspension, *241*, **241**
switches, 668, *668*, 669, *669*, 692
   transistors, 685, 698
synthetic compounds, 132–133
synthesis reaction, 201, **201**
systems. See energy, conservation of; momentum, conservation of.

T

tables, R23
taking notes. See note-taking strategies.
tarnish, 46, *46*
technology
   acoustical engineering, 535, *535*
   alloys, 156, **262**, 262–267, *263*
   alternative energy, 4–5, 88–90, *88*, 99
   applications of Bernoulli's Principle, 405
   audiogram, 537, *537*
   cameras and photography, 614, *615*, 619
   carbon nanotubes, 281, *281*
   cars, electric and hybrid, 77, 87
   catalytic converter, 224, *225*
   catapult, 412

cell phone, 563, 567
cells, electric and electrochemical, 233, **655**, *655*
cells, primary and storage, 656, *657*
cells, solar, 4, **88,** 88–89, 658, *658*
chemical technology, 224
circuit, **667**, 667–673, 675–679
cochlear implants, 484–485
compound machines, **468**, 468–470, *470*
computer modeling, 415
computer, *xli*, 683, **685**, 685–689, *686–687*, 698–699
corrective lenses, 609–610
digital devices, 627–628, 683–684, 718, *718*
electric energy, 80, 83, *83*, 88–89
electrical energy and appliances, xxxv, 439, *439*
electrician, 674
electrolysis, 199, *199*
electromagnets, **714,** 714–717, *717*
electronic products, 226–227, *227*
electronics, **681**, 681–684
electrostatic air filter, 640
elements in industry, 155–158
energy conversions, 80, *81*, 86–87
energy efficiency, **83,** 91
engineering and thermal expansion, 108
fiber optics, **617**
gamma rays, *561*, **566**
generator, **720,** *720–721*, 720–722, 726–727
holograms, 588
hydraulics, 407
hydrogen fuel cells, xliii
infrared light, *560*, **564,** 564–565
insulators, 117, *120*, 121–123
Internet, 688–689
lasers, *xl*, 589, **615,** 615–616, 618
light-emitting diode (LED), 87, *87*
lighting, 570–572
machines, **449**
maglev train, 704, *704*
magnets for medical use, 711
microchips, 226–227, 685
microscopes, xl, *xl,* 612, *613*
microwaves, *560*, **563**
miniaturization, 470
motor, 716–718, *717*
multimeter, 654, *654*
Musical Instrument Digital Interface (MIDI), 629
musical instruments, 540–541, *541*
nanotechnology, **471**
nature of, xlii–xliii
objects used to do work, 423, *423*
oscilloscope, 529, *529*
particle accelerator, 235, *235*
particle detector, *xxxviii*
petroleum, 292, *293*
photocopier, 639, *639*
plastics, **295,** 295–296, *296*
polymers, **294,** 294–297, *295*

propulsion, ion and beamed energy, 3, *3*, 4
radar, 563
radio waves, *560,* **562**
radioactivity in medicine, 159
recorded sound devices, 543
robot, 306–309, *306, 308, 472,* **473**
scanning electron micrograph, *543*
scanning tunneling microscope, xl, *xl,* 20, *20, 183,* 235
semiconductor, 158, 226
sonar, **539,** *539*
sonic boom, 524, *524*
spacecraft, *2,* 3–4, 333, *385,* 386, 415
spectroscopy, 132
steam engine, 413–414
superconductor, 648
telephone, 542, *542*
telescope, reflecting and refracting, 587, 612, *613*
thermometer, 97, **107**
transformer, **723,** *723*
transistor, 685, 698
ultrasound, *483,* 483–485, **526,** 538–540
ultraviolet light, *561,* **565**
water treatment, 62
x-rays, *561,* **566**
Teflon, 296
telephone, 542, *542,* 563
telescope, *560,* 612, *613*
television, 560, 562
temperature, 48, 96–98, **105,** 203, *203. See also* heat.
   convection and, 118
   conversion, 109, R21, *R21*
   in cooking, 115
   vs. heat, 110
   kinetic energy and, 105, *105,* 124
   of lakes, 114, 118
   measuring, 106–107, 124
   reaction rate and, 203, *203*
   scales, 106, *106*
   solubility and, 248–249, *249*
   specific heat and, 113
   speed of sound and, 523
   vs. thermal energy, 111
   unit conversion, R21, *R21*
terminal velocity, 393, 394
Thales of Miletus, 696
thermal energy, *73,* **73,** *111,* **111,** 432
   heat and, 111, 124
   mass and, 114
   from ponds, 99
thermal expansion, 108
thermite reaction, 215, *215*
thermometer, 97, **107**
thermos, 98, *120*, 121
third law of motion. *See* Newton's laws of motion.

Index **R89**

Thompson, Benjamin, 98
Thomson, Joseph John, 233
timbre, 529
time
    distance, speed, and, 320–327, *321*, *322*, *324*, *325*, *328*, *338*
    distance-time graph, 324, *325*, 334, *335*, *338*
    energy, power, and, 437–439, *438*, *439*, 442
    velocity, acceleration, and, 329, *330*, 331–335, *332*, *334*, *338*
    velocity-time graph, 334, 335, *394*
    work, power, and, 434–436, *436*, 442
titanium alloy, 265, *265*, 266
total internal reflection, 617, *617*
transformer, *723*, **723**
    in a power plant, 727, *727*
transistors, 685, 698
transition metals, *155*, 155–156
translucent materials, 574, *574*
transmission, **573**, 574–575
transparent materials, 574, *574*
transportation, alloys and, 264
transverse waves, **493**, 510
    graph of, 498, *499*
trough, **497**, 510
tsunamis, 509, *509*
tungsten, 571, *571*

U

ultrasound, 482–485, **526**, 527, 538–540
ultrasound scanner, 482–485, 540, *540*
ultraviolet light, 561, *561*, **565**, *565*
units of measurement, 328. *See also* metric system.
    ampere (amp), **653**
    British thermal unit (BTU), 91
    calorie, **112**
    centimeter, 12
    coulomb, 635, 643
    decibel, **532**
    degree, **106**
    gram, 10
    hertz, **526**, 527, 561
    horsepower, 436
    joule, **112**, 421
    kilogram, 10, 355
    kilogram-meter per second (kg·m/s), 369
    kilometers per hour (km/h), 327
    kilowatt, **728**
    kilowatt-hour, **729**
    meter, 12
    meters per second (m/s), 322, 328
    meters per second squared (m/s^2), 332, 355
    newton, 11, 355–357
    ohm, **647**
    pascal, 396
    pound, 11
    volt, **643**, 653
    watt, 435, **728**
    wavelength, **497**, 510
unsaturated fat, 285

V

vacuum, **521**, 555
    acceleration in, 383
    EM waves and, 555
vacuum flask, 98, *120*, 121
vacuum tubes, 698
Van de Graaff generator, 636, *636*
vanillin, 278, *279*, 300
variables, 659, **R30**, R31, R32
    controlling, R17
    dependent, **R30**, R31
    independent, R30
    isolating, 433
vector, **326**, 326
    acceleration, 330
    of force, 346
    momentum, 369
    velocity, 326
velocity, **326**, *326*, 329–335, *330*, *338*. *See also* speed.
    acceleration, time, and, 329, *330*, 331–335, *332*, *334*, *338*
    average, 327
    escape, 386
    kinetic energy, mass, and, 428, 430
    momentum, mass, and, 368–369, *369*, *374*
    needed to achieve orbit, 386
    relation to speed, 326–327
    terminal, *393*, 394
    velocity-time graph, *334*, 335, *393*, *394*
vibration, **517**, 518–519, 520
visible light, 432, 561, *561*, **564**, 615. *See also* optics.
vision, 606–610
    correction of, 609–610
    farsightedness, 609, *609*, 610
    formation of images, *607*, 608
    nearsightedness, 609, *609*, 610
vitamin E molecule, 18
vocabulary strategies, R50–R51
    choose your own strategy, 238, *238*
    description wheel, 102, *102*, 168, *168*, 312, 418, 516, *516*, 592, *592*, 702, *702*, R50, *R50*
    four square, 8, *8*, 196, *196*, 380, 418, 488, *488*, 592, *592*, 632, *632*, R50, *R50*
    frame game, 70, *70*, 136, *136*, 552, *552*, 592, *592*, 666, *666*, R51, *R51*
    magnet word, 40, *40*, 274, *274*, 344, 418, R51, *R51*
    word triangle, 448, R51, *R51*
vocal cords, 518, *518*
volt, **643**, 653
Volta, Alessandro, 233, 697

voltage
  drop, 680
  magnetic control of, 723
  source, 668, *668*, 676, 692
voltmeter, 654
volume, xxxi, **xxxi**, **11**, 34, 41, R43, **R43**
  buoyancy, 413
  calculating, 12–13
  Chapter Investigation, 14–15
  displacement, 13, *13*, 403, 408
  of liquid, 13
  mass, density and, 403
  as physical property, 41, 42

W

water, **xxxiii**, 28, 172, 173, *173*, 179, *179*, 180, 397, 398, 399. *See also* ice; buoyancy; hydraulics.
  electrolysis, 199, *199*, 217, *217*
  heat and temperature and, 110
  molecule, 18, *18*, 19, 30, *30*
  molecular structure, 182, *182*
  oil and, 24, 250–251, *251*
  pH, *258*
  physical changes of, 44, 50
  physical states, 198, *198*
  pressure in, 397, *399*
  as solution, 252
  as solvent, 250–251, *251*, 254
  specific heat of, 113
  used to power machines, *423*
  vapor, xxxiii
water-treatment plants, 62
water wheels, *423*
Watt, James, 414, 436
watt (unit of power), **435**, **728**
wavelength, 496, *497*, **497**, 510
  color and, 576–579, 580–581
  frequency and, 498, *498*, 526
waves, 486–509, **489**. *See also* light; medium; sound; sound waves.
  AM (amplitude modulation), 562, *562*
  amplitude, 496, *497*, **497**
  behavior, 504–508
  classification, 492–494
  compressional, 494
  diffraction, **506**, *506*, 506–507, *507*, 510
  electromagnetic, 550–581. *See also* electromagnetic waves.
  energy and, 489–494
  FM (frequency modulation), 562, *562*
  frequency, 496, *497*, **497**, 498, 510, 525–546
  height, 495, 496
  Internet activity, 487
  longitudinal, **494**, 498, *498*, 510
  mechanical, **491**, 517, 521
  model, *492*

  ocean, 490, 492, 493, 495, 500–501
  properties, 496–501
  reflection, *505*, **505**, 510, 594–597, *594*, *596*, *597*
  refraction, *505*, **505**, 510, 600, *600*, *602*
  rope, 489, 490, *490*, 493, *493*
  sound, 494, 514–545
  speed of, 496, 500–501, 524
  transverse, **493**, 498, *499*, 510
  wavelength, 496, *497*, **497**, 498, 510, 526, 576–581
wedge, 458, **462**, *462*, 463
  compound machines using, 469, *476*
  real-world examples, *462*, 463
  used to hold objects together, 463
  used to separate objects, 463
weight, **11**, **383**
  difference between mass and, 11
  friction and, *391*
  gravitation and, 383–384, *384*
  mass and, compared, 383–384, *384*
  measuring, 11
weightlessness, 387
wet cell. *See* electrochemical cell.
wet mount, making a, R15, *R15*
whales, 399
wheel and axle, 458, **460**, *460*, 465, *476*
  compound machines using, 468–469, *469*, 470, *476*
  mechanical advantage of, *465*, 469
  real-world examples, 460, 463, 465
white light, 576
wide-angle lens, 619, *619*
wind
  convection cycle, 118, *118*
  energy, 88, 90
  used to power machines, 423
windmills, 90, *90*, 423
wings, 405
wool, physical changes in, 44, 45, *45*
work, **419**, 419–439, *422*, 442
  distance, force, and, 419–423, *420*, *422*, 442, 452–453, *453*
  energy transfer and, 425, 430, *431*
  gravitation and, 422–423, *423*
  input, 454–456, *454*, 457
  Internet activity, 417
  machines, force, and, 449–456, *450*, *451*, 459–466, *459*, *476*
  output, 454–456, *454*, 457
  time, power, and, 434–436, *436*, 442
World Wide Web, 689

X, Y, Z

x-rays, 73, 132, 561, *561*, **566**, *566*
zero, absolute, 98

Acknowledgments

Photography

Cover © Scott T. Smith/Corbis; **i** © Scott T. Smith/Corbis; **iii** *left (top to bottom)* Photograph of James Trefil by Evan Cantwell; Photograph of Rita Ann Calvo by Joseph Calvo; Photograph of Linda Carnine by Amilcar Cifuentes; Photograph of Sam Miller by Samuel Miller; *right (top to bottom)* Photograph of Kenneth Cutler by Kenneth A. Cutler; Photograph of Donald Steely by Marni Stamm; Photograph of Vicky Vachon by Redfern Photographics; **vi** © David Leahy/Getty Images; **vii** AP/Wide World Photos; **viii** © Digital Vision/PictureQuest; **x** © Arthur Tilley/Getty Images; **xi** © Mike Chew/Corbis; **xii** © Chip Simons/Getty Images; **xiii** © Alan Kearney/Getty Images; **xiv** © 2003 Barbara Ries; **xv** © Philip & Karen Smith/age fotostock america, inc.; **xx–xxi** Photographs by Sharon Hoogstraten; **xxx–xxxi** © Larry Hamill/age fotostock america, inc.; **xxxii–xxxiii** © Fritz Poelking/age fotostock america, inc.; **xxxiv–xxxv** © Galen Rowell/Corbis; **xxxvi–xxxvii** © Jack Affleck/SuperStock; **xxxviii** AP/Wide World Photos; **xxxix** © David Parker/IMI/University of Birmingham High, TC Consortium/Photo Researchers; **xl** *left* AP/Wide World Photos; *right* *Washington University Record*; **xli** *top* © Kim Steele/Getty Images; *bottom* Reprinted with permission from S. Zhou et al., *SCIENCE* 291:1944–47. © 2001 AAAS; **xlii–xliii** © Mike Fiala/Getty Images; **xliii** *left* © Derek Trask/Corbis; *right* AP/Wide World Photos; **xlviii** © The Chedd-Angier Production Company.

Matter and Energy

Divider © Scott T. Smith/Corbis; **2–3, 3** Courtesy of NASA/JPL/Caltech; **4** *top* © Babakin Space Center, The Planetary Society; *bottom* © The Chedd-Angier Production Company; **6–7** © Steve Allen/Brand X Pictures; **7, 9** Photographs by Sharon Hoogstraten; **10** *left* © Antonio Mo/Getty Images; *right* © ImageState/Alamy; **11** © Tom Stewart/Corbis; **12, 13** Photographs by Sharon Hoogstraten; **14** *top* © Stewart Cohen/Getty Images; *bottom* Photograph by Sharon Hoogstraten; **14–15, 15** Photographs by Sharon Hoogstraten; **16** © Royalty-Free/Corbis; **17** Photograph by Sharon Hoogstraten; **18** © NatPhotos/Tony Sweet/Digital Vision; **19** © Jake Rajs/Getty Images; **20** Courtesy IBM Archives; **21** Photograph by Sharon Hoogstraten; **22** *left* © James L. Amos/Corbis; *right* © Omni Photo Communications, Inc./Index Stock; **23** © Richard Laird/Getty Images; **24** Photograph by Sharon Hoogstraten; **25** © Royalty-Free/Corbis; **26** © Nik Wheeler/Corbis; **27** Photograph by Sharon Hoogstraten; **30** © Robert F. Sisson/Getty Images; **31** Photograph by Sharon Hoogstraten; **34** *top* Photograph by Sharon Hoogstraten; *bottom left* © James L. Amos/Corbis; *bottom right* © Royalty-Free/Corbis; **36** Photographs by Sharon Hoogstraten; **38–39** © David Leahy/Getty Images; **39, 41** Photographs by Sharon Hoogstraten; **42** *left* Photograph by Sharon Hoogstraten; *right* © Dan Lim/Masterfile; **45** *top left* © Maryellen McGrath/Bruce Coleman Inc.; *top center* © Jean-Bernard Vernier/Corbis Sygma; *top right* © Angelo Cavalli/Getty Images; *bottom* © Garry Black/Masterfile; *inset* Photograph by Sharon Hoogstraten; **46** © Mark C. Burnett/Stock, Boston Inc./PictureQuest; **47** Photograph by Sharon Hoogstraten; **48** © J. Westrich/Masterfile; **49** *left* © Owen Franken/Corbis; *right* © Erich Lessing/Art Resource, New York; **50** © ImageState/Alamy; **51** *left* © Brand X Pictures; *right* © Peter Bowater/Alamy; **52** © Royalty-Free/Corbis; **53** © Winifred Wisniewski/Frank Lane Picture Agency/Corbis; **54** © A. Pasieka/Photo Researchers; **55** © Sean Ellis/Getty Images; **56** *top* © Royalty-Free/Corbis; *bottom* Photograph by Sharon Hoogstraten; **57, 58** Photographs by Sharon Hoogstraten; **59** © Lawrence Livermore National Laboratory/Photo Researchers; **60** *top left* © SPL/Photo Researchers; *top right* © Felix St. Clair Renard/Getty Images; *bottom* © David Young-Wolff/PhotoEdit; **61** Photograph by Sharon Hoogstraten; **62** © Alan Towse/Ecoscene/Corbis; **63** © Robert Essel NYC/Corbis; *inset* © The Cover Story/Corbis; **64** *top left* © Dan Lim/Masterfile; *top right* © Mark C. Burnett/Stock, Boston Inc./PictureQuest; *bottom* © David Young-Wolff/PhotoEdit; **66** © Winifred Wisniewski/Frank Lane Picture Agency/Corbis; **68–69** AP/Wide World Photos; **69, 71** Photographs by Sharon Hoogstraten; **72** © Alan Schein Photography/Corbis; **73** *top* © Patrick Ward/Corbis; *bottom* © NASA/Photo Researchers; **74** AP/Wide World Photos; **75** *top* © George H. H. Huey/Corbis; *bottom* Photograph by Sharon Hoogstraten; **76** *top* © Vladimir Pcholkin/Getty Images; *bottom* © Thomas Beach; **77** © Adam Gault/Digital Vision; **78** © Bill Aron/PhotoEdit; **79** © TempSport/Corbis; **80** © Robert Cameron/Getty Images; **81** *left* © Gunter Marx Photography/Corbis; *right* © Lester Lefkowitz/Corbis; **82** © Left Lane Productions/Corbis; **83** © Dorling Kindersley; **84** *top* © Grant Klotz/Alaska Stock Images/PictureQuest; *bottom* Photograph by Sharon Hoogstraten; **85, 86** Photographs by Sharon Hoogstraten; **87** *top left* © Royalty-Free/Corbis; *top right* Thinkstock, LLC; *bottom* AP/Wide World Photos; **88** © AFP/Corbis; *inset* © John Farmar; Cordaiy Photo Library Ltd./Corbis; **89** *top* © Sally A. Morgan; Ecoscene/Corbis; *bottom* Photograph by Sharon Hoogstraten; **90** © Joe Sohm/Visions of America, LLC/PictureQuest; **91** © Michael S. Lewis/Corbis; **92** *top* © Vladimir Pcholkin/Getty Images; *bottom* © AFP/Corbis; **96** © Don Farrall/Getty Images; **97** *top left* © Sheila Terry/Photo Researchers; *top center, top right* © Dorling Kindersley; *bottom* © SEF/Art Resource, New York; **98** *top left* Mary Evans Picture Library; *top right, bottom* © Dorling Kindersley; **99** © Mark Wiens/Masterfile; **100–101** © Steve Bloom/stevebloom.com; **101, 103** Photographs by Sharon Hoogstraten; **104** © Tracy Frankel/Getty Images; **105** Photographs by Sharon Hoogstraten; **106** © Daryl Benson/Masterfile; *inset* © Spencer Grant/PhotoEdit; **107** Photograph by Sharon Hoogstraten; **108** *top* © Steve Vidler/SuperStock; *bottom* © Chase Jarvis/Getty Images; **109** ©

FogStock/Alamy; *inset* © Gordon Wiltsie/Getty Images; **110** © David Bishop/Getty Images; **111** Thinkstock, LLC; **112** Photograph by Sharon Hoogstraten; **113** © Richard Bickel/Corbis; **115** *top left* © Jeremy Samuelson/FoodPix; *bottom left* © William Reavell-StockFood Munich/StockFood; *right* © Martin Jacobs/FoodPix; **116** Photograph by Sharon Hoogstraten; **117** © Brand X Pictures/Alamy; **119** © ImageState Royalty Free/Alamy; **120** *top left* E.C. Humphrey; *top right* Creatas®; *bottom* © Uwe Walz Gdt/age fotostock america, inc.; **122** *top* © Nancy Ney/Corbis; *bottom* Photograph by Sharon Hoogstraten; **123** Photograph by Sharon Hoogstraten; **124** *top* Photographs by Sharon Hoogstraten; *bottom* Thinkstock, LLC.

Chemical Interactions
Divider © Photodisc/Getty Images; **130–131** © David Cavagnaro/Peter Arnold, Inc.; **131** Joel Sartore/National Geographic Image Collection; **132** © The Chedd-Angier Production Company; **133** © Colin Cuthbert/Photo Researchers; **134–135** IBM Research, Almaden Research Center; **135, 137** Photographs by Sharon Hoogstraten; **138** NASA; **140** © Pascal Goetgheluck/Photo Researchers; **141** Photograph by Sharon Hoogstraten; **144** © Cnri/Photo Researchers; **145** Photograph by Sharon Hoogstraten; **146** *left, right* The Granger Collection, New York; **152** *top* © A. Hart-Davis/Photo Researchers; *bottom* Photograph by Sharon Hoogstraten; **154** Photograph by Sharon Hoogstraten; **155** *left* © Charles D. Winters/Photo Researchers; *center* © Rich Treptow/Visuals Unlimited; *right* © Corbis Images/PictureQuest; **156** © Peter Christopher/Masterfile; **157** © M. Gibbon/Robertstock.com; **158** © Superstock; **159** *top* © Simon Fraser/Photo Researchers; *bottom* Photograph by Sharon Hoogstraten; **161** © Alfred Pasieka/Photo Researchers; *inset* © John Walsh/Photo Researchers; **166–167** © Digital Vision/PictureQuest; **167, 169** Photographs by Sharon Hoogstraten; **170** *left* © Rich Treptow/Visuals Unlimited; *center, right* © E. R. Degginger/Color-Pic, Inc.; **171, 173** Photograph by Sharon Hoogstraten; **174** © Lawrence M. Sawyer/Photodisc/PictureQuest; **175** © IFA/eStock Photography (PQ price control)/PictureQuest; **177** © Runk and Schoenberger/Grant Heilman Photography, Inc.; **180** © The Image Bank/Getty Images; **181** Photograph by Sharon Hoogstraten; **183** © Astrid & Hanns-Frieder Michler/Photo Researchers; *inset* © Volker Steger/Photo Researchers; **184** Photograph by Sharon Hoogstraten; **185** © David Wrobel/Visuals Unlimited; **186** © Rob Blakers/photolibrary/PictureQuest; **187** *left* © E. R. Degginger/Robertstock.com; *right* © C. Swartzell/Visuals Unlimited; **188** *top* © David Young-Wolff/Getty Images; *bottom* Photograph by Sharon Hoogstraten; **189** Photograph by Sharon Hoogstraten; **190** *left* © Rich Treptow/Visuals Unlimited; *center, right* © E. R. Degginger/Color-Pic, Inc.; **194–195** From *General Chemistry* by P. W. Atkins, © 1989 by Peter Atkins. Used with permission of W.H. Freeman and Company; **195, 197** Photographs by Sharon Hoogstraten; **198** © Daryl Benson/Masterfile; **200** *top left* © Science VU/Visuals Unlimited; *top right* © 1992 Richard Megna/Fundamental Photographs, NYC; *bottom left* © E. R. Degginger/Color-Pic, Inc.; *bottom right* © Larry Stepanowicz/Visuals Unlimited; **202** Photograph by Sharon Hoogstraten; **205** © Corbis Images/PictureQuest; *inset* © Andrew Lambert Photography/Photo Researchers; **206** © Wally Eberhart/Visuals Unlimited; **207** *top* The Granger Collection, New York; *bottom* Photograph by Sharon Hoogstraten; **208** © William Ervin/Photo Researchers; **210** © Maximilian Stock Ltd./Photo Researchers; **212** © Index Stock; **213** *left, inset* Courtesy of Chicago Fire Department; *center* Uline; *bottom right* Photograph by Sharon Hoogstraten; **214** Photograph by Sharon Hoogstraten; **215** *top* NASA; *bottom* © 1992 Richard Megna/Fundamental Photographs, NYC; **216** © Jeffrey L. Rotman/Corbis; **217** Thomas Eisner and Daniel Aneshansley, Cornell University; **219** © Harald Sund/Brand X Pictures/PictureQuest; **220** *top* AP/Wide World Photos; *bottom* Photographs by Sharon Hoogstraten; **221** Photograph by Sharon Hoogstraten; **222** © Runk and Schoenberger/Grant Heilman Photography, Inc.; **223** Photograph by Sharon Hoogstraten; **224** © Tom Yhlman/Visuals Unlimited; **225** *background* © Conor Caffrey/Photo Researchers; **226** © Arnold Fisher/Photo Researchers; **227** *left to right* © Bruce Forster/Getty Images; © Colin Cuthbert/Photo Researchers; © Fontarnau-Gutiérrez/age fotostock america, inc.; © D. Roberts/Photo Researchers; **228** © 1992 Richard Megna/Fundamental Photographs, NYC; **232** From Hales, *Vegetable Statiks* [1727]; **233** *top* The Granger Collection, New York; *bottom* Mary Evans Picture Library; **234** *top* AP/Wide World Photos; *bottom* © Dorling Kindersley; **235** *top, bottom* © David Parker/Photo Researchers; **236–237** © Stephen Frink/Index Stock; **237, 239** Photographs by Sharon Hoogstraten; **240** © Richard Cummins/Corbis; **241, 243** Photographs by Sharon Hoogstraten; **244** © Peter & Georgina Bowater/Stock Connection/PictureQuest; *inset* © 2001 Kim Fennema/Visuals Unlimited; **245, 246** Photographs by Sharon Hoogstraten; **247** *left, right* © 1990 Richard Megna/Fundamental Photographs, NYC; **248–249** Photographs by Sharon Hoogstraten; **250** © Stephen Frink/StephenFrink.com; **251** Photograph by Sharon Hoogstraten; **252** © Thom Lang/Corbis; **253, 255, 257** Photographs by Sharon Hoogstraten; **258** *top left* © Martyn F. Chillmaid/Photo Researchers; *top right* © Chuck Swartzell/Visuals Unlimited; *center left* © E. R. Degginger/Color-Pic, Inc.; *center right* © Phil Degginger/Color-Pic, Inc.; *bottom left* © Stockbyte; *bottom right* © E. R. Degginger/Color-Pic, Inc.; **260** © Runk and Schoenberger/Grant Heilman Photography, Inc.; **260–261, 261, 262** Photographs by Sharon Hoogstraten; **263** *top to bottom* © Photodisc/Getty Images; © Greg Pease/Stock Connection/PictureQuest; © Stockbyte; © S. Feld/Robertstock.com; Jellinek & Sampson, London/Bridgeman Art Library; **264** © Joachim Messerschmidt/Bruce Coleman, Inc.; **265** *top* © Princess Margaret Rose Hospital/Photo Researchers; *inset* © Klaus Rose/Okapia/Photo Researchers; *bottom* Photograph by Sharon Hoogstraten; **266** NASA; **267** © IFA/eStock Photography (PQ price control)/PictureQuest; **268** © Joachim Messerschmidt/Bruce Coleman, Inc.; **272–273** © Jeff Greenberg/Index Stock/PictureQuest; **273, 275** Photographs by Sharon Hoogstraten; **276** *left* © E. R. Degginger/Color-Pic, Inc.; *right* © Charles D. Winters/Photo Researchers; **277** Photograph by Sharon Hoogstraten; **279** *top* © Claver Carroll/age fotostock america, inc.; *bottom left* © Fabio Cardoso/age fotostock america, inc.; *bottom right* Photograph by

Sharon Hoogstraten; **281** *left* © S. J. Tans et al., Delft University of Technology/Photo Researchers; *right* Georgia Institute of Technology; **282** Photograph by Sharon Hoogstraten; **283** © Marcialis/StockFood; **284** © John Durham/Photo Researchers; **285** *top* © Meyer/StockFood; *bottom* © SPL/Photo Researchers; **286** Photograph by Sharon Hoogstraten; **287** *left* © Andrew Syred/Photo Researchers; *right* © SCIMAT 2000/Photo Researchers; **290** © Eising/StockFood; **291** Photograph by Sharon Hoogstraten; **293** *top* © Thomas Kitchin/Tom Stack & Associates; *center* © Superstock; *bottom left* © Bob Krist/Corbis; *bottom center* © Omni Photo Communications/Index Stock; *bottom right* © Gary Rhijnsburger/Masterfile; **295** *top* Image Club Graphics; *bottom* © 1994 CMCD, Inc.; **296** *bottom left* © J. Blank/Robertstock.com; **297** *left* © SuperStock; *right* © Cheryl A. Ertelt/Visuals Unlimited; **298** *top* © E. R. Degginger/Color-Pic, Inc.; *bottom* Photograph by Sharon Hoogstraten; **299** Photograph by Sharon Hoogstraten; **300** © SuperStock.

Motion and Forces

Divider © Brett Froomer/Getty Images, **306–307** Courtesy of NASA/JPL/Caltech; **307** © Stocktrek/Corbis; **308** *top* Courtesy of NASA/JPL/Caltech; *bottom* © The Chedd-Angier Production Company; **310–311** © Lester Lefkowitz/Corbis; **311** Photographs by Sharon Hoogstraten; **313** © Royalty-Free/Corbis; **315** © Globus, Holway & Lobel/Corbis; **316** *top* Photograph by Sharon Hoogstraten; *bottom* © The Image Group/Getty Images; **318** *top* © Georgina Bowater/Corbis; *bottom* © SuperStock; **319** © Graham Wheatley/The Military Picture Library/Corbis; **320, 321** Photographs by Sharon Hoogstraten; **322** © Gunter Marx Photography/Corbis; **323** Photograph by Sharon Hoogstraten; **325** © Tom Brakefield/Corbis; **326** © David M. Dennis/Animals Animals; **327** © Kelly-Mooney Photography/Corbis; **328** © Gallo Images/Corbis; **329** © 1986 Richard Megna/Fundamental Photographs, NYC; **331** Photograph by Sharon Hoogstraten; **332** © Royalty-Free/Corbis; **333** Courtesy of NASA/JPL/Caltech; **334** © Robert Essel NYC/Corbis; **336** *top* © Mark Jenkinson/Corbis; *bottom* Photographs by Sharon Hoogstraten; **338** *top* © Globus, Holway & Lobel/Corbis; *center* Photograph by Sharon Hoogstraten; **340** © David M. Dennis/Animals Animals; **342–343** © Arthur Tilley/Getty Images; **343, 345** Photographs by Sharon Hoogstraten; **346** © John Kelly/Getty Images; **347** *left* © AFP/Corbis; *right* © Reuters NewMedia Inc./Corbis; **348** © Michael Kevin Daly/Corbis; **349** *left* © Jim Cummins/Getty Images; *right* © Piecework Productions/Getty Images; **350** Photograph by Sharon Hoogstraten; **351** © Jeffrey Lynch/Mendola Ltd.; **352** *left, inset* © Bill Ross/Corbis; *right* Dr. Paula Messina, San Jose State University; **353, 354** Photographs by Sharon Hoogstraten; **356** AP/Wide World Photos; **357** NASA; **358** Photograph by Sharon Hoogstraten; **359** AP/Wide World Photos; **360** *top* Clare Hirn, Jewish Hospital, University of Louisville and ABIOMED; *bottom* John Lair, Jewish Hospital, University of Louisville and ABIOMED; **361** © Danny Lehman/Corbis; **362–363** Photographs by Sharon Hoogstraten; **364** © Photodisc/Getty Images; *background* © David C. Fritts/Animals Animals; **366** *top* Digital image © 1996 Corbis/Original image courtesy of NASA/Corbis; *bottom* Photographs by Sharon Hoogstraten; **368, 370** Photographs by Sharon Hoogstraten; **372** © TRL Ltd./Photo Researchers; **373** © Charles O'Rear/Corbis; **374** *top* © Photodisc/Getty Images; *bottom* Photographs by Sharon Hoogstraten; **375** © Siede Preis/Getty Images; **376** Photographs by Sharon Hoogstraten; **378–379** © Mike Chew/Corbis; **379, 381** Photographs by Sharon Hoogstraten; **384, 385** Photographs of models by Sharon Hoogstraten; **384** *left* NASA; *right* © Photodisc/Getty Images; **C385** *top, bottom, background* NASA; **386** Photograph by Sharon Hoogstraten; **387** NASA; **388** *left* © Royalty-Free/Corbis; *right* NASA/ESA; **389** © John Beatty/Getty Images; **390, 391** Photographs by Sharon Hoogstraten; **392** *top* © Al Francekevich/Corbis; *bottom* Photograph by Sharon Hoogstraten; **393** © Joe McBride/Getty Images; **394** © NatPhotos/Tony Sweet/Digital Vision; *inset* © Michael S. Yamashita/Corbis; **395** Photograph by Sharon Hoogstraten; **396** © Wilson Goodrich/Index Stock; **397** © Royalty-Free/Corbis; **398** © Philip & Karen Smith/Getty Images; **399** © Ralph A. Clevenger/Corbis; **400** *top* © Stephen Frink/Corbis; *bottom* Photographs by Sharon Hoogstraten; **402, 403, 404** Photographs by Sharon Hoogstraten; **405** Photograph of prairie dogs © W. Perry Conway/Corbis; **407** © Omni Photo Communications Inc./Index Stock; **408** *top, bottom* Photographs by Sharon Hoogstraten; *center* © Royalty-Free/Corbis; **409** Photograph by Sharon Hoogstraten; **410** *left* © Joe McBride/Getty Images; *right* Photograph by Sharon Hoogstraten; **412** *top* © Erich Lessing/Art Resource, New York; *bottom* © Dagli Orti/The Art Archive; **413** *top left* © SPL/Photo Researchers; *top right* Sam Fogg Rare Books & Manuscripts; *bottom* © Dorling Kindersley; **414** *left* © Victoria & Albert Museum, London/Art Resource, New York; *top right* Photo Franca Principe, Institute and Museum of the History of Science; *center right* © Scala/Art Resource, New York; *bottom right* © Dorling Kindersley; **415** *top* © Gerald L. Schad/Photo Researchers; *bottom* NASA; **416–417** © Digital Vision; **417** *top* Image Club Graphics; *center* Photograph by Sharon Hoogstraten; **419, 420** Photographs by Sharon Hoogstraten; **421** © Rob Lewine/Corbis; **422** Photograph by Sharon Hoogstraten; **423** © Reinhard Eisele/Corbis; **424** © Roger Allyn Lee/SuperStock; **425** Chris Wipperman/KCPDSA; **427** © Patrik Giardino/Corbis; **428** © Tony Anderson/Getty Images; **429** Photograph by Sharon Hoogstraten; **430** © 1988 Paul Silverman/Fundamental Photographs, NYC; **431** © Tony Donaldson/Icon Sports Media; **433** © AFP/Corbis; **434** Photograph by Sharon Hoogstraten; **435** © Pete Saloutos/Corbis; **436** © Digital Vision; **437** Photograph by Sharon Hoogstraten; **438** © Walter Hodges/Corbis; **439** © Grantpix/Index Stock; **440** *top* © David Young-Wolff/PhotoEdit; *bottom* Photographs by Sharon Hoogstraten; **442** © Pete Saloutos/Corbis; **444** Photographs by Sharon Hoogstraten; **446–447** © Balthazar Korab; **449** Photograph by Sharon Hoogstraten; **450** © David Young-Wolff/PhotoEdit; **451** © Joseph Sohm/ChromoSohm Inc./Corbis; **453** © Brad Wrobleski/Masterfile; **454** © Michael Macor/San Francisco Chronicle/Corbis SABA; **455** Photograph by Sharon Hoogstraten; **456** © Jean-Yves Ruszniewski/Corbis; **457** © Royalty-Free/Corbis; *inset* © Felicia Martinez/PhotoEdit; **458, 459** Photographs by

Sharon Hoogstraten; **460** © Tom Stewart/Corbis; **461** Photograph by Sharon Hoogstraten; **462** *top* © David Butow/Corbis SABA; *bottom* © Peter Beck/Corbis; **463** © Henryk T. Kaiser/Index Stock; **464** © Tony Freeman/PhotoEdit; **465** © Todd A. Gipstein/Corbis; **467** AP/Wide World Photos; **468** © Tony Freeman/PhotoEdit; **469** © Lester Lefkowitz/Corbis; **470** Hurst Jaws of Life; **471** © David Parker/Photo Researchers; **472** *top* AP/Wide World Photos; *bottom* © Robert Caputo/Stock Boston; *background* © Royalty-Free/Corbis; **474** *top* © Photodisc/Getty Images; *bottom* Photograph by Sharon Hoogstraten; **476** © ThinkStock/SuperStock; **477** *top left* Photograph by Sharon Hoogstraten; **478** © Tony Freeman/PhotoEdit.

Waves, Sound, and Light
Divider © David Pu'u/Corbis; **482–483** © Paul Kuroda/SuperStock; **483** *left* © B. Benoit/Photo Researchers; *right* © Powerstock/SuperStock; **484** *top* © Stephen Frink/Corbis; *bottom* © The Chedd-Angier Production Company; **485** © George Stetten, M.D., Ph.D; **486–487** © Peter Sterling/Getty Images; **487, 489** Photographs by Sharon Hoogstraten; **491** Photograph courtesy of Earthquake Engineering Research Institute Reconnaissance Team; **492** © Michael Krasowitz/Getty Images; **493** Photograph by Sharon Hoogstraten; **495** © John Lund/Getty Images; **496** © Greg Huglin/Superstock; **497** © Arnulf Husmo/Getty Images; **499** Richard Olsenius/National Geographic Image Collection; **500** Photograph by Sharon Hoogstraten; **502** *top* © 1990 Robert Mathena/Fundamental Photographs, NYC; *bottom* Photographs by Sharon Hoogstraten; **503, 504** Photographs by Sharon Hoogstraten; **505** © 2001 Richard Megna/Fundamental Photographs, NYC; **506** *top* © 1972 FP/Fundamental Photographs, NYC; *bottom* Photograph by Sharon Hoogstraten; **507** © 1998 Richard Megna/Fundamental Photographs, NYC; **508** © Hiroshi Hara/Photonica; **509** Takaaki Uda, Public Works Research Institute, Japan/NOAA; **510** *bottom center* © 2001 Richard Megna/Fundamental Photographs, NYC; *bottom right* © 1972 FP/Fundamental Photographs, NYC; **514–515** © Chip Simons/Getty Images; **515, 517** Photographs by Sharon Hoogstraten; **519** © Susumu Nishinaga/Photo Researchers; **521** Photographs by Sharon Hoogstraten; **522** © Jeff Rotman/Getty Images; **523** © John Terence Turner/Getty Images; **524** *left* © Reuters NewMedia Inc./Corbis; *background* © Jason Hindley/Getty Images; **525** Photograph by Sharon Hoogstraten; **527** *left (top to bottom)* © Will Crocker/Getty Images; © Dorling Kindersley; © Photodisc/Getty Images; © Dorling Kindersley; © Photodisc/Getty Images; © Stephen Dalton/Animals Animals; © Steve Bloom/Getty Images; *top right* © Don Smetzer/Getty Images; *bottom right* Brian Gordon Green/National Geographic Image Collection; **528** Photograph by Sharon Hoogstraten; **529** © Dorling Kindersley; **530** © Michael Melford/Getty Images; **532** © Tom Main/Getty Images; **533** Photograph by Sharon Hoogstraten; **535** *left* © Roger Ressmeyer/Corbis; *right* Symphony Center, Home of the Chicago Symphony Orchestra; **536** © Yehoash Raphael, Kresge Hearing Research Institute, The University of Michigan; **537** © Chris Shinn/Getty Images; **538** Photograph by Sharon Hoogstraten; **539** *top left* © Stephen Dalton/OSF/Animals Animals; *top right* © Paulo de Oliveira/Getty Images; *bottom left* © AFP/Corbis; *bottom right* U.S. Navy photo by Photographer's Mate 3rd Class Lawrence Braxton/Department of Defense; **540** © Fetal Fotos; **543** © Andrew Syred/Photo Researchers; **544** *top left* © Reuters NewMedia Inc./Corbis; *bottom* Photographs by Sharon Hoogstraten; **545** Photograph by Sharon Hoogstraten; **546** *bottom left* © Stephen Dalton/OSF/Animals Animals; *bottom right* © Paulo de Oliveira/Getty Images; **548** © Photodisc/Getty Images; **550–551** © Alan Kearney/Getty Images; **551** *top, center* Photographs by Sharon Hoogstraten; *bottom* The EIT Consortium/NASA; **553** Photograph by Sharon Hoogstraten; **555** NASA, The Hubble Heritage Team, STScI, AURA; **556** Photograph by Sharon Hoogstraten; **558** *top* Palomar Observatory/Caltech; *center* NASA/MSFC/SAO; *bottom* NASA/CXC/ASU/J. Hester et al; *background* NASA/JHU/AUI/R. Giacconi et al.; **559** Photograph by Sharon Hoogstraten; **560** *left* © China Tourism Press/Getty Images; *center* © David Nunuk/Photo Researchers; *right* © Dr. Arthur Tucker/Photo Researchers; **561** *left to right* © Jeremy Woodhouse/Getty Images; © Sinclair Stammers/Photo Researchers; © Hugh Turvey/Photo Researchers; © Alfred Pasieka/Photo Researchers; **564** Photograph by Sharon Hoogstraten; **565** *top* © Dr. Arthur Tucker/Photo Researchers; *bottom* © Thomas Eisner, Cornell University; **566** © Martin Spinks; **567** © Photodisc/Getty Images; *inset* © David Young-Wolff/Getty Images; **568** Robert F. Sisson/National Geographic Image Collection; **569** © George D. Lepp/Corbis; **570** *top* © Raymond Blythe/OSF/Animals Animals; *bottom* Photograph by Sharon Hoogstraten; **572** © Traffic Technologies; **573** Photograph by Sharon Hoogstraten; **574** © Jeff Greenberg/Visuals Unlimited; **575** © Raymond Gehman/Corbis; **576** © Charles Swedlund; **577** *top* © Ace Photo Agency/Phototake; *bottom* © Dorling Kindersley; **578** Photograph by Sharon Hoogstraten; **580** *top* © Michael Newman/PhotoEdit; *bottom* Photographs by Sharon Hoogstraten; **581** Photographs by Sharon Hoogstraten; **582** *center right* Robert F. Sisson/National Geographic Image Collection; *bottom* © Ace Photo Agency/Phototake; **586** *top* The Granger Collection, New York; *bottom* © Jack and Beverly Wilgus; **587** *top* The Granger Collection, New York; *center left* Diagram of the eye from the *Opticae thesaurus. Alhazeni Arabis libri septem, nunc primum editi* by Ibn al-Haytham (Alhazen). Edited by Federico Risnero (Basleae, 1572), p. 6. Private collection, London; *center right* Courtesy of NASA/JPL/Caltech; *bottom* © Royal Greenwich Observatory/Photo Researchers; **588** *top* © Stock Connection/Alamy; *center* © Florian Marquardt; *bottom* © Museum of Holography, Chicago; **589** *top* © Bettmann/Corbis; *bottom* © Bob Masini/Phototake; **590–591** © Tom Raymond/Getty Images; **591** *top, center* Photographs by Sharon Hoogstraten; *bottom* © Philippe Plaily/Photo Researchers; **592** Photograph by Sharon Hoogstraten; **594** © Laura Dwight/Corbis; **595** Photograph by Sharon Hoogstraten; **596** © Michael Newman/PhotoEdit; **597** Photographs by Sharon Hoogstraten; **598** Peter McBride/Aurora; **599** Photograph by Sharon Hoogstraten; **600** © Richard H. Johnston/Getty Images; **602** © Kim Heacox/Getty Images; *background* ©

Photodisc/Getty Images; **603** © T. R. Tharp/Corbis; **604** *top* © Ruddy Gold/age photostock america, inc.; *bottom* Photograph by Sharon Hoogstraten; **605** Photographs by Sharon Hoogstraten; **606** © CMCD, 1994; **608** Photograph by Sharon Hoogstraten; **610** © Argentum/Photo Researchers; **611** Photograph by Sharon Hoogstraten; **613** *top* © Andrew Syred/Photo Researchers; *center* Luna and Planetary Institute, CIRS/Library; *bottom* NASA; **614** Photograph by Sharon Hoogstraten; **615** Use of Canon Powershot S45 courtesy of Canon USA; **616** © Philippe Psaila/Photo Researchers; **617** *top* © Photodisc/Getty Images; *bottom* © Tom Stewart/corbisstockmarket.com; **618** Bradley C. Edwards, Ph.D.; **619** *top* © Photodisc/Getty Images; *center* © PhotoFlex.com; *bottom* © Michael Goldman/Photis/PictureQuest; **620** © Michael Newman/PhotoEdit.

Electricity and Magnetism
Divider © Nick Koudis/Getty Images; **626–627** © PHISH 2003; 3 © Jacques M. Chenet/Corbis; **628** *top* © John Foxx/ImageState; *bottom* © The Chedd-Angier Production Company; **629** © Stuart Hughes/Corbis; **630–631** AP/Wide World Photos; **631, 633** Photographs by Sharon Hoogstraten; **634** © Roger Ressmeyer/Corbis; **636** © Charles D. Winters/Photo Researchers; **638** Photograph by Sharon Hoogstraten; **640** © Maximilian Stock Ltd./Photo Researchers; **641** *left* © Ann and Rob Simpson; *right* © Patrice Ceisel/Visuals Unlimited; **642** Photograph by Sharon Hoogstraten; **643** © Steve Crise/Corbis; **645** © A & J Verkaik/Corbis; **646** Photograph by Sharon Hoogstraten; **647** *top* © Tim Wright/Corbis; *bottom* © Leland Bobb/Corbis; **648** © James D. Hooker/*Lighting Equipment News (UK)*; **650** *top left* © Scott T. Smith; All other photographs by Sharon Hoogstraten; **651, 652, 654, 655** Photographs by Sharon Hoogstraten; **657** © Chip Simons 2003; **658** Photo Courtesy of NASA/Getty Images; **659** © Julian Hirshowitz/Corbis; **660** © James D. Hooker/*Lighting Equipment News (UK)*; **664–665** © 2003 Barbara Ries; **665, 667** Photographs by Sharon Hoogstraten; **672** *left* © 1989 Paul Silverman/Fundamental Photographs, NYC; *right* Photograph by Sharon Hoogstraten; **673** © Creative Publishing International, Inc.; **674** *top left* © Gary Rhijnsburger/Masterfile; *center left* © Creative Publishing International, Inc.; **675, 676, 677, 678** Photographs by Sharon Hoogstraten; **680** © Robert Essel NYC/Corbis; **681** Photograph by Sharon Hoogstraten; **683** *top* AP/Wide World Photos; *bottom* Photograph by Sharon Hoogstraten; **685** © Kurt Stier/Corbis; **686, 687** © Gen Nishino/Getty Images; **688** © Donna Cox and Robert Patterson/National Center for Supercomputing Applications, University of Illinois, Urbana; **689** AP/Wide World Photos; **690** *top* © Sheila Terry/Photo Researchers; *bottom* Photograph by Sharon Hoogstraten; **696** *top* © SPL/Photo Researchers; *bottom* The Granger Collection, New York; **697** *top left* © Philadelphia Museum of Art/Corbis; *top right* © Archivo Iconografico, S.A./Corbis; *bottom* © Adam Hart-Davis/Photo Researchers; **698** *top* Science Museum/Science & Society Picture Library; *center left* © Bettmann/Corbis; *center right* © Tony Craddock/Photo Researchers; *bottom* © Bettmann/Corbis; **699** *top* © Alfred Pasieka/Photo Researchers; *bottom* AP/Wide World Photos; **700–701** © Philip & Karen Smith/age fotostock america, inc.; **701, 703** Photographs by Sharon Hoogstraten; **704** *top* © Michael S. Yamashita/Corbis; *bottom* Photograph by Sharon Hoogstraten; **705** Photographs by Sharon Hoogstraten; **706** © The Natural History Museum, London; **707** Photograph by Sharon Hoogstraten; **708** NASA; **709** Photograph by Sharon Hoogstraten; **710** © Chris Madeley/Photo Researchers; **711** © Brian Bahr/Getty Images; *inset* Courtesy of Discover Magnetics; **712, 714** Photographs by Sharon Hoogstraten; **715** *top* © George Haling/Photo Researchers; *bottom* © Dick Luria/Photo Researchers; **717** © G. K. & Vikki Hart/Getty Images; **719** Photograph by Sharon Hoogstraten; **721** © Ondrea Barbe/Corbis; **722** Photograph by Sharon Hoogstraten; **723** © Randy M. Ury/Corbis; **724** *top* © Christopher Gould/Getty Images; *bottom* Photographs by Sharon Hoogstraten; **725** Photographs by Sharon Hoogstraten; **726** Bureau of Reclamation; **728** Courtesy of General Electric; **729** *top* Photograph by Sharon Hoogstraten; *bottom* © Maya Barnes/The Image Works; **731** © Mark Richards/PhotoEdit; **732** *top* Photograph by Sharon Hoogstraten.

Backmatter
R28 © Photodisc/Getty Images.

Illustrations and Maps

Accurate Art, Inc. **127, 411, 479, 513;** Ampersand Design Group **29, 115, 213, 225, 319, 619, 674;** Argosy **490, 493, 494, 498, 499, 505, 510, 535, 541;** Eric Chadwick **578, 579;** Steve Cowden **426, 492, 531, 534, 562, 684, 686–687, 692;** Stephen Durke **10, 11, 18, 20, 22, 30, 32, 33, 34, 81, 139, 140, 141, 142, 143, 162, 176, 177, 178, 179, 180, 182, 187, 190, 192, 198, 199, 201, 216, 217, 225, 230, 242, 270, 276, 286, 287, 288, 300, 302, 635, 636, 637, 645, 649, 655, 660, 663, 668, 670, 677, 692, 727, 732, 734;** Patrick Gnan **288;** Gary Hincks **252;** KO Studios **288;** Debbie Maizels **288;** MapQuest.com, Inc. **114, 314, 364, 433, 472;** Precision Graphics **293;** Tony Randazzo/American Artists Rep. Inc. **317;** Dan Stuckenschneider **406, 439, 460, 461, 462, 463, 465, 466, 469, 476, 477, 542, 557, 571, 582, 613, 615, 616, 620, 639, 657, 671, 673, 679, 716, 717, 718, 720, 721, 732, R11–R19, R22, R32;** Dan Stukenschneider based on an illustration by Matt Cioffi **472;** Bart Vallecoccia **518, 519, 606, 607, 609, 615, 620.**

National Science Education Standards

Content Standards: 5–8

A. Science as Inquiry

As a result of activities in grades 5–8, all students should develop

Abilities Necessary to do Scientific Inquiry

A.1 Identify questions that can be answered through scientific investigations. Students should develop the ability to refine and refocus broad and ill-defined questions. An important aspect of this ability consists of students' ability to clarify questions and inquiries and direct them toward objects and phenomena that can be described, explained, or predicted by scientific investigations. Students should develop the ability to identify their questions with scientific ideas, concepts, and quantitative relationships that guide investigation.

A.2 Design and conduct a scientific investigation. Students should develop general abilities, such as systematic observation, making accurate measurements, and identifying and controlling variables. They should also develop the ability to clarify their ideas that are influencing and guiding the inquiry, and to understand how those ideas compare with current scientific knowledge. Students can learn to formulate questions, design investigations, execute investigations, interpret data, use evidence to generate explanations, propose alternative explanations, and critique explanations and procedures.

A.3 Use appropriate tools and techniques to gather, analyze, and interpret data. The use of tools and techniques, including mathematics, will be guided by the question asked and the investigations students design. The use of computers for the collection, summary, and display of evidence is part of this standard. Students should be able to access, gather, store, retrieve, and organize data, using hardware and software designed for these purposes.

A.4 Develop descriptions, explanations, predictions, and models using evidence. Students should base their explanation on what they observed, and as they develop cognitive skills, they should be able to differentiate explanation from description—providing causes for effects and establishing relationships based on evidence and logical argument. This standard requires a subject matter knowledge base so the students can effectively conduct investigations, because developing explanations establishes connections between the content of science and the contexts within which students develop new knowledge.

A.5 Think critically and logically to make the relationships between evidence and explanations. Thinking critically about evidence includes deciding what evidence should be used and accounting for anomalous data. Specifically, students should be able to review data from a simple experiment, summarize the data, and form a logical argument about the cause-and-effect relationships in the experiment. Students should begin to state some explanations in terms of the relationship between two or more variables.

A.6 Recognize and analyze alternative explanations and predictions. Students should develop the ability to listen to and respect the explanations proposed by other students. They should remain open to and acknowledge different ideas and explanations, be able to accept the skepticism of others, and consider alternative explanations.

National Science Education Standards

A.7 Communicate scientific procedures and explanations. With practice, students should become competent at communicating experimental methods, following instructions, describing observations, summarizing the results of other groups, and telling other students about investigations and explanations.

A.8 Use mathematics in all aspects of scientific inquiry. Mathematics is essential to asking and answering questions about the natural world. Mathematics can be used to ask questions; to gather, organize, and present data; and to structure convincing explanations.

Understandings about Scientific Inquiry

A.9.a Different kinds of questions suggest different kinds of scientific investigations. Some investigations involve observing and describing objects, organisms, or events; some involve collecting specimens; some involve experiments; some involve seeking more information; some involve discovery of new objects and phenomena; and some involve making models.

A.9.b Current scientific knowledge and understanding guide scientific investigations. Different scientific domains employ different methods, core theories, and standards to advance scientific knowledge and understanding.

A.9.c Mathematics is important in all aspects of scientific inquiry.

A.9.d Technology used to gather data enhances accuracy and allows scientists to analyze and quantify results of investigations.

A.9.e Scientific explanations emphasize evidence, have logically consistent arguments, and use scientific principles, models, and theories. The scientific community accepts and uses such explanations until displaced by better scientific ones. When such displacement occurs, science advances.

A.9.f Science advances through legitimate skepticism. Asking questions and querying other scientists' explanations is part of scientific inquiry. Scientists evaluate the explanations proposed by other scientists by examining evidence, comparing evidence, identifying faulty reasoning, pointing out statements that go beyond the evidence, and suggesting alternative explanations for the same observations.

A.9.g Scientific investigations sometimes result in new ideas and phenomena for study, generate new methods or procedures for an investigation, or develop new technologies to improve the collection of data. All of these results can lead to new investigations.

National Science Education Standards

B. Physical Science

As a result of their activities in grades 5–8, all students should develop an understanding of

Properties and Changes of Properties in Matter

B.1.a   A substance has characteristic properties, such as density, a boiling point, and solubility, all of which are independent of the amount of the sample. A mixture of substances often can be separated into the original substances using one or more of the characteristic properties.

B.1.b   Substances react chemically in characteristic ways with other substances to form new substances (compounds) with different characteristic properties. In chemical reactions, the total mass is conserved. Substances often are placed in categories or groups if they react in similar ways; metals is an example of such a group.

B.1.c   Chemical elements do not break down during normal laboratory reactions involving such treatments as heating, exposure to electric current, or reaction with acids. There are more than 100 known elements that combine in a multitude of ways to produce compounds, which account for the living and nonliving substances that we encounter.

Motions and Forces

B.2.a   The motion of an object can be described by its position, direction of motion, and speed. That motion can be measured and represented on a graph.

B.2.b   An object that is not being subjected to a force will continue to move at a constant speed and in a straight line.

B.2.c   If more than one force acts on an object along a straight line, then the forces will reinforce or cancel one another, depending on their direction and magnitude. Unbalanced forces will cause changes in the speed or direction of an object's motion.

Transfer of Energy

B.3.a   Energy is a property of many substances and is associated with heat, light, electricity, mechanical motion, sound, nuclei, and the nature of a chemical. Energy is transferred in many ways.

B.3.b   Heat moves in predictable ways, flowing from warmer objects to cooler ones, until both reach the same temperature.

B.3.c   Light interacts with matter by transmission (including refraction), absorption, or scattering (including reflection). To see an object, light from that object—emitted by or scattered from it—must enter the eye.

B.3.d   Electrical circuits provide a means of transferring electrical energy when heat, light, sound, and chemical changes are produced.

B.3.e   In most chemical and nuclear reactions, energy is transferred into or out of a system. Heat, light, mechanical motion, or electricity might all be involved in such transfers.

B.3.f   The sun is a major source of energy for changes on the earth's surface. The sun loses energy by emitting light. A tiny fraction of that light reaches the earth, transferring energy from the sun to the earth. The sun's energy arrives as light with a range of wavelengths, consisting of visible light, infrared, and ultraviolet radiation.

National Science Education Standards

C. Life Science

As a result of their activities in grades 5–8, all students should develop understanding of

Structure and Function in Living Systems

C.1.a Living systems at all levels of organization demonstrate the complementary nature of structure and function. Important levels of organization for structure and function include cells, organs, tissues, organ systems, whole organisms, and ecosystems.

C.1.b All organisms are composed of cells—the fundamental unit of life. Most organisms are single cells; other organisms, including humans, are multicellular.

C.1.c Cells carry on the many functions needed to sustain life. They grow and divide, thereby producing more cells. This requires that they take in nutrients, which they use to provide energy for the work that cells do and to make the materials that a cell or an organism needs.

C.1.d Specialized cells perform specialized functions in multicellular organisms. Groups of specialized cells cooperate to form a tissue, such as a muscle. Different tissues are in turn grouped together to form larger functional units, called organs. Each type of cell, tissue, and organ has a distinct structure and set of functions that serve the organism as a whole.

C.1.e The human organism has systems for digestion, respiration, reproduction, circulation, excretion, movement, control, and coordination, and for protection from disease. These systems interact with one another.

C.1.f Disease is a breakdown in structures or functions of an organism. Some diseases are the result of intrinsic failures of the system. Others are the result of damage by infection by other organisms.

Reproduction and Heredity

C.2.a Reproduction is a characteristic of all living systems; because no individual organism lives forever, reproduction is essential to the continuation of every species. Some organisms reproduce asexually. Other organisms reproduce sexually.

C.2.b In many species, including humans, females produce eggs and males produce sperm. Plants also reproduce sexually—the egg and sperm are produced in the flowers of flowering plants. An egg and sperm unite to begin development of a new individual. That new individual receives genetic information from its mother (via the egg) and its father (via the sperm). Sexually produced offspring never are identical to either of their parents.

C.2.c Every organism requires a set of instructions for specifying its traits. Heredity is the passage of these instructions from one generation to another.

C.2.d Hereditary information is contained in genes, located in the chromosomes of each cell. Each gene carries a single unit of information. An inherited trait of an individual can be determined by one or by many genes, and a single gene can influence more than one trait. A human cell contains many thousands of different genes.

C.2.e The characteristics of an organism can be described in terms of a combination of traits. Some traits are inherited and others result from interactions with the environment.

National Science Education Standards

Regulation and Behavior

C.3.a All organisms must be able to obtain and use resources, grow, reproduce, and maintain stable internal conditions while living in a constantly changing external environment.

C.3.b Regulation of an organism's internal environment involves sensing the internal environment and changing physiological activities to keep conditions within the range required to survive.

C.3.c Behavior is one kind of response an organism can make to an internal or environmental stimulus. A behavioral response requires coordination and communication at many levels, including cells, organ systems, and whole organisms. Behavioral response is a set of actions determined in part by heredity and in part from experience.

C.3.d An organism's behavior evolves through adaptation to its environment. How a species moves, obtains food, reproduces, and responds to danger are based in the species' evolutionary history.

Populations and Ecosystems

C.4.a A population consists of all individuals of a species that occur together at a given place and time. All populations living together and the physical factors with which they interact compose an ecosystem.

C.4.b Populations of organisms can be categorized by the function they serve in an ecosystem. Plants and some microorganisms are producers—they make their own food. All animals, including humans, are consumers, which obtain food by eating other organisms. Decomposers, primarily bacteria and fungi, are consumers that use waste materials and dead organisms for food. Food webs identify the relationships among producers, consumers, and decomposers in an ecosystem.

C.4.c For ecosystems, the major source of energy is sunlight. Energy entering ecosystems as sunlight is transferred by producers into chemical energy through photosynthesis. That energy then passes from organism to organism in food webs.

C.4.d The number of organisms an ecosystem can support depends on the resources available and abiotic factors, such as quantity of light and water, range of temperatures, and soil composition. Given adequate biotic and abiotic resources and no disease or predators, populations (including humans) increase at rapid rates. Lack of resources and other factors, such as predation and climate, limit the growth of populations in specific niches in the ecosystem.

Diversity and Adaptations of Organisms

C.5.a Millions of species of animals, plants, and microorganisms are alive today. Although different species might look dissimilar, the unity among organisms becomes apparent from an analysis of internal structures, the similarity of their chemical processes, and the evidence of common ancestry.

C.5.b Biological evolution accounts for the diversity of species developed through gradual processes over many generations. Species acquire many of their unique characteristics through biological adaptation, which involves the selection of naturally occurring variations in populations. Biological adaptations include changes in structures, behaviors, or physiology that enhance survival and reproductive success in a particular environment.

C.5.c Extinction of a species occurs when the environment changes and the adaptive characteristics of a species are insufficient to allow its survival. Fossils indicate that many organisms that lived long ago are extinct. Extinction of species is common; most of the species that have lived on the earth no longer exist.

National Science Education Standards

D. Earth and Space Science

As a result of their activities in grades 5–8, all students should develop an understanding of

Structure of the Earth System

- D.1.a The solid earth is layered with a lithosphere; hot, convecting mantle; and dense, metallic core.

- D.1.b Lithospheric plates on the scales of continents and oceans constantly move at rates of centimeters per year in response to movements in the mantle. Major geological events, such as earthquakes, volcanic eruptions, and mountain building, result from these plate motions.

- D.1.c Land forms are the result of a combination of constructive and destructive forces. Constructive forces include crustal deformation, volcanic eruption, and deposition of sediment, while destructive forces include weathering and erosion.

- D.1.d Some changes in the solid earth can be described as the "rock cycle." Old rocks at the earth's surface weather, forming sediments that are buried, then compacted, heated, and often recrystallized into new rock. Eventually, those new rocks may be brought to the surface by the forces that drive plate motions, and the rock cycle continues.

- D.1.e Soil consists of weathered rocks and decomposed organic material from dead plants, animals, and bacteria. Soils are often found in layers, with each having a different chemical composition and texture.

- D.1.f Water, which covers the majority of the earth's surface, circulates through the crust, oceans, and atmosphere in what is known as the "water cycle." Water evaporates from the earth's surface, rises and cools as it moves to higher elevations, condenses as rain or snow, and falls to the surface where it collects in lakes, oceans, soil, and in rocks underground.

- D.1.g Water is a solvent. As it passes through the water cycle it dissolves minerals and gases and carries them to the oceans.

- D.1.h The atmosphere is a mixture of nitrogen, oxygen, and trace gases that include water vapor. The atmosphere has different properties at different elevations.

- D.1.i Clouds, formed by the condensation of water vapor, affect weather and climate.

- D.1.j Global patterns of atmospheric movement influence local weather. Oceans have a major effect on climate, because water in the oceans holds a large amount of heat.

- D.1.k Living organisms have played many roles in the earth system, including affecting the composition of the atmosphere, producing some types of rocks, and contributing to the weathering of rocks.

Earth's History

- D.2.a The earth processes we see today, including erosion, movement of lithospheric plates, and changes in atmospheric composition, are similar to those that occurred in the past. Earth history is also influenced by occasional catastrophes, such as the impact of an asteroid or comet.

- D.2.b Fossils provide important evidence of how life and environmental conditions have changed.

National Science Education Standards

Earth in the Solar System

D.3.a   The earth is the third planet from the sun in a system that includes the moon, the sun, eight other planets and their moons, and smaller objects, such as asteroids and comets. The sun, an average star, is the central and largest body in the solar system.

D.3.b   Most objects in the solar system are in regular and predictable motion. Those motions explain such phenomena as the day, the year, phases of the moon, and eclipses.

D.3.c   Gravity is the force that keeps planets in orbit around the sun and governs the rest of the motion in the solar system. Gravity alone holds us to the earth's surface and explains the phenomena of the tides.

D.3.d   The sun is the major source of energy for phenomena on the earth's surface, such as growth of plants, winds, ocean currents, and the water cycle. Seasons result from variations in the amount of the sun's energy hitting the surface, due to the tilt of the earth's rotation on its axis and the length of the day.

E. Science and Technology

As a result of activities in grades 5–8, all students should develop

Abilities of Technological Design

E.1   Identify appropriate problems for technological design. Students should develop their abilities by identifying a specified need, considering its various aspects, and talking to different potential users or beneficiaries. They should appreciate that for some needs, the cultural backgrounds and beliefs of different groups can affect the criteria for a suitable product.

E.2   Design a solution or product. Students should make and compare different proposals in the light of the criteria they have selected. They must consider constraints—such as cost, time, trade-offs, and materials needed—and communicate ideas with drawings and simple models.

E.3   Implement a proposed design. Students should organize materials and other resources, plan their work, make good use of group collaboration where appropriate, choose suitable tools and techniques, and work with appropriate measurement methods to ensure adequate accuracy.

E.4   Evaluate completed technological designs or products. Students should use criteria relevant to the original purpose or need, consider a variety of factors that might affect acceptability and suitability for intended users or beneficiaries, and develop measures of quality with respect to such criteria and factors; they should also suggest improvements and, for their own products, try proposed modifications.

E.5   Communicate the process of technological design. Students should review and describe any completed piece of work and identify the stages of problem identification, solution design, implementation, and evaluation.

National Science Education Standards

Understandings about Science and Technology

E.6.a Scientific inquiry and technological design have similarities and differences. Scientists propose explanations for questions about the natural world, and engineers propose solutions relating to human problems, needs, and aspirations. Technological solutions are temporary; technologies exist within nature and so they cannot contravene physical or biological principles; technological solutions have side effects; and technologies cost, carry risks, and provide benefits.

E.6.b Many different people in different cultures have made and continue to make contributions to science and technology.

E.6.c Science and technology are reciprocal. Science helps drive technology, as it addresses questions that demand more sophisticated instruments and provides principles for better instrumentation and technique. Technology is essential to science, because it provides instruments and techniques that enable observations of objects and phenomena that are otherwise unobservable due to factors such as quantity, distance, location, size, and speed. Technology also provides tools for investigations, inquiry, and analysis.

E.6.d Perfectly designed solutions do not exist. All technological solutions have trade-offs, such as safety, cost, efficiency, and appearance. Engineers often build in back-up systems to provide safety. Risk is part of living in a highly technological world. Reducing risk often results in new technology.

E.6.e Technological designs have constraints. Some constraints are unavoidable, for example, properties of materials, or effects of weather and friction; other constraints limit choices in the design, for example, environmental protection, human safety, and aesthetics.

E.6.f Technological solutions have intended benefits and unintended consequences. Some consequences can be predicted, others cannot.

F. Science in Personal and Social Perspectives

As a result of activities in grades 5–8, all students should develop understanding of

Personal Health

F.1.a Regular exercise is important to the maintenance and improvement of health. The benefits of physical fitness include maintaining healthy weight, having energy and strength for routine activities, good muscle tone, bone strength, strong heart/lung systems, and improved mental health. Personal exercise, especially developing cardiovascular endurance, is the foundation of physical fitness.

F.1.b The potential for accidents and the existence of hazards imposes the need for injury prevention. Safe living involves the development and use of safety precautions and the recognition of risk in personal decisions. Injury prevention has personal and social dimensions.

F.1.c The use of tobacco increases the risk of illness. Students should understand the influence of short-term social and psychological factors that lead to tobacco use, and the possible long-term detrimental effects of smoking and chewing tobacco.

F.1.d Alcohol and other drugs are often abused substances. Such drugs change how the body functions and can lead to addiction.

F.1.e Food provides energy and nutrients for growth and development. Nutrition requirements vary with body weight, age, sex, activity, and body functioning.

National Science Education Standards

F.1.f   Sex drive is a natural human function that requires understanding. Sex is also a prominent means of transmitting diseases. The diseases can be prevented through a variety of precautions.

F.1.g   Natural environments may contain substances (for example, radon and lead) that are harmful to human beings. Maintaining environmental health involves establishing or monitoring quality standards related to use of soil, water, and air.

Populations, Resources, and Environments

F.2.a   When an area becomes overpopulated, the environment will become degraded due to the increased use of resources.

F.2.b   Causes of environmental degradation and resource depletion vary from region to region and from country to country.

Natural Hazards

F.3.a   Internal and external processes of the earth system cause natural hazards, events that change or destroy human and wildlife habitats, damage property, and harm or kill humans. Natural hazards include earthquakes, landslides, wildfires, volcanic eruptions, floods, storms, and even possible impacts of asteroids.

F.3.b   Human activities also can induce hazards through resource acquisition, urban growth, land-use decisions, and waste disposal. Such activities can accelerate many natural changes.

F.3.c   Natural hazards can present personal and societal challenges because misidentifying the change or incorrectly estimating the rate and scale of change may result in either too little attention and significant human costs or too much cost for unneeded preventive measures.

Risks and Benefits

F.4.a   Risk analysis considers the type of hazard and estimates the number of people that might be exposed and the number likely to suffer consequences. The results are used to determine the options for reducing or eliminating risks.

F.4.b   Students should understand the risks associated with natural hazards (fires, floods, tornadoes, hurricanes, earthquakes, and volcanic eruptions), with chemical hazards (pollutants in air, water, soil, and food), with biological hazards (pollen, viruses, bacterial, and parasites), social hazards (occupational safety and transportation), and with personal hazards (smoking, dieting, and drinking).

F.4.c   Individuals can use a systematic approach to thinking critically about risks and benefits. Examples include applying probability estimates to risks and comparing them to estimated personal and social benefits.

F.4.d   Important personal and social decisions are made based on perceptions of benefits and risks.

> **National Science Education Standards**

Science and Technology in Society

F.5.a Science influences society through its knowledge and world view. Scientific knowledge and the procedures used by scientists influence the way many individuals in society think about themselves, others, and the environment. The effect of science on society is neither entirely beneficial nor entirely detrimental.

F.5.b Societal challenges often inspire questions for scientific research, and social priorities often influence research priorities through the availability of funding for research.

F.5.c Technology influences society through its products and processes. Technology influences the quality of life and the ways people act and interact. Technological changes are often accompanied by social, political, and economic changes that can be beneficial or detrimental to individuals and to society. Social needs, attitudes, and values influence the direction of technological development.

F.5.d Science and technology have advanced through contributions of many different people, in different cultures, at different times in history. Science and technology have contributed enormously to economic growth and productivity among societies and groups within societies.

F.5.e Scientists and engineers work in many different settings, including colleges and universities, businesses and industries, specific research institutes, and government agencies.

F.5.f Scientists and engineers have ethical codes requiring that human subjects involved with research be fully informed about risks and benefits associated with the research before the individuals choose to participate. This ethic extends to potential risks to communities and property. In short, prior knowledge and consent are required for research involving human subjects or potential damage to property.

F.5.g Science cannot answer all questions and technology cannot solve all human problems or meet all human needs. Students should understand the difference between scientific and other questions. They should appreciate what science and technology can reasonably contribute to society and what they cannot do. For example, new technologies often will decrease some risks and increase others.

G. History and Nature of Science

As a result of activities in grades 5–8, all students should develop understanding of

Science as a Human Endeavor

G.1.a Women and men of various social and ethnic backgrounds—and with diverse interests, talents, qualities, and motivations—engage in the activities of science, engineering, and related fields such as the health professions. Some scientists work in teams, and some work alone, but all communicate extensively with others.

G.1.b Science requires different abilities, depending on such factors as the field of study and type of inquiry. Science is very much a human endeavor, and the work of science relies on basic human qualities, such as reasoning, insight, energy, skill, and creativity—as well as on scientific habits of mind, such as intellectual honesty, tolerance of ambiguity, skepticism, and openness to new ideas.

National Science Education Standards

Nature of Science

G.2.a Scientists formulate and test their explanations of nature using observation, experiments, and theoretical and mathematical models. Although all scientific ideas are tentative and subject to change and improvement in principle, for most major ideas in science, there is much experimental and observational confirmation. Those ideas are not likely to change greatly in the future. Scientists do and have changed their ideas about nature when they encounter new experimental evidence that does not match their existing explanations.

G.2.b In areas where active research is being pursued and in which there is not a great deal of experimental or observational evidence and understanding, it is normal for scientists to differ with one another about the interpretation of the evidence or theory being considered. Different scientists might publish conflicting experimental results or might draw different conclusions from the same data. Ideally, scientists acknowledge such conflict and work towards finding evidence that will resolve their disagreement.

G.2.c It is part of scientific inquiry to evaluate the results of scientific investigations, experiments, observations, theoretical models, and the explanations proposed by other scientists. Evaluation includes reviewing the experimental procedures, examining the evidence, identifying faulty reasoning, pointing out statements that go beyond the evidence, and suggesting alternative explanations for the same observations. Although scientists may disagree about explanations of phenomena, about interpretations of data, or about the value of rival theories, they do agree that questioning, response to criticism, and open communication are integral to the process of science. As scientific knowledge evolves, major disagreements are eventually resolved through such interactions between scientists.

History of Science

G.3.a Many individuals have contributed to the traditions of science. Studying some of these individuals provides further understanding of scientific inquiry, science as a human endeavor, the nature of science, and the relationships between science and society.

G.3.b In historical perspective, science has been practiced by different individuals in different cultures. In looking at the history of many peoples, one finds that scientists and engineers of high achievement are considered to be among the most valued contributors to their culture.

G.3.c Tracing the history of science can show how difficult it was for scientific innovators to break through the accepted ideas of their time to reach the conclusions that we currently take for granted.

Project 2061
Benchmarks for Science Literacy

1. The Nature of Science

By the end of the 8th grade, students should know that

1.A The Scientific World View

1.A.1 When similar investigations give different results, the scientific challenge is to judge whether the differences are trivial or significant, and it often takes further studies to decide. Even with similar results, scientists may wait until an investigation has been repeated many times before accepting the results as correct.

1.A.2 Scientific knowledge is subject to modification as new information challenges prevailing theories and as a new theory leads to looking at old observations in a new way.

1.A.3 Some scientific knowledge is very old and yet is still applicable today.

1.A.4 Some matters cannot be examined usefully in a scientific way. Among them are matters that by their nature cannot be tested objectively and those that are essentially matters of morality. Science can sometimes be used to inform ethical decisions by identifying the likely consequences of particular actions but cannot be used to establish that some action is either moral or immoral.

1.B Scientific Inquiry

1.B.1 Scientists differ greatly in what phenomena they study and how they go about their work. Although there is no fixed set of steps that all scientists follow, scientific investigations usually involve the collection of relevant evidence, the use of logical reasoning, and the application of imagination in devising hypotheses and explanations to make sense of the collected evidence.

1.B.2 If more than one variable changes at the same time in an experiment, the outcome of the experiment may not be clearly attributable to any one of the variables. It may not always be possible to prevent outside variables from influencing the outcome of an investigation (or even to identify all of the variables), but collaboration among investigators can often lead to research designs that are able to deal with such situations.

1.B.3 What people expect to observe often affects what they actually do observe. Strong beliefs about what should happen in particular circumstances can prevent them from detecting other results. Scientists know about this danger to objectivity and take steps to try and avoid it when designing investigations and examining data. One safeguard is to have different investigators conduct independent studies of the same questions.

Project 2061 Benchmarks

1.C The Scientific Enterprise

1.C.1 Important contributions to the advancement of science, mathematics, and technology have been made by different kinds of people, in different cultures, at different times.

1.C.2 Until recently, women and racial minorities, because of restrictions on their education and employment opportunities, were essentially left out of much of the formal work of the science establishment; the remarkable few who overcame those obstacles were even then likely to have their work disregarded by the science establishment.

1.C.3 No matter who does science and mathematics or invents things, or when or where they do it, the knowledge and technology that result can eventually become available to everyone in the world.

1.C.4 Scientists are employed by colleges and universities, business and industry, hospitals, and many government agencies. Their places of work include offices, classrooms, laboratories, farms, factories, and natural field settings ranging from space to the ocean floor.

1.C.5 In research involving human subjects, the ethics of science require that potential subjects be fully informed about the risks and benefits associated with the research and of their right to refuse to participate. Science ethics also demand that scientists must not knowingly subject coworkers, students, the neighborhood, or the community to health or property risks without their prior knowledge and consent. Because animals cannot make informed choices, special care must be taken in using them in scientific research.

1.C.6 Computers have become invaluable in science because they speed up and extend people's ability to collect, store, compile, and analyze data, prepare research reports, and share data and ideas with investigators all over the world.

1.C.7 Accurate record-keeping, openness, and replication are essential for maintaining an investigator's credibility with other scientists and society.

3. The Nature of Technology

By the end of the 8th grade, students should know that

3.A Technology and Science

3.A.1 In earlier times, the accumulated information and techniques of each generation of workers were taught on the job directly to the next generation of workers. Today, the knowledge base for technology can be found as well in libraries of print and electronic resources and is often taught in the classroom.

3.A.2 Technology is essential to science for such purposes as access to outer space and other remote locations, sample collection and treatment, measurement, data collection and storage, computation, and communication of information.

3.A.3 Engineers, architects, and others who engage in design and technology use scientific knowledge to solve practical problems. But they usually have to take human values and limitations into account as well.

Project 2061 Benchmarks

3.B Design and Systems

3.B.1   Design usually requires taking constraints into account. Some constraints, such as gravity or the properties of the materials to be used, are unavoidable. Other constraints, including economic, political, social, ethical, and aesthetic ones, limit choices.

3.B.2   All technologies have effects other than those intended by the design, some of which may have been predictable and some not. In either case, these side effects may turn out to be unacceptable to some of the population and therefore lead to conflict between groups.

3.B.3   Almost all control systems have inputs, outputs, and feedback. The essence of control is comparing information about what is happening to what people want to happen and then making appropriate adjustments. This procedure requires sensing information, processing it, and making changes. In almost all modern machines, microprocessors serve as centers of performance control.

3.B.4   Systems fail because they have faulty or poorly matched parts, are used in ways that exceed what was intended by the design, or were poorly designed to begin with. The most common ways to prevent failure are pretesting parts and procedures, overdesign, and redundancy.

3.C Issues in Technology

3.C.1   The human ability to shape the future comes from a capacity for generating knowledge and developing new technologies—and for communicating ideas to others.

3.C.2   Technology cannot always provide successful solutions for problems or fulfill every human need.

3.C.3   Throughout history, people have carried out impressive technological feats, some of which would be hard to duplicate today even with modern tools. The purposes served by these achievements have sometimes been practical, sometimes ceremonial.

3.C.4   Technology has strongly influenced the course of history and continues to do so. It is largely responsible for the great revolutions in agriculture, manufacturing, sanitation and medicine, warfare, transportation, information processing, and communications that have radically changed how people live.

3.C.5   New technologies increase some risks and decrease others. Some of the same technologies that have improved the length and quality of life for many people have also brought new risks.

3.C.6   Rarely are technology issues simple and one-sided. Relevant facts alone, even when known and available, usually do not settle matters entirely in favor of one side or another. That is because the contending groups may have different values and priorities. They may stand to gain or lose in different degrees, or may make very different predictions about what the future consequences of the proposed action will be.

3.C.7   Societies influence what aspects of technology are developed and how these are used. People control technology (as well as science) and are responsible for its effects.

Project 2061 Benchmarks

4. The Physical Setting

By the end of the 8th grade, students should know that

4.A The Universe

4.A.1 The sun is a medium-sized star located near the edge of a disk-shaped galaxy of stars, part of which can be seen as a glowing band of light that spans the sky on a very clear night. The universe contains many billions of galaxies, and each galaxy contains many billions of stars. To the naked eye, even the closest of these galaxies is no more than a dim, fuzzy spot.

4.A.2 The sun is many thousands of times closer to the earth than any other star. Light from the sun takes a few minutes to reach the earth, but light from the next nearest star takes a few years to arrive. The trip to that star would take the fastest rocket thousands of years. Some distant galaxies are so far away that their light takes several billion years to reach the earth. People on earth, therefore, see them as they were that long ago in the past.

4.A.3 Nine planets of very different size, composition, and surface features move around the sun in nearly circular orbits. Some planets have a great variety of moons and even flat rings of rock and ice particles orbiting around them. Some of these planets and moons show evidence of geologic activity. The earth is orbited by one moon, many artificial satellites, and debris.

4.A.4 Large numbers of chunks of rock orbit the sun. Some of those that the earth meets in its yearly orbit around the sun glow and disintegrate from friction as they plunge through the atmosphere—and sometimes impact the ground. Other chunks of rocks mixed with ice have long, off-center orbits that carry them close to the sun, where the sun's radiation (of light and particles) boils off frozen material from their surfaces and pushes it into a long, illuminated tail.

4.B The Earth

4.B.1 We live on a relatively small planet, the third from the sun in the only system of planets definitely known to exist (although other, similar systems may be discovered in the universe).

4.B.2 The earth is mostly rock. Three-fourths of its surface is covered by a relatively thin layer of water (some of it frozen), and the entire planet is surrounded by a relatively thin blanket of air. It is the only body in the solar system that appears able to support life. The other planets have compositions and conditions very different from the earth's.

4.B.3 Everything on or anywhere near the earth is pulled toward the earth's center by gravitational force.

4.B.4 Because the earth turns daily on an axis that is tilted relative to the plane of the earth's yearly orbit around the sun, sunlight falls more intensely on different parts of the earth during the year. The difference in heating of the earth's surface produces the planet's seasons and weather patterns.

4.B.5 The moon's orbit around the earth once in about 28 days changes what part of the moon is lighted by the sun and how much of that part can be seen from the earth—the phases of the moon.

4.B.6 Climates have sometimes changed abruptly in the past as a result of changes in the earth's crust, such as volcanic eruptions or impacts of huge rocks from space. Even relatively small changes in atmospheric or ocean content can have widespread effects on climate if the change lasts long enough.

Project 2061 Benchmarks

4.B.7   The cycling of water in and out of the atmosphere plays an important role in determining climatic patterns. Water evaporates from the surface of the earth, rises and cools, condenses into rain or snow, and falls again to the surface. The water falling on land collects in rivers and lakes, soil, and porous layers of rock, and much of it flows back into the ocean.

4.B.8   Fresh water, limited in supply, is essential for life and also for most industrial processes. Rivers, lakes, and groundwater can be depleted or polluted, becoming unavailable or unsuitable for life.

4.B.9   Heat energy carried by ocean currents has a strong influence on climate around the world.

4.B.10 Some minerals are very rare and some exist in great quantities, but—for practical purposes—the ability to recover them is just as important as their abundance. As minerals are depleted, obtaining them becomes more difficult. Recycling and the development of substitutes can reduce the rate of depletion but may also be costly.

4.B.11 The benefits of the earth's resources—such as fresh water, air, soil, and trees—can be reduced by using them wastefully or by deliberately or inadvertently destroying them. The atmosphere and the oceans have a limited capacity to absorb wastes and recycle materials naturally. Cleaning up polluted air, water, or soil or restoring depleted soil, forests, or fishing grounds can be very difficult and costly.

4.C Processes that Shape the Earth

4.C.1   The interior of the earth is hot. Heat flow and movement of material within the earth cause earthquakes and volcanic eruptions and create mountains and ocean basins. Gas and dust from large volcanoes can change the atmosphere.

4.C.2   Some changes in the earth's surface are abrupt (such as earthquakes and volcanic eruptions) while other changes happen very slowly (such as uplift and wearing down of mountains). The earth's surface is shaped in part by the motion of water and wind over very long times, which act to level mountain ranges.

4.C.3   Sediments of sand and smaller particles (sometimes containing the remains of organisms) are gradually buried and are cemented together by dissolved minerals to form solid rock again.

4.C.4   Sedimentary rock buried deep enough may be reformed by pressure and heat, perhaps melting and recrystallizing into different kinds of rock. These re-formed rock layers may be forced up again to become land surface and even mountains. Subsequently, this new rock too will erode. Rock bears evidence of the minerals, temperatures, and forces that created it.

4.C.5   Thousands of layers of sedimentary rock confirm the long history of the changing surface of the earth and the changing life forms whose remains are found in successive layers. The youngest layers are not always found on top, because of folding, breaking, and uplift of layers.

4.C.6   Although weathered rock is the basic component of soil, the composition and texture of soil and its fertility and resistance to erosion are greatly influenced by plant roots and debris, bacteria, fungi, worms, insects, rodents, and other organisms.

4.C.7   Human activities, such as reducing the amount of forest cover, increasing the amount and variety of chemicals released into the atmosphere, and intensive farming, have changed the earth's land, oceans, and atmosphere. Some of these changes have decreased the capacity of the environment to support some life forms.

Project 2061 Benchmarks

4.D Structure of Matter

4.D.1   All matter is made up of atoms, which are far too small to see directly through a microscope. The atoms of any element are alike but are different from atoms of other elements. Atoms may stick together in well-defined molecules or may be packed together in large arrays. Different arrangements of atoms into groups compose all substances.

4.D.2   Equal volumes of different substances usually have different weights.

4.D.3   Atoms and molecules are perpetually in motion. Increased temperature means greater average energy, so most substances expand when heated. In solids, the atoms are closely locked in position and can only vibrate. In liquids, the atoms or molecules have higher energy, are more loosely connected, and can slide past one another; some molecules may get enough energy to escape into a gas. In gases, the atoms or molecules have still more energy and are free of one another except during occasional collisions.

4.D.4   The temperature and acidity of a solution influence reaction rates. Many substances dissolve in water, which may greatly facilitate reactions between them.

4.D.5   Scientific ideas about elements were borrowed from some Greek philosophers of 2,000 years earlier, who believed that everything was made from four basic substances: air, earth, fire, and water. It was the combinations of these "elements" in different proportions that gave other substances their observable properties. The Greeks were wrong about those four, but now over 100 different elements have been identified, some rare and some plentiful, out of which everything is made. Because most elements tend to combine with others, few elements are found in their pure form.

4.D.6   There are groups of elements that have similar properties, including highly reactive metals, less-reactive metals, highly reactive nonmetals (such as chlorine, fluorine, and oxygen), and some almost completely nonreactive gases (such as helium and neon). An especially important kind of reaction between substances involves combination of oxygen with something else—as in burning or rusting. Some elements don't fit into any of the categories; among them are carbon and hydrogen, essential elements of living matter.

4.D.7   No matter how substances within a closed system interact with one another, or how they combine or break apart, the total weight of the system remains the same. The idea of atoms explains the conservation of matter: If the number of atoms stays the same no matter how they are rearranged, then their total mass stays the same.

4.E Energy Transformations

4.E.1   Energy cannot be created or destroyed, but only changed from one form into another.

4.E.2   Most of what goes on in the universe—from exploding stars and biological growth to the operation of machines and the motion of people—involves some form of energy being transformed into another. Energy in the form of heat is almost always one of the products of an energy transformation.

4.E.3   Heat can be transferred through materials by the collisions of atoms or across space by radiation. If the material is fluid, currents will be set up in it that aid the transfer of heat.

4.E.4   Energy appears in different forms. Heat energy is in the disorderly motion of molecules; chemical energy is in the arrangement of atoms; mechanical energy is in moving bodies or in elastically distorted shapes; gravitational energy is in the separation of mutually attracting masses.

Project 2061 Benchmarks

4.F Motion

4.F.1   Light from the sun is made up of a mixture of many different colors of light, even though to the eye the light looks almost white. Other things that give off or reflect light have a different mix of colors.

4.F.2   Something can be "seen" when light waves emitted or reflected by it enter the eye—just as something can be "heard" when sound waves from it enter the ear.

4.F.3   An unbalanced force acting on an object changes its speed or direction of motion, or both. If the force acts toward a single center, the object's path may curve into an orbit around the center.

4.F.4   Vibrations in materials set up wavelike disturbances that spread away from the source. Sound and earthquake waves are examples. These and other waves move at different speeds in different materials.

4.F.5   Human eyes respond to only a narrow range of wavelengths of electromagnetic radiation—visible light. Differences of wavelength within that range are perceived as differences in color.

4.G Forces of Nature

4.G.1   Every object exerts gravitational force on every other object. The force depends on how much mass the objects have and on how far apart they are. The force is hard to detect unless at least one of the objects has a lot of mass.

4.G.2   The sun's gravitational pull holds the earth and other planets in their orbits, just as the planets' gravitational pull keeps their moons in orbit around them.

4.G.3   Electric currents and magnets can exert a force on each other.

Project 2061 Benchmarks

5. The Living Environment

By the end of the 8th grade, students should know that

5.A Diversity of Life

5.A.1 One of the most general distinctions among organisms is between plants, which use sunlight to make their own food, and animals, which consume energy-rich foods. Some kinds of organisms, many of them microscopic, cannot be neatly classified as either plants or animals.

5.A.2 Animals and plants have a great variety of body plans and internal structures that contribute to their being able to make or find food and reproduce.

5.A.3 Similarities among organisms are found in internal anatomical features, which can be used to infer the degree of relatedness among organisms. In classifying organisms, biologists consider details of internal and external structures to be more important than behavior or general appearance.

5.A.4 For sexually reproducing organisms, a species comprises all organisms that can mate with one another to produce fertile offspring.

5.A.5 All organisms, including the human species, are part of and depend on two main interconnected global food webs. One includes microscopic ocean plants, the animals that feed on them, and finally the animals that feed on those animals. The other web includes land plants, the animals that feed on them, and so forth. The cycles continue indefinitely because organisms decompose after death to return food material to the environment.

5.B Heredity

5.B.1 In some kinds of organisms, all the genes come from a single parent, whereas in organisms that have sexes, typically half of the genes come from each parent.

5.B.2 In sexual reproduction, a single specialized cell from a female merges with a specialized cell from a male. As the fertilized egg, carrying genetic information from each parent, multiplies to form the complete organism with about a trillion cells, the same genetic information is copied in each cell.

5.B.3 New varieties of cultivated plants and domestic animals have resulted from selective breeding for particular traits.

5.C Cells

5.C.1 All living things are composed of cells, from just one to many millions, whose details usually are visible only through a microscope. Different body tissues and organs are made up of different kinds of cells. The cells in similar tissues and organs in other animals are similar to those in human beings but differ somewhat from cells found in plants.

5.C.2 Cells repeatedly divide to make more cells for growth and repair. Various organs and tissues function to serve the needs of cells for food, air, and waste removal.

5.C.3 Within cells, many of the basic functions of organisms—such as extracting energy from food and getting rid of waste—are carried out. The way in which cells function is similar in all living organisms.

5.C.4 About two-thirds of the weight of cells is accounted for by water, which gives cells many of their properties.

Project 2061 Benchmarks

5.D Interdependence of Life

5.D.1 In all environments—freshwater, marine, forest, desert, grassland, mountain, and others—organisms with similar needs may compete with one another for resources, including food, space, water, air, and shelter. In any particular environment, the growth and survival of organisms depend on the physical conditions.

5.D.2 Two types of organisms may interact with one another in several ways: They may be in a producer/consumer, predator/prey, or parasite/host relationship. Or one organism may scavenge or decompose another. Relationships may be competitive or mutually beneficial. Some species have become so adapted to each other that neither could survive without the other.

5.E Flow of Matter and Energy

5.E.1 Food provides molecules that serve as fuel and building material for all organisms. Plants use the energy in light to make sugars out of carbon dioxide and water. This food can be used immediately for fuel or materials or it may be stored for later use. Organisms that eat plants break down the plant structures to produce the materials and energy they need to survive. Then they are consumed by other organisms.

5.E.2 Over a long time, matter is transferred from one organism to another repeatedly and between organisms and their physical environment. As in all material systems, the total amount of matter remains constant, even though its form and location change.

5.E.3 Energy can change from one form to another in living things. Animals get energy from oxidizing their food, releasing some of its energy as heat. Almost all food energy comes originally from sunlight.

5.F Evolution of Life

5.F.1 Small differences between parents and offspring can accumulate (through selective breeding) in successive generations so that descendants are very different from their ancestors.

5.F.2 Individual organisms with certain traits are more likely than others to survive and have offspring. Changes in environmental conditions can affect the survival of individual organisms and entire species.

5.F.3 Many thousands of layers of sedimentary rock provide evidence for the long history of the earth and for the long history of changing life forms whose remains are found in the rocks. More recently deposited rock layers are more likely to contain fossils resembling existing species.

Project 2061 Benchmarks

6. The Human Organism

By the end of the 8th grade, students should know that

6.A Human Identity

6.A.1   Like other animals, human beings have body systems for obtaining and providing energy, defense, reproduction, and the coordination of body functions.

6.A.2   Human beings have many similarities and differences. The similarities make it possible for human beings to reproduce and to donate blood and organs to one another throughout the world. Their differences enable them to create diverse social and cultural arrangements and to solve problems in a variety of ways.

6.A.3   Fossil evidence is consistent with the idea that human beings evolved from earlier species.

6.A.4   Specialized roles of individuals within other species are genetically programmed, whereas human beings are able to invent and modify a wider range of social behavior.

6.A.5   Human beings use technology to match or excel many of the abilities of other species. Technology has helped people with disabilities survive and live more conventional lives.

6.A.6   Technologies having to do with food production, sanitation, and disease prevention have dramatically changed how people live and work and have resulted in rapid increases in the human population.

6.B Human Development

6.B.1   Fertilization occurs when sperm cells from a male's testes are deposited near an egg cell from the female ovary, and one of the sperm cells enters the egg cell. Most of the time, by chance or design, a sperm never arrives or an egg isn't available.

6.B.2   Contraception measures may incapacitate sperm, block their way to the egg, prevent the release of eggs, or prevent the fertilized egg from implanting successfully.

6.B.3   Following fertilization, cell division produces a small cluster of cells that then differentiate by appearance and function to form the basic tissues of an embryo. During the first three months of pregnancy, organs begin to form. During the second three months, all organs and body features develop. During the last three months, the organs and features mature enough to function well after birth. Patterns of human development are similar to those of other vertebrates.

6.B.4   The developing embryo—and later the newborn infant—encounters many risks from faults in its genes, its mother's inadequate diet, her cigarette smoking or use of alcohol or other drugs, or from infection. Inadequate child care may lead to lower physical and mental ability.

6.B.5   Various body changes occur as adults age. Muscles and joints become less flexible, bones and muscles lose mass, energy levels diminish, and the senses become less acute. Women stop releasing eggs and hence can no longer reproduce. The length and quality of human life are influenced by many factors, including sanitation, diet, medical care, sex, genes, environmental conditions, and personal health behaviors.

Project 2061 Benchmarks

6.C Basic Functions

6.C.1 Organs and organ systems are composed of cells and help to provide all cells with basic needs.

6.C.2 For the body to use food for energy and building materials, the food must first be digested into molecules that are absorbed and transported to cells.

6.C.3 To burn food for the release of energy stored in it, oxygen must be supplied to cells, and carbon dioxide removed. Lungs take in oxygen for the combustion of food and they eliminate the carbon dioxide produced. The urinary system disposes of dissolved waste molecules, the intestinal tract removes solid wastes, and the skin and lungs rid the body of heat energy. The circulatory system moves all these substances to or from cells where they are needed or produced, responding to changing demands.

6.C.4 Specialized cells and the molecules they produce identify and destroy microbes that get inside the body.

6.C.5 Hormones are chemicals from glands that affect other body parts. They are involved in helping the body respond to danger and in regulating human growth, development, and reproduction.

6.C.6 Interactions among the senses, nerves, and brain make possible the learning that enables human beings to cope with changes in their environment.

6.D Learning

6.D.1 Some animal species are limited to a repertoire of genetically determined behaviors; others have more complex brains and can learn a wide variety of behaviors. All behavior is affected by both inheritance and experience.

6.D.2 The level of skill a person can reach in any particular activity depends on innate abilities, the amount of practice, and the use of appropriate learning technologies.

6.D.3 Human beings can detect a tremendous range of visual and olfactory stimuli. The strongest stimulus they can tolerate may be more than a trillion times as intense as the weakest they can detect. Still, there are many kinds of signals in the world that people cannot detect directly.

6.D.4 Attending closely to any one input of information usually reduces the ability to attend to others at the same time.

6.D.5 Learning often results from two perceptions or actions occurring at about the same time. The more often the same combination occurs, the stronger the mental connection between them is likely to be. Occasionally a single vivid experience will connect two things permanently in people's minds.

6.D.6 Language and tools enable human beings to learn complicated and varied things from others.

Project 2061 Benchmarks

6.E Physical Health

6.E.1 The amount of food energy (calories) a person requires varies with body weight, age, sex, activity level, and natural body efficiency. Regular exercise is important to maintain a healthy heart/lung system, good muscle tone, and bone strength.

6.E.2 Toxic substances, some dietary habits, and personal behavior may be bad for one's health. Some effects show up right away, others may not show up for many years. Avoiding toxic substances, such as tobacco, and changing dietary habits to reduce the intake of such things as animal fat increases the chances of living longer.

6.E.3 Viruses, bacteria, fungi, and parasites may infect the human body and interfere with normal body functions. A person can catch a cold many times because there are many varieties of cold viruses that cause similar symptoms.

6.E.4 White blood cells engulf invaders or produce antibodies that attack them or mark them for killing by other white cells. The antibodies produced will remain and can fight off subsequent invaders of the same kind.

6.E.5 The environment may contain dangerous levels of substances that are harmful to human beings. Therefore, the good health of individuals requires monitoring the soil, air, and water and taking steps to keep them safe.

6.F Mental Health

6.F.1 Individuals differ greatly in their ability to cope with stressful situations. Both external and internal conditions (chemistry, personal history, values) influence how people behave.

6.F.2 Often people react to mental distress by denying that they have any problem. Sometimes they don't know why they feel the way they do, but with help they can sometimes uncover the reasons.

8. The Designed World

By the end of the 8th grade, students should know that

8.A Agriculture

8.A.1 Early in human history, there was an agricultural revolution in which people changed from hunting and gathering to farming. This allowed changes in the division of labor between men and women and between children and adults, and the development of new patterns of government.

8.A.2 People control the characteristics of plants and animals they raise by selective breeding and by preserving varieties of seeds (old and new) to use if growing conditions change.

8.A.3 In agriculture, as in all technologies, there are always trade-offs to be made. Getting food from many different places makes people less dependent on weather in any one place, yet more dependent on transportation and communication among far-flung markets. Specializing in one crop may risk disaster if changes in weather or increases in pest populations wipe out that crop. Also, the soil may be exhausted of some nutrients, which can be replenished by rotating the right crops.

8.A.4 Many people work to bring food, fiber, and fuel to U.S. markets. With improved technology, only a small fraction of workers in the United States actually plant and harvest the products that people use. Most workers are engaged in processing, packaging, transporting, and selling what is produced.

Project 2061 Benchmarks

8.B Materials and Manufacturing

8.B.1 The choice of materials for a job depends on their properties and on how they interact with other materials. Similarly, the usefulness of some manufactured parts of an object depends on how well they fit together with the other parts.

8.B.2 Manufacturing usually involves a series of steps, such as designing a product, obtaining and preparing raw materials, processing the materials mechanically or chemically, and assembling, testing, inspecting, and packaging. The sequence of these steps is also often important.

8.B.3 Modern technology reduces manufacturing costs, produces more uniform products, and creates new synthetic materials that can help reduce the depletion of some natural resources.

8.B.4 Automation, including the use of robots, has changed the nature of work in most fields, including manufacturing. As a result, high-skill, high-knowledge jobs in engineering, computer programming, quality control, supervision, and maintenance are replacing many routine, manual-labor jobs. Workers therefore need better learning skills and flexibility to take on new and rapidly changing jobs.

8.C Energy Sources and Use

8.C.1 Energy can change from one form to another, although in the process some energy is always converted to heat. Some systems transform energy with less loss of heat than others.

8.C.2 Different ways of obtaining, transforming, and distributing energy have different environmental consequences.

8.C.3 In many instances, manufacturing and other technological activities are performed at a site close to an energy source. Some forms of energy are transported easily, others are not.

8.C.4 Electrical energy can be produced from a variety of energy sources and can be transformed into almost any other form of energy. Moreover, electricity is used to distribute energy quickly and conveniently to distant locations.

8.C.5 Energy from the sun (and the wind and water energy derived from it) is available indefinitely. Because the flow of energy is weak and variable, very large collection systems are needed. Other sources don't renew or renew only slowly.

8.C.6 Different parts of the world have different amounts and kinds of energy resources to use and use them for different purposes.

8.D Communication

8.D.1 Errors can occur in coding, transmitting, or decoding information, and some means of checking for accuracy is needed. Repeating the message is a frequently used method.

8.D.2 Information can be carried by many media, including sound, light, and objects. In this century, the ability to code information as electric currents in wires, electromagnetic waves in space, and light in glass fibers has made communication millions of times faster than is possible by mail or sound.

8.E Information Processing

8.E.1   Most computers use digital codes containing only two symbols, 0 and 1, to perform all operations. Continuous signals (analog) must be transformed into digital codes before they can be processed by a computer.

8.E.2   What use can be made of a large collection of information depends upon how it is organized. One of the values of computers is that they are able, on command, to reorganize information in a variety of ways, thereby enabling people to make more and better uses of the collection.

8.E.3   Computer control of mechanical systems can be much quicker than human control. In situations where events happen faster than people can react, there is little choice but to rely on computers. Most complex systems still require human oversight, however, to make certain kinds of judgments about the readiness of the parts of the system (including the computers) and the system as a whole to operate properly, to react to unexpected failures, and to evaluate how well the system is serving its intended purposes.

8.E.4   An increasing number of people work at jobs that involve processing or distributing information. Because computers can do these tasks faster and more reliably, they have become standard tools both in the workplace and at home.

8.F Health Technology

8.F.1   Sanitation measures such as the use of sewers, landfills, quarantines, and safe food handling are important in controlling the spread of organisms that cause disease. Improving sanitation to prevent disease has contributed more to saving human life than any advance in medical treatment.

8.F.2   The ability to measure the level of substances in body fluids has made it possible for physicians to make comparisons with normal levels, make very sophisticated diagnoses, and monitor the effects of the treatments they prescribe.

8.F.3   It is becoming increasingly possible to manufacture chemical substances such as insulin and hormones that are normally found in the body. They can be used by individuals whose own bodies cannot produce the amounts required for good health.

Project 2061 Benchmarks

9. The Mathematical World

By the end of the 8th grade, students should know that

9.A Numbers

9.A.1 There have been systems for writing numbers other than the Arabic system of place values based on tens. The very old Roman numerals are now used only for dates, clock faces, or ordering chapters in a book. Numbers based on 60 are still used for describing time and angles.

9.A.2 A number line can be extended on the other side of zero to represent negative numbers. Negative numbers allow subtraction of a bigger number from a smaller number to make sense, and are often used when something can be measured on either side of some reference point (time, ground level, temperature, budget).

9.A.3 Numbers can be written in different forms, depending on how they are being used. How fractions or decimals based on measured quantities should be written depends on how precise the measurements are and how precise an answer is needed.

9.A.4 The operations + and – are inverses of each other—one undoes what the other does; likewise x and ÷ .

9.A.5 The expression *a/b* can mean different things: *a* parts of size *1/b* each, *a* divided by *b*, or *a* compared to *b*.

9.A.6 Numbers can be represented by using sequences of only two symbols (such as 1 and 0, on and off); computers work this way.

9.A.7 Computations (as on calculators) can give more digits than make sense or are useful.

9.B Symbolic Relationships

9.B.1 An equation containing a variable may be true for just one value of the variable.

9.B.2 Mathematical statements can be used to describe how one quantity changes when another changes. Rates of change can be computed from differences in magnitudes and vice versa.

9.B.3 Graphs can show a variety of possible relationships between two variables. As one variable increases uniformly, the other may do one of the following: increase or decrease steadily, increase or decrease faster and faster, get closer and closer to some limiting value, reach some intermediate maximum or minimum, alternately increase and decrease indefinitely, increase or decrease in steps, or do something different from any of these.

9.C Shapes

9.C.1 Some shapes have special properties: triangular shapes tend to make structures rigid, and round shapes give the least possible boundary for a given amount of interior area. Shapes can match exactly or have the same shape in different sizes.

9.C.2 Lines can be parallel, perpendicular, or oblique.

9.C.3 Shapes on a sphere like the earth cannot be depicted on a flat surface without some distortion.

9.C.4 The graphic display of numbers may help to show patterns such as trends, varying rates of change, gaps, or clusters. Such patterns sometimes can be used to make predictions about the phenomena being graphed.

Project 2061 Benchmarks

9.C.5   It takes two numbers to locate a point on a map or any other flat surface. The numbers may be two perpendicular distances from a point, or an angle and a distance from a point.

9.C.6   The scale chosen for a graph or drawing makes a big difference in how useful it is.

9.D Uncertainty

9.D.1   How probability is estimated depends on what is known about the situation. Estimates can be based on data from similar conditions in the past or on the assumption that all the possibilities are known.

9.D.2   Probabilities are ratios and can be expressed as fractions, percentages, or odds.

9.D.3   The mean, median, and mode tell different things about the middle of a data set.

9.D.4   Comparison of data from two groups should involve comparing both their middles and the spreads around them.

9.D.5   The larger a well-chosen sample is, the more accurately it is likely to represent the whole. But there are many ways of choosing a sample that can make it unrepresentative of the whole.

9.D.6   Events can be described in terms of being more or less likely, impossible, or certain.

9.E Reasoning

9.E.1   Some aspects of reasoning have fairly rigid rules for what makes sense; other aspects don't. If people have rules that always hold, and good information about a particular situation, then logic can help them to figure out what is true about it. This kind of reasoning requires care in the use of key words such as if, and, not, or, all, and some. Reasoning by similarities can suggest ideas but can't prove them one way or the other.

9.E.2   Practical reasoning, such as diagnosing or troubleshooting almost anything, may require many-step, branching logic. Because computers can keep track of complicated logic, as well as a lot of information, they are useful in a lot of problem-solving situations.

9.E.3   Sometimes people invent a general rule to explain how something works by summarizing observations. But people tend to overgeneralize, imagining general rules on the basis of only a few observations.

9.E.4   People are using incorrect logic when they make a statement such as "If A is true, then B is true; but A isn't true, therefore B isn't true either."

9.E.5   A single example can never prove that something is always true, but sometimes a single example can prove that something is not always true.

9.E.6   An analogy has some likenesses to but also some differences from the real thing.

Project 2061 Benchmarks

10. Historical Perspectives

By the end of the 8th grade, students should know that

10.A Displacing the Earth from the Center of the Universe

10.A.1 The motion of an object is always judged with respect to some other object or point and so the idea of absolute motion or rest is misleading.

10.A.2 Telescopes reveal that there are many more stars in the night sky than are evident to the unaided eye, the surface of the moon has many craters and mountains, the sun has dark spots, and Jupiter and some other planets have their own moons.

10.F Understanding Fire

10.F.1 From the earliest times until now, people have believed that even though millions of different kinds of material seem to exist in the world, most things must be made up of combinations of just a few basic kinds of things. There has not always been agreement, however, on what those basic kinds of things are. One theory long ago was that the basic substances were earth, water, air, and fire. Scientists now know that these are not the basic substances. But the old theory seemed to explain many observations about the world.

10.F.2 Today, scientists are still working out the details of what the basic kinds of matter are and of how they combine, or can be made to combine, to make other substances.

10.F.3 Experimental and theoretical work done by French scientist Antoine Lavoisier in the decade between the American and French revolutions led to the modern science of chemistry.

10.F.4 Lavoisier's work was based on the idea that when materials react with each other many changes can take place but that in every case the total amount of matter afterward is the same as before. He successfully tested the concept of conservation of matter by conducting a series of experiments in which he carefully measured all the substances involved in burning, including the gases used and those given off.

10.F.5 Alchemy was chiefly an effort to change base metals like lead into gold and to produce an elixir that would enable people to live forever. It failed to do that or to create much knowledge of how substances react with each other. The more scientific study of chemistry that began in Lavoisier's time has gone far beyond alchemy in understanding reactions and producing new materials.

10.G Splitting the Atom

10.G.1 The accidental discovery that minerals containing uranium darken photographic film, as light does, led to the idea of radioactivity.

10.G.2 In their laboratory in France, Marie Curie and her husband, Pierre Curie, isolated two new elements that caused most of the radioactivity of the uranium mineral. They named one radium because it gave off powerful, invisible rays, and the other polonium in honor of Madame Curie's country of birth. Marie Curie was the first scientist ever to win the Nobel prize in two different fields—in physics, shared with her husband, and later in chemistry.

Project 2061 Benchmarks

11. Common Themes

By the end of the 8th grade, students should know that

11.A Systems

11.A.1 A system can include processes as well as things.

11.A.2 Thinking about things as systems means looking for how every part relates to others. The output from one part of a system (which can include material, energy, or information) can become the input to other parts. Such feedback can serve to control what goes on in the system as a whole.

11.A.3 Any system is usually connected to other systems, both internally and externally. Thus a system may be thought of as containing subsystems and as being a subsystem of a larger system.

11.B Models

11.B.1 Models are often used to think about processes that happen too slowly, too quickly, or on too small a scale to observe directly, or that are too vast to be changed deliberately, or that are potentially dangerous.

11.B.2 Mathematical models can be displayed on a computer and then modified to see what happens.

11.B.3 Different models can be used to represent the same thing. What kind of a model to use and how complex it should be depends on its purpose. The usefulness of a model may be limited if it is too simple or if it is needlessly complicated. Choosing a useful model is one of the instances in which intuition and creativity come into play in science, mathematics, and engineering.

11.C Constancy and Change

11.C.1 Physical and biological systems tend to change until they become stable and then remain that way unless their surroundings change.

11.C.2 A system may stay the same because nothing is happening or because things are happening but exactly counterbalance one another.

11.C.3 Many systems contain feedback mechanisms that serve to keep changes within specified limits.

11.C.4 Symbolic equations can be used to summarize how the quantity of something changes over time or in response to other changes.

11.C.5 Symmetry (or the lack of it) may determine properties of many objects, from molecules and crystals to organisms and designed structures.

11.C.6 Cycles, such as the seasons or body temperature, can be described by their cycle length or frequency, what their highest and lowest values are, and when these values occur. Different cycles range from many thousands of years down to less than a billionth of a second.

10.I Discovering Germs

10.I.1 Throughout history, people have created explanations for disease. Some have held that disease has spiritual causes, but the most persistent biological theory over the centuries was that illness resulted from an imbalance in the body fluids. The introduction of germ theory by Louis Pasteur and others in the 19th century led to the modern belief that many diseases are caused by microorganisms—bacteria, viruses, yeasts, and parasites.

10.I.2 Pasteur wanted to find out what causes milk and wine to spoil. He demonstrated that spoilage and fermentation occur when microorganisms enter from the air, multiply rapidly, and produce waste products. After showing that spoilage could be avoided by keeping germs out or by destroying them with heat, he investigated animal diseases and showed that microorganisms were involved. Other investigators later showed that specific kinds of germs caused specific diseases.

10.I.3 Pasteur found that infection by disease organisms—germs—caused the body to build up an immunity against subsequent infection by the same organisms. He then demonstrated that it was possible to produce vaccines that would induce the body to build immunity to a disease without actually causing the disease itself.

10.I.4 Changes in health practices have resulted from the acceptance of the germ theory of disease. Before germ theory, illness was treated by appeals to supernatural powers or by trying to adjust body fluids through induced vomiting, bleeding, or purging. The modern approach emphasizes sanitation, the safe handling of food and water, the pasteurization of milk, quarantine, and aseptic surgical techniques to keep germs out of the body; vaccinations to strengthen the body's immune system against subsequent infection by the same kind of microorganisms; and antibiotics and other chemicals and processes to destroy microorganisms.

10.I.5 In medicine, as in other fields of science, discoveries are sometimes made unexpectedly, even by accident. But knowledge and creative insight are usually required to recognize the meaning of the unexpected.

10.J Harnessing Power

10.J.1 Until the 1800s, most manufacturing was done in homes, using small, handmade machines that were powered by muscle, wind, or running water. New machinery and steam engines to drive them made it possible to replace craftsmanship with factories, using fuels as a source of energy. In the factory system, workers, materials, and energy could be brought together efficiently.

10.J.2 The invention of the steam engine was at the center of the Industrial Revolution. It converted the chemical energy stored in wood and coal, which were plentiful, into mechanical work. The steam engine was invented to solve the urgent problem of pumping water out of coal mines. As improved by James Watt, it was soon used to move coal, drive manufacturing machinery, and power locomotives, ships, and even the first automobiles.

11.D Scale

11.D.1 Properties of systems that depend on volume, such as capacity and weight, change out of proportion to properties that depend on area, such as strength or surface processes.

11.D.2 As the complexity of any system increases, gaining an understanding of it depends increasingly on summaries, such as averages and ranges, and on descriptions of typical examples of that system.

12. Habits of Mind

By the end of the 8th grade, students should know that

12.A Values and Attitudes

12.A.1 Know why it is important in science to keep honest, clear, and accurate records.

12.A.2 Know that hypotheses are valuable, even if they turn out not to be true, if they lead to fruitful investigations.

12.A.3 Know that often different explanations can be given for the same evidence, and it is not always possible to tell which one is correct.

12.B Computation and Estimation

12.B.1 Find what percentage one number is of another and figure any percentage of any number.

12.B.2 Use, interpret, and compare numbers in several equivalent forms such as integers, fractions, decimals, and percents.

12.B.3 Calculate the circumferences and areas of rectangles, triangles, and circles, and the volumes of rectangular solids.

12.B.4 Find the mean and median of a set of data.

12.B.5 Estimate distances and travel times from maps and the actual size of objects from scale drawings.

12.B.6 Insert instructions into computer spreadsheet cells to program arithmetic calculations.

12.B.7 Determine what unit (such as seconds, square inches, or dollars per tankful) an answer should be expressed in from the units of the inputs to the calculation, and be able to convert compound units (such as yen per dollar into dollar per yen, or miles per hour into feet per second).

12.B.8 Decide what degree of precision is adequate and round off the result of calculator operations to enough significant figures to reasonably reflect those of the inputs.

12.B.9 Express numbers like 100, 1,000, and 1,000,000 as powers of 10.

12.B.10 Estimate probabilities of outcomes in familiar situations, on the basis of history or the number of possible outcomes.

Project 2061 Benchmarks

12.C Manipulation and Observation

12.C.1 Use calculators to compare amounts proportionally.

12.C.2 Use computers to store and retrieve information in topical, alphabetical, numerical, and key-word files, and create simple files of their own devising.

12.C.3 Read analog and digital meters on instruments used to make direct measurements of length, volume, weight, elapsed time, rates, and temperature, and choose appropriate units for reporting various magnitudes.

12.C.4 Use cameras and tape recorders for capturing information.

12.C.5 Inspect, disassemble, and reassemble simple mechanical devices and describe what the various parts are for; estimate what the effect that making a change in one part of a system is likely to have on the system as a whole.

12.D Communication Skills

12.D.1 Organize information in simple tables and graphs and identify relationships they reveal.

12.D.2 Read simple tables and graphs produced by others and describe in words what they show.

12.D.3 Locate information in reference books, back issues of newspapers and magazines, compact disks, and computer databases.

12.D.4 Understand writing that incorporates circle charts, bar and line graphs, two-way data tables, diagrams, and symbols.

12.D.5 Find and describe locations on maps with rectangular and polar coordinates.

12.E Critical-Response Skills

12.E.1 Question claims based on vague attributions (such as "Leading doctors say...") or on statements made by celebrities or others outside the area of their particular expertise.

12.E.2 Compare consumer products and consider reasonable personal trade-offs among them on the basis of features, performance, durability, and cost.

12.E.3 Be skeptical of arguments based on very small samples of data, biased samples, or samples for which there was no control sample.

12.E.4 Be aware that there may be more than one good way to interpret a given set of findings.

12.E.5 Notice and criticize the reasoning in arguments in which (1) fact and opinion are intermingled or the conclusions do not follow logically from the evidence given, (2) an analogy is not apt, (3) no mention is made of whether the control groups are very much like the experimental group, or (4) all members of a group (such as teenagers or chemists) are implied to have nearly identical characteristics that differ from those of other groups.

Formulas

Word Form	Symbolic Form	Purpose
Volume = length · width · height	$V = lwh$	to calculate the volume of a rectangular object
Density = $\dfrac{\text{mass}}{\text{Volume}}$	$D = \dfrac{m}{V}$	to calculate the density of an object
Speed = $\dfrac{\text{distance}}{\text{time}}$	$S = \dfrac{d}{t}$	to calculate the speed of an object
acceleration = $\dfrac{\text{final velocity} - \text{initial velocity}}{\text{time}}$	$a = \dfrac{v_{final} - v_{initial}}{t}$	to calculate the acceleration of an object
Force = mass · acceleration	$F = ma$	to calculate the force, mass, or acceleration of an object; called Newton's second law
momentum = mass · velocity	$p = mv$	to calculate the momentum of an object
Pressure = $\dfrac{\text{Force}}{\text{Area}}$	$P = \dfrac{F}{A}$	to calculate the pressure on an object
Work = Force · distance	$W = Fd$	to calculate work
Gravitational Potential Energy = mass · gravitational acceleration · height	$GPE = mgh$	to calculate the gravitational potential energy of an object
Kinetic Energy = $\dfrac{\text{mass} \cdot \text{velocity}^2}{2}$	$KE = \dfrac{1}{2}mv^2$	to calculate the kinetic energy of an object
Mechanical Energy = Potential Energy + Kinetic Energy	$ME = PE + KE$	to calculate the mechanical energy of an object
Power = $\dfrac{\text{Work}}{\text{time}}$	$P = \dfrac{W}{t}$	to calculate power based on work
Power = $\dfrac{\text{Energy}}{\text{time}}$	$P = \dfrac{E}{t}$	to calculate power based on energy
Efficiency (%) = $\dfrac{\text{Output work}}{\text{Input work}} \cdot 100$		to calculate the efficiency of a machine
Mechanical Advantage = $\dfrac{\text{Output work}}{\text{Input work}}$	$MA = \dfrac{F_{out}}{F_{in}}$	to calculate a machine's mechanical advantage
Speed = wavelength · frequency	$S = \lambda \cdot f$	to calculate the speed of a wave
Current = $\dfrac{\text{Voltage}}{\text{Resistance}}$	$I = \dfrac{V}{R}$	to calculate the relationships among current, voltage, and resistance; called Ohm's law
Electrical Power = Voltage · Current	$P = VI$	to calculate power
Energy used = Power · time	$E = Pt$	to calculate the total energy used

The Periodic Table of the Elements

Period	1	2	3	4	5	6	7	8	9
1	1 **H** Hydrogen 1.008								
2	3 **Li** Lithium 6.941	4 **Be** Beryllium 9.012							
3	11 **Na** Sodium 22.990	12 **Mg** Magnesium 24.305							
4	19 **K** Potassium 39.098	20 **Ca** Calcium 40.078	21 **Sc** Scandium 44.956	22 **Ti** Titanium 47.87	23 **V** Vanadium 50.942	24 **Cr** Chromium 51.996	25 **Mn** Manganese 54.938	26 **Fe** Iron 55.845	27 **Co** Cobalt 58.933
5	37 **Rb** Rubidium 85.468	38 **Sr** Strontium 87.62	39 **Y** Yttrium 88.906	40 **Zr** Zirconium 91.224	41 **Nb** Niobium 92.906	42 **Mo** Molybdenum 95.94	43 **Tc** Technetium (98)	44 **Ru** Ruthenium 101.07	45 **Rh** Rhodium 102.906
6	55 **Cs** Cesium 132.905	56 **Ba** Barium 137.327	57 **La** Lanthanum 138.906	72 **Hf** Hafnium 178.49	73 **Ta** Tantalum 180.95	74 **W** Tungsten 183.84	75 **Re** Rhenium 186.207	76 **Os** Osmium 190.23	77 **Ir** Iridium 192.217
7	87 **Fr** Francium (223)	88 **Ra** Radium (226)	89 **Ac** Actinium (227)	104 **Rf** Rutherfordium (261)	105 **Db** Dubnium (262)	106 **Sg** Seaborgium (266)	107 **Bh** Bohrium (264)	108 **Hs** Hassium (269)	109 **Mt** Meitnerium (268)

Period
Each row of the periodic table is called a **period**. As read from left to right, one proton and one electron are added from one element to the next.

Group
Each column of the table is called a **group**. Elements in a group share similar properties. Groups are read from top to bottom.

58 **Ce** Cerium 140.116	59 **Pr** Praseodymium 140.908	60 **Nd** Neodymium 144.24	61 **Pm** Promethium (145)	62 **Sm** Samarium 150.36
90 **Th** Thorium 232.038	91 **Pa** Protactinium 231.036	92 **U** Uranium 238.029	93 **Np** Neptunium (237)	94 **Pu** Plutonium (244)

 Metal Metalloid Nonmetal  Solid  Liquid Gas